Features and Benefits

Merrill Advanced Mathematical Concepts
Precalculus with Applications

1. **NCTM Standards**   As the correlation on pages T18–T19 shows, strict attention was paid to the *NCTM Standards* in developing this program. Each lesson in the *Teacher's Wraparound Edition* includes a list of *NCTM Standards* covered by that lesson

2. **Applications and Problem Solving**   Because the ability to grasp concepts and skills is greatly enhanced when they are tied to applications, most lessons open with an application (page 524). Application examples are also included in most lessons (page 528, example 5). This is strengthened by including *Applications and Problem Solving* and *Critical Thinking* problems in every set of exercises (pages 252–253, exercises 39–47).

   Each chapter opener (pages 300–301) emphasizes the need for mathematics in a variety of chosen professions. *Decision Making* and *Case Study Follow-Up* features (pages 97, 604) provide students with opportunities to use mathematics when solving problems dealing with relevant issues

3. **Graphing Calculator**   Each of the 24 *Graphing Calculator Lessons* is directly related to the lesson that precedes or follows it Having access to this powerful tool will help students more readily understand the related concepts (pages 577–578)

   Students also have the opportunity to use graphing calculators in *Explorations* (page 198), in exercises (page 193, exercises 38–40), and in graphing calculator programs (page 183, exercise 39).

4. **Review**   To help maintain previously-learned skills and concepts, a *Mixed Review* is included in every set of exercises with a College Entrance Exam practice question in each set (page 207, note exercise 37). Each exercise is referenced to the lesson where the concept was first introduced. The *Mid-Chapter Review* in each chapter provides a review of the concepts taught thus far in the chapter (page 383).

5. **Calculus Concepts and Skills**   By integrating concepts and skills related to calculus throughout the program, such as the concepts of *limit* and *derivative*, students will be better prepared for a course in calculus (pages 149–154). Chapter 17 presents a formal introduction to calculus (pages 910–955).

6. **Discrete Mathematics**   Unit 4 contains five chapters (Chapters 12–16) that give students the opportunity to explore this branch of mathematics. Students will construct models, discover and use algorithms, and examine exciting new concepts that will help them solve real-world problems.

7. **Teacher Support**   The unique *Teacher's Wraparound Edition* includes a complete lesson plan for each lesson. Of particular note are the *5-Minute Check, Chalkboard Examples, Teaching Tips*, and selected pages from the *Teacher's Classroom Resources* package (pages T12–T18). The four-page interleaf section preceding each chapter gives a complete overview of the concepts taught and the materials available for each lesson. Additional information on cooperative learning and technology are also provided with pages from the *Activity Masters* and *Technology Masters* from the *Teacher's Classroom Resources* (pages 4A–4D).

8. **Teacher's Classroom Resources**   This package contains an extensive set of supplementary materials that are designed to meet the complete spectrum of student needs and interests. Of note are the *Technology Masters, Teacher's Guide for Software Resources, Graphing Calculator Instruction Guide, SAT and ACT Study Guide*, and an extraordinary *Transparency Package* that contains a full color transparency for every lesson. See the brochure that follows for a description of each component.

A WHOLE NEW LOOK FOR A PROVEN PRECALCULUS PROGRAM

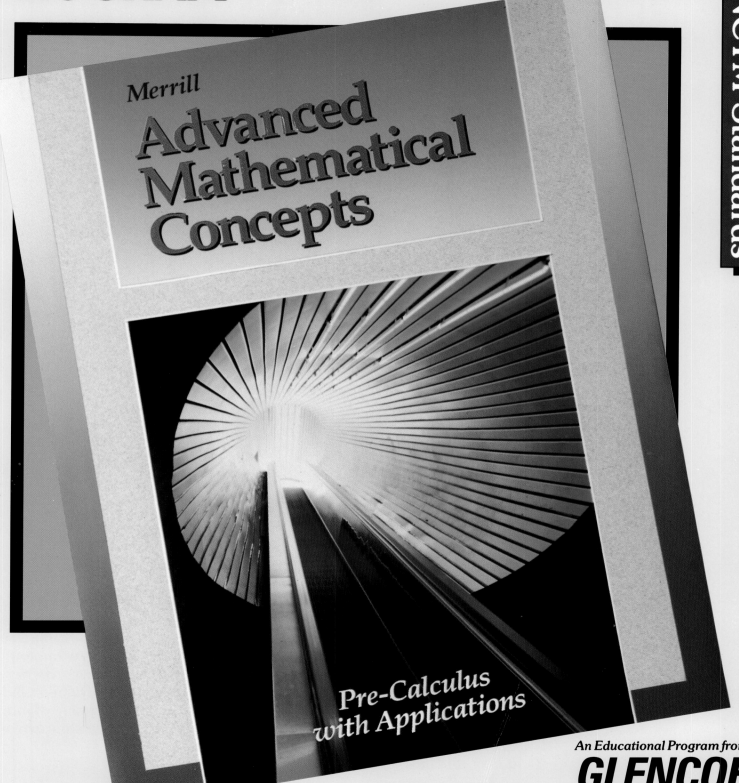

Merrill

Advanced Mathematical Concepts

Pre-Calculus with Applications

An Educational Program from
GLENCOE

Clarity. Flexibility. Relevance. You'l
in this Classroom-Tested Precalculu

MERRILL ADVANCEI
PRECALCULUS WITH

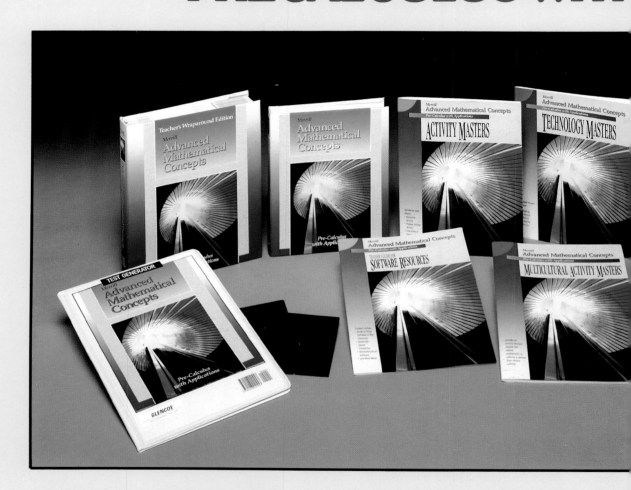

This comprehensive revision of **Merrill Advanced Mathematical Concepts** *retains the logical, flexible chapter organization of the previous text, while enhancing the mathematical content with meaningful applications to non-mathematics disciplines, such as science, social studies, and business.*

A full-color design, a wide range of exercise sets, relevant special features, and an emphasis on graphing and technology invite your students to experience the excitement of understanding and applying higher level mathematics skills. Five units explore:

Find Them All
Curriculum

MATHEMATICAL CONCEPTS: APPLICATIONS

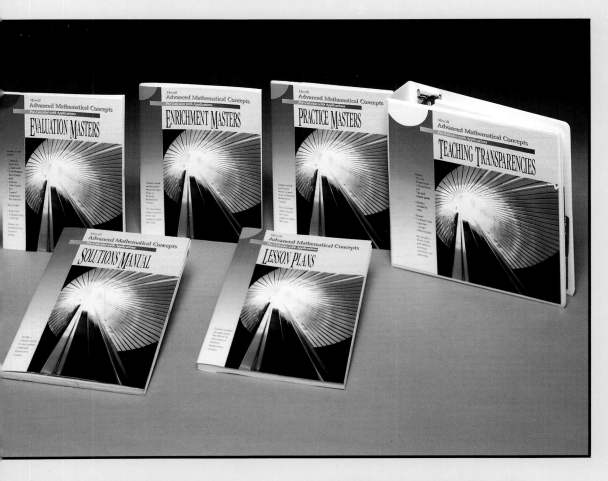

- *Relations, Functions, and Graphs (Chapters 1–4)*
- *Trigonometry (Chapters 5–8)*
- *Advanced Functions and Graphing (Chapters 9–11)*
- *Discrete Mathematics (Chapters 12–16)*
- *Introduction to Calculus (Chapter 17)*

Combine the newly-revised Student Edition with the exclusive Teacher's Wraparound Edition and an extensive array of ancillary materials, and you have a complete learning program that leads the way in advanced mathematics instruction and helps you teach with ease and confidence.

A Logical Presentation Helps You Guide Your Students from Algebra Topics to the Intricacies of Calculus

*The format of every lesson strengthens student learning. Each lesson begins with an **Objective**, so students know what to expect, and an **Application** to engage student interest. Concepts are then reinforced with plenty of **examples**, highlighting of important **concepts**, and a substantial **exercise set** that enhances student skills by encouraging them to write, read, practice, think logically, and review.*

By integrating calculus concepts, such as those of **limit** and the **derivative**, and the skills related to calculus throughout the course, this program assists you in preparing your students for a course in calculus.

Let's consider the slope of the line tangent to the graph of $f(x) = 3x^2 - 4x + 1$ at $(2, 5)$. The slope of the secant line through two general points $A(x, f(x))$ and $B(x + h, f(x + h))$ is equal to $\frac{f(x+h) - f(x)}{h}$, where $h \neq 0$. Find the slope of the secant line to the graph of $f(x) = 3x^2 - 4x + 1$. That is, find $f(x + h)$.

$$f(x + h) = 3(x + h)^2 - 4(x + h) + 1$$
$$= 3x^2 + 6xh + 3h^2 - 4x - 4h + 1$$

Now, find the slope of $\overleftrightarrow{AB}$.

$$m = \frac{f(x+h) - f(x)}{h} \quad \text{Definition of slope}$$
$$= \frac{(3x^2 + 6xh + 3h^2 - 4x - 4h + 1) - (3x^2 - 4x + 1)}{h}$$
$$= \frac{6xh + 3h^2 - 4h}{h}$$
$$= 6x + 3h - 4$$

A general expression for the slope of the secant line for $f(x) = 3x^2 - 4x + 1$ is $6x + 3h - 4$. The slope of the secant line through specific points can be found by substituting values for x and h.

x	h	slope of the secant line
2	2	$6(2) + 3(2) - 4 = 14$
2	1	$6(2) + 3(1) - 4 = 11$
2	0.5	$6(2) + 3(0.5) - 4 = 9.5$
2	0.25	$6(2) + 3(0.25) - 4 = 8.75$
2	0.1	$6(2) + 3(0.1) - 4 = 8.3$
2	0.01	$6(2) + 3(0.01) - 4 = 7.97$

As h approaches zero, the middle term of $6x + 3h - 4$ also approaches zero, which means that $6x + 3h - 4$ approaches $6x - 4$. As h approaches zero, the secant line approaches the tangent; so, as h approach—— the slope of the secant line approaches the slope of the tangent. Then——— tangent to the graph of $f(x) = 3x^2 - 4x + 1$ at $(x, f(x)$———

The slope of the tangent at $(2, 5)$ can be found by——— expression $6x - 4$. The slope of the tangent at $(2——$

The symbol $f'(x)$ is often used to denote the——— defined as follows.

$$f'(x) = \lim_{h \to 0} \frac{f(x+h) - f(x)}{h} \qquad \lim_{h \to 0} \text{ is read "the l———}$$

The symbol $\lim_{h \to 0} \frac{f(x+h) - f(x)}{h}$ means the lim——— value of h approaches zero. The function $f'(x——$

$f'(x)$ is read "f prime of x."

150 CHAPTER 3 THE NATURE OF GRAPHS

3-6 Tangent to a Curv———

Objectives

After studying this lesson, you should be able t———
- find the derivative of a function, and
- find the slope and the equation of a line tange——— a given point.

Application

The Department of Transportation in each——— hills with restrictions on the weight of vehicl——— are allowed on the hill. One of the factors aff——— or slope of the hill at given points. The steepn——— from the slope of the line tangent to the hill———

A line tangent to a curve at a point on the curve is the line that passes through that point and has a slope that is the same as the slope of the curve at that point. In the figure at the right, two lines tangent to the graph of $f(x) = x^2$ are shown. One line is tangent at $(-1, 1)$, and the other line is tangent at $(2, 4)$. Lines that are tangent to a curve are also called **tangents** to a curve.

$y = f(x)$

Suppose you graph a function $y = f(x)$. Suppose points A and B are two points on the graph near each other. The slope of line AB can be found by using the coordinates of A and B. Let the coordinates of A and B be $(x, f(x))$ and $(x + h, f(x + h))$, respectively. The slope is

$$\frac{f(x+h) - f(x)}{(x+h) - x} \text{ or } \frac{f(x+h) - f(x)}{h}.$$

Line AB is called a **secant line** because it intersects the curve more than once.

Suppose A remains fixed while you move B along the curve toward A. As B approaches A, the values of h become smaller and smaller, approaching zero. When $h = 0$, B coincides with A. Then the secant line becomes the line tangent to the curve at point A.

In the expression for the slope of $\overleftrightarrow{AB}$, notice that $\frac{f(x+h) - f(x)}{h}$ is undefined when $h = 0$. However, the secant is a tangent when $h = 0$. So, the definition of the slope of the tangent line must be defined in a special way.

LESSON 3-6 TANGENT TO A CURVE 149

As you saw, finding the derivative of a function can be time consuming and complex. There are rules that will make the process easier.

ches zero"

Rules for Derivatives

Constant Rule:	The derivative of a constant function is zero. If $f(x) = c$, then $f'(x) = 0$.
Power Rule:	If $f(x) = x^n$, where n is a rational number, then $f'(x) = n \cdot x^{n-1}$.
Constant Multiple of a Power Rule:	If $f(x) = cx^n$, where c and n are rational numbers, $f'(x) = n \cdot cx^{n-1}$.
Sum Rule:	If $f(x) = g(x) + h(x)$, then $f'(x) = g'(x) + h'(x)$.

Example 1

Find the derivative of each function.

a. $f(x) = 6$
b. $f(x) = \frac{1}{x}$
c. $f(x) = 6x^3 - 4x^2 + 2x - 9$

a. $f(x) = 6$
   $f'(x) = 0$ *Use the constant rule.*

b. $f(x) = \frac{1}{x}$
   $f(x) = x^{-1}$
   $f'(x) = -1x^{-2}$ *Use the power rule.*

c. $f(x) = 6x^3 - 4x^2 + 2x - 9$
   Use the power rule and constant rule for each term.
   Then use the sum rule.
   $f(x) = 3 \cdot 6x^{3-1} - 2 \cdot 4x^{2-1} + 1 \cdot 2x^{1-1} - 0$
   $f'(x) = 18x^2 - 8x + 2$

Since the derivative is also the expression for the slope of the line tangent to the graph of a function, you can use the derivative to find the slope of the line tangent at a given point on the graph.

Example 2

Find the slope of the line tangent to the graph of $f(x) = x^4 - 2x^3 + 5x^2 - 8$ at the point $(-2, 44)$.

Use the rules for derivatives to find $f'(x)$.
$f'(x) = 4x^{4-1} - 2(3)x^{3-1} + 5(2)x^{2-1} - 0$
$= 4x^3 - 6x^2 + 10x$

Now evaluate $f'(x)$ for $x = -2$.
$f'(-2) = 4(-2)^3 - 6(-2)^2 + 10(-2)$
$= -32 - 24 - 20 \text{ or } -76$

The slope of the line tangent to the graph of $f(x) = x^4 - 2x^3 + 5x^2 - 8$ at the point $(-2, 44)$ is -76.

LESSON 3-6 TANGENT TO A CURVE 151

Planning Your Precalculus Course

Merrill Advanced Mathematical Concepts includes a wide variety of topics, more than can normally be studied in one year. Most classes can study the entire text in three semesters. Outlines for two possible one-year courses and four possible one-semester courses are shown below. Selection of a plan is dependent on the background and ability level of the students and on the objectives and interests of the school district.

Course Y1   A one-year course for students who have had little or no trigonometry (includes trigonometry, advanced algebra, theory of equations, and analytic geometry)

Course Y2   A one-year course for students who have previously studied trigonometry, designed as a precalculus course for the student who is preparing for a rigorous course in calculus

Course S1   A one-semester course emphasizing trigonometry

Course S2   A one-semester course emphasizing algebra and elementary functions

Course S3   A one-semester course emphasizing analytic geometry

Course S4   A one-semester course emphasizing discrete mathematics

The charts on these two pages denote which chapters should be covered for each course. They also suggest time schedules for both 6-week and 9-week grading periods. The maximum and minimum number of days required for each chapter are given. Notice that most chapters can be covered in about three weeks.

COURSE PLANNING CALENDAR - ONE YEAR COURSES

6-Week Grading Periods

Grading Period	Y1 Chapter	Y1 Days	Y2 Chapter	Y2 Days
1	1	11-13	3	11-15
	3	13-17		12-15
2	4	11-14	3	12-16
	5	13-16	4	11-14
3	12-15	12-15	5 Lessons 5-6 to 5-8	
	6 7	12-15	6	2 Lesson 6-2
			7 Lessons 7-6 to 7-9	5-7
			8	13-15
4	9	13-15	9	13-15
	10	13-15	10	13-15
5	11	11-14	11	11-14
	12	13-16	12	13-16
6	13	11-16	13	11-16
	17	12-15	17	11-14

9-Week Grading Periods

Grading Period	Y1 Chapter	Y1 Days	Y2 Chapter	Y2 Days
1	1	11-14	1	11-14
	3	13-17	2	12-14
	4	12-15	3	12-17
2	5	13-16	4	11-15
	6	12-14	5	6-8
	7	12-15	6	2 Lesson 6-2
			7 Lessons 7-6 to 7-9	
			8	13-15
3	9	13-15	9	13-15
	10	13-15	10	13-15
	11	11-15	11	11-15
4	12	13-16	12	13-16
	13	11-15	13	11-15
	17	11-14	17	11-14

Merrill Advanced Mathematical Concepts includes a wide variety of topics — more than usually can be studied in one year. The Course Planning Guide offers outlines for two possible one-year courses and four possible one-semester courses. You can select your own plan, based on your teaching objectives and the ability levels of your students.

COURSE PLANNING CALENDAR - ONE SEMESTER COURSES

6-Week Grading Periods

Grading Period	S1 Chapter	S1 Days	S2 Chapter	S2 Days	S3 Chapter	S3 Days	S4 Chapter	S4 Days
1	3	13-15	1	8-9	1	11-15	2	11-13
	5	13-15	3	8-9	2	11-15	12	13-17
2	6	12-15	4	11-14	3	13-15	13	11-13
	7	12-15	10	13-16	5	13-15	14	13-17
3	8	12-14	11	11-14	9	13-15	15	11-15
		13-16	13	13-16	10	13-15	16	11-15

9-Week Grading Periods

Grading Period	S1 Chapter	S1 Days	S2 Chapter	S2 Days	S3 Chapter	S3 Days	S4 Chapter	S4 Days
1	3	13-16	1	8-9	1	11-14	2	11-14
	5	13-15	2	8-9	2	12-14	12	12-17
	6	12-14	3	8-9	3	12-17	13	11-14
			4	10-13 11-14				
2	7	12-15	10	13-16	5	13-15	14	13-16
	8	13-16	11	11-14	9	13-15	15	11-14
			13	13-15	10	13-15	16	11-13

The following one-quarter courses are also possible.

COURSE	CHAPTERS
Trigonometry	5 - 8
Analytic Geometry	1, 2, 3, and 10
Discrete Mathematics	13 - 16
Limits, Sequences, and An Introduction to Calculus	4, 12, 17

In the **discrete mathematics** unit, students construct models, discover and use algorithms, and examine new concepts that will help them solve real-world problems. This study involves concepts such as discontinuity, iteration, recursion, and induction, that will prepare students for college-level courses.

12-8 Mathematical Induction

Objective
After studying this lesson, you should be able to:
■ use mathematical induction to prove the validity of formulas.

Application
Consider the series $1 + 3 + 5 + 7 + \cdots$. What is the first term? What is the sum of the first two terms? the first three terms? the first four terms? Look for a pattern by finding the first five partial sums.

$$1 = 1 = 1^2$$
$$1 + 3 = 4 = 2^2$$
$$1 + 3 + 5 = 9 = 3^2$$
$$1 + 3 + 5 + 7 = 16 = 4^2$$
$$1 + 3 + 5 + 7 + 9 = 25 = 5^2$$

Notice that each partial sum is the square of the number of terms being added, or n^2. Even though we know that this rule is true for the first five partial sums, we do not know if this rule will be true for a partial sum having 1,000,000 odd numbers or n odd numbers.

A method of proof called **mathematical induction** can be used to prove certain formulas or conjectures. Mathematical induction depends on a recursive process that is much like climbing a ladder. First, you must climb onto the first step. Then, you must be able to climb from one step to the next. Thus, if you can get onto the first step, you can certainly climb to the second. If you are on the second step, you can climb to the third. If you are on the third step, you can climb to the fourth, and so on indefinitely, for all steps.

In general, the following steps are used to prove a result by mathematical induction.

Proof by Mathematical Induction	1. First, verify that S_n is valid for the first possible case, usually $n = 1$. 2. Then, assume that S_n is valid for $n = k$ and prove that it is also valid for $n = k + 1$.

Thus, since S_n is valid for $n = 1$ (or any other first case), it is valid for $n = 2$. Since it is valid for $n = 2$, it is valid for $n = 3$, and so on, indefinitely.

Let's use mathematical induction to prove the conjecture that was made at the beginning of the lesson. Notice that this sequence of numbers is arithmetic with a common difference of 2. The general formula for the nth term is $2n - 1$.

$$S_n: 1 + 3 + 5 + 7 + \cdots + (2n - 1) = n^2$$

1. First, verify that S_n is valid for the first possible case, $n = 1$.
If $n = 1$, then S_1 is 1. The sum is 1 and $1^2 = 1$, so the formula, S_n, is valid for the first case.

2. Then, assume that S_n is valid for $n = k$ and prove that it is also valid for $n = k + 1$.

It must be proven that if S_k: $1 + 3 + 5 + 7 + \cdots = k^2$, then S_{k+1}: $1 + 3 + 5 + 7 + \cdots = (k + 1)^2$ is also valid.

The kth term of the series is $2k - 1$. Substitute $k + 1$ for k. Then $2(k + 1) - 1 = 2k + 1$. You can write a formula for S_{k+1} by adding the next term, $2k + 1$, to each side.

$$S_k: 1 + 3 + 5 + 7 + \cdots + (2k - 1) = k^2$$
$$S_{k+1}: 1 + 3 + 5 + 7 + \cdots + (2k - 1) + (2k + 1) = k^2 + (2k + 1)$$
$$= (k + 1)^2$$

Since the formula for the sum for $n = k + 1$ produces the same result as the direct computation of the sum of the series, the formula is valid for $n = k + 1$ if it is valid for $n = k$. Thus, it can be concluded that since the formula is valid for $n = 1$, it is also valid for $n = 2$. Since it is valid for $n = 2$, it is valid for $n = 3$, and so on, indefinitely. Therefore, the following formula is valid for any positive integer n.

$$S_n: 1 + 3 + 5 + 7 + \cdots + (2n - 1) = n^2$$

Example

Prove $S_n: 1 + 4 + 7 + \cdots + (3n - 2) = \dfrac{n(3n - 1)}{2}$.

1. First, verify that S_n is valid for $n = 1$.
Since $S_1 = 1$ and $\dfrac{1[3(1) - 1]}{2} = 1$, the formula is valid for $n = 1$.

2. Then, assume that S_n is valid for $n = k$ and prove that it is also valid for $n = k + 1$.

$$S_k: 1 + 4 + 7 + \cdots + (3k - 2) = \frac{k(3k - 1)}{2}$$
$$S_{k+1}: 1 + 4 + 7 + \cdots + (3k - 2) + (3k + 1) = \frac{k(3k - 1)}{2} + (3k + 1)$$
$$= \frac{k(3k - 1)}{2} + \frac{2(3k + 1)}{2}$$
$$= \frac{3k^2 - k + 6k + 2}{2}$$
$$= \frac{3k^2 + 5k + 2}{2}$$
$$= \frac{(k + 1)(3k + 2)}{2}$$

If $k + 1$ is substituted into the original formula, the same result is obtained.

$$S_{k+1} = \frac{(k + 1)[3(k + 1) - 1]}{2} \text{ or } \frac{(k + 1)(3k + 2)}{2}$$

Thus, if the formula is valid for $n = k$, it is also valid for $n = k + 1$. Since S_n is valid for $n = 1$, it is also valid for $n = 2$, $n = 3$, and so on.

Table of Contents

5

Applications Strengthen Your Students' Understanding of Mathematics in the Real World

Merrill Advanced Mathematical Concepts isn't just theory taught in a vaccum. Because the text continually applies and connects mathematical principles to real-world situations, students come to appreciate the importance of mathematics in their daily lives.

Almost every lesson begins with an **Application** of the concept being presented. These applications help students see how the chapter content relates to their everyday experience.

"This standard emphasizes the importance of... modeling connections between problem situations that may arise in the real world or in disciplines other than mathematics; and mathematical connections between two equivalent representations..."
—NCTM Standards

CHAPTER 10

CONICS

HISTORICAL SNAPSHOT

	First Barometer ("Torricelli Tube") Florence, Italy	Celsius temperature scale developed in Uppsala, Sweden	University of North Carolina established at Asheville	
Conic Sections Apollonius (The "Great Geometer"), Alexandria	Fahrenheit temperature scale developed in Holland	Beaufort Wind Scale developed in England		First Weather Satellite NASA's TIROS-I, USA
262–190 BC	AD 1644	1714 1742	1806	1955 1960

522

CHAPTER OBJECTIVES

In this chapter, you will:
- Write equations of circles, parabolas, ellipses, and hyperbolas.
- Graph circles, parabolas, ellipses, and hyperbolas.
- Recognize conic sections by their equations.
- Write equations of tangents and normals to conic sections.

CAREER GOAL: Meteorology

James Martin was born with spinal muscular atrophy, a disorder in which there is a bad connection between the nerves and muscles in his legs and arms. He credits his family with being his inspiration. "My mom and dad put me in public school and always encouraged me to pursue my dreams."

James hasn't wasted any time pursuing his dreams. He works part-time as a computer specialist at the National Climatic Center in Asheville, part of the National Oceanic and Atmospheric Administration. At the University of North Carolina, James majors in computer sciences and atmospheric sciences "so that I can become more familiar with the climate that I work with every day." James hopes that with a bachelor's degree, he will achieve a higher grade in civil service, with supervisory responsibilities. Having the title of meteorologist will also lead to more career opportunities.

Meteorologists use conics and vectors, especially in the study of the cone-shaped hurricane. If you cut horizontally across a hurricane, you would find a circle. A velocity vector drawn tangent to this circle represents the circulation speed of the hurricane. James says that the algebra, geometry, and trigonometry courses he took in high school prepared him well for his college mathematics courses.

From James' perspective, both computer science and atmospheric science offer opportunities for the physically challenged. "I hope that I can encourage other people who are physically challenged to be active in society. I also want to show society that we who are physically challenged don't have to be pushed back into a corner. We have a lot to offer if just given the opportunity."

READ MORE ABOUT IT

Bohren, Craig F. *What Light Through Yonder Window Breaks? More Experiments in Atmospheric Physics.* New York: John Wiley & Sons, 1991.
Carpenter, Clive. *The Changing World of Weather.* New York: Facts on File, 1991.
Spiegel, Herbert J. and Arnold Gruber. *From Weather Vanes to Satellites.* New York: John Wiley & Sons, 1991.

SPOTLIGHT ON...

James Martin
Age: 31
Class: Senior
School: University of North Carolina Asheville, North Carolina
Majors: Computer Science and Atmospheric Sciences

"I hope that I can encourage other people who are physically challenged to be active in society."

FOR MORE INFORMATION

If you would like more information about meteorology, contact:

American Meteorological Society (AMS)
45 Beacon Street
Boston, MA 02108

Each of the 17 **Chapter Openers** offers a career focus, featuring actual college students. These students share their college major, the high school mathematics courses they took to prepare for college, and those they are presently studying. The student-to-student advice on courses and careers brings relevance to the study of mathematics.

DECISION MAKING

Choosing a Home Computer

Since the introduction of the personal computer, millions of Americans have purchased computers for home use. Many buyers have been happy with their purchases, but others have discovered that they bought too much or too little, or worse yet, that they didn't need a computer at all.

1. Describe the features you would look for in a home computer. Include such factors as capacity, capabilities, programs you want to run, type of printer, and any other features you feel are important.
2. Research computers and costs. Talk to computer owners and retailers, read articles and ads, and contact computer manufacturers. Then make a list of three computers that would adequately meet your needs.
3. Outline a plan for financing the cost of each computer on your list.
4. **Project** Work with your group to complete one of the projects listed at the right based on the information you gathered in Exercises 1–3.

PROJECTS
- *Conduct an interview.*
- *Write a book report.*
- *Write a proposal.*
- *Write an article for the school paper.*
- *Write a report.*
- *Make a display.*
- *Make a graph or chart.*
- *Plan an activity.*
- *Design a checklist.*

Decision Making features encourage cooperative learning and provide practice in exploring today's pressing issues. They also give your students an opportunity to complete long-range projects that focus on these issues.

CASE STUDY FOLLOW-UP

Refer to Case Study 3: *The Legal System*, on pages 962–965.

An elliptical rotunda on the north side of the building that symbolizes the American legal system is a "whispering gallery." The major axis of the rotunda measures 44.4 feet. The minor axis measures 35.6 feet.

1. Where is the rotunda?
2. Two people standing at the two foci can easily hear each other whispering, even if there is other noise in the room. How far apart are the whisperers standing?
3. **Research** Find out about the size and shape of the dome of the U.S. Capitol. Can the dome be described in terms of conic sections? Write about your findings in a 1-page paper.

Four Case Studies focus on topics of interest to today's students. In each chapter, students are asked to make connections between the mathematics in that chapter and the case study topics.

7

A Wealth of Opportunities to Explore and Understand Graphing and Technology

*Graphing in the coordinate plane drives the content of the text. Using this unique program, you'll present most concepts in the context of graphing **before** you introduce traditional methods.*

Twenty-four graphing calculator lessons present the keystroking required to use the TI-81 and the Casio calculators as tools.

Graphing Calculator Explorations offer practice in using the technology for problem-solving. Investigative in nature, these features contain no keying instructions.

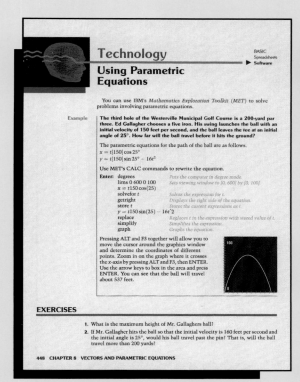

Technology

► BASIC
  Spreadsheets
► Software

Using Parametric Equations

You can use IBM's *Mathematics Exploration Toolkit* (MET) to solve problems involving parametric equations.

Example

The third hole of the Westerville Municipal Golf Course is a 200-yard par three. Ed Gallagher chooses a five iron. His swing launches the ball with an initial velocity of 150 feet per second, and the ball leaves the tee at an initial angle of 25°. How far will the ball travel before it hits the ground?

The parametric equations for the path of the ball are as follows.
$x = t|150| \cos 25°$
$y = t|150| \sin 25° - 16t^2$

Use MET's CALC commands to rewrite the equation.

Enter: degrees — *Puts the computer in degree mode.*
lims 0 600 0 100 — *Sets viewing window to [0, 600] by [0, 100].*
x = t150 cos(25)
solvefor t — *Solves the expression for t.*
getright — *Displays the right side of the equation.*
store t — *Stores the current expressions as t.*
y = t150 sin(25) − 16t^2
replace — *Replaces t in the expression with stored value of t.*
simplify — *Simplifies the expression.*
graph — *Graphs the equation.*

Pressing ALT and F3 together will allow you to move the cursor around the graphics window and determine the coordinates of different points. Zoom in on the graph where it crosses the x-axis by pressing ALT and F3, then ENTER. Use the arrow keys to box in the area and press ENTER. You can see that the ball will travel about 537 feet.

EXERCISES

1. What is the maximum height of Mr. Gallagher's ball?
2. If Mr. Gallagher hits the ball so that the initial velocity is 160 feet per second and the initial angle is 25°, would his ball travel past the pin? That is, will the ball travel more than 200 yards?

448 CHAPTER 8 VECTORS AND PARAMETRIC EQUATIONS

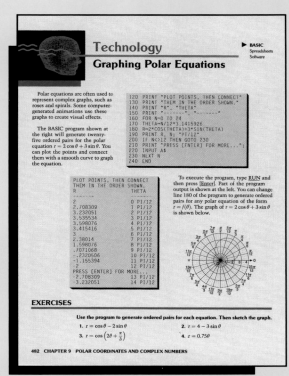

Technology

► BASIC
  Spreadsheets
  Software

Graphing Polar Equations

Polar equations are often used to represent complex graphs, such as roses and spirals. Some computer-generated animations use these graphs to create visual effects.

The BASIC program shown at the right will generate twenty-five ordered pairs for the polar equation $r = 2 \cos \theta + 3 \sin \theta$. You can plot the points and connect them with a smooth curve to graph the equation.

```
120 PRINT "PLOT POINTS, THEN CONNECT"
130 PRINT "THEM IN THE ORDER SHOWN."
140 PRINT "R", "THETA"
150 PRINT "-------", "-------"
160 FOR N=0 TO 24
170 THETA=N/12*3.1415926
180 R=2*COS(THETA)+3*SIN(THETA)
190 PRINT R, N; PI/12"
200 IF N<>12 THEN GOTO 230
210 PRINT "PRESS [ENTER] FOR MORE...";
220 INPUT A$
230 NEXT N
240 END
```

To execute the program, type RUN and then press [Enter]. Part of the program output is shown at the left. You can change line 180 of the program to generate ordered pairs for any polar equation of the form $r = f(\theta)$. The graph of $r = 2 \cos \theta + 3 \sin \theta$ is shown below.

```
PLOT POINTS, THEN CONNECT
THEM IN THE ORDER SHOWN.
R               THETA
2                0 PI/12
2.708309         1 PI/12
3.232051         2 PI/12
3.535534         3 PI/12
3.598076         4 PI/12
3.415416         5 PI/12
3                6 PI/12
2.38014          7 PI/12
1.598076         8 PI/12
.7071068         9 PI/12
-.2320506       10 PI/12
-1.155394       11 PI/12
-2              12 PI/12
PRESS [ENTER] FOR MORE...
-2.708309       13 PI/12
-3.232051       14 PI/12
```

EXERCISES

Use the program to generate ordered pairs for each equation. Then sketch the graph.

1. $r = \cos \theta - 2 \sin \theta$
2. $r = 4 - 3 \sin \theta$
3. $r = \cos\left(2\theta + \frac{\pi}{3}\right)$
4. $r = 0.75\theta$

482 CHAPTER 9 POLAR COORDINATES AND COMPLEX NUMBERS

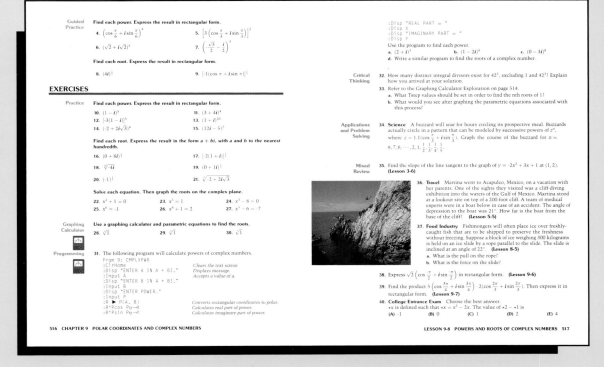

Guided Practice

Find each power. Express the result in rectangular form.

4. $\left(\cos \frac{\pi}{6} + i \sin \frac{\pi}{6}\right)^4$
5. $\left[3\left(\cos \frac{\pi}{3} + i \sin \frac{\pi}{3}\right)\right]^2$
6. $(\sqrt{2} + i\sqrt{2})^5$
7. $\left(-\frac{\sqrt{3}}{2} - \frac{i}{2}\right)^4$

Find each root. Express the result in rectangular form.

8. $(4i)^{\frac{1}{3}}$
9. $[-1(\cos \pi + i \sin \pi)]^{\frac{1}{3}}$

EXERCISES

Practice

Find each power. Express the result in rectangular form.

10. $(1 - i)^5$
11. $(3 + 4i)^4$
12. $[-3(1 - i)]^3$
13. $(1 + i)^{20}$
14. $(-2 + 2i\sqrt{3})^4$
15. $(12i - 5)^2$

Find each root. Express the result in the form $a + bi$, with a and b to the nearest hundredth.

16. $(0 + 8i)^{\frac{1}{3}}$
17. $[-2(1 + i)]^{\frac{1}{3}}$
18. $\sqrt[3]{-4i}$
19. $(0 + 1i)^{\frac{1}{3}}$
20. $(-1)^{\frac{1}{5}}$
21. $\sqrt[3]{-2 + 2i\sqrt{3}}$

Solve each equation. Then graph the roots on the complex plane.

22. $x^3 - 1 = 0$
23. $x^5 = 1$
24. $x^3 - 8 = 0$
25. $x^6 = -1$
26. $x^4 + 1 = 2$
27. $x^5 - 6 = -7$

Graphing Calculator

Use a graphing calculator and parametric equations to find the roots.

28. $\sqrt[3]{1}$
29. $\sqrt[4]{1}$
30. $\sqrt[5]{1}$

Programming

31. The following program will calculate powers of complex numbers.

```
Prgm 9: CMPLXPWR
:ClrHome              Clears the text screen
:Disp "ENTER A IN A + BI."   Displays message.
:Input A
:Disp "ENTER B IN A + BI."
:Input B              Accepts a value of a.
:Disp "ENTER POWER."
:Input P
:R ► P(A, B)          Converts rectangular coordinates to polar.
:R^Pcos Pη→X          Calculates real part of power.
:R^Psin Pη→Y          Calculates imaginary part of power.
```

516 CHAPTER 9 POLAR COORDINATES AND COMPLEX NUMBERS

```
:Disp "REAL PART = "
:Disp X
:Disp "IMAGINARY PART = "
:Disp Y
```
Use the program to find each power.
a. $(2 + i)^5$
b. $(1 - 2i)^4$
c. $(0 - 3i)^8$
d. Write a similar program to find the roots of a complex number.

Critical Thinking

32. How many distinct integral divisors exist for 42^3, excluding 1 and 42^3? Explain how you arrived at your solution.

33. Refer to the Graphing Calculator Exploration on page 514.
   a. What Tstep values should be set in order to find the nth roots of 1?
   b. What would you see after graphing the parametric equations associated with this process?

Applications and Problem Solving

34. **Science** A buzzard will soar for hours circling its prospective meal. Buzzards actually circle in a pattern that can be modeled by successive powers of z^n, where $z = 1.1(\cos \frac{\pi}{3} + i \sin \frac{\pi}{3})$. Graph the course of the buzzard for $n = 8, 7, 6, \cdots, 2, 1, \frac{1}{2}, \frac{1}{3}, \frac{1}{4}, \frac{1}{5}$.

Mixed Review

35. Find the slope of the line tangent to the graph of $y = -2x^2 + 3x + 1$ at (1, 2). **(Lesson 3-6)**

36. **Travel** Martina went to Acapulco, Mexico, on a vacation with her parents. One of the sights they visited was a cliff-diving exhibition into the waters of the Gulf of Mexico. Martina stood at a lookout site on top of a 200-foot cliff. A team of medical experts were in a boat below in case of an accident. The angle of depression to the boat was 21°. How far is the boat from the base of the cliff? **(Lesson 5-5)**

37. **Food Industry** Fishmongers will often place ice over freshly-caught fish that are to be shipped to preserve the freshness without freezing. Suppose a block of ice weighing 300 kilograms is held on an ice slide by a rope parallel to the slide. The slide is inclined at an angle of 22°. **(Lesson 8-5)**
   a. What is the pull on the rope?
   b. What is the force on the slide?

38. Express $\sqrt{2}\left(\cos \frac{\pi}{2} + i \sin \frac{\pi}{2}\right)$ in rectangular form. **(Lesson 9-6)**

39. Find the product $5\left(\cos \frac{3\pi}{4} + i \sin \frac{3\pi}{4}\right) \cdot 2(\cos \frac{2\pi}{3} + i \sin \frac{2\pi}{3})$. Then express it in rectangular form. **(Lesson 9-7)**

40. **College Entrance Exam** Choose the best answer.
   *x is defined such that *x = x^2 - 2x. The value of *2 - *1 is
   (A) -1 (B) 0 (C) 1 (D) 2 (E) 4

LESSON 9-8 POWERS AND ROOTS OF COMPLEX NUMBERS 517

9

Continuous Review Keeps Learning Fresh and Students Motivated

*The **Exercise Sets** in each lesson have a new organization. Each set begins with **Checking for Understanding**; then the students **Practice** the concepts, learn to use and apply the mathematics through **Applications and Problem Solving**, and reinforce previously learned concepts with the **Mixed Review.***

32. Prove that $\vec{a} \cdot \vec{b} = \vec{b} \cdot \vec{a}$ for two-dimensional vectors.
33. Prove that $\vec{a} \cdot \vec{b} = \vec{b} \cdot \vec{a}$ for three-dimensional vectors.
34. Prove that $\vec{a} \times \vec{a} = 0$.
35. Use the definition of cross product to prove that $\vec{a} \times (\vec{b} + \vec{c}) = (\vec{a} \times \vec{b}) + (\vec{a} \times \vec{c})$.
36. Is it true that $\vec{a} \times \vec{b} = \vec{b} \times \vec{a}$? Explain.

Programming

37. The program below calculates the cross product of two vectors.
```
:Prgm8:XPRODUCT
:ClrHome
:Disp "1ST VECTOR, A1="        Clears the text screen.
:Input A                       Displays the quoted message.
:Disp "A2="                    Accepts a value for A.
:Input B
:Disp "A3="
:Input C
:Disp "2ND VECTOR, B1="
:Input D
:Disp "B2="
:Input E
:Disp "B3="
:Input F
:BF-EC→I
:DC-AF→J
:AE-BD→K                       Calculates i coefficient, stores in I.
:Disp "CROSS PRODUCT"
:Disp "COEFF. OF I="
:Disp I
:Disp "COEFF. OF J="           Displays the value stored in I.
:Disp J
:Disp "COEFF. OF K="
:Disp K
```
Find each cross product.
a. $(1, 3, -2) \times (1, -1, 2)$ b. $(-3, 6, 5) \times (-2, -7, 2)$

Critical Thinking

38. If $\vec{a} \neq 0$, $\vec{a} \cdot \vec{b} = \vec{a} \cdot \vec{c}$, and $\vec{a} \times \vec{b} = \vec{a} \times \vec{c}$, must it be true that $\vec{b} = \vec{c}$? Justify your answer.

Applications and Problem Solving

39. **Physics** The handle of a jack is at an angle of 30° with the horizontal. A downward force of 55 pounds is applied to the jack at a point 1.5 feet from the point where the handle meets the body of the jack.
a. Find the moment of the force.
b. Find the torque of the force.
c. An object tends to rotate around the line that passes through the point P and is parallel to the moment. This line is called the axis of rotation. Find the axis of rotation for the force applied to the jack handle.

434 CHAPTER 8 VECTORS AND PARAMETRIC EQUATIONS

CHECKING FOR UNDERSTANDING

Communicating Mathematics

Read and study the lesson to answer each question.

1. If the inner product of $\vec{w}$ and $\vec{v}$ is nonzero, what can you say about $\vec{w}$ and $\vec{v}$?
2. Could the inner product of a nonzero vector and itself ever be zero? Explain.
3. Show that $\vec{i} \times \vec{j} = \vec{k}$.

Guided Practice

Find each inner product and state whether the vectors are perpendicular. Write *yes* or *no*.

4. $(3, 5) \cdot (4, -2)$
5. $(8, 4) \cdot (2, 4)$
6. $(5, -1) \cdot (2, 3)$
7. $(-6, 3) \cdot (1, 2)$
8. $(4, 2) \cdot (-3, 6)$
9. $(11, 2) \cdot (-3, 16)$
10. $(7, -2, 4) \cdot (3, 8, 1)$
11. $(-2, 4, 8) \cdot (16, 4, 2)$

Find each cross product.

12. $(7, 2, 1) \times (2, 5, 3)$
13. $(-2, -3, 1) \times (2, 3, -4)$
14. $(1, -3, 2) \times (5, 1, -2)$
15. $(-1, 0, 4) \times (5, 2, -1)$

EXERCISES

Practice

Find each inner product and state whether the vectors are perpendicular. Write *yes* or *no*.

16. $(-6, 1) \cdot (-1, 2)$
17. $(2, 0) \cdot (0, 4)$
18. $(2, -2) \cdot (5, -5)$
19. $(2, 5) \cdot (0, 1)$
20. $(5, 2) \cdot (-3, 7)$
21. $(-8, 2) \cdot (4.5, 18)$
22. $(3, -2, 4) \cdot (1, -4, 0)$
23. $(-4, 9, 8) \cdot (3, 2, -2)$
24. $(4, 9, -3) \cdot (-6, 7, 5)$
25. $(-6, 2, 10) \cdot (4, 1, 9)$

Find each cross product. Then verify that the resulting vector is perpendicular to the given vectors.

26. $(1, 3, 2) \times (2, -1, -1)$
27. $(2, 1, 2) \times (1, -1, 3)$
28. $(1, -3, 2) \times (-2, 1, -5)$
29. $(4, 0, -2) \times (-7, 1, 0)$

Find a vector perpendicular to the plane containing the given points.

30. $(1, 2, 3), (-4, 2, -1)$, and $(5, -3, 0)$
31. $(0, 1, 2), (-2, 2, 4)$, and $(-1, -1, -1)$

LESSON 8-4 PERPENDICULAR VECTORS 433

Every exercise set begins with Communicating Mathematics. These exercises provide opportunities for students to express mathematical concepts verbally, in writing, or through the use of models, tables, or graphs.

To improve higher order thinking skills, Critical Thinking and Applications exercises are included in *every* lesson.

"All students need extensive experience listening to, reading about, writing about, speaking about, reflecting on, and demonstrating mathematical ideas."

—NCTM Standards

Each chapter also includes a **Chapter Summary and Review.** This unique feature contains objectives, examples, and exercises to help your students understand and retain what they've learned.

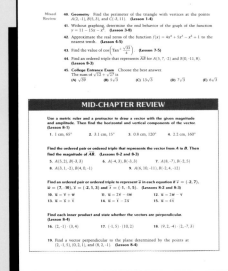

To keep previously learned skills and concepts alive, each lesson includes a **Mixed Review** with practice provided for college entrance exam questions. Every problem is referenced to the related lesson, so students can restudy important concepts easily. Exercises in the **Mid-Chapter Reviews** also are referenced to the appropriate lessons.

There are four 2-page **Unit Reviews** that provide a comprehensive study of the material covered in each of the first four units.

You'll Find All You Need to Organize and Enhance the Content in Every Chapter is at Your Fingertips, Right at the Point of Instruction

Merrill Advanced Mathematical Concepts is the only precalculus program that offers you the advantages of a Teacher's Wraparound Edition. A variety of unique teaching strategies are offered that enable you to reach your goals while helping you create the most conducive atmosphere for learning.

Four **Interleaf Pages** precede each chapter and provide a quick, easy reference for **Previewing, Organizing,** and **Enhancing the Chapter.**

Within the **Interleaf Pages,** you'll also find an abundance of cooperative learning strategies and technology activities to deepen your students' learning experience. Worksheets from the Multicultural Activity, Technol-ogy, and Activity Masters Booklets are shown at a reduced size to help you plan the chapter activities. The interleaf pages also help you identify the available resources at a glance.

This Unique Teacher's Edition is Organized Around a 6-Step Teaching Program

The **6-Step Teaching Plan** provides a myriad of interesting, time-saving activities that help you Introduce, Teach, Evaluate, Reteach, Apply, and Extend each lesson.

Worksheets, related to each lesson, are conveniently displayed at a reduced size in the margins. Answers are shown in red, helping you evaluate students' worksheets quickly and easily.

A challenging **Math Power** question is provided for each lesson, offering interesting ways to engage your students in problem solving, connections, communication, and reasoning.

13

Unique, Challenging, and Thought-Provoking Resources Make it Easy to Support and Extend Program Content

No other precalculus program provides such an array of resource materials. From practice enrichment masters to transparencies, all you need to teach Merrill Advanced Mathematical Concepts has been carefully prepared for your use.

Practice Masters give your students additional practice to reinforce their mathematical skills. One master is included for every lesson. Full-size answers are provided on the back of each Practice Master sheet.

Enrichment Masters extend and enrich every lesson. These masters contain extensions, challenges, games, puzzles, and other activities to encourage further study. Full-size answers are found on the back of each sheet.

Multicultural Activity Masters offer an activity for each chapter that relates mathematics to cultures or persons from various cultures.

Activity Masters help your students get the most out of every lesson. An Application Activity, a Problem-Solving Activity, and a Case Study or Decision-Making Activity are provided for every chapter.

Evaluation Masters save time while offering a wide range of testing options for each chapter. They include:

- 2 multiple-choice tests
- 2 free-response tests
- 4 quizzes
- 1 mid-chapter test, and
- 1 page of standardized test questions for each chapter.

In addition, there are:

- 4 unit tests
- 2 semester tests, and
- 1 final test.

Full-size answers are provided for ease in grading.

Technology Masters help students feel at home with the technology required in advanced mathematics. There is a Graphing Calculator Activity and a Computer Activity for each chapter.

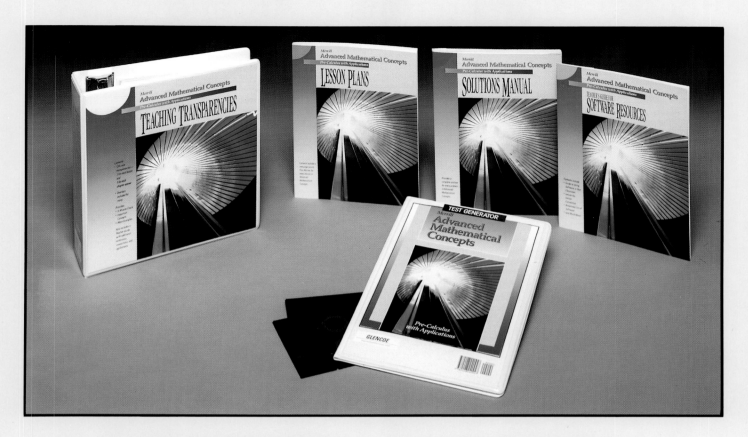

Lesson Plans, a one-page plan for each lesson, help you make the best use of your time and materials.

A **Solutions Manual** provides a complete solution for every problem in the Student Edition.

The **Teacher's Guide for Software Resources** contains *A Guide to Using Software in Your Classroom*, a lesson-by-lesson correlation of commercial software, and an annotated list of commerical software.

The **Graphing Calculator Instruction Guide** allows you to teach the capabilities of the TI-81 and the Casio graphing calculators.

An **SAT and ACT Preparation Guide** helps you prepare your students to succeed on the mathematics portions of the SAT and ACT college entrance examinations.

The **Transparency Package** contains a full-color transparency for every lesson and each chapter opener. Each transparency includes a 5-Minute Check, important concepts, and additional examples. *A Teacher's Guide* that offers additional extensions, connections, and applications is also included.

A **Test and Review Generator** enables you to create an almost infinite number of problems for review and testing situations, all correlated to text objectives (in Apple, Macintosh, and IBM formats).

Merrill

Advanced Mathematical Concepts

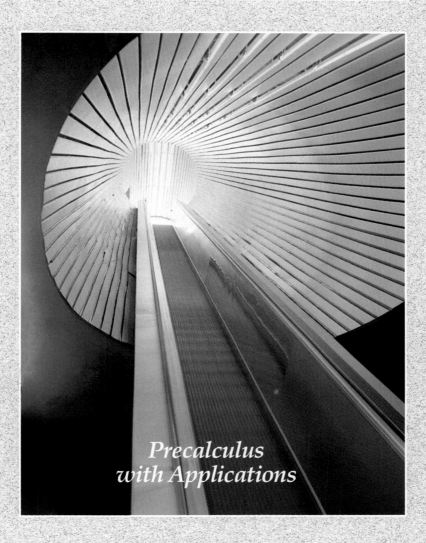

*Precalculus
with Applications*

GLENCOE

Macmillan/McGraw–Hill

New York, New York   Columbus, Ohio   Mission Hills, California   Peoria, Illinois

Send all inquiries to:
GLENCOE DIVISION
Macmillan/McGraw-Hill
936 Eastwind Drive
Westerville, Ohio 43081

ISBN: 0-02-824286-6 (Student Edition)
ISBN: 0-02-824287-4 (Teacher's Wraparound Edition)

Printed in the United States of America.

  2 3 4 5 6 7 8 9 10 VH 00 99 98 97 96 95 94

AUTHORS

Berchie W. Gordon is a Mathematics/Computer coordinator for the Northwest Local School District in Cincinnati, Ohio. Dr. Gordon has taught mathematics at every level from junior high school to college. She received her B.S. degree in mathematics from Emory University in Atlanta, Georgia, and her M.A.T. in education from Northwestern University, in Evanston, Illinois. She has done further study at the University of Illinois and the University of Cincinnati, where she received her doctorate in curriculum and instruction. Dr. Gordon has developed and conducted numerous in-service workshops in mathematics and computer applications and has traveled nationally to make presentations on graphing calculators to various groups. She has also served as a consultant for IBM and is a coauthor of *Merrill Algebra 1* and *Merrill Algebra 2 with Trigonometry*.

Lee E. Yunker is a teacher and chairperson of the Mathematics Department at West Chicago Community High School, West Chicago, Illinois. Mr. Yunker obtained his B.S. degree from Elmhurst College in Elmhurst, Illinois, and his M.Ed. in mathematics from the University of Illinois. Mr. Yunker frequently speaks or conducts workshops on a variety of topics. Recently, he participated in the first U.S./Korea Seminar on a Comparative Analysis of Mathematics Education in the United States and Korea at The Seoul National University. Mr. Yunker is a past member of the boards of directors of both the National Council of Teachers of Mathematics and the National Council of Supervisors of Mathematics. Mr. Yunker is a 1985 State Presidential Award Winner for Excellence in Mathematics Teaching and is a coauthor of *Merrill Geometry* and *Fractals for the Classroom: Strategic Activities, Volumes One and Two*, co-published by the NCTM and Springer-Verlag.

F. Joe Crosswhite is professor emeritus of mathematics education at The Ohio State University. He obtained his B.S. degree in mathematics education and M.Ed. degree in secondary administration from Missouri University and his Ph.D. degree in mathematics education from The Ohio State University. Dr. Crosswhite served as president of the National Council of Teachers of Mathematics from 1984–1986. During his tenure, the Commission on Standards for School Mathematics was formed, on which he served. Dr. Crosswhite has also served on the Mathematical Sciences Education Board of the National Research Council and as the chairperson of the Conference Board of Mathematical Sciences. Dr. Crosswhite has published widely in professional journals and is a coauthor of *Merrill Pre-Calculus Mathematics*.

Glen D. Vannatta was a mathematics teacher, department chairperson, and supervisor of mathematics for the Indianapolis Public Schools in Indianapolis, Indiana. He received his B.S., M.S., and Ed.D. degrees in mathematics education from Indiana University. Dr. Vannatta has authored or co-authored over 30 mathematics textbooks from junior high school to the freshman college level. He has provided leadership in mathematics contests and has supervised extensive achievement testing programs. In addition, he has written numerous articles for mathematics publications, including the *Mathematics Teacher*. Dr. Vannatta has also served as president or vice-president of several local, state, and national mathematics organizations.

iii

CONSULTANTS

William Collins
Mathematics Teacher and
  Department Chairperson
James Lick High School
San Jose, California

Dr. Christian Hirsch
Professor of Mathematics and
  Mathematics Education
Western Michigan University
Kalamazoo, Michigan

Valarie Elswick
Mathematics and Computer
  Science Teacher
Roy C. Ketcham High School
Wappingers Falls, New York

Dalia Trevino
Secondary Instructional Facilitator
United High School
Laredo, Texas

TECHNOLOGY WRITERS/CONSULTANTS

Graphing Calculator Explorations and Exercises
Dr. Leo Edwards
Vice Chancellor for Academic Affairs
Fayetteville State University
Fayetteville, North Carolina

Technology Pages
Dr. Jeff Gordon
Director of Instructional Technology
University of Cincinnati
Cincinnati, Ohio

Graphing Calculator Programs
Babs Merket
Mathematics Teacher
Waukesha South High School
Waukesha, Wisconsin

Technology Pages
Dwayne Hickman
Developmental Mathematics Specialist
Columbus State Community College
Columbus, Ohio

Graphing Calculator Lessons
Jill Baumer-Piña
Former Program Assistant
Department of Mathematics
The Ohio State University
Columbus, Ohio

REVIEWERS

Stephanie A. Allison
Mathematics Department
  Chairperson
C. D. Hylton High School
Woodbridge, Virginia

Margaret G. Couvillon
Mathematics Teacher
Bellaire High School
Houston, Texas

Richard F. Dube
Mathematics Supervisor
Taunton High School
Taunton, Massachusetts

Barbara A. Baker
Mathematics Teacher
Thomas A. Edison High School
Alexandria, Virginia

Bill Diedrich
Mathematics Teacher and
  Department Chairperson
Minnetonka High School
Minnetonka, Minnesota

Ron England
Mathematics Department
  Chairperson
Rangeview High School
Aurora, Colorado

Russell Chappell
Mathematics Department
  Chairperson
Granite City Senior High School
Granite City, Illinois

Reid L. Dillon
Mathematics Teacher
Brighton High School
Salt Lake City, Utah

Bill Fisher
Mathematics Teacher and
  Department Chairperson
Emmerich Manual High School
Indianapolis, Indiana

TABLE OF CONTENTS

TECHNOLOGY

W hat would your life be like without technology? Imagine the absence of computer games, grocery store scanners, digital watches, microwaves, VCRs, or CDs. It's hard to imagine! The technology features in this text will expose you to very powerful applications of mathematics you'll be able to use for a lifetime.

Graphing Calculator Technology

There are 43 pages of **Graphing Calculator Lessons** in this text covering 24 topics. These lessons allow you to use the Casio fx-7000G and the Texas Instruments TI-81 as tools for learning and doing mathematics. For example, see page 369 to find out how to use a graphing calculator to determine whether an equation is a trigonometric identity. Also see page 844 to learn how a graphing calculator can be used to draw a scatter plot and a line that best represents the relationship of the points in the scatter plot.

Graphing calculator technology is also integrated in many lessons through **Graphing Calculator Explorations** and **Graphing Calculator and Programming** exercises. For example, in Exercise 38 on page 26, you use a graphing calculator program to plot points in a relation.

Computer Technology

The **Technology** pages in this text let you use technology to explore patterns, make conjectures, and discover mathematics. You will learn to use programs written in BASIC as well as computer software and spreadsheets.

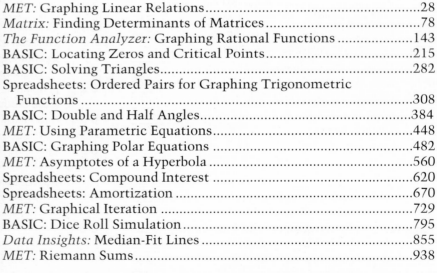

Mathematics Exploration Toolkit (MET) was developed for IBM by Wicat Systems, Inc. *Matrix* was developed by The North Carolina School of Science and Mathematics. *The Function Analyzer* and *Data Insights* were developed by Sunburst Communications, Inc.

Unit 4 Discrete Mathematics ...652

MAKING A DIFFERENCE WITH MATHEMATICS

Whan are you ever going to use this stuff? It may be sooner than you think. At the beginning of each chapter, you'll meet real college students and learn about the careers each of them is pursuing. In the **Decision Making** and **Case Study Follow-Up** features, you'll find situations that will enable you to connect mathematics to your real-life experiences as a consumer and a citizen.

WE RECYCLE

Teacher's Handbook

The purpose of this 20-page Teacher's Handbook is to provide an introduction to the format and philosophy of the *Merrill Advanced Mathematical Concepts: Precalculus with Applications* Teacher's Wraparound Edition. It is also intended to relate some background information on several contemporary issues facing mathematics educators in the 1990s, such as the use of technology and alternate assessment strategies. Suggested time schedules for six-week and nine-week grading periods and clearly-defined instructional objectives are included to further make the learning of precalculus smooth for both students and teachers.

Teacher's Handbook Table of Contents

How to Use the Six-Step Teaching Plan in *Merrill Advanced Mathematical Concepts*

What do you search for when making a new textbook selection? You may search for a total program that is easy to teach. Your ***Merrill Advanced Mathematical Concepts* Teacher's Wraparound Edition** delivers the collective teaching experience of its authors, consultants, and reviewers so that you will have the wealth of reliable information for which you search. By furnishing you with an effective teaching model, this book saves you preparation time and energy. You, in turn, are free to spend that time and energy on your most important responsibility—your students.

As a professional, you will be pleased to find this program provides you with readily-available activities to engage your students throughout the entire class period.

Each Unit Opener provides an overview of the concepts in that unit as

Applications provide you with real-world examples and exercises found in the chapter.

well as a description of how the concepts are related to other units in the text. The **Multicultural Notes** give additional information about the contributions of other cultures to related topics in the unit. A list of **Decision Making**, **Case Study Follow-Ups**, and **Technology** features are provided.

Each Chapter Opener begins with a **More About...** section, which provides more information about the college student highlighted in the Chapter

Opener. A **Class Project** is also provided that is intended to be on-going throughout the chapter. The **Applications** chart provides you with a list of real-world examples and exercises found in the chapter.

Each lesson includes a comprehensive six-part teaching plan that, when utilized consistently, makes it easy for you to teach and easy for your students to learn.

OBJECTIVES AND EXAMPLES

- find the composition of functions
  (Lesson 1-2)

  Find $[f \circ g](x)$ if $f(x) = -5x + 4$ and $g(x) = 2x - 3$.

  $[f \circ g](x) = f(2x - 3)$
  $= -5(2x - 3) + 4$
  $= -10x + 19$

- find and revise functions
  (Lesson 1-2)

  Given $f(x) = \frac{1}{2}x^3 + 5$, find $f^{-1}(x)$.

REVIEW EXERCISES

Find $[f \circ g](x)$ and $[g \circ f](x)$.

9. $f(x) = 3x - 5$
   $g(x) = x + 2$

10. $f(x) = -3x^2$
    $g(x) = 2x^3$

11. $f(x) = x^2 + 2x - 3$
    $g(x) = x + 1$

12. $f(x) = \frac{1}{2x}$
    $g(x) = \frac{1}{2}x - 1$

Find the inverse of each function. Then state whether the inverse is a function.

13. $f(x) = x^2 - 12$

14. $f(x) = 6 - 3x$

15. $f(x) = 8x^3$

16. $f(x) = 3x^3 - 2$

2-4	**LESSON PLAN**

Teacher's Name _____ Date _____

Grade _____ Class _____ Dates _____

Materials/resources needed: _____

Objectives
- ____ 2-4A: Determine the slope and intercepts of a line.
- ____ 2-4B: Use the slope and intercepts to graph a linear equation.
- ____ 2-4C: Determine if two lines are parallel, perpendicular, or neither.
- ____ State/local objectives: _____

NCTM Curriculum Standards: 1, 2, 3, 4, 5, 6, 7, 8

INTRODUCING THE LESSON
5-Minute Check, *TWE*, p. 66
▶ Teaching Aid, Transparency 2-4
Motivating the Lesson, *TWE*, p. 66

TEACHING THE LESSON
Chalkboard Examples, *TWE*, pp. 67-69
Alternate Teaching Strategies, *TWE*, p. 66

1 INTRODUCING THE LESSON

INTRODUCING THE LESSON, or the anticipatory set as it is sometimes called, is the first step of the *Merrill Advanced Mathematical Concepts* teaching plan.

INTRODUCING THE LESSON begins with two pre-lesson activities to engage your students. The **5-Minute Check** includes one to five questions from the previous lesson. This allows you to check retention of skills and concepts. The 5-Minute Check is also available on the transparency that accompanies each lesson. **Prerequisite Skills** (in appropriate lessons) provides an opportunity for students to refresh their memories on skills learned in other mathematics courses that are necessary to the lesson. **Motivating the Lesson** helps prepare students for learning the day's lesson by piquing their interest. It is intended to help focus the attention of the class so the lesson can begin.

The latter activity may also provide time for students to interact with you, thus enabling you to modify the lesson to fit what students already know. This activity usually can be completed within the first five minutes of class and should be a direct lead-in to the concepts that will be presented. By focusing your students, you will provide the structural framework for what is to come.

2 TEACHING THE LESSON

TEACHING THE LESSON, the second step of the teaching plan, is the heart of any lesson. The primary aim of the *Merrill Advanced Mathematical Concepts* teaching plan is to give you the tools to accomplish the admittedly difficult task of enabling your students to learn the concepts. Effective **Teaching Tips** as well as **Chalkboard Examples** are provided in this part of the teaching cycle. **Using Technology** sections provide helpful suggestions for implementing graphing calculators into the lesson presentation.

ALTERNATE TEACHING STRATEGIES provides you various methods of teaching the content of the lesson. These strategies include Using Cooperative Groups, Using Technology, and Using Critical Thinking, just to name a few.

With the materials presented in the TEACHING THE LESSON step of the six-part teaching plan, your efficiency and productivity as a teacher will increase. The TEACHING THE LESSON step brings together the major elements that form a sound teaching approach.

3 EVALUATING THE LESSON

As a teacher, you work hard at making the transfer of knowledge as efficient and productive as it can be. One finding of educational researchers is that teachers who closely guide their students during a lesson are more effective. This third step provides **Checking for Understanding** to assist you in identifying and correcting common student errors. **Closing the Lesson** provides you with a quick way of determining if students have mastered the objectives of the lesson and gives students an opportunity for direct communication in written, spoken, or modeled form.

4 RETEACHING THE LESSON

No matter how thoroughly a subject is covered in the classroom, there may be students who do not understand the lesson the first time it is taught. A **RETEACHING THE LESSON** activity is provided for every lesson as a way to teach the same concepts or facts differently so they will be more amenable to students' individual learning styles.

Research shows that teachers who closely guide their students during a lesson are more effective.

5 APPLYING THE LESSON

A suggested **HOMEWORK ASSIGNMENT GUIDE** for two levels - Average and Enriched - is provided for each lesson. In addition, **Exercise Notes** may be provided that give insight and hints into specific exercises. Additional **Using Technology** notes provide helpful suggestions for implementing the graphing calculator exercises.

6 EXTENDING THE LESSON

Every lesson has an **EXTENDING THE LESSON** activity that enriches and extends the concepts taught in the lesson. **Decision Making** and **Case Study Follow-Up** features appear in each chapter.

As you review the **Teacher's Wraparound Edition** of *Merrill Advanced Mathematical Concepts*, you will discover that you and your students are considered very important. With the enormous number of teaching tips and strategies provided by the **Teacher's Wraparound Edition**, you should be able to accomplish the goals of your curriculum with a minimum of time and effort. This is true whether you are teaching precalculus for the first time, or whether you are a master teacher. The materials allow adaptability and flexibility so that student and curricular needs can be met. ∎

How *Merrill Advanced Mathematical Concepts* Meets the NCTM Standards

Content that relates to specific NCTM Standards is found on the following student edition pages:

STANDARD 1: *Mathematics As Problem Solving*

6-47, 54-97, 104-171, 178-229, 240-295, 302-351, 358-405, 412-455, 466-517, 524-591, 598-645, 656-705, 712-745, 752-795, 802-859, 866-903, 914-951

STANDARD 2: *Mathematics As Communication*

6-47, 54-97, 104-171, 178-229, 240-295, 302-351, 358-405, 412-455, 466-517, 524-591, 598-645, 656-705, 712-745, 752-795, 802-859, 866-903, 914-951

STANDARD 3: *Mathematics As Reasoning*

6-47, 54-97, 104-171, 178-229, 240-295, 302-351, 358-405, 412-455, 466-517, 524-591, 598-645, 656-705, 712-745, 752-795, 802-859, 866-903, 914-951

STANDARD 4: *Mathematical Connections*

6-47, 54-97, 104-171, 178-229, 240-295, 302-351, 358-405, 412-455, 466-517, 524-591, 598-645, 656-705, 712-745, 752-795, 802-859, 866-903, 914-951

STANDARD 5: *Algebra*

6-47, 54-97, 104-171, 178-229, 247-262, 269-295, 309-320, 328-333, 345-351, 358-405, 466-517, 524-591, 598-613, 730-745

STANDARD 6: *Functions*

6-47, 54-61, 84-97, 104-143, 149-171, 178-229, 247-295, 302-351, 358-405, 442-448, 466-517, 524-591, 605-645, 712-745, 914-951

STANDARD 7: *Geometry From A Synthetic Perspective*

54-61, 91-97, 104-124, 149-154, 247-254, 263-295, 412-418

STANDARD 8: *Geometry From An Algebraic Perspective*
6-11, 19-47, 104-124, 240-246, 255-262, 288-295, 302-333, 345-351, 358-376, 392-405, 419-455, 466-493, 501-505, 510-517, 524-591, 717-721

STANDARD 9: *Trigonometry*
247-295, 302-351, 358-405, 436-441, 568-576

STANDARD 10: *Statistics*
802-859

STANDARD 11: *Probability*
768-795

STANDARD 12: *Discrete Mathematics*
62-83, 91-97, 656-705, 752-795, 866-903

STANDARD 13: *Conceptual Underpinnings of Calculus*
117-143, 149-171, 670-705, 914-951

STANDARD 14: *Mathematical Structure*
6-12, 126-131, 134-142, 195-207, 494-517, 570-576, 598-603, 896-903

CURRICULUM AND EVALUATION STANDARDS FOR SCHOOL MATHEMATICS

Cooperative Learning

"The best answer to the question, 'What is the most effective method of teaching?' is that it depends on the goal, the student, the content, and the teacher. But the next best answer is, 'Students teaching other students'. There is a wealth of evidence that peer teaching is extremely effective for a wide range of goals, content, and students of different levels and personalities."

Wilbert McKeachie, et al, 1986

Cooperative learning groups learn things together, not just do things together. Studies show that cooperative learning promotes more learning than competitive or individual learning experiences regardless of student age, subject matter, or learning activity. More difficult learning tasks, such as problem solving, critical thinking, and conceptual learning, come our far ahead when cooperative strategies are used. Studies also show that in classroom settings, adolescents learn more from each other about subject matter than from the teacher.

The basic elements of a cooperative learning group are as follows:

- Students must perceive that they "sink or swim together."
- Students are responsible for everyone else in the group, as well as themselves, in learning the assigned material.
- Students must see that they all have the same goal, that they need to divide up the tasks and share the responsibility equally, and that they will be given one evaluation or reward that will apply to all members of the group.

General guidelines and suggestions for implementing cooperative learning in your geometry classroom are provided on this page and the next. A list of specific tasks in cooperative learning is provided in the teacher material that precedes Chapter 1. In the subsequent chapters, each of these tasks are explained in

More difficult learning tasks, such as problem solving and critical thinking, come out far ahead when cooperative strategies are used.

detail. The **Teacher's Classroom Resources** package contains an Activity Masters Booklet in which you will find a Decision Making Activity or a Case-Study Follow-Up for each chapter. These activities provide an excellent arena for cooperative learning.

Additional information and activities for using cooperative groups are also available in Glencoe's **Cooperative Learning in the Mathematics Classroom**.

Preparation and Social Skills

1. *Arrange your room.* Students in groups should face each other as they work together. It is helpful to number the tables so you can refer to groups by number, or have groups choose a name.

2. *Decide on the size of the group.* Groups work best when teams are composed of two to five students. The materials available might dictate the size of the group.

3. *Assign students to groups.* Each group should be mixed socially, racially, ethnically, sexually, and by learning abilities. Occasionally a student may insist on working alone. This student usually changes his or her mind when seeing that everyone else's grades are better, and that the groups are having more fun.

4. *Prepare students for cooperation.* This is a critical step. Tell students about the rationale, procedures, and expected outcomes of this method of instruction. Students need to know that you are not forcing them to be friends, but asking them to work together as they will later on in life with people who come together for a specific purpose.

5. *Plan Teaching Materials.* Distributing materials can help you communicate that the activity is to be a group and not an individual activity. You can provide only one set of materials or one copy of the worksheet to the group. Group members will quickly realize that they need to work

together if they are to be successful. You can vary this by providing each member with a worksheet but collecting only one of them.

6. _Explain group tasks._ For some activities, each group will need someone to take notes, someone to summarize as the group progresses, and someone to make sure everyone is involved. Classes that have less experience using these methods may need these roles assigned to group members at the beginning of each activity. These jobs should be done by different students each time, so that one student does not feel burdened doing the same job all the time.

7. _Explain the day's lesson._ On the chalkboard or overhead, write the following headings:

■ **_Form Groups_:** List the number of students in each group.

■ **_Topic of the Day:_** general academic topic.

■ **_Task:_** title of activity. At this time, go over instructions and relate the work to previous learning.

■ **_Goal:_** Indicate whether students will all do individual work of which you will select one person's paper or product to grade, or whether they will produce only one product per group. Student signatures on all the work indicates that they will accept the collected work for their grade.

■ **_Cooperative Skills_:** List the specific group skills you will be checking. Start with one or two basic skills. The following skills start from basic and move to more advanced.

a. Use quiet voices.

b. Encourage each other to participate.

c. Use each other's names. Use eye contact.

d. Ask your teacher for help only after you have decided as a group that you all need help.

e. Stress that all student contributions are valuable.

After students have some experience working in cooperative groups, you can expect group members to exhibit some or all of the following higher level cooperative skills.

a. Express support and acceptance, both verbal and nonverbal, through eye contact, enthusiasm, and praise.

b. Ask for help or clarification about what is happening.

c. Suggest new ideas.

d. Use appropriate humor that stays on task.

e. Describe feelings using "I messages," such as, "I like the way you praised my idea."

f. Summarize and elaborate on what others have contributed.

g. Develop memory aids and analogies that are clever ways of remembering important points.

h. Criticize ideas, not people.

i. Go beyond the first answer to a question.

Teacher Responsibilities During Cooperative Group Work

1. _Monitor student behavior._ Use a formal observation sheet to count the number of times you observe the behavior expected on that particular assignment for each group. Start with a few behaviors at the beginning and move up to many different behaviors when you feel comfortable doing so. Share your observations with each group.

2. _Provide assistance with the task._ Clarify instructions, review concepts, or answer questions. You will find students who see you nearby will automatically start asking questions. Your first response should be, "Have you asked everyone in the group?"

Your role will be supportive supervisor rather than direct supervisor; you will help a group that has gotten stuck and is experiencing a high level of frustration. You might do this by asking a few open-ended questions. In a conflict situation, you might ask the group to identify the reason for the difficulty and ask them to come up with some strategies for handling the conflict.

3. _Intervene to teach cooperative skills._ As you observe that some groups have more problems than others with cooperative skills, you may wish to intervene by asking the group to think about why they are not being effective and have them work toward a solution.

4. _Provide closure for the lesson._ Students should be asked to summarize what they have learned and be able to relate it to what they have previously studied. You may want to review the main points and ask students to give examples. You should also answer any final questions.

5. _Evaluate the group process._ In order for groups to be aware of their progress in learning to work together, they must be given time to evaluate or process how they are working together. Allow a few minutes at the end of the lesson for groups to decide if they achieved the criterion you set up. Have them rate themselves on a scale of one to ten and write down specific ways they could improve. Keep in mind that cooperative learning does not just "happen". The first few days may seem like bedlam, with some students upset, others mistrustful, and others off task. Both you and your students will make mistakes. Be patient and keep at it. ■

Integrating Technology Into Your Precalculus Classroom

"Students today can't prepare bark to calculate their problems. They depend upon their slates which are more expensive. What will they do when their slate is dropped and it breaks? They will be unable to write!"

Teachers' Conference, 1703

The above quote seems ridiculous today, but in 1703, it was not. Many people may ask, "Couldn't they see enough into the future to know that slates would be required?"; but as the old adage goes, hindsight is 20/20. The difficulty lies in foreseeing the future.

A similar situation today is in regard to computers and calculators. While most people agree that technology should be used in the mathematics classroom, few are offering ideas on incorporation, testing, appropriate use, and other areas where teachers have questions. Some have used the testing issue as an argument against using technology, but in the spring of 1994, students will be allowed to use nonprogrammable scientific calculators to complete a portion of the Scholastic Aptitude Test (SAT).

Appropriate Use of Technology

There are many different ideas and definitions of the "appropriate use of technology," and rightly so. Every class and every teacher is different. What is appropriate and works for one may not be appropriate or work for another. However, at the precalculus level, the use of technology is generally accepted. Keep in mind that many of your students are just learning the technology. It is with that in mind that **Merrill Advanced Mathematical Concepts** has provided ample instruction and examples of technology incorporated in the program at point-of-use.

Using Technology in Your Classroom

Technology opens up many new ideas and opportunities. It is up to you to decide how to present and use technology in your classroom. Many of the standard teaching techniques are appropriate, such as using cooperative groups, or having students work with a partner, but there are also new ways of teaching that are appropriate when using technology in you classroom. For example, instead of drawing a graph on the chalkboard or making an overhead transparency, a computer screen or projection instrument can be used for classroom demonstrations.

Teaching Aids

There are many technological teaching aids as well as numerous products to assist in the teaching of technology. One of them is a projection panel for the overhead projector that is attached to a graphing calculator or computer modem. This can be used for demonstration of new concepts or as a follow-along visual when students are learning new keying strokes on their personal graphing calculators.

Overhead projector calculators are also available for most models. They can serve the same purpose as a projection panel and demonstration computer.

Overhead transparencies can be made of the calculator keyboard template found in the manual for Texas Instrument and Casio graphing calculators. This template may prove helpful when demonstrating a sequence of keystrokes to use to perform a given task.

Changes in the Classroom

There will be some changes in your classroom with the onset of technology. One will be your role, which will most likely change from leader to guide. Students will begin to do things on their own and it will be up to you to keep them headed in the right direction. Students will also begin to ask more questions, including more higher-order questions, than before. You may not have all the answers, but the investigation can be enjoyable and

Graphing calculators can often pique your students' curiosity about mathematics topics. You may begin to hear, "Why did it do that?" or "What's happening?" instead of "What's the answer?" or "I don't understand."

enlightening for both you and your students.

Another change will be the students' perception of traditional graphs, such as parabolas, circles, ellipses, and polar graphs. With manipulation of the range values on a graphing calculator, the shape of the graph shown on a square coordinate grid becomes different on the calculator. Students' mastery of analyzing graphs strengthens their knowledge of functions and their characteristics.

Advantages of Technology

Probably the biggest advantage of technology is the amount of time it can save you. The ease of editing errors, the number of graphs and pictures that can be drawn in a short amount of time, the speed of calculating; all these and other time-saving advantages make technology a major plus for the mathematics classroom.

With each year, the price of technology decreases. This makes technology more easily accessible for individual students as well as schools purchasing classroom sets.

There are numerous other advantages. One is that students will have a deeper understanding of the concepts being taught. As we move toward a more pictorial society, students are becoming visual learners. Technology teaches them in a way that piques their interest and leads to questions that show a desire to learn.

Another advantage of technology is the cooperative efforts that develop among students. Since students will most likely need to work with others when they become members of the work force, it is best for them to learn to work with others while they are in school. With technology, you can teach your students to work cooperatively, which will benefit them in college and in their careers.

Technology Fears

Perhaps the biggest fear, and certainly one that is most often expressed, is that of the technology taking the place of the teacher. This will never happen. There is no way that a computer can do what a teacher does, and in particular, sense what a teacher can. For example, no computer can sense uncertainty of an answer in a student's tone of voice. Few students will be able to turn on a calculator or computer and teach themselves with it.

They need teachers to explain the technology and to help them make connections.

You can also see the evidence of needing the teacher when you relate the use of technology in education to its use in the business world. Computers have been in the mainstream of business for quite sometime now, and there has not been a reduction in the number of persons needed. Yet a large number of business executives will tell you they would not want to do their job without the use of a computer. Many teachers who have incorporated technology into their classrooms are saying the same thing.

Computers and calculators are excellent tools for teaching mathematics concepts. Technology can teach students in ways that were never before possible. In the past, teachers could only dream of being able to do some of the things that they can now do with ease, thanks to technology. While incorporating technology into your mathematics classroom may be difficult at first, in the long run, it will definitely pay off for both you and your students.

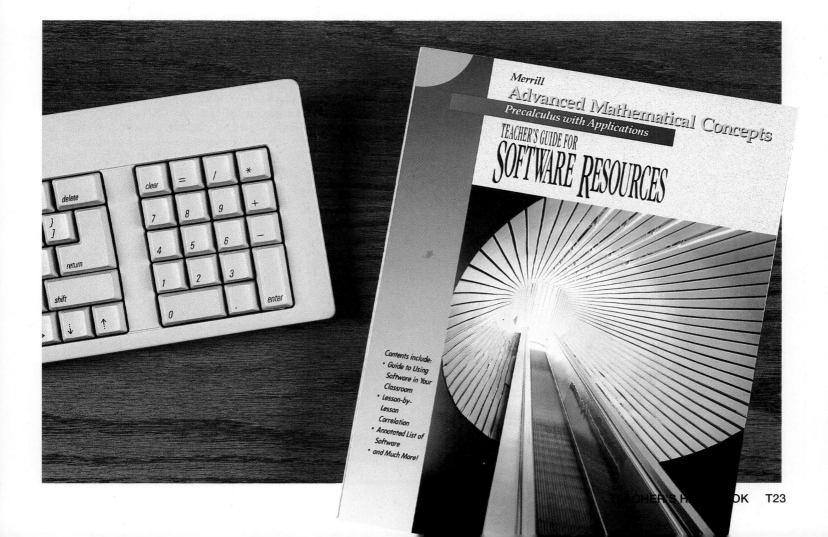

Using the Graphing Calculator

"Innovative instruction based on a new symbiosis of machine calculation and human thinking can shift the balance of learning toward understanding, insight, and mathematical intuition."

Everybody Counts. (1989, p. 63)

An introduction to the use of graphing calculators is presented in the Student Edition just prior to the first chapter (pp. xiv, 1). This section gives students and teachers an introduction to the basics of calculator operation. In addition to this introduction, there are numerous **Graphing Calculator Explorations** and **Graphing Calculator Lessons** throughout that give detailed instruction in calculator use for specific tasks.

The instructions in this text are specific to the TI-81 and the Casio fx-7000G graphing calculators. Newer versions of these calculators offer more advanced features. However, these features are often specific to one calculator and not general to the family of calculators. If your students have calculators other than the TI-81 or Casio fx-7000G, have them consult their owner's manual for the procedures to perform individual tasks.

Why Should I Use Graphing Calculators in my Precalculus Classroom?

The graphing calculator offers you much more flexibility than before. Some people may not understand that it is okay to solve problems with a calculator and that most of the time the calculator does not "find the answer" for you but merely helps you to find appropriate solutions to problems. If students do not understand how to interpret the information the calculator provides, it is of no use. For example, if you look at the graph of a line and ask what the slope of the graph is, some students may tell you they do not know how to find it. Still others will look at 2.718281828... and not recognize it as the decimal approximation of *e*. It is still up to you as the teacher to make connections with the technology and to teach with it. The calculator simply saves time and effort and allows you to go deeper into mathematical concepts with your students than you could in the past.

The calculator is not the solve-all instrument for precalculus, but a tool for completing the tedious tasks that used to take hours and lots of paper to achieve before you could get to the real meat of the problem. Encourage students to experiment with their calculators to find applications that are appropriate to the topic being studied.

It may be difficult for each of your students to have his/her own graphing calculator. If this is a problem, you can have your students work in pairs like lab partners.

Even if each of your students has his or her own graphing calculator, there are times when you may want to have them work together. This can often lead to students answering other students' questions and solving problems on their own. You can also have them work in small groups on some of the graphing calculator lessons. If some students are having difficulty with the material, those students who understand it can help explain the concepts in this situation.

The graphing calculator allows you to look at many new areas of mathematics that until now were restricted at this level because of difficulty. While it may take time to feel comfortable with using graphing calculators in your classroom, and you may be just beginning to learn how to use them, it is important to keep trying and to keep learning. Teaching your students to know when and how to use a graphing calculator to solve problems will help your students become better problem solvers, and in the end, this is what we really want them to become.

In addition to the **Graphing Calculator Exercises** and the **Graphing Calculator Programs** presented in the Student Edition, *Merrill Advanced Mathematical Concepts* provides a **Technology Masters Booklet** that contains one graphing calculator activity and one computer activity for each chapter. A preview of the technology in the chapter, as well as pictures of the activity pages, are found on the

Teaching your students to know when and how to use a graphing calculator to solve problems will help your students become better problem solvers, and in the end, this is what we really want them to become.

fourth page of the material preceding each chapter in the **Teacher's Wraparound Edition**.

For additional information on graphing calculator instruction, you may wish to consult Glencoe's **Graphing Calculator Instruction Guide**.

Should I use graphing calculators along with computers?

A precalculus course taught effectively with graphing calculators alone can provide an excellent mathematical education. The addition of appropriate computer software activities can further enhance teacher demonstrations and students' mathematical investigations. Some specialized types of software offer capabilities not possible on a graphing calculator. In the **Technology** features in the student text, different software programs are introduced. These include the *Mathematical Exploration Toolkit (MET)*, spreadsheets, data analysis software, and BASIC programs.

Many graphing utilities offer the same capabilities as graphing calculators. Commonly-used graphing utilities software products are listed below with the computer formats available. For more information on these and other software products that can be used with *Merrill Advanced Mathematical Concepts*, refer to the **Teacher's Guide for Software Resources** in the Teacher Classroom Resource package.

Graphing Utility	Format
Algebra XPresser	M
Bradford GraphMaker	A
Calculus	I, M
Cactusplot	A, I
Visualizing Algebra: Function Analyzer	I
Function Probe	M
Function Supposer	I
Function Workshop	AGS
Graph Wiz	M
GraphExplorer	I, M
Graphic Approach to Calculus	A, I
Graphitti	M
Green Globs and Graphing Equations	A, I
IBM Mathematics Exploration Toolkit	I
Master Grapher & 3D Grapher	A, I, M
MathTools for Advanced Algebra	M
MathTools for Precalculus/Calculus	M
Precalculus Plotter Plus	A, I, M
Pre-Calculus with Trigonometry	I, M
TEMath: Tools for Exploring Math	M
Trig Pak	I

I = IBM, M = Macintosh, A = Apple II, AGS = Apple II GS

The graphing calculator allows you to look at many new area of mathematics that until now were restricted at this level because of difficulty.

Alternate Assessment Strategies

Most students today will agree that the test is seen as the bottom line of the educational enterprise. Most of them will also agree that the present tests used to determine a student's accomplishment often fall short of the goal of measuring a student's understanding of ideas.

The vast array of testing devices today which, for the most part, center around multiple choice answers, true/false responses, and objective one-word answers, may be little more than mechanical ways of evaluating that focus on a student's ability to cough up answers on cue. They may reveal little to either the student or the teacher of the student's capabilities.

"Mathematics teachers are participating in a major restructuring of the goals and practices of mathematics education. It is essential that assessment strategies be found that can adequately reflect this new conception of the subject."[1]

Many formal assessment strategies may be rooted in informal assessment: that is, the garnering of information concomitant with instruction. Informal assessments are invaluable in the sense that they provide a realistic picture of student ability in a context where such ability is put to immediate use.

When educational goals are confined to the duplication of mathematical procedures, then conventional paper-and-pencil tests are adequate for assessing a learner's level of performance. But as our educational objectives broaden in scope, assessment should go beyond this. Assessments should now be extended for the purpose of guiding the actions of not just the student but of all those persons involved in the learning experience.

What Are the Alternatives?

There is a plethora of devices whereby the teacher of mathematics may expand his or her repertoire of assessment strategies. These include the use of questioning, observation, and journals.

Open-ended Questions Perhaps one of the easiest strategies to employ is that of open-ended questions which will permit students to more fully elaborate their knowledge of mathematical concepts and principles. In an assessment of this nature, students are forced to think for themselves and to express mathematical ideas in language that corresponds with their mathematical development.

The teacher has several options for scoring open-ended questions but the two most frequently used methods are analytic and holistic. Holistic scoring seems to be favored because judgement is based on the response as a whole, as opposed to analytic scoring, which

The Likelihood Of Sharing a Birthday

y as a Percent — 100 90 80 70 60 50 40

Number Of Persons — 10 20 30 40 50 60

Informal assessments provide a realistic picture of student ability in a context where such ability is put to immediate use.

evaluates answers on the basis of specific points that have been addressed in the student's responses.

Classroom Observation
Documenting classroom observations is another strategic device for assessing student achievement. During the course of the instructional process, most teachers are quite adept at forming rather accurate opinions concerning the capabilities of their students which, in many instances, a later formal assessment will bear out or validate. Such observations, however, are very often not accorded the status of a test because they have not been formally structured and systematically recorded. Yet the quality of such informal assessment is in many cases superior to that obtained by formal testing. By simply implementing some structure into such observations, teachers can capitalize on this information for assessment purposes and at the same time dispense with other time-consuming and often unproductive forms of evaluation. Recording observations can frequently be done while students work in cooperative groups.

Questioning provides an excellent tool for assessing the competence of students as well as for monitoring the development of meaningful understanding. Dialogue of this nature between teacher and student is most beneficial in identifying errors in comprehension (reading and otherwise), in transformation, and in the use of process skills. "Research has indicated that at least 40% of students' errors on written mathematical problems occur before they even get to use the process skills their teachers have so laboriously stressed."[2]

Self-evaluation One of the most valuable strategies we might implement is that of enabling students to monitor their own progress. This procedure calls for the student to write confidential answers to teacher questions regarding the way he or she feels in the class, what he or she would most like help with, and how mathematics class might be changed with an eye toward improving his or her skills.
Along the same lines, utilizing tests to which students have contributed questions not only makes for an effective revision strategy, it also provides students with a sense of ownership in the assessment process.

Portfolios and Journals Yet another means to assess student progress is to require students to periodically submit samples of their work in portfolios. Again, students might be asked to keep a daily journal in which they describe what they have learned and reflect on the material covered. Regular perusal of the journal can guide teaching

procedures and serve as the basis for individual student-teacher conferences.

Daily Assessment Lastly, the mathematics class lends itself quite easily to carrying out practical tests—demonstrating skills in a practice situation. Your *Merrill Advanced Mathematical Concepts* **Teacher's Wraparound Edition** contains an assessment option in the Closing the Lesson section of each lesson plan. Student understanding can be evaluated through writing, modeling, or speaking activities. Since the skills are assessed in practice, they provide immediate feedback as well as enhanced motivation for students who are usually most eager to show off (correctly or not!) what they can do.

Although there are undoubtedly situations when the written test is effective, we must guard against using it to the exclusion of other forms of assessment. The examiner must select, from among the many strategic techniques available, that one which will best indicate what his or her students can do.

For additional information and suggestions for utilizing alternate assessment strategies in your precalculus classroom, you may wish to consult Glencoe's **Alternate Assessment in the Mathematics Classroom**. ■

1. Clarke, David J., Doug M. Clarke, and Charles J. Lovitt, "Changes in Mathematics Teaching Call for Assessment Alternatives," *Teaching and Learning Mathematics in the 1990s*, (1990 Yearbook, Reston VA: NCTM, 1990), p. 118.
2. Ibid., p. 123.

Meeting Individual Needs

"We cannot afford to have the majority of our population mathematically illiterate: Equity has become an economic necessity."

NCTM Standards (1989, p. 4)

Multicultural Perspective

There is no doubt that the United States is a multicultural society. Changing demographics, and changing economic and social orders are having a tremendous impact on the schools in this country. From the 1980 census to the 1990 census, we saw a significant increase in the population of all minority groups, with the greatest increases among the Asian and Hispanic populations.

The term *multicultural* represents more than just *many cultures*. There is a multicultural basis to all knowledge, including mathematics.

From the ancient Egyptians, who used the "Pythagorean" theorem 1500 years *before* Pythagoras, to the ancient Chinese, who calculated the value of π to ten places 1200 years *before* the Europeans, mathematics as we know it today has been shaped by many cultures. Even the term *algebra* was contributed by an Arabian mathematician, Al-Khowarizmi.

Multicultural education in mathematics first means that curricula and other materials must accurately reflect the contributions of all cultures and women in a realistic, non-stereotypical, positive

manner. It strives to make cultural differences, and their contributions to mathematics, accessible to all. Psychologically, there is a strong and positive relationship between accepting oneself and accepting others.

Mathematics teachers should seek out and actively incorporate curricula and other materials that accurately represent all cultures and women. For example, the sophisticated sand tracings of the Bushoong people in Africa or the Malekulas of the Republic of Vanuatu in the South Pacific are examples of graph theory.

Multicultural curriculum products provide a positive foundation from which to launch an effective mathematics program for reaching minorities, women, and people with

disabilities. However, multicultural education must also fully enter the teaching process. As such, the value and importance of all cultures must be recognized and infused into the total process of teaching mathematics. In this respect, multicultural education is nothing more than good teaching and good education.

Until the 1990s, the role of minorities, women, and people with disabilities in the work force had been widely seen as an equity issue. Today, reaching out and bringing members of these under-represented groups into the technological work force is the key to our future national strength, security, and quality of life.

By the year 2000, it is estimated that 85% of new entrants to the nation's work force will be members of minority groups and women, and the number of people with disabilities who can go out into the work place will rise.

In addition, most jobs will require greater

mathematical skills, and other numbers of jobs requiring post-secondary education will increase dramatically.

By the year 2010, we could suffer a shortfall of as many as 560,000 science and engineering professionals alone, because of decreased interest in mathematics-associated professions. America in the 1990s is a very different country demographically from the one that produced our current mathematicians, scientists, and engineers. The professional work force that put America in a position of technological, economic, and military leadership is eroding as a result of retirements and declining student interest. The level of mathematics literacy needed to participate fully in the early years of the 21st century, its jobs, its economic and social orders, and its democratic institutions is steadily increasing. There is little doubt that our ability to reach America's minorities, women, and people with disabilities, and to help them become skilled and productive contributors to the economy will determine our success or failure in the global marketplace.

Students should have the opportunity to learn about persons from all cultures who have contributed to the development of mathematics.

What is the role of the mathematics educator in all of this? Students should have the opportunity to learn about persons from all cultures who have contributed to or are presently active in the development of mathematics. Additionally, students should learn about the individuals from all cultures who have been successful in their respective careers.

That is, multicultural teaching in mathematics simply means striving for excellence from students irrespective of race, sex, or disability. Cultural behaviors and cultural differences become teaching and learning tools for eliciting excellence as an expectation for *all* students.

Finally, beyond each teacher's own curriculum, classroom, and multicultural perspective, the mathematics teacher should pursue every opportunity to actively be in the vanguard of those who demand that *all* students be given the opportunity to study and excel in the more advanced forms of mathematics. America's leadership role in the global economy and security of the 21st century depends on how successful we are in raising the mathematics literacy of *all* students.

To this end, each chapter of **Merrill Advanced Mathematical Concepts** opens with an introduction to a real college student who is utilizing mathematics in his or her chosen major. This group of students reflects the multicultural nature of America and shows your precalculus students the many fields of endeavor that rely on a good background in mathematics. In addition, each lesson of **Merrill Advanced Mathematical Concepts** contains numerous real-life situations in which mathematics can applied.

The **Merrill Advanced Mathematical Concepts Multicultural Activity Masters Booklet** contains a worksheet for each chapter to further highlight the fact that mathematics is a universal human endeavor. ∎

Limited English Proficiency Needs

One of the greatest factors contributing to the under-achievement in mathematics education for the language-minority student is his or her failure to understand the language of instruction. There are, however, strategies which the mathematics teacher can employ to help overcome the obstacles that beset language-minority students.

Ideally, these students will have the opportunity of having new concepts and skills reinforced by discussing them in their native language, whatever that language might be. It may be that a bilingual teacher can meet this need, or perhaps a tutor proficient in the language can be procured to provide this service.

If the student is proficient in his or her native language, perhaps materials written in that language can be provided to supplement classroom instruction.

Teachers in parts of the country with rapidly expanding Hispanic populations have no doubt encountered students who are fully bilingual in English and Spanish and others who definitely feel more secure when additional explanation can be provided in Spanish. You may find it helpful to select the members of your cooperative groups so that a fully bilingual student is paired with a student less secure in the English language to facilitate learning.

If the student is not especially literate in his or her own language, perhaps an oral approach using pictorial materials and/or manipulative devices would be feasible.

When a student does not respond to the prescribed expectations of the school, the teacher needs to substitute developmentally-equivalent tasks to shape development. For example, if the student does not participate in classroom discussion, the wise teacher will observe his or her verbal interaction with other students in informal, less structured environments. Because students coming from diverse cultural backgrounds lack common educational experiences, the teacher soon recognizes that the only way to establish a basis for communication is to begin instruction with content that is familiar to everyone.

"The challenge is to find personally interesting and culturally relevant ways of creating new contexts for children, contexts in which the mastery of school skills can be meaningful and rewarding."[1]

By integrating the development of language in such new contexts, we may be able to open the door to the challenging and exciting world of mathematics for the language-minority student.

Using Technology

Students of all cultural backgrounds share a fascination with technology. Teachers should be alert to opportunities to use graphing calculators, BASIC programming, graphing and statistical software, and other technological innovations to motivate students and circumvent language difficulties. Technology is one area in which figures and mathematical symbolism can be used to great advantage, since they tend to be relatively language independent.

Suggestions for implementing technology into your mathematics classroom can be found on pages T22-T25, as well as in the Lesson Notes for each chapter. The **Merrill Advanced Mathematical Concepts Teacher's Guide for Software Resources** provides additional guidelines, activities, and suggested software for use with your precalculus course. ∎

1 Bowman, Barbara, T., "Educating Language-Minority Children: Challenges and Opportunities," *Phi Delta Kappan*, October 1989, p. 120.

Learning Objectives

1 Linear Relations and Functions

1-1A: Determine whether a given relation is a function.

1-1B: Identify the domain and range of any relation or function.

1-2A: Perform operations with functions.

1-2B: Find composite functions.

1-2C: Find and recognize inverse functions.

1-3A: Find zeros of linear functions.

1-3B: Graph linear equations and inequalities.

1-4A: Find the distance between two points.

1-4B: Find the slope of a line through two points.

1-4C: Prove geometric theorems involving slope, distance, and midpoints analytically.

1-5A: Write linear equations using slope-intercept form.

1-5B: Write linear equations using point-slope form.

1-6A: Write equations of parallel and perpendicular lines.

1-6B: Prove geometric theorems involving parallel and perpendicular lines analytically.

2 Systems of Equations and Inequalities

2-1A: Solve systems of equations graphically.

2-1B: Solve systems of equations algebraically.

2-2: Add, subtract, and multiply matrices.

2-3A: Evaluate determinants.

2-3B: Find inverses of matrices.

2-3C: Solve systems of equations by using inverses of matrices.

2-4: Solve systems of equations by using matrices.

2-5A: Graph systems of inequalities.

2-5B: Find the maximum or minimum value of a function defined for a polygonal convex set.

2-6A: Use linear programming procedures to solve problems.

2-6B: Recognize situations where exactly one solution to a linear programming problem may not exist.

3 The Nature of Graphs

3-1A: Identify symmetrical graphs.

3-1B: Use symmetry to complete a graph.

3-1C: Identify an odd function and an even function.

3-2A: Identify the graphs of simple polynomial functions, absolute value functions, and step functions.

3-2B: Sketch the graphs of these functions.

3-3A: Determine the inverse of a relation or function.

3-3B: Graph a function and its inverse.

3-4A: Determine horizontal, vertical, and slant asymptotes.

3-4B: Graph rational functions.

1-5: Graph polynomial, absolute value, and radical inequalities.

3-6A: Find the derivative of a function.

3-6B: Find the slope and the equation of a line tangent to the graph of a function at a given point.

3-7: Find the critical points of the graph of a polynomial function and determine if each is a minimum, maximum, or point of inflection.

3-8A: Determine continuity or discontinuity of functions.

3-8B: Identify the end behavior of graphs.

4 Polynomial and Rational Functions

4-1A: Determine roots of polynomial equations.

4-1B: Apply the fundamental theorem of algebra.

4-2A: Solve quadratic equations.

4-2B: Use the discriminant to describe the roots of quadratic equations.

4-2C: Graph quadratic equations and inequalities.

4-3: Find the factors of polynomials using the remainder and factor theorems.

4-4A: Identify all possible rational roots of a polynomial equation by using the rational root theorem.

4-4B: Determine the number of positive and negative real zeros a polynomial function has.

14 Combinatorics and Probability

14-1A: Solve problems related to the basic counting principle.
14-1B: Distinguish between dependent and independent events.
14-2A: Solve problems involving permutations with repetitions.
14-2B: Solve problems involving circular permutations.
14-3: Solve problems involving combinations.
14-4A: Find the probability of an event.
14-4B: Find the odds for the success and failure of an event.
14-5: Find the probability of independent and dependent events.
14-6A: Identify mutually exclusive events.
14-6B: Find the probability of mutually exclusive and inclusive events.
14-7: Find the probability of an event given the occurrence of another event.
14-8: Find the probability of an event by using the binomial theorem.

15 Statistics and Data Analysis

15-1A: Draw, analyze, and use bar graphs and histograms.
15-1B: Organize data into a frequency distribution table.
15-2A: Find the mean, mode, and median of a set of data.
15-2B: Find the mean and median of data organized in a stem-and-leaf plot or a frequency distribution table.
15-3A: Find the mean deviation, semi-interquartile range, and standard deviation of a set of data.
15-3B: Organize and compare data using box-and-whisker plots.
15-4: Use the normal distribution curve.
15-5: Find the standard error of the mean to predict the true mean of a population with a certain level of confidence.
15-6A: Draw and analyze scatter plots.
15-6B: Draw regression lines.
15-6C: Compute correlation values to determine goodness of fit.

16 Graph Theory

16-1A: Distinguish between multigraphs and simple graphs.
16-1B: Determine whether a graph is complete.
16-2A: Distinguish among walks, trails, paths, circuits, and cycles.
16-2B: Determine whether a graph is connected.
16-3: Find Euler paths and circuits.
16-4: Use the breadth-first search algorithm and Dijkstra's algorithm to find a shortest path.
16-5A: Find spanning trees.
16-5B: Find minimal spanning trees.
16-6A: Use digraphs to solve problems.
16-6B: Represent digraphs as matrices and vice versa.

17 Limits, Derivatives, and Integrals

17-1: Use limit theorems to evaluate the limit of a polynomial function.
17-2: Find the derivative of a function.
17-3: Find the area between a curve and the x-axis by using the limit of areas of rectangles.
17-4: Use integration formulas.
17-5: Use the fundamental theorem of calculus to evaluate definite integrals and to find area.

Planning Your Precalculus Course

Merrill Advanced Mathematical Concepts includes a wide variety of topics, more than can normally be studied in one year. Most classes can study the entire text in three semesters. Outlines for two possible one-year courses and four possible one-semester courses are shown below. Selection of a plan is dependent of the background and ability level of the students and on the objectives and interests of the school district.

Course Y1 A one-year course for students who have had little or no trigonometry (includes trigonometry, advanced algebra, theory of equations, and analytic geometry)

Course Y2 A one-year course for students who have previously studied trigonometry, designed as a precalculus course for the student who is preparing for a vigorous course in calculus

Course S1 A one-semester course emphasizing trigonometry

Course S2 A one-semester course emphasizing algebra and elementary functions

Course S3 A one-semester course emphasizing analytic geometry

Course S4 A one-semester course emphasizing discrete mathematics

The charts on these two pages denote which chapters should be covered for each course. They also suggest time schedules for both 6-week and 9-week grading periods. The maximum and minimum number of days required for each chapter are given. Notice that most chapters can be covered in about three weeks.

COURSE PLANNING CALENDAR - ONE YEAR COURSES

6-Week Grading Periods

Grading Period	TYPE OF COURSE			
	Y1		Y2	
	Chapter	Days	Chapter	Days
1	1	11-13	1	11-15
	3	13-17	2	12-15
2	4	11-14	3	12-16
	5	13-16	4	11-14
3	6	12-15	5	6-8
	7	12-15	Lessons 5-6 to 5-8	
			6	2
			Lesson 6-7	
			7	5-7
			Lessons 7-6 to 7-8	
			8	13-15
4	9	13-15	9	13-15
	10	13-15	10	13-15
5	11	11-14	11	11-14
	12	13-16	12	13-16
6	13	11-16	13	11-16
	17	11-14	17	11-14

9-Week Grading Periods

Grading Period	TYPE OF COURSE			
	Y1		Y2	
	Chapter	Days	Chapter	Days
1	1	11-13	1	11-14
	3	13-17	2	12-14
	4	12-15	3	12-17
2	5	13-16	4	11-15
	6	12-14	5	6-8
	7	12-15	Lessons 5-6 to 5-8	
			6	2
			Lesson 6-7	
			7	5-7
			Lessons 7-6 to 7-7	
			8	13-15
3	9	13-15	9	13-15
	10	13-15	10	13-15
	11	11-15	11	11-15
4	12	13-16	12	13-16
	13	11-15	13	11-15
	17	11-14	17	11-14

COURSE PLANNING CALENDAR - ONE SEMESTER COURSES

6-Week Grading Periods

Grading Period	TYPE OF COURSE							
	S1		S2		S3		S4	
	Chapter	Days	Chapter	Days	Chapter	Days	Chapter	Days
1	3	13-15	1	8-9	1	11-15	2	11-13
	5	13-15	2	8-9	2	11-15	12	13-17
			3	10-12				
2	6	12-15	4	11-14	3	13-15	13	11-13
	7	12-15	10	13-16	5	13-15	14	13-17
3	8	12-14	11	11-14	9	13-15	15	11-15
	9	13-16	13	13-16	10	13-15	16	11-15

9-Week Grading Periods

Grading Period	TYPE OF COURSE							
	S1		S2		S3		S4	
	Chapter	Days	Chapter	Days	Chapter	Days	Chapter	Days
1	3	13-16	1	8-9	1	11-14	2	11-14
	5	13-15	2	8-9	2	12-14	12	12-17
	6	12-14	3	10-13	3	12-17	13	11-14
			4	11-14				
2	7	12-15	10	13-16	5	13-15	14	13-18
	8	12-14	11	11-14	9	13-15	15	11-14
	9	13-16	12	13-15	10	13-15	16	11-13

The following one-quarter course are also possible.

COURSE	CHAPTERS
Trigonometry	5 - 8
Analytic Geometry	1, 2, 3, and 10
Discrete Mathematics	13 - 16
Limits, Sequences, and An Introduction to Calculus	4, 12, 17

A Message to Students About Graphing Calculators

What is it?

What does it do?

How is it going to help me learn math?

These are just a few of the questions many students ask themselves when they first see a graphing calculator. Some students may think, "Oh, no! Do we **have** to use one?", while others may think, "All right! We get to use these neat calculators!" There are as many thoughts and feelings about graphing calculators as there are students, but one thing is for sure: a graphing calculator *can* help you learn mathematics.

So what is a graphing calculator? Very simply, it is a calculator that draws graphs. This means that it will do all of the things that a "regular" calculator will do, *plus* it will draw graphs of simple or very complex equations. In pre-calculus, this capability is nice to have because the graphs of some complex equations take a lot of time to sketch by hand. Some are even considered impossible to draw by hand. This is where a graphing calculator can be very useful.

But a graphing calculator can do more than just calculate and draw graphs. You can program it, work with matrices, and perform statistical computations, just to name a few things. If you need to generate random numbers, you can do that on the graphing calculator. If you need to find the absolute value of numbers, you can do that, too. You can use it to help you with algebra and geometry as well. It's really a very powerful tool—so powerful that is often called a pocket computer. But don't let that intimidate you. A graphing calculator can save you time and make doing mathematics easier.

If you are already familiar with graphing calculators, you may remember some of the difficulty you had at first. They can seem a bit confusing and overwhelming, but you can overcome those feelings by watching others who are familiar with these calculators and know how to use them, or by trying to use them yourself and reading the instruction manual. In some ways, using a graphing calculator is like playing a video game. With a video game, you may not be familiar with the controls or understand the game in the beginning, but the more you play it, the more you understand. This is also true of using a graphing calculator. It can feel awkward at first, but it's fun once you get the hang of it.

As you have probably noticed, graphing calculators have some keys that other calculators do not. The up and down arrow keys ($\boxed{\blacktriangle}$ and $\boxed{\blacktriangledown}$) can be used to move from one graph to another when you graph more than one equation at a time and to move up or down when editing or entering a calculation. The left and right arrow keys ($\boxed{\blacktriangleleft}$ and $\boxed{\blacktriangleright}$) can be used to move (or trace) along a graph and to move left or right when editing or entering a calculation. The $\boxed{\text{2nd}}$ and $\boxed{\text{ALPHA}}$ keys allow you to access whatever is typed in blue (2nd) or gray (ALPHA) above the keys on the keyboard. For example, pressing the $\boxed{\text{2nd}}$ key followed by the $\boxed{x^2}$ key will result in the square root symbol "$\sqrt{}$" appearing on the screen. This is because "$\sqrt{}$" is in blue above the $\boxed{x^2}$ key on the keyboard. Pressing $\boxed{\text{ALPHA}}$ followed by $\boxed{x^2}$ will result in the letter "I" appearing on the screen. This is because "I" is in gray above the $\boxed{x^2}$ key on the keyboard. In this text, however, the keystrokes with the blue or gray characters will be written in the keystroke boxes, not the specific keys that you need to press. For example, to find "$\sqrt{3}$", the text will give a keying sequence of $\boxed{\text{2nd}}$ $\boxed{\sqrt{}}$ 3 instead of $\boxed{\text{2nd}}$ $\boxed{x^2}$ 3.

There are some keystrokes that can save you time when you are using a graphing calculator. A few of them are listed on the next page.

- 2nd ON turns the calculator off.
- 2nd ENTRY copies the previous calculation so you can edit and use it again.
- Pressing ON while the calculator is graphing stops the calculator from completing the graph.
- 2nd A-LOCK locks the ALPHA key, which is like pressing "shift lock" or "caps locks" on a typewriter or computer. The result is that all caps will be typed and you do not have to hold the shift key down. (This is good for programming.)
- ZOOM 6 redraws a graph in the standard viewing window of [-10, 10] by [-10, 10].
- 2nd QUIT will return you to the home (or text) screen.

Now that we have discussed what a graphing calculator is and some of the things that it can do, we still have the question, "How can it help me learn math?" This may not be an easy question to answer because every student learns things in his or her own way. But one way that a graphing calculator can help everyone learn is by giving you a pictorial representation (that is, a picture) of the equations. The ease of changing the graphs and making new ones can also help you understand what changes in the equations mean. In this way, a graphing calculator can also help you make connections in mathematics that before were difficult to see, and even more difficult to demonstrate.

The advantages of a graphing calculator can be seen if you try to put things in perspective. For example, would you rather use a washing machine or wash clothes by hand? Would you rather cook in an oven or over a fireplace? Would you rather cut wood with a hand saw or a power saw? These may seem like silly questions, but the same type of question can be asked about graphing calculators: Would you rather draw graphs by hand or use a graphing calculator? You may say, "Draw them by hand" now, but once you learn how to use a graphing calculator, it can make learning math easier and more fun. So many things that used to take a lot of time and effort can be done so much more quickly. A graphing calculator can help you gain understanding without some of the frustrations that you face when you draw graphs with paper and a pencil.

While a graphing calculator cannot do everything, it can make some things easier. It would be nice to be able to look ahead and see what we will be doing 10, 20, or even 30 years from now, but none of us can do that. So, to prepare for whatever lies ahead, you should try to learn as much as you can. This future will definitely involve technology, and using a graphing calculator is a good start toward becoming familiar with technology. Who knows? Maybe one day you will be designing the next satellite, building the next skyscraper, or helping students learn mathematics with the aid of a graphing calculator!

RELATIONS, FUNCTIONS, AND GRAPHS

The word *relation* is from the Latin root word *relatus*. From this word we get *relate*, which is what you do when you share a story with another person; *related*, as in being a member of someone's family; *relationship*, or an attachment between two people; and *relative*, as in being kin to another person. No matter what form of the word is used, you can see that there is a pairing between things that are related.

In mathematics, the word *relation* also refers to a pairing. A relation is most often represented by a set of ordered pairs. With these ordered pairs, we can examine the concept of function, which is a special kind of relation, and we can graph relations and functions to analyze trends and relationships.

Throughout this text, you will see that many real-world phenomena can be modeled by relations and functions. A mathematical model is a simplified version of a complex problem. Each of the lessons in this unit will contain a real-world problem and its mathematical model. As you work with these models, we hope that you will see the value of using mathematics to solve problems of all types and that you will become more comfortable with using relations and functions to solve these problems.

2

Unit 1 Focus

The key theme of Unit 1 is the relationship of different types of functions and their graphs. Some of these concepts may be a review of topics from previous algebra courses. Graphing is an integral part of the exploration of the characteristics and relationships of these functions.

Connections to Other Units

The concepts developed in this unit are related to concepts in Units 2, 3, and 5. The transformations of graphs presented in this unit also apply to the graphs of trigonometric functions in Unit 2 and to the conic sections and exponential functions in Unit 3. The concepts of maximum and minimum of a function are further explored in Units 2 and 5.

Multicultural Notes

France   Near Carnac lie thousands of stones in nearly parallel rows. They are believed to have acted as giant dot paper for astronomers who used them to plot the movements of celestial bodies about 5000 years ago. Using the alignment of the stones, they were able to establish sighting lines and to predict heavenly events such as eclipses.

Egypt   The slopes of ancient Egyptian pyramids vary with their location. Scientists have concluded that pyramids were sloped for the particular latitude of their location. The shadow patterns were used to measure the length of a year.

A level shadow-floor was found on the north side of the Great Pyramid. The paving blocks were cut in widths very near to the measurement by which the noon-time shadows varied from day to day. These shadows were used to plot the movement of the sun over the years. From this, ancient priests determined the exact length of a year to within 6 hours.

Cooperative Learning

The **Decision Making** activities offer students an opportunity to explore real-world questions while working in cooperative groups. These questions require students to do research and come to a viable conclusion.

Problem Solving

The **Case Study Follow-Ups** provide an arena for problem solving, applying mathematics, and becoming more aware of issues that may face students in their adult lives. These questions require research and applications of the mathematics of the chapter.

Using Technology

Computer and calculator literacy is a growing part of our everyday lives. The features in this unit give students exposure to different technology tools available to facilitate their study of mathematics.

3

1 LINEAR RELATIONS AND FUNCTIONS

PREVIEWING THE CHAPTER

This chapter begins by having students identify relations and determine which relations are also functions. Students discover the properties of functions by performing operations, finding composite and inverse functions, and determining zeros of functions. After representing linear equations and inequalities as graphs, students find the distances between two points and the slopes of lines. Students use the slope and a point on a line to write linear equations in point-slope and slope-intercept forms. The chapter closes with students using definitions of parallel and perpendicular lines to prove theorems by applying analytic methods.

Lesson Objective Chart

Lesson (Pages)	Lesson Objectives		State/Local Objectives
1-1 (6-11)	**1-1A:**	Determine whether a given relation is a function.	
	1-1B:	Identify the domain and range of any relation or function.	
1-2 (12-18)	**1-2A:**	Perform operations with functions.	
	1-2B:	Find composite functions.	
	1-2C:	Find and recognize inverse functions.	
1-3 (21-27)	**1-3A:**	Find zeros of linear functions.	
	1-3B:	Graph linear equations and inequalities.	
1-4 (29-35)	**1-4A:**	Find the distance between two points.	
	1-4B:	Find the slope of a line through two points.	
	1-4C:	Prove geometric theorems involving slope, distance, and midpoints analytically.	
1-5 (36-41)	**1-5A:**	Write linear equations using slope-intercept form.	
	1-5B:	Write linear equations using point-slope form.	
1-6 (42-47)	**1-6A:**	Write equations of parallel and perpendicular lines.	
	1-6B:	Prove geometric theorems involving parallel and perpendicular lines analytically.	

ORGANIZING THE CHAPTER

You may want to refer to the **Course Planning Guide Calendar** on pages T34-T35 for a complete pacing chart.

Lesson Planning Guide

					Blackline Masters Booklets								
						Technology			Activity Masters				
Lesson	Pages	Practice	Enrichment	Evaluation	Graphing Calculator	Computer	Multicultural Activity	Applications	Problem Solving	Case Study Follow-Up	Decision Making	Transparencies
1-1	6-11	p. 1	p. 1								p. 3	1-1
1-2	12-18	p. 2	p. 2	Quiz A, p. 9	p. 1							1-2
1-3	21-27	p. 3	p. 3	Quiz B, p. 9 Mid-Chapter Test, p. 11		p. 2						1-3
1-4	29-35	p. 4	p. 4	Quiz C, p. 10					p. 2			1-4
1-5	36-41	p. 5	p. 5					p. 1				1-5
1-6	42-47	p. 6	p. 6	Quiz D, p. 10		p. 1						1-6
Review	48-50	Multiple Choice Tests, Forms 1A and 1B, pp. 1-4 Free Response Tests, Forms 2A and 2B, pp. 5-8 Standardized Test Questions, p. 12										
Test	51											

Other Chapter Resources

Student Edition

Case Study Follow-Up, p. 11
Decision Making, p. 47
Technology, p. 28

Other Supplements

Transparency 1-0 for Chapter Opener
Alternate Assessment in the Mathematics Classroom,
    Glencoe Publishing Co., 1993
Cooperative Learning in the Mathematics Classroom,
    Glencoe Publishing Co., 1993

Software

Test and Review Generator Software
    Available for Apple, IBM, and Macintosh
Teacher's Guide for Software Resources

ENHANCING THE CHAPTER

Cooperative Learning

An Overview

For successful cooperative-learning experiences, research indicates that the teacher's responsibilities include:
1. Deciding on the size of the groups.
2. Assigning students to the groups.
3. Arranging the room.
4. Describing the subject-matter and cooperative-skills objectives.
5. Planning teaching materials to promote group interdependence.
6. Assigning roles to students in the group.
7. Explaining the specific task to be performed.
8. Describing the student's responsibilities to the group.
9. Establishing individual accountability.
10. Explaining the criteria for success.
11. Specifying desired student behaviors.
12. Monitoring students' behavior.
13. Providing task assistance.
14. Intervening to teach cooperative-learning skills.
15. Providing closure to the lesson.
16. Evaluating the quality of students' learning.
17. Assessing how well the group functioned.

Each of these will be discussed in detail in subsequent pre-chapter materials.

For more information on cooperative learning, see pages T20-T21. Additional information on using cooperative groups is available in Glencoe's *Cooperative Learning in the Mathematics Classroom,* ©1993.

Multicultural

Multicultural Activity Masters, p. 1

Activity Masters

Applications, p. 1

Problem Solving, p. 2

Decision Making, p. 3

Technology

Before beginning the first chapter, you may wish to refer to pages T22-T25 on *Integrating Technology into Your Precalculus Classroom*. Additional instructions on the use of graphing calculators begins on page xiv of the student text.

The Technology Feature after Lesson 1-3 illustrates how to use the *Mathematics Exploration Toolkit (MET)* to determine whether two given functions are inverses. *MET* is a powerful calculator, symbolic manipulator, and graphing utility for IBM and IBM compatible personal computers. HELP screens are available at any point in the program by pressing the F1 key. Other Technology Features using *MET* appear in Chapters 8, 10, 13, and 17.

The Exploration in Lesson 1-1 examines the excluded values that may appear when certain functions are graphed on a graphing calculator. Lesson 1-3A instructs students on graphing linear equations and inequalities. Throughout the chapter students learn to use the calculator to determine the domain and range of functions and to compare and contrast functions.

Graphing Calculator Exercises, pp. 11, 18, 26, 40
Graphing Calculator Program, p. 26

Outside Resources

Books/Periodicals

Heid, M. K. "Resequencing Skills and Concepts in Applied Calculus Using the Computer as a Tool, *"Journal of Research in Mathematics Education,* January 1988, pp. 3-25.

Hughes-Hallet, Deborah. *The Math Workshop: Elementary Functions,* Norton, NY, 1980

Films/Videotapes/Videodiscs

Mathematics: Intermediate Algebra. Great Plains National, University of Nebraska-Lincoln

Software

Graphing utilities (see list on page T25)

Green Globs and Graphing Equations. Wings for Learning/Sunburst (Apple II, IBM)

IBM Mathematics Exploration Toolkit. IBM

Technology Masters

Graphing Calculator, p. 1

Computer, p. 2

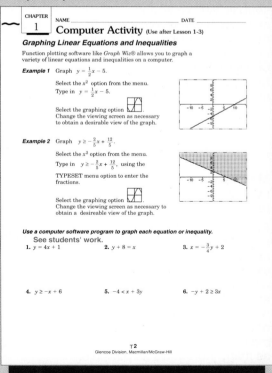

CHAPTER 1

LINEAR RELATIONS AND FUNCTIONS

HISTORICAL SNAPSHOT

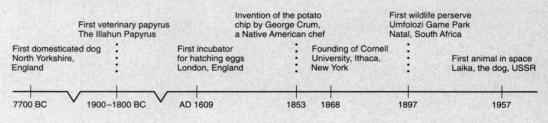

First domesticated dog
North Yorkshire,
England

First veterinary papyrus
The Illahun Papyrus

First incubator
for hatching eggs
London, England

Invention of the potato
chip by George Crum,
a Native American chef

Founding of Cornell
University, Ithaca,
New York

First wildlife perserve
Umfolozi Game Park
Natal, South Africa

First animal in space
Laika, the dog, USSR

7700 BC   1900–1800 BC   AD 1609   1853   1868   1897   1957

4

then plot weight as a function of height and draw a curve connecting the data points. As a check on their work, students should attempt to predict the weight of an unmeasured animal using their graph.

In this chapter, you will:
■ Define relations, functions, composites, and inverses.
■ Write equations of lines.
■ Find the distance between two points, the slope of the line through two points, and the midpoint of a line segment.

CAREER GOAL: Veterinary Medicine

Perhaps it was because she was inspired by James Herriot's touching book *All Creatures Great and Small*. Or maybe she was inspired by growing up with her best friend, her dog Duchess. But whatever the reason, Julie Ferguson has wanted to be a veterinarian since she was in the fifth grade.

Julie studied algebra, geometry, trigonometry, and calculus in high school. She also studied biology, which was one of her favorite subjects. After working in a veterinary clinic for two years while in high school, Julie says "I saw how rewarding the job was. It was a way to use my biology experience, so I decided that veterinary medicine was the career for me."

Julie is currently working as a research assistant at Cornell University, which helps her learn practical applications of her classwork. For example, she often operates a photospectrometer in her job. "In animal science, we learn to generate a standard curve for use in comparing unknown quantities of various substances. For example, suppose we have a fluid with an unknown amount of nitrogen. We would first use fluids with known amounts of nitrogen and read the concentration of nitrogen on a photospectrometer. This equipment measures the absorption of light versus the concentration of nitrogen. We would plot the concentrations of nitrogen onto a graph. This becomes our standard curve." It is then possible to use the graph and photospectrometer to find the concentration of nitrogen in the unknown quantity.

After graduating with a degree in animal science, Julie expects to spend four more years in veterinary school at Cornell. "As a veterinarian, I hope that I will be in the community's eye as a health professional and as a community volunteer. I hope to provide comfort to pet owners wherever I can."

READ MORE ABOUT IT

Herriot, James. *All Creatures Great and Small*. New York: St. Martins Press, 1972.
Lee, Mary Price and Richard. *Opportunities in Animal and Pet Care Careers*. Lincolnwood, Illinois: VGM Career Horizons, 1989.
Schwabe, Calvin W. *Veterinary Medicine and Human Health*. Baltimore, Maryland: Williams & Wilkins, 1984.

SPOTLIGHT ON...

Julie Ferguson
Age: 19
Class: Junior
School: Cornell University
 Ithaca, New York
Major: Animal Science

"I hope to provide comfort to pet owners wherever I can."

FOR MORE INFORMATION

If you would like more information about veterinary medicine, contact:

American Veterinary Medical
 Association (AVMA)
930 N. Meacham Road
Schaumburg, IL 60196

Applications

Lesson	Application	Examples	Exercises
1-1	Recycling Finance		59 60
1-2	Sales Employment	3	37
1-3	Business Economics	4	40, 41
1-4	Economics Consumer Products	2	36, 37 38
1-5	Economics Manufacturing Anatomy	4 6	33 34, 35
1-6	Sales Sports	2	34 35

NCTM Standards: 1–6, 8, 14

Lesson Resources

- Practice Master 1–1
- Enrichment Master 1–1
- Activity Master, p. 3

 Transparency 1–1 contains the 5-Minute Check and a teaching aid for this lesson.

INTRODUCING THE LESSON

5-Minute Check

1. Find the value of the expression $x^2 + 4x + 4$ for $x = -2$. **0**
2. Solve $5n + 6 = -3n - 10$. **−2**
3. Evaluate $|x - 2y| - |2x - y| - xy$ if $x = -2$ and $y = 7$. **19**
4. Factor $8xy^2 - 4xy$. **$4xy(2y - 1)$**
5. Simplify $\frac{12x^5y^3}{21xy^4} \cdot \frac{4x^4}{7y}$.

Prerequisite Skills

Students should be able to evaluate algebraic expressions for given values of the variable.

Evaluate for $x = -3$.
1. $x^2 - 2x - 5$ **10**
2. $\frac{-5x}{x^2}$ **$\frac{5}{3}$**
3. $\sqrt{6x + 34}$ **4**
4. $|x - 4|$ **7**

1-1   Relations and Functions

Objectives	After studying this lesson, you should be able to:
1–1A	■ determine whether a given relation is a function, and
1–1B	■ identify the domain and range of any relation or function.

Application

 FYI...

The first artificial satellite to be placed in orbit was Sputnik 1, launched on October 4, 1957, by the former Soviet Union.

A satellite is a natural or artificial object that revolves around a celestial body. The moon is an example of a natural satellite. Artificial satellites are used for scientific research, communication, weather forecasting, and military reconnaissance. The time that it takes an artifical satellite to complete a revolution around Earth depends on its speed and altitude. For a satellite orbiting at 100 miles above Earth, the following equation shows the relationship between speed (s) and time (t).

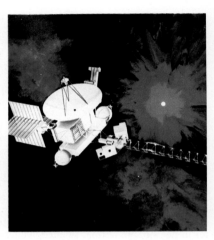

$$t = \frac{1540}{s}$$

The table below contains values for s, in thousands of miles per hour, and corresponding values for t, in minutes, given the equation above.

s	15	20	25	30
t	102.7	77	61.6	51.3

We can write the values in the table as a set of ordered pairs. A pairing of elements of one set with elements of a second set is called a **relation.** The first element of an ordered pair is the *abscissa*. The second element is the *ordinate*.

The following set, from the example above, represents a relation.

$$\{(15, 102.7), (20, 77), (25, 61.6), (30, 51.3)\}$$

The set of abscissas $\{15, 20, 25, 30\}$ of the ordered pairs is called the **domain** of the relation. The set of ordinates $\{102.7, 77, 61.6, 51.3\}$ is called the **range**.

Definition of Relation, Domain, and Range	**A relation is a set of ordered pairs. The domain is the set of all abscissas of the ordered pairs. The range is the set of all ordinates of the ordered pairs.**

ALTERNATE TEACHING STRATEGIES

Using Models

Use a small box to represent a "function machine." Explain that a function acts on a variable as a machine acts on raw materials, turning it into something new. Write $f(x) = x^2 + 5$ on the side of the box and poke holes in the top and side. Illustrate putting $x = 3$ in the top hole. The machine acts on the 3 and turns it into $f(3) = 14$.

Using Connections

Ask students to write the satellite equation at the beginning of the lesson as a function. $f(s) = \frac{1540}{s}$

Then have them give other examples of real-world functions. **Sample answer: Amount earned at \$5/hour is a function of the number of hours worked. $f(h) = 5h$**

A relation can be presented as a set of ordered pairs, a table of values, a graph, or by a rule in words or symbols that determines pairs of values.

Example 1

If x is a positive integer less than 6, state the relation representing the equation $y = 5 + x$ by listing a set of ordered pairs. Also, state the domain and range of the relation.

The relation is $\{(1, 6), (2, 7), (3, 8), (4, 9), (5, 10)\}$.

The domain is $\{1, 2, 3, 4, 5\}$.

The range is $\{6, 7, 8, 9, 10\}$.

The relation in Example 1 is a special type of relation called a **function**.

Definition of Function	**A function is a relation in which each element of the domain is paired with exactly one element in the range.**

All functions are relations, but not all relations are functions.

Example 2

The table below shows the number of students enrolled in U.S. high schools from 1960 through 2000.

1960	1970	1980	1990	2000 (projected)
13,000,000	19,700,000	18,000,000	16,700,000	19,700,000

Does this relation represent a function? Why or why not?

This table represents the following set of ordered pairs.

$(1960, 13, 000, 000), (1970, 19, 700, 000), (1980, 18, 000, 000),$
$(1990, 16, 700, 000), (2000, 19, 700, 000)$

For each member of the domain, there is only one corresponding element in the range. Thus, this relation is a function.

A function can also be defined as a set of ordered pairs in which no two pairs have the same first element. This definition can be applied when a relation is represented by a graph. If every vertical line drawn on the graph of a relation passes through no more than one point of the graph, then the relation is a function. This is called the **vertical line test.** Thus, the graph at the right does not show a function, but it does show a relation.

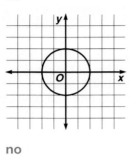
Example 3 | **Determine if the graph of each relation is that of a function.**

a.

b.

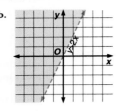

a. Each element of the domain is paired with exactly one element of the range. Therefore, this graph does represent a function.

b. A vertical line would pass through infinitely many points on the graph. Therefore, this graph does not represent a function.

x is called the independent variable, and y is called the dependent variable.

A function is commonly denoted by f. In *function notation*, the symbol $f(x)$ is read "f of x" and should be interpreted as the value of the function f at x. The expression $y = f(x)$ indicates that for each element in the domain that replaces x, the function assigns one and only one replacement for y. The ordered pairs of the function are written in the form (x, y) or $(x, f(x))$.

Example 4 | **Find $f(3)$ if $f(x) = 4x^2 - 2x + 5$.**

$f(3) = 4(3)^2 - 2(3) + 5$ *x = 3*

$= 35$

Example 5 | **Find $f(4)$ if $f(x) = |-3x + 8|$.**

$f(4) = |-3(4) + 8|$ *The vertical bars denote absolute value.*

$= |-4|$

$= 4$

Often an equation for a function is given, but the domain is not specified. In cases such as this, the domain consists of all the real numbers for which the corresponding values in the range are also real numbers.

Example 6 | **Name all values of x that are not in the domain of f.**

a. $f(x) = \dfrac{3x}{x^2 - 5}$

a. Any value that makes the denominator equal zero must be excluded from the domain of f, since division by zero is undefined. To determine the excluded values, let $x^2 - 5 = 0$ and solve.

$x^2 - 5 = 0$

$x^2 = 5$

$x = \pm\sqrt{5}$

Therefore, the domain includes all real numbers except $+\sqrt{5}$ and $-\sqrt{5}$.

8   CHAPTER 1   LINEAR RELATIONS AND FUNCTIONS

Additional Answers

1. Relations and functions can both be represented by sets of ordered pairs. Unlike a relation, however, a function cannot pair any member of the domain with more than one member of the range.

2. The vertical line test is a quick visual way of determining whether or not a graph of a relation is a function. If a vertical line drawn on the graph of a relation passes through no more than one point of the graph, then the relation is a function.

4. Since a relation can be represented by a set of ordered pairs, a function is always a relation. However, in a function, there is exactly one y-value for every x-value. Not all relations have this constraint.

b. $f(x) = \sqrt{x + 1}$

b. Any value that makes the radicand negative must be excluded from the domain of f, since the square root of a negative number is not a real number. Let $x + 1 < 0$ and solve for the excluded values.

$$x + 1 < 0$$
$$x < -1$$

Therefore, the domain excludes all real numbers less than –1.

You can use a graphing calculator to help determine the excluded values in a function by examining the graph of the function.

EXPLORATION: Graphing Calculator

Determine the excluded values in the domain of
$$f(x) = \frac{x}{x^2 - x - 12} \text{ with a graphing calculator.}$$

1. Establish the viewing window by using the settings below.

XMIN: -10   XMAX: 10   XSCL: 1
YMIN: -5   YMAX: 5   YSCL: 1

2. Press the $\boxed{Y=}$ key. Enter the function.

3. Press $\boxed{\text{GRAPH}}$.

4. What do you notice about the vertical lines on the graph? They are the asymptotes.

CHECKING FOR UNDERSTANDING

Communicating Mathematics

Read and study the lesson to answer each question. 1, 2, 4. See margin.

1. **Compare and contrast** the meanings of the words *relation* and *function*.

2. **Describe** what the vertical line test does.

3. See students' work.

3. **Draw** the graph of a function on a set of coordinate axes.

4. **Explain** why all functions are relations, but not all relations are functions.

LESSON 1-1   RELATIONS AND FUNCTIONS   9

Guided Practice

State whether each graph represents a function. Write *yes* or *no*.

5.

yes

6.

no

7.

yes

Given $f(x) = 7 - x^2$, find each value.

8. $f(0)$ 7
9. $f(4)$ −9
10. $f(-3)$ −2
11. $f(11)$ −114
12. $f\left(\frac{1}{2}\right)$ $6\frac{3}{4}$
13. $f(3.7)$ −6.69
14. $f(2a)$ $7 - 4a^2$
15. $f(6 + n)$ $-29 - 12n - n^2$

16. What value(s) of x are not in the domain of $f(x) = \dfrac{x^3 + 5x}{4x}$? 0

17. What value(s) of x are not in the domain of $f(x) = \dfrac{1}{\sqrt{x - 4}}$? $x \le 4$

EXERCISES

Practice

State the domain and range of each relation. Then state whether the relation is a function. Write *yes* or *no*. 18–25. See margin for domain and range.

18. $\{(-3, 0), (4, -2), (2, -6)\}$ yes
19. $\{(1, 2), (2, 4), (-3, -6), (0, 0)\}$ yes
20. $\{(0, 3), (5, 3), (6, 3), (2, 3)\}$ yes
21. $\{(-2, 9), (-2, 8), (-2, 7)\}$ no
22. $\{(5, 5), (6, 6)\}$ yes
23. $\{(1, 5), (2, 6), (3, 7), (4, 8)\}$ yes
24. $\{(4, -2), (4, 2), (9, -3), (9, 3)\}$ no
25. $\{(8, -3), (7, 3), (6, -3)\}$ yes

Given that x is an integer, state the relation representing each of the following by listing a set of ordered pairs. Then state whether the relation is a function. Write *yes* or *no*. 26–31. See margin for relations.

26. $y = 3x - 3$ and $0 < x < 6$ yes
27. $y = 2.5x$ and $4 \le x \le 8$ yes
28. $y = 5$ and $4 \le x \le 9$ yes
29. $y^2 = x - 2$ and $x = 11$ no
30. $|2y| = x$ and $x = 4$ no
31. $y = |x| - 1.5$ and $-2 \le x < 4$ yes

The symbol $[x]$ means the greatest integer not greater than x. If $f(x) = [x] + 4$, find each value.

32. $f(-4)$ 0
33. $f(2.5)$ 6
34. $f(-6.3)$ −3
35. $f(\sqrt{2})$ 5
36. $f(-\sqrt{3})$ 2
37. $f(\pi)$ 7
38. $f(-4 + t)$ $[t]$
39. $f(q + 1)$ $[q] + 5$

Given $f(x) = |x^2 - 13|$, find each value.

40. $f(0)$ 13
41. $f(-4)$ 3
42. $f(-\sqrt{13})$ 0
43. $f(2)$ 9
44. $f(4.8)$ 10.04
45. $f\left(1\frac{1}{2}\right)$ $10\frac{3}{4}$
46. $f(n + 4)$ $|n^2 + 8n + 3|$
47. $f(5m)$ $|25m^2 - 13|$

Name all values of x that are not in the domain of the given function.

48. $f(x) = \dfrac{3}{x - 1}$ 1
49. $f(x) = \dfrac{3 - x}{5 + x}$ −5
50. $f(x) = \dfrac{x^2 - 18}{32 - x^2}$ $\pm 4\sqrt{2}$
51. $f(x) = \dfrac{15}{|2x| - 9}$ $\pm 4\frac{1}{2}$
52. $f(x) = \sqrt{x^2 - 9}$ $-3 < x < 3$
53. $f(x) = \dfrac{x + 2}{\sqrt{x^2 - 7}}$ $-\sqrt{7} \le x \le \sqrt{7}$

Graphing Calculator

Use a graphing calculator to determine whether each equation is a relation or a function.

54. $y = 3x^2 + 1$ **55.** $y = (x-5)^{\frac{1}{2}}$ **56.** $x^2 + y^2 = 25$ **57.** $\dfrac{x^2}{9} + \dfrac{y^2}{16} = 1$

function   function   relation   relation

Critical Thinking

58. Find $P(6)$ if $P(x)$ is a function for which $P(1) = 1$, $P(2) = 2$, $P(3) = 3$, and $P(x+1) = \dfrac{P(x-2)P(x-1) + 1}{P(x)}$ for $x > 3$. $\dfrac{4}{7}$

Applications and Problem Solving

59–60. See margin.

59. Recycling   A recycling center accepts aluminum cans for recycling. A weekly record from the center is shown at the right. Can you use the information in the second and third columns of the chart to illustrate a function? Can you use this information to illustrate a relation that is not a function? Explain.

Day	Number of Cans Recycled	Pounds of Aluminum Produced
M	75,000	3000
T	80,000	3150
W	70,000	2850
Th	75,000	3100
F	85,000	3400

60. Finance   The formula for the simple interest earned on an investment is $I = prt$, where I is the interest earned, p is the principal, r is the interest rate, and t is the time in years. Assume that $5000 is invested at an annual interest rate of 8% and that the interest is added to the principal at the end of each year.
  a. Find the amount of interest that will be earned each year for five years.
  b. State the domain and range of the relation.
  c. Is this relation a function? Why or why not?

CASE STUDY FOLLOW-UP

Refer to Case Study 2: *Trashing the Planet*, on pages 959–961.

Let x = the number of non-federal hazardous waste sites in a given state, and let y = the number of federal hazardous waste sites in that state. The following ordered pairs (x, y) represent the numbers of sites in the six states with a total of at least 11, but not greater than 15, hazardous waste sites.

Connecticut (14,1)   Tennessee (12,2)   Georgia (11,2)
Alabama (10,2)   Rhode Island (9,2)   Utah (7,4)

1. Is the set of ordered pairs a relation? Is it a function? yes; yes

2. Let $f(x) = -240x + 482,640$, where x is the year and $f(x)$ is the number of active trash landfills in the United States that year. Evaluate the function for the years 1986, 1993, and 2006. $f(1986) = 6000, f(1993) = 4320, f(2006) = 1200$ a. 1986, 2006
  a. For which years does the function yield the estimates given in the case study?
  b. Is the function that specifies the number of landfills in the United States as a function of the year a linear function? yes

3. Research   Write a one-page paper on the Superfund, the federal program to clean up hazardous waste sites. See students' work.

EXTENDING THE LESSON

Math Power: Problem Solving

Find a function $g(x)$ in which the abscissa and ordinate of each ordered pair satisfying the function are the reverse of the abscissa and ordinate of an ordered pair satisfying the function $f(x) = 4x - 5$.

$g(x) = \dfrac{x + 5}{4}$

Case Study Follow-Up

This activity provides an opportunity to do research and apply mathematics in solving problems related to issues that may face students in their adult lives. Case Study 2 is located on pages 959–961.

Using Technology

If students cannot visually determine whether each equation is a function or not, have them use the edge of a piece of paper to perform the vertical line test over the calculator screen.

Additional Answers

59. If the x-coordinate represents the pounds of aluminum produced and the y-coordinate represents the number of cans recycled, the relation is a function. If the x-coordinate represents the number of cans recycled and the y-coordinate represents the pounds of aluminum produced, the relation is not a function because the x-coordinate 75,000 would be paired with 2 y-coordinates, 3000 and 3100.

60a. (year, interest): (1, $400), (2, $432), (3, $466.56), (4, $503.89), (5, $544.20)

60b. Domain = {1, 2, 3, 4, 5}
Range = {$400, $432, $466.56, $503.89, $544.20}

60c. Yes, the relation is a function. For each member of the domain, there is only one corresponding element in the range.

Enrichment Masters Booklet, p. 1

NCTM Standards: 1–6, 14

Lesson Resources

- Practice Master 1–2
- Enrichment Master 1–2
- Evaluation Master, Quiz A, p. 9
- Technology Master, p. 1

 Transparency 1–2 contains the 5-Minute Check and a teaching aid for this lesson.

INTRODUCING THE LESSON

 5-Minute Check

(over Lesson 1–1)

1. $f(x) = 6 - x^2$. Find $f(-2)$.   **2**
2. Consider the relation {(−2, 2), (1, 2), (2, 3)}. State the domain and range of the relation. **domain {−2, 1, 2}; range {2, 3}**
3. Is the relation in Exercise 2 a function?   **yes**

Name all values of x that are not in the domain of the function.

4. $f(x) = \dfrac{5}{2-x}$ **x = 2**

5. $f(x) = \sqrt{x^2 - 4}$
   −2 < x < 2

Motivating the Lesson

Have students read the application. Ask them to describe the two steps they must perform in order to solve the problem.   **First, take 20% off of $39.99. Then add 7%.**

1-2 Composition and Inverses of Functions

Objectives

After studying this lesson, you should be able to:

- 1–2A ■ perform operations with functions,
- 1–2B ■ find composite functions, and
- 1–2C ■ find and recognize inverse functions.

Application

Joyce Wallace is buying a pair of jeans for $39.99. The jeans are on sale at a 20% discount and the sales tax in Joyce's area is 7%. How much will Joyce have to pay for the jeans? *This problem will be solved in Example 3.*

To solve the problem above, two functions, one involving a discount and the other involving sales tax, can be used. If you have two functions f and g, you can form new functions by adding, subtracting, multiplying, or dividing.

Operations With Functions		
	Sum:	$(f + g)(x) = f(x) + g(x)$
	Difference:	$(f - g)(x) = f(x) - g(x)$
	Product:	$(f \cdot g)(x) = f(x) \cdot g(x)$
	Quotient:	$\left(\dfrac{f}{g}\right)(x) = \dfrac{f(x)}{g(x)}, g(x) \neq 0$

The domain of each new function consists of those values of x common to the domains of f and g. The domain of the quotient function is further restricted by excluding any values that make the denominator, $g(x)$, zero.

Example 1

Given $f(x) = x + 3$ and $g(x) = \dfrac{2x}{x-5}$, find each function below. Name all values of x that are not in the domain of the new function.

a. $(f + g)(x)$

b. $(f - g)(x)$

a. $(f + g)(x) = f(x) + g(x)$

$$= x + 3 + \dfrac{2x}{x-5}$$

$$= \dfrac{(x+3)(x-5) + 2x}{x-5}$$

$$= \dfrac{x^2 - 15}{x-5}, \; x \neq 5$$

b. $(f - g)(x) = f(x) - g(x)$

$$= x + 3 - \dfrac{2x}{x-5}$$

$$= \dfrac{(x+3)(x-5) - 2x}{x-5}$$

$$= \dfrac{x^2 - 4x - 15}{x-5}, \; x \neq 5$$

12 CHAPTER 1 LINEAR RELATIONS AND FUNCTIONS

ALTERNATE TEACHING STRATEGIES

Using Cooperative Groups

Have students work in pairs. Each student thinks of a function. Then they work together to find the sum, difference, product, and quotient of their functions; the composite of the two functions in both orders; and the inverse of each function.

Using Charts

Have students find the inverse of $f(x)$.

x	3	7	−1	−4	9	5	0
f(x)	2	−6	3	8	1	−2	7

x	2	−6	3	8	1	−2	7
f(x)	3	7	−1	−4	9	5	0

c. $(f \cdot g)(x)$
                            d. $\left(\dfrac{f}{g}\right)(x)$

c. $(f \cdot g)(x) = f(x) \cdot g(x)$
                d. $\left(\dfrac{f}{g}\right)(x) = \dfrac{f(x)}{g(x)}$

$$= (x+3) \cdot \dfrac{2x}{x-5} \qquad\qquad\qquad = (x+3) \div \dfrac{2x}{x-5}$$

$$= \dfrac{2x^2 + 6x}{x-5}, x \neq 5 \qquad\qquad\qquad = \dfrac{x^2 - 2x - 15}{2x}, x \neq 0, 5$$

Another way of combining two functions is through **composition** of functions. A function g maps the elements in set R to those in set S. Another function f maps the elements in set S to those in set T. Thus, the range of g is the same as the domain of f. A diagram is shown below.

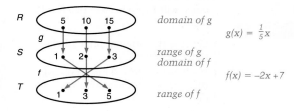

By combining f and g in this way, a function from R to T is defined, since each element of R is associated with exactly one element of T. For example, $g(15) = 3$ and $f(3) = 1$. This new function that maps R onto T is called the **composite** of f and g. It is denoted by $f \circ g$, as shown below.

$f \circ g$ is read "f composition g," or "f of g."

Composition of Functions

Given functions f and g, the composite function $f \circ g$ can be described by the following equation.

$$[f \circ g](x) = f(g(x))$$

The domain of $f \circ g$ includes all of the elements x in the domain of g for which $g(x)$ is in the domain of f.

LESSON 1-2 COMPOSITION AND INVERSES OF FUNCTIONS 13

Chalkboard Example

For Example 1

Given $f(x) = 2x - 1$ and $g(x) = x^2$, find each function.
a. $(f + g)(x)$ $x^2 + 2x - 1$
b. $(f - g)(x)$ $-x^2 + 2x - 1$
c. $(f \cdot g)(x)$ $2x^3 - x^2$
d. $\left(\dfrac{f}{g}\right)(x)$ $\dfrac{2x-1}{x^2}, x \neq 0$

Teaching Tip When discussing composition of functions, point out that $[f \circ g](x)$ is found by substituting $g(x)$ for x in $f(x)$.

Example 2

If $f(x) = x + 1$ and $g(x) = \dfrac{1}{x-1}$, find $[f \circ g](x)$.

$$[f \circ g](x) = f(g(x))$$

$$= f\left(\frac{1}{x-1}\right) \qquad \text{\textit{Replace g(x) with} } \frac{1}{x-1}.$$

$$= \frac{1}{x-1} + 1 \qquad \text{\textit{Substitute} } \frac{1}{x-1} \text{ \textit{for x in x + 1.}}$$

$$= \frac{1}{x-1} + \frac{x-1}{x-1} \qquad \text{\textit{The least common denominator is x} - 1.}$$

$$= \frac{x}{x-1}$$

You can use composition of functions to solve the application problem presented at the beginning of the lesson.

Example 3

APPLICATION

Sales

Refer to the application at the beginning of the lesson. How much will Joyce have to pay for the jeans?

Let x = the original price of the jeans, or $39.99.

Let $T(x) = 1.07x$. This represents the cost of an item with a 7% sales tax rate.

Let $S(x) = 0.80x$. This represents the cost of an item with a 20% discount.

The cost of Joyce's jeans is $[T \circ S](x)$.

$$[T \circ S](x) = T(S(x))$$

$$= T(0.80x)$$

$$= T(0.80(39.99)) \qquad \text{\textit{Substitute 39.99 for x.}}$$

$$\approx T(31.99) \qquad \text{\textit{Simplify. Round to the nearest cent.}}$$

$$\approx 1.07(31.99) \qquad \text{\textit{Evaluate T when x is 31.99.}}$$

$$\approx 34.23 \qquad \text{\textit{Round to the nearest cent.}}$$

Joyce will have to pay $34.23 for the jeans.

In the examples above, the range of g was the same as the domain of f.

The composite function $f \circ g$ exists only when the range of g is a subset of the domain of f. Otherwise, the composite is undefined. For example, $[f \circ g](x)$ does not exist for the following functions.

$$g(x) = -\sqrt{x}$$
$$f(x) = \sqrt{x} + 1$$

$$[f \circ g](x) = f(g(x)) = \sqrt{(-\sqrt{x})} + 1 \qquad \text{\textit{Does [g \circ f](x) exist?}}$$

Iteration is a special type of composition, the composition of a function to itself. Chapter 13 is devoted to this topic.

Now consider two functions $f(x) = 3x - 2$ and $g(x) = \frac{x+2}{3}$. You can find functions $[f \circ g](x)$ and $[g \circ f](x)$ as follows.

$$[f \circ g](x) = f\left(\frac{x+2}{3}\right) \qquad\qquad [g \circ f](x) = g(3x - 2)$$

$$= 3\left(\frac{x+2}{3}\right) - 2 \qquad\qquad\qquad = \frac{(3x-2)+2}{3}$$

$$= x \qquad\qquad\qquad\qquad\qquad\qquad = x$$

Since $[f \circ g](x) = [g \circ f](x) = x$ for all values of x, f and g are called **inverse functions**.

Inverse Functions

> **Two functions f and g are inverse functions if and only if**
> $$[f \circ g](x) = [g \circ f](x) = x.$$

The notation f^{-1} is read "f inverse," or "the inverse of f." The –1 is not an exponent.

The inverse function of f, if it exists, is denoted by f^{-1}. If f and g are inverse functions, then $f = g^{-1}$ and $g = f^{-1}$.

The inverse of a function can be shown as a mapping.

 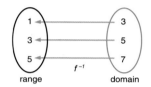

If $f = \{(1,3),(3,5),(5,7)\}$, then $f^{-1} = \{(3,1),(5,3),(7,5)\}$.

Notice that the inverse is found by reversing the order of the coordinates of each ordered pair for the function. The mapping shown above is one-to-one. The mapping shown at the right is not one-to-one. The inverse of f is a function only if f represents a one-to-one mapping.

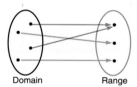

Property of Inverse Functions

> **Suppose f and f^{-1} are inverse functions. Then, $f(x) = y$ if and only if $f^{-1}(y) = x$.**

EVALUATING THE LESSON

Checking for Understanding

Exercises 1–11 are designed to help you assess students' understanding through reading, writing, speaking, and modeling. You should work through Exercises 1–3 with your students and then monitor their work on Exercises 4–11.

Practice Masters Booklet, p. 2

Example 4 | Given $f(x) = 4x - 9$, find $f^{-1}(x)$, and show that f and f^{-1} are inverse functions.

$y = 4x - 9$ $\qquad f(x) = y$

$x = 4y - 9$ $\qquad$ *Exchange x and y.*

$x + 9 = 4y$ $\qquad$ *Solve for y.*

$\dfrac{x+9}{4} = y$

$\dfrac{x+9}{4} = f^{-1}(x)$ $\qquad$ *Replace y with $f^{-1}(x)$.*

Then, show that $[f \circ f^{-1}](x) = [f^{-1} \circ f](x) = x$.

$[f \circ f^{-1}](x) = f\left(\dfrac{x+9}{4}\right)$ $\qquad\qquad$ $[f^{-1} \circ f](x) = f^{-1}(4x - 9)$

$\qquad\qquad = 4\left(\dfrac{x+9}{4}\right) - 9$ $\qquad\qquad\qquad\qquad = \dfrac{(4x-9)+9}{4}$

$\qquad\qquad = x$ $\qquad\qquad\qquad\qquad\qquad\qquad = x$

Since $[f \circ f^{-1}](x) = [f^{-1} \circ f](x) = x$, f and f^{-1} are inverse functions.

Not all functions have inverses that are functions. *Note that the notation f^{-1} is used whether or not the inverse is a function.*

Example 5 | Given $f(x) = x^2 - 1$, find $f^{-1}(x)$.

$y = x^2 - 1$ $\qquad f(x) = y$

$x = y^2 - 1$ $\qquad$ *Exchange x and y.*

$x + 1 = y^2$ $\qquad$ *Solve for y.*

$\pm\sqrt{x+1} = y$

$\pm\sqrt{x+1} = f^{-1}(x)$ $\qquad$ *Replace y with $f^{-1}(x)$*

The equation $f^{-1}(x) = \pm\sqrt{x+1}$ does not define a function. Therefore, $f(x) = x^2 - 1$ does not have an inverse that is a function.

CHECKING FOR UNDERSTANDING

Communicating Mathematics

Read and study the lesson to answer each question. 1–3. See margin.

1. Is $[f \circ g](x)$ always equal to $[g \circ f](x)$ for two functions $f(x)$ and $g(x)$? Explain your answer.

2. Why does the equation for the inverse in Example 5 not represent a function?

3. **Graph** $f(x) = 4x - 9$ and $f^{-1}(x) = \dfrac{x+9}{4}$ on the same set of axes, along with $y = x$. What do you notice about the graphs of $f(x)$ and $f^{-1}(x)$?

RETEACHING THE LESSON

Before students find the inverse of a function, have them list the operations that "undo" each operation in the function. For example, "divide by 5" undoes multiplication by 5, and "take the square root" undoes squaring the variable. When students have found the inverse, have them check to see that it includes each undoing operation.

Additional Answers

1. No. In fact, $[f \circ g](x)$ and $[g \circ f](x)$ are almost never equal.

2. Because each value of x has two values of $y = f^{-1}(x)$. For example, let $x = 2$. Then $y = +\sqrt{3}$ and $-\sqrt{3}$.

3. See students' graphs; $f(x)$ and $f^{-1}(x)$ are reflections of each other about the line $y = x$.

Guided Practice

Given $f(x) = \dfrac{x}{x+1}$ and $g(x) = x^2 - 1$, find each function below.

4. $(f+g)(x)$ **5.** $(f-g)(x)$ **6.** $(f \cdot g)(x)$ **7.** $\left(\dfrac{f}{g}\right)(x)$

Find $[f \circ g](x)$ and $[g \circ f](x)$.

8. $f(x) = x + 3$
$g(x) = 2x + 5$ $2x + 8, 2x + 11$

9. $f(x) = x^2 - 9$ $x^2 + 8x + 7,$
$g(x) = x + 4$ $x^2 - 5$

Determine if the given functions are inverses of each other. Write *yes* or *no*. Show your work.

10. $f(x) = 3x + 1$ yes
$g(x) = \dfrac{x-1}{3}$

11. $f(x) = \dfrac{1}{2}x - 5$ no
$g(x) = 2x + 5$

EXERCISES

Practice

Given $f(x) = \dfrac{3}{x-7}$ and $g(x) = x^2 + 5x$, find each function below.

12. $(f+g)(x)$ **13.** $(f-g)(x)$ **14.** $(f \cdot g)(x)$ **15.** $\left(\dfrac{f}{g}\right)(x)$
12–15. See margin.

Find $[f \circ g](x)$ and $[g \circ f](x)$.

16. $f(x) = \dfrac{1}{2}x - 7$ $\dfrac{1}{2}x - 4, \dfrac{1}{2}x - 1$
$g(x) = x + 6$

17. $f(x) = 3x^2$ $3x^2 - 24x + 48,$
$g(x) = x - 4$ $3x^2 - 4$

18. $f(x) = x^3$ $x^3 + 3x^2 + 3x + 1,$
$g(x) = x + 1$ $x^3 + 1$

19. $f(x) = 5x^2$ $5x^4 - 10x^2 + 5,$
$g(x) = x^2 - 1$ $25x^4 - 1$

20. $f(x) = x^3 + x^2 + 1$
$g(x) = 2x$
$8x^3 + 4x^2 + 1, 2x^3 + 2x^2 + 2$

21. $f(x) = x^2 + 5x + 6$
$g(x) = x + 1$
$x^2 + 7x + 12, x^2 + 5x + 7$

Determine if the given functions are inverses of each other. Write *yes* or *no*. Show your work.

22. $f(x) = 5x - 6$ yes
$g(x) = \dfrac{x+6}{5}$

23. $f(x) = x + 5$ yes
$g(x) = x - 5$

24. $f(x) = \dfrac{x-1}{2}$ yes
$g(x) = 2x + 1$

25. $f(x) = -x$ no
$g(x) = x$

26. $f(x) = -3x + 7$ no
$g(x) = 3x - 7$

27. $f(x) = \dfrac{1}{3}x + 2$ yes
$g(x) = 3(x - 2)$

30. $f^{-1}(x) = \pm\sqrt{x+9}$, not a function

Find the inverse of each function. Then state whether the inverse is a function.

28. $f(x) = 4x + 4$
$f^{-1}(x) = \dfrac{1}{4}x - 1,$
function

29. $f(x) = x^3$
$f^{-1}(x) = \sqrt[3]{x}$, function

30. $f(x) = x^2 - 9$

LESSON 1-2   COMPOSITION AND INVERSES OF FUNCTIONS   17

Closing the Lesson

Speaking Activity   Let $f(x) = x + 1$ and let $g(x) = 2x - 3$. Have students explain the difference between $(f \cdot g)(x)$ and $[f \circ g](x)$. $(f \cdot g)(x)$ means to multiply $f(x)$ and $g(x)$. That is, $(x + 1)(2x - 3)$ or $2x^2 - x - 3$. $[f \circ g](x)$ means to evaluate $f(x)$ for $x = 2x - 3$. That is, $(2x - 3) + 1$ or $2x - 2$.

APPLYING THE LESSON

Homework Exercises

Assignment Guide

Average: 12–29, 33–42
Enriched: 15–42

The red A, B, and C flags, printed only in the Teacher's Wraparound Edition, indicate the level of difficulty of the exercises.

Chapter 1, Quiz A, (Lessons 1–1 through 1–2), is available in the *Evaluation Masters*, p. 9.

Additional Answers

4. $\dfrac{x^3 + x^2 - 1}{x + 1}$

5. $\dfrac{-x^3 - x^2 + 2x + 1}{x + 1}$

6. $x^2 - x$

7. $\dfrac{x}{x^3 + x^2 - x - 1}, x \neq 1$

12. $\dfrac{x^3 - 2x^2 - 35x + 3}{x - 7}, x \neq 7$

13. $-\dfrac{x^3 - 2x^2 - 35x - 3}{x - 7}, x \neq 7$

14. $\dfrac{3x^2 + 15x}{x - 7}, x \neq 7$

15. $\dfrac{3}{x^3 - 2x^2 - 35x}, x \neq -5, 0, 7$

Show students how to use parentheses to enter $f \circ g$ and $g \circ f$ as an equation on the graphing calculator. Point out that the expression following $Y =$ does not have to be in simplified form for execution.

31. Find two functions, $f(x)$ and $g(x)$, such that $[f \circ g](x) = [g \circ f](x)$.

32. Given $f(x) = 2x + 1$, find each value.

31. See students' work.

a. $f(f(2))$ 11   **b.** $f(f(f(-1)))$ -1 **c.** $f(f(f(3)))$ 31

Graphing Calculator

Given $f(x) = x^{\frac{1}{2}}$ and $g(x) = x - 4$, use a graphing calculator to graph each function. Then determine the domain and range.

33. $f \circ g$ d: $x \geq 4$; r: $y \geq 0$

34. $g \circ f$ d: $x \geq 0$; r: $y \geq -4$

Critical Thinking

35. If $[f \circ g](x) = \dfrac{x^4 + x^2}{1 + x^2}$ and $g(x) = 1 - x^2$, find $f\left(\dfrac{1}{2}\right)$. $\dfrac{1}{2}$

Applications and Problem Solving

36. Sales On the same shopping trip described on page 12, Joyce Wallace spotted a sweater that would go perfectly with her new jeans. The original price of the sweater, $59.99, is marked 25% off. Use composition of functions to determine how much Joyce would have to pay for the sweater, including sales tax. $48.14

37. Sales Jason and Heather Paulsen bought a vase with a $50 gift certificate that they had received as a present. The vase was marked 33% off, and the sales tax in their area was 5.5%. If they paid $45.95 for the vase, use composition of functions to determine the original price of the vase. $65

Mixed Review

38. No, most elements in the domain are paired with two elements in the range.

38. Does the graph at the right represent a function? Write *yes* or *no*. Then explain your answer. **(Lesson 1-1)**

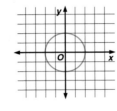

39. Given that x is an integer, state the relation representing $y = 11 - x$ and $-3 \leq x \leq 0$ by listing a set of ordered pairs. Then state whether this relation is a function. **(Lesson 1-1)**
$\{(-3, 14), (-2, 13), (-1, 12), (0, 11)\}$, yes

40. Given $f(x) = 4 + 6x - x^3$, find $f(14)$. **(Lesson 1-1)** -2656

41. Name all values of x that are not in the domain of $f(x) = \dfrac{x}{x^2 - 6}$. **(Lesson 1-1)**
$\pm\sqrt{6}$

42. College Entrance Exam Choose the best answer. $\dfrac{9^5 - 9^4}{8} = D$

(A) $\dfrac{1}{8}$ **(B)** $\dfrac{9}{8}$ **(C)** $\dfrac{9^3}{8}$ **(D)** 9^4 **(E)** $\dfrac{9^9}{8}$

18   CHAPTER 1   LINEAR RELATIONS AND FUNCTIONS

EXTENDING THE LESSON

Math Power: Problem Solving

$f(x) = 2x + 7$
$g(x) = 3x + n$
Find n so that $f(g(x)) = g(f(x))$.
14

Enrichment Masters Booklet, p. 2

1-3A Graphing Calculators: Graphing Linear Equations and Inequalities

The graphing calculator is a powerful tool for use in mathematics and other areas of life. On a graphing calculator, the **viewing window** for a graph is that portion of the coordinate grid displayed on the **graphics screen** of the calculator. Sometimes the viewing window is written as [left, right] by [bottom, top] or [Xmin, Xmax] by [Ymin, Ymax]. This means that a viewing window of [–5, 7] by [–10, 10] denotes the domain values of $-5 \leq x \leq 7$ and the range values of $-10 \leq y \leq 10$. A viewing window of [–10, 10] by [–10, 10] is called the **standard viewing window** and is a good viewing window to start with to solve a problem. This standard viewing window can be easily obtained on the TI-81 by pressing ZOOM 6.

Any viewing window can be set on both the Casio *fx*-7000G and the TI-81 by pressing the RANGE key. The **range screen** will appear and display the current settings for your viewing window as well as the **Xscl** and **Yscl**, or **scl**, which indicate the *x*-scale and *y*-scale. These labels set the frequency of the tick marks along each of the axes. For example, Xscl = 1 means that there will be a tick mark for every one unit along the *x*-axis. The **Xres** on the TI-81 establishes the quality of the resolution on the graphics screen. The Xres value can be set between 1 and 8, with 1 being the best resolution.

Example 1

Graph $y = -2x + 33$.

Use the standard viewing window.

TI-81: Y= (−) 2 X|T + 33
GRAPH

Casio: Graph (−) 2 ALPHA
X + 33 EXE

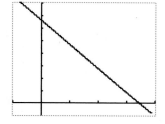

None of the graph is shown when you graph this equation in the standard viewing window. Pressing the RANGE key and setting the viewing window to [–5, 20] by [–5, 40] with scale factors of 5 for each scale will allow you to see where the graph intersects both the *x*- and the *y*-axes.

When the equation in Example 1 is graphed in the viewing window [–5, 20] by [–5, 40], it is a **complete graph**. A complete graph is a graph that shows all of the important characteristics of the graph on the graphics screen. For a linear equation, these are the *x*- and *y*-intercepts.

Once you have plotted a graph on the graphics screen of the Casio, it remains on the screen until it is cleared by pressing SHIFT Cls EXE or until the range values are changed.

Objective   Solve linear equations and inequalities on a graphing calculator.

Motivating the Lesson

In this lesson, students can devote their time to selecting an appropriate viewing rectangle for the graph of a linear function. Ask students to experiment with large and small view rectangles. Encourage them to discuss which viewing rectangle is more appropriate for graphing a particular equation.

Teaching Tip   Ask students to use their knowledge of the information from an equation to find the *x*- and *y*-intercepts of the graph before selecting a viewing window.

More Examples

1. Graph $y = -7x + 15$ on a graphing calculator.

[–5, 5] by [–5, 20]

More Examples

2. Use a graphing calculator to graph $y \geq -3x + 5$.

[−5, 5] by [−10, 10]

EVALUATING THE LESSON

Closing the Lesson

Ask students which of the following viewing windows they would choose to graph $y = 3x + 9$.
a. [−10, 10] by [−10, 10]
b. [−5, 5] by [−5, 5]
c. [−2, 2] by [−10, 10]
d. [−4, 4] by [−4, 20]
Ask students to discuss their reasoning.

APPLYING THE LESSON

Homework Exercises

Assignment Guide

All: 1–12

Additional Answers

Answers may vary. Sample answers are given.
1. [−10, 10] Xscl: 1, [−10, 10] Yscl: 1
2. [−10, 10] Xscl: 1, [−10, 10] Yscl: 1
3. [−10, 10] Xscl: 1, [−0.1, 0.1] Yscl: 0.01
4. [−5, 5] Xscl: 1, [−500, 500] Yscl: 100
5. [−10, 10] Xscl: 1, [−150, 50] Yscl: 10
6. [−20, 100] Xscl: 10, [−50, 50] Yscl: 10

Linear inequalities can be graphed on the TI-81 by using the "Shade(" command and entering a function for a lower boundary and a function for the upper boundary of the inequality. The calculator first graphs both functions and then shades above the first function entered and below the second function entered.

Before graphing an inequality, reset the range values to the standard viewing window and clear any functions in the Y = list. Do this by pressing Y= and then using the arrow keys and the CLEAR key to select and clear all functions. Next, return to the text screen by pressing 2nd and QUIT.

When graphing a linear inequality, you can use the Ymin range value as the lower boundary if the inequality asks for "$y \leq$," since the points that satisfy the inequality are below the graph of the related equation. Use the Ymax range value as the upper boundary if the inequality asks for "$y \geq$," since the points that satisfy the inequality are above the graph of the related equation.

Before graphing any inequality, first clear the graphics screen by pressing 2nd DRAW 1 ENTER.

Example 2

Graph $y \leq 3x + 4$ in the standard viewing window.

The inequality asks for points "less than or equal to", so we will use Ymin or −10 as the lower boundary and the expression for the related equation, $3x + 4$, as the upper boundary. Enter a comma between each boundary.

2nd DRAW 7 (−) 10 ALPHA
. 3 X|T + 4) ENTER

Since both the x- and the y-intercept of the line $y = 3x + 4$ are within the standard viewing window, this is a complete graph of the inequality.

You can use values other than Ymin or Ymax as the boundaries of an inequality. Any value below Ymin for "less than or equal to" and any value above Ymax for "greater than or equal to" will allow the calculator to graph the inequality in the viewing window that is set.

EXERCISES 1–12. See margin.

Use a graphing calculator to graph each equation. State the range values that you used to view a complete graph for each equation.

1. $y = 4x - 4$ 2. $y = -5x + 7$ 3. $y = 0.02x$
4. $y = 150x + 5$ 5. $y = -23x - 91$ 6. $y = 0.8x - 43$

Graph each linear inequality on a TI-81 and sketch the graph on a piece of paper.

7. $y \geq 2x + 5$ 8. $y \leq -3x + 6$ 9. $y \leq 0.3x - 0.47$
10. $y \geq 50x - 4$ 11. $y \leq 0.45x$ 12. $y \geq 24$

20 CHAPTER 1   LINEAR RELATIONS AND FUNCTIONS

For graphs for Exercises 7–12, see Teacher's Answer Key.

1-3 Linear Functions and Inequalities

Objectives
1–3A
1–3B

After studying this lesson, you should be able to:
- find zeros of linear functions, and
- graph linear equations and inequalities.

Application

Most VCRs allow you to record programs in three modes. They are the two-hour standard-play mode (SP), the four-hour long-play mode (LP), and the six-hour super-long-play mode (SLP). The two-hour mode, which allows you to record two hours of programs on the videotape, produces the highest-quality recording; the six-hour mode, which allows you to record six hours of programs, produces the lowest-quality recording.

Toshiki wants to fill a videotape with a movie that is three hours long. He wants the best quality possible. Since the two-hour mode would not be long enough to record the whole movie, and the four-hour mode would not fill the tape, Toshiki decides to begin in the four-hour mode and switch to the two-hour mode sometime during the program. Let's call the time that he switches the "switching time."

Let x = the switching time in hours. Since the movie is recorded for x hours in the four-hour mode, the fraction of the videotape filled in this mode is $\frac{x}{4}$. That means that $3 - x$ hours of the movie are to be recorded in the two-hour mode. Thus, the fraction of the videotape filled in the two-hour mode is $\frac{3-x}{2}$. Since the entire videotape will be filled with the movie, the sum of the two fractions must be 1. The following equation represents the situation.

$$\frac{x}{4} + \frac{3-x}{2} = 1$$
$$x + 2(3 - x) = 4 \qquad \textit{Multiply each side by 4.}$$
$$x = 2$$

The switching time is 2 hours. Thus, Toshiki should record the first two hours in the four-hour mode and the last hour in the two-hour mode.

NCTM Standards: 1–6, 8

Lesson Resources

- Practice Master 1–3
- Enrichment Master 1–3
- Evaluation Master, Quiz B, p. 9
- Technology Master, p. 2

 Transparency 1–3 contains the 5-Minute Check and a teaching aid for this lesson.

INTRODUCING THE LESSON

 5-Minute Check

(over Lesson 1–2)

Given $f(x) = 3x$ and $g(x) = x^2 - 1$, find each function.
1. $(f + g)(x)$ $x^2 + 3x - 1$
2. $(f - g)(x)$ $-x^2 + 3x + 1$
3. $[f \circ g](x)$ $3x^2 - 3$
4. $[g \circ f](x)$ $9x^2 - 1$
5. $f(x) = 5x - 4$. Find $f^{-1}(x)$.
   $f^{-1}(x) = \frac{x+4}{5}$

Motivating the Lesson

On the chalkboard or the overhead projector, graph a straight line crossing the x-axis at $x = 2$. Say that the line is the graph of the function $f(x)$. Ask students to give the value of x for which $f(x) = 0$.
2

ALTERNATE TEACHING STRATEGIES

Using Logical Reasoning

Students learn that $y = 0$ at the point where the graph of a linear equation crosses the x-axis. Point out that, for analogous reasons, $x = 0$ where the graph crosses the y-axis. For a given equation, students can easily find these points and use them to draw the graph of the equation.

Using Calculators

After they isolate one variable, students can use their calculators to find ordered pairs.
Example: $y = 2\frac{1}{4}x - 3\frac{3}{4}$, for $x = 1\frac{1}{2}$

Calculator:
2.25 ⓧ 1.5 ⊟ 3.75 ⊜ −0.375
ordered pair: (1.5, −0.375)

point out that it is very easy to find
ordered pairs by choosing simple
values of the independent variable
(for example, $x = 0$ and $x = 1$).
Have students find and graph a
third ordered pair as a check of
the first two.

Chalkboard Example

For Example 1

Graph $x + 2y - 4 = 0$.

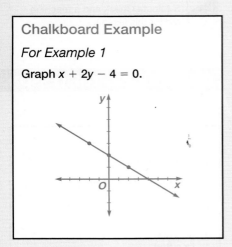

The equations on the previous page are **linear equations**. A linear equation has the form $Ax + By + C = 0$, where A and B are not both 0. Its graph is always a straight line. The graph of the equation $x = 2$ is shown at the right. *Does this equation represent a function?*

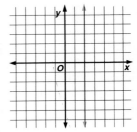

Each solution of a linear equation is an ordered pair. Each ordered pair corresponds to a point in the coordinate plane. Since two points determine a line, only two points are needed to graph a linear equation.

Example 1

Graph $3x - 2y = 6$.

Solve for y. Then find two ordered pairs that are solutions of the equation.

$$-2y = -3x + 6$$
$$y = \frac{3}{2}x - 3$$

x	y	(x, y)
0	-3	$(0, -3)$
1	$-\frac{3}{2}$	$\left(1, -\frac{3}{2}\right)$

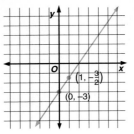

Graph the ordered pairs and connect them with a line.
Does this equation represent a function?

Not all linear equations represent functions, as shown by the example of $x = 2$ above. A **linear function** is defined as follows.

Linear Function

A linear function is defined by $f(x) = mx + b$, where m and b are real numbers.

Values of x for which $f(x) = 0$ are called **zeros** of the function f. For a linear function, the zeros can be found by solving the equation $mx + b = 0$. If $m \neq 0$, then $-\frac{b}{m}$ is the only zero of the function. The graph of the function crosses, or intercepts, the x-axis at the point with coordinates $\left(-\frac{b}{m}, 0\right)$. Thus, $-\frac{b}{m}$ is called the **x-intercept**.

If $m = 0$, then $f(x) = b$. The graph is a horizontal line. This function is called a **constant function**. A constant function either has *no* zeros ($b \neq 0$), or every value of x is a zero ($b = 0$).

Example 2

Find the zero of each function. Then graph the function.

a. $f(x) = 3x - 1$

a. To find the zeros of $f(x)$, set $f(x)$ equal to 0 and solve for x.

$$3x - 1 = 0$$
$$x = \frac{1}{3}$$

$\frac{1}{3}$ is a zero of the function. So, the coordinates of one point on the graph are $\left(\frac{1}{3}, 0\right)$. Find the coordinates of a second point. When $x = 1$, $f(x) = 3(1) - 1$, or 2. Thus, the coordinates of a second point are $(1, 2)$.

b. $f(x) = 3$

b. Since $m = 0$ and $b = 3$, this function has no zeros. The graph of this function is a horizontal line 3 units above the x-axis.

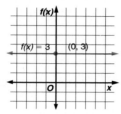

The graph of a **linear inequality** is not a linear function. However, you can use the graphs of linear functions to help graph linear inequalities. The graph of $y = -\frac{1}{2}x + 2$ is a line that separates the coordinate plane into two regions, as shown at the right. The line described by $y = -\frac{1}{2}x + 2$ is called the **boundary** of each region. If the boundary is part of a graph, it is drawn as a solid line. If the boundary is not part of a graph, it is drawn as a dashed line. The graph of $y > -\frac{1}{2}x + 2$ is the region above the line. The graph of $y < -\frac{1}{2}x + 2$ is the region below the line.

LESSON 1-3   LINEAR FUNCTIONS AND INEQUALITIES   23

LESSON 1–3   LINEAR FUNCTIONS AND INEQUALITIES   23

Example 3 | **Graph** $8 - y \geq 3x$.

$$8 - y \geq 3x$$
$$-y \geq 3x - 8$$
$$y \leq -3x + 8$$

Remember to reverse the direction of the inequality symbol when you multiply by a negative number.

Notice that the boundary line is included since the inequality symbol is less than or equal to.

Example 4

APPLICATION

Business

Mike Welz can spend up to \$35 per day plus \$0.30 per mile when renting a car to use on company business. The total cost of the daily rental (C) is a function of the total miles driven (m).

a. **Write a linear inequality that expresses the acceptable daily rental car cost.**

b. **Graph the inequality.**

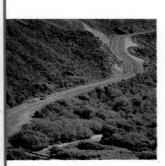

a. A linear equation that expresses the acceptable daily cost of a rental car is $C = 35 + 0.30m$. Since Mr. Welz's company will only pay up to that amount, the inequality would be $C \leq 35 + 0.30m$.

b. The graph of the inequality is shown at the right. Since costs cannot be negative, the graph is only in the first quadrant.

Relations such as $2 < x + y \leq 5$ can also be graphed. The graph of this relation is the intersection of the graph of $2 < x + y$ and the graph of $x + y \leq 5$. Notice that the boundary $x + y = 5$ is part of the graph, but the boundary $2 = x + y$ is not part of the graph.

CHECKING FOR UNDERSTANDING

Communicating Mathematics

Read and study the lesson to answer each question. 1–2. See margin.

1. **Describe** the process you would use to graph $-5 \leq x - 5y \leq 6$.

2. **Describe** how Mike Welz (in Example 4) could determine if he would be completely reimbursed for his rental car travel, if his rental car bill was \$72.45 on Thursday, and he drove 186 miles.

Guided Practice

Name the zero of each function whose graph is shown.

3.

(0, 3)
(2, 0)

$f(x)=-\frac{3}{2}x+3$

4.

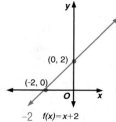

(0, 2)
(-2, 0)

-2 $f(x)=x+2$

5.

(0, 5)

none $f(x)=5$

Of $(0,0)$, $(3,2)$, $(-4,2)$, or $(-2,4)$, name the ordered pair(s) that satisfy each inequality.

6. $3x-4y \geq -5$
$(0,0), (3,2)$

7. $y \neq x-5$
all points

8. $x > 4y+3$
none

Write an inequality that describes each graph.

9.

x=2

$x > 2$

10.

y=3

$y \leq 3$

11.

y=x+2

$y \leq x+2$

Graph each equation or inequality. 12–13. See Teacher's Answer Key.

12. $3x = 2y$

13. $2 < 2x + y < 8$

EXERCISES

Practice

Write an inequality that describes each graph.

14.

y = -2x - 3

$y > -2x - 3$

15.

y=4
y=1

$1 \leq y \leq 4$

16.

-x+y=3
-x+y=-2

$-2 \leq -x + y \leq 3$

Find the zero of each function.

17. $f(x) = 0.5x + 6$ -12

18. $f(x) = 14x$ 0

19. $f(x) = 9x + 5$ $-\frac{5}{9}$

20. $f(x) = 5x - 8$ $\frac{8}{5}$

21. $f(x) = 19$ none

22. $f(x) = 3x + 1$ $-\frac{1}{3}$

LESSON 1–3   LINEAR FUNCTIONS AND INEQUALITIES   25

Closing the Lesson

Modeling Activity   Have students give an example of a linear function. Have them describe how to graph the function and where on the graph they would find the zeros of the function.   **Graph by connecting two points. The zero is the x-intercept.**

APPLYING THE LESSON

Homework Exercises

Assignment Guide

Average: 14–34, 38, 39, 41–47
Enriched: 16–38, 40–47
All: Mid-Chapter Review, 1–10

The red A, B, and C flags, printed only in the Teacher's Wraparound Edition, indicate the level of difficulty of the exercises.

Chapter 1, Quiz B, (Lesson 1–3), is available in the *Evaluation Masters*, p. 9.

Practice Masters Booklet, p. 3

RETEACHING THE LESSON

Show students that they can easily find two ordered pairs and graph an equation by using the *x*- and *y*-intercepts of the graph. Substitute *x* = 0 in the equation to find the *y*-intercept. Substitute *y* = 0 in the equation to find the *x*-intercept. Graph the intercepts and draw a line through them.

1-3 Practice Worksheet
NAME _____ DATE _____

Linear Functions and Inequalities
Write an inequality that describes each graph.

1. $y \geq -2x - 4$

2. $-2 \leq y \leq 4$

3. $\frac{3}{4}x - 3 \leq y \leq \frac{4}{5}x + 4$

Find the zero of each function.

4. $f(x) = 0.2x + 10$ -50

5. $f(x) = 11.5x$ 0

6. $f(x) = 13x - 9$ $\frac{9}{13}$

7. $f(x) = -3$ none

8. $f(x) = -5x + 6$ $\frac{6}{5}$

9. $f(x) = 0.3x + 0.2$ $-\frac{2}{3}$

Graph each equation or inequality.

10. $y = 3x - 2$

11. $1 - y = 2x$

12. $x \geq -2$

13. $y = |2x + 4|$

14. $-y > 2x + 2$

15. $-4 \leq x - 2y \leq 6$

T3
Glencoe Division, Macmillan/McGraw-Hill

LESSON 1–3   LINEAR FUNCTIONS AND INEQUALITIES   25

Exercise Note

For Exercises 36–37, students should graph ordered pairs as in the earlier exercises. Remind them that the absolute value of all values of a variable is positive.

Using Technology

The program given in Exercise 38 is for use with a TI–81 graphing calculator. For other programmable calculators, have students consult their owner's manual for commands similar to those presented here.

Additional Answers

40b. $D(6.15)$ represents the demand for soybeans, given that the price of soybeans for that month is $6.15 per bushel.

41a.

$y = 0.82x + 24$

41c. If the nation had no disposable income, personal consumption expenditures would be $24 billion.

Graph each equation or inequality. 23–37. See Teacher's Answer Key.

23. $y = 3x - 2$ **24.** $y - 7 = x$ **25.** $x + 2y = 5$

26. $x = -\frac{1}{2}y$ **27.** $4y = 2 + 3x$ **28.** $y = |3x - 2|$

29. $x < 5$ **30.** $y > -x$ **31.** $x - y < 5$

32. $2y \leq x - 5$ **33.** $-y < 2x + 1$ **34.** $y \geq \frac{2}{5}x + \frac{19}{5}$

35. $-2 \leq x + 2y \leq 4$ **36.** $y > |x|$ **37.** $|x + 3| < y - 1$

Programming

38. The following program will plot points in a relation.

```
Prgm 1: PLOTPTS
:All-Off                          Deactivates all current functions.
:ClrDraw                          Clears the graphing screen.
:Lbl 1                            Sets the marker at position 1.
:Disp "X="                        Displays the message "X=".
:Input X                          Accepts an X value.
:Disp "Y="                        Displays the message "Y=".
:Input Y                          Accepts a Y value.
:PT-ON(X,Y)                       Plots the point (X, Y).
:Pause                            Waits until the user presses the ENTER key.
:Disp "PRESS 0 TO QUIT OR 1       Displays memory.
 TO PLOT MORE POINTS"
:Input A                          Accepts an A value.
:If A = 0                         Tests whether A is 0.
:End                              Ends program if A = 0.
:Goto 1                           Goes back to the line Lbl "1" and continues.
```

38. See students' work.

Find three ordered pairs that are solutions of each equation and graph them.
a. $2x + 5y = 8$ **b.** $y = 4x - 9$

Critical Thinking

39. A linear function may have zero, one, or infinitely many zeros. Illustrate all three of these situations. See margin.

Applications and Problem Solving

40. Economics The average daily demand for the sale of soybean futures may be represented by a function known as a *demand function*. For example, in September of 1990, the average number of bushels demanded daily was 103.7 million. The function $D(p) = \dfrac{560}{p}$ represents the demand for soybeans that particular month, where p is the price in dollars per bushel ($p > 0$). See margin.
a. Find $D(6.15)$. 91.06   **b.** Interpret the meaning of $D(6.15)$.

26   CHAPTER 1   LINEAR RELATIONS AND FUNCTIONS

Additonal Answers

39.

$y = x + 1$

one zero

$y = 3$

no zeros

$y = 0$

infinitely many zeros

41. Economics The equation $y = 0.82x + 24$, where $x \geq 0$, expresses a relationship between a nation's disposable income, x (in billions of dollars), and personal consumption expenditures, y (in billions of dollars). Economists call this type of equation a *consumption function*.

   a. Graph the consumption function. See margin.

   b. Name the y-intercept. $24 billion

   c. Explain the significance of the y-intercept. See margin.

Mixed Review

42. $\{(-4, 16), (-3, 9), (-2, 4)\}$, yes

42. Given that x is an integer, state the relation representing $y = x^2$ and $-4 \leq x \leq -2$ by listing a set of ordered pairs. Then state whether this relation is a function. **(Lesson 1-1)**

43. Given $f(x) = 4 + 6x - x^3$, find $f(2 + a)$. **(Lesson 1-1)** $8 - 6a - 6a^2 - a^3$

44. $x^2 + 2x - 4$, $-x^2 + 2x + 4$

44. Given $f(x) = 2x$ and $g(x) = x^2 - 4$, find $(f + g)(x)$ and $(f - g)(x)$. **(Lesson 1-2)**

45. Find $[f \circ g](x)$ if $f(x) = \frac{2}{5}x$ and $g(x) = 40x - 10$. **(Lesson 1-2)** $16x - 4$

46. Determine if $f(x) = 3x + 5$ and $g(x) = \frac{x + 5}{3}$ are inverses of each other. Write *yes* or *no*. **(Lesson 1-2)** no

47. College Entrance Exam Choose the best answer.

   If $\dfrac{2x - 3}{x} = \dfrac{3 - x}{2}$, which of the following could be a value for x? A

   (A) -3 **(B)** -1 **(C)** 37 **(D)** 5 **(E)** 15

MID-CHAPTER REVIEW

1. Consider the relation $\{(2, 3), (5, 2), (3, 0), (6, 1), (5, -1)\}$. **(Lesson 1-1)**

   a. State the domain and range of the relation. d: $\{2, 3, 5, 6\}$; r : $\{-1, 0, 1, 2, 3, \}$

   b. Is the relation a function? Why or why not?
     No, the element 5 in the domain is paired with both 2 and −1 in the range.

Given $f(x) = 4 + 6x - x^3$, find each value. **(Lesson 1-1)**

2. $f(0)$ 4   **3.** $f(-1)$ −1   **4.** $f\left(\frac{1}{2}\right)$ $6\frac{7}{8}$ **5.** $f(3k)$ $4 + 18k - 27k^3$

6. Name all values of x that are not in the domain of $f(x) = \dfrac{x + 1}{x^2 - 5}$. **(Lesson 1-1)** $\pm\sqrt{5}$

7. If $f(x) = x^2$ and $g(x) = \dfrac{1}{x}$, find $[f \circ g](x)$ and $[g \circ f](x)$. **(Lesson 1-2)** $\frac{1}{x^2}$, $\frac{1}{x^2}$

8. Find the inverse of $f(x) = \dfrac{7 - x}{4}$. **(Lesson 1-2)** $f^{-1}(x) = 7 - 4x$

Graph each equation or inequality. **(Lesson 1-3)** 9 –10. See margin.

9. $2x - 4y = 8$ **10.** $-2x + 7 \geq y$

EXTENDING THE LESSON

Math Power: Communication

Write a paragraph explaining why a linear inequality is not a linear function.

Sample answer: The graph of a linear inequality is a half plane. Any vertical line will pass through an infinite number of points in the half plane. Therefore, the graph fails the vertical line test, and the inequality is not a function.

Mid-Chapter Review

The Mid-Chapter Review provides students with a brief review of the concepts and skills in Lessons 1–1 through 1–3. Lesson numbers are given at the end of problems or instruction lines so students may review concepts not yet mastered.

Additional Answers
Mid-Chapter Review

9.

$2x - 4y = 8$

10.

$-2x + 7 \geq y$

Enrichment Masters Booklet, p. 3

1-3 | NAME _____ DATE _____
Enrichment Worksheet

Inverses and Symmetry

1. Use the coordinate axes at the right to graph the function $f(x) = x$ and the points $A(2, 4)$, $A'(4, 2)$, $B(-1, 3)$, $B'(3, -1)$, $C(0, -5)$, and $C'(-5, 0)$.

2. Describe the apparent relationship between the graph of the function $f(x) = x$ and any two points with interchanged abscissas and ordinates.
Sample answers: The points are mirror images of each other in the graph of $f(x) = x$; the points are symmetric to each other with respect to the graph of $f(x) = x$; the points are the same distance from but on opposite sides of the graph of $f(x) = x$.

3. Find the inverse of the function $f(x) = 2x - 4$. Then graph $f(x)$ and $f^{-1}(x)$ on the coordinate axes at the right.

4. Describe the apparent relationship between the graphs you have drawn and the graph of the function $f(x) = x$.
Sample answers: They are mirror images of each other in the graph of $f(x) = x$; they intersect $f(x) = x$ at the same point and at the same angle.

Recall from your earlier math courses that two points P and Q are said to be *symmetric* about line ℓ provided that P and Q are equidistant from ℓ and on a perpendicular through ℓ. The line ℓ is the *axis of symmetry* and P and Q are *images* of each other in ℓ. The image of the point $P(a, b)$ in the line $y = x$ is the point $Q(b, a)$.

5. Explain why the graphs of a function $f(x)$ and its inverse, $f^{-1}(x)$, are symmetric about the line $y = x$.
The graph of $f^{-1}(x)$ consists of ordered pairs formed by interchanging the coordinates of the ordered pairs of $f(x)$. Therefore, each point $P(a, b)$ in $f(x)$ has an image $Q(b, a)$ in $f^{-1}(x)$ that is symmetric with it about the line $y = x$.

T 3
Glencoe Division, Macmillan/McGraw-Hill

Using Technology

Objective This optional page shows how graphing software can be used to determine if two functions are inverses of each other.

Teaching Suggestions

Point out to students that they may also use the software to visualize if two functions are inverses of each other. Have them graph each function separately with the line $y = x$. Functions that are inverses of each other are reflections of each other over the line $y = x$. If the graph of one function intersects the line $y = x$, then the inverse of that function also intersects the line $y = x$ at the same point(s). Have them verify each pair of inverses visually.

Note that the sequence of commands given in the example has the computer perform the algebraic steps to verify that two functions are inverses of each other.

Additional Answers

4. If $g(x)$ and $f(x)$ are inverses and one of the graphs intersects the line $y = x$, the other graph will also intersect the line at the same point.

Technology

Graphing Linear Relations

BASIC
Spreadsheets
► Software

You can use IBM's *Mathematics Exploration Toolkit (MET)* to determine if two functions are inverses.

Example

Determine if $f(x) = \dfrac{x-5}{4}$ and $g(x) = 4x + 5$ are inverses.

First, enter the expression on the right side of the equation. Then, define the function. The steps for $f(x)$ are shown. Follow the same procedure for $g(x)$.

Enter	Result	
$(x-5)/4$	$\dfrac{x-5}{4}$	
def f	$f(x) = \dfrac{x-5}{4}$	*Defines the function f(x).*
sto p		*Stores f(x) in p.*

Then, find $[f \circ g](x)$ and $[g \circ f](x)$.

Enter	Result	Enter	Result
$f(g(x))$	$f(g(x))$	$g(f(x))$	$g(f(x))$
simp	$\dfrac{f(x)-5}{4}$	simp	$4g(x) + 5$
simp	$\dfrac{4x+5-5}{4}$	simp	$4\left(\dfrac{x-5}{4}\right) + 5$
simp	x	simp	x

Therefore, since $[f \circ g](x) = [g \circ f](x) = x$, the functions are inverses. Graph the two equations on the same screen. The steps for $f(x)$ are shown.

Enter	Result	
p	$f(x) = \dfrac{x-5}{4}$	*Recalls p to the screen.*
subs y $f(x)$	$y = \dfrac{x-5}{4}$	*Replaces f(x) with y.*
gra		*Graphs p.*

EXERCISES

Use *MET* to determine if the given functions are inverses of each other. Write *yes* or *no*. 4. See margin for graphs.

1. $f(x) = 3x + 7$
$g(x) = \dfrac{x-7}{3}$ yes

2. $f(x) = x + 4$
$g(x) = x - 4$ yes

3. $f(x) = -5x + 2$
$g(x) = 5x - 2$ no

4. Graph each pair of functions and $y = x$ on the same screen. What is true about the intersection of the graphs of $f(x)$ and $g(x)$? The intersection is always on the line $y = x$.

1-4 Distance and Slope

Objectives
1–4A
1–4B
1–4C

After studying this lesson, you should be able to:
- find the distance between two points,
- find the slope of a line through two points, and
- prove geometric theorems involving slope, distance, and midpoints analytically.

Application

The concept of distance is one we use daily in so many different ways that we almost take it for granted. We use distance to estimate the desired number of car lengths between us and the car in front of us, to decide whether a basket made in a basketball game is worth two points or three, to determine the margin of victory in the Indianapolis 500, or to estimate our arrival time when we travel.

In mathematics, the concept of distance is extremely useful and very important. The distance between two points on a number line can be found by using absolute value. Let A and B be two points on a line with coordinates a and b, respectively. The distance between A and B is $|a - b|$ or $|b - a|$.

Recall that RT denotes the length of $\overline{RT}$, the segment with endpoints R and T.

The distance between points in the coordinate plane can also be found. Consider points $R(-3, 2)$ and $S(4, 12)$. To find RS, first choose a point T such that $\overline{RT}$ is parallel to the x-axis and $\overline{ST}$ is parallel to the y-axis. T has coordinates $(4, 2)$. Since S has the same abscissa as T, ST is equal to the absolute value of the difference in the ordinates of S and T, $|12 - 2|$. Similarly, RT is equal to the absolute value of the difference in the abscissas of R and T, $|4 - (-3)|$.

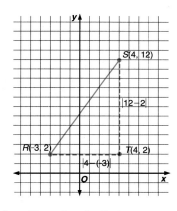

Since $\triangle RST$ is a right triangle, RS can be found by using the Pythagorean theorem, which is illustrated on the next page.

LESSON 1-4 DISTANCE AND SLOPE 29

NCTM Standards: 1–6, 8

Lesson Resources

- Practice Master 1–4
- Enrichment Master 1–4
- Evaluation Master, Quiz C, p. 10
- Activity Master, p. 2
- Transparency 1–4 contains the 5-Minute Check and a teaching aid for this lesson.

INTRODUCING THE LESSON

Five-Minute Check
(over Lesson 1–3)

1. Find the zero of the function $f(x) = 9x - 3$. $\frac{1}{3}$
2. The graph of a function is a line that crosses the x–axis at $(5, 0)$ and the y–axis at $(0, -3)$. Name the zero of the function.   5
3. Graph $2x + y - 4 = 0$.

Prerequisite Skills

Students should be able to use the Pythagorean Theorem.
1. The two legs of a right triangle measure 16 units and 12 units. Find the length of the hypotenuse.   **20 units**
2. The hypotenuse of a right triangle measures 29 units. Find the length of one leg if the other leg measures 21 units.   **20 units**

Motivating the Lesson

Ask students to find four points in the coordinate plane that are exactly 5 units from the point $(3, -2)$.   **(8, –2), (–2, –2), (3, 3), and (3, –7)**

ALTERNATE TEACHING STRATEGIES

Using Connections

Point out the connection between slope and rate of change. For example, suppose a tree increases in height 3 feet per year. The height of the tree (h) is a function of its age in years (y). That is, $h = 3y$. The graph of h will have a slope of 3. Have students name other common rates, define them as functions, and specify the slopes of the graphs of the functions.

Using Communication

Mention the mnemonic device "rise over run" as a means of finding the slope of a line. The slope is the vertical "rise" between two points on the line, divided by the horizontal "run" from one point to the other.

Teaching Tip Before Example 1, point out that in order to use the distance formula, either point can be designated as (x_1, y_1). The other point will be (x_2, y_2). That is, students can find the difference between abscissas and ordinates in either order in the formula. Also, point out that distance always requires a unit of measure.

Chalkboard Example

For Example 1

Find the distance between (–2, –5) and (10, 0). **13**

$$(RS)^2 = (RT)^2 + (ST)^2 \qquad \textit{Pythagorean theorem}$$

$$RS = \sqrt{(RT)^2 + (ST)^2}$$

$$= \sqrt{|4 - (-3)|^2 + |12 - 2|^2}$$

$$= \sqrt{7^2 + 10^2}$$

$$= \sqrt{149} \text{ or about } 12.2 \qquad \overline{RS} \text{ is about 12.2 units long.}$$

Assume (x_1, y_1) and (x_2, y_2) represent the coordinates of any two points in the plane. The figure at the right illustrates how the formula for finding the distance between (x_1, y_1) and (x_2, y_2) is derived.

$$d = \sqrt{|x_2 - x_1|^2 + |y_2 - y_1|^2} \qquad \textit{Pythagorean theorem}$$

$$= \sqrt{(x_2 - x_1)^2 + (y_2 - y_1)^2}$$

Why does $|x_2 - x_1|^2 = (x_2 - x_1)^2$?

Distance Formula for Two Points	The distance, *d* units, between two points with coordinates (x_1, y_1) and (x_2, y_2) is given by the following formula. $$d = \sqrt{(x_2 - x_1)^2 + (y_2 - y_1)^2}$$

Example 1

Find the distance between (**4**, **–5**) and (**–2**, **3**).

$$d = \sqrt{(x_2 - x_1)^2 + (y_2 - y_1)^2}$$

$$= \sqrt{(-2 - 4)^2 + (3 - (-5))^2} \qquad \textit{Let } (x_1, y_1) = (4, -5) \textit{ and } (x_2, y_2) = (-2, 3).$$

$$= \sqrt{(-6)^2 + 8^2}$$

$$= \sqrt{100} \text{ or } 10$$

The distance is 10 units.

Slope is often defined as $\frac{rise}{run}$.

Any two distinct points determine a line. The **slope** of the line is the ratio of the change in the ordinates of the coordinates of the points to the corresponding change in the abscissas. The slope of a line is constant.

Definition of Slope	The slope, *m*, of the line through (x_1, y_1) and (x_2, y_2) is given by the following equation, if $x_2 \neq x_1$. $$m = \frac{y_2 - y_1}{x_2 - x_1}$$

---

30   CHAPTER 1   LINEAR RELATIONS AND FUNCTIONS

Example 2

APPLICATION

Economics

A relationship between a nation's disposable income, x (in billions of dollars), and personal consumption expenditures, y (in billions of dollars), is shown in the table at the right. Find the rate of change of personal consumption expenditures with respect to disposable income.

x	y
56	50
76	67.2

The rate of change is the slope of the line containing points at $(56, 50)$ and $(76, 67.2)$. Find the slope of this line.

$$m = \frac{y_2 - y_1}{x_2 - x_1}$$
$$= \frac{67.2 - 50}{76 - 56} \quad \textit{Let } x_1 = 56, y_1 = 50, x_2 = 76, \textit{ and } y_2 = 67.2.$$
$$= \frac{17.2}{20} \text{ or } 0.86$$

Economists call this result the *marginal propensity to consume (MPC)*. An MPC of 0.86 means that for each \$1 increase in disposable income, consumption increases \$0.86. In other words, 86% of each additional dollar earned is spent and 14% is saved.

Example 3

Graph the line through $(4, 5)$ and $(4, -3)$. Then, find the slope of the line.

$$m = \frac{-3 - 5}{4 - 4}$$
$$= -\frac{8}{0} \quad \textit{Division by zero is undefined.}$$

Because the abscissas of the two points are the same, the slope is undefined. Any line parallel to the y-axis has undefined slope and is of the form $x = c$.

Many theorems from plane geometry can be more easily proven by analytic methods. That is, they can be proven by placing the figure in a coordinate system and using algebra to express and draw conclusions about the geometric relationships. The study of coordinate geometry from an algebraic perspective is called **analytic geometry**.

The formulas for distance, slope, and midpoints are frequently used in analytic geometry. The distance formula can be used to find the coordinates of the midpoint of a line segment. In the figure at the right, the midpoint of $\overline{P_1P_2}$ is P_m.

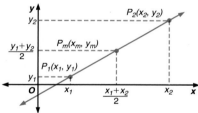

LESSON 1-4 DISTANCE AND SLOPE 31

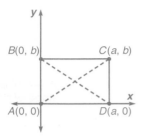
Midpoint of a Line Segment	If the coordinates of P_1 and P_2 are (x_1, y_1) and (x_2, y_2), respectively, then the midpoint of $\overline{P_1 P_2}$ has coordinates $\left(\dfrac{x_1 + x_2}{2}, \dfrac{y_1 + y_2}{2}\right)$.

Example 4

Find the midpoint of the segment that has endpoints at (5, 8) and (2, 6).

The midpoint is at $\left(\dfrac{5+2}{2}, \dfrac{8+6}{2}\right)$ or $\left(\dfrac{7}{2}, 7\right)$.

How can you show that the midpoint is equidistant from the endpoints?

When using analytic methods to prove theorems from geometry, the position of the figure in the coordinate plane can be arbitrarily selected as long as size and shape are preserved. This means that the figure may be translated, rotated, or reflected from its original position. For polygons, a vertex is usually located at the origin and one side is made to coincide with the *x*-axis, as shown below.

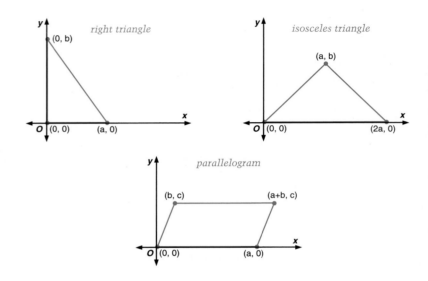

Example 5

Prove that the medians to the congruent sides of an isosceles triangle are congruent.

In $\triangle ABC$, let the vertices be $A(0, 0)$ and $B(a, 0)$. Since $\overline{AC}$ and $\overline{BC}$ are congruent sides, let the third vertex be $C\left(\dfrac{a}{2}, b\right)$. Let D be the midpoint of $\overline{AC}$ and let E be the midpoint of $\overline{BC}$. First, find the coordinates of D and E by using the midpoint formula.

The coordinates of D are: $\left(\dfrac{\frac{a}{2}+0}{2}, \dfrac{b+0}{2}\right)$ or $\left(\dfrac{a}{4}, \dfrac{b}{2}\right)$.

The coordinates of E are: $\left(\dfrac{\frac{a}{2}+a}{2}, \dfrac{b+0}{2}\right)$ or $\left(\dfrac{3a}{4}, \dfrac{b}{2}\right)$.

Then find the measure of each median using the distance formula.

$$AE = \sqrt{\left(\frac{3a}{4}-0\right)^2 + \left(\frac{b}{2}\right)^2} = \frac{1}{2}\sqrt{\frac{9a^2}{4}+b^2}$$

$$BD = \sqrt{\left(a-\frac{a}{4}\right)^2 + \left(0-\frac{b}{2}\right)^2} = \frac{1}{2}\sqrt{\frac{9a^2}{4}+b^2}$$

Since $AE = BD$, the medians to the congruent sides of an isosceles triangle are congruent.

CHECKING FOR UNDERSTANDING

Communicating Mathematics

Read and study the lesson to answer each question. 2–3. See margin.

1. **Describe** three other ways, not mentioned in this lesson, that you use distance in your everyday life. Answers will vary.

2. If you were given the coordinates of two points, $(-2, 3)$ and $(7, -9)$, describe how you would decide which point is (x_1, y_1) and which is (x_2, y_2) when finding the slope of the line passing through them.

3. **Research** the meaning of the term *disposable income*.

Guided Practice

5. 10, undefined   6. $2\sqrt{10}$, 3

Find the distance between the points with the given coordinates. Then, find the slope of the line passing through each pair of points.

4. $(4, 1), (7, 1)$ 3, 0
5. $(5, 1), (5, 11)$
6. $(1, 3), (-1, -3)$

7. $(0, 0), (-4, -3)$ $5, \dfrac{3}{4}$
8. $(-1, 1), (4, 13)$ $13, \dfrac{12}{5}$
9. $(-2, 2), (0, 4)$ $2\sqrt{2}$, 1

Find the perimeter of the triangle having vertices with the given coordinates.

10. $(2, 3), (14, 3), (14, 8)$ 30
11. $(2, 2), (5, 2), (2, 6)$ 12
12. $(1, -1), (1, 3), (-2, -1)$ 12
13. $(3, 3), (3, -9), (-2, 3)$ 30

14. The vertices of a rectangle are at $(-3, 1), (-1, 3), (3, -1), (1, -3)$. Find the area of the rectangle. 16 square units

15. The vertices of a triangle are at $(5, 0), (-3, 2)$, and $(-1, -4)$. Find the coordinates of the midpoints of the sides. $(1, 1), (-2, -1), (2, -2)$

RETEACHING THE LESSON

Encourage students to estimate slopes, coordinates of midpoints, and distances between points. Distance can be estimated with a rough sketch. Point out that lines with positive slopes slant up to the right, those with negative slopes slant up to the left. The greater the absolute value of the slope, the steeper the line.

Checking for Understanding

Exercises 1–15 are designed to help you assess students' understanding through reading, writing, speaking, and modeling. You should work through Exercises 1–3 with your students and then monitor their work on Exercises 4–15.

Closing the Lesson

Writing Activity   Write the coordinates of two points on the chalkboard. Have students find the distance between the points, the slope of the line passing through the points, and the midpoint of the segment connecting the points.

Additional Answers

2. It does not matter which point is (x_1, y_1) and which point is (x_2, y_2). Either way, the slope is $-\dfrac{4}{3}$.

3. Disposable income is the money that households have left to spend or save after taxes have been paid.

Practice Masters Booklet, p. 4

Assignment Guide

Average: 16–32, 35, 36, 39–44
Enriched: 22–35, 37–44

The red A, B, and C flags, printed only in the Teacher's Wraparound Edition, indicate the level of difficulty of the exercises.

Chapter 1, Quiz C, (Lesson 1–4), is available in the *Evaluation Masters,* p. 10.

Exercise Note

In Exercises 24–27, students should check to see whether opposite sides of the figure are parallel (that is, they have the same slope) or, alternatively, whether they are the same length.

Additional Answers

32a. $BD = \sqrt{(c - 0)^2 + (a - 0)^2}$
$= \sqrt{c^2 + a^2}$
$AC = \sqrt{(c - 0)^2 + (0 - a)^2}$
$= \sqrt{c^2 + a^2}$
Thus, $\overline{AC} \cong \overline{BD}$.

32b. The midpoint of $\overline{AC}$ is $\left(\frac{c}{2}, \frac{a}{2}\right)$. The midpoint of $\overline{BD}$ is $\left(\frac{c}{2}, \frac{a}{2}\right)$. Therefore, the diagonals intersect at their common midpoint, $E\left(\frac{c}{2}, \frac{a}{2}\right)$.
Thus, $\overline{AE} \cong \overline{EC}$ and $\overline{BE} \cong \overline{ED}$.

32c. The diagonals of a rectangle bisect each other.

EXERCISES

Practice **Find the distance between the points with the given coordinates. Then, find the slope of the line passing through each pair of points.**

16. $(5, -3), (-1, -6)$ $3\sqrt{5}, \frac{1}{2}$

17. $(6, 0), (0, 6)$ $6\sqrt{2}, -1$

18. $(5, 7), (0, 0)$ $\sqrt{74}, \frac{7}{5}$

19. $(1, -5), (-7, 11)$ $8\sqrt{5}, -2$

20. $(3, a), (8, a)$ $5, 0$

21. $(b, 6 + a), (b, a + 3)$ 3, undefined

22. $(r, s), (r + 2, s - 1)$ $\sqrt{5}, -\frac{1}{2}$

23. $(n, 4n), (n + 1, n)$
$\sqrt{1 + 9n^2}, -3n$

Determine whether the figure with vertices with the given coordinates is a parallelogram.

24. $(3, 4), (6, 2), (8, 7), (5, 9)$ yes

25. $(4, 11), (8, 14), (4, 19), (0, 15)$ no

26. $(-2, 1), (-1, 5), (-5, 6), (-6, 2)$ yes

27. $(2, -3), (-2, 3), (-3, -2), (3, 2)$ yes

Collinear points lie on the same line. Find the value of k for which points with each set of coordinates is collinear. *Remember, the slope of each line is constant.*

28. $(4, 0), (k, 3), (4, -3)$ 4

29. $(2, -5), (-4, -11), (k, 1)$ 8

30. $(7, -2), (0, 5), (3, k)$ 2

31. $(15, 1), (-3, -8), (3, k)$ -5

32. See margin.

32. Consider rectangle $ABCD$.
   a. Prove that $\overline{AC} \cong \overline{BD}$.
   b. Prove that $\overline{AE} \cong \overline{EC}$ and $\overline{BE} \cong \overline{ED}$.
   c. What can you conclude about the diagonals of a rectangle?

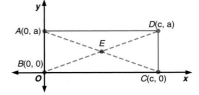

Prove using analytic methods. 33–35. See Teacher's Answer Key.

33. The line segment joining the midpoints of two sides of a triangle is equal in length to one-half the third side.

34. The median of a trapezoid is equal in length to one-half the sum of the lengths of the parallel sides.

Critical Thinking **35.** Prove analytically that the segments joining midpoints of successive sides of an isosceles trapezoid form a rhombus.

33. Prove that $DE = \frac{1}{2}AB = \frac{1}{2}a$.

$D = \left(\frac{b + 0}{2}, \frac{c + 0}{2}\right) = \left(\frac{b}{2}, \frac{c}{2}\right)$

$E = \left(\frac{a + b}{2}, \frac{0 + c}{2}\right) = \left(\frac{a + b}{2}, \frac{c}{2}\right)$

$DE = \sqrt{\left(\frac{b}{2} - \frac{a + b}{2}\right)^2 + \left(\frac{c}{2} - \frac{c}{2}\right)^2}$

$= \sqrt{\left(-\frac{a}{2}\right)^2}$

$= \frac{a}{2}$

34. Prove that $EF = \frac{1}{2}(AD + BC)$.

The coordinates of E are $\left(\frac{b}{2}, \frac{c}{2}\right)$.

The coordinates of F are $\left(\frac{a + d}{2}, \frac{c}{2}\right)$.

$AD = a \qquad BC = d - b$

Therefore, $EF = \sqrt{\left(\frac{a + d}{2} - \frac{b}{2}\right)^2 + \left(\frac{c}{2} - \frac{c}{2}\right)^2}$

$= \frac{a + d - b}{2}$

$= \frac{1}{2}\left(a + (d - b)\right)$

$= \frac{1}{2}(AD + BC)$

36. Economics In the table at the right, a nation's disposable income is represented by x and its personal consumption expenditures are represented by y. All figures represent billions of dollars.

x	y
48	44
68	60

   a. Calculate the marginal propensity to consume. 0.8

   b. Suppose the average disposable income per family increases \$1805 in a year. Based on the MPC, by how much would consumption increase? \$1444

37. Economics In Example 2, a rate of change called the marginal propensity to consume (MPC) was presented. Another rate of change is the *marginal propensity to save* (MPS): MPS = 1 − MPC.

   a. Calculate the MPS for the data in Exercise 36. 0.2

   b. If disposable income were to increase as in Exercise 36b, how many additional dollars would the average family save? \$361

38. Consumer Products Citydog Screen Printers of Staten Island, New York, makes special-order T-shirts. Recently, Citydog received two orders for a special T-shirt designed for a mathematics symposium. The first order was for 40 T-shirts at a total cost of \$295, and the second order was for an additional 80 T-shirts at a total cost of \$565. Each order included a standard shipping and handling charge.

   a. Write a linear equation to represent the situation. $y = 6.75x + 25$

   b. What is the cost per T-shirt? \$6.75

   c. What is the standard shipping and handling charge? \$25

Mixed Review

39. Given $f(x) = 5 - x^2$, find $f(3)$. **(Lesson 1-1)** −4

40. If $f(x) = -2x + 11$ and $g(x) = x - 6$, find $[f \circ g](x)$ and $[g \circ f](x)$. **(Lesson 1-2)** $-2x + 23, -2x + 5$

41. If $f(x) = x^3$ and $g(x) = x^2 - 3x + 7$, find $(f \cdot g)(x)$ and $\left(\dfrac{f}{g}\right)(x)$. **(Lesson 1-2)** 41. $x^5 - 3x^4 + 7x^3, \dfrac{x^3}{x^2 - 3x + 7}$

42. Find the zero of $f(x) = 5x - 3$. **(Lesson 1-3)** $\dfrac{3}{5}$

43. Graph $y = \dfrac{1}{2}x - 1\dfrac{1}{2}$. **(Lesson 1-3)** See margin.

44. College Entrance Exam Choose the best answer. C
In the figure at the right, the area of square $OXYZ$ is 2. What is the area of the circle?

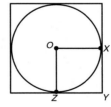

   (A) $\dfrac{\pi}{4}$ **(B)** $\pi\sqrt{2}$ **(C)** 2π **(D)** 4π **(E)** 8π

LESSON 1-4 DISTANCE AND SLOPE 35

EXTENDING THE LESSON

Math Power: Problem Solving

A segment connects (x_1, y_1) and (x_2, y_2). Ask students to write a formula for distance from the midpoint of the segment to (x_1, y_2).

$d = \dfrac{1}{2}\sqrt{(x_2 - x_1)^2 + (y_2 - y_1)^2}$

Additional Answers

35. Let the vertices of the isosceles trapezoid have the coordinates $A(0, 0)$, $B(2a, 0)$, $C(2a - 2c, 2b)$, $D(2c, 2b)$.

The coordinates of the midpoints are: $P(a, 0)$, $Q(2a - c, b)$, $R(a, 2b)$, $S(c, b)$.

$$PQ = \sqrt{(2a - c - a)^2 + (b - 0)^2}$$
$$= \sqrt{(a - c)^2 + b^2}$$
$$QR = \sqrt{(2a - c - a)^2 + (b - 2b)^2}$$
$$= \sqrt{(a - c)^2 + b^2}$$
$$RS = \sqrt{(a - c)^2 + (2b - b)^2}$$
$$= \sqrt{(a - c)^2 + b^2}$$
$$PS = \sqrt{(a - c)^2 + (0 - b)^2}$$
$$= \sqrt{(a - c)^2 + b^2}$$

So, all of the sides are congruent and quadrilateral $PQRS$ is a rhombus.

43.

$y = \dfrac{1}{2}x - 1\dfrac{1}{2}$

(3, 0), (−1, −2)

Enrichment Masters Booklet, p. 4

NCTM Standards: 1–6, 8

Lesson Resources

- Practice Master 1–5
- Enrichment Master 1–5
- Activity Master, p. 1

 Transparency 1–5 contains the 5-Minute Check and a teaching aid for this lesson.

INTRODUCING THE LESSON

 5-Minute Check

(over Lesson 1–4)

1. Find the distance between (–6, 2) and (–2, –1).   **5**
2. Find the slope of the line through (5, 2) and (–1, 6). $-\frac{2}{3}$
3. Find the midpoint of the segment that has endpoints at (–6, 5) and (–16, –1).   **(–11, 2)**
4. Determine whether the triangle with vertices at (0, –1), (–4, –4), and (–1, –8) is isosceles.   **yes**

Motivating the Lesson

Have students read the application. Ask them to estimate the percent of gross national product devoted to medical expenses in 1993 and to explain their reasoning.
Sample answer: From 1984 to 1987, the percent rose 0.2% per year. At that rate, it would reach 12.1% in 1993.

1-5 Forms of Linear Equations

Objectives
1–5A
1–5B

After studying this lesson, you should be able to:
- write linear equations using slope-intercept form, and
- write linear equations using point-slope form.

Application

 FYI...

The average American pays about $2000 a year for health insurance.

From 1984 to 1987, medical expenses in the United States rose in a linear pattern from 10.3% of the gross national product in 1984 to 10.9% of the gross national product in 1987. Assuming that the level of growth continues at that rate, write a linear equation to describe the percent of the gross national product devoted to medical expenses, *y*, in year **x**. *This problem will be solved in Example 4.*

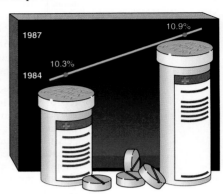

Sometimes the slope and **y-intercept** of a line are easy to determine just by looking at the equation of the line. For example, the graph of $y = 3.5x - 9$ has slope 3.5 and y-intercept –9. The equation $y = 3.5x - 9$ is said to be in **slope-intercept form**.

Slope-Intercept Form	The slope-intercept form of an equation of a line is $y = mx + b$. The slope is *m* and the y-intercept is *b*.

Example 1

Write the equation $4x - 3y + 7 = 0$ in slope-intercept form. Then, name the slope and y-intercept.

$$4x - 3y + 7 = 0$$
$$-3y = -4x - 7$$
$$y = \frac{4}{3}x + \frac{7}{3}$$

The slope is $\frac{4}{3}$ and the y-intercept is $\frac{7}{3}$.

If one point and the slope of a line are known, the slope-intercept form can be used to find the equation of the line.

ALTERNATE TEACHING STRATEGIES

Using Logical Reasoning

A line has a slope of 3. Ask students to find an equation of the line without using paper and pencil, under each of these conditions:
- the y-intercept is (0, –2) (use y-intercept form).   *y* = 3*x* – 2
- (4, 5) is on the graph (use point-slope form).   *y* – 5 = 3(*x* – 4)

Using Critical Thinking

Ask students to give an example of an equation that cannot be graphed by finding its intercepts and drawing the line that passes through them.
y = 2*x* (both intercepts are the same point, the origin)

Example 2 | **Write the slope-intercept form of the equation of the line through $(3, 7)$ that has a slope of 2.**

Substitute the slope and coordinates of the point in the general slope-intercept form of a linear equation. Then, solve for b.

$$y = mx + b$$
$$7 = 2(3) + b$$
$$1 = b$$

The slope-intercept form of the equation of the line is $y = 2x + 1$.

The slope formula can also be used to find the equation of a line when a point and the slope are known.

Example 3 | **Find the equation of the line through $(-2, 4)$ that has a slope of -1. Then, write the equation in slope-intercept form.**

Suppose a second point on the line is at (x, y). Substitute the values into the slope formula.

$$m = \frac{y_2 - y_1}{x_2 - x_1}$$
$$-1 = \frac{y - 4}{x - (-2)}$$
$$-1(x + 2) = y - 4$$
$$-x - 2 = y - 4$$
$$-x + 2 = y$$

The slope-intercept form of the equation is $y = -x + 2$.

The form of a linear equation derived from the slope formula is called the **point-slope form** of the equation. If $\frac{y_2 - y_1}{x_2 - x_1} = m$, then $y - y_1 = m(x - x_1)$.

Point-Slope Form | If the point with coordinates (x_1, y_1) lies on a line having slope m, the point-slope form of the equation of the line can be written as follows.

$$y - y_1 = m(x - x_1)$$

If the coordinates of two points on a line are known, the slope can be found. Then the equation of the line can be written using slope-intercept form or point-slope form.

LESSON 1-5   FORMS OF LINEAR EQUATIONS   37

Teaching Tip   Before Example 1, explain why b is the y-intercept in the equation $y = mx + b$. The y-intercept is the point where $x = 0$. Substituting $x = 0$ in $y = mx + b$ gives $y = m(0) + b$ or b.

Chalkboard Examples

For Example 1

Write the equation $-2x + 5y - 6 = 0$ in slope-intercept form. Then, name the slope and y-intercept.
$$y = \frac{2}{5}x + \frac{6}{5}$$
$$\text{slope} = \frac{2}{5}; y\text{-intercept} = \frac{6}{5}$$

For Example 2

Write the slope-intercept form of the equation of the line through $(-2, 3)$ that has a slope of $\frac{3}{5}$.
$$y = \frac{3}{5}x + \frac{21}{5}$$

For Example 3

Find the equation of the line through $(4, 3)$ that has a slope of 3. Then, write the equation in slope-intercept form.
$$y = 3x - 9$$

Example 4

 APPLICATION

Economics

In 1984, medical expenses were 10.3% of the gross national product (GNP), and in 1987, medical expenses were 10.9% of the gross national product. Assuming that the level of growth continues at that rate, write a linear equation in slope-intercept form to describe the percent of the gross national product devoted to medical expenses, y, in year x.

Since y represents the percent of the GNP devoted to medical expenses and x represents the year, let $x_1 = 1984$, $y_1 = 10.3$, $x_2 = 1987$, and $y_2 = 10.9$. Then find the slope of the line through the points $(1984, 10.3)$ and $(1987, 10.9)$.

$$m = \frac{y_2 - y_1}{x_2 - x_1}$$
$$= \frac{10.9 - 10.3}{1987 - 1984}$$
$$= \frac{0.6}{3} \quad \text{or} \quad 0.2$$

Substitute the slope and coordinates of a point in the general slope-intercept form. Then, solve for b.

$$y = mx + b$$
$$10.9 = 0.2(1987) + b \qquad x = 1987, y = 10.9, \text{ and } m = 0.2$$
$$10.9 = 397.4 + b$$
$$-386.5 = b$$

The slope-intercept form of the equation of the line is $y = 0.2x - 386.5$.

Example 5

Find the point-slope form of the equation of the line through $(3, 7)$ and $(4, -1)$. Then, write the equation in slope-intercept form.

First, find the slope.
$$m = \frac{-1 - 7}{4 - 3} \text{ or } -8$$

Then, substitute values into the general point-slope form of a linear equation.
$$y - y_1 = m(x - x_1)$$
$$y - 7 = -8(x - 3) \qquad \textit{The coordinates of either point can be used for } (x_1, y_1)$$
$$y = -8x + 31$$

The slope-intercept form of the equation is $y = -8x + 31$.

Additional Answers

1. The gross national product is the total value of the goods and services produced by the residents of a nation during a specified period, such as a year.
2. 5.5 represents the hourly wage and −10 represents a fixed amount taken from the paycheck, such as taxes or insurance.
3. Solve the equation for y and use the slope-intercept form to graph the line. Graph the y-intercept and use the slope to find a second point, then sketch a line through them.
4. Use the slope-intercept form when you know the slope and the coordinates of a point. Use the point-slope form when you know the coordinates of two points.
5. Overhead costs include rent, utilities, office supplies, and so on. They are fixed costs, and are often paid monthly.

Example 6

The Fluff Detergent Company manufactures detergent with a fixed overhead cost of $5000. In addition, each box of Fluff Detergent costs $0.40 to produce. Write an equation that represents the total cost, $C(x)$, of producing x boxes of Fluff. Then find the fixed cost and the variable cost per box of Fluff.

The equation is $C(x) = 0.40x + 5000$. This equation is called a *cost function*.

The slope of the function is called the *variable cost*. In this example, $m = 0.40$. The cost of producing 0 boxes is called the *fixed cost*.

$C(x) = 0.40x + 5000$
$C(0) = 0.40(0) + 5000$
$\quad\quad = 5000$

Therefore, the fixed cost is $5000, and the variable cost is $0.40.

CHECKING FOR UNDERSTANDING

Communicating Mathematics

Read and study the lesson to answer each question. 1–5. See margin.

1. **Research** the meaning of the term *gross national product*.

2. If the equation $S = 5.5H - 10$ represents the weekly salary (S) earned by an employee at a fast-food restaurant for H hours worked, explain what 5.5 and –10 represent.

3. **Describe** how you could quickly graph the line $3x + 5y = 30$.

4. **Explain** when you would use the slope-intercept form to find the equation of a line and when you would use the point-slope form to find the equation of a line.

5. **Research** the meaning of the term *overhead costs*.

Guided Practice

Write each equation in slope-intercept form. Then name the slope and y-intercept.

6. $3x - 2y = 7$
   $y = \frac{3}{2}x - \frac{7}{2}, \frac{3}{2}, -\frac{7}{2}$

7. $8x = 2y - 1$
   $y = 4x + \frac{1}{2}, 4, \frac{1}{2}$

8. $4x + 3y = 0$
   $y = -\frac{4}{3}x, -\frac{4}{3}, 0$

Write the slope-intercept form of the equation of the line through the point with the given coordinates and having the given slope.

9. $(3, 2), 4$
   $y = 4x - 10$

10. $(5, 7), 0$
    $y = 7$

11. $(-3, -4), -6$
    $y = -6x - 22$

LESSON 1-5   FORMS OF LINEAR EQUATIONS   39

RETEACHING THE LESSON

Ask students to name the most appropriate form to use to find the equation of a line under each condition:
- they know the slope and the y-intercept   **slope-intercept**
- they know two points   **point-slope**
- they know the slope and a point   **point-slope**

Homework Exercises

Assignment Guide

Average: 15–23, 27, 29, 30, 32–40
Enriched: 18–29, 31–40

The red A, B, and C flags, printed only in the Teacher's Wraparound Edition, indicate the level of difficulty of the exercises.

Using Technology

In Exercises 27–30, point out that each exercise should have three graphs on the screen. Encourage students to sketch the graphs from the screen onto their paper for discussion and later referral.

Additional Answers

21. Point-slope form is undefined, $x = -1$
For exercises 22–26, equations are formed using (x_1, y_1).
22. $y + 5 = -4(x - 3)$, $y = -4x + 7$
23. $y - 2 = \frac{7}{2}(x - 5)$,

$y = \frac{7}{2}x - \frac{31}{2}$

24. $y - 5 = \frac{3}{5}(x - 2)$,

$y = \frac{3}{5}x + \frac{19}{5}$

25. $y - 1 = -\frac{3}{5}(x - 3)$,

$y = -\frac{3}{5}x + \frac{14}{5}$

26. $y + 1 = -\frac{1}{11}(x + 7)$,

$y = -\frac{1}{11}x - \frac{18}{11}$

27. The graphs are all lines. When m is positive, the graph slopes up to the right. When m is negative, the graph slopes down to the right. All three graphs cross the y-axis at $(0, -1)$.
28. The graphs are all lines. When m is positive, the graph slopes up to the right. When m is negative, the graph slopes down to the right. All three graphs cross the y-axis at $(0, -3)$.
29. The graphs are all lines. When m is positive, the graph slopes up to the right. When m is negative, the graph slopes down to the right. All three graphs cross the y-axis at $(0, 2)$.

30. The graphs are all lines. When m is positive, the graph slopes up to the right. When m is negative, the graph slopes down to the right. All three graphs cross the y-axis at $(0, 4)$.

Write the point-slope form of the equation of the line through the points with the given coordinates. Then write the equation in slope-intercept form.

12. $(6, 6), (-6, -6)$
$y - 6 = x - 6; y = x$

13. $(-2, 0), (1, -3)$
$y - 0 = -1(x+2); y = -x - 2$

14. $(4, 2), (7, 2)$
$y - 2 = 0; y = 2$

EXERCISES

Practice

Write the slope-intercept form of the equation of the line through the point with the given coordinates and having the given slope.

A
15. $(-6, 2), 8$ $y = 8x + 50$
16. $(-5, -12), -5$ $y = -5x - 37$
17. $(3, 5), -3$ $y = -3x + 14$
18. $(-10, 4), \frac{3}{4}$ $y = \frac{3}{4}x + \frac{23}{2}$

B
19. $(-7, 3), -\frac{1}{4}$ $y = -\frac{1}{4}x + \frac{5}{4}$
20. $(9, 11), \frac{2}{3}$ $y = \frac{2}{3}x + 5$

Write the point-slope form of the equation of the line through the points with the given coordinates. Then write the equation in slope-intercept form.

21–26. See margin.

C
21. $(-1, 4), (-1, 7)$
22. $(3, -5), (2, -1)$
23. $(5, 2), (7, 9)$
24. $(2, 5), (7, 8)$
25. $(3, 1), (-2, 4)$
26. $(-7, -1), (4, -2)$

27–30. See margin for explanations.

Graphing Calculator

Use a graphing calculator to graph each function, without erasing, for $m = 1$, $m = -3$, and $m = 5$. Explain how the graphs are alike or different.

27. $f(x) = mx - 1$
28. $f(x) = mx - 3$
29. $f(x) = mx + 2$
30. $f(x) = mx + 4$

31–32. See margin.

Critical Thinking

31. Write equations for the sides of the triangle that has vertices $A(2, -7)$, $B(5, 1)$, and $C(-3, 2)$.

32. Write equations for the sides of the square that has vertices $P(1, 4)$, $Q(4, -1)$, $R(-1, -4)$, and $S(-4, 1)$.

Applications and Problem Solving

33. **Manufacturing** It costs Consolidated Cereals Corporation $1050 to produce 100 boxes of corn flakes and $1250 to produce 500 boxes of corn flakes.
a. Find the cost function. $C(x) = 0.5x + 1000$
b. Determine the fixed cost and the variable cost per box. $1000, $0.50
c. Sketch the graph of the cost function. See margin.

34. **Anatomy** The tibia is a bone in the human that connects the knee and the ankle. A man with a tibia 38.5 centimeters long should be about 173 centimeters tall, and a man with a tibia 44.125 centimeters long should be about 188 centimeters tall.
$y = 2\frac{2}{3}x + 70\frac{1}{3}$
a. Write a linear equation relating height, y, to the length of the tibia, x.
b. About how tall should a man be whose tibia is 40 cm long? 177 cm

35. Anatomy The radius is a bone in the human that connects the elbow and the wrist. A woman with a radius 22 centimeters long should be about 160 centimeters tall, and a woman with a radius 26 centimeters long should be about 174 centimeters tall.

35a.
$y = \frac{7}{2}x + 83$

  a. Write a linear equation relating height, y, to the length of the radius, x.

  b. About how long should the radius be of a woman who is 157.5 centimeters tall? 21.286 cm

Mixed Review

37. $4x^2 - 7$, $4x^2 - 7$

36. Does the graph at the right represent a function? **(Lesson 1-1)** yes

37. If $f(x) = x$ and $g(x) = 4x^2 - 7$, find $f \circ g(x)$ and $g \circ f(x)$. **(Lesson 1-2)**

38. Graph $y \leq -\frac{1}{3}x + 2$. **(Lesson 1-3)** See margin.

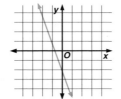

39. Demographics The population of the Dallas-Fort Worth metropolitan area was 2,352,000 in 1970. The population grew to 3,885,000 in 1990. If x represents the year and y represents the population, find the rate of increase for the growth of the population. **(Lesson 1-4)** 76,650 people per year

40. College Entrance Exam Compare quantities A and B below. A
Write A if the quantity in Column A is greater.
Write B if the quantity in Column B is greater.
Write C if the two quantities are equal.
Write D if there is not enough information to determine the relationship.

(A) 5×6^{12} **(B)** 6×5^{12}

EXTENDING THE LESSON

Math Power: Connections

Suppose $f(x) = 4x - 3$ and $g(x) = 2x + 5$. Find the slope and y-intercept of the graph of each function.

- $[f \circ g](x)$ slope = 8; y-intercept = 17
- $[g \circ f](x)$ slope = 8; y-intercept = –1

Additional Answers

31. $y = \frac{8}{3}x - \frac{37}{3}, y = -\frac{1}{8}x + \frac{13}{8},$
$y = -\frac{9}{5}x - \frac{17}{5}$

32. $y = -\frac{5}{3}x + \frac{17}{3}, y = \frac{3}{5}x - \frac{17}{5},$
$y = -\frac{5}{3}x - \frac{17}{3}, y = \frac{3}{5}x + \frac{17}{5}$

33c.

38.

$y \leq -\frac{1}{3}x + 2$

Enrichment Masters Booklet, p. 5

NCTM Standards: 1–6, 8

Lesson Resources

- Practice Master 1–6
- Enrichment Master 1–6
- Evaluation Master, Quiz D, p. 10
- Multicultural Activity Master, p. 1

 Transparency 1–6 contains the 5-Minute Check and a teaching aid for this lesson.

INTRODUCING THE LESSON

5-Minute Check

(over Lesson 1–5)

1. Write the equation $6x - 2y + 7 = 0$ in slope-intercept form.

   $y = 3x + \frac{7}{2}$

2. Write the slope-intercept form of the equation of the line through $(-6, -9)$ that has a slope $\frac{2}{3}$.

   $y = \frac{2}{3}x - 5$

3. Write the point-slope form of the equation of the line through $\left(-\frac{1}{2}, 4\right)$ and $\left(\frac{1}{2}, 6\right)$.

   $y - 4 = 2\left(x + \frac{1}{2}\right)$ or

   $y - 6 = 2\left(x - \frac{1}{2}\right)$

Motivating the Lesson

Have students work in small groups. Each group should graph the following equations on a single coordinate axes.

$y = 2x - 5 \qquad y = 2x - 1$
$y = 2x + 2 \qquad y = 2x + 4$

Ask students what conclusions they can draw.

It appears that lines with the same slope are parallel.

1-6 Parallel and Perpendicular Lines

Objectives

After studying this lesson, you should be able to:

1–6A
- write equations of parallel and perpendicular lines, and

1–6B
- prove geometric theorems involving parallel and perpendicular lines analytically.

Application

The contrails of an airplane are the streaks of condensed water vapor that follow the airplane when the airplane flies at high altitudes. The contrails of the jet aircraft pictured at the right represent a family of lines. Families of lines always have a common feature. In this case, the contrails all represent lines that have the same slope.

Lines that are parallel or perpendicular can be studied by examining their equations and slopes. Lines that are **parallel** have the same slope. That is, if m_1 is the slope of ℓ_1 and m_2 is the slope of ℓ_2, then ℓ_1 and ℓ_2 are parallel if and only if $m_1 = m_2$. Vertical lines are parallel even though the slope of a vertical line is undefined.

Parallel Lines	**Two nonvertical lines are parallel if and only if their slopes are equal. Any two vertical lines are always parallel.**

A convenient way to write a linear equation is in **standard form.** The standard form of a linear equation will be used to develop relationships among slope and parallel and perpendicular lines.

Standard Form of a Linear Equation	**The standard form of a linear equation is $Ax + By + C = 0$, where $A, B,$ and C are real numbers and A and B are not both zero.**

What is the slope of the line if B is 0?

The slope of a line can be obtained directly from the standard form of the linear equation if B is not 0. By solving $Ax + By + C = 0$ $(B \neq 0)$ for y, the result is $y = -\frac{A}{B}x - \frac{C}{B}$. Therefore, the slope is $-\frac{A}{B}$. For example, the slope of the line $2x - 4y + 7 = 0$ is $-\frac{2}{-4}$ or $\frac{1}{2}$. *The expression "the line $2x - 4y + 7 = 0$" means "the line that is the graph of $2x - 4y + 7 = 0$."*

Since parallel lines have the same slope, the equation of a line parallel to a given line and through a given point can be written using point-slope form.

ALTERNATE TEACHING STRATEGIES

Using Discussion

Informally discuss the terms *parallel* and *perpendicular*. Review the geometric meanings of the terms. Ask students to give everyday examples of parallel and perpendicular lines.

Using Cooperative Groups

Have small groups of students derive a formula for the slope of a line parallel to the line $Ax + By + C = 0$ and for the slope of a line perpendicular to it.

parallel: $m = -\frac{A}{B}$

perpendicular: $m = \frac{B}{A}$

Example 1

Write the standard form of the equation of the line that passes through $(2, -3)$ and is parallel to the line $4x - y + 3 = 0$.

Since $-\dfrac{A}{B} = -\left(\dfrac{4}{-1}\right)$, the slope is 4.

$y - y_1 = m(x - x_1)$ *Use the point-slope form.*

$y + 3 = 4(x - 2)$ *Replace y_1 with –3, m with 4, and x_1 with 2.*

$y + 3 = 4x - 8$

$4x - y - 11 = 0$

The equation is $4x - y - 11 = 0$.

Example 2

APPLICATION
Sales

During the month of January, Fransworth Computer Center sold 24 Macintosh IIci computers and 40 Personal LaserWriter NT printers. The total sales on these two items for the month of January was $213,600. In February, they sold 30 Macintosh IIci computers and 50 Personal LaserWriter NT printers. Assuming the prices stayed consistent during the months of January and February, is it possible that their February sales could have totaled $283,000 on these two items?

The sales function for the month of January is $24x + 40y = 213,600$ or $y = -\dfrac{3}{5}x + 5340$. The sales function for the month of February is $30x + 50y = 283,000$ or $y = -\dfrac{3}{5}x + 5660$. Since these two equations have the same slope, their graphs are parallel lines. As a result, the ratio of total sales should be proportional to the ratio of computer sales or printer sales from month to month. However, since $\dfrac{64}{80} \neq \dfrac{213,600}{283,000}$, the February sales could not have been $283,000.

Quadrilateral $ABCD$ at the right is a rhombus. A rhombus has perpendicular diagonals. The slope of diagonal $\overline{AC}$ is $\dfrac{4}{8}$ or $\dfrac{1}{2}$. The slope of diagonal $\overline{BD}$ is $\dfrac{4}{-2}$ or –2. The two slopes, $\dfrac{1}{2}$ and –2, are negative reciprocals of each other. That is, the product of the slopes is –1. This is true for the slopes of any two nonvertical **perpendicular** lines.

LESSON 1-6   PARALLEL AND PERPENDICULAR LINES   43

LESSON 1-6   PARALLEL AND PERPENDICULAR LINES   43

TEACHING THE LESSON

Teaching Tip   In Example 2, point out that *x* represents the cost of a computer and *y* the cost of a printer. Therefore, total sales for January, the *sales function*, is $24x + 40y = 213,600$.

Chalkboard Examples

For Example 1

Write the standard form of the equation of the line that passes through (10, –2) and is parallel to the line $2x - 5y - 8 = 0$.
$2x - 5y - 30 = 0$

For Example 2

Assuming that the prices stayed consistent through March, is it possible that March sales of 32 Macintosh computers and 36 LaserWriter printers could have totaled $244,240?   **yes**

Chalkboard Examples

For Example 3

Write the standard form of the equation of the line that passes through (2, –3) and is perpendicular to the line $6x - 8y - 5 = 0$.
$4x + 3y + 1 = 0$

For Example 4

Prove that the line segments joining the consecutive midpoints of a quadrilateral form a parallelogram.

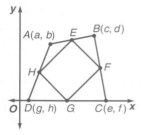

$E\left(\dfrac{a+c}{2}, \dfrac{b+d}{2}\right)$,

$F\left(\dfrac{c+e}{2}, \dfrac{d+f}{2}\right)$,

$G\left(\dfrac{g+e}{2}, \dfrac{h+f}{2}\right)$, and

$H\left(\dfrac{a+g}{2}, \dfrac{b+h}{2}\right)$ are midpoints.

Slope of $\overline{EH}$ = slope of $\overline{FG}$ = $\dfrac{d-h}{c-g}$. Slope of $\overline{EF}$ = slope of $\overline{HG}$ = $\dfrac{b-f}{a-e}$. Therefore, the opposite sides of quadrilateral $EFGH$ are parallel, making it a parallelogram.

Thus, when ℓ_1 is perpendicular to ℓ_2, the following is true.

$$m_1 m_2 = -1 \text{ or } m_1 = -\frac{1}{m_2}$$

Perpendicular Lines	**Two nonvertical lines are perpendicular if and only if their slopes are negative reciprocals.**

The equation of a line perpendicular to a given line and through a given point can be written using the point-slope form.

Example 3

Write the standard form of the equation of the line that passes through (3, –5) and is perpendicular to the line $2x - 3y + 6 = 0$.

Since $m = -\dfrac{A}{B}$, the line $2x - 3y + 6 = 0$ has slope $\dfrac{2}{3}$. Therefore, the slope of a line that is perpendicular to the line $2x - 3y + 6 = 0$ would be $-\dfrac{3}{2}$.

$$y - y_1 = m(x - x_1) \quad \textit{Use the point-slope form.}$$
$$y + 5 = -\frac{3}{2}(x - 3) \quad \textit{Replace } y_1 \textit{ with –5, m with } -\frac{3}{2}, \textit{ and } x_1 \textit{ with 3.}$$
$$2y + 10 = -3x + 9$$
$$3x + 2y + 1 = 0$$

The equation is $3x + 2y + 1 = 0$.

You can use the definitions of parallel and perpendicular lines to prove theorems by using analytic methods.

Example 4

Prove that the line segment joining the midpoints of two sides of a triangle
a. is parallel to the third side and
b. has a length that is one-half the length of the third side.

a. In $\triangle ABC$, let the vertices be $A(0,0), B(a,0)$, and $C(b,c)$. Then, $M\left(\dfrac{b}{2}, \dfrac{c}{2}\right)$ and $N\left(\dfrac{a+b}{2}, \dfrac{c}{2}\right)$ are the midpoints of $\overline{AC}$ and $\overline{BC}$, respectively. The slope of $\overline{AB}$ is $\dfrac{0}{a}$ or 0. The slope of $\overline{MN}$ is as follows.

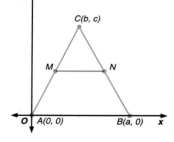

$$\frac{\frac{c}{2} - \frac{c}{2}}{\frac{a+b}{2} - \frac{b}{2}} = \frac{0}{\frac{a}{2}} \text{ or } 0$$

Since the slopes are the same, $\overline{AB}$ is parallel to $\overline{MN}$.

Additional Answers

1. The definition says that the slopes of any two parallel lines are equal. Vertical lines have no slope, yet they are parallel.
2. $267,000; This makes the proportion $\dfrac{24}{30} = \dfrac{213,600}{267,000}$ true.
3. No; the slopes must be negative reciprocals and thus, their signs must be opposite.
4. All vertical lines have undefined slope and only horizontal lines are perpendicular to them. The slope of all horizontal lines is 0.

b. To find the lengths of the horizontal line segments, use the distance formula.

$$MN = \sqrt{\left(\frac{b}{2} - \frac{a+b}{2}\right)^2 + \left(\frac{c}{2} - \frac{c}{2}\right)^2}$$

$$= \sqrt{\left(\frac{b-a-b}{2}\right)^2 + (0)^2}$$

$$= \sqrt{\left(-\frac{a}{2}\right)^2}$$

$$= \frac{a}{2} \text{ or } \frac{1}{2}a$$

$$AB = \sqrt{(a-0)^2 + (0-0)^2}$$

$$= \sqrt{a^2 + 0}$$

$$= a$$

Therefore, the line segment joining the midpoints of two sides of a triangle is parallel to the third side of the triangle, and its length is one-half the length of the third side.

CHECKING FOR UNDERSTANDING

Communicating Mathematics

Read and study the lesson to answer each question. 1–4. See margin.

1. **Explain** why the definition of parallel lines begins with the wording "Two nonvertical lines...."

2. What should have been the sales for the month of February in Example 2? Describe how you reached your solution.

3. **Discuss** whether it is possible for two perpendicular lines to have slopes that are either both positive or both negative. Explain your answer.

4. **Describe** the slope of a line that is perpendicular to a line that has an undefined slope. Verify that your description of this line is correct.

Guided Practice

Find the slope of each line whose equation is given. Then, determine whether the lines are _parallel_, _perpendicular_, or _neither_.

5. $y = 3x - 2$ $3, -3$
$y = -3x + 2$ neither

6. $y = 6x - 2$ $6, 6$
$y = 6x + 7$ parallel

7. $y = x - 9$ $1, -1$
$x + y + 9 = 0$ perpendicular

8. $y = 2x + 4$ $2, -\frac{1}{2}$
$x + 2y + 10 = 0$ perpendicular

9. $y + 4x - 2 = 0$ $-4, -4$
$y + 4x + 1 = 0$ parallel

10. $y = 8x - 1$ $8, 7$
$7x - y - 1 = 0$ neither

Write the standard forms of the equations of the lines that are parallel and perpendicular to $y = 2x - 3$ and pass through the point with the given coordinates.

12. $2x - y + 12 = 0$;
$x + 2y - 9 = 0$
13. $2x - y - 18 = 0$;
$x + 2y - 4 = 0$
14. $2x - y + 3 = 0$;
$x + 2y + 19 = 0$

11. $(4, 2)$ 12. $(-3, 6)$ 13. $(8, -2)$ 14. $(-5, -7)$

11. $2x - y - 6 = 0$;
$x + 2y - 8 = 0$

LESSON 1-6 PARALLEL AND PERPENDICULAR LINES 45

15.

$WZ = \sqrt{(2+1)^2 + (-1-3)^2} = 5$

$YZ = \sqrt{(2-6)^2 + (-1-2)^2} = 5$

$XY = \sqrt{(6-3)^2 + (2-6)^2} = 5$

$WX = \sqrt{(3+1)^2 + (6-3)^2} = 5$

Thus, *WXYZ* is a rhombus.

The slope of $\overline{WX} = \frac{6-3}{3+1} = \frac{3}{4}$

and the slope of $\overline{WZ} =$
$\frac{3+1}{-1-2} = -\frac{4}{3}$.

Thus, $\overline{WX}$ is perpendicular to $\overline{WZ}$ and *WXYZ* is a square.

16.

Slope of $\overline{AC} = \frac{a-0}{a-0} = 1$.

Slope of $\overline{BD} = \frac{0-a}{a-0} = -1$.

Since the slope of $\overline{BD}$ is the negative reciprocal of the slope of $\overline{AC}$, $\overline{AC}$ is perpendicular to $\overline{BD}$.

15–16. See margin.

15. Show that quadrilateral *WXYZ* is a square if its vertices are $W(-1, 3)$, $X(3, 6)$, $Y(6, 2)$, and $Z(2, -1)$.

16. Prove analytically that the diagonals of a square are perpendicular.

EXERCISES

Practice
Write the standard form of the equation of the line that is parallel to the given line and passes through the given point.

17. $y = 3x - 5; (0, 6)$ $3x - y + 6 = 0$
18. $y = 2x + 6; (-1, -2)$ $2x - y = 0$
19. $y = 6x + 7; (0, -3)$ $6x - y - 3 = 0$
20. $y = -4x - 3; (5, -7)$ $4x + y - 13 = 0$
21. $2x + 3y - 5 = 0; (2, 4)$
$2x + 3y - 16 = 0$
22. $2x - 7y = 3; (8, 0)$
$2x - 7y - 16 = 0$

Write the standard form of the equation of the line that is perpendicular to the given line and passes through the given point.

25. $5x + 4y + 43 = 0$
26. $3x - 2y + 15 = 0$

23. $y = -2x + 5; (0, -3)$ $x - 2y - 6 = 0$
24. $y = 4x - 2; (3, 4)$ $x + 4y - 19 = 0$
25. $5y - 4x = 10; (-15, 8)$
26. $3y + 2x = 3; (-9, -6)$
27. $6x - 4y + 8 = 0; (2, 12)$
$2x + 3y - 40 = 0$
28. $3x - y = 8; (-1, 5)$
$x + 3y - 14 = 0$

29. $4, -\frac{49}{4}$

30. $-\frac{14}{3}, \frac{6}{7}$

31–34. See margin.

29. For what value of k is the graph of $kx - 7y + 10 = 0$ parallel to the graph of $8x - 14y + 3 = 0$? For what value of k are the graphs perpendicular?

30. For what value of k is the graph of $2x - ky + 5 = 0$ parallel to the graph of $3x + 7y + 15 = 0$? For what value of k are the graphs perpendicular?

31. Show that triangle *ABC* is a right triangle if its vertices are $A(-1, 2)$, $B(4, -3)$, and $C(-2, -1)$.

32. Show that quadrilateral *PQRS* is a rhombus if its vertices are $P(3, 1)$, $Q(8, 1)$, $R(12, 4)$, and $S(7, 4)$.

Critical Thinking
33. Prove analytically that the line joining the midpoints of the nonparallel sides of a trapezoid is parallel to the bases of the trapezoid.

Applications and Problem Solving
34. Sales   Lisa owns and operates a pizza and calzone concession at a county fair each summer. On two consecutive days in July, Lisa reported the following sales: on the first day, she sold 520 slices of pizza and 280 calzones; on the second day, she sold 390 slices of pizza and 210 calzones. Write a convincing argument to show whether her sales on the second day could have been $1057.50 if her sales on the first day were $1410. (Assume that the prices remained the same over the two days.) See margin.

---

31. slope of $\overline{AB} = \frac{2-(-3)}{-1-4} = -1$

slope of $\overline{BC} = \frac{-1-(-3)}{-2-4} = -\frac{1}{3}$

slope of $\overline{CA} = \frac{-1-2}{-2-(-1)} = 3$

The slopes of $\overline{BC}$ and $\overline{CA}$ have a product of –1, so the lines are perpendicular. Therefore, △*ABC* is a right triangle.

32. $\overline{PQ} = \sqrt{(3-8)^2 + (1-1)^2} = 5$

$\overline{QR} = \sqrt{(12-8)^2 + (4-1)^2} = 5$

$\overline{RS} = \sqrt{(12-7)^2 + (4-4)^2} = 5$

$\overline{SP} = \sqrt{(7-3)^2 + (4-1)^2} = 5$

slope of $\overline{PQ} = \frac{1-1}{3-8} = \frac{0}{-5} = 0$

slope of $\overline{QR} = \frac{4-1}{12-8} = \frac{3}{4}$

slope of $\overline{RS} = \frac{4-4}{12-7} = 0$

slope of $\overline{SP} = \frac{4-1}{7-3} = \frac{3}{4}$

The opposite sides are parallel, and all sides are congruent. The figure is a rhombus.

35. Sports Marquita starts riding her bicycle at 10 miles per hour. At the same time, Heather starts riding her bicycle in the same direction from a point 5 miles north of Marquita. Heather also rides at a rate of 10 miles per hour. If the girls continue to ride at the same speed, will Marquita ever catch up with Heather? Why or why not? No, they are riding along parallel lines or the same line, 5 miles apart.

Mixed Review

36. If $f(x) = 3x^2 - 4$ and $g(x) = 5x + 1$, find $f \circ g(4)$ and $g \circ f(4)$. **(Lesson 1-2)** 1319, 221

37. Graph $-6 \le 3x - y \le 12$. **(Lesson 1-3)** See Teacher's Answer Key.

38. Find the distance between $(4, -3)$ and $(-2, 6)$. **(Lesson 1-4)** $\sqrt{117}$

39. Manufacturing It costs ABC Corporation $3000 to produce 20 color televisions and $5000 to produce 60 of the same color televisions. **(Lesson 1-5)**
  a. Find the cost function. $C(x) = 50x + 2000$
  b. Determine the fixed cost and the variable cost per unit. $2000, $50
  c. Sketch the graph of the cost function. See Teacher's Answer Key.

40. College Entrance Exam If $2x + y = 12$ and $x + 2y = -6$, then find the value of $2x + 2y$. 4

DECISION MAKING

Recycling

Americans throw away more than 600 million pounds of paper and 100 million pounds of plastic every day. Much of this material could be recycled. However, some materials are easier and less expensive than others to recycle. How can you best use your resources to start a recycling campaign? Should you decide on one or two materials and try to get others to recycle these? Or should you concentrate your efforts on education by publicizing the importance of recycling?

1. Find out which kinds of materials can be recycled most efficiently. Are there companies or organizations in your city that will buy recycled materials from you? Are there companies that will recycle materials without paying for them? How would you organize a recycling campaign if you were in charge of it?

2. Describe steps you could take to raise student or public awareness of the need to recycle.

3. **Project** Work with your group to complete one of the projects listed at the right based on the information you gathered in Exercises 1–2. 1–3. See students' work.

PROJECTS

- *Conduct an interview.*
- *Write a book report.*
- *Write a proposal.*
- *Write an article for the school paper.*
- *Write a report.*
- *Make a display.*
- *Make a graph or chart.*
- *Plan an activity.*
- *Design a checklist.*

LESSON 1-6 PARALLEL AND PERPENDICULAR LINES   47

EXTENDING THE LESSON

Math Power: Reasoning

Suppose a line has x- and y-intercepts of a and b, respectively. Show that the equation of the line is $\frac{x}{a} + \frac{y}{b} = 1$. slope $= -\frac{b}{a}$

equation (point-slope form):

$y - 0 = -\frac{b}{a}(x - a)$

$y = -\frac{bx}{a} + b$

$\frac{y}{b} = -\frac{x}{a} + 1$ or $\frac{x}{a} + \frac{y}{b} = 1$

Decision Making

This activity provides students an opportunity to work together on a given problem. You may wish to refer to pages T20–T21 and page 4c for the various elements of cooperative groups and specific goals and strategies for using them.

Additional Answers

33.

The coordinates of E are $\left(\frac{b}{2}, \frac{c}{2}\right)$. The coordinates of F are $\left(\frac{a+d}{2}, \frac{c}{2}\right)$. Slope of $\overline{EF}$

$= \dfrac{\frac{c}{2} - \frac{c}{2}}{\frac{b}{2} - \frac{a+d}{2}} = 0$. Since the

slopes of $\overline{BC}$ and $\overline{AD}$ are also zero, $\overline{BC}$, $\overline{AD}$, and $\overline{EF}$ are parallel.

34. The two equations are $y = -\frac{13}{7}x + \frac{141}{28}$ and $y = -\frac{13}{7}x + \frac{423}{42}$. Since they have the same slope, the graphs are parallel lines. As a result, the ratio of the total sales should be proportional to the ratio of calzones sold from day to day. Since $\frac{1057.50}{1410} = \frac{210}{280}$, her sales on the second day could have been $1057.50.

Enrichment Masters Booklet, p. 6

1-6 NAME _____ DATE _____
Enrichment Worksheet

Finding Equations From Area

A right triangle in the first quadrant is bounded by the x-axis, the y-axis, and a line intersecting both axes. The point $(1, 2)$ lies on the hypotenuse of the triangle. The area of the triangle is 4 square units.

Follow these instructions to find the equation of the line containing the hypotenuse. Let m represent the slope of the line.

1. Write the equation, in point-slope form, of the line containing the hypotenuse.
   $y - 2 = m(x - 1)$
2. Find the x-intercept and the y-intercept of the line.
   x-intercept: $\frac{m-2}{m}$ y-intercept: $2 - m$
3. Write the measures of the legs of the triangle.
   $\frac{2-m}{m}$ and $2 - m$
4. Use your answers to Exercise 3 and the formula for the area of a triangle to write an expression for the area of the triangle in terms of the slope of the hypotenuse. Set the expression equal to 4, the area of the triangle, and solve for m.
   $m = -2$
5. Write the equation of the line, in point-slope form, containing the hypotenuse of the triangle.
   $y - 2 = -2(x - 1)$
6. Another right triangle in the first quadrant has an area of 4 square units. The point $(2, 1)$ lies on the hypotenuse. Find the equation of the line, in point-slope form, containing the hypotenuse.
   $y - 1 = -\frac{1}{2}(x - 2)$
7. A line with negative slope passes through the point $(6, 1)$. A triangle bounded by the line and the coordinate axes has an area of 16 square units. Find the slope of the line.
   $m = -\frac{1}{2}$ or $m = -\frac{1}{18}$

T6
Glencoe Division, Macmillan/McGraw-Hill

Additional Answers

1. {(0, –7), (1, –2), (2, 3), (3, 8)}; yes
2. {(–1, –3), (0, 0), (1, 3), (2, 24)}; yes
3. {(5, 1), (5, –1), (6, 2), (6, –2)}; no
4. {(–8, 4), (–7, 3), (–6, 2), (–5, 1), (–4, 0), (–3, 1)}; yes
9. $[f \circ g](x) = 3x + 1$; $[g \circ f](x) = 3x - 3$
10. $[f \circ g](x) = -12x^6$; $[g \circ f](x) = -54x^6$
11. $[f \circ g](x) = x^2 + 4x + 6$; $[g \circ f](x) = x^2 + 2x + 4$
12. $[f \circ g](x) = \frac{1}{x-2}$;

    $[g \circ f](x) = \frac{1}{4x} - 1$
13. $f^{-1}(x) = \pm\sqrt{x + 12}$; no
14. $f^{-1}(x) = 2 - \frac{1}{3}x$; yes
15. $f^{-1}(x) = \frac{1}{2}\sqrt[3]{x}$; yes
16. $f^{-1}(x) = \sqrt[3]{\frac{x+2}{3}}$; yes

VOCABULARY

Upon completing this chapter, you should be familiar with the following terms:

analytic geometry	**31**	**42**	parallel
boundary	**23**	**43**	perpendicular
composite	**13**	**37**	point-slope form
composition	**13**	**6**	range
constant function	**23**	**6**	relation
domain	**6**	**30**	slope
function	**7**	**36**	slope-intercept form
inverse functions	**15**	**42**	standard form
iteration	**15**	**7**	vertical line test
linear equation	**22**	**23**	x-intercept
linear function	**22**	**30**	y-intercept
linear inequality	**23**	**22**	zero of a function

SKILLS AND CONCEPTS

OBJECTIVES AND EXAMPLES	REVIEW EXERCISES
Upon completing this chapter, you should be able to:	Use these exercises to review and prepare for the chapter test.
■ determine whether a given relation is a function **(Lesson 1-1)**	**Given that x is an integer, state the relation representing each of the following by listing a set of ordered pairs. Then state whether the relation is a function. Write yes or no.**
If x is a positive integer between 1 and 4, determine whether $y^2 = x - 1$ is a function.	**1.** $y = 5x - 7$ and $0 \leq x \leq 3$ 1–4. See
The relation is $\{(2, 1), (2, -1), (3, \sqrt{3}), (3, -\sqrt{3})\}$. Since 3 is paired with $\sqrt{3}$ and $-\sqrt{3}$, the relation is not a function.	**2.** $y = 3x^3$ and $-2 < x < 3$ margin.
	3. $|y| = x - 4$ and $5 \leq x < 7$
	4. $y = |4 + x|$ and $-8 \leq x < -2$
■ identify the domain and range of any relation or function **(Lesson 1-1)**	**Name all values of x that are not in the domain of the given function.**
Name all values of x that are not in the domain of $f(x) = \frac{7x - 1}{x^3 + 1}$.	**5.** $f(x) = \frac{5}{x}$ 0 **6.** $f(x) = \frac{x^2}{x^2 - 3}$ $\pm\sqrt{3}$
$x^3 + 1 = 0$	
$\quad x = -1 \quad$ –1 is not in the domain of f.	**7.** $f(x) = \frac{2(x^2 - 9)}{x + 3}$ –3 **8.** $f(x) = \frac{2x^3 - 5}{2|x| - 5}$ $\pm\frac{5}{2}$

OBJECTIVES AND EXAMPLES	REVIEW EXERCISES

■ find the composition of functions **(Lesson 1-2)**

Find $[f \circ g](x)$ if $f(x) = -5x + 4$ and $g(x) = 2x - 3$.

$$[f \circ g](x) = f(2x - 3)$$
$$= -5(2x - 3) + 4$$
$$= -10x + 19$$

Find $[f \circ g](x)$ and $[g \circ f](x)$.

9. $f(x) = 3x - 5$
$g(x) = x + 2$

10. $f(x) = -3x^2$
$g(x) = 2x^3$

11. $f(x) = x^2 + 2x + 3$
$g(x) = x + 1$

12. $f(x) = \dfrac{1}{2x}$
$g(x) = \dfrac{1}{2}x - 1$

9–12. See margin.

■ find and recognize inverse functions **(Lesson 1-2)**

Given $f(x) = \dfrac{1}{2}x^3 + 5$, find $f^{-1}(x)$.

$$x = \dfrac{1}{2}y^3 + 5$$
$$2x - 10 = y^3$$
$$\sqrt[3]{2x - 10} = y \;\rightarrow\; f^{-1}(x) = \sqrt[3]{2x - 10}$$

Find the inverse of each function. Then state whether the inverse is a function.

13. $f(x) = x^2 - 12$

14. $f(x) = 6 - 3x$

15. $f(x) = 8x^3$

16. $f(x) = 3x^3 - 2$

13–16. See margin.

■ find the zeros of linear functions **(Lesson 1-3)**

Find the zero of $f(x) = 4x + 3$.

$$4x + 3 = 0$$
$$x = -\dfrac{3}{4} \qquad \text{The zero is } -\dfrac{3}{4}.$$

Find the zero of each function. Then graph the function. 17–20. For graphs, see Teacher's Answer Key.

17. $f(x) = 3x - 8$ $\;-\dfrac{8}{3}$

18. $f(x) = 19$ none

19. $f(x) = 0.25x - 5$ 20

20. $f(x) = 7x + 1$ $\;-\dfrac{1}{7}$

■ find the distance between two points **(Lesson 1-4)**

Find the distance between $(3, 8)$ and $(-5, 11)$.

$$d = \sqrt{(x_2 - x_1)^2 + (y_2 - y_1)^2}$$
$$= \sqrt{(-5 - 3)^2 + (11 - 8)^2}$$
$$= \sqrt{73}$$

Find the distance between the points with the given coordinates.

21. $(0, 0), (5, 12)$ 13

22. $(1, -6), (-3, -4)$ $2\sqrt{5}$

23. $(a, b), (a + 3, b + 4)$ 5

24. $(2k, 4k), (3k, 6k)$ $|k|\sqrt{5}$

■ write linear equations using slope-intercept form **(Lesson 1-5)**

Write the slope-intercept form of the line through $(2, -4)$ that has a slope of $\dfrac{1}{2}$.

$$m = \dfrac{y_2 - y_1}{x_2 - x_1}$$
$$\dfrac{1}{2} = \dfrac{y - (-4)}{x - 2}$$
$$x - 2 = 2y + 8$$
$$y = \dfrac{1}{2}x - 5$$

Write the slope-intercept form of the equation of the line through the point with the given coordinates and having the given slope.

25. $(5, 5), 2$ $\;y = 2x - 5$

26. $(-2, 3), -1$ $\;y = -x + 1$

27. $(0, 0), \dfrac{3}{5}$ $\;y = \dfrac{3}{5}x$

28. $(1, 4), -\dfrac{4}{3}$ $\;y = -\dfrac{4}{3}x + \dfrac{16}{3}$

Alternative Review Strategy

To provide a brief in-class review, you may wish to read the following questions to your students and have them answer verbally.

1. State whether the relation {(2, 1), (3, 5), (2, 6)} is a function. **no**
2. Name all values of x that are not in the domain of the function $f(x) = \sqrt{x}$. **$x < 0$**
3. If $f(x) = x + 5$, what is $f^{-1}(x)$? **$x - 5$**
4. If $f(x) = 2x$ and $g(x) = 6$, what is $[f \circ g](x)$? **12**
5. Find the zero of the function $f(x) = 2x + 10$. **−5**
6. Find the distance between $(-8, 6)$ and $(16, -4)$. **26**
7. Find the slope of the line $y = -\dfrac{3}{4}x + 12$. **$-\dfrac{3}{4}$**
8. Find the equation of a line through the points $(3, 4)$ and $(4, 6)$. **$y = 2x - 2$**
9. Find the slope of the line parallel to the line $5x - 8y - 4 = 0$ **$\dfrac{5}{8}$**
10. Find the slope of a line perpendicular to a line with slope $-\dfrac{3}{7}$. **$\dfrac{7}{3}$**

For more information on other methods of alternate assessment, you may wish to refer to Glencoe's *Alternate Assessment in the Mathematics Classroom*.

Two multiple-choice tests (Forms 1A and 1B) and two free-response tests (Form 2A and 2B) are provided in the *Evaluation Masters*. Chapter 1 Test, Form 1A is shown below. Chapter1 Test, Form 2A is shown on the next page.

Evaluation Masters Booklet, pp. 1–2

	OBJECTIVES AND EXAMPLES	REVIEW EXERCISES

OBJECTIVES AND EXAMPLES

■ write equations of lines using point-slope form **(Lesson 1-5)**

Write the slope-intercept form of the line through the points $(5, -2)$ and $(3, -8)$.

$$m = \frac{-8 - (-2)}{3 - 5}$$
$$= 3$$

$$y - y_1 = m(x - x_1)$$
$$y - (-2) = 3(x - 5)$$
$$y = 3x - 17$$

■ write the equations of parallel and perpendicular lines **(Lesson 1-6)**

Write the standard form of the equation of the line that passes through $(-1, 3)$ and is perpendicular to the line $y = \frac{1}{5}x + 2$.

$$y - y_1 = m(x - x_1)$$
$$y - 3 = -5(x - (-1))$$
$$y = -5x - 2 \quad \text{or} \quad 5x + y + 2 = 0$$

REVIEW EXERCISES

Find the point-slope form of the equation of the line through the points with the given coordinates. Then write the equation in slope-intercept form.

29. $(3, 7), (6, 10)$ $y = x + 4$
30. $(-1, 0), (5, 9)$ $y = \frac{3}{2}x + \frac{3}{2}$
31. $(4, 4), (2, -3)$ $y = \frac{7}{2}x - 10$
32. $(11, -6), (10, -9)$ $y = 3x - 39$

Write the standard form of the equation of the line described below.

33. parallel to $y = 4x - 7$, passes through $(-2, 3)$ $4x - y + 11 = 0$
34. parallel to $-2x + 3y - 5 = 0$, passes through $(2, 4)$ $2x - 3y + 8 = 0$
35. perpendicular to $6x = 2y - 4$, y-intercept 4 $x + 3y - 12 = 0$
36. perpendicular to $5y = 4x + 2$, x-intercept 5 $5x + 4y - 25 = 0$

APPLICATIONS AND PROBLEM SOLVING

37. **Aviation**   A jet plane starts from rest on a runway. It accelerates uniformly at a rate of 20 m/s². The equation for computing the distance traveled is $d = \frac{1}{2}at^2$. **(Lesson 1-1)**   37a. 10 m, 40 m, 90 m, 160 m, 250 m
    a. Find the distance traveled at the end of each second for 5 seconds.
    b. Is this relation a function? Why or why not?   Yes, each element of the domain is paired with exactly one element of the range.

38. Prove that the diagonals of a parallelogram bisect each other. **(Lesson 1-4)**   See margin.

39. **Manufacturing**   The Yummy Candy Company can produce 100 candy bars at a cost of $150 and 600 candy bars at a cost of $200. Find the cost function and determine the fixed cost and the variable cost per candy bar. **(Lesson 1-5)** $y = 0.1x + 140$; $140, $0.10

Additional Answer

38.

The midpoint of $\overline{AC}$ is

$$\left(\frac{a + b + 0}{2}, \frac{0 + c}{2}\right) \text{ or } \left(\frac{a + b}{2}, \frac{c}{2}\right).$$

The midpoint of $\overline{BD}$ is

$$\left(\frac{a + b}{2}, \frac{c + 0}{2}\right) \text{ or } \left(\frac{a + b}{2}, \frac{c}{2}\right).$$

Since the coordinates of the midpoint of $\overline{AC}$ are the same as those of $\overline{BD}$, the diagonals bisect each other.

Given that x is an integer, state the relation representing each of the following by listing a set of ordered pairs. Then state whether the relation is a function. Write yes or no. 1–2. See margin.

1. $y = 3x - 1$ and $-3 < x \leq 2$

2. $|y| = 2x + 5$ and $0 \leq x \leq 4$

Given $f(x) = x - 3x^2$, find each value.

3. $f(0)$ 0

4. $f(4)$ −44

5. $f(-6)$ −114

6. $f(7.1)$ −144.13

Find $[f \circ g](x)$ and $[g \circ f](x)$. 8. $50x^2 + 120x + 72, 10x^2 + 6$

7. $f(x) = \sqrt{x}\ \sqrt{2x^2 - 5}$,
$g(x) = 2x^2 - 5\ 2x - 5$

8. $f(x) = 2x^2$
$g(x) = 5x + 6$

9. $f(x) = -x - 7\ 3x - 7$,
$g(x) = -3x\ 3x + 21$

Find the inverse of each function. Then state whether the inverse is a function.
10 – 12. See margin.

10. $f(x) = \dfrac{x^2 + 5}{3}$

11. $f(x) = \dfrac{1}{4}x + 1$

12. $f(x) = -2(x^3 - 1)$

Graph each equation or inequality. 13 – 16. See Teacher's Answer Key.

13. $y = 3x - 6$

14. $2x = y + 1$

15. $y + 4x \leq 12$

16. $y > 2x - 2$

Find the distance between the points with the given coordinates. Then, find the slope of the line passing through each pair of points. 19. $\sqrt{k^2 + 4}, \dfrac{2}{k}$

17. $(-1, 2), (3, 1)$ $\sqrt{17}, -\dfrac{1}{4}$

18. $(5, 11), (12, 12)$ $5\sqrt{2}, \dfrac{1}{7}$

19. $(3k, k + 1), (2k, k - 1)$

20. Write the slope-intercept form of the equation of the line through $(-1, 3)$ that has a slope of $\dfrac{5}{3}$. $y = \dfrac{5}{3}x + \dfrac{14}{3}$

21. Write the slope-intercept form of the equation of the line through $(0, 4)$ and $(8, -2)$. $y = -\dfrac{3}{4}x + 4$

22. Write the standard form of the equation of the line parallel to the line $3x + 2y - 3 = 0$ and passing through $(3, 4)$. $3x + 2y - 17 = 0$

23. Write the standard form of the equation of the line perpendicular to the line $-x + 5y = -3$ and passing through the origin. $5x + y = 0$

24. Prove that the midpoint of the hypotenuse of a right triangle is equidistant from all of the vertices. See Teacher's Answer Key.

25. **Physics** The equation of the illuminance, E, of a small light source is $E = \dfrac{P}{4\pi d^2}$, where P is the luminous flux (lm) of the source and d is its distance from the surface. Suppose the luminous flux of a desk lamp is 750 lm.
   a. What is the illuminance (in lm/m^2) on a desktop if the lamp is 2.5 m above it? 9.5 lm/m^2 b. d cannot be negative or zero.
   b. Name the values of d, if any, that are not in the domain of the given function.

Bonus

The function f is defined by $f(x) = \dfrac{kx}{4x + 2}$, where k is a constant and $x \neq -\dfrac{1}{2}$. What is the value of k when $f(f(x)) = x$ for all real numbers except $-\dfrac{1}{2}$? −2

This page may be used as a test or as a review. All answers to this test appear in the Selected Answers in the student text.

Standardized Test Practice Questions are also provided in the Evaluation Masters.

Evaluation Masters Booklet, pp. 5–6

Test Generator Software is provided in Apple, IBM, and Macintosh versions. You may use this software to create your own tests, based on the needs of your students.

Additional Answers

1. {(2, 5), (1, 2), (0, −1), (−1, −4), (−2, −7)}; yes

2. {(4, 13), (3, 11), (2, 9), (1, 7), (0, 5), (4, −13), (3, −11), (2, −9), (1, −7), (0, −5)} no

10. $f^{-1}(x) = \pm\sqrt{3x - 5}$; no

11. $f^{-1}(x) = 4x - 4$; yes

12. $f^{-1}(x) = \sqrt[3]{\dfrac{-x}{2}} + 1$; yes

2 SYSTEMS OF EQUATIONS AND INEQUALITIES

PREVIEWING THE CHAPTER

This chapter includes further work with equations to include methods for solving systems of equations graphically and algebraically. Matrices and operations on matrices are introduced. After students learn to evaluate determinates and find inverses of matrices, they are shown the connection of using matrices as a tool for solving systems of equations. Students also solve systems of inequalities by graphing. They also find maximum and minimum values for graphs of convex polygonal sets and extend this concept to linear programming where graphs of inequalities are used to model real-life situations.

Lesson Objective Chart

Lesson (Pages)	Lesson Objectives		State/Local Objectives
2-1 (56-61)	**2-1A:**	Solve systems of equations graphically.	
	2-1B:	Solve systems of equations algebraically.	
2-2 (64-70)	**2-2:**	Add, subtract, and multiply matrices.	
2-3 (71-77)	**2-3A:**	Evaluate determinants.	
	2-3B:	Find inverses of matrices.	
	2-3C:	Solve systems of equations by using inverses of matrices.	
2-4 (79-83)	**2-4:**	Solve systems of equations by using matrices.	
2-5 (86-90)	**2-5A:**	Graph systems of inequalities.	
	2-5B:	Find the maximum or minimum value of a function defined for a polygonal convex set.	
2-6 (91-97)	**2-6A:**	Use linear programming procedures to solve problems.	
	2-6B:	Recognize situations where exactly one solution to a linear programming problem may not exist.	

ORGANIZING THE CHAPTER

You may want to refer to the **Course Planning Guide Calendar** on pages T34-T35 for a complete pacing chart.

Lesson Planning Guide

| | | | | | Blackline Masters Booklets | | | | | | | | |
| | | | | | | | Technology | | | | Activity Masters | | | |
Lesson	Pages	Practice	Enrichment	Evaluation	Graphing Calculator	Computer	Multicultural Activity	Applications	Problem Solving	Case Study Follow-Up	Decision Making	Transparencies
2-1	56-61	p. 7	p. 7								p. 6	2-1
2-2	64-70	p. 8	p. 8	Quiz A, p. 21			p. 4					2-2
2-3	71-77	p. 9	p. 9	Quiz B, p. 21 Mid-Chapter Test, p. 23								2-3
2-4	79-83	p. 10	p. 10	Quiz C, p. 22					p. 5			2-4
2-5	86-90	p. 11	p. 11			p. 4						2-5
2-6	91-97	p. 12	p. 12	Quiz D, p. 22	p. 3		p. 2					2-6
Review	98-100	Multiple Choice Tests, Forms 1A and 1B, pp. 13-16 Free Response Tests, Forms 2A and 2B, pp. 17-20 Standardized Test Questions, p. 24										
Test	101											

Other Chapter Resources

Student Edition
Case Study Follow-Up, p. 97
Decision Making, p. 70
Technology, p. 78

Other Supplements
Transparency 2-0 for Chapter Opener
Alternate Assessment in the Mathematics Classroom,
    Glencoe Publishing Co., 1993
Cooperative Learning in the Mathematics Classroom,
    Glencoe Publishing Co., 1993

Software
Test and Review Generator Software
    Available for Apple, IBM, and Macintosh
Teacher's Guide for Software Resources

ENHANCING THE CHAPTER

Cooperative Learning

Arranging the Room

Providing a physical environment conducive to cooperative-learning activities is important if success is to be achieved when using this learning technique. How the room is arranged should indicate to students what is expected of them as well as make it easy for both you and the groups to accomplish the defined goals. Since you will want to monitor the groups, they should be arranged in a way that permits you to pass among them, unobtrusively if possible. They should also be placed apart far enough so that the groups do not interfere with each other's learning. The students in each group must be able to see all of the pertinent materials, see one another, and converse without disturbing students in other groups, and exchange ideas and materials with other members of the group in a convenient manner. Among the best arrangements is one where the group members sit in a circle, although any arrangement that permits each group member to have eye contact with and easy access to all other members of the group also would be satisfactory.

For more information on cooperative learning, see pages T20–T21. Additional information on using cooperative groups is available in Glencoe's *Cooperative Learning in the Mathematics Classroom,* ©1993.

Multicultural

Multicultural Activity Masters, p. 2

CHAPTER 2
NAME _____ DATE _____

Multicultural Activity (Use after Lesson 2-6)

Solving Linear Programming Problems

The method for solving linear programming problems you studied in this lesson is based upon the *corner principle,* which states that the highest profit value on a polygonal region can always be found at a corner point. This method is useful for a problem involving two variables and a few corner points.

Real-world problems often involve many variables and corner points. George Dantzig, an American mathematician and a professor of operations research and computer science at Stanford University, invented a linear-programming technique called the *simplex method.* This method has been used for many years to solve complex linear-program problems.

In about 1980, the Russian mathematician L. K. Khachian invented a technique for solving linear-programming problems called the *ellipsoid method,* which works better than the simplex method for problems involving a large number of variables. It has great significance at the theoretical level.

Narenda Karmarkar, a research mathematician who solves problems for American businesses and industries, has created a powerful new linear programming algorithm that solves complex industrial problems faster and more efficiently than any previous method. His method is currently being applied to problems in telecommunications and in airline routing. One problem recently solved by his algorithm involved about 800,000 variables and required 10 hours of computer time.

Make a graph for the following problem. Then use the corner principle to solve the problem.

A breakfast-food manufacturer has 800 pounds of oats and 40 pounds of honey. She can make a box of Oats Power from 0.5 pounds of oats and no honey. She can make a box of Honey Oats Power from 0.4 pounds of oats and 0.1 pounds of honey. She will make a 10¢ profit on a box of Oats Power and a 13¢ profit on a box of Honey Oats Power. How many boxes of each should she make with the available ingredients to maximize her profit?

Profit = $0.10x + 0.13y$
Profit is maximum at (1280, 400).
She should make 1280 boxes of Oats Power and 400 boxes of Honey Oats Power.

T 2
Glencoe Division, Macmillan/McGraw-Hill

Activity Masters

Applications, p. 4

CHAPTER 2
NAME _____ DATE _____

Application (Use after Lesson 2-2)

Matrix Multiplication

A furniture manufacturer makes upholstered chairs and wooden tables. Matrix A shows the number of hours spent on each item by three different workers. One day the factory receives an order for 10 chairs and 3 tables. This is shown in matrix B.

$$\begin{array}{c} \quad\quad\quad \text{hours} \\ \quad\text{woodworker finisher upholsterer} \\ \begin{array}{l} \text{chair} \\ \text{table} \end{array} \left[\begin{array}{ccc} 4 & 2 & 12 \\ 18 & 15 & 0 \end{array}\right] = A \quad \begin{array}{l}\text{number ordered} \end{array} \begin{array}{c} \text{chair table} \\ [\,10 \quad 3\,] \end{array} = B \end{array}$$

$$[10\ 3]\begin{bmatrix}4 & 2 & 12 \\ 18 & 15 & 0\end{bmatrix} = [10(4) + 3(18)\ \ 10(2) + 3(15)\ \ 10(12) + 3(0)] = [94\ \ 65\ \ 120]$$

The product of the two matrices shows the number of hours needed for each type of worker to complete the order: 94 hours for woodworking, 65 hours for finishing, and 120 hours for upholstering.

To find the total labor cost, multiply by a matrix that shows the hourly rate for each worker: $15 for woodworking, $9 for finishing, and $12 for upholstering.

$$C = \begin{bmatrix} 15 \\ 9 \\ 12 \end{bmatrix}; \ [\,94\ \ 65\ \ 120\,]\begin{bmatrix} 15 \\ 9 \\ 12 \end{bmatrix} = [94(15) + 65(9) + 120(12)] = \$3435$$

Use matrix multiplication to solve this problem.

A candy company packages caramels, chocolates, and hard candy in three different assortments: traditional, deluxe, and superb. For each type of candy the table below gives the number in each assortment, the number of calories per piece, and the cost to make each piece.

	traditional	deluxe	superb	calories per piece	cost per piece in cents
caramels	10	16	15	60	10
chocolates	12	8	25	70	12
hard candy	10	16	8	55	6

The company receives an order for 300 traditional, 180 deluxe and 100 superb assortments.

1. Find the number of each type of candy needed to fill the order.
   7380 caramels; 7540 chocolates; 6680 hard candies
2. Find the total number of calories in each type of assortment.
   1990 traditional; 2400 deluxe; 3090 superb
3. Find the cost of production for each type of assortment.
   $3.04 traditional; $3.52 deluxe; $4.98 superb
4. Find the cost to fill the order.
   $2043.60

T 4
Glencoe Division, Macmillan/McGraw-Hill

Problem Solving, p. 5

CHAPTER 2
NAME _____ DATE _____

Problem Solving (Use after Lesson 2-4)

Use Subgoals

One technique for solving problems is to define appropriate subgoals. As each subgoal is reached, you are that much closer to solving the original problem.

Problems that require two or more steps to solve are often successfully attacked using subgoals.

Here is one such problem.

Use the elimination method to solve this system of equations.
$$\begin{aligned} 2x + y - 3z &= 1 \\ x + 2y + 5z &= 9 \\ 3x - 3y - 10z &= 4 \end{aligned}$$

Answer these questions to solve the problem.

1. A first subgoal is to derive a system involving two equations in the same two variables. Derive such a system. **Answers will vary. One answer is $-3y - 13z = -17$ and $-9y - 25z = -23$.**
2. Now, solve the two-system equation to get two equations, each in one unknown. This is the second subgoal.
   Answers will vary. One answer is $z = 2$ and $y = -3$.
3. Complete the solution to the problem.
   $x = 5$, $y = -3$, and $z = 2$
   Explain how the subgoal method can be used to solve this problem.
4. The system of equations at the right is solved using transformations of an augmented matrix. $\begin{aligned} 2x + y - 3z &= 1 \\ x + 2y + 5z &= 9 \\ 3x - 3y - 10z &= 4 \end{aligned}$
   Answers will vary. Possible answer is to get the third row in the form 0, 0, 1; then the second row in the form 0, 1, 0.
5. Five circular chips are laid on a rectangular grid as shown in the Given State below. The goal is to move the counters to the Goal State. Any counter may be moved to any adjacent empty square.

Given State			Subgoal 1			Subgoal 2			Goal State		
A	A	C		B	C		B	C		A	B
A		B	A	A	A	A	A	A	A		C

a. Show how to get from the beginning of the problem to Subgoal 1.
   Possible answer: Rotate all 5 counters counter-clockwise to get B in upper left; move bottom middle A up and C to right; rotate 4 righthand counters to get C in upper right; move bottom middle A left and top middle A down.
b. How does the use of subgoals help in this problem?
   Sample answer: There are fewer steps in each subproblem.

T 5
Glencoe Division, Macmillan/McGraw-Hill

Decision Making, p. 6

CHAPTER 2
NAME _____ DATE _____

Decision Making (Use after Lesson 2-1)

Designing a Study Space

Few students are lucky enough to have a separate room for homework. Some students use part of a bedroom for their studies; others choose to work at a library.

In these exercises, you will work with others to plan the ideal space for doing schoolwork at home.
   Answers will vary.

Factors for an Ideal Study Space
(Reference Books, Quiet, Paper, Pens and Pencils, Light, Furniture, Computer or Calculator)

1. The circle graph shows one way to represent the key variables in an ideal space to study. Make a list of the variables that are important to you. Then construct a circle graph showing the relative importance of each variable.

2. Work in a small group to choose the best lighting, furniture, calculator, and computer. Assume that you will use one side of a bedroom for your study area. Each member of the group should collect advertisements and catalogues to share during the discussion. Include floor plans in your summary of the best set-up.

3. Now, consider budgetary constraints. With your group, determine three different budgets. Pick the best physical equipment for each budget. Are there ways a student could save money by building items or buying at garage sales?

4. Analyze your current study area. First, describe what resources you already have. Devise at least three ways to improve your working conditions without spending any money. (Often, reorganizing your equipment can result in a better working environment.) Then, list three improvements that involve some expenditures.

5. Prepare a logical argument to convince another student that it is not advantageous to do homework in front of the television.

6. Organize a debate on this issue: Listening to music while doing homework is helpful. For example, if you are working in a group of 5 students, 2 students could argue the "pro" side; 2 students could argue the "con" side; and 1 student could act as moderator.

7. Create and take a survey of students at your school to find out their current study conditions. Make sure you choose a representative sample for the survey so that your findings will be indicative of the entire school. What suggestions would you make to other students based on your investigations?

T 6
Glencoe Division, Macmillan/McGraw-Hill

Technology

The Technology feature following Lesson 2-3 utilizes *Matrix,* a computer program formatted for IBM and IBM compatible computers. The software evaluates the determinants of matrices.

The Exploration in Lesson 2-1 illustrates how to estimate solutions of systems of equations by using a graphing calculator. The program included in Exercise 28 of that lesson will solve a system of two linear equations written in standard form. Students who have graphing calculators with a matrix feature can utilize this function to perform operations with matrices, and find their inverses and determinants.

Graphing Calculator Exercises, pp. 76, 89
Graphing Calculator Program, p. 60-61

Outside Resources

Books/Periodicals

North Carolina School of Science and Mathematics. *New Topics for Secondary School Mathematics: Matrices,* Reston, VA, NCTM, 1988.

Hanson, Viggo P., and Zweng, Marilyn J., editors. *Computers in Mathematics Education.* 1984 Yearbook of the National Council of Teachers of Mathematics, Reston VA, NCTM, 1984.

Films/Videotapes/Videodiscs

Mathematics: College Algebra. Great Plains National, University of Nebraska-Lincoln

The Mechanical Universe...and Beyond, Part I. California Institute of Technology and the Southern California Consortium

Software

Graphing utilities (see list on page T25)

Function at Your Best: With Linear Programming Applications. Wings for Learning/Sunburst (IBM)

Matrix. North Carolina School of Science and Mathematics, NCTM (IBM)

Matrix Theory. Addison-Wesley Publishing Co. (Apple II)

Supplementary MathTools. MacNumerics by Spring Branch Software, Inc., William K. Bradford Publishing (Macintosh)

Technology Masters

Graphing Calculator, p. 3

Computer, p. 4

This two-page introduction to the chapter provides students with an opportunity to see how college students use the mathematics presented in this chapter in their chosen majors. It also gives students a glimpse of the college majors that are available to them.

Transparency 2–0, available in the *Advanced Mathematical Concepts* Teaching Transparency Package, provides another full-color visual and motivational activity that you can use to engage your students in the mathematical content of the chapter.

More About Juan Porras

Juan Porras has studied linear programming to help him maximize profits and minimize costs for agricultural activities. He is studying agricultural economics at Texas A & M University and is interested in management or research. He has done an internship on a farm and would like to help agriculture expand in South Texas.

Chapter Project

Materials paper and pencil

Procedure Organize students into cooperative groups. Each group will create a manufacturing company for which a linear programming model can be applied. Have each group describe the costs and profits of manufactured products in terms of a system of inequalities. Have them describe the polygonal region determined by the inequalities, write a profit equation for the company, and then find the maximum or minimum profits of the company can expect from the constraints created. Finally, have each group prepare a report and present it to the class.

CHAPTER 2

SYSTEMS OF EQUATIONS AND INEQUALITIES

HISTORICAL SNAPSHOT

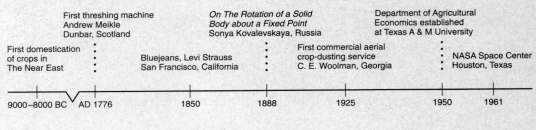

First threshing machine
Andrew Meikle
Dunbar, Scotland

On The Rotation of a Solid Body about a Fixed Point
Sonya Kovalevskaya, Russia

Department of Agricultural Economics established
at Texas A & M University

First domestication
of crops in
The Near East

Bluejeans, Levi Strauss
San Francisco, California

First commercial aerial
crop-dusting service
C. E. Woolman, Georgia

NASA Space Center
Houston, Texas

| 9000–8000 BC | AD 1776 | 1850 | 1888 | 1925 | 1950 | 1961 |

52

CHAPTER OBJECTIVES

In this chapter, you will:
- Solve systems of equations and inequalities.
- Define matrices.
- Add, subtract, and multiply matrices.
- Use linear programming procedures to solve problems.

CAREER GOAL: Agricultural Management

Ask Juan Porras what his career goal is, and you'll be presented with a flurry of options. He says that he is interested in getting into the management of a large agri-business corporation. Or, he may go to law school. Or, he may pursue a research position with the United States Dairy Association (USDA). Or, he may go into farm and ranch management. And oh, by the way, he is also interested in real estate.

Where did all of this ambition come from? Juan says it began with the family business. His father owns several farms and ranches. In his home county, Texas's Starr County, agriculture is big business. "I have always felt that agriculture is a basic profession," Juan says. "That is, no matter what else happens, we will always need agriculture."

In the summer of 1991, Juan did an internship with the Starr County Agricultural Extension agent. He says, "My internship gave me lots of hands-on experiences. Being in the classroom is entirely different from actually being out on the farm, applying what you learn in textbooks." One of the things that Juan has learned is how to use linear programming to maximize return. "For example, assume you know your available constraints in terms of land, labor, and capital. You then identify your potential agricultural activities, such as raising wheat and corn, or having a cow-calf operation, or growing and selling cotton. Linear programming helps you to determine the combination of your potential agricultural activities that will maximize your profit and minimize your costs."

In the future, Juan "would really like to help to expand agriculture in South Texas. The people here are quiet, good, hardworking individuals. If we could attract more agricultural industries to South Texas, there would be many more jobs, and the financial stability of the area would improve greatly."

READ MORE ABOUT IT

Atak, Jeremy and Fred Bateman. *To Their Own Soil*. Ames, Iowa: Iowa State University Press, 1987.

Hurt, R. Douglas. *The Department of Agriculture*. New York: Chelsea House, 1987.

White, William C. and Donald N. Collins. *Opportunities in Agriculture Careers*. Lincolnwood, Illinois: VGM Career Horizons, 1991.

SPOTLIGHT ON...

Juan Porras
Age: 21
Class: Senior
School: Texas A & M University
    College Station, Texas
Major: Agricultural Economics

"Agriculture is a basic profession; no matter what else happens, we will always need agriculture."

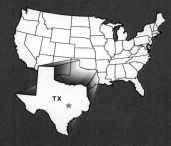

TX

FOR MORE INFORMATION

If you would like more information about agricultural economics, contact:

International Association of Agricultural Economists (IAAE)
1211 W. 22nd Street, Suite 216 Oak Brook, IL 60521

Applications

Lesson	Application	Examples	Exercises
2–1	Sales Agriculture Real Estate	4	30 31 32
2–2	Agriculture Entertainment Geometry	6	47 48
2–3	Metallurgy Landscaping	5	35 36
2–4	Restaurants Consumer Purchasing		22 23
2–5	Education Business		21 22
2–6	Manufacturing	1	15, 16, 18, 20, 22
	Nutrition Contracting Energy Marketing		17 19 21 23

Objective   Solve a system of two linear equations in two variables graphically.

Motivating the Lesson

Ask students to discuss whether the system of linear equations graphed below has a solution.

Call upon students to justify their responses.

Teaching Tip   Ask students if they can tell before using a graphing calculator whether a system of equations has a solution. For example, ask "How do you know that the system $y = 2x + 5$ and $y = 3x$ has exactly one solution?"

Students should respond that since the lines have different slopes they are not parallel, so they must intersect at some point.

Teaching Tip   Have student practice using the ZOOM feature to more closely examine points of intersection.

2-1A   Graphing Calculators: Graphing Systems of Linear Equations

You can use a graphing calculator to graph and solve systems of linear equations since several equations can be graphed on the screen at the same time. If the graphs of the two equations intersect, then the system has a solution and the solution is the coordinates of the point of intersection of the two lines. These coordinates, (x, y), can be determined to a great degree of accuracy on the graphing calculator by using the TRACE and ZOOM functions.

Graph the system of equations $y = 3.4x + 2.1$ and $y = -5.1x + 8.3$ in the standard viewing window.

Now use the trace function to determine the coordinates of the intersection point. On the TI-81, press TRACE, and on the Casio press SHIFT Trace. Then use the left and right arrow keys to move along the function to the intersection point. The TI-81 allows you to move from one function to another by pressing the up and down arrow keys. The Casio will only access the last function graphed.

The TI-81 has a special "zoom" feature that is very useful for determining the coordinates of a solution or point to a great degree of accuracy. With the blinking dot or cursor on the point of intersection, zoom in by pressing ZOOM 2 and ENTER. This magnifies a portion of the previous graphics screen and creates a new smaller screen with the coordinates of the cursor at the center. Checking your range now will help to illustrate what is happening.

You can continue zooming in until the coordinates of the point of intersection are found to the degree of accuracy that you desire or need. If you would like to zoom in faster, you can set the zoom factors of the calculator higher and zoom in on the point again. Setting the factors to 10 will allow you to zoom in fairly quickly.

TI-81:   ZOOM 4   10 ENTER 10 ZOOM 2 ENTER

On the Casio, you can zoom in by tracing to the point of intersection and pressing SHIFT X. This will zoom in on the point of intersection by a factor of 2. If you want to zoom in quicker, you can insert the zoom factor in the text screen.

Casio: $\boxed{\text{G}\leftrightarrow\text{T}}$ $\boxed{\rightarrow}$ $\boxed{\text{SHIFT}}$ $\boxed{\text{INS}}$ $\boxed{\text{SHIFT}}$ $\boxed{\text{Factor}}$ 10 $\boxed{:}$ $\boxed{\text{EXE}}$

Once the lines have been replotted, trace to the point of intersection again and check the coordinates. If you need to zoom in again, simply press $\boxed{\text{EXE}}$. You can alternate between the x- and y-coordinates by pressing $\boxed{\text{SHIFT}}$ $\boxed{\text{X}\leftrightarrow\text{Y}}$.

This process determines that the x- and y-coordinates of the point of intersection of the system $y = 3.4x + 2.1$ and $y = 5.1x + 8.3$ are (0.73, 4.58) to the nearest hundredth.

Example

Graph the system of equations below and find the solution to the nearest hundredth.

$$y = 3.27x + 2.87$$
$$y = -2.55x - 4.58$$

TI-81: $\boxed{\text{Y=}}$ 3.27 $\boxed{\text{X|T}}$ $\boxed{+}$ 2.87 $\boxed{\text{ENTER}}$ $\boxed{(-)}$ 2.55 $\boxed{\text{X|T}}$ $\boxed{-}$ 4.58 $\boxed{\text{GRAPH}}$

Casio: $\boxed{\text{GRAPH}}$ 3.27 $\boxed{\text{ALPHA}}$ $\boxed{\text{X}}$ $\boxed{+}$ 2.87 $\boxed{:}$ $\boxed{\text{GRAPH}}$ $\boxed{(-)}$ 2.55 $\boxed{\text{ALPHA}}$ $\boxed{\text{X}}$ $\boxed{-}$ 4.58 $\boxed{\text{EXE}}$

TI-81: $\boxed{\text{TRACE}}$ to the point of intersection, then $\boxed{\text{ZOOM}}$ 2 and $\boxed{\text{ENTER}}$

Casio: $\boxed{\text{SHIFT}}$ $\boxed{\text{Trace}}$ to the point of intersection, then set the zoom factor by pressing $\boxed{\text{G}\leftrightarrow\text{T}}$ $\boxed{\rightarrow}$ $\boxed{\text{SHIFT}}$ $\boxed{\text{INS}}$ $\boxed{\text{SHIFT}}$ $\boxed{\text{Factor}}$ 10 $\boxed{:}$ $\boxed{\text{EXE}}$.

The solution is (–1.28, –1.32) to the nearest hundredth.

EXERCISES

Use a graphing calculator to solve the following systems of equations by graphing. Determine the coordinates of the solution to the nearest hundredth.

1. $y = 6x + 3$ (–0.78, –1.67)
   $y = -3x - 4$

2. $y = 4x + 0.342$ (–0.92, –3.37)
   $y = 0.5x - 2.905$

3. $y = 7.65x + 3.85$ (–0.88, –2.86)
   $y = 4.957x + 1.492$

4. $y = 2.34x - 2$ (3.93, 7.19)
   $y = 5.39x - 14$

5. $4.9x + 0.3y = 1.6$ (0.37, –0.70)
   $-6.2x + 3.2y = -4.4$

6. $8.33x + 3.492y = 3.8$ (0.46, –0.01)
   $4.8x - 1.074y = 2.3$

More Examples

Use a graphing calculator to solve the system of equations.
2.33x + 5.67y = 12
2.87x − 4.35y = 10
Determine the coordinates of the solution to the nearest hundredth.
(4.12, 0.42)

EVALUATING THE LESSON

Closing the Lesson

Ask students which of the following systems can be solved graphically.
a. $3x + 2y = 6$
   $3x + 2y = 7$ no
b. $4x - 5y = 10$
   $3x + 5y = 7$ yes

EVALUATING THE LESSON

Homework Exercises

Assignment Guide

All: 1–6

Lesson Resources

- Practice Master 2–1
- Enrichment Master 2–1
- Activity Master, p. 6

Transparency 2–1 contains the 5-Minute Check and a teaching aid for this lesson.

INTRODUCING THE LESSON

5–Minute Check

(over Chapter 1)

1. State the domain and range of {(–2, 4), (1, 3), (–2, –2)}. Is it a function? **D = {–2, 1}, R = {4, 3, –2}; no**

2. If $f(x) = 2x - 4$ and $g(x) = x^2$, find $g(f(x))$. **$4x^2 - 16x + 16$**

3. A manufacturer of compact discs has $1000 in fixed costs per day and a cost of $4 for each compact disc produced. Express the cost of the total number of discs produced per day, $C(x)$, as a linear function. What is the domain of the function? **$C(x) = 4x + 1000$; positive integers**

4. Find the slope of the line connecting the points at (–4, 3) and (–2, –5). Then find the distance between the points. **–4; $2\sqrt{17}$ units**

5. Write the equation of a line parallel to the line $2x - 3y = 8$ with y-intercept –6. **$y = \frac{2}{3}x - 6$**

Motivating the Lesson

Discuss the idea of the *break-even* point in putting on a school dance. How many tickets must be sold to cover expenses, such as the cost of food, the cost of hiring a disk jockey to play music, the cost of decorations, and so on?

2-1 Solving Systems of Equations

Objectives
2–1A
2–1B

After studying this lesson, you should be able to:
- solve systems of equations graphically, and
- solve systems of equations algebraically.

Application

Heather Washington, a recent mechanical engineering graduate, plans to start her own business manufacturing custom touring bicycle frames. She

is planning to call her business Tour de Force, Inc. After careful research, she has decided that in order to be successful, she will need $12,500 for overhead (fixed costs like labor, rent, utilities, and so on), an additional $200 per frame for materials (variable cost), and in order to be competitive, a selling price of $700 per bicycle frame. How many frames must Heather sell in order to break even?

Let's write two equations to represent the constraints in the problem. The equation that represents the cost to produce the frames, called the *cost equation*, is $y = 200x + 12,500$. The equation that represents the sales price of the frames, called the *revenue equation*, is $y = 700x$.

> FYI...
>
> In 1990, there were 55.3 million bikers in the United States.

The intersection of the graphs of the cost and revenue equations is called the *break-even point*. The graph at the right shows the break-even point for Tour de Force, Inc. Thus, if Heather sells 25 bicycle frames, she will break even.

As you can see, graphing more than one linear equation on the same coordinate system has practical applications. If the graphs intersect, the ordered pair for the point of intersection is the solution to the **system of equations**.

Example 1

Solve the system of equations by graphing.
$y = 5x - 2$
$y = -2x + 5$

Since the two lines have different slopes, the graphs of the equations are intersecting lines.

The solution of the system is $(1, 3)$.

ALTERNATE TEACHING STRATEGIES

Using Computers

A computer can be used to find the break-even point of the two equations in the application. Then the graphs can be *traced* to find other values. Have students explain what the other values represent.

Using Charts

Have students make charts of other possible values of the cost and revenue equations. Students can use the charts to determine if certain domain values represent a loss or a profit to the Tour de Force, Inc. business.

A **consistent** system of equations has at least one solution. If there is exactly one solution, the system is **independent**. If there are infinitely many solutions, the system is **dependent**.

Consider the equations $2y + 3x = 6$ and $4y + 6x = 12$. The equations written in slope-intercept form are $y = -\frac{3}{2}x + 3$ and $y = -\frac{3}{2}x + 3$. The graphs of these equations are the same line. Since any ordered pair on the graph satisfies both equations, there are infinitely many solutions to this system of equations.

Some systems of equations have no ordered pairs as the solution. Consider the equations $y = -3x - 2$ and $y = -3x + 3$. The graphs of these two equations are two lines with slopes of -3 and different y-intercepts. These lines are parallel and do not intersect. Therefore, there is no solution to this system of equations. This is called an **inconsistent** system of equations.

The chart below gives a summary of the possibilities for the graphs of two linear equations in two variables.

Graphs of Equations	Slopes of Lines	Type of System	Number of Solutions
lines intersect	different slopes	consistent and independent	one
lines coincide	same slope, same intercepts	consistent and dependent	infinitely many
lines parallel	same slope, different intercepts	inconsistent	none

Systems of linear equations may also be solved algebraically. Two ways of solving systems algebraically are the **elimination method** and the **substitution method**. In some situations, one method may be easier to use than the other.

Example 2

Use the elimination method to solve the system of equations.

$3x - 4y = 360$
$5x + 2y = 340$

To solve this system, first multiply the second equation by 2. Then add the two equations.

$3x - 4y = 360$
$\underline{10x + 4y = 680}$
$13x \qquad = 1040$
$\qquad x = 80$

Now substitute 80 for x in either of the original equations.

$5x + 2y = 340$
$5(80) + 2y = 340$
$y = -30$

The solution is $(80, -30)$.

Teaching Tip   In discussing the application, point out that the constraints come from the conditions in the problem itself. The key phrases that lead to the constraints are *in order to be successful* and *in order to be competitive*. The actual constraints are expressed mathematically. Also discuss the possible domain and range values of the break-even point.
D = {positive integers}, R = {positive integers}

Chalkboard Example

For Example 1

Solve the system of equations by graphing.
$y = -\frac{1}{2}x$

$y = \frac{3}{2}x + 4$ $-2, 1$

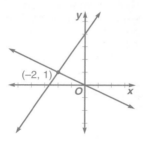

For Example 2

Use the elimination method to solve the system of equations.
$3x - 4y = 1200$
$-2x + y = -550$ $(200, -150)$

Teaching Tip   Evaluating the number of solutions possible for a system of equations is easier if the equations are written in slope-intercept form. You may need to review this form of an equation.

Teaching Tip   In discussing Example 2, point out that either variable can be eliminated first by using the elimination method. Also stress the importance of substituting the first value obtained into the *original* equations. The final solution should also be checked with the original equations.

Teaching Tip As shown in Example 3, point out that the substitution method is usually the easier method when the system of equations has one variable expressed in terms of another.

Teaching Tip For Example 4, discuss how the algebraic solutions are interpreted in terms of the original problem.

Chalkboard Examples

For Example 3

Use the substitution method to solve the system of equations.
$x = -3y - 2$
$3x + 10y = -4$ (-8, 2)

For Example 4

The Music Booster Club of Central High sells compact discs and cassette tapes to raise money. During the last fund-raiser, 48 compact discs and 32 cassettes sold for $1,040. This time, they hope to sell three times as many discs and four times as many cassettes for $3,440. What is the selling price of each disc and cassette? disc: $15, cassette: $10

Example 3

Use the substitution method to solve the system of equations.
$x = 7y + 3$
$2x - y = -7$

The first equation is stated in terms of x, so substitute $7y + 3$ for x in the second equation.

$$2x - y = -7$$
$$2(7y + 3) - y = -7$$
$$13y = -13$$
$$y = -1$$

Now solve for x by substituting -1 for y in either of the original equations.

$$x = 7y + 3$$
$$x = 7(-1) + 3$$
$$x = -4$$

The solution is $(-4, -1)$.

You can also use elimination and substitution to solve real-world problems.

Example 4

HomeMade Toys manufactures solid pine trucks and cars and usually sells four times as many trucks as cars. The net profit from each truck is $6 and from each car, $5. If the company wants a total profit of $29,000, how many trucks and cars should they sell?

Let t represent the number of trucks sold.
Let c represent the number of cars sold.
Because they usually sell four times as many trucks as cars, $t = 4c$.
The total profit can be represented by the equation $6t + 5c = 29,000$.

The first equation is stated in terms of t, so substitute $4c$ for t in the second equation.

$$6t + 5c = 29,000$$
$$6(4c) + 5c = 29,000$$
$$29c = 29,000$$
$$c = 1000$$

Now solve for w by substituting 1000 for c in either of the original equations.

$$t = 4c$$
$$= 4(1000)$$
$$= 4000$$

HomeMade Toys must sell 4000 trucks and 1000 cars to make a total profit of $29,000.

You can use a graphing calculator to show solutions of systems of equations.

Additional Answers

1. The substitution method is usually easier whenever one or both of the equations are already solved for one variable in terms of the other (for example, $y = 2x - 7$).

3. A system of equations is inconsistent when it represents two parallel lines; since they have no points in common, there is no solution.

EXPLORATION: Graphing Calculator

Suppose the cost function for producing a widget is $y = 3x + \$80$, and the revenue function is $y = 8x$.

1. Complete the table below to find when cost is equal to revenue.

Number of Widgets	Cost	Revenue
4	$3(4) + 80 = 92$	$8(4) = 32$
8	$3(8) + 80 = 104$	$8(8) = 64$
12	? 116	? 96
16	? 128	? 128
20	? 140	? 160

2. Graph the two functions.
   Make sure you use appropriate range values.

3. What is the relationship between the graph and the results in the table?
   Cost equals revenue when $c = 16$. This point is at the intersection of the graphs of the functions.

CHECKING FOR UNDERSTANDING

Communicating Mathematics

Read and study the lesson to answer each question. 1, 3. See margin.

1. **Describe** the circumstances under which it would be easier to solve a system of equations by using the substitution method rather than the elimination method.

2. What is the name for the point of intersection of the graph of a revenue equation and the graph of a cost equation? break-even point

3. When is a system of equations inconsistent?

4. **Describe**, as you would to a friend, how to solve a system of equations by using the elimination method. Answers may vary.

Guided Practice

A possible solution is given for each system of equations. Is it the correct solution? Write *yes* or *no*.

5. $\left(\frac{1}{2}, 6\right)$ yes
$4x + y = 8$
$6x - 2y = -9$

6. $\left(\frac{1}{3}, \frac{2}{3}\right)$ no
$2x + 3y = 3$
$12x - 15y = -4$

7. $(2, 5)$ no
$-3x + 10y = 5$
$2x + 7y = 24$

8. $(4, 3)$ yes
$\frac{1}{2}x + 5y = 17$
$3x + 2y = 18$

9. $(-6, -4)$ no
$\frac{1}{3}x - \frac{3}{2}y = -4$
$5x - 4y = 14$

10. $(4, 7)$ yes
$1.5x + 2y = 20$
$2.5x - 5y = -25$

LESSON 2-1 SOLVING SYSTEMS OF EQUATIONS 59

RETEACHING THE LESSON

Have students work in cooperative groups to solve each problem below. Have them discuss the strategies as they solve the problems.

Solve the system of equations by graphing.
$y = 4x - 18$
$y = \frac{3}{4}x - 5$ **(4, –2)**

Use the elimination method to solve the system of equations.
$3x - 4y = 2$
$-4x + 3y = -5$ **(2, 1)**

Use the substitution method to solve the system of equations.
$y = 3x - 8$
$2x + y = 22$ **(6, 10)**

Using Technology

In the Exploration, students use the graphing calculator to observe the behavior of the graphs of two linear equations. Have them use the TRACE function to determine or verify the break-even point.

EVALUATING THE LESSON

Checking for Understanding

Exercises 1–12 are designed to help you assess students' understanding through reading, writing, speaking, and modeling. You should work through Exercises 1–4 with your students and then monitor their work on Exercises 5–12.

Closing the Lesson

Writing Activity Write a brief paragraph discussing the different possibilities for the graphs of two linear equations in two variables.

Practice Masters Booklet, p. 7

The red A, B, and C flags, printed only in the Teacher's Wraparound Edition, indicate the level of difficulty of the exercises.

Using Technology

For Exercise 28, have students refer their calculator manuals for specifics on entering programs. Encourage them to use the ZOOM and TRACE features to more closely identify the solutions to the system of equations.

Additional Answers

16.

17.

18.

---

11. Solve the system of equations by graphing. See Teacher's Answer Key for graph.
$3x - y - 1 = 0$
$x + y - 3 = 0$ $(1, 2)$

12. Solve the system of equations algebraically.
$5x - y = 16$
$2x + 3y = 3$ $(3, -1)$

EXERCISES

Practice

State whether each system is *consistent and independent, consistent and dependent,* or *inconsistent.*

 A

13. $5x - 7y = 70$ I
$-10x + 14y = 120$

14. $7x - 8y = -11$ CD
$-35x + 40y = 55$

15. $3x - 8y = 10$ CI
$16x - 32y = 75$

16–21. See margin for graphs.
Solve each system of equations by graphing.

16. $x = 0$ $(0, 1)$
$y = 1$

17. $x = 0$ $(0, 4)$
$4x + 5y = 20$

 B

18. $x + 4y = 12$ $(0, 3)$
$3x - 2y = -6$

19. $3x - 2y = -6$ $(-2, 0)$
$x + y = -2$

20. $x + y = -2$ $(2, -4)$
$3x - y = 10$

21. $3x - y = 10$ $(4, 2)$
$x + 4y = 12$

Solve each system of equations algebraically.

22. $x + 2y = 1$ $(-1, 1)$
$3x - 5y = -8$

23. $2x - y = -7$ $(-2, 3)$
$x = 2y - 8$

C

24. $3x + 5y = 7$ $\left(\frac{97}{28}, -\frac{19}{28}\right)$
$2x - 6y = 11$

25. $3x + 2y = 40$ $(12, 2)$
$x - 7y = -2$

26. $2x + 3y = 8$ $\left(\frac{14}{5}, \frac{4}{5}\right)$
$x - y = 2$

27. $x + y = 6$ $(5.25, 0.75)$
$x = y + 4.5$

Programming

28. The following program will solve a system of two linear equations written in the form $Ax + By = C$ and $Dx + Ey = F$.

```
Prgm 2: SlvSystm
:Disp "FIRST X-COEFF="
:Input A
:Disp "FIRST Y-COEFF="
:Input B
:Disp "FIRST CONSTANT="
:Input C
:Disp "SECOND X-COEFF="
:Input D
:Disp "SECOND Y-COEFF="
:Input E
:Disp "SECOND CONSTANT="
:Input F
:If AE-BD = 0
:Goto 1
```

Displays the quoted message.
Accepts a value for A.

Accepts a value for B.

Accepts a value for C.

Accepts a value for D.

Accepts a value for E.

Accepts a value for F.
If the determinant of coefficients is 0,
program will go to line "Lbl 1."

60   CHAPTER 2   SYSTEMS OF EQUATIONS AND INEQUALITIES

19.

20.

21.

```
:(CE-BF)/(AE-BD)→ X       Value is calculated and stored for X.
:Disp "X="
:Disp X                   Displays the value of X.
:(AF-CD)/(AE-BD)→ Y       Value is calculated and stored for Y.
:Disp "Y="
:Disp Y
:Goto 2                   Program will go to line "Lbl 2."
:Lbl 1
:Disp "INCONSISTENT OR DEPENDENT"
:Lbl 2
:End
```

Use the program above to solve each system of equations.

a. $x - y = 1$
$3x - y = 3$ $\ (1, 0)$

b. $x + y = 6$
$3x + 3y = 3$
inconsistent or dependent

c. $a - b = 0$
$3a + 2b = -15$
$(-3, -3)$

29. Find the coordinates of the vertices of the triangle with sides determined by the graphs of the following equations: $4x + 3y + 1 = 0, 4x - 3y - 17 = 0$, and $4x - 9y + 13 = 0$.
$(2, -3), (-1, 1), (8, 5)$

Applications and Problem Solving

30. Sales The Cotton Club, a small manufacturer of sweatshirts, has fixed costs of $2000 and a variable cost of $5 per sweatshirt. They sell their sweatshirts for $15 apiece.

30b. 201 sweatshirts

a. Find their break-even point. $(200, 3000)$
b. What is the least number of sweatshirts they must sell to make a profit?

31. Agriculture Mrs. Griffin wants to plant soybeans and corn on 100 acres of land. Soybeans require 6 hours of labor per acre, and corn requires 8 hours of labor per acre. If Mrs. Griffin has 660 hours available, how many acres of each crop should she plant? 70 soybeans, 30 corn

32. Real Estate AMC Homes, Inc. is planning to build three- and four-bedroom homes in a housing development called Chestnut Hills. Public demand indicates a need for three times as many three-bedroom homes as four-bedroom homes. The net profit from each three-bedroom home is $6000 and from each four-bedroom home, $7000. If AMC Homes must net a total profit of $2,500,000 from this development, how many of each type of home should they build? 300 three-bedroom, 100 four-bedroom

Mixed Review

33. State the domain and range of the relation $\{(16, -4), (16, 4)\}$. Is this relation a function? **(Lesson 1-1)** $\{16\}, \{-4, 4\}$; no

34. Of $(0, 0), (3, 2), (-4, 2)$, or $(-2, 4)$, which satisfy $x + y \geq 3$? **(Lesson 1-3)** $(3, 2)$

35. Write the slope-intercept form of the equation of the line through $(1, 4)$ and $(5, 7)$. **(Lesson 1-5)**

35. $y = \frac{3}{4}x + 3\frac{1}{4}$

36. Show that the points with coordinates $(-1, 3), (3, 6), (6, 2)$, and $(2, -1)$ are the vertices of a square. **(Lesson 1-6)** See margin.

37. College Entrance Exam Choose the best answer. D
How old was a person exactly 1 year ago if exactly x years ago the person was y years old?

(A) $y - 1$ **(B)** $y - x - 1$ **(C)** $x - y - 1$ **(D)** $y + x - 1$ **(E)** $x - 1$

LESSON 2-1 SOLVING SYSTEMS OF EQUATIONS 61

EXTENDING THE LESSON

Math Power: Reasoning

Solve the system of linear equations.
$3x - 2y + z = -3$
$-x + y - 2z = -5$
$x + y + z = 5$ $\quad (-1, 2, 4)$

Additional Answers

36.

$D(3, 6)$
$A(-1, 3)$
$C(6, 2)$
$B(2, -1)$

$AB = \sqrt{(2 + 1)^2 + (-1 - 3)^2} = 5$
$BC = \sqrt{(2 - 6)^2 + (-1 - 2)^2} = 5$
$CD = \sqrt{(6 - 3)^2 + (2 - 6)^2} = 5$
$AD = \sqrt{(3 + 1)^2 + (6 - 3)^2} = 5$
Thus, **ABCD** is a rhombus.
The slope of $\overline{AD} = \frac{6 - 3}{3 + 1} = \frac{3}{4}$

and the slope of $\overline{AB} = \frac{3 + 1}{-1 - 2} =$

$-\frac{4}{3}$. Thus, $\overline{AD}$ is perpendicular to

$\overline{AB}$ and **ABCD** is a square.

Enrichment Masters Booklet, p. 7

NAME _____ DATE _____
2-1 Enrichment Worksheet

Set Theory and Venn Diagrams

Set theory, which was developed by the nineteenth century German logician and mathematician, Georg Cantor, became a fundamental unifying principle in the study of mathematics in the middle of this century. The use of sets permits the precise description of mathematical concepts.

The intersection of two sets determines the elements common to the two sets. Thus, the intersection of two lines in a system of equations refers to the point or points that are common to the sets of points belonging to each of the lines. We can use Venn diagrams, which are named for the British logician, John Venn, to visually represent the intersection of two sets.

Example

Let U = the set of all points in the Cartesian coordinate plane.
Let A = the set of all points that satisfy the equation $x = 4$.
Let B = the set of all points that satisfy the equation $y = -2$.

The shaded region represents the intersection of sets A and B, written $A \cap B$. In this example, $A \cap B = \{(4, -2)\}$.

Since the solution sets of two parallel lines have no points in common, the sets are called **disjoint sets**. In a Venn diagram, such sets are drawn as circles that do not overlap.

 $A \cap B = \varnothing$.

Use the diagram at the right to answer the following questions.
Let A = the set of all points that satisfy the equation for line p.
Let B = the set of all points that satisfy the equation for line q.

1. In which numbered region do the points that satisfy only the equation for line p lie? 1
2. In which numbered region do the points that satisfy only the equation for line q lie? 3
3. In which numbered region do the points that satisfy the equations for neither line p nor line q lie? 4
4. If the equation of line p is $2x - y = 4$ and the equation of line q is $3x + y = 6$, which point lies in region 2? $(2, 0)$

T7
Glencoe Division, Macmillan/McGraw-Hill

LESSON 2–1 SOLVING SYSTEMS OF EQUATIONS 61

2-2A   Graphing Calculators: Matrices

The TI-81 graphing calculator can help you with many algebraic and mathematical tasks. One of these is performing operations with matrices. The TI-81 can find determinants and inverses of matrices, as well as perform operations with matrices.

The MATRX key accesses the matrix operations menus. There are two: the MATRIX menu and the EDIT menu. The first to appear is the MATRIX menu, which lists the matrix functions available. The EDIT menu allows you to define matrices. You can access the EDIT menu by using the left or right arrow key (◀ or ▶). This menu displays the dimensions of the matrices A, B, and C. A matrix with a dimension of 2×3 indicates a matrix with 2 rows and 3 columns. The TI-81 will accommodate a maximum of 6 rows and 6 columns in a matrix.

To enter a matrix into your calculator, choose the EDIT menu and select matrix [A]. Then enter the dimensions and elements of the matrix. As you enter the dimensions, notice the small graphics box to the right of the dimensions definition. Each dot of the box stands for a position in the matrix. The dimensions of the box change as you change the dimensions of the matrix. The dot that is blank represents the current element position.

Example 1

Enter matrix $A = \begin{bmatrix} 1 & 3 \\ 2 & -2 \end{bmatrix}$ **on a TI-81 graphing calculator.**

Enter: MATRX ▶ ENTER 2 ENTER 2 ENTER
1 ENTER 3 ENTER 2 ENTER (−) 2

You can display the matrix by pressing 2nd QUIT to return to the text screen, then 2nd [[A]] ENTER to display the matrix.

The TI-81 graphing calculator can be used to find the determinant and the inverse of a matrix.

Example 2

Find the determinant and the inverse of matrix A.

First, find the determinant.

Enter: MATRX 5 2nd [[A]] ENTER *-8*

Then, find the inverse.

Enter: 2nd [[A]] x^{-1} ENTER $\begin{bmatrix} 0.25 & 0.375 \\ 0.25 & -0.125 \end{bmatrix}$

The determinant of matrix A is –8 and the inverse is $\begin{bmatrix} 0.25 & 0.375 \\ 0.25 & -0.125 \end{bmatrix}$.

Objective   Use a graphing calculator to perform operations on matrices.

Motivating the Lesson

This lesson provides an excellent opportunity for students to appreciate how graphing calculators can greatly reduce the risk of calculation error and facilitate the solution of many problems involving matrices. For example, once a square matrix has been entered into the calculator, students need only press x^2 to obtain the square of a given matrix. For a greater appreciation of technology, you may wish to present this lesson after the paper-and-pencil instruction in Lesson 2-2.

TEACHING THE LESSON

Teaching Tip   Remind students to enter the elements of the matrix row by row, not column by column.

Teaching Tip   Students may need some time to familiarize themselves with the keying sequences necessary to perform matrix operations. For example, to find the determinant, they must select the determinant function from the menu and then name the matrix. To find the inverse, they must name the matrix first and then press x^{-1}.

Additional Answers

1. $\begin{bmatrix} -10 & -4 & -8 \\ -2 & 8 & 6 \\ 0 & -12 & -6 \end{bmatrix}$

2. 48

3. $\begin{bmatrix} 0.125 & 0.375 & 0.2083 \\ -0.0625 & 0.3125 & 0.39583 \\ 0.125 & -0.625 & -0.4583 \end{bmatrix}$

4. $\begin{bmatrix} 6 & 24 \\ 21 & -15 \\ 6 & 3 \end{bmatrix}$

5. $\begin{bmatrix} 32 & 34 \\ -32 & 25 \\ 48 & -27 \end{bmatrix}$

6. $\begin{bmatrix} 56 & -34 & 50 \\ -35 & 46 & -23 \\ 7 & 1 & 8 \end{bmatrix}$

7. 0

8. $\begin{bmatrix} 23 & -14 \\ -9 & 87 \end{bmatrix}$

9. 1875

You can also use a graphing calculator to perform operations on matrices.

Example 3

Enter matrix $B = \begin{bmatrix} 2 & 3 & 6 \\ 4 & -8 & 5 \end{bmatrix}$. Then find $\frac{1}{2}B$, AB, A^2, and $AB + B$.

First enter matrix B.

Enter: MATRX ▶ ▼ ENTER 2 ENTER 3 ENTER
 2 ENTER 3 ENTER 6 ENTER 4 ENTER (−) 8 ENTER 5
 2nd QUIT

Find $\frac{1}{2}B$.

Enter: .5 2nd [B] ENTER $\qquad \begin{bmatrix} 1 & 1.5 & 3 \\ 2 & -4 & 2.5 \end{bmatrix}$

Then find AB.

Enter: 2nd [A] 2nd [B] ENTER $\qquad \begin{bmatrix} 14 & -21 & 21 \\ -4 & 22 & 2 \end{bmatrix}$

Next find A^2.

Enter: 2nd [A] x² ENTER $\qquad \begin{bmatrix} 7 & -3 \\ -2 & 10 \end{bmatrix}$

Now find $AB + B$.

Enter: 2nd [A] 2nd [B] + 2nd [B] ENTER $\qquad \begin{bmatrix} 16 & -18 & 27 \\ 0 & 14 & 7 \end{bmatrix}$

Therefore, $\frac{1}{2}B = \begin{bmatrix} 1 & 1.5 & 3 \\ 2 & -4 & 2.5 \end{bmatrix}$, $AB = \begin{bmatrix} 14 & -21 & 21 \\ -4 & 22 & 2 \end{bmatrix}$, $A^2 = \begin{bmatrix} 7 & -3 \\ -2 & 10 \end{bmatrix}$,

and $AB + B = \begin{bmatrix} 16 & -18 & 27 \\ 0 & 14 & 7 \end{bmatrix}$.

EXERCISES

Enter the matrices into a graphing calculator in the appropriate locations. Then find each of the following. 1-18. See margin.

$A = \begin{bmatrix} 5 & 2 & 4 \\ 1 & -4 & -3 \\ 0 & 6 & 3 \end{bmatrix}$ $\qquad B = \begin{bmatrix} 2 & 8 \\ 7 & -5 \\ 2 & 1 \end{bmatrix}$ $\qquad C = \begin{bmatrix} 0 & 3 & 1 \\ 7 & -5 & 6 \end{bmatrix}$

1. $-2A$
2. determinant of A
3. A^{-1}
4. $3B$
5. AB
6. BC
7. determinant of BC
8. CB
9. determinant of CB
10. CA
11. $C + CA$
12. $BC - A$
13. $(CB)^2$
14. $(CB)^{-1}$
15. $A + BC$
16. ABC
17. $B + AB$
18. $4BC$

Lesson Resources

- Practice Master 2–2
- Enrichment Master 2–2
- Evaluation Master, Quiz A, p. 21
- Activity Master, p. 4

 Transparency 2–2 contains the 5-Minute Check and a teaching aid for this lesson.

INTRODUCING THE LESSON

 5-Minute Check

(over Lesson 2–1)

1. Solve the system of equations by graphing.
   $y = \frac{2}{3}x + 3$
   $y = -3x - 8$ **(–3, 1)**

2. Solve the system of equations by elimination.
   $-2x - y = -5$
   $5x + 4y = 8$ **(4, –3)**

3. Solve the system of equations by substitution.
   $y = -2x - 4$
   $3x - 4y = 10$ $\left(\frac{-6}{11}, \frac{-32}{11}\right)$

4. The daily revenue of the Sweats Unlimited Company is $21,200 and the daily fixed cost is $9800. Sweatshirts sell for $28 and sweatpants sell for $18. The cost of producing the shirts is $18 each, and the cost for the pants is $6 per pair. Find the break-even point for the daily sales.   **500 sweatshirts and 400 sweatpants**

5. Solve the system of equations.
   $2x - 3y = -10.5$
   $4x + y = 38.5$ **(7.5, 8.5)**

Prerequisite Skills

Students should be familiar with the associative and commutative properties of multiplication before beginning this lesson.

1. Give an example of the associative property of multiplication.   **Sample:**
   $-8 \cdot (-2 \cdot 3) = (-8 \cdot -2) \cdot 3$

2. Give an example of the commutative property of addition.   **Sample:**
   $-8 \cdot (-2 + 3) = -8 (3 + -2)$

2-2 Introduction to Matrices

Objective
2–2

After studying this lesson, you should be able to:
- add, subtract, and multiply matrices.

Application

Edwin Yunker, the father of one of the authors of this textbook, is a grain farmer in Mokena, Illinois. Mr. Yunker sold most of his fall harvest for 1992 on the grain futures market for delivery in the summer of 1993. He scheduled his delivery of corn, soybeans, and oats (in bushels) on a wall chart as shown below.

$$\begin{array}{c} \\ \text{June} \\ \text{July} \\ \text{August} \end{array} \begin{array}{ccc} \text{corn} & \text{soybeans} & \text{oats} \\ \left[\begin{array}{ccc} 15,000 & 2000 & 500 \\ 13,500 & 6000 & 1000 \\ 14,000 & 5500 & 1500 \end{array}\right. & & \left.\begin{array}{c} \\ \\ \\ \end{array}\right] \end{array}$$

This display is called a **matrix**. A matrix is any rectangular array of terms called **elements**. The elements of a matrix are arranged in rows and columns and are usually enclosed by brackets. A matrix with m rows and n columns is an **$m \times n$ matrix** (read "m by n"). The **dimensions** of the matrix are m and n.

$$\begin{bmatrix} -2 & 3 \\ 11 & -4 \end{bmatrix} \qquad \begin{bmatrix} 7 & \frac{1}{2} & 4 & 12 \\ -3 & 6 & 15 & -2 \end{bmatrix} \qquad \begin{bmatrix} 2 & -8 \\ 0 & 5 \\ -3 & 6 \end{bmatrix}$$

2 × 2 matrix   **2 × 4 matrix**   **3 × 2 matrix**

Certain matrices have special names. A matrix that has only one row is called a **row matrix**, and a matrix that has only one column is called a **column matrix**. A **square matrix** has the same number of rows as columns. Sometimes square matrices are called matrices of **nth order**, where n is the number of rows and columns. The elements of an $m \times n$ matrix can be represented using double subscript notation, as shown below.

$$\begin{bmatrix} a_{11} & a_{12} & a_{13} & \ldots & a_{1n} \\ a_{21} & a_{22} & a_{23} & \ldots & a_{2n} \\ \ldots & \ldots & \ldots & \ldots & \ldots \\ a_{m1} & a_{m2} & a_{m3} & \ldots & a_{mn} \end{bmatrix}$$

a_{ij} is the element in the ith row and the jth column.

ALTERNATE TEACHING STRATEGIES

Using Communication

Matrix is a word used in fields other than mathematics. Encourage students to find other uses of the word matrix, such as *dot-matrix*. Have them discuss any similarities between these definitions and the mathematical definition.

Using Critical Thinking

Have students discuss the situation presented in the application. Have them discuss how the matrix is organized, how the elements of the rows and columns are related to each other, and how each element is referenced by the row number and column number.

Definition of Equal Matrices	Two matrices are equal if and only if they have the same dimensions and are identical, element by element.

Example 1

Find the values of x and y for which the following equation is true.

$$\begin{bmatrix} y - 3 \\ y \end{bmatrix} = \begin{bmatrix} x \\ 2x \end{bmatrix}$$

Since corresponding elements must be equal, the following equations are true.

$y - 3 = x$
$\quad y = 2x$

Solve the system of equations.

$2x - 3 = x$ *Substitute 2x for y in the first equation.*
$\quad\quad x = 3$ *Solve for x.*
$y = 2(3)$ or 6   *Substitute 3 for x in the second equation to find y.*

The matrices are equal if $x = 3$ and $y = 6$.

Matrices with the same dimensions can be added. The ijth element of the sum of matrices A and B is $a_{ij} + b_{ij}$.

Definition of Addition of Matrices	The sum of two $m \times n$ matrices is an $m \times n$ matrix in which the elements are the sum of the corresponding elements of the given matrices.

Example 2

Find $A + B$ if $A = \begin{bmatrix} 3 & 5 & -7 \\ -1 & 0 & 4 \end{bmatrix}$ and $B = \begin{bmatrix} -2 & 8 & 6 \\ 5 & -9 & 10 \end{bmatrix}$.

$$A + B = \begin{bmatrix} 3 + (-2) & 5 + 8 & -7 + 6 \\ -1 + 5 & 0 + (-9) & 4 + 10 \end{bmatrix} = \begin{bmatrix} 1 & 13 & -1 \\ 4 & -9 & 14 \end{bmatrix}$$

Matrices, like real numbers, have identity elements. For every matrix A, another matrix can be found such that their sum is A. For example, if $A = \begin{bmatrix} a_{11} & a_{12} \\ a_{21} & a_{22} \end{bmatrix}$, then $\begin{bmatrix} a_{11} & a_{12} \\ a_{21} & a_{22} \end{bmatrix} + \begin{bmatrix} 0 & 0 \\ 0 & 0 \end{bmatrix} = \begin{bmatrix} a_{11} & a_{12} \\ a_{21} & a_{22} \end{bmatrix}$. The matrix $\begin{bmatrix} 0 & 0 \\ 0 & 0 \end{bmatrix}$ is called a **zero matrix**. Thus, the identity matrix for addition for any $m \times n$ matrix is the $m \times n$ zero matrix.

Teaching Tip For Example 3, have students try to find the matrix C so that $A + C$ equals the zero matrix. What might be another name for C?

$C = \begin{bmatrix} -3 & -6 \\ 2 & -4 \end{bmatrix}$, additive inverse matrix

Chalkboard Examples

For Example 3

Find $A - B$ if $A = \begin{bmatrix} -2 & 4 \\ -1 & 5 \end{bmatrix}$ and

$B = \begin{bmatrix} -4 & -3 \\ 8 & 2 \end{bmatrix}$. $\begin{bmatrix} 2 & 7 \\ -9 & 3 \end{bmatrix}$

For Example 4

Multiply $\begin{bmatrix} 1 & -4 \\ -4 & 9 \\ -2 & 6 \end{bmatrix}$ by 3.

$\begin{bmatrix} 3 & -12 \\ -12 & 27 \\ -6 & 18 \end{bmatrix}$

Matrices also have additive inverses. If $A = \begin{bmatrix} a_{11} & a_{12} \\ a_{21} & a_{22} \end{bmatrix}$, the matrix that must be added to A in order to obtain a zero matrix is $\begin{bmatrix} -a_{11} & -a_{12} \\ -a_{21} & -a_{22} \end{bmatrix}$ or $-A$. Therefore, $-A$ is the additive inverse of A. The additive inverse is used when subtracting matrices.

Definition of Subtraction of Matrices

The difference $A - B$ of two $m \times n$ matrices is equal to the sum $A + (-B)$, where $-B$ represents the additive inverse of B.

Example 3

Find $A - B$ if $A = \begin{bmatrix} 3 & 6 \\ -2 & 4 \end{bmatrix}$ and $B = \begin{bmatrix} 1 & 5 \\ -7 & 8 \end{bmatrix}$.

$A - B = A + (-B)$

$= \begin{bmatrix} 3 & 6 \\ -2 & 4 \end{bmatrix} + \begin{bmatrix} -1 & -5 \\ 7 & -8 \end{bmatrix}$

$= \begin{bmatrix} 3 + (-1) & 6 + (-5) \\ -2 + 7 & 4 + (-8) \end{bmatrix}$

$= \begin{bmatrix} 2 & 1 \\ 5 & -4 \end{bmatrix}$

A matrix can be multiplied by a number called a **scalar.** The product of a scalar k and a matrix A is defined as follows.

Scalar Product

The product of a scalar k and an $m \times n$ matrix A is an $m \times n$ matrix denoted by kA. Each element of kA is equal to k times the corresponding element of A.

Example 4

Multiply $\begin{bmatrix} 5 & 3 & -1 \\ -2 & 8 & -9 \end{bmatrix}$ by 4.

$4 \begin{bmatrix} 5 & 3 & -1 \\ -2 & 8 & -9 \end{bmatrix} = \begin{bmatrix} 4(5) & 4(3) & 4(-1) \\ 4(-2) & 4(8) & 4(-9) \end{bmatrix}$

$= \begin{bmatrix} 20 & 12 & -4 \\ -8 & 32 & -36 \end{bmatrix}$

A matrix can also be multiplied by another matrix, provided that the first matrix has the same number of columns as the second matrix has rows. The product of the two matrices is found by multiplying rows and columns.

Suppose $A = \begin{bmatrix} a_1 & b_1 \\ a_2 & b_2 \end{bmatrix}$ and $X = \begin{bmatrix} x_1 & y_1 \\ x_2 & y_2 \end{bmatrix}$. Each element of matrix AX is the product of one row of matrix A and one column of matrix X.

$$AX = \begin{bmatrix} a_1 & b_1 \\ a_2 & b_2 \end{bmatrix} \begin{bmatrix} x_1 & y_1 \\ x_2 & y_2 \end{bmatrix} = \begin{bmatrix} a_1 x_1 + b_1 x_2 & a_1 y_1 + b_1 y_2 \\ a_2 x_1 + b_2 x_2 & a_2 y_1 + b_2 y_2 \end{bmatrix}$$

In general, the product of two matrices is defined as follows.

Product of Two Matrices	The product of an $m \times n$ matrix A and an $n \times r$ matrix B is an $m \times r$ matrix AB. The ijth element of AB is the sum of the products of the corresponding elements in the ith row of A and the jth column of B.

Example 5

Find AB if $A = \begin{bmatrix} 4 & 3 \\ 5 & 2 \end{bmatrix}$ and $B = \begin{bmatrix} 8 & 0 \\ 9 & -6 \end{bmatrix}$.

$$AB = \begin{bmatrix} 4(8) + 3(9) & 4(0) + 3(-6) \\ 5(8) + 2(9) & 5(0) + 2(-6) \end{bmatrix} = \begin{bmatrix} 59 & -18 \\ 58 & -12 \end{bmatrix}$$

Example 6

Agriculture

Refer to the application at the beginning of the lesson. If Mr. Yunker is paid for his delivery of grain at the end of the month, how much will he receive each month if the prices per bushel are as follows: corn, \$2.85, soybeans, \$6.10, and oats, \$1.85?

Multiply the delivery matrix by a column matrix that contains the grain prices.

$$\begin{matrix} \text{June} \\ \text{July} \\ \text{August} \end{matrix} \begin{bmatrix} 15{,}000 & 2000 & 500 \\ 13{,}500 & 6000 & 1000 \\ 14{,}000 & 5500 & 1500 \end{bmatrix} \times \begin{bmatrix} 2.85 \\ 6.10 \\ 1.85 \end{bmatrix}$$

$$= \begin{bmatrix} 15{,}000(2.85) + 2000(6.10) + 500(1.85) \\ 13{,}500(2.85) + 6000(6.10) + 1000(1.85) \\ 14{,}000(2.85) + 5500(6.10) + 1500(1.85) \end{bmatrix}$$

$$= \begin{bmatrix} 55{,}875 \\ 76{,}925 \\ 76{,}225 \end{bmatrix}$$

Notice that the product has as many rows as the first matrix and as many columns as the second matrix. The resulting 3×1 matrix shows that Mr. Yunker will receive \$55,875 for grain delivered in June, \$76,925 for grain delivered in July, and \$76,225 for grain delivered in August.

LESSON 2-2   INTRODUCTION TO MATRICES   67

Checking for Understanding

Exercises 1–15 are designed to help you assess students' understanding through reading, writing, speaking, and modeling. You should work through Exercises 1–4 with your students and then monitor their work on Exercises 5–15.

Closing the Lesson

Writing Activity Give an example of two matrices whose product is commutative. Give a counterexample to prove that multiplication of matrices is not commutative in general.

Communicating Mathematics

Read and study the lesson to answer each question.

1. **Define** the dimensions of a matrix. See margin.

2. **Write** the element in the fifth column and the fourth row of matrix B using double subscript notation. b_{45}

3. Give an example of a matrix of 5th order. Answers will vary.

4. **Write** two 3×4 matrices that are additive inverses of each other. Explain how you know that they are additive inverses. Answers will vary.

Guided Practice

Use matrices A, B, and C to find each of the following. 5–13. See margin.

$$A = \begin{bmatrix} 3 & 0 \\ -1 & 5 \end{bmatrix} \qquad B = \begin{bmatrix} 5 & 1 \\ -3 & 4 \end{bmatrix} \qquad C = \begin{bmatrix} 3 \\ -1 \end{bmatrix}$$

5. $A + B$ 6. $A - B$ 7. $B - A$

8. $5C$ 9. $-3B$ 10. AC

11. AB 12. ABC 13. BB

Find the values of x and y for which each matrix equation is true.

14. $\begin{bmatrix} y \\ x \end{bmatrix} = \begin{bmatrix} 2x - 6 \\ 2y \end{bmatrix}$ $(4, 2)$ 15. $\begin{bmatrix} 5x - 3y \\ 3y \end{bmatrix} = \begin{bmatrix} 8 \\ 27 \end{bmatrix}$ $(7, 9)$

Homework Exercises

Assignment Guide

Average: 16–28, 29–39 odd, 41–43, 46, 47, 49–53
Enriched: 16–24 even, 25–28, 30–40 even, 41–53

The red A, B, and C flags, printed only in the Teacher's Wraparound Edition, indicate the level of difficulty of the exercises.

Chapter 2, Quiz A (Lessons 2–1 through 2–2), is available in the *Evaluation Masters*, p. 21.

Additional Answers

1. The dimensions of a matrix are given by $m \times n$, where m is the number of rows in the matrix and n is the number of columns.

EXERCISES

16–24. See Teacher's Answer Key.

Practice

Use matrices A, B, and C to find each sum or difference.

$$A = \begin{bmatrix} 1 & 5 & 7 \\ 5 & 2 & -6 \\ 3 & 0 & -2 \end{bmatrix} \qquad B = \begin{bmatrix} -3 & 6 & -9 \\ 4 & -3 & 0 \\ 8 & -2 & 3 \end{bmatrix} \qquad C = \begin{bmatrix} 6 & 9 & -4 \\ -11 & 13 & -8 \\ 20 & 4 & -2 \end{bmatrix}$$

16. $A + B$ 17. $A + C$ 18. $B + C$

19. $(A + B) + C$ 20. $B + (-A)$ 21. $C - B$

22. $B - C$ 23. $C - A$ 24. $B - A$

Find the values of x and y for which each matrix equation is true.

B

25. $[x \quad 2y] = [y + 5 \quad x - 3]$ $(7, 2)$ 26. $[5 \quad 4x] = [2x \quad 5y]$ $\left(\frac{5}{2}, 2\right)$

27. $\begin{bmatrix} 2x \\ 0 \\ 16 \end{bmatrix} = \begin{bmatrix} 8 - y \\ y \\ 4x \end{bmatrix}$ $(4, 0)$ 28. $\begin{bmatrix} y \\ 8x \end{bmatrix} = \begin{bmatrix} 15 + x \\ 2y \end{bmatrix}$ $(5, 20)$

68   CHAPTER 2   SYSTEMS OF EQUATIONS AND INEQUALITIES

5. $\begin{bmatrix} 8 & 1 \\ -4 & 9 \end{bmatrix}$ 6. $\begin{bmatrix} -2 & -1 \\ 2 & 1 \end{bmatrix}$ 7. $\begin{bmatrix} 2 & 1 \\ -2 & -1 \end{bmatrix}$ 8. $\begin{bmatrix} 15 \\ -5 \end{bmatrix}$

9. $\begin{bmatrix} -15 & -3 \\ 9 & -12 \end{bmatrix}$ 10. $\begin{bmatrix} 9 \\ -8 \end{bmatrix}$ 11. $\begin{bmatrix} 15 & 3 \\ -20 & 19 \end{bmatrix}$ 12. $\begin{bmatrix} 42 \\ -79 \end{bmatrix}$ 13. $\begin{bmatrix} 22 & 9 \\ -27 & 13 \end{bmatrix}$

Use matrices **D, E,** and **F** to find each product. 29–40. See margin.

$$D = \begin{bmatrix} 7 & 0 \\ 5 & 3 \end{bmatrix} \quad E = \begin{bmatrix} 2 & 4 \\ 8 & -4 \\ -2 & 6 \end{bmatrix} \quad F = \begin{bmatrix} 3 & -3 & 6 \\ 5 & 4 & -2 \end{bmatrix}$$

29. $3D$

30. $4E$

31. $2F$

32. $-5D$

33. ED

34. EF

35. FE

36. DF

37. DD

38. $(FE)D$

39. $E(DF)$

40. $-4EF$

41. Find $2A - 3B$ if $A = \begin{bmatrix} 1 & -7 \\ 3 & 2 \end{bmatrix}$ and $B = \begin{bmatrix} -4 & 5 \\ 1 & -1 \end{bmatrix}$. $\begin{bmatrix} 14 & -29 \\ 3 & 7 \end{bmatrix}$

Prove or disprove each statement. 42–45. See Teacher's Answer Key.

42. Addition of 2×2 matrices is commutative.

43. Addition of 2×2 matrices is associative.

44. Multiplication of two second-order matrices is commutative.

45. Multiplication of three second-order matrices is associative.

Critical Thinking

46. All integers n, such that $n \geq 0$, except 1, are arranged in a five-column matrix as shown at the right. In which column will the number 1992 be found? 2

$$\begin{bmatrix} 0 & 2 & 3 & 4 & 5 \\ 9 & 8 & 7 & 6 & 0 \\ 0 & 10 & 11 & 12 & 13 \\ 17 & 16 & 15 & 14 & 0 \\ 0 & 18 & 19 & 20 & 21 \\ \dots & \dots & \dots & \dots & 0 \end{bmatrix}$$

Applications and Problem Solving

47. Entertainment On the opening weekends for *Patriot Games, Lethal Weapon 3,* and *Batman Returns,* the Foxfield Theater reported the following ticket sales.

	Adults	Children
Patriot Games	1021	523
Lethal Weapon 3	2547	785
Batman Returns	3652	2456

If the ticket prices were $6 for each adult and $4 for each child, what were the weekend sales for each movie? PG, $8218; LW3, $18,422; BR, $31,736

48. Geometry Scalar multiplication can be used to find the coordinates of the vertices of a geometric figure after the figure has been reduced or enlarged. This type of transformation is called a **dilation**. Find the vertices of $\triangle DEF$, if the perimeter of $\triangle DEF$ is three times the perimeter of $\triangle ABC$, and the vertices of $\triangle ABC$ are $A(2, 5)$, $B(-4, 5)$, and $C(3, -7)$. *Hint: Put the coordinates in a 3×2 matrix.* $D(6, 15), E(-12, 15), F(9, -21)$

LESSON 2-2 INTRODUCTION TO MATRICES 69

RETEACHING THE LESSON

Have students make up a matrix to solve the following problem: The Terrific Toy Suppliers sells 1000 dolls, 540 trains, and 842 trucks in December, 612 dolls, 112 trains, and 154 trucks in January, and 175 dolls, 110 trains, and 118 trucks in February. The cost of a doll is $18.95, of a train is $29.95, and of a truck is $12.95. What is the amount of sales the company has each month?

$$\begin{bmatrix} 1000 & 540 & 842 \\ 612 & 112 & 154 \\ 175 & 110 & 118 \end{bmatrix} \cdot \begin{bmatrix} 18.95 \\ 29.95 \\ 12.95 \end{bmatrix}$$

Exercise Notes

For Exercises 33–40, stress the importance of multiplying the matrices in the correct order, since multiplication is not commutative.

For Exercises 42–45, have students think of specific examples that can help them with each problem.

Additional Answers

29. $\begin{bmatrix} 21 & 0 \\ 15 & 9 \end{bmatrix}$

30. $\begin{bmatrix} 8 & 16 \\ 32 & -16 \\ -8 & 24 \end{bmatrix}$

31. $\begin{bmatrix} 6 & -6 & 12 \\ 10 & 8 & -4 \end{bmatrix}$

32. $\begin{bmatrix} -35 & 0 \\ -25 & -15 \end{bmatrix}$

33. $\begin{bmatrix} 34 & 12 \\ 36 & -12 \\ 16 & 18 \end{bmatrix}$

34. $\begin{bmatrix} 26 & 10 & 4 \\ 4 & -40 & 56 \\ 24 & 30 & -24 \end{bmatrix}$

35. $\begin{bmatrix} -30 & 60 \\ 46 & -8 \end{bmatrix}$

36. $\begin{bmatrix} 21 & -21 & 42 \\ 30 & -3 & 24 \end{bmatrix}$

37. $\begin{bmatrix} 49 & 0 \\ 50 & 9 \end{bmatrix}$

38. $\begin{bmatrix} 90 & 180 \\ 282 & -24 \end{bmatrix}$

39. $\begin{bmatrix} 162 & -54 & 180 \\ 48 & -156 & 240 \\ 138 & 24 & 60 \end{bmatrix}$

40. $\begin{bmatrix} -104 & -40 & -16 \\ -16 & 160 & -224 \\ -96 & -120 & 96 \end{bmatrix}$

Practice Masters Booklet, p. 8

Additional Answer

50.

$y < -2x + 8$

Enrichment Masters Booklet, p. 8

Mixed Review

49. Find $[f \circ g](x)$ and $[g \circ f](x)$ if $f(x) = x^2 + 3x + 2$ and $g(x) = x - 1$. **(Lesson 1-2)** $[f \circ g](x) = x^2 + x, [g \circ f](x) = x^2 + 3x + 1$

50. Graph $y < -2x + 8$. **(Lesson 1-3)** See margin.

51. Find the distance between points at $(2t, t)$ and $(5t, 5t)$. Then, find the slope of the line passing between these points. **(Lesson 1-4)** $5|t|, \frac{4}{3}$

52. Write the slope-intercept form of the equation of the line through $(1, 5)$ that has a slope of -2. **(Lesson 1-5)** $y = -2x + 7$

53. Solve the system of equations. **(Lesson 2-1)**
$3x + 4y = 375$
$5x + 2y = 345$ $(45, 60)$

54. College Entrance Exam Choose the best answer. A
If $xy = 1$, then x is the reciprocal of y. Which of the following equals the arithmetic mean of x and y?

(A) $\dfrac{y^2 + 1}{2y}$ (B) $\dfrac{y + 1}{2y}$ (C) $\dfrac{y^2 + 2}{2y}$ (D) $\dfrac{y^2 + 1}{y}$ (E) $\dfrac{x^2 + 1}{y}$

DECISION MAKING

Choosing a College Major

Which college is best for you? There are more than 3600 colleges and junior colleges in the United States, so you have a wide range of options open to you. Would you like a small, intimate college in the east, or a large, bustling university in the midwest? Are there schools with special programs in the field you wish to pursue? How much financial aid is available to you? There are a number of things to consider.

1. Describe a college you think you would like to attend. Include such factors as size, location, proximity to your home, academic credentials, and any other factors you think are important.

2. Go to the library and find a book with descriptions of colleges. Make a list of schools that fit the description that you wrote for Exercise 1.

3. **Project** Work with your group to complete one of the projects listed at the right, based on the information you gathered in Exercises 1–2 above. 1–3. See students' work.

PROJECTS

- Conduct an interview.
- Write a book report.
- Write a proposal.
- Write an article for the school paper.
- Write a report.
- Make a display.
- Make a graph or chart.
- Plan an activity.
- Design a checklist.

70 CHAPTER 2 SYSTEMS OF EQUATIONS AND INEQUALITIES

EXTENDING THE LESSON

Math Power: Connections

Find the value of x and y such that
$$\begin{bmatrix} x & y \\ -x & -2y \end{bmatrix} \cdot \begin{bmatrix} 2 \\ -1 \end{bmatrix} = \begin{bmatrix} 4 \\ 8 \end{bmatrix}.$$
$(8, 12)$

Decision Making

This activity provides students an opportunity to work together on a given problem. You may wish to refer to pages T20–T21 and page 52c for the various elements of cooperative groups and specific goals and strategies for using them.

2-3 Determinants and Multiplicative Inverses of Matrices

Objectives
2–3A
2–3B
2–3C

After studying this lesson, you should be able to:
- evaluate determinants,
- find inverses of matrices, and
- solve systems of equations by using inverses of matrices.

Application

To make 20 kilograms of aluminum alloy with 70% aluminum, Kim Troy, a metallurgist, wants to use two metals with 55% and 80% aluminum content. How much of each metal should she use? *This problem will be solved in Example 5.*

The term __determinant__ is often used to mean the value of the determinant.

Each square matrix has a **determinant**. The determinant of $\begin{bmatrix} 8 & 7 \\ 4 & 5 \end{bmatrix}$ is denoted by $\begin{vmatrix} 8 & 7 \\ 4 & 5 \end{vmatrix}$ or $\det \begin{bmatrix} 8 & 7 \\ 4 & 5 \end{bmatrix}$. The value of a second-order determinant is a number and is defined as follows.

Second-Order Determinant

The value of $\det \begin{bmatrix} a_1 & b_1 \\ a_2 & b_2 \end{bmatrix}$ is $\begin{vmatrix} a_1 & b_1 \\ a_2 & b_2 \end{vmatrix} = a_1 b_2 - a_2 b_1.$

A matrix that has a nonzero determinant is called a __nonsingular matrix__.

Example 1

Find the value of $\begin{vmatrix} 7 & 9 \\ 3 & 6 \end{vmatrix}$.

$$\begin{vmatrix} 7 & 9 \\ 3 & 6 \end{vmatrix} = 7(6) - 3(9)$$
$$= 42 - 27$$
$$= 15$$

FYI...

Aluminum was first displayed as "silver from clay" at the 1855 exposition in Paris by its discoverer, chemist Henri-Etienne Saint-Claire Deville.

The **minor** of an element of an nth-order determinant is a determinant of $(n-1)$th order. This minor can be found by deleting the row and column containing the element.

$$\begin{vmatrix} a_1 & b_1 & c_1 \\ a_2 & b_2 & c_2 \\ a_3 & b_3 & c_3 \end{vmatrix} \qquad \text{The minor of } a_1 \text{ is } \begin{vmatrix} b_2 & c_2 \\ b_3 & c_3 \end{vmatrix}.$$

To evaluate a determinant of the nth order, expand the determinant by minors, using the elements in one of the rows. Find the product of each term in the row and its respective minor, and then add. The signs of the terms alternate. If the first row is used, the first term will be positive, as shown on the next page.

LESSON 2-3 DETERMINANTS AND MULTIPLICATIVE INVERSES OF MATRICES 71

ALTERNATE TEACHING STRATEGIES

Using Graphing Calculators

You may want to show students how to manipulate matrices using a graphing calculator such as the TI–81 that performs matrix operations.

Using Critical Thinking

Does every 2×2 matrix have an inverse? Have students give examples to verify their answers.

2–3 Lesson Notes

NCTM Standards: 1, 2, 3, 4, 5, 12

Lesson Resources

- Practice Master 2–3
- Enrichment Master 2–3
- Evaluation Master, Quiz B, p. 21

Transparency 2–3 contains the 5-Minute Check and a teaching aid for this lesson.

INTRODUCING THE LESSON

 5-Minute Check

(over Lesson 2–2)

1. Find the values of x and y for which the following equation is true.
$$\begin{bmatrix} x + 3 \\ x \end{bmatrix} = \begin{bmatrix} y \\ -2y \end{bmatrix} \quad (-2, 1)$$

2. Find $A + B$ if $A = \begin{bmatrix} -3 & 4 & -1 \\ 4 & -2 & 9 \end{bmatrix}$ and $B = \begin{bmatrix} 8 & 1 & 4 \\ -3 & -9 & -2 \end{bmatrix}$.
$$\begin{bmatrix} 5 & 5 & 3 \\ 1 & -11 & 7 \end{bmatrix}.$$

3. Find $A - B$ for Exercise 2 above.
$$\begin{bmatrix} -11 & 3 & -5 \\ 7 & 7 & 11 \end{bmatrix}$$

4. Multiply matrix B in Exercise 2 by –2.
$$\begin{bmatrix} -16 & -2 & -8 \\ 6 & 18 & 4 \end{bmatrix}$$

5. Find AB if $A = \begin{bmatrix} -1 & 4 \\ -3 & 8 \end{bmatrix}$ and $B = \begin{bmatrix} 4 & 1 \\ -2 & 9 \end{bmatrix}$. $\begin{bmatrix} -12 & 35 \\ -28 & 69 \end{bmatrix}$

Motivating the Lesson

Tell students that they will learn an alternate way of solving a system of equations in this lesson. This method can be used to solve real-life applications of systems of equations.

Third-Order Determinant

$$\begin{vmatrix} a_1 & b_1 & c_1 \\ a_2 & b_2 & c_2 \\ a_3 & b_3 & c_3 \end{vmatrix} = a_1 \begin{vmatrix} b_2 & c_2 \\ b_3 & c_3 \end{vmatrix} - b_1 \begin{vmatrix} a_2 & c_2 \\ a_3 & c_3 \end{vmatrix} + c_1 \begin{vmatrix} a_2 & b_2 \\ a_3 & b_3 \end{vmatrix}$$

Example 2

Find the value of $\begin{vmatrix} 8 & 9 & 3 \\ 3 & 5 & 7 \\ -1 & 2 & 4 \end{vmatrix}$.

$$\begin{vmatrix} 8 & 9 & 3 \\ 3 & 5 & 7 \\ -1 & 2 & 4 \end{vmatrix} = 8 \begin{vmatrix} 5 & 7 \\ 2 & 4 \end{vmatrix} - 9 \begin{vmatrix} 3 & 7 \\ -1 & 4 \end{vmatrix} + 3 \begin{vmatrix} 3 & 5 \\ -1 & 2 \end{vmatrix}$$
$$= 8(6) - 9(19) + 3(11)$$
$$= -90$$

The identity matrix for multiplication for any square matrix A is the matrix, I, such that $IA = A$ and $AI = A$. A second-order matrix can be represented by

For any m × m matrix, the identity matrix, I, must be m × m.

$\begin{bmatrix} a_1 & b_1 \\ a_2 & b_2 \end{bmatrix}$. Since $\begin{bmatrix} a_1 & b_1 \\ a_2 & b_2 \end{bmatrix} \cdot \begin{bmatrix} 1 & 0 \\ 0 & 1 \end{bmatrix} = \begin{bmatrix} 1 & 0 \\ 0 & 1 \end{bmatrix} \cdot \begin{bmatrix} a_1 & b_1 \\ a_2 & b_2 \end{bmatrix} = \begin{bmatrix} a_1 & b_1 \\ a_2 & b_2 \end{bmatrix}$, the

matrix $\begin{bmatrix} 1 & 0 \\ 0 & 1 \end{bmatrix}$ is the identity matrix for multiplication for any second-order matrix.

Identity Matrix under Multiplication

The identity matrix of nth order, I_n, is the square matrix whose elements in the main diagonal, from upper left to lower right, are 1s, while all other elements are 0s.

Multiplicative inverses exist for some matrices. Suppose A is equal to $\begin{bmatrix} a_1 & b_1 \\ a_2 & b_2 \end{bmatrix}$, a nonzero matrix of second order. The inverse matrix A^{-1} can be designated as $\begin{bmatrix} x_1 & y_1 \\ x_2 & y_2 \end{bmatrix}$. The product of a matrix A and its inverse A^{-1} must equal the identity matrix, I, for multiplication.

$$\begin{bmatrix} a_1 & b_1 \\ a_2 & b_2 \end{bmatrix} \begin{bmatrix} x_1 & y_1 \\ x_2 & y_2 \end{bmatrix} = \begin{bmatrix} 1 & 0 \\ 0 & 1 \end{bmatrix}$$

$$\begin{bmatrix} a_1x_1 + b_1x_2 & a_1y_1 + b_1y_2 \\ a_2x_1 + b_2x_2 & a_2y_1 + b_2y_2 \end{bmatrix} = \begin{bmatrix} 1 & 0 \\ 0 & 1 \end{bmatrix}$$

From the previous matrix equation, two systems of linear equations can be written as follows.

$$a_1x_1 + b_1x_2 = 1 \qquad\qquad a_1y_1 + b_1y_2 = 0$$
$$a_2x_1 + b_2x_2 = 0 \qquad\qquad a_2y_1 + b_2y_2 = 1$$

By solving each system of equations, values for x_1, x_2, y_1, and y_2 can be obtained.

$$x_1 = \frac{b_2}{a_1 b_2 - a_2 b_1} \qquad\qquad y_1 = \frac{-b_1}{a_1 b_2 - a_2 b_1}$$

$$x_2 = \frac{-a_2}{a_1 b_2 - a_2 b_1} \qquad\qquad y_2 = \frac{a_1}{a_1 b_2 - a_2 b_1}$$

The denominator $a_1 b_2 - a_2 b_1$ is equal to the determinant of A. If the determinant of A is not equal to 0, the inverse exists and can be defined as follows.

Inverse of a Second-Order Matrix	If $A = \begin{bmatrix} a_1 & b_1 \\ a_2 & b_2 \end{bmatrix}$ and $\begin{vmatrix} a_1 & b_1 \\ a_2 & b_2 \end{vmatrix} \neq 0$, then $A^{-1} = \dfrac{1}{\begin{vmatrix} a_1 & b_1 \\ a_2 & b_2 \end{vmatrix}} \begin{bmatrix} b_2 & -b_1 \\ -a_2 & a_1 \end{bmatrix}$.

$A \cdot A^{-1} = A^{-1} \cdot A = I$, where I is the identity matrix.

Example 3

Find the multiplicative inverse of the matrix $\begin{bmatrix} 3 & -1 \\ 4 & 2 \end{bmatrix}$.

First, find the determinant.

$$\begin{vmatrix} 3 & -1 \\ 4 & 2 \end{vmatrix} = 3(2) - 4(-1) = 10$$

The inverse is $\dfrac{1}{10} \begin{bmatrix} 2 & 1 \\ -4 & 3 \end{bmatrix}$ or $\begin{bmatrix} \frac{1}{5} & \frac{1}{10} \\ -\frac{2}{5} & \frac{3}{10} \end{bmatrix}$.   *Check to see if $A \cdot A^{-1} = A^{-1} \cdot A = I$.*

You can solve systems of equations by using matrix equations.

Example 4

Solve the system of equations by using matrix equations.
$5x + 4y = -3$
$3x - 5y = -24$

Write the system as a matrix equation.

$$\begin{bmatrix} 5 & 4 \\ 3 & -5 \end{bmatrix} \cdot \begin{bmatrix} x \\ y \end{bmatrix} = \begin{bmatrix} -3 \\ -24 \end{bmatrix}$$

To solve the matrix equation, first find the inverse of the coefficient matrix.

$$\frac{1}{\begin{vmatrix} 5 & 4 \\ 3 & -5 \end{vmatrix}} \begin{bmatrix} -5 & -4 \\ -3 & 5 \end{bmatrix} = -\frac{1}{37} \begin{bmatrix} -5 & -4 \\ -3 & 5 \end{bmatrix} \qquad \begin{vmatrix} 5 & 4 \\ 3 & -5 \end{vmatrix} = 5(-5) - 3(4) \text{ or } -37$$

(continued on the next page)

LESSON 2-3   DETERMINANTS AND MULTIPLICATIVE INVERSES OF MATRICES   73

EVALUATING THE LESSON

Checking for Understanding

Exercises 1–12 are designed to help you assess students' understanding through reading, writing, speaking, and modeling. You should work through Exercises 1–4 with your students and then monitor their work on Exercises 5–12.

Closing the Lesson

Modeling Activity   Have each student create his or her own problem situation for which a 2×2 system of equations can be used to solve the problem. Then ask for a demonstration of how to solve the problem.

Practice Masters Booklet, p. 9

Now multiply each side of the matrix equation by the inverse and solve.

$$-\frac{1}{37}\begin{bmatrix} -5 & -4 \\ -3 & 5 \end{bmatrix} \cdot \begin{bmatrix} 5 & 4 \\ 3 & -5 \end{bmatrix} \cdot \begin{bmatrix} x \\ y \end{bmatrix} = -\frac{1}{37}\begin{bmatrix} -5 & -4 \\ -3 & 5 \end{bmatrix} \cdot \begin{bmatrix} -3 \\ -24 \end{bmatrix}$$

$$\begin{bmatrix} x \\ y \end{bmatrix} = \begin{bmatrix} -3 \\ 3 \end{bmatrix}$$

The solution is $(-3, 3)$.

Example 5

APPLICATION

Metallurgy

Refer to the application at the beginning of the lesson. How much of the metals with 55% aluminum and 80% aluminum content should Kim Troy use to make 20 kilograms of a 70% aluminum alloy?

Let x represent the amount of metal with 55% aluminum content, and let y represent the amount of metal with 80% aluminum content. Then $x + y = 20$, since 20 kg are needed.

Write an equation in standard form that represents the proportions of each metal needed.

$$55\%x + 80\%y = 70\%(x + y)$$
$$0.55x + 0.8y = 0.7(x + y)$$
$$0.55x + 0.8y = 0.7x + 0.7y$$
$$0.15x - 0.1y = 0$$
$$15x - 10y = 0$$

Write the system as a matrix equation and solve.

$$\begin{array}{l} x + y = 20 \\ 15x - 10y = 0 \end{array} \longrightarrow \begin{bmatrix} 1 & 1 \\ 15 & -10 \end{bmatrix} \cdot \begin{bmatrix} x \\ y \end{bmatrix} = \begin{bmatrix} 20 \\ 0 \end{bmatrix}$$

$$-\frac{1}{25}\begin{bmatrix} -10 & -1 \\ -15 & 1 \end{bmatrix} \cdot \begin{bmatrix} 1 & 1 \\ 15 & -10 \end{bmatrix} \cdot \begin{bmatrix} x \\ y \end{bmatrix} = -\frac{1}{25}\begin{bmatrix} -10 & -1 \\ -15 & 1 \end{bmatrix} \cdot \begin{bmatrix} 20 \\ 0 \end{bmatrix}$$

$$\begin{bmatrix} x \\ y \end{bmatrix} = \begin{bmatrix} 8 \\ 12 \end{bmatrix}$$

The solution is $(8, 12)$. So, Kim should use 8 kg of metal with 55% aluminum content and 12 kg of metal with 80% aluminum content. *Check the solution by substituting these values in the original problem.*

RETEACHING THE LESSON

Students having difficulty with finding the discriminant of a 3×3 matrix may find the lattice method easier to master. An alternate way to calculate the determinant in Example 2 on p. 72 is to use the following pattern.

Add the product of the "positive" diagonals and subtract the product of the "negative" diagonals to get $160 + (-63) + 18 - (-15) - 112 - 108 = -90$.

CHECKING FOR UNDERSTANDING

Communicating Mathematics

Read and study the lesson to answer each question. 1–4. See margin.

1. Do all matrices have a determinant? Explain.

2. When is a matrix considered to be nonsingular?

3. **Describe** the identity matrix under multiplication for any nth order matrix.

4. **Explain** why the inverse matrix under multiplication exists only when the determinant is nonzero.

Guided Practice

Find the value of each determinant.

5. $\begin{vmatrix} 3 & -5 \\ 7 & 9 \end{vmatrix}$ 62

6. $\begin{vmatrix} 10 & 50 \\ -5 & 25 \end{vmatrix}$ 500

7. $\begin{vmatrix} 7 & 1 & 6 \\ 3 & -1 & 4 \\ -2 & 3 & 0 \end{vmatrix}$ −50

8. $\begin{vmatrix} 2 & 4 & 6 \\ 1 & 2 & 3 \\ 3 & -1 & 4 \end{vmatrix}$ 0

Find the multiplicative inverse of each matrix, if it exists.

9. $\begin{bmatrix} -2 & 3 \\ -4 & 1 \end{bmatrix}$ $\frac{1}{10}\begin{vmatrix} 1 & -3 \\ 4 & -2 \end{vmatrix}$

10. $\begin{bmatrix} 8 & 4 \\ -4 & -2 \end{bmatrix}$ does not exist

Solve each matrix equation.

11. $\begin{bmatrix} 4 & 8 \\ 2 & -3 \end{bmatrix} \cdot \begin{bmatrix} x \\ y \end{bmatrix} = \begin{bmatrix} 7 \\ 0 \end{bmatrix}$ $\left(\frac{3}{4}, \frac{1}{2}\right)$

12. $\begin{bmatrix} 5 & 4 \\ 3 & -5 \end{bmatrix} \cdot \begin{bmatrix} x \\ y \end{bmatrix} = \begin{bmatrix} -3 \\ -24 \end{bmatrix}$ (−3, 3)

EXERCISES

Practice

Find the value of each determinant.

13. $\begin{vmatrix} 7 & 16 \\ 3 & 8 \end{vmatrix}$ 8

14. $\begin{vmatrix} -4 & 8 \\ 0 & 2 \end{vmatrix}$ −8

15. $\begin{vmatrix} 16 & 17 \\ 15 & 16 \end{vmatrix}$ 1

16. $\begin{vmatrix} 6 & 7 & 4 \\ -2 & -4 & 3 \\ 1 & 1 & 1 \end{vmatrix}$ 1

17. $\begin{vmatrix} 3 & 0 & 2 \\ 0 & -1 & 5 \\ 6 & 7 & 0 \end{vmatrix}$ −93

18. $\begin{vmatrix} 4 & 2 & -3 \\ 5 & 1 & 0 \\ -2 & 1 & 11 \end{vmatrix}$ −87

Find the multiplicative inverse of each matrix, if it exists.

19. $\begin{bmatrix} -1 & -2 \\ 0 & -1 \end{bmatrix}$ $\begin{bmatrix} -1 & 2 \\ 0 & -1 \end{bmatrix}$

20. $\begin{bmatrix} -2 & 2 \\ 1 & -1 \end{bmatrix}$ does not exist

21. $\begin{bmatrix} 1 & 1 \\ 2 & -3 \end{bmatrix}$ $-\frac{1}{5}\begin{bmatrix} -3 & -1 \\ -2 & 1 \end{bmatrix}$

22. $\begin{bmatrix} 2 & -5 \\ 6 & 1 \end{bmatrix}$ $\frac{1}{32}\begin{bmatrix} 1 & 5 \\ -6 & 2 \end{bmatrix}$

23. $\begin{bmatrix} 3 & 1 \\ -4 & 1 \end{bmatrix}$ $\frac{1}{7}\begin{bmatrix} 1 & -1 \\ 4 & 3 \end{bmatrix}$

24. $\begin{bmatrix} 1 & 2 \\ 2 & 1 \end{bmatrix}$ $-\frac{1}{3}\begin{bmatrix} 1 & -2 \\ -2 & 1 \end{bmatrix}$

Solve each system by using matrix equations.

25. $5x + y = 26$ (7, −9)
    $2x - 3y = 41$

26. $5x + y = 1$ $\left(\frac{1}{3}, -\frac{2}{3}\right)$
    $9x + 3y = 1$

LESSON 2-3 DETERMINANTS AND MULTIPLICATIVE INVERSES OF MATRICES   75

Additional Answers

1. No, a matrix must be square in order for it to have a determinant.

2. A matrix is nonsingular when its determinant is nonzero.

3. All elements are 0s except for the elements on the main diagonal, which are 1s.

4. If the determinant is zero, then part of the inverse is $\frac{1}{0}$, which is undefined.

APPLYING THE LESSON

Homework Exercises

Assignment Guide

Average: 13–29, 32, 34, 36–40
Enriched: 16–40
All: Mid-Chapter Review, 1–10

The red A, B, and C flags, printed only in the Teacher's Wraparound Edition, indicate the level of difficulty of the exercises.

Using Technology

The TI–81 and the Casio 7700 are two calculators that have matrix functions. Students may need to refer to Lesson 2–2A for instructions for inputing a matrix, before attempting Exercise 32.

Chapter 2, Quiz B (Lesson 2–3), is available in the *Evaluation Masters*, p. 21.

Exercise Note

For Exercises 29–31, discuss how to determine the minors for determinants of order higher than three.

Additional Answers

33. Let $A = \begin{bmatrix} a_{11} & a_{12} \\ a_{21} & a_{22} \end{bmatrix}$ and $I = \begin{bmatrix} 1 & 0 \\ 0 & 1 \end{bmatrix}$.

$AI = \begin{bmatrix} a_{11} & a_{12} \\ a_{21} & a_{22} \end{bmatrix} \cdot \begin{bmatrix} 1 & 0 \\ 0 & 1 \end{bmatrix} =$

$\begin{bmatrix} a_{11}+0 & 0+a_{12} \\ a_{21}+0 & 0+a_{22} \end{bmatrix} =$

$\begin{bmatrix} a_{11} & a_{12} \\ a_{21} & a_{22} \end{bmatrix} = A.$

$IA = \begin{bmatrix} 1 & 0 \\ 0 & 1 \end{bmatrix} \cdot \begin{bmatrix} a_{11} & a_{12} \\ a_{21} & a_{22} \end{bmatrix} =$

$\begin{bmatrix} a_{11}+0 & a_{12}+0 \\ 0+a_{21} & 0+a_{22} \end{bmatrix} =$

$\begin{bmatrix} a_{11} & a_{12} \\ a_{21} & a_{22} \end{bmatrix} = A.$

34. Let $A = \begin{bmatrix} a_{11} & a_{12} \\ a_{21} & a_{22} \end{bmatrix}$ and $I = \begin{bmatrix} 1 & 0 \\ 0 & 1 \end{bmatrix}$.

$A^{-1} = \begin{bmatrix} \dfrac{a_{22}}{a_{11}a_{22}-a_{21}a_{12}} & \dfrac{-a_{12}}{a_{11}a_{22}-a_{21}a_{12}} \\ \dfrac{-a_{21}}{a_{11}a_{22}-a_{21}a_{12}} & \dfrac{a_{11}}{a_{11}a_{22}-a_{21}a_{12}} \end{bmatrix}$

$AA^{-1} = \begin{bmatrix} \dfrac{a_{11}a_{22}-a_{12}a_{21}}{a_{11}a_{22}-a_{21}a_{12}} & \dfrac{-a_{11}a_{12}+a_{12}a_{11}}{a_{11}a_{22}-a_{21}a_{12}} \\ \dfrac{a_{21}a_{22}-a_{21}a_{22}}{a_{11}a_{22}-a_{21}a_{12}} & \dfrac{-a_{21}a_{12}+a_{11}a_{22}}{a_{11}a_{22}-a_{21}a_{12}} \end{bmatrix}$

$= \begin{bmatrix} 1 & 0 \\ 0 & 1 \end{bmatrix} = I$

Thus, $AA^{-1} = I.$

Solve each matrix equation.

27. $\begin{bmatrix} 1 & 2 & 2 \\ 2 & -1 & 1 \\ 3 & -2 & 3 \end{bmatrix} \cdot \begin{bmatrix} x \\ y \\ z \end{bmatrix} = \begin{bmatrix} 0 \\ -1 \\ -4 \end{bmatrix}$, if the inverse is $-\dfrac{1}{9}\begin{bmatrix} -1 & -10 & 4 \\ -3 & -3 & 3 \\ -1 & 8 & -5 \end{bmatrix}$ $\left(\dfrac{2}{3}, 1, -\dfrac{4}{3}\right)$

28. $\begin{bmatrix} 3 & 1 & 1 \\ -6 & 5 & 3 \\ 9 & -2 & -1 \end{bmatrix} \cdot \begin{bmatrix} x \\ y \\ z \end{bmatrix} = \begin{bmatrix} -1 \\ -9 \\ 5 \end{bmatrix}$, if the inverse is $-\dfrac{1}{9}\begin{bmatrix} 1 & -1 & -2 \\ 21 & -12 & -15 \\ -33 & 15 & 21 \end{bmatrix}$ $\left(\dfrac{2}{9}, -\dfrac{4}{3}, -\dfrac{1}{3}\right)$

Find the value of each determinant by using expansion by minors.

29. $\begin{vmatrix} 1 & 2 & 3 & 1 \\ 4 & 3 & -1 & 0 \\ 2 & -5 & 4 & 4 \\ 1 & -2 & 0 & 2 \end{vmatrix}$ -109

30. $\begin{vmatrix} 7 & 0 & 9 & 5 \\ 8 & 2 & -1 & 2 \\ -5 & 3 & 7 & 9 \\ 0 & -1 & -4 & -6 \end{vmatrix}$ -890

31. $\begin{vmatrix} 3 & 0 & 0 & 4 & 0 \\ 6 & -3 & 2 & 0 & 7 \\ 0 & 4 & 3 & 0 & 5 \\ 0 & 2 & 1 & 3 & -4 \\ 6 & 0 & -2 & -3 & 0 \end{vmatrix}$ 3411

Graphing Calculator

32. Use the MATRIX feature on a graphing calculator to solve the system below.

$3x - 3y + 6z = 30$
$x - 3y + 10z = 50$
$-x + 3y - 5z = 40$ $(26, 52, 18)$

Critical Thinking

Prove each statement. 33–34. See margin.

33. $AI = IA = A$ for second-order matrices.

34. $AA^{-1} = A^{-1}A = I$ for second-order matrices.

Applications and Problem Solving

35. Metallurgy George Johnson is a chemist who is preparing an acid solution to be used as a cleaner for machine parts. The machine shop needs 200 mL of the solution at a 48% concentration. George has only 60% and 40% solutions. How much of each solution should George combine to make 200 mL of the 48% solution?

35. 80 mL of the 60% solution, 120 mL of the 40% solution

36. Landscaping Two dump trucks have capacities of 10 tons and 12 tons. They make a total of 20 round trips to haul 226 tons of topsoil to be used to landscape the new skyscraper. How many round trips did each truck make? 7 trips by the 10-ton truck, 13 trips by the 12-ton truck

EXTENDING THE LESSON

Math Power: Problem Solving

What would be the order of a minor for a sixth-order determinant? What would be the minor of a_1 for the following determinant?

$\begin{vmatrix} a_1 & b_1 & c_1 & d_1 & e_1 & f_1 \\ a_2 & b_2 & c_2 & d_2 & e_2 & f_2 \\ a_3 & b_3 & c_3 & d_3 & e_3 & f_3 \\ a_4 & b_4 & c_4 & d_4 & e_4 & f_4 \\ a_5 & b_5 & c_5 & d_5 & e_5 & f_5 \\ a_6 & b_6 & c_6 & d_6 & e_6 & f_6 \end{vmatrix}$

$5; \begin{vmatrix} b_2 & c_2 & d_2 & e_2 & f_2 \\ b_3 & c_3 & d_3 & e_3 & f_3 \\ b_4 & c_4 & d_4 & e_4 & f_4 \\ b_5 & c_5 & d_5 & e_5 & f_5 \\ b_6 & c_6 & d_6 & e_6 & f_6 \end{vmatrix}$

Mixed
Review

37. Find $[f \circ g](4)$ and $[g \circ f](4)$ if $f(x) = x^2 - 1$ and $g(x) = x + 1$. **(Lesson 1-2)** 24, 16

38. Write the slope-intercept form of the equation of the line that passes through $(1, 6)$ and has a slope of 2. **(Lesson 1-4)** $y = 2x + 4$

39. Solve the system of equations below. **(Lesson 2-1)**
$x = 5y - 2$
$3x + y = 10$ $\quad\quad (3, 1)$

40. Find two square matrices A and B for which $(A + B)^2$ does not equal $A^2 + 2AB + B^2$. **(Lesson 2-2)** Answers may vary.

41. **College Entrance Exam** Compare quantities A and B below. B
Write A if the quantity in Column A is greater.
Write B if the quantity in Column B is greater.
Write C if the two quantities are equal.
Write D if there is not enough information to determine the relationship.

(A) $3^2 + 4^2$ $\quad\quad\quad\quad$ **(B)** 7^2

MID-CHAPTER REVIEW

Solve each system of equations by graphing. (Lesson 2-1)

1. $3x - y - 1 = 0$
$x + y - 3 = 0$ $\ (1, 2)$

2. $3x - 2y = 5$
$x + 7y = -6$ $\ (1, -1)$

Solve each system of equations algebraically. (Lesson 2-1)

3. $5x - y - 16 = 0$
$2x + 3y - 3 = 0$ $\ (3, -1)$

4. $-2x + 4y = 3$
$5x - 7y = 11$ $\ \left(\frac{65}{6}, \frac{37}{6}\right)$

Let $A = \begin{bmatrix} 3 & 0 \\ -1 & 5 \end{bmatrix}$ and let $B = \begin{bmatrix} 5 & 1 \\ -3 & 4 \end{bmatrix}$. **Find each of the following. (Lesson 2-2)**

5. $A + B$ $\begin{bmatrix} 8 & 1 \\ -4 & 9 \end{bmatrix}$
6. $A - B$ $\begin{bmatrix} -2 & -1 \\ 2 & 1 \end{bmatrix}$
7. AB $\begin{bmatrix} 15 & 3 \\ -20 & 19 \end{bmatrix}$

8. Find the value of $\begin{vmatrix} 5 & 3 & 2 \\ 6 & 1 & 8 \\ 4 & 2 & 2 \end{vmatrix}$. **(Lesson 2-3)** 6

Solve each matrix equation. (Lesson 2-3)

9. $\begin{bmatrix} -2 & -4 \\ 2 & 3 \end{bmatrix} \cdot \begin{bmatrix} x \\ y \end{bmatrix} = \begin{bmatrix} 6 \\ 5 \end{bmatrix}$ $(19, -11)$

10. $\begin{bmatrix} -1 & 14 \\ 6 & 12 \end{bmatrix} \cdot \begin{bmatrix} x \\ y \end{bmatrix} = \begin{bmatrix} 4 \\ 0 \end{bmatrix}$ $\left(-\frac{1}{2}, \frac{1}{4}\right)$

LESSON 2-3 DETERMINANTS AND MULTIPLICATIVE INVERSES OF MATRICES 77

Enrichment Masters Booklet, p. 9

Mid-Chapter Review

The Mid-Chapter Review provides students with a brief review of the concepts and skills in Lessons 2–1 through 2–3. Lesson numbers are given at the end of problems or instructions lines so students may review concepts not yet mastered.

Objective This optional page shows how computer software can be used to perform matrix operations, including finding the determinant of a matrix.

Teaching Suggestions

You may also want to use the software to verify the following properties of determinants.
1. Only square matrices have determinants.
2. If each entry in any one row or column of the matrix is 0, then the determinant of the matrix is 0.
3. If any two rows or two columns of a matrix are interchanged, the resulting determinant has the opposite sign of the original determinant.
4. If any two rows or two columns of a matrix have identical entries, then the determinant of the matrix is 0.
5. If each of the entries in a row or column is multiplied by a constant k, then the determinant is multiplied by k.

Technology

Finding Determinants of Matrices

Matrix software accompanies Introduction to College Mathematics, developed by the North Carolina School of Science and Mathematics.

The calculations used to evaluate determinants can be very tedious, if done using paper and a pencil. Fortunately, there are computer programs that can calculate determinants for you. One such program is *Matrix*, for IBM-compatible computers. To evaluate the determinant of a 5×5 matrix using *Matrix*, use the following steps.

- Select **F1. Define/Edit Matrix** from the main menu.
- Select **1. Define a Matrix (Static)**.
- When the computer prompts you to enter the number of rows and columns of the matrix, type in **5, 5** and press **[Enter]**.
- You enter a matrix by entering its rows at the prompts.

  ROW1: 1, 4, 3, 2, 3 **ROW4: 0, 5, 2, –1, 1**
  ROW2: –4, 2, –9, 0, 1 **ROW5: 0, 0, 4, 2, 5**
  ROW3: 1, 1, 4, 3, 4

- When requested, name the matrix **A**.
- Select **F3. Matrix Calculator Menu** from the main menu.
- Select **1. Calculator**.
- At the prompt, type in **DET(A)** and press **[Enter]** to find the determinant of matrix A.
- The computer will respond with **Number result = –110**.

The menu system used by *Matrix* is as follows.

EXERCISES

Use *Matrix* to evaluate the determinant for each matrix.

1. $\begin{bmatrix} 3 & 5 \\ 6 & -3 \end{bmatrix}$ –39

2. $\begin{bmatrix} 1 & 6 & -2 \\ 8 & -2 & 0 \\ 5 & 9 & -1 \end{bmatrix}$ –114

3. $\begin{bmatrix} 1 & 4 & 8 & 1 \\ 0 & 1 & -3 & 0 \\ -4 & 2 & 8 & 1 \\ 6 & -5 & 8 & 9 \end{bmatrix}$ 917

2-4 Solving Systems of Equations by Using Matrices

Objective
2–4

After studying this lesson, you should be able to:
- solve systems of equations by using matrices.

Application

The *K'iu-ch'ang*, or *Arithmetic in Nine Sections*, is the greatest of the ancient Chinese books on mathematics. A mathematician named Ch'ang Ts'ang is thought to have collected and edited these writings of the ancients around 213 B.C. Chapter 8 was called *Fang cheng*, or *Method of Tables*, and dealt with the solution of systems of equations with two or three unknowns using matrices. This work indicates that Chinese mathematicians were pioneers in establishing the early science of mathematics.

The coefficients and constants of the system of equations shown below can be written in the form of a 3×4 **augmented matrix**. An augmented matrix is an array of the coefficients and constants of a system of equations.

System of Equations

$$\left.\begin{array}{r} x - 2y + z = 7 \\ 3x + y - z = 2 \\ 2x + 3y + 2z = 7 \end{array}\right\} \longrightarrow \left.\begin{array}{r} 1x - 2y + 1z = 7 \\ 3x + 1y - 1z = 2 \\ 2x + 3y + 2z = 7 \end{array}\right\} \longrightarrow$$

Augmented Matrix

$$\begin{bmatrix} 1 & -2 & 1 & \vdots & 7 \\ 3 & 1 & -1 & \vdots & 2 \\ 2 & 3 & 2 & \vdots & 7 \end{bmatrix}$$

This system can be solved by transforming the rows of the matrix, since each row represents an equation. Each change in the matrix represents a corresponding change in the system of equations. Any operation that results in an equivalent system of equations is permitted for the matrix. The objective is to obtain the identity matrix on the left side. That is, we want to obtain

$$\begin{bmatrix} 1 & 0 & 0 & \vdots & x \\ 0 & 1 & 0 & \vdots & y \\ 0 & 0 & 1 & \vdots & z \end{bmatrix}$$ for which the solution is (x, y, z). In general, any of the

following row operations can be used to transform an augmented matrix.

Row Operations on Matrices
- **Interchange any two rows.**
- **Replace any row with a nonzero multiple of that row.**
- **Replace any row with the sum of that row and a multiple of another row.**

LESSON 2-4 SOLVING SYSTEMS OF EQUATIONS BY USING MATRICES 79

There is no single correct order in which to perform row operations to arrive at the solution. That is, the order in which you transform rows in a matrix may be different from the way your classmate does it, but you may both be correct.

Example 1

Solve the system of equations by using row operations.

$$x - 2y + z = 7$$
$$3x + y - z = 2$$
$$2x + 3y + 2z = 7$$

First, write the augmented matrix.

$$\begin{bmatrix} 1 & -2 & 1 & \vdots & 7 \\ 3 & 1 & -1 & \vdots & 2 \\ 2 & 3 & 2 & \vdots & 7 \end{bmatrix}$$

Multiply row one by –3 and add the result to row two.

$$\begin{bmatrix} 1 & -2 & 1 & \vdots & 7 \\ 0 & 7 & -4 & \vdots & -19 \\ 2 & 3 & 2 & \vdots & 7 \end{bmatrix}$$

Multiply row one by –2 and add the result to row three.

$$\begin{bmatrix} 1 & -2 & 1 & \vdots & 7 \\ 0 & 7 & -4 & \vdots & -19 \\ 0 & 7 & 0 & \vdots & -7 \end{bmatrix}$$

Multiply row two by –1 and add the result to row three.

$$\begin{bmatrix} 1 & -2 & 1 & \vdots & 7 \\ 0 & 7 & -4 & \vdots & -19 \\ 0 & 0 & 4 & \vdots & 12 \end{bmatrix}$$

Add row three to row two.

$$\begin{bmatrix} 1 & -2 & 1 & \vdots & 7 \\ 0 & 7 & 0 & \vdots & -7 \\ 0 & 0 & 4 & \vdots & 12 \end{bmatrix}$$

Multiply row two by $\frac{1}{7}$.

$$\begin{bmatrix} 1 & -2 & 1 & \vdots & 7 \\ 0 & 1 & 0 & \vdots & -1 \\ 0 & 0 & 4 & \vdots & 12 \end{bmatrix}$$

Multiply row three by $\frac{1}{4}$.

$$\begin{bmatrix} 1 & -2 & 1 & \vdots & 7 \\ 0 & 1 & 0 & \vdots & -1 \\ 0 & 0 & 1 & \vdots & 3 \end{bmatrix}$$

Multiply row two by 2 and add the result to row one.

$$\begin{bmatrix} 1 & 0 & 1 & \vdots & 5 \\ 0 & 1 & 0 & \vdots & -1 \\ 0 & 0 & 1 & \vdots & 3 \end{bmatrix}$$

Multiply row three by –1 and add the result to row one.

$$\begin{bmatrix} 1 & 0 & 0 & \vdots & 2 \\ 0 & 1 & 0 & \vdots & -1 \\ 0 & 0 & 1 & \vdots & 3 \end{bmatrix}$$

The solution is $(2, -1, 3)$.   *Notice that the left side is the identity matrix. Check the solution by substituting in the original equations.*

Chalkboard Example

For Example 2

Find the equation of a parabola that contains the points (1, 4), (2, 6), and (–3, 8).

$y = \frac{3}{5}x^2 + \frac{1}{5}x + \frac{16}{5}$

Augmented matrices can be used to solve a variety of problems.

Example 2

Find the equation of a parabola that contains the points at $(1, 9)$, $(4, 6)$, and $(6, 14)$.

The general form of the equation of a parabola is $y = ax^2 + bx + c$. Since each of the ordered pairs satisfies the general equation, the following can be generated.

$a(1)^2 + b(1) + c = 9$ *Use (1, 9).*
$a(4)^2 + b(4) + c = 6$ *Use (4, 6).*
$a(6)^2 + b(6) + c = 14$ *Use (6, 14).*

Simplify.

$a + b + c = 9$
$16a + 4b + c = 6$
$36a + 6b + c = 14$

Use an augmented matrix and row operations to solve.

$$\begin{bmatrix} 1 & 1 & 1 & \vdots & 9 \\ 16 & 4 & 1 & \vdots & 6 \\ 36 & 6 & 1 & \vdots & 14 \end{bmatrix} \rightarrow \begin{bmatrix} 1 & 0 & 0 & \vdots & 1 \\ 0 & 1 & 0 & \vdots & -6 \\ 0 & 0 & 1 & \vdots & 14 \end{bmatrix}$$

The solution is $(1, -6, 14)$, so $a = 1$, $b = -6$, and $c = 14$. Therefore, the equation of the parabola is $y = x^2 - 6x + 14$.   *Check this equation by substituting the original three points.*

LESSON 2-4   SOLVING SYSTEMS OF EQUATIONS BY USING MATRICES   81

CHECKING FOR UNDERSTANDING

Communicating Mathematics

Read and study the lesson to answer each question.

1. **State** the objective desired when you use augmented matrices to solve systems of equations. Obtain the identity matrix on the left side.

2. Could the system of equations in Example 2 have been solved by using another method? If so, show how it could have been done. Answers may vary.

Guided Practice

State the row operations you would use to get a zero in the second column of row one. Then state the row operations you would use to get a zero in the first column of row two. 3–5. See margin.

3. $\begin{bmatrix} 3 & 5 & 7 \\ 6 & -1 & -8 \end{bmatrix}$

4. $\begin{bmatrix} 4 & -7 & -2 \\ 1 & 2 & 7 \end{bmatrix}$

5. $\begin{bmatrix} 5 & -3 & 0 \\ 3 & 6 & -6 \end{bmatrix}$

Solve each system of equations by using augmented matrices.

6. $5x - 2y = 5$
$x + y = 8$
$(3, 5)$

7. $2x + y - 2z - 7 = 0$
$x - 2y - 5z + 1 = 0$
$4x + y + z + 1 = 0$ $(-1, 5, -2)$

EXERCISES

Practice

Solve each system of equations by using augmented matrices.

8. $3x + 5y = 7$ $(-1, 2)$
$6x - y = -8$

9. $4x - 7y = -2$ $(3, 2)$
$x + 2y = 7$

10. $3x + 3y = -9$ $\left(\frac{1}{3}, -\frac{10}{3}\right)$
$-2x + y = -4$

11. $5x = 3y - 50$ $\left(-\frac{97}{19}, \frac{155}{19}\right)$
$2y = 1 - 3x$

12. $x - y + z = 3$ $(3, 1, 1)$
$2y - z = 1$
$2y - x + 1 = 0$

13. $x + y + z = -2$ $(-1, 2, -3)$
$2x - 3y + z = -11$
$-x + 2y - z = 8$

14. $2x + 6y + 8z = 5$ $\left(\frac{1}{2}, \frac{1}{3}, \frac{1}{4}\right)$
$-2x + 9y - 12z = -1$
$4x + 6y - 4z = 3$

15. $x + y + z - 6 = 0$ $(7, 1, -2)$
$2x - 3y + 4z - 3 = 0$
$4x - 8y + 4z - 12 = 0$

16. $x + 2y = 5$
$3x + 4z = 2$
$2y + 3w = -2$
$3z - 2w = 1$ $\left(-\frac{61}{35}, \frac{62}{35}, \frac{113}{70}, -\frac{29}{35}\right)$

17. $w + x + y + z = 0$
$2w + x - y - z = 1$
$-w - x + y + z = 0$
$2x + y = 0$ $(1, -1, 2, -2)$

Find the equation of a parabola that contains the points given.

18. $(1, 4), (5, 40),$ and $(3, 14)$
$y = 2x^2 - 3x + 5$

19. $(2, 3), (3, 6),$ and $(-2, 31)$
$y = 2x^2 - 7x + 9$

82 CHAPTER 2 SYSTEMS OF EQUATIONS AND INEQUALITIES

The system is dependent; there is no unique solution.

Critical Thinking

20. What does it mean when an augmented matrix has a row containing all zeros?

21. What does it mean when an augmented matrix has a row containing all zeros, except for the last element? The system is inconsistent; there is no solution.

Applications and Problem Solving

22. Restaurants At Morgan's Fine Cuisine, meals are served *a la carte*. That is, each item on the menu is priced separately. Jackie and Ted Parris went to Morgan's to celebrate their anniversary. Jackie ordered prime rib, 2 side dishes, and a roll. Ted ordered prime rib, 3 side dishes, and 2 rolls. Jackie's meal came to $36 and Ted's meal came to $44. If the prime rib is three times as expensive as a side dish, what is the cost of each item? prime rib, $21; side dish, $7; roll, $1

23. Consumer Purchasing Janet is spending her clothes allowance on school clothes. If she buys 3 blouses, 2 skirts, and 4 pairs of jeans, she will spend $292. If she buys 4 blouses, 1 skirt, and 3 pairs of jeans, she will spend $252. If jeans cost $4 more than skirts, what is the price of each item? blouse, $28; skirt, $32; jeans, $36

Mixed Review

24. Does the graph at the right represent a function? **(Lesson 1-1)** yes

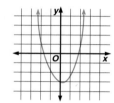

25. Solve the system of equations below. **(Lesson 2-1)**
$x + 2y = 11$
$3x - 5y = 11$ $(7, 2)$

26. Find $A + B$ if $A = \begin{bmatrix} 3 & 8 \\ -2 & 4 \end{bmatrix}$ and $B = \begin{bmatrix} 1 & 5 \\ -2 & 8 \end{bmatrix}$. **(Lesson 2-2)** $\begin{bmatrix} 4 & 13 \\ -4 & 12 \end{bmatrix}$

27. Find the value of $\begin{vmatrix} 2 & 3 & 4 \\ 5 & 6 & 7 \\ 8 & 9 & 10 \end{vmatrix}$. **(Lesson 2-3)** 0

28. College Entrance Exam
What is the sum of four integers whose average is 15? 60

Exercise Notes

For Exercises 16–17, point out that the matrix equation method of solving a system of equations of order higher than three may be easier than the algebraic method.

For Exercises 22—23, you might want students to work on the problems in cooperative groups.

Additional Answers

3. Multiply row 2 by 5 and add it to row 1.
Multiply row 1 by –2 and add it to row 2.

4. Multiply row 1 by 2 and row 2 by 7. Add row 2 to row 1.
Multiply row 2 by –4 and add row 1 to it.

5. Multiply row 1 by 2. Add row 2 to row 1.
Multiply row 1 by –3 and row 2 by 5. Add row 1 to row 2.

Enrichment Masters Booklet, p. 10

2-4 **Enrichment Worksheet**
NAME _____ DATE _____

Area of a Triangle

Determinants can be used to find the area of a triangle on the coordinate plane. For a triangle with vertices $P_1(x_1, y_1), P_2(x_2, y_2),$ and $P_3(x_3, y_3)$, the area is given by the following formula.

$$\text{Area} = \pm \frac{1}{2}\begin{vmatrix} x_1 & y_1 & 1 \\ x_2 & y_2 & 1 \\ x_3 & y_3 & 1 \end{vmatrix}$$

The sign is chosen so that the result is positive.

Example Find the area of the triangle with vertices $A(3, 8), B(-2, 5),$ and $C(0, -1)$.

$$\text{Area} = \pm \frac{1}{2}\begin{vmatrix} 3 & 8 & 1 \\ -2 & 5 & 1 \\ 0 & -1 & 1 \end{vmatrix} = \pm \frac{1}{2}\left[3\begin{vmatrix} 5 & 1 \\ -1 & 1 \end{vmatrix} - 8\begin{vmatrix} -2 & 1 \\ 0 & 1 \end{vmatrix} + 1\begin{vmatrix} -2 & 5 \\ 0 & -1 \end{vmatrix}\right]$$

$$= \pm \frac{1}{2}[3(5 - (-1)) - 8(-2 - 0) + 1(2 - 0)]$$

$$= \pm \frac{1}{2}[36] = 18$$

The area is 18 square units.

Find the area of the triangle having vertices with the given coordinates.

1. $A(0, 6), B(0, -4), C(0, 0)$
Points are collinear; there is no triangle.

2. $A(5, 1), B(-3, 7), C(-2, -2)$
33 square units

3. $A(8, -2), B(0, -4), C(-2, 10)$
58 square units

4. $A(12, 4), B(-6, 4), C(3, 16)$
108 square units

5. $A(-1, -3), B(7, -5), C(-3, 9)$
46 square units

6. $A(1.2, 3.1), B(5.7, 6.2), C(8.5, 4.4)$
8.39 square units

7. What is the sign of the determinant in the formula when the points are taken in clockwise order? in counterclockwise order?
negative; positive

T10
Glencoe Division, Macmillan/McGraw-Hill

EXTENDING THE LESSON

Math Power: Connections

The method presented in Example 2 can also be used to generate the equation of a circle through three (noncollinear) points, using the general form of the equation of a circle $x^2 + y^2 + ax + by + c = 0$. Find the equation of the circle through $(-3, 4), (4, 5),$ and $(1, -4)$.
$x^2 + y^2 - 2x - 2y - 23 = 0$

INTRODUCING THE LESSON

Objective   Graph a system of linear inequalities on a graphing calculator.

Motivating the Lesson

In this lesson, students can see how to combine paper-and-pencil calculations with their skills on the TI-81 graphing calculator to graph systems of linear inequalities.

TEACHING THE LESSON

Teaching Tip   Point out that the order in which the inequalities are entered on the TI-81 is important. Students may wish to write the inequalities in order before entering them with the SHADE function.

Teaching Tip   If students have a Casio *fx-7700GB* graphing calculator, point out that it has an inequality mode accessed by pressing the MODE key twice and pressing ÷ . When GRAPH is pressed, they can choose the appropriate inequality symbol and the shading will appear automatically.

Additional Answers

1.

2.

3.
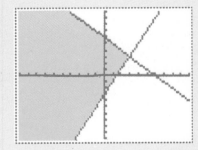

2-5A   Graphing Calculators: Graphing Systems of Linear Inequalities

Graphing a system of linear inequalities on the TI-81 is similar to graphing one linear inequality, which is explained in Lesson 1-3A. The "Shade(" command is still used to graph a system of inequalities, but the two equations of the system are used as the upper and lower boundaries instead of entering a minimum or a maximum value.

Once again, prepare to graph by resetting the range values to the standard viewing window and clearing any functions from the Y = list. You will also need to clear the graphics screen before graphing an inequality.

Since the TI-81 graphs functions and shades above the first function entered and below the second function entered, the first step in solving a system is deciding which function to enter first as the lower boundary and which to enter second as the upper boundary.

A "greater than or equal to" symbol indicates that values on and above the line of the related equation will satisfy the inequality. Similarly, a "less than or equal to" symbol indicates that values on and below the line of the related equation satisfy the inequality. Therefore, the related equation of the inequality with the sign "$y \geq$" will be entered first, and the related equation of the inequality with the sign "$y \leq$" will be entered second.

Example 1

Graph the system of inequalities below.
$$y \leq 2x - 3$$
$$y \geq -0.5x - 4$$

Values below the line $y = 2x - 3$ will satisfy the inequality $y \leq 2x - 3$.

Values above the line $y = -0.5x - 4$ will satisfy the inequality $y \geq -0.5x - 4$.

So, we will enter the equation $y = -0.5x - 4$ first and the equation $y = 2x - 3$ second.

Enter: 2nd DRAW 7 (−) 0.5 XT − 4
ALPHA , 2 XT − 3
) ENTER

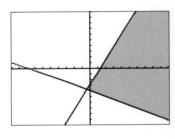

The points in the shaded area satisfy both $y \leq 2x - 3$ and $y \geq -0.5x - 4$.

84   CHAPTER 2   SYSTEMS OF EQUATIONS AND INEQUALITIES

You may have to solve some inequalities for y first to find a solution to the system graphically. Also, remember to clear the graphics screen by pressing [2ND] [DRAW] 1 and [ENTER] before graphing another inequality.

Example 2

Graph the system of inequalities below.
$$5x - y \geq 2$$
$$6x + 2y \geq 4$$

Solving both inequalities for y, we obtain $y \leq 5x - 2$ for the first inequality and $y \geq -3x + 2$ for the second inequality.

Values above the line $y = -3x + 2$ will satisfy the inequality $6x + 2y \geq 4$.

Values below the line $y = 5x - 2$ will satisfy the inequality $5x - y \geq 2$.

So, we will enter the equation $y = -3x + 2$ first and the equation $y = 5x - 2$ second.

Enter: [2ND] [DRAW] 7
[(−)] 3 [X|T] [+] 2 [ALPHA] [.] 5 [X|T] [−] 2 [)] [ENTER]

The points in the shaded area satisfy both $5x - y \geq 2$ and $6x + 2y \geq 4$.

EXERCISES

Graph each system of inequalities and sketch the graph on a piece of paper. Solve the inequalities for y first if necessary. 1–8. See margin.

1. $y \leq x$
   $y \geq -4$

2. $y \leq -3x$
   $y \geq 4x$

3. $y \geq 2x - 3$
   $y \leq -x + 6$

4. $y \geq -2x + 0.5$
   $y \leq 0.5x - 5$

5. $x + y \leq -1$
   $-x + y \geq 5$

6. $y \geq -2$
   $2x + y \leq 8$

7. $2x - 2y \geq 9$
   $-3x - y \leq -4$

8. $3x + 3y \leq 6$
   $2x - y \leq 5$

GRAPHING CALCULATORS: GRAPHING SYSTEMS OF LINEAR INEQUALITIES 85

More Examples

Graph the system of inequalities.
$$12x - 5y \leq 6$$
$$-3x + 4y \geq 5$$

EVALUATING THE LESSON

Closing the Lesson

Ask students in which order they would enter the system of inequalities to use the SHADE feature. Then graph.
$$3x - 5y \leq 10$$
$$5x + 4y \geq 11$$

APPLYING THE LESSON

Homework Exercises

Assignment Guide

All: 1-8

Additional Answers

5.

6.

7.

8.

Lesson Resources

- Practice Master 2–5
- Enrichment Master 2–5
- Technology Master p. 4

Transparency 2–5 contains the 5–Minute Check and a teaching aid for this lesson.

INTRODUCING THE LESSON

5–Minute Check

(over Lesson 2–4)

1. State the row operations you would use to get a zero in the second row of column 1.
$$\begin{bmatrix} -3 & 4 & 7 \\ 6 & 2 & -5 \end{bmatrix}$$
   Multiply the first row by 2 and add it to the second row.

2. Give the augmented matrix that you would use to solve the system of equations.
$-3x - y + 2z = 8$
$-x + 7y - 8z = 2$
$3x - 2y + z = -4$
$$\begin{bmatrix} -3 & -1 & 2 & 8 \\ -1 & 7 & -8 & 2 \\ 3 & -2 & 1 & -4 \end{bmatrix}$$

3. Solve the system of equations in Exercise 2 by using augmented matrices.
$\left(-4\frac{1}{2}, -8\frac{1}{6}, -6\frac{5}{6}\right)$

4. Solve the system of equations by using augmented matrices.
$-2x + 4y = 5$ $\left(\frac{1}{2}, \frac{3}{2}\right)$
$-x + 3y = 4$

Motivating the Lesson

Use grid paper and spaghetti or toothpicks to help students create various polygons on the grid paper. Have them try to determine the coordinates of points of intersection of the side of the polygons. If possible, also have them give the equations of the sides.

2-5 Solving Systems of Inequalities

Objectives

After studying this lesson, you should be able to:

2–5A
- graph systems of inequalities, and

2–5B
- find the maximum or minimum value of a function defined for a polygonal convex set.

Application

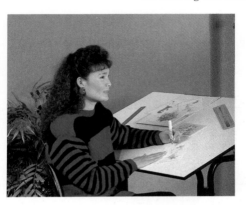

Belan Chu, a recent graphic arts graduate, has been doing some research on starting her own custom greeting card business. She will have initial start-up costs of $1500. Belan figures that it will cost 45¢ to produce each card. In order for Belan to remain competitive with the large greeting card manufacturers, she must sell her cards for no more than $1.70 per card, and her income must exceed her costs. Belan needs to determine if and when she might make a profit.

This situation can be modeled by a **system of linear inequalities**. To solve a system of inequalities, you must find the ordered pairs that satisfy both inequalities. One way to do this is to graph both inequalities on the same coordinate plane. The intersection of the two graphs contains points with the ordered pairs in the solution set. If the graphs do not intersect, then the system has no solution.

FYI...

In ancient Rome, young girls dropped love messages into a large urn in the center of the city. Men of the city drew messages and dated the girls whose messages they had drawn. Hence, the valentine card was born.

In order to solve the application described above, write a system of inequalities to represent the situation. Let x represent the number of greeting cards sold. Let y represent the income in dollars.

$x \geq 0$
$y \geq 0$
$y \geq 0.45x + 1500$ *Income must exceed costs.*

$y \leq 1.70x$ *Cards will be sold for no more than $1.70 each.*

Graph the system of inequalities. The ordered pair for any point in the intersection of the two graphs is a solution to the system. Belan's break-even point is where the lines intersect. She will begin making a profit after she sells 1200 cards. Notice that as the number of cards sold increases beyond 1200, her profit region expands, allowing her an opportunity for greater profit.

ALTERNATE TEACHING STRATEGIES

Using Computers

The graph given for the application can be shown using a computer. Then students can change various quantities (like the start-up cost) and show how the solution region is affected.

Using Critical Thinking

Is it possible that systems of inequalities have infinitely many solutions? Explain why this is true. Use graphs of several cases to explain your answer.

Not every system of inequalities has a solution.

Example 1

Solve the system of inequalities by graphing.
$$y > x + 5$$
$$y < x - 2$$

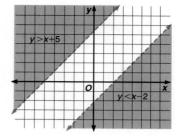

The graphs have no points in common. Therefore, no ordered pairs satisfy both inequalities.

Often the solution set of the system of linear inequalities is a **polygonal convex set**. Such a set consists of all points on or inside a convex polygon.

Example 2

Solve the system of inequalities by graphing. Then name the coordinates of the vertices of the polygonal convex set.
$$x \geq 0$$
$$y \geq 0$$
$$x + y \leq 5$$

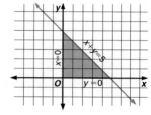

Points in the shaded region satisfy all three inequalities. The coordinates of the vertices of the set are $(0, 0)$, $(5, 0)$, and $(0, 5)$.

f(x, y) represents a function of two variables, x and y.

Sometimes it is necessary to find the maximum or minimum value that a function has for the points of a polygonal convex set. Consider the function $f(x, y) = 5x - 3y$, with the following inequalities forming a polygonal convex set.

$$y \geq 0 \qquad -x + y \leq 2 \qquad 0 \leq x \leq 5 \qquad x + y \leq 6$$

By graphing the inequalities and finding the intersection of the graphs, you can determine a polygonal convex set of points for which the function can be evaluated. The region shown at the right is the polygonal convex set determined by the inequalities listed above. Since the polygonal convex set has infinitely many points, it would be impossible to evaluate the function for all of them. However, according to the **vertex theorem**, a function such as $f(x, y) = 5x - 3y$ need only be evaluated for the coordinates of the vertices of the polygonal boundary in order to find the maximum and minimum values.

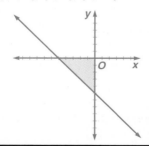

EVALUATING THE LESSON

Checking for Understanding

Exercises 1–10 are designed to help you assess students' understanding through reading, writing, speaking, and modeling. You should work through Exercises 1–2 with your students and then monitor their work on Exercises 3–10.

Closing the Lesson

Modeling Activity Use grid paper and spaghetti or toothpicks to construct a polygon on the coordinate plane. Explain how the polygon relates to the lesson. What do the interior points of the polygon represent?

Vertex Theorem	The maximum or minimum value of $f(x, y) = ax + by + c$ on a polygonal convex set occurs at a vertex of the polygonal boundary.

The value of $f(x, y) = 5x - 3y$ at each vertex can be found as follows.

$f(x, y) = 5x - 3y$ $f(2, 4) = 5(2) - 3(4) = -2$
$f(0, 0) = 5(0) - 3(0) = 0$ $f(5, 1) = 5(5) - 3(1) = 22$
$f(0, 2) = 5(0) - 3(2) = -6$ $f(5, 0) = 5(5) - 3(0) = 25$

Therefore, the maximum value of $f(x, y)$ is 25, and the minimum is -6. The maximum occurs at $(5, 0)$, and the minimum occurs at $(0, 2)$.

Example 3

Find the maximum and minimum values of $f(x, y) = x + 2y + 1$ for the polygonal convex set determined by the following inequalities.

$x \geq 0$ $y \geq 0$ $2x + y \leq 4$ $x + y \leq 3$

First, graph the inequalities and find the coordinates of the vertices of the resulting polygon.

The coordinates of the vertices are $(0, 0)$, $(2, 0)$, $(1, 2)$, and $(0, 3)$.

Then, evaluate the function $f(x, y) = x + 2y + 1$ at each vertex.

$f(0, 0) = 0 + 2(0) + 1 = 1$ $f(1, 2) = 1 + 2(2) + 1 = 6$
$f(2, 0) = 2 + 2(0) + 1 = 3$ $f(0, 3) = 0 + 2(3) + 1 = 7$

Thus, the maximum value of the function is 7, and the minimum value is 1.

CHECKING FOR UNDERSTANDING

Communicating Mathematics

Read and study the lesson to answer each question. 1–2. See margin.

1. Is it possible to have more than one ordered pair that produces a maximum or minimum for a given function? Explain your answer.

2. Can a function within a polygonal convex set have no maximum? Explain your answer.

Additional Answers

1. Yes, if the function passes through two vertices or coincides with an edge of the polygonal convex set representing the constraints in the problem.

2. Yes, there may not be a maximum if the region is not bounded.

Guided Practice

Given $f(x, y) = 3x + 2y + 1$, find each value.

3. $f(3, 2)$ 14

4. $f\left(\frac{1}{3}, \frac{1}{2}\right)$ 3

5. $f(-1.5, 4)$ 4.5

Find the maximum and minimum values of each function defined for the polygonal convex set having vertices at $(0, 0), (4, 0), (3, 5),$ and $(0, 5)$.

6. $f(x, y) = x + y$
8, 0

7. $f(x, y) = 8x + y$
32, 0

8. $f(x, y) = 4y - 3x$
20, -12

Solve each system of inequalities by graphing and name the coordinates of the vertices of each polygonal convex set. Then, find the maximum and minimum values for the given function on that set. 9–10. See Teacher's Answer Key for graphs.

9. $x + 4y \leq 12$ $(-2, 0), (2, -4)$
$3x - 2y \geq -6$ $(4, 2), (0, 3);$
$x + y \geq -2$ $8, -1$
$3x - y \leq 10$
$f(x, y) = x - y + 2$

10. $x \leq 3$ $(1, 0), (3, 0), (3, 5),$
$y \leq 5$ $(0, 5), (0, 1); 56, 12$
$x + y \geq 1$
$x \geq 0$
$y \geq 0$
$f(x, y) = 2x + 8y + 10$

EXERCISES

Practice

Solve each system of inequalities by graphing and name the coordinates of the vertices of each polygonal convex set. Then, find the maximum and minimum values for the given function on that set. 11–16. See Teacher's Answer Key for graphs.

11. $x \geq 0$ $(0, 0), (2, 0), (0, 4);$
$y \geq 0$ 4, -2
$2x + y \leq 4$
$f(x, y) = y - x$

12. $x \leq 0$ $(0, 0), (0, -3), (-3, -3);$
$y + 3 \geq 0$ 0, -9
$y \leq x$
$f(x, y) = x + 2y$

13. $x \geq 0$ $(0, 1), (3, 1), (0, 4);$
$y \geq 1$ 21, 9
$x + y \leq 4$
$f(x, y) = 4x + 2y + 7$

14. $x + y \leq 5$ $(0, 5), (15, -10), (-15, -10);$
$y - x \leq 5$ $\frac{65}{6}, -\frac{25}{6}$
$y \geq -10$
$f(x, y) = \frac{1}{2}x - \frac{1}{3}y$

15. $y \geq 0$ $(0, 0), (5, 0), (5, 1),$
$0 \leq x \leq 5$ $(2, 4), (0, 2);$
$-x + y \leq 2$ 15, -14
$x + y \leq 6$
$f(x, y) = 3x - 5y$

16. $x \geq 1$ $(1, 4), (3, 2), (6, 2),$
$y \geq 2$ $(3, 8), (1, 8); 11, -5$
$y \leq 8$
$x + y \geq 5$
$2x + y \leq 14$
$f(x, y) = y - 2x + 5$

17. Write a system of inequalities that determines the polygonal convex set with vertices at $(0, 0), (5, 1), (1, 6),$ and $(6, 4)$.

$y \geq \frac{1}{5}x, y \leq -\frac{2}{5}x + \frac{32}{5}, y \geq 3x - 14, y \leq 6x$

Graphing Calculator

Solve each system of inequalities. Use the ZOOM feature on a graphing calculator to check your solution. Assume that $x, y \geq 0$. 18–19. See students' work.

18. $x - y \leq 4$
$2x + y \leq 14$

19. $2x + 2y \geq 40$
$xy \geq 100$

LESSON 2-5 SOLVING SYSTEMS OF INEQUALITIES 89

Exercise Notes

You might want to make Exercise 21 an open-ended research problem. Let each student find the minimum ACT and SAT score for the school of his or her own choice.

For Exercise 22, remind students to consider only integer values of the number of tires.

Additional Answer

20. $[5\frac{1}{2}, 0]$, $[6\frac{1}{2}, 0]$, $[\frac{29}{3}, \frac{19}{3}]$,

$[7\frac{1}{2}, 8\frac{1}{2}]$, $[2\frac{1}{2}, 8\frac{1}{2}]$, $[\frac{6}{5}, \frac{23}{5}]$,

$[2\frac{1}{2}, 2]$;

maximum at $[7\frac{1}{2}, 8\frac{1}{2}] = 88\frac{1}{2}$,

minimum at $[2\frac{1}{2}, 2] = 24\frac{1}{2}$

Enrichment Masters Booklet, p. 11

Critical Thinking

20. Graph the following system to form a polygonal convex set. Determine which lines intersect and solve pairs of equations to determine the coordinates of each vertex. Then, find the maximum and minimum values of $f(x, y) = 5x + 6y$ for each region. See margin.

$0 \leq 2y \leq 17$
$y \geq 2x - 13$
$y \leq 3x + 1$
$3y \leq -2x + 11$
$y \geq 7 - 2x$
$y \leq 16 - x$

21–22. See Teacher's Answer Key.

Applications and Problem Solving

21. **Education** Bob Chase intends to major in medicine at the Harvard Medical School. He has been told that he must have two outstanding admissions scores in order to be admitted. He needs an ACT score of at least 30 and an SAT score of at least 1200. Write two inequalities to represent this situation, and graph the inequalities to show the solution.

22. **Business** Henry Jackson, a recent college graduate, plans to start his own business manufacturing bicycle tires. Henry knows that his start-up costs are going to be $3000 and that each tire will cost him $2 to manufacture. In order to remain competitive, Henry cannot charge more than $5 per tire. Draw a graph to show when Henry will make a profit.

Mixed Review

23. State whether the system below is *consistent and independent*, *consistent and dependent*, or *inconsistent*. (**Lesson 2-1**) consistent and dependent

$4x - 2y = 7$
$-12x + 6y = -21$

24. Find the values of x and y for which $\begin{bmatrix} 4x + y \\ x \end{bmatrix} = \begin{bmatrix} 6 \\ 2y - 12 \end{bmatrix}$ is true. (**Lesson 2-2**) $(0, 6)$

25. Find the determinant for $\begin{bmatrix} 1 & 3 \\ 2 & 5 \end{bmatrix}$. Does an inverse exist for this matrix? (**Lesson 2-3**) -1, yes

26. Solve the system below by using augmented matrices. (**Lesson 2-4**)

$4x + 2y + 3z = 6$
$2x + 7y = 3z$
$-3x - 9y + 13 = -2z$ $\left(-\frac{91}{11}, \frac{68}{11}, \frac{98}{11}\right)$

27. **College Entrance Exam** Choose the best answer.
$\triangle ABC$ and $\triangle ABD$ share side $\overline{AB}$. $\triangle ABC$ has area x and $\triangle ABD$ has area y. If $\overline{AD}$ is longer than $\overline{AC}$ and $\overline{BD}$ is longer than $\overline{BC}$, which of the following cannot be true? B

(A) $y > x$ (B) $y < x$ (C) $y \geq x$ (D) $y \neq x$ (E) $y \leq x$

90 CHAPTER 2 SYSTEMS OF EQUATIONS AND INEQUALITIES

EXTENDING THE LESSON

Math Power: Reasoning

Could the graph of a polygonal region ever contain more than one maximum or minimum value of a function? yes, if the graph of the function also contains a side of the polygonal region

2-6 Linear Programming

Objectives

After studying this lesson, you should be able to:

2–6A ■ use linear programming procedures to solve problems, and

2–6B ■ recognize situations where exactly one solution to a linear programming problem may not exist.

Application

Farmers often have a difficult time in late winter trying to determine exactly what crops to plant in the spring. There are so many factors to be considered: new government regulations on maximum crop production, seed costs, labor costs, fertilizer expenses, fluctuating prices on the grain market, and weather. Joe Washington has a choice of planting a combination of two different crops on 20 acres of land. For crop A, seed costs $120 per acre, and for crop B, seed costs $200 per acre.

Government restrictions limit acreage of crop A to 15 acres but do not limit crop B. Crop A will take 15 hours of labor per acre at a cost of $5.60 per hour, and crop B will require 10 hours of labor per acre at $5.00 per hour. If the expected income from crop A is $600 per acre and from crop B is $520 per acre, how should the 20 acres be apportioned between the two crops in order to maximize profit?

Mr. Washington can use a procedure called **linear programming** to help him maximize his profit. Many practical problems can be solved by using this method. The nature of these problems is that certain **constraints** exist or are placed upon the variables, and some function of these variables must be maximized or minimized. The constraints are often written as a system of linear inequalities.

The following procedure can be used to solve linear programming problems.

Linear Programming Procedure

1. **Define variables.**
2. **Write the constraints as a system of inequalities.**
3. **Graph the system and find the coordinates of the vertices of the polygon formed.**
4. **Write an expression to be maximized or minimized.**
5. **Substitute values from the coordinates of the vertices into the expression.**
6. **Select the greatest or least result.**

LESSON 2-6   LINEAR PROGRAMMING   91

NCTM Standards: 1, 2, 3, 4, 5, 6, 7, 12

Lesson Resources

- Practice Master 2–6
- Enrichment Master 2–6
- Evaluation Master, Quiz D, p. 22
- Multicultural Activity Master, p. 2
- Technology Master p. 3

 Transparency 2–6 contains the 5-Minute Check and a teaching aid for this lesson.

INTRODUCING THE LESSON

 5-Minute Check

(over Lesson 2–5)

1. Does point (–2, 4) satisfy the system of inequalities?
   $y \leq 3x - 4$
   $y \geq 3x + 4$ **no**
2. Solve the system of inequalities by graphing.
   $y > x + 2$
   $y < x - 4$ **no solution**

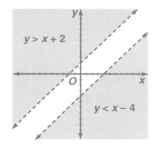

3. Solve the system of inequalities by graphing. Then name the vertices of the polygonal convex set.
   $x \geq 0$
   $y \geq 0$
   $x + y \leq 6$
   (0, 0), (6, 0), (0, 6)
4. Find the maximum and minimum values of $f(x, y) = 2x + y + 1$ for the polygonal convex set determined by the following inequalities.
   $x \geq 0$
   $y \geq 0$
   $y \leq -x + 5$
   $y \leq -\frac{2}{3}x + 4$
   max: 11, min: 5

ALTERNATE TEACHING STRATEGIES

Using Cooperative Groups

Have students in cooperative groups discuss how to express each constraint below in mathematical language.
1. The number of packages produced is less than 300.
2. The daily production rate is between 900 and 1000.
3. More than 92 hours of time on machine A is needed to produce the object.

Using Charts

Using charts to help organize the information given in an application can be very helpful. Have students make a chart of the vertices. Put the ordered pairs in one column and the value of the function in another column.

Motivating the Lesson

Find a system of inequalities that would determine a polygonal region for the graph shown below.

$$x \geq 0, y \geq 0, y \leq -\frac{3}{5}x + 8,$$
$$y \leq -5x + 30$$

Let's use this procedure to solve the application presented at the beginning of the lesson.

Define variables.

Let x = the number of acres of crop A.
Let y = the number of acres of crop B.

Write inequalities.

$x \geq 0, \ y \geq 0$ *Acreage cannot be less than 0.*
$x \leq 15$ *No more than 15 acres of crop A are permitted.*
$x + y \leq 20$ *No more than 20 acres can be planted in all.*

Graph the system.

The constraints $x \geq 0$ and $y \geq 0$ tell you to consider only those points that are in Quadrant I.

The vertices are at $(0,0)$, $(15,0)$, $(15,5)$, and $(0,20)$.

Write an expression.

Profit equals income less costs. The profit from crop A equals $600x - 120x - 15(5.60)x$, or $396x$. The profit from crop B equals $520y - 200y - 10(5.00)y$, or $270y$. Thus, the profit function is $P(x, y) = 396x + 270y$.

Substitute values.

$P(0,0) = 396(0) + 270(0) = 0$
$P(15,0) = 396(15) + 270(0) = 5940$
$P(15,5) = 396(15) + 270(5) = 7290$
$P(0,20) = 396(0) + 270(20) = 5400$

Answer the problem.

The maximum occurs at $(15, 5)$. Thus, Mr. Washington should plant 15 acres of crop A and 5 acres of crop B to obtain the maximum profit of $7290.

In certain circumstances, the use of linear programming is not helpful. Consider the graph at the right, based on the following constraints.

$x \geq 0$
$y \geq 0$
$y \geq 6$
$4x + 3y \leq 12$

The constraints do not define a region with any points in common in Quadrant I. When the constraints of a linear programming problem cannot be satisfied simultaneously, then **infeasibility** is said to occur. This may mean that the constraints have been formulated incorrectly, certain requirements need to be changed, or that additional resources are required before the problem can be solved.

The solution of a linear programming problem is **unbounded** if the region defined by the constraints is infinitely large. Consider the graph at the right. While this graph would be helpful in a problem where the objective is to minimize cost, it is not possible to determine how to maximize revenue.

$x \geq 0$ and $y \geq 0$

It is also possible for a linear programming problem to have two or more optimal solutions. When this occurs, the problem is said to have **alternate optimal solutions**. This usually occurs when the function to be maximized or minimized is parallel to one side of the polygonal convex set.

Example

The AC Telephone Company manufactures two styles of cordless telephones, deluxe and standard. Each deluxe telephone nets the company $9 in profit, and each standard telephone nets $6. Machines A and B are used to make both styles of telephones. Each deluxe telephone requires three hours of machine A time and one hour of machine B time. Each standard telephone requires two hours of machine A time and two hours of machine B time. An employee has an idea that frees twelve hours of machine A time and eight hours of machine B time. Determine the mix of telephones that can be made during the free time that most effectively generates profit for the company within the given constraints.

Define variables.

Let d = the number of deluxe telephones.
Let s = the number of standard telephones.

Write inequalities.

$$d \geq 0$$
$$s \geq 0$$
$$3d + 2s \leq 12 \quad \text{machine A}$$
$$d + 2s \leq 8 \quad \text{machine B}$$

Graph the system.

Write an expression.

Since the profit on each deluxe telephone is $9 and the profit on each standard telephone is $6, the profit function is $P(d, s) = 9d + 6s$.

(continued on the next page)

LESSON 2-6 LINEAR PROGRAMMING 93

Checking for Understanding

Exercises 1–14 are designed to help you assess students' understanding through reading, writing, speaking, and modeling. You should work through Exercises 1–3 with your students and then monitor their work on Exercises 4–14.

Closing the Lesson

Speaking Activity Have students explain the difference between an infeasible region, an unbounded region, or a region that has alternate optimal solutions.

Practice Masters Booklet, p. 12

$$P(0,0) = 9(0) + 6(0) = 0$$
Substitute values. $$P(0,4) = 9(0) + 6(4) = 24$$
$$P(2,3) = 9(2) + 6(3) = 36$$
$$P(4,0) = 9(4) + 6(0) = 36$$

Answer the problem. This problem has alternate optimal solutions. The company will make the same profit if they make and sell 2 deluxe telephones and 3 standard telephones as it will from making and selling 4 deluxe telephones and no standard telephones.

CHECKING FOR UNDERSTANDING

Communicating Mathematics

Read and study the lesson to answer each question. 1–3. See margin.

1. **Define** linear programming in your own words.
2. **Explain** why the vertex theorem is useful when solving linear programming problems.
3. **Explain**, in your own words, under what conditions a linear programming problem has alternate optimal solutions.

Guided Practice

The Champion Lumber Company converts logs into lumber or plywood. In a given week, the total production cannot exceed 800 units, of which 200 units of lumber and 300 units of plywood are required by regular customers. The profit on a unit of lumber is $20, and the profit on a unit of plywood is $30. Let x represent the units of lumber and let y represent the units of plywood.

4. Write an inequality to represent the total production. $x + y \leq 800$
5. Write an inequality to represent the production of lumber. $x \geq 200$
6. Write an inequality to represent the production of plywood. $y \geq 300$
7. Write an equation to represent the total profit. $P(x, y) = 20x + 30y$
8. Graph the polygonal convex set determined by the inequalities. See margin.
9. Name the vertices of the polygon. $(200, 600)$, $(500, 300)$, $(200, 300)$
10. Find the number of units each of lumber and plywood that should be produced to maximize profit. 200 lumber, 600 plywood
11. What is the maximum profit? $22,000

Graph each system of inequalities. Then, state whether the situation is *infeasible*, has *alternate optimal solutions*, or is *unbounded*. In each system, assume that $x \geq 0$ and $y \geq 0$.

12. $3y \geq 25$
$x + y \leq 30$
$f(x, y) = 3x + 3y$
alternate optimal

13. $2x + y \geq 15$
$3x + y \leq 12$
$f(x, y) = 2x + 2y$
infeasible

14. $2x + 2y \geq 10$
$2x + y \geq 8$
$2x + 3y \geq 30$
$f(x, y) = x + y$
unbounded

RETEACHING THE LESSON

Would linear programming be appropriate to find the maximum and minimum values for each graph below? Explain.

A. **B.** **C.**

You could find the minimum value in the first and third graphs, but you cannot find the maximum value in the third graph because it is an unbounded region. The second region is an infeasible solution because it does not show the intersection of the inequalities.

EXERCISES

Applications and Problem Solving

Solve each problem, if possible. If not possible, state whether the problem is *infeasible*, has *alternate optimal solutions*, or is *unbounded*.

15. Manufacturing The Cruiser Bicycle Company makes two styles of bicycles: the Traveler, which sells for $200, and the Tourister, which sells for $600. Each bicycle has the same frame and tires, but the assembly and painting time required for the Traveler is only one hour, while it takes three hours for the Tourister. There are 300 frames and 360 hours of labor available for production. How many of each model should be produced to maximize revenue? alternate optimal

16. Manufacturing A manufacturer makes widgets and gadgets. At least 500 widgets and 700 gadgets are needed to meet minimum daily demands. The machinery can produce no more than 1200 widgets and 1400 gadgets per day. The combined number of widgets and gadgets that the packaging department can handle is 2300 per day. b. 1200 w, 1100 g, $748

   a. If the company sells widgets for 40 cents each and gadgets for 50 cents each, how many of each item should be produced for maximum daily income? What is the maximum daily income? 900 w, 1400 g, $1060

   b. Suppose the cost of producing a widget is 7 cents and the cost of producing a gadget is 18 cents. How many widgets and gadgets should be produced for maximum daily profit? What is the maximum daily profit?

17. $9\frac{2}{3}$ of Y and 0 of X

17. Nutrition A diet is to include at least 140 mg of Vitamin A and at least 145 mg of Vitamin B. These requirements can be obtained from two types of food. Type X contains 10 mg of Vitamin A and 20 mg of Vitamin B per pound. Type Y contains 30 mg of Vitamin A and 15 mg of Vitamin B per pound. If type X food costs $12 per pound and type Y food cost $8 per pound, how many pounds of each type of food should be purchased to satisfy the requirements at the minimum cost?

18. Manufacturing The SwingWell Company produces two types of golf clubs: the Driver, which sells for $30, and the Master, which sells for $40. SwingWell has more orders for the upcoming month than it is capable of producing. Using the production schedule below, what is the maximum revenue that SwingWell should anticipate for the coming month? $170,000

Process	Driver	Master	Time Available
Cutting	2 min	2 min	$166\frac{2}{3}$ h
Assembly	1 min	3 min	150 h
Finishing	2 min	3 min	200 h

Homework Exercises

Assignment Guide

Average: 15–20, 23–28
Enriched: 15, 17–28

The red A, B, and C flags, printed only in the Teacher's Wraparound Edition, indicate the level of difficulty of the exercises.

Chapter 2, Quiz D, (Lessons 2–5 through 2–6), is available in the *Evaluation Masters*, p. 22.

Exercise Note

For Exercises 18–23, consider letting students work in cooperative groups.

Using Technology

Graphing utilities may be helpful to demonstrate the graphs of the inequalities used in the applications.

Additional Answers

1. Answers will vary, but most should say that linear programming is the process used to find the maximum and minimum values of a function.
2. Answers will vary, but students should focus on the fact that only the vertices of the region have to be checked to find the maximum or minimum values.
3. Answers will vary, but students should say that a linear programming problem has alternate optimal solutions usually when the function to be maximized or minimized is parallel to one side of the polygonal convex set.

8.

19. Contracting The BJ Electrical Company needs to hire master electricians and apprentices for a one-week project. Master electricians receive a salary of $750 per week and apprentices receive $350 per week. As part of its contract, the company has agreed to hire at least 30 workers. The local Building Safety Council recommends that each master electrician spend three hours for inspection time during the project. This project should require 25 hours of inspection time. How many of each type of worker should be hired to accomplish the project and still meet the contract safety requirements? unbounded

20. Manufacturing A company makes two models of light fixtures, A and B, each of which must be assembled and packed. The time required to assemble model A is 12 minutes, and model B takes 18 minutes. It takes 2 minutes to package model A and 1 minute to package model B. Each week there are available 240 hours of assembly time and 20 hours for packing.

a. If model A sells for $1.50 and model B sells for $1.70, how many of each model should be made to obtain the maximum weekly income? What is the maximum weekly income? 300 A, 600 B, $1470

b. Suppose the cost to produce model A is 75¢ and the cost to produce model B is 85¢. How many model A light fixtures and model B light fixtures should be produced for maximum weekly profit? What is the maximum weekly profit? 300 A, 600 B, $735

21. Energy A chemical company uses two types of fuel for heating and processing. At least 3800 gallons of fuel are used each day. The burning of each gallon of #1 crude leaves a residue of 0.02 pounds of ash and 0.06 pounds of soot. Each gallon of #2 crude leaves a residue of 0.05 pounds of ash and 0.01 pounds of soot. The factory needs at least 120 pounds of ash and at least 136 pounds of soot each day. If #1 crude costs $1.50 per gallon and #2 crude costs $1.10 per gallon, then how many gallons of each type should be purchased in order to minimize costs?

21. 1960 of #1, 1840 of #2

22. Manufacturing The File-Away Company sells letter-size file cabinets for $138 and legal-size file cabinets for $176.50. The company has 120,000 square feet of sheet metal in stock. It takes 36 square feet to make the letter-size file cabinet and 54 square feet to make the legal-size file cabinet. The board of directors has allocated the following labor costs.

Cost	Letter Size	Legal Size	Total Available
Direct Labor	$42	$52	$375,000
Indirect Labor	$18	$21	$194,500

Determine the optimum number of each type of cabinet the company should make to maximize their revenues. 3333 letter-size only

23. Marketing Yummy Ice Cream conducted a survey and found that people liked their black walnut flavor three times more than their tutti-frutti flavor. One distributor wants to order at least 20,000 gallons of the tutti-frutti flavor. The company has all of the ingredients to produce both flavors, but it has only 45,000 gallon-size containers available. If each gallon of ice cream sells for $2.95, how many gallons of each type flavor should the company produce? infeasible

Additional Answer

27. Multiply row 2 by –3 and add it to row 1. Multiply row 1 by 2 and row 2 by 3 and add row 1 to row 2.

Critical Thinking

24. The system below forms a polygonal convex set.

$x \le 0$

$y \le 10$

$y \ge -x$, when $-6 \le x \le 0$

$2x + 3y \ge 6$ when $-12 \le x \le -6$

What is the area of the closed figure? 54 square units

Mixed Review

25. Multiply $\begin{bmatrix} 8 & -7 \\ -4 & 0 \end{bmatrix}$ by $\frac{3}{4}$. **(Lesson 2-2)** $\begin{bmatrix} 6 & -\frac{21}{4} \\ -3 & 0 \end{bmatrix}$

26. Find the multiplicative inverse of $\begin{bmatrix} 2 & 1 \\ -3 & 2 \end{bmatrix}$. **(Lesson 2-3)** $\frac{1}{7}\begin{bmatrix} 2 & -1 \\ 3 & 2 \end{bmatrix}$

27. See margin.

27. State the row operations you would use to get a zero in the second column of row one of $\begin{bmatrix} 3 & 3 & -9 \\ -2 & 1 & -4 \end{bmatrix}$. Then state the row operations you would use to get a zero in the first column of row two. **(Lesson 2-4)**

28. Find the maximum and minimum values of $f(x, y) = x + 2y$ if it is defined for the polygonal convex set having vertices at $(0, 0)$, $(4, 0)$, $(3, 5)$, and $(0, 5)$. **(Lesson 2-5)** 13, 0

29. College Entrance Exam Choose the best answer. $\sqrt{\dfrac{\sqrt{25}}{5}} = A$

(A) 1   **(B)** $\sqrt{2}$ **(C)** 2   **(D)** 5   **(E)** $5\sqrt{2}$

CASE STUDY FOLLOW-UP

Refer to Case Study 1: *Buying a Home*, on pages 956–958.

Manuel Tijera plans to rent one house and purchase another. He estimates that mortgage interest deductions on his federal income tax will save him 25% on his mortgage payments. He wants to spend no more than $800 per month on rent and no more than $2000 per month on rent and mortgage payments, including tax savings, combined.

1. Use linear programming to find the maximum total monthly amount he might have to pay, factoring in his tax savings. $900+$800 =$1700

2. If he chooses this option, what is the maximum amount he can borrow on a 15-year 9% FRM? about $120,000

3. **Research** Find out about local median rental costs and new home prices. Write a 1-page paper analyzing the advantages and disadvantages of renting versus buying a home in your city. See students' work.

LESSON 2-6   LINEAR PROGRAMMING   97

EXTENDING THE LESSON

Math Power: Problem Solving

Let x and y be positive integers so that $x + y \le 9$ and $3x + 2y \le 22$. What is the maximum value of $3x + 4y$? of $x + 5y$?
36; 45

Case Study Follow-Up

This activity provides an opportunity to do research and apply mathematics in solving problems related to issues that may face students in their adult lives. Case Study 1 is located on pages 956–958.

Additional Answers

5. $\begin{bmatrix} 4 & 3 \\ 2 & -6 \end{bmatrix}$ 6. $\begin{bmatrix} -10 & -13 \\ 2 & 2 \end{bmatrix}$

7. $\begin{bmatrix} -9 & -15 \\ 6 & -6 \end{bmatrix}$ 8. $\begin{bmatrix} -8 \\ 20 \end{bmatrix}$

9. $\begin{bmatrix} -5 & -51 \\ -8 & 8 \end{bmatrix}$ 10. $\begin{bmatrix} 19 \\ 14 \end{bmatrix}$

20.

(1, 5), (4, 2), (6, –2), (1, –2)
maximum at (1, 5) = 13,
minimum at (1 –2) = –8

21.

(0, 9), (4, 7), (6, 5), (6, 4), (0, 4)
maximum at (4, 7) = 25,
minimum at (0, 4) = 8

CHAPTER 2   # SUMMARY AND REVIEW

VOCABULARY

Upon completing this chapter, you should be
familiar with the following terms:

alternate optimal solutions	**93**	**91**	linear programming
augmented matrix	**79**	**64**	matrix
column matrix	**64**	**71**	minor
consistent	**57**	**64**	nth order
constraint	**91**	**87**	polygonal convex set
dependent	**57**	**64**	row matrix
determinant	**71**	**66**	scalar
dimensions	**64**	**64**	square matrix
element	**64**	**57**	substitution method
elimination method	**57**	**56**	system of equations
inconsistent	**57**	**86**	system of linear inequalities
independent	**57**	**93**	unbounded
infeasibility	**92**	**87**	vertex theorem
$m \times n$ matrix	**64**	**65**	zero matrix

SKILLS AND CONCEPTS

OBJECTIVES AND EXAMPLES	REVIEW EXERCISES

Upon completing this chapter, you should be able to:

Use these exercises to review and prepare for the chapter test.

- solve systems of equations algebraically **(Lesson 2-1)**

  Solve the system of equations below.
  $y = -x + 2$
  $3x + 4y = 2$

  $3x + 4y = 2 \qquad y = -x + 2$
  $3x + 4(-x + 2) = 2 \qquad = -6 + 2$
  $x = 6 \qquad = -4 \qquad (6, -4)$

Solve each system of equations algebraically.

1. $y = -2x$
   $x + y = -2$ (2, –4)

2. $x - y = 5$
   $x = 6y$ (6, 1)

3. $5y - 2x = 0$
   $3y + x = -1$
   $\left(-\dfrac{5}{11}, -\dfrac{2}{11}\right)$

4. $y - 6x = 1$
   $-15x + 2y = -4$
   (2, 13)

- add, subtract, and multiply matrices **(Lesson 2-2)**

  $-2 \begin{bmatrix} 1 & -4 \\ 0 & 3 \end{bmatrix} = \begin{bmatrix} -2(1) & -2(-4) \\ -2(0) & -2(3) \end{bmatrix}$

  $= \begin{bmatrix} -2 & 8 \\ 0 & -6 \end{bmatrix}$

Use matrices A, B, and C to find each sum, difference, or product. 5–10. See margin.

$A = \begin{bmatrix} 7 & 8 \\ 0 & -4 \end{bmatrix}$ $B = \begin{bmatrix} -3 & -5 \\ 2 & -2 \end{bmatrix}$ $C = \begin{bmatrix} 2 \\ -5 \end{bmatrix}$

5. $A + B$ 6. $B - A$ 7. $3B$
8. $-4C$ 9. AB 10. BC

OBJECTIVES AND EXAMPLES	REVIEW EXERCISES

OBJECTIVES AND EXAMPLES

■ evaluate determinants **(Lesson 2-3)**

Find the value of $\begin{vmatrix} -2 & 5 \\ 6 & -7 \end{vmatrix}$.

$\begin{vmatrix} -2 & 5 \\ 6 & -7 \end{vmatrix} = (-2)(-7) - 6(5) = -16$

■ solve systems of equations by using inverses of matrices. **(Lesson 2-3)**

Solve $\begin{bmatrix} 3 & -5 \\ -2 & 2 \end{bmatrix} \cdot \begin{bmatrix} x \\ y \end{bmatrix} = \begin{bmatrix} 1 \\ -2 \end{bmatrix}$.

$-\frac{1}{4}\begin{bmatrix} 2 & 5 \\ 2 & 3 \end{bmatrix} \cdot \begin{bmatrix} 3 & -5 \\ -2 & 2 \end{bmatrix} \cdot \begin{bmatrix} x \\ y \end{bmatrix} = -\frac{1}{4}\begin{bmatrix} 2 & 5 \\ 2 & 3 \end{bmatrix} \cdot \begin{bmatrix} 1 \\ -2 \end{bmatrix}$

$\begin{bmatrix} x \\ y \end{bmatrix} = \begin{bmatrix} 2 \\ 1 \end{bmatrix}$

■ solve systems of equations by using augmented matrices **(Lesson 2-4)**

The solution represented by the reduced

augmented matrix $\begin{bmatrix} 1 & 0 & 0 & -4 \\ 0 & 1 & 0 & \frac{1}{3} \\ 0 & 0 & 1 & 6 \end{bmatrix}$ is

$(-4, \frac{1}{3}, 6)$.

■ find the maximum or minimum value of a function defined for a polygonal convex set **(Lesson 2-5)**

Find the maximum and minimum values of $f(x, y) = 4y + x - 3$ for the polygonal convex set graphed at right.

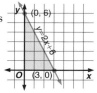

$f(0, 0) = 4(0) + 1(0) - 3 = -3$ *minimum*

$f(3, 0) = 4(0) + 1(3) - 3 = 0$

$f(0, 6) = 4(6) + 1(0) - 3 = 21$ *maximum*

REVIEW EXERCISES

Find the value of each determinant.

11. $\begin{vmatrix} 7 & -4 \\ 5 & -3 \end{vmatrix}$ -1

12. $\begin{vmatrix} 8 & -4 \\ -6 & 3 \end{vmatrix}$ 0

13. $\begin{vmatrix} 5 & 0 & 4 \\ 7 & 3 & -1 \\ 2 & -2 & 6 \end{vmatrix}$ 0

14. $\begin{vmatrix} 3 & -1 & 4 \\ 5 & -2 & 6 \\ 7 & 3 & -4 \end{vmatrix}$ 24

Solve each matrix equation.

15. $\begin{bmatrix} 2 & 5 \\ -1 & -3 \end{bmatrix} \cdot \begin{bmatrix} x \\ y \end{bmatrix} = \begin{bmatrix} 1 \\ 2 \end{bmatrix}$ $(13, -5)$

16. $\begin{bmatrix} 3 & 2 \\ -6 & 4 \end{bmatrix} \cdot \begin{bmatrix} x \\ y \end{bmatrix} = \begin{bmatrix} -3 \\ 6 \end{bmatrix}$ $(-1, 0)$

17. $\begin{bmatrix} -3 & 5 \\ -2 & 4 \end{bmatrix} \cdot \begin{bmatrix} x \\ y \end{bmatrix} = \begin{bmatrix} 1 \\ -2 \end{bmatrix}$ $(-7, -4)$

Solve each system of equations by using augmented matrices.

18. $x - 2y - 3z = 2$
$x - 4y + 3z = 14$
$-3x + 5y + 4z = 0$ $(-10, -6, 0)$

19. $2x + 3y - 4z = 5$
$x + y + 2z = 3$
$-x + 2y - 6z = 4$ $(-1, 3, \frac{1}{2})$

Solve each system of inequalities by graphing and name the coordinates of the vertices of each polygonal convex set. Then, find the maximum and minimum values for the function $f(x, y) = 3y + 2x - 4$.

20. $x \geq 1$
$y \geq -2$
$y \leq 6 - x$
$y + 2x \leq 10$

21. $x \geq 0$
$y \geq 4$
$2y \leq 18 - x$
$x \leq 6$
$y \leq 11 - x$

20–21. See margin.

Two multiple-choice tests (Forms 1A and 1B) and two free-response tests (Forms 2A and 2B) are provided in the *Evaluation Masters*. Chapter 2 Test, Form 1A is shown below. Chapter 2 Test, Form 2A is shown on the next page.

Evaluation Masters Booklet, pp. 13–14

- recognize situations where exactly one solution to a linear programming problem may not exist **(Lesson 2-6)**

The system of inequalities graphed at the right represents an *unbounded* situation because the constraints cannot be satisfied simultaneously.

Graph each system of inequalities. Then, state whether the situation is *infeasible*, has *alternate optimal solutions*, or is *unbounded*. In each system, assume that $x \geq 0$ and $y \geq 0$.

22. $x + 3y \leq 9$
$6x + 3y \leq 18$ alternate optimal
$f(x, y) = x + y$ solutions

23. $2x \geq 14$
$x + 3y \leq 6$
$f(x, y) = 2x + y$ infeasible

22–23. For graphs, see Teacher's Answer Key.

APPLICATIONS AND PROBLEM SOLVING

24. Sports   In a three-team track meet, the following numbers of first-, second-, and third-place finishes were recorded.

School	First Place	Second Place	Third Place
Boardman	2	5	5
Girard	8	2	3
Niles	6	4	1

Boardman: 30; Girard: 49; Niles: 43

Use matrices to find the final scores for each school if 5 points are awarded for first place, 3 for second place, and 1 for third place.   **(Lesson 2-2)**

25. Geometry   The perimeter of a triangle is 83 inches. The longest side is three times the length of the shortest side and 17 inches more than one-half the sum of the other two sides. Find the length of each side.   **(Lesson 2-4)**   39 inches, 31 inches, 13 inches

26. Manufacturing   A toy manufacturer produces two types of model spaceships, the Voyager and the Explorer. Each of the toys requires the same three operations: plastic molding, machining, and bench assembly. Each Voyager requires 5 minutes for molding, 3 minutes for machining, and 5 minutes for assembly. Each Explorer requires 6 minutes for molding, 2 minutes for machining, and 18 minutes for assembly. The manufacturer can afford a daily schedule of not more than 4 hours for molding, 2 hours for machining, and 9 hours for assembly. **(Lesson 2-6)**

a. If the profit is $2.40 on each Voyager and $5.00 on each Explorer, how many of each toy should be produced for maximum profit?   18 Voyagers, 25 Explorers

b. What is the maximum daily profit? $168.20

Additional Answers
Chapter Test

17. (0, 0), (0, 3), $\left(1\frac{2}{3}, 4\frac{2}{3}\right)$, (4, 0)

maximum at $\left(1\frac{2}{3}, 4\frac{2}{3}\right) = 28\frac{1}{3}$

minimum at (0, 0) = 0

18. (1, 5), (3, 3), (1, 0), (4, 0)
maximum at (1, 5) = 28
minimum at (1, 0) = 3

19. $\left(-\frac{5}{2}, 5\right)$, (3, 5), (3, 1), $\left(\frac{2}{3}, -\frac{4}{3}\right)$

maximum at (3, 5) = 34,

minimum at $\left(\frac{2}{3}, -\frac{4}{3}\right) = -4\frac{2}{3}$

For graphs, see Teacher's Answer Key.

Solve each system of equations.

1. $x - 4 = y$
$y = 2x - 8$ (4, 0)

2. $x + 5 = y$
$3x = y - 1$ (2, 7)

3. $y - 3x = 8$
$x + y = 4$ (-1, 5)

4. $5 - 6x = y$
$2x + 7y = 5$ $\left(\frac{3}{4}, \frac{1}{2}\right)$

Use matrices A, B, C, and D to find each sum, difference, or product. 5–9. See margin.

$$A = \begin{bmatrix} 5 & 4 \\ -1 & -2 \end{bmatrix} \quad B = \begin{bmatrix} -1 & -2 \\ 5 & 4 \end{bmatrix} \quad C = \begin{bmatrix} -2 & 4 & 6 \\ 5 & -7 & -1 \end{bmatrix} \quad D = \begin{bmatrix} 1 & -2 \\ 0 & 4 \\ -3 & 4 \end{bmatrix}$$

5. $5D$ **6.** $2A + B$ **7.** $2B - A$ **8.** CD **9.** $AB + CD$

Find the value of each determinant.

10. $\begin{vmatrix} -3 & 5 \\ 1 & -4 \end{vmatrix}$ 7

11. $\begin{vmatrix} 8 & 5 \\ -3 & -2 \end{vmatrix}$ -1

12. $\begin{vmatrix} 2 & 1 & -1 \\ 6 & 4 & -3 \\ 0 & 2 & -2 \end{vmatrix}$ -4

13. $\begin{vmatrix} 3 & 1 & 2 \\ -2 & 0 & 4 \\ 3 & 5 & 2 \end{vmatrix}$ -64

14. Solve $\begin{bmatrix} -1 & 4 \\ 7 & 0 \end{bmatrix} \cdot \begin{bmatrix} x \\ y \end{bmatrix} = \begin{bmatrix} -1 \\ -14 \end{bmatrix}$. $\left(-2, -\frac{3}{4}\right)$

Solve each system of equations using augmented matrices.

15. $x + 2y + z = 3$
$2x - 3y + 2z = -1$
$x - 3y + 2z = 1$ (-2, 1, 3)

16. $-3x + y + z = 2$
$5x + 2y - 4z = 21$
$x - 3y - 7z = -10$ (1, 6, -1)

Solve each system of inequalities by graphing and name the coordinates of the vertices of each polygonal convex set. Then, find the maximum and minimum values for the function $f(x, y) = 5y + 3x$. 17–19. See margin.

17. $x \geq 0$
$y \geq 0$
$y \leq x + 3$
$2x + y \leq 8$

18. $y \geq 0$
$x \geq 1$
$x + y \leq 6$
$y + 3x \leq 12$

19. $y \leq 5$
$x \leq 3$
$y + 2x \geq 0$
$y \geq x - 2$

20. Carpentry Emilio has a small carpentry shop in his basement to make bookcases. He makes two sizes, large and small. His profit on a large bookcase is $80, and his profit on a small bookcase is $50. It takes Emilio 6 hours to make a large bookcase and 2 hours to make a small one. He can spend only 24 hours each week on his carpentry work. He must make at least two of each size each week. What is the maximum weekly profit? $460

Bonus

Name the polygonal boundary formed by the set of all points with coordinates (x, y) that satisfy all of the constraints below when n is a positive number. pentagon

$n \leq 2y \leq 4n$ $\qquad$ $x + n \geq y$
$2n \leq x + y \leq 5n$ $\qquad$ $y + n \geq x$
$n \leq 2x \leq 4n$

This page may be used as a test or as a review. All answers to this test appear in the Selected Answers in the student text.

Standardized Test Practice Questions are also provided in the *Evaluation Masters*.

Evaluation Masters Booklet, pp. 17-18

Test Generator Software is provided in Apple, IBM, and Macintosh versions. You may use this software to create your own tests, based on the needs of your students.

Additional Answers

5. $\begin{bmatrix} 5 & -10 \\ 0 & 20 \\ -15 & 20 \end{bmatrix}$

6. $\begin{bmatrix} 9 & 6 \\ 3 & 0 \end{bmatrix}$

7. $\begin{bmatrix} -7 & -8 \\ 11 & 10 \end{bmatrix}$

8. $\begin{bmatrix} -20 & 44 \\ 8 & -42 \end{bmatrix}$

9. $\begin{bmatrix} -5 & 50 \\ -1 & -48 \end{bmatrix}$

PREVIEWING THE CHAPTER

In this chapter, the concept of symmetry is reviewed and extended to include the symmetry of graphs with respect to a point or line on a coordinate plane. Students identify and sketch families of graphs based on a parent graph. The parent graphs include graphs of monomials, absolute value functions, step functions, rational functions, and radical functions. The families of graphs are formed by translations and transformations on the coordinate plane. Students also find and graph inverses of functions and identify asymptotes associated with rational functions. Tangents to graphs are explored, and students learn to find the slopes and equations of lines tangent to a given graph. Building on these skills, students identify the critical points and the end behavior of the graphs of polynomial functions.

Lesson Objective Chart

Lesson (Pages)	Lesson Objectives		State/Local Objectives
3-1 (106-116)	**3-1A:**	Identify symmetrical graphs.	
	3-1B:	Use symmetry to complete a graph.	
	3-1C:	Identify an odd function and an even function.	
3-2 (117-124)	**3-2A:**	Identify the graphs of simple polynomial functions, absolute value functions, and step functions.	
	3-2B:	Sketch the graphs of these functions.	
3-3 (126-131)	**3-3A:**	Determine the inverse of a relation or function.	
	3-3B:	Graph a function and its inverse.	
3-4 (134-142)	**3-4A:**	Determine horzontal, vertical, and slant asymptotes.	
	3-4B:	Graph rational functions.	
3-5 (144-148)	**3-5:**	Graph polynomial, absolute value, and radical inequalities.	
3-6 (149-154)	**3-6A:**	Find the derivative of a function.	
	3-6B:	Find the slope and the equation of a line tangent to the graph of a function at a given point.	
3-7 (156-163)	**3-7:**	Find the critical points of the graph of a polynomial function and determine if each is a minimum, maximum, or point of inflection.	
3-8 (164-171)	**3-8A:**	Determine continuity or discontinuity of functions.	
	3-8B:	Identify the end behavior of graphs.	

ORGANIZING THE CHAPTER

You may want to refer to the **Course Planning Guide Calendar** on pages T34-T35 for a complete pacing chart.

Lesson Planning Guide

					Technology				Activity Masters			
Lesson	Pages	Practice	Enrichment	Evaluation	Graphing Calculator	Computer	Multicultural Activity	Applications	Problem Solving	Case Study Follow-Up	Decision Making	Transparencies
3-1	106-116	p. 13	p. 13									3-1
3-2	117-124	p. 14	p. 14	Quiz A, p. 33		p. 6	p. 3					3-2
3-3	126-131	p. 15	p. 15									3-3
3-4	134-142	p. 16	p. 16	Quiz B, p. 33 Mid-Chapter Test, p. 35				p. 7				3-4
3-5	144-148	p. 17	p. 17									3-5
3-6	149-154	p. 18	p. 18	Quiz C, p. 34					p. 8			3-6
3-7	156-163	p. 19	p. 19		p. 5							3-7
3-8	164-171	p. 20	p. 20	Quiz D, p. 34						p. 9		3-8
Review	172-174	Multiple Choice Tests, Forms 1A and 1B, pp. 25-28										
Test	175	Free Response Tests, Forms 2A and 2B, pp. 29-32 Standardized Test Questions, p. 36										

Other Chapter Resources

Student Edition

Case Study Follow-Up, p. 163
Decision Making, p. 116
Technology, p. 143

Other Supplements

Transparency 3-0 for Chapter Opener
Alternate Assessment in the Mathematics Classroom,
   Glencoe Publishing Co., 1993
Cooperative Learning in the Mathematics Classroom,
   Glencoe Publishing Co., 1993

Software

Test and Review Generator Software
   Available for Apple, IBM, and Macintosh
Teacher's Guide for Software Resources

ENHANCING THE CHAPTER

Cooperative Learning

Describing the Objectives

Before students engage in any cooperative-learning activity, it is important that you specify two types of objectives and make sure that both are clearly understood by all members of the groups. The first objective is the mathematical or content objective. For this you clearly describe the mathematical task or experiment that is to be completed. The second objective describes the cooperative-learning skills that will be emphasized during the activity. Examples of these skills include: stay with the group; use quiet voices; communicate support; encourage every-member participation; expand on other member's answers or explanations; criticize ideas, not people; and so on. Usually no more than one or two of these skills should be stressed per session while maintaining other skills that were introduced and emphasized earlier.

For more information on cooperative learning, see pages T20-T21. Additional information on using cooperative groups is available in Glencoe's *Cooperative Learning in the Mathematics Classroom*, ©1993.

Multicultural

Multicultural Activity Masters, p. 3

3 **Multicultural Activity** (Use after Lesson 3-2)

Luis W. Alvarez

Luis Alvarez (1911–) is an American physicist and inventor who has made remarkable contributions in many diverse fields. Among his inventions is a ground control approach radar system that has increased the safety of airplane landings and a variable-focus thin lens that has led to advances in the field of eye care. He also devised a way to use X-rays to search for hidden chambers in the pyramids of Egypt, produced an extensive study of the film of the assassination of President Kennedy, and collaborated in formulating the asteroid theory of dinosaur extinction. In 1968, Dr. Alvarez was awarded the Nobel Prize for physics.

In studying the Kennedy assassination film, Dr. Alvarez utilized several physical formulas. For example, to analyze the behavior of a bullet fired under given conditions, he used the family of functions given by the formula $p = \sqrt{2mk}$, where p is the momentum of a particle with mass m when it is propelled by k units of kinetic energy. When a numerical value is assigned to one of the variables m or k, p is a function of the other variable.

1. Sketch the graph of $p = \sqrt{2mk}$ for $m = 1$, $m = 2$, and $m = 3$.

2. Sketch the graph of $p = \sqrt{2mk}$ for $k = 10$, $k = 20$, and $k = 30$.

3. The graph at the right shows three members of a family of functions. Write an equation for each function. Then write an equation involving the variables x, y, and t to describe the complete family of functions.
$y = x^2$, $y = 2x^2$, $y = 3x^2$, $y = tx^2$

T 3
Glencoe Division, Macmillan/McGraw-Hill

Activity Masters

Applications, p. 7

3 **Applications** (Use after Lesson 3-4)

Finding Maximum or Minimum Values

Many problems require finding a maximum or minimum value. Such problems often can be solved by first writing a system of equations and then writing a function of one variable. By finding and classifying the critical points of the function, the maximum or minimum value is found. Diagrams are often helpful for writing the initial system of equations.

Example A road-salt storage shed is to be built with two square sides, a back, and a top. The shed is to be constructed of 900 square feet of corrugated steel. Find the dimensions for which the volume will be a maximum.

Let x represent the height and depth. Let y represent the width. Since the surface area is to be 900 square feet, $2x^2 + 2xy = 900$. Therefore, $y = \frac{450 - x^2}{x}$. The volume is given by $V = x^2y$. Substituting for y gives $V = 450x - x^3$. The critical values for V are $\pm\sqrt{150}$. When $x = \sqrt{150}$, there is a relative maximum for V. Therefore, $x = \sqrt{150} \approx 12.25$ and $y = \frac{450 - 150}{\sqrt{150}} \approx 24.5$. The dimensions for maximum volume are 12.25 feet by 12.25 feet by 24.5 feet.

Solve each problem.

1. A store owner wants to construct a 1000-square-foot rectangular display enclosure in the store's parking lot. Three sides are to be chainlink fencing which costs $9.00 per running foot. The fourth side is to be a brick wall which costs $18.75 per running foot. Find the dimensions that will minimize the cost.
length = 39.3 ft; width = 25.5 ft

2. Gloria wants to make a rectangular patio along the back of her house. She plans to surround the patio on three sides with one foot square flagstones. She has 118 flagstones. Find the maximum area of the patio not including the area of the flagstones.
1740.5 sq ft

T 7
Glencoe Division, Macmillan/McGraw-Hill

Problem Solving, p. 8

3 **Problem Solving** (Use after Lesson 3-1)

List the Possibilities

Lesson 3-1 discussed symmetry about the origin and symmetry with respect to four different lines. You can determine which types of symmetry, if any, characterize the graph of a function by making an organized list of possibilities.

Example Determine the symmetries of the graph of $y^2 = x^2 + 1$.

Each type of symmetry can be detected by substituting the coordinates of a test point in the function. If the function remains unaltered through substitution, the graph has the given symmetry.

Test for symmetry about:	Test point	Result of substitution in $y^2 = x^2 + 1$	Same?
x-axis	$(x, -y)$	$(-y)^2 = (x)^2 + 1$ $y^2 = x^2 + 1$	Yes
y-axis	$(-x, y)$	$(y)^2 = (-x)^2 + 1$ $y^2 = x^2 + 1$	Yes
origin	$(-x, -y)$	$(-y)^2 = (-x)^2 + 1$ $y^2 = x^2 + 1$	Yes
line $y = x$	(y, x)	$(x)^2 = (y)^2 + 1$ $x^2 = y^2 + 1$	No
line $y = -x$	$(-y, -x)$	$(-x)^2 = (-y)^2 + 1$ $x^2 = y^2 + 1$	No

The graph is symmetric with respect to the x-axis, the y-axis, and the origin.

Determine the symmetries, if any, of each graph by making an organized list of possibilities.

1. $y^2 = x^2$ x-axis, y-axis, origin, $y = x$, $y = -x$

2. $y^2 = x^3$ x-axis

3. $3y = \frac{5}{x}$ origin, $y = x$, $y = -x$

4. $|x| + |y| = 7$ x-axis, y-axis, origin, $y = x$, $y = -x$

5. $x^2 + y^2 = 25$ x-axis, y-axis, origin, $y = x$, $y = -x$

6. $y = 4x^2 + 3x + 1$ none

T 8
Glencoe Division, Macmillan/McGraw-Hill

Case Study Follow-Up, p. 9

3 **Case Study Follow-Up** (Use after Lesson 3-8)

Graphing Home-Sale Prices

Refer to Case Study 2: *Buying a Home*, on pages 959-961 in your textbook.

Because real-world data can rarely be collected constantly or continuously, graphs of such data are usually discontinuous. In order to analyze discontinuous data, mathematicians create continuous functions that model the data as closely as possible. Graphs of these functions can be studied like those of any function, used to understand the data they model, and used to predict future trends.

1. Graph the following data on a separate sheet of paper. Assume that the data are collected continuously and connect the points with a smooth curve.

Median Sales Price, New Privately Owned One-Family Houses Sold in the Western United States, 1970-1990

Year	Price $	Year	Price $	Year	Price $
1970	24,000	1977	53,500	1984	87,300
1971	25,500	1978	61,300	1985	92,600
1972	27,500	1979	69,600	1986	95,700
1973	32,400	1980	72,300	1987	111,000
1974	35,800	1981	77,800	1988	126,500
1975	40,600	1982	75,000	1989	139,000
1976	47,200	1983	80,100	1990	148,000

See students' work.

2. Compare the median sales price of new privately owned one-family houses in the Western United States in 1980 with the median sales price nationwide that same year.
Homes in the western United States averaged $7700 higher.

Assume that f is a continuous function that models the data.

3. In which interval(s) does f increase? In which interval(s) does it decrease?
increase: 1970-1981, 1982-1990; decrease: 1981-1982

4. Identify the critical points of the function.
relative maximum, 1981; relative minimum, 1982; possible points of inflection, 1980, 1985

5. Where would you expect the derivative of f to equal zero? 1981, 1982

T 9
Glencoe Division, Macmillan/McGraw-Hill

The Technology feature following Lesson 3-4 uses *The Function Analyzer* to generate graphs of functions and find equations of asymptotes. *The Function Analyzer* is a graphing program that is able to represent holes that sometimes occur in the graphs of rational functions.

This chapter makes extensive use of the graphing calculator. In Lesson 3-1, students are introduced to the TRACE function of the calculator to estimate the coordinates of any point on a graph. The graphing calculator is used to determine whether a function is odd or even. Students learn to compare members of a family of graphs by graphing all the functions on the same screen. In Lesson 3-4, students learn how to recognize asymptotes that appear on the screen of a graphing calculator. In Lesson 3-7, they learn to estimate critical points of the graphs of polynomial functions. Exercises throughout the chapter give students the opportunity to use a graphing calculator to more fully understand the nature of graphs.

Graphing Calculator Exercises, pp. 114, 123, 130, 147, 154, 162, 170
Graphing Calculator Program, p. 115

Books/Periodicals

Dion, Gloria. The Graphics Calculator. A Tool for Critical Thinking, *Mathematics Teacher*, Vol. 83 (October 1990), pp. 564-571.

The Spode Group. *Motivating A-Level Mathematics,* Oxford University Press, New York, New York, 1986.

Films/Videotapes/Videodiscs

Mathematics: College Algebra. Great Plains National, University of Nebraska-Lincoln

Software

Graphing utilities (see list on page T25)

The Function Analyzer, Wings for Learning/Sunburst (IBM)

Graphing Calculator, p. 5

Computer, p. 6

CHAPTER 3

THE NATURE OF GRAPHS

HISTORICAL SNAPSHOT

	Chiu-Chang Suan-Shu, or Nine Chapters on the Mathematical Art, China	Sphygmomanometer (blood pressure device) Dr. Scipione Riva, Italy	Department of Biomedical Engineering established at Duke University
First medical diagnosis Hippocrates of Greece		Stethoscope with wood-turned cylinder Rene Laennec, France	Defibrillator (to restore heart rhythm) Johns Hopkins University	Artificial Heart Dr. Robert Jarvik Utah Medical Center

| 460 BC | 250 BC | AD 1816 | 1896 | 1932 | 1970 | 1982 |

102

CHAPTER OBJECTIVES

In this chapter, you will:

- Graph relations and functions.
- Analyze families of graphs.
- Study about symmetry, continuity, and transformations of graphs.
- Find asymptotes, intercepts, and critical points of graphs.

CAREER GOAL: Biomedical Research

Around the world, more than 3 million people live with artificial body parts. Sheila Chuang wants to be a part of this emerging technology. As a biomedical researcher, Sheila wants "to help people and to have an impact on the health system." She is also considering going to medical school because "I dream of developing and implanting artificial organs."

Sheila wanted to choose a field that would combine her love for mathematics with her interests in chemistry and biology. She found that "biomedical engineering provided the challenge of engineering, yet it was the one area of engineering that seemed to have the most direct contact with human beings."

Biomedical researchers use mathematics in many ways. For example, Sheila says, "After angioplasty to open up a clogged artery, a permanent metal *stent* is implanted to hold the artery open. Duke is currently working on the development of a bioabsorbable stent that will degrade over time and be eliminated by the body. However, we want to be able to put drugs into the stent for delivery into the body. We use graphs to measure the rate at which a given drug will be delivered by the stent."

One summer, Sheila worked in biomechanics under a fellowship from the University of Minnesota Biomedical Engineering Center. She worked with orthopedic surgeons on advances in prostheses for knees and hips, like the one shown in the photo. She says, "I really saw the close relationship between biomedical engineering and medicine."

Most biomedical experts agree that sometime in the near future, an artificial part will be able to take the place of almost any part of the human anatomy, except the brain. Sheila says, "Biomedical engineering is a new and growing field, and it is really neat to be a part of it!"

READ MORE ABOUT IT

Cradts-Lighty, Anita. *Information Sources in Biotechnology.* Stockton, California: Stockton Press, 1986.

Plantz, Scott H. *Getting Into Medical School: Strategies for the 90's.* New York: Prentice Hall, 1990.

Swanson, Barbara M. *Careers in Health Care.* Homewood, Illinois: Dow Jones-Irwin, 1984.

SPOTLIGHT ON...

Sheila Chuang
Age: 20
Class: Junior
School: Duke University
   Durham, North Carolina
Major: Biomedical Engineering

"Biomedical engineering is a new and growing field, and it is really neat to be a part of it."

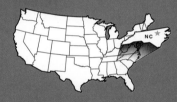

FOR MORE INFORMATION

If you would like more information about biomedical engineering, contact:

Biomedical Engineering
   Society
P.O. Box 2399
Culver City, CA 90231

Applications

Lesson	Application	Examples	Exercises
3–1	Astronomy	4	
	Physics		43
	Gardening		44
3–2	Business	3	
	Service		
	Charges		33
	Geometry		34
3–3	Academics		31
	Fire Fighting		32
3–4	Physics	3	42
	Amusements		40
	Music		41
3–5	Manufacturing	4	
	Woodworking		34
	Elections		35
3–6	Amusement	3	
	Physics		44
	Entertainment		45
3–7	Aviation	1	
	Manufacturing	5	
	Horticulture		33
	Agriculture		34
3–8	Manufacturing		35
	Government		36

INTRODUCING THE LESSON

Objective Graph polynomial functions and approximate the real zeros of the function.

Motivating the Lesson

Have students find various ordered pairs that satisfy the equation $y = x^2 - 4x + 4$. Have them graph these ordered pairs and connect them with a smooth curve. Discuss how the graphing calculator could help them save time and increase their accuracy.

TEACHING THE LESSON

Teaching Tip It may be helpful to remind students of the meaning of *a zero of a function*. Have them review concepts in Chapters 1 and 2 if they do not remember the meaning.

Teaching Tip Ask students what they might know about the graph of a cubic function before using a graphing calculator in Example 1.

More Examples

1. Graph $f(x) = x^5 - 3x - 1$ so that a complete graph is shown. Then approximate each of the real zeros to the nearest hundredth.

−1.21, −0.33, 1.39

3-1A Graphing Calculators: Graphing Polynomial Functions

You can use a graphing calculator to graph polynomial functions and approximate the real zeros of a function. When using a graphing calculator to approximate zeros, it is important to view a complete graph of the function before zooming in on a certain point. Zeros may be overlooked if they are not in the original viewing window. A complete graph of a polynomial function shows all of the important characteristics of the graph, such as all the x- and y-intercepts, all relative minimum and maximum points, and the end behavior of the graph.

Example 1

Graph $f(x) = 2x^3 + 5x^2 - 8x + 4$ so that a complete graph appears. Then approximate each of the real zeros to the nearest hundredth.

First, graph the function in the standard viewing window.

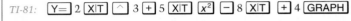

TI-81: [Y=] 2 [X|T] [^] 3 [+] 5 [X|T] [x²] [−] 8 [X|T] [+] 4 [GRAPH]

Casio: [Graph] 2 [ALPHA] [X] [xʸ] 3 [+] 5
[ALPHA] [X] [x²] [−] 8
[ALPHA] [X] [+] 4 [EXE]

This viewing window does not accommodate a complete graph because the relative maximum cannot be seen. Change the viewing window to [−5, 4] by [−5, 30] with a scale factor of 1 for the x-axis and a scale factor of 5 for the y-axis. Regraph by pressing [GRAPH] on the TI-81 and [EXE] on the Casio.

This viewing window accommodates the complete graph. We can tell by the graph that there is exactly one real zero. Tracing and zooming in reveals that the real zero is approximately −3.72.

The function in Example 1 is a third-degree function because the highest power of x in the equation is 3. A third-degree function has three zeros. For a second-degree function, the highest power of x in the equation is 2, and a second-degree function has two zeros, and so on. When using your graphing calculator to approximate real zeros, it is helpful to know that a function of degree n has n zeros. The zeros may not all be real, however. Complex zeros, or imaginary zeros, occur in conjugate pairs, but they do not lie on the x-axis in the coordinate plane.

You can always determine the number of real zeros of a function by finding the number of times the graph crosses the x-axis. Functions of odd degree must have at least one real zero because they must cross the x-axis at least once. Looking at various graphs of linear and cubic equations can illustrate this point. Functions of even degree, however, may not have any real roots and may not cross the x-axis at all. The graph of a parabola, such as $y = x^2 + 4$, is one such function. Graphs of polynomial functions of degree 2 or higher can cross the x-axis more than once.

More Examples

Example 2

Graph $p(x) = x^4 - 3x^3 - 7x^2 - x + 2$ so that a complete graph is shown. Then approximate each of the real zeros to the nearest hundredth.

First, try the standard viewing window.

A complete graph is not shown in the standard viewing window. Try changing the range to $[-4, 6]$ by $[-70, 10]$ with a scale factor of 1 for the x-axis and a scale factor of 10 for the y-axis.

This shows a complete graph. Now trace and zoom in on the real zeros. They are $-1, 4.56,$ and 0.44 to the nearest hundredth.

More Examples

2. Graph $f(x) = x^4 - 5x^2 + 7$ so that a complete graph is shown. Then approximate each of the real zeros to the nearest hundredth.

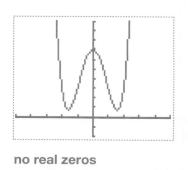

no real zeros

EVALUATING THE LESSON

Closing the Lesson

Ask students if there is a connection between the degree of the polynomial function and the maximum number of real zeros of the function.

APPLYING THE LESSON

Homework Exercises

Assignment Guide

All: 1–10

Additional Answers

For graphs for Exercises 1–10, see Teacher's Answer Key.

EXERCISES

Graph each function so that a complete graph is shown. Then approximate each of the real zeros to the nearest hundredth and sketch the graph on a piece of paper.

6. 0.22, 0.76, 6.03

7. $-5.33, -0.71, -0.39, 1.39$

1. $f(x) = x^5 + 2x^2 - 4$ 1.10

2. $h(x) = x^4 - 3x^3 + x - 4$ $-1.08, 3.05$

3. $p(x) = 3x^3 + 4x^2 - 8$ 1.06

4. $m(x) = 2x^4 - 3x^2 + 9$ none

5. $g(x) = x^3 - 2x^2 - 3x + 6$ $-1.73, 1.75, 1.89$

6. $f(x) = x^3 - 7x^2 + 6x - 1$

7. $r(x) = x^4 + 5x^3 - 3x^2 - 7x - 2$

8. $g(x) = 4x^4 + 7x + 2$ $-1.08, -0.29$

9. $q(x) = x^5 + 2x^4 - 11x^3 + 4x^2 - 3x + 4$ $-4.61, 0.76, 2.24$

10. $p(x) = -x^5 - 3x^4 + 9x^3 + 18x^2 - 7x - 13$ $-4.04, -1.51, -0.88, 0.91, 2.59$

NCTM Standards: 1–8

Lesson Resources

- Practice Master 3–1
- Enrichment Master 3–1

 Transparency 3–1 contains the 5-Minute Check and a teaching aid for this lesson.

INTRODUCING THE LESSON

5–Minute Check

(over Chapter 2)

1. Solve the system of equations.
   $x + y = 2$
   $3x = y - 10$ (–2, 4)

2. If $A = \begin{bmatrix} -3 & 4 \\ 2 & 7 \end{bmatrix}$ and $B = \begin{bmatrix} -1 & 5 \\ -3 & 2 \end{bmatrix}$,
   find $A + B$.
   $\begin{bmatrix} -4 & 9 \\ -1 & 9 \end{bmatrix}$

3. Find the value of $\begin{vmatrix} 5 & -4 \\ -3 & 9 \end{vmatrix}$.   33

4. Solve the system of equations by using augmented matrices.
   $x + y - 2z = -7$
   $2x - y - z = 4$
   $-x + 2y + 3z = -3$ (1, –4, 2)

5. Solve the system of inequalities by graphing. Then name the vertices of the polygonal convex set.
   $x \geq 0, y \geq 0$
   $y \leq x + 2$
   $y \leq -x + 8$
   (0, 0), (0, 2), (3, 5), (8, 0)

Motivating the Lesson

Symmetry is a familiar notion to many students. Open the lesson by bringing old magazines to class and have students pick out interesting photographs that display various types of symmetry.

3-1 Symmetry

Objectives
3–1A
3–1B
3–1C

After studying this lesson, you should be able to:
- identify symmetrical graphs,
- use symmetry to complete a graph, and
- identify an odd function and an even function.

Application

 FYI...

Butterflies cannot fly if their body temperature is less than 86° F. They warm themselves in the sun or flutter their wings while perched to generate enough body heat to fly when the air temperature is below 86°.

One of the smallest butterflies is the Western Pygmy Blue butterfly of North America. Its wingspan is only 1 centimeter. The largest butterfly, the Queen Alexandra Birdwing butterfly of Papua, New Guinea, has a wingspan of 28 centimeters. All butterflies have wings that are symmetrical.

A knowledge of symmetry can often help you sketch and analyze graphs. A graph may have **point symmetry**, **line symmetry**, neither, or both. If a graph has point or line symmetry, you can plot points to sketch part of the graph, then use symmetry to sketch the rest.

Point Symmetry

> **Two distinct points P and P' are symmetric with respect to a point, M, if and only if M is the midpoint of $\overline{PP'}$. Point M is symmetric with respect to itself.**

When the definition of symmetry is extended to a set of points, it must be true for each point in the set. A figure with point symmetry can be turned about a center point and, in less than a full turn, the image coincides with the original figure. Each of the figures below has point symmetry with respect to the point labeled in the diagram.

Symmetry with respect to a given point M can also be expressed as symmetry about point M.

The graph of a function is a set of points. The graph of a function may or may not have point symmetry.

ALTERNATE TEACHING STRATEGIES

Using Critical Thinking

Which regular polygons with eight or less sides have point symmetry? line symmetry?

point: triangle, square, pentagon, hexagon, heptagon, octagon;
line: triangle, square, pentagon, hexagon, heptagon, octagon

Using Manipulatives

Have students create shapes that have either line or point symmetry. Encourage them to manipulate the shapes in order to explore their symmetries. This could include folding the shapes or turning them about a fixed axis. Making shapes out of waxed paper is very convenient for doing folding exercises.

EXPLORATION: Paper Folding

Determine if the graph of $f(x) = x - 3$ has point symmetry about the x-intercept 3.

1. Graph the function.
2. Draw a vertical line, v, through the x-intercept parallel to the y-axis. Fold the graph paper along the x-axis. Then fold it along line v.
3. Hold the paper up to the light. Notice that the part of the graph above the x-axis now matches up with the part of the graph below the x-axis. This shows that the graph of $f(x)$ has point symmetry about the x-intercept.

One of the most common points of symmetry is the origin. Observe that the graph of $f(x) = \frac{1}{x}$, shown below, has symmetry with respect to the origin. Use this table to compare the range of $f(x)$ when the domain is positive with the range of $f(x)$ when the domain is negative.

$f(x), x > 0$	$f(x), x < 0$
$f(1) = 1$	$f(-1) = -1$
$f(2) = \frac{1}{2}$	$f(-2) = -\frac{1}{2}$
$f(3) = \frac{1}{3}$	$f(-3) = -\frac{1}{3}$
$f(4) = \frac{1}{4}$	$f(-4) = -\frac{1}{4}$
$f(n) = \frac{1}{n}, n \neq 0$	$f(-n) = -\frac{1}{n}, n \neq 0$

The values in the table above suggest that $f(-x) = -f(x)$, when a function is symmetric with respect to the origin.

Symmetry with Respect to the Origin	**The graph of a relation S is symmetric with respect to the origin if and only if $(-a, -b) \in S$ whenever $(a, b) \in S$. A function $f(x)$ has a graph that is symmetric with respect to the origin if and only if $f(-x) = -f(x)$.**

∈ means belongs to.

You can verify symmetry with respect to the origin algebraically, as shown in Example 1.

Prerequisite Skills

Students should be familiar with the concept of reflections.

1. Find the image of P reflected over line m.

2. Find the image of triangle ABC reflected over line m.

TEACHING THE LESSON

Teaching Tip After discussing the figures with symmetry, encourage students to come up with other examples of symmetry about a point M. Include a discussion of any symmetries in arbitrary curves that students may draw.

Teaching Tip After defining *function*, remind students that each element in the domain of a function is paired with exactly one element in the range.

Teaching Tip Use the methods in the Exploration to find line symmetry in other figures and functions. Paperfolding can also be used to create figures with symmetry.

Using Technology

Demonstrate the function $f(x) = \frac{1}{x}$ by using technology. Use the TRACE features of a graphing calculator or computer to compare the range of $f(x)$ when the domain is positive versus the range of $f(x)$ when the domain is negative.

Teaching Tip After defining *symmetry with respect to the origin*, students may need to see several numerical examples to help them understand the difference between $f(-x)$ and $-f(x)$. For example, if $f(x) = x^2 - 2x - 1$, then $f(-x) = x^2 + 2x - 1$, while $-f(x) = -x^2 + 2x + 1$.

Chalkboard Examples

For Example 1

Determine whether the graph of $f(x) = x^6$ is symmetric with respect to the origin.   **no**

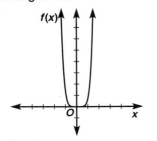

Example 1

Determine whether the graph of $f(x) = x^5$ is symmetric with respect to the origin.

The graph of $f(x) = x^5$ appears to be symmetric with respect to the origin. Verify this algebraically.

$$f(x) = x^5$$
$f(-x) = (-x)^5$ *Replace x with -x.*
$f(-x) = -(x^5)$
$f(-x) = -f(x)$ *Replace x^5 with f(x).*

Since $f(-x) = -f(x)$, the graph of $f(x) = x^5$ is symmetric with respect to the origin.

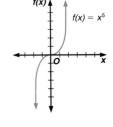

Another type of symmetry is line symmetry.

Line Symmetry

Two distinct points P and P' are symmetric with respect to a line ℓ if and only if ℓ is the perpendicular bisector of $\overline{PP'}$. A point P is symmetric to itself with respect to line ℓ if and only if P is on ℓ.

Each of the graphs below has line symmetry. The equation of each line of symmetry is given. Graphs that have line symmetry can be folded along the line of symmetry so that the two halves match exactly. Some graphs, such as the graph of an ellipse, have more than one line of symmetry.

$x = 0$

$y = 7$

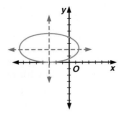

$x = -3$ and $y = 2$

Some common lines of symmetry are the x-axis, the y-axis, the line $y = x$, and the line $y = -x$. The following table shows how the coordinates of symmetric points are related for each of these common lines of symmetry.

Teaching Tip Before defining each type of symmetry listed on this page, point out that S is the set of points making up the graph itself.

Symmetry with Respect to	Definition	Sample Graph
x-axis	$(a, -b) \in S$ if and only if $(a, b) \in S$. Example: $(2, \sqrt{6})$, and $(2, -\sqrt{6})$ are on the graph.	 $x = y^2 - 4$
y-axis	$(-a, b) \in S$ if and only if $(a, b) \in S$. Example: $(2, 8)$ and $(-2, 8)$ are on the graph.	 $y = -x^2 + 12$
the line $y = x$	$(b, a) \in S$ if and only if $(a, b) \in S$. Example: $(2, 3)$ and $(3, 2)$ are on the graph.	 $xy = 6$
the line $y = -x$	$(-b, -a) \in S$ if and only if $(a, b) \in S$. Example: $(4, 5)$ and $(-5, -4)$ are on the graph.	 $y = -x$

LESSON 3-1 SYMMETRY 109

Example 2

**Determine whether the graph of
$f(x) = x^4 + 3x^2 + 8$ is symmetric with
respect to the x-axis, the y-axis, neither,
or both.**

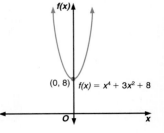

The graph appears to be symmetric with
respect to the y-axis, but not the x-axis.

Test for symmetry with respect to
the x-axis. For the graph of $f(x)$ to be
symmetric with respect to the x-axis,
point (a, b) is on the graph if and only if
point $(a, -b)$ is on the graph.

Suppose $a = 2$. Then $b = 2^4 + 3(2)^2 + 8$ or 36, and $-b = -36$. The point $(2, 36)$
is on the graph. However, $(2, -36)$ cannot be on the graph since b is never
negative. While a single point cannot show symmetry, it can show that
symmetry does not exist. Thus, there is no symmetry with respect to the
x-axis.

Test for symmetry with respect to the y-axis. For the graph of $f(x)$ to be
symmetric with respect to the y-axis, point (a, b) is on the graph if and only
if point $(-a, b)$ is on the graph.

For a: $b = a^4 + 3a^2 + 8$
For $-a$: $b = (-a)^4 + 3(-a)^2 + 8$
$= a^4 + 3a^2 + 8$

So, in general, point $(-a, b)$ is on the graph if and only if point (a, b) is on the
graph. Thus, the graph is symmetric with respect to the y-axis.

The line $y = x$ includes the origin and forms a 45° angle with both the x- and
y-axes. It has a slope of 1. The line $y = -x$ also includes the origin and forms a
45° angle with both the axes, but its slope is -1.

Example 3

**Determine whether the graph of the function
$xy = 6$ is symmetric with respect to the line
$y = x$, the line $y = -x$, neither, or both.**

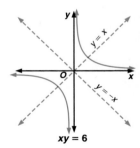

If the graph is symmetric with repect to the
line $y = x$, (a, b) and (b, a) must both be on the
graph. The point (a, b) is on the graph if $ab = 6$.
The point (b, a) is on the graph if $ba = 6$. Since
both of these statements are true, the graph is
symmetric with respect to the line $y = x$.

If the graph is symmetric with respect to the line $y = -x$, (a, b) and $(-b, -a)$ must both be on the graph. The point (a, b) is on the graph if $ab = 6$. The point $(-b, -a)$ is on the graph if $(-b)(-a) = 6$. But $(-b)(-a) = ba$ and $ba = ab$. So both of these statements are true, and the graph is symmetric with respect to the line $y = -x$.

Symmetry can be used to sketch the graph of a function. If you have part of the graph and know what types of symmetry the function has, the rest of the graph can be sketched without graphing more ordered pairs.

Example 4

APPLICATION

Astronomy

The path of a moon orbiting a planet can be modeled by the graph of an ellipse with the equation $\dfrac{x^2}{25} + \dfrac{y^2}{16} = 1$. The graph is symmetric with respect to both the x- and y-axes. If the moon travels through $(5, 0)$, $(0, -4)$, and $(-3, -3.2)$ on the model, complete a sketch of the path of the moon.

Graph the given ordered pairs.

Since the graph is symmetric with respect to the x-axis, every point on one side of the x-axis has a corresponding point on the other side of the axis.

$$(0, -4) \quad \rightarrow \quad (0, 4)$$
$$(-3, -3.2) \quad \rightarrow \quad (-3, 3.2)$$

Graph these ordered pairs.

Since the graph is symmetric with respect to the y-axis, every point on either side of the y-axis has a corresponding point on the other side of the axis.

$$(-3, -3.2) \quad \rightarrow \quad (3, -3.2)$$
$$(-3, 3.2) \quad \rightarrow \quad (3, 3.2)$$
$$(5, 0) \quad \rightarrow \quad (-5, 0)$$

Graph these ordered pairs.
Connect all the points to form the ellipse.

LESSON 3-1   SYMMETRY   111

Using Technology

Stress that in order to use the approach shown in the Exploration for any function, students should find numerous examples of points that suggest symmetry. Then they should *always* verify the symmetry algebraically.

Additional Answers

2.

4. Each term containing *x* has an even power. When evaluating the function, this always results in a positive number. A positive number is added to this. This result must always be positive.

14.

14a. (3, −4)	14b. (−3, 4)
14c. (4, 3)	14d. (−4, −3)

15.

15a. (−2, 5)	15b. (2, −5)
15c. (−5, −2)	15d. (5, 2)

16.

16a. (4, 8)	16b. (−4, −8)
16c. (−8, 4)	16d. (8, −4)

You will learn more about polynomial functions in Lesson 4.1.

Functions whose graphs are symmetric with respect to the *y*-axis are **even functions**. If a function of the form $f(x) = a_0x^n + a_1x^{n-1} + \ldots + a_{n-2}x^2 + a_{n-1}x + a_n$, called a polynomial function, has exponents that are all even, then the function is an even function. Functions whose graphs are symmetric with respect to the origin are **odd functions**. Odd polynomial functions have exponents that are all odd. Some functions are neither even nor odd.

even functions
$f(-x) = f(x)$

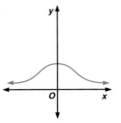

odd functions
$f(-x) = -f(x)$

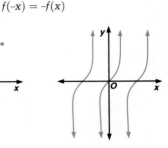

You can check whether a function is odd, even, or neither by using the TRACE feature on a graphing calculator.

EXPLORATION: Graphing Calculator

Determine whether $f(x) = x^8 - 3x^4 + 2x^2 + 2$ is odd, even, or neither.

1. Press the $\boxed{Y=}$ key and enter the equation. Press $\boxed{\text{GRAPH}}$.

2. The graph appears to be symmetric about the *y*-axis. Check this by determining whether $f(-x) = f(x)$. Use the TRACE function.

   X= .94736842   Y=2.0273182
   X=−.94736842   Y=2.0273182

   These are sample comparisons.

3. It appears that $f(-x) = f(x)$. Verify this algebraically.

$$f(x) = x^8 - 3x^4 + 2x^2 + 2$$
$$f(-x) = (-x)^8 - 3(-x)^4 + 2(-x)^2 + 2 \quad \text{\textit{Replace x with −x.}}$$
$$f(-x) = x^8 - 3x^4 + 2x^2 + 2 \quad \text{\textit{Simplify.}}$$
$$f(-x) = f(x) \quad \text{\textit{Replace } x^8 - 3x^4 + 2x^2 + 2 \text{ with } f(x).}$$

The graph is symmetric about the *y*-axis and all the exponents of the polynomial are even. So, $f(x) = x^8 - 3x^4 + 2x^2 + 2$ is an even function.

CHECKING FOR UNDERSTANDING

Communicating Mathematics

Read and study the lesson to answer each question.

1. **Tell** what point is one of the most common points of symmetry. the origin
2. **Sketch** a graph that has more than one line of symmetry. See margin.
3. **Complete** each sentence.
   a. If a graph of a function $f(x)$ is symmetric with respect to the origin, then $f(-x) = $? . $-f(x)$
   b. If a graph of a function $f(x)$ is symmetric with respect to the y-axis, then $f(-x) = $? . $f(x)$
   c. The line $y = x$ forms a ? angle with both the x- and y-axes. $45°$
4. **Explain** why $f(x)$ cannot be negative in Example 2. See margin.

Guided Practice

State whether each figure has point symmetry, line symmetry, neither, or both.

5.

both

6.

neither

7.

point

8.

both

9.

line

10.

line

Determine the line(s) of symmetry for each graph.

11.
(2, 3)
$x = 2$

12.
(−2, −5)
$y = -5$

13.
(2, −2)
$x = 2, y = -2$

Graph each point. Then graph and record the coordinates of the point P' for each of the following conditions: P and P' are symmetric with respect to (a) the x-axis, (b) the y-axis, (c) the line $y = x$, and (d) the line $y = -x$. 14–16. See margin.

14. $P(3, 4)$ 15. $P(-2, -5)$ 16. $P(4, -8)$

LESSON 3-1 SYMMETRY 113

RETEACHING THE LESSON

Have students work in cooperative groups to determine the point and/or line symmetries for each graph below.

$y = x$

point (0, 0)

EVALUATING THE LESSON

Checking for Understanding

Exercises 1–16 are designed to help you assess students' understanding through reading, writing, speaking, and modeling. You should work through Exercises 1–4 with your students and then monitor their work on Exercises 5–16.

Closing the Lesson

Writing Activity Write a paragraph discussing when a relation is symmetric with respect to the x-axis, the y-axis, the line $y = x$, or the line $y = -x$.

Practice Masters Booklet, p. 13

3-1 NAME _____ DATE _____
Practice Worksheet

Symmetry

Find the coordinates of P' if P and P' are symmetric with respect to point M.

1. $P(-7, 4)$, $M(0, 0)$
   $(7, -4)$
2. $P(5, 4)$, $M(-3, 2)$
   $(-11, 0)$
3. $P(-5, 5)$, $M(10, 12)$
   $(25, 19)$

The graphs below are portions of complete graphs. Sketch a complete graph for each of the following symmetries: with respect to (a) the x-axis, (b) the y-axis, (c) the line y = x, and (d) the line y = −x.

4.
5.
6.

Determine if each function is an even function, an odd function, or neither.

7. $y = x^2 + x - 2$
   neither
8. $y = \sqrt{4x^2 - 25}$
   even
9. $y = -2x^7 + x^5 - x^3$
   odd

Determine whether the graph of each equation is symmetric with respect to the origin, the x-axis, the y-axis, the line y = x, or the line y = −x.

10. $xy = -12$
    $y = x$, origin
11. $y = \pm\sqrt{x + 6}$
    x-axis
12. $y^2 = \frac{x^2}{9} - 16$
    x-axis, y-axis, origin

T13
Glencoe Division, Macmillan/McGraw-Hill

Assignment Guide

Average: 17–33, 38, 40–43, 45–51
Enriched: 17, 20, 23, 41, 42, 44–51

The red A, B, and C flags, printed only in the Teacher's Wraparound Edition, indicate the level of difficulty of the exercises.

Using Technology

For Exercises 37–39, remind students that they may need to adjust the range intervals in order to see a complete graph. They can start with the standard intervals for their calculators and make adjustments as necessary. In Exercise 39, BOX refers to a specific zoom feature on some graphing calculators.

Additional Answers

20. a.

b.

c.

d.

21. a.

b.

c.

d.

EXERCISES

Practice Find the coordinates of P' if P and P' are symmetric with respect to point M.

17. $P(-2, -2), M(1, 1)$
$P'(4, 4)$

18. $P(-3, 2), M(0, 0)$
$P'(3, -2)$

19. $P(-3, 7), M(-3, 1)$
$P'(-3, -5)$

The graphs below are portions of complete graphs. Sketch a complete graph for each of the following symmetries: with respect to (a) the x-axis, (b) the y-axis, (c) the line $y = x$, and (d) the line $y = -x$. 20–25. See margin.

20.

21.

22.

23.

24.

25.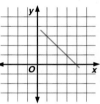

Determine whether each function is an even function, an odd function, or neither.

27. neither

26. $y = x^5 - 4x$ odd

27. $y = 6x^3 - 3x + 5$

28. $y = x^2 - 64$ even

29. $y = 6 - 6x^2 + x^8$ even

30. $y = 5x^2 + 6x - 9$
neither

31. $y = -3x^9 + 4x^5$
odd

Determine whether the graph of each equation is symmetric with respect to the origin, the x-axis, the y-axis, the line $y = x$, or the line $y = -x$.

33. y-axis

34. x-axis

32. $y = -6x$ origin

33. $y = 6x^4 - 3x^2 + 1$

34. $x = y^2 + 4$

35. $y = 2x^9 - 7x^2 + 4$
no symmetry

36. $x^2 + y^2 = 9$ all

37. $y^2 = \dfrac{4x^2}{9} - 4$
x-axis, y-axis, origin

Graphing Calculator

Use a graphing calculator to graph each function and determine any lines of symmetry. 38–40. For graphs, see margin.

38. $y = -(x - 2)^{-2}$ $x = 2$

39. $y = \dfrac{4x^2}{1 + x^2}$ $x = 0$

40. Graph $y = \dfrac{1}{4}x^2 - x + 1$ and $y = x^2 - 7$ on the same screen. Use the ZOOM and TRACE functions to determine their points of intersection.
Answers are approximate: $(-3.9, 8.2)$, $(2.8, 0.8)$.

Critical Thinking
41. Plot points to graph the parabola whose equation is $y = 3x^2 - 4x - 4$ and the circle whose equation is $(x - 2)^2 + (y - 4)^2 = 16$. One of the points of intersection of these two graphs is at $(2, 0)$. Do you expect another point of intersection to be at $(-2, 0)$? Why or why not? See margin.

22. a. $(-2, 1)$, $(-2, -1)$

b. $(-2, 1)$, $(2, 1)$

c. $(-2, 1)$

d. $(-2, 1)$, $(1, 2)$, $(1, -2)$

23. a. $(-1, 3)$, $(-3, -1)$

b. $(-1, 3)$, $(1, 3)$

c. $(-1, 3)$

d. $(-3, 3)$, $(3, -1)$

42. The following program can be used to check whether a function is even, odd, or neither. The function to be checked must be in Y_1. You may get an error message if –A is not in the domain of the function. If this occurs, the function is neither even nor odd.

```
Prgm 3: ODDREVEN
:ClrHome
:Disp "X-COOR OF POINT ON GRAPH"
:Disp "(NOT 1 OR 0)"
:Input A
:A → X            Stores the value of A in X.
:Y₁ → B           Calculates Y₁, stores in B.
:-A → X           Stores the opposite of A in X.
:Y₁ → C           Calculates Y₁, stores in C.
:If B = C         If f(A) = f(– A),
:Disp "EVEN FUNCTION"   calculator displays the message.
:If B = C         If f(A) = f(– A),
:Goto 1           program goes to line "Lbl 1."
:If C = -B        If f(– A) = – f(A),
:Disp "ODD FUNCTION"    calculator displays the message.
:If C = -B        If f(– A) = – f(A),
:Goto 1           program goes to line "Lbl 1."
:Disp "NOT ODD OR EVEN"
:Lbl 1
:End
```

Determine whether each function is an even function, an odd function, or neither.
a. $y = x + 1$ neither **b.** $y = 3x^9 + 4x^7 - x^3 + 2x$ odd

Applications and Problem Solving

43. Physics The light pattern from a fog light at the airport can be modeled by the equation $\frac{x^2}{4} - \frac{y^2}{16} = 1$. One of the points on the graph is at (3,4.5), and one of the x-intercepts is –2. Find the coordinates of three additional points on the graph and the other x-intercept. x-intercept: $(2, 0)$; other points: $(-3, 4.5), (3, -4.5), (-3, -4.5)$

44. Gardening A garden containing flowers called impatiens is planted in a region shaped like a parabola. Since impatiens grow better in shade, the gardener is designing a circular arbor for a climbing vine that will be placed above the garden. Four posts, placed on the circle, support the arbor. The gardener models this plan with the graphs of a circle whose equation is $x^2 + y^2 = 25$ and a parabola whose equation is $y = x^2 - 6$. The two poles are positioned at (3.2, 3.9) and (1.1, –4.9). Find the coordinates of the position of the other two poles. $(-3.2, 3.9)$ and $(-1.1, -4.9)$

LESSON 3-1 SYMMETRY 115

Using Technology

The program given in Exercise 42 is for use with a TI-81 graphing calculator. For other programmable calculators, have students consult their owner's manual for commands similar to those presented here.

Additional Answers

38.

39.

40.

41. No, neither the parabola nor the circle are symmetric with respect to the y-axis, so they do not follow the rules for points with that symmetry.

24.
a.   b.

c. d.

25.
a.   b.

c. d.

Mixed Review

45. 1, 3
47. Parallel; the lines have the same slope.

45. Find $[f \circ g](4)$ and $[g \circ f](4)$ if $f(x) = x^2 - 4x + 5$ and $g(x) = x - 2$. **(Lesson 1-2)**

46. Find the coordinates of the midpoint of $\overline{FG}$ given its endpoints $F(-3, -2)$ and $G(8, 4)$. **(Lesson 1-4)** $(2.5, 1)$

47. The slope of $\overleftrightarrow{AB}$ is 0.6. The slope of $\overleftrightarrow{CD}$ is $\frac{3}{5}$. State whether the lines are parallel, perpendicular, or neither. Explain. **(Lesson 1-6)**

48. Find the multiplicative inverse of $\begin{bmatrix} 8 & -3 \\ 4 & -5 \end{bmatrix}$. **(Lesson 2-3)** $\frac{1}{28}\begin{bmatrix} 5 & -3 \\ 4 & -8 \end{bmatrix}$

49. Use matrices to solve the system of equations. **(Lesson 2-4)**
$$8m - 3n - 4p = 6$$
$$4m + 9n - 2p = -4 \quad \left(\frac{3}{4}, -\frac{2}{3}, \frac{1}{2}\right)$$
$$6m + 12n + 5p = -1$$

a. $a \geq 0, b \geq 0, 4a + b \leq 32, a + 6b \leq 54$

50. Retail Amanda Haines, a sales associate at a paint store, plans to mix as many gallons as possible of colors A and B. She has exactly 32 units of blue dye and 54 units of red dye. Each gallon of color A requires 4 units of blue dye and 1 unit of red dye. Each gallon of color B requires 1 unit of blue dye and 6 units of red dye. Use linear programming to answer the following questions. **(Lesson 2-6)**

   a. Let a be the number of gallons of color A and let b be the number of gallons of color B. Write the inequalities that describe this situation.

   b. Find the maximum number of gallons possible. 14 gallons

51. College Entrance Exam Student A is 15 years old. Student B is one-third older. How many years ago was student B twice as old as student A? 10

DECISION MAKING

The Ozone Layer

Earth's ozone layer blocks ultraviolet rays that can cause skin cancer and other serious environmental hazards. Many scientists believe that some commonly-used chemicals, especially chlorofluorocarbons (CFCs), are destroying the ozone layer. What are your responsibilities as a citizen in the face of this evidence? How can we weigh the benefits that would accrue from banning CFCs against the financial losses that companies which produce CFCs will suffer?

1. Research the evidence for ozone-layer destruction by CFCs and other chemicals.

2. If you were a legislator, what steps would you take to resolve the conflict between the need for environmental safety and the need to protect businesses and jobs?

3. List three things you can do to address the problem.

4. **Project** Work with your group to complete one of the projects listed at the right, based on the information you gathered in Exercises 1–3. 1–4. See students' work.

PROJECTS

- Conduct an interview.
- Write a book report.
- Write a proposal.
- Write an article for the school paper.
- Write a report.
- Make a display.
- Make a graph or chart.
- Plan an activity.
- Design a checklist.

Enrichment Masters Booklet, p. 13

EXTENDING THE LESSON

Math Power: Reasoning

Suppose $f(x)$ is an even function and $g(x)$ is an odd function. Is $h(x) = f(x) \cdot g(x)$ an even function, an odd function, or neither? Justify your answer.

It is odd because $h(-x) = f(-x) \cdot g(-x) = f(x) \cdot (-g(x)) = -f(x) \cdot g(x)$. This is $-h(x)$.

Decision Making

This activity provides students an opportunity to work together on a given problem. You may wish to refer to pages T20–T21 and page 102c for the various elements of cooperative groups and specific goals and strategies for using them.

3-2 Families of Graphs

Objectives

3–2A
After studying this lesson, you should be able to:
- identify the graphs of simple polynomial functions, absolute value functions, and step functions, and

3–2B
- sketch the graphs of these functions.

Application

Max Dunn of Protem, Missouri, has a dog breeding business. One of his beagles, Belle, recently had a litter of puppies. Mr. Dunn's children noticed that all the puppies looked like Belle and the father, King. However, they could tell the puppies apart because each has distinctively different characteristics from its parents and from the other puppies.

As a member of a family, the puppies have physical characteristics similar to those of their parents as well as their siblings. However, each puppy also has physical characteristics that makes it look different from the other members of the family. Graphs can also be related in a similar manner.

A **parent graph** is an anchor graph from which other graphs in the family are derived. Some different types of parent graphs are shown below. Notice that the coefficient of x in each parent graph is 1.

$y = x^2$ $y = x^3$ $y = x^4$ $y = x^5$

   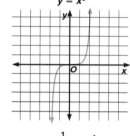

polynomial functions

$y = \sqrt{x}$ $y = |x|$ $y = [x]$ $y = \frac{1}{x}$ or x^{-1}

square root function   *absolute value function*   *greatest integer function*   *rational function*

LESSON 3-2   FAMILIES OF GRAPHS   117

NCTM Standards: 1–8, 13

Lesson Resources

- Practice Master 3–2
- Enrichment Master 3–2
- Evaluation Master, Quiz A, p. 33
- Multicultural Activity Master, p. 3
- Technology Master, p. 6

 Transparency 3–2 contains the 5-Minute Check and a teaching aid for this lesson.

INTRODUCING THE LESSON

⏱ 5-Minute Check

(over Lesson 3–1)

1. Find the coordinates of P' if $P(-3, 4)$ and P' are symmetric with respect to point $M(2, 2)$. **(7, 0)**

2. Complete the graph using symmetry with respect to the line $y = x$.

3. Determine if $f(x) = 3x^3 + 2x + 2$ is even, odd, or neither. **neither**

4. Determine whether the graph of $4x^2 + 9y^2 = 36$ is symmetric with respect to the x-axis, the y-axis, the line $y = x$, the line $y = -x$, or the origin. **x-axis, y-axis, origin**

5. Determine the line of symmetry of the graph the function $y = (x + 3)^2$.   **$x = -3$**

ALTERNATE TEACHING STRATEGIES

Using Graphing Calculators

Use graphing calculators and a visual display to demonstrate the reflections, translations, and dilations of the families of functions discussed in this lesson.

Using Cooperative Groups

Have students work in groups to determine if families of functions have the same symmetries as the parent function. Encourage students to use computers or graphing calculators to help them discuss and answer conjectures which they may make.

Motivating the Lesson

Use technology to help you motivate the lesson. Display the graph of a simple function such as $y = x^2$ and ask students to predict the vertex of $y = (x - 2)^2$, $y = (x + 3)^2$, and so on. Tell students that they will learn how to do transformations of functions in this lesson.

Teaching Tip After discussing the parent graphs, encourage students to memorize them. It is much easier to do transformations of a function if the parent graph is known. Students should consider the eight functions given on page 126 as a *basic toolkit*.

Chalkboard Examples

For Example 1

Graph $f(x) = x^3$ and $g(x) = -x^3$. Describe how the graphs of $g(x)$ and $f(x)$ are related.

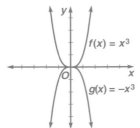

They are reflections of each other over the x-axis.

For Example 2

Use the parent graph $y = x^3$ to sketch the graph of each function. Describe how each graph is related to the parent graph.

a. $y = x^3 - 1$ The point of symmetry is now $(0, -1)$.

b. $y = (x - 1)^3$ The point of symmetry is now $(1, 0)$.

c. $y = (x - 1)^3 + 3$ The point of symmetry is now $(1, 3)$.

Changes to the equation of the parent graph affect the appearance of the graph. The changed graph still resembles the parent graph, but it may appear in a different location on the coordinate plane.

One way to relocate the graph is by using a **reflection**. A reflection *flips* a figure over a line called the *axis of symmetry*. Every point in the original figure has a corresponding point in the reflected image on the opposite side of the axis of symmetry. The exception is any point that lies on the axis of symmetry. Then the point is its own reflected image.

The axis of symmetry is also called the line of symmetry.

Example 1

Graph $f(x) = x^2$ and $g(x) = -x^2$. Describe how the graphs of $g(x)$ and $f(x)$ are related.

$f(x) = x^2$		$g(x) = -x^2$	
x	$f(x)$	x	$g(x)$
-2	4	-2	-4
-1	1	-1	-1
0	0	0	0
1	1	1	-1
2	4	2	-4

The graph of $g(x)$ is a reflection of the graph of $f(x)$ over the x-axis, and vice versa. The symmetry of these two graphs is shown algebraically by $g(x) = -f(x)$, or $f(x) = -g(x)$. *Notice that when the function has a negative coefficient, the graph turns downward.*

The reflection in Example 1 is one type of **linear transformation**. A linear transformation relocates the graph on the coordinate plane, but does not change its shape or size. Another example of a linear transformation is a **translation**. A translation *slides* the graph vertically and/or horizontally, but does not change the shape.

Example 2

Use the parent graph $y = x^3$ given on the previous page to sketch the graphs of each function. Describe how each graph is related to the parent graph.

You can use a graphing calculator to graph the parent function and the related function at the same time.

Notice that the point at $(0, 0)$ is the point of symmetry for the parent graph.

a. $y = x^3 + 3$

a. When a number is added to the parent function, the result is a translation up or down, the y-axis. Since 3 is added to the original function or $y = f(x) + 3$, the graph of the parent function slides 3 units up. The point of symmetry is now at $(0, 3)$.

b. $y = (x + 3)^3$

b. When a positive number is added to x in the parent function, the result is a translation to the left along the x-axis. Since 3 is added to x in the original function or $y = f(x + 3)$, the graph of the parent function slides 3 units left. The point of symmetry is now at $(-3, 0)$.

(-3, 0) $y = (x + 3)^3$

c. $y = (x + 3)^2 - 4$

c. In $y = (x + 3)^3 - 4$, two translations occur. The 3 added to x indicates a slide 3 units to the left. The 4 subtracted indicates a slide 4 units down from the graph of the function $y = (x + 3)^3$. The point of symmetry is now at $(-3, -4)$.

(-3, -4) $y = (x + 3)^3 - 4$

The **greatest integer function**, $f(x) = [x]$, is a type of step function. The symbol $[x]$ means the greatest integer not greater than x. For example, $[5.3]$ is 5 and $[-2.9]$ is -3. The graphs of step functions are often used to model real-world problems.

Example 3

APPLICATION

Business

InfoSystem is a database company that organizes payroll files for other companies. They charge for their services by the minute. If they work on your files for less than 1 minute, you pay nothing. If they work for at least 1 minute but less than 2 minutes, the charge is $1. If they work for at least 2 minutes but less than 3 minutes, the charge is $2, and so on. If you require them to service your files more than once in a calendar week, a $25 charge is added. Graph the function that would determine the cost for 12.8 minutes of service occurring the second time during the week.

The function $f(x) = [x]$ describes the charges for servicing accounts once a week.

x	$f(x)$
0.75	0
1	1
1.5	1
1.9	1
2	2
2.9	2
3.5	3
4	4

$f(x) = [x]$

(continued on the next page)

LESSON 3-2   FAMILIES OF GRAPHS   119

LESSON 3-2   FAMILIES OF GRAPHS   119

Chalkboard Example

For Example 3

The U. S. Postal Service charges their third-class mail customers a rate that depends on the weight of the item being mailed. An item not exceeding one ounce costs $0.29. Over one ounce but less than two ounces costs $0.52, and so on, as shown in the table below. Graph the function that would determine the cost of mailing an 8.5-ounce item.   **$1.44**

Ounces	Rate ($)
$0 < x \leq 1$	0.29
$1 < x \leq 2$	0.52
$2 < x \leq 3$	0.75
$3 < x \leq 4$	0.98
$4 < x \leq 6$	1.21
$6 < x \leq 8$	1.33
$8 < x \leq 10$	1.44
$10 < x \leq 12$	1.56
$12 < x \leq 14$	1.67
$14 < x \leq 16$	1.79

For Example 4

Graph each function. Then describe how each graph is related to the parent graph.
a. $f(x) = |x|$

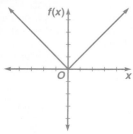

This is the parent function.

b. $g(x) = -3|x|$

The graph has a V-shape like the parent but is narrower. It is also reflected over the x-axis because the parent function was multiplied by a negative number.

c. $h(x) = 0.4|x| + 2$

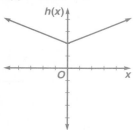

The graph has a V-shape but is broader because multiplying by a number less than one shrinks the graph vertically. It is also translated up two units.

A charge of $25 added to the function translates the function 25 units up. The function $f(x) = [x] + 25$ describes these charges.

The cost of their services for 12.8 minutes the second time during the week would be $37 since $f(12.8) = [12.8] + 25$ or 37.

A geometric transformation of a linear graph changes the slope of the line.

Another way in which a parent graph can be modified is by a **geometric transformation**. With a geometric tranformation, a nonlinear graph is *stretched* or *shrunk*. This results from multiplying the function by a number. *Geometric transformations are sometimes called <u>dilations</u>.*

Example 4

Graph each function. Then describe how each graph is related to the parent graph.

a. $f(x) = |x|$

a. $f(x) = |x|$ is the absolute value function.

x	f(x)
-2	2
-1	1
0	0
1	1
2	2

This is the parent function. Notice that the vertex is at $(0, 0)$.

b. $g(x) = 2|x|$

b.

x	g(x)
-2	4
-1	2
0	0
1	2
2	4

The graph has a V-shape like the parent graph. However, the graph is narrower. Multiplying a function by a number greater than 1 stretches the graph vertically. The vertex of the graph is still at $(0, 0)$.

120 CHAPTER 3 THE NATURE OF GRAPHS

c. $h(x) = -0.5|x| - 3$

c. Multiplying by a negative number reflects the graph over the *x*-axis. Multiplying by 0.5 widens the graph. Subtracting 3 translates the graph 3 units down. The vertex of the graph is now at $(0, -3)$.

x	-0.5|x|	h(x)
-2	-1	-4
-1	-0.5	-3.5
0	0	-3
1	-0.5	-3.5
2	-1	-4

Notice that multiplying by a positive number less than 1 shrinks the graph vertically.

The following chart summarizes the relationships in families of graphs. The parent graph may differ, but the transformations of the graphs have the same effect. Remember that more than one transformation may affect a parent graph.

Change to the Parent Function $y = f(x)$, $c \geq 0$	Change to Parent Graph	Examples
Reflections $y = -f(x)$ $y = f(-x)$	Is reflected over the *x*-axis. Is reflected over the *y*-axis.	
Translations $y = f(x) + c$ $y = f(x) - c$	Translates the graph *c* units up. Translates the graph *c* units down.	
$y = f(x + c)$ $y = f(x - c)$	Translates the graph *c* units left. Translates the graph *c* units right.	

LESSON 3-2   FAMILIES OF GRAPHS   121

Checking for Understanding

Exercises 1–12 are designed to help you assess students' understanding through reading, writing, speaking, and modeling. You should work through Exercises 1–4 with your students and then monitor their work on Exercises 5–12.

Closing the Lesson

Writing Activity   Show the graphs resulting from each type of reflection, translation, and dilation discussed in this lesson, performed on each parent function shown on page 117.

Additional Answers

1. Reflection flips the figure over a line of symmetry. The shape remains the same. Translations move the figure from one location to another. The shape and orientation of the figure remains the same. Dilations change the shape of the figure.
2. It is closer to the y-axis than the graph of $f(x) = x^4$.
3. It moves 2 units right and 7 units up, resulting in (6, 12).

Practice Masters Booklet, p. 14

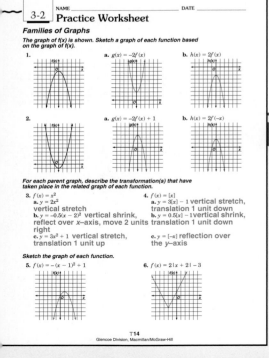

Dilations		
$y = c \cdot f(x),\ c > 1$	Stretches the graph vertically.	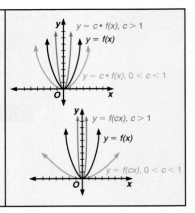
$y = c \cdot f(x),\ 0 < c < 1$	Shrinks the graph vertically.	
$y = f(cx),\ c > 1$	Shrinks the graph horizontally.	
$y = f(cx),\ 0 < c < 1$	Stretches the graph horizontally.	

CHECKING FOR UNDERSTANDING

Communicating Mathematics

Read and study the lesson to answer each question. 1–3. See margin.

1. **Explain** the similarities and differences among reflections, translations, and dilations.

2. **Describe** the changes in the parent graph $f(x) = x^4$ for the function $f(x) = 3x^4$.

3. **Show** how the point at (4, 5) on the graph of $f(x)$ translates for $f(x - 2) + 7$.

4. **Draw** one of the parent graphs on page 117 and then draw a related graph that is stretched horizontally. Write the equation for the related graph.

4. See students' work.

Guided Practice

The graph on the left in each set of graphs is the parent graph. Describe how the other graphs in the set are related to the parent graph.

5a. shrunk vertically
5b. moved 2 units up
5c. shrunk horizontally

5. $f(x) = |x|$ a. $f(x) = 0.5|x|$ b. $f(x) = |x| + 2$ c. $f(x) = |3x|$

6. $f(x) = x^2$ a. $f(x) = -x^2 + 3$ b. $f(x) = (x + 1)^2$ c. $f(x) = (x - 3)^2$

6a. reflected over x-axis, moved 3 units up   6b. moved 1 unit left   6c. moved 3 units right

RETEACHING THE LESSON

Have students graph one of the parent graphs on page 117. Then have them fold the paper along the axis of symmetry. Next, trace the parent by placing paper against a window or light table. For translations, have students trace the parent graph on tracing paper. Then let them move their tracing to the translated position.

Express each function graphed at the right in terms of $f(x)$.

7. $g(x)$ $f(x) + 2$

8. $h(x)$ $f(x - 6)$

9. $m(x)$ $-f(x - 4)$

10. $p(x)$ $-f(x) - 2$

11. $q(x)$ $f(x + 5) - 2$

12. $k(x)$ $-f(x + 6) - 3$

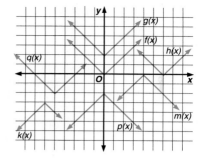

EXERCISES

Practice

A

The graph of $f(x)$ is shown at the right. Sketch a graph of each function based on the graph of $f(x)$.

13. $g(x) = f(x + 3)$

14. $h(x) = f(x) - 4$

15. $j(x) = -f(x)$

16. $k(x) = 3f(x)$

17. $s(x) = -0.5f(x)$

18. $m(x) = 2f(x) + 3$

19. $n(x) = f(x - 5) + 4$

20. $p(x) = 3f(x + 2) - 7$ 13–20. See Teacher's Answer Key.

For each parent graph, describe the transformation(s) that have taken place in the related graph of each function.   21–23. See margin.

21. $f(x) = x^2$
   a. $y = 3x^2$
   b. $y = -1.4x^2$
   c. $y = 4(x - 2)^2$
   d. $y = \frac{1}{2}(x + 1)^2$
   e. $y = 2x^2 - 5$

22. $f(x) = [x]$
   a. $y = [x] - 5$
   b. $y = [x + 7]$
   c. $y = 3[x]$
   d. $y = 2[x] + 4$
   e. $y = -[x]$

23. $f(x) = |x|$
   a. $y = |x| + 6$
   b. $y = |x - 4|$
   c. $y = 0.4|x|$
   d. $y = 2|x + 3| - 8$
   e. $y = -|x - 3| + 6$

Sketch the graph of each function.   24–27. See Teacher's Answer Key.

24. $f(x) = 2(x - 3)^4 - 7$

25. $h(x) = -4|x - 5| - 1$

26. $p(x) = 0.33(x + 2)^3 + 2$

27. $q(x) = -(x + 2)^2 + 5$

28–30. For graphs, see Teacher's Answer Key.

Graphing Calculator

Use a graphing calculator to graph each set of functions on the same screen. Name the x-intercepts of the graphs.

28. $y = x^2$ 0
    $y = (2x + 5)^2$ $-\frac{5}{2}$
    $y = (3x - 1)^2$ $\frac{1}{3}$

29. $y = x^3$ 0
    $y = (2x + 1)^3$ $-\frac{1}{2}$
    $y = (5x - 2)^3$ $\frac{2}{5}$

30. $y = |x|$ 0
    $y = |4x - 2|$ $\frac{1}{2}$
    $y = |5x + 1|$ $-\frac{1}{5}$

APPLYING THE LESSON

Homework Exercises

Assignment Guide

Average: 13–24, 28, 32, 33, 35–39
Enriched: 14, 17, 22–39

The red A, B, and C flags, printed only in the Teacher's Wraparound Edition, indicate the level of difficulty of the exercises.

Chapter 3, Quiz A, (Lessons 3–1 through 3–2), is available in the *Evaluation Masters*, p. 33.

Using Technology

For Exercises 28–30, have students predict the x-intercepts, and then use a graphing calculator to check their predictions. The graphs appear in the Teacher's Answer Key.

Additional Answers

21a. narrower than the parent
21b. narrower and reflected over the x-axis
21c. narrower and moved 2 units right
21d. wider and moved 1 unit left
21e. narrower and moved 5 units down

22a. moved down 5 units
22b. moved left 7 units
22c. narrower
22d. narrower, moved up 4 units
22e. inverted

23a. moved up 6 units
23b. moved right 4 units
23c. wider
23d. narrower, moved 3 units left and 8 units down
23e. inverted, moved 3 units right and 6 units up

31. Study the coordinates of the x-intercepts you found in the related graphs in Exercises 28–30. Make a conjecture about the x-intercept of $y = (ax + b)^n$ if $y = x^n$ is the parent function. The x-intercept will be $-\frac{b}{a}$.

Critical Thinking

32. Study the parent graphs at the beginning of this lesson.
   a. Select a parent graph or a modification of the parent graph that meets each of the following specifications. 32a–c. See margin.
      (1) positive at its leftmost points and positive at its rightmost points
      (2) negative at its leftmost points and positive at its rightmost points
      (3) negative at its leftmost points and negative at its rightmost points
      (4) positive at its leftmost points and negative at its rightmost points
   b. Sketch the related graph for each parent graph that is translated 3 units right and 5 units down.
   c. Write an equation for each related graph.

Applications and Problem Solving

33. **Service Charges** Gatsby's Automotive Shop charges $35 per hour or any fraction of an hour for labor when servicing cars.
   a. Graph the function that would determine the cost of 5.25 hours of labor.
   b. Graph the function that would show a $15 discount if you leave your car overnight. 33a–b. See Teacher's Answer Key. 33c. $125
   c. What would be the cost of 3.45 hours labor on a car left overnight?

34. **Geometry** The length of a rectangular prism is 3 inches greater than the width. The height is 2 inches less than the width.
   a. Write the volume of the prism as the function $V(w)$, where w represents the width. $V(w) = w^3 + w^2 - 6w$
   b. Sketch the graph of $V(w)$.
   c. Sketch the graph of the function describing the volume of a prism whose width is 2 inches greater than that of the prism described by $V(w)$. 34b–c. See Teacher's Answer Key.
   d. In reality, which values of w would not be considered in the domain of $V(w)$? Why? $w < 0$ because the width cannot be negative and $0 \le w \le 2$ because the volume cannot be negative

Mixed Review

35. Determine whether the graph at the right is the graph of a function. **(Lesson 1-1)** not a function

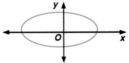

36. $y = \frac{1}{15}x + \frac{1}{15}$

36. Write the equation $15y - x = 1$ in slope-intercept form. **(Lesson 1-5)**

37. Find the determinant of $\begin{bmatrix} 5 & 9 \\ 7 & -3 \end{bmatrix}$. Then state whether an inverse exists for the matrix. **(Lesson 2-3)** -78, yes

38. y-axis

38. Determine whether the graph of $6x^4 - 3x^2 + 1$ is symmetric with respect to the x-axis, the y-axis, the line $y = x$, the line $y = -x$, or the origin. **(Lesson 3-1)**

39. **College Entrance Exam** Choose the best answer. B
   The product of 75^3 and 75^7 is
   (A) 75^5 **(B)** 75^{10} **(C)** 150^{10} **(D)** 5625^{10} **(E)** 75^{21}

EXTENDING THE LESSON

Math Power: Connections

Find a point of symmetry for the graph of $y = x^3 + 3x^2$. $(-1, 2)$

3-3A Graphing Calculators: Graphing Radical Functions

You can use a graphing calculator to graph various types of radical functions quickly and easily. To graph a radical function on the Casio graphing calculator, you can use the $\boxed{\sqrt[x]{}}$ key. The TI-81 graphing calculator does not have an $\boxed{\sqrt[x]{}}$ key, so you will need to rewrite some radical equations to enter them into the calculator. If you have an equation of the form $y = \sqrt[n]{x}$, enter it into the calculator as $y = x^{\frac{1}{n}}$. For example, the equation $y = \sqrt[4]{x^3}$ can be graphed on the TI-81 by entering the equivalent equation of $y = x^{\frac{3}{4}}$ using the $\boxed{\wedge}$ key and parentheses around the $\frac{3}{4}$. The parentheses are very important because without them, the calculator will graph $y = x^3 \div 4$.

Example

Graph $y = \sqrt{x - 3} + 1$ in the viewing window [-1, 6] by [-1, 6], with a scale factor of 1 for both axes. Determine the domain and range.

TI-81: $\boxed{Y=}$ $\boxed{2nd}$ $\boxed{\sqrt{}}$ $\boxed{((}$ $\boxed{X|T}$ $\boxed{-}$ 3 $\boxed{)}$ $\boxed{+}$ 1 $\boxed{GRAPH}$

Casio: $\boxed{Graph}$ $\boxed{\sqrt{}}$ $\boxed{((}$ $\boxed{ALPHA}$ $\boxed{X}$ $\boxed{-}$ 3 $\boxed{)}$ $\boxed{+}$ 1 $\boxed{EXE}$

Tracing and zooming in on the initial point of the graph shows that there are only values for $x \geq 3$ and $y \geq 1$. So the domain is $x \geq 3$, and the range is $y \geq 1$.

It may be difficult to find the domain and range on a calculator using TRACE and ZOOM. If you have a TI-81, try using the ZOOM "box" command to keep the initial point in the box.

EXERCISES

Graph each function so that a complete graph is shown. Then state the domain and range of each function and sketch the graph on a piece of paper.

1. $y = \sqrt{x - 1} + 5$ d: $x \geq 1$; r: $y \geq 5$

2. $y = \sqrt{x + 2} - 6$ d: $x \geq 2$; r: $y \geq -6$

3. $y = \sqrt[3]{x - 2}$ d: all reals; r: all reals

4. $y = \sqrt{6x + 5}$ d: $x \geq -\frac{5}{6}$; r: $y \geq 0$

5. $y = \sqrt[4]{x} + 2$ d: $x \geq 0$; r: $y \geq 2$

6. $y = \sqrt[5]{3x + 4} - 4$ d; all reals; r: all reals

INTRODUCING THE LESSON

Objective Graph and analyze a radical function by using a graphing calculator.

Motivating the Lesson

Show students the graph of $y^2 = x$. Remind students that a graphing calculator will only graph functions. Then ask them how they could create this parabola on a graphing calculator.

TEACHING THE LESSON

Teaching Tip The function $y = \sqrt{x - 3} + 1$ in the Example is not defined for many values of x in the interval [-1, 6]. The graphing calculator will only plot ordered pairs of real numbers that satisfy the equation.

More Examples

Graph $y = \sqrt{4x + 3} + 1$.
Determine the domain and range.
D: $x \geq -0.75$, R: $y \geq 1$

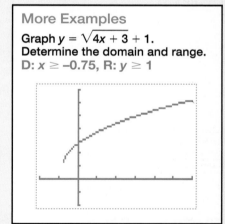

EVALUATING THE LESSON

Closing the Lesson

Ask students to describe the difference between the graphs of $y = x$ and $y = \sqrt[3]{x}$.

APPLYING THE LESSON

Homework Exercises

Assignment Guide

All: 1–6

NCTM Standards: 1–6, 13, 14

Lesson Resources

- Practice Master 3–3
- Enrichment Master 3–3

 Transparency 3–3 contains the 5-Minute Check and a teaching aid for this lesson.

INTRODUCING THE LESSON

 5-Minute Check

(over Lesson 3–2)

The graph of *f(x)* is shown. Sketch a graph of each function based on *f(x)*.

1. *f(x + 2)*

2. *f(x) − 2*

3. *2f(x)*

4. *−2f(x − 1)*

3-3 Inverse Functions and Relations

Objectives
3–3A
3–3B

After studying this lesson, you should be able to:
- determine the inverse of a relation or function, and
- graph a function and its inverse.

Application

FYI...
In 1905, 17,000 bankruptcy petitions were filed. In 1988, 594,000 bankruptcy petitions were filed—nearly 35 times as many!

The economic recession of the early 1990s caused many businesses to declare bankruptcy and, in some cases, collapse totally. In an attempt to avoid bankruptcy, Burdette's Clothing Store had a storewide sale. Every item was marked 20% off at the register. In order to satisfy the bankruptcy lawyers, they had to calculate what their income would have been if that merchandise had been sold at retail value.

To find the reduced price of each sale, the registers' computer had been programmed with the formula $S = x(1 − R)$, where S is the sale price, x is the original price and R is the rate of discount. Since $R = 0.20$, the formula that results is $S = 0.80x$.

In order to find the original price if you are given the reduced price, you would have to work backward, reversing the procedure. Instead of multiplying the original cost by 0.80 to find the sale price, you divide the sale price by 0.80 to arrive at the original price. These two procedures are examples of inverse operations.

Relations also have inverses, and these inverses are themselves relations. Since functions are relations, all functions have inverses, but the inverse may not be a function.

Definition of Inverse Relations

Two relations are inverse relations if and only if one relation contains the element (b, a), whenever the other relation contains the element (a, b).

The inverse of f(x) is written $f^{-1}(x)$.

126 CHAPTER 3 THE NATURE OF GRAPHS

ALTERNATE TEACHING STRATEGIES

Using Manipulatives

Have each student use a square piece of grid paper with the origin at the center to draw the graph of some function. Then fold the grid paper along a diagonal of the square. This represents the line $y = x$. Have students trace the inverse on the other side of the fold. Repeat this for various examples.

Using Discussion

Have students describe the relationship between a relation and its inverse. Discuss how to determine if a relation is a function and whether the function has an inverse.

Example 1

You can review more about inverses in Lesson 1-2.

Graph $f(x) = x^3$ and its inverse.

To graph the inverse of a function, the first step is to interchange the x- and y-coordinates of the ordered pairs of the original function. Then graph $f(x)$ and $f^{-1}(x)$.

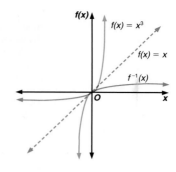

$f(x) = x^3$		$f^{-1}(x)$	
x	**y**	**x**	**y**
-3	-27	-27	-3
-2	-8	-8	-2
-1	-1	-1	-1
0	0	0	0
1	1	1	1
2	8	8	2
3	27	27	3

Notice that $f^{-1}(x)$ is a function.

The graph of $f^{-1}(x)$ is the reflection of $f(x)$ over the line $f(x) = x$.

You can find the inverse of a function algebraically. Review the property of inverse functions in Lesson 1-2 and then study the following example.

Example 2

Find the inverse of $f(x) = x^2 + 2$. Then graph $f(x)$ and its inverse.

Let $f(x) = y$. $y = x^2 + 2$

Interchange x and y. $x = y^2 + 2$

Solve for y. $x - 2 = y^2$

$$\pm\sqrt{x - 2} = y$$

Replace y with $f^{-1}(x)$. $f^{-1}(x) = \pm\sqrt{x - 2}$

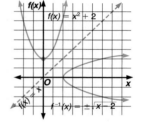

You can use a graphing calculator to graph $f(x) = x^2 + 2$ and $f^{-1}(x) = \pm\sqrt{x - 2}$.

Press the $\boxed{Y =}$ key. Enter the three equations: $y = x^2 + 2$, $y = \sqrt{x - 2}$, and $y = -\sqrt{x - 2}$.

Press $\boxed{\text{GRAPH}}$.

Sketch the images shown on your screen.

Remember to use the vertical line test to verify that a graph represents a function.

Notice that $f^{-1}(x)$ is *not* a function.

LESSON 3-3   INVERSE FUNCTIONS AND RELATIONS   127

Motivating the Lesson

Have students practice reflecting various graphs of known functions over the line $y = x$. Then have them try to give the equations of the reflected graphs. Tell them that the objective of the lesson is to learn how to determine these equations.

TEACHING THE LESSON

Chalkboard Examples

For Example 1

Graph $f(x) = x^2$ and its inverse.

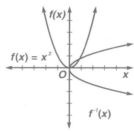

For Example 2

Find the inverse of $f(x) = x^2 - 4$. Then graph $f(x)$ and its inverse.
$f^{-1}(x) = \pm\sqrt{x + 4}$

Teaching Tip   Before Example 2, remind students that the graph of an inverse relation will be a reflection of the original graph over the line $y = x$.

Chalkboard Example

For Example 3

Sketch $y = -\sqrt[4]{x}$.

You have learned to use the vertical line test to determine if a graph is the graph of a function. You can use the **horizontal line test** to determine if the graph of the inverse of a function is also a function. If any horizontal line drawn on the graph of a function passes through no more than one point of the graph, then the function has an inverse that is also a function.

The inverse is not a function.

As a general rule for polynomial functions,
- *if n is even, the inverse of $f(x) = x^n$ is not a function;*
- *if n is odd, the inverse of $f(x) = x^n$ is a function.*

The inverse is a function.

The transformations you learned in Lesson 3-2 can also be applied to graphing inverses. Recall that the inverse of $y = x^5$ is the radical function $y = \sqrt[5]{x}$.

Example 3

Sketch $y = -\sqrt[5]{x}$.

First sketch the parent graph of $y = x^5$.

Reflect the graph over the line $y = x$.

A coefficient of –1 indicates that the graph should be reflected over the x-axis.

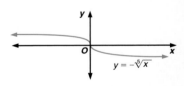

RETEACHING THE LESSON

Have each student create an arbitrary function $f(x)$, graph it, find the inverse of the function, and graph the inverse. Students can then use a group environment to explain their problems to other members of the group.

Practice Masters Booklet, p. 15

NAME _____ DATE _____

3-3 Practice Worksheet

Inverse Functions and Relations

Find the inverse of each function.

1. $y = -5x + 7$
   $y = \frac{-x + 7}{5}$

2. $y = -4x^2 + 1$
   $y = \pm \frac{1}{2}\sqrt{1-x}$

Find the inverse of each function. Sketch the function and its inverse. Is the inverse a function? Write yes or no.

3. $y = (x-1)^3 + 1$ $y = \sqrt[3]{x-1} + 1$; yes

4. $y = 4x^2 - 1$ $y = \pm \frac{1}{2}\sqrt{1-x}$; no

5. $y = 4(x+1)^2 - 2$ $y = \pm \frac{1}{2}\sqrt{x+2} - 1$; no

6. $y = \sqrt[3]{x-1}$ $y = x^3 + 1$; yes

For the parent graph $f(x) = x^2$, describe the transformation(s) that have taken place in the related graph of each function.

7. $y = \pm\sqrt{x-1}$
   translates the inverse 1 unit to the right

8. $y = \pm\sqrt{x} + 1$
   translates the inverse 1 unit up

9. $y = \pm 2\sqrt{x}$
   vertically stretches the inverse

10. $y = \pm 2\sqrt{x-1}$
    translates the inverse 1 unit to the right; then vertically stretches the graph

T15
Glencoe Division, Macmillan/McGraw-Hill

Example 4

Sketch the graph of $y = \pm 2\sqrt{x + 3} - 6$.

The parent graph is the graph of $y = x^2$.

Reflect the parent graph over the line $y = x$ to obtain its inverse whose equation is $y = \pm\sqrt{x}$.

Sketch the graph of $y = \pm 2\sqrt{x}$, which is wider than the reflection of the parent graph.

The graph of $y = \pm 2\sqrt{x + 3}$ is the graph of $y = \pm 2\sqrt{x}$, translated 3 units left. Subtracting 6 translates the graph 6 units down.

EVALUATING THE LESSON

Checking for Understanding

Exercises 1–12 are designed to help you assess students' understanding through reading, writing, speaking, and modeling. You should work through Exercises 1–4 with your students and then monitor their work on Exercises 5–12.

Closing the Lesson

Modeling Activity Make up several sample graphs with their inverses shown on a sheet of transparency acetate. Draw in the line $y = x$, and show students how the graph of the inverse of a function is a reflection of the graph of the function over the line $y = x$.

CHECKING FOR UNDERSTANDING

Communicating Mathematics

Read and study the lesson to answer each question. 1–4. See margin.

1. **Describe** the relationship between the coordinates of the ordered pairs of a relation and its inverse.
2. **Demonstrate** how transformations are used to graph $y = \sqrt[3]{x - 2} + 3$.
3. **Find a counterexample** to this statement: The inverse of a function is also a function.
4. **Show** how you know whether the inverse of a function is also a function without graphing the inverse.

Guided Practice

Given point P of the function $f(x)$, state the corresponding point P' in the inverse of the function.

5. $P(-4, 5)$ $P'(5, -4)$ 6. $P(-3, -2)$ $P'(-2, -3)$ 7. $P(-2, 8)$ $P'(8, -2)$ 8. $P(3t, 8u)$
$P'(8u, 3t)$

LESSON 3-3   INVERSE FUNCTIONS AND RELATIONS   129

Additional Answers

1. The ordered pair (a, b) corresponds to the ordered pair (b, a) in the inverse.
2. Graph $y = x^3$. Reflect over line $y = x$, move 2 units right and 3 units up.
3. Sample answer: The inverse of $f(x) = x^2$ is $f^{-1}(x) = \pm\sqrt{x}$ which is not a function.

4. If you can draw a horizontal line through the function and it intersects the graph more than once, the inverse of the function will not be a function.

Homework Exercises

Assignment Guide

Average: 13–25, 27, 30, 31, 33–37
Enriched: 15–26, 28–37

The red A, B, and C flags, printed only in the Teacher's Wraparound Edition, indicate the level of difficulty of the exercises.

Using Technology

For Exercises 27–29, suggest that students check the equation of the inverse of the first equation by graphing it on the same screen as the original relation. It should be a reflection of the original equation over the line $y = x$.

Additional Answers

12.

$y = \pm\sqrt{x+7}$

$y = x^2 - 7$

For Exercises 25 and 26, each graph involves a reflection over the line $y = x$.

25a. reflection
25b. reflection, moved 3 units right
25c. reflection, moved 6 units up
25d. narrower version of the reflection
25e. wider version of the reflection, moved 4 units up
25f. reflection, moved 5 units right and 3 units up

26a. reflection
26b. reflection, moved 6 units up
26c. reflection, moved 4 units right
26d. wider version of the reflection
26e. reflection, moved 3 units left and 8 units down
26f. reflection, then reflected over the x-axis, moved 3 units right and 6 units up

---

Determine if the inverse of each relation graphed below is a function. Write *yes* or *no*.

9.
yes

10.
yes

11.
no

12. Find the inverse of $y = x^2 - 7$. Graph the function and its inverse.
$y = \pm\sqrt{x + 7}$ For graphs, see margin.

EXERCISES

Practice

Find the inverse of each function.

13. $y = 2x + 3$ $y = \dfrac{x-3}{2}$

14. $y = 0.5x - 8$ $y = 2(x + 8)$

15. $y = 4 - 3x^2$ $y = \pm\dfrac{1}{3}\sqrt{3(4-x)}$

16. $y = x^2 + 4$ $y = \pm\sqrt{x - 4}$

17. $y = (x - 2)^3$ $y = \sqrt[3]{x} + 2$

18. $y = (x + 3)^4 - 5$
$y = \pm\sqrt[4]{x + 5} - 3$

Find the inverse of each function. Sketch the function and its inverse. Is the inverse a function? Write *yes* or *no*. 22. $y = \pm\sqrt{x + 5} - 2$; no 23. $y = \sqrt[3]{x} - 6 + 3$; yes

19. $y = x^2 + 2$ $y = \pm\sqrt{x - 2}$; no

20. $y = (x + 3)^3$ $y = \sqrt[3]{x} - 3$; yes

21. $y = (x - 4)^4$ $y = \pm\sqrt[4]{x} + 4$; no

22. $y = (x + 2)^2 - 5$

23. $y = (x - 3)^3 + 6$

24. $y = x^5 + 5$ $y = \sqrt[5]{x - 5}$; yes

For graphs for Exercises 19–24, see Teacher's Answer Key.

For each parent graph, describe the transformation(s) that have taken place in the related graph of each function. 25–26. See margin.

25. $y = x^2$
   a. $y = \pm\sqrt{x}$
   b. $y = \pm\sqrt{x - 3}$
   c. $y = \pm\sqrt{x + 6}$
   d. $y = \pm 3\sqrt{x}$
   e. $y = \pm 0.2\sqrt{x} + 4$
   f. $y = \pm\sqrt{x - 5} + 3$

26. $y = x^3$
   a. $y = \sqrt[3]{x}$
   b. $y = \sqrt[3]{x} + 6$
   c. $y = \sqrt[3]{x} - 4$
   d. $y = 0.4\sqrt[3]{x}$
   e. $y = \sqrt[3]{x + 3} - 8$
   f. $y = -\sqrt[3]{x - 3} + 6$

Graphing Calculator

Graph the two relations on the same screen. Determine if the two relations are inverses. Write *yes* or *no*. If the answer is no, write the equation that is the inverse of the first equation. 27–29. For graphs, see Teacher's Answer Key.

27. $y = (x + 1)^2$
   $y = \pm\sqrt{x - 1}$
   no, $y = \sqrt{x} - 1$

28. $y = x^2 - 2$
   $y = \pm\sqrt{x + 2}$ yes

29. $y = x^3 - 5$
   $y = \sqrt[3]{x} + 5$
   no, $y = \sqrt[3]{x + 5}$

Critical Thinking

30. Find a function that is its own inverse. Can you find more than one?
$f(x) = x$ and $f(x) = -x$

Applications and Problem Solving

31. Academics In Beth's physics class, the lab work score counts the same as a test score when the grades are averaged for the quarter. No other scores are used to find the average grade. She scored 75%, 80% and 72% on her tests. What lab work score must she receive to average 80% for the quarter? 93%

32. a. $v = 8\sqrt{h}$

32. Fire Fighting The Fairfield Fire Department must purchase a pump that is powerful enough to propel water 80 feet into the air. One pump is advertised to project water with a velocity of 75 feet/second. The velocity of the water can be described by the equation $v = \sqrt{2gh}$, where v is the velocity of the water, g is the acceleration due to gravity ($32\,\text{ft/s}^2$), and h is the maximum height of water flow.

a. Write the simplified equation after replacing g with 32.

b. Graph the relation. See margin.

c. Use the graph to determine the maximum height of the water possible from this pump. 88 feet

d. Does this pump meet the department's needs? yes

e. Another pump is being considered that propels water with a velocity of 70 feet/second. Will this pump meet the department's needs? Explain. No, it only propels water up to 76.6 feet.

Mixed Review

33. Graph $0 < x - y < 2$. **(Lesson 1-3)** See margin.

34. Solve the system of equations by graphing. **(Lesson 2-1)** No solution.

$$3x - 8y = 4$$
$$6x - 42 = 16y$$

35. State whether the figure at the right has point symmetry, line symmetry, neither, or both. **(Lesson 3-1)** both

36. Describe the transformation(s) that have taken place between the parent graph of $y = x^2$ and the graph of $y = 0.5(x + 1)^2$. **(Lesson 3-2)** See margin.

37. College Entrance Exam Choose the best answer. A
If $d = m - \dfrac{50}{m}$, and m is a positive number that increases in value, then d

(A) increases in value.
(B) decreases in value.
(C) remains unchanged.
(D) increases, then decreases.
(E) decreases, then increases.

LESSON 3-3   INVERSE FUNCTIONS AND RELATIONS   131

EXTENDING THE LESSON

Math Power: Problem Solving

State whether the function $f(x) = [x]$ has an inverse which is a function. Explain.

No; the graph does not pass the horizontal line test.

Exercise Note

For Exercise 30, encourage students to verify numerically that $f(x) = x$ is its own inverse.
If $f^{-1}(x) = x$, then $f(f^{-1}(x)) = x$ and $f^{-1}(f(x)) = x$.

Additional Answers

32b.

33.

36. wider than parent graph moved 1 unit left

Enrichment Masters Booklet, p. 15

INTRODUCING THE LESSON

Objective Graph rational functions on a graphing calculator.

Motivating the Lesson

Show students the graph of a rational function. Ask them how the appearance of this graph differs from the other graphs in this chapter.

TEACHING THE LESSON

Teaching Tip Before graphing the equations in Examples 1 and 2, ask students to find those values for which the rational expression is undefined. These values are sometimes called *singularities* because the graph exhibits special behavior in the vicinity of such values.

Teaching Tip Remind students to use parentheses to group the numerator and denominator when entering an equation into a graphing calculator.

More Examples

1. Graph the function $y = \frac{x-1}{x^2-4}$.

   Determine the equations of the vertical and horizontal asymptotes and the points of discontinuity, if they exist.
   vertical asymptotes: $x = -2$, $x = 2$; horizontal asymptote: $y = 0$

3-4A Graphing Calculators: Graphing Rational Functions

A rational function is an equation in which one polynomial is divided by another, or in mathematical terms, $f(x) = \frac{p(x)}{q(x)}$, where $q(x) \neq 0$. Rational functions have some features that other polynomial functions do not have, and the graphing calculator is a good tool to use to explore these graphs.

Some graphs of rational functions are **discontinuous.** Discontinuous means that if you had to draw the graph with a piece of paper and a pencil, you would have to pick up your pencil at least once in order to completely draw the graph. These breaks in continuity can appear as asymptotes or as point discontinuities. A point discontinuity is like a hole in a graph. A break in continuity may not be visible in the first viewing window. You may have to zoom in to see it.

Example 1

Graph $y = \dfrac{x^2-1}{x+1}$. **Use the viewing window** $[-5, 5]$ **by** $[-5, 5]$ **with scale factors of 1 for both axes.**

TI-81: [Y=] [(] [X|T] [x²] [−] [1] [)] [÷] [(] [X|T] [+] [1] [)] [GRAPH]

Casio: [Graph] [(] [ALPHA] [X] [x²] [−] [1] [)] [÷] [(] [ALPHA] [X] [+] [1] [)] [EXE]

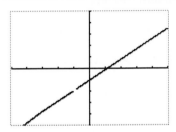

The graph looks like a line with a break in continuity at $x = -1$. Remember that the denominator cannot be zero, so $x + 1 \neq 0$, or $x \neq -1$. The rest of the graph looks like the line $y = x - 1$ because the function $y = \dfrac{x^2-1}{x+1}$ simplifies to $y = x - 1$.

Rational functions can also have asymptotes at values of x for which discontinuities occur. An asymptote can either be vertical or horizontal. Vertical asymptotes can be found algebraically by finding where the denominator of the function equals zero. Horizontal asymptotes can be found algebraically by solving the equation for x and looking where y is undefined in the denominator of the function. Both asymptotes can also be found graphically by using the TRACE and ZOOM functions.

Example 2

Graph $y = \dfrac{2x+3}{x-1}$. Use the viewing window [–7, 7] by [–5, 10] with scale factors of 1 on both axes. Then find the vertical and horizontal asymptotes.

TI-81: `Y=` `((` `2` `XIT` `+` `3` `)` `÷` `((` `XIT` `–` `1` `))` `GRAPH`

Casio: `Graph` `((` `2` `ALPHA` `X` `+` `3` `()`
`÷` `((` `ALPHA` `X` `–` `1` `))` `EXE`

First, find the vertical asymptote by tracing along the graph and observing the x-values near the discontinuity. As |y| increases, x approaches 1. On the TI-81, you can trace to a point where $x = 1$ and the calculator gives no y-value. This shows that the vertical asymptote is at $x = 1$.

The horizontal asymptotes can be found by looking at the end behavior of the function. You can trace along the function to find that as |x| increases, y approaches 2. This can also be seen by graphing the function in a viewing window with large values of x, such as [1000, 1001] by [–5, 10], and tracing along the function. The horizontal asymptote is at $y = 2$.

Sometimes it may appear as though the graphing calculator has drawn a vertical asymptote on the screen, but this is not the case. If it appears as though a vertical asymptote has been drawn, notice that the calculator does not plot the line through the exact point where the vertical asymptote occurs. In Example 2, the calculator appeared to draw the asymptote, but not at $x = 1$.

EXERCISES

Graph each function on a graphing calculator so that a complete graph is shown. Then sketch the graph on a piece of paper. Determine the vertical and horizontal asymptotes and the point discontinuities, if any. 1–10. See margin for graphs.

1. $y = \dfrac{1}{x^2}$ $x = 0; y = 0$

2. $y = \dfrac{5}{x^3}$ $x = 0; y = 0$

3. $y = \dfrac{x^2 + 6}{2x + 3}$ $x = -1.5$

4. $y = \dfrac{x + 3}{x^3 - 2x^2 - 8x}$ $x = -2, x = 0, x = 4; y = 0$

5. $y = \dfrac{4x}{x^2 + 9}$ none

6. $y = \dfrac{x^2 - 4}{x - 2}$ hole at $x = 2$

7. $y = \dfrac{x - 5}{3x}$ $x = 0; y = \dfrac{1}{3}$

8. $y = \dfrac{x^2 + 2x + 5}{2x^2}$ $x = 0; y = \dfrac{1}{2}$

9. $y = \dfrac{3x^2 + 1}{0.5x^2 + x}$ $x = 0, x = -2; y = 6$

10. $y = \dfrac{x^3 - 1}{x^3 + 1}$ $x = -1; y = 1$

More Examples

2. Graph the function
$y = \dfrac{(x - 1)(x - 2)(x - 3)}{(x - 1)(x - 2)}$.

Determine the equations of the vertical and horizontal asymptotes and the points of discontinuity, if they exist.

points of discontinuity:
$x = 1, x = 2$

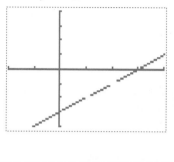

EVALUATING THE LESSON

Closing the Lesson

Ask students to write a rational function that has vertical asymptotes at $x = 1$ and $x = 2$, and has a horizontal asymptote at $y = 0$.

Sample answer: $y = \dfrac{x + 1}{(x - 1)(x - 2)}$

APPLYING THE LESSON

Homework Exercises

Assignment Guide

All: 1–10

Additional Answers

For the graphs for Exercise 1–10, see Teacher's Answer Key.

Lesson Resources

- Practice Master 3–4
- Enrichment Master 3–4
- Evaluation Master, Quiz B, p. 33
- Activity Master, p. 7

 Transparency 3–4 contains the 5-Minute Check and a teaching aid for this lesson.

INTRODUCING THE LESSON

 5-Minute Check

(over Lesson 3–3)

1. Find the inverse of $y = -3x + 4$.
   $y = -\dfrac{x-4}{3}$

2. Find the inverse of $y = x^2 + 1$.
   $y = \pm\sqrt{x-1}$

3. Sketch the graph of $f(x) = (x + 1)^2$ and its inverse. Is the inverse a function?   **no**

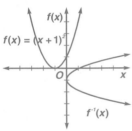

$f(x) = (x + 1)^2$

4. Describe the transformation that has taken place in graphing the family of graphs for $y = x^2$.
   a. $y = \pm\sqrt{x}$
      The reflection over the line $y = x$ yields the inverse.
   b. $y = \pm\sqrt{x-1}$ **The inverse is translated one unit to the right.**
   c. $y = \pm\sqrt{x-1}+2$
      The inverse is translated one unit to the right and two units up.

3-4 Rational Functions and Asymptotes

Objectives

3–4A

3–4B

After studying this lesson, you should be able to:
- determine horizontal, vertical, and slant asymptotes, and
- graph rational functions.

Application

Music stars on tour often use specialized buses to travel from one concert city to the next. On her first solo tour in 1992, Wynona Judd traveled in her bus from Live Oak, Florida, where she did a concert on October 31, to Atlanta for a concert at the Fox Theater the next day. The trip is 297 miles long and lasted approximately 5.5 hours. Her bus driver keeps a record of their average travel time in order to better plan future tours.

The average speed for this part of the trip can be determined by the formula $r = \dfrac{d}{t}$. In this case, $d = 297$. You could use your graphing calculator to graph $r = \dfrac{297}{t}$. Then find the point at which the t-coordinate is 5.5 and read the r-coordinate. In this case, the point is at (5.5, 54). The average speed of the bus for this part of the tour was 54 miles per hour.

t=5.5   r=54

The function $r = \dfrac{297}{t}$ is an example of a **rational function**. A rational function is the quotient of two polynomials. It has the form $f(x) = \dfrac{g(x)}{h(x)}$, where $h(x) \neq 0$. The parent rational function is $f(x) = \dfrac{1}{x}$. The graph of $f(x) = \dfrac{1}{x}$ consists of two parts, one in Quadrant I and one in Quadrant III. Neither part of the graph has a point on the y-axis, where $x = 0$. The parent function $f(x) = \dfrac{1}{x}$ is undefined at $x = 0$, since division by zero is undefined. Also neither part of the graph has a point on the x-axis, where $y = 0$, since $\dfrac{1}{x} \neq 0$.

For a rational function $f(x) = \dfrac{g(x)}{h(x)}$, where $h(x) \neq 0$, the branches of the graph of a rational function approach lines called **asymptotes**. If the function is not defined when $x = a$, then the line with the equation $x = a$ is a **vertical asymptote**.

ALTERNATE TEACHING STRATEGIES

Using Critical Thinking

Have students graph each of the following rational functions and determine their horizontal asymptotes:

$y = \dfrac{x}{x-4}$; $y = \dfrac{x^2}{x^2-4}$; $y = \dfrac{x^3}{x^3-8}$.

Make a conjecture about a horizontal asymptote of $y = \dfrac{x^4}{x^4-16}$.

It will have a horizontal asymptote $y = 1$.

Using Computers

Have students use computers to graph, trace asymptotes, and transform the graphs of various rational functions.

"x approaches ∞" is usually written x → ∞.

Notice that as the value of x approaches zero in the first quadrant of the graph, the value of $f(x)$ increases without bound toward positive infinity (∞). In the third quadrant, as x approaches zero, the value of $f(x)$ decreases without bound toward negative infinity ($-\infty$).

Vertical Asymptote	The line $x = a$ is a vertical asymptote for a function $f(x)$ if $f(x) \to \infty$ or $f(x) \to -\infty$ as $x \to a$ from either the left or the right.

Also notice that as the value of x increases and approaches positive infinity in the first quadrant, the value of $f(x)$ approaches zero. The same pattern can be observed in the third quadrant. As the value of x decreases and approaches negative infinity, the value of $f(x)$ approaches zero. Since there is no value of x such that $y = 0$, the line $y = 0$, which is the x-axis, is a **horizontal asymptote**.

Horizontal Asymptote	The line $y = b$ is a horizontal asymptote for a function $f(x)$ if $f(x) \to b$ as $x \to \infty$ or as $x \to -\infty$.

Example 1

Determine the asymptotes for the graph of $f(x) = \dfrac{x}{x+2}$.

$f(-2)$ is not defined. So there is a vertical asymptote at $x = -2$.

You can use the TRACE function on your graphing calculator to approximate the horizontal asymptote.

To find the horizontal asymptote, let $f(x) = y$ and solve for x in terms of y. Then find where the function is undefined for values of y.

$$y = \frac{x}{x+2}$$
$$y(x+2) = x$$
$$xy + 2y = x$$
$$2y = x - xy$$
$$2y = x(1-y)$$
$$\frac{2y}{1-y} = x$$

The rational expression $\dfrac{2y}{1-y}$ is undefined for $y = 1$. The horizontal asymptote is the line $y = 1$, or $f(x) = 1$.

LESSON 3-4 RATIONAL FUNCTIONS AND ASYMPTOTES 135

Prerequisite Skills

Students should be familiar with factoring.
1. Factor $x^2 - 1$. $(x+1)(x-1)$
2. Factor $x^2 - 5x - 6$. $(x-6)(x+1)$
3. Factor $x^3 + 8x^2 + 7x$. $x(x+7)(x+1)$

Motivating the Lesson

Inflate a balloon to demonstrate Boyle's law: *If the temperature of a gas remains constant, the pressure P of the gas varies inversely as the volume V of the gas, or PV = k.* If $k = 130$, use technology to demonstrate the graph of $P = \dfrac{k}{V}$.

TEACHING THE LESSON

Teaching Tip After discussing rational functions, tell students that the graph of many rational functions is called a *hyperbola*.

Chalkboard Example

For Example 1

Determine the asymptotes for the graph of $f(x) = \dfrac{x}{x-1}$. $x = 1, y = 1$

Example 2

Use the parent graph $f(x) = \frac{1}{x}$ to graph each equation. Describe the transformation(s) that have taken place.

a. $g(x) = \dfrac{1}{x+1}$

a. To graph $g(x) = \dfrac{1}{x+1}$, translate the parent graph 1 unit to the left. When the parent graph is translated, the asymptote it approaches is also translated in the same direction. The new vertical asymptote is $x = -1$. Since the graph did not move up or down, horizontal asymptote is still $y = 0$.

b. $j(x) = \dfrac{3}{x}$

b. The graph of $j(x) = \dfrac{3}{x}$ does not come as close to the origin as the parent graph, but no translation has taken place. The vertical asymptote is still $x = 0$, and the horizontal asymptote is $y = 0$.

c. $k(x) = \dfrac{-2}{x}$

c. The graph of $k(x) = \dfrac{-2}{x}$ involves two transformations. The graph is not as close to the origin as the parent graph, and because it is multiplied by -1, it is reflected over the x-axis. The asymptotes remain the same.

d. $m(x) = \dfrac{1}{x-4} + 3$

d. The graph of $m(x) = \dfrac{1}{x-4} + 3$ is the parent graph translated 4 units to the right and 3 units up. The new vertical asymptote is $x = 4$, and the new horizontal asymptote is $y = 3$.

Example 3

APPLICATION

Physics

As you get farther from Earth's surface, gravity has less effect and you actually weigh less at higher altitudes. A person's weight, $W(h)$, at a specific height h above Earth's surface can be found by the formula $W(h) = \dfrac{r}{h + r}(w)$, where r is Earth's radius and w is the person's weight at sea level. Earth's radius is about 6400 kilometers. Graph this function for a person weighing 50 kilograms at sea level, and explain the meaning of the asymptotes.

Substitute all known values into the formula.

$$W(h) = \left(\frac{6400}{h + 6400} \right) 50$$

$$= \frac{320{,}000}{h + 6400}$$

The vertical asymptote of the function is $h = -6400$. However, for this problem, we will only consider values for which $h \geq 0$.

The horizontal asymptote of the function is $W(h) = 0$, because the weight of a person cannot be zero.

A third type of asymptote is the **slant asymptote**. Slant asymptotes occur when the degree of the numerator is exactly one greater than that of the denominator. For example, in $f(x) = \dfrac{x^2}{x - 6}$, the exponents are 2 and 1 and $2 - 1 = 1$. Thus, this function has a slant asymptote, as shown in the graph at the right.

When the degrees are the same or the denominator has the greater degree, the function has vertical and horizontal asymptotes.

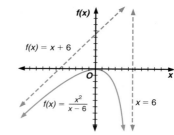

Slant Asymptote

The oblique line ℓ is a slant asymptote for a function $f(x)$ if the graph of $f(x)$ approaches ℓ as $x \to \infty$ or as $x \to -\infty$.

An oblique line is a line that is neither vertical nor horizontal.

Example 4

Determine the slant asymptote for $f(x) = \dfrac{x^2 - 2x + 1}{x}$.

First use division to rewrite the rational expression as a quotient. *Remember to use the same procedure as with whole numbers. That is, $7 \div 3 = 2$ R 1 or $2\frac{1}{3}$.*

Therefore, $f(x) = x - 2 + \dfrac{1}{x}$.

$$\begin{array}{r} x - 2 \\ x\overline{)x^2 - 2x + 1} \\ \underline{x^2} \\ -2x + 1 \\ \underline{-2x} \\ 1 \end{array}$$

(continued on the next page)

Chalkboard Examples

For Example 3

As the pressure P on a gas increases, the volume V of the gas decreases according to Boyle's law, $V = \dfrac{k}{P}$, where k is a known constant for the gas. Graph this function for a gas with a constant of 162.

For Example 4

Determine the slant asymptote for $f(x) = \dfrac{x^2 + x + 1}{x}$.

$y = x + 1$

As the value of x increases positively and negatively, the value of $\frac{1}{x}$ approaches zero. Therefore, the value of $x - 2 + \frac{1}{x}$ approaches $x - 2$. So, the line $g(x) = x - 2$ is the slant asymptote for $f(x)$.

The line $x = 0$ is a vertical asymptote for $f(x)$, because $f(x)$ increases or decreases without bound close to $x = 0$.

Whenever the denominator and numerator of a rational function contain a common factor, a **hole** may appear in the graph of the funtion. For example, in $f(x) = \frac{x^2 - 9}{x + 3}$, the numerator and denominator both have a factor of $x + 3$. The function is undefined if $x = -3$. If numerator and denominator are both divided by the common factor, the function $f(x) = x - 3$ results. The graph of $f(x) = \frac{x^2 - 9}{x + 3}$ looks like the graph of $f(x) = x - 3$, but it has a hole at $x = -3$.

Example 5

Graph $y = \frac{x^2 + 3x - 10}{x - 2}$.

$y = \frac{x^2 + 3x - 10}{x - 2}$

$= \frac{(x + 5)(x - 2)}{x - 2}$

$= x + 5, x \neq 2$

The graph is the graph of $y = x + 5$ with a hole at $(2, 7)$.

Example 6

Graph $y = \frac{(x - 4)(x - 2)}{x(x - 3)^2(x - 4)}$.

$y = \frac{(x - 4)(x - 2)}{x(x - 3)^2(x - 4)}$

$= \frac{x - 2}{x(x - 3)^2}, x \neq 4$

Since $x - 4$ is a common factor, there is a hole at $x = 4$. Because y increases or decreases without bound close to $x = 0$ and $x = 3$, there are vertical asymptotes at $x = 0$ and $x = 3$. There is also a horizontal asymptote at $y = 0$ for $x > 3$ and $x < 0$.

The graph is the graph of $y = \frac{x - 2}{x(x - 3)^2}$, with a hole at $(4, 0.5)$.

CHECKING FOR UNDERSTANDING

Communicating Mathematics

Read and study the lesson to answer each question. 1–2. See margin.

1. **Describe** how a graph behaves when an asymptote is present.

2. **Explain** under what conditions a rational function has a slant asymptote and how you find its equation.

3. **Graph** $f(x) = \frac{1}{x}$ after it has been translated 2 units right and 6 units down.
   a. What are its asymptotes? $x = 2, y = -6$
   b. Write the equation of the translated graph. $f(x) = \frac{1}{x-2} - 6$

4. **Explain** why only values for $h \geq 0$ were considered in Example 3.
   At 0, you are at sea level. Values less would put you below sea level.

Guided Practice

Given the graphs of transformations of $f(x) = \frac{1}{x}$, write the equation of each graph.

5.

$f(x) = \frac{1}{x-1}$

6.

$f(x) = \frac{1}{x+4}$

7.

$f(x) = \frac{1}{x} + 5$

8.

$f(x) = \frac{1}{x-2} - 3$

9.

$f(x) = -\frac{1}{x}$

10.

$f(x) = \frac{-1}{x+5}$

LESSON 3-4 RATIONAL FUNCTIONS AND ASYMPTOTES 139

RETEACHING THE LESSON

Graph the rational function $y = \frac{(x-2)(x+3)}{x(x-2)}$ and give the equations of its asymptotes. Check the solution by using a graphing calculator. $x = 0, y = 1$

Additional Answer

3.

Homework Exercises

Assignment Guide

Average: 15–23, 24–38 even, 39, 40, 43–48
Enriched: 18–23, 25–35 odd, 36–48

The red A, B, and C flags, printed only in the Teacher's Wraparound Edition, indicate the level of difficulty of the exercises.

Chapter 3, Quiz B, (Lessons 3–3 through 3–4), is available in the *Evaluation Masters*, p. 33.

Additional Answers

For graphs for Exercises 19 and 20, see Teacher's Answer Key.

19a. translated 1 unit down
19b. translated 5 units left
19c. closer to the axes
19d. wider, translated 8 units up
19e. translated 3 units right, 7 units up

20a. translated 3 units up
20b. translated 9 units right
20c. wider
20d. translated 5 units left, 1 unit down
20e. reflected, translated 2 units right, 4 units up

21. $y = \dfrac{x}{x(x-4)}$

22. $y = \dfrac{x+1}{(x+1)(x+5)(x-1)}$

23. $y = \dfrac{x(x-3)(x+7)}{(x-3)(x+7)}$

24.

$y = \dfrac{3}{x+2}$

Determine the asymptotes for each function.

11. $y = \dfrac{-2}{(x+1)^2}$

$x = -1, y = 0$

12. $y = \dfrac{x}{x-2}$

$x = 2, y = 1$

Determine the values of x for which a hole appears in the graph of each function.

13. $y = \dfrac{(x-3)(x+5)}{(x+5)(x-1)}$ $x = -5$

14. $y = \dfrac{x^2 + 3x - 28}{x^3 - 11x^2 + 28x}$ $x = 4$

EXERCISES

Practice

Determine any horizontal, vertical, or slant asymptotes in the graph of each function.   16. $x = \pm 1.7, x = 0, y = 0$

15. $y = \dfrac{x}{x^2 + x - 6}$ $x = 2, x = -3, y = 0$

16. $y = \dfrac{2}{x^5 - 3x^3}$

17. $y = \dfrac{3x^3 - 2x + 1}{2x^2}$ $y = \dfrac{3}{2}x, x = 0$

18. $y = \dfrac{x^2 + 4x + 4}{x^2 - 11x + 30}$
$x = 5, x = 6, y = 1$

For each parent graph, describe the transformation(s) that have taken place in the related graph of each function. Then sketch each graph.   19–20. See margin.

19. $y = \dfrac{1}{x}$

a. $y = \dfrac{1}{x} - 1$

b. $y = \dfrac{1}{x+5}$

c. $y = \dfrac{1}{4x}$

d. $y = \dfrac{1}{0.2x} + 8$

e. $y = \dfrac{1}{x-3} + 7$

20. $y = \dfrac{1}{x^2}$

a. $y = \dfrac{1}{x^2} + 3$

b. $y = \dfrac{1}{(x-9)^2}$

c. $y = \dfrac{1}{0.4x^2}$

d. $y = \dfrac{1}{(x+5)^2} - 1$

e. $y = \dfrac{-1}{(x-2)^2} + 4$

Create a function of the form $y = f(x)$ that satisfies each set of conditions.

21. vertical asymptote at $x = 4$, hole at $x = 0$ 21–23. See margin.

22. vertical asymptotes at $x = -5$ and $x = 1$, hole at $x = -1$

23. holes at $x = 3$ and $x = -7$, resembles $y = x$

140   CHAPTER 3   THE NATURE OF GRAPHS

25.

$y = \dfrac{x-5}{x+1}$

26.

$y = \dfrac{-4}{x-1}$

27.

$y = \dfrac{(x+2)(x-2)}{x-12}$

28.

$y = \dfrac{x}{x-5}$

29.

$y = \dfrac{-2}{(x-3)^2}$

Graph each rational function. 24–38. See margin.

24. $y = \dfrac{3}{x+2}$

25. $y = \dfrac{x-5}{x+1}$

26. $y = \dfrac{-4}{x-1}$

27. $y = \dfrac{(x+2)(x-2)}{x-2}$

28. $y = \dfrac{x}{x-5}$

29. $y = \dfrac{-2}{(x-3)^2}$

30. $y = \dfrac{x^2-x}{x}$

31. $y = \dfrac{-5}{(x-3)(x+1)}$

32. $y = \dfrac{x^2}{x(x-1)}$

33. $y = \dfrac{3}{(x-4)^2}$

34. $y = \dfrac{x^2+3x}{x}$

35. $y = \dfrac{x^2+3x-4}{x}$

36. $y = \dfrac{x}{1-x^2}$

37. $y = \dfrac{-x}{x^2-4}$

38. $y = \dfrac{x-1}{x^2-9}$

Critical Thinking
39. Graph $y = \dfrac{3x^2(x+1)}{2(x-2)^2(x-1)}$. See margin.

Applications and Problem Solving
40. Amusements Louis was baby-sitting his neighbor's two children and decided to take them to the park. The children wanted to play on the seesaw. When they got on the seesaw, the older child was too heavy for the younger one. Louis knew that if the older child sat closer to the center of the seesaw, it would work better. The equation relating the two weights and the distances from the center of the seesaw is $w_1 d_1 = w_2 d_2$, where w_1 is the weight of one child and d_1 is the distance of that child from the center of the seesaw and w_2 and d_2 are the weight and distance for the other child.

a. Suppose the children are balanced on the seesaw. One child weighs 30 pounds and sits 6 feet from the center of the seesaw. Write a rational function to find the weight of the other child. 40a–b. See margin.

b. Graph the function in part a.

40d. If a person is heavier than the other person, that person should sit closer to the center of the seesaw.

c. If the older child weighs 45 pounds, how far must she sit from the center of the seesaw? 4 feet

d. Make a general conjecture about the relationship of a person's weight to the distance from the center of the seesaw in order to make it work properly.

LESSON 3-4 RATIONAL FUNCTIONS AND ASYMPTOTES 141

Additional Answers continued on next page.

Additional Answers

40a. $w = \dfrac{180}{d}$

40b.

41a.

43. Sample answer: {(2, 4), (2, –4), (1, 2), (1, –2), (0, 0)}; because there is more than one member of the domain paired with the range.

Enrichment Masters Booklet, p. 16

---

41. Music The frequency of a sound wave is called its pitch. The pitch p of a musical tone and its wavelength w are related by the equation $p = \dfrac{v}{w}$, where v is the velocity of sound through air. Suppose a sound wave has a velocity of 1056 feet/second.

41a. x- and y-axes; for graph, see margin.

a. Graph the equation $p = \dfrac{v}{w}$. What lines are close to the maximum values for the pitch and the wavelength?

41b. It increases.

b. What happens to the pitch of the tone as the wavelength decreases?

41c. It is half.

c. If the wavelength is doubled, what happens to the pitch of the tone?

42. Physics The average speed v of a certain particle in meters per second is given by the equation $v = \dfrac{2t^2 + 7t + 5}{t + 3}$, where t is the time in seconds.

a. For what values of t would an asymptote exist? *$t = -3$*

b. What is the value of v if $t = 2$? *5.4*

c. Use a graphing calculator to graph this function. Describe the appearance of the graph. *It has a vertical asymptote at $t = -3$ and seems to also have a slant asymptote approximated by $y = 2t$.*

Mixed Review

43. See margin.

43. Write an example of a relation that is not a function. Tell why. **(Lesson 1-1)**

44. Find the length of the sides of a triangle whose vertices are $A(-1, 3)$, $B(-1, -3)$, and $C(3, 0)$. **(Lesson 1-4)** *$AB = 6, BC = 5, AC = 5$*

45. Find the slope of a line perpendicular to a line whose equation is $3x - 4y = 0$. **(Lesson 1-6)** *$-\dfrac{4}{3}$*

46. Find the maximum and minimum values of $f(x, y) = y - x$ defined for the polygonal convex set having vertices at $(0, 0)$, $(4, 0)$, $(3, 5)$, and $(0, 5)$. **(Lesson 2-5)** *5, –4*

47. Find the inverse of $x^2 - 9 = y$. **(Lesson 3-3)** *$y = \pm\sqrt{x + 9}$*

48. College Entrance Exam Compare quantities A and B below. *A*
   Write A if quantity A is greater.
   Write B if quantity B is greater.
   Write C if the two quantities are equal.
   Write D if there is not enough information to determine the relationship.

   (A) the volume of a cube with side $x, x > 1$

   (B) the volume of a rectangular solid with sides measuring x, $x + 1$, and $x - 1$, $x > 1$

142   CHAPTER 3   THE NATURE OF GRAPHS

EXTENDING THE LESSON

Math Power: Connections

The graph of a rational function can never cross one of its vertical asymptotes, but it can cross a horizontal one. Find the point where the graph of $y = \dfrac{x^2 + 1}{x^2 - 2x - 1}$ crosses its horizontal asymptote.

(–1, 1)

Technology

Graphing Rational Functions

BASIC
Spreadsheets
▶ **Software**

Using Technology

Objective This optional page shows how graphing software can be used to explore the graphs of a rational function and to find the equation(s) of the asymptotes of the function.

The graphs of rational functions are intriguing. However, much time can be spent sketching a single graph by hand. Graphing calculators and graphing software graph rational functions, but not always correctly. Many graphing utilities fail to properly represent the asymptotes and holes that occur when you graph rational functions. *The Function Analyzer*, by Sunburst Communications, correctly graphs rational functions.

To generate the graph of the rational function $f(x) = \dfrac{x^3 + 4x^2 - 2x + 3}{x^3 - 4x^2 - x - 1}$ using *The Function Analyzer*, use the following steps.

- Select **Function** from the menu and then press **N** to use a new function.
- Type in the function: **(X^3 + 4X^2 − 2X + 3)/(X^3 − 4X^2 − X−1)**. Then press **[Enter]**. *The caret symbol (^) does not show on the screen when typed.*

After the graph is drawn, find the equation of the vertical asymptote between $x = 4$ and $x = 5$.

- Press **[Esc]** twice to return to the main menu.
- Select **Scale** and then select **Enter New Coordinate Values**.
- To set the scale, type **100[↓] - 100 [←] 4 [→] 5** and press **[Enter]**. The graph will be redrawn using the new scale.
- Then set the scale to **500[↓] - 500 [←] 4.2 [→] 4.4** and press **[Enter]**.
- Finally, set the scale the **2000 [↓] −2000 [←] 4.25 [→] 4.35** and press **[Enter]**.
- Press **[Esc]** twice to return to the main menu and then select **Values**.
- Press **[←]** eight times to show the coordinates of the points that are near the asymptote.

We can conclude that the asymptote is somewhere between $x = 4.286$ and $x = 4.288$. *The equation of the asymptote is actually $x = 4.28762526163747$.*

Teaching Suggestions

Point out to students that in the case of a rational function with a factorable denominator, the vertical asymptote(s) of the function are predictably at the values for which the expression is undefined. This software also enables you to find the asymptotes of rational functions with denominators that do not factor.

You may wish to follow up the lesson by having students compare the graph of a rational function on a graphing calculator with the graph produced by the software package. Make sure the scale is the same for both screens. Have students interpret each graph in terms of what information it gives about the rational function.

EXERCISES

Use *The Function Analyzer* to graph each rational function. Select the Clear Screen option before beginning each exercise. Then find the equation(s) of the asymptote(s) for each function.

1. $f(x) = \dfrac{(x-3)(x+5)}{(x+1)(x+3)}$ $x = -1, x = -3, y = 1$

2. $g(x) = \dfrac{x^2 + x - 6}{x^2 - x - 2}$ $x = -1, y = 1$

3. $h(x) = \dfrac{3.12x^3 - 4.5x + 8.92}{-1.02x^4 + 11.41x^2 - 9.15x + 7.11}$ $x = -4, x = 3, y = 0$

CHAPTER 3   TECHNOLOGY: GRAPHING RATIONAL FUNCTIONS   143

NCTM Standards: 1–5

Lesson Resources

- Practice Master 3–5
- Enrichment Master 3–5

 Transparency 3–5 contains the 5-Minute Check and a teaching aid for this lesson.

INTRODUCING THE LESSON

 5-Minute Check

(over Lesson 3–4)

1. Determine any horizontal, vertical, or slant asymptotes in the graph of $y = \dfrac{(x - 2)(x + 3)}{x(x + 4)}$.

   $x = -4, x = 0, y = 1$

2. Describe the transformation(s) that have taken place in graphing the family of graphs if $y = \dfrac{1}{x}$ is the parent graph.

   a. $y = \dfrac{1}{x} - 2$ **the parent graph shifted 2 units down**

   b. $y = \dfrac{1}{x - 2}$ **the parent graph shifted 2 units right**

3. Graph the rational function $y = \dfrac{(x - 3)(x + 1)}{x(x + 1)}$.

Motivating the Lesson

Suppose the cost of putting on a school play is $500. The tickets will cost $4 for adults and $3 for students. Have students put together a spreadsheet to determine different combinations of how many tickets of each type need to be sold in order to make a profit.

3-5 Graphs of Inequalities

Objective
3–5

After studying this lesson, you should be able to:
- graph polynomial, absolute value, and radical inequalities.

Application

Call it Magic Mitts®, Scatch®, Katch-a-Roo®, or Super Grip Ball®. It's basically a Velcro™ ball with Velcro™ paddles and lots of imagination. (The photo at the left is a close-up of Velcro™ magnified 18 times.) Mark Paliafito was 26 when he founded Paliafito America Inc. in 1990. His company distributes Super Grip Ball®. In July of 1991, they had sold 650,000 of their product and had orders for one million more.

Recreation Limited sells sports equipment. According to their accountants, their profits $f(x)$ from the sale of Super GripBall® can be modeled by the relation $f(x) < -0.003x^2 + 9x - 1500$, where x is the number of sets of Super Grip Ball® sold in a week and $0 \leq x < 1500$.

To graph this inequality, first graph the function $f(x) = -0.003x^2 + 9x - 1500$. Since the inequality does not contain the equality, graph the function as a broken graph. Next, draw a dotted line at $x = 1500$ to show that the boundary we are considering is the graph of the function up to $x = 1500$.

The inequality contains infinitely many solutions. These solutions are indicated in the graph as a shaded region. To find which region should be shaded, test a point that is not on the boundary.

Test (1000,0): *This point is inside the boundary.*

Is $0 < -0.003(1000)^2 + 9(1000) - 1500$?
  $0 < 4500$ *true*

Since $(1000, 0)$ is a point that satisfies the inequality and $0 \leq 1000 < 1500$, the region that contains this point should be shaded.

Notice that the graph is a member of the $y = x^2$ family of graphs. You can use the skills that you learned with families of graphs to graph other inequalities.

144 CHAPTER 3 THE NATURE OF GRAPHS

ALTERNATE TEACHING STRATEGIES

Using Logical Reasoning

Have students draw a graph of $y < x^2 - 2x + 1$.

1. What is the first step in drawing the graph?
2. Which side of the boundary should be shaded? Are the boundary points solutions?
3. What is a convenient point to test?

Using Communication

Suppose a corporation has found an inequality that represents its profit. Why is it still possible for the company to lose money even though the model does not show a loss?

The model may only give a general prediction for profit. It may not fit when actual values are used to determine the profit.

Example 1

Graph $y \leq \sqrt[3]{x + 2} - 4$.

First graph the inverse of the parent function $y = x^3$.
Then translate the inverse 2 units left and 4 units down.
Since the boundary is included in the inequality, the graph is drawn as a solid line.

The origin is often used as a test point because (0, 0) is easily tested in any inequality.

Test a point not on the boundary.

Test $(0, 0)$:

$y \leq \sqrt[3]{x + 2} - 4$

$0 \overset{?}{\leq} \sqrt[3]{0 + 2} - 4$ *Replace (x, y) with (0, 0).*

$0 \overset{?}{\leq} \sqrt[3]{2} - 4$ *$\sqrt[3]{2} \approx 1.26$*

$0 \not\leq -2.74$

Since $(0, 0)$ does not satisfy the inequality, the region containing $(0, 0)$ should *not* be shaded. So, shade the region below the graph.

Check your solution by testing a point in the region you shaded.

Some inequalities involve absolute value functions. The same process used in Example 1 is used for determining which region should be included in the solution.

Example 2

Graph $y > |x - 3| - 5$.

Graph the parent function $y = |x|$ and translate it 3 units right and 5 units down. The boundary is not included in the inequality, so it is dashed.

Test a point not on the boundary to determine which region should be included in the graph.

Test $(0, 0)$:

$y > |x - 3| - 5$

$0 \overset{?}{>} |0 - 3| - 5$ *Let (x, y) = (0, 0).*

$0 > -2$ *true*

Since $(0, 0)$ satisfies the inequality, the region containing the origin is included in the graph and is shaded.

Teaching Tip   Before discussing the examples, ask students why they should check solutions by testing points in the shaded region.

Chalkboard Examples

For Example 1

Graph $y \leq \sqrt[3]{x - 1} + 2$.

For Example 2

Graph $y > |x + 2| + 4$.

Chalkboard Examples

For Example 3

Solve $|x - 2| < 0.1$.
$\{x \mid 1.9 < x < 2.1\}$

For Example 4

The Top Machine Tool Company makes 3.750-inch diameter pistons for automobile engines. In order for the pistons to work properly in each engine, the diameter of a piston can vary by no more than 0.0001 inch.
a. Write an inequality to represent the diameter of a piston.
   $|x - 3.75| \leq 0.0001$
b. What is the largest and smallest diameter allowable for a piston?   as small as 3.7499 inches and as large as 3.7501 inches
c. Sketch a graph to represent the range of values allowed for the diameter of a piston.

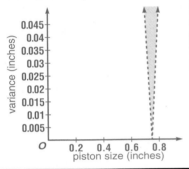

EVALUATING THE LESSON

Checking for Understanding

Exercises 1–9 are designed to help you assess students' understanding through reading, writing, speaking, and modeling. You should work through Exercises 1–2 with your students and then monitor their work on Exercises 3–9.

Closing the Lesson

Speaking Activity Explain how to graph an inequality. Describe how to determine where the graph should be shaded.

Example 3

An inequality in the form $|x| < n$, where $n \leq 0$, has no solution.

Solve $|x - 4| < 0.1$.

There are two cases that must be solved. In one case, $x - 4$ is negative, and in the other, it is positive.

$$
\begin{array}{l|l}
\textit{If } a < 0, \textit{ then } |a| = -a. & \textit{If } a > 0, \textit{ then } |a| = a. \\
-(x - 4) < 0.1 & x - 4 < 0.1 \\
{-x + 4} < 0.1 & x < 4.1 \\
{-x} < -3.9 & \\
{x} > 3.9 &
\end{array}
$$

The solution set is $\{x \mid 3.9 < x < 4.1\}$ *$\{x \mid 3.9 < x < 4.1\}$ is read "the set of all numbers x such that x is between 3.9 and 4.1."*

Example 4

APPLICATION
Manufacturing

The AccuData Company makes 3.5-inch computer disks. So the disks can fit into the drives of various computers, the dimensions of the plastic case about the magnetic disk can vary by no more than 0.11 inch.
a. Write an inequality to represent the width of the plastic case.
b. What are the largest and smallest lengths of the case allowable?
c. Sketch a graph to represent the range of values allowed for the case.

a. If x represents the width of the new disk, then $|x - 3.5|$ equals the acceptable variance from the 3.5-inch norm. This variance can be no more than 0.11 inches. So, $|x - 3.5| \leq 0.11$.

b. $\begin{array}{l|l} \textit{If } a < 0, \textit{ then } |a| = -a. & \textit{If } a > 0, \textit{ then } |a| = a. \\ -(x - 3.5) \leq 0.11 & x - 3.5 \leq 0.11 \\ {-x + 3.5} \leq 0.11 & x \leq 3.61 \\ {-x} \leq -3.39 & \\ {x} \geq 3.39 & \end{array}$

The solution is $\{x \mid 3.39 \leq x \leq 3.61\}$. The length of the disk can be as great as 3.61 inches and as small as 3.39 inches.

c. The function $|x - 3.5| < y$ describes all variances less than y. The values of the function below the line $y = 0.11$ describe the acceptable variances.

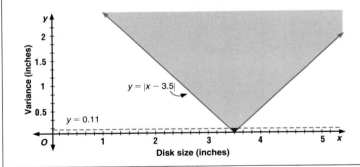

Additional Answers

1. **After graphing the boundary function, test a point not on the boundary. If the point satisfies the inequality, shade that region. If not, test a point in the other region.**

33.

CHECKING FOR UNDERSTANDING

Communicating Mathematics

Read and study the lesson to answer each question.

1. **Describe** how you determine which region of the graph of an inequality should be shaded. See margin.

2. **Write** an absolute value inequality that has no solution. Sample answer: $|x| < -4$

Guided Practice

Determine if each ordered pair is a solution for the given inequality. Write *yes* or *no*.

3. $y > x^4 - 5x^2 + 2, (2, 3)$ yes

4. $y < -0.2x^2 + 9x - 7, (10, 20)$ yes

5. $y < |x - 2| + 7, (3, 8)$ no

6. $y > -\sqrt{x + 11} + 1, (-2, -4)$ no

Graph each inequality. 7–9. See Teacher's Answer Key.

7. $y < |x + 4|$

8. $y > \sqrt[3]{x} + 3$

9. $x^3 - 5x^2 + 6x - 9 > y$

EXERCISES

Practice

Graph each inequality. 10–21. See Teacher's Answer Key.

10. $y > 2x + 3$

11. $y < -4x + 9$

12. $y > \sqrt{x + 2}$

13. $y > x^2 - 5$

14. $|x - 5| < 0.05 + y$

15. $|x + 2| > 5 + y$

16. $y < |x + 9|$

17. $y > |x + 3| - 2$

18. $y > |x| + 2$

19. $y > (x - 4)^2$

20. $y < |3x - 4| + 5$

21. $y < \sqrt[3]{x + 8} - 8$

Solve each inequality.   22. $\{x | x < -5 \text{ or } x > 1\}$ 24. $\{x | x < -18 \text{ or } x > 10\}$

22. $|x + 2| > 3$

23. $|2x + 7| < 0$ ∅

24. $|3x + 12| > 42$

25. $|x| \le x$
   $\{x | x \ge 0\}$

26. $|x| > x$
   $\{x | x < 0\}$

27. $|x + 2| - x \ge 0$
   all real numbers

Graphing Calculator

Use a TI-81 calculator to graph the boundaries of each inequality. Then use the SHADE feature to complete the graph. 28–31. See Teacher's Answer Key.

28. $y > 3x + 2$

29. $y < x^2 + 2x - 3$

30. $y < x^3 + 5x^2 - 18x - 72$

31. $y < |x| + 2$

Critical Thinking

32. Solve $|x + 1| + |x - 1| \le 2$. $\{x | -1 \le x \le 1\}$

33. Solve the system of inequalities by graphing.
   $y > 2(x - 2)^2 - 5$
   $y < -(x - 2)^2$ See margin.

Applications and Problem Solving

34. **Woodworking** Marcia Gardlik makes customized picture frames. A customer came into her shop and requested that she make a square frame that used wood 1.5 inches wide and was sized so that the area of the family crest was at most two-thirds the total area of the picture and frame. Write an inequality to describe the possible lengths of one side of the frame.
   $\frac{1}{3}x^2 - 6x + 9 \le 0$

LESSON 3-5   GRAPHS OF INEQUALITIES   147

RETEACHING THE LESSON

Determine if the boundary and shading are correct for each graph.

a. $y > -3x + 4$ yes

b. $y \le |x - 2|$ boundary: yes; shading: yes

35. Elections The 1992 presidential campaign had three prominent candidates. In April, a television news program poll stated that Ross Perot was favored by 35% of the American voters, with a margin of error of 3.3%. Write an inequality to describe the range of the percents of American voters who favored Ross Perot at that time. $31.7\% < v < 38.3\%$

Mixed Review

36. Find $[f \circ g](x)$ if $f(x) = x - 0.2x$ and $g(x) = x - 0.3x$. **(Lesson 1-2)** $0.56x$

37. Name the slope and y-intercept of the graph of $x - 2y - 4 = 0$. **(Lesson 1-5)**

38. Find $3A + 2B$ if $A = \begin{bmatrix} 4 & -2 \\ 5 & 7 \end{bmatrix}$ and $B = \begin{bmatrix} -3 & 5 \\ -4 & 3 \end{bmatrix}$. **(Lesson 2-2)**

$37.\ \frac{1}{2}, -2$

39. Solve $\begin{bmatrix} -1 & 2 \\ -4 & 3 \end{bmatrix} \cdot \begin{bmatrix} x \\ y \end{bmatrix} = \begin{bmatrix} 0 \\ 15 \end{bmatrix}$. **(Lesson 2-3)** $(-6, -3)$

40. Graph $y = \frac{4x}{x - 1}$. **(Lesson 3-4)** See margin.

41. College Entrance Exam Choose the best answer. Nine playing cards from the same deck are placed to form a large rectangle whose area is 180 in². There is no space between the cards and no overlap. What is the perimeter of this rectangle? B

(A) 29 in. **(B)** 58 in. **(C)** 64 in.
(D) 116 in. **(E)** 210 in.

MID-CHAPTER REVIEW

For graphs for Exercises 3–6, see Teacher's Answer Key.

1. Determine whether the graph of $y = |x| + 1$ is symmetric with respect to the x-axis, the y-axis, the line $y = x$, the line $y = -x$, or the origin. In your answer, include all symmetries that apply. **(Lesson 3-1)** y-axis

2. For each parent graph, describe the transformations that have taken place in the related graph of each function. **(Lesson 3-2)**
$f(x) = x^3$
   a. $y = x^3 + 3$ moved up 3 units
   b. $y = (x + 2)^3$ moved left 2 units
   c. $y = 2x^3 - 4$ narrower and moved down 4 units

3. Sketch the graph of $y = |2x - 1| + 2$ reflected over the line $y = x$. **(Lesson 3-2)**

4. Find the inverse of $y = x^2 + 6$. Then sketch the function and its inverse. **(Lesson 3-3)** $y = \pm\sqrt{x - 6}$

5. Determine any holes in the graph of $y = \frac{x^2 - x}{x^2 - 1}$. Then graph the function. **(Lesson 3-4)** $x = 1$

6. Graph $y \le |x + 2| - 5$. **(Lesson 3-5)**

---

148 CHAPTER 3 THE NATURE OF GRAPHS

EXTENDING THE LESSON

Math Power: Communication

Describe the solution to following system of inequalities by graphing: $y > |x - 2|$ *and* $y < |x + 1|$. The solution is the region determined by graphing the inequalities on the same coordinate plane. It is the region between the parallel lines that are the right branches of the absolute value graphs.

Mid-Chapter Review

The Mid-Chapter Review provides students with a brief review of the concepts and skills in Lessons 3–1 through 3–5. Lesson numbers are given at the end of problems or instructions lines so students may review concepts not yet mastered.

3-6 Tangent to a Curve

Objectives

3–6A
3–6B

After studying this lesson, you should be able to:
- find the derivative of a function, and
- find the slope and the equation of a line tangent to the graph of a function at a given point.

Lesson Resources

- Practice Master 3–6
- Enrichment Master 3–6
- Evaluation Master, Quiz C, p. 34
- Activity Master, p. 8

Transparency 3–6 contains the 5-Minute Check and a teaching aid for this lesson.

Application

The Department of Transportation in each state is responsible for marking hills with restrictions on the weight of vehicles, such as trucks or buses, that are allowed on the hill. One of the factors affecting this limit is the steepness or slope of the hill at given points. The steepness of the hill can be determined from the slope of the line tangent to the hill at those points.

A line tangent to a curve at a point on the curve is the line that passes through that point and has a slope that is the same as the slope of the curve at that point. In the figure at the right, two lines tangent to the graph of $f(x) = x^2$ are shown. One line is tangent at $(-1, 1)$, and the other line is tangent at $(2, 4)$. Lines that are tangent to a curve are also called **tangents** to a curve.

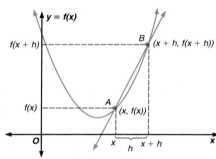

Suppose you graph a function $y = f(x)$. Suppose points A and B are two points on the graph near each other. The slope of line AB can be found by using the coordinates of A and B. Let the coordinates of A and B be $(x, f(x))$ and $(x + h, f(x + h))$, respectively. The slope is

$$\frac{f(x + h) - f(x)}{(x + h) - x} \text{ or } \frac{f(x + h) - f(x)}{h}.$$

Line AB is called a **secant line** because it intersects the curve more than once.

Suppose A remains fixed while you move B along the curve toward A. As B approaches A, the values of h become smaller and smaller, approaching zero. When $h = 0$, B coincides with A. Then the secant line becomes the line tangent to the curve at point A.

In the expression for the slope $\overleftrightarrow{AB}$, notice that $\frac{f(x + h) - f(x)}{h}$ is undefined when $h = 0$. However, the secant is a tangent when $h = 0$. So, the definition of the slope of the tangent line must be defined in a special way.

LESSON 3-6 TANGENT TO A CURVE 149

ALTERNATE TEACHING STRATEGIES

Using Discussion

Have students explore their own notions about what *finding a limit* or *reaching a limit* may be.

Using Computers

Use a spreadsheet to demonstrate that as *h* approaches zero, the slope of the secant line approaches the slope of the tangent line.

INTRODUCING THE LESSON

5-Minute Check
(over Lesson 3–5)

1. Graph the inequality
   $y < x - 3$.

2. Graph the inequality
   $y < |x + 4|$.

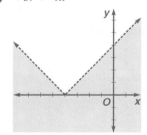

3. Solve $|x - 1| > 4$.
   $\{x \mid x > 5 \text{ or } x < -3\}$

4. Graph $y \geq \sqrt{x + 2}$.

Students should be familiar with evaluating a function for any domain value of the function.
1. If $f(x) = x^2 + 4$, find $f(-3)$.   13
2. If $f(x) = x^2 - 2x + 1$, find $f(1 - h)$. h^2

Motivating the Lesson

Have students label a 10 × 10 piece of grid paper with the integers 1 through 10 as they move to the right on the horizontal axis and 10 through 1 as they go up on the vertical axis. Now have them fold the paper along the line segments matching each integer. They have created the tangent lines to a curve, a hyperbola.

TEACHING THE LESSON

Teaching Tip   After introducing tangents and secants, remind students about the geometric definition of *tangent to a circle* and *secant*.

Teaching Tip   Before defining *derivative of f(x)*, ask those students who have studied physics if they can recall the definition of *instantaneous velocity at time x*. Compare the definition

$$\lim_{\Delta x \to 0} \frac{f(x + \Delta x) - f(x)}{\Delta x}$$ to the one that will be presented.

Let's consider the slope of the line tangent to the graph of $f(x) = 3x^2 - 4x + 1$ at $(2, 5)$. The slope of the secant line through two general points $A(x, f(x))$ and $B(x + h, f(x + h))$ is equal to $\frac{f(x + h) - f(x)}{h}$, where $h \neq 0$. Find the slope of the secant line to the graph of $f(x) = 3x^2 - 4x + 1$. That is, find $f(x + h)$.

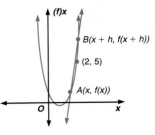

$$f(x + h) = 3(x + h)^2 - 4(x + h) + 1$$
$$= 3x^2 + 6xh + 3h^2 - 4x - 4h + 1$$

Now, find the slope of $\overleftrightarrow{AB}$.

$$m = \frac{f(x + h) - f(x)}{h} \quad \textit{Definition of slope}$$
$$= \frac{(3x^2 + 6xh + 3h^2 - 4x - 4h + 1) - (3x^2 - 4x + 1)}{h}$$
$$= \frac{6xh + 3h^2 - 4h}{h}$$
$$= 6x + 3h - 4$$

A general expression for the slope of the secant line for $f(x) = 3x^2 - 4x + 1$ is $6x + 3h - 4$. The slope of the secant line through specific points can be found by substituting values for x and h.

x	h	slope of the secant line
2	2	$6(2) + 3(2) - 4 = 14$
2	1	$6(2) + 3(1) - 4 = 11$
2	0.5	$6(2) + 3(0.5) - 4 = 9.5$
2	0.25	$6(2) + 3(0.25) - 4 = 8.75$
2	0.1	$6(2) + 3(0.1) - 4 = 8.3$
2	0.01	$6(2) + 3(0.01) - 4 = 7.97$

As h approaches zero, the middle term of $6x + 3h - 4$ also approaches zero, which means that $6x + 3h - 4$ approaches $6x - 4$. As h approaches zero, the secant line approaches the tangent; so, as h approaches zero, the slope of the secant line approaches the slope of the tangent. Therefore, the slope of the line tangent to the graph of $f(x) = 3x^2 - 4x + 1$ at $(x, f(x))$ is $6x - 4$.

The slope of the tangent at $(2, 5)$ can be found by substituting 2 for x in the expression $6x - 4$. The slope of the tangent at $(2, 5)$ is $6(2) - 4$, or 8.

$f'(x)$ is read "f prime of x."

The symbol $f'(x)$ is often used to denote the slope of the tangent line. It is defined as follows.

$$f'(x) = \lim_{h \to 0} \frac{f(x + h) - f(x)}{h} \qquad \textit{lim is read "the limit as h approaches zero"}$$

The symbol $\lim_{h \to 0} \frac{f(x + h) - f(x)}{h}$ means the limiting value of the slope as the value of h approaches zero. The function $f'(x)$ is called the **derivative** of $f(x)$.

As you saw, finding the derivative of a function can be time consuming and complex. There are rules that will make the process easier.

Rules for Derivatives	**Constant Rule:**	The derivative of a constant function is zero. If $f(x) = c$, then $f'(x) = 0$.
	Power Rule:	If $f(x) = x^n$, where n is a rational number, then $f'(x) = n \cdot x^{n-1}$.
	Constant Multiple of a Power Rule:	If $f(x) = cx^n$, where c and n are rational numbers, $f'(x) = n \cdot cx^{n-1}$.
	Sum Rule:	If $f(x) = g(x) + h(x)$, then $f'(x) = g'(x) + h'(x)$.

Example 1

Find the derivative of each function.

a. $f(x) = 6$ b. $f(x) = \dfrac{1}{x}$ c. $f(x) = 6x^3 - 4x^2 + 2x - 9$

a. $f(x) = 6$
$f'(x) = 0$ *Use the constant rule.*

b. $f(x) = \dfrac{1}{x}$
$f(x) = x^{-1}$
$f'(x) = -1x^{-2}$ *Use the power rule.*

c. $f(x) = 6x^3 - 4x^2 + 2x - 9$
Use the power rule and constant rule for each term. Then use the sum rule.
$f(x) = 3 \cdot 6x^{3-1} - 2 \cdot 4x^{2-1} + 1 \cdot 2x^{1-1} - 0$
$f'(x) = 18x^2 - 8x + 2$

Since the derivative is also the expression for the slope of the line tangent to the graph of a function, you can use the derivative to find the slope of the tangent at a given point on the graph.

Example 2

Find the slope of the line tangent to the graph of $f(x) = x^4 - 2x^3 + 5x^2 - 8$ at the point $(-2, 44)$.

Use the rules for derivatives to find $f'(x)$.

$f'(x) = 4x^{4-1} - 2(3)x^{3-1} + 5(2)x^{2-1} - 0$
$\quad\;\; = 4x^3 - 6x^2 + 10x$

Now evaluate $f'(x)$ for $x = -2$.

$f'(-2) = 4(-2)^3 - 6(-2)^2 + 10(-2)$
$\quad\quad\;\; = -32 - 24 - 20 \text{ or } -76$

The slope of the line tangent to the graph of $f(x) = x^4 - 2x^3 + 5x^2 - 8$ at the point $(-2, 44)$ is -76.

LESSON 3-6   TANGENT TO A CURVE   151

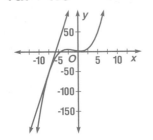
The derivative is also useful in many real-life applications.

Example 3

Cedar Point Amusement Park in Sandusky, Ohio, holds the Guinness World Record for the most roller coasters at a single site, with 10. The slope of one of the hills on the *Mean Streak*, a wooden roller coaster, can be modeled by the graph of the function $f(x) = \frac{-x^2}{2} + 5x + 50$. Find the slope of the line tangent to this curve at the point where $x = 1$.

$f(x) = \frac{-x^2}{2} + 5x + 50$

$f'(x) = 2(-\frac{1}{2})x^{2-1} + 1(5)x^{1-1} + 0$

$f'(x) = -x + 5$

$f'(1) = -(1) + 5$

$\qquad = 4 \qquad$ The slope of the tangent line at the point where $x = 1$ is 4.

If you know the coordinates of one point on a curve and the slope of the line tangent to a curve at that point, you can find the equation of the tangent line. This process uses the point-slope form of the equation.

Example 4

Find the equation of the line tangent to the graph of $y = 3x^3 - 2x^2 + 4x - 2$ at the point $(-2, -42)$. Write the equation in slope-intercept form. Then graph the function and the tangent line.

First, use the derivative to find the slope of the tangent line. Then, evaluate the derivative for $x = -2$.

$f(x) = 3x^3 - 2x^2 + 4x - 2$

$f'(x) = 9x^2 - 4x + 4$

$f'(-2) = 9(-2)^2 - 4(-2) + 4$

$f'(-2) = 48 \qquad$ *The slope of the tangent at $(-2, -42)$ is 48.*

Use the slope and the point $(-2, -42)$ to write the equation of the tangent line in slope-intercept form.

You can review the point-slope form of an equation in Lesson 1-5.

$y - y_1 = m(x - x_1)$

$y - (-42) = 48(x - (-2)) \qquad$ *(x, y) = (-2, -42), m = 48*

$\qquad y = 48x + 54$

You can use your graphing calculator to graph the function and the tangent line. You can use the ZOOM and TRACE features to verify that the line is tangent to the graph at $(-2, -42)$.

CHECKING FOR UNDERSTANDING

Communicating Mathematics

Read and study the lesson to answer each question. 1–2. See margin.

1. **Explain** the difference between a secant line and a tangent line.

2. **Describe** how to find the derivative of a function.

3. **Illustrate** at what point the line tangent to the graph of a function representing a highway hill would have a slope of zero. the point at the top of the hill

4. **Write** the symbol for the derivative of $f(x)$. $f'(x)$

Guided Practice

Find the derivative of each function.

5. $f(x) = x^2 + 5$ $f'(x) = 2x$

6. $f(x) = 2x^2 - 11$ $f'(x) = 4x$

7. $\frac{1}{2}x^4$ $f'(x) = 2x^3$

8. $f(x) = -2x^2 + 3x + 1$ $f'(x) = -4x + 3$

9. $f(x) = 0.6x^4 - 0.4x^2 - 0.8$
$f'(x) = 2.4x^3 - 0.8x$

10. $f(x) = 2x^6 + 8x^3 + 4x - 120$
$f'(x) = 12x^5 + 24x^2 + 4$

Find the slope of the line tangent to the graph of each function at the given point.

11. $y = x^2$, $(3, 9)$ 6

12. $y = x^2 + 4$, $(0, 4)$ 0

13. $y = 2x^2$, $(0, 0)$ 0

14. Find the equation of the line tangent to the graph of $y = x^2$ at $(2, 4)$. Write the equation in slope-intercept form. $y = 4x - 4$

EXERCISES

Practice

Find the derivative of each function. 15–20. See margin.

15. $f(x) = x^3 - 2x^2 + 4x$

16. $f(x) = 3x^2 - 8x + 5$

17. $f(x) = 0.3x^3 - 4x^2 + 5$

18. $f(x) = 4x^{-2} + 2x^{-3} + 4$

19. $f(x) = -4x^5 + 7x^3 + x$

20. $f(x) = \frac{3}{x^4} + x^2 - \frac{6}{13}$

Find the slope of the line tangent to the graph of each function at the given point.

21. $y = 2x^2$, $(-2, 8)$ –8

22. $y = \frac{1}{2}x^2 + 12$, $(-3, 16\frac{1}{2})$ –3

23. $y = -2x^2 + 3x + 10$, $(1, 11)$ –1

24. $y = 0.5x^2 - 0.4x - 0.5$, $(1, -0.4)$ 0.6

25. $y = x^2 + \frac{1}{6}x + 1$, $\left(\frac{1}{2}, \frac{4}{3}\right)$ $1\frac{1}{6}$

26. $y = \frac{x^3 - 4}{6}$, $\left(2, \frac{2}{3}\right)$ 2

27. Find the slope of the line tangent to the graph of $y = 2x^2 - 3x - 4$ at the point where $x = -2$. –11

28. Find the slope of the line tangent to the graph of $y = \frac{1}{2}x^2 + \frac{1}{4}x + \frac{1}{8}$ at the point where $x = \frac{1}{2}$. $\frac{3}{4}$

For graphs for Exercises 29–34, see Teacher's Answer Key.

30. $y = -x + 1$
31. $y = -2x + 2.25$
32. $y = -0.25$

Find the equation of the line tangent to the graph of each function at the given point. Write the equation in slope-intercept form. Graph the function and the tangent.

29. $y = x^2 - 3$, $(3, 6)$ $y = 6x - 12$

30. $y = x^2 - 3x + 2$, $(1, 0)$

31. $y = -x^2 - x + 2$, $(0.5, 1.25)$

32. $y = x^2 - 5x + 6$, $(2.5, -0.25)$

33. $y = 0.5x^2 + x - 1$, $(-4, 3)$
$y = -3x - 9$

34. $y = -3x^2 + x + 5$, $\left(\frac{1}{6}, 5\frac{1}{12}\right)$
$y = 5\frac{1}{12}$

RETEACHING THE LESSON

Ask students to discuss how they would find the equation of a line tangent to the graph of $f(x) = -2x^3 + 4x^2 - 3x + 6$ at the point $(-1, 15)$.

APPLYING THE LESSON

Homework Exercises

Assignment Guide

Average: 15–28, 29–37 odd, 39–41, 42, 44, 46–52

Enriched: 16–26 odd, 27–52

The red A, B, and C flags, printed only in the Teacher's Wraparound Edition, indicate the level of difficulty of the exercises.

Chapter 3, Quiz C, (Lessons 3–5 thorough 3–6), is available in the *Evaluation Masters*, p. 34.

Using Technology

For Exercises 39–41, remind students that they may need to use the ZOOM feature as well as the TRACE feature in order to determine the range of x values for which the slope is positive, negative, or zero.

Practice Masters Booklet, p. 18

NAME _____ DATE _____

3-6 **Practice Worksheet**

Tangent to a Curve

Find the derivative of each function.

1. $f(x) = 1.2x^4 - 3.5x^3 + 2.4x$

   $4.8\ x^3 - 10.5x^2 + 2.4$

2. $f(x) = 3x^{-3} - 5x^{-2} - 4x$

   $-9x^{-4} + 10x^{-3} - 4$

3. $f(x) = \frac{2}{x^5} - \frac{5}{x^2}$

   $-10x^{-6} + 10x^{-3}$

4. $f(x) = \frac{1}{3}x^3 + \frac{1}{2}x^2 + 3$

   $x^2 + x$

Find the slope of the line tangent to the graph of each function at the given point.

5. $y = 3x^2$, $(1, 3)$

   6

6. $y = \frac{1}{2}x^2 - 4$, $(2, -2)$

   2

7. $y = \frac{4x^3 - 7}{2}$, $(1, 0)$

   6

Find the equation of the line tangent to the graph of each function at the given point. Write the equation in slope-intercept form. Graph the function and the tangent.

8. $y = 2x^2 - 1$, $(-1, 1)$
   $y = -4x - 3$

9. $y = x^2 - 5x + 1$, $(0, 1)$
   $y = -5x + 1$

10. Find the coordinates of the point(s) at which the line tangent to the graph of $f(x) = x^2 - 1$ has slope –2.
    (–1, 0)

T18
Glencoe Division, Macmillan/McGraw-Hill

Find the coordinates of the point(s) at which the line tangent to the graph of the function $f(x)$ has the designated slope.

35. $f(x) = x^2 + 4x + 4, m = -2$ $(-3, 1)$

36. $f(x) = 3x^3 - 36x, m = 0$ $(2, -48), (-2, 48)$

37. $f(x) = \frac{-4}{x}, m = 1$ $(2, -2), (-2, 2)$

38. $f(x) = 4x^4 - 8x^2 - 5, m = 0$
    $(0, -5), (1, -9), (-1, -9)$

Graphing Calculator

Use a graphing calculator to graph the derivative of each function. Use the TRACE function to find the values of x for which the slope of the tangent line (Y) is positive, negative, and zero. 39–41. See margin.

39. $y = x^2 + 2x$

40. $y = 12 - x^2$

41. $y = x^3 - 3x^2 - 7$

42. See margin.

Critical Thinking

42. Write a convincing argument to prove that the derivative of a constant is zero.

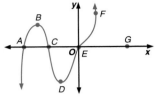

43. The graph of $g(x)$ is shown at the right. At which of the labeled points on the graph does $g'(x)$ appear to equal 0? Explain your reasoning. B and D, because at each of these points, the tangent line appears to be horizontal.

Applications and Problem Solving

44. **Physics** Instantaneous velocity is the instantaneous rate of change in position of a particle with respect to time, t seconds. If $f(t)$ is a function describing the position of the particle, then $f'(t)$ is the instantaneous velocity of that particle. Find the instantaneous velocity in meters per second of a particle whose function is $f(t) = 2t^2 - 8t + 3$, when $t = 5$. 12 m/s

45. **Entertainment** Blimpy is a clown who entertains at children's birthday parties. One of his tricks is magically blowing up spherical balloons with the tip of his finger. Actually, Blimpy has a hose from an air tank connected to his finger tip.

    a. Find the instantaneous rate of change in the volume of a balloon Blimpy is inflating with respect to the radius when the radius is 2 inches. *The formula for volume is* $V = \frac{4}{3}\pi r^3$. 16π in^3

    b. What does this rate of change mean? For each inch of increase in the radius, the volume increases 16π, or about 50.3 cubic inches.

Mixed Review

46. Graph $y + 6 \geq 4$. **(Lesson 1-3)** See margin.

47. Find the solution to the system of equations. **(Lesson 2-1)**
    $x + y = 1$
    $3x + 5y = 7$ $(-1, 2)$

48. Use an augmented matrix to solve the system of equations. **(Lesson 2-4)**
    $2x + y + z = 0$
    $3x - 2y - 3z = -21$
    $4x + 5y + 3z = -2$ $(-2, -3, 7)$

49. Find $f(-7, 4)$ if $f(x, y) = 5x - 2y + 1$. **(Lesson 2-5)** -42

50. Graph $y = (x + 2)^2 - 3$ and its inverse. **(Lesson 3-3)** See margin.

51. Graph $y \geq x^2 - 25$. **(Lesson 3-5)** See margin.

52. **College Entrance Exam** Choose the best answer. E
    A rectangular block of metal weighs 3 ounces. How many pounds will a similar block of the same metal weigh if the edges are twice as long?
    (A) 0.375   **(B)** 0.75   **(C)** 1.5   **(D)** 3   **(E)** 24

EXTENDING THE LESSON

Math Power: Connections

To find the derivative of the product of two functions, use the following rule: the derivative of $(f(x) \cdot g(x)) = f(x) \cdot g'(x) + g(x) \cdot f'(x)$. Find the derivative of $f(x) \cdot g(x)$ where $f(x) = x$ and $g(x) = x^2 + x + 1$.
$3x^2 + 2x + 1$

Additional Answer

51.

$(0, -25)$

3-7A Graphing Calculators: Locating Critical Points of Polynomial Functions

A graphing calculator can help you locate critical points of a polynomial function. A critical point is a point where the graph of the function changes direction or where the graph changes concavity. A critical point can be a relative minimum, a relative maximum, or a point of inflection.

Using the zoom function is a good way to locate critical points of a function. You can use the ZOOM key if you are using a TI-81 graphing calculator. You can also reset your range values manually or zoom in by a factor on both graphing calculators.

Example

Approximate the critical points on the graph of $y = x^4 - 3x^3 + 2x + 4$ to the nearest hundredth.

TI-81: [Y=] [X|T] [^] 4 [−] 3 [X|T] [^] 3 [+] 2 [X|T] [+] 4 [GRAPH]

Casio: [Graph] [ALPHA] [X] [x^y] 4 [−] 3 [ALPHA] [X] [x^y] 3 [+] 2 [ALPHA] [X] [+] 4 [EXE]

The viewing window of $[-5, 5]$ by $[-5, 10]$ contains a complete graph of the function. Looking at the graph, we can see that there are three critical points: one relative maximum and two relative minima.

Using TRACE and ZOOM, we find that the relative maximum occurs at $(0.54, 4.69)$, to the nearest hundredth. To find the y-coordinate on the Casio, press [SHIFT] [X↔Y].

The same process can be used to find the two relative minima. They are at $(-0.43, 3.41)$ and $(2.14, -0.15)$, to the nearest hundredth.

EXERCISES

Graph each function so that a complete graph is shown. Then approximate each of the critical points to the nearest hundredth and sketch the graph on a piece of paper.

5. $(-0.91, 0.04)$, $(2.23, -15.22)$
6. $(-0.71, 3.69)$, $(0, 4)$, $(0.31, 3.93)$

1. $y = x^2 + 2$ $(0, 2)$
3. $y = (x - 4)^3$ $(4, 0)$
5. $y = x^3 - 2x^2 - 6x - 3$
7. $y = -x^4 + 3x^2 - 4$
$(-1.23, -1.75), (0, -4), (1.23, -1.75)$

2. $y = x^2 + 3x - 6$ $(-1.5, -8.25)$
4. $y = x^3 - 4x + 1$ $(-1.15, 4.08)$,
6. $y = 2x^4 + x^3 - x^2 + 4$ $(1.15, -2.08)$
8. $y = x^5 + 4x^3 + 2$ $(0, 2)$

Objective Approximate the coordinates of relative maxima, relative minima, and point of inflection of the graph of a polynomial function.

Motivating the Lesson

Have students imagine the graph of a polynomial function that linearly models the path of a roller coaster track. Have them sketch the path and identify maximum and minimum points and the effect on the rider at those points.

Teaching Tip Students may ask whether the graph in Example 1 has another peak or valley outside the viewing window presented. Point out that a polynomial of degree 4 can have, at most, a total of three relative maxima and minima points.

More Examples

Approximate the critical points on the graph of $y = x^3 + x + 3$ to the nearest hundredth.
point of inflection: $(0, 3)$, no maxima or minima

Closing the Lesson

Ask students to predict the most maxima and minima points possible for different degree polynomials.

Homework Exercises

Assignment Guide

All: 1–8

NCTM Standards: 1–6, 13

Lesson Resources

- Practice Master 3–7
- Enrichment Master 3–7
- Technology Master, p. 5

 Transparency 3–7 contains the 5-Minute Check and a teaching aid for this lesson.

INTRODUCING THE LESSON

 5-Minute Check

(over Lesson 3–6)

1. Find the derivative of $f(x) = x^3 + 2x^2 - 4x + 1$.
   $3x^2 + 4x - 4$
2. Find the slope of the line tangent to the graph of $y = -3x^2$ at the point $(-2, -12)$.   12
3. Find the equation of the line tangent to the graph of $y = 3x^2 - 4x + 2$ at the point $(-1, 9)$. Write the equation in slope-intercept form. Graph the function and the tangent.
   $y = -10x - 1$

Motivating the Lesson

Have cooperative groups of students throw balls to each other outside of school. One student in each group should try to determine the maximum height of the ball. Another student should draw the path of the ball.

3-7 Graphs and Critical Points of Polynomial Functions

Objective
3–7

After studying this lesson, you should be able to:
- find the critical points of the graph of a polynomial function and determine if each is a minimum, maximum, or point of inflection.

Application

 FYI...

The first man in space was Soviet cosmonaut Yuri Gagarin. He made a single orbit around Earth on April 12, 1961.

On May 5, 1961, astronaut Alan B. Shepard, Jr. was launched from Cape Canaveral, Florida, on the first manned space flight from the United States. The Redstone booster rocket launched him into flight at an initial velocity of 6274 feet per second. Then the Project Mercury spacecraft fell to Earth off the coast of Florida. How long into the flight did the spacecraft, *Freedom 7*, reach its maximum height? *This problem will be solved in Example 1.*

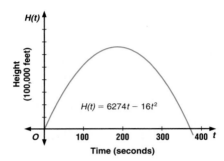

$H(t) = 6274t - 16t^2$

As an object is propelled upward, gravity tends to pull it back to Earth. This relationship can be expressed by the formula $H(t) = v_0t - 0.5gt^2$, where $H(t)$ is the distance above the starting point, v_0 is the initial velocity, t is the time elapsed, and g is the acceleration due to gravity. Earth has a constant acceleration of 32 feet/second^2 (9.8 meters/second ^{2}).

If 6274 ft/s is substituted for v_0 and 32 ft/s^2 for g, the formula becomes $H(t) = 6274t - 16t^2$. The graph of this function is shown at the left.

Remember that this is a graph of the function, not the actual path of the object being projected into the air.

Look at the graph of $H(t)$. The highest point on the graph is the point at which the slope of the tangent at that point is zero. We can use the derivative to determine the t-coordinate or time of that point.

$$H(t) = 6274t - 16t^2$$
$$H'(t) = 6274 - 32t \quad \textit{Find the derivative.}$$
$$0 = 6274 - 32t \quad \textit{Replace the slope with 0.}$$
$$-6274 = -32t \quad \textit{Solve for t.}$$
$$196 \approx t$$

The spacecraft reached its maximum height at 196 seconds after liftoff.

ALTERNATE TEACHING STRATEGIES

Using Models

To help students understand that the slope of the tangent line at a maximum or minimum point of a graph is 0, have them draw a graph on grid paper and then fold the paper so that the crease is a line tangent to the maximum or minimum point of the graph. Determine two points on the line and calculate its slope.

Using Graphing Calculators

Use graphing calculators to graph a function, trace a maximum (or minimum) value of the function, and to find other critical values of a function.

Example 1

APPLICATION

Aviation

Refer to the application at the beginning of the lesson. Find the maximum height of the Freedom 7 spacecraft.

We found that the maximum height occurred at 196 seconds. To find the maximum height, find $H(196)$.

$$H(t) = 6274t - 16t^2$$
$$H(196) = 6274(196) - 16(196)^2 \qquad t = 196$$
$$H(196) = 615{,}048$$

The maximum height is 615,048 feet which is about 116.5 miles.

The coordinates of the maximum point on the graph of $H(t)$ are $(196, 615{,}048)$.

A curve may possess three types of points called **critical points.** They are called critical points because at these points the nature of the graph changes. A critical point may be a **maximum**, a **minimum**, or a **point of inflection.** For a maximum, the curve changes from an increasing curve to a decreasing curve. For a minimum, the curve changes from a decreasing curve to an increasing curve. A point of inflection is a point where the graph changes its curvature as described below.

maximum

minimum

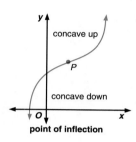

point of inflection

Some graphs may have more than one critical point. In the graph at the right, points A, B, and C are critical points. Point A is called a **relative maximum.** The y-coordinate of A is not the greatest value of the function, but it does represent the greatest value in an interval. Point B is a **relative minimum.** Likewise, its y-coordinate is not the least value of the function, but is a least value for an interval. Point C is a point of inflection.

The plural of maximum is maxima. *The plural of minimum is* minima.

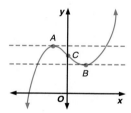

When $f'(x) = 0$, the line tangent to the curve at $(x, f(x))$ is parallel to the x-axis. To find the relative maximum or relative minimum of a function, you need to find the points on the graph where the slope of the tangent is 0. To do this, find the derivative, which is the function for the slope of the tangent. Then set it equal to zero and solve.

LESSON 3-7   GRAPHS AND CRITICAL POINTS OF POLYNOMIAL FUNCTIONS   157

TEACHING THE LESSON

Chalkboard Example

For Example 1

Refer to the application at the beginning of the lesson. Find the maximum height achieved by a rocket that follows a path described by $D(t) = 5856t - 16t^2$.
535,824 ft

Teaching Tip   After discussing *relative maximum* and *relative minimum points*, point out that a graph can have many relative maxima or minima.

To find the point of inflection, you need to find the derivative of the derivative and set it equal to zero and solve. This is called the second derivative and is represented by $f''(x)$.

Example 2 | **Determine the critical points for the graph of $f(x) = 3x^3 - 9x + 5$.**

$f(x) = 3x^3 - 9x + 5$

$f'(x) = 9x^2 - 9$ *Find the derivative.*

$0 = 9x^2 - 9$ *Replace $f'(x)$ with 0.*

$9 = 9x^2$ *Solve for x.*

$\pm 1 = x$

$f'(x) = 9x^2 - 9$

$f''(x) = 18x$ *Find the second derivative.*

$0 = 18x$ *Replace $f''(x)$ with 0.*

$0 = x$ *Solve for x.*

The graph of the function has three critical points, one when $x = 1$, one when $x = -1$, and one when $x = 0$. To find the y-coordinates of each point, find $f(1), f(-1)$, and $f(0)$.

$f(1) = 3(1)^3 - 9(1) + 5$

$f(1) = -1$

$f(-1) = 3(-1)^3 - 9(-1) + 5$

$f(-1) = 11$

$f(0) = 3(0)^3 - 9(0) + 5$

$= 5$

The critical points are at $(1, -1)$, at $(-1, 11)$, and at $(0, 5)$.   *Use your graphing calculator to verify the critical points.*

Once you have found the critical points of the graph of a function, you can determine if each point is a minimum, maximum, or point of inflection. You can determine this by testing points to either side of the critical point.

For $f(x)$ with $(a, f(a))$ as a critical point and h is a small value greater than zero:		
$f(a - h)$	$f(a + h)$	type of critical point
$f(a - h) < f(a)$	$f(a + h) < f(a)$	maximum
$f(a - h) > f(a)$	$f(a + h) > f(a)$	minimum
$f(a - h) < f(a)$	$f(a + h) > f(a)$	point of inflection
$f(a - h) > f(a)$	$f(a + h) < f(a)$	point of inflection

158   CHAPTER 3   THE NATURE OF GRAPHS

Example 3

The point at $(1, -4)$ is a critical point of the graph of $f(x) = x^3 - 3x - 2$. Determine whether this point represents a maximum, a minimum, or a point of inflection.

Evaluate the function for a point on either side of $(1, -4)$.

$f(1) = -4$

Let $h = 0.01$. Now find $f(1 + 0.01)$ and $f(1 - 0.01)$.

$f(1.01) = -3.9997$ *f(1.01) > f(1)*
$f(0.99) = -3.9997$ *f(0.99) > f(1)*

The point at $(1, -4)$ is a minimum of the graph.

Chalkboard Examples

For Example 3

The point at (2, 15) is a critical point of the graph of $f(x) = -4x^2 + 16x - 1$. Determine whether this point represents a maximum, a minimum, or a point of inflection.
maximum

For Example 4

Find the critical points of the graph of $f(x) = -2x^3 + 3x^2 - 5$. Then determine whether each point represents a maximum, a minimum, or a point of inflection.
(0, –5), relative minimum; (1, –4), relative maximum; (0.5, –4.5), point of inflection

Example 4

Find the critical points of the graph of $f(x) = 3x^3 - 18x^2 - 4$. Then determine whether each point represents a maximum, a minimum, or a point of inflection.

$f(x) = 3x^3 - 18x^2 - 4$
$f'(x) = 9x^2 - 36x$
$\quad 0 = 9x^2 - 36x$ *Replace f'(x) with 0.*
$\quad 0 = x^2 - 4x$ *Solve for x.*
$\quad 0 = x(x - 4)$ *Factor.*
$x = 0 \quad$ or $\quad x - 4 = 0$
$\qquad\qquad\qquad x = 4$

$f'(x) = 9x^2 - 36x$
$f''(x) = 18x - 36$ *Find the second derivative.*
$\quad 0 = 18x - 36$ *Replace f''(x) with 0.*
$\quad 2 = x$ *Solve for x.*

The critical points occur when $x = 0$, $x = 4$, and $x = 2$. Find $f(0)$, $f(4)$, and $f(2)$ to determine the y-coordinates of the points.

$f(0) = 3(0)^3 - 18(0)^2 - 4$
$f(0) = -4$
$f(4) = 3(4)^3 - 18(4)^2 - 4$
$f(4) = -100$
$f(2) = 3(2)^3 - 18(2)^2 - 4$
$f(2) = -52$

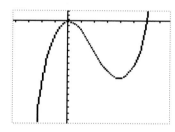

The critical points are at $(0, -4)$, at $(4, -100)$, and at $(2, -52)$. Now test points on each side of the critical points to determine their nature.

$f(0) = -4$ $f(4) = -100$
$f(0.01) = -4.0018$ *f(0.01) < f(0)* $f(4.01) = -99.9982$ *f(4.01) > f(4)*
$f(-0.01) = -4.0018$ *f(-0.01) < f(0)* $f(3.99) = -99.9982$ *f(3.99) > f(4)*
$(0, -4)$ is a relative maximum. $(4, -100)$ is a relative minimum.

(continued on the next page)

LESSON 3-7 GRAPHS AND CRITICAL POINTS OF POLYNOMIAL FUNCTIONS 159

$f(2) = -52$

$f(2.01) = -52.3600$ *f(2.01) < f(2)*

$f(1.99) = -51.6400$ *f(1.99) > f(2)*

$(2, -52)$ is a point of inflection.

The graphing calculator screen shown above verifies these results.

You can use critical points from the graphs of a function to solve real-life problems involving maximum and minimum.

Example 5

APPLICATION

Manufacturing

The Ripe and Juicy Fruit Company is developing plans for an open fruit bin that is 6 feet high and has a volume of 294 cubic feet. What are the dimensions of a rectangular base that will minimize the amount of material used (and thus, the cost of the material) to manufacture the open bin?

Let ℓ = the length of the base of the bin.
Find the value of ℓ terms of its width (w).

$V = \ell w h$

$294 = \ell w(6)$

$\dfrac{49}{w} = \ell$

Only positive values for ℓ and w are shown in the graph of $\ell = \dfrac{49}{w}$ at the right. Why?

The amount of material used to manufacture the bin is the surface area of the base plus the four sides.

surface area = area of base + area of front/back + area of 2 sides

$S(w) =$	ℓw	+	$2\ell h$	+	$2wh$
=	$\left(\dfrac{49}{w}\right)w$	+	$2\left(\dfrac{49}{w}\right)(6)$	+	$2w(6)$

$S(w) = 12w + 588w^{-1} + 49$

Now, find $S'(w)$ to determine maxima and/or minima.

$S'(w) = 12 - 588w^{-2}$

$0 = 12 - 588w^{-2}$ *Replace S'(w) with 0.*

$\dfrac{588}{w^2} = 12$ *Solve for w.*

$588 = 12w^2$

$\pm 7 = w$ *Disregard the negative value.*

If the width is 7 feet, the surface area is 217 square feet.

Now determine what type of critical point $(7, 217)$ is.

$f(7) = 217$

$f(6.99) = 217.0002$ *f(6.99) > f(7)*

$f(7.01) = 217.0002$ *f(7.01) > f(7)*

$(7, 217)$ are the coordinates of a minimum point.

If the width is 7 feet, the length is $\frac{49}{7}$ or 7 feet. The dimensions of the bin should be 7 feet by 7 feet by 6 feet.

Other important points on a graph are the x-intercepts and y-intercepts. Remember that a y-intercept of a relation is the y-coordinate of the point where $x = 0$. The x-intercept is the x-coordinate of the point where $y = 0$. It is possible for a graph to have no x- or y-intercept. Functions have at most one y-intercept. The number of x-intercepts may vary depending on the function.

In Chapter 1, you learned that the zero of a linear function is the point where $f(x) = 0$. The same is true for other types of functions. The zeros of a function are also the x-intercepts. The y-intercept can be determined by finding $f(0)$.

Example 6

Find the x-intercept(s) and y-intercept for $f(x) = x^3 + 6x^2 + 5x$. Then use a graphing calculator to verify your results.

To find the x-intercept(s), find the values of x for which $f(x) = 0$.

$f(x) = x^3 + 6x^2 + 5x$
$0 = x^3 + 6x^2 + 5x$ *Replace f(x) with 0.*
$0 = x(x + 5)(x + 1)$ *Factor.*

$x = 0$ or $x + 5 = 0$ or $x + 1 = 0$
                  $x = -5$ $x = -1$

The three x-intercepts are 0, -5, and -1.

To find the y-intercept, find $f(0)$.

$f(x) = x^3 + 6x^2 + 5x$
$f(0) = (0)^3 + 6(0)^2 + 5(0)$
$f(0) = 0$

The y-intercept is 0.

Use your graphing calculator to graph the function. Use the TRACE function to check the accuracy of the intercepts you found algebraically.

X=-5 Y=0

Chalkboard Example

For Example 6

Find the x-intercept(s) and y-intercept for $f(x) = 2x^3 - 5x^2 + 3x$. Then use a graphing calculator to verify your results.
x-intercepts: 0, 1, 1.5;
y-intercept: 0

EVALUATING THE LESSON

Checking for Understanding

Exercises 1–9 are designed to help you assess students' understanding through reading, writing, speaking, and modeling. You should work through Exercises 1–3 with your students and then monitor their work on Exercises 4–9.

Closing the Lesson

Modeling Activity   Have each student make an open box from a sheet of 8.5 in. × 11 in. paper. Discuss how to find the dimensions that result in the maximum volume of the box.

Practice Masters Booklet, p. 19

CHECKING FOR UNDERSTANDING

Communicating Mathematics

Read and study the lesson to answer each question. 1–3. See margin.

1. **Describe** the three types of critical points.

2. **Explain** how you determine each type of critical point.

3. **Sketch** an example of a function with two relative maxima and one relative minimum.

LESSON 3-7   GRAPHS AND CRITICAL POINTS OF POLYNOMIAL FUNCTIONS   161

Additional Answers

1. maximum: a point where the y-value is the maximum for the function; minimum: point where the y-value is the minimum for the function; point of inflection: point where the graph of the function changes curvature.

2. After determining the coordinates of the critical points, test values on each side of the point to determine if it is a maximum, minimum, or point of inflection.

3.

3-7 **Practice Worksheet**

NAME _____ DATE _____

Graphs and Critical Points of Polynomial Functions

Find the critical points for each function. Then determine whether each point is a minimum, a maximum, or a point of inflection.

1. $f(x) = x^2 - 6x + 1$
   $(3, -8)$, min

2. $f(x) = 2x^2 - 10x + 3$
   $\left(\frac{5}{2}, -\frac{19}{2}\right)$, min

3. $f(x) = -3x^2 + 9x$
   $\left(\frac{3}{2}, \frac{27}{4}\right)$, max

4. $f(x) = -x^2 + 5x - 1$
   $\left(\frac{5}{2}, \frac{21}{4}\right)$ max

5. $f(x) = x^3 + x^2 - x$
   $(-1, 1)$, max
   $\left(\frac{1}{3}, -\frac{5}{27}\right)$, min

6. $f(x) = x^4 - 10x^2 + 9$
   $(-\sqrt{5}, -16)$, min
   $(0, 9)$, max
   $(\sqrt{5}, -16)$, min

Find the x- and y-intercepts of the graph of each function.

7. $f(x) = 2x^2 + 5x - 3$
   x-intercepts: $-3, \frac{1}{2}$
   y-intercept: -3

8. $f(x) = x^2 - 10x + 21$
   x-intercepts: 3,7
   y-intercept: 21

9. $f(x) = (x + 1)(x - 1)(x + 2)$
   x-intercepts: $-2, -1, 1$
   y-intercept: -2

10. $f(x) = x^3 + 5x^2 + 6x$
    x-intercepts: $-3, -2, 0$
    y-intercept: 0

11. $f(x) = (x - 2)^3$
    x-intercept: 2
    y-intercept: -8

12. $f(x) = x^4 + 2x^2 + 1$
    x-intercepts: none
    y-intercept: 1

13. Graph $f(x) = 2x^3 + 3x$.

T19
Glencoe Division, Macmillan/McGraw-Hill

Homework Exercises

Assignment Guide

Average: 10–17, 18–26 even, 27, 28,
31, 33, 35–40
Enriched: 16–40

The red A, B, and C flags, printed only in the Teacher's Wraparound Edition, indicate the level of difficulty of the exercises.

Using Technology

For Exercises 27–30, remind students that they may need to adjust the range intervals in order to see a *complete* graph. They can start with the standard intervals for their calculators and make adjustments as necessary.

Additional Answers

14. rel max: (0, 3), rel min:
$\left(\frac{2}{3}, 2\frac{23}{27}\right)$, pt of inf: $\left(\frac{1}{3}, \frac{79}{27}\right)$

15. rel min: $\left(\frac{1}{3}, \frac{26}{27}\right)$, rel max:

(0, 1), pt of inf: $\left(\frac{1}{6}, \frac{53}{54}\right)$

16. rel max: (0, 16), rel min:
$(\pm 2, 0)$, pt of inf: $\left(\pm\frac{2\sqrt{3}}{3}, 7\frac{1}{9}\right)$

20. x: –3, 3, –1; y: –9
21. x: 0, 5, 7; y: 0

24.

25.

26.

Guided Practice   Find the critical points for each function. Then determine whether each point is a *minimum*, a *maximum*, or a *point of inflection*.

4. $f(x) = x^2 + 4x - 12$ (–2, –16), min
5. $f(x) = -2x^2 - 6x + 5$ $\left(-\frac{3}{2}, \frac{19}{2}\right)$, max
6. $f(x) = x^2 - x - 6$ (0.5, –6.25), min
7. $f(x) = 12x^3$ (0, 0), inflection

Find the x- and y-intercepts of the graph of each function.

8. $f(x) = 3x^2 - 8x + 5$ $x: \frac{5}{3}, 1; y: 5$
9. $f(x) = x^2 - x$ $x: 0, 1; y: 0$

EXERCISES

Practice   Find the critical points for each function. Then determine whether each point is a *minimum*, a *maximum*, or a *point of inflection*. 14–16. See margin.

10. $f(x) = x^2 - 8x + 10$ (4, –6), min
11. $g(t) = t^2 + 2t - 15$ (–1, –16), min
12. $D(r) = -r^2 - 2r + 8$ (–1, 9), max
13. $f(x) = 3x^2 - 4x + 1$ $\left(\frac{2}{3}, -\frac{1}{3}\right)$, min
14. $S(w) = w^3 - w^2 + 3$
15. $f(x) = 2x^3 - x^2 + 1$
16. $D(r) = r^4 - 8r^2 + 16$
17. $V(w) = w^5 - 28$
(0, –28), inflection

Find the x- and y-intercepts of the graph of each function.   19. $x: -\frac{3}{2}, -\frac{5}{2}; y: 15$

20–21. See margin.

18. $f(x) = x^2 + 12x + 32$ x: –8, –4; y: 32
19. $f(x) = 4x^2 + 16x + 15$
20. $f(x) = (x + 3)(x - 3)(x + 1)$
21. $f(x) = x^3 - 12x^2 + 35x$
22. $f(x) = (x + 7)^5$ x: –7, y: 16,807
23. $f(x) = x^4 - 13x^2 + 36$
x: 2, –2, 3, –3; y: 36

Graph each function. 24–26. See margin.

24. $f(x) = x^4 - 2x^2 - 8$
25. $D(t) = t^3 + t$
26. $S(w) = w^3 - 7w - 6$
27–30. See margin.

Graphing Calculator   Use a graphing calculator to graph each function. Use the TRACE and BOX functions to determine the x-intercept(s), y-intercept, relative minima, and relative maxima.

27. $y = x^4 - 26x^2 + 25$
28. $y = 6x^3 + x^2 - 5x - 2$
29. $y = x^3 - 4x^2 - 25x + 28$
30. $y = x^4 + 4x^3 + 3x^2 - 4x - 4$

Critical Thinking   31. Find the derivative of $f(x) = 2\sqrt{x} + 3\sqrt[3]{x^2} - 4\sqrt[4]{x}$. $x^{-\frac{1}{2}} + 2x^{-\frac{1}{3}} - x^{-\frac{3}{4}}$

32. Which families of graphs have points of inflection but no maximum or minimum points? equations in the form $y = (x + a)^n + b$, where n is odd, and a and b are real numbers

33. **Horticulture**   *Ameriflora* was an international flower exhibit held in Columbus, Ohio, in 1992. A rectangular region of the exhibit was fenced off to landscape for the fall season. The area of the region was 125,000 square feet. A type of fence costing \$20 per foot was used along the back and front of the region because these were high-traffic areas. A less expensive fence costing \$10 per foot was used for the other sides. What were the dimensions of the region that minimized the cost of the fence? 500 ft by 250 ft

---

Additional Answers

27–30. For graphs, see Teacher's Answer Key. Decimal answers are approximations.

27. x: 1, –1, 5, –5; y: 25
rel max: (0, 25)
rel min: (3.6, –144),
(–3.6, –144)

28. x: $-\frac{1}{2}$, 1, $-\frac{2}{3}$, y: –2

rel max: (–0.6, 0.07)
rel min: (0.5, –3.5)

29. x: 1, –4, 7; y: 28
rel max: (–1.8, 54)
rel min: (4.5, –74.4),
(3.1, –52.1)

30. x: –2, –1, 1; y: –4
rel max: (–1.4, 0.35)
rel min: (–2, 0), (0.4, –4.8)

34. Agriculture Marta Yoshiki raises cotton. If she harvests her crop now, the yield will average 120 pounds of cotton per acre and will sell for $0.48 per pound. However, she knows that if she waits, her yield will increase by about 10 pounds per week, but the price will decrease by $0.03 per pound per week.

  a. How many weeks should she wait in order to maximize her profit? 2 weeks

  b. What is the maximum profit? $58.80 per acre

Mixed Review

35. Show that $P(4, 2)$ is the midpoint of $\overline{AB}$ that has endpoints $A(9, 3)$ and $B(-1, 1)$. (**Lesson 1-4**) See margin.

36. Explain how you perform scalar multiplication on a 2×2 matrix. Give an example. (**Lesson 2-2**) See margin.

37. Find the determinant for $\begin{bmatrix} -15 & 5 \\ -9 & 3 \end{bmatrix}$. Tell whether an inverse exists for the matrix. (**Lesson 2-3**) 0, no

38. Describe the transformation(s) of the parent graph of $f(x) = x^2$ that are required to graph $(x + 4)^2 - 8 = y$. (**Lesson 3-2**) 4 units left and 8 units down

39. Find the equation of the line tangent to the graph of $y = 2x^2 - 3x$ at $(-1, 5)$. (**Lesson 3-6**) $y = -7x - 2$

40. College Entrance Exam Choose the best answer. C

The area of a right triangle is 12 in². The ratio of the lengths of its legs is 2:3. Find the length of the hypotenuse.

  (A) $\sqrt{13}$ in.   (B) 26 in.   (C) $2\sqrt{13}$ in.   (D) 52 in.   (E) $4\sqrt{13}$ in.

CASE STUDY FOLLOW-UP

Refer to Case Study 4: *The U.S. Economy* on pages 966–969.

Spider Industries, a U.S.-based company, test-marketed an electronic cobweb destroyer in Japan. The function $R = 160x - \frac{1}{5}x^2$ specifies the company's revenues (R) in terms of the number of destroyers sold.

1. Find the revenue generated by sales of the following number of destroyers.

  a. 20 $3120   **b.** 100 $14,000   **c.** 500 $30,000

2. How many destroyers must the company sell to maximize the revenue? At what selling price must they sell destroyers to accomplish this? 400 destroyers; $80

3. The company sold all of its destroyers, maximizing its revenue. How many times would they have to repeat their accomplishment to make up the United States' 1990 trade imbalance with Japan? 1,281,250 times

4. Research Find out about the U.S. trade imbalance with Japan. What is its cause? What are U.S. companies doing to overcome it? Summarize your findings in a 1-page paper. See students' work.

EXTENDING THE LESSON

Math Power: Reasoning

Give an example of a function whose second derivative is $18x - 8$.

Answers will vary. Sample: $3x^3 - 4x^2 + x - 1$

Case Study Follow-Up

This activity provides an opportunity to do research and apply mathematics in solving problems related to issues that may face students in their adult lives. Case Study 4 is located on pages 966–969.

Additional Answers

35. Sample answer:
P lies on $\overline{AB}$.
$$AP \stackrel{?}{=} PB$$
$$\sqrt{(9 - 4)^2 + (3 - 2)^2}$$
$$\stackrel{?}{=} \sqrt{(4 + 1)^2 + (2 - 1)^2}$$
$$\sqrt{26} = \sqrt{26}$$
$$AP = PB$$
So P is midpoint of $\overline{AB}$.

36. Multiply each element of the matrix by the scalar.
$$2\begin{bmatrix} 1 & 2 \\ 3 & 4 \end{bmatrix} = \begin{bmatrix} 2 & 4 \\ 6 & 8 \end{bmatrix}$$

Enrichment Masters Booklet, p. 19

3-7 NAME _____ DATE _____
Enrichment Worksheet

"Unreal" Equations

There are some equations that cannot be graphed on the real-number coordinate system. One example is the equation $x^2 - 2x + 2y^2 + 8y + 14 = 0$. Completing the squares in x and y gives the equation $(x - 1)^2 + 2(y + 2)^2 = -5$.

For any real numbers, x and y, the values of $(x - 1)^2$ and $2(y + 2)^2$ are nonnegative. So, their sum cannot be -5. Thus, no real values of x and y satisfy the equation; only imaginary values can be solutions.

Determine whether each equation can be graphed on the real number plane. Write yes or no.

1. $(x + 3)^2 + (y - 2)^2 = -4$ no

2. $x^2 - 3x + y^2 + 4y = -7$ no

3. $(x + 2)^2 + y^2 - 6y + 8 = 0$ yes

4. $x^2 + 16 = 0$ no

5. $x^4 + 4y^2 + 4 = 0$ no

6. $x^2 + 4y^2 + 4xy + 16 = 0$ no

In Exercises 7 and 8, for what values of k :
a. will the solutions of the equation be imaginary?
b. will the graph be a point?
c. will the graph be a curve?
d. Choose a value of k for which the graph is a curve and sketch the curve on the axes provided.

7. $x^2 - 4x + y^2 + 8y + k = 0$
a. $k > 20$; b. $k = 20$;
c. $k < 20$;
d.

8. $x^2 + 4x + y^2 - 6y - k = 0$
a. $k < -13$; b. $k = -13$;
c. $k > -13$;
d.

T19
Glencoe Division, Macmillan/McGraw-Hill

Lesson Resources

- Practice Master 3–8
- Enrichment Master 3–8
- Evaluation Master, Quiz D, p. 34
- Activity Master, p. 9

 Transparency 3–8 contains the 5-Minute Check and a teaching aid for this lesson.

INTRODUCING THE LESSON

 5-Minute Check

(over Lesson 3–7)

1. Find the critical points for the graph of $f(x) = x^2 - 6x + 8$. Determine whether each point represents a minimum, maximum, or a point of inflection.   **(3, –1), minimum**
2. Find the *x*- and *y*-intercepts of the graph of $f(x) = x^2 - x - 6$.   **x: –2, 3; y: –6**
3. Graph $f(x) = x^3 + x$.

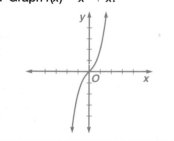

Motivating the Lesson

Have the students study a map of their city. Look for streets that may appear in discontinuous sections. For example:

Elm street cannot be followed by your finger without lifting your finger from the map.

3-8   Continuity and End Behavior

Objectives
3–8A
3–8B

After studying this lesson, you should be able to:
- determine continuity or discontinuity of functions, and
- identify the end behavior of graphs.

Application

Jeffry Stuart developed an interactive videodisc that is used to assist diabetic teenagers understand their disease better. Each videodisc sells for $600. Mr. Stuart receives an 8% royalty for every disc sold up to 200 discs. For the 200th disc sold, he will receive a one-time payment of $100. For every disc sold after the 200th, he will receive a 16% royalty.

The graph at the left demonstrates the relationship between the number of discs sold and the amount of money Jeffry Stuart receives for each disk.

If $0 < x < 200$, $f(x) = 0.08(\$600)$ or $48.

If $x = 200$, $f(x) = \$100$.

If $x > 200$, $f(x) = 0.16(\$600)$ or $96.

All polynomial functions are continuous.

This graph represents a type of step function. Step functions have breaks in the function. That is, you cannot trace the graph of the function without lifting your pencil. A function is said to be **continuous** at point (x, y) if it is defined at that point and passes through that point without a break. If there is a break in the graph through that point, the function is said to be **discontinuous** at that point. In the function shown above, $f(x)$ is discontinuous at the point where $x = 200$.

Each of the functions graphed below are discontinuous at some point. Each illustrates a different type of discontinuity.

Infinite Discontinuity   **Jump Discontinuity**   **Point Discontinuity**

Asymptotes in a graph indicate discontinuity.

The application above illustrates a function with jump discontinuity.

ALTERNATE TEACHING STRATEGIES

Using Communication

Describe the behavior of $f(x) = \dfrac{x^2 - 4}{x + 2}$ near $x = -2$.

Using Computers

Create a spreadsheet of values to help determine the end behavior of a graph. In one column, enter values of *x* that get increasingly greater. In the other column, enter the value of the function at *x*.

A function may have discontinuity but be continuous over an interval. A function is continuous on an interval if it is continuous at every point in that interval without exception. In the graph of $f(x) = \dfrac{1}{x^2}$ on the previous page, the function is continuous for $x > 0$ and $x < 0$, but is discontinuous for $x = 0$.

The function $f(x) = \begin{cases} x^2 + 1 \text{ if } x \le 0 \\ x \text{ if } x > 0 \end{cases}$, shown on the previous page, has a segmented definition. That is, it includes different expressions for different parts of its domain. While this function is discontinuous, other segmented functions are continuous. The graph of $f(x) = \begin{cases} x \text{ if } x \ge 0 \\ x^2 \text{ if } x < 0 \end{cases}$, shown at the right, is an example of a segmented function that is continuous.

Chalkboard Example

For Example 1

Determine whether each function is continuous.
a. $y = 3x^2 + x - 7$ yes

b. $f(x) = \dfrac{|3x|}{x}$ no

c. $y = \dfrac{-1}{3x^2}$ no

d. $f(x) = \dfrac{x^2 - 4}{x + 2}$ no

Continuity on an Interval	A function $f(x)$ is continuous on an interval if it is continuous for each value of x in that interval.

There are functions that are impossible to graph in the real number system. Some of these functions are said to be *everywhere discontinuous*. An example of such a function is $f(x)$, where $\begin{cases} f(x) = 1 \text{ when } x \text{ is rational} \\ f(x) = 2 \text{ when } x \text{ is irrational} \end{cases}$.

Example 1

Determine whether each function is continuous.

a. $y = 3x^2 + 7$

a. Graph the function.
   The function is defined for every point in the domain.

   The function is continuous.

b. $f(x) = \dfrac{|2x|}{x}$

b. When $x > 0$, $f(x) = 2$.
   When $x < 0$, $f(x) = -2$.
   This function is undefined at $x = 0$ in both intervals.

   This function has jump discontinuity at $x = 0$.

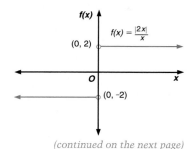

(continued on the next page)

LESSON 3-8   CONTINUITY AND END BEHAVIOR   165

c. $y = \dfrac{1}{2x^2}$

c. The graph of this function has an asymptote at $x = 0$.
For $x > 0$, as $x \to 0$, $y \to \infty$.
For $x < 0$, as $x \to 0$, $y \to \infty$.

This function has infinite discontinuity at $x = 0$.

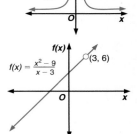

d. $f(x) = \dfrac{x^2 - 9}{x - 3}$

d. This function is undefined at $x = 3$.
Since $\dfrac{x^2 - 9}{x - 3} = x + 3$, the graph of
$f(x)$ resembles $g(x) = x + 3$, but has a point discontinuity at $x = 3$.

The **end behavior** of the graph of a function refers to the behavior of $f(x)$ as $|x|$ becomes very large. Notice in the graph of $f(x) = \dfrac{x^2 - 9}{x - 3}$ shown above, as $x \to \infty$, $f(x) \to \infty$ and as $x \to -\infty$, $f(x) \to -\infty$.

Example 2

Describe the end behavior of the graphs of $f(x) = 4x^3$ and $g(x) = 4x^3 - 3x^2 + 2x - 5$.

Use your calculator to observe what happens to $f(x)$ and $g(x)$ as $|x|$ becomes increasingly great in each function.

Values for f(x) and g(x) may vary for different calculators. However, the pattern remains the same.

x	$f(x)$
−100,000	-4×10^{15}
−10,000	-4×10^{12}
−1000	−4,000,000,000
−100	−4,000,000
−10	−4000
−1	−4
0	0
1	4
10	4000
100	4,000,000
1000	4,000,000,000
10,000	4×10^{12}
100,000	4×10^{15}

x	$g(x)$
−100,000	-4.00003×10^{15}
−10,000	-4.0003×10^{12}
−1000	−4,003,002,005
−100	−4,030,205
−10	−4325
−1	−14
0	−5
1	−2
10	3715
100	3,970,195
1000	3,997,001,995
10,000	3.9997×10^{12}
100,000	3.99997×10^{15}

Notice that $f(x)$ and $g(x)$ have relatively small absolute values in the $-10 < x < 10$ interval. However, as the x values become increasingly greater (or less), the values of the two functions approach the same two extremes. That is, as $x \to \infty$, $f(x) \to \infty$ and $g(x) \to \infty$. As $x \to -\infty$, $f(x) \to -\infty$ and $g(x) \to -\infty$.

As you can see from Example 2, calculations of $f(x)$ and $g(x)$ for $|x|$ are tedious and time-consuming. The behavior of $g(x)$ was the same as its related function $f(x)$. Suppose $P(x) = a_0x^n + a_1x^{n-1} + a_2x^{n-2} + ... + a_{n-1}x + a_n$ with $n \geq 1$. The end behavior of $P(x)$ will be the same as the end behavior of $f(x) = a_0x^n$. The values of a_0 and n can indicate the end behavior of the graph of any polynomial function.

Using Technology

A graphing calculator can be used to determine the end behavior of a function. Students should reset the range values to successively larger values and view the function. The ZOOM feature of some calculators may also be helpful.

End Behavior of Graphs of Polynomial Functions ($n \geq 1$)

a_0	n	$x \rightarrow$	$P(x) \rightarrow$
positive	even	∞	∞
positive	even	$-\infty$	∞
positive	odd	∞	∞
positive	odd	$-\infty$	$-\infty$

a_0	n	$x \rightarrow$	$P(x) \rightarrow$
negative	even	∞	$-\infty$
negative	even	$-\infty$	$-\infty$
negative	odd	∞	$-\infty$
negative	odd	$-\infty$	∞

EXPLORATION: Graphing Calculator

Determine the end behavior of $f(x) = x^3 + 5x^2 - 4$ with a graphing calculator.

To determine the end behavior of a function using a graphing calculator, view the graph of $f(x)$ using successively larger viewing windows. Establish the viewing windows by setting and resetting the range values.

1. XMIN: -10   XMAX: 10   XSCL: 1
   YMIN: -10   YMAX: 10   YSCL: 1

2. XMIN: -10   XMAX: 10   XSCL: 1
   YMIN: -100   YMAX: 100   YSCL: 10

3. XMIN: -20   XMAX: 20   XSCL: 2
   YMIN: -400   YMAX: 400   YSCL: 40

4. XMIN: -100   XMAX: 100   XSCL: 10
   YMIN: -10000   YMAX: 10000
   YSCL: 1000

LESSON 3-8   CONTINUITY AND END BEHAVIOR   167

Chalkboard Example

For Example 3

Graph each function. Determine the interval(s) for which the function is increasing and the interval(s) for which the function is decreasing.

a. $f(x) = x^2 - 7$ For $x < 0$, the function is decreasing. For $x > 0$, the function is increasing.

b. $f(x) = -\frac{1}{x}$ The function has asymptotes at $x = 0$ and $y = 0$. For $x < 0$, the function is decreasing. For $x > 0$, the function is increasing.

c. $h(x) = x^3 + x^2 - x + 4$ The graph has critical points at $x = \frac{1}{3}$ and $x = -1$. For $x < -1$, the graph is increasing. For $-1 < x < \frac{1}{3}$, the function is decreasing. For $x > \frac{1}{3}$, the function is increasing.

Additional Answers

1. Infinite discontinuity occurs when a graph has an asymptote. Jump discontinuity occurs when the graph is defined for all values of x, but the graph itself is broken for a given value of x. Point discontinuity occurs when the function is defined for all values of x, except one, and would be continuous if that point were included.

2. If $a > b$, and $f(a) > f(b)$, the function is increasing. If $a > b$, and $f(a) < f(b)$, the function is decreasing.

3. If you can trace a graph without lifting your pencil, it is continuous.

4. The end behavior of the function is similar to the end behavior of the parent function defined by the first term.

5. As $x \to \infty, y \to -\infty$. As $x \to -\infty$, $y \to -\infty$.

6. As $x \to \infty, y \to \infty$. As $x \to -\infty$, $y \to -\infty$.

7. As $x \to \infty, y \to \pm\infty$. As $x \to -\infty$, $y \to \pm\infty$.

8. As $x \to \infty, y \to -\infty$. As $x \to -\infty$, $y \to \infty$.

In Lesson 3-7, you learned how to determine whether a critical point was a maximum, a minimum, or a point of inflection by testing points on each side of the critical point. Functions can also be described as increasing or decreasing functions.

Increasing and Decreasing Functions	A function $f(x)$ is increasing if and only if $f(x_1) < f(x_2)$ whenever $x_1 < x_2$. A function $f(x)$ is decreasing if and only if $f(x_1) > f(x_2)$ whenever $x_1 < x_2$.

The function must be defined for the values x_1 and x_2.

Observe the two graphs below. The graph of $f(x) = x^3$ illustrates an increasing function. That is, as you trace the function from left to right, $f(x)$ increases. The graph of $f(x) = (-x)^3$ illustrates a decreasing function. As you trace the function from left to right, $f(x)$ decreases.

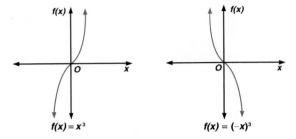

The graphs of many functions illustrate characteristics of both increasing and decreasing functions for different intervals of the function. These intervals often occur between the relative maximum(s) and relative minimum(s).

Example 3 | **Graph each function. Determine the interval(s) for which the function is increasing and the interval(s) for which the function is decreasing.**

a. $f(x) = -x^2 + 12$

a. The graph has a relative maximum at $x = 0$.
For $x < 0$, the function is increasing.
For $x > 0$, the function is decreasing.

b. $g(x) = \frac{1}{x}$

b. The graph has asymptotes at $x = 0$ and $y = 0$.
For $x < 0$, the function is decreasing.
For $x > 0$, the function is decreasing.

9. As $x \to \infty, y \to 0$. As $x \to -\infty$, $y \to 0$.

10. As $x \to \infty, y \to -\infty$. As $x \to -\infty$, $y \to \infty$.

c. $h(x) = 2x^3 + 8x^2 + 8x + 5$

c. $h'(x) = 6x^2 + 16x + 8$
$0 = 6x^2 + 16x + 8$
$0 = 3x^2 + 8x + 4$
$0 = (3x + 2)(x + 2)$

The graph has a relative maximum at $x = -2$ and a relative minimum at $x = -\frac{2}{3}$.

For $x < -2$, the function is increasing.

For $-2 < x < -\frac{2}{3}$, the function is decreasing.

For $x > -\frac{2}{3}$, the function is increasing.

$(-2, 5)$

$\left(-\frac{2}{3}, 2\frac{17}{27}\right)$

$h(x) = 2x^3 + 8x^2 + 8x + 5$

EVALUATING THE LESSON

Checking for Understanding

Exercises 1–13 are designed to help you assess students' understanding through reading, writing, speaking, and modeling. You should work through Exercises 1–4 with your students and then monitor their work on Exercises 5–13.

Closing the Lesson

Writing Activity   Write a paragraph that explains how to determine the end behavior of a function.

CHECKING FOR UNDERSTANDING

Communicating Mathematics

Read and study the lesson to answer each question. 1–4. See margin.

1. **Describe** three kinds of discontinuity.

2. **Explain** when a function is decreasing and when it is increasing.

3. **Demonstrate** how to tell if the graph of a function is continuous.

4. **Compare** the end behavior of $g(x) = x^5 + 4x^4 + 3x^2 + 8$ with the end behavior of the parent function $f(x) = x^5$. Make a conjecture about the end behavior of any function $g(x)$ and its parent function $f(x)$.

Guided Practice

Determine whether each graph has *infinite discontinuity*, *jump discontinuity*, or *point discontinuity*, or is *continuous*. Then describe the end behavior of each graph. 5–10. For end behavior, see margin.

5.

point discontinuity

6.

jump discontinuity

7.

infinite discontinuity

8.

continuous

9.

infinite discontinuity

10.

jump discontinuity

LESSON 3-8   CONTINUITY AND END BEHAVIOR   169

RETEACHING THE LESSON

Give students a list of functions to graph on their graphing calculator. Have them describe the end behavior and look for characteristics in the equation of the function to correspond with the behavior.

Practice Masters Booklet, p. 20

APPLYING THE LESSON

Homework Exercises

Assignment Guide

Average: 14–28, 31, 32, 34, 35, 37–42
Enriched: 14–22 even, 24–42

The red A, B, and C flags, printed only in the Teacher's Wraparound Edition, indicate the level of difficulty of the exercises.

Chapter 3, Quiz D, (Lessons 3–7 through 3–8), is available in the *Evaluation Masters*, p. 34.

Exercise Note

For Exercises 27–30, encourage students to graph the function without the use of a calculator or computer. It is difficult to see an *open* point on a graphics screen.

Using Technology

For Exercises 31–33, remind students that they may need to adjust the range intervals in order to see the end behavior of the graph.

Additional Answers

24. $x \to \infty$, $f(x) \to \infty$; $x \to -\infty$, $f(x) \to -\infty$
25. $x \to \infty$, $f(x) \to \infty$; $x \to -\infty$, $f(x) \to \infty$
26. $x \to \infty$, $f(x) \to -\infty$; $x \to -\infty$, $f(x) \to \infty$
31a. continuous
31b. decreasing: $-\infty < x < 2.5$
     increasing: $2.5 < x < \infty$
32a. no
32b. decreasing for all x, $x \neq -1$
33a. continuous
33b. decreasing: $-\infty < x < -9$
     increasing: $-9 < x < \infty$

Determine the intervals for which each function is *increasing* or *decreasing*.

11. all reals: increasing

11. $y = 2x + 5$ 12. $y = \dfrac{1}{x}$ 13. $y = x^2$

12. $x > 0$: decreasing, $x < 0$: decreasing   13. $x < 0$: decreasing, $x > 0$ increasing

EXERCISES

Practice   For graphs for Exercises 14–23, see Teacher's Answer Key.
Determine whether each graph has *infinite discontinuity*, *jump discontinuity*, or *point discontinuity*, or is *continuous*. Then graph each function.

14. $y = \dfrac{12}{5x^2}$ infinite discontinuity   15. $y = \dfrac{x^2 - 4}{x + 2}$ point discontinuity

16. $y = \dfrac{|x|^3}{x}$ point discontinuity   17. $y = 8 - 2x - x^2$ continuous

18. $y = \begin{cases} 3x - 6, & \text{if } x > 0 \\ 3x^2 - 6, & \text{if } x < 0 \end{cases}$ point discontinuity   19. $y = \begin{cases} x, & \text{if } x < 0 \\ 0, & \text{if } x = 0 \\ x, & \text{if } x > 0 \end{cases}$ continuous

20. point discontinuity

20. $y = \begin{cases} -x + 5, & \text{if } x < 1 \\ x^2 - 2x + 5, & \text{if } x > 1 \end{cases}$ 21. $y = \dfrac{6}{x^2} - 4$ infinite discontinuity

22. $y = x^3 - x^2 - 14x + 16$ continuous   23. $y = \dfrac{4}{x^2} + x$ infinite discontinuity

Without graphing, describe the end behavior of each function. 24–26. See margin.

24. $y = 6x^5 + 7x^3 + 1$ 25. $y = x^2 - 25$ 26. $y = 24 - 18x - 45x^3$

Complete each segmented function so that the function is continuous.

27. $y = \begin{cases} \dfrac{x^2 - 11x + 28}{x - 4} \\ \underline{?}, & \text{if } x = \underline{?} \end{cases}$ $-3, 4$ 28. $y = \begin{cases} \dfrac{x^2 - 11}{x + \sqrt{11}} \\ \underline{?}, & \text{if } x = \underline{?} \end{cases}$ $-2\sqrt{11}, -\sqrt{11}$

29. $y = \begin{cases} x^3, & \text{if } x < 4 \\ 68 - x, & \text{if } x > 4 \\ \underline{?}, & \text{if } x = \underline{?} \end{cases}$ $64, 4$ 30. $y = \begin{cases} \dfrac{x^3 + 27}{x + 3} \\ \underline{?}, & \text{if } x = \underline{?} \end{cases}$ $27, -3$

31–33. See margin. For graphs, see Teacher's Answer Key.

Graphing Calculator   Use a graphing calculator to graph each function.
a. Determine whether the graph is continuous.
b. State the intervals for which the function is increasing or decreasing.

31. $y = x^2 - 5x + 4$ 32. $y = \dfrac{1}{x + 1}$ 33. $y = |x + 9|$

Critical Thinking   34. Find the value for p and q so that the function is continuous if
$f(x) = \begin{cases} x - 2, & \text{if } x \geq 2 \\ \sqrt{p - x^2}, & \text{if } -2 < x < 2 \\ q - x, & \text{if } x \leq -2 \end{cases}$ $p = 4, q = -2$

Applications and Problem Solving   35. **Manufacturing** The Twin Forks packing plant is developing a new type of can that will contain peaches. The can is made of a special alloy that reduces the number of preservatives needed to keep the fruit fresh. If the can has to have a volume of 300 cm³, determine the radius, height, and minimum surface area needed to manufacture the most cost effective can. $r = 3.6$ cm, $h = 7.4$ cm, $S = 248.8$ cm²

36. Government The table below appeared in the Federal Income Tax instructions booklet for 1991.

Schedule Y-1 Use if your filing status is Married filing jointly or Qualifying widow(er)

If the amount on Form 1040, line 37, is: Over	But not over	Enter on Form 1040, line 38	of the amount over
$0	$34,000	. . . . . . 15%	$0
34,000	82,150	$5,100.00 + 28%	34,000
82,150	. . . . . .	18,582.00 + 31%	82,150

a. Write a function that relates the three different income levels. See margin.
b. Graph the function. See margin.
c. Determine if the graph is continuous. Explain. It is continuous.
d. Determine the amount of tax individuals owe if the amount on line 37 of Form 1040 is:

(1) $73,000   **(2)** $32,050   **(3)** $22,174   **(4)** $87,234
$16,020 $4807.50 $3326.10 $20,158.04

Mixed Review

37. Find $[f \circ g](4)$ if $f(x) = 5x + 9$ and $g(x) = 0.5x - 1$. **(Lesson 1-2)** 14

38. Manufacturing Picto Inc. makes console and wide-screen televisions. The equipment in the factory allows for making at most 450 console televisions and 200 wide-screen televisions in one month. The console television costs $600 per unit to produce and is sold at $125 profit. The wide-screen television costs $900 per unit to produce and is sold at $200 profit. During the month of November, the company can spend $3,600,000 to produce these televisions. **(Lesson 2-6)**

38a. 450 console, 200 wide-screen

a. To maximize profit, how many of each type should they make?
b. What is the maximum profit possible with these amounts? $96,250

39. Find the inverse of $f(x) = (x - 9)^2$. **(Lesson 3-3)** $f^{-1}(x) = \pm\sqrt{x} + 9$

40. Graph $y \geq \sqrt[3]{x + 4} - 2$. **(Lesson 3-5)** See margin.

41. Find the critical points for the graph of $y = x^3 - x^2 + 3$. Determine whether each point is a relative maximum, a relative minimum, or a point of inflection. **(Lesson 3-7)** max: (0,3), min: (0.67, 2.85), inflection: (0.33, 2.93)

42. College Entrance Exam Choose the best answer. B
A college graduate goes to work for $x per week. After several months the company falls on hard times and gives all the employees a 10% pay cut. A few months later, business picks up and the company gives all the employees a 10% raise. What is the college graduate's new salary?

(A) $0.90x$ **(B)** $0.99x$ **(C)** x **(D)** $1.01x$ **(E)** $1.11x$

LESSON 3-8   CONTINUITY AND END BEHAVIOR   171

EXTENDING THE LESSON

Math Power: Problem Solving

Find a value of m and b so that
$$f(x) = \begin{cases} -x^2 & \text{if } x \leq 0 \\ mx + b & \text{if } 0 < x < 1 \\ x^2 & \text{if } x \geq 1 \end{cases}$$
is continuous. $m = 1, b = 0$

Additional Answers

1. origin, $y = \pm x$, odd
2. x-axis, neither
3. none, neither
4. y-axis, even
5.
6.
7.
8.

VOCABULARY

Upon completing this chapter, you should be familiar with the following terms:

134 asymptote	**138** hole	**106** point symmetry
164 continuous	**135** horizontal asymptote	**134** rational function
157 critical points	**128** horizontal line test	**118** reflection
150 derivative	**126** inverse relations	**157** relative maximum
164 discontinuous	**108** line symmetry	**157** relative minimum
166 end behavior	**118** linear transformation	**149** secant line
112 even function	**157** maximum	**137** slant asymptote
120 geometric transformation	**157** minimum	**149** tangent
	112 odd function	**118** translation
119 greatest integer function	**117** parent graph	**134** vertical asymptote
	157 point of inflection	

SKILLS AND CONCEPTS

OBJECTIVES AND EXAMPLES	REVIEW EXERCISES
Upon completing this chapter, you should be able to:	Use these exercises to review and prepare for the chapter test.
■ identify an odd function and an even function **(Lesson 3-1)**	**Determine whether the graph of each relation is symmetric with respect to the x-axis, the y-axis, the line $y = x$, the line $y = -x$, or the origin. Then, state whether each relation is *even, odd,* or *neither.***
Determine whether $f(x) = x^3 + x$ is odd, even, or neither.	1–4. See margin.
$f(-x) = -x^3 - x$	**1.** $xy = 8$
$-f(x) = -x^3 - x$	**2.** $x = y^2 - 3$
Since $f(-x) = -f(x), f(x) = x^3 + x$ is odd.	**3.** $y = -2x^3 + x^2 - 3$
	4. $y = 8 - 4x^2$

■ identify the graphs of simple polynomial functions, absolute value functions, and step functions. **(Lesson 3-2)**	Use the graph of $f(x) = x^4$ to sketch a graph for each function. Then, describe the transformation(s) of $f(x)$ that have taken place.
The graph of $g(x) = (x-2)^2$ is the translation of the graph of $f(x) = x^2$ two units to the right.	**5.** $y = -f(x)$ reflect across x-axis
	6. $y = f(x) - 3$ translate down 3 units
	7. $y = f(x + 5)$ translate left 5 units
	8. $y = 6(f(-x))$ thinner, reflect across y-axis
	5–8. For graphs, see margin.

OBJECTIVES AND EXAMPLES	REVIEW EXERCISES

OBJECTIVES AND EXAMPLES

■ determine the inverse of a function or relation   (Lesson 3-3)

Suppose $f(x) = 4(x-3)^2$. Find f^{-1}.

$x = 4(y-3)^2$ *Interchange x and y.*

$\frac{x}{4} = (y-3)^2$ *Solve for y.*

$\pm\frac{\sqrt{x}}{2} + 3 = y \quad \rightarrow \quad f^{-1}(x) = \pm\frac{\sqrt{x}}{2} + 3$

■ determine horizontal, vertical, and slant asymptotes   (Lesson 3-4)

Determine the asymptotes for the graph of $f(x) = \frac{x-1}{x}$.

vertical asymptote: $x = 0$

Solve for x in terms of y: $x = \frac{1}{1-y}$

horizontal asymptote: $y = 1$

■ graph polynomial, absolute value, and radical inequalities   (Lesson 3-5)

Graph $y < x^2 + 1$.

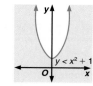

■ find the slope and the equation of a line tangent to the graph of a function at a given point   (Lesson 3-6)

Find the slope of the tangent to the graph of $y = x^2 + 3x - 7$ at the point $(5, 33)$.

$f'(x) = 2x + 3$ *Find the derivative.*

$f'(5) = 2(5) + 3$ or 13

The slope is 13.

REVIEW EXERCISES

Find the inverse of each function. Sketch the function and its inverse. Is the inverse a function? Write *yes* or *no*.

9. $y = 6 - 2x$ $y = \frac{6-x}{2}$; yes

10. $y = \frac{1}{4}(x-3)^2$ $y = \pm 2\sqrt{x} + 3$; no

11. $y = (x+1)^3 - 2$ $y = \sqrt[3]{x+2} - 1$; yes

9–11. For graphs, see Teacher's Answer Key.

Determine any horizontal, vertical, or slant asymptotes or holes for each function. Then, graph each function.   12. $x = \frac{1}{3}, y = \frac{1}{3}$,

12. $y = \frac{(x+2)(x+1)}{(3x-1)(x+2)}$ hole: $x = -2$

13. $y = \frac{x}{(x+3)(x-4)}$ $x = -3, 4, y = 0$

14. $y = \frac{x^2-9}{x-3}$ hole: $x = 3$

12–14. For graphs, see Teacher's Answer Key.

Graph each inequality.   15–18. See Teacher's Answer Key.

15. $y < \sqrt[3]{x+2}$

16. $y \geq |x| - 3$

17. $y > (x-3)^2$

18. $y \leq x^2 - 4x - 5$

Find the equation of the line tangent to the graph of each function at the given point. Write the equation in slope-intercept form.

19. $y = x^2 + 5x - 2, (1,4)$ $y = 7x - 3$

20. $y = -x^2 + 6x + 11, (-2,-5)$ $y = 10x + 23$

21. $y = 3x^2 + 4x - 2, (1,5)$ $y = 10x - 5$

22. $y = 2x^2 - 9x + 5, (2,-5)$ $y = -x - 3$

For more information on other methods of alternate assessment, you may wish to refer to Glencoe's *Alternate Assessment in the Mathematics Classroom.*

Alternate Review Strategy

To provide a brief in-class review, you may wish to read the following questions to your students and have them answer verbally.

1. Determine whether the function $y = -6x^2$ is symmetric with respect to the origin, the x-axis, or the y-axis.   **y-axis**

2. Describe the transformation that has taken place if you graph $y = x^2$ and then graph $y = 2(x-1)^2$.   **In the second graph, the parent graph $y = x^2$ has been shifted to the right one unit and is narrower.**

3. Find the inverse of $f(x) = 3x - 4$. $y = \frac{x+4}{3}$

4. Describe the transformation that has taken place if you graph $y = \frac{1}{x}$ and then graph $y = \frac{1}{x-2}$.   **In the second graph, the parent graph $y = \frac{1}{x}$ has been shifted two units to the right.**

5. Describe the graph of the rational function $y = \frac{1}{(x-4)^2}$.

It has asymptotes at $x = 4$ and $y = 0$. The y-values are positive. y increases dramatically as x approaches 4 from either side.

6. Find the derivative of $f(x) = x^3 - 3x^2 + 2x - 1$.   **$3x^2 - 6x + 2$**

7. Find the critical points of $y = 3x^2 + 12x - 2$. Then determine whether each point is a maximum, a minimum, or a point of inflection.   **$(-2, -14)$; minimum**

8. Determine whether the graph of $y = x^3 - 3x^2 + 2x - 1$ is continuous.   **yes**

Two multiple-choice tests (Forms 1A and 1B) and two free-response tests (Forms 2A and 2B) are provided in the *Evaluation Masters*. Chapter 3 Test, Form 1A is shown below. Chapter 3 Test, Form 2A is shown on the next page.

Evaluation Masters Booklet, pp. 25–26

■ find the critical points of a graph and determine if each is a minimum, maximum, or point of inflection **(Lesson 3-7)**

Determine whether the point at $(-1, 4)$ on the graph of $f(x) = 2x^3 + x^2 - 4x + 1$ is a minimum or a maximum.

$f(-1) = 4$
$f(-1.01) = 3.9995 \quad \rightarrow \quad f(-1.01) < f(-1)$
$f(-0.99) = 3.9995 \quad \rightarrow \quad f(-0.99) < f(-1)$

The point at $(-1, 4)$ is a maximum.

Find the critical points of each function. Then, determine whether each point represents a *maximum*, a *minimum*, or a *point of inflection*.

23. $f(x) = 4 + x - x^2$ $\left(\frac{1}{2}, \frac{17}{4}\right)$, max
24. $f(x) = x^3 - 6x^2 + 9x$
25. $f(x) = x^3 + 3x^2 - 4$
26. $f(x) = 2x^3 - 5$ $(0, -5)$, inflection
24. $(3, 0)$, min; $(1, 4)$, max; $(2, 2)$, inflection
25. $(0, -4)$, min; $(-2, 0)$, max; $(-1, -2)$, inflection

■ determine continuity or discontinuity of functions **(Lesson 3-8)**

Determine whether $y = \dfrac{x(x - 3)}{x - 3}$ is continuous.

The graph resembles the graph of $y = x$, but has a hole at $x = 3$. It has point discontinuity.

Determine whether each graph has *infinite discontinuity*, *jump discontinuity*, *point discontinuity*, or is *continuous*. Then graph each function.

27. $y = \dfrac{-x}{(x - 2)^2}$ infinite

28. $y = \begin{cases} \dfrac{|x|}{x} \text{ if } x \neq 0 \\ 1 \text{ if } x = 0 \end{cases}$ jump

29. $y = \begin{cases} x + 1 \text{ if } x < 0 \\ 1 - x \text{ if } x \geq 0 \end{cases}$ continuous
27–29. For graphs, see Teacher's Answer Key.

APPLICATIONS AND PROBLEM SOLVING

30. Sports One of the most spectacular long jumps ever performed was by Bob Beaman in the 1968 Olympics. His jump of 29 feet 2.5 inches surpassed the world record at that time by over 2 feet! The function $h(t) = 4.6t - 4.9t^2$ describes the height of Beaman's jump (in meters) with respect to time (in seconds). **(Lesson 3-7)**
  a. Draw a graph of this function. See margin.
  b. What was the maximum height of his jump? 1.08 m

Center of Gravity
h
Start — Maximum Height

31. Physics The position of a particle with respect to time can be described by the function $f(t) = 3t^2 + 5t - 8$, where $f(t)$ is in meters and t is in seconds. **(Lesson 3-7)**
  a. Find the instantaneous velocity, $f'(t)$, of the particle when $t = 4.29$m/s. 30.74 m/s
  b. The acceleration of the particle can be found by finding the second derivative of the function, $f''(t)$. Find the acceleration of the particle. 6 m/s^2

Additional Answers

Chapter Review

30.

Chapter Test

18.

$y = 3x^3 - 2x^2 - 5x$

$x: -1, 0, \frac{5}{3}; y: 0$

Use the graph of $f(x) = x^2 + 1$ to sketch a graph for each function. Describe the transformations of $f(x)$ that have taken place. 1–3. See Teacher's Answer Key.

1. $y = f(x - 5)$

2. $y = -f(x) + 2$

3. $y = \frac{1}{2}(f(x + 3))$

Find the inverse of each function. Sketch the function and its inverse. Is the inverse a function? Write *yes* or *no*. 4–6. See Teacher's Answer Key.

4. $y = (x - 4)^2$

5. $y = 8x^3 + 1$

6. $y = (x + 3)^4 - 7$

Find the asymptotes, if they exist, and determine whether each relation is *even*, *odd*, or *neither*. 7. $x = -1, 3, y = 0$; neither 8. $x = \pm 2, y = 0$; odd 9. no asymptotes; neither

7. $y = \dfrac{x + 5}{(x - 3)(x + 1)}$

8. $y = \dfrac{x}{x^2 - 4}$

9. $y = x^7 - 5x^3 - 8$

Graph each inequality. 10–11. See Teacher's Answer Key.

10. $y > |x - 4|$

11. $y \leq 2x^2 + 3$

Find the equation of the line tangent to the graph of each function at the given point. Write the equation in slope-intercept form.

12. $y = x^2 - 4x + 1, (1, -2)$ $y = -2x$

13. $y = 3x^2 - 2x + 1, (2, 9)$ $y = 10x - 11$

Find the critical points of each function. Then, determine whether each point represents a *maximum*, a *minimum*, or a *point of inflection*. 15. $(0, 3)$, max; $(-2, -1)$, min; $(-1, 1)$, inflection

14. $y = x^2 - 8x + 4$ $(4, -12)$, min

15. $y = -x^3 - 3x^2 + 3$

Determine whether each relation has *infinite discontinuity, jump discontinuity, point discontinuity,* or is *continuous*. Then graph each function. 16–17. For graphs, see Teacher's Answer Key.

16. $y = \dfrac{-x^2(x - 2)}{x - 2}$ point

17. $y = \begin{cases} x + 1, & \text{if } x > 0 \\ 3, & \text{if } x \leq 0 \end{cases}$ jump

18–19. See Teacher's Answer Key.
18. Find the x- and y- intercepts of $y = 3x^3 - 2x^2 - 5x$. Then, graph the function.

19. Without graphing, describe the end behavior of the graph of $y = x^4 - 2x^2 - 1$.

20. Auto Safety Airbags are becoming a standard safety feature in many cars today. They protect people from experiencing the full impact of a collision. Without airbags, a person or object would move forward at the velocity that the car is traveling, v_i, and then after impact, be repelled backward at a velocity of $v_f = \dfrac{m_1 - m_2}{m_1 + m_2} \cdot v_i$, where m_1 and m_2 are the masses of the person and the car meeting.

a. Graph the function if $v_i = 5$ m/s and $m_1 = 7$ kg. See margin.

b. Find the value of v_f when the value of m_2 is 5 kg. 0.83 m/s

Bonus Determine the constants b and c so that the function
$$f(x) = \begin{cases} x + 1 & \text{if } 1 < x < 3 \\ x^2 + bx + c & \text{if } |x - 2| \geq 1 \end{cases} \text{ is continuous. } b = -3, c = 4$$

This page may be used as a test or as a review. All answers to this test appear in the Selected Answers in the student text.

Standardized Test Practice Questions are also provided in the *Evaluation Masters*.

Evaluation Masters Booklet, pp. 29–30

Test Generator Software is provided in Apple, IBM, and Macintosh versions. You may use this software to create your own tests, based on the needs of your students.

Additional Answers

19. $x \to \infty, f(x) \to \infty; x \to -\infty, f(x) \to \infty$

20a.

$m_1 = -7$

$v_f = 5\left(\dfrac{m_1 - 7}{m_1 + 7}\right)$

4 POLYNOMIAL AND RATIONAL FUNCTIONS

PREVIEWING THE CHAPTER

This chapter builds on the concepts of polynomial and rational functions introduced in Chapter 3. Students determine the number of complex zeros for polynomial functions by using the fundamental theorem of algebra and then find the zeros. Students solve and graph quadratic equations. The remainder and factor theorems are used to find binomial factors of polynomials. Students then use the rational root theorem to identify the possible rational roots of a polynomial equation. They also use Descartes' rule of signs to determine how many positive and negative real zeros a polynomial function has. The location principle is used to estimate the zeros of a polynomial function. Throughout the chapter, students use the information they gain from analyzing a polynomial function to graph the function. In the final lessons of the chapter, students solve rational and radical equations and inequalities.

Lesson Objective Chart

Lesson (Pages)		Lesson Objectives	State/Local Objectives
4-1 (178-184)	4-1A:	Determine roots of polynomial equations.	
	4-1B:	Apply the fundamental theorem of algebra.	
4-2 (187-194)	4-2A:	Solve quadratic equations.	
	4-2B:	Use the discriminant to describe the roots of quadratic equations.	
	4-2C	Graph quadratic equations and inequalities.	
4-3 (195-200)	4-3:	Find the factors of polynomials using the remainder and factor theorems.	
4-4 (201-207)	4-4A:	Identify all possible rational roots of a polynomial equation by using the rational root theorem.	
	4-4B:	Determine the number of positive and negative real zeros a polynomial function has.	
4-5 (209-214)	4-5A:	Approximate the real zeros of a polynomial function.	
	4-5B:	Graph polynomial functions.	
4-6 (216-222)	4-6A:	Find the least common denominator of rational expressions.	
	4-6B:	Solve rational equations and inequalities.	
	4-6C:	Decompose a fraction into partial fractions.	
4-7 (225-229)	4-7:	Solve radical equations and inequalities.	

ORGANIZING THE CHAPTER

You may want to refer to the **Course Planning Guide Calendar** on pages T34-T35 for a complete pacing chart.

Lesson Planning Guide

Blackline Masters Booklets

Lesson	Pages	Practice	Enrichment	Evaluation	Graphing Calculator	Computer	Multicultural Activity	Applications	Problem Solving	Case Study Follow-Up	Decision Making	Transparencies
4-1	178-184	p. 21	p. 21		p. 7			p. 10				4-1
4-2	187-194	p. 22	p. 22	Quiz A, p. 45								4-2
4-3	195-200	p. 23	p. 23								p. 12	4-3
4-4	201-207	p. 24	p. 24	Quiz B, p. 45 Mid-Chapter Test, p. 47								4-4
4-5	209-214	p. 25	p. 25			p. 8	p. 4					4-5
4-6	216-222	p. 26	p. 26	Quiz C, p. 46								4-6
4-7	225-229	p. 27	p. 27	Quiz D, p. 46					p. 11			4-7
Review	230-232	Multiple Choice Tests, Forms 1A and 1B, pp. 37-40 Free Response Tests, Forms 2A and 2B, pp. 41-44 Standardized Test Questions, p. 48										
Test	233											

Other Chapter Resources

Student Edition

Case Study Follow-Up, p. 184
Decision Making, p. 194
Technology, p. 215
Unit Review, pp. 234-235

Other Supplements

Transparency 4-0 for Chapter Opener
Evaluation Masters, Unit Test, pp. 49-52
Alternate Assessment in the Mathematics Classroom,
    Glencoe Publishing Co., 1993
Cooperative Learning in the Mathematics Classroom,
    Glencoe Publishing Co., 1993

Software

Test and Review Generator Software
    Available for Apple, IBM, and Macintosh
Teacher's Guide for Software Resources

ENHANCING THE CHAPTER

Cooperative Learning

Deciding on the Size of Groups

Considerable research indicates that, for most schools, six is the maximum number of students to assign to a cooperative-learning group. A group of this size provides opportunities to have members with different cooperative-learning skills that are helpful to the whole group. It also can decrease the time required to do the assigned task since there are more members with more talents to do the work. However, because group skills must be learned by students, few may have the skills required for a group of this size. Therefore, if your students lack these skills, it is advisable to begin with groups of no more than two or three students each. A small group can be more effective in these cases because it takes less time for the members to get organized, and it provides more opportunity for each member to participate and to develop cooperative-learning skills.

For more information on cooperative learning, see pages T20-T21. Additional information on using cooperative groups is available in Glencoe's *Cooperative Learning in the Mathematics Classroom*, ©1993.

Multicultural

Multicultural Activity Masters, p. 4

CHAPTER 4	NAME _____ DATE _____

Multicultural Activity (Use after Lesson 4-5)

Qín Jiǔsháo

Qín Jiǔsháo (ca. 1202–1261) was a civil servant who held a variety of administrative government positions in the provinces of central China. But Qín was also accomplished in many fields other than government, among them poetry, music, architecture, astronomy, and mathematics. His great mathematical work was the *Shūshū jiǔzhāng* (*Mathematical Treatise in Nine Sections*), which covered topics ranging from astronomy, surveying, and taxation to indeterminate analysis. Because of his remarkable mathematical insights, Qín is considered to be one of the greatest mathematicians of all time.

In the *Shūshū*, Qín described methods for solving polynomial equations. The steps below give some insight into how Qín used estimation and repeated addition and multiplication to approximate the real roots of an equation like $x^2 - x = 11$.

Step 1 Since $3^2 - 3 < 11 < 4^2 - 4$, x is between 3 and 4. Thus, $x = 3 + a$, where $0 < a < 1$.

Step 2 Substitute $3 + a$ for x. Expand and simplify.

$$
\begin{array}{ll}
x^2 - x = 11 & \leftarrow \text{original equation} \\
(3 + a)^2 - (3 + a) = 11 & \\
a^2 + 5a = 5 & \leftarrow \text{transformed equation}
\end{array}
$$

Step 3 Using trial and error, you can determine that the greatest one-place decimal such that $a^2 + 5a \le 5$ is 0.8. Thus, $a = 0.8 + b$, where $0 < b < 0.1$.

After Step 3, the positive solution of $x^2 - x = 11$ has been computed to one decimal place: $x = 3.8 + b$. To continue the root-finding process to two decimal places, repeat Steps 2 and 3 by using substitution and another transformed equation.

1. Continue the process above to approximate the positive root of $x^2 - x = 11$ to two decimal places.
   3.85
2. Use the process above to approximate the positive root of $x^2 + 4x - 35 = 0$ to two decimal places.
   4.24
3. Use the process above to approximate the positive root of $x^3 + 2x^2 - 3x = 6$ to one decimal place.
   1.7

T4
Glencoe Division, Macmillan/McGraw-Hill

Activity Masters

Applications, p. 10

CHAPTER 4	NAME _____ DATE _____

Application (Use after Lesson 4-1)

Approximation by Means of Polynomials

Many scientific experiments produce pairs of numbers $(x, f(x))$ that become more meaningful if they can be related by some kind of formula. If the pairs form a function, you can fit a polynomial to the pairs in exactly one way. Consider the pairs given by the following table.

x	1	2	4	7
$f(x)$	6	11	39	−54

We will assume that the polynomial is of degree three. Substitute the given values into this expression. Let $x_0 = 1$; $x_1 = 2$; $x_2 = 4$.

$$f(x) = A + B(x - x_0) + C(x - x_0)(x - x_1) + D(x - x_0)(x - x_1)(x - x_2)$$

You will get the system of equations shown at the right. You can solve this system and use the values for $A, B, C,$ and D to find the desired polynomial.

$$
\begin{aligned}
6 &= A \\
11 &= A + B \\
39 &= A + 3B + 6C \\
-54 &= A + 6B + 30C + 90D
\end{aligned}
$$

Answers may vary slightly due to rounding.

Solve each problem.

1. Solve the system of equations given above for the values $A, B, C,$ and D.
   $A = 6$; $B = 5$, $C = 3$, $D = -2$
2. Find the polynomial function that represents the four ordered pairs given in the example. Write your answer in the form $f(x) = a + bx + cx^2 + dx^3$.
   $f(x) = 23 - 32x + 17x^2 - 2x^3$
3. Find the polynomial function that gives the following values. Assume that the polynomial is of degree three.

x	8	12	15	20
$f(x)$	−207	169	976	3801

   $A = -207$, $B = 94$, $C = 25$, $D = 1$; $f(x) = x^3 - 10x^2 - 10x + 1$
4. A scientist measured the volume $f(x)$ of carbon dioxide gas that can be absorbed by one cubic centimeter of charcoal at pressure x.

x	120	340	534	698
$f(x)$	3.1	5.5	7.1	8.3

   Find the values for $A, B, C,$ and D.
   $A = 3.1$, $B = 0.01091$, $C = -0.00000643$, $D = 0.0000000081$

T10
Glencoe Division, Macmillan/McGraw-Hill

Problem Solving, p. 11

CHAPTER 4	NAME _____ DATE _____

Problem Solving (Use after Lesson 4-7)

Use Contradiction

Solving problems by contradiction is useful when you know that exactly one of a small number of alternatives can be true. In particular, this technique is used to prove statements that must be either true or false. You start by assuming that the opposite of the statement is true and then derive a contradiction. Since only one of two alternatives leads to a contradiction, the other alternative—the statement that is true—has been proved. Here is an example of such a problem.

An isosceles right triangle has legs of measure 1. Prove that the measure of the hypotenuse of this triangle is an irrational number.

Answer these questions to solve the problem.

1. Use the Pythagorean theorem to find the measure of the hypotenuse. Then, assume that the measure of the hypotenuse is irrational and that it thus can be expressed as a ratio, in simplest form, of two integers $\frac{a}{b}$. Simplify the resulting equation to remove the radical sign.
   $\sqrt{2}$; $\sqrt{2} = \frac{a}{b}$; $2b^2 = a$
2. How do you know that a must be an even number?
   a^2 has a factor of 2 so it is even and so is a.
3. Since a is an even number, you can substitute $2n$ for a. Do so. What can you conclude about b?
   $2b^2 = (2n)^2$; $b^2 = 2n^2$; b^2 is even and so is b.
4. If both a and b are even, how does that contradict the assumption you made in Exercise 1?
   Since $\frac{a}{b}$ is in simplest form, a and b have no common factors; no, we find that they have 2 as a common factor.
5. State the conclusion of Exercises 1–4.
   $\sqrt{2}$ must be an irrational number.

Use contradiction to solve each problem.

6. Assume that you have already proved that the squares of all nonzero integers are positive numbers. Prove that $x^2 + 1 = 0$ has no integer solution. Assume $x = c$, where c is an integer. Substitute c for x to get $c^2 + 1 = 0$. Subtracting 1 from both sides gives $c^2 = -1$. This contradicts the statement that was already proved.
7. A solution of $x^4 + 4x^3 - 7x^2 - 34x - 24 = 0$ is
   (A) 1 (B) 0 (C) −3 (D) 3 (E) 24   (D)
8. The solution of $\sqrt{x} + \sqrt{x - 3} = \frac{3}{\sqrt{x-3}}$ is
   (A) 3 (B) 0 (C) 4 (D) 3 (E) $\frac{1}{3}$ (C)

T11
Glencoe Division, Macmillan/McGraw-Hill

Decision Making, p. 12

CHAPTER 4	NAME _____ DATE _____

Decision Making (Use after Lesson 4-3)

Improving Test-Taking Skills

Many students have "test phobia." Taking a test makes them so nervous that they do not do their best.

In these exercises, you will research some ways to become better prepared for taking tests. As you feel more confident in your test-taking skills, any fear you have of tests will probably decrease.
Answers will vary.

1. Survey a fairly large sample of the students at your school. What percent have "test phobia"? What are the physical, mental, and emotional signs of this condition? Your survey might also include questions on techniques students use to overcome fear of tests.
2. Which type of test is most difficult for you, a free-response test in which you write a brief answer for each question, a multiple-choice test, a true-false test, or an essay test? Discuss this issue with a partner or a group. Give reasons for your conclusions.
3. Work with a small group. Research the reference materials available at your school and public libraries on test preparation. (You may be surprised at how many different products there are!) Why do you think there is a big market for materials of this type?
4. Describe a typical college entrance exam. How long does it take? Where is it given? What materials can you take to the testing site?
5. Research the recommendations of testing experts on whether you should guess on a multiple-choice test. What is meant by a "guessing penalty"? If you can eliminate at least 1 option out of 4, do you think you should guess? Give reasons for your answer.
6. One type of question found on college-entrance tests is the *quantitative comparison*. The directions are similar to the following.

   Questions 8–27 each consist of two quantities, one in Column A and one in Column B. You are to compare the two quantities and on the answer sheet blacken space
   A if the quantity in Column A is greater;
   B if the quantity in Column B is greater;
   C if the two quantities are equal;
   D if the relationship cannot be determined from the information given.

   Prepare a tutoring session in which you would coach another student in techniques on quantitative-comparison questions.
7. Organize a debate on the following issue: "It is not a good idea to cram for a test the night before." If you are working in a group of 5 students, 2 students can argue the "pro" side; 2 students can argue the "con" side; and 1 student can act as moderator.

T12
Glencoe Division, Macmillan/McGraw-Hill

Technology

The Technology feature following Lesson 4-5 provides a computer program in the BASIC programming language that helps students locate zeros and critical points of polynomial functions.

As in Chapter 3, the graphing calculator can be a fundamental tool in studying the characteristics of polynomial equations and the graphs of their related functions. After learning to graph quadratic functions, students learn to graph other polynomial functions. Students use what they have learned about the number and type of zeros of a function to help them determine the range and ZOOM features they need to use to locate zeros and critical points of polynomial functions on a graphing calculator. In the Graphing Calculator Exploration in Lesson 4-3, students use the calculator to investigate polynomials and their factors. In Lesson 4-7A, students learn to solve radical equations and inequalities by graphing the related function.

Graphing Calculator Exercises, pp. 182, 193, 206
Graphing Calculator Program, p. 183

Outside Resources

Books/Periodicals

Dilcher, Karl. *Zeros of Bernoulli, Generalized Bernoulli and Euler Polynomials,* American Mathematical Society, Providence, RI, 1988.

Marden, Morris. *Geometry of Polynomials,* American Mathematical Society, Providence, RI, 1989.

Films/Videotapes/Videodiscs

Concepts in Mathematics, Solving Quadratic Equations, TV Ontario, The Ontario Educational Communications Authority

Polynomials, National Council of Teachers of Mathematics, Washington, DC

Software

Graphing utilities (see list on page T25)

Technology Masters

Graphing Calculator, p. 7

Computer, p. 8

CHAPTER 4

POLYNOMIAL AND RATIONAL FUNCTIONS

HISTORICAL SNAPSHOT

	Translation and analysis of Newton's *Principia* Emilie du Chatelet, France		First Oil Well "Colonel" Edwin L. Drake Titusville, Pennsylvania			First offshore oil well Superior Oil Co. and Pure Oil Co., Gulf of Mexico
Oil first used to keep armour from rusting England and Germany		Battle of The Alamo		University of Texas established at Austin, Texas		First computer-controlled refinery by Texaco Oil Co., Texas
AD 1617	1759	1835	1859	1883	1937	1959

176

CHAPTER OBJECTIVES

In this chapter, you will:
- Solve polynomial equations.
- Solve inequalities.
- Solve rational equations.

CAREER GOAL: Petroleum Engineering

Imagine doing something you love while living in a faraway, exotic land. Deborah Hempel would like to live and work in Russia for five to ten years. "I really want to work internationally," she says. "The oil company for which a petroleum engineer works must prove that each petroleum engineer it sends to work in that country is better than any of that country's own citizens. Therefore, five years of experience is necessary."

Deborah says that "the petroleum industry is really dynamic and ever-changing." However, she adds, "I do dislike the job uncertainty. For example, in 1986, the petroleum industry hit rock bottom. Then during 1990 and 1991, it was on the upswing. It seems to have stabilized, but where will it go from here?"

Deborah uses equations in her daily work. For example, "Each oil reservoir is made of sand and shale. Two characteristics of the reservoir are porosity and permeability. Porosity refers to the size of the pores in the shale. The greater the porosity, the more oil it can store. Permeability refers to how the pores are interconnected. Unless the pores are interconnected well, you can't get the oil out.

"Sometimes it's necessary to drill a second well next to a potential oil well. Then, water is pumped down the second well to create enough pressure to drive the oil up the first well. Petroleum engineers use an equation to calculate when the water will push the oil through the first well and up to the surface. The equation includes the variables of porosity, permeability, viscosity, or stickiness of the oil, the change in pressure between the two wells, and the distance between the two wells."

Deborah wants to be "a petroleum engineer who doesn't have a lax attitude about the environment," she says. "These days, petroleum engineers are learning more about how they can drill for valuable supplies of oil and, at the same time, protect the environment."

READ MORE ABOUT IT

Butterworth, W.E. *Black Gold: The Story of Oil.* New York: Four Winds Press, 1975.
Hobson, G.D., ed. *Modern Petroleum Technology.* London: Institute of Petroleum, 1973.
Krueger, Gretchen Dewailly. *Opportunities in Petroleum Careers.* Lincolnwood, Illinois: VGM Career Horizons, 1990.

SPOTLIGHT ON...

Deborah Hempel
Age: 22
Class: Senior
School: University of Texas
 Austin, Texas
Major: Petroleum Engineering

"I want to be a petroleum engineer who doesn't have a lax attitude about the environment."

FOR MORE INFORMATION

If you would like more information about petroleum engineering, contact:

Society of Petroleum Engineers
P.O. Box 833836
Richardson, TX 75083-3836

Lesson	Application	Examples	Exercises
4–1	Construction	5	
	Aeronautics		40
	Finance		41
	Entertainment		42
4–2	Entertainment	1	
	Stationery	4	
	Gardening		43
	Physics		44
	Baseball		45
4–3	Cycling	4	
	Physics		32
	Manufacturing		33
4–4	Fire Fighting	1	
	Manufacturing	5	
	Driving		30
	Cardiology		31
	Business		32
4–5	Packaging	1	
	Ecology		28
	Pets		29
	Astronomy		30
4–6	Recreation	2	
	Number Theory		36
	Candle Making		36
	Neighborhoods		37
4–7	History	5	
	Physics		27
	Demolition		28

Lesson Resources

- Practice Master 4-1
- Enrichment Master 4-1
- Technology Master, p. 7
- Activity Master, p. 10

 Transparency 4-1 contains the 5-Minute Check and a teaching aid for this lesson.

INTRODUCING THE LESSON

 5-Minute Check

(over Chapter 3)

1. State what types of symmetry are exhibited by the graph.

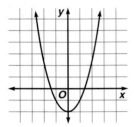

symmetry with respect to the y-axis

2. Let $f(x) = \dfrac{2}{x-3}$.

   a. Determine the asymptotes for the function.
      horiz., $y = 0$; vert., $x = 3$
   b. Find the inverse of f(x).

   $f^{-1}(x) = \dfrac{2}{x} + 3$

3. Graph $y < 4 - 3x$.

$y < 4 - 3x$

4-1 Polynomial Functions

Objectives

After studying this lesson, you should be able to:

4–1A ■ determine roots of polynomial equations, and

4–1B ■ apply the fundamental theorem of algebra.

Application

Instead of investing in the stock market or other financial institutions, many people invest in collectibles, such as antiques. Lesley Yoshito is an investor in vintage automobiles. Three years ago, she purchased a 1953 Chevrolet Corvette roadster for $99,000. Two years ago, she purchased a 1929 Pierce-Arrow Model 125 for $55,000. A year ago, she purchased a 1909 Cadillac Model Thirty for $65,000. If the cars appreciate at a rate of 15% per year, determine the current value of her total investment.

Appreciation is the increase in value of an item over a period of time. The formula for compound interest can be used to find the value of Ms. Yoshito's cars after appreciation. The formula is $A = P(1 + R)^t$, where P is the original amount of money invested, R is the rate of return (written as a decimal), and t is the time invested (in years). The value of her total investment in the cars is the sum of the current value of her investments.

The rate of appreciation in this case is 15%. So $R = 0.15$. Let $x = 1 + R$ or 1.15. Let $T(x)$ represent the total current value of the three cars. Then find $T(x)$.

$$
\begin{array}{rclcccccc}
Total & = & Corvette & + & Pierce\text{-}Arrow & + & Cadillac & \\
T(x) & = & 99{,}000(x)^3 & + & 55{,}000(x)^2 & + & 65{,}000(x)^1 & \\
T(1.15) & = & 99{,}000(1.15)^3 & + & 55{,}000(1.15)^2 & + & 65{,}000(1.15) & & x = 1.15 \\
T(1.15) & = & 298{,}054.13 & & & & &
\end{array}
$$

The present value of Ms. Yoshito's investment is $298,054.13.

The function above, $T(x)$, contains a **polynomial in one variable**.

Definition of Polynomial in One Variable	A polynomial in one variable, x, is an expression of the form $a_0x^n + a_1x^{n-1} + \ldots + a_{n-2}x^2 + a_{n-1}x + a_n$. The coefficients $a_0, a_1, a_2, \ldots, a_n$ represent complex numbers (real or imaginary), a_0 is not zero, and n represents a nonnegative integer.

Complex numbers are defined on the next page.

The terms of a polynomial are usually written in order of decreasing degree.

The **degree** of a polynomial in one variable is the greatest exponent of its variable. The coefficient of the variable with the greatest exponent is called the *leading coefficient*. The degree of the polynomial developed above, $99{,}000x^3 + 55{,}000x^2 + 65{,}000x$, is 3. The leading coefficient is 99,000.

ALTERNATE TEACHING STRATEGIES

Using Calculators

Students may enjoy finding values of polynomial functions using the expanded form $axn + bxn^{-1} + cxn^{-2} + \ldots = \{[(ax + b)x + c]x + \ldots\}$. This method is particularly well suited for computing values when using a calculator or computer. The keystrokes needed are a ☒ x ⊞ b ☒ ⊟ x ⊞ c ⊟ ☒ x, and so on.

Using Cooperative Groups

Have students work together in groups to create polynomial functions having a particular degree and number of real roots; for example, degree 3 and 3 real roots or degree 3 and only 1 real root. Each group could generate a list of such functions, one in each category.

Example 1

Determine if each expression is a polynomial in one variable. If the expression is a polynomial in one variable, state the degree.

$$\text{a. } c^4 + 2a^2 + 4c \qquad \text{b. } w^4 - w^2 + 5w^5 - 6w^3 \qquad \text{c. } 3x^2 + \frac{3}{x} + 8$$

a. $c^4 + 2a^2 + 4c$ is not a polynomial in one variable, because it has two variables.

b. $w^4 - w^2 + 5w^5 - 6w^3$ is a polynomial in one variable. It has a degree of 5.

c. $3x^2 + \frac{3}{x} + 8$ is not a polynomial in one variable, because $\frac{3}{x}$ is equivalent to $3x^{-1}$. A polynomial cannot have a term in which the variable has a negative exponent.

If a function f is a polynomial in one variable, then f is a **polynomial function**. If a domain value for the function is known, then a unique range value can be determined.

A root of $P(x) = 0$ is a zero, where $f(x) = P(x)$.

If $P(x)$ represents a polynomial, then $P(x) = 0$ is called a **polynomial equation**. A **root**, or solution, of the equation is a value of x for which the value of the polynomial $P(x)$ is 0. Thus, 5 is a root of the equation $x^2 - 6x + 5 = 0$, since $5^2 - 6(5) + 5 = 0$; 5 is also called a **zero** of the function $f(x) = x^2 - 6x + 5$. On the graph of a function, the zeros are the x-intercepts.

Example 2

Determine whether 3 is a root of $x^3 - 2x^2 - 5x + 6 = 0$.

Evaluate the function $P(x) = x^3 - 2x^2 - 5x + 6$ for $P(3)$.

$$P(3) = 3^3 - 2(3)^2 - 5(3) + 6$$
$$= 27 - 18 - 15 + 6$$
$$= 0$$

Since $P(3) = 0$, 3 is a root of $x^3 - 2x^2 - 5x + 6 = 0$.

The root of a polynomial function may be an **imaginary number**, such as $2i$. By definition, the imaginary unit, i, equals $\sqrt{-1}$. The imaginary numbers combined with the real numbers make up the set of **complex numbers**. A complex number is any number in the form $a + bi$, where a and b are real numbers. If $b = 0$, then the complex number is a real number. If $a = 0$ and $b \neq 0$, then the complex number is called a *pure imaginary number*.

One of the most important theorems in mathematics is the **fundamental theorem of algebra**.

Fundamental Theorem of Algebra

Every polynomial equation with degree greater than zero has at least one root in the set of complex numbers.

LESSON 4-1   POLYNOMIAL FUNCTIONS   179

Prerequisite Skills

Students need to be familiar with factoring polynomial expressions.
1. $x^4 - 81$ $(x - 3)(x + 3)(x^2 + 9)$
2. $x^2 + 6x - 16$ $(x + 8)(x - 2)$
3. $x^3 + 3x^2 - 4x$ $x(x - 1)(x + 4)$
4. $6x^2 - 11x - 10$ $(3x + 2)(2x - 5)$
5. $3x^3 + 81$ $3(x + 3)(x^2 - 3x + 9)$

Motivating the Lesson

Ask students to write an equation that gives the value of an IRA, starting with an initial deposit, adding a contribution for each of three successive years, and using a constant annual yield.

TEACHING THE LESSON

Chalkboard Examples

For Example 1

Determine if each expression is a polynomial in one variable. If the expression is a polynomial in one variable, state the degree.
a. $x^2 + 3xy - 5y^3$ not a poly.
b. $8 - x - 4x^2 + \frac{7}{x}$ not a poly.
c. $z^2 - z^3 - z + 3z^4 - 1$ a poly. of deg. 4.

For Example 2

Determine whether −3 is a root of $x^3 + 3x^2 - 3x + 6 = 0$.
$(-3)^3 + 3(-3)^2 - 3(-3) + 6 \neq 0$

The degree of a polynomial indicates how many roots are possible. This is stated in a corollary to the fundamental theorem of algebra.

Corollary to the Fundamental Theorem of Algebra

Every polynomial $P(x)$ of degree n $(n > 0)$ can be written as the product of a constant k $(k \neq 0)$ and n linear factors.

$$P(x) = k(x - r_1)(x - r_2)(x - r_3) \ldots (x - r_n)$$

Thus, a polynomial equation of degree n has exactly n complex roots, namely $r_1, r_2, r_3, \ldots, r_n$.

The general shapes of the graphs for polynomial functions with positive leading coefficients and degree greater than 0 are shown below. These graphs also show the maximum number of times the graph of each type of polynomial may cross the x-axis.

Degree 1   **Degree 2**   **Degree 3**   **Degree 4**   **Degree 5**

The graph of a polynomial function with odd degree *must* cross the x-axis at least once. The graph of a function with even degree may or may not cross the x-axis. If it does, it will be an even number of times. Each x-intercept represents a real root of the corresponding polynomial equation.

Example 3

State the number of complex roots of the equation $x^3 + 2x^2 - 8x = 0$. Then find the roots and graph the related polynomial function.

The polynomial has degree 3, so there are 3 complex roots. In this case, you can factor the equation to find these roots.

$$x^3 + 2x^2 - 8x = 0$$
$$x(x^2 + 2x - 8) = 0$$
$$x(x + 4)(x - 2) = 0$$

To find each root, set each factor equal to zero.

$$x = 0 \qquad x + 4 = 0 \qquad x - 2 = 0$$
$$x = -4 \qquad x = 2$$

The roots are 0, −4, and 2.

The graph of $f(x) = x^3 + 2x^2 - 8x$ crosses the x-axis at −4, 0, and 2.

Example 4

Write the polynomial equation of least degree with roots –3, 2*i*, and –2*i*.

The linear factors for the polynomial are $x - (-3)$, $x - 2i$, and $x - (-2i)$. Now find the product of these factors.

$0 = (x + 3)(x - 2i)(x + 2i)$
$0 = (x + 3)(x^2 - 4i^2)$ $i^2 = -1$
$0 = (x + 3)(x^2 + 4)$ $-4i^2 = -4(-1)$
$0 = x^3 + 3x^2 + 4x + 12$

The simplest polynomial equation with roots –3, 2*i*, and –2*i* is
$0 = x^3 + 3x^2 + 4x + 12$.

Example 5

APPLICATION

Construction

The Santa Fe Recreation Department has a 50 foot by 70 foot area for construction of a new public swimming pool. The pool will be surrounded by a concrete sidewalk of constant width. Because of water restrictions, the pool can have a maximum area of 2400 square feet. What should be the width of the sidewalk that surrounds the pool?

Let x = the width of the sidewalk.
The length of the pool would be $70 - 2x$ feet.
The width of the pool would be $50 - 2x$ feet.

$A = \ell w$
$2400 = (70 - 2x)(50 - 2x)$
$2400 = 3500 - 240x + 4x^2$
$0 = 1100 - 240x + 4x^2$
$0 = 275 - 60x + x^2$
$0 = (55 - x)(5 - x)$

$55 - x = 0$ or $5 - x = 0$
$x = 55$ $x = 5$

Use $x = 5$, since 55 is an unreasonable solution. The sidewalk around the pool should be 5 feet wide.

CHECKING FOR UNDERSTANDING

Communicating Mathematics

Read and study the lesson to answer each question. 1–3. See margin.

1. **Explain** the relationship between a polynomial equation and its corresponding function.

2. **Define** a complex number and tell under what conditions it will be a real number.

3. **Sketch** the general graph of a sixth degree function.

4. **Explain** why the solution of 55 is unreasonable in Example 5. 55 feet is greater than the width of the entire area on which the pool is to be built.

Guided Practice

Determine if each expression is a polynomial in one variable. If the expression is a polynomial in one variable, state the degree.

5. $a^3 + 2a + \sqrt{3}$ yes, 3   6. $\frac{1}{x} = \frac{1}{2x}$ no   7. $2m^3 + 5m^7 + 9$ yes, 7

LESSON 4-1 POLYNOMIAL FUNCTIONS 181

Teaching Tip In Example 4, point out that $(x - 2i)(x + 2i)$ is in the form $(a - b)(a + b)$ and thus equals $x^2 - (2i)^2$.

Chalkboard Examples

For Example 4

Write the polynomial equation of least degree with roots 2, 3*i*, and −3*i*.
$x^3 - 2x^2 + 9x - 18 = 0$

For Example 5

The Santa Fe Park Department has a 110-foot by 130-foot area for a new garden. The garden will be surrounded by a dirt pathway of consistent width. Because of water restrictions, the garden can have a maximum area of 12,000 square feet. What should be the width of the pathway that surrounds the garden? 5 feet

EVALUATING THE LESSON

Checking for Understanding

Exercises 1-14 are designed to help you assess students' understanding through reading, writing, speaking, and modeling. You should work through Exercises 1-4 with your students and then monitor their work on Exercises 5-14.

Additional Answers

1. The solutions to a polynomial equation are the values for which the function $P(x) = 0$.

2. A complex number is any number in the form $a + bi$, where a and b are real numbers and i is the imaginary unit. A complex number is a real number when $b = 0$.

3.

RETEACHING THE LESSON

Have each student give an example of a function that is not a polynomial function, and then a function that is a polynomial function. Have students give its degree, its leading coefficient, and number of complex roots.

Writing Activity   Give an example of a polynomial function and state what the corollary to the Fundamental Theorem of Algebra means for your particular function.

APPLYING THE LESSON

Homework Exercises

Assignment Guide

Average: 15-27, 29, 33-35, 38-40, 43-49

Enriched: 17-25 odd, 26-49

The red A, B, and C flags, printed only in the Teacher's Wraparound Edition, indicate the level of difficulty of the exercises.

Exercise Note

For Exercise 24, remind students that it will be easier to expand the polynomial if they first multiply the factor $(x + 0.5)$ by 2. Point out that since the equation is of the form $P(x) = 0$, this operation is valid.

Practice Masters Booklet, p. 21

Determine whether each number is a root of $x^4 - 4x^3 - x^2 + 4x = 0$.

8. 2 no   9. 0 yes   10. –1 yes   11. –2 no   12. 4 yes

13. Write the polynomial equation of least degree whose roots are $1, -1, 2,$ and -2.
$x^4 - 5x^2 + 4 = 0$

14. Solve $(u + 2)(u^2 - 4) = 0$ and graph the related polynomial function. $-2, -2, 2$
For graph, see margin.

EXERCISES

Practice

State the number of complex roots of each equation. Then find the roots and graph the related function. 15–22. For graphs, see Teacher's Answer Key.

15. $x - 2 = 0$ 1; 2

16. $x^2 - 144 = 0$ 2; 12, –12

17. $r^2 - 14r + 49 = 0$ 2; 7

18. $x^2 + 25 = 0$ 2; $\pm 5i$

19. $12x^2 + 8x - 15 = 0$ 2; $\frac{5}{6}, -\frac{3}{2}$

20. $18x^2 + 3x - 1 = 0$ 2; $\frac{1}{6}, -\frac{1}{3}$

21. $6c^3 - 3c^2 - 45c = 0$ 3; $0, 3, -2.5$

22. $n^3 - 9n = 0$ 3; $0, -3, 3$

24. $2x^3 - 3x^2 - 18x - 8 = 0$

25. $x^5 - 10x^4 + 25x^3 + 20x^2 - 80x - 64 = 0$

Write the polynomial equation of least degree for each set of roots given.

23. $-3, 2$ $x^2 + x - 6 = 0$

24. $-2, -0.5, 4$

25. $-1, -1, 4, 4, 4$

26. $-5i, 5i, i, -i$
$x^4 + 26x^2 + 25 = 0$

27. $1, -1, 1 + i, 1 - i$
$x^4 - 2x^3 + x^2 + 2x - 2 = 0$

28. $2, 2 \pm 3i, -1 \pm i$
$x^5 - 4x^4 + 11x^3 + 4x^2 - 10x - 52 = 0$

Solve each equation and graph the related function.

29. $x^3 - 6x^2 + 10x - 8 = 0$ $4, 1 \pm i$

30. $x^4 - 10x^2 + 9 = 0$ $-1, 1, -3, 3$

31. $x^4 + x^2 - 2 = 0$ $-1, 1, \pm\sqrt{2}i$

32. $4m^4 + 17m^2 + 4 = 0$ $\pm 2i, \pm\frac{i}{2}$

For graphs for Exercises 29–32, see Teacher's Answer Key.

33. Sketch a fourth degree equation for each situation. See Teacher's Answer Key.
   a. no x-intercept
   b. one x-intercept
   c. two x-intercepts
   d. three x-intercepts
   e. four x-intercepts
   f. five x-intercepts

Graphing Calculator

Graph the related function for each equation. Use the TRACE and BOX functions to find the roots of each equation to the nearest hundredth. State the range values for the window that shows both the x-intercepts and the y-intercept.

34. $x^2 + 4x + 4 = 0$

35. $x^3 - 4x^2 - 320x = 0$

36. $x^4 - 26x^2 + 25 = 0$

34–36. See margin.

37. Graph the function $f(x) = x^5 - 15x^3 - 10x^2 + 60x + 72$.
   a. What is the maximum number of x-intercepts possible for this function? 5
   b. How many x-intercepts are there and what are they? 2; –2 and 3
   c. Why are there fewer x-intercepts than the maximum number? *Hint: The factored form of the polynomial is $(x + 2)^3(x - 3)^2$.* See margin.

Critical Thinking

38. If B and C are the real roots of $x^2 + Bx + C = 0$, where $B \neq 0$ and $C \neq 0$, find the product of B and C. –2

Additional Answers

14.

For graphs for Exercises 34-36, see students' work. Sample answers:
34. –2; Xmin: –10, Xmax: 10, Ymin: –10, Ymax: 10
35. 0, 20, –16; Xmin: –20, Xmax: 25, Ymin: –400, Ymax: 400
36. –1, –5, 1, 5; Xmin: –10, Xmax: 10, Ymin: –50, Ymax: 50
37c. There are 5 real roots. However, there is a triple root at –2 and a double root at 3.

Programming

39. The following program will compute the value of a function that is stored in Y_1, given a value for X. To end the program, press 2nd QUIT.

```
Prgm4: TABLE
:Lbl 1
:Disp "X="
:Input X
:Disp "Y="
:Disp Y₁     Displays the value of Y₁ using the input value for X.
:Goto 1
```

Given $f(x) = x^4 + 3x^3 - 2x^2 + x - 4$, use the program shown above to find each value.

a. $f(2)$ 30   **b.** $f(-3)$ –25   **c.** $f(0.5)$ –3.5625

Applications and Problem Solving

40. Aeronautics At liftoff, the space shuttle *Discovery* has a constant acceleration, a, of 16.4 ft/s². The initial velocity, v_0, due to the rotation of Earth is 1341 ft/s. Use the function $d(t) = v_0 t + \frac{1}{2}at^2$ to determine the distance from Earth for each time interval, t, after liftoff.

a. 30 seconds 47,610 ft
b. 1 minute 109,980 ft
c. 2 minutes 279,000 ft
d. If the time the space shuttle is in flight doubles, does the distance double? Explain. No, the relationship is not linear.

41. Finance The Lancaster Art Commission has invested in works by American painters. Three years ago, they bought a painting for $30,000. Two years ago, another painting was bought for $55,000. Last year, a third painting was purchased for $75,000.

a. If the appreciation of the paintings is approximately 13% per year, write a function that represents the commission's total investment and calculate the current value. $f(x) = 30{,}000x^3 + 55{,}000x^2 + 75{,}000x$; $198,266.41

b. Suppose each year the commission deposited the money in a savings account rather than purchasing works of art. If the rate of interest was 6.5%, what would be the value of the investment now? How does this differ from the art investment? $178,495.86; $19,770.55 less

42. Entertainment The scenery for a new children's show has a playhouse with painted window panes. A special gloss paint covers the area of the painted windows to make them look like glass. If the gloss only covers 315 square inches and the window must be 6 inches taller than it is wide, how large should the scenery painters make the window? 15 in. by 21 in.

LESSON 4-1 POLYNOMIAL FUNCTIONS 183

Using Technology

For Exercises 34–37, it may help students to know that any integer roots of the equation must be less than or equal to $|a_n|$ in absolute value.

Using Technology

The program given in Exercise 39 is for use with a TI-81 graphing calculator. For other programmable calculators, have students consult their owner's manual for commands similar to those presented here.

Additional Answers

47.

48.

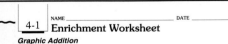
4-1 NAME _____ DATE _____
Enrichment Worksheet

Graphic Addition

One way to sketch the graphs of some polynomial functions is to use *addition of ordinates*. This method is useful when a polynomial function f can be written as the sum of two other functions, g and h, that are easier to graph. Then, each $f(x)$ can be found by mentally adding the corresponding $g(x)$ and $h(x)$. The graph at the right shows how to construct the graph of $f(x) = -\frac{1}{2}x^3 + \frac{1}{2}x^2 - 8$ from the graphs of $g(x) = -\frac{1}{2}x^3$ and $h(x) = \frac{1}{2}x^2 - 8$.

In each problem, the graphs of g(x) and h(x) are shown. Use addition of ordinates to graph a new polynomial function, f(x), such that f(x) = g(x) + h(x). Then write the equation for f(x).

1. $f(x) = -\frac{1}{2}x^3 - \frac{1}{2}x^2 + 8$
2. $f(x) = \frac{1}{2}x^3 + \frac{1}{2}x^2 - 12$
3. $f(x) = \frac{1}{2}x^3 - \frac{1}{2}x^2 + 8$
4. $f(x) = \frac{1}{2}x^3 + \frac{1}{2}x^2 - 8$
5. $f(x) = -\frac{1}{2}x^3 + \frac{1}{2}x^2 - 12$
6. $f(x) = -\frac{1}{2}x^3 - \frac{1}{2}x^2 + 4$

T 21
Glencoe Division, Macmillan/McGraw-Hill

---

43. Find $[g \circ h](x)$ if $g(x) = x - 1$ and $h(x) = x^2$. **(Lesson 1-2)** $x^2 - 1$

44. Write the slope-intercept form of the equation of the line that passes through $(0, 7)$ and $(5, 2)$. **(Lesson 1-5)** $y = -x + 7$

45. Solve the system of equations algebraically. **(Lesson 2-1)**
$x - 2y = -1$
$2x + 3y = -16$ $(-5, -2)$

46. Find the values of x, y, and z for which $\begin{bmatrix} x^2 & 7 & 9 \\ 5 & 12 & 6 \end{bmatrix} = \begin{bmatrix} 25 & 7 & y \\ 5 & 2z & 6 \end{bmatrix}$ is true.
(Lesson 2-2) $x = \pm 5, y = 9, z = 6$

47. Graph $y = \dfrac{2}{x^2 - x - 2}$ **(Lesson 3-4)** See margin.

48. Determine whether the graph of $y = \dfrac{x^2 - 1}{x + 1}$ has infinite discontinuity, jump discontinuity, or point discontinuity, or is continuous. Then graph the function. **(Lesson 3-8)** Point discontinuity; for graph, see margin.

49. College Entrance Exam Compare quantities A and B below. B
Write A if quantity A is greater.
Write B if quantity B is greater.
Write C if the two quantities are equal.
Write D if there is not enough information to determine the relationship.
(A) the slope of $2x + 3y = 7$ **(B)** the slope of $3x - 2y = 7$

CASE STUDY FOLLOW-UP

Refer to Case Study 3: *The Legal System*, on pages 962–965.

Alcohol may be involved in as many as half of all fatal traffic accidents. Police routinely test drivers suspected of drinking to find their blood-alcohol levels, the portion of their blood that is alcohol.

1. Assuming that the overall male/female arrest proportion holds for all crimes, how many men were arrested for drunken driving in 1990? 1.5 million

2. The polynomial function $A(x) = -0.0015x^2 + 0.1058x$ approximates a person's blood-alcohol level x hours after drinking 8 ounces of 100-proof whiskey.
    a. Find the blood-alcohol level after 5 hours. 0.4915
    b. In five states—California, Maine, Oregon, Utah, and Vermont—the legal blood-alcohol level is 0.08. In all other states, it is 0.1. Calculate the blood-alcohol level in fifths of an hour beginning with $c = 0.2$ to find the first time after drinking 8 ounces of 100-proof whiskey that a person could be arrested for drunken driving in these five states. after 0.8 h

3. **Research** Collect statistics on drunken driving and accidents in your state and write a 1-page paper summarizing your findings. In your paper, give your ideas about what can be done to reduce the amount of drinking and driving. See students' work.

184   CHAPTER 4   POLYNOMIAL AND RATIONAL FUNCTIONS

EXTENDING THE LESSON

Math Power: Reasoning

Three of the roots of a polynomial function are 3, 2*i*, and −5*i*.
a. What is the minimum degree of the function? 5
b. Write an equation of a function with these roots. Answers may vary.

Case Study Follow-Up

This activity provides an opportunity to do research and apply mathematics in solving problems related to issues that may face students in their adult lives. Case Study 3 is located on pages 962–965.

4-2A Graphing Calculators: Graphing Quadratic Functions

A graphing calculator can graph many different types of equations and can be used to analyze many different types of functions. In Chapter 3, we examined polynomial, radical, and rational functions. In this lesson, we will graph quadratic functions.

A quadratic function is a function of the form $y = ax^2 + bx + c$. This means that any equation in one variable, where the highest power is two is a quadratic equation. The graph of a quadratic equation is called a **parabola**.

Example 1

Graph $y = -16x^2 + 11$.

TI-18: [Y=] [(−)] 16 [X|T] [x²] [+] 11 [GRAPH]

Casio: [GRAPH] [(−)] 16 [ALPHA] [X] [x²] [+] 11 [EXE]

The standard viewing window does not show a complete graph of the equation. Try the viewing window [-3, 3] by [-5, 15] with a scale factor of 1 for the x- and y-axes.

This view shows a complete graph of the function because you can see the x- and y-intercepts, the maximum point, and the end behavior of the graph.

Notice from the graph that the shape of the graph of a quadratic equation is a parabola. Any quadratic equation will have this same general shape, although it may be thinner, fatter, shorter, or taller. Also, a parabola can open up, down, to the left, or to the right. However, graphs of quadratic equations that are functions open up or down.

Quadratic equations can also be solved. That is, you can let y equal 0 and solve the equation for x. The equation is of the form $0 = ax^2 + bx + c$, and you can use a graphing calculator to find the solutions if they are real. The **solutions** are the points where the graph crosses the x-axis because these are the points where $y = 0$.

There are three possible outcomes when solving a quadratic equation. The equation will have either two real solutions, one real solution, or no real solutions. Each of these outcomes is illustrated on the next page.

GRAPHING CALCULATORS: GRAPHING QUADRATIC FUNCTIONS 185

INTRODUCING THE LESSON

Objective Graph quadratic functions and solve quadratic equations on a graphing calculator.

Motivating the Lesson

Make one transparency that is a coordinate plane. On another transparency, draw a parabola. Have students place the parabola on the coordinate plane so that the parabola has two x-intercepts, then one x-intercept, and finally no x-intercept.

TEACHING THE LESSON

Teaching Tip Before discussing Example 1, ask students to list everything they know about the graph of a quadratic function. Make a list of observations and conclusions on the chalkboard.

More Examples

1. Graph $y = -2x^2 - 3x + 4$.

two real solutions   one real solution   no real solutions

Example 2

Solve $0 = 2x^2 - 5x + 1$ by using the graphing calculator. Round solutions to the nearest hundredth.

Graph the equation in the standard viewing window. Remember to first clear the graphics screen on the Casio.

TI-81: $\boxed{Y=}$ 2 $\boxed{X|T}$ $\boxed{x^2}$ $\boxed{-}$ 5 $\boxed{X|T}$ $\boxed{+}$ 1 $\boxed{GRAPH}$

Casio: $\boxed{Graph}$ 2 $\boxed{ALPHA}$ $\boxed{X}$ $\boxed{x^2}$ $\boxed{-}$ 5 $\boxed{ALPHA}$ $\boxed{X}$ $\boxed{+}$ 1 $\boxed{EXE}$

The standard viewing window shows a complete graph of the equation. Now zoom in on each of the x-intercepts to find the solutions to the equation. The solutions of this equation are 0.22 and 2.28 to the nearest hundredth.

It should be noted that solving quadratic equations graphically produces only approximate solutions. While approximations are adequate for most applications, if an exact solution is needed, the equation should be solved by factoring or by using the quadratic formula.

EXERCISES 1–6. See Teacher's Answer Key.

Use a graphing calculator to show a complete graph of each function. Then sketch the graph on a piece of paper.

1. $y = x^2 + 2x + 9$
2. $y = -3x^2 - 0.5x + 8$
3. $y = 1.1x^2 + 6.3x - 2.4$
4. $y = 12x^2 + 44x + 192$
5. $y = 0.9x^2 - 0.21x - 0.643$
6. $y = -\frac{1}{4}x^2 + 2x - 4$

Find the solutions of each quadratic equation to the nearest hundredth by using a graphing calculator.

7. $\frac{1}{2}x^2 + 3x - 5 = 0$ −7.36, 1.36
8. $14x^2 + 3.5x - 12.1 = 0$ −1.06, 0.81
9. $x^2 + 36.15x + 209.31 = 0$ −28.91, −7.24
10. $22x^2 + 35x - 19 = 0$ −2.02, 0.43
11. $0.3x^2 - 0.225x - 0.068 = 0$ −0.23, 0.98
12. $-5x^2 + 3.27x + 19.11 = 0$ −1.66, 2.31

4-2 Quadratic Equations and Inequalities

Objectives
4–2A
4–2B
4–2C

After studying this lesson, you should be able to:
- solve quadratic equations,
- use the discriminant to describe the roots of quadratic equations, and
- graph quadratic equations and inequalities.

NCTM Standards: 1-6

Lesson Resources

- Practice Master 4-2
- Enrichment Master 4-2
- Evaluation Master, Quiz A, p. 45

 Transparency 4-2 contains the 5-Minute Check and a teaching aid for this lesson.

Application

The Thespian Club at Colerain Senior High School needs to purchase an additional wireless microphone for the character Albert in the play *Bye Bye Birdie*. Each cast member will contribute an equal share for the cost of the microphone, which is $300. If 5 more students had joined the original cast, the cost per cast member would have been $10 less. How many cast members are there in this production of *Bye Bye Birdie*?

Let x = the number of cast members, and let y = the contribution of each student.

$$(x + 5)(y - 10) = 300$$
$$(x + 5)\left(\frac{300}{x} - 10\right) = 300 \qquad y = \frac{300}{x}$$
$$(x + 5)(300 - 10x) = 300x$$
$$300x - 10x^2 + 1500 - 50x = 300x$$
$$-10x^2 - 50x + 1500 = 0$$

 FYI...

The musical *Bye Bye Birdie* opened on Broadway on April 14, 1960, at the Martin Beck Theater. The show completed 607 performances.

One way to determine the roots, or solutions, of this quadratic equation would be to examine the graph of the related function, $y = -10x^2 - 50x + 1500$. The x-intercepts of the graph are the zeros of the function, which are also the solutions of the quadratic equation. So, the solutions are $x = 10$ and $x = -15$. Since the number of cast members cannot be negative, there must be 10 members in the cast of *Bye Bye Birdie*.

The graph of a quadratic function is called a parabola. The vertex of the parabola is its critical point.

You have solved quadratic equations by factoring and by graphing. Another method for solving a quadratic equation is by **completing the square**. Completing the square is a helpful method to use when the quadratic is not easily factorable. It can be used to solve any quadratic equation. Remember that, for any number b, the square of the binomial $x + b$ has the form $x^2 + 2bx + b^2$. When completing the square, you know the first term and middle term and need to supply the last term. This term equals the square of half the coefficient of the middle term. The leading coefficient must be 1.

LESSON 4-2 QUADRATIC EQUATIONS AND INEQUALITIES 187

INTRODUCING THE LESSON

 5-Minute Check
(over Lesson 4-1)

1. Determine if each expression is a polynomial in one variable. If the expression is a polynomial in one variable, state the degree.
   a. $a^3 - 2a^2b + b^2$ **not a poly. in one variable**
   b. $x^2 + 4x^4 - 5x + x^3$ **poly. of deg. 4**
2. Determine whether 2 is a root of $x^3 + x^2 - 4x - 4 = 0$. **yes**
3. State the number of complex roots of the equation $x^4 - 81 = 0$. Find the roots and graph the related polynomial function. **4; ±3, ±3i**

4. Write the polynomial equation of least degree with roots -1, and $\pm i$. $x^3 + x^2 + x + 1 = 0$

ALTERNATE TEACHING STRATEGIES

Using Problem Solving

Students may be interested in seeing some of the applications involving quadratic equations that exist. A physics book would be one good source for finding such examples. Students could work on one or two such problems in pairs and then give a report to the class.

Using Charts

Classify the set of quadratic equations according to some of their distinguishing characteristcs, such as the sign of the leading coefficient and the value of the discriminant. Make a chart showing the general shape of the graph for each type.

From Lesson 4-1, students know that a quadratic equation has two roots. What is the quickest way of discovering if those roots are real? List a set of quadratic equations on the chalkboard and have students try to decide how many real roots each one has. They should be interested in seeing how efficiently the discriminant answers this question.

TEACHING THE LESSON

Chalkboard Examples

For Example 1

A projectile has an initial velocity of 256 ft/s and an initial height of 576 ft. Its height at time t is given by the equation: $h(t) = -16t^2 + 256t + 576$. When does the projectile hit the ground? **after 18 s**

For Example 2

Solve $3x^2 + x - 2 = 0$ using the quadratic formula. Then graph the related function. $\frac{2}{3}, -1$

Example 1

Refer to the application at the beginning of the lesson. Solve the problem by completing the square.

$$0 = -10x^2 - 50x + 1500$$
$$0 = x^2 + 5x - 150 \qquad \textit{Divide each side by -10.}$$
$$150 = x^2 + 5x \qquad \textit{Add 150 to each side.}$$
$$150 + 6.25 = x^2 + 5x + 6.25 \qquad \textit{Add } \left(\frac{5}{2}\right)^2 \textit{ or 6.25 to each side.}$$
$$156.25 = (x + 2.5)^2 \qquad \textit{Factor the perfect square trinomial.}$$
$$\pm 12.5 = x + 2.5 \qquad \textit{Take the square root of each side.}$$

$$12.5 = x + 2.5 \qquad \text{or} \qquad -12.5 = x + 2.5$$
$$10 = x \qquad\qquad\qquad -15 = x$$

The solutions for the equation are $x = 10$ and $x = -15$. Since the number of cast members cannot be negative, the number is 10. *This agrees with the previous solution.*

Completing the square can be used to develop a general formula for solving any quadratic equation of the form $ax^2 + bx + c = 0$. This formula is called the **quadratic formula**.

Quadratic Formula

The roots of a quadratic equation of the form $ax^2 + bx + c = 0$ with $a \neq 0$ are given by the following formula.

$$x = \frac{-b \pm \sqrt{b^2 - 4ac}}{2a}$$

You will be asked to derive this formula in Exercise 42.

The quadratic formula can be used to find the roots of any quadratic equation.

Example 2

Solve $4x^2 - 8x + 3 = 0$ using the quadratic formula. Then graph the related function.

$$x = \frac{-b \pm \sqrt{b^2 - 4ac}}{2a}$$
$$= \frac{-(-8) \pm \sqrt{(-8)^2 - 4(4)(3)}}{2(4)} \qquad \begin{array}{l} a = 4, \\ b = -8, \\ c = 3 \end{array}$$
$$= \frac{8 \pm \sqrt{16}}{8}$$
$$= \frac{8 \pm 4}{8}$$

$$x = \frac{8 + 4}{8} \qquad \text{or} \qquad x = \frac{8 - 4}{8}$$
$$x = \frac{12}{8} \text{ or } \frac{3}{2} \qquad\qquad x = \frac{4}{8} \text{ or } \frac{1}{2}$$

To graph the related function, you need to know the x-intercepts, y-intercept, and the vertex. You already know the x-intercepts: $\frac{3}{2}$ and $\frac{1}{2}$.

To find the y-intercept, find $f(0)$ for $f(x) = 4x^2 - 8x + 3$.
$f(0) = 4(0)^2 - 8(0) + 3$ or 3

To find the vertex, find the derivative.

$f(x) = 4x^2 - 8x + 3$
$f'(x) = 8x - 8$ *Find the derivative.*
$\quad 0 = 8x - 8$ *Replace $f'(x)$ with 0.*
$\quad 1 = x$ *Solve for x.*
$f(1) = 4(1)^2 - 8(1) + 3$
$\quad\quad = -1$

The vertex is at $(1, -1)$.

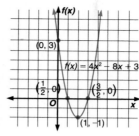

Graph the ordered pairs corresponding to the intercepts and the vertex. These are the points at $(\frac{3}{2}, 0)$, $(\frac{1}{2}, 0)$, $(0, 3)$, $(1, -1)$.

The graph shows there is an x-intercept at $\frac{3}{2}$ and one at $\frac{1}{2}$.

In the quadratic formula, the expression under the radical, $b^2 - 4ac$, is called the **discriminant**. The discriminant tells us the nature of the roots of a quadratic equation.

Nature of the Roots of a Quadratic Equation

Discriminant	Nature of the Roots
$b^2 - 4ac > 0$	two distinct real roots
$b^2 - 4ac = 0$	exactly one real root
$b^2 - 4ac < 0$	no real roots (two distinct imaginary roots)

In Example 2, the discriminant has a value of 16. Therefore, there are two distinct real roots, namely $\frac{3}{2}$ and $\frac{1}{2}$.

Example 3

Determine the discriminant of $x^2 - 6x + 13 = 0$. Use the quadratic formula to find the roots. Then graph the related function.

The value of the discriminant, $b^2 - 4ac$, is $(-6)^2 - 4(1)(13)$ or -16. Since the value of the discriminant is less than 0, there are no real roots. Verify this by using the quadratic formula.

$$x = \frac{-b \pm \sqrt{b^2 - 4ac}}{2a}$$

$$= \frac{-(-6) \pm \sqrt{-16}}{2} \quad\quad b^2 - 4ac = -16$$

$$= \frac{6 \pm 4i}{2}$$

$$= 3 \pm 2i \quad\quad \text{Both roots are imaginary.}$$

(continued on the next page)

Chalkboard Example

For Example 4

Determine if a rectangular piece of wrapping paper with a perimeter of 50 inches can have an area of 136 square inches. State the dimensions of the paper if it does exist.   8 in. by 17 in.

Find the y-intercept.
$f(0) = (0)^2 - 6(0) + 13$ or 13

Find the vertex.
$$f'(x) = 2x - 6$$
$$0 = 2x - 6$$
$$3 = x$$

$$f(3) = 3^2 - 6(3) + 13$$
$$= 4$$

The vertex is at $(3, 4)$.

Use the y-intercept and vertex to graph the function.

The graph has no x-intercepts, verifying there are no real roots.

The roots of the equation in Example 3 are the complex numbers $3 + 2i$ and $3 - 2i$. Complex numbers in the form $a + bi$ and $a - bi$ are called **conjugates**. Imaginary roots of polynomial equations always occur in conjugate pairs.

Complex Conjugates Theorem	Suppose a and b are real numbers with $b \neq 0$. If $a + bi$ is a root of a polynomial equation with real coefficients, then $a - bi$ is also a root of the equation.

Example 4

Stationery

Determine if a rectangular piece of wrapping paper with a perimeter of 36 inches can have an area of 81 square inches. State the dimensions of the paper if it does exist.

Use the perimeter and area formulas to produce a quadratic equation.

$$P = 2\ell + 2w \qquad \textit{Perimeter formula}$$
$$36 = 2\ell + 2w \qquad \textit{P = 36}$$
$$36 - 2w = 2\ell \qquad \textit{Subtract 2w from each side.}$$
$$18 - w = \ell \qquad \textit{Divide each side by 2.}$$

Now substitute the value of ℓ into the area formula.

$$A = \ell w \qquad \textit{Area formula}$$
$$81 = (18 - w)w \qquad \textit{$\ell = 18 - w$ and A = 81}$$
$$0 = -81 + 18w - w^2 \qquad \textit{Subtract 81 from each side and multiply.}$$
$$0 = w^2 - 18w + 81 \qquad \textit{Multiply each side by –1.}$$

Now use the discriminant to determine how many roots there are.

$$b^2 - 4ac = (-18)^2 - 4(1)(81) \text{ or } 0$$

Because the discriminant is 0, there will be one distinct real root.

The quadratic is a perfect square trinomial. You can solve this equation by factoring.

190   CHAPTER 4   POLYNOMIAL AND RATIONAL FUNCTIONS

$$w^2 - 18w + 81 = 0$$
$$(w - 9)^2 = 0 \qquad \textit{Factor the trinomial.}$$
$$w = 9 \qquad \textit{The width of the rectangle is 9 inches.}$$

Since the width is 9 inches and $81 = \ell w$, the length is also 9 inches.
The dimensions of the paper are 9 inches by 9 inches.

In Chapter 3, you learned to graph different types of inequalities. You can use the methods of graphing quadratic equations in this lesson to graph **quadratic inequalities**.

Example 5

Graph $y > x^2 + 8x - 20$.

First graph the related function, $f(x) = x^2 + 8x - 20$, by finding the x- and y-intercepts and vertex.

Find the x-intercepts.

$$x = \frac{-(8) \pm \sqrt{8^2 - 4(1)(-20)}}{2(1)}$$
$$x = -10 \text{ or } x = 2$$

Find the y-intercept.

$$f(0) = (0)^2 + 8(0) - 20 \text{ or } -20$$

Find the vertex.

$$f'(x) = 2x + 8$$
$$0 = 2x + 8$$
$$-4 = x$$

$$f(-4) = (-4)^2 + 8(-4) - 20$$
$$= -36$$

The vertex is at $(-4, -36)$.

Graph the parabola. Because the inequality does not include the equation $y = x^2 + 8x - 20$, the parabola is dashed.

Determine which region is shaded by testing a point inside the parabola.

Test $(0, 0)$: $y > x^2 + 8x - 20$
$$0 > 0^2 + 8(0) - 20$$
$$0 > -20$$

The inequality is true, so $(0, 0)$ is a solution. Shade the region that contains $(0, 0)$.

Test a point outside the parabola to check your solution.

EVALUATING THE LESSON

Checking for Understanding

Exercises 1–14 are designed to help you assess students' understanding through reading, writing, speaking, and modeling. You should work through Exercises 1–3 with your students and then monitor their work on Exercises 4–14.

Closing the Lesson

Writing Activity Have students explain what the discriminant of a quadratic equation is and tell what its value reveals.

Additional Answers

1. Graphing, completing the square, quadratic formula; The graphing solution may be less exact, since exact values are harder to determine on a coordinate plane.
3. If the discriminant is positive, there are two distinct real roots. If it is 0, there is one distinct real root. If it is negative, there are two imaginary roots.

Practice Masters Booklet, p. 22

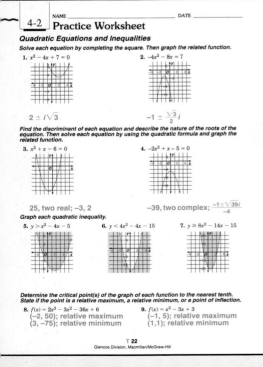

CHECKING FOR UNDERSTANDING

Communicating Mathematics

Read and study the lesson to answer each question.

1. **Discuss** three different methods for determining the zeros of a quadratic equation and the ways in which the solutions might differ. See margin.

2. **Write** the expression for the discriminant of a quadratic equation $ax^2 + bx + c = 0$. $b^2 - 4ac$

3. **Explain** how the discriminant can be used to describe the nature of the roots of a quadratic equation. See margin.

Guided Practice

Find the value of c that makes each trinomial a perfect square.

4. $x^2 + 4x + c$ 4
5. $p^2 - p + c$ $\frac{1}{4}$
6. $y^2 + \frac{3}{2}y + c$ $\frac{9}{16}$

7–8. For graphs, see Teacher's Answer Key.

Solve each equation by completing the square. Then graph the related function.

7. $x^2 - 5x + 9 = 0$ $\frac{5 \pm i\sqrt{11}}{2}$
8. $z^2 - 10z + 10 = -11$ 3, 7

Find the discriminant of each equation and describe the nature of the roots of the equation.

9. $4x^2 + 6x + 25 = 0$ -364
2 imaginary roots
10. $x^2 + 12x + 36 = 0$ 0
1 distinct real root

11. Name the conjugate of $5 - i\sqrt{2}$. $5 + i\sqrt{2}$

Solve each equation by using the quadratic formula.

12. $t^2 - 3t - 28 = 0$ 7, -4
13. $3x^2 - 5x + 9 = 0$ $\frac{5 \pm i\sqrt{83}}{6}$

14. Graph $10 - 3x - x^2 \ge y$. See margin.

EXERCISES

15–20. For graphs see Teacher's Answer Key.

Practice

A

Solve each equation by completing the square. Then graph the related function.

15. $x^2 - 3x - 88 = 0$ $-8, 11$
16. $x^2 - \frac{3}{4}x + \frac{1}{8} = 0$ $\frac{1}{2}, \frac{1}{4}$
17. $2x^2 + 11x - 21 = 0$ $\frac{3}{2}, -7$
18. $x^2 - 3x - 7 = 0$ $\frac{3 \pm \sqrt{37}}{2}$
19. $z^2 - 2z = 24$ 6, -4
20. $3x^2 - 12x = -4$ $2 \pm \frac{2\sqrt{6}}{3}$

For discriminants and descriptions for Exercises 21–26, see margin.

Find the discriminant of each equation and describe the nature of the roots of the equation. Then solve each equation by using the quadratic formula and graph the related function. For graphs for Exercises 21–26, see Teacher's Answer Key.

B

21. $4x^2 + 19x - 5 = 0$ $\frac{1}{4}, -5$
22. $3 - 7m - 6m^2 = 0$ $-\frac{3}{2}, \frac{1}{3}$
23. $2w^2 + 3w + 3 = 0$ $\frac{-3 \pm i\sqrt{15}}{4}$
24. $2k^2 + 5k - 9 = 0$ $\frac{-5 \pm \sqrt{97}}{4}$
25. $6b^2 - 39b + 45 = 0$ $\frac{3}{2}, 5$
26. $4x^2 - 2x + 9 = 0$ $\frac{1 \pm i\sqrt{35}}{4}$

Graph each quadratic inequality. 27–32. See Teacher's Answer Key.

27. $y < 3 + 7x - 6x^2$
28. $y < 3x^2 + 7x + 4$
29. $y \ge 2x^2 - 9x - 5$
30. $y > 4x^2 - 8x + 3$
31. $y \le -x^2 - 7x + 10$
32. $y > -4x^2 - 3x - 6$

192 CHAPTER 4 POLYNOMIAL AND RATIONAL FUNCTIONS

RETEACHING THE LESSON

Give students a list of quadratic equations and have them choose the best method of finding the roots of each. See if they can come up with some rules of thumb for deciding when to apply each method.

Additional Answer

14.

Determine the critical point(s) of the graph of each function to the nearest tenth. State if the point is a relative maximum, a relative minimum, or a point of inflection. 33–36. See margin.

33. $f(x) = x^3 - 2x^2 - 35x$

34. $f(x) = 15x^3 - 16x^2 - x + 2$

35. $f(x) = x^3 - 9x^2 + 23x - 15$

36. $f(x) = x^3 + 6x^2 + 8x$

37. Consider the functions $f(x) = x^2 - 3x - 54$ and $g(x) = 54 + 3x - x^2$.
  a. Determine the zeros of each function. $(-6, 0), (9, 0)$
  b. Sketch a graph of each function. See margin.
  c. Write a paragraph in which you compare and contrast the two graphs.
  See margin.

Graphing Calculator

Use the TRACE and BOX commands to graph each function and determine the x-intercepts. State the Xmin, Xmax, Ymin, and Ymax of the window that shows the x-intercepts and y-intercept. 38–40. See margin.

38. $x^2 - 6x + 9 = y$

39. $x^2 - 3x - 700 = y$

40. $x^4 - 50x^2 + 49 = y$

Critical Thinking

41. Find the difference of the roots of the quadratic equation below.
$(3 + 2\sqrt{2})x^2 + (1 + \sqrt{2})x = 2$ $\dfrac{3}{\sqrt{3 + 2\sqrt{2}}}$

42. Derive the quadratic formula by completing the square.
See Teacher's Answer Key.

Applications and Problem Solving

43. Gardening The length of Mary Adam's rectangular flower garden is 6 feet more than its width. A walkway 3 feet wide surrounds the outside of the garden. The total area of the walkway itself is 288 square feet. Find the dimensions of the garden. 18 ft by 24 ft

44. Physics The distance, $d(t)$, fallen by a free-falling body can be represented by the formula $d(t) = v_0 t - \dfrac{1}{2} gt^2$, where v_0 is the initial velocity and g represents the acceleration due to gravity. The acceleration due to gravity is 9.8 m/s². If a rock is thrown downward with an initial velocity of 4 m/s from the edge of the North Rim of the Grand Canyon, which is 1750 meters deep, determine how long it will take the rock to reach the bottom of the Grand Canyon. 19.3 seconds

45. Baseball When an object is projected upward, its height in feet above the ground, $d(t)$, is given as a function of time, t in seconds, by the formula $d(t) = v_0 t - \dfrac{1}{2} gt^2$. The acceleration due to gravity g is 32 ft/s². If Andy Van Slyke of the Pittsburgh Pirates hits a ball straight upward with an initial velocity, v_0, of 80 ft/s, determine the time that the ball is in the air.

45. 5 seconds

Mixed Review

46. Graph $2y - 5x \leq 8$. **(Lesson 1-3)** See margin.

47. Write the standard form of an equation of the line that passes through $(4, 2)$ and is parallel to the line whose equation is $y = 2x - 4$. **(Lesson 1-6)** $2x - y - 6 = 0$

48. Solve the system of equations by using augmented matrices. **(Lesson 2-4)**
$6r + s = 9$
$3r + 2s = 0$ $(2, -3)$

Additional Answers

21. 441, 2 real distinct roots
22. 121, 2 real distinct roots
23. –15, 2 imaginary roots
24. 97, 2 real distinct roots
25. 441, 2 real distinct roots
26. –140, 2 imaginary roots

33. (4.1, –108.2), rel min;
 (–2.8, 60.4), rel max; (0.7, –24.3),
 pt of infl
34. (0.7, –1.4), rel min;
 (–0.03, 2.0), rel max; (0.4, 0),
 pt of infl
35. (4.2, –3.1), rel min;
 (1.8, 3.1), rel max; (3, 0), pt of infl
36. (–0.8, –3.1), rel min;
 (–3.2, 3.1), rel max; (–2, 0), pt of infl

Additional Answers continued on next page

46.

Enrichment Masters Booklet, p. 22

4-2 | NAME _____ DATE _____

Enrichment Worksheet

Conjugates and Absolute Value

When studying complex numbers, it is often convenient to represent a complex number by a single variable. For example, we might let $z = x + yi$. We denote the conjugate of z by $\bar{z}$. Thus, $\bar{z} = x - yi$. We can define the absolute value of a complex number as follows.

$$|z| = |x + yi| = \sqrt{x^2 + y^2}$$

There are many important relationships involving conjugates and absolute values of complex numbers.

Example   Show that $z^2 = z\bar{z}$ for any complex number z.

Let $z = x + yi$. Then,

$z\bar{z} = (x + yi)(x - yi)$

$= x^2 + y^2$

$= \left(\sqrt{x^2 + y^2}\right)^2$

$= |z|^2$

Example   Show that $\frac{\bar{z}}{|z|^2}$ is the multiplicative inverse for any nonzero complex number z.

We know that $|z|^2 = z\bar{z}$. If $z \neq 0$, then we have

$z\left(\frac{\bar{z}}{|z|^2}\right) = 1$. Thus, $\frac{\bar{z}}{|z|^2}$ is the multiplicative inverse of z.

For each of the following complex numbers, find the absolute value and multiplicative inverse.

1. $2i$
2. $\frac{-i}{2}$

2. $-4 - 3i$
5; $\frac{-4 + 3i}{25}$

3. $12 - 5i$
13; $\frac{12 + 5i}{169}$

4. $5 - 12i$
13; $\frac{5 + 12i}{169}$

5. $1 + i$
$\sqrt{2}$; $\frac{1 - i}{2}$

6. $\sqrt{3} - i$
2; $\frac{\sqrt{3} + i}{4}$

7. $\frac{\sqrt{3}}{3} + \frac{\sqrt{3}}{3}i$
$\frac{\sqrt{6}}{3}$; $\frac{\sqrt{3} - i\sqrt{3}}{2}$

8. $\frac{\sqrt{2}}{2} - \frac{\sqrt{2}}{2}i$
1; $\frac{\sqrt{2}}{2} + \frac{\sqrt{2}}{2}i$

9. $\frac{1}{2} - \frac{\sqrt{3}}{2}i$
1; $\frac{1}{2} + \frac{\sqrt{3}}{2}i$

T 22
Glencoe Division, Macmillan/McGraw-Hill

49. Determine whether the graph of $y = |x| + 1$ is symmetric with respect to the x-axis, the y-axis, the line $y = x$, the line $y = -x$, or the origin. Include all symmetries in your answer. **(Lesson 3-1)** y-axis

50. Find the equation of the tangent to the graph of $y = -3x^2 + 5$ at $(-2, -7)$. **(Lesson 3-6)** $y = 12x + 17$

51. Write the simplest polynomial equation with roots $-5, -6$, and 10. **(Lesson 4-1)**

51. $x^3 + x^2 - 80x - 300 = 0$

52. College Entrance Exam   Compare quantities A and B below.   B
Write A if quantity A is greater.
Write B if quantity B is greater.
Write C if the quantities are equal.
Write D if there is not enough information to determine the relationship.

Given: $p > 0, q < 0$

    (A) $p + q$ **(B)** $p - q$

COOPERATIVE LEARNING

DECISION MAKING

Choosing a Vacation Spot

Where is the best place in the United States for you to spend a two-week vacation? What do you want to accomplish on a vacation? Should fun and relaxation be your only goals, or should you try to learn something about America's history, culture, or nature at the same time? Planning for a vacation includes thinking not only about destinations but about food, lodging, methods of transportation, and, of course, how you are going to pay for it all! 1–4. See students' work.

1. Without naming a specific place, describe your ideal vacation. Tell what kinds of activities you most want to participate in during your trip and what goals you want to accomplish.

2. Research possible places that will meet your vacation needs. Talk to friends, consult books in the library, contact state tourism departments, or talk to a travel agent. Make a list of three potential vacation destinations.

3. For each destination, outline a two-week agenda and prepare a budget specifying anticipated costs for the entire trip.

4. **Project**   Work with your group to complete one of the projects listed at the right, based on the information you gathered in Exercises 1–3.

PROJECTS

- *Conduct an interview.*
- *Write a book report.*
- *Write a proposal.*
- *Write an article for the school paper.*
- *Write a report.*
- *Make a display.*
- *Make a graph or chart.*
- *Plan an activity.*
- *Design a checklist.*

194 CHAPTER 4 POLYNOMIAL AND RATIONAL FUNCTIONS

EXTENDING THE LESSON

Math Power: Reasoning

Show that if a and c have different signs, then $ax^2 + bx + c = 0$, $a \neq 0$, has two real roots.   If a and c have different signs, then $ac < 0$. Thus, $-4ac > 0$. $b^2 - 4ac$ would have a positive value indicating two real roots.

Decision Making

This activity provides students an opportunity to work together on a given problem. You may wish to refer to pages T20-T21 and page 176c for the various elements of cooperative groups and specific goals and strategies for using them.

4-3 The Remainder and Factor Theorems

Objective
4–3
After studying this lesson, you should be able to:
- find the factors of polynomials using the remainder and factor theorems.

Application

On July 26, 1992, Miguel Indurain of Spain won his second consecutive Tour de France competition in cycling. He averaged a record-setting speed of almost 40 km/h or about 11 m/s. The average recreational cyclist pedals at a rate of about 4 m/s. Suppose you were cycling along at the speed of 4 m/s and headed down a hill, accelerating at a rate of 0.4 m/s^2. How far down the hill would you be after 5 seconds?

The formula that represents this relationship is $D(t) = v_i t + \frac{1}{2}at^2$, where $D(t)$ is the distance from the starting point, v_i is the initial velocity, t is time, and a is the acceleration. By substituting the initial velocity and the acceleration from this problem into the formula, we get $D(t) = 4t + \frac{1}{2}(0.4)t^2$, or $D(t) = 4t + 0.2t^2$.

To find the distance after 5 seconds, evaluate this function for $t = 5$.

$$D(5) = 4(5) + 0.2(5)^2 \text{ or } 25$$

After 5 seconds, you would be 25 meters down the hill.

Suppose you divide the polynomial $4t + 0.2t^2$ by $t - 5$.

$$
\begin{array}{r}
0.2t + 5 \\
t - 5 \overline{)\, 0.2t^2 + 4t + 0} \\
\underline{0.2t^2 - 1t} \\
5t + 0 \\
\underline{5t - 25} \\
25
\end{array}
$$

From arithmetic, you may remember that the dividend equals the product of the divisor and the quotient plus the remainder. For example, $32 \div 5 = 6$ R2, so $32 = 5(6) + 2$. This relationship can be applied to polynomials.

$$D(t) = (t - 5)(0.2t + 5) + 25$$

Now let $t = 5$. What do you find?

$$D(5) = (5 - 5)[0.2(5) + 5] + 25 \text{ or } 25$$

Notice that the value of $D(5)$ is the same as the remainder when the polynomial is divided by $t - 5$. This example illustrates the **remainder theorem**.

LESSON 4-3   THE REMAINDER AND FACTOR THEOREMS   195

ALTERNATE TEACHING STRATEGIES

Using Cooperative Groups

Give each group of students a piece of paper on which the long division and synthetic division versions of the same problem are worked out side by side. Have each group look for similarities between the two methods and see if they can discover how synthetic division is done.

Using Computers

Write a flow chart showing how to do synthetic division. Input should include the dividend and the divisor. The quotient and remainder should be output.

For Example 1

Let $P(x) = 2x^3 + x^2 - 4x + 3$.
Show that $P(-1)$ is the remainder
when $P(x)$ is divided by $x + 1$.

$$
\begin{array}{r}
2x^2 - x - 3 \\
x + 1 \overline{)2x^3 + x^2 - 4x + 3} \\
\underline{2x^3 + 2x^2} \\
-x^2 - 4x \\
\underline{-x^2 - x} \\
-3x + 3 \\
\underline{-3x - 3} \\
6
\end{array}
$$

$P(-1) = 2(-1)^3 + (-1)^2 - 4(-1) + 3 = 6$

Teaching Tip Emphasize the importance of leaving space in a long division problem or inserting a zero in a synthetic division problem if any powers of x in the dividend have zero coefficients. Then have each student do a few synthetic division problems independently when the concept is first presented so that the necessary steps will be learned.

The Remainder Theorem

If a polynomial $P(x)$ is divided by $x - r$, the remainder is a constant, $P(r)$, and
$$P(x) = (x - r) \cdot Q(x) + P(r)$$
where $Q(x)$ is a polynomial with degree one less than the degree of $P(x)$.

The remainder theorem provides another way to find the value of the polynomial function $P(x)$ for a given value r. The value will be the remainder when $P(x)$ is divided by $x - r$.

Example 1

Let $P(x) = x^3 + 3x^2 - 2x - 8$. Show that the value of $P(-2)$ is the remainder when $P(x)$ is divided by $x + 2$.

Use long division to find the remainder.

$$
\begin{array}{r}
x^2 + x - 4 \\
x + 2 \overline{)x^3 + 3x^2 - 2x - 8} \\
\underline{x^3 + 2x^2} \\
x^2 - 2x \\
\underline{x^2 + 2x} \\
-4x - 8 \\
\underline{-4x - 8} \\
0
\end{array}
$$

Evaluate $P(x)$ for $x = -2$.

$P(x) = x^3 + 3x^2 - 2x - 8$
$P(-2) = (-2)^3 + 3(-2)^2 - 2(-2) - 8$
$P(-2) = -8 + 12 + 4 - 8$
$P(-2) = 0$

The remainder after division is 0, and the value of $P(-2)$ is also 0.

Long division can be very time consuming. **Synthetic division** is a shortcut for dividing a polynomial by a binomial of the form $x - r$. Let's divide the polynomial $x^3 + 3x^2 - 2x - 8$ by $x + 2$ using synthetic division. For $x + 2$, the value of r is -2.

Step 1 Arrange the terms of the polynomial in descending powers of x. Then, write the coefficients as shown.

$x^3 + 3x^2 - 2x - 8$
1   3   -2   -8

Step 2 Write the constant r of the divisor $x - r$. In this case, write -2.

$-2 \rfloor$ 1   3   -2   -8

Step 3 Bring down the first coefficient.

$-2 \rfloor$ 1   3   -2   -8
1

Step 4 Multiply the first coefficient by r. Then write the product under the second coefficient. Add.

$-2 \rfloor$ 1   3   -2   -8
         -2
1   1

Step 5 Multiply the sum by r. Then write the product under the next coefficient. Add.

$-2 \rfloor$ 1   3   -2   -8
         -2   -2
1   1   -4

Step 6 Repeat Step 5 until all coefficients in the dividend have been used.

$$\begin{array}{r|rrr} -2 & 1 & 3 & -2 & -8 \\ & & -2 & -2 & 8 \\ \hline & 1 & 1 & -4 & 0 \end{array}$$

The final sum represents the remainder, which in this case, is zero. The other numbers are the coefficients of the polynomial that is the quotient.

Step 7 Remember that the quotient has a degree one less than the dividend. Write the quotient as $x^2 + x - 4$.

So, $x^3 + 3x^2 - 2x - 8 = (x + 2)(x^2 + x - 4)$. This result agrees with the long division in Example 1.

Example 2

Use synthetic division to divide $m^5 - 3m^2 - 20$ by $m - 2$.

$$\begin{array}{r|rrrrrr} 2 & 1 & 0 & 0 & -3 & 0 & -20 \\ & & 2 & 4 & 8 & 10 & 20 \\ \hline & 1 & 2 & 4 & 5 & 10 & 0 \end{array}$$

Notice there are no m^4, m^3, or m terms. Zeros are placed in their positions as place holders.

The quotient is $m^4 + 2m^3 + 4m^2 + 5m + 10$.

If the remainder is zero when $P(x)$ is divided by $x - r$, then $x - r$ is a factor of $P(x)$. A corollary to the remainder theorem, called the **factor theorem**, states this more formally.

The Factor Theorem

The binomial $x - r$ is a factor of the polynomial $P(x)$ if and only if $P(r) = 0$.

Example 3

Let $P(x) = x^3 - 4x^2 - 7x + 10$. Determine if $x - 5$ is a factor of $P(x)$.

Let's use synthetic division. In this case, $r = 5$.

$$\begin{array}{r|rrr} 5 & 1 & -4 & -7 & 10 \\ & & 5 & 5 & -10 \\ \hline & 1 & 1 & -2 & 0 \end{array}$$

Since the remainder is 0, $x - 5$ is a factor of $x^3 - 4x^2 - 7x + 10$.

Check: $P(5) = 5^3 - 4(5^2) - 7(5) + 10$
$= 125 - 100 - 35 + 10$ or 0

When a polynomial is divided by one of its binomial factors, the quotient is called a **depressed polynomial**. A depressed polynomial has a degree less than the original polynomial. In Example 3, $x^2 + x - 2$ is the depressed polynomial. This polynomial may also be factorable, which would give you other zeros of the function. In this case, $x^2 + x - 2$ can be factored as $(x + 2)(x - 1)$. So, the other zeros of the function are -2 and 1.

LESSON 4-3   THE REMAINDER AND FACTOR THEOREMS   197

You can also find factors of a polynomial such as $x^3 - 4x^2 - 7x + 10$ by using a shortened form of synthetic division to test several values of r.

r	1	-4	-7	10
1	1	-3	-10	0
2	1	-2	-11	-12
3	1	-1	-10	-20
4	1	0	-7	-18
5	1	1	-2	0
-1	1	-5	-2	12
-2	1	-6	5	0

In the table at the left, the first column contains various values for r. The next three columns show the coefficients of the depressed polynomial in the last line of the synthetic division and the fifth column shows the remainder. Any value of r that results in a remainder of zero indicates a factor of the polynomial. The factors of the original polynomial are $x - 1$, $x - 5$, and $x + 2$.

Look at the pattern of values in the last column. Notice that when $r = 2, 3,$ and 4, the values of $f(x)$ decrease and then increase. This indicates that there is an x-coordinate of a critical point between 2 and 4.

You can use a graphing calculator to investigate polynomials and their factors.

EXPLORATION: Graphing Calculator

1. Graph each polynomial on the same screen. What do you notice about these graphs? They are the same.

   a. $P(x) = (x - 1)(x + 2)(x + 3)$
   b. $P(x) = (x^2 + x - 2)(x + 3)$
   c. $P(x) = x^3 + 4x^2 + x - 6$

2. Graph $P(x) = \dfrac{(x^3 + 4x^2 + x - 6)}{(x - 1)}$.

   a. Use the TRACE function to find $P(-2)$ and $P(-3)$. 0; 0
   b. Graph $y = (x + 2)(x + 3)$.

2c. They are the same.

   c. How does this compare with the graph of
   $P(x) = \dfrac{(x^3 + 4x^2 + x - 6)}{(x - 1)}$?
   d. What does this indicate?
   $(x + 2)(x + 3)$ or $x^2 + x + 6$ is a depressed polynomial after division by $(x - 1)$.

Example 4

APPLICATION

Cycling

Refer to the application at the beginning of the lesson. If the hill on which you were riding is 55 meters long, how long will it take you to reach the bottom of the hill?

Use the formula for the distance and replace $D(t)$ with 55.

$D(t) = 4t + 0.2t^2$

$55 = 4t + 0.2t^2$ *Replace $D(t)$ with 55.*

$0 = 0.2t^2 + 4t - 55$ *Subtract 55 from each side.*

$0 = t^2 + 20t - 275$ *Multiply each side by 5 so the coefficient of t^2 is 1.*

You could use synthetic division to factor this polynomial. However, since 275 is such a large number, it may be easier to use the quadratic formula to find the values of t.

$t = \dfrac{-20 \pm \sqrt{(20)^2 - 4(1)(-275)}}{2(1)}$

$t = \dfrac{-20 \pm \sqrt{1500}}{2}$ $\sqrt{1500} \approx 38.73$

$t \approx 9.4$ or -29.4

The value of -29.4 is not a reasonable answer. So you will reach the bottom of the hill in about 9.4 seconds.

CHECKING FOR UNDERSTANDING

Communicating Mathematics

Read and study the lesson to answer each question.

1. **Write** the expression that completes this sentence: When a polynomial is divided by the factor $(x - r)$, the remainder is the same as __?__. $P(r)$

2. **Define** a depressed polynomial. See margin.

3. **Explain** what is meant by synthetic division. See margin.

Guided Practice

Find $P(3)$ for each polynomial. State whether $x - 3$ is a factor of the polynomial. Write *yes* or *no*.

4. $P(x) = x^2 - 6x + 0$ -9, no

5. $P(x) = x^2 + 2x - 15$ 0, yes

6. $P(x) = x^2 - 5x + 6$ 0, yes

7. $P(x) = x^4 + x^2 - 2$ 88, no

8. Let $f(x) = x^7 + x^9 + x^{12} - 2x^2$.
   a. State the degree of $f(x)$.   12
   b. State the number of complex zeros that $f(x)$ has.   12
   c. State the degree of the depressed polynomial that would result from dividing $f(x)$ by $x - a$.   11
   d. Find one factor of $f(x)$. x, x^2, or $x^{10} + x^7 + x^5 - 2$

9. Use synthetic division to find all the factors of $x^3 + 7x^2 - x - 7$ if one of the factors is $x + 1$. $(x + 1)(x - 1)(x + 7)$

EXERCISES

Practice

Divide using synthetic division.   12. $x^2 - 4x + 3$ 13. $x^3 + 3x^2 + 6x + 12$, R 23

10. $(x^2 - x - 56) \div (x + 7)$ $x - 8$

11. $(x^2 - x + 4) \div (x - 2)$ $x + 1$, R6

12. $(x^3 + x^2 - 17x + 15) \div (x + 5)$

13. $(x^4 + x^3 - 1) \div (x - 2)$

14. $(x^3 - 9x^2 + 27x - 28) \div (x - 3)$ $x^2 - 6x + 9$, R -1

15. $(2x^3 - 2x - 3) \div (x - 1)$ $2x^2 + 2x$, R -3

LESSON 4-3 THE REMAINDER AND FACTOR THEOREMS 199

RETEACHING THE LESSON

Students having difficulty understanding the remainder theorem might benefit from seeing some examples worked out in arithmetic, such as $235 \div 22 = 10$, R15 and $235 = 22 \times 10 + 15$. Working through a few examples, first with numbers and then with polynomials, should make the concepts clearer.

Additional Answers

2. A depressed polynomial is the quotient resulting from dividing a polynomial by one of its binomial factors of degree 1.

3. Synthetic division is a shorthand version of long division of a polynomial, when the divisor is a binomial in the form $x - r$. This process uses only the coefficients of the dividend.

Chalkboard Example

For Example 4

Refer to the application at the beginning of the lesson. If the hill on which you were riding is 45 meters long, how long will it take you to reach the bottom of the hill?   **about 8 seconds**

EVALUATING THE LESSON

Checking for Understanding

Exercises 1–9 are designed to help you assess students' understanding through reading, writing, speaking and modeling. You should work through Exercises 1–3 with your students and then monitor their work on Exercises 4–9.

Closing the Lesson

Speaking Activity   Have students take turns explaining the process and uses of synthetic division.

Practice Masters Booklet, p. 23

Find the remainder for each division. Is the divisor a factor of the polynomial?

16. $(x^3 - 30x) \div (x + 5)$ 25, no

17. $(x^4 - 6x^2 + 8) \div (x - \sqrt{2})$ 0, yes

18. $(5x^2 - 2x + 6) \div \left(x - \frac{2}{5}\right)$ 6, no

19. $(x^5 + 32) \div (x + 2)$ 0, yes

Use the remainder theorem to find the remainder for each division. State whether the binomial is a factor of the polynomial.

20. $(x^2 + 1) \div (x + 1)$ 2, no

21. $(x^2 + 5x - 2) \div (x + 3)$ –2, no

22. $(2x^2 - x + 3) \div (x - 3)$ 18, no

23. $(2x^3 - 3x + x) \div (x - 1)$ 0, yes

24. $(x^4 + x^2 + 2) \div (x - 3)$ 92, no

25. $(2x^4 - x^3 + 1) \div (x + 3)$ 190, no

Find the value of k so that each remainder is zero.

26. $(x^3 + 8x^2 + kx + 4) \div (x + 2)$ 14

27. $(x^3 + kx^2 + 4x + 1) \div (x + 1)$ 4

28. Determine how many times 1 is a root of $x^3 - 3x + 2 = 0$.   twice

29. Determine how many times 2 is a root of $x^6 - 9x^4 + 24x^2 - 16 = 0$.   twice

30. Determine how many times –1 is a root of $x^3 + 2x^2 - x - 2 = 0$. Then find the other roots.   once; 1, –2

Critical Thinking

31. Find a, b, and c for $P(x) = ax^2 + bx + c$ if $P(3 + 4i) = 0$ and $P(3 - 4i) = 0$. $a = 1, b = -6, c = 25$

Applications and Problem Solving

32. Physics   As an object moves farther from Earth, its weight decreases due to the diminished effect of Earth's gravity. The force of gravity decreases with the square of the distance from the center of Earth. The distance, R, from the center of Earth to the surface is about 3960 miles. The relationship between the weight of a body on earth, w_E, and the weight of a body a certain distance, r, from Earth, w_S, is $(R + r)^2 = \frac{R^2 \cdot w_E}{w_S}$. Determine the distance the spacecraft is from Earth if an astronaut weighs 200 pounds on Earth and 175 pounds in space.   273.4 miles

33. Manufacturing   A soft drink can has a height 4 inches greater than the radius of its lid. Determine the length of the radius of the lid and the height of the can if the volume of the can is about 15.71 cubic inches. *Use $V = \pi r^2 h$.* $r \approx 1$ inch, $h \approx 5$ inches

Mixed Review

34. If $f(x) = x^3$ and $g(x) = 3x$, find $g[f(-2)]$.   **(Lesson 1-2)**   –24

35. Find the critical points of the graph of $f(x) = x^5 - 32$. Determine whether each represents a maximum, a minimum, or a point of inflection.   **(Lesson 2-5)**

36. Graph $y = \frac{x - 3}{x - 2}$.   **(Lesson 3-4)**   See margin.   35.(0,–32), inflection

37. Solve $z^2 + 4z = 96$ by completing the square.   **(Lesson 4-2)**   8 or –12

38. College Entrance Exam   Choose the best answer.   B
The distance from City A to City B is 150 miles. From City A to City C is 90 miles. Therefore, it is necessarily true that

(A) the distance from B to C is 60 miles.

(B) six times the distance from A to B equals 10 times the distance from A to C.

(C) the distance from B to C is 240 miles.

(D) the distance from A to B exceeds by 30 miles twice the distance from A to C.

(E) three times the distance from A to C exceeds by 30 miles twice the distance from A to B.

EXTENDING THE LESSON

Math Power: Connections

Name all the information you can gather from a polynomial equation that may be helpful in graphing the related polynomial function.   The roots are the x-intercepts. $P(0)$ is the y-intercept. The derivative can help find maxima or minima.

4-4 The Rational Root Theorem

Objectives
4–4A
■ identify all possible rational roots of a polynomial equation by using the rational root theorem, and

4–4B
■ determine the number of positive and negative real zeros a polynomial function has.

After studying this lesson, you should be able to:

Application

Universal Studios Hollywood has built a new ride called *Backdraft*, patterned after the movie by the same name. The special effects in the ride include scenes where fire fighters must battle blazes that reach temperatures of 2000°F. Most fire departments do not battle blazes of this intensity.

The traditional fire truck is capable of pumping 750–1500 gallons of water per minute. The truck draws water from a fire hydrant or other water source and boosts the water pressure before pumping it through smaller diameter water hoses called booster hoses. As water fills the hose from the fire hydrant to the truck, it becomes a long cylinder. Suppose the volume of the hose is 11,775 cubic inches and the length of the hose is 150 inches less than 300 times the radius of the hose. What are the radius and length of the hose? *This problem will be solved in Example 1.*

> **FYI...**
> The first successful steam fire engine was built in 1852 by Moses Latta of Cincinnati, Ohio.

Let's write an equation in terms of r, the radius. The length of the hose is the height of the cylinder. So, $h = 300r - 150$.

$V = \pi r^2 h$	*Volume of a cylinder*
$11,775 = 3.14r^2(300r - 150)$	*Let $\pi = 3.14$, $r = r$, $V = 11,775$ and $h = 300r - 150$.*
$11,775 = 942r^3 - 471r^2$	*Multiply.*
$0 = 942r^3 - 471r^2 - 11,775$	*Subtract 11,775 from each side.*
$0 = 2r^3 - r^2 - 25$	*Divide each side by 471.*

We know there are three complex roots for this polynomial equation. You could use synthetic division to test the possible roots. However, you may have to test hundreds of values before finding a rational root, if it exists. The **rational root theorem** provides a means for dramatically lowering the number of rational values that you might test to find rational roots of a polynomial equation with integral coefficients.

Rational Root Theorem

Let $a_0x^n + a_1x^{n-1} + \cdots + a_{n-1}x + a_n = 0$ represent a polynomial equation of degree n with integral coefficients. If a rational number $\frac{p}{q}$, where p and q have no common factors, is a root of the equation, then p is a factor of a_n and q is a factor of a_0.

LESSON 4-4 THE RATIONAL ROOT THEOREM 201

NCTM Standards: 1- 6, 14

Lesson Resources

- Practice Master 4-4
- Enrichment Master 4-4
- Evaluation Master, Quiz B, p. 45

 Transparency 4-4 contains the 5-Minute Check and a teaching aid for this lesson.

INTRODUCING THE LESSON

 5-Minute Check

(over Lesson 4-3)

Divide using synthetic division.
1. $(x^4 - 3x^2 + 6) \div (x + 1)$.
   $x^3 - x^2 - 2x + 2$; R 4
2. $(x^3 + 2x^2 - 5x - 6) \div (x - 2)$
   $x^2 + 4x + 3$; R 0
3. $(x^4 - x^3 + 2x + 5) \div (x + 2)$
   $x^3 - 3x^2 + 6x - 10$; R 25

Use the remainder theorem to find the remainder for each division. State whether the binomial is a factor of the polynomial.
4. $(x^3 - 2x^2 - 33x + 10) \div (x + 5)$
   yes
5. $(x^3 - 7x + 5) \div (x + 3)$ no

Motivating the Lesson

Ask students what the factors of $3x^2 + 14x - 24$ might be. After some possibilities have been listed on the chalkboard, point out that they involve x or $3x$ as linear terms, and factors of 24 as constant terms. Tell students that extending this fact to the case of higher-degree polynomials is one of the key ideas of this lesson.

ALTERNATE TEACHING STRATEGIES

Using Critical Thinking

Have students compare the products of $(x - 3)(x - 2)(x - 1)$ and $(x + 3)(x + 2)(x + 1)$. Note that one of these polynomials has only positive roots while the other has only negative roots. What features of the polynomials themselves give us a clue to this fact? **The second product has all positive coefficients, while the first has alternating signs.**

Using Connections

Have students write down each polynomial equation in the Exercises 15–22 from Lesson 4–1 along with its rational roots, if any. Have them search for a relationship between the coefficients of each polynomial and the values of those roots.

Teaching Tip   Point out to students that they should be careful when applying the rational root theorem that they not confuse the roles of p and q. It is more important that they learn what p and q represent rather than memorizing symbols.

Chalkboard Example

For Example 1

A cylindrical water tower has a volume of 24,727.5 cubic feet. Its height is 20 feet more than its radius. What are its dimensions?
radius, 15 ft; height, 35 ft

For the polynomial equation $0 = 2r^3 - r^2 - 25$ in the fire hose problem, if $\frac{p}{q}$ is a rational root, then p is a factor of 25 and q is a factor of 2.

possible values for p: $\pm1, \pm5, \pm25$

possible values for q: $\pm1, \pm2$

possible rational roots, $\frac{p}{q}$: $\pm1, \pm\frac{1}{2}, \pm5, \pm\frac{5}{2}, \pm25, \pm\frac{25}{2}$

Example 1

APPLICATION

Firefighting

Refer to the application at the beginning of the lesson. Find the radius and the length of the fire hose.

Use the shortened form of synthetic division to determine which of the possible roots listed above, if any, are roots of the equation $0 = 2r^3 - r^2 - 25$.

root	2	–1	0	–25
1	2	1	1	–24
5	2	9	45	200
25	2	49	1225	30,600
0.5	2	0	0	–25
2.5	2	4	10	0

To simplify computation, write the fractions as decimals.

← 2.5 is a root of the equation.

You need not continue the process of synthetic division to find roots, since the depressed polynomial is a quadratic. Use the discriminant to determine the nature of the other two roots.

Remember the roots of a polynomial equation are the zeros of the polynomial function.

The discriminant of the depressed polynomial $2r^2 + 4r + 10$ is $(4)^2 - 4(2)(10)$ or -64. A negative discriminant tells us that the two other roots are imaginary. The graph of the function $V(r) = 2r^3 - r^2 - 25$ is shown at the right. There is one real zero at the r-intercept, 2.5. The other two zeros of the function are imaginary, so the graph intersects the r-axis once.

Since the only real root of the equation is 2.5, the radius of the fire hose is 2.5 inches, and the length of the hose is $300(2.5) - 150$ or 600 inches.

A corollary to the rational root theorem, called the **integral root theorem**, states that if the leading coefficient (a_0) has a value of 1, then any rational roots must be factors of a_n, $a_n \neq 0$.

Integral Root Theorem	**Let $x^n + a_1x^{n-1} + \cdots + a_{n-1}x + a_n = 0$ represent a polynomial equation that has leading coefficient of 1, integral coefficients, and $a_n \neq 0$. Any rational roots of this equation must be integral factors of a_n.**

Example 2

Find the roots of $x^3 + 6x^2 + 10x + 3 = 0$.

There are three complex roots. According to the integral root theorem, the possible rational roots of the equation are factors of 3. The possibilities are ± 3 and ± 1.

r	1	6	10	3
3	1	9	37	114
-3	1	3	1	0

← There is one root at $x = -3$.

The depressed polynomial is $x^2 + 3x + 1$. Use the quadratic formula to find the other two roots.

$$x = \frac{-b \pm \sqrt{b^2 - 4ac}}{2a}$$

$$= \frac{-3 \pm \sqrt{3^2 - 4(1)(1)}}{2(1)} \qquad a = 1, b = 3, c = 1$$

$$= \frac{-3 \pm \sqrt{5}}{2}$$

The three roots of the equation are -3, $\dfrac{-3 + \sqrt{5}}{2}$, and $\dfrac{-3 - \sqrt{5}}{2}$.

Descartes' rule of signs can be used to determine the possible numbers of positive real zeros a polynomial has. It is named after the French mathematician René Descartes, who first proved the theorem in 1637. *In Descartes' rule of signs, when we speak of a zero of the polynomial, we mean a zero of the corresponding polynomial function.*

Descartes' Rule of Signs	Suppose $P(x)$ is a polynomial whose terms are arranged in descending powers of the variable. Then the number of positive real zeros of $P(x)$ is the same as the number of changes in sign of the coefficients of the terms, or is less than this by an even number. The number of negative real zeros of $P(x)$ is the same as the number of changes in sign of the coefficients of the terms of $P(-x)$, or is less than this number by an even number.

Ignore zero coefficients when using this rule.

Example 3

State the number of possible complex zeros, the number of positive real zeros, and the number of possible negative real zeros for $h(x) = x^4 - 2x^3 + 7x^2 + 4x - 15$.

Because the degree of $h(x)$ is 4, $h(x)$ has four complex zeros.
To determine the number of possible positive real zeros, count the sign changes for the coefficients.

$$h(x) = x^4 - 2x^3 + 7x^2 + 4x - 15$$

$$\begin{array}{ccccc} 1 & -2 & 7 & 4 & -15 \\ & \text{yes} & \text{yes} & \text{no} & \text{yes} \end{array}$$

(continued on the next page)

There are 3 changes. So, there are either 3 positive real zeros or 1 positive real zero.

To determine the number of possible negative real zeros, find $h(-x)$ and count the number of sign changes.

$$h(-x) = (-x)^4 - 2(-x)^3 + 7(-x)^2 + 4(-x) - 15$$

$$x^4 \quad + \quad 2x^3 \quad + \quad 7x^2 \quad - \quad 4x \quad - \quad 15$$

$$1 \qquad 2 \qquad 7 \qquad -4 \qquad -15$$

$$\text{no} \qquad \text{no} \qquad \text{yes} \qquad \text{no}$$

There is 1 change. So, there is 1 negative real zero.
The polynomial $h(x)$ has either 3 or 1 positive real zeros and exactly 1 negative real zero.

Example 4

Find the zeros of $M(x) = x^4 + 4x^3 + 3x^2 - 4x - 4$. Then graph the function.

There are 4 complex zeros. Using Descartes' rule of signs, we find that there is 1 positive real zero and 3 or 1 negative real zeros. The integral root theorem tells us the possible rational zeros are ± 1, ± 2, and ± 4.

Let's use synthetic division to test our possibilities.

The remainder is 0. So, 1 is a zero and $x - 1$ is one factor of the polynomial.

The depressed polynomial is $x^3 + 5x^2 + 8x + 4$. Use this polynomial and synthetic division to find other factors of the polynomial.

r	1	5	8	4
−1	1	4	4	0

The remainder is 0. So, −1 is a zero and $x + 1$ is another factor of the polynomial.

The depressed polynomial from this division is $x^2 + 4x + 4$, which can be factored as $(x + 2)(x + 2)$. This means that both zeros of $x^2 + 4x + 4$ are at $x = -2$.

$$M(x) = (x - 1)(x + 1)(x + 2)^2$$

The zeros of $M(x)$ are 1, −1, and −2.

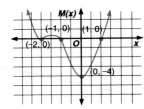

The graph of $M(x)$ is shown at the right. Notice that because there is a double zero at $x = -2$, the graph is tangent to the x-axis at that point and does not cross it. Thus, Descartes' rule of signs holds.

Example 5

A manufacturing company produces rectangular polystyrene packing fillers for an electronics firm that produces computer parts. The filler has a length (in cm) that is the square of the width and a height three times the width. In developing a new filler for another product, the width is increased by 1 cm, the length is increased by 2 cm, and the height is increased by 3 cm. The volume of the new filler is 162 cm². Find the dimensions of the original filler.

Let's define the measurements of each filler.

	original filler	new filler
width	x	$x + 1$
length	x^2	$x^2 + 2$
height	$3x$	$3x + 3$

Volume of new filler $= (x + 1)(x^2 + 2)(3x + 3)$
$$162 = 3x^4 + 6x^3 + 9x^2 + 12x + 6$$
$$0 = x^4 + 2x^3 + 3x^2 + 4x - 52$$

There are 4 complex roots. There is one possible positive real root and 3 or 1 possible negative real roots. The possible rational roots are $\pm 1, \pm 2, \pm 4, \pm 13, \pm 26,$ and ± 52.

Use synthetic division to test the possibilities.

r	1	2	3	4	-52
1	1	3	6	10	-42
2	1	4	11	26	0

2 is a root. Since there is only one possible positive root and negative roots are not reasonable for this problem, we can end our search for roots. The original filler is 2 cm by 4 cm by 6 cm.

CHECKING FOR UNDERSTANDING

Communicating Mathematics

Read and study the lesson to answer each question. 1–4. See margin.

1. **Discuss** why you may not need to use synthetic division to find more zeros of a polynomial function once you have found one zero of the function.

2. **Sketch** a graph of a polynomial function with zeros at –3 and 0 and a double zero at 5.

3. **Show** how the integral root theorem is derived from the rational root theorem.

4. **Demonstrate** how Descartes' rule of signs works.

Guided Practice

List all possible rational zeros of each function. Then determine the rational zeros.

5. $f(x) = x^3 + 2x^2 - 5x - 6$
$\pm 1, \pm 2, \pm 3, \pm 6; -3, -1, 2$

6. $f(x) = 2x^3 + 3x^2 - 8x + 3$
$\pm 0.5, \pm 1, \pm 1.5, \pm 3; -3, 0.5, 1$

LESSON 4-4   THE RATIONAL ROOT THEOREM   205

APPLYING THE LESSON

Homework Exercises

Assignment Guide

Average: 11-24, 28-30, 32-37
Enriched: 15-37
All: Mid-Chapter Review, 1-5

The red A, B, and C flags, printed only in the Teachers' Wraparound Edition, indicate the level of difficulty of the exercises.

Chapter 4, Quiz B, (Lessons 4-3 through 4-4), is available in the *Evaluation Masters,* p. 45.

Using Technology

For Exercises 25-28, point out how the magnitude of the leading coefficient affects the shape of the graph.

Additional Answers

7. 1 pos.; 2 or 0 neg.; –3, –1, 2
8. 2 or 0 pos.; 1 neg.; –3, 1, 0.5
9. 2 or 0 pos.; 1 neg.; –1.5, $\frac{1}{3}$, 3
10. 1 pos.; 2 or 0 neg.; 0.75
11. ±6, ±3, ±2, ±1; –3, –2, –1, 1
12. ±2, ±1; 1
13. ±20, ±10, ±5, ±4, ±2, ±1; 2, –2, 5
14. ±18, ±9, ±6, ±3, ±2, ±1; –2
15. ±2, ±1; 1, 2
16. ±3, ±1.5, ±1, ±0.5; 0.5

Practice Masters Booklet, p. 24

State the number of possible positive real zeros and the number of possible negative real zeros of each function. Then find the rational zeros. 7–10. See margin.

7. $f(x) = x^3 + 2x^2 - 5x - 6$
8. $f(x) = 2x^3 + 3x^2 - 8x + 3$
9. $f(x) = 6x^3 - 11x^2 - 24x + 9$
10. $f(x) = 4x^3 + 5x^2 + 2x - 6$

EXERCISES

Practice

A

List all possible rational zeros of each function. Then determine the rational zeros.

11. $f(x) = x^4 + 5x^3 + 5x^2 - 5x - 6$
12. $f(x) = x^3 - 4x^2 + x + 2$
13. $f(x) = x^3 - 5x^2 - 4x + 20$
14. $f(x) = x^3 - 2x^2 + x + 18$

B

15. $f(x) = x^4 - 5x^3 + 9x^2 - 7x + 2$
16. $f(x) = 2x^4 - x^3 - 6x + 3$
   11–16. See margin.

Find the number of possible positive real zeros and the number of possible negative real zeros. Determine all of the rational zeros. 17–24. See margin.

17. $f(x) = x^3 - 2x^2 - 8x$
18. $f(x) = x^3 + 7x^2 + 7x - 15$
19. $f(x) = 8x^3 - 6x^2 - 23x + 6$
20. $f(x) = 2x^3 - 5x^2 - 28x + 15$
21. $f(x) = 6x^3 + 19x^2 + 2x - 3$
22. $f(x) = x^3 - 7x - 6$

C

23. $f(x) = x^4 - 5x^2 + 4$
24. $f(x) = x^4 + 2x^3 - 9x^2 - 2x + 8$

Graphing Calculator

Use the rational root theorem and Descartes' rule of signs to determine the nature of the possible rational roots for each equation. Use this information and the graphs of the related functions to approximate all the rational roots to the nearest tenth.

25. $24x^3 - 26x^2 + 9x - 1 = 0$ 0.5, 0.$\overline{3}$, 0.25
26. $25x^3 + 105x^2 - 96x + 20 = 0$ 0.4, –5
27. $6x^3 - 7x^2 - 29x - 12 = 0$
   –0.5, 3, –1.$\overline{3}$
28. $x^4 - 10x^3 + 35x^2 - 50x + 24 = 0$
   1, 2, 3, 4

Critical Thinking

29. Write a third-degree polynomial function for each restriction.
   a. no positive real roots Sample answer: $f(x) = x^3 + 2x^2 + 3x + 53$
   b. no negative real roots Sample answer: $f(x) = x^3 - 2x^2 + 3x - 7$

Applications and Problem Solving

30. **Driving** The formula for calculating the distance traveled for a given time is $D(t) = v_i t + 0.5at^2$, where v_i is the initial velocity and a is the acceleration. A car is moving at 12 m/s and coasts up a hill with an acceleration of –1.6 m/s^2.
   a. Explain what negative acceleration is. deceleration
   b. For what values of t does $D(t) = 43$? 6 seconds or 9 seconds
   c. Explain why there are two times for the same distance. See margin.

31. **Cardiology** Doctors can measure cardiac output in potential heart attack patients by monitoring the concentration of dye after a known amount is injected in a vein near the heart. In a normal heart, the concentration of the dye is given by the function $g(x) = -0.006x^4 + 0.140x^3 - 0.053x^2 + 1.79x$, where x is the time in seconds.
   a. Graph $g(x)$. See margin.
   b. Find all the zeros of this function. 0, 23.5

206 CHAPTER 4 POLYNOMIAL AND RATIONAL FUNCTIONS

Additional Answers

17. 1 pos. and 1 neg.; 0, 4, –2
18. 1 pos. and 2 or 0 neg.; 1, –3, –5
19. 2 or 0 pos. and 1 neg.; $\frac{1}{4}$, $-\frac{3}{2}$, 2
20. 2 or 0 pos. and 1 neg; 5, –3, 0.5
21. 1 pos. and 2 or 0 neg.; –0.5, –3, $\frac{1}{3}$
22. 1 pos. and 2 or 0 neg.; –1, –2, 3
23. 2 or 0 pos. and 2 or 0 neg.; –2, 2, –1, 1
24. 2 or 0 pos. and 2 or 0 neg.; 1, –1, 2, –4

30c. For 6 seconds the car is rolling up the hill, reaching a maximum point at 7.5 seconds. Then it rolls back down the hill. After 9 seconds, the car is at the same point it was going up the hill.

32. Business Crystal Clear Water Company delivers spring water in water coolers to companies in the Cincinnati area. They also deliver cone-shaped drinking cups, whose volume is approximately 84.82 cm³. The height of each cup is 6 cm more than the radius. Determine the dimensions of the cone-shaped cup if $V = \frac{1}{3}\pi r^2 h$. *r*, 3 cm; *h*, 9 cm

Mixed Review

33. Explain three types of discontinuity in graphs. Sketch an example of each. **(Lesson 3-8)** See margin.

34. Find the slope of the tangent to $y = x^2 + 4x - 5$ at $(1, 0)$. **(Lesson 3-6)** 6

35. Find the value of the discriminant for $3m^2 + 5m + 10 = 0$. Fully describe the nature of its roots. **(Lesson 4-2)** −95, 2 imaginary roots

36. Use synthetic division to determine if $x + 2$ is a factor of $x^3 + 6x^2 + 12x + 12$. Explain your answer. **(Lesson 4-3)** No, there is a remainder of 4.

37. College Entrance Exam Refer to the figure at the right. Choose the best answer. B
What percent of the area of rectangle *PQRS* is shaded?

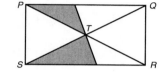

(A) 20% (B) 25% (C) 30%
(D) $33\frac{1}{3}$% (E) 40%

4. Since $R = 2$, $x - 4$ is not a factor.   5. $\pm 12, \pm 6, \pm 4, \pm 3, \pm 2, \pm 1, \pm\frac{3}{2}, \pm\frac{1}{2}$; no rational zero

MID-CHAPTER REVIEW

1. Find the roots of $x^3 + 2x^2 - 80x = 0$. **(Lesson 4-1)** $0, -10, 8$

2. Solve $p^2 + 6p + 3 = 0$ by completing the square. **(Lesson 4-2)** $-3 \pm \sqrt{6}$

3. Find the discriminant of $7m^2 - 13m + 2 = 0$. Fully describe the nature of its roots. Then solve the equation. **(Lesson 4-2)** 113; 2 real roots; $\frac{13 \pm \sqrt{113}}{14}$

4. Use the remainder theorem to find the remainder for $(x^3 - 4x^2 + 2x - 6) \div (x - 4)$. State whether the binomial is a factor of the polynomial. **(Lesson 4-3)**

5. List all the possible rational zeros of $n(x) = 2x^3 - 13x^2 - 17x + 12$. Then determine the rational zeros. **(Lesson 4-4)**

EXTENDING THE LESSON

Math Power: Reasoning

Explain why the theorems in this lesson deal exclusively with real, rather than imaginary, roots.
Imaginary numbers are not rational. Thus, they cannot satisfy the hypotheses of the theorems.

Mid-Chapter Review

The Mid-Chapter Review provides students with a brief review of the concepts and skills in Lessons 4–1 through 4–4. Lesson numbers are given at the end of problems or instruction lines so students may review concepts not yet mastered.

Enrichment Masters Booklet, p. 24

4-5A **Graphing Calculators: Locating Zeros of Polynomial Functions**

INTRODUCING THE LESSON

Objective Approximate the real zeros of a polynomial function by using a graphing calculator.

Motivating the Lesson

Ask students whether an even function, other than a member of the family $y = (x - a)^n$, where n is even, can have an odd number of real zeros. For example, $y = x^2(x + 1)^2(x - 1)^2$ is even and has 3 real zeros.

TEACHING THE LESSON

Teaching Tip Remind students that the number of real zeros of a function cannot exceed the degree of the polynomial.

More Examples

Approximate the zeros of the function $f(x) = x^4 - 5x^2 + 6$ to the nearest hundredth.

$\pm 1.41,\ \pm 1.73$

A graphing calculator can be used to find the coordinates of a point to a great degree of accuracy. This feature is a big advantage when you are trying to locate the zeros of a polynomial function. With some knowledge of polynomials and the ZOOM and TRACE functions on a graphing calculator, you can locate the zeros of polynomial functions without using paper and a pencil.

A **zero** of a function is the x-coordinate of the point where the graph crosses the x-axis. It is also called a root, or a solution, of the equation. Since $y = 0$ on the x-axis, the x-coordinate is the solution.

Example

Approximate the zeros of the function $y = 2x^3 + x^2 - 5x - 3$ to the nearest hundredth.

TI-81: [Y=] 2 [X|T] [^] 3 [+] [X|T] [^] 2 [−] 5 [X|T] [−] 3 [GRAPH]

Casio: [GRAPH] 2 [ALPHA] [X] [x^y] 3 [+] [ALPHA] [X] [x^y] 2
[−] 5 [ALPHA] [X] [−] 3 [EXE]

The standard viewing window contains a complete graph of the function. Looking at the graph, we can see that the graph crosses the x-axis three times.

Using TRACE and ZOOM, we find that the zeros are at –1.50, –0.62, and 1.62.

After you have zoomed in on one zero and need to find another, it helps to regraph the function in the original viewing window. Then zoom in and trace again to locate the next zero.

EXERCISES

Use a graphing calculator to approximate the real zeros of each equation to the nearest hundredth.

1. $y = x^3 - 4x$ –2, 0, 2
2. $y = -x^3 + 4x^2 - 6x + 8$ 2.88
3. $y = 4x^4 - 6x^2 - 2x + 1$ 0.28, 1.32
4. $y = 2x^5 + 3x^4 - 12x + 4$
    4. –2.17, 0.34, 1.17
5. $y = -2x^4 + 5$
    –1.26, 1.26
6. $y = 3x^3 - x^2 + 6x - 1$ 0.17

208 CHAPTER 4 POLYNOMIAL AND RATIONAL FUNCTIONS

EVALUATING THE LESSON

Closing the Lesson

Ask students whether the polynomial function in the Example is odd, even, or neither. Have them verify their answers.

APPLYING THE LESSON

Homework Exercises

Assignment Guide

All: 1-6

4-5 Locating the Zeros of a Function

Objectives
4–5A
4–5B

After studying this lesson, you should be able to:
- approximate the real zeros of a polynomial function, and
- graph polynomial functions.

Application

The earliest jigsaw puzzles were made as "dissected maps" by John Spilsbury in London about 1762. Today there are hundreds of companies making jigsaw puzzles of varying difficulty and size.

The Fully-Interlocking Puzzle Company has been producing 1000-piece jigsaw puzzles. These puzzles have sold so well that they would like to market 1500-piece puzzles. Before manufacturing these puzzles, the company needs to determine the size of the box in which the puzzles will be marketed. The 1000-piece puzzle is packaged in a box 25 cm by 30 cm by 5 cm. The marketing department would like to increase each of these dimensions by the same amount to create the box for the 1500-piece puzzle. The volume of the new box must be 1.5 times the volume of the original box. What should be the dimensions of the box for the 1500-piece puzzle?

Use the information from the problem to write a polynomial function that describes the volume of the 1500-piece puzzle box.

Dimension	Original Box	New Box
width	25 cm	$25 + x$ cm
length	30 cm	$30 + x$ cm
height	5 cm	$5 + x$ cm
volume	3750 cm^3	1.5(3750) or 5625 cm^3

We can substitute the dimensions of the new box into the formula $V = \ell w h$ to find a polynomial equation to solve this problem.

$$V = \ell w h$$
$$5625 = (30 + x)(25 + x)(5 + x)$$
$$5625 = x^3 + 60x^2 + 1025x + 3750$$
$$0 = x^3 + 60x^2 + 1025x - 1875$$

ALTERNATE TEACHING STRATEGIES

Using Charts

Write a polynomial function on the chalkboard and have students find values of the function for each of several x-values, including possible rational roots. Organize the information in a chart and graph the function. Use the table of function values and the graph to illustrate the location principle.

Using Logical Reasoning

Write a polynomial function on the chalkboard and have students test various positive values of x as possible roots using synthetic division. When the values get very great, help students to understand the idea behind the upper bound theorem.

NCTM Standards: 1- 6

Lesson Resources

- Practice Master 4-5
- Enrichment Master 4-5
- Technology Master, p. 8
- Multicultural Activity Master, p. 4

 Transparency 4-5 contains the 5-Minute Check and a teaching aid for this lesson.

INTRODUCING THE LESSON

5-Minute Check

(over Lesson 4–4)

Let $f(x) = 2x^4 - x^3 - 3x^2 - 31x - 15$.

1. List all possible rational zeros of $f(x)$. $\pm 1, \pm 3, \pm 5, \pm 15,$ $\pm \frac{1}{2}, \pm \frac{3}{2}, \pm \frac{5}{2}, \pm \frac{15}{2}$

2. Find the roots of $f(x)$. $3, -\frac{1}{2}, -1 \pm 2i$

3. State the number of possible positive real zeros and the number of possible negative real zeros for $g(x) = 3x^4 + 16x^3 - 7x^2 - 64x - 20$. Then find the rational roots.
   1 pos. real zero, 1 or 3 neg. real zeros, $-5, -\frac{1}{3}, \pm 2$

4. Write a third-degree polynomial function with one positive real zero.   Sample answer: $f(x) = x^3 - 2x - 1$

Motivating the Lesson

Have students consider the polynomial function $f(x) = x^4 + 2x^3 + 3x^2 + 2x - 2$. How many possible positive real zeros does it have? 1 Use a graphing calculator to graph the function. Between what two integers does this positive real zero lie? between 0 and 1

Chalkboard Example

For Example 1

Suppose the company decides to add twice as much to the length of the box as to its other two dimensions. What are the dimensions of the new box?

33 cm by 26.5 cm by 6.5 cm

Let $V(x) = x^3 + 60x^2 + 1025x - 1875$. There are three complex zeros, with one possible positive zero and two possible negative zeros. The possible rational zeros are $\pm1, \pm3, \pm5, \pm15, \pm25, \pm75, \pm125, \pm375, \pm625$, and ±1875. The company used a spreadsheet to evaluate these values and found that none of these values is a zero of the function. This means that the zeros are not rational values. We can use another method to help you approximate the zeros of this function. This method is called **the location principle**.

The Location Principle	**Suppose $y = f(x)$ represents a polynomial function. If a and b are two numbers with $f(a)$ negative and $f(b)$ positive, the function has at least one real zero between a and b.**

If $f(a) > 0$ and $f(b) < 0$, then the function also has at least one real zero between a and b.

This principle is illustrated by the graph at the right. The graph of $y = f(x)$ is a continuous curve. At $x = a$, $f(a)$ is negative. At $x = b$, $f(b)$ is positive. As we watch the curve go from negative to positive, we see that it must cross the x-axis. Thus, a zero exists somewhere between a and b.

Example 1

APPLICATION

Packaging

Find the dimensions of the box for the 1500-piece puzzle.

When you test the possible rational roots for an equation, you can often narrow down the range of values in which a zero exists. The value of $V(1)$ is -789. The value of $V(3)$ is 1767. A zero must exist somewhere between $V(1)$ and $V(3)$. Let's try other values in that range.

x	$V(x)$
1	−789
1.5	−199.125
2	423
2.5	1078.125
3	1767

The sign change indicates there is a zero between 2 and 1.5.

You can use the location principle again to fine tune your search for the zero between 2 and 1.5.

x	$V(x)$
1.5	−199.125
1.6	−77.304
1.7	45.813

The sign change indicates there is a zero between 1.6 and 1.7.

You could again use the location principle to find the zero to the nearest hundredth. However, finding the zero to the nearest tenth is appropriate for the problem. Since $V(1.7)$ is closer to zero than $V(1.6)$, we will use 1.7.

To find the dimensions of the puzzle box, add 1.7 cm to each measurement. The box for the 1500-piece puzzle will be 26.7 cm by 31.7 cm by 6.7 cm.

Example 2

Determine between which consecutive integers the real zeros of $f(x) = x^3 + 2x^2 - 3x - 5$ are located.

By Descartes' rule of signs, the function must have 1 positive real zero and 2 or 0 negative real zeros. Use substitution or synthetic division to evaluate the function for successive integral values of x. Since the greatest possible integral zero is 5 and the least possible integral zero is –5, we will test values in that range until we locate the three possible zeros.

You could also use your graphing calculator to find the range of values in which to find a zero.

r	1	2	-3	-5
-5	1	-3	12	-65
-4	1	-2	5	-25
-3	1	-1	0	-5
-2	1	0	-3	1
-1	1	1	-4	-1
0	1	2	-3	-5
1	1	3	0	-5
2	1	4	5	5

Changes in sign indicate that the three zeros are located between –3 and –2, between –2 and –1, and between 1 and 2. According to Descartes' rule of signs, this result is reasonable.

Example 3

Approximate to the nearest tenth the real zeros of $f(x) = x^4 - 3x^3 - 2x^2 + 3x - 5$. Then sketch the graph of the function, given that the relative maximum is at $(0.4, -4.3)$, and the relative minima are at $(-0.7, -6.8)$ and $(2.5, -17.8)$.

By Descartes' rule of signs, the function must have 3 or 1 positive real zeros and 1 negative real zero. The possible rational zeros are ± 1 and ± 5. Use substitution or synthetic division to evaluate the function for several values of x between 5 and –5 until you locate the zeros.

r	1	-3	-2	3	-5
5	1	2	8	43	210
4	1	1	2	11	39
3	1	0	-2	-3	-14
2	1	-1	-4	-5	-15
1	1	-2	-4	-1	-6
0	1	-3	-2	3	-5

r	1	-3	-2	3	-5
-1	1	-4	2	1	-6
-2	1	-5	8	-13	21
-3	1	-6	16	-45	130
-4	1	-7	26	-101	399
-5	1	-8	38	-187	930

By the location principle, there is a negative zero between –1 and –2 and a positive zero between 3 and 4. Evaluate values between these pairs of integers to the nearest tenth.

x	f(x)
-1.1	-5.3
-1.2	-4.2
-1.3	-2.8
-1.4	-1.0
-1.5	1.2

x	f(x)
3.1	-11.9
3.2	-9.3
3.3	-6.1
3.4	-2.2
3.5	2.4

The real zeros are approximately –1.4 and 3.4.

(continued on the next page)

LESSON 4-5 LOCATING THE ZEROS OF A FUNCTION 211

Teaching Tip In Example 4, some students may need to see a few more steps to find $f(-x)$. Then have them find $f(-x)$ for another function.

Using Technology

Remind students that they can use their calculators to find the remainder for any value of r by evaluating $P(x)$ for $x = r$.

EVALUATING THE LESSON

Checking for Understanding

Exercises 1–8 are designed to help you assess students' understanding through reading, writing, speaking, and modeling. You should work through Exercises 1–4 with your students and then monitor their work on Exercises 5–8.

Practice Masters Booklet, p. 25

Now sketch the graph using the maximum and minima given and the zeros. You can also use the values you found in evaluating the function to give you other points to sketch the graph.

In Example 3, the function $f(x) = x^4 - 3x^3 - 2x^2 + 3x - 5$ had 3 or 1 positive real zeros. Instead of testing greater values of x to determine if additional positive zeros exist, the **upper bound theorem** can be used to determine an **upper bound** of the zeros of a function. An upper bound is the integer greater than or equal to the greatest real zero.

Upper Bound Theorem	Suppose c is a positive integer and $P(x)$ is divided by $x - c$. If the resulting quotient and remainder have no change in sign, then $P(x)$ has no real zeros greater than c. Thus, c is an upper bound of the zeros of $P(x)$.

Zero coefficients are ignored when counting sign changes.

The synthetic division in Example 3 indicates that 4 and 5 are upper bounds of the zeros of $f(x) = x^4 - 3x^3 - 2x^2 + 3x - 5$ because there are no change of signs in the quotient and remainder. In this case, the least positive integral upper bound of the zeros is 4.

A **lower bound** of the zeros of $P(x)$ can be found by determining an upper bound for the zeros of $P(-x)$. Therefore, if c is an upper bound of the zeros of $P(-x)$, then $-c$ is a lower bound of the zeros of $P(x)$.

Example 4 | Find a lower bound of the zeros of $f(x) = x^4 - 3x^3 - 2x^2 + 3x - 5$.

$f(-x) = x^4 + 3x^3 - 2x^2 - 3x - 5$

r	1	3	-2	-3	-5
1	1	4	2	−1	−6
2	1	5	8	13	21

The last row has no changes in sign, so 2 is an upper bound of $f(-x)$.

Since 2 is an upper bound of $f(-x)$, –2 is a lower bound of $f(x)$.

212 CHAPTER 4 POLYNOMIAL AND RATIONAL FUNCTIONS

RETEACHING THE LESSON

Students may find it more natural to apply the location principle after first graphing the function with a graphing calculator. This should suggest a pair of integers between which a root lies, and then students can go on to approximate its value more closely.

CHECKING FOR UNDERSTANDING

Communicating Mathematics

Read and study the lesson to answer each question. 2. Volume cannot be negative.

1. **Explain** the location principle and why it works. See margin.
2. **Tell** why negative zeros of the function $V(x)$ in Example 1 were not determined.
3. **Explain** how to use the location principle to find the real zeros of a function to the nearest hundredth. See margin.
4. **Describe** how you find an upper bound and a lower bound for the zeros of a polynomial function. See margin.

Guided Practice

Use the synthetic division for each function to determine between which two consecutive x-values the zeros occur. State the location of the real zeros. State the least integral upper bound.

5. 3 zeros; between −2 and −1, at 1, between 3 and 4; UB: 4

5. $f(x) = x^3 - 3x^2 - 2x + 4$

r	1	−3	−2	4
−2	1	−5	8	−12
−1	1	−4	2	2
0	1	−3	−2	4
1	1	−2	−4	0
2	1	−1	−4	−4
3	1	0	−2	−2
4	1	1	2	12
5	1	2	8	44

6. 4 zeros; between −3 and −2, −2 and −1, 1 and 2, 2 and 3; UB: 3

6. $f(x) = x^4 - 8x^2 + 10$

r	1	0	−8	0	10
−4	1	−4	8	−32	138
−3	1	−3	1	−3	19
−2	1	−2	−4	8	−6
−1	1	−1	−7	7	3
0	1	0	−8	0	10
1	1	1	−7	−7	3
2	1	2	−4	−8	−6
3	1	3	1	3	19

7. Use substitution or synthetic division to find the zeros of $f(x) = x^2 + 3x + 1$ to the nearest tenth. −0.4 and −2.6

8. Find the least integral upper bound and the greatest integral lower bound of the zeros of $f(x) = x^2 - x - 1$. 2 and −1

EXERCISES

Practice

Determine between which consecutive integers the real zeros of each function are located.

12. 0 and 1, 1 and 2, −2 and −1

9. $f(x) = x^2 - 4x - 2$ 4 and 5, −1 and 0
10. $f(x) = 2x^2 - 5x + 1$ 0 and 1, 2 and 3
11. $f(x) = x^3 - 2$ 1 and 2
12. $f(x) = x^3 - 3x + 1$
13. $f(x) = x^4 - 2x^3 + x - 2$ at 2, at −1
14. $f(x) = 2x^4 + x^2 - 3x + 3$ no real zeros

Approximate the real zeros of each function to the nearest tenth.

15. $f(x) = x^2 + 3x + 2$ −2, −1
16. $f(x) = 2x^3 - 4x^2 - 3$ 2.3
17. $f(x) = x^3 - 4x + 6$ −2.5
18. $f(x) = 3x^4 + x^2 - 1$ 0.7, −0.7

19. $f(x) = 2x^4 - x^3 + x - 2$ 1, −1
20. $f(x) = -x^3 + x^2 - x + 1$ 1

Use the upper bound theorem to find the least integral upper bound and the greatest integral lower bound of the zeros of each function.

21. $f(x) = x^3 + 3x^2 - 5x - 10$ 2, −5
22. $f(x) = x^4 - 8x + 2$ 2, 0
23. $f(x) = 3x^3 - 2x^2 + 5x - 1$ 1, 0
24. $f(x) = x^5 + 5x^4 - 3x^3 + 20x^2 - 15$ 1, −7

LESSON 4-5   LOCATING THE ZEROS OF A FUNCTION   213

Closing the Lesson

Speaking Activity Have the class compare and contrast the role of synthetic division in finding the rational roots of a polynomial function and finding approximations to its other roots using the location principle.

APPLYING THE LESSON

Homework Exercises

Assignment Guide

Average: 9-22, 25, 27, 29-35
Enriched: 13-35

The red A, B, and C flags printed only in the Teacher's Wraparound Edition, indicate the level of difficulty of the exercises.

Exercise Notes

For Exercises 9–24, remind students to first apply Descartes' rule of signs. Along with a quick sketch of the general shape of the graph, this should help them to direct their other work on each function.

Additional Answers

1. The location principle is a method of estimation by which the zero of a function can be approximated. Repeated applications of the technique can produce an estimate to the decimal place desired. It works because a zero is the place where $f(x) = 0$. Values of $f(x)$ evaluated for x greater than and less than the target zero indicate the direction the graph is taking without graphing the function.

3. First find between which two integers each zero is found. Use the two nearest integers to find between which two tenths the zero is found. Then find the zero to the nearest hundredth using the numbers between the tenths.

4. Use synthetic division to test values of r for $f(x)$ until there are no sign changes in the row. This value of r is the least positive upper bound. Repeat the process for values of r for $f(-x)$. When you find this upper bound, you can say that $-r$ is the greatest negative lower bound.

For each function, determine the number and type of possible complex zeros. Use the location principle to determine the real zeros to the nearest tenth. Determine the relative maxima and relative minima. Then sketch the graph. 25–26. See margin.

C

25. $f(x) = 2x^3 + 9x^2 - 12x - 40$ 26. $f(x) = x^4 - 3x^2 - 9$

Critical Thinking

27. Suppose the graph of $g(x)$ has two relative maxima and one relative minimum.
    a. What is the minimum degree of $g(x)$? fourth degree
    b. Draw a graph to support your answer. See margin.

Applications and Problem Solving

28. **Ecology** In the early 1900s, the deer population of the Kaibab Plateau in Arizona experienced a rapid increase because hunters had reduced the number of natural predators. The food supply was not great enough to support the increased population, eventually causing the population to decline. The deer population for the period 1905–1930 can be approximated by the function $f(x) = -0.125x^5 + 3.125x^4 + 4000$, where x is the number of years from 1905.
    a. Graph this function. See Teacher's Answer Key.
    b. Describe the pattern of the deer population in terms of the concepts you have learned in this lesson. See margin.

29. **Pets** Rick Glatfelter built a kennel for his dog by attaching two sides of fencing to the existing corner of the yard to create a rectangle that is 4 meters wide by 6 meters long. As his dog has grown, he wishes to double the kennel's area by increasing each side of the rectangle by the same amount. By how much should the dimensions be increased? 2 meters

30. **Astronomy** In 1609, Johannes Kepler discovered two of his three laws that describe the behavior of every planet and satellite in our solar system. His third law, discovered in 1618, states that the ratio of the squares of the periods of any two moons revolving about a planet is equal to the ratio of the cubes of their average distances from the planet. This can be written as $\left(\frac{T_a}{T_b}\right)^2 = \left(\frac{r_a}{r_b}\right)^3$, where T_a and T_b are the periods of the moons and r_a and r_b are their average distances from the planet. In 1610, Galileo discovered four moons of Jupiter. The first moon, Io, has a period of 1.8 days. Another moon, Ganymede, shown at the left, has a period of 7.3 days and is 6.5 units farther from Jupiter than Io is from Jupiter. Use Kepler's third law to determine the distance of Io and Ganymede from Jupiter. Ganymede: 10.7 units, Io: 4.2 units

Mixed Review

31. Find the slope of the line whose equation is $3y + 8x = 12$. **(Lesson 1-4)** $-\frac{8}{3}$

32. Graph the parent function and the translated function $f(x) = |x + 2| - 4$. **(Lesson 3-2)** See Teacher's Answer Key.

33. Graph $x^2 + 8x - 20 > 0$. **(Lesson 4-1)** See Teacher's Answer Key.

34. Determine the zeros and critical points of $f(x) = x^3 - 4x^2 - 25x + 28$. Then graph the function. **(Lesson 4-4)** See Teacher's Answer Key.

35. **College Entrance Exam** If 15 cans of food are needed for seven men for two days, how many are needed for four men for seven days? 30

214   CHAPTER 4   POLYNOMIAL AND RATIONAL FUNCTIONS

EXTENDING THE LESSON

Math Power: Reasoning

Is it possible for a polynomial function to have a real zero greater than its greatest possible rational root? If so, give an example. **Yes, one example is the function given in Exercise 10.**

Additional Answer

27b.

sample answer

Technology

Locating Zeros and Critical Points

▶ **BASIC**
Spreadsheets
Software

```
100  PRINT
110  PRINT "F(X) = Ax^4+Bx^3+Cx^2+Dx+E"
120  PRINT "ENTER A, B, C, D, E";
130  INPUT A, B, C, D, E
140  PRINT "ENTER STARTING X POINT";
150  INPUT MINIMUM
160  PRINT "ENTER STOPPING X POINT";
170  INPUT MAXIMUM
180  PRINT "ENTER INCREMENT SIZE";
190  INPUT INC
200  PRINT "FINDING ZEROS..."
210  SIGN = 0
220  FOR X = MINIMUM TO MAXIMUM STEP INC
230  F = E+X*(D+X*(C+X*(B+X*A)))
240  OLDSIGN = SIGN
250  IF F = 0 THEN SIGN = 0
260  IF F < 0 THEN SIGN = -1
270  IF F > 0 THEN SIGN = 1
280  IF F = 0 THEN PRINT "ZERO AT X="; X:GOTO 310
290  IF SIGN * OLDSIGN <> -1 THEN GOTO 310
300  PRINT "ZERO BETWEEN X="; X - INC;" AND X=";X
310  NEXT X
320  PRINT "NOW FINDING CRITICAL POINTS..."
330  SIGN = 0
340  FOR X = MINIMUM TO MAXIMUM STEP INC
350  F = D+X*(2*C+X*(3*B+X*4*A))
360  OLDSIGN = SIGN
370  IF F = 0 THEN SIGN = 0
380  IF F < 0 THEN SIGN = -1
390  IF F > 0 THEN SIGN = 1
400  IF F = 0 THEN PRINT "CRITICAL POINT AT X=";X:
     GOTO 430
410  IF SIGN * OLDSIGN <> -1 THEN GOTO 430
420  PRINT "CRITICAL POINT BETWEEN X="; X -INC;"
     AND X=";X
430  NEXT X
440  PRINT "DONE!"
450  END
```

Engineers and scientists use computer programs to find zeros and critical points of large polynomial functions. The programs that they use are powerful, accurate, and fast. A printout of one of these programs might exceed one hundred pages!

The BASIC program shown at the left can help you find zeros and critical points of polynomial functions of degree four or less. This program will either find the zeros or critical points, or it will tell you where possible zeros or critical points may be found. Then you can refine your search to find the exact values.

To execute the program, type **RUN** and then press **[Enter]**. The sample shown below uses $f(x) = x^3 - x^2 - 17x + 20$.

```
RUN

F(X) = Ax^4 + Bx^3 + Cx^2 + Dx + E
ENTER A, B, C, D, E? 0,1,-1,-17,20
ENTER STARTING X POINT? -5
ENTER STOPPING X POINT? 5
ENTER INCREMENT SIZE? .1
FINDING ZEROS...
ZERO BETWEEN X=-4.20000001 AND X=-4.1
ZERO BETWEEN X=1.09999999 AND X=1.19999999
ZERO BETWEEN X=3.99999999 AND X=4.09999999
NOW FINDING CRITICAL POINTS...
CRITICAL POINT BETWEEN X=-2.10000001
AND X=-2.00000001
CRITICAL POINT BETWEEN X=2.69999999
AND X=2.79999999
DONE!
```

Using Technology

Objective This optional page shows how a computer program in BASIC can be used to find the zeros and other critical points of a polynomial function.

Teaching Suggestions

Point out that the expression given in line 230 is equivalent to evaluating a 4th-degree polynomial function for a given value in the program loop. Have students verify this. For zeros that are not rational, run the program as many times as necessary to approximate each zero, each time decreasing the increment size by a factor of 10.

Additional Answers

1. zeros: –2, 1, 2; critical points:
   (1.535184, –0.879420),
   (0.333333, 2.592593),
   (–0.868517, 6.065605)
2. zeros: –2, 2; no real critical points
3. zero: 0.865244; critical point: (0, –8)

EXERCISES

Use the BASIC program to find the zeros and critical points for each polynomial.

1. $f(x) = x^3 - x^2 - 4x + 4$ **2.** $f(x) = x^4 + x^3 + x^2 - 4x - 20$ **3.** $f(x) = 3x^3 + 7x - 8$

Lesson Resources

- Practice Master 4-6
- Enrichment Master 4-6
- Evaluation Master, Quiz C, p. 46

 Transparency 4-6 contains the 5-Minute Check and a teaching aid for this lesson.

INTRODUCING THE LESSON

 5-Minute Check

(over Lesson 4-5)

Determine between which consecutive integers the real zeros of each function are located.
1. $f(x) = x^3 - 2x^2 + 5x - 3$
   between 0 and 1
2. $f(x) = x^4 + 4x^3 + 8x^2 + 36x - 9$
   between 0 and 1, between −4 and −5
3. Approximate the real zeros of the function in Exercise 2 above to the nearest tenth.
   0.2, −4.2
4. Use the upper bound theorem to find the least integral upper bound and the greatest integral lower bound of the zeros of $f(x) = 2x^4 - 3x - 6$. 2, −2

Prerequisite Skills

Students must be able to find the least common multiple of a set of expressions.
Find the least common multiple of each set below.
1. $2a, 3ab^2, 12b$ $12ab^2$
2. $x - 3, x + 2, x^2 + 2x$
   $x^3 - x^2 - 6x$
3. $x - 1, x + 1, x^2 - 1$ $x^2 - 1$

4-6 Rational Equations and Partial Fractions

Objectives
4–6A
4–6B
4–6C

Application

 FYI...

In 1963 and 1964, 70-year-old William Willis of the United States sailed 10,850 miles from Peru to Australia on his raft, the *Age Unlimited* The trip took him 204 days.

After studying this lesson, you should be able to:
- find the least common denominator of rational expressions,
- solve rational equations and inequalities, and
- decompose a fraction into partial fractions.

At Wet and Wild Water Park, the Raging River is one of the most popular rides. The ride involves a wide stream of water in which your raft meanders downstream for 3 kilometers in the same amount of time that it takes the park workers to return the rafts directly upstream 2 kilometers to the beginning of the ride. If the raft travels at a rate of 1.5 km/h in still water, what is the rate of the current of the water in the ride?

Each way on the ride involves the same amount of time. So, solve the formula $d = rt$ for t. Thus, $t = \dfrac{d}{r}$. The current works with the raft going downstream and against the raft going upstream, but the rate, c, of the current is constant. So for the rate downstream, add the rate of the current, and for the rate upstream, subtract the rate of the current.

	d	r	t
downstream	3	$1.5 + c$	$\dfrac{3}{1.5 + c}$
upstream	2	$1.5 - c$	$\dfrac{2}{1.5 - c}$

$$t_d = t_u \qquad t_d = \text{time downstream}, \ t_u = \text{time upstream}$$

$$\frac{3}{1.5 + c} = \frac{2}{1.5 - c}$$

$$(1.5 + c)(1.5 - c)\left(\frac{3}{1.5 + c}\right) = \left(\frac{2}{1.5 - c}\right)(1.5 + c)(1.5 - c) \qquad \text{\textit{Multiply by the common denominator.}}$$

$$3(1.5 - c) = 2(1.5 + c) \qquad \text{\textit{Simplify each side.}}$$

$$4.5 - 3c = 3 + 2c$$

$$1.5 = 5c$$

$$0.3 = c \qquad \text{The rate of the current is 0.3 km/h.}$$

An equation, like the one above, that consists of one or more rational expressions is called a **rational equation**. One way to solve a rational equation is to multiply each side of the equation by the least common denominator (LCD). The LCD is the least common multiple of the denominators.

ALTERNATE TEACHING STRATEGIES

Using Applications

Have each student report how much time he or she spent on last night's homework and write each time on the chalkboard. Then pose questions such as "Jane did the assignment in 45 minutes while Mio did it in 30. How long would it have taken them if they had been working together?"

Using Discussion

Write a rational equation on the chalkboard and have students suggest steps that could be taken to obtain its solution. Write the steps down as they are given and ask students to give a good, clear presentation of the techniques used.

You should always check your solutions by substituting them into the original equation. Remember that the denominator in a fraction can never be equal to zero. Any possible solution that results in a zero in the denominator must be excluded from your list of solutions.

Example 1

Solve $\dfrac{t+4}{t} + \dfrac{3}{t-4} = \dfrac{-16}{t^2-4t}$.

$$\dfrac{t+4}{t} + \dfrac{3}{t-4} = \dfrac{-16}{t^2-4t} \qquad \textit{The LCD is } t(t-4).$$

$$t(t-4)\left(\dfrac{t+4}{t}\right) + t(t-4)\left(\dfrac{3}{t-4}\right) = t(t-4)\left(\dfrac{-16}{t^2-4t}\right)$$

$$(t-4)(t+4) + t(3) = -16$$

$$t^2 - 16 + 3t = -16$$

$$t^2 + 3t = 0$$

$$t(t+3) = 0$$

$$t = 0 \text{ or } t = -3$$

When you check your solutions, you find that t cannot equal 0, so $t = 0$ cannot be a solution. Therefore, the only solution is –3.

Example 2

The Northern Hills swimming pool can be filled by a vent in 10 hours. It can be emptied by a drain pipe in 20 hours. The pool manager mistakenly leaves the drain pipe open while trying to fill the pool before Memorial Day. How long will it take to fill the pool?

Let h represent the number of hours it will take to fill the pool.

The fact that it takes 10 hours to fill the pool means that in 1 hour, $\dfrac{1}{10}$ of the pool is filled; 20 hours to drain the pool means that in 1 hour, $\dfrac{1}{20}$ of the pool is drained. A full pool can be represented by 1. The equation that represents this situation is $\dfrac{1}{10}h - \dfrac{1}{20}h = 1$ or $\dfrac{h}{10} - \dfrac{h}{20} = 1$.

$$\dfrac{h}{10} - \dfrac{h}{20} = 1$$

$$20\left(\dfrac{h}{10}\right) - 20\left(\dfrac{h}{20}\right) = 20(1) \qquad \textit{The LCD is 20.}$$

$$2h - h = 20$$

$$h = 20$$

It will take 20 hours to fill the pool.

When adding or subtracting fractions with unlike denominators, you must first find a common denominator. Suppose you have a rational expression and you want to know what fractions were added or subtracted and resulted in that expression. This process is called decomposing a fraction into **partial fractions**. You can use a rational equation to do this.

LESSON 4-6   RATIONAL EQUATIONS AND PARTIAL FRACTIONS   217

Motivating the Lesson

The ancient Egyptians wrote fractions as sums of unit fractions. For example, $\dfrac{2}{3} = \dfrac{1}{2} + \dfrac{1}{6}$ and $\dfrac{2}{29} = \dfrac{1}{24} + \dfrac{1}{58} + \dfrac{1}{174} + \dfrac{1}{232}$. This cumbersome method seems to be just a curiosity now, but how about decomposing an algebraic fraction into its component parts? How can $\dfrac{x}{(x-2)(x+3)}$ be written as a sum of fractions? This question is not a matter of curiosity but a necessary technique in the study of integral calculus.

$$\dfrac{x}{(x-2)(x+3)} = \dfrac{2}{5(x-2)} + \dfrac{3}{5(x+3)}$$

TEACHING THE LESSON

Chalkboard Examples

For Example 1

Solve $\dfrac{1}{t-2} + \dfrac{t-3}{7-t} = \dfrac{t+1}{-t^2+9t-14}$.

3, 4

For Example 2

Two brothers run a lawn mowing business for the summer. When working alone, the older brother can mow Mr. Wilson's lawn in three hours, while the younger brother can do the job in two hours, twenty minutes. How long would it take the two of them working together?   **1.3125 hours or about 1 hour 19 minutes**

Teaching Tip   After discussing Example 1, tell students that when solving rational equations and inequalities, they should write down any restrictions on the domain immediately so that only actual solutions are considered.

Example 3

Decompose $\dfrac{x - 11}{x^2 - 2x - 3}$ **into partial fractions.**

First factor the denominator.

$$\dfrac{x - 11}{x^2 - 2x - 3} = \dfrac{x - 11}{(x - 3)(x + 1)}$$

Express the factored form as the sum of two fractions using A and B as numerators and the factors as denominators.

$$\dfrac{x - 11}{(x - 3)(x + 1)} = \dfrac{A}{x - 3} + \dfrac{B}{x + 1}$$

Eliminate the denominators by multiplying each side by the LCD.

$$x - 11 = A(x + 1) + B(x - 3)$$

The excluded values for this rational function are –1 and 3. By substituting each of these values into the equation, you can find the values of A and B.

Let x = -1.

$$x - 11 = A(x + 1) + B(x - 3)$$
$$-1 - 11 = A(-1 + 1) + B(-1 - 3)$$
$$-12 = -4B$$
$$3 = B$$

Let x = 3.

$$3 - 11 = A(3 + 1) + B(3 - 3)$$
$$-8 = 4A$$
$$-2 = A$$

Now substitute the values for A and B into the original fractions.

$$\dfrac{A}{x - 3} + \dfrac{B}{x + 1} = \dfrac{-2}{x - 3} + \dfrac{3}{x + 1}$$

So, $\dfrac{x - 11}{x^2 - 2x - 3} = \dfrac{-2}{x - 3} + \dfrac{3}{x + 1}.$

The processes used in solving rational equations can also be used in determining the solutions of rational inequalities.

Example 4

Solve $\dfrac{(x - 3)(x - 4)}{(x - 5)(x - 6)^2} < 0.$

Let a number line represent all possible values for x. Plot all values of x that cause $f(x) = \dfrac{(x - 3)(x - 4)}{(x - 5)(x - 6)^2}$ to equal 0. Those zeros are 3 and 4. Then plot 5 and 6 as circles since they must be excluded from the list of possible solutions.

Draw vertical lines to separate the number line as shown below.

Select a sample value within each region and test it in the rational expression to see if it yields a positive or negative result. It is not necessary to find the exact value of the expression.

Test $f(0)$: $\dfrac{(0-3)(0-4)}{(0-5)(0-6)^2}$ → $\dfrac{(-)(-)}{(-)(-)(-)}$ → −

So in the region $x < 3, f(x) < 0$. Thus, $x < 3$ is a solution.

Test $f(3.5)$: $\dfrac{(3.5-3)(3.5-4)}{(3.5-5)(3.5-6)^2}$ → $\dfrac{(+)(-)}{(-)(-)(-)}$ → +

In the region $3 < x < 4, f(x) > 0$. This is not a solution.

Continue to test a value in each region of the number line to determine all regions in which $f(x) < 0$.

The solution is $x < 3$ or $4 < x < 5$.

Chalkboard Example

For Example 5

Solve $\dfrac{1}{3b} - \dfrac{2}{5b} < 1.$

$b > -\dfrac{1}{15},\ b \neq 0$

Example 5

Solve $\dfrac{1}{4a} + \dfrac{5}{8a} > \dfrac{1}{2}.$

The inequality can be written as $\dfrac{1}{4a} + \dfrac{5}{8a} - \dfrac{1}{2} > 0$. The related function is $f(a) = \dfrac{1}{4a} + \dfrac{5}{8a} - \dfrac{1}{2}$. Find the zeros of this function.

$$\dfrac{1}{4a} + \dfrac{5}{8a} - \dfrac{1}{2} = 0$$

$$8a\left(\dfrac{1}{4a}\right) + 8a\left(\dfrac{5}{8a}\right) - 8a\left(\dfrac{1}{2}\right) = 8a(0) \qquad \textit{The LCD is 8a.}$$

$$2 + 5 - 4a = 0$$

$$a = \dfrac{7}{4}$$

The value $a = 0$ is a point of discontinuity. Graph the zero and the point of discontinuity on a number line. Draw vertical lines to separate the number line into regions.

Now test a sample value in each region to determine if the values in the region satisfy the inequality.

(continued on the next page)

LESSON 4-6   RATIONAL EQUATIONS AND PARTIAL FRACTIONS   219

Checking for Understanding

Exercises 1–12 are designed to help you assess students' understanding through reading, writing, speaking, and modeling. You should work through Exercises 1–4 with your students and then monitor their work on Exercises 5–12.

Closing the Lesson

Writing Activity Have each student add two rational expressions to form a single fraction. Then have students exchange fractions and decompose them into partial fractions.

Practice Masters Booklet, p. 26

Test $a = -1$: $\dfrac{1}{4(-1)} + \dfrac{5}{8(-1)} \overset{?}{>} \dfrac{1}{2}$

$$-\dfrac{1}{4} - \dfrac{5}{8} \overset{?}{>} \dfrac{1}{2}$$

$$-\dfrac{7}{8} > \dfrac{1}{2} \quad \textit{false}$$

$a < 0$ is not a solution.

Test $a = 1$: $\dfrac{1}{4(1)} + \dfrac{5}{8(1)} \overset{?}{>} \dfrac{1}{2}$

$$\dfrac{1}{4} + \dfrac{5}{8} \overset{?}{>} \dfrac{1}{2}$$

$$\dfrac{7}{8} > \dfrac{1}{2} \quad \textit{true}$$

$0 < a < \dfrac{7}{4}$ is a solution.

Test $a = 2$: $\dfrac{1}{4(2)} + \dfrac{5}{8(2)} \overset{?}{>} \dfrac{1}{2}$

$$\dfrac{1}{8} + \dfrac{5}{16} \overset{?}{>} \dfrac{1}{2}$$

$$\dfrac{7}{16} > \dfrac{1}{2} \quad \textit{false}$$

$a \geq \dfrac{7}{4}$ is not a solution.

The solution is $0 < a < \dfrac{7}{4}$.

CHECKING FOR UNDERSTANDING

Communicating Mathematics

Read and study the lesson to answer each question. 1–4. See margin.

1. **Demonstrate** how to find the LCD of two or more fractions.

2. **Explain** why all solutions of a rational equation must be checked.

3. **Describe** what is meant by decomposing into partial fractions.

4. **Compare** the two methods used to solve rational inequalities presented in Examples 4 and 5.

Guided Practice

Find the LCD for the rational expressions in each equation. Solve each equation.

5. $\dfrac{1}{m} = \dfrac{m - 34}{2m^2}$

6. $\dfrac{9}{b + 5} = \dfrac{3}{b - 3}$

7. $\dfrac{7a}{3(a + 1)} - \dfrac{5}{4(a - 1)} = \dfrac{3a}{2(a + 1)}$

$2m^2; -34$ $(b + 5)(b - 3); 7$ $12(a + 1)(a - 1); 3$ and $-\dfrac{1}{2}$

Solve each equation. Check your solution.

8. $\dfrac{3}{x} + \dfrac{7}{x} = 8 \quad \dfrac{5}{4}$

9. $1 + \dfrac{5}{a - 1} = \dfrac{7}{6} \quad 31$

10. $\dfrac{3y + 2}{4} = \dfrac{9}{4} - \dfrac{3 - 2y}{6} \quad 3$

220   CHAPTER 4   POLYNOMIAL AND RATIONAL FUNCTIONS

RETEACHING THE LESSON

Have students work through the solution of one or more equations and inequalities involving ordinary fractions so they can review finding and using the LCD. Then work on an equation that involves rational expressions.

T26
Glencoe Division, Macmillan/McGraw-Hill

11. Decompose $\dfrac{-x+5}{(x-1)(x+1)}$ into partial fractions. $\dfrac{2}{x-1} - \dfrac{3}{x+1}$

12. Solve $\dfrac{2}{w} + 3 > \dfrac{29}{w}$. $w < 0, w > 9$

EXERCISES

Solve each equation. Check your solution.

13. $b - \dfrac{5}{b} = 4$ $-1, 5$

14. $\dfrac{6}{p+3} + \dfrac{p}{p-3} = 1$ 1

15. $\dfrac{2}{x+2} + \dfrac{3}{x} = \dfrac{-x}{x+2}$ -3

16. $\dfrac{12}{t} + t - 8 = 0$ $2, 6$

17. $1 = \dfrac{1}{1-y} + \dfrac{y}{y-1}$ all reals except 1

18. $\dfrac{1}{3m} + \dfrac{6m-9}{3m} = \dfrac{3m-3}{4m}$ $\dfrac{23}{15}$

19. $1 + \dfrac{n+6}{n+1} = \dfrac{4}{n-2}$ $\dfrac{1 \pm \sqrt{145}}{4}$

20. $\dfrac{2q}{2q+3} - \dfrac{2q}{2q-3} = 1$ $\dfrac{-3 \pm 3\sqrt{2}}{2}$

Solve each inequality.

21. $5 + \dfrac{1}{x} > \dfrac{16}{x}$ $x < 0, x > 3$

22. $\dfrac{2y+1}{5} - \dfrac{2+7y}{15} < \dfrac{2}{3}$ $y > -9$

23. $1 + \dfrac{5}{a-1} < \dfrac{7}{6}$ $a < 1, a > 31$

24. $\dfrac{2a-5}{6} - \dfrac{a-5}{4} < \dfrac{3}{4}$ $a < 4$

25. $x^3 - 11x^2 + 18x \geq 0$
$0 \leq x \leq 2, x \geq 9$

26. $x^5 + x^4 - 16x - 16 < 0$
$x < -2, -1 < x < 2$

Decompose each expression into partial fractions. 27–29. See margin.

27. $\dfrac{3p-1}{p^2-1}$

28. $\dfrac{-4y}{3y^2-4y+1}$

29. $\dfrac{2m+1}{m^2+m}$

30. Solve $\dfrac{1}{2a-2} = \dfrac{a}{a^2-1} + \dfrac{2}{a+1}$. no real solutions

31. Solve $\dfrac{x^2-16}{x^2-4x-5} > 0$. $x < -4, -1 < x < 4, x > 5$

32. Tell how you could use the graph of $f(x) = 8x^3 - 22x^2 - 5x + 12$ to solve $8x^3 - 22x^2 - 5x + 12 \geq 0$. See margin.

33. Solve $\dfrac{7}{y+1} > 7$. $-1 < y < 0$

34. A dish of mixed nuts contains cashews and peanuts. Two more ounces of peanuts are added to the dish, making the new mixture 20% cashews. Sarah likes cashews, so she adds 2 ounces of them to the dish. The mixture in the dish is now $33\dfrac{1}{3}$% cashews. What percent of the original mixture of nuts was cashews? 25%

Assignment Guide

Average: 13-27, 30, 33, 35, 36, 38-43
Enriched: 19-43

The red A, B, and C flags, printed only in the Teacher's Wraparound Edition, indicate the level of difficulty of the exercises.

Chapter 4, Quiz C, (Lessons 4-5 through 4-6), is available in the *Evaluation Masters,* p. 46.

Additional Answers

1. For an equation $\dfrac{1}{a} + \dfrac{1}{b} = \dfrac{1}{c}$, the LCD is the product of the factors of a, b, and c with no duplication of common factors.

2. All solutions must be checked because some may result in a zero in the denominator.

3. Decomposing a rational expression into partial fractions means to use factors and solving rational equations to find what terms were added/subtracted to arrive at the expression.

4. In both examples you are testing values for which the inequality is true. However, in Example 4, an expression less than 0 means a negative expression. Since the expression involves factors, you need only consider the combinations of signs that produce a negative rather than the exact numerical value of the function.

27. $\dfrac{2}{p+1} + \dfrac{1}{p-1}$

28. $\dfrac{-2}{y-1} + \dfrac{2}{3y-1}$

29. $\dfrac{1}{m+1} + \dfrac{1}{m}$

32. Graph the function $f(x)$. Anywhere the graph is above the x-axis, the value of $f(x)$ is positive. Those values where $f(x)$ is positive are solutions to the inequality.

Additional Answers

38. A relation relates members of a set called the domain to members of a set called the range. In a function, the relation must be such that each member of the domain is related to one and only one member of the range.

40.

41. $\pm\dfrac{1}{6},\ \pm\dfrac{1}{3},\ \pm\dfrac{1}{2},\ \pm\dfrac{2}{3},\ \pm 1,\ \pm 2$

Enrichment Masters Booklet, p. 26

NAME _____ DATE _____

4-6 Enrichment Worksheet

Cycle Quadruples

Four nonnegative integers are arranged in cyclic order to make a "cyclic quadruple." In the example, this quadruple is 23, 8, 14, and 32.

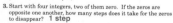

The next cyclic quadruple is formed from the absolute values of the four differences of adjacent integers:

$|23-8|=15$ $|8-14|=6$ $|14-32|=18$ $|32-23|=9$

By continuing in this manner, you will eventually get four equal integers. In the example, the equal integers appear in three steps.

Solve each problem.

1. Start with the quadruple 25, 17, 55, 47. In how many steps do the equal integers appear? **4 steps**

2. Some interesting things happen when one or more of the original numbers is 0. Draw a diagram showing a beginning quadruple of three zeros and one nonnegative integer. Predict how many steps it will take to reach 4 equal integers. Also, predict what that integer will be. Complete the diagram to check your predictions. **3 steps; a**

3. Start with four integers, two of them zero. If the zeros are opposite one another, how many steps does it take for the zeros to disappear? **1 step**

4. Start with two equal integers and two zeros. The zeros are next to one another. How many steps does it take for the zeros to disappear? **2 steps**

5. Start with two nonequal integers and two zeros. The zeros are next to one another. How many steps does it take for the zeros to disappear? **3 steps**

6. Start with three equal integers and one zero. How many steps does it take for the zero to disappear? **3 steps**

7. Describe the remaining cases with one zero and tell how many steps it takes for the zero to disappear.
   (1) all integers different; 1 step
   (2) opposite nonzero integers equal, but different from third integer; 1 step
   (3) two adjacent integers equal, but different from third integer; 2 steps

T 26
Glencoe Division, Macmillan/McGraw-Hill

Applications and Problem Solving

35. Number Theory Four times the multiplicative inverse of a number is added to the number. The result is $10\frac{2}{5}$. What is the number? $\frac{2}{5}$ or 10

36. Candle Making A beeswax candle is made by repeatedly dipping the wick into the molten wax. Paraffin candles are usually made by pouring the molten wax into forms with wick shafts, and the wick is added as the last step. One type of beeswax candle burns up in 6 hours. Another paraffin candle of the same length burns up in 9 hours. If both candles are lit at the same time, how much time will pass before one is twice as long as the other? **4.5 hours**

37. Neighborhoods Rosea and Tai live on the same street in the same neighborhood in West Branch, Iowa, the birthplace of President Herbert Hoover. When Rosea jogs to Tai's house, it takes 10 minutes. When Tai rides his bike to Rosea's house, it takes 6 minutes. Suppose they both leave their houses at the same time headed for the other person's house. In how many minutes will they meet? **3.75 min**

Mixed Review

38. Describe the difference between a relation and a function. How do you test a graph to determine if it is the graph of a function? **(Lesson 1-1)** See margin.

39. Education You may answer up to 30 questions on your final exam in history class. It consists of multiple-choice and essay questions. Two 48-minute class periods have been set aside for taking the test. It will take you 1 minute to answer each multiple-choice question and 12 minutes for each essay question. Correct answers on multiple-choice questions earn 5 points and correct essay answers earn 20 points. If you are confident that you will answer all of the questions you attempt correctly, how many of each type of question should you answer to receive the highest score? **(Lesson 2-6)** 24 multiple choice, 6 essay

40. Graph the inverse of $f(x) = x^2 - 16$. **(Lesson 3-3)** See margin.   41. See margin.

41. List all possible rational roots for $6x^3 + 6x^2 - 15x - 2 = 0$. **(Lesson 4-4)**

42. Approximate the real zeros of $h(x) = 3x^3 - 16x^2 + 12x + 6$ to the nearest tenth. **(Lesson 4-5)** $-0.3, 4.3, 1.4$

43. College Entrance Exam Choose the best answer. E
An automobile travels m miles in h hours. At this rate, how far will it travel in x hours?

(A) $\dfrac{m}{x}$ (B) $\dfrac{m}{xh}$ (C) $\dfrac{m}{h}$ (D) $\dfrac{mh}{x}$ (E) $\dfrac{mx}{h}$

222 CHAPTER 4 POLYNOMIAL AND RATIONAL FUNCTIONS

EXTENDING THE LESSON

Math Power: Problem Solving

Suppose you are told that $-\dfrac{2x+1}{(x^2+x-2)^2}$ is the derivative of a function $f(x)$. What information does this give you about the graph of $f(x)$?
The function is increasing for $x < -\frac{1}{2}$, decreasing for $x > -\frac{1}{2}$, and has a relative maximum at $x = -\frac{1}{2}$.

4-7A Graphing Calculators: Solving Radical Equations and Inequalities

You can use a graphing calculator to graph and solve many types of equations and inequalities. In Lesson 3-3A, we graphed radical functions on the graphing calculator. In this lesson, we will solve radical equations and inequalities by graphing.

Radical equations can be solved on the graphing calculator by using two different methods, but both methods will produce the same solution. One method is to look at each side of the equation and graph both of them as a separate function. The solution is where the two equations intersect on the graph. The other method is to first solve the equation so that it equals zero and then graph it. In this case, the solution is where the graph crosses the x-axis.

Example 1

Solve $\sqrt{3x + 7} - \sqrt{4x - 3} = 1$.

Try the separate function method. Use the viewing window $[-2, 8]$ by $[-3, 6]$ with a scale factor of 1 for both axes.

TI-81: [Y=] [2nd] [√] [(] 3 [X|T] [+] 7 [)] [−] [2nd] [√]
[(] 4 [X|T] [−] 3 [)] [ENTER] 1 [GRAPH]

Casio: [Graph] [√] [(] 3 [ALPHA] [X] [+]
7 [)] [−] [√] [(] 4 [ALPHA] [X] [−] 3
[)] [:] [Graph] 1 [EXE]

Trace to the intersection point of the two graphs and zoom in. Use the [ZOOM] key on the TI-81 and [SHIFT] [×] or [Factor] to zoom in on the Casio. This method produces a solution of 3.

Now try to solve the equation by setting it equal to zero and graphing the equation. The equation is then $\sqrt{3x + 7} - \sqrt{4x - 3} - 1 = 0$.

TI-81: [Y=] [2nd] [√] [(] 3 [X|T] [+] 7 [)] [−] [2nd] [√]
[(] 4 [X|T] [−] 3 [)] [−] 1 [GRAPH]

Casio: [Graph] [√] [(] 3 [ALPHA] [X]
[+] 7 [)] [−] [√] [(] 4 [ALPHA]
[X] [−] 3 [)] [−] 1 [EXE]

Tracing to the zero of the function and zooming in produces a solution of 3, which is identical to the solution from the first method.

GRAPHING CALCULATORS: SOLVING RADICAL EQUATIONS AND INEQUALITIES   223

Objective   Solve radical equations and inequalities on a graphing calculator.

Motivating the Lesson

Ask students how they would solve the following system.
$y = \sqrt{2x - 2}$
$y = 1 - x$
Then ask them how they would solve the equation $\sqrt{2x - 2} = 1 - x$.

Teaching Tip   Point out that the method used to solve the equation in Example 1 is to let each side of the equation equal y. Then graph those equations. The solutions are those points the two graphs have in common.

More Examples

1. Solve $\sqrt{2x - 2} = 1 - x$ for x. **1**

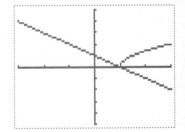

2. Solve $\sqrt{3x - 4} \geq 4$. Round your solution to the nearest hundredth.
   $x \geq 6.67$

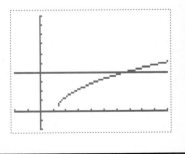

Ask students how many solutions they might expect when solving $\sqrt{3x - 5} = \sqrt{x - 3}$.

Homework Exercises

Assignment Guide

All: 1-12

Additional Answers

For graphs for Exercises 1-12, see Teacher's Answer Key.

The equation in Example 1 has a solution, namely 3. However, some radical equations do not have a solution in the set of real numbers. This happens when there are no x-values that will satisfy the equation. You can tell if an equation has no real solution on a graph if the graph does not cross the x-axis.

The TI-81 graphing calculator can also be used to solve radical inequalities by shading the area on the graph that makes the inequality true. Using each side of the inequality as a separate function, use the "Shade(" command and enter the "lesser" expression first as the lower bound and the "greater" expression second as the upper bound.

Example 2

Solve $\sqrt{5x - 3} \leq 4$. Round your solution to the nearest hundredth.

First, clear any functions listed in the ⎡Y=⎤ list and clear the graphics screen by pressing ⎡2nd⎤ ⎡DRAW⎤ 1 ⎡ENTER⎤. Then, enter the inequality. For example, $\sqrt{5x - 3}$ is the lesser expression and 4 is the greater expression.

TI-81: ⎡2nd⎤ ⎡DRAW⎤ 7 ⎡2nd⎤ ⎡√⎤ ⎡(⎤ 5 ⎡X|T⎤ ⎡−⎤ 3 ⎡)⎤ ⎡ALPHA⎤ ⎡,⎤ 4 ⎡)⎤ ⎡ENTER⎤

A good graph of the inequality can be seen in the viewing window of [–2, 8] by [–3, 6] with scale factors of 1 for both axes.

You can use the arrow keys and zoom in to approximate a solution to the inequality. After moving the cursor to the edge of the shade with an arrow key, zoom in. Then press ⎡2nd⎤ ⎡QUIT⎤ and ⎡ENTER⎤ to redraw the graph.

The solution is $0.63 \leq x \leq 3.79$.

EXERCISES

Graph and solve each equation to the nearest hundredth. Then sketch the graph on a piece of paper.

1. $\sqrt{10x - 1} = 7$ 5

2. $\sqrt{6x - 2} - 1 = 3$ 3

3. $\sqrt{5x - 4} - \sqrt{16x - 7} = -2$ 1, 0.91

4. $\sqrt{\frac{1}{2}x + 2} + \sqrt{x} = 4$ 4

5. $\sqrt{3x} - \sqrt{\frac{1}{3}x} = 1$ 0.75

6. $\sqrt{x + 5} + \sqrt{2x + 7} = 2\sqrt{3}$ –2

7. $\sqrt[3]{4x + 13} - 6 = -9$ –10

8. $\sqrt{9 - 3x} + \sqrt{2 - 5x} = -5$ no solution

Use a TI-81 graphing calculator to graph each inequality. Then sketch the graph on a piece of paper.

9. $\sqrt{x + 1} \leq 3$

10. $\sqrt{2x - 5} \leq 6$

11. $\sqrt{4x - 7} \geq 5$

12. $\sqrt[3]{x + 3} \geq -2$

4-7 Radical Equations and Inequalities

Objective
4–7

After studying this lesson, you should be able to:
■ solve radical equations and inequalities.

Application

The Media Arts class at a local university created a science fiction movie to enter in the state film contest. In their film, Lucky Winslow falls asleep on her space ship and awakens to find that she has landed on a planet. However, she doesn't know whether she has landed on Venus or Mars. The Media Arts class sought the help of the physics classes to add authenticity to their film. They asked how Lucky could figure out where she had landed.

The physics class told them that if Lucky could make a pendulum, she could use a formula to determine the acceleration of gravity of the planet and then use her charts to discover where she was. Suppose Lucky makes a 1-meter pendulum. When she allows the pendulum to oscillate, the period of the oscillation is 3.27 seconds. The local acceleration due to gravity can be determined by the formula,

$T = 2\pi\sqrt{\dfrac{\ell}{g}}$, where T is the period of the oscillation

of the pendulum, ℓ is the length of the pendulum, and g is acceleration due to gravity. Suppose the acceleration due to gravity on the surface of Mars is 3.7 m/s² and on the surface of Venus is 8.9 m/s². On which planet did Lucky land?

$$T = 2\pi\sqrt{\frac{\ell}{g}}$$

$$3.27 = 2\pi\sqrt{\frac{1}{g}} \qquad \textit{T = 3.27, } \ell\textit{ = 1}$$

$$\frac{3.27}{2\pi} = \sqrt{\frac{1}{g}} \qquad \textit{Divide each side by } 2\pi.$$

$$\left(\frac{3.27}{2\pi}\right)^2 = \left(\sqrt{\frac{1}{g}}\right)^2 \qquad \textit{Square each side.}$$

$$\left(\frac{3.27}{2\pi}\right)^2 = \frac{1}{g}$$

$$g = \frac{1}{\left(\frac{3.27}{2\pi}\right)^2}$$

$$g = 3.692021585 \qquad \textit{Use your calculator.}$$

Since this number rounds to 3.7, Lucky must be on Mars.

LESSON 4-7   RADICAL EQUATIONS AND INEQUALITIES   225

NCTM Standards: 1-6

Lesson Resources

- Practice Master 4-7
- Enrichment Master 4-7
- Evaluation Master, Quiz D, p. 46
- Activity Master, p. 11

 Transparency 4-7 contains the 5-Minute Check and a teaching aid for this lesson.

INTRODUCING THE LESSON

5-Minute Check
(over Lesson 4–6)

1. Solve $\dfrac{1}{2t-1} + \dfrac{1}{t+1} = \dfrac{3}{2}$.

   $-\dfrac{1}{2}$, 1

2. Solve $\dfrac{2}{y} - 1 > \dfrac{6}{y-1}$.

   $-2 < y < -1$

3. Decompose $\dfrac{5x+7}{x^2+x-20}$ into

   partial fractions. $\dfrac{2}{x+5} + \dfrac{3}{x-4}$

Motivating the Lesson

Have students work in small groups. Each group needs a stopwatch, a weight, and a piece of string. Have students use the string and weight as a pendulum, and use the stopwatch to time its period for different lengths of string. Make a chart listing the period for each length, and observe how the period and the square root of the length are related.

ALTERNATE TEACHING STRATEGIES

Using Computers

Have students make a flow chart of the steps involved in solving a radical equation. It should include a loop for the steps involved in isolating and eliminating the radicals.

Using Models

Have students consider the following problem. *What point in the coordinate plane is twice as far from (0, 2) as from (3, 7) and has an x-coordinate of 5?* Encourage students to try some sort of graphical solution first, and then use the distance formula.
There are two such points; one has a y-coordinate of 7.634, and the other has a y-coordinate of about 4.367.

Teaching Tip   Have students review the solution of Example 1 and see if they can identify an earlier point at which it was clear that no real solution exists.
Sample answer: $\sqrt{x - 4}$ cannot be negative.

Teaching Tip   In Example 2, remind students that odd roots (cube, fifth, and so on) can be negative, while even roots cannot be negative.

Equations, such as $T = 2\pi\sqrt{\dfrac{\ell}{g}}$, in which the variables occur in radical expressions are known as **radical equations**. To solve radical equations, you must isolate the radical on one side of the equation and raise each side of the equation to the proper power to eliminate the radical expression.

The process of raising each side of an equation to a power sometimes produces extraneous solutions. These are solutions that do not satisfy the original equation. Therefore, it is important to check all possible solutions in the original equation to determine if any of them should be eliminated from the solution set.

Example 1

Solve $-5 + \sqrt{x - 4} = -2.$

$$-5 + \sqrt{x - 4} = -2$$
$$\sqrt{x - 4} = 3 \qquad \textit{Isolate the radical.}$$
$$x - 4 = 9 \qquad \textit{Square each side.}$$
$$x = 13$$

Now check the possible solution.   **Check:**
$$5 + \sqrt{x - 4} = 2$$
$$5 + \sqrt{13 - 4} \overset{?}{=} 2 \qquad x = 13$$
$$5 + \sqrt{9} \overset{?}{=} 2$$
$$5 + 3 \neq 2$$

The solution does not check. The equation has no real solutions.

Example 2

Solve $3 = \sqrt[3]{x + 4} + 12.$

$$3 = \sqrt[3]{x + 4} + 12$$
$$-9 = \sqrt[3]{x + 4} \qquad \textit{Isolate the cube root.}$$
$$(-9)^3 = \left(\sqrt[3]{x + 4}\right)^3 \qquad \textit{Cube each side.}$$
$$-729 = x + 4$$
$$-733 = x \qquad \textit{–733 is a possible solution.}$$

Check :
$$3 = \sqrt[3]{x + 4} + 12$$
$$3 \overset{?}{=} \sqrt[3]{-733 + 4} + 12 \qquad x = -733$$
$$3 \overset{?}{=} \sqrt[3]{-729} + 12$$
$$3 \overset{?}{=} -9 + 12$$
$$3 = 3$$

The solution checks. The solution of the equation is –733.

If there is more than one radical in an equation, you may need to repeat the process for solving radical equations until all radicals have been eliminated.

Example 3

Solve $\sqrt{3x + 4} - \sqrt{2x - 7} = 3$.

$$\sqrt{3x + 4} - \sqrt{2x - 7} = 3$$

$$\sqrt{3x + 4} = 3 + \sqrt{2x - 7} \qquad \textit{Isolate one of the radicals.}$$

$$3x + 4 = 9 + 6\sqrt{2x - 7} + 2x - 7 \qquad \textit{Square each side.}$$

$$x + 2 = 6\sqrt{2x - 7} \qquad \textit{Simplify.}$$

$$x^2 + 4x + 4 = 36(2x - 7) \qquad \textit{Square each side.}$$

$$x^2 - 68x + 256 = 0 \qquad \textit{Simplify.}$$

$$x = \frac{-(-68) \pm \sqrt{(-68^2 - 4(1)(256)}}{2(1)} \qquad \textit{Use the quadratic formula.}$$

$$x = 4 \text{ or } 64$$

Check both possible solutions.

Check $x = 4$:	**Check $x = 64$:**
$\sqrt{3x + 4} - \sqrt{2x - 7} = 3$	$\sqrt{3x + 4} - \sqrt{2x - 7} = 3$
$\sqrt{3(4) + 4} - \sqrt{2(4) - 7} \stackrel{?}{=} 3$	$\sqrt{3(64) + 4} - \sqrt{2(64) - 7} \stackrel{?}{=} 3$
$\sqrt{16} - \sqrt{1} \stackrel{?}{=} 3$	$\sqrt{196} - \sqrt{121} \stackrel{?}{=} 3$
$4 - 1 \stackrel{?}{=} 3$	$14 - 11 \stackrel{?}{=} 3$
$3 = 3$	$3 = 3$

Both solutions check. The solutions are 4 and 64.

To determine the solution set of radical inequalities, use the same procedures that you used to solve radical equations.

Example 4

Solve $\sqrt{5x + 4} \leq 8$.

$$\sqrt{5x + 4} \leq 8$$

$$5x + 4 \leq 64 \qquad \textit{Square each side.}$$

$$5x \leq 60$$

$$x \leq 12$$

In order for $\sqrt{5x + 4}$ to be a real number, $5x + 4$ must be greater than or equal to zero.

$$5x + 4 \geq 0$$

$$5x \geq -4$$

$$x \geq -0.8$$

So, the solution is $-0.8 \leq x \leq 12$.

You can check the solution by substituting values of x from each interval into the original inequality.

EVALUATING THE LESSON

Checking for Understanding

Exercises 1–7 are designed to help you assess students' understanding through reading, writing, speaking, and modeling. You should work through Exercises 1–4 with your students and then monitor their work on Exercises 5–7.

Closing the Lesson

Speaking Activity   Have students explain the major steps involved in solving a radical equation that contains only one radical. Then have them compare this to the steps necessary if two radicals are present.

Practice Masters Booklet, p. 27

Example 5

APPLICATION

History

Argentine cowboys called gauchos rode the Argentine plains in the 18th and 19th centuries. One of the tools used by the gauchos was the bola. Bolas were made of three iron balls or stones attached to strings that met at the other end. The gauchos would use these bolas to entangle their prey's feet. If a gaucho swung his bola over his head forming a circle, the relationship between the period of the revolution T, the mass, m, of the ball, the length of the string, r, and the force, F (in newtons), exerted on the string could be expressed as $T=2\pi\sqrt{\dfrac{mr}{F}}$. Suppose one of the balls of the bola has a mass of 0.2 kg and the string is 0.8 meters long. If you wanted the bola to make at least one complete revolution every second, what is the minimum force exerted on the string?

$$T\ge 2\pi\sqrt{\frac{mr}{F}}$$

$$1\ge 2\pi\sqrt{\frac{(0.2)(0.8)}{F}}$$

$T = 1,$
$m = 0.2,$
$r = 0.8$

$$\frac{1}{2\pi}\ge\sqrt{\frac{0.16}{F}}$$

$$\frac{1}{4\pi^2}\ge\frac{0.16}{F}\quad\text{\textit{Square each side.}}$$

$$F\ge(0.16)(4\pi^2)$$

$$F\ge 6.316546817$$

The force must be at least 6.32 newtons.

CHECKING FOR UNDERSTANDING

Communicating Mathematics

Read and study the lesson to answer each question.

1. Refer to the application at the beginning of the lesson.
   a. **Determine** what the period (in oscillations/second) of a 1-meter pendulum is on Earth if the acceleration due to gravity at Earth's surface is 9.8 m/s². 2.01 s
   b. **Calculate** the period of the pendulum if Lucky had landed on Venus. 2.11 s

2. **Demonstrate** how you would solve $\sqrt{x+5}=2$. See margin.

3. **Explain** the difference between solving an equation with one radical and solving an equation with more than one radical. See margin.

4. What should be the last step in solving any radical equation or inequality? Check each possible solution.

Guided Practice

Solve each equation. Check your solutions.

5. $\sqrt{x+8}-5=0$ 17

6. $\sqrt[3]{y-7}=4$ 71

7. $\sqrt[4]{3x}-2=0$ $\frac{16}{3}$

228   CHAPTER 4   POLYNOMIAL AND RATIONAL FUNCTIONS

RETEACHING THE LESSON

Have students work together on the following pair of equations:

$8+\sqrt{x-3}=5$ and $8+\sqrt[3]{x-3}=5$.

Ask them to consider these questions: Why does the first equation have no solution while the second has −24 as its solution? What are some ways to change the first equation so that it does have a solution?

Additional Answers

2. First square each side of the equation. Then solve for x.

3. When there is more than one radical expression in an equation, you isolate one of the radicals and then square each side. Then you isolate the radical again and square each side. Finally solve for the variable.

EXERCISES

Practice

Solve each equation. Check your solution.

8. $\sqrt{8n-5}-1=2$ $\frac{7}{4}$

9. $\sqrt{1-4t}=2$ $-\frac{3}{4}$

10. $\sqrt[4]{7v-2}+12=7$ no real solution

11. $\sqrt[3]{6u-5}+2=-3$ -20

12. $\sqrt{6x-4}=\sqrt{2x+10}$ 3.5

13. $\sqrt{9u-4}=\sqrt{7u-20}$ no real solution

14. $\sqrt{k+9}-\sqrt{k}=\sqrt{3}$ 3

15. $\sqrt{x+10}+\sqrt{x-6}=8$ 15

16. $\sqrt{x+2}-7=\sqrt{x+9}$ no real solutions

17. $\sqrt{4x^2-3x+2}-2x-5=0$ -1

18. $\sqrt{x+4}+\sqrt{x-3}=7$ 12

19. $\sqrt{x-9}-\sqrt{x+7}=2$ no real solution

Solve each inequality. Check your solution.

20. $\sqrt{x+4}\le 6$ $-4 \le x \le 32$

21. $\sqrt{2x-7}\ge 5$ $x \ge 16$

22. $\sqrt[3]{3x-8}\ge 1$ $x \ge 3$

23. $\sqrt[4]{5x-9}\le 2$ $1.8 \le x \le 5$

Solve each equation. Check your solution.

24. $\sqrt{3x+10}=\sqrt{x+11}-1$ -2

25. $\sqrt{2x+1}+\sqrt{2x+6}=5$ $\frac{3}{2}$

Critical Thinking

26. **Physics** Refer to the application at the beginning of the lesson. See margin.
   a. On Earth, if a pendulum has a length of 0.5 meters, what is its period? If the length of the pendulum is doubled, does the period double? Explain.
   b. Suppose you doubled the period you found in part a. What would be the length of the new pendulum and how does it relate to the original length?
   c. Suppose you triple the period you found in part a. What would be the length of the new pendulum and how does it relate to the original length?
   d. Write a conjecture about the relationship of the original pendulum length and the new pendulum length for n times the period T.

27. 0.64 meters

Applications and Problem Solving

27. **Physics** Acceleration due to gravity on Earth is 9.8 m/s². If a pendulum has an oscillation period on Earth of 1.6 seconds, determine the length of the pendulum.

28. **Demolition** A wrecking ball suspended from a crane is a type of pendulum. Determine the force on a 14-meter chain that is attached to a 60-kilogram ball, if the ball moves at a rate of 0.5 revolutions/second. 132,647.5 newtons

Mixed Review

29. Write $y=-7x+2$ in standard form. **(Lesson 1-5)** $7x+y=2$

30. Find the determinant of $\begin{bmatrix} 5 & -4 \\ 8 & 2 \end{bmatrix}$. **(Lesson 2-3)** 42

31. max: $(-1, 7)$, min: $(1, 3)$, inflection: $(0, 5)$

31. Find the critical points of the graph of $y=x^3-3x+5$. Determine if each point is a maximum, a minimum, or a point of inflection. **(Lesson 3-7)**

32. Solve $\frac{x-4}{x-2}=\frac{x-2}{x+2}+\frac{1}{x-2}$. **(Lesson 4-6)** 14

33. **College Entrance Exam** Choose the best answer. E
   John is now three times Pat's age. Four years from now John will be x years old. In terms of x, how old is Pat now?
   (A) $\frac{x+4}{3}$ (B) $3x$ (C) $x+4$ (D) $x-4$ (E) $\frac{x-4}{3}$

EXTENDING THE LESSON

Math Power: Communication

Have students look up the definitions of parabola, ellipse, hyperbola, and circle as a locus of points and see if they can derive the equation by using the definition and the distance formula. Students can report their results to the class.

Additional Answers

26b. Length = 2.0 meters; if you double the period, the length is 4 times the original.

26c. Length = 4.5 meters; if you triple the period, the length is 9 times the original.

26d. For $n(T)$, the length of the new pendulum equals n^2 times the original length.

APPLYING THE LESSON

Homework Exercises

Assignment Guide

Average: 8-19, 21-25 odd, 26, 28, 29-33
Enriched: 12-20 even, 22-33

The red A, B, and C flags, printed only in the Teacher's Wraparound Edition, indicate the level of difficulty of the exercises.

Chapter 4, Quiz D, (Lesson 7), is available in the *Evaluaton Masters*, p. 46.

Exercise Notes

For Exercises 20–25, remind students that even roots must be nonnegative; for example, $\sqrt{x+4} \ge 0$. This places some additional restrictions on the solution set.

Additional Answers

26a. 1.419 oscillations/second; If the length is doubled, T = 2.01 oscillations/second, which is not 2(1.419).
For 26b–26d, see below.

Enrichment Masters Booklet, p. 27

Using the Chapter Summary and Review

The Chapter Summary and Review begins with an alphabetical listing of the new terms that were presented in the chapter. Have students define each term and provide an example of it, if appropriate.

The Skills and Concepts presented in the chapter are reviewed using a side-by-side format. Encourage students to refer to the Objectives and Examples on the left as they complete the Review Exercises on the right.

The Chapter Summary and Review ends with exercises that review Applications and Problem Solving.

Additional Answers

1.

2.

3.

4.

VOCABULARY

Upon completing this chapter, you should be familiar with the following terms:

187 completing the square	179 imaginary number	191 quadratic inequality
179 complex number	202 integral root theorem	226 radical equation
190 conjugate	210 location principle	216 rational equation
203 Decartes' rule of signs	212 lower bound	201 rational root theorem
178 degree	217 partial fraction	196 remainder theorem
197 depressed polynomial	179 polynomial equation	179 root
189 discriminant	179 polynomial function	196 synthetic division
197 factor theorem	178 polynomial in one	212 upper bound
179 fundamental theorem	variable	212 upper bound theorem
of algebra	188 quadratic formula	179 zero

SKILLS AND CONCEPTS

OBJECTIVES AND EXAMPLES	REVIEW EXERCISES
Upon completing this chapter, you should be able to:	Use these exercises to review and prepare for the chapter test.

■ determine roots of polynomial equations **(Lesson 4-1)**

Solve $x^2 - 3x = 0$.

$x^2 - 3x = 0$

$x(x - 3) = 0$

$x = 0$ or $x - 3 = 0$

$x = 3$

The roots are 0 and 3.

Solve each equation and sketch a graph of the related function.

1. $a + 4 = 0$ -4

2. $0 = t^2 + 6t + 9$ -3

3. $6y^2 + y - 2 = 0$ $\frac{1}{2}, -\frac{2}{3}$

4. $x^3 + 2x^2 - 3x = 0$ $-3, 1, 0$

1–4. For graphs, see margin.

■ solve quadratic equations   **(Lesson 4-2)**

Solve $3x^2 - 2x - 5 = 0$ using the quadratic formula.

$x = \dfrac{-b \pm \sqrt{b^2 - 4ac}}{2a}$

$= \dfrac{-(-2) \pm \sqrt{(-2)^2 - 4(3)(-5)}}{2(3)}$

$= \dfrac{2 \pm \sqrt{64}}{6}$ or $\dfrac{2 \pm 8}{6}$

$x = \dfrac{10}{6}$ or $\dfrac{5}{3}$ $x = \dfrac{-6}{6}$ or -1

Find the discriminant of each equation and describe the nature of the roots of the equation. Then solve each equation using the quadratic formula. 5–8. See margin.

5. $2x^2 - 7x - 4 = 0$

6. $3m^2 - 10m + 5 = 0$

7. $4a^2 + a + 4 = 0$

8. $-2y^2 + 3y + 8 = 0$

5. 81; 2 distinct real roots; $4, -\frac{1}{2}$

6. 40; 2 distinct real roots; $\dfrac{5 \pm \sqrt{10}}{3}$

7. −63; no real roots; $\dfrac{-1 \pm 3i\sqrt{7}}{8}$

8. 73; 2 distinct real roots; $\dfrac{-3 \pm \sqrt{73}}{-4}$

13. 3; 1 pos; 2 or 0 neg; −2, −4, 7

14. 3; 2 or 0 pos, 1 neg; $3, 3, -\frac{1}{2}$

15. 4; 2 or 0 pos, 2 or 0 neg; 2, −2, 3, −3

16. 4; 1 pos, 3 or 1 neg; −1

OBJECTIVES AND EXAMPLES	REVIEW EXERCISES

- find the factors of polynomials using the remainder and factor theorems **(Lesson 4-3)**

Use the Remainder Theorem to determine if $x + 3$ is a factor of $P(x)$ if $P(x) = x^3 + 2x^2 - 5x - 9$.

$$P(-3) = (-3)^3 + 2(-3)^2 - 5(-3) - 9$$
$$= -3$$

The remainder is not 0, so $x + 3$ is not a factor of $P(x)$.

Find the remainder for each division. Is the divisor a factor of the polynomial?

9. $(x^3 - x^2 - 10x - 8) \div (x + 2)$ 0; yes

10. $(2x^3 - 5x^2 + 7x + 1) \div (x - 5)$ 161; no

11. $(4x^3 - 7x + 1) \div (x + \frac{1}{2})$ 4; no

12. $(x^4 - 10x^2 + 9) \div (x - 3)$ 0; yes

- determine the number of positive and negative real zeros a polynomial function has   **(Lesson 4-4)**

$f(x) = 3x^4 - 9x^3 + 4x - 6$

Since $f(x)$ has 3 sign changes, there are 3 or 1 positive real zeros.

$f(-x) = 3x^4 + 9x^3 - 4x - 6$

Since $f(-x)$ has 1 sign change, there is 1 negative real zero.

State the number of complex zeros for each function. Then find the number of possible positive real zeros and the number of possible negative real zeros. Determine all of the rational zeros. 13–16. See margin.

13. $f(x) = x^3 - x^2 - 34x - 56$

14. $f(x) = 2x^3 - 11x^2 + 12x + 9$

15. $f(x) = x^4 - 13x^2 + 36$

16. $f(x) = x^4 + x^3 - 9x^2 - 17x - 8$

- approximate the real zeros of a polynomial function   **(Lesson 4-5)**

Determine between which successive integers the real zeros of $f(x) = x^3 + 4x^2 + x - 2$ are located.

r	1	4	1	-2	
-4	1	0	1	-6	] a zero
-3	1	1	-2	4	
-2	1	2	-3	4	
-1	1	3	-2	0	← a zero
0	1	4	1	-2	] a zero
1	1	5	6	4	

One zero is –1. Another is located between –4 and –3. The other is between 0 and 1.

Determine between which successive integers the real zeros of each function are located.

17. $g(x) = x^2 - 3x - 3$ –1 and 0, 3 and 4

18. $f(x) = x^3 - x^2 + 1$ –1 and 0

19. $g(x) = 4x^3 + x^2 - 11x + 3$

20. $f(x) = x^4 - 9x^3 + 25x^2 - 24x + 6$
19.   –2 and –1, 0 and 1, 1 and 2
20.   0 and 1, 1 and 2, 2 and 3, 4 and 5

Alternate Review Strategy

To provide a brief in-class review, you may wish to read the following questions to your students and have them answer verbally.

1. What are the roots of $x^2 - 6x + 9 = 0$?   **3, 3 (double root)**
2. What is the nature of the roots of the quadratic equation $x^2 + 4x + 5 = 0$?   **complex conjugate pair**
3. Is $x + 2$ a factor of $P(x) = x^3 + 6x^2 + 13x + 10$?   **yes**
4. State the number of possible positive real zeros and the number of possible negative real zeros of $x^4 - 3x^2 + 6x + 8 = 0$.   **0 or 2 pos.; 0 or 2 neg.**
5. What, if anything, can be concluded about the zeros of the polynomial function $f(x)$ if $f(1.4) = 9$ and $f(1.5) = -2.5$?   **There is at least one real zero between 1.4 and 1.5.**
6. What would be a reasonable first step in solving the rational equation below.
$$\frac{5}{m-3} + \frac{4}{m+6} = \frac{9}{(m-3)(m+6)}$$
   Sample answer: Find the LCD.
7. Give an example of a radical equation whose solution will require two squaring operations.
   Sample answer: $3 - \sqrt{x + 2} = \sqrt{x - 5}$

For more information on other methods of alternate assessment, you may wish to refer to Glencoe's *Alternate Assessment in the Mathematics Classroom.*

Two multiple-choice tests (Forms 1A and 1B) and two free-response tests (Forms 2A and 2B) are provided in the *Evaluation Masters*. Chapter 4 Test, Form 1A is shown below. Chapter 4 Test, Form 2A is shown on the next page.

Evaluation Masters Booklet, pp. 37–38

NAME _____ DATE _____

~~ Chapter 4 Test, Form 1A

Write the letter for the correct answer in the blank at the right of each problem.

1. Find the complex roots of $x^3 + x^2 - 10x + 8 = 0$.
   A. 1, 2, 4   B. -1, -2, -4   C. 1, 2, -4   D. -1, 2, -4   1. __C__

2. Write the polynomial equation of least degree for the roots $2i, -2i, -4$.
   A. $x^3 - 4x^2 + 4x - 16$ B. $x^2 + 4x^2 - 4x - 16$
   C. $x^3 + 4x^2 + 4x + 16$ D. $x^3 - 4x^2 - 4x + 16$ 2. __C__

3. Find the discriminant of $3m^2 - 4m - 1 = 0$ and describe the nature of the roots.
   A. 4; real   B. 1; real   C. -4; imaginary   D. -28; imaginary   3. __A__

4. Which inequality represents the graph?
   A. $y \geq x^2 - 6x - 1$
   B. $y \geq x^2 + 7x + 6$
   C. $y \geq x^2 - 6x - 3.5$
   D. $y > x^2 + 6x - 6$ 4. __B__

5. Solve $x^2 - 4x - 9 = 0$ by completing the square.
   A. $2 \pm \sqrt{13}$ B. $2 \pm \sqrt{5}$ C. $-2 \pm \sqrt{13}$ D. $-2 \pm \sqrt{5}$ 5. __A__

6. Solve $-3x^2 + 4 = 0$ by using the quadratic formula.
   A. $\pm \sqrt{\frac{3}{6}}$ B. $\frac{2\sqrt{2}i}{3}$ C. $\frac{2\sqrt{3}}{3}$ D. 0, $\frac{4}{3}$ 6. __C__

7. Divide $x^3 - 4x^2 + 12x - 9$ by $(x - 2)$ using synthetic division.
   A. $x^2 - 2x + 8$ R 7   B. $x^2 - 2x + 15$ R -41
   C. $3x^2 + 2x + 16$ R 23   D. $x^2 - 6x$ R 9   7. __A__

8. Use the remainder theorem to find the remainder of $(2x^3 - 4x^2 + 5x) \div (x + 2)$.
   A. 10   B. 5   C. -11   D. -42   8. __D__

9. List all possible rational zeros of $f(x) = 2x^3 - x^2 + 3x - 4$.
   A. $\pm 1, \pm 4$ B. $\pm 1, \pm 2, \pm 4, \pm 0.5, \pm 0.25$
   C. $\pm 1, \pm 2, \pm 4, \pm 0.5$ D. $\pm 1, \pm 2, \pm 4$ 9. __C__

10. Which of the following is a rational zero of $f(x) = 2x^3 - 3x^2 + 17$.
    A. $-\frac{1}{2}$ B. $\frac{1}{2}$ C. 2   D. -1   10. __D__

11. Find the number of possible positive real zeros of $f(x) = 6 + x^4 + 2x^2 - 5x^3 - 12x$.
    A. 4, 2 or 0   B. 3 or 1   C. 4   D. 1   11. __A__

12. Determine between which consecutive integers the real zeros of $f(x) = 3x^4 + x^3 - 2x^2 + 4$ are located.
    A. -1 and 0   B. 0 and 1   C. -2 and -3   D. no real zeros   12. __D__

T37
Glencoe Division, Macmillan/McGraw-Hill

NAME _____ DATE _____

~~ Chapter 4 Test, Form 1A (continued)

13. Find the greatest integral lower bound of the zeros of $f(x) = 4x^3 - 2x^2 - 12x + 1$.
    A. -1   B. -2   C. 1   D. 2   13. __B__

14. Solve $\frac{2x - 5}{x} + \frac{4x - 1}{x + 2} = -\frac{3x + 8}{x(x + 2)}$.
    A. ± 1 B. $-\frac{2}{9}$ C. $-\frac{2}{3}, \frac{1}{2}$ D. $\frac{-1 \pm \sqrt{433}}{12}$ 14. __C__

15. Solve $2 + \frac{6}{a - 4} > \frac{1}{3}$.
    A. $a > 4$ B. $a < \frac{2}{5}$ and $a > 4$
    C. $\frac{2}{5} < a < 4$ D. $\frac{2}{5} < a$ 15. __B__

16. Decompose $\frac{5x + 1}{x^2 - x - 12}$ into partial fractions.
    A. $\frac{3}{x + 3} + \frac{-2}{x - 4}$ B. $\frac{3}{x + 3} + \frac{2}{x - 4}$
    C. $\frac{2}{x + 3} + \frac{3}{x - 4}$ D. $\frac{-2}{x + 3} + \frac{3}{x - 4}$ 16. __C__

17. Solve $\sqrt{6x - 1} - 4 = -2$.
    A. $\frac{1}{3}$ B. $\frac{5}{3}$ C. 9   D. $\frac{3}{2}$ 17. __D__

18. Solve $\sqrt{7x + 2} < 4$.
    A. $x > 2$ B. $x > 1$ C. $x < 2$ D. $x < 1$ 18. __C__

19. Gretchen's garden measured 10 feet long by 12 feet wide. Gretchen decreased the length of each side by the same amount and this reduced the area of her garden by one third. By how much did Gretchen reduce each side of her garden?
    A. 2 feet   B. 3 feet   C. 4 feet   D. 20 feet   19. __A__

20. Which equation represents the graph of the function?
    A. $y = x^2 + 1$
    B. $y = x^2 + x + 4$
    C. $y = x^2 - 2x - 3$
    D. $y = x^2 - 4x + 1$ 20. __D__

Bonus
Find the discriminant of $(2 + \sqrt{3})x^2 - (4 - \sqrt{3})x = 1$.
    A. $11 - 12\sqrt{3}$ B. $-16 - 9\sqrt{3}$ C. $-2 + 2\sqrt{3}$ D. $27 - 4\sqrt{3}$ Bonus: __D__

T38
Glencoe Division, Macmillan/McGraw-Hill

OBJECTIVES AND EXAMPLES	REVIEW EXERCISES

- solve rational equations and inequalities (Lesson 4-6)

   Solve $\frac{1}{9} + \frac{1}{2a} = \frac{1}{a^2}$.

   $$\frac{1}{9} + \frac{1}{2a} = \frac{1}{a^2}$$
   $$(18a^2)\left(\frac{1}{9} + \frac{1}{2a}\right) = \left(\frac{1}{a^2}\right)(18a^2)$$
   $$2a^2 + 9a = 18$$
   $$2a^2 + 9a - 18 = 0$$
   $$(2a - 3)(a + 6) = 0$$
   $$a = \frac{3}{2} \text{ or } a = -6$$

Solve each equation or inequality. Check your solution.

21. $n + 5 = \frac{6}{n}$ -6, 1

22. $\frac{5}{6} - \frac{2m}{2m + 3} = \frac{19}{6}$ $-\frac{21}{20}$

23. $3x^2 - x - 4 \geq 0$ $x \leq -1, x \geq \frac{4}{3}$

24. $\frac{2}{x + 1} - 1 < \frac{1}{6}$ $x < -1, x > \frac{5}{7}$

- solve radical equations and inequalities (Lesson 4-7)

   Solve $9 + \sqrt{x - 1} = 1$.

   $$9 + \sqrt{x - 1} = 1$$
   $$\sqrt{x - 1} = -8$$
   $$x - 1 = 64$$
   $$x = 65$$

Solve each equation or inequality. Check your solution.

25. $5 - \sqrt{x + 2} = 0$ 23

26. $\sqrt[3]{4a - 1} - 3 = 0$ 7

27. $\sqrt{x + 8} - \sqrt{x + 35} = -3$ 1

28. $\sqrt{x - 5} - 7 < 0$ $5 \leq x < 54$

APPLICATIONS AND PROBLEM SOLVING

29. **Sports**   Shalonda hit a home run that traveled in a path whose height is described by the function $h(x) = -0.003x^2 + x + 4$, where x represents the number of feet the ball has traveled from the plate and $h(x)$ represents the height of the ball. If the scoreboard is 30 feet high and 410 feet from the plate, show that Shalonda's home run ball did not hit the scoreboard. **(Lesson 4-2)** Substitute values for x and $h(x)$; $30 \neq -460.3$; the ball hits the ground about 337 feet from the plate.

30. **Art**   James wants to paint a watercolor for his living room. He has 6 feet of framing material to frame the finished painting. What should the dimensions of his canvas be for the painting to be of maximum area?   **(Lesson 4-5)** 1.5 ft × 1.5 ft

Additional Answers
Chapter Test

10.

15. 3; 1 pos, 2 or 0 neg; $\frac{1}{2}, -\frac{1}{3}, -2$

16. 4; 1 pos, 3 or 1 neg; -1, -1

17. 4; 1 pos, 2 or 0 neg; 0, 9

18. 3; 2 or 0 pos, 1 neg; $-\frac{1}{2}, \frac{3}{2}, \frac{7}{2}$

Solve each equation or inequality. Check your solution.

1. $n^2 - 5n + 4 = 0$ 1, 4

2. $6z^3 - 7z^2 - 3z = 0$ $-\frac{1}{3}, 0, \frac{3}{2}$

3. $2a^2 - 5a + 4 = 0$ $\frac{5 \pm i\sqrt{7}}{4}$

4. $\frac{1}{80} + \frac{1}{a} = \frac{1}{10}$ $\frac{80}{7}$

5. $3y^2 + 4y - 15 \le 0$ $-3 \le y \le \frac{5}{3}$

6. $\frac{5}{x+2} > \frac{5}{x} + \frac{2}{3x}$ $x < -17,$ $-2 < x < 0$

7. $\sqrt{y-2} - 3 = 0$ 11

8. $\sqrt{2x+2} = \sqrt{3x-5}$ 7

9. $\sqrt{11 - 10m} > 9$ $m < -7$

10. Graph $y \le -3x^2 + 11x + 4$. See margin.

Divide using synthetic division.

11. $(2x^3 - 3x^2 + 3x - 4) \div (x - 2)$ $2x^2 + x + 5, R6$

12. $(x^4 - 5x^3 - 13x^2 + 53x + 60) \div (x + 1)$ $x^3 - 6x^2 - 7x + 60$

Use the remainder theorem to find the remainder of each division. State whether the binomial is a factor of the polynomial.

13. $(x^3 + 8x^2 + 2x - 11) \div (x + 2)$ 9; no

14. $(4x^4 - 2x^2 + x - 3) \div (x - 1)$ 0; yes

State the number of complex zeros for each function. Then find the number of possible positive real zeros and the number of possible negative zeros. Determine all of the rational zeros. 15–18. See margin.

15. $f(x) = 6x^3 + 11x^2 - 3x - 2$

16. $p(x) = x^4 + x^3 - 9x^2 - 17x - 8$

17. $h(x) = x^4 - 3x^3 - 53x^2 - 9x$

18. $g(x) = 8x^3 - 36x^2 + 22x + 21$

Decompose each expression into partial fractions.

19. $\frac{5z - 11}{2z^2 + z - 6}$ $\frac{3}{z+2} - \frac{1}{2z-3}$

20. $\frac{7x^2 + 18x - 1}{(x^2 - 1)(x + 2)}$ $\frac{6}{x+1} - \frac{3}{x+2} + \frac{4}{x-1}$

Approximate the real zeros of each function to the nearest tenth.

21. $g(x) = x^2 - 3x - 3$ 3.8, –0.8

22. $f(x) = x^3 - x + 1$ –1.3

23. Find the greatest integral lower bound of the zeros of $f(x) = x^3 + 3x^2 - 5x - 10$. –5

24. **Manufacturing** The volume of a fudge tin must be 120 cubic centimeters. The tin is 7 centimeters longer than it is wide and six times longer than it is tall. Find the dimensions of the tin. 5 cm by 12 cm by 2 cm

25. **Travel** A car travels 300 km in the same time that a freight train travels 200 km. The speed of the car is 20 km/h more than the speed of the train. Find the speed of the freight train. 40 km/h

Bonus
Determine the values of k such that $x^3 - 4x^2 - 2x + k = 0$ has a root between –1 and –2. $3 < k < 20$

This page may be used as a test or as a review. All answers to this test appear in the Selected Answers in the student text.

Standardized Test Practice Questions are also provided in the *Evaluation Masters*.

Evaluation Masters Booklet, pp. 41–42

Test Generator Software is provided in Apple, IBM, and Macintosh versions. You may use this software to create your own tests, based on the needs of your students.

Using the Unit Review

These two pages review the skills and concepts presented in Unit 1. In addition, a four-page unit test, shown below and on the next page, is provided in the *Evaluations Masters Booklet*.

Evaluation Masters Booklet, pp. 49–50

Given that x is an integer, state the relation representing each of the following by listing a set of ordered pairs. Then, state whether the relation is a function. Write *yes* or *no*. **(Lesson 1-1)**

1. $y = 3x + 1$ and $-1 \le x \le 3$ yes
2. $y = |2 - x|$ and $-2 < x \le 2$ yes

1–2. For relations, see Teacher's Answer Key.

Find $[f \circ g](x)$ and $[g \circ f](x)$. **(Lesson 1-2)**

3. $f(x) = 2x - 1$ $2x + 5$,
   $g(x) = x + 3$ $2x + 2$

4. $f(x) = 4x^2$ $16x^6$,
   $g(x) = -2x^3$ $-128x^6$

5. $f(x) = x^2 - 25$ $4x^2 - 16x - 9$,
   $g(x) = 2x - 4$ $2x^2 - 54$

Find the zero of each function. (Lesson 1-3)

6. $f(x) = 4x - 10$ $\dfrac{5}{2}$
7. $f(x) = 15x$ 0
8. $f(x) = 0.75x + 3$ -4

Graph each equation or inequality. (Lesson 1-3) 9–11. See Teacher's Answer Key.

9. $4 - 3x = y$
10. $x + 3y < 12$
11. $y \ge -\dfrac{2}{3}x + 5$

Find the distance between the points with the given coordinates. Then, write the slope-intercept form of the equation of the line through those points. **(Lessons 1-4, 1-5)**

12. $(2, 5), (-1, 3)$ $\sqrt{13}, y = \dfrac{2}{3}x + \dfrac{11}{3}$
13. $(-3, 2), (0, -5)$ $\sqrt{58}, y = -\dfrac{7}{3}x - 5$
14. $(4, -4), (6, -10)$ $2\sqrt{10}, y = -3x + 8$

Write the standard form of the equation of each line described below. **(Lesson 1-6)**

15. parallel to $y = 3x - 1$, passes through $(-1, 4)$ $3x - y + 7 = 0$
16. perpendicular to $2x - 3y = 6$, x-intercept 2 $3x + 2y - 6 = 0$

Solve each system of equations. (Lesson 2-1)

17. $y = -4x$
    $x - y = 5$ $(1, -4)$
18. $x + y = 12$
    $2x - y = -4$ $\left(\dfrac{8}{3}, \dfrac{28}{3}\right)$
19. $3x - 2y = 10$
    $4x + 3y = 2$ $(2, -2)$

Use matrices A, B, C, and D to find each sum, difference, or product. **(Lessons 2-2, 2-3)**

$$A = \begin{bmatrix} 6 & 2 \\ 3 & -3 \end{bmatrix} \quad B = \begin{bmatrix} -4 & 6 \\ 5 & 7 \end{bmatrix} \quad C = \begin{bmatrix} 3 & 2 & -1 \\ -5 & -8 & 1 \end{bmatrix}$$

$$D = \begin{bmatrix} 2 & 0 \\ 6 & -3 \\ -5 & -1 \end{bmatrix} \quad E = \begin{bmatrix} -3 & 1 & 5 \\ -1 & -4 & -2 \\ 3 & 2 & -1 \end{bmatrix}$$

20. $A + B$
21. $2A - B$
22. CD
23. $AB + CD$
24. Evaluate the determinant of matrix A.
25. Evaluate the determinant of matrix E.
26. Find the inverse of matrix B.

20–26. See margin.

Solve each system of equations by using augmented matrices. **(Lesson 2-4)**

27. $x - 3y + z = 0$
    $x + 3y - z = 2$
    $-2x + 6y + 2z = 1$
    $1, \dfrac{5}{12}, \dfrac{1}{4}$

28. $2x + 2y - 2z = 3$
    $3x - y + z = 2$
    $x - 3y - z = 5$
    $\dfrac{7}{8}, -\dfrac{7}{8}, -\dfrac{3}{2}$

Solve each system of inequalities by graphing and name the coordinates of the vertices of each polygonal convex set. Then, find the maximum and minimum values for the function $f(x, y) = 2y - 2x - 3$. **(Lesson 2-5)** 29–30. See margin.

29. $x \ge 0$
    $y \ge 0$
    $2y + x \le 1$

30. $x \ge 2$
    $y \ge -3$
    $y \le 5 - x$
    $y + 2x \le 8$

Additional Answers

1. $\{(-1, -2), (0, 1), (1, 4), (2, 7), (3, 10)\}$
2. $\{(-1, 3), (0, 2), (1, 1), (2, 0)\}$

20. $\begin{bmatrix} 2 & 8 \\ 8 & 4 \end{bmatrix}$

21. $\begin{bmatrix} 16 & -2 \\ 1 & -13 \end{bmatrix}$

22. $\begin{bmatrix} 23 & -5 \\ -63 & 23 \end{bmatrix}$

23. $\begin{bmatrix} 9 & 45 \\ -90 & 20 \end{bmatrix}$

24. -24
25. 19

26. $\begin{bmatrix} -\dfrac{7}{58} & \dfrac{3}{29} \\ \dfrac{5}{58} & \dfrac{2}{29} \end{bmatrix}$

29.

$(0, 0), (1, 0), \left(0, \dfrac{1}{2}\right); -2, -5$

Determine whether each function is an even function, an odd function, or neither. (Lesson 3-1)

31. $y = -3x^3$ odd

32. $y = 2x^4 - 5$ even

33. $y = x^3 + 3x^2 - 6x - 8$ neither

Use the graph of $f(x) = x^3$ to sketch a graph for each function. Then, describe the transformations that have taken place in the related graphs. (Lesson 3-2)

34. $y = -f(x)$ **35.** $y = f(x - 2)$
34–35. See margin.

Find the inverse of each function. Sketch the function and its inverse. Is the inverse a function? Write *yes* or *no*. (Lesson 3-3)

36. $y = \frac{1}{2}x - 5$ $y = 2(x + 5)$; yes

37. $y = (x - 1)^3 + 2$ $y = \sqrt[3]{x - 2} + 1$; yes
36–37. For graphs, see Teacher's Answer Key.

Determine any horizontal, vertical, or slant asymptotes or holes in the graph of each function. Then, graph each function. (Lesson 3-4)

38. $y = \frac{x}{(2x + 1)(x + 2)}$ $x = -\frac{1}{2}, -2$

39. $y = \frac{x^2 - 9}{x + 3}$ hole: $x = -3$
38–39. For graphs, see Teacher's Answer Key.

Graph each inequality. (Lesson 3-5)

40. $y \le |x + 3|$

41. $y > \sqrt[3]{x + 4}$
40–41. See Teacher's Answer Key.

Find the equation of the line tangent to the graph of each function at the given point. Write the equation in slope-intercept form. (Lesson 3-6)

42. $y = x^2 + 3x - 7$, $(1, -3)$ $y = 5x - 8$

43. $y = -2x^2 + 5x + 1$, $(-1, -6)$ $y = 9x + 3$

Find the critical points for each function. Then, determine whether each point is a *maximum*, a *minimum*, or a *point of inflection*. (Lesson 3-7)

44. $f(x) = 2 + x + x^2$ $\left(-\frac{1}{2}, 1\frac{3}{4}\right)$, min

45. $f(x) = x^3 - 3x + 4$
$(1, 2)$, min; $(-1, 6)$, max; $(0, 4)$ inf

Determine whether each graph has *infinite discontinuity, jump discontinuity, point discontinuity*, or is *continuous*. Then, graph each function. (Lesson 3-8)

46. $y = \frac{x^2 - 1}{x + 1}$ point

47. $y = \begin{cases} x - 1, & \text{if } x < 0 \\ x - 3, & \text{if } x \ge 0 \end{cases}$ jump
46–47. For graphs, see Teacher's Answer Key.

Solve each equation or inequality. (Lessons 4-1, 4-2, 4-6, 4-7)

48. $x^2 - 8x + 16 = 0$ 4

49. $4x^2 - 4x - 10 = 0$ $\frac{1 \pm \sqrt{11}}{2}$

50. $\frac{x + 2}{4} + \frac{x - 3}{4} = 6$ $\frac{25}{2}$

51. $2 + \frac{1}{x - 1} > \frac{1}{2}$ $x < \frac{1}{3}, x > 1$

52. $9 + \sqrt{x - 1} = 1$ no real solution

53. $\sqrt{x + 8} - \sqrt{x + 35} \le -3$ $-8 \le x \le 1$

Use the remainder theorem to find the remainder for each division. (Lesson 4-3)

54. $(x^2 - x + 4) \div (x - 6)$ 34

55. $(2x^3 - 3x + 1) \div (x - 2)$ 11

Find the number of possible positive real zeros and the number of possible negative real zeros. Determine all of the rational zeros. (Lesson 4-4)

56. $f(x) = 3x^2 + x - 2$ 1; 1; $-1, \frac{2}{3}$

57. $f(x) = x^4 + x^3 - 2x^2 + 3x - 1$ 3 or 1; 1; none

Approximate the real zeros of each function to the nearest tenth. (Lesson 4-5)

58. $f(x) = x^2 - 2x - 5$ $-1.4, 3.4$

59. $f(x) = x^3 + 4x^2 + x - 2$ $-1, -3.6, 0.6$

30.

$(2, -3)$, $(5.5, -3)$, $(3, 2)$, $(2, 3)$; $-1, -20$

34.

reflected over *x*-axis

35.

moved 2 units right

The key theme of Unit 2 is the relationship among various trigonometric functions and their graphs. Some of the trigonometric concepts may have been introduced in previous courses. Those concepts are reviewed and extended in this unit's exploration of the characteristics of trigonometric functions and graphs.

Connections to Other Units

The concepts developed in this unit are related to concepts in Units 1, 3, and 5. The transformations of graphs presented in Units 1 and 5 are also applied to trigonometric graphs in this unit. The concept of maximum and minimum of a function presented in Unit 1 is also explored in this unit.

Multicultural Notes

Portugal The fifteenth century is often called the Great Age of Discovery. The advent of ships capable of ocean voyages coupled with improved knowledge of currents, wind, and navigational methods made distant journeys feasible. The Portuguese lead the way with expeditions south along the coast of Africa. Portuguese cartographers and navigators were the first to correct the error of plane charts which did not recognize the curvature of Earth. Their ability to map positions with greater precision enabled the Portuguese to determine the latitudes of locations along Africa/s coast. These advances culminated in the discovery of a route around the Cape or Good Hope to India.

Greece A cam is a device for converting rotary motion into linear motion. The idea of the cam goes back to the first century A.D. when it was made popular by Hero of Alexandria. It has been used throughout history in bellows, windmills, and valves. It is used today in internal combustion engines and machinery of all kinds.

Cams may be disk, plate, cylindrical, or drum. The output arm, which is kept in contact with the cam surface, is the follower.

UNIT 2

TRIGONOMETRY

Chapter 5 The Trigonometric Functions
Chapter 6 Graphs and Inverses of the Trigonometric Functions
Chapter 7 Trigonometric Identities and Equations
Chapter 8 Vectors and Parametric Equations

The simplest definition of trigonometry would go something like this: Trigonometry is the study of angles and triangles. The word *trigonometry* literally means "triangle measurement." However, the study of trigonometry is much more complex and comprehensive than that. In this unit alone, you will find trigonometric functions of angles, solve triangles, find the area of triangles, verify trigonometric identities, solve trigonometric equations, graph the trigonometric functions, and use vectors to solve parametric equations and to model motion.

Trigonometry has applications in construction, geography, physics, acoustics, medicine, meteorology, and navigation, among other fields. As a result, you will very likely use trigonometry in your chosen field, no matter what it may be. Such was the case in ancient times. Navigators, surveyors, and astonomers have used triangles to measure distances for thousands of years. Ancient Egyptian papyri and Babylonian clay tablets, dating from around 1600 B.C., also show evidence of practical problem solving by using triangle measurement.

As you can see, trigonometry has many applications to many fields of study. As you study this unit, it is our hope that you will become more familiar with the opportunities that await you when you master this powerful area of mathematics.

236

The motion of the cam follower can be represented by a displacement-time diagram. Depending on the cam contour, possible displacement-time diagrams illustrate simple harmonic motion, cycloidal motion, and catenoidal motion.

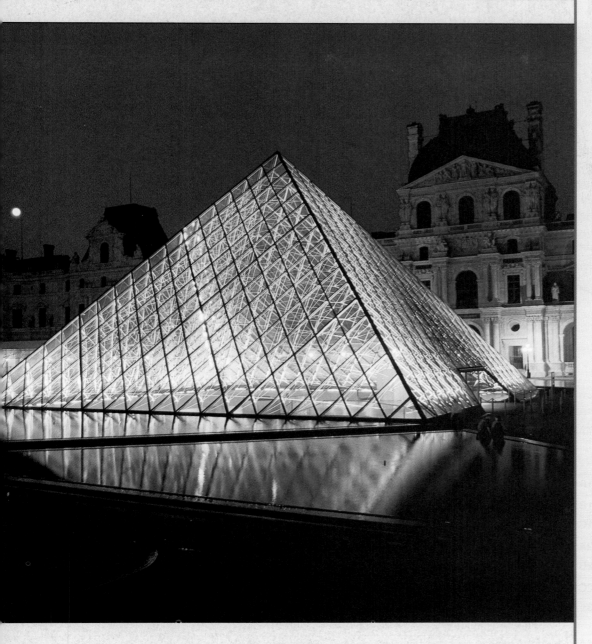

Cooperative Learning

The **Decision Making** activities offer students an opportunity to explore real-world questions while working in cooperative groups. These questions require students to do research and come to a viable conclusion.

Problem Solving

The **Case Study Follow-Ups** provide an arena for problem solving, applying mathematics, and becoming more aware of issues that may face students in their adult lives. These questions require research and applications of the mathematics of the chapter.

Using Technology

Computer and calculator literacy is a growing part of our everyday lives. The features in this unit give students exposure to different technology tools available to facilitate their study of mathematics.

237

5 THE TRIGONOMETRIC FUNCTIONS

PREVIEWING THE CHAPTER

This chapter reviews angles and angle measurement and builds on that knowledge to explore trigonometric functions. After changing degree measure to radians and vice versa, students find coterminal and reference angles and the measures of arcs. Students use these skills to find linear and angular velocities and areas of sectors. Students begin their study of trigonometry by investigating trigonometric functions for an angle in standard position on the unit circle. After studying trigonometric functions of special angles and right triangles, students solve triangles using the law of sines and the law of cosines. These two laws are also used to find the area of a triangle.

Lesson Objective Chart

Lesson (Pages)	Lesson Objectives		State/Local Objectives
5-1 (240-246)	**5-1A:**	Change from radian to degree measure and vice versa.	
	5-1B:	Find angles that are coterminal with a given angle.	
	5-1C:	Find the reference angle for a given angle.	
5-2 (247-254)	**5-2A:**	Find the length of an arc, given the measure of the central angle.	
	5-2B:	Find linear and angular velocities.	
	5-2C:	Find the area of a sector.	
5-3 (255-262)	**5-3:**	Find the values of the six trigonometric functions of an angle in standard position given a point on its terminal side.	
5-4 (263-268)	**5-4A:**	Find the exact values for the six trigonometric functions of special angles.	
	5-4B:	Find decimal approximations for the values of the six trigonometric functions of any angle.	
5-5 (269-275)	**5-5:**	Solve right triangles.	
5-6 (276-281)	**5-6A:**	Determine whether a triangle has zero, one, or two solutions.	
	5-6B:	Solve triangles by using the law of sines.	
5-7 (283-287)	**5-7:**	Solve triangles by using the law of cosines.	
5-8 (288-295)	**5-8:**	Find the area of triangles.	

ORGANIZING THE CHAPTER

You may want to refer to the **Course Planning Guide Calendar** on pages T34-T35 for a complete pacing chart.

Lesson Planning Guide

Lesson	Pages	Practice	Enrichment	Evaluation	Graphing Calculator	Computer	Multicultural Activity	Applications	Problem Solving	Case Study Follow-Up	Decision Making	Transparencies
5-1	240-246	p. 28	p. 28						p. 14			5-1
5-2	247-254	p. 29	p. 29	Quiz A, p. 61						p. 15		5-2
5-3	255-262	p. 30	p. 30									5-3
5-4	263-268	p. 31	p. 31	Quiz B, p. 61 Mid-Chapter Test, p. 63			p. 5					5-4
5-5	269-275	p. 32	p. 32					p. 13				5-5
5-6	276-281	p. 33	p. 33	Quiz C, p. 62		p. 10						5-6
5-7	283-287	p. 34	p. 34		p. 9							5-7
5-8	288-295	p. 35	p. 35	Quiz D, p. 62								5-8
Review	296-298	Multiple Choice Tests, Forms 1A and 1B, pp. 53-56 Free Response Tests, Forms 2A and 2B, pp. 57-60 Standardized Test Questions, p. 64										
Test	299											

Blackline Masters Booklets — Technology — Activity Masters

Other Chapter Resources

Student Edition
Case Study Follow-Up, p. 275
Decision Making, p. 254
Technology, p. 282

Other Supplements
Transparency 5-0 for Chapter Opener
Alternate Assessment in the Mathematics Classroom,
   Glencoe Publishing Co., 1993
Cooperative Learning in the Mathematics Classroom,
   Glencoe Publishing Co., 1993

Software
Test and Review Generator Software
   Available for Apple, IBM, and Macintosh
Teacher's Guide for Software Resources

ENHANCING THE CHAPTER

Cooperative Learning

Assigning Students to Groups

Research indicates that a heterogeneous group will allow for a more effective cooperative-learning situation than will a homogeneous group. Therefore, it is inadvisable to allow students to choose their own groups. A more desirable method would be to randomly assign students by having them count off and placing the 1s in one group, the 2s in another, and so on. A better method is to form groups so that each group has members of varying levels of ability. It is not necessary that students remain members of the same group for the entire year. In fact, it may be desirable if membership is changed periodically, giving students the opportunity and experience of working with most of their classmates during the school year.

For more information on cooperative learning, see pages T20-T21. Additional information on using cooperative groups is available in Glencoe's *Cooperative Learning in the Mathematics Classroom*, ©1993.

Multicultural

Multicultural Activity Masters, p. 5

CHAPTER 5   NAME _____ DATE _____

Multicultural Activity (Use after Lesson 5-4)

Hugh Nathaniel Mulzac

Born on Union Island in the Caribbean, Hugh Mulzac (1886 – 1971) was the first African-American to become commander of an United States Merchant Marine ship. During World War I, Mulzac served as a deck officer on four different vessels that carried supplies to Allied troops in Europe. He passed his examination for a master's license in 1918, astounding his examiners with his extensive knowledge of navigation, meteorology, ship construction, nautical astronomy, and general seamanship. However, it was not until the United States became involved in World War II that he was given command of his own ship. From 1942 to 1945, as captain of the *Libertyship Booker T. Washington*, Mulzac transported more than 18,000 Allied troops to the Mediterranean, France, England, and the Pacific.

The captain of a ship needs to have considerable knowledge of mathematics in order to keep a ship safely afloat. For example, the diagram at the right shows how a ship can list to one side due to waves traveling perpendicular to the course of the ship. The angle, θ, of the list of the ship is called the **heel** of the ship.

1. A ship 54-feet wide sits 18 feet deep in still water. (In the diagram, this is indicated by line segment RS.) Waves produce a heel of 6°. Find AE to the nearest tenth of a foot.
   20.8 feet
2. A ship 54 feet wide sits 20 feet deep in still water. Waves produce a new depth, AE, of 24 feet. What heel, θ, to the nearest tenth of a degree, did the waves produce?
   8.4°
3. A ship 54-feet wide sits 22 feet deep in still water. Waves produce a heel of 7.2°. If the distance from sea level to the sea bed is 28 feet, will the bottom of the ship clear the sea bed?
   yes
4. In the diagram at the right, ships A and B are 100 miles apart. Their captains wish to rendezvous at point C. If ship A is sailing at 18 miles per hour, at what speed, to the nearest tenth of a mile per hour, would the captain of ship B have to sail in order to make the rendezvous?
   22.2 miles per hour

T5
Glencoe Division, Macmillan/McGraw-Hill

Activity Masters

Applications, p. 13

CHAPTER 5   NAME _____ DATE _____

Applications (Use after Lesson 5-5)

Navigation

For short distances in navigation, the curvature of the earth may be disregarded and the ideas of plane trigonometry may be used.

The bearing or course of a watercraft is given simply as the number of degrees clockwise from north that it is heading. Or, the bearing may be given as an acute angle, mentioning the compass directions. At the right, the bearing of the craft is 155°, or the bearing is S25°E, or 25° east of south.

Example   A boat A sights the lighthouse B in the direction N65°E and the spire of a church C in the direction S75°E. According to the map, B is 7 miles from C in the direction N30°W. In order for A to avoid running aground, find the bearing it should keep to pass B at 4 miles distance.

In $\triangle ABC$, $m\angle \alpha = 180° - 65° - 75°$ or 40°
$m\angle C = 180° - 30° - (180° - 75°)$ or 45°
$a = 7$ miles
With the law of sines, $AB = \frac{a\sin C}{\sin \alpha} = \frac{7(\sin 45°)}{\sin 40°} = 7.7$ mi.

The bearing of A must be tangent at X to circle B with radius $BX = 4$. Thus, $\triangle ABX$ is a right triangle.
Then $\sin \theta = \frac{BX}{AB} = \frac{4}{7.7} \approx 0.519$. Therefore,

$m\angle \theta = 31°18'$. The bearing of A should be $65° - 31°18' = 33°42'$.

Solve.

1. Suppose the lighthouse B in the example is sighted at S30°W by a ship P due north of the church C. Find the bearing P should keep to pass B at 4 miles distance. **S64°51'W**

2. In the fog, the lighthouse keeper determines by radar that a boat 18 miles away is heading to the shore. The direction of the boat from the lighthouse is S80°W. What bearing should the lighthouse keeper radio the boat to take to come ashore 4 miles south of the lighthouse? **S87°10'E or N92°50'E**

3. To avoid a rocky area along a shoreline, a ship at A travels 7 km to B, bearing 22°15', then 8 km to C, bearing 60°30', then 6 km to D, bearing 109°15'. Find the distance from A to D. **1742km**

T13
Glencoe Division, Macmillan/McGraw-Hill

Problem Solving, p. 14

CHAPTER 5   NAME _____ DATE _____

Problem Solving (Use after Lesson 5-1)

Write a Formula

Some processes in mathematics that are used repeatedly can often be represented by a formula. The process of converting feet, f, to inches, i, can be represented by the formula $i = 12f$. The formula becomes a model of the process that can be used as an evaluation tool. How many inches are there in 4 feet?

$i = 12(4)$
$i = 48$ inches

Lesson 5-1 introduced several types of conversions. You can model each using a formula.

Example   Write a formula for converting degrees, minutes, and seconds to a decimal number of degrees.

First, choose variables to represent quantities that will be involved in conversions.
Let D = decimal number of degrees,
   d = whole number of degrees,
   m = whole number of minutes, and
   s = whole number of seconds.

Next, carry out examples of the conversion to determine the process. In Lesson 5-1, Example 1 showed that the following process is used to change 29° 45' 26" to a decimal number of degrees.

$29° 45' 26" = 29 + 45\left(\frac{1°}{60}\right) + 26\left(\frac{1°}{3600}\right)$

$= 29.757°$

Finally, model the process with a formula.

$D = d + \frac{1}{60}m + \frac{1}{3600}s$

Write a formula to model each process.

1. converting degrees (d) to radians (r) $r = d\left(\frac{\pi}{180}\right)$

2. converting radians (r) to degrees (d) $d = r\left(\frac{180}{\pi}\right)$

3. finding measures of angles, α, coterminal with an angle with degree measure d
   $a = d + 360k°$ **where k is an integer**

4. finding the slope, m, of a line perpendicular to the line $Ax + By + C = 0$ $m =$

5. finding the solution (x, y) of this system: $\begin{aligned} a_1x + b_1y &= c_1 \\ a_2x + b_2y &= c_2 \end{aligned}$ $\left(\frac{b_2c_1 - b_1c_2}{a_1b_2 - a_2b_1}, \frac{a_1c_2 - \cdots}{a_1b_2 - \cdots}\right)$

T14
Glencoe Division, Macmillan/McGraw-Hill

Case Study Follow-Up, p. 15

CHAPTER 5   NAME _____ DATE _____

Case Study Follow-Up (Use after Lesson 5-2)

Constructing a Circle Graph

Refer to Case Study 3: The Legal System, on pages 962-965 in your textbook.

A crime watch citizens group produced a billboard detailing crime statistics for the United States in 1990. One section of the billboard consisted of a circle graph with a radius of 2 meters that showed the major categories of larceny and the percent of all larcenies represented by each category.

1. Complete the chart. Round your answers to the nearest hundredth.

1990 U.S. larcenies

Type	Percent of total	Measure of central angle(°)	Length of arc (m)	Area of sector (m²)
Purse snatching	1	3.60	0.13	0.13
Pocket picking	1	3.60	0.13	0.13
Coin machines	1	3.60	0.13	0.13
Shoplifting	16	57.60	2.01	2.01
Bicycles	6	21.60	0.75	0.75
From motor vehicles	22	79.20	2.76	2.76
From buildings	14	50.40	1.76	1.76
Motor vehicle accessories	15	54.00	1.88	1.88
All others	24	86.40	3.01	3.01

2. Draw a circle graph displaying the larceny data.

1990 U.S. Larcenies

T15
Glencoe Division, Macmillan/McGraw-Hill

Technology

The Technology feature preceding Lesson 5-7 presents a program in BASIC computer language that solves triangles using the law of sines.

In the Exploration in Lesson 5-3, students investigate trigonometric functions by using a graphing calculator. The graphing calculator program in Lesson 5-8 will find the area of any triangle, given the lengths of its sides. Any scientific calculator that has trigonometric function keys is recommended as a tool in problem solving in this chapter.

Graphing Calculator Exercises, p. 261
Graphing Calculator Program, p. 294

Outside Resources

Books/Periodicals

Girard, Joan E. *A Guide to Using Texas Instrument Calculators with Precalculus Series,* Dellen Publishers, 1990.

Research and Education Association Staff. *Essentials of Algebra and Trigonometry,* Research and Education Association, Piscataway City, NJ, 1992.

Films/Videotapes/Videodiscs

Concepts in Mathematics, Trigonometric Functions: Solving Triangles, TV Ontario, The Ontario Educational Communications Authority

Mathematics, Trigonometry, Great Plains National, University of Nebraska-Lincoln.

Trigonometry, Educational Solutions, Inc.

Software

The Geometer's Sketchpad. Key Curriculum Press (Macintosh)

The Geometric Supposer: Triangles. Sunburst (Apple II, IBM, Macintosh)

GeoExplorer. Scott Foresman (IBM, Macintosh)

Technology Masters

Graphing Calculator, p. 9

Computer, p. 10

This two-page introduction to the chapter provides students with an opportunity to see how college students use the mathematics presented in this chapter in their chosen majors. It also gives students a glimpse of the college majors that are available to them.

Transparency 5–0, available in the *Advanced Mathematical Concepts* Teaching Transparency Package, provides another full-color visual and motivational activity that you can use to engage your students in the mathematical content of the chapter.

More About Marlene Watson

Marlene Watson's interest in all phases of building construction was inspired by an interest in Native American architecture. She has used her courses in mathematics to help design buildings. She is studying construction engineering and management at the University of California at Berkeley and is interested in becoming an architect and a civil engineer.

Chapter Project

Materials paper, pencil, and posterboard

Procedure Organize students into cooperative groups. Assign each group one or more buildings or land areas of a small town such as a grocery store, an elementary school, a high school, residential houses, parks, and so on to design. Have students draw the shapes of their components using the same scale and then find the areas. Point out that most of the shapes can be estimated by using triangles. Put all the components together on poster board to form a town plan. Find the total area of all the components in the town.

CHAPTER 5

THE TRIGONOMETRIC FUNCTIONS

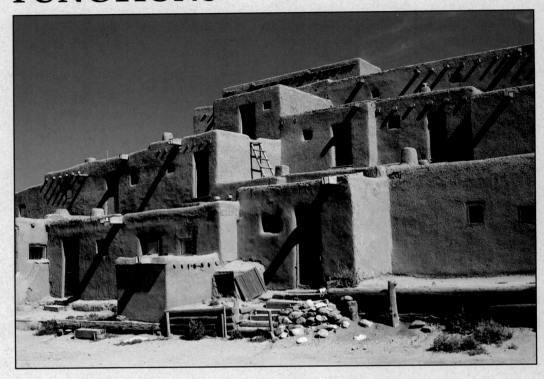

HISTORICAL SNAPSHOT

| Hipparchus, founder of trigonometry Alexandria | Pueblo Bonito, multi-storied Anasazi settlement Chaco Canyon, New Mexico | California Gold Rush ("Forty-Niners") Begun July 28, 1848 | First skyscraper, 10-story Home Insurance Company building, Chicago | School of Architecture established at University of California, Berkeley | Geodesic Dome, by Richard Buckminster Fuller Baton Rouge, Louisiana | Computer-aided architectural design, Cornell University, New York |

| 161–125 BC | AD 1050–1250 | 1848 | 1882 | 1894 | 1958 | 1984 |

238

CHAPTER OBJECTIVES

In this chapter, you will:
- Measure angles in radians and degrees.
- Evaluate the trigonometric functions.
- Solve triangles and find the area of triangles.

CAREER GOAL: Construction Engineering Management

Marlene Watson is pursuing a master's degree in construction engineering and management. She would like to become registered as both an architect and a civil engineer. "I eventually intend to become a construction engineering manager for an architectural/engineering firm. This will allow me to be involved in all phases of building construction, including the initial design phase, the final design, budgeting, scheduling, and final construction.

Marlene was inspired to choose this area of study because she has always been interested in traditional Native American architecture. "Most people think Indians only lived in teepees and huts. But Native American architecture was structurally designed for adaption to each group's respective environment. For example, the Miwok Indians of California designed their pithouse to provide protection during earthquakes. The beams rested in Y-shaped supports with enough overlap to allow the roof to move back and forth during an earthquake."

Marlene took courses in algebra, geometry, and trigonometry in high school. She says that "architects use trigonometry a great deal in building design. For example, it is used to measure sunlight and shade at different times of each day of the year in a given geographical location. We use a sun-angle calculator to measure the azimuth angle and bearing angle for a building. Bearing angles indicate where a building will cast a shadow at a given time of the day. Applying trigonometric functions to the bearing angle determines the length of the building's shadow."

Marlene is the only American Indian to have graduated from her high school and gone on to Berkeley. She says, "I want to help change that by serving as a role model for American Indian students. I want them to know that mathematics and science have always been a significant part of Native American cultures."

READ MORE ABOUT IT

Deep Foundations. New York: American Society of Civil Engineers, 1980.
Lorenz, Clare. *Women in Architecture.* New York: Rizzoli International Publications, Inc., 1990.
Piper, Robert J. *Opportunities in Architecture.* Lincolnwood, Illinois: VGM Career Horizons, 1985.

SPOTLIGHT ON...

Marlene Watson
Age: 30
Class: Graduate
School: University of California
 Berkeley, California
Majors: Architecture and Civil
 Engineering

"Mathematics and science have always been a significant part of Native American cultures."

FOR MORE INFORMATION

If you would like more information about architecture or civil engineering, contact:

American Institute of
 Architects
1735 New York Avenue NW
Washington, DC 20006

American Society of Civil
 Engineers (ASCE)
345 E. 47th Street
New York, NY 10017

Applications

Lesson	Application	Examples	Exercises
5–1	Geography		63
	Navigation		64
	Mechanics		65
	Manufacturing		71
5–2	Civil Engineering	2	45
	Astronomy		40
	Mechanics		41
	Geography		42
	Interior Design		43
	Sports		44
	Physics		46
	Manufacturing		47
	Landscaping		52
5–3	Surveying		49
	Construction		50
	Mechanics		57
5–4	Optics	4	38
	Physics		37
5–5	Fire Fighting	4	
	Engineering	6	
	Geometry		13, 25, 26, 27
	Home Maintenance		29
	Aeronautics		30, 34
	National Landmarks		31
	Geography		32
	Cartography		33
5–6	Mechanics	2	
	Navigation		30
	Landscaping		31
5–7	Landscaping	1	
	Aviation		13
	Carpentry		26
	Navigation		27
	Surveying		28, 33
5–8	Land Measure	5	
	Exterior Design		33
	Model Building		34
	Manufacturing		35
	Mechanics		39

NCTM Standards: 1–4

Lesson Resources

- Practice Master 5–1
- Enrichment Master 5–1
- Activity Master, p. 14

 Transparency 5–1 contains the 5-Minute Check and a teaching aid for this lesson.

INTRODUCING THE LESSON

 5–Minute Check

(over Chapter 4)

1. Solve $t^2 + 8t + 16 = 0$ and sketch a graph of the related function.   −4

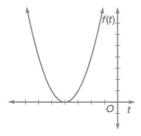

2. Solve $x^2 + 9x - 28 = 0$ by using the quadratic formula.
   $$\frac{-9 \pm \sqrt{193}}{2}$$

3. Find the remainder of $(x^3 - x^2 + 4x - 2) \div (x - 1)$ and tell whether the divisor is a factor of the polynomial. **2, no**

4. State the number of complex zeros for $f(x) = x^3 - 2x^2 - 4x + 8$. State the real zeros. **3; 2, −2**

5. Determine between which successive integers the real zeros of $f(x) = 2x^3 - 4x^2 + x + 2$ are located. **−1 and 0**

5-1   Angles and Their Measure

Objectives	After studying this lesson, you should be able to:
5–1A	■ change from radian to degree measure, and vice versa,
5–1B	■ find angles that are coterminal with a given angle, and
5–1C	■ find the reference angle for a given angle.

Application

 FYI...

The oldest map ever found was drawn on a clay tablet. It was found in northern Mesopotamia, now Iraq, in 2250 B.C. The earliest printed map is one of western China, dated A.D. 1115.

In order to locate every point on Earth, cartographers use a grid that contains circles through the poles, called longitude lines, and circles parallel to the equator, called latitude lines. Point *P* is located by traveling north from the equator through a central angle of $a°$ to a circle of latitude and then west along that circle through an angle of $b°$. If you consult an atlas, you will see, for example, that Houston, Texas, is located at north latitude 29°45′26″ and west longitude 95°21′37″.

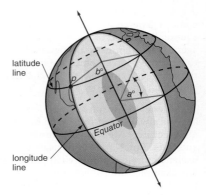

An angle may be generated by the rotation of two rays that share a fixed endpoint. Let one ray remain fixed to form the *initial side* of the angle, and let the second ray rotate to form the *terminal side*. If the rotation is in a counterclockwise direction, the angle formed is a *positive angle*. If the rotation is clockwise, it is a *negative angle*. An angle with its vertex at the origin and its initial side along the positive *x*-axis is said to be in **standard position**. If the terminal side of an angle in standard position coincides with one of the axes, the angle is called a **quadrantal angle**.

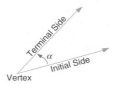

In the figures below, all of the angles are in standard position. The measure of angle *A* is positive, angle *B* has a negative measure, and angle *C* is a quadrantal angle with a positive measure.

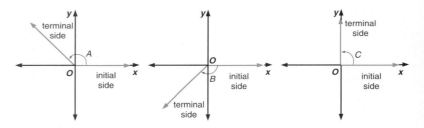

240   CHAPTER 5   THE TRIGONOMETRIC FUNCTIONS

ALTERNATE TEACHING STRATEGIES

Using Cooperative Groups

Have pairs of students play "Battleship" by having them draw *x*- and *y*-axes on a piece of paper. Then have them draw a large circle on the paper using the origin as its center. Ask students to divide the circle into 36 equal parts (every 10°). Each student should place each of three ships on the circle. The other student then has to guess the location of each ship by giving its coordinates in degrees.

Using Manipulatives

Make a Cartesian plane of heavy black poster board and a brightly colored terminal ray that swings freely around the quadrants. Give an angle of rotation and have a student rotate the ray about the plane. Ask another student for the reference angle for this angle. Experiment with various angles. Encourage students to construct their own smaller versions of this manipulative.

The two most common units used to measure angles are **degrees** and **radians**. You may be more familiar with degree measure. An angle has a measure of one degree (written 1°) if it results from $\frac{1}{360}$ of a complete revolution in the positive direction. Each degree is comprised of 60 **minutes** (written 60') and each minute is comprised of 60 **seconds** (written 60"). The latitude of Houston, Texas, shown in the application at the beginning of the lesson, would be read "29 degrees, 45 minutes, 26 seconds."

Example 1

> **Change 29°45'26" to a decimal number of degrees to the nearest thousandth.**
>
> $29°45'26" = 29° + 45'\left(\frac{1°}{60'}\right) + 26"\left(\frac{1°}{3600"}\right)$
>
> $= 29.757°$

Some scientific calculators have keys that allow you to change automatically from degrees, minutes, and seconds to decimal values of degrees, and vice versa. Check your calculator's instruction booklet to see if your calculator does this.

Another unit of angle measure is the radian. The definition of a radian is based on the concept of a **unit circle**. A unit circle is a circle of radius 1 whose center is at the origin of a rectangular coordinate system. The unit circle is symmetric with respect to the x-axis, the y-axis, and the origin. A point $P(x, y)$ is on the unit circle if and only if its distance from the origin is 1. Thus, for each point $P(x, y)$ on the unit circle, the distance from the origin is represented by the following equation.

$$\sqrt{(x - 0)^2 + (y - 0)^2} = 1$$

If each side of this equation is squared, the result is an equation of the unit circle.

$$x^2 + y^2 = 1$$

Consider an angle α in standard position, shown at the right. Let $P(x, y)$ be the point of intersection of its terminal side with the unit circle. The radian measure of an angle in standard position is defined as the length of the corresponding arc on the unit circle. Thus, the measure of angle α is s radians.

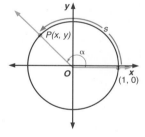

Prerequisite Skills

Students should be familiar with terminology related to the coordinate plane.
1. Name the quadrant for each point below.

A: III, B: I, C: IV
2. Describe the signs of the coordinates of a point located in each of the four quadrants.
I: (+, +), II: (−, +), III: (−, −), IV: (+, −)

Motivating the Lesson

An air traffic controller tells the pilot of an airplane flying east to turn the plane so that it has a heading of 120° east of north. What angle does the airplane turn?
30°

TEACHING THE LESSON

Teaching Tip After discussing latitude and longitude, ask students to determine the latitude and longitude of their hometown.

Teaching Tip Before defining radian as the measure of an angle in standard position, remind students that the circumference of a circle is $2\pi r$, where r is the radius of the circle. The length s of an arc is a fraction of the circumference.

> **Chalkboard Example**
>
> *For Example 1*
>
> Change 34°29'19" to a decimal number of degrees to the nearest thousandth. **34.489°**

There is an important relationship between radian and degree measure. Since an angle of one complete revolution can be represented either by 360° or by 2π radians, $360° = 2\pi$ radians. Thus, $180° = \pi$ radians, and $90° = \dfrac{\pi}{2}$ radians. The following formulas relate degree and radian measures.

Degree/Radian Conversion Formulas	1 radian $= \dfrac{180}{\pi}$ degrees or about 57.3°
	1 degree $= \dfrac{\pi}{180}$ radians or about 0.017 radians

Angles expressed in radians are often written in terms of π. The term *radians* is also usually omitted when writing angle measures. However, the degree symbol is always used in this book to express the measure of angles in degrees.

Examples

2 **Change 30° to radian measure in terms of π.**

$$30° = 30° \times \dfrac{\pi}{180°}$$

$$= \dfrac{\pi}{6}$$

3 **Change $\dfrac{3\pi}{4}$ radians to degree measure.**

$$\dfrac{3\pi}{4} = \dfrac{3\pi}{4} \times \dfrac{180°}{\pi}$$

$$= 135°$$

Angles whose measures are multiples of 30° and 45° are commonly used in trigonometry. These angle measures correspond to radian measures of $\dfrac{\pi}{6}$ and $\dfrac{\pi}{4}$, respectively. The diagrams below can help you to make these conversions mentally.

Multiples of 30° and $\dfrac{\pi}{6}$

Multiples of 45° and $\dfrac{\pi}{4}$

Two angles in standard position are called **coterminal angles** if they have the same terminal side. Since angles differing in radian measure by multiples of 2π are equivalent, and angles differing in degree measure by multiples of 360° are equivalent, every angle has infinitely many coterminal angles.

Coterminal Angles

If α is the degree measure of an angle, then all angles of the form $\alpha + 360k°$, where k is an integer, are coterminal with α. If β is the radian measure of an angle, then all angles of the form $\beta + 2k\pi$, where k is an integer, are coterminal with β.

k is generally assumed to be nonzero.

Example 4

Find one positive angle and one negative angle that are coterminal with an angle having measure $\frac{11\pi}{4}$.

A positive angle is $\frac{11\pi}{4} - 2\pi$ or $\frac{3\pi}{4}$.

A negative angle is $\frac{11\pi}{4} - 4\pi$ or $-\frac{5\pi}{4}$.

Example 5

Identify all angles that are coterminal with a 60° angle.

All angles having a measure $60 + 360k°$, where k is an integer, are coterminal with a 60° angle.

If α is a nonquadrantal angle in standard position, its **reference angle** is defined as the acute angle formed by the terminal side of the given angle and the x-axis. You can use the figures and the rule below to find the reference angle for any angle α that $0 < \alpha < 2\pi$. If the measure of α is greater than 2π or less than 0, it can be associated with a coterminal angle of positive measure between 0 and 2π.

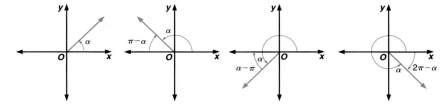

Reference Angle Rule

For any angle α, $0 < \alpha < 2\pi$, its reference angle α' is defined by
a. α, when the terminal side is in Quadrant I,
b. $\pi - \alpha$, when the terminal side is in Quadrant II,
c. $\alpha - \pi$, when the terminal side is in Quadrant III, and
d. $2\pi - \alpha$, when the terminal side is in Quadrant IV.

LESSON 5-1   ANGLES AND THEIR MEASURE   243

Chalkboard Example

For Example 6

Find the measure of the reference angle for each angle.

a. $\frac{7\pi}{8}$ $\frac{\pi}{8}$

b. 425°   65°

c. $-\frac{17\pi}{6}$ $\frac{\pi}{6}$

EVALUATING THE LESSON

Checking for Understanding

Exercises 1–23 are designed to help you assess students' understanding through reading, writing, speaking, and modeling. You should work through Exercises 1–4 with your students and then monitor their work on Exercises 5–23.

Closing the Lesson

Writing Activity   Have students write a paragraph discussing how to find the reference angle of any angle.

Practice Masters Booklet, p. 28

NAME _____ DATE _____

5-1 Practice Worksheet

Angles and Their Measure

If each angle has the given measure and is in standard position, determine the quadrant in which its terminal side lies.

1. $\frac{7\pi}{12}$ II
2. $-\frac{2\pi}{3}$ III
3. 371°   I
4. $\frac{14\pi}{5}$ II
5. $-156°$ III
6. 1000°   IV
7. 332°   IV
8. $-240°$ II

Change each degree measure to radian measure in terms of π.

9. 36° $\frac{\pi}{5}$
10. $-250°$ $-\frac{25\pi}{18}$
11. $-145°$ $-\frac{29\pi}{36}$
12. 6° $\frac{\pi}{30}$
13. 870° $\frac{87\pi}{18}$
14. 18° $\frac{\pi}{10}$
15. $-820°$ $-\frac{41\pi}{9}$
16. 345° $\frac{23\pi}{12}$

Change each radian measure to degree measure.

17. -1 $-57°$
18. 4π $720°$
19. -2.56 $-147°$
20. 12.85 $736°$
21. $\frac{3\pi}{16}$ $33.75°$
22. $-\frac{7\pi}{9}$ $-140°$
23. $\frac{13\pi}{30}$ $78°$
24. $-\frac{17\pi}{3}$ $-1020°$

25–28 Answers may vary. Sample answers are given.
Find one positive angle and one negative angle that are coterminal with each angle.

25. 70°   430°, $-290°$
26. $-\frac{2\pi}{5}$ $\frac{8\pi}{5}, -\frac{12\pi}{5}$
27. $-300°$ 60°, $-660°$
28. $\frac{3\pi}{4}$ $\frac{11\pi}{4}, -\frac{5\pi}{4}$

Find the reference angle for each angle with the given measure.

29. $-20°$ 20°
30. 160°   20°
31. $-545°$ 5°
32. 300°   60°
33. $\frac{10\pi}{3}$ $\frac{\pi}{3}$
34. $-\frac{5\pi}{8}$ $\frac{3\pi}{8}$
35. $-\frac{\pi}{4}$ $\frac{\pi}{4}$
36. $-\frac{7\pi}{3}$ $\frac{\pi}{3}$

T28
Glencoe Division, Macmillan/McGraw-Hill

Example 6

Find the measure of the reference angle for each angle.

a. $\frac{5\pi}{4}$

b. $-\frac{13\pi}{3}$

a. $\alpha = \frac{5\pi}{4}$, so its terminal side is in Quadrant III.

$\alpha' = \alpha - \pi$ *Reference Rule c*

$= \frac{5\pi}{4} - \pi$

$= \frac{\pi}{4}$

b. $-\frac{13\pi}{3}$ is coterminal with $\frac{5\pi}{3}$ in Quadrant IV.

$\alpha' = 2\pi - \alpha$ *Reference Rule d*

$= 2\pi - \frac{5\pi}{3}$

$= \frac{\pi}{3}$

c. **510°**

c. 510° is coterminal with 150° in Quadrant II.

$\alpha' = \pi - \alpha$ *Reference Rule b*

$= 180° - 150$ *$\pi = 180°$*

$= 30°$

CHECKING FOR UNDERSTANDING

Communicating Mathematics

Read and study the lesson to answer each question. 1–4. See margin.

1. **Define** the terms *positive angle* and *negative angle* in your own words.

2. **Explain** how to change the measure of an angle from degrees to radians and from radians to degrees.

3. **Sketch** a 30° angle in standard position and a positive angle greater than 360° that is coterminal with it.

4. **Write** an expression for the measures of all angles that are coterminal with an angle whose measure is θ.

Guided Practice

If each angle has the given measure and is in standard position, determine the quadrant in which its terminal side lies.

5. $\frac{15\pi}{4}$ IV
6. 210° III
7. –220° II
8. $\frac{11\pi}{6}$ IV

9. $-\frac{4\pi}{3}$ II
10. 750° I
11. $\frac{14\pi}{3}$ II
12. –475° III

Change each degree measure to radian measure in terms of π.

13. 18° $\frac{\pi}{10}$
14. 240° $\frac{4\pi}{3}$
15. 1° $\frac{\pi}{180}$
16. –45° $-\frac{\pi}{4}$

244   CHAPTER 5   THE TRIGONOMETRIC FUNCTIONS

RETEACHING THE LESSON

Have students cut quartered circles to model a given angle. Use semicircles of a different color to help students relate to angles.

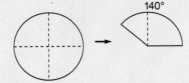

Place angle on top of semicircle.

Change each radian measure to degree measure.

17. π 180°   **18.** $\frac{3\pi}{2}$ 270°   **19.** $-\frac{7\pi}{6}$ −210°   **20.** $\frac{5\pi}{4}$ 225°

State whether each pair of angles is coterminal. Write *yes* or *no*.

21. $\frac{\pi}{4}, \frac{9\pi}{4}$ yes   **22.** −30°, 390° no   **23.** 120°, $\frac{14\pi}{3}$ yes

EXERCISES

Practice

If each angle has the given measure and is in standard position, determine the quadrant in which its terminal side lies.

24. $-\frac{8\pi}{3}$ III   **25.** −167° III   **26.** $\frac{7\pi}{8}$ II   **27.** 227° III

28. $\frac{13\pi}{3}$ I   **29.** −730° IV   **30.** $-\frac{3\pi}{5}$ III   **31.** $-\frac{11\pi}{5}$ IV

Change each degree measure to radian measure in terms of π. **39.** $-\frac{125\pi}{18}$

32. 200° $\frac{10\pi}{9}$ **33.** −150° $-\frac{5\pi}{6}$ **34.** 75° $\frac{5\pi}{12}$ **35.** 105° $\frac{7\pi}{12}$

36. 570° $\frac{19\pi}{6}$ **37.** −450° $-\frac{5\pi}{2}$ **38.** 405° $\frac{9\pi}{4}$ **39.** −1250°

Change each radian measure to degree measure.

40. $\frac{\pi}{3}$ 60°   **41.** −3.5 −200°32′   **42.** $\frac{4\pi}{3}$ 240°   **43.** $-\frac{\pi}{2}$ −90°

44. 1.75 100°16′   **45.** $-\frac{7\pi}{12}$ −105°   **46.** 17.46 1000°23′   **47.** $\frac{17\pi}{6}$ 510°

48–51. Answers may vary; sample answers are given.
Find one positive angle and one negative angle that are coterminal with each angle.

48. −60° 300°, −420°   **49.** $\frac{5\pi}{12}$ $\frac{29\pi}{12}, -\frac{19\pi}{12}$ **50.** $\frac{11\pi}{6}$ $\frac{23\pi}{6}, -\frac{\pi}{6}$ **51.** −310° 50°, −670°

Find the reference angle for each angle with the given measure.

52. −30° 30°   **53.** $\frac{12\pi}{5}$ $\frac{2\pi}{5}$ **54.** 130° 50°   **55.** −210° 30°

56. $\frac{9\pi}{4}$ $\frac{\pi}{4}$ **57.** −420° 60°   **58.** $\frac{23\pi}{6}$ $\frac{\pi}{6}$ **59.** $-\frac{5\pi}{3}$ $\frac{\pi}{3}$

Change each degree measure to radian measure to the nearest thousandth.

60. 55°22′ 0.966   **61.** −110°50′28″ −1.935   **62.** 250°49′15″ 4.378

Homework Exercises

Assignment Guides

Average: 25–47 odd, 48–51,
          53–59 odd, 60–64, 66–76
Enriched: 24–58 even, 60–76

The red A, B, and C flags, printed only in the Teacher's Wraparound Edition, indicate the level of difficulty of the exercises.

Additional Answers

1. **Sample answer: A positive angle is formed when the terminal side of an angle is rotated in a counterclockwise direction. A negative angle is formed when the terminal side of an angle is rotated in a clockwise direction.**

2. **If you know the degree measure of an angle and you need to find the radian measure, multiply the number of degrees by $\frac{\pi}{180}$. If you know the radian measure of an angle and you need to find the degree measure, multiply the number of radians by $\frac{180}{\pi}$.**

3.

4. **If θ is the degree measure of an angle, then $\theta + 360k°$, where k is an integer, is the measure of all angles that are coterminal with the angle. If θ is the radian measure of an angle, then $\theta + 2k\pi$, where k is an integer, is the measure of all angles that are coterminal to the angle.**

63. Geography Earth rotates on its axis every 24 hours. Through how many degrees does a point on the equator travel in one hour? in one week? 15°, 2520°

Applications
and Problem
Solving

64. Navigation Navigators often use angles measured clockwise from due north. A ship sets sail from port with a heading of 35° east of north. After sailing for many hours, the ship's captain changes the heading to 154°15′ east of north. At what angle did the ship turn? 60°45′

154°15′
turn angle
35°

65. Mechanics A lathe is a machine in which wood or metal is rotated about a horizontal axis and shaped by a tool that is fixed. A point on the rim of a lathe pulley turns at the rate of 2.22×10^4 degrees per second. 65a. 3700 revolutions per minute

a. How many revolutions per minute is this?

b. How many radians per minute is this? Express your answer in terms of π. 7400π radians per minute

Mixed
Review

66. Find $f(3)$ if $f(x) = 4 + 6x - x^3$. **(Lesson 1-1)** –5

67. Find the slope of the line through $(-3, 2)$ and $(5, 7)$. **(Lesson 1-4)** $\frac{5}{8}$

68. Write the standard form of the equation of the line through $(3, -2)$ that is parallel to the line $3x - y + 7 = 0$. **(Lesson 1-6)** $3x - y - 11 = 0$

69. Solve the system of equations $3x + y = 6$ and $4x + y = 7$. **(Lesson 2-1)** $(1, 3)$

70. Find matrix X in the equation $\begin{bmatrix} 1 & 1 \\ 1 & 1 \end{bmatrix} \begin{bmatrix} 3 & 5 \\ -3 & -5 \end{bmatrix} = X$. **(Lesson 2-3)** $\begin{bmatrix} 0 & 0 \\ 0 & 0 \end{bmatrix}$

71. Manufacturing A manufacturer can show a profit of $6 on a bicycle and a profit of $4 on a tricycle. Department A requires 3 hours to manufacture the parts for a bicycle and 4 hours to manufacture parts for a tricycle. Department B takes 5 hours to assemble a bicycle and 2 hours to assemble a tricycle. How many bicycles and tricycles should be produced to maximize the profit if the total time available in department A is 450 hours and in department B is 400 hours? **(Lesson 2-6)** 50 bicycles, 75 tricycles

72. Create a function of the form $y = f(x)$ that has a vertical asymptote at $x = 5$ and a hole at $x = 0$. **(Lesson 3-4)** Sample answer: $y = \dfrac{x}{x(x - 5)}$

73. Is 6 a root of $x^3 - 5x^2 - 3x - 18 = 0$? Write *yes* or *no*. **(Lesson 4-1)** yes

74. Solve $\dfrac{3}{x} + \dfrac{5}{x} = 10$. **(Lesson 4-6)** $\frac{4}{5}$

75. Solve $5 - \sqrt{b + 2} = 0$. **(Lesson 4-7)** 23

76. College Entrance Exam If a walker can cover 2 miles in 25 minutes, what is the rate in miles per hour? 4.8

RETEACHING THE LESSON

Math Power: Problem Solving

The radius of Earth is about 4000 miles. Suppose you ride directly north from your town to another town. How many miles away is the other town if you traveled along an arc of 1°?

about 69.8 miles

Enrichment Masters Booklet, p. 28

5-2 Central Angles and Arcs

Objectives
5–2A
5–2B
5–2C

After studying this lesson, you should be able to:
- find the length of an arc, given the measure of the central angle,
- find linear and angular velocities, and
- find the area of a sector.

Application

Civil engineers must deal with angle measures and distances frequently when they design roadways. The map below shows a stretch of Route 3 outside of Boston, Massachusetts. Two portions of the roadway are arcs of circles.

FYI...

The longest driveable road is the Pan American Highway, extending from northwest Alaska to Santiago, Chile, then east to Buenos Aires, Argentina, and ending in Brasilia, Brazil.

How many miles is it along the roadway from point *A* to point *E*? To solve this problem, you need to be familiar with central angles. *This problem will be solved in Example 2.*

A **central angle** of a circle is an angle whose vertex lies at the center of the circle. If two central angles in different circles are congruent, the ratio of the lengths of their intercepted arcs is equal to the ratio of the measures of their radii. For example, given $\odot O$ and $\odot Q$,

if $\angle O \cong \angle Q$, then $\dfrac{m\widehat{AB}}{m\widehat{CD}} = \dfrac{OA}{QC}$.

INTRODUCING THE LESSON

Lesson Resources

- Practice Master 5–2
- Enrichment Master 5–2
- Evaluation Master, Quiz A, p. 61
- Activity Master, p. 15

Transparency 5–2 contains the 5-Minute Check and a teaching aid for this lesson.

⏱ 5-Minute Check

(over Lesson 5–1)

1. Determine the quadrant in which the terminal side of an angle of 324° lies.   **IV**
2. Change 320° to radian measure in terms of π.
   $\dfrac{16\pi}{9}$
3. Change $-\dfrac{13\pi}{3}$ radians to degree measure.   **−780°**
4. Find one positive and one negative angle that are coterminal with an angle of −200°.   **Answers may vary. Sample: positive: 160°, negative: −560°**
5. Find the reference angle for an angle of $-\dfrac{9\pi}{4}$ radians. $\dfrac{\pi}{4}$

Prerequisite Skills

Students should be familiar with formulas related to circles.
1. What is the circumference of a circle with radius 8 cm?
   16π cm
2. Find the area of circle O.
   36π in²

ALTERNATE TEACHING STRATEGIES

Mini-Math Lab

Materials: string, paper circles, ruler, and protractor. Carefully place the string along an arc of the circle. Cut the string to match the length of the arc. Measure the string and the radius of the circle. Measure the central angle of the arc. Verify that the arc length in radians is equal to the product of the radius and the radian measure of the central angle.

Using Discussion

Have students discuss how to find the relationship between the linear and angular velocity of an object moving in a circular path. Encourage students who have studied physics to offer their explanations.

Airplanes travel a *great circle route* between continents because it is shorter than the distance along a straight line. That is, pilots fly along a line of longitude rather than a line of latitude. Discuss the distance between two points on Earth along a great circle route. A globe can be used to demonstrate the route.

TEACHING THE LESSON

Chalkboard Examples

For Example 1

Find the length of an arc that subtends a central angle of 38° in a circle of radius 5 cm.
≈ **3.316 cm**

For Example 2

Refer to the application at the beginning of the lesson. Suppose you ride a bicycle with wheels 30 inches in diameter along the path from point *A* to point *E*. Calculate the number of revolutions that the tire makes.
≈ **1250 revolutions**

θ is the Greek letter theta.

We say that an arc <u>subtends</u> its central angle.

Let *O* be the center of two concentric circles. Let *r* be the measure of the radius of the larger circle, and let the smaller circle be a unit circle. A central angle of *θ* radians is drawn in the two circles that intercept $\overset{\frown}{RT}$ on the unit circle and $\overset{\frown}{SW}$ on the other circle. Suppose $\overset{\frown}{SW}$ is *s* units long. $\overset{\frown}{RT}$ is *θ* units long since it is an arc of a unit circle intercepted by a central angle of *θ* radians. Thus, we can write the following proportion.

$$\frac{s}{\theta} = \frac{r}{1} \text{ or } s = r\theta$$

Length of an Arc	The length of any circular arc, *s*, is equal to the product of the measure of the radius of the circle, *r*, and the radian measure of the central angle, *θ*, that it subtends. $$s = r\theta$$

Example 1

Find the length of an arc that subtends a central angle of 42° in a circle of radius 8 cm.

$42° = 42 \times \dfrac{\pi}{180}$ *Find the radian measure of the central angle.*

$\quad = \dfrac{7\pi}{30}$

$s = r\theta$ *Find the length of the arc.*

$\quad = (8)\left(\dfrac{7\pi}{30}\right)$

$\quad \approx 5.86$

The length of the arc is approximately 5.86 centimeters.

Example 2

APPLICATION

Civil Engineering

Refer to the application at the beginning of the lesson. How far is it along the roadway from point *A* to point *E*?

To find the length of $\overset{\frown}{BC}$, change 90.5° to radians   90.5° ≈ 1.58 radians
Thus, the length of $\overset{\frown}{BC}$ is about 0.30 × 1.58 or 0.47 miles   *r* = 0.30

To find the length of $\overset{\frown}{CD}$, change 52.5° to radians.   52.5° ≈ 0.92 radians
Thus, the length of $\overset{\frown}{CD}$ is about 0.50 × 0.92, or 0.46 miles.   *r* = 0.50

Find the sum of the distances.   0.43 + 0.50 + 0.47 + 0.46 = 1.86

Therefore, the distance from point *A* to point *E* is about 1.86 miles.

The arc length formula can be used to find the relationship between the linear and angular velocities of an object moving in a circular path. If the object moves with constant **linear velocity** (v) for a period of time(t), the distance (s) it travels is given by the formula $s = vt$. Thus, the linear velocity is $v = \frac{s}{t}$.

As the object moves along the circular path, the radius, r, forms a central angle of measure θ. The change in the central angle with respect to time, $\frac{\theta}{t}$, is the **angular velocity** of the object. Since the length of the arc is $s = r\theta$, the following is true.

$$s = r\theta$$

$$\frac{s}{t} = \frac{r\theta}{t} \qquad \textit{Divide each side by t.}$$

$$v = r\frac{\theta}{t} \qquad \textit{Remember that } v = \frac{s}{t}.$$

Linear and Angular Velocity	If an object moves along a circle of radius r units, then its linear velocity, v, is given by $$v = r\frac{\theta}{t},$$ where $\frac{\theta}{t}$ represents the angular velocity in radians per unit of time.

Example 3

A pulley of radius 12 cm turns at 7 revolutions per second. What is the linear velocity of the belt driving the pulley in meters per second?

$$v = r\frac{\theta}{t}$$

$$= 12\frac{(7 \cdot 2\pi)}{1} \qquad \textit{One revolution is } 2\pi, \textit{ so 7 revolutions is } 7 \cdot 2\pi \textit{ radians.}$$

$$= 168\pi$$

$$\approx 527.788$$

$$\approx 5.278 \qquad \textit{Divide by 100 to change cm to m.}$$

The linear velocity of the belt is approximately 5.28 m/s.

Example 4

A trucker drives 55 miles per hour. His truck's tires have a diameter of 26 inches. What is the angular velocity of the wheels in revolutions per second?

First, convert 55 miles per hour to inches per second.

$$\frac{55 \text{ miles}}{1 \text{ hour}} \cdot \frac{5280 \text{ feet}}{1 \text{ mile}} \cdot \frac{12 \text{ inches}}{1 \text{ foot}} \cdot \frac{1 \text{ hour}}{3600 \text{ seconds}} = \frac{968 \text{ inches}}{1 \text{ second}}$$

(continued on the next page)

LESSON 5-2 CENTRAL ANGLES AND ARCS 249

Then use the formula for linear velocity to find θ.

$$v = r\frac{\theta}{t}$$

$$968 = 13\frac{\theta}{1}$$ *Since the diameter is 26 inches, the radius is 13 inches.*

$$\frac{968}{13} = \theta$$

Since $\theta = \frac{968}{13}$ radians, the angular velocity is $\frac{968}{13} \div 2\pi$, or about 12 revolutions per second.

A **sector** of a circle is a region bounded by a central angle and the intercepted arc. For example, figure $ORTS$ is a sector of $\odot O$. The ratio of the area of a sector to the area of a circle is equal to the ratio of its arc length to the circumference. Let A represent the area of the sector. Then, $\frac{A}{\pi r^2} = \frac{\text{length of } \widehat{RTS}}{2\pi r}$. But the length of $\widehat{RTS}$ is $r \cdot \theta$. Thus, the following formula is true.

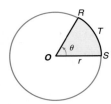

Area of a Circular Sector	If θ is the measure of the central angle expressed in radians and r is the measure of the radius of the circle, then the area of the sector, A, is as follows. $$A = \frac{1}{2}r^2\theta$$

Example 5

A sector has arc length of 16 cm and a central angle measuring 0.95 radians. Find the radius of the circle and the area of the sector.

First, find the radius of the circle.

$$s = r\theta$$
$$16 = r \cdot 0.95$$
$$r = 16.84 \qquad \text{The radius is about 16.84 cm long.}$$

Then find the area of the sector.

$$A = \frac{1}{2}r^2\theta$$
$$= \frac{1}{2}(16.84)^2(0.95)$$
$$= 134.70 \qquad \text{The area is about 134.70 cm}^2.$$

CHECKING FOR UNDERSTANDING

Communicating
Mathematics

Read and study the lesson to answer each question. 1–5. See margin.

1. **Describe** how the length of an arc is a proportional part of the circumference of a circle and the area of a sector is a proportional part of the area of the circle.

2. **Compare and contrast** linear and angular velocity.

3. **Describe** how to change an angular velocity from revolutions per minute to degrees per second.

4. **Explain** why an ice skater at the outside of a chain of skaters must skate faster than a skater near the inside of the chain in order to keep all of the skaters in line.

5. **Show** that when the radius of a circle is doubled, the length of the arc subtended and the linear velocity of a point on the circle are also doubled.

Guided
Practice

Find the arc length in terms of π for each central angle shown.

6.

7.

8.

Complete.

9. $60 \text{ mph} = \blacksquare \text{ ft/s}$ 88

10. $8 \text{ rpm} = \blacksquare \text{ rad/s}$ $\frac{4\pi}{15}$

11. $10 \text{ ft/min} = \blacksquare \text{ in./s}$ 2

12. $15 \text{ cm/s} = \blacksquare \text{ m/min}$ 9

Find the area of each sector, given its central angle, θ, and the radius of the circle. Round answers to the nearest tenth.

13. $\theta = \frac{\pi}{8}, r = 7 \text{ m}$ 9.6 m^2

14. $\theta = 48°, r = 22 \text{ in.}$ 202.7in^2

15. Find the area of the sector swept by the spoke of a wheel of radius 15 cm as the wheel rotates through an angle of 270°. Round your answer to the nearest tenth.
530.1 cm^2

EXERCISES

Practice

Given the radian measure of a central angle, find the measure of its intercepted arc in terms of π in a circle of radius 10 cm.

16. $\frac{\pi}{4}$ $\frac{5\pi}{2}$ cm

17. $\frac{2\pi}{3}$ $\frac{20\pi}{3}$ cm

18. $\frac{5\pi}{6}$ $\frac{25\pi}{3}$ cm

19. $\frac{2\pi}{5}$ 4π cm

Given the measurement of a central angle, find the measure of its intercepted arc in terms of π in a circle of diameter 30 in.

20. $30°$ $\frac{5\pi}{2}$ in.

21. $5°$ $\frac{5\pi}{12}$ in.

22. $77°$ $\frac{77\pi}{12}$ in.

23. $57°18'$ $\frac{191\pi}{40}$ in.

RETEACHING THE LESSON

Have students work in cooperative groups to solve each problem. Have them discuss the strategies as they are solving the problems.

1. An arc is 8 cm long and subtends an angle of 60°. Find the radius of the circle. $\approx 7.6 \text{ cm}$

2. A sector has an area of 12 cm² and a central angle of 0.8 radians. Find the radius of the circle.
$\approx 5.5 \text{ cm}$

3. Find the area of a sector of a circle with central angle $\frac{\pi}{2}$ radians and radius 2.9 cm. $\approx 6.6 \text{ cm}^2$

EVALUATING THE LESSON

Checking for Understanding

Exercises 1–15 are designed to help you assess students' understanding through reading, writing, speaking, and modeling. You should work through Exercises 1–5 with your students and then monitor their work on Exercises 6–15.

Closing the Lesson

Speaking Activity Have students explain how to find the linear velocity of an object moving along a circle in terms of its angular velocity.

APPLYING THE LESSON

Homework Exercises

Assignment Guides

Average: 16–34, 36, 39–41, 45, 48–55
Enriched: 18–32 even, 34–55

The red A, B, and C flags, printed only in the Teacher's Wraparound Edition, indicate the level of difficulty of the exercises.

Chapter 5, Quiz A, (Lessons 5–1 through 5–2), is available in the *Evaluation Masters,* p. 61.

Practice Masters Booklet, p. 29

5-2 NAME _____ DATE _____
Practice Worksheet

Central Angles and Arcs
Given the radian measure of a central angle, find the measure of its intercepted arc in terms of π in a circle of radius 10 cm.

1. $\frac{\pi}{6}$ $\frac{5\pi}{3}$ cm
2. $\frac{\pi}{3}$ $\frac{10\pi}{3}$ cm
3. $\frac{\pi}{2}$ 5π cm
4. $\frac{\pi}{5}$ 2π cm

5. $\frac{3\pi}{5}$ 6π cm
6. $\frac{4\pi}{7}$ $\frac{40\pi}{7}$ cm
7. $\frac{\pi}{12}$ $\frac{5\pi}{6}$ cm
8. $\frac{\pi}{24}$ $\frac{5\pi}{12}$ cm

Given the measurement of a central angle, find the measure of its intercepted arc in terms of π in a circle of diameter 60 in.

9. $10°$ $\frac{5\pi}{3}$ in.
10. $60°$ 10π in.
11. $42°$ 7π in.
12. $50°$ $\frac{25\pi}{3}$ in.

13. $72°$ 12π in.
14. $110°$ $\frac{55\pi}{3}$ in.
15. $35°$ $\frac{35\pi}{6}$ in.
16. $65°$ $\frac{65\pi}{6}$ in.

Given the measure of an arc, find the degree measure to the nearest tenth of the central angle it subtends in a circle of radius 16 cm.

17. 87 $311.5°$
18. 5.6 $20.1°$
19. 12 $43.0°$
20. 25 $89.5°$

21. 10.24 $36.7°$
22. 7.9 $28.3°$
23. 11 $39.4°$
24. 6 $21.5°$

Find the area of each sector to the nearest tenth, given its central angle, θ, and the radius of the circle.

25. $\theta = \frac{\pi}{6}, r = 14 \text{ cm}$
51.3 cm^2

26. $\theta = \frac{\pi}{6}, r = 12 \text{ ft}$
37.7 ft^2

T29
Glencoe Division, Macmillan/McGraw-Hill

Exercise Note

For Exercise 40, point out that the angle subtended by the width of the sun is also known as the object's *apparent size*. We perceive an object that is farther away to be smaller because of the smaller angle it subtends with our eyes.

Additional Answer

39. The angular velocity of r is $\frac{R}{r}$ times a.

Given the measure of an arc, find the degree measure to the nearest tenth of the central angle it subtends in a circle of radius 8 cm.

24. 5   35.8°   25. 14   100.3°   26. 24   171.9°   27. 12.5   89.5°

Find the area of each sector to the nearest tenth, given its central angle, θ, and the radius of the circle.

28. $\theta = \frac{5\pi}{12}, r = 10$ ft   65.4 ft^2

29. $\theta = 54°, r = 6$ in.   17.0 in^2

30. $\theta = \frac{2\pi}{3}, r = 1.36$ m   1.9 m^2

31. $\theta = 82°, r = 7.3$ km   38.1 km^2

32. $\theta = 45°, r = 9.75$ mm
37.3 mm^2

33. $\theta = 12°, r = 14$ yd   20.5 yd^2

For Exercises 34-38, round answers to the nearest tenth.

34. An arc is 6.5 cm long and it subtends a central angle of 45°. Find the radius of the circle.   8.3 cm

35. An arc is 70.7 m long and it subtends a central angle of $\frac{2\pi}{7}$. Find the diameter of the circle.   157.5 m

36. A sector has arc length 6 ft and central angle of 1.2 radians. Find the radius and area of the circle.   5 ft, 78.5 ft^2

37. A sector has area of 15 in^2 and central angle of 0.2 radians. Find the radius of the circle and arc length of the sector.   12.2 in., 2.4 in.

38. A sector has a central angle of 20° and arc length of 3.5 mm. Find the radius and area of the circle.   10.0 mm, 314.2 mm^2

Critical Thinking

39. The figure at the right shows two gears that mesh. Make a conjecture about the angular velocity of the gear with radius r if the angular velocity of the gear with radius R is a.   See margin.

Applications and Problem Solving

40. **Astronomy**   Earth revolves around the sun in an elliptical orbit. However, for this problem, you can assume that the orbit is circular with a radius of about 9.3×10^7 miles. a. 9.80×10^4 ft/s

   a. At what speed in feet per second does Earth travel around the sun?

   b. An astronomer estimates the angle subtended by the width of the sun as 0.5°. If this is the case, what is the approximate diameter of the sun?   810,000 miles

41. **Mechanics**   A wheel has a radius of 3.5 feet. As it turns, a cable connected to a box winds onto the wheel. To the nearest foot, how far does the box move if the wheel turns 130° in the counterclockwise direction?   8 feet

42. Geography The position of a point on Earth is often given in terms of the latitude and longitude. Jackson, Mississippi, and St. Louis, Missouri, lie along the same longitude line. The latitude of Jackson, Mississippi, is 32°17′ N, and the latitude of St. Louis, Missouri, is 38°37′ N. The radius of Earth is about 4000 miles.

   a. About how far apart are the two cities? about 442 miles

   b. If Earth makes one revolution every 24 hours, what is the linear velocity of a point near the equator? about 1050 mph

43. Interior Design A carpenter is building a window frame that consists of a semi-circular region, divided as shown at the right. Find the area of panes A, B, and C to the nearest hundredth of a square foot.
A, 0.39 ft²; B, 1.18 ft²; C, 1.96 ft²

1 ft   1 ft   1 ft

44. Sports Jason's bicycle wheel is 26 inches in diameter.

   a. To the nearest revolution, how many times will the wheel turn if it is ridden for 1 mile? 776 times

   b. Suppose the wheel turns at a constant rate of 2.5 revolutions per second. To the nearest tenth, what is the linear speed of a point on the tire in feet per second? in miles per hour? 17 ft/s, 11.6 mph

45. Civil Engineering The figure below shows a stretch of roadway where the curves are arcs of circles.

How many miles is it along the road from point A to point E? 5.23 mi

46. Physics A pendulum hangs on a 2.5-meter rod. Every two seconds, the pendulum swings 5° left and then 5° right of center. How many meters does the pendulum swing in one hour? 785 m

47. Manufacturing The figure at the right is a side view of three rollers that are tangent to one another. 47a. B, clockwise; C, counterclockwise

   a. If roller A turns counterclockwise, in which directions do rollers B and C turn?

   b. If roller A turns at 120 revolutions per minute, at what angular velocities do rollers B and C turn? 180 rpm, 75 rpm

Mixed Review

48. If $f(x) = \dfrac{1}{x-1}$ and $g(x) = x + 1$, find $[f \circ g](x)$. **(Lesson 1-2)** $\dfrac{1}{x}$

49. Find the value of the determinant for $\begin{bmatrix} 4 & 3 \\ 8 & 6 \end{bmatrix}$. Then state whether an inverse exists for the matrix. Write *yes* or *no*. **(Lesson 2-3)** 0, no

50. Find the slope of the line tangent to the graph of $f(x) = 2x^2 - 3x + 3$ at the point $(-2, 17)$. **(Lesson 3-6)** –11

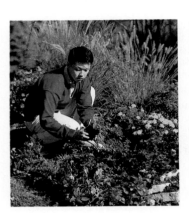

51. Solve $6x^2 + 7x + 2 = 0$ using the quadratic formula. $-\frac{1}{2}, -\frac{2}{3}$
(**Lesson 4-2**)

52. Landscaping A landscaper works on a job for 10 days and is then joined by a helper. Together they finish the job in 6 more days. The helper could have done the job alone in 30 days. How long would it have taken the landscaper to do the job alone?
(**Lesson 4-6**) 20 days

53. Solve $\sqrt[3]{3y - 1} - 2 = 0$. (**Lesson 4-7**) 3

54. Change 60° to radian measure in terms of π. (**Lesson 5-1**) $\frac{\pi}{3}$

55. College Entrance Exam Choose the best answer. A
The volume of a cylinder can be found by using the formula $V = \pi r^2 h$. How many cubic inches of sand can be placed into a cylindrical can that has a radius of 4 inches and a height of 1.5 feet?
(A) 288π **(B)** 144π **(C)** 96π **(D)** 24π **(E)** 6π

DECISION MAKING

Education and Literacy

No resource is more important to a democratic nation than an educated citizenry. Yet more than one fourth of American high school students drop out before graduation, and 20% of Americans are functionally illiterate—that is, they are unable to deal with everyday life because of inadequate education. What can you do to help alleviate this problem? How can you turn your talents in a positive direction by working to raise the educational level of your community?

1. Describe the personal skills you have that you might be able to apply to the problem of illiteracy in your community. Do you enjoy working with children? senior citizens? Could you best use your talents by working directly with people seeking to learn to read or to improve their math skills, or should you channel your efforts toward educating the public or politicians about the critical need for educational reform?

2. Find out what organizations and agencies in your community are concerned with this problem. Contact several of them to find out what they do and whether they can use the help of volunteers.

3. Project Work with your group to complete one of the projects listed at the right based on the information you gathered in Exercises 1–2. 1–3. See students' work.

PROJECTS

- *Conduct an interview.*
- *Write a book report.*
- *Write a proposal.*
- *Write an article for the school paper.*
- *Write a report.*
- *Make a display.*
- *Make a graph or chart.*
- *Plan an activity.*
- *Design a checklist.*

Enrichment Masters Booklet, p. 29

EXTENDING THE LESSON

Math Power: Reasoning

Compact disc players use lasers to read digital codes, which they translate into sound waves. The actual rotational speed of the disc depends on the laser's position on the disc. If the slowest speed of the disc is about 200 rpm when the laser is at the outer edge of the disc, how many degrees does the disc turn in one second? **about 1200°**

Decision Making

This activity provides students an opportunity to work together on a given problem. You may wish to refer to pages T20–T21 and page 238c for the various elements of cooperative groups and specific goals and strategies for using them.

5-3 Circular Functions

Objective
5–3

After studying this lesson, you should be able to:
- find the values of the six trigonometric functions of an angle in standard position given a point on its terminal side.

Application

At the scene of many traffic accidents, police officers often use a trundle wheel to determine the length of skid marks. When the wheel is turned through one complete revolution, there is a one-to-one correspondence between the points on the rim of the wheel and the real numbers representing the length of the skid marks on the ground. As the wheel completes more revolutions, there is a many-to-one correspondence between the points on the rim of the wheel and the real numbers.

In a similar manner, two important **trigonometric functions**, the sine and cosine functions, can be defined in terms of the unit circle.

Consider an angle θ standard position. The terminal side of the angle intersects the unit circle at a unique point, $P(x, y)$. The y-coordinate of this point is called **sine θ**. The abbreviation for sine is *sin*. The x-coordinate of this point is called **cosine θ**. The abbreviation for cosine is *cos*.

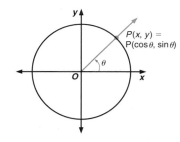

Definition of Sine and Cosine	If the terminal side of an angle θ in standard position intersects the unit circle at $P(x, y)$, then $\cos\theta = x$ and $\sin\theta = y$.

Since there is exactly one point $P(x, y)$ for any angle θ, the relations $\cos\theta = x$ and $\sin\theta = y$ are functions of θ. Because they are both defined using a unit circle, they are often called **circular functions**.

Example 1

Find each value.
a. sin 90°

a. The terminal side of a 90° angle in standard position is the positive y-axis, which intersects the unit circle at $(0, 1)$. The y-coordinate of this ordered pair is sin 90°.

Therefore, sin 90° = 1.

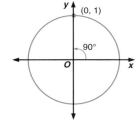

LESSON 5-3 CIRCULAR FUNCTIONS 255

ALTERNATE TEACHING STRATEGIES

Using Graphing Calculators

Set the TI-81 calculator to radian, parametric, and simultaneous mode. Range: Tmin: 0, Tmax: 7, Tstep: 0.1, Xmin: –1, Xmax: 6.3, Xscl: 1.57, Ymin: –3, Ymax: 3, Yscl: 1.

Press Y= . Enter $X_{1T} = \cos T$, $Y_{1T} = \sin T$, $X_{2T} = T$, $Y_{2T} = \sin T$.
Press GRAPH . The unit circle and the sine function are graphed simultaneously.

Using Critical Thinking

Use the unit circle to justify the following statement.
$(\sin\theta)^2 + (\cos\theta)^2 = 1$

NCTM Standards: 1–6, 8, 9

Lesson Resources

- Practice Master 5–3
- Enrichment Master 5–3
   Transparency 5–3 contains the 5-Minute Check and a teaching aid for this lesson.

INTRODUCING THE LESSON

 5-Minute Check
(over Lesson 5–2)

1. Find the area of a sector given that its central angle is $\frac{\pi}{3}$ and the radius of the circle is 8 m.
   $\frac{32\pi}{3} \approx$ **33.5 m²**

2. Given the radian measure $\frac{\pi}{8}$ of the central angle of a circle with radius 4 cm, find the measure of its intercepted arc.
   $\frac{\pi}{2} \approx$ **1.6 cm**

3. Given the measure 12° of the central angle of a circle with diameter 14 in., find the measure of its intercepted arc.
   $\frac{7\pi}{15} \approx$ **1.5 in.**

4. An arc of a circle with radius 10 has measure 18 units. Find the degree measure of the central angle it subtends. $\approx$ **103°**

5. Find the area of a sector of a circle of radius 6 in. with central angle 36°.
   $\frac{18\pi}{5} \approx$ **11.3 in²**

Motivating the Lesson

The line voltage V of an alternating current can be described by the equation $V = 115\sqrt{2}\cos(120\pi t)$, where t is in seconds. An equation for simple harmonic motion is $y = A\sin 2\pi ft$, where A is the amplitude of vibration, f the frequency, and t the length of time. These examples suggest the need to express sine t and cosine t as real numbers.

TEACHING THE LESSON

Teaching Tip The use of similar triangles to define sine and cosine imply that the size of the triangle (and therefore the size of the circle) does not affect the value of the sine or cosine of an angle.

Chalkboard Example

For Example 1

Find each value.
a. $\sin \pi$ **0**
b. $\cos 90°$ **0**

Using Technology

Remind students to put their calculators in parametric mode before attempting this exploration.

---

b. $\cos \pi$

b. The terminal side of an angle in standard position measuring π radians is the negative x-axis, which intersects the unit circle at $(-1, 0)$. The x-coordinate of this ordered pair is $\cos \pi$.

Therefore, $\cos \pi = -1$.

EXPLORATION: Graphing Calculator

1. Use the range values below to set up a viewing window.

TMIN = 0	XMIN = -2.4	YMIN = -1.6
TMAX = 360	XMAX = 2.35	YMAX = 1.55
TSTEP = 15	XSCL = 0.5	YSCL = 0.5

2. Define the unit circle with the definition $X_{1T} = \cos T$ and $Y_{1T} = \sin T$.

3. Activate the TRACE function to move around the circle.
   a. What does T represent? the measure of the angle
   b. What does the x-value represent? the cosine of the angle
   c. What does the y-value represent? the sine of the angle

4. Determine the trigonometric functions of the angles whose terminal sides lie at $0°$, $90°$, $180°$, and $360°$. $(1, 0), (0, 1), (-1, 0), (0, -1)$

The sine and cosine functions of an angle in standard position may be defined in terms of the ordered pair for *any* point on its terminal side and the distance between that point and the origin.

Suppose $P(x, y)$ and $P'(x', y')$ are two points on the terminal side of an angle with measure θ, where P' is on the unit circle. Let $OP = r$. By the Pythagorean theorem, $r = \sqrt{x^2 + y^2}$. Since P' is on the unit circle, $OP' = 1$. Triangles $OP'Q'$ and OPQ are similar. Thus, the lengths of corresponding sides are proportional.

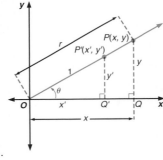

$$\frac{x'}{1} = \frac{x}{r} \text{ and } \frac{y'}{1} = \frac{y}{r}$$

Therefore, $\cos \theta = x'$ or $\frac{x}{r}$ and $\sin \theta = y'$ or $\frac{y}{r}$.

The ratios $\frac{x}{r}$ and $\frac{y}{r}$ do not depend on the choice of P. They depend only on the measure of θ and thus, are the basic trigonometric functions of θ.

Find the values of the sine and cosine functions of an angle in standard position with measure θ if the point with coordinates (5, 12) lies on its terminal side.
$\frac{12}{13}$, $\frac{5}{13}$

For Example 3

Find $\sin \theta$ when $\cos \theta = \frac{8}{17}$ and the terminal side of θ is in the first quadrant. $\frac{15}{17}$

Sine and Cosine Functions of an Angle in Standard Position	For any angle in standard position with measure θ, a point $P(x, y)$ on its terminal side, and $r = \sqrt{x^2 + y^2}$, the sine and cosine functions of θ are as follows. $$\sin \theta = \frac{y}{r} \qquad \cos \theta = \frac{x}{r}$$

Example 2

Find the values of the sine and cosine functions of an angle in standard position with measure θ if the point with coordinates (3, 4) lies on its terminal side.

You know that $x = 3$ and $y = 4$. You need to find r.

$$r = \sqrt{x^2 + y^2}$$
$$= \sqrt{3^2 + 4^2}$$
$$= 5$$

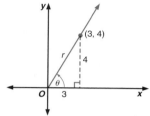

Then write the sine and cosine ratios.

$$\sin \theta = \frac{y}{r} \text{ or } \frac{4}{5} \qquad \cos \theta = \frac{x}{r} \text{ or } \frac{3}{5}$$

Example 3

Find $\sin \theta$ when $\cos \theta = \dfrac{5}{13}$ and the terminal side of θ is in the first quadrant.

Since $\cos \theta = \frac{x}{r} = \frac{5}{13}$ and r is always positive, $r = 13$ and $x = 5$. Now, find y.

$$r = \sqrt{x^2 + y^2}$$
$$13 = \sqrt{5^2 + y^2}$$
$$169 = 25 + y^2$$
$$144 = y^2$$
$$\pm 12 = y$$

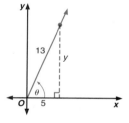

Since θ is in the first quadrant, y must be positive.

Thus, $\sin \theta = \frac{y}{r}$ or $\frac{12}{13}$.

LESSON 5-3 CIRCULAR FUNCTIONS 257

In addition to the ratios $\dfrac{y}{r}$ and $\dfrac{x}{r}$ that are used to define the sine and cosine functions, four other ratios may be formed using x, y, and r. These are the **tangent**, **cotangent**, **secant**, and **cosecant** functions, which are abbreviated *tan*, *cot*, *sec*, and *csc*, respectively. These ratios depend only on the measure of θ and thus, provide additional trigonometric functions.

Trigonometric Functions of an Angle in Standard Position

> For any angle in standard position with measure θ, a point $P(x, y)$ on its terminal side, and $r = \sqrt{x^2 + y^2}$, the trigonometric functions of θ are as follows.
>
> $$\sin \theta = \frac{y}{r} \qquad \cos \theta = \frac{x}{r} \qquad \tan \theta = \frac{y}{x}$$
>
> $$\csc \theta = \frac{r}{y} \qquad \sec \theta = \frac{r}{x} \qquad \cot \theta = \frac{x}{y}$$

We can write the tangent, cosecant, secant, and cotangent functions in terms of the sine, cosine, and tangent.

$$\tan \theta = \frac{\sin \theta}{\cos \theta} \qquad \csc \theta = \frac{1}{\sin \theta} \qquad \sec \theta = \frac{1}{\cos \theta} \qquad \cot \theta = \frac{1}{\tan \theta}$$

Thus, $\sin \theta$ and $\csc \theta$ are reciprocals, as are $\sec \theta$ and $\cos \theta$, and $\tan \theta$ and $\cot \theta$.

Example 4

> **The terminal side of an angle θ in standard position contains the point with coordinates $(8, -15)$. Find $\tan \theta$, $\cot \theta$, $\sec \theta$, and $\csc \theta$.**
>
> You know that $x = 8$ and $y = -15$. You need to find r.
>
> $r = \sqrt{x^2 + y^2}$
>
> $ = \sqrt{8^2 + (-15)^2}$
>
> $ = \sqrt{289}$ or 17
>
> Now, write the ratios.
>
> $\tan \theta = \dfrac{y}{x}$ or $\dfrac{-15}{8}$ $\qquad$ $\cot \theta = \dfrac{x}{y}$ or $\dfrac{8}{-15}$
>
> $\sec \theta = \dfrac{r}{x}$ or $\dfrac{17}{8}$ $\qquad$ $\csc \theta = \dfrac{r}{y}$ or $\dfrac{17}{-15}$

If you know the value of one of the trigonometric functions and the quadrant in which the terminal side of θ lies, you can find the values of the remaining five functions.

Additional Answers

1. Since $a + 360k°$ is coterminal with a, $\sin(a° + 360k°)$ is the same as $\sin a°$. For example, $\sin 90° = 1$ and $\sin(90° + 720°) = \sin 810° = 1$.

2. first quadrant

3. By definition $\cos \theta = \dfrac{x}{r}$. Let $r = 1$.

   If the measure of θ is $0°$, $x = r$. Thus, $\cos \theta = \dfrac{1}{1}$ or 1. As θ increases r remains 1 and x decreases. Therefore, $\dfrac{x}{r}$ decreases. When r is vertical, $x = 0$. Thus, $\cos \theta = \dfrac{0}{1}$ or 0.

4. $\sin 13°$

Example 5

If $\csc \theta = -2$ and θ lies in Quadrant III, find $\sin \theta$, $\cos \theta$, $\tan \theta$, $\cot \theta$, and $\sec \theta$.

Since $\csc \theta$ and $\sin \theta$ are reciprocals, $\sin \theta = -\dfrac{1}{2}$.

To find the other function values, you must find the coordinates of a point on the terminal side of θ. Since $\sin \theta = -\dfrac{1}{2}$ and r is always positive, let $r = 2$ and let $y = -1$. Find x.

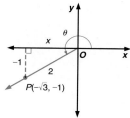

$$r^2 = x^2 + y^2$$
$$2^2 = x^2 + (-1)^2$$
$$3 = x^2$$
$$\pm\sqrt{3} = x$$

Since the terminal side of θ lies in Quadrant III, $x = -\sqrt{3}$.

Now, write the ratios.

$$\cos \theta = \frac{-\sqrt{3}}{2} \text{ or } -\frac{\sqrt{3}}{2}$$

$$\tan \theta = \frac{-1}{-\sqrt{3}} \text{ or } \frac{\sqrt{3}}{3}$$

$$\sec \theta = \frac{2}{-\sqrt{3}} \text{ or } -\frac{2\sqrt{3}}{3}$$

$$\cot \theta = \frac{-\sqrt{3}}{-1} \text{ or } \sqrt{3}$$

As illustrated in Examples 4 and 5, the values of the trigonometric functions may be either positive, negative, or 0. Since r is always positive, the signs of the functions are determined by the signs of x and y.

CHECKING FOR UNDERSTANDING

Communicating Mathematics

Read and study the lesson to answer each question. 1–4 See margin.

1. **Explain** why the $\sin a°$ and $\sin(a° + 360k°)$, where k is an integer, are equal. Use an example as part of your explanation.

2. **State** the quadrant or quadrants in which $\sin \theta$ and $\cos \theta$ are both positive.

3. **Show** that as the measure of θ increases from $0°$ to $90°$, the value of $\cos \theta$ decreases from 1 to 0.

4. **Tell** which is greater, $\sin 12°$ or $\sin 13°$.

LESSON 5-3   CIRCULAR FUNCTIONS   259

Homework Exercises

Assignment Guide

Average: 22–37, 43–49 odd, 51–58
Enriched: 26–41, 42–48 even, 49–58
All: Mid-Chapter Review, 1–8

The red A, B, and C flags, printed only in the Teacher's Wraparound Edition, indicate the level of difficulty of the exercises.

Additional Answers

6. $\sin \theta = \frac{-4}{5}$, $\cos \theta = \frac{3}{5}$,

$\tan \theta = \frac{-4}{3}$, $\csc \theta = \frac{5}{-4}$,

$\sec \theta = \frac{5}{3}$, $\cot \theta = \frac{3}{-4}$

7. $\sin \theta = \frac{\sqrt{2}}{2}$, $\cos \theta = \frac{\sqrt{2}}{2}$,

$\tan \theta = 1$, $\csc \theta = \sqrt{2}$,
$\sec \theta = \sqrt{2}$, $\cot \theta = 1$

8. $\sin \theta = 0$, $\cos \theta = -1$,
$\tan \theta = 0$, $\csc \theta =$ undefined,
$\sec \theta = -1$, $\cot \theta =$ undefined

22. $\sin \alpha = \frac{12}{13}$ $\csc \alpha = \frac{13}{12}$

$\cos \alpha = \frac{5}{13}$ $\sec \alpha = \frac{13}{5}$

$\tan \alpha = \frac{12}{5}$ $\cot \alpha = \frac{5}{12}$

23. $\sin \alpha = \frac{8}{17}$ $\csc \alpha = \frac{17}{8}$

$\cos \alpha = \frac{15}{17}$ $\sec \alpha = \frac{17}{15}$

$\tan \alpha = \frac{8}{15}$ $\cot \alpha = \frac{15}{8}$

24. $\sin \alpha = \frac{4}{5}$ $\csc \alpha = \frac{5}{4}$

$\cos \alpha = \frac{3}{5}$ $\sec \alpha = \frac{5}{3}$

$\tan \alpha = \frac{4}{3}$ $\cot \alpha = \frac{3}{4}$

25. $\sin \alpha = -\frac{8\sqrt{65}}{65}$ $\csc \alpha = -\frac{\sqrt{65}}{8}$

$\cos \alpha = \frac{\sqrt{65}}{65}$ $\sec \alpha = \sqrt{65}$

$\tan \alpha = -8$ $\cot \alpha = -\frac{1}{8}$

26. $\sin \alpha = 0$ $\csc \alpha =$ undefined
$\cos \alpha = -1$ $\sec \alpha = -1$
$\tan \alpha = 0$ $\cot \alpha =$ undefined

27. $\sin \alpha = \frac{\sqrt{2}}{2}$ $\csc \alpha = \sqrt{2}$

$\cos \alpha = -\frac{\sqrt{2}}{2}$ $\sec \alpha = -\sqrt{2}$

$\tan \alpha = -1$ $\cot \alpha = -1$

28. $\sin \alpha = -\frac{3\sqrt{34}}{34}$ $\csc \alpha = -\frac{\sqrt{34}}{3}$

$\cos \alpha = \frac{5\sqrt{34}}{34}$ $\sec \alpha = \frac{\sqrt{34}}{5}$

$\tan \alpha = -\frac{3}{5}$ $\cot \alpha = -\frac{5}{3}$

29. $\sin \alpha = 1$ $\csc \alpha = 1$
$\cos \alpha = 0$ $\cot \alpha = 0$
$\tan \alpha =$ undefined
$\sec \alpha =$ undefined

30. $\cos \theta = \frac{3}{5}$, $\tan \theta = \frac{-4}{3}$,

$\csc \theta = \frac{5}{-4}$, $\sec \theta = \frac{5}{3}$,

$\cot \theta = \frac{3}{-4}$

---

5. **Complete** the chart below that indicates the sign of the trigonometric functions in each quadrant.

Function	Quadrant			
	I	II	III	IV
$\sin \alpha$ or $\csc \alpha$	+	+	−	−
$\cos \alpha$ or $\sec \alpha$	+	−	−	+
$\tan \alpha$ or $\cot \alpha$	+	−	+	−

Guided Practice

Find the values of the six trigonometric functions of an angle in standard position if a point with the given coordinates lies on its terminal side. 6–8. See margin.

6. $(3, -4)$ 7. $(3, 3)$ 8. $(-4, 0)$

Suppose $\sin \theta = \frac{1}{2}$ **and the terminal side is in the second quadrant. Find each value.**

9. $\cos \theta$ $-\frac{\sqrt{3}}{2}$ 10. $\tan \theta$ $-\frac{\sqrt{3}}{3}$ 11. $\sec \theta$ $-\frac{2\sqrt{3}}{3}$

Suppose θ **is an angle in standard position with the given conditions. State the quadrant or quadrants in which the terminal side of** θ **lie.**

12. $\sin \theta > 0$ I, II   13. $\tan \theta < 0$ II, IV

14. $\sin \theta > 0$, $\cos \theta < 0$ II   15. $\tan \theta > 0$, $\cos \theta < 0$ III

Find two values of x **that make each statement true.** 16–21. Answers may vary.

16. $\cos x = 1$ 17. $\sin x = 1$

18. $\cos x = 0$ 19. $\sin x = 0$

20. $\cos x = -1$ 21. $\sin x = -1$

EXERCISES

Practice

Find the values of the six trigonometric functions of an angle in standard position if a point with the given coordinates lies on its terminal side. 22–29. See margin.

22. $(5, 12)$ 23. $(15, 8)$ 24. $(3, 4)$ 25. $(1, -8)$

26. $(-3, 0)$ 27. $(-\sqrt{2}, \sqrt{2})$ 28. $(5, -3)$ 29. $(0, 2)$

Suppose θ **is an angle in standard position whose terminal side lies in the given quadrant. For each function, find the values of the remaining five trigonometric functions of** θ**.** 30–33. See margin.

30. $\sin \theta = -\frac{4}{5}$; Quadrant IV   31. $\cos \theta = -\frac{1}{2}$; Quadrant II

32. $\tan \theta = 2$; Quadrant I   33. $\sec \theta = \sqrt{3}$; Quadrant IV

260   CHAPTER 5   THE TRIGONOMETRIC FUNCTIONS

Tell whether the value of each trigonometric function is *positive, negative, zero*, or *undefined*.

34. $\sin 2\pi$ 0

35. $\cos \dfrac{\pi}{4}$ +

36. $\tan 315°$ −

37. $\cos \dfrac{5\pi}{4}$ −

38. $\sin \dfrac{11\pi}{4}$ +

39. $\tan 90°$
undefined

40. $\cos 450°$ 0

41. $\sin (-45°)$ −

Graphing
Calculator

42–45. Graph each angle described in Exercises 34–37 on a unit circle, using the method described in the Exploration. Use the TRACE function to verify whether the value of each trigonometric function is *positive, negative, zero*, or *undefined*.
See students' work.

46–48. See margin.

**Critical
Thinking**

46. Explain why the statement $\sin \theta = 2$ is not possible.

47. Show that $\sin 90k° = 0$, if k is any even integer.

48. Show that $\cos 90k° = 0$, if k is any odd integer.

**Applications
and Problem
Solving**

49. Surveying Two surveyors at points R and S sight a marker at point T. Write an equation that relates $\tan 35°$ with the distance across Hidden Lake (d) and the distance between the surveyors.
$\tan 35° = \dfrac{d}{250}$

Hidden
Lake

50. Construction A ramp is designed to help people in wheelchairs move more easily from one level to another. If a ramp 16 feet long forms an angle of 12° with the level ground, write an equation that relates $\sin 12°$ with the length of the ramp and the vertical rise, v. $\sin 12° = \dfrac{v}{16}$

**Mixed
Review**

51. Name all values of x that are not in the domain of f for $f(x) = \dfrac{3x}{x^2 - 5}$.
(Lesson 1-1) $\pm\sqrt{5}$

52. Find the additive inverse of $\begin{bmatrix} 6 & 5 \\ 8 & 4 \end{bmatrix}$.
(Lesson 2-2) $\begin{bmatrix} -6 & -5 \\ -8 & -4 \end{bmatrix}$

53. Solve $3x^2 - 7x - 20 = 0$ using the quadratic formula. **(Lesson 4-2)** $4, -\dfrac{5}{3}$

54. Find the critical points of the graph of $y = x^4 - 8x^2 + 16$. Then determine whether each point represents a maximum, a minimum, or a point of inflection.
(Lesson 3-7) $(0, 16)$, max; $(\pm 2, 0)$, min; $\left(\pm\dfrac{2\sqrt{3}}{3}, \dfrac{64}{9} \right)$, point of inflection

55. Use synthetic division to divide $(x^3 + 2x + 3)$ by $(x - 2)$. **(Lesson 4-3)**
55. $x^2 + 2x + 6$ R15

Exercise Note

For Exercises 47 and 48, start a discussion about the periodicity of the trigonometric functions.

Using Technology

You may wish to refer students to the Graphing Calculator Exploration on page 256 before they attempt Exercises 42–45 Remind students that the T-range values need to be altered for expression being evaluated for radian measure as well as the mode.

Additional Answers

46. If $\sin \theta = 2$, then $y = 2$ and $r = 1$. Since $r^2 = x^2 + y^2$, $1 = x^2 + 4$ or $x^2 = -3$ which is not possible.

47. Let $k = 2n$, where n is any integer. Then, $\sin (90k°) = \sin (90 \cdot 2n°) = \sin (180n°)$. But $\sin (180n°) = \sin 0°$ for all integers n. Since $\sin 0° = 0$, $\sin (90k°) = 0$.

48. Let $k = 2n + 1$ where n is any integer. Then $\cos (90k°) = \cos [90°(2n + 1)] = \cos (180n° + 90°)$. The related angle for $(180n° + 90°) = 90°$. Thus, $\cos (180n° + 90°) = \cos 90° = 0$.

Additional Answers

31. $\sin \theta = \dfrac{\sqrt{3}}{2}$, $\tan \theta = -\sqrt{3}$,

$\csc \theta = \dfrac{2\sqrt{3}}{3}$, $\sec \theta = -2$,

$\cot \theta = -\dfrac{\sqrt{3}}{3}$

32. $\sin \theta = \dfrac{2\sqrt{5}}{5}$, $\cos \theta = \dfrac{\sqrt{5}}{5}$,

$\csc \theta = \dfrac{\sqrt{5}}{2}$, $\sec \theta = \sqrt{5}$,

$\cot \theta = \dfrac{1}{2}$

33. $\sin \theta = \dfrac{-\sqrt{6}}{3}$, $\cos \theta = \dfrac{\sqrt{3}}{3}$,

$\tan \theta = -\sqrt{2}$, $\csc \theta = \dfrac{-\sqrt{6}}{2}$,

$\cot \theta = \dfrac{-\sqrt{2}}{2}$

Additional Answer

Mid-Chapter Review

8. $\sin \theta = \dfrac{3}{5}$, $\cos \theta = \dfrac{4}{5}$,

$\tan \theta = \dfrac{3}{4}$, $\csc \theta = \dfrac{5}{3}$,

$\sec \theta = \dfrac{5}{4}$, $\cot \theta = \dfrac{4}{3}$

56. Change $\dfrac{5\pi}{6}$ to degree measure. **(Lesson 5-1)** 150°

57. **Mechanics** A pulley of radius 10 cm turns at 5 revolutions per second. Find the linear velocity of the belt driving the pulley in meters per second. **(Lesson 5-2)**
3.14 m/s

58. **College Entrance Exam** Compare quantities A and B below. B
Write A if quantity A is greater.
Write B if quantity B is greater.
Write C if the two quantities are equal.
Write D if there is not enough information to determine the relationship.

   (A) the maximum number of boxes of pens costing $2.98 each that can be bought for $15, with no tax

   (B) the maximum number of boxes of pens costing $3.25 each that can be bought for $20, with no tax

MID-CHAPTER REVIEW

1. Change $-\dfrac{3\pi}{4}$ to degree measure. **(Lesson 5-1)** −135°

2. Change 405° to radian measure in terms of π. **(Lesson 5-1)** $\dfrac{9\pi}{4}$

3. Find one positive angle and one negative angle that are coterminal with an angle measuring 225°. **(Lesson 5-1)** Answers may vary; a sample answer is 585° and −135°.

4. Find the reference angle for $\dfrac{5\pi}{8}$. **(Lesson 5-1)** $\dfrac{3\pi}{8}$

5. Find the length of an arc to the nearest tenth that intercepts a central angle of 32° in a circle of radius 11 cm. **(Lesson 5-2)** 6.1 cm

6. A sector has a central angle of 0.8 radians and a radius of 7.5 cm. Find the area of the sector to the nearest tenth. **(Lesson 5-2)** 22.5 cm²

7. A flashlight has a range of 100 feet and casts its beam through an angle of 100°. To the nearest 100 square feet, what area is illuminated by the flashlight? **(Lesson 5-2)** 8700 ft²

8. Find the values of the six trigonometric functions of an angle α in standard position if the point with coordinates (4, 3) lies on its terminal side. **(Lesson 5-3)** See margin.

262 CHAPTER 5 THE TRIGONOMETRIC FUNCTIONS

Enrichment Masters Booklet, p. 30

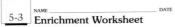

NAME _____ DATE _____

5-3 Enrichment Worksheet

Areas of Polygons and Circles

A regular polygon has sides of equal length and angles of equal measure. A regular polygon can be inscribed in or circumscribed about a circle. For n-sided regular polygons, the following area formulas can be used.

Area of circle $\qquad A_C = \pi r^2$

Area of inscribed polygon $\qquad A_I = \dfrac{nr^2}{2} \times \sin \dfrac{360°}{n}$

Area of circumscribed polygon $A_C = nr^2 \times \tan \dfrac{180°}{n}$

Use a calculator to complete the chart below for a unit circle (a circle of radius 1).

	Number of Sides	Area of Inscribed Polygon	Area of Circle less Area of Polygon	Area of Circumscribed Polygon	Area of Polygon less Area of Circle
	3	1.2990381	1.8425545	5.1961524	2.0545598
1.	4	2	1.1415927	4	0.8584073
2.	8	2.8284271	0.3131655	3.3137085	0.1721158
3.	12	3	0.1415927	3.2153903	0.0737977
4.	20	3.0901699	0.0514227	3.1676888	0.0260961
5.	24	3.1058285	0.0357641	3.1596599	0.0180673
6.	28	3.1152931	0.0262996	3.1548423	0.0132496
7.	32	3.1214452	0.0201475	3.1517249	0.0101322
8.	1000	3.1415720	0.0000207	3.1416030	0.0000103

9. What number do the areas of the circumscribed and inscribed polygons seem to be approaching as the number of sides of the polygon increases?
π

T30
Glencoe Division, Macmillan/McGraw-Hill

EXTENDING THE LESSON

Math Power: Communication

At what points does the line $x = \dfrac{1}{2}$ intersect the unit circle? Explain how you can use these points to find $\sin \theta$ if $\cos \theta = \dfrac{1}{2}$. The line $x = \dfrac{1}{2}$ intersects the circle at $\left(\dfrac{1}{2}, \dfrac{\sqrt{3}}{2} \right)$ and $\left(\dfrac{1}{2}, -\dfrac{\sqrt{3}}{2} \right)$. Since points on the unit circle have coordinates $(\cos \theta, \sin \theta)$, $\sin \theta = \dfrac{\sqrt{3}}{2}$ or $-\dfrac{\sqrt{3}}{2}$.

Mid-Chapter Review

The Mid-Chapter Review provides students with a brief review of the concepts and skills in Lessons 5–1 through 5–3. Lesson numbers are given at the end of problems or instruction lines so students may review concepts not yet mastered.

5-4 Trigonometric Functions of Special Angles

Objectives

After studying this lesson, you should be able to:

5–4A ■ find exact values for the six trigonometric functions of special angles, and

5–4B ■ find decimal approximations for the values of the six trigonometric functions of any angle.

Application

You see an object because light is reflected from the object into your eyes. However, light travels faster in air than it does in water. This can be a bit confusing if you are about to step on a submerged rock while crossing a stream. The rock is not exactly where it appears to be. The displacement of the light ray depends on the angle at which the light strikes the surface of the water from below, A, the depth of the rock, t, and the angle at which the light leaves the surface of the water, B. The measure of displacement, x, is given by the formula below.

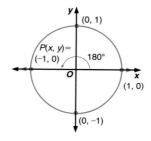

$$x = t \left(\frac{\sin (B - A)}{\cos A} \right)$$

Find the displacement if t measures 10 centimeters, the measure of angle A is 30°, and the measure of angle B is 42°. *This problem will be solved in Example 4.*

Before you find the values of the trigonometric functions in the formula above, it is helpful to study the values of trigonometric functions of special angles. One such group of angles are quadrantal angles. It is easy to find the trigonometric functions for quadrantal angles since their terminal sides lie along an axis. Using a unit circle, let (x, y) be the coordinates of the point of intersection of the circle with the terminal side of the angle. For example, $\cos 180° = -1$ and $\sin 180° = 0$.

LESSON 5-4 TRIGONOMETRIC FUNCTIONS OF SPECIAL ANGLES 263

ALTERNATE TEACHING STRATEGIES

Using Charts

Have students draw a large circle on a sheet of typing paper. Tell them to mark off all multiples of 30° and 45° along the circle. Mark the same points with radian measures as well. Then label each point with its coordinates. Use the coordinates on the circle to create a chart of all the trigonometric values of the special angles from 0° to 360° and from 0 radians to 2π radians.

Using Critical Thinking

Have the students extend the charts on page 265 to include the values of $\tan \theta$, $\sec \theta$, $\csc \theta$, and $\cot \theta$.

NCTM Standards: 1–4, 6, 7, 9

Lesson Resources

- Practice Master 5–4
- Enrichment Master 5–4
- Evaluation Master, Quiz B, p. 61
- Multicultural Activity Master, p. 5

 Transparency 5–4 contains the 5-Minute Check and a teaching aid for this lesson.

INTRODUCING THE LESSON

> **5-Minute Check**
> *(over Lesson 5–3)*
>
> 1. Suppose θ is an angle in standard position whose terminal side lies in the second quadrant. If $\cos \theta = -\frac{1}{2}$, find $\sin \theta$. $\frac{\sqrt{3}}{2}$
>
> 2. Suppose θ is an angle in standard position with $\sin \theta < 0$. State the quadrant(s) in which the terminal side of θ could lie.   **III or IV**
>
> 3. Find a positive value of x that makes the equation $\sin x = -1$ true.   **270°**
>
> 4. Find the values of the six trigonometric functions of an angle in standard position if the point at (–5, 12) lies on its terminal side.
> $\sin \theta = \frac{12}{13}$, $\cos \theta = \frac{5}{-13}$,
> $\tan \theta = -\frac{12}{5}$, $\cot \theta = -\frac{5}{12}$,
> $\sec \theta = -\frac{13}{5}$, $\csc \theta = \frac{13}{12}$
>
> 5. Tell whether $\sin 400°$ is positive, negative, or zero.   **positive**

Show students that trigonometry can be used to solve some real-life applications by bringing in a glass container with a rock or other object placed on the bottom. Fill it with water and have a student volunteer point to the object by putting his or her finger into the water. Use a stick to demonstrate that the student may not be pointing directly at the object. Have several other students also try the experiment. Point out that finding the displacement of the light is an application they will study.

TEACHING THE LESSON

Teaching Tip   Before discussing the table of trigonometric values for the quadrantal angles, draw the unit circle on the chalkboard and show how the values in the table translate into points along the unit circle.

Chalkboard Examples

For Example 1

Find the values of the six trigonometric functions for an angle in standard position that measures 180°.
sin 180° = 0, cos 180° = –1, tan 180° = 0, cot 180° is undefined, sec 180° = –1, csc 180° is undefined.

For Example 2

Find sin 30°, cos 30°, and tan 30°.
$\sin 30° = \frac{1}{2}$, $\cos 30° = \frac{\sqrt{3}}{2}$,

$\tan 30° = \frac{\sqrt{3}}{3}$

Example 1   **Find the values of the six trigonometric functions for an angle in standard position that measures 90°.**

$\sin 90° = 1$ $\cos 90° = 0$

tan 90° is undefined because division by zero is undefined.

$\cot 90° = 0$ $\csc 90° = 1$

sec 90° is undefined because division by zero is undefined.

The domain of the sine and cosine functions is the set of real numbers, since sin θ and cos θ are defined for any angle θ. The range of the sine and cosine functions is the set of real numbers between –1 and 1 inclusive, since (sin θ, cos θ) are the coordinates of points on the unit circle. Since division by zero is undefined, there are several angle measures that are excluded from the domain of the tangent, cotangent, secant, and cosecant functions. The table below summarizes the values of the trigonometric functions of common quadrantal angles. The dashes represent undefined values.

Angle	sin	cos	tan	csc	sec	cot
0°	0	1	0	—	1	—
90° or $\frac{\pi}{2}$	1	0	—	1	—	0
180° or π	0	–1	0	—	–1	—
270° or $\frac{3\pi}{2}$	–1	0	—	–1	—	0
360° or 2π	0	1	0	—	1	—

You can find the trigonometric functions of other special angles by using relationships from geometry. Recall that in a 30°–60° right triangle, the lengths of the sides are in the ratio $1 : \sqrt{3} : 2$. In a 45°–45° right triangle, the lengths of the sides are in the ratio $1 : 1 : \sqrt{2}$.

Example 2   **Find sin 60°, cos 60°, and tan 60°.**

Sketch a 30°–60° right triangle so that the 60° angle is in standard position.

Choose $P(x, y)$ on the terminal side of the angle so that $r = 2$. It follows that $x = 1$ and $y = \sqrt{3}$.

$\sin 60° = \dfrac{\sqrt{3}}{2}$

$\cos 60° = \dfrac{1}{2}$

$\tan 60° = \sqrt{3}$

264   CHAPTER 5   THE TRIGONOMETRIC FUNCTIONS

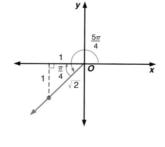
The values found in Example 2 are also those for angles of radian measure $\frac{\pi}{3}$ since $60° = \frac{\pi}{3}$. The chart below summarizes the sine and cosine values for selected angles from 0 to π. *It is a good idea to memorize these values since you will use them frequently.*

θ (in radians)	0	$\frac{\pi}{6}$	$\frac{\pi}{4}$	$\frac{\pi}{3}$	$\frac{\pi}{2}$	$\frac{2\pi}{3}$	$\frac{3\pi}{4}$	$\frac{5\pi}{6}$	π
θ (in degrees)	0	30°	45°	60°	90°	120°	135°	150°	180°
$\cos \theta$	1	$\frac{\sqrt{3}}{2}$	$\frac{\sqrt{2}}{2}$	$\frac{1}{2}$	0	$-\frac{1}{2}$	$-\frac{\sqrt{2}}{2}$	$-\frac{\sqrt{3}}{2}$	-1
$\sin \theta$	0	$\frac{1}{2}$	$\frac{\sqrt{2}}{2}$	$\frac{\sqrt{3}}{2}$	1	$\frac{\sqrt{3}}{2}$	$\frac{\sqrt{2}}{2}$	$\frac{1}{2}$	0

You can also use the reference angle for certain angles to find the value of trigonometric functions. Recall that the reference angle is the acute angle formed by the terminal side of a given angle and the x-axis.

Example 3

You may wish to review the reference angle rules in Lesson 5–1.

Find each value.

a. $\cos \dfrac{5\pi}{6}$

a. $\alpha = \dfrac{5\pi}{6}$, so its terminal side is in Quadrant II.

$\alpha' = \pi - \alpha$ *Reference rule b*

$\quad = \pi - \dfrac{5\pi}{6}$

$\quad = \dfrac{\pi}{6}$ *$\dfrac{\pi}{6} = 30°$*

$\cos \dfrac{5\pi}{6} = -\cos \dfrac{\pi}{6}$ *$\cos \alpha < 0$ in Quadrant II*

$\qquad = -\dfrac{\sqrt{3}}{2}$

b. $\tan \left(-\dfrac{11\pi}{4} \right)$

b. $-\dfrac{11\pi}{4}$ is coterminal with $\dfrac{5\pi}{4}$ in Quadrant III.

$\alpha' = \alpha - \pi$ *Reference rule c*

$\quad = \dfrac{5\pi}{4} - \pi$

$\quad = \dfrac{\pi}{4}$ *$\dfrac{\pi}{4} = 45°$*

Teaching Tip Students should be familiar with the commonly used angles and their sine and cosine. Remind them that all of these can be determined by using 30°–60°–90° and 45°–45°–90° triangles and reference angles.

Chalkboard Example

For Example 3

Find each value.

a. $\sin \dfrac{7\pi}{4}$ $-\dfrac{\sqrt{2}}{2}$

b. $\tan -\dfrac{8\pi}{3}$ $\sqrt{3}$

c. $\sec -\dfrac{13\pi}{4}$ $-\sqrt{2}$

$$\tan\left(-\frac{11\pi}{4}\right) = \tan\frac{\pi}{4} \qquad \text{tan } \alpha > 0 \text{ in Quadrant III}$$
$$= 1$$

c. $\csc\dfrac{29\pi}{3}$

c. $\dfrac{29\pi}{3}$ is coterminal with $\dfrac{5\pi}{3}$ in Quadrant IV.

$$\alpha' = 2\pi - \alpha \qquad \textit{Reference rule d}$$
$$= 2\pi - \frac{5\pi}{3}$$
$$= \frac{\pi}{3}$$

$$\csc\frac{29\pi}{3} = -\csc\frac{\pi}{3} \qquad \text{csc} < 0 \text{ in Quadrant IV}$$
$$= -\frac{1}{\sin\frac{\pi}{3}}$$
$$= -\frac{2}{\sqrt{3}} \text{ or } -\frac{2\sqrt{3}}{3}$$

The values of the trigonometric functions of *any* angle can be approximated using a scientific calculator. Most approximate values are given to four decimal places. Always check to see whether the calculator is in radian or degree mode.

Example 4

APPLICATION

Optics

Refer to the application at the beginning of the lesson. Find the displacement if *t* measures 10 cm, the measure of angle *A* is 30°, and the measure of angle *B* is 42°.

$$x = t\left(\frac{\sin(B - A)}{\cos A}\right)$$
$$= 10\left(\frac{\sin(42° - 30°)}{\cos 30°}\right)$$
$$= 10\left(\frac{\sin 12°}{\cos 30°}\right) \qquad \textit{Use your calculator. Make sure it is in degree mode.}$$

$$10 \boxed{\times} \boxed{(} 12 \boxed{\text{SIN}} \boxed{\div} 30 \boxed{\text{COS}} \boxed{)} \boxed{=} \; 2.4007574$$

The rock submerged 10 centimeters under water is actually about 2.4 centimeters from where it appears.

RETEACHING THE LESSON

Have each student make up a set of *flash cards* with each of the sine and cosine values for special angles from 0 to π. Then have students pair up to use the flash cards.

Practice Masters Booklet, p. 31

NAME _____ DATE _____

5-4   Practice Worksheet

Trigonometric Functions of Special Angles

Find each exact value. Do not use a calculator.

1. $\sin\frac{\pi}{4}$ $\frac{\sqrt{2}}{2}$
2. $\cos\frac{\pi}{4}$ $\frac{\sqrt{2}}{2}$
3. $\tan\frac{\pi}{4}$ 1

4. $\cos 210°$ $-\frac{\sqrt{3}}{2}$
5. $\sin 300°$ $-\frac{\sqrt{3}}{2}$
6. $\tan 330°$ $-\frac{\sqrt{3}}{3}$

7. $\sin\frac{3\pi}{4}$ $\frac{\sqrt{2}}{2}$
8. $\cos\frac{3\pi}{4}$ $-\frac{\sqrt{2}}{2}$
9. $\tan\frac{3\pi}{4}$ -1

10. $\sin 90°$ 1
11. $\csc 270°$ -1
12. $\tan 45°$ 1

13. $\cos\frac{3\pi}{2}$ 0
14. $\tan\frac{3\pi}{2}$ undefined
15. $\sin\frac{3\pi}{2}$ -1

Use a calculator to approximate each value to four decimal places.

16. $\cot(-75°)$ -0.2679
17. $\sin 634°$ -0.9976
18. $\cos 235°$ -0.5736

19. $\sin 2$ 0.9093
20. $\sec 4.28$ -2.3864
21. $\cot 0.23$ 4.2709

T31
Glencoe Division, Macmillan/McGraw-Hill

CHECKING FOR UNDERSTANDING

Communicating Mathematics

Read and study the lesson to answer each question. 1–4. See margin.

1. **Explain** why some of the trigonometric functions for quadrantal angles are undefined. Use an example as part of your explanation.

2. **Explain** how you would evaluate sec 79° using a calculator.

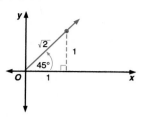

3. **Show** how you can use the figure at the right to find the value of the trigonometric functions for a 45° angle.

4. **Name** three angle measures that are excluded from the domain of the tangent function.

Guided Practice

Find each exact value. Do not use a calculator.

5. tan 60° $\sqrt{3}$

6. cos 450° 0

7. $\sin\left(-\frac{3\pi}{4}\right)$ $-\frac{\sqrt{2}}{2}$

8. csc $\frac{\pi}{2}$ 1

9. sec 30° $\frac{2\sqrt{3}}{3}$

10. cot $\frac{8\pi}{3}$ $-\frac{\sqrt{3}}{3}$

Use a calculator to approximate each value to four decimal places.

11. cos 42° 0.7431

12. csc 36.7° 1.6733

13. tan $\frac{7\pi}{6}$ 0.5774

14. Find the values of the six trigonometric functions of an angle in standard position with measure $\frac{3\pi}{2}$. See margin.

EXERCISES

Practice

Find each exact value. Do not use a calculator.

15. csc 90° 1

16. cos 60° $\frac{1}{2}$

17. sin $\frac{\pi}{3}$ $\frac{\sqrt{3}}{2}$

18. tan $\frac{9\pi}{4}$ 1

19. sec $\frac{7\pi}{3}$ 2

20. cot 45° 1

21. sec 270° undefined

22. cos $\frac{5\pi}{6}$ $-\frac{\sqrt{3}}{2}$

23. sin $\frac{7\pi}{6}$ $-\frac{1}{2}$

24. csc $\left(-\frac{7\pi}{2}\right)$ 1

25. tan 3π 0

26. cot $\frac{19\pi}{3}$ $\frac{\sqrt{3}}{3}$

Use a calculator to approximate each value to four decimal places.

27. cot $\left(-\frac{4\pi}{9}\right)$ −0.1763

28. sin 710° −0.1736

29. sec (−112°) −2.6695

30. sin 7 0.6570

31. cot 11.55π −0.1584

32. csc 34.78° 1.7531

33. tan 115°40′ −2.0809

34. cos 72°30′30″ 0.3006

35. tan (16.4 + π) 0.8288

LESSON 5-4 TRIGONOMETRIC FUNCTIONS OF SPECIAL ANGLES 267

EVALUATING THE LESSON

Checking for Understanding

Exercises 1–14 are designed to help you assess students' understanding through reading, writing, speaking, and modeling. You should work through Exercises 1–4 with your students and then monitor their work on Exercises 5–14.

Closing the Lesson

Writing Activity Have students write a paragraph describing how they would find the values of the six trigonometric functions of an angle in each of the four quadrants.

APPLYING THE LESSON

Homework Exercises

Assignment Guide

Average: 15–31, 36, 37, 39–45
Enriched: 16–26 even, 27–45

The red A, B, and C flags printed only in the Teacher's Wraparound Edition, indicate the level of difficulty of the exercises.

Chapter 5, Quiz B, (Lessons 5–3 through 5–4), is available in the *Evaluation Masters*, p. 61.

Additional Answer

36. $\sin \theta = \dfrac{-5\sqrt{26}}{26}$,

$\cos \theta = \dfrac{-\sqrt{26}}{26}$, $\tan \theta = 5$,

$\csc \theta = \dfrac{\sqrt{26}}{-5}$, $\sec \theta = -\sqrt{26}$,

$\cot \theta = \dfrac{1}{5}$

Critical Thinking

36. The terminal side of an angle θ in standard position coincides with the line $y = 5x$ and lies in Quadrant III. Find the six trigonometric functions of θ.
See margin.

Applications and Problem Solving

37. Physics The application at the beginning of the lesson suggests that as light passes from air to water, the light ray is bent toward the normal, the line perpendicular to the boundary between the two substances. The relation between the angle of incidence θ_1 and angle of refraction θ_2 is given by Snell's Law, $\dfrac{\sin \theta_1}{\sin \theta_2} = k$, where k is a constant called the index of refraction. Suppose a ray of light passes from air to glass. The measure of the angle of incidence is $52°$ and the measure of the angle of refraction is $31.3°$. Find the index of refraction for glass. 1.52

38. Optics Refer to the application at the beginning of the lesson. Suppose a fisherman is trying to net a fish under water. Find the measure of displacement if t measures 10 centimeters, the measure of angle A is $41°$, and the measure of angle B is $60°$.
4.31 cm

Mixed Review

39. Write the slope-intercept form of the equation of the line that passes through $(2, 5)$ and $(6, 3)$. **(Lesson 1-5)** $y = -\dfrac{1}{2}x + 6$

40. Find the slope of the line tangent to the graph of $y = 2x^2$ at $(2, 8)$. **(Lesson 3-6)** 8

41. Solve $\dfrac{1}{9} + \dfrac{1}{2a} = \dfrac{1}{a}$. **(Lesson 4-6)** $\dfrac{9}{2}$

42. Change $35°20'55''$ to a decimal number of degrees to the nearest thousandth. **(Lesson 5-1)** $35.349°$

43. Agriculture A center-pivot irrigation system with a 75-meter radial arm completes one revolution every 6 hours. Find the linear velocity of a nozzle at the end of the arm. **(Lesson 5-2)** 25π m/h

44. Find $\sin \theta$ when $\tan \theta = -\dfrac{3}{4}$ and the terminal side of θ is in Quadrant IV. **(Lesson 5-3)** $-\dfrac{3}{5}$

45. College Entrance Exam Choose the best answer. C

x, y, and z are different positive integers. $\dfrac{x}{y}$ and $\dfrac{y}{z}$ are also positive integers. Which of the following cannot be a positive integer?

(A) $\dfrac{x}{z}$ **(B)** $(x)(y)$ **(C)** $\dfrac{z}{x}$ **(D)** $(x + y)z$ **(E)** $(x - z)y$

268 CHAPTER 5 THE TRIGONOMETRIC FUNCTIONS

EXTENDING THE LESSON

Math Power: Connections

A Ferris wheel is 40 feet wide and 4 feet off the ground. If the wheel revolves at 5 revolutions per minute, then you are $24 + 20 \sin (30t - 90)°$ feet above ground, where t is the time in seconds. How far are you above the ground after 3 seconds?
about 24 ft after 5 seconds?
about 41.3 ft About how long does it take to reach the highest point, 44 feet off the ground? 6 seconds

5-5 Right Triangles

Objective
5-5

After studying this lesson, you should be able to:
■ solve right triangles.

Application

The longest truck-mounted ladder used by the Dallas Fire Department is 108 feet long and consists of four hydraulic sections. Gerald Travis, aerial expert for the department, indicates that the optimum operating angle of this ladder is 60°. Outriggers, with an 18-foot span between each, are used to stabilize the ladder truck and permit operating angles greater than 60°, allowing the ladder truck to be closer to buildings in the downtown streets of Dallas. Assuming the ladder is mounted 8 feet off the ground, how far from an 84-foot burning building should the base of the ladder be placed to achieve the optimum operating angle of 60°? How far should the ladder be extended to reach the roof? *This problem will be solved in Example 4.*

Right triangles can be used to define trigonometric functions. Let A, B, and C designate the vertices of a right triangle and the angles at those vertices. The measures of the sides opposite angles A, B, and C are designated by a, b, and c, respectively. All right triangles having acute angles congruent to angles A and B are similar. Thus, the ratios of corresponding sides are equal. These ratios are determined by the measures of the acute angles. Therefore, any two congruent angles of different right triangles will have the same ratios associated with them.

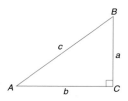

Trigonometric Functions in a Right Triangle

For an acute angle A in right triangle ABC, the trigonometric functions are as follows.

$$\sin A = \frac{\text{side opposite}}{\text{hypotenuse}} = \frac{a}{c} \qquad \csc A = \frac{\text{hypotenuse}}{\text{side opposite}} = \frac{c}{a}$$

$$\cos A = \frac{\text{side adjacent}}{\text{hypotenuse}} = \frac{b}{c} \qquad \sec A = \frac{\text{hypotenuse}}{\text{side adjacent}} = \frac{c}{b}$$

$$\tan A = \frac{\text{side opposite}}{\text{side adjacent}} = \frac{a}{b} \qquad \cot A = \frac{\text{side adjacent}}{\text{side opposite}} = \frac{b}{a}$$

SOH-CAH-TOA is a mnemonic device commonly used for remembering the first three equations.

$$\text{Sin } \theta = \frac{\text{Opposite}}{\text{Hypotenuse}} \qquad \text{Cos } \theta = \frac{\text{Adjacent}}{\text{Hypotenuse}} \qquad \text{Tan } \theta = \frac{\text{Opposite}}{\text{Adjacent}}$$

LESSON 5-5   RIGHT TRIANGLES   269

ALTERNATE TEACHING STRATEGIES

Using Manipulatives

Give each group of four students four different right triangles to solve. Have each student solve one of the triangles using trigonometry and explain how it was solved to the other group members.

Using Applications

Have students estimate the height of the school building using only a yardstick and a protractor.

NCTM Standards: 1–7, 9

Lesson Resources

- Practice Master 5–5
- Enrichment Master 5–5
- Activity Master, p. 13

 Transparency 5–5 contains the 5-Minute Check and a teaching aid for this lesson.

INTRODUCING THE LESSON

5-Minute Check

(over Lesson 5–4)

1. Find the exact value of sin 60°. Do not use a calculator. $\frac{\sqrt{3}}{2}$

2. Find the exact value of tan 270°. Do not use a calculator.   **undefined**

3. Use a calculator to approximate the value of sec 42.8° to four decimal places.   **1.3629**

4. Find the values of the six trigonometric functions of an angle in standard position with measure $\frac{\pi}{2}$.

   $\sin \frac{\pi}{2} = 1$, $\cos \frac{\pi}{2} = 0$,

   $\tan \frac{\pi}{2}$: undefined,

   $\cot \frac{\pi}{2} \geq 0$, $\sec \frac{\pi}{2}$:

   undefined,

   $\csc \frac{\pi}{2} = 1$

5. Use a calculator to approximate the value of sin $(12.2 + \pi)$ to four decimal places.   **0.3582**

Motivating the Lesson

Place the end of a yardstick at various heights along a stack of books on the floor to show students how the angle of elevation (the angle the yardstick makes with the floor) changes with the height of the stack. Calculate the angle of elevation by using the height of the stack, the length of the yardstick, and the tangent ratio.

Chalkboard Examples

For Example 1

A right triangle has sides whose lengths are 8 cm, 15 cm, and 17 cm. Find the values of the six trigonometric functions of α.

$\sin \alpha = \dfrac{8}{17}$, $\cos \alpha = \dfrac{15}{17}$,

$\tan \alpha = \dfrac{8}{15}$, $\csc \alpha = \dfrac{17}{8}$,

$\sec \alpha = \dfrac{17}{15}$, $\cot \alpha = \dfrac{15}{8}$

For Example 2

Solve right triangle ABC. Round angle measures to the nearest degree and side measures to the nearest tenth.

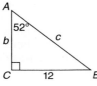

$B = 38°$, $c = 15.2$, $b = 9.4$

For Example 3

In $\triangle RST$, find the measure of $\angle R$ to the nearest degree. **34°**

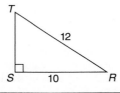

Teaching Tip After doing Example 3, ask students to explain how they would solve the problem using the csc ratio.

Example 1

A right triangle has sides whose lengths are 5 cm, 12 cm, and 13 cm. Find the values of the six trigonometric functions of α.

$\sin \alpha = \dfrac{\text{side opposite}}{\text{hypotenuse}} = \dfrac{5}{13}$

$\cos \alpha = \dfrac{\text{side adjacent}}{\text{hypotenuse}} = \dfrac{12}{13}$

$\tan \alpha = \dfrac{\text{side opposite}}{\text{side adjacent}} = \dfrac{5}{12}$

$\csc \alpha = \dfrac{\text{hypotenuse}}{\text{side opposite}} = \dfrac{13}{5}$

$\sec \alpha = \dfrac{\text{hypotenuse}}{\text{side adjacent}} = \dfrac{13}{12}$

$\cot \alpha = \dfrac{\text{side adjacent}}{\text{side opposite}} = \dfrac{12}{5}$

You can use trigonometric functions to solve right triangles. To **solve a triangle** means to find all of the measures of its sides and angles. Usually, two measures, such as a side and an angle, are given. Then you can find the remaining measures.

Example 2

Solve right triangle *ABC*. Round angle measures to the nearest degree and side measures to the nearest tenth.

$49° + B = 90°$ *Angles A and B are complementary.*

$\qquad B = 41°$

$\sin 49° = \dfrac{7}{c}$ $\qquad$ $\tan 49° = \dfrac{7}{b}$

$0.7547 \approx \dfrac{7}{c}$ $\qquad$ $1.1504 \approx \dfrac{7}{b}$

$\qquad c \approx 9.3$ $\qquad\qquad b \approx 6.1$

Therefore, $B = 41°$, $c = 9.3$, and $b = 6.1$.

Example 3

In $\triangle RST$, find the measure of $\angle R$ to the nearest degree.

$\sin R = \dfrac{\text{side opposite}}{\text{hypotenuse}}$

$\qquad = \dfrac{8}{14}$ *Use your calculator.*

$8 \boxed{\div} 14 \boxed{=} \boxed{\text{2nd}} \boxed{\text{SIN}}$ *34.849905*

$R \approx 35°$

There are many useful applications of trigonometry involving right triangles.

Example 4

APPLICATION

Fire Fighting

Refer to the application at the beginning of the lesson. Assume that the ladder is mounted 8 feet off the ground.
a. How far from an 84-foot burning building should the base of the ladder be placed to achieve the optimum operating angle of 60°?
b. How far should the ladder be extended to reach the roof?

a. Begin by drawing a diagram. In the diagram at the right, d feet represents the distance between the base of the truck-mounted ladder and the base of the wall of the building, and ℓ feet represents the length of the ladder when it is extended.

Use the trigonometric ratios to find d.

$$\tan 60° = \frac{76}{d}$$

$$1.7321 \approx \frac{76}{d}$$

$$d \approx 43.9$$

So, the base of the ladder should be placed 43.9 feet from the wall.

b. Then use the trigonometric ratios to find ℓ.

$$\sin 60° = \frac{76}{\ell}$$

$$0.8660 \approx \frac{76}{\ell}$$

$$\ell \approx 87.8$$ The hydraulic ladder should be extended 87.8 feet.

You can use right triangle trigonometry to solve problems involving geometric figures. The *apothem* of a regular polygon is the measure of a line segment from the center of the polygon to the midpoint of one of its sides.

Example 5

A regular hexagon is inscribed in a circle with diameter 7.52 cm. Find the apothem. Round the answer to the nearest hundredth.

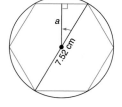

First, draw a diagram.

If the diameter of the circle is 7.52 cm, the radius is 7.52 ÷ 2 or 3.76 cm.

The measure of the central angle is 360° ÷ 12 or 30°.

(continued on the next page)

LESSON 5-5 RIGHT TRIANGLES 271

Write an equation using trigonometric ratios.

$$\cos 30° = \frac{a}{3.76} \qquad \cos = \frac{side\ adjacent}{hypotenuse}$$

$$3.76 \cos 30° = a$$

$$3.2562 \approx a$$

Thus, the apothem of the hexagon is about 3.26 cm.

There are many other applications that require trigonometric solutions. For example, surveyors use special instruments to find the measures of angles of elevation and angles of depression. An **angle of elevation** is the angle between a horizontal line and the line of sight from an observer to an object at a higher level. An **angle of depression** is the angle between a horizontal line and the line of sight from the observer to an object at a lower level.

Example 6

A flagpole 40 feet high stands on top of the Wentworth Building. From a point P in front of Bailey's Drugstore, the angle of elevation of the top of the pole is 54°54′, and the angle of elevation of the bottom of the pole is 47°30′. To the nearest foot, how high is the building?

Draw a diagram to model the situation.
Let *x* = the height of the building.
Let *a* = the distance from P to the foot of the building.

$$\tan 47°30′ = \frac{x}{a} \qquad \tan \alpha = \frac{side\ opposite}{side\ adjacent}$$

$$\tan 54°54′ = \frac{40 + x}{a}$$

Solve each equation for *a*. Then, the following is true.

$$\frac{40 + x}{\tan 54°54′} = \frac{x}{\tan 47°30′}$$

$$\tan 47°30′(40 + x) = x(\tan 54°54′)$$

$$40\tan 47°30′ = x(\tan 54°54′ - \tan 47°30′)$$

$$43.6523 = 0.3315x$$

$$x = 131.68$$

Use your calculator to change degrees and minutes to a decimal.

So, the building is about 132 feet tall.

CHECKING FOR UNDERSTANDING

Communicating Mathematics

Read and study the lesson to answer each question.

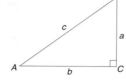

1. **Write** an equation that relates sin A and cos B. Describe the equation in words. Use the drawing at the right. See margin.

2. **Sketch** a right triangle in which $\sin A = \frac{3}{7}$ and $\tan B = \frac{2\sqrt{10}}{3}$. See margin.

3. **Describe** one way to use trigonometry and right triangles to find the height of your school building. Answers may vary.

Guided Practice

Write an equation that would enable you to solve for the indicated measures. Do *not* solve.

4. If $A = 20°$ and $c = 35$, find a. $\sin 20° = \frac{a}{35}$

5. If $b = 13$ and $A = 76°$, find a. $\tan 76° = \frac{a}{13}$

6. If $a = 6$ and $c = 12$, find B. $\cos B = \frac{1}{2}$

7. If $a = 21.2$ and $b = 9$, find A. $\tan A = \frac{21.2}{9}$

8. If $B = 16°$ and $c = 13$, find a. $\cos 16° = \frac{a}{13}$

9. If $A = 49°13'$ and $a = 10$, find b. $\tan 49°13' = \frac{10}{b}$

10. If $c = 16$ and $a = 7$, find b. $7^2 + b^2 = 16^2$

11. If $a = 7$ and $b = 12$, find A. $\tan A = \frac{7}{12}$

12. If $a = 5$ and $b = 6$, find c. $5^2 + 6^2 = c^2$

13. **Geometry** The base angles of an isosceles triangle measure $57°30'$ and the base is 7.5 cm long. Find the lengths of the congruent sides and the altitude to the base to the nearest tenth. 7.0 cm, 5.9 cm

14. A tower 250 meters high casts a shadow 176 meters long. Find the angle of elevation of the sun to the nearest minute. $54°51'$

EXERCISES

Practice

Solve each triangle described, given the triangle below. Round angle measures to the nearest minute and side measures to the nearest tenth. 15–24. See margin.

15. $A = 41°$, $b = 7.44$
16. $B = 42°10'$, $a = 9$
17. $b = 22$, $A = 22°22'$
18. $a = 21$, $c = 30$

19. $A = 45°$, $c = 7\sqrt{2}$
20. $a = 31.2$, $c = 42.4$
21. $A = 37°15'$, $b = 11$
23. $A = 55°55'$, $c = 16$

22. $a = 11$, $b = 21$
24. $B = 78°8'$, $a = 41$

LESSON 5-5   RIGHT TRIANGLES   273

RETEACHING THE LESSON

Ask students to explain how to find the height of a tall building. Have them use models in their explanation.

25. Geometry A regular pentagon has an apothem of 7.43 centimeters. Find the length of a side of the pentagon and the length of the radius of the circumscribed circle to the nearest hundredth. 10.80 cm, 9.18 cm

26. Geometry A rectangle is 17.5 centimeters by 26.2 centimeters. Find the angle formed by the longer side and a diagonal to the nearest minute. 33°44′

27. Geometry A 7.4-centimeter chord subtends a central angle of 41° in a circle. Find the length of the radius of the circle to the nearest hundredth. 10.57 cm

Critical Thinking

28. Derive two formulas for the length of the altitude of the triangle shown at the right, given that a, b, and θ are known. Justify each of the steps you take in your reasoning. See margin.

Applications and Problem Solving

29. Home Maintenance Mrs. James is using a 6-meter ladder to clean the windows on her second floor. Her ladder stands on level ground and rests against the side of her house at a point 4 meters from the ground. How far from the side of her house is the foot of the ladder? Round your answer to the nearest hundredth. 4.47 m

30. Aeronautics A hot air balloon rises at the rate of 70 feet per minute. An observer 420 feet from the place of ascent watches the balloon rise.

30a. $\tan \theta = \frac{70t}{420}$

30b. 245 ft, 1540 ft, 4200 ft

a. Write an expression for the altitude of the balloon in terms of time, t minutes, and the angle of elevation, θ.

b. What is the altitude of the balloon after 3.5 minutes, 22 minutes, and 1 hour?

c. What are the angles of elevation to the nearest minute for each amount of time? 30°15′, 74°45′, 84°17′

31. National Landmarks The Washington Monument is 169.29 meters tall and, at a particular time, casts a shadow 201.2 meters long. Find the approximate angle of elevation of the sun at that time. about 40°

32. Geography To find the height of the Charles Mound in Illinois, Jim located two points, C and D, on a plain in line with the mound. The angle of depression from the mound to C is 49°42′, and the angle of depression to D is 26°27′. Jim reads in an encyclopedia that the mound is 1235 feet high. Find the distance from C to D to the nearest foot. 1435 ft

33. Cartography Find the bearing of a road that runs directly from A to B, with B being 3 miles north and 1.7 miles east of A. (The bearing of B from A is the positive angle with vertex at A measured clockwise from north to B.) 60°28′

34. Aeronautics A satellite S is in a geosynchronous orbit; that is, it stays over the same point T on Earth as Earth rotates on its axis. From the satellite, a spherical cap of Earth is visible. The circle bounding this cap is called the horizon circle. The line of sight from the satellite is tangent to a point Q on the surface of Earth. If the radius of Earth, CQ, is 3963 miles and the satellite is 23,300 miles from the surface of Earth at Q, what is the radius of the horizon circle, PQ, in miles?

3907 miles

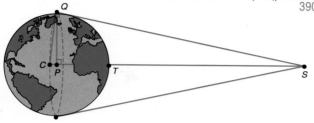

Mixed Review

35. Determine if –2 is a root of $x^3 - 3x^2 - 2x + 4 = 0$.   **(Lesson 4-1)** no

36. Find the measure of the reference angle for an angle of 210°.   **(Lesson 5-1)** 30°

37. Suppose θ is an angle in standard position and $\tan \theta > 0$. State the quadrants in which the terminal side of θ can lie.   **(Lesson 5-3)** I, III

38. Find $\sin \frac{\pi}{4}$, $\cos \frac{\pi}{4}$, and $\tan \frac{\pi}{4}$.   **(Lesson 5-4)** $\frac{\sqrt{2}}{2}, \frac{\sqrt{2}}{2}, 1$

39. College Entrance Exam Choose the best answer. C
In the figure at the right, four semicircles are drawn on the four sides of a rectangle. What is the total area of the shaded regions?

(A) 5π **(B)** $\frac{5\pi}{2}$ **(C)** $\frac{5\pi}{4}$ **(D)** $\frac{5\pi}{8}$ **(E)** $\frac{5\pi}{16}$

CASE STUDY FOLLOW-UP

Refer to Case Study 1: *Buying a Home*, on pages 956–958.

The angle of elevation of a roof is called the pitch.

1. The pitch of the roof shown is 28°. The width of the house is 48 feet. Find h, the maximum height of the attic. 12.8 ft

2. The area of a one-story square house with a pitched roof is the same as the mean area of a one-family dwelling built in 1990. The pitch of the roof is 20°. Find the maximum height of the attic. 8.3 ft

3. See students' work.

3. Research Adobe homes in New Mexico have flat roofs. Farm houses in Maine have roofs with steep pitches. Research the relationship between local weather and roof design. Then write a 1-page paper describing your findings.

EXTENDING THE LESSON

Math Power: Connections

If the height of a rectangular prism is 10 inches and the sides of the square base are each 5 inches, find the angle formed by the diagonal of the prism with a diagonal of a base of the prism.
54.8°

10 in.

5 in.

Case Study Follow-Up

This activity provides an opportunity to do research and apply mathematics in solving problems related to issues that may face students in their adult lives. Case Study 1 is located on pages 956–958.

Enrichment Masters Booklet, p. 32

NAME _____ DATE _____

5-5 Enrichment Worksheet

Using Right Triangles to Find the Area of Another Triangle

You can find the area of a right triangle by using the formula $A = \frac{1}{2}bh$. In the formula, one leg of the right triangle can be used as the base, and the other leg can be used as the height.

The vertices of a triangle can be represented on the coordinate plane by three ordered pairs. In order to find the area of a general triangle, you can **encase** the triangle in a rectangle as shown in the diagram below.

A rectangle is placed around the triangle so that the vertices of the triangle all touch the sides of the rectangle.

Example Find the area of a triangle whose vertices are $A(-1, 3)$, $B(4, 8)$, and $C(8, 5)$.

Plot the points and draw the triangle. Encase the triangle in a rectangle whose sides are parallel to the axes, then find the coordinates of the vertices of the rectangle.

$D(-1, 8)$ $B(4, 8)$ $E(8, 8)$
$C(8, 5)$
$A(-1, 3)$ $F(8, 3)$

Area $\triangle ABC$ = area $ADEF$ − area $\triangle ADB$ − area $\triangle BEC$ − area $\triangle CFA$, where $\triangle ADB$, $\triangle BDC$, and $\triangle CFA$ are all right triangles.

Area $\triangle ABC$ = $5(9) - \frac{1}{2}(5)(5) - \frac{1}{2}(4)(3) - \frac{1}{2}(2)(9)$
= 17.5 square units

Find the area of the triangle having vertices with each set of coordinates.
1. $A(4, 6), B(-1, 2), C(6, -5)$ 31.5
2. $A(-2, -4), B(4, 7), C(6, -1)$ 35
3. $A(4, 2), B(6, 9), C(-1, 4)$ 19.5
4. $A(2, -3), B(6, -8), C(3, 5)$ 13.5

T32
Glencoe Division, Macmillan/McGraw-Hill

NCTM Standards: 1–7, 9

Lesson Resources

- Practice Master 5–6
- Enrichment Master 5–6
- Evaluation Master, Quiz C, p. 62
- Technology Master, p. 10

 Transparency 5–6 contains the 5-Minute Check and a teaching aid for this lesson.

INTRODUCING THE LESSON

 5-Minute Check

(over Lesson 5–5)

1. Write an equation that would enable you to find *c* for triangle *ABC*.

$$\sin 38° = \frac{14}{c}$$

2. Find *b* to the nearest tenth in triangle *ABC* above. ≈ **17.9**
3. Given triangle *ABC* with right angle *C*, *B* = 29°, and *c* = 27. Solve the triangle. Round side measures to the nearest tenth.
   A = **61°**, *a* = **23.6**, *b* = **13.1**
4. A regular hexagon has side length 8 cm. Find the length of the apothem to two decimal places. **6.93 cm**

Prerequisite Skills

Students should be familiar with the necessary conditions for two triangles to be congruent.

1. Name the triangle congruence theorems from geometry.
   SAS, ASA, AAS, SSS
2. Name the case from geometry that is not true in general. **SSA**

5-6   The Law of Sines

Objectives

After studying this lesson, you should be able to:

5–6A ■ determine whether a triangle has zero, one, or two solutions, and
5–6B ■ solve triangles by using the law of sines.

Application

The blades of many power lawn mowers are rotated by a two-stroke engine with a piston sliding back and forth in the engine cylinder. As the piston moves back and forth, the connecting rod rotates the circular crankshaft. In order to ensure smooth operation of your lawn mower, design engineers synchronize the linear motion of the piston with the circular motion of the crankshaft. Suppose that the crankshaft rotates at 1200 revolutions per minute and that P is at the vertical position when it begins to rotate. How many centimeters is the piston from the rim of the crankshaft after 0.01 second? *This problem will be solved in Example 2.*

The law of sines can be used to solve triangles that are not right triangles. Consider △*ABC* inscribed in ⊙*O* with diameter $\overline{DB}$. Let 2*r* be the measure of the diameter. Draw $\overline{AD}$. Then ∠*D* ≅ ∠*C* since they intercept the same arc. So, sin *C* = sin *D*. ∠*BAD* is inscribed in a semicircle, so it is a right angle. So, sin $D = \frac{c}{2r}$. Thus, since sin *D* = sin *C*, it follows that sin $C = \frac{c}{2r}$ or $\frac{c}{\sin C} = 2r$.

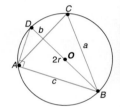

Similarly, by drawing diameters through *A* and *C*, $\frac{b}{\sin B} = 2r$ and $\frac{a}{\sin A} = 2r$. Thus, the following is true.

$$\frac{a}{\sin A} = \frac{b}{\sin B} = \frac{c}{\sin C}$$

These equations state that the ratio of any side of a triangle to the sine of the angle opposite that side is a constant for a given triangle. These equations are collectively called the law of sines.

ALTERNATE TEACHING STRATEGIES

Using Models

Have students draw various triangles. Measure the sides with a ruler and the angles with a protractor. Verify the law of sines for each triangle.

Using Manipulatives

Place three objects on the floor so that they form a large triangle. Use a ruler and a protractor to determine the two sides and an angle of the triangle. Solve the triangle using the law of sines. Repeat the activity by forming a different triangle and measuring two angles and a side.

Law of Sines

Let $\triangle ABC$ be any triangle with a, b, and c representing the measures of the sides opposite the angles with measurements A, B, and C respectively. Then, the following is true.

$$\frac{a}{\sin A} = \frac{b}{\sin B} = \frac{c}{\sin C}$$

For example, in a $30° - 60°$ right triangle with sides measuring 1, $\sqrt{3}$, and 2, the ratios are as follows.

$$\frac{1}{\sin 30°} = \frac{\sqrt{3}}{\sin 60°} = \frac{2}{\sin 90°}$$

Example 1

Solve $\triangle ABC$ if $A = 29°10'$, $B = 62°20'$, and $c = 11.5$. Round angle measures to the nearest minute and side measures to the nearest tenth.

First, find the measure of angle C.
$C = 180° - (29°10' + 62°20')$ or $88°30'$

Use the law of sines to find a and b.

$$\frac{a}{\sin A} = \frac{c}{\sin C} \qquad\qquad \frac{b}{\sin B} = \frac{c}{\sin C}$$

$$\frac{a}{\sin 29°10'} = \frac{11.5}{\sin 88°30'} \qquad\qquad \frac{b}{\sin 62°20'} = \frac{11.5}{\sin 88°30'}$$

$$a = \frac{11.5\sin 29°10'}{\sin 88°30'} \qquad\qquad b = \frac{11.5\sin 62°20'}{\sin 88°30'}$$

$$\approx \frac{11.5(0.4874)}{0.9997} \qquad\qquad \approx \frac{11.5(0.8857)}{0.9997}$$

$$\approx 5.6 \qquad\qquad\qquad\qquad \approx 10.2$$

Therefore, $C = 88°30'$, $a \approx 5.6$, and $b \approx 10.2$.

Example 2

APPLICATION

Mechanics

Refer to the application at the beginning of the lesson. How many centimeters is the piston from the rim of the crankshaft after 0.01 second? Round your answer to the nearest tenth.

The crankshaft rotates at 1200 revolutions per minute or 20 revolutions per second. So, point P turns through $20(360°)$ or $7200°$ every second or $72°$ every 0.01 second. Thus, the measure of $\angle O$ is $90° - 72°$ or $28°$.

$$\frac{PQ}{\sin O} = \frac{OP}{\sin Q}$$

Apply the law of sines to $\angle Q$.

$$\frac{15}{\sin 28°} = \frac{5}{\sin Q}$$

$$\sin Q = \frac{5\sin 28°}{15}$$

$$\sin Q \approx 0.1565$$

$$Q \approx 9°$$

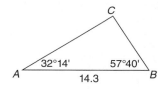

(continued on the next page)

Motivating the Lesson

Draw the picture below on the chalkboard. Tell students that they will learn how to find the distance across the lake in this lesson.

TEACHING THE LESSON

Teaching Tip   Before doing Example 1, verify the law of sines for a $45°–45°–90°$ triangle with sides measuring 1, 1, and $\sqrt{2}$.

Chalkboard Examples

For Example 1

Solve $\triangle ABC$ if $A = 32°14'$, $B = 57°40'$, and $c = 14.3$. Round angle measures to the nearest minute and side measures to the nearest tenth.

$C = 90°6'$, $a = 7.6$, $b = 12.1$

For Example 2

Refer to the application at the beginning of the lesson. How many centimeters is the piston from the rim of the crankshaft after 5 seconds? Round to the nearest tenth.   38.2 cm

So after 0.01 second, $\angle P = 180° - (28° + 9°)$ or $143°$. Apply the law of sines again.

$$\frac{QO}{\sin 143°} = \frac{15}{\sin 28°}$$

$$QO = \frac{15 \sin 143°}{\sin 28°}$$

$$\approx \frac{15(0.6018)}{0.4695}$$

$$\approx 19.2$$

Therefore, the piston is about $19.2 - 5$ or 14.2 centimeters from the rim of the crankshaft after 0.01 second.

When the measures of two sides of a triangle and the measure of the angle opposite one of them are given, there may not always be one solution. However, one of the following will be true.

1. No triangle exists.
2. Exactly one triangle exists.
3. Two triangles exist.

In other words, there may be no solution, one solution, or two solutions. Suppose you know the measures of a, b, and A. Consider the following cases.

Case 1: $m \angle A < 90°$

If $a = b \sin A$, one solution exists.
The solution is a right triangle.

If $a > b \sin A$ and $a \geq b$,
one solution exists.

If $a < b \sin A$, no solution exists.

If $b \sin A < a < b$, two solutions exist.

Case 2: $m \angle A \geq 90°$

If $a \leq b$, no solution exists.

If $a > b$, one solution exists.

Example 3 | **Solve △ABC if A = 63°10′, b = 18, and a = 17. Round angle measures to the nearest minute and side measures to the nearest tenth.**

To determine the number of solutions, first compare a with $b \sin A$.

$$b \sin A = 18 \sin 63°10′$$
$$= 18(0.8923)$$
$$= 16.1$$

Since $63°10′ < 90°$ and $b \sin A < a < b$ $(16.1 < 17 < 18)$, two solutions exist. Use the law of sines to find B.

$$\frac{17}{\sin 63°10′} = \frac{18}{\sin B}$$

$$\sin B = \frac{18 \sin 63°10′}{17}$$

$$\sin B \approx \frac{18(0.8923)}{17}$$

$$\sin B \approx 0.9448 \qquad \textit{Use a calculator to find B.}$$

$$B \approx 70°52′ \qquad \textit{Round to the nearest minute.}$$

Since we know that there are two solutions, another measurement for B is about $180° - 70°52′$ or $109°8′$. Now, solve each triangle.

Solution 1

$$C \approx 180° - (63°10′ + 70°52′)$$
$$\approx 45°58′$$

$$\frac{17}{\sin 63°10′} \approx \frac{c}{\sin 45°58′}$$

$$c \approx \frac{17 \sin 45°58′}{\sin 63°10′}$$

$$\approx \frac{17(0.7189)}{0.8923}$$

$$\approx 13.7$$

One solution is $B \approx 70°52′$, $C \approx 45°58′$, and $c \approx 13.7$.

Solution 2

$$C \approx 180° - (63°10′ + 109°8′)$$
$$\approx 7°42′$$

$$\frac{17}{\sin 63°10′} \approx \frac{c}{\sin 7°42′}$$

$$c \approx \frac{17 \sin 7°42′}{\sin 63°10′}$$

$$\approx \frac{17(0.1340)}{0.8923}$$

$$\approx 2.6$$

Another solution is $B \approx 109°8′$, $C \approx 7°42′$, and $c \approx 2.6$.

LESSON 5-6   THE LAW OF SINES   279

LESSON 5–6   THE LAW OF SINES   279

Example 4 | Solve $\triangle ABC$ if $A = 43°$, $b = 20$, and $a = 11$. Round angle measures to the nearest minute and side measures to the nearest tenth.

$$b \sin A = 20 \sin 43°$$
$$\approx 20(0.6820)$$
$$\approx 13.64$$

Since $43° < 90°$ and $11 < 13.64$, no solution exists.

EVALUATING THE LESSON

Checking for Understanding

Exercises 1–13 are designed to help you assess students' understanding through reading, writing, speaking, and modeling. You should work through Exercises 1–3 with your students and then monitor their work on Exercises 4–13.

Closing the Lesson

Modeling Activity   Have each student draw an arbitrary triangle, measure one angle and two sides, determine whether the triangle can be solved, and state how many solutions exist.

Practice Masters Booklet, p. 33

CHECKING FOR UNDERSTANDING

Communicating Mathematics

Read and study the lesson to answer each question. 1–3. See margin.

1. **Describe** one set of conditions for which the law of sines can be used to solve a triangle.

2. **Explain** how you know that a triangle has no solution.

3. **Sketch** $\triangle ABC$ if $m\angle ABC = 40°$, BC measures 4 inches, and $m\angle BCA = 60°$.

Guided Practice

Write an equation that would enable you to solve for the indicated measures. Do *not* solve.

4. If $A = 40°$, $B = 60°$, and $a = 20$, find b.

5. If $b = 2.8$, $A = 53°$, and $B = 61°$, find a. $\dfrac{2.8}{\sin 61°} = \dfrac{a}{\sin 53°}$

6. If $b = 10$, $a = 14$, and $A = 50°$, find B.

7. If $b = 16$, $c = 12$, and $B = 42°$, find C. $\dfrac{16}{\sin 42°} = \dfrac{12}{\sin C}$

4. $\dfrac{20}{\sin 40°} = \dfrac{b}{\sin 60°}$

6. $\dfrac{14}{\sin 50°} = \dfrac{10}{\sin B}$

Determine the number of possible solutions. If a solution exists, solve the triangle. Round angle measures to the nearest minute and side measures to the nearest tenth. 8–13. See Teacher's Answer Key.

8. $A = 140°$, $b = 10$, $a = 3$

9. $C = 17°$, $a = 10$, $c = 11$

10. $A = 30°$, $a = 4$, $b = 8$

11. $B = 160°$, $a = 10$, $A = 41°$

12. $A = 60°$, $b = 2$, $a = \sqrt{3}$

13. $A = 38°$, $b = 10$, $a = 8$

EXERCISES

Practice

Determine the number of possible solutions. If a solution exists, solve the triangle. Round angle measures to the nearest minute and side measures to the nearest tenth. 14–21. See Teacher's Answer Key.

14. $a = 8$, $A = 49°$, $B = 57°$

15. $a = 6$, $b = 8$, $A = 150°$

16. $a = 26$, $b = 29$, $A = 58°$

17. $A = 40°$, $B = 60°$, $c = 20$

18. $B = 70°$, $C = 58°$, $a = 84$

19. $a = 12$, $b = 14$, $A = 90°$

20. $A = 25°$, $a = 125$, $b = 150$

21. $A = 76°$, $a = 5$, $b = 20$

22. $A = 37°20'$, $B = 51°30'$, $c = 125$ one; $C = 91°10'$, $a = 75.8$, $b = 97.8$

23. $b = 40$, $a = 32$, $A = 125°20'$ none

24. $A = 107°13'$, $a = 17.2$, $c = 12.2$ one; $C = 42°39'$, $B = 30°8'$, $b = 9.0$

280   CHAPTER 5   THE TRIGONOMETRIC FUNCTIONS

RETEACHING THE LESSON

Have students discuss how to determine whether a triangle can be solved and how many solutions exist.

Additional Answers

1. Sample answer: The law of sines can be used to solve $\triangle ABC$ when the measure of A and the values of a and b are also known.

2. Sample answer: When the values of a, b, and A are known, $m\angle A < 90°$, and $a < b\sin A$, the triangle has no solution. If $m\angle A \geq 90°$ and $a \leq b$, the triangle also has no solution.

Use the law of sines to show that each statement is true.

25. $\dfrac{a-c}{c} = \dfrac{\sin A - \sin C}{\sin C}$

26. $\dfrac{b+c}{b-c} = \dfrac{\sin B + \sin C}{\sin B - \sin C}$

27. $\dfrac{a}{b} = \dfrac{\sin A}{\sin B}$

28. $\dfrac{b}{a+b} = \dfrac{\sin B}{\sin A + \sin B}$

Critical Thinking

29. Suppose the angle measures of $\triangle ABC$ are equal to the angle measures of $\triangle XYZ$. Use the law of sines to show that the triangles are similar, but not necessarily congruent. See Teacher's Answer Key.

Applications and Problem Solving

30. Navigation A ship's captain plans to sail to a port that is 450 miles away and 12° east of north. The captain sails the ship due north, turns the ship, and sails 316 miles.

a. Through what angle should the captain turn the ship to arrive at port? 17°13′ east of north

b. How many hours will it take to arrive at the turning point if the captain chooses a speed of 23 miles per hour? 6 hours

c. Instead of the plan above, the captain decides to sail 200 miles north, turn through an angle of 20° east of north, and then sail along a straight course. Will the ship reach the port by following this plan? no

31. Landscaping A corner of McCormick Park occupies a triangular area that faces two streets that meet at an angle measuring 85°. The sides of the area facing the streets are each 60 feet in length. The park's landscaper wants to plant begonias around the edges of the triangular area. Find the perimeter of the triangular area. 201.1 ft

Mixed Review

32. Solve $\dfrac{8}{x-3} = \dfrac{x+5}{x-3}$. **(Lesson 4-6)** no solution

33. Identify all angles that are coterminal with a 45° angle. **(Lesson 5-1)** $45° + 360k°$, where k is an integer

34. Find $\sin \dfrac{13\pi}{6}$. **(Lesson 5-4)** $\dfrac{1}{2}$

35. When the angle of elevation of the sun is 27°, the shadow of a tree is 25 meters long. How tall is the tree? Round to the nearest tenth. **(Lesson 5-5)** 12.7 meters

36. College Entrance Exam Choose the best answer. D
A person is hired for a job that pays $500 per month and receives a 10% raise in each following month. In the fourth month, how much will that person earn?

(A) 550   **(B)** 600.50   **(C)** 650.50   **(D)** 665.50   **(E)** 700

EXTENDING THE LESSON

Math Power: Reasoning

Have students derive the law of sines from the following figure.

Since $\sin A = \dfrac{h}{c}$ and $\sin C = \dfrac{h}{a}$, solving each equation for h and setting the answers equal to each other gives $c \sin A = a \sin C$. Divide each side by $\sin A \sin C$ to get $\dfrac{a}{\sin A} = \dfrac{c}{\sin C}$. Since vertices B and C can be switched,

$\dfrac{a}{\sin A} = \dfrac{b}{\sin B}$. Therefore,

$\dfrac{a}{\sin A} = \dfrac{b}{\sin B} = \dfrac{c}{\sin C}$.

The red A, B, and C flags, printed only in the Teacher's Wraparound Edition, indicate the level of difficulty of the exercises.

Chapter 5, Quiz C (Lessons 5–5 through 5–6) is available in the *Evaluation Masters*, p. 62

Exercise Note

The answers for the exercises involving the law of sines may vary because of rounding and the measures of the angles or sides used to do each calculation.

Additional Answer

3.

Enrichment Masters Booklet, p. 33

5-6   **Enrichment Worksheet**
NAME _____ DATE _____

Triangle Challenge

A surveyor took the following measurements from two irregularly-shaped pieces of land. Some of the lengths and angle measurements are missing. Find all missing lengths and angle measurements. Round lengths to the nearest tenth and angle measurements to the nearest minute.

1.

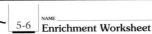

$a \approx 49.5$; $b \approx 52.7$; $c \approx 66.7$
$A \approx 103°58'$; $B \approx 50°8'$; $C \approx 76°52'$;
$D \approx 76°8'$; $E \approx 50°52'$; $F \approx 54°8'$

2.

$a \approx 107.5$; $b \approx 40.5$; $c \approx 52.3$; $d \approx 113.4$
$A \approx 32°37'$; $B \approx 100°$; $C \approx 71°23'$;
$D \approx 55°37'$; $E \approx 82°23'$

T 33
Glencoe Division, Macmillan/McGraw-Hill

Objective This optional page shows how a computer program in BASIC can be used to simulate solving a triangle using the law of sines.

Teaching Suggestions

Point out to students that the program converts the degree measure of an angle to radian measure so that the computer can process the calculations. As an extension, have students modify the program to include applying the law of sines to solve a triangle in which two sides and a non-included angle are known.

Technology

Solving Triangles

▶ **BASIC**
Spreadsheets
Software

```
10  INPUT AA, AB, SA
15  IF AA=0 THEN 180
20  LET AC=180 - AA - AB
30  IF AC < = 0 THEN 130
40  LET SB = SA*SIN (AB*3.14159/180)/
    SIN(AA*3.14159/180)
50  LET SC = SA*SIN (AC*3.14159/180)/
    SIN(AA*3.14159/180)
60  PRINT "ANGLE A = ";AA
70  PRINT "ANGLE B = ";AB
80  PRINT "ANGLE C = ";AC
90  PRINT "SIDE A = ";SA
100 PRINT "SIDE B = ";INT (SB + .5)
110 PRINT "SIDE C = ";INT (SC + .5)
120 GOTO 10
130 PRINT "ANGLE A = ";AA
140 PRINT "ANGLE B = ";AB
150 PRINT "SIDE A = ";SA
160 PRINT "NO TRIANGLE EXISTS."
170 GOTO 10
180 END
```

The BASIC program shown at the left solves triangles by using the law of sines, if solutions exist. In the program, AA represents the degree measure of angle A and SA represents the measure of side a. To begin using the program, enter the degree measures of two angles and the measure of a side opposite one of the angles. To exit the program, enter **0,0,0** at the prompt and then press **[Enter]**.

For a triangle in which the measure of angle A is 35°, the measure of angle B is 45°, and the measure of side A is 6 units, the display is as shown at the right.

```
RUN
ANGLE A = 35
ANGLE B = 45
ANGLE C = 100
SIDE A = 6
SIDE B = 8
SIDE C = 17
```

EXERCISES

Use the BASIC program to solve each triangle.

1. $A = 43°, B = 58°, a = 17$ $C = 79°, b = 21, c = 24$
2. $A = 40°, B = 60°, a = 20$ $C = 80°, b = 27, c = 31$
3. $A = 53°, B = 61°, a = 2.8$ $C = 66°, b = 4, c = 3$

282 CHAPTER 5 THE TRIGONOMETRIC FUNCTIONS

5-7   The Law of Cosines

Objective
5–7

After studying this lesson, you should be able to:
- solve triangles by using the law of cosines.

Application

Suzanne Chu made the diagram at the right based on the measurements listed on the deed to her property. She wants to lay a gravel pathway as shown by the dashed line in the diagram. The pathway will lead from two opposite corners to a circular fountain in the center. The circular region is to have a radius of 10 feet. How long will the pathway be, not including the fountain area? *This problem will be solved in Example 1.*

If either two sides and the included angle or three sides of a triangle are given, the law of sines cannot be used to solve the triangle. Another formula is needed. Consider $\triangle ABC$ with a height of h units and sides measuring a units, b units, and c units. Suppose $\overline{DC}$ is x units long. Then $\overline{BD}$ is $(a - x)$ units long.

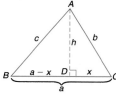

The Pythagorean theorem and the definition of the cosine function can be used to show how $\angle C$, a, b, and c are related.

$c^2 = (a - x)^2 + h^2$ *Apply the Pythagorean theorem to $\triangle ADB$.*

$c^2 = a^2 - 2ax + x^2 + h^2$ *Expand $(a - x)^2$.*

$c^2 = a^2 - 2ax + b^2$ $b^2 = x^2 + h^2$ *in $\triangle ADC$.*

$c^2 = a^2 - 2a(b \cos C) + b^2$ $\cos C = \dfrac{x}{b}$, *so $x = b \cos C$.*

$c^2 = a^2 + b^2 - 2ab \cos C$

By drawing altitudes from B and C, you can derive similar formulas for a^2 and b^2. All three formulas, which make up the law of cosines, can be summarized as follows.

Law of Cosines

Let $\triangle ABC$ be any triangle with a, b, and c representing the measures of sides opposite angles with measurements A, B, and C, respectively. Then, the following are true.

$$a^2 = b^2 + c^2 - 2bc \cos A$$
$$b^2 = a^2 + c^2 - 2ac \cos B$$
$$c^2 = a^2 + b^2 - 2ab \cos C$$

LESSON 5-7   THE LAW OF COSINES   283

ALTERNATE TEACHING STRATEGIES

Using Models

Have students draw various triangles. Measure two sides with a ruler and the angle between them with a protractor. Verify the law of cosines.

Using Communication

Have students discuss how to solve triangles knowing various combinations of sides and angles. They should tell if there is no solution or whether the triangle can be solved using right triangle trigonometry, the law of sines, or the law of cosines.

NCTM Standards: 1–7, 9

Lesson Resources

- Practice Master 5–7
- Enrichment Master 5–7
- Technology Master, p. 9

Transparency 5–7 contains the 5-Minute Check and a teaching aid for this lesson.

INTRODUCING THE LESSON

5-Minute Check
(over Lesson 5–6)

1. Write an equation that would enable you to find b in $\triangle ABC$ if $A = 50°$, $B = 48°$, and $a = 14$.
$$\dfrac{14}{\sin 50°} = \dfrac{b}{\sin 48°}$$

2. Find b to the nearest tenth in triangle ABC in Exercise 1.
≈ 13.6

3. Determine the number of possible solutions if $A = 120°$, $b = 9$, and $a = 6$.   **none**

4. Given $\triangle ABC$ with $B = 41°$, $C = 52°$, and $c = 27$, solve the triangle. Round angle measures to the nearest minute and side measures to the nearest tenth.
$A = 87°$, $a = 34.2$, $b = 22.5$

5. For $\triangle ABC$, determine the number of possible solutions if $A = 124°$, $b = 38$, and $a = 30$. If a solution exists, solve the triangle. Round angle measures to the nearest minute and side measures to the nearest tenth.
none

Motivating the Lesson

Suppose a roof is built so that the angle at the peak and the length of each side is known. How would the width of the house be determined? Tell students that the *SAS case* of congruent triangles cannot be solved with the law of sines.

Chalkboard Examples

For Example 1

Suppose you want to fence a triangular lot as shown below. If two sides measure 84 feet and 78 feet and the angle between the two sides is 102°, what is the length of the fence to the nearest foot?   **288 ft**

For Example 2

Solve △*ABC* if *A* = 39°24′, *b* = 12, *c* = 14. Round angle measures to the nearest degree and side measures to the nearest tenth.
***a* = 9.0, *B* = 58°, *C* = 83°**

Teaching Tip After discussing Example 2, point out that the entire question can be solved by using the law of cosines only.

Additional Answers

1. Sample answer: In any triangle, the length of a side squared is the sum of the squares of the other two sides minus the product of twice the other two sides and the cosine of the angle opposite the first side.
2. Sample answer: If the included angle measures 90°, the equation becomes $c^2 = a^2 + b^2 - 2ab \cos 90°$. Since $\cos 90° = 0$, $c^2 = a^2 + b^2 - 2ab(0)$ or $c^2 = a^2 + b^2$.
3. Use the law of cosines to find *a*. Then use the law of sines to find *C*.

4a.

4b. **no**

You can use the law of cosines to solve the application at the beginning of the lesson.

Example 1

How many feet long is the pathway on Suzanne Chu's property, not including the fountain area, which has a radius of 10 feet?

The proposed gravel pathway is the third side of a triangle whose other two sides measure 107.8 feet and 204 feet with an included angle of 79°. Use the law of cosines to find its length, ℓ, in feet.

$$\ell^2 = (204)^2 + (107.8)^2 - 2(204)(107.8) \cos 79°$$
$$\ell^2 \approx 41{,}616 + 11{,}620.84 - 43{,}982.4(0.1908)$$
$$\ell^2 \approx 44{,}844.998$$
$$\ell \ \approx 211.8$$

Since the fountain will have a diameter of 20 feet, the length of the gravel pathway, exclusive of the fountain area, is about $212 - 20$ or 192 feet.

Many times, you will have to use both the law of cosines and the law of sines to solve triangles.

Example 2

Solve △*ABC* if *A* = 52°10′, *b* = 6, and *c* = 8. Round angle measures to the nearest minute and side measures to the nearest tenth.

Use the law of cosines to find *a*.

$$a^2 = b^2 + c^2 - 2bc \cos A$$
$$a^2 = 6^2 + 8^2 - 2(6)(8) \cos 52°10′$$
$$a^2 \approx 36 + 64 - 96(0.6134)$$
$$a^2 \approx 41.11$$
$$\ a \approx 6.4$$

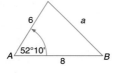

Use the law of sines to find *B*.

$$\frac{6.4}{\sin 52°10′} = \frac{6}{\sin B}$$
$$\sin B = \frac{6 \sin 52°10′}{6.4}$$
$$\sin B \approx \frac{6(0.7898)}{6.4}$$
$$\sin B \approx 0.7404$$
$$B \approx 47°46′ \qquad \textit{Round to the nearest minute.}$$

$$C = 180° - (52°10′ + 47°46′) \text{ or } 80°4′$$

Therefore, $a = 6.4$, $B = 47°46′$, and $C = 80°4′$.

Example 3

Solve △ABC if a = 21, b = 16.7, and c = 10.3. Round angle measures to the nearest minute.

Use the law of cosines.

$$a^2 = b^2 + c^2 - 2bc \cos A$$
$$(21)^2 = (16.7)^2 + (10.3)^2 - 2(16.7)(10.3) \cos A$$
$$441 = 278.89 + 106.09 - 344.02 \cos A$$

$$\cos A = \frac{441 - 278.89 - 106.09}{-344.02}$$

$$\cos A \approx -0.1628$$
$$A \approx 99°22' \qquad \textit{Round to the nearest minute.}$$

Use the law of sines.

$$\frac{21}{\sin 99°22'} = \frac{16.7}{\sin B}$$

$$\sin B = \frac{16.7 \sin 99°22'}{21}$$

$$\sin B \approx \frac{16.7(0.9867)}{21}$$

$$\sin B \approx 0.7847$$
$$B \approx 51°42' \qquad \textit{Round to the nearest minute.}$$

$$C \approx 180° - (99°22' + 51°42')$$
$$\approx 28°56'$$

Therefore, $A \approx 99°22'$, $B \approx 51°42'$ and $C \approx 28°56'$.

CHECKING FOR UNDERSTANDING

Communicating Mathematics

Read and study the lesson to answer each question. 1–4. See margin.

1. **State** the law of cosines in your own words.

2. **Explain** how the Pythagorean theorem is a special case of the law of cosines.

3. **Explain** how to find C in the triangle below. Do not solve.

4. **a. Sketch** a triangle in which AC is 4 inches, AB is 6 inches, and $C = 53°$.
   b. Are there any other triangles that satisfy these conditions?

LESSON 5-7   THE LAW OF COSINES   285

RETEACHING THE LESSON

Suppose the distance between A and B in the diagram at the right cannot be measured directly. Explain how the law of cosines can be used to find the distance between A and B.
The law of cosines can be used directly.
$AB^2 = 100^2 + 140^2 - 2(100)(140)\cos 120°$
$AB \approx 208.8$ ft

Homework Exercises

Assignment Guide

Average: 14–24, 26, 27, 29–34
Enriched: 17–34

The red A, B, and C flags, printed only in the Teacher's Wraparound Edition, indicate the level of difficulty of the exercises.

Exercise Note

The answers for the exercises involving the law of cosines may vary because of rounding and the measures of the angles or sides used to do each calculation.

Additional Answers

5. $A = 53°35'$,
   $B = 59°33'$, $C = 66°52'$
6. $c = 6.5$, $A = 76°5'$, $B = 68°55'$
7. $C = 30°57'$, $B = 109°3'$,
   $b = 14.7$
8. $a = 4.5$, $B = 58°59'$, $C = 81°1'$
9. $b = 18.5$, $C = 79°3'$, $A = 40°57'$
10. $a = 9.6$, $B = 70°$, $b = 14$
11. $A = 30°13'$, $C = 104°19'$,
    $c = 23.1$
12. $a = 2.0$, $B = 105°18'$,
    $C = 45°52'$
14. $A = 34°3'$, $B = 44°25'$,
    $C = 101°32'$
15. $a = 7.8$, $B = 44°13'$,
    $C = 84°47'$
16. $a = 459.1$, $B = 69°16'$,
    $C = 58°4'$
17. $A = 44°25'$, $B = 57°7'$,
    $C = 78°28'$
18. $a = 202.6$, $B = 55°53'$,
    $C = 62°42'$
19. $A = 21°47'$, $B = 120°$,
    $C = 38°13'$
20. $c = 14.1$, $A = 104°53'$,
    $B = 35°47'$
21. $A = 51°50'$, $B = 70°53'$,
    $C = 57°17'$
22. $C = 81°$, $a = 9.1$, $b = 12.1$
23. $b = 12.3$, $A = 39°19'$,
    $C = 20°41'$

Guided Practice The measures of three parts of a triangle are given. Determine whether the law of sines or the law of cosines should be used to solve the triangle. Then solve each triangle. Round angle measures to the nearest minute and side measures to the nearest tenth. 5–12. See margin for solutions.

5. $a = 14, b = 15, c = 16$ cosines
6. $C = 35°, a = 11, b = 10.5$ cosines
7. $a = 10, A = 40°, c = 8$ sines
8. $A = 40°, b = 6, c = 7$ cosines
9. $c = 21, a = 14, B = 60°$ cosines
10. $A = 40°, C = 70°, c = 14$ sines
11. $b = 17, B = 45°28', a = 12$ sines
12. $A = 28°50', b = 4, c = 2.9$ cosines

13. **Aviation** Natalie is flying from Dallas to Little Rock, a distance of 319 miles. She starts her flight 15° off course and flies on this course for 75 miles. How far is she from Little Rock? 247.3 miles

EXERCISES

Practice Solve each triangle. Round angle measures to the nearest minute and side measures to the nearest tenth. 14–23. See margin.

14. $a = 4, b = 5, c = 7$
15. $b = 7, c = 10, A = 51°$
16. $A = 52°40', b = 540, c = 490$
17. $a = 5, b = 6, c = 7$

18. $A = 61°25', b = 191, c = 205$
19. $a = 3, b = 7, c = 5$
20. $b = 13, a = 21.5, C = 39°20'$
21. $a = 11.4, b = 13.7, c = 12.2$
22. $A = 40°, B = 59°, c = 14$
23. $a = 9, c = 5, B = 120°$

24. The sides of a triangle measure 6.8 cm, 8.4 cm, and 4.9 cm. Find the measure of the smallest angle to the nearest minute. 35°41'

25. A parallelogram has sides of 55 cm and 71 cm. Find the length of each diagonal to the nearest tenth if the largest angle measures 106°. 101.1 cm, 76.9 cm

26. 25.5 ft

Critical Thinking 26. **Carpentry** Two carpenters are trying to carry a board down a corridor and around a corner in the Lawson Building. The figure at the right is an overhead view of the corridor. What is the length of the longest board that can be carried parallel to the floor through the corridor, to the nearest tenth of a foot? *Hint: You may want to make a scale drawing and experiment with thin strips of paper.*

27. Navigation   Two ships leave San Francisco at the same time. One travels 40° west of north at a speed of 20 knots. The other travels 10° west of south at a speed of 15 knots. How far apart are they after 11 hours? *1 knot = 1 nautical mile per hour.* 349.7 nautical miles

28. Surveying   A triangular plot of land was measured as shown in the figure at the right. Trigonometry was used to calculate *BC*. However, it was discovered that the measure of angle *A* was really 36.95°. By how many feet was the calculation of *BC* in error? 1.17 feet

Mixed Review

29. Find the slope of the line through (–3, 2) and (5, 7).   **(Lesson 1-4)** $\frac{5}{8}$

30. Find the value of $\begin{vmatrix} 7 & 9 \\ 3 & 6 \end{vmatrix}$.   **(Lesson 2-3)**   15

31. Find the reference angle for an angle that measures 150°.   **(Lesson 5-1)**   30°

32. Find sin θ when the point with coordinates (–7, 24) lies on the terminal side of the angle in standard position.   **(Lesson 5-3)** $\frac{24}{25}$

33. Surveying   Two surveyors 560 yards apart sight a boundary marker C on the other side of a canyon at angles of 27° and 38°. Their measurements will be used to plan a bridge that spans the canyon. How long will the bridge be, to the nearest tenth of a yard? **(Lesson 5-6)** 172.7 yd

34. College Entrance Exam   Sue's average score for three bowling games was 162. In the second game, Sue scored 10 less than in the first game. In the third game, she scored 13 less than in the second game. What was her score in the first game? 173

LESSON 5-7   THE LAW OF COSINES   287

EXTENDING THE LESSON

Math Power: Connections

Have students derive the law of cosines by using the coordinate system shown at the right and the relationship $(\sin A)^2 + (\cos A)^2 = 1$.

Sample: Since $h = c \sin A$ and $b - x = c \cos A$, the coordinates of *B* are ($c \cos A$, $c \sin A$).

$a^2 = (c \cos A - b)^2 + (c \sin A - 0)^2 = c^2 (\cos A)^2 - 2 bc \cos A + b^2 + c^2 (\sin A)^2$
$= c^2 ((\sin A)^2 + (\cos A)^2) - 2 bc \cos A + b^2 = c^2 (1) - 2 bc \cos A + b^2$
$= b^2 + c^2 - 2 bc \cos A$

Enrichment Masters Booklet, p. 34

NAME _____   DATE _____

5-7   Enrichment Worksheet

The Law of Cosines and the Pythagorean Theorem

The law of cosines bears strong similarities to the Pythagorean theorem. According to the law of cosines, if two sides of a triangle have lengths *a* and *b* and if the angle between them has a measure of *x*°, then the length, *y*, of the third side of the triangle can be found by using the equation

$$y^2 = a^2 + b^2 - 2ab \cos x°.$$

Answer the following questions to clarify the relationship between the law of cosines and the Pythagorean theorem.

1. If the value of *x*° becomes less and less, what number is cos *x*° close to?
   1
2. If the value of *x*° is very close to zero but then increases, what happens to cos *x*° as *x*° approaches 90°?
   decreases, approaches 0
3. If *x*° equals 90°, what is the value of cos *x*°? What does the equation of $y^2 = a^2 + b^2 - 2ab \cos x°$ simplify to if *x*° equals 90°?
   0, $y^2 = a^2 + b^2$
4. What happens to the value of cos *x*° as *x*° increases beyond 90° and approaches 180°?
   decreases to −1
5. Consider some particular value of *a* and *b*, say 7 for *a* and 19 for *b*. Use a graphing calculator to graph the equation you get by solving $y^2 = 7^2 + 19^2 - 2(7)(19) \cos x°$ for *y*.
   See students graphs.
   a. In view of the geometry of the situation, what range of values should you use for *X*?
   X min = 0°; *X* max = 360°
   b. Display the graph and use the TRACE function. What do the maximum and minimum values appear to be for the function?
   See students' graphs;
   Y min = −26, *Y* max = −12.
   c. How do the answers for part b relate to the lengths 7 and 19? Are the maximum and minimum values from part b ever actually attained in the geometric situation?
   min = −(19 + 7); max = −(19 − 7); no

T34
Glencoe Division, Macmillan/McGraw-Hill

NCTM Standards: 1–7, 9

Lesson Resources

- Practice Master 5–8
- Enrichment Master 5–8
- Evaluation Master, Quiz D, p. 62

Transparency 5–8 contains the 5-Minute Check and a teaching aid for this lesson.

INTRODUCING THE LESSON

5-Minute Check

(over Lesson 5-7)

1. For △ABC, a = 12, b = 14, c = 16. Determine whether the law of sines or the law of cosines should be used first to solve the triangle.
   law of cosines
2. Solve the triangle in Exercise 1. Round angle measures to the nearest minute.
   **A = 46°36′,
   B = 57°58′, C = 75°26′**
3. Solve △ABC with A = 62°40′, b = 112, and c = 198. Round angle measures to the nearest minute and side measures to the nearest tenth.   **a = 177.2,
   B = 34°12′, C = 83°8′**

Motivating the Lesson

Ask students to sketch a model for the following problem.

Suppose a crop-dusting airplane flies 400 km on a bearing of 60° east of due north and then flies south for 350 km. The plane then flies on a northwest course to return to its starting point. What is the area of the field it dusted?

Sample answer:

5-8   Area of Triangles

Objective
5–8

After studying this lesson, you should be able to:
- find the area of triangles.

Application

Surveyors calculate measures of distances and angles so that they can represent boundary lines of parcels of land. The diagram at the right is a plot of John and Reneé Walters' land. What is the area of the region to the nearest square foot? *This problem will be solved in Example 5.*

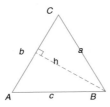

The area of any triangle can be expressed in terms of two sides of the triangle and the measure of the included angle. Suppose you know the measures of $\overline{AC}$ and $\overline{AB}$ and the measure of the included angle A in $\triangle ABC$, shown at the left. Let K represent the measure of the area of $\triangle ABC$ and let h represent the measure of the altitude from B. Then, $K = \frac{1}{2}bh$.

But, $\sin A = \frac{h}{c}$ or $h = c \sin A$. If you substitute $c \sin A$ for h, the result is the following formula.

$$K = \frac{1}{2}bc \sin A$$

If you drew altitudes from A and C, you could also develop the formulas $K = \frac{1}{2}ab \sin C$ and $K = \frac{1}{2}ac \sin B$.

Example 1

Find the area of $\triangle ABC$ if $a = 7.5$, $b = 9$, and $C = 100°$. Round your answer to the nearest tenth.

$K = \frac{1}{2}ab \sin C$

$\quad = \frac{1}{2}(7.5)(9) \sin 100°$

$\quad \approx (33.75)(0.9848)$

$\quad \approx 33.237$

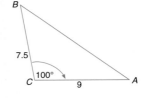

The area is about 33.2 square units.

ALTERNATE TEACHING STRATEGIES

Using Connections

Have students find the area of $\triangle ABC$ using two different methods.
≈ 31.2 square units

Using Connections

Explain how the area formula $K = \frac{1}{2}bc \sin A$ becomes the area formula $A = \frac{1}{2}bh$ for a right triangle.

Answers will vary. Sample answer: Since sin 90° = 1, $\frac{1}{2}bc \sin A$ becomes $\frac{1}{2}bh$ for $\triangle ABC$ with right angle A.

You can also find the area of a triangle if you know the measures of one side of the triangle and two angles. By the law of sines, $\frac{b}{\sin B} = \frac{c}{\sin C}$ or $b = \frac{c \sin B}{\sin C}$. If you substitute $\frac{c \sin B}{\sin C}$ for b in $K = \frac{1}{2}bc \sin A$, the result is the following formula.

$$K = \frac{1}{2}c^2 \frac{\sin A \sin B}{\sin C}$$

Similarly, $K = \frac{1}{2}a^2 \frac{\sin B \sin C}{\sin A}$ and $K = \frac{1}{2}b^2 \frac{\sin A \sin C}{\sin B}$.

Example 2

Find the area of $\triangle ABC$ if $a = 18.6$, $A = 19°20'$, and $B = 63°50'$. Round your answer to the nearest tenth.

First, find the measure of angle C.

$C = 180° - (19°20' + 63°50')$
$\quad = 96°50'$

Then, find the area of the triangle.

$K = \frac{1}{2}a^2 \frac{\sin B \sin C}{\sin A}$

$\quad = \frac{1}{2}(18.6)^2 \frac{\sin 63°50' \sin 96°50'}{\sin 19°20'}$

$\quad \approx \frac{1}{2}(345.96)\frac{(0.8975)(0.9929)}{(0.3311)}$

$\quad \approx 465.6$

The area is about 465.6 square units.

If you know the measures of three sides of a triangle, you can find the area by using the law of cosines and the formula $K = \frac{1}{2}bc \sin A$.

Example 3

Find the area of $\triangle ABC$ if $a = \sqrt{2}$, $b = 2$, and $c = 3$. Round your answer to the nearest tenth.

First, solve for A by using the law of cosines.

$a^2 = b^2 + c^2 - 2bc \cos A$
$(\sqrt{2})^2 = 2^2 + 3^2 - 2(2)(3) \cos A$
$\cos A = \frac{(\sqrt{2})^2 - 2^2 - 3^2}{-2(2)(3)}$
$\cos A \approx 0.9167$
$\quad A \approx 23°33' \qquad \textit{Round to the nearest minute.}$

(continued on the next page)

LESSON 5-8   AREA OF TRIANGLES   289

TEACHING THE LESSON

Chalkboard Examples

For Example 1

Find the area of $\triangle ABC$ if $a = 8.4$, $b = 10$, and $C = 108°$. Round to the nearest tenth.   **39.9 square units**

For Example 2

Find the area of $\triangle ABC$ if $a = 14.2$, $A = 18°50'$, and $B = 69°18'$. Round to the nearest tenth. **292.0 square units**

For Example 3

Find the area of $\triangle ABC$ if $a = \sqrt{3}$, $b = 4$, and $c = 5$. Round to the nearest tenth.   **3.1 square units**

Then, find the area.

$$K = \frac{1}{2} bc \sin A$$
$$\approx \frac{1}{2}(2)(3) \sin 23°33'$$
$$\approx 3(0.3995)$$
$$\approx 1.199$$

The area is about 1.2 square units.

If you know the measures of three sides of any triangle, you can also use Hero's formula to find the area of a triangle.

Hero's Formula

If the measures of the sides of a triangle are a, b, and c, then the area, K, of the triangle is found as follows.

$$K = \sqrt{s(s - a)(s - b)(s - c)}, \text{ where } s = \frac{1}{2}(a + b + c)$$

s is called the <u>semiperimeter</u>.

Example 4

Use Hero's formula to find the area of $\triangle ABC$ if $a = 20$, $b = 30$, and $c = 40$. Round your answer to the nearest tenth.

$$s = \frac{1}{2}(20 + 30 + 40)$$
$$= 45$$

$$K = \sqrt{s(s - a)(s - b)(s - c)}$$
$$= \sqrt{45(45 - 20)(45 - 30)(45 - 40)}$$
$$= \sqrt{84,375}$$
$$\approx 290.5$$

The area is about 290.5 square units.

To solve application problems, you may have to use more than one formula for the area of a triangle.

Example 5

APPLICATION

Land Measure

Refer to the application at the beginning of the lesson. What is the area of the Walters' land to the nearest square foot?

Separate the region as shown at the right. The area of region $ABCDE$ is the sum of the areas of $\triangle ABC$, $\triangle ACE$, and $\triangle ECD$. Let a be the side with measure 202 ft, let b be the side with measure 158 ft, let c be the side with measure 201.5 ft, and let e be the side with measure 180.25 ft.

Area of $\triangle ABC = \frac{1}{2}ac \sin B$

$$= \frac{1}{2}(202)(201.5) \sin 82.5°$$
$$\approx (20,351.5)(0.9914)$$
$$\approx 20,176.5$$

Area of $\triangle ECD = \frac{1}{2}eb \sin D$

$$= \frac{1}{2}(180.25)(158) \sin 75°$$
$$\approx (14,239.75)(0.9659)$$
$$\approx 13,754.2$$

To find the area of $\triangle ACE$, first use the law of cosines to find AC and AE.

$$AC = \sqrt{(202)^2 + (201.5)^2 - 2(202)(201.5) \cos 82.5°}$$
$$\approx 266.0$$

$$CE = \sqrt{(180.25)^2 + (158)^2 - 2(180.25)(158) \cos 75°}$$
$$\approx 206.7$$

Then apply Hero's formula. $\quad s \approx \frac{1}{2}(125 + 266 + 206.7)$ or 298.85

$$K = \sqrt{s(s-a)(s-b)(s-c)}$$
$$\approx \sqrt{298.85(298.85 - 125)(298.85 - 266)(298.85 - 206.7)}$$
$$\approx 12,540.9$$

Area $ABCDE$ = area of $\triangle ABC$ + area of $\triangle ECD$ + area of $\triangle ACE$
$\qquad\qquad \approx \quad\;\; 20,176.5 \quad + \quad 13,754.2 \quad + \quad 12,540.9$
$\qquad\qquad \approx \quad\;\; 46,471.6$

So, the area of region $ABCDE$ is about 46,472 square feet, which is a little more than 1 acre.

A **segment** of a circle is the region bounded by an arc and its chord. If the arc is a minor arc, then the area of the segment can be found by subtracting the area of $\triangle ODE$ from the area of sector $ODFE$, where F is a point on the arc. Let S represent the area of the segment.

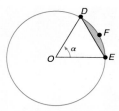

$S = $ (area of sector $ODFE$) $- ($ area of $\triangle ODE)$
$$= \frac{1}{2}r^2\alpha - \frac{1}{2}de \sin O$$
$$= \frac{1}{2}r^2\alpha - \frac{1}{2}r \cdot r \sin \alpha \qquad d = r, e = r, \text{ and } C = \alpha$$
$$= \frac{1}{2}r^2(\alpha - \sin \alpha)$$

Area of a Circular Segment

If α is the measure of the central angle expressed in radians and the radius of the circle measures r units, then the area of the segment, S, is as follows.

$$S = \frac{1}{2}r^2(\alpha - \sin \alpha)$$

Example 6

A sector has a central angle of **150°** in a circle with a radius of **11.5 inches**. Find the area of the circular segment to the nearest tenth.

First, convert 150° to radian measure.

$$150° = 150 \times \frac{\pi}{180}$$
$$= \frac{5\pi}{6} \text{ or } 2.6180 \quad \textit{Round to four decimal places.}$$

Then, find the area of the segment.

$$S = \frac{1}{2}r^2(\alpha - \sin \alpha)$$
$$\approx \frac{1}{2}(11.5)^2(2.6180 - \sin 2.6180)$$
$$\approx \frac{1}{2}(132.25)(2.6180 - 0.5000)$$
$$\approx 140.1$$

The area of the circular segment is 140.1 in².

CHECKING FOR UNDERSTANDING

Communicating Mathematics

Read and study the lesson to answer each question.

1. **Explain** how to use triangle area formulas to find the area of the parallelogram $ABCD$ shown below. Do *not* solve. See margin.

2. **Describe** how to find the length of the third side of a triangle if its area is known and the length of two sides are known.
   See margin.
3. **Sketch** the plot of land on which your school is located. List the measurements you would take to find its area. What is the fewest number of measurements needed?
   Answers may vary; see students' work.

292   CHAPTER 5   THE TRIGONOMETRIC FUNCTIONS

4–9. See margin for equations. All area answers are in square units.

Write an equation that can be used to find the area of each triangle described below. Then find the area of each triangle to the nearest tenth.

4. $a = 3, b = 4, C = 120°$ 5.2

5. $c = 20, A = 45°, B = 30°$ 73.2

6. $a = 4, b = 6, c = 8$ 11.6

7. $A = 43°, b = 16, c = 12$ 65.5

8. $a = 6, B = 52°, c = 4$ 9.5

9. $b = 12, B = 135°, C = 30°$ 13.2

10–11. All answers are in square units.
Find the area of each circular segment to the nearest tenth, given its central angle θ, and the measure of the radius of the circle.

10. $\theta = 81°, r = 16$ 54.5

11. $\theta = \dfrac{5\pi}{6}, r = 15$ 238.3

EXERCISES

Find the area of each triangle to the nearest tenth.

12. $c = 3.2, A = 16°, B = 31°45'$ 1.0   12–20. All answers are in square units.

13. $a = 2, b = 7, c = 8$ 6.4

14. $A = 60°, a = 2, B = 75°$ 1.6

15. $a = 174, b = 138, c = 188$ 11,486.3

16. $a = 8, B = 60°, C = 75°$ 37.9

17. $a = 11, B = 50°6', c = 5$ 21.1

18. $a = 17, b = 13, c = 19$ 107.8

19. $b = 146.2, c = 209.3, A = 62°12'$ 13,533.9

20. $a = 19.42, c = 19.42, B = 31°16'$ 97.9

21–26. All answers are in square units.

Find the area of each circular segment to the nearest tenth, given its central angle, θ, and the measure of the radius of the circle.

21. $\theta = \dfrac{3\pi}{4}, r = 24$ 474.9

22. $\theta = 120°, r = 8$ 39.3

23. $\theta = 85°, r = 2.1$ 1.1

24. $\theta = \dfrac{5\pi}{8}, r = 6$ 18.7

25. $\theta = 26°, r = 42$ 13.6

26. $\theta = \dfrac{\pi}{5}, r = 16.25$ 5.4

For Exercises 27—30, round all answers to the nearest tenth.

27. The adjacent sides of a parallelogram measure 8 cm and 12 cm, and one angle measures 60°. Find the area of the parallelogram. $83.1\ cm^2$

28. A rhombus has sides of 5 cm each and one diagonal is 6 cm long. Find the area of the rhombus. $24.0\ cm^2$

29. A regular pentagon is inscribed in a circle whose radius measures 7 cm. Find the area of the pentagon. $116.5\ cm^2$

30. A regular octagon is inscribed in a circle with a radius of 5 cm. Find the area of the octagon. $70.7\ cm^2$

LESSON 5-8 AREA OF TRIANGLES 293

APPLYING THE LESSON

Homework Exercises

Assignment Guide

Average: 12–27, 32, 33, 36–41
Enriched: 19–41

The red A, B, and C flags, printed only in the Teacher's Wraparound Edition, indicate the level of difficulty of the exercises.

Chapter 5, Quiz D, (Lessons 5–7 through 5–8), is available in the *Evaluation Masters*, p. 62.

Additional Answers

1. Separate the parallelogram into two triangles, △*ABC* and △*ACD*. Use the law of cosines to find the length of $\overline{AC}$. Then use Hero's formula to find the area of △*ACD* and double it to find the area of the parallelogram.

2. Sample answer: Let *K* be the measure of the area of △*ABC* and let *b* and *c* be the two known lengths. Substitute *K*, *b*, and *c* into the formula $K = \dfrac{1}{2}bc\sin A$ and solve for *A*.

Then use the law of cosines to find the length of the third side, *a*.

4. $K = \dfrac{1}{2} \cdot 3 \cdot 4 \sin 120°$

5. $K = \dfrac{1}{2} \cdot 20^2 \cdot \dfrac{\sin 45° \cdot \sin 30°}{\sin 105°}$

6. $K = \sqrt{9(9-4)(9-6)(9-8)}$

7. $K = \dfrac{1}{2} \cdot 16 \cdot 12 \sin 43°$

8. $K = \dfrac{1}{2} \cdot 6 \cdot 4 \sin 52°$

9. $K = \dfrac{1}{2} \cdot 12^2 \cdot \dfrac{\sin 30° \cdot \sin 15°}{\sin 135°}$

294 CHAPTER 5 THE TRIGONOMETRIC FUNCTIONS

Using Technology

The program given in Exercise 31 is for use with a TI-81 graphing calculator. For other programmable calculators, have students consult their owner's manual for commands similar to those presented here.

Programming

31. The program below finds the area of a triangle given the lengths of all three sides of the triangle.

```
Prgm 5:HEROS
:ClrHome                          Clears the text screen.
:Disp "SIDE 1 ="                  Displays the quoted message.
:Input A                          Accepts a value for A.
:Disp "SIDE 2 ="
:Input B
:Disp "SIDE 3 ="
:Input C
:If A+B≤C                         Checks for the sum of 2 sides less than or equal
:Goto 1                           to the third side; goes to line Lbl 1.
:If A+C≤B
:Goto 1
:If B+C≤A
:Goto 1
:(A+B+C)/2→S                      Calculates the semiperimeter, stores it in S.
:√(S(S−A)(S−B)(S−C))→K            Calculates the area, stores it in K.
:Disp "AREA="
:Disp K                           Displays the value stored in K.
:Goto 2
:Lbl 1                            Sets a marker at position 1.
:Disp "NO TRIANGLE"
:Lbl 2
:End                              Ends the program.
```

Use the program to find the area of each triangle to the nearest tenth. First, find the lengths of the three sides.

a. $a = 17.7$, $b = 21$, $C = 78°10'$ 181.9 square units

b. $a = 10$, $A = 75°20'$, $B = 49°40'$ 32.3 square units

Critical Thinking

32. Derive a formula for the area of $\triangle ABC$ if you know the measures of $\angle B$, $\angle C$ and side AC. See margin.

Applications and Problem Solving

33. Model Building The diagram below shows the dimensions for a sail on a wooden model ship.

a. Find the area of the sail to the nearest square inch. 302 in²

b. If the scale of the length of the real ship to the model ship is 1 foot : $\frac{1}{2}$ inch, find the area of the real sail in square feet. 1208 ft²

12.5 in.

26 in.

18 in.

75°

16.5 in.

Additional Answer

32. $K = \left(\dfrac{b^2 \sin C}{2 \sin B} \right) \cdot \sin(180 - (m\angle B + m\angle C))$

34. Exterior Design The diagram below is of the covering for an exterior doorway to a home. The owner wants to cover it with copper sheeting. Find the area to be covered to the nearest square foot. 1331 ft²

40 in.
23 in.
22.5 in.
23 in.
15 in.
46 in.
15 in.

35. Manufacturing The diagram at the right shows a storage bin with a hopper at the bottom. The storage bin is shaped like a rectangular prism.

5 ft
8.6 ft
2.25 ft
2 ft
114°
154°
5.4 ft
1.7 ft

a. Find the area of a vertical cross section to the nearest square foot. 17 ft²

b. Find the total volume of the bin and hopper. 146 ft³

Mixed Review

36. Write the standard form of the equation of the line through $(3, -2)$ that is parallel to the line $3x - y + 7 = 0$. **(Lesson 1-6)** $3x - y - 11 = 0$

37. Determine whether the graph of $f(x) = x^4 + 3x^2 + 2$ is symmetric with respect to the x-axis, the y-axis, neither, or both. **(Lesson 3-1)** y-axis

38. Use the remainder theorem to find the remainder when $x^3 + 8x + 1$ is divided by $x - 2$. **(Lesson 4-3)** 25

39. 139,000 cm/s

39. Mechanics A circular saw 18.4 cm in diameter rotates at 2400 revolutions per second. What is the linear velocity at which a saw tooth strikes the cutting surface in centimeters per second? **(Lesson 5-2)**

40. $a \approx 11.9$, $B = 39°57'$, $C = 104°3'$

40. Solve $\triangle ABC$ if $A = 36°$, $b = 13$, and $c = 6$. Round angle measures to the nearest minute and side measures to the nearest tenth. **(Lesson 5-7)**

41. College Entrance Exam Compare quantities A and B below. A
Write A if quantity A is greater.
Write B if quantity B is greater.
Write C if the two quantities are equal.
Write D if there is not enough information to determine the relationship.

$x - y = 4$
$x + y = 3$

(A) x **(B)** y

EXTENDING THE LESSON

Math Power: Problem Solving

Find the area of the field described in Motivating the Lesson for this lesson.
60,622 km²

Enrichment Masters Booklet, p. 35

Using the Chapter Summary and Review

The Chapter Summary and Review begins with an alphabetical listing of the new terms that were presented in the chapter. Have students define each term and provide an example of it, if appropriate.

The Skills and Concepts presented in the chapter are reviewed using a side-by-side format. Encourage students to refer to the Objectives and Examples on the left as they complete the Review Exercises on the right.

The Chapter Summary and Review ends with exercises that review Applications and Problem Solving.

VOCABULARY

Upon completing this chapter, you should be familiar with the following terms:

angle of depression	272	241	minute
angle of elevation	272	240	quadrantal angle
angular velocity	249	241	radian
central angle	247	243	reference angle
circular functions	255	241	second
coterminal angle	242	250	sector
degree	241	291	segment
Hero's formula	290	240	standard position
law of cosines	283	255	trigonometric functions
law of sines	277	241	unit circle
linear velocity	249		

SKILLS AND CONCEPTS

OBJECTIVES AND EXAMPLES	REVIEW EXERCISES

Upon completing this chapter, you should be able to:

Use these exercises to review and prepare for the chapter test.

■ change from radian to degree measure, and vice versa **(Lesson 5-1)**

Change $-\dfrac{5\pi}{3}$ radians to degree measure.

$$-\frac{5\pi}{3} = -\frac{5\pi}{3} \times \frac{180°}{\pi} = -300°$$

Change each radian measure to degree measure.

1. $\dfrac{\pi}{3}$ 60°   2. $-\dfrac{5\pi}{12}$ –75°   3. $\dfrac{4\pi}{3}$ 240°

Change each degree measure to radian measure in terms of π.

4. 150° $\dfrac{5\pi}{6}$ 5. –315° $-\dfrac{7\pi}{4}$ 6. 270° $\dfrac{3\pi}{2}$

■ find the reference angle for a given angle **(Lesson 5-1)**

Find the measure of the reference angle for $\dfrac{8\pi}{3}$.

$\dfrac{8\pi}{3}$ is coterminal with $\dfrac{2\pi}{3}$ in Quadrant II.

$\alpha' = \pi - \dfrac{2\pi}{3}$

$\quad = \dfrac{\pi}{3}$ *Reference rule b*

Find the reference angle for each angle with the given measure.

7. $\dfrac{7\pi}{4}$ $\dfrac{\pi}{4}$ 8. 405° 45°

9. $-\dfrac{4\pi}{3}$ $\dfrac{\pi}{3}$ 10. –60° 60°

11. $\dfrac{11\pi}{6}$ $\dfrac{\pi}{6}$ 12. 870° 30°

296   CHAPTER 5   THE TRIGONOMETRIC FUNCTIONS

- find the length of an arc, given the measure of the central angle **(Lesson 5-2)**

  Find the length of the arc intercepted by a central angle of $\frac{2\pi}{3}$ in a circle of radius 10 in.

  $s = r\theta$

  $= 10\left(\frac{2\pi}{3}\right)$

  ≈ 20.9 The length is about 20.9 in.

Given the measure of a central angle, find the measure of its intercepted arc in terms of π in a circle of diameter 30 cm.

13. $\frac{3\pi}{4}$ $\frac{45\pi}{4}$ 14. $\frac{\pi}{5}$ 3π

15. $75°$ $\frac{25\pi}{4}$ 16. $150°$ $\frac{25\pi}{2}$

- find the values of the six trigonometric functions of an angle **(Lesson 5-3)**

  Find $\tan\theta$ if θ is in standard position and the point with coordinates $(5, 8)$ lies on the terminal side of the angle in standard position.

  $\tan\theta = \dfrac{y}{x}$

  $= \dfrac{8}{5}$

Find the value of the given trigonometric function of an angle in standard position if a point with the given coordinates lies on its terminal side.

17. $\sin\theta$; $(3, 3)$ $\frac{\sqrt{2}}{2}$

18. $\cos\theta$; $(-5, 12)$ $\frac{-5}{13}$

19. $\cot\theta$; $(8, -2)$ -4

20. $\sec\theta$; $(-2, 0)$ -1

- find the values of the six trigonometric functions of special angles **(Lesson 5-4)**

  Find $\sin\frac{4\pi}{3}$.

  $\sin\frac{4\pi}{3} = -\sin\frac{\pi}{3}$

  $= -\frac{1}{2}$

Find each exact value. Do not use a calculator.

21. $\cos\frac{3\pi}{4}$ $-\frac{\sqrt{2}}{2}$ 22. $\tan\frac{7\pi}{3}$ $\sqrt{3}$

23. $\csc 120°$ $\frac{2\sqrt{3}}{3}$ 24. $\cot 315°$ -1

25. $\sin\frac{18\pi}{4}$ 1 26. $\sec\frac{-5\pi}{6}$ $-\frac{2\sqrt{3}}{3}$

- solve right triangles **(Lesson 5-5)**

  Solve $\triangle ABC$ if $C = 90°$, $c = 10$, and $A = 74°$.

  $\dfrac{a}{10} = \sin 74°$ $\dfrac{b}{10} = \cos 74°$

  $a \approx 9.6$ $b \approx 2.8$

  $B = 90° - 74° = 16°$

Solve each triangle ABC described below. Angle C is the right angle. Round angle measures to the nearest minute and side measures to the nearest tenth.

27. $A = 63°$, $a = 9.7$

28. $a = 2$, $b = 7$

29. $B = 83°$, $b = \sqrt{31}$

30. $a = 44$, $B = 44°44'$ 27–30. See margin.

Additional Answers

27. $B = 27°$, $c = 10.9$, $b = 4.9$
28. $c = 7.3$, $A = 15°57'$, $B = 74°3'$
29. $A = 7°$, $c = 5.6$, $a = 0.7$
30. $A = 45°16'$, $c = 61.9$, $b = 43.6$

Alternate Review Strategy

To provide a brief in-class review, you may wish to read the following questions to your students and have them answer verbally.

1. Change $\frac{5\pi}{3}$ radians to degrees.
   300°
2. Change $-270°$ to radians. $\frac{3\pi}{2}$
3. Find the reference angle for an angle of 600°.   **60°**
4. Given the central angle of a circle with radius 8 has measure $\frac{\pi}{4}$, find the measure of the intercepted arc in terms of π.
   2π
5. If θ is in standard position, find the value of $\sin\theta$ for the point $(-5, -12)$. $-\frac{12}{13}$
6. Find $\sec\frac{-5\pi}{4}$ without using a calculator. $-\sqrt{2}$
7. Solve $\triangle ABC$ if $A = 64°$, $a = 12.3$, and C is a right angle. Round angle measures to the nearest minute and side measures to the nearest tenth.
   $B = 26°$, $b = 6$, $c = 13.7$
8. If a solution exists, solve the triangle with $A = 42°12'$, $a = 184$, and $b = 200$. Round angle measures to the nearest minute and side measures to the nearest tenth.
   ($B = 46°54'$, $C = 90°54'$, $c = 273.9$) or ($B = 133°48'$, $C = 4°$, $c = 19.1$)
9. Find the area of $\triangle ABC$ with $A = 68°$, $b = 12$, and $c = 18$.
   100.1 square units

Two multiple-choice tests (Forms 1A and 1B) and two free-response tests (Forms 2A and 2B) are provided in the *Evaluation Masters*. Chapter 5 Test, Form 1A is shown below. Chapter 5 Test, Form 2A is shown on the next page.

Evaluation Masters Booklet, pp. 53–54

NAME _____ DATE _____

Chapter 5 Test, Form 1A

Write the letter for the correct answer in the blank at the right of each problem.

1. Find one positive and one negative angle that are coterminal with an angle measuring $\frac{2\pi}{3}$.
   A. $\frac{5\pi}{3}, -\frac{2\pi}{3}$ B. $\frac{4\pi}{3}, -\frac{\pi}{3}$ C. $\frac{11\pi}{3}, -\frac{7\pi}{3}$ D. $\frac{8\pi}{3}, -\frac{4\pi}{3}$ 1. **D**

2. Find the reference angle for an angle measuring 125°.
   A. 35°   B. 225°   C. 135°   D. 55°   2. **D**

3. Change –62°11′45″ to radian measure to the nearest thousandth.
   A. –1.084   B. –1.085   C. –1.086   D. –1.087   3. **C**

4. Find the degree measure, to the nearest tenth, of the central angle whose intercepted arc measures 16 in. in a circle of radius 12 in.
   A. 76.4°   B. 270.0°   C. 283.6°   D. 43.0°   4. **A**

5. Find the area, to the nearest tenth, of a sector of a circle defined by a central angle measuring 105° if the radius of the circle is 4.2 m.
   A. 7.7 m²   B. 16.2 m²   C. 32.3 m²   D. 926.1 m²   5. **B**

For Exercises 6-8, suppose csc θ = –2 and the terminal side of the angle lies in Quadrant III. Find each value.

6. sin θ
   A. $-\frac{1}{2}$ B. $\frac{1}{2}$ C. $-\frac{\sqrt{3}}{2}$ D. $\frac{\sqrt{3}}{2}$ 6. **A**

7. cos θ
   A. $-\frac{1}{2}$ B. $\frac{1}{2}$ C. $-\frac{\sqrt{3}}{2}$ D. $\frac{\sqrt{3}}{2}$ 7. **C**

8. tan θ
   A. $-\frac{\sqrt{3}}{3}$ B. $\frac{\sqrt{3}}{3}$ C. $-\sqrt{3}$ D. $\sqrt{3}$ 8. **B**

9. Find the exact value of tan $\frac{9\pi}{3}$ without using a calculator.
   A. 1   B. –1   C. 0   D. undefined   9. **C**

10. Find the exact value of csc 315° without using a calculator.
    A. $-\sqrt{2}$ B. –2   C. –1   D. $-\frac{2\sqrt{3}}{2}$ 10. **A**

11. Use a calculator to approximate tan (–122°) to four decimal places.
    A. –0.5754   B. 0.5754   C. –1.6003   D. 1.6003   11. **D**

12. State the number of possible solutions to $\triangle PQR$ if $P = 43°$, $p = 13.3$, and $q = 9.1$.
    A. no solutions   B. 1 solution   C. 2 solutions   D. 3 solutions   12. **B**

13. There are 20 rollers under a conveyor belt and each roller has a radius of 8 cm. The rollers turn at a rate of 2 revolutions per second. What is the linear velocity of the belt driving the rollers in meters per second?
    A. 0.50 m/s   B. 50.26 m/s   C. 100.53 m/s   D. 1.005 m/s   13. **D**

T53
Glencoe Division, Macmillan/McGraw-Hill

NAME _____ DATE _____

Chapter 5 Test, Form 1A (continued)

For Exercises 14-16, use right triangle ABC to find each value. Round angle measures to the nearest degree and side measures to the nearest tenth.

14. the measure of angle C
    A. 112°   B. 79°   C. 68°   D. 58°   14. **C**

15. the measure of side b
    A. 10.8   B. 26.7   C. 3.7   D. 24.8   15. **A**

16. the measure of side a
    A. 9.3   B. 4.0   C. 3.7   D. 24.8   16. **B**

17. In $\triangle ABC$, $A = 55°14′$, $B = 27°19′$, and $c = 12.3$. Find C to the nearest minute.
    A. 98°   B. 98°27′   C. 97°5′   D. 97°27′   17. **D**

18. In $\triangle ABC$, $A = 63°$, $B = 19°$, and $a = 2.4$. Find b to the nearest tenth.
    A. 0.9   B. 3.6   C. 6.6   D. 3.6   18. **A**

19. In $\triangle ABC$, $B = 112°2′$, $C = 21°46′$, and $c = 18$. Find a to the nearest tenth.
    A. 35.0   B. 4.8   C. 9.2   D. 35.6   19. **A**

For Exercises 20-22, find each value for $\triangle ABC$ if $a = 5$, $b = 6$, and $c = 8$.

20. the measure of angle A
    A. 141°   B. 124°   C. 39°   D. 20°   20. **C**

21. the measure of angle B
    A. 131°   B. 160°   C. 28°   D. 49°   21. **D**

22. the measure of angle C
    A. 87°   B. 93°   C. 152°   D. 160°   22. **B**

23. Find the area of $\triangle ABC$ to the nearest tenth if $a = 8$, $b = 5$, and $c = 4$.
    A. 5.8 units²   B. 8.2 units²   C. 16.4 units²   D. 13.1 units²   23. **B**

24. Find the area of $\triangle ABC$ to the nearest tenth if $b = 11.9$, $A = 44°30′$, and $B = 56°12′$.
    A. 58.7 units²   B. 117.4 units²   C. 42.0 units²   D. 4.9 units²   24. **A**

25. Find the area of a circular segment to the nearest tenth if the measure of its central angle is 135° and the measure of its radius is 6.9 units.
    A. 39.3 units²   B. 78.5 units²   C. 5.7 units²   D. 72.9 units²   25. **A**

Bonus

How many possible solutions are there for a triangle whose sides measure 1, 9, and 15?
    A. no solutions   B. 1 solution   C. 2 solutions   D. 3 solutions   Bonus: **A**

T 54
Glencoe Division, Macmillan/McGraw-Hill

■ solve triangles by using the law of sines **(Lesson 5-6)**
In $\triangle ABC$, find a if $A = 51°$, $C = 32°$, and $c = 18$.
$$\frac{a}{\sin A} = \frac{c}{\sin C}$$
$$\frac{a}{\sin 51°} = \frac{18}{\sin 32°}$$
$$a = 26.4$$

Determine the number of possible solutions. If a solution exists, solve the triangle. Round angle measures to the nearest minute and side measures to the nearest tenth.

31. $A = 38°42′$, $a = 172$, $c = 203$
32. $a = 12$, $b = 19$, $A = 57°$
33. $A = 29°$, $a = 12$, $b = 15$
34. $A = 45°$, $a = 83$, $b = 79$ 31-34. See margin.

■ solve triangles by using the law of cosines **(Lesson 5-7)**
In $\triangle ABC$, find a if $A = 63°$, $b = 20$, and $c = 14$.
$$a^2 = b^2 + c^2 - 2bc \cos A$$
$$a^2 = 20^2 + 14^2 - 2(20)(14) \cos 63°$$
$$a^2 \approx 341.77$$
$$a \approx 18.5$$

Solve each triangle. Round angle measures to the nearest minute and side measures to the nearest tenth. 35 – 38. See margin.

35. $A = 51°$, $b = 40$, $c = 45$
36. $B = 19°$, $a = 51$, $c = 61$
37. $a = 11$, $b = 13$, $c = 20$
38. $B = 24°$, $a = 42$, $c = 6.5$

■ find the area of triangles   **(Lesson 5-8)**
Find the area of $\triangle ABC$ if $a = 6$, $b = 4$, and $C = 54°$.
$$K = \frac{1}{2}ab \sin C$$
$$= \frac{1}{2}(6)(4) \sin 54°$$
$$\approx 9.7$$

Find the area of each triangle to the nearest tenth. All answers are in square units.

39. $A = 20°$, $a = 19$, $C = 64°$ 471.7
40. $a = 5$, $b = 7$, $c = 9$ 17.4
41. $a = 11.7$, $b = 13.5$, $C = 81°20′$ 78.1
42. $A = 42°$, $B = 65°$, $a = 63$ 2570.5

APPLICATIONS AND PROBLEM SOLVING

43. **Entertainment**   Shannon rides the Ferris wheel at the Franklin County Fair. She makes 12 revolutions during a 3-minute ride. If the diameter of the Ferris wheel is 30 feet, what is Shannon's linear velocity in miles per hour? Round your answer to the nearest tenth.   **(Lesson 5-2)**   4.3 mph

44. **Landscaping**   Rusty wants to plant a circular flower bed around a tree in his front yard. He wants it to look like the drawing at the right.   **(Lesson 5-8)**

    a. If the radius of the entire flower bed measures 4 feet, and each chord is the same length, what is the area of each circular segment where he plans to plant impatiens? Round your answer to the nearest tenth. 9.8 ft²

    b. A flat of impatiens holds 24 plants. If he can plant 3 plants per square foot, how many flats should he buy?   4 flats

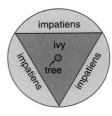

Additional Answers

31. two; $C = 47°33′$, $B = 93°45′$, and $b = 274.5$ or $C = 132°27′$, $B = 8°51′$, $b = 42.3$
32. none
33. two; $B = 37°18′$, $C = 113°42′$, and $c = 22.7$ or $B = 142°42′$, $C = 8°18′$, and $c = 3.6$
34. one; $B = 42°18′$, $C = 92°42′$, $c = 117.2$
35. $a = 36.9$, $B = 57°24′$, $C = 71°36′$
36. $b = 21.0$, $A = 52°15′$, $C = 108°45′$
37. $A = 30°31′$, $B = 36°53′$, $C = 112°36′$
38. $b = 36.2$, $A = 151°51′$, $C = 4°9′$

Change each degree measure to radian measure in terms of π. Change each radian measure to degree measure.

1. $135°$ $\frac{3\pi}{4}$ **2.** $-\frac{\pi}{5}$ $-36°$ **3.** $480°$ $\frac{8\pi}{3}$ **4.** $\frac{7\pi}{12}$ $105°$

Use the circle at the right to answer the following questions to the nearest tenth.

5. What is the length of the intercepted arc? 16.5 cm

6. What is the area of the sector? 52.0 cm²

7. What is the area of the circular segment? 42.0 cm²

$r = 6.3$ cm

$150°$

Find each exact value. Do not use a calculator.

8. $\sin\frac{5\pi}{6}$ $\frac{1}{2}$ **9.** $\cot 210°$ $\sqrt{3}$ **10.** $\sec 135°$ $-\sqrt{2}$ **11.** $\cos -\frac{\pi}{6}$ $\frac{\sqrt{3}}{2}$ **12.** $\tan 225°$ 1

Solve each right triangle. Angle C is the right angle. Round angle measures to the nearest minute and side measures to the nearest tenth. 13–15. See margin.

13. $b = 42, A = 77°$ **14.** $c = 13, a = 12$ **15.** $c = 14, B = 32°$

Determine the number of possible solutions. If a solution exists, solve the triangle. Round angle measures to the nearest minute and side measures to the nearest tenth. 16–19. See margin.

16. $a = 64, c = 90, C = 98°$ **17.** $a = 9, b = 20, A = 31°$

18. $a = 13, b = 7, c = 15$ **19.** $a = 20, c = 24, B = 47°$

Find the area of each triangle to the nearest tenth. Answers are in square units.

20. $A = 70°11', B = 43°55', b = 16.7$ 172.7   **21.** $b = 11.5, c = 14, A = 20°$ 27.5

22. Astronomy The linear velocity of Earth's moon is about 2300 mph. If the average distance from the center of Earth to the center of the moon is 2.4×10^5 miles, how long does it take the moon to make one revolution about Earth? Assume the orbit is circular. 656 hours or 27.3 days

23. Recreation At ground level, the measurement of the angle of elevation of a kite is 70°. It is held by a string 65 meters long. How far is the kite above the ground? 61.1 meters

24. Navigation A ship at sea is 70 miles from one radio transmitter and 130 miles from another. The measurement of the angle between signals is 130°. How far apart are the transmitters? 183.0 miles

25. Geometry An isosceles triangle has a base of 22 centimeters and a vertex angle measuring 36°. Find its perimeter. 93.2 cm

Bonus   In $\triangle ABC$, where a, b, and c are measures of the sides, $\frac{a+b+c}{2+\sqrt{3}} = \frac{ab}{a+b-c}$. Find the measure of $\angle C$. $30°$ or $\frac{\pi}{6}$

Test Generator Software is provided in Apple, IBM, and Macintosh versions. You may use this software to create your own tests, based on the needs of your students.

Additional Answers

13. $B = 13°, c = 186.7, a = 181.9$

14. $A = 67°23', B = 22°37', b = 5$

15. $A = 58°, b = 7.4, a = 11.9$

16. one; $A = 44°46', B = 37°14', b = 55.0$

17. none

18. one; $A = 60°, B = 27°48', C = 92°12'$

19. one; $b = 17.9, C = 78°41', A = 54°19'$

This page may be used as a test or as a review. All answers to this test appear in the Selected Answers in the student text.

Standardized Test Practice Questions are also provided in the *Evaluation Masters*.

Evaluation Masters Booklet, pp. 57–58

NAME _____ DATE _____

Chapter 5 Test, Form 2A

1. Find the reference angle for the angle measuring $-42°$.   1. ___42°___

2. Find the reference angle for the angle measuring $\frac{21\pi}{4}$ radians.   2. ___$\frac{\pi}{4}$___

3. If an angle in standard position measures $-\frac{12\pi}{5}$ radians, in which quadrant does its terminal side lie?   3. ___Quadrant IV___

4. Change 675° to radian measure in terms of π.   4. ___$\frac{15\pi}{4}$___

5. Change $\frac{11\pi}{9}$ radians to degree measure.   5. ___220°___

6. Change 246°19'24" to radian measure. Round your answer to the nearest thousandth.   6. ___4.299___

7. Find the degree measure, to the nearest tenth, of the central angle whose intercepted arc measures 14 in. in a circle of radius 12 in.   7. ___66.8°___

8. Find the area, to the nearest tenth, of the sector of a circle defined by a central angle measuring 52° if the radius of the circle is 8 cm.   8. ___29.0 cm²___

9. Find the length of an arc that subtends an angle of 36° in a circle of diameter 10 in. Write your answer in terms of π.   9. ___π in.___

Suppose $\sin\theta = -\frac{5}{13}$ and the terminal side of the angle lies in Quadrant IV. Find each value.

10. $\cos\theta$ 10. ___$\frac{12}{13}$___

11. $\tan\theta$ 11. ___$-\frac{5}{12}$___

12. $\cot\theta$ 12. ___$-\frac{12}{5}$___

13. $\sec\theta$ 13. ___$\frac{13}{12}$___

14. $\csc\theta$ 14. ___$-\frac{13}{5}$___

Find the exact value of each function without using a calculator.

15. $\cot\frac{24\pi}{6}$ 15. ___undefined___

16. $\sec 150°$ 16. ___$-\frac{2\sqrt{3}}{3}$___

T 57

Glencoe Division, Macmillan/McGraw-Hill

NAME _____ DATE _____

Chapter 5 Test, Form 2A (continued)

Use a calculator to approximate each value to four decimal places.

17. $\sin 725°$ 17. ___0.0872___

18. $\sec 12$ 18. ___1.1850___

For Exercises 19-21, use right triangle ABC to find each value. Round angle measures to the nearest degree and side measures to the nearest tenth.

19. the measure of angle B 19. ___38°___

20. the length of side b 20. ___3.1___

21. the length of side c 21. ___5.1___

22. State the number of possible solutions to $\triangle DEF$ if $F = 121°$, $d = 12$, and $f = 12$.   22. ___no solutions___

Find each value for $\triangle ABC$ if $a = 3.6$, $A = 7°34'$, $B = 74°6'$, and $C = 98°20'$. Round the measures to the nearest tenth.

23. the measure of side b 23. ___26.3___

24. the measure of side c 24. ___27.1___

For Exercises 25-27, find each value for $\triangle ABC$ if $a = 13$, $b = 10$, and $C = 56°$. Round angle measures to the nearest degree and side measures to the nearest tenth.

25. the measure of side c 25. ___11.1___

26. the measure of angle A 26. ___76°___

27. the measure of angle B 27. ___48°___

28. Find the area of $\triangle ABC$, to the nearest tenth, if $a = 12$, $b = 10$, and $c = 4$.   28. ___18.7 units²___

29. Find the area of a circular segment, to the nearest tenth, if its central angle measures 60° and the radius of the circle is 10.6 units.   29. ___10.2 units²___

30. Mr. Allen needs to rent a ladder to paint the outside of his house. The painted part of his house is 20 feet high, and the ladder must reach the top of the painted part. How long must the ladder be if the angle formed by the ladder and level ground is 75°?   30. ___20.71 feet___

Bonus

The terminal side of an angle θ in standard position coincides with the line $2x + y = 0$ in Quadrant II. Find $\sec\theta$.   Bonus: ___$-\sqrt{5}$___

T 58

Glencoe Division, Macmillan/McGraw-Hill

CHAPTER 6

GRAPHS AND INVERSES OF THE TRIGONOMETRIC FUNCTIONS

PREVIEWING THE CHAPTER

This chapter continues the study of trigonometric functions with an emphasis on graphing. First students familiarize themselves with the graphs of the six basic trigonometric functions. They learn to find the amplitude, period, and phase shift of a graph, including writing equations of graphs and drawing graphs given these values. Evaluation of inverse functions is succeeded by finding principle values, writing equations, and graphing inverses of trigonometric functions. With these skills, students are able to solve problems involving simple harmonic motion.

Lesson Objective Chart

Lesson (Pages)	Lesson Objectives		State/Local Objectives
6-1 (302-307)	6-1:	Use graphs of the trigonometric functions.	
6-2 (309-318)	6-2A:	Find the amplitude, period, and phase shift for a trigonometric function.	
	6-2B:	Write equations of trigonometric functions given the amplitude, period, and phase shift.	
6-3 (321-327)	6-3:	Graph various trigonometric functions.	
6-4 (328-333)	6-4:	Evaluate inverse trigonometric functions.	
6-5 (334-338)	6-5:	Find principal values of inverse trigonometric functions.	
6-6 (340-344)	6-6A:	Write equations for inverses of trigonometric functions.	
	6-6B:	Graph inverses of trigonometric functions.	
6-7 (345-351)	6-7:	Solve problems involving simple harmonic motion.	

ORGANIZING THE CHAPTER

You may want to refer to the **Course Planning Guide Calendar** on pages T34-T35 for a complete pacing chart.

Lesson Planning Guide

Lesson	Pages	Practice	Enrichment	Evaluation	Graphing Calculator	Computer	Multicultural Activity	Applications	Problem Solving	Case Study Follow-Up	Decision Making	Transparencies
6-1	302-307	p. 36	p. 36									6-1
6-2	309-318	p. 37	p. 37	Quiz A, p. 73						p. 18		6-2
6-3	321-327	p. 38	p. 38		p. 11			p. 16				6-3
6-4	328-333	p. 39	p. 39	Quiz B, p. 73 Mid-Chapter Test, p. 75					p. 17			6-4
6-5	334-338	p. 40	p. 40									6-5
6-6	340-344	p. 41	p. 41	Quiz C, p. 74		p. 12						6-6
6-7	345-351	p. 42	p. 42	Quiz D, p. 74			p. 6					6-7
Review	352-354	Multiple Choice Tests, Forms 1A and 1B, pp. 65-68 Free Response Tests, Forms 2A and 2B, pp. 69-72 Standardized Test Questions, p. 76										
Test	355											

Blackline Masters Booklets — **Technology** (Graphing Calculator, Computer), **Activity Masters** (Multicultural Activity, Applications, Problem Solving, Case Study Follow-Up, Decision Making)

Other Chapter Resources

Student Edition

Case Study Follow-Up, p. 318
Decision Making, p. 307
Technology, p. 308

Other Supplements

Transparency 6-0 for Chapter Opener
Alternate Assessment in the Mathematics Classroom,
    Glencoe Publishing Co., 1993
Cooperative Learning in the Mathematics Classroom,
    Glencoe Publishing Co., 1993

Software

Test and Review Generator Software
    Available for Apple, IBM, and Macintosh
Teacher's Guide for Software Resources

ENHANCING THE CHAPTER

Cooperative Learning

Specifying Desired Student Behavior

To make sure that students exhibit the group skills required for a successful cooperative-learning experience, you should clearly define the expected behaviors at the outset. Initially, skills will include the more obvious, such as "stay with your group," "use quiet voices," and "take turns when speaking." As groups begin to operate more effectively, add other expected behaviors, such as "criticize ideas, not people," "encourage everyone to participate," "use names and look at other members when speaking," "paraphrase statements made by others," "ask for elaboration," "probe by asking in-depth questions," "check to make sure every member understands and can explain the material," and so on. Research indicates that it is more effective if you define and focus on only one or two of these skills in each session.

For more information on cooperative learning, see pages T20-T21. Additional information on using cooperative groups is available in Glencoe's *Cooperative Learning in the Mathematics Classroom*, ©1993.

Multicultural

Multicultural Activity Masters, p. 6

CHAPTER 6 NAME _____ DATE _____

Multicultural Activity (Use after Lesson 6-7)

Otis Boykin

Otis Boykin (1920–1982) was an African-American scientist and inventor who began his career as a laboratory assistant testing automatic controls for airplanes. He invented more than two dozen electronic devices, among them a control unit for artificial heart stimulators (pacemakers), a burglar-proof cash register, and a type of resistor that is presently used in many computers, television sets, and radios. From 1964 to 1982, he worked as a private consultant for several electronics firms in the United States and France.

In his work with radio waves, Boykin dealt with equations of the form $f(t) = A \sin(Bt)$, where either A or B is a function of t. If A, which is the amplitude, is a function of t, the radio wave is called an **amplitude modulation (AM) wave**. In the exercises that follow, you will have an opportunity to explore the way in which variable amplitudes affect the graph of the sine function.

1. Let $f(t) = t \sin t$.
   a. Complete the table. Leave your answers in fraction form.

t	0	$\frac{\pi}{2}$	π	$\frac{3\pi}{2}$	2π	$\frac{5\pi}{2}$	3π	$\frac{7\pi}{2}$	4π	$\frac{9\pi}{2}$	5π
$f(t)$	0	$\frac{\pi}{2}$	0	$-\frac{3\pi}{2}$	0	$\frac{5\pi}{2}$	0	$-\frac{7\pi}{2}$	0	$\frac{9\pi}{2}$	0

   b. Based on the table in part a, write a sentence or two to describe the graph of $f(t) = t \sin t$ for positive values of t.
      The graph is similar to a sine wave. However, the relative maxima and minima get farther and farther above and below the t-axis because of the increasing amplitude.
   c. Use a graphing calculator to check your conjecture.
      See students' work.
2. Let $f(t) = (3 \sin 15t) \sin t$.
   a. Show that $-3 \le (3 \sin 15t) \sin t \le 3$. That is, show that $f(t)$ lies between the curves $y = 3 \sin t$ and $y = -3 \sin t$.
      $-3 \le 3 \sin 15t \le 3$ and $-1 \le \sin t \le 1$.
      Hence, $-3 \le (3 \sin 15t) \sin t \le 3$
   b. Use a graphing calculator to graph $f(t) = (3 \sin 15t) \sin t$.
      See students' work.

T 6
Glencoe Division, Macmillan/McGraw-Hill

Activity Masters

Applications, p. 16

CHAPTER 6 NAME _____ DATE _____

Applications (Use after Lesson 6-3)

Business Cycles

Success in business depends on many factors. Consumer buying habits, trends in fashion and taste, seasonal trends, the strength of competition, and the state of the national and international economies all affect the fortunes of a business. The result of all these factors is that businesses often show a broad overall pattern of growth or decline superimposed over a continuing series of small ups and downs. Such business cycles can often be modeled by using trigonometric functions.

The economist for a large sporting-goods manufacturer developed the following trigonometric function for the company's sales.

$$S = 8 + \frac{t}{52} - 6 \cos \frac{\pi t}{26},$$

where S represents sales in millions of dollars during week t of a year, beginning January 1.

1. Which term in the equation increases steadily as t increases? $\frac{t}{52}$
2. a. Which term in the equation cycles through a recurring pattern of growth and decline? $6 \cos \frac{\pi t}{26}$
   b. Find the maximum and minimum values of this term. $6; -6$
3. Describe the sales cycle over several years.
   Sales begin at $2 million/week at $t = 0$ and increase steadily to $14.5 million/week at $t = 26$, then decline to $3 million/week at the end of year 1. This pattern continues annually—increase to week 26, decrease to week 52, with each annual maximum and minimum higher than the previous one. The overall pattern is growth.

Find the sales for each of the following weeks.

4. $t = 13$ $8.25 million
5. $t = 26$ $14.5 million
6. $t = 39$ $8.75 milli
7. $t = 52$ $3 million
8. $t = 65$ $9.25 million
9. $t = 78$ $15.5 milli
10. Graph the sales function for four years.

T 16
Glencoe Division, Macmillan/McGraw-Hill

Problem Solving, p. 17

CHAPTER 6 NAME _____ DATE _____

Problem Solving (Use after Lesson 6-4)

Make a Sketch

When a method of solving a problem is not immediately evident, try drawing a sketch. A sketch helps you to visualize a problem and see how the parts of a problem relate to one another. Drawing a sketch is an especially valuable but often overlooked strategy for solving problems in trigonometry. By turning back to the basic definitions of the trigonometric functions, you can often model complex problems and gain insights into their solutions.

Example Find $\sin\left(\cos^{-1}\frac{5}{8}\right)$.

Trigonometric functions and inverse functions can be represented in terms of the measures of angles or the lengths of sides of a triangle. Use these representations to create sketches.

$\cos^{-1}\frac{5}{8}$ is "the angle whose cosine is $\frac{5}{8}$."

The angle is depicted in the sketch as $\angle A$.
The sketch shows that the problem is one of finding the sine of $\angle A$. Since by the Pythagorean theorem, the length of the side opposite $\angle A$ is $\sqrt{39}$,
$\sin A = \frac{\text{opposite}}{\text{hypotenuse}} = \frac{\sqrt{39}}{8}$.

Draw a sketch to model each problem. Then solve. Assume that all angles are in Quadrant I.

1. Find $\tan\left(\sin^{-1}\frac{4}{9}\right)$. $\frac{4\sqrt{65}}{65}$

2. Find $\sec(\arctan 1.3)$. 1.64

3. The measure of the altitude to the hypotenuse of a right triangle whose sides are in the proportion 3:4:5 is $\frac{12}{5}$. The altitude divides the right angle of the triangle into two angles. Find the cosine of each. $\cos \angle DCA = \frac{3}{5}$; $\cos \angle DCB = \frac{4}{5}$

4. In right triangle $\triangle ABC$, $\cos B = \frac{2}{5}$, $\angle C$ is the right angle, and $\overline{AD}$ bisects $\angle A$. Find $m \angle DAC$. $11.8°$

T 17
Glencoe Division, Macmillan/McGraw-Hill

Case Study Follow-Up, p. 18

CHAPTER 6 NAME _____ DATE _____

Case Study Follow-Up (Use after Lesson 6-2)

Modeling Energy Prices

Refer to Case Study 4: *The U.S. Economy*, on pages 966-969 in your textbook.

Of all the goods and services tracked by the Commerce Department in recent years, energy has shown some of the greatest instability in prices.

1. The average price of a gallon of gasoline in January, 1986, was $1.14. Find the average price at the end of 1986.
   $0.89 per gallon
2. Plot the following points on the graph.

Annual Percent Change in Consumer Price Index for Energy

1978	1979	1980	1981	1982	1983	1984	1985	1986	1987	1988	1989	1990
6.9	10.8	16.4	14.6	9.8	5.6	3.5	1.6	-2.3	-1.1	-1.4	3.3	3.5

3. Draw a smooth trigonometric curve that connects the points as closely as possible.

Answer these questions about the curve you have drawn.

4. Which trigonometric function could be used to describe your graph? Sample answer: sine
5. What is the period of the curve? about 12 years
6. What is the amplitude of the curve? about 9 percent
7. If the curve is an accurate model of an energy-price cycle, when would you next expect the annual change in energy prices to drop below 2 percent? around 1998

T 18
Glencoe Division, Macmillan/McGraw-Hill

The Technology feature following Lesson 6-1 describes how to use a computer spreadsheet program to generate ordered pairs for trigonometric functions.

As in Chapter 5, students are encouraged to use any scientific calculator with trigonometric function features to evaluate functions and their inverses. Students use graphing calculators throughout the chapter to study the different characteristics of the graphs of trigonometric functions. The Graphing Calculator Exploration in Lesson 6-2 allows students to investigate the change in the graph of a function as its coefficient changes. Another Exploration investigates the change in the graph of a function when a quantity is added to the angle measure. Students also use the graphing calculator to graph the inverses of trigonometric functions.

Graphing Calculator Exercises, pp. 305, 316

Graphing Calculator, p. 11

Computer, p. 12

Outside Resources

Books/Periodicals

Barndorff-Nielson, O.E. *Parametric Statistical Models and Likelihood* (Lecture Notes in Statistics, Ser. Vol 50), Springer-Verlag New York, Inc. 1988.

I.M. Gelfand, et al. *Functions and Graphs,* Berkhauser, 1990.

Films/Videotapes/Videodiscs

Concepts in Mathematics, Trigonometric Functions 2: Sinusoidal Waves, TV Ontario, The Ontario Educational Communications Authority

Software

Graphing utilities that include trigonometric functions (see list on page T25)

Pre-Calculus 4.0 with Trigonometry. True BASIC (IBM, Macintosh)

Trig Pak, Version 2.0. Brooks/Cole, Wadsworth School Group (IBM)

CHAPTER 6

GRAPHS AND INVERSES OF THE TRIGONOMETRIC FUNCTIONS

HISTORICAL SNAPSHOT

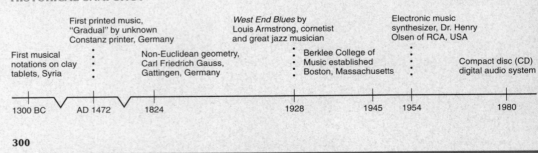

First musical notations on clay tablets, Syria	First printed music, "Gradual" by unknown Constanz printer, Germany	Non-Euclidean geometry, Carl Friedrich Gauss, Gattingen, Germany	*West End Blues* by Louis Armstrong, cornetist and great jazz musician	Berklee College of Music established Boston, Massachusetts	Electronic music synthesizer, Dr. Henry Olsen of RCA, USA	Compact disc (CD) digital audio system
1300 BC	AD 1472	1824	1928	1945	1954	1980

300

Through experimentation, they should find and mark the 12 places to fret or touch the string to raise the pitch one octave. The frequency of the string at each point is $\sqrt[12]{2}$ times the frequency at the next lower point. Students should make a list of the starting frequency and the 12 higher frequencies leading to the octave. Then they should calculate the period of the string at each point.

CHAPTER OBJECTIVES

In this chapter, you will:
- Graph trigonometric functions and compound functions.
- Determine the amplitude, period, and phase shift for a graph.
- Evaluate and graph inverse trigonometric functions.
- Solve problems involving simple harmonic motion.

CAREER GOAL: Independent Music Production

Did you ever take music lessons? Eric Essix began playing the guitar when he was ten years old. Then ten years ago, he began "dabbling in studio work," and today, he has two record albums to his credit. Although Eric has been a performer for over half of his life, he says, "I like the challenge of taking sounds that you hear in your head and reproducing them on tape. I like the challenge of taking an abstract idea and turning it into something that other people can hear and enjoy." Eric's goal is to "produce contemporary jazz music as an independent producer. As such, I will have opportunities to produce jazz music for advertising companies, recording companies, television, and films."

You may not think that musicians use mathematics in their work, but Eric disagrees. "Music production is so computer-based that it is impossible to produce music in the '90s without the use of mathematics," Eric says. "We frequently use mathematics to derive a particular sound or effect. For instance, we can place music in a sonic environment that is totally different from the one in which it was recorded. You may listen to a CD that sounds like the artist was in a large concert hall. However, he may have been performing in a small recording studio.

"If you shout into the Grand Canyon, you can count the number of times that your echo repeats. That is called the *delay time*. Delay times are different for sounds produced in a large concert hall versus sound produced in a small recording studio. However, we can mathematically change the number and frequency of delay times of a sound recorded in a small studio to make the sound simulate that produced in a large concert hall."

As to why he loves music, Eric says, "Music is probably the most powerful force in the universe. Nothing else affects people and covers the entire spectrum of emotions as music does. I want to be a part of that."

READ MORE ABOUT IT

Baskervi, N. David. *Music Business Handbook & Career Guide.* Los Angeles: The Sherwood Company, 1985.

Csida, Joseph. *The Music/Record Career Handbook.* New York: Billboard Publications, 1980.

Shemel, Sidney and M. William Krasilovsky. *This Business of Music.* New York: Billboard Publications, 1985.

SPOTLIGHT ON...

Eric Essix
Age: 32
Class: Junior
School: Berklee College of Music, Boston, Massachusetts
Major: Music Production and Engineering

"Music production is so computer based that it is impossible to produce music in the '90s without the use of mathematics."

FOR MORE INFORMATION

If you would like more information about music production, contact:

National Academy of Recording Artists and Sciences
303 N. Glenoaks Boulevard,
Suite 140
Burbank, CA 91502-1178

Applications

Lesson	Application	Examples	Exercises
6–1	Electronics		53
	Physics		54
6–2	Physics	5	
	Zoology		47
	Entertainment		48
	Hydraulics		49
6–3	Music	5	
	Acoustics		32
	Electronics		33
	Physics		34
6–4	Aerospace	2	
	Navigation		47
	Optics		48
	Civil		
	Engineering		49
6–5	Optics	2	
	Electronics		47
	Optics		48
6–6	Medicine	3	
	Navigation		34
	Coordinate		
	Geometry		35
	History		36
6–7	Navigation	1	
	Entertainment	2	25
	Automotive		
	Engineering		26
	Physics		24, 27
	Zoology		28

Lesson Resources

- Practice Master 6–1
- Enrichment Master 6–1

 Transparency 6–1 contains the 5-Minute Check and a teaching aid for this lesson.

INTRODUCING THE LESSON

 ### 5-Minute Check

(over Chapter 5)

1. Change $\frac{4\pi}{3}$ radians to degrees.
   240°
2. Find cos –60° without using a calculator. **0.5**
3. In a circle of diameter 10 cm, find the length of the arc intercepted by a central angle of $\frac{3\pi}{4}$. $\frac{15\pi}{4}$
4. Solve $\triangle ABC$ if $A = 34°$, $a = 15$, and $b = 22$. Round angle measures to the nearest degree and side measures to the nearest unit.
   $B = 55°$, $C = 91°$, $c = 27$

Motivating the Lesson

Have students use calculators to find values of the sine and cosine functions in the interval 0 to π. Ask them to describe the behavior of the two functions in the interval.

sine: increases from 0 to 1 at $\frac{\pi}{2}$, then decreases to 0; cosine: decreases from 1 to 0 at $\frac{\pi}{2}$ and continues to decrease to –1

6-1 Graphs of the Trigonometric Functions

Objective
6–1

After studying this lesson, you should be able to:
- use the graphs of the trigonometric functions.

Application

 FYI...

An electrocardiograph is a special device that uses an oscilloscope to monitor the activity of the heart. Dutch physician Willem Einthoven was the first to consider using an oscilloscope in this way. He received the 1924 Nobel Prize for Medicine for his research.

We live in an electronic age. Electricity powers our lights, heats our homes, and even runs our cars. However, unlike light or sound, under normal circumstances we cannot sense this form of energy directly. We must use tools, like an oscilloscope, to measure the behavior of electric currents.

The electric power that is used in American homes is delivered in alternating current. An alternating current surges in one direction and then the other in a way that can be represented on the oscilloscope by a sine curve.

You could generate the coordinates of points on the parent graphs of trigonometric functions with a calculator or spreadsheet program. The graphs may be generated by using a graphing calculator or graphing software. The parent graphs of the six basic trigonometric functions are shown below and on the next page.

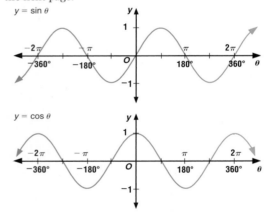

302 CHAPTER 6 GRAPHS AND INVERSES OF THE TRIGONOMETRIC FUNCTIONS

ALTERNATE TEACHING STRATEGIES

Using Connections

Ask students to give examples of periodic functions in everyday life and to compare and contrast them with the sine or cosine function. **Sample answer: The time of sunset through an entire year. The latest sunset (June 21) corresponds to the maximum at (0°, 1) on the cosine curve. The earliest (December 21) corresponds to the minimum at (180°, –1).**

Using Critical Thinking

Ask students to explain the asymptote in the graph of the tangent at $x = \frac{\pi}{2}$ by using the definition of the tangent function. **For $x = \frac{\pi}{2}$, the side adjacent to x is 0. Thus, the fraction $\frac{\text{opposite}}{\text{adjacent}}$ is undefined value, yielding the asymptote at $\frac{\pi}{2}$.**

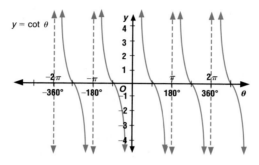

Do you notice a similarity between the sine and cosine curves? The cosine curve is the sine curve translated 90° to the left along the θ-axis. Since the cosecant and secant ratios are the reciprocals of the sine and cosine ratios, the same relationship holds true for their curves. However, this does not hold true for the tangent and cotangent curves. *Why?*

A quadrantal angle is an angle in standard position whose terminal side coincides with one of the coordinate axes. So the measures of the quadrantal angles are ⋯, −270°, −180°, −90°, 0°, 90°, 180°, 270°, ⋯. Knowing the characteristics of the basic trigonometric graphs can help you quickly determine quadrantal values of the trigonometric functions. The value of the sine function is 0 at −360°, −180°, 0°, 180°, 360°, and at all other integral multiples of 180°. The maximum value of the sine function is 1 for 90° or −270°, and the minimum is −1 for 270° or −90°. The fact that the trigonometric functions are **periodic** allows us to find more function values easily.

Periodic Function and Period	A function is periodic if, for some real number α, $f(x + \alpha) = f(x)$ for each x in the domain of f. The least positive value of α for which $f(x) = f(x + \alpha)$ is the period of the function.

Teaching Tip When discussing the graphs of the sine and cosine functions, point out that since the sine and cosine are not linear functions, the graphs curve continuously. From 0 to 90°, and in each succeeding 90° interval on either of the curves, no three points are collinear.

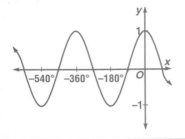
Since the sine function is periodic, its graph repeats itself every 360°. So we can find other zero, maximum, and minimum values easily. For example, since we know that $\sin 90° = 1$, $\sin(90° + 360k°) = 1$ for any integral value of k. The same methods can be used to find special values of the other functions.

Example 1

Use the graph of the cosine function to find the values of θ for which $\cos\theta = 1$.

When $\cos\theta = 1$ and $-360 \le \theta \le 360°$, the value of θ is $-360°, 0°$, or $360°$. Since the cosine function has a period of $360°$, the values of θ for which $\cos\theta = 1$ are given by $0° + 360k°$ or simply $360k°$, where k is any integer.

The graph of a trigonometric function may be drawn from the knowledge of its shape and the values of the function at integral multiples of 90°.

Example 2

Graph the sine curve in the interval $-540° \le \theta \le 0°$.

Find the value of sine θ for $\theta = -540°, -450°, -270°, -180°, -90°$, and $0°$.

Plot the points from these ordered pairs.
$(-540°, 0), (-450°, -1), (-360°, 0), (-270°, 1), (-180°, 0), (-90°, -1), (0°, 0)$

Connect these points with a smooth continuous curve.

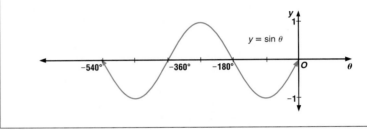

CHECKING FOR UNDERSTANDING

Communicating Mathematics

Read and study the lesson to answer each question.

1. **Describe** how a cosine curve can be translated to coincide with the graph of a sine curve. shift to the right 90° or shift to the left 270°

2. $f(\theta)$ is undefined for that value of θ.

2. The vertical lines in the graphs of the tangent, cotangent, secant, and cosecant functions are asymptotes. What do they indicate about the values of θ where the asymptotes cross the θ-axis?

304   CHAPTER 6   GRAPHS AND INVERSES OF THE TRIGONOMETRIC FUNCTIONS

3. at $\theta = -270°$, $-90°$, $90°$, and $270°$

3. **Explore** the graphs of the trigonometric functions on your graphing calculator. What are the values of θ, for which the graphs of the sine and the cosecant functions are tangent to each other in the interval from $-360°$ to $360°$?

4. **Explain** which transformation(s) changes the graph of the tangent curve to the graph of the cotangent curve. reflection and translation

Guided Practice

Find each value by referring to the graphs of the sine and cosine functions.

5. $\cos 270°$ 0

6. $\sin 90°$ 1

7. $\sin 360°$ 0

8. $\cos 450°$ 0

9. $\cos 90°$ 0

10. $\cos(-90°)$ 0

11. $\sin 180°$ 0

12. $\sin 450°$ 1

13. $\sin(-90°)$ –1

Find the values of θ for which each equation is true. 14–17. k is any integer.

14. $\cos \theta = 1$ $360k°$

15. $\tan \theta = 1$ $45° + 180k°$

16. $\sin \theta = 0$ $180k°$

17. $\cot \theta = 0$ $90° + 180k°$

18. Graph the function $y = \cos x$ on the interval $-360°$ to $360°$. See margin.

EXERCISES

Practice

Find each value by referring to the graphs of the trigonometric functions.

19. $\sin 810°$ 1

20. $\cos(-540°)$ –1

21. $\tan 45°$ 1

22. $\cot(-45°)$ –1

23. $\csc(-90)°$ –1

24. $\sec 0°$ 1

25. $\tan 720°$ 0

26. $\csc 270°$ –1

27. $\cot 180°$ undefined

Find the values of θ for which each equation is true. 28–33. k is any integer.

28. $\sin \theta = 1$ $90° + 360k°$

29. $\cos \theta = -1$ $180° + 360k°$

30. $\csc \theta = -1$ $270° + 360k°$

31. $\tan \theta = -1$ $135° + 180k°$

32. $\sec \theta = 1$ $360k°$

33. $\cot \theta = -1$ $135° + 180k°$

State the domain and range for each function. 34–39. See margin.

34. $y = \sin \theta$

35. $y = \cos x$

36. $y = \cot x$

37. $y = \sec \theta$

38. $y = \tan \theta$

39. $y = \csc \theta$

Graph each function on the given interval. 40–45. See Teacher's Answer Key.

40. $y = \sin x$; $-180° \le x \le 180°$

41. $y = \cos x$; $270° \le x \le 630°$

42. $y = \tan x$; $90° \le x \le 450°$

43. $y = \csc x$; $-540° \le x \le 0°$

44. $y = \sec x$; $-180° \le x \le 360°$

45. $y = \cot x$; $-90° \le x \le 360°$

Graphing Calculator

Use a graphing calculator to graph the sine and cosine functions on the same set of axes for $0° \le x \le 360°$. Use the graphs to find values of x, if any, for which each of the following is true. 46–51. See margin.

46. $\sin x = -\cos x$

47. $\sin x \le \cos x$

48. $\sin x \cos x > 1$

49. $\sin x \cos x \le 0$

50. $\sin x + \cos x = 1$

51. $\sin x - \cos x = 0$

Additional Answers

34. real numbers; $-1 \le y \le 1$

35. real numbers; $-1 \le y \le 1$

36. real numbers except $\theta = k \cdot 180°$; reals

37. real numbers except $\theta = k \cdot 180° + 90°$; $y \le -1, y \ge 1$, k is any integer

38. real numbers except $\theta = k \cdot 180° + 90°$; reals

39. real numbers except $\theta = k \cdot 180°$; $y \le -1, y \ge 1$, k is any integer

46–51. For graphs, see Teacher's Answer Key.

46. $x = 135°, 315°$

47. $0° \le x \le 45°, 225° \le x \le 360°$

48. none

49. $90° \le x \le 180°, 270° \le x \le 360°$

50. $x = 0°, 90°, 360°$

51. $x = 45°, 225°$

APPLYING THE LESSON

Homework Exercises

Assignment Guide

Average: 19–39, 40–48 even, 52, 53, 55–64

Enriched: 26–64

The red A, B, and C flags, printed only in the Teacher's Wraparound Edition, indicate the level of difficulty of the exercises.

Exercise Note

In Exercises 18–26, point out that students can recognize 3-digit multiples of 90° by noting the first two digits in the measure of an angle. These will be divisible by 9 if the measure is a multiple of 90°. For example, for 810°, $81 = 9 \cdot 9$, so 810° is a multiple of 90°.

Using Technology

In Exercises 46 and 51, show how students can use the TRACE function to solve the equation. In Exercise 46, they should graph $y = \sin x$ and $y = -\cos x$, then trace to approximate the point of intersection. In Exercise 51, they should graph $y = \sin x$ and $y = \cos x$, and do the same.

Practice Masters Booklet, p. 36

NAME _____ DATE _____

6-1 **Practice Worksheet**

Graphs of the Trigonometric Functions

Find each value by referring to the graphs of the trigonometric functions.

1. $\sin(-720°)$ 0

2. $\tan(-180°)$ 0

3. $\cos(540°)$ –1

4. $\tan(180°)$ 0

5. $\csc(720°)$ undefined

6. $\sec(180°)$ –1

Find the values of θ for which each equation is true.

7. $\sin \theta = -1$ $270° + 360k°$ where k is any integer

8. $\sec \theta = -1$ $180° + 360k°$ where k is any integer

9. $\tan \theta = 0$ $180k°$ where k is any integer

Graph each function on the given interval.

10. $y = \sin x$; $-90° \le x \le 90°$

11. $y = \tan x$; $-90° \le x \le 270°$

12. $y = \cos x$; $-360° \le x \le 360°$

13. $y = \sec x$; $-360° \le x \le 360°$

T36
Glencoe Division, Macmillan/McGraw-Hill

Additional Answers

52.

The graphs of $y = \sin x$ and $y = 2 \sin x$ have the same x-intercepts, but different maximum and minimum values, 1 to –1 and 2 to –2, respectively. The graph of $y = 3 \sin x$ has the same x-intercepts as the other two graphs, but its maximum is 3 and its minimum is –3.

53b.

Critical Thinking

52. Graph the functions $y = \sin x$ and $y = 2 \sin x$ on the same set of axes on a graphing calculator. How do the graphs differ? Make a conjecture as to the shape of the graph of $y = 3 \sin x$. Then graph this function on the same axes. Was your conjecture correct? **See margin.**

Applications and Problem Solving

53. Electronics The frequency of an alternating current is the number of complete back-and-forth cycles it goes through each second. The frequency is measured in hertz. The formula for the effective current, I_{eff}, of a maximum current of I_{max} volts with a frequency of f hertz is $I_{eff} = I_{max}\sqrt{2}\sin(2\pi ft)$, where t is measured in seconds.

a. The electric power delivered for household use in the United States is 110 volts and has a frequency of 60 hertz. Write the function that describes the effective current related to time. $I_{eff} = 110\sqrt{2}\sin(120\pi t)$

b. Graph the function on a graphing calculator using a range representing $\frac{1}{60}$ of a second. Then sketch the graph. **See margin.**

c. Use the TRACE function of the calculator to find the times when the effective current is zero. $t = \frac{1}{30}k$, where k is any integer

54a. $\theta = \frac{\pi}{4}\cos \pi t$

54. Physics A torsion pendulum is an object suspended by a wire or rod so that its plane is horizontal and it rotates back and forth around the wire without losing energy. Suppose that the pendulum is rotated θ_m radians and released. Then the angular displacement, or the angle of rotation, θ, at time t is $\theta = \theta_m \cos \omega t$, where ω is the angular frequency in radians per second. Suppose the angular frequency of a certain torsion pendulum is π radians per second and its initial rotation is $\frac{\pi}{4}$ radians.

a. Write the equation for the angular displacement of the pendulum.

b. What are the first two values of t for which the angular displacement of the pendulum is 0? **0.5 seconds and 1.5 seconds**

Mixed Review

55. Write the slope-intercept form of the equation of the line through $(5, 2)$ and $(-1, 4)$. **(Lesson 1-5)** $y = -\frac{1}{3}x + \frac{11}{3}$

56. Solve the system of equations below by using augmented matrices. **(Lesson 2-4)**

$4x + 2y = 10$
$y = 6 - x$ $(-1, 7)$

57. Determine whether the graph of $y = \pm\sqrt{x - 49}$ is symmetric with respect to the x-axis, the y-axis, the line $y = x$, the line $y = -x$, or the origin. **(Lesson 3-1)** x-axis

58. Is –4 a root of $x^4 + 3x^3 + 10x - 20 = 0$? **(Lesson 4-1)** no

59. Solve $\dfrac{4}{x+1} = \dfrac{6}{x-3}$. **(Lesson 4-6)** $x = -9$

60. Change $\dfrac{5\pi}{16}$ radians to degree measure to the nearest minute. **(Lesson 5-1)**
$56°15'$

61. Solve $\triangle ABC$ if $A = 40°$, $b = 16$, and $a = 9$. **(Lesson 5-6)** No solution exists.

62. Navigation Two boats carrying marine researchers leave McMurdo port at the same time. One boat travels east at a speed of 12 mph. The other boat travels northeast at 16 mph. If both boats keep on the same course, how far apart will they be after 2 hours? **(Lesson 5-7)** 22.67 mi

63. Find the area to the nearest square unit of $\triangle ABC$ if $a = 17$, $b = 13$, and $c = 19$. **(Lesson 5-8)** 108 square units

64. College Entrance Exam A certain fraction is equivalent to $\dfrac{2}{5}$. If the numerator is decreased by 2 and the denominator is increased by 1, then the new fraction is equivalent to $\dfrac{1}{4}$. What is the numerator of the original fraction? 6

DECISION MAKING

Drunk Driving

Drunk driving has become epidemic in the United States, particularly among teenagers. About 43% of deaths of 16- to 20-year-olds result from motor vehicle accidents, about half of which are alcohol related. In that age group there were about 3000 alcohol-related deaths in 1991. What can you do to raise awareness of the problem among your fellow students and help avert a tragedy in your community? 1–3. See students' work.

1. Describe some of the reasons that teenagers drink and drive. Outline an argument you could use to refute each of these reasons.

2. Research the problem locally. Find local statistics or stories you could use to illustrate the seriousness of the problem. Contact members of the community who have expertise in this area to come to your school to speak about what you can do to help.

3. **Project** Work with your group to complete one of the projects listed at the right based on the information you gathered in Exercises 1–2.

PROJECTS

- *Conduct an interview.*
- *Write a book report.*
- *Write a proposal.*
- *Write an article for the school paper.*
- *Write a report.*
- *Make a display.*
- *Make a graph or chart.*
- *Plan an activity.*
- *Design a checklist.*

LESSON 6-1 GRAPHS OF THE TRIGONOMETRIC FUNCTIONS 307

EXTENDING THE LESSON

Math Power: Communication

Research *direct current* and write a paper discussing your findings. In your paper, compare and contrast direct and alternating current and explain whether direct current can be represented graphically using trigonometric curves.

Decision Making

This activity provides students an opportunity to work together on a given problem. You may wish to refer to pages T20–T21 and page 300c for the various elements of cooperative groups and specific goals and strategies for using them.

Enrichment Masters Booklet, p. 36

Using Technology

Objective This optional page shows how spreadsheet software can be used to examine ordered pairs of a function.

Teaching Suggestions

Point out that a spreadsheet can use built-in mathematical functions like $y = \sin x$ to write mathematical expressions. The built-in functions are called the *function library* of the spreadsheet. Have students determine other functions in the library.

Note that the first character in a mathematical expression (like +, @, =, and so on) is an instruction to the computer that the expression following is not text, but an expression which can be evaluated. Check your software manual to determine the proper way to enter a mathematical expression.

Additional Answers

1.

2.

3.

4.

Technology

Ordered Pairs for Graphing Trigonometric Functions

Spreadsheet programs are among the most popular software for businesses. Spreadsheets are used in accounting, for generating charts, and when working with databases. Spreadsheets are also used in mathematics, mainly to examine functions by generating ordered pairs.

```
= = = = = A = = = = = = B = = = = = = C = = = = =
1    START  X =        -2
2    STOP   X =         2
3    STEP     =    (B2-B1)/10
4
5         ^X                        ^Y
6    +B1+0*B3                  @SIN(A6+@PI/3)
7    +B1+1*B3                  @SIN(A7+@PI/3)
8    +B1+2*B3                  @SIN(A8+@PI/3)

16   +B1+10*B3                 @SIN(A16+@PI/3)
```

The spreadsheet shown at the left calculates and displays a list of ordered pairs for the function $y = \sin\left(x + \frac{\pi}{3}\right)$. While only eleven ordered pairs are shown on the screen, you can generate others by changing the **Start X** and **Stop X** values. As soon as you change an X value, new ordered pairs are calculated and displayed.

The display at the right shows what the spreadsheet looks like for the domain $-2 \leq x \leq 2$. Only the first four ordered pairs are shown.

If you want to generate ordered pairs for a trigonometric function that is different from the one used, you can change

```
= = = = =A= = = = =B= = = =C= = =
1    START  X =      -2
2    STOP   X =       2
3    STEP     =      0.4
4
5           X                    Y
6          -2                -0.81504
7          -1.6              -0.52507
8          -1.2              -0.15220
9          -0.8               0.244687
```

the function when typing in the new information. Note that you will have to change all of the expressions in cells C6 through C16.

EXERCISES   1–4. See margin for graphs.

Make a detailed graph of the function $y = \sin\left(x + \frac{\pi}{3}\right)$ by using the spreadsheet to generate ordered pairs over the following domains.

1. $-4 \leq x \leq -2$ **2.** $-2 \leq x \leq 0$ **3.** $0 \leq x \leq 3$ **4.** $2 \leq x \leq 4$

Amplitude, Period, and Phase Shift

Objectives

6–2A

6–2B

After studying this lesson, you should be able to:
- find the amplitude, period, and phase shift for a trigonometric function, and
- write equations of trigonometric functions given the amplitude, period, and phase shift.

Application

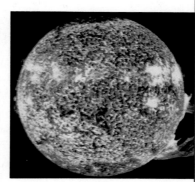

A *sunspot* is a relatively dark area on the surface of the sun. These spots are cooler areas, with temperatures of about 7000°F, compared with temperatures of about 11,000°F on the rest of the sun's surface. Astronomers have long been studying the number of sunspots that occur on the surface of the sun each year. They have found that the number of sunspots counted in a given year varies periodically from about 10 to 110 per year. The most sunspots occurred in the years 1750 and 1948, and 18 complete cycles occurred between these years. If the number of sunspots, y, is graphed with respect to years since 1750, x, the graph is similar to a modified cosine curve.

Recall from Chapter 3 that changes to the equation of the parent graph affect the appearance of the graph. One way that the parent graphs of the trigonometric functions can be modified is to multiply by constants. Let's consider an equation of the form $y = A \sin \theta$. We know that the maximum absolute value of $\sin \theta$ is 1. If every value of $\sin \theta$ is multiplied by A, the maximum value of $A \sin \theta$ is $|A|$. Similarly, the maximum value of $A \cos \theta$ is $|A|$. The absolute value of A, or $|A|$, is called the **amplitude** of the functions $y = A \sin \theta$ and $y = A \cos \theta$.

If $A < 0$ in the equation $y = A \sin \theta$ or $y = A \cos \theta$, the curve is the reflection of the graph of the function $y = |A| \sin \theta$ or $y = |A| \cos \theta$ over the θ-axis.

LESSON 6-2 AMPLITUDE, PERIOD, AND PHASE SHIFT 309

NCTM Standards: 1–6, 8, 9

Lesson Resources

- Practice Master 6–2
- Enrichment Master 6–2
- Evaluation Master, Quiz A, p. 73
- Activity Master, p. 18
   Transparency 6–2 contains the 5-Minute Check and a teaching aid for this lesson.

INTRODUCING THE LESSON

 5-Minute Check

(over Lesson 6–1)

Find each value by referring to the graphs of the trigonometric functions.
1. sin 450°   **1**
2. cos –270°   **0**
3. tan 675°   **–1**
4. Find the values of θ for which sin θ = –1 is true.
   270° + 360k°
5. Give the domain and range of $y = \cos x$.   **real numbers; –1 ≤ y ≤ 1**

Prerequisite Skills

Students should know how to find the absolute value of a number. Find each absolute value.
1. |−14| **14**   2. |9| **9**
3. |3.67| **3.67**   4. $\left|2\frac{3}{4}\right|$ **$2\frac{3}{4}$**

Motivating the Lesson

Have students read the application at the beginning of the lesson. Then ask these questions.
- How is the graph like the cosine curve?
  It is periodic. Each increasing section appears to be a reflection of the decreasing section that follows.
- How does it differ from the cosine?
  It appears to increase and decrease more sharply. It does not cross the x-axis.
- How is it more like the cosine than the sine?
  It begins at its maximum.

ALTERNATE TEACHING STRATEGIES

Using Cooperative Groups

Have each student sketch a graph of $y = A \sin x$. Assign each student a different value of A. Then have them compare the graphs to see how the amplitude is affected by the value of A. Repeat with graphs of $y = \sin Ax$ to see how the period is affected. Repeat with graphs of $y = \sin (x + A°)$ to see how the phase is affected.

Using Questioning

After discussing amplitude, period, and phase shift, refer to the graph above.
- What is the amplitude of the graph?
  40
- What is the period? **11 years**
- Suppose the 18 cycles described had occurred between 1753 and 1951. How would the phase of the graph change? **It would shift three years to the right.**

Teaching Tip When discussing the definition of amplitude, suggest that students picture the graph as an ocean wave and the x-axis as sea level. The amplitude is the height of the wave above (or below) sea level.

Chalkboard Example

For Example 1

State the amplitude of the function y = –2 sin x. Graph y = –2 sin x and y = sin x on the same set of axes. Compare the graphs. The amplitude is |–2| or 2.

The graphs cross the x-axis at 0°, 180°, and 360°. The graphs of y = –2 sin x and y = sin x reach critical values at 90° (–2 and 1, respectively) and 270° (2 and –1, respectively).

Amplitude of Sine Cosine Functions

The amplitude of the functions $y = A \sin \theta$ and $y = A \cos \theta$ is the absolute value of A, or $|A|$.

The amplitude can also be described as the absolute value of one-half the difference of the maximum and minimum function values.

$$\left| \frac{A - (-A)}{2} \right| = |A|$$

The tangent, cotangent, secant, and cosecant functions do not have amplitudes because their values increase and decrease without bound for values that approach certain multiples of 90°.

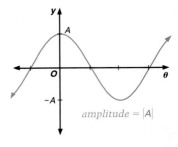

amplitude = $|A|$

Example 1

State the amplitude of the function $y = 3 \cos \theta$. Graph $y = 3 \cos \theta$ and $y = \cos \theta$ on the same set of axes. Compare the graphs.

According to the definition of amplitude, the amplitude of $y = A \cos \theta$ is $|A|$. So the amplitude of $y = 3 \cos \theta$ is $|3|$ or 3.

Make a table of values. Then graph the points and draw a smooth curve.

θ	0°	45°	90°	135°	180°	225°	270°	315°	360°
$\cos \theta$	1	$\frac{\sqrt{2}}{2}$	0	$-\frac{\sqrt{2}}{2}$	-1	$-\frac{\sqrt{2}}{2}$	0	$\frac{\sqrt{2}}{2}$	1
$3 \cos \theta$	3	$\frac{3\sqrt{2}}{2}$	0	$-\frac{3\sqrt{2}}{2}$	-3	$-\frac{3\sqrt{2}}{2}$	0	$\frac{3\sqrt{2}}{2}$	3

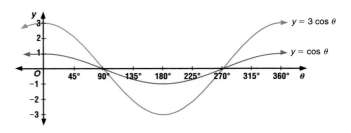

The graphs cross the θ-axis at $\theta = 90°$ and $\theta = 270°$. Also, both functions reach their maximum value at $\theta = 0°$ and $\theta = 360°$ and their minimum value at $\theta = 180°$. But the maximum and minimum values of the function $y = \cos \theta$ are 1 and –1, and the maximum and minimum values of the function $y = 3 \cos \theta$ are 3 and –3.

EXPLORATION: Graphing Calculator

1. Use the range values below to set up a viewing window. Mode should be in radians.

   $-4.7 \le X \le 4.8$ $-3 \le Y \le 3$ $XSCL = 1$ $YSCL = 1$

2. Graph the following functions on the same screen.
   a. $\sin x$ **b.** $2 \sin x$ **c.** $3 \sin x$

3. Describe the change in the graph of $f(x) = A \sin x$, where $A > 0$, as A increases. The amplitude increases.

4. Make a conjecture about the behavior of the graph of $f(x) = A \sin x$, if $A < 0$. Test your conjecture. See margin.

The graphs of trigonometric functions can be modified by changing the amplitude of the function. We can modify graphs of trigonometric functions in a second way. Consider an equation of the form $y = \sin k\theta$, where k is any integer. Since the period of the sine function is 360°, the following identity can be developed.

If θ is expressed in radians, the period of $y = \sin k\theta$ and $y = \cos k\theta$ is $\frac{2\pi}{k}$. The period of $y = \tan k\theta$ is $\frac{\pi}{k}$.

$$y = \sin k\theta$$
$$= \sin(k\theta + 360°)$$
$$= \sin k\left(\theta + \frac{360°}{k}\right)$$

Therefore, the period of $y = \sin k\theta$ is $\frac{360°}{k}$. Similarly, the period of $y = \cos k\theta$ is $\frac{360°}{k}$. The period of $y = \tan k\theta$ is $\frac{180°}{k}$ since the period of the tangent function is 180°.

Period of Sine, Cosine, and Tangent Functions

The period of the functions $y = \sin k\theta$ and $y = \cos k\theta$ is $\frac{360°}{k}$. The period of the function $y = \tan k\theta$ is $\frac{180°}{k}$.

Example 2

State the period of the function $y = \sin 4\theta$. Then graph the function and $y = \sin \theta$ on the same set of axes.

The definition of the period of $y = \sin k\theta$ is $\frac{360°}{k}$. Therefore, the period of $y = \sin 4\theta$ is $\frac{360°}{4}$ or 90°.

If you are using a graphing calculator, set the range first: Xmin = 0, Xmax = 360, Xscl = 30, Ymin = -1.5, Ymax = 1.5, Yscl = 1, Xres = 1. Mode should be in degrees.

(continued on the next page)

LESSON 6-2   AMPLITUDE, PERIOD, AND PHASE SHIFT   311

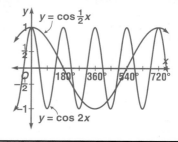

Using Technology

After students graphs the family of functions $f(x) = \sin(x + c)$, ask them how the behavior of this graph compares with the parent graph, $f(x) = \sin x$. Ask them how this compares with the behavior changes from $f(x) = x$ to $f(x + c)$.

Then enter both $y = \sin x$ and $y = \sin 4x$ and press GRAPH.

EXPLORATION: Graphing Calculator

1. Use the range values below to set up a viewing window. Mode should be in radians.

$$-4.7 \le X \le 4.8 \qquad -3 \le Y \le 3 \qquad XSCL = 1 \qquad YSCL = 1$$

2. Graph the following functions on the same screen.
   a. $\sin x$ **b.** $\sin\left(x + \dfrac{\pi}{2}\right)$ **c.** $\sin\left(x + \dfrac{\pi}{3}\right)$

3. Describe the behavior of the graph of $f(x) = \sin(x + c)$, where $c > 0$, as c increases. Graph shifts right by amount c decreases.

4. Make a conjecture about what happens to the graph of $f(x) = \sin(x + c)$ if $c < 0$ and continues to decrease. Test your conjecture.

4. See students' work.

The phase shift is the least value of $|k\theta + c|$ for which $y = 0$.

In addition to changing the amplitude or period, the third way that a trigonometric graph can be modified is by a **phase shift**. Consider an equation of the form $y = A \sin(k\theta + c)$, where $A \ne 0$, $k \ne 0$, and $c \ne 0$. To find a zero of the function, find a value of θ for which $0 = A \sin(k\theta + c)$. Since $\sin 0 = 0$, solving $k\theta + c = 0$ will yield a zero of the function.

$$k\theta + c = 0$$
$$\theta = -\frac{c}{k}$$

Therefore, $y = 0$ when $\theta = -\dfrac{c}{k}$. The value of $-\dfrac{c}{k}$ is the phase shift. When $c > 0$, the graph of $y = A \sin(k\theta + c)$ is the graph of $y = A \sin k\theta$, shifted $\left|\dfrac{c}{k}\right|$ to the left. When $c < 0$, the graph of $y = A \sin(k\theta + c)$ is the graph of $y = A \sin k\theta$ shifted $\left|\dfrac{c}{k}\right|$ to the right.

312 CHAPTER 6 GRAPHS AND INVERSES OF THE TRIGONOMETRIC FUNCTIONS

Phase Shift of All Trigonometric Functions

The phase shift of the function $y = A \sin (k\theta + c)$ is $-\dfrac{c}{k}$. If $c > 0$, the shift is to the left. If $c < 0$, the shift is to the right. This definition applies to all of the trigonometric functions.

Example 3

State the phase shift of the function $y = \tan (\theta - 45°)$. Then use a graphing calculator to graph the function and $y = \tan \theta$ on the same set of axes.

The phase shift is $-\dfrac{c}{k} = -\dfrac{-45°}{1}$ or $45°$. Since c is less than 0, the shift is to the right.

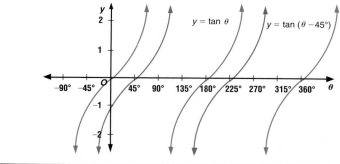

We can write an equation for a trigonometric function if we are given the amplitude, period, and phase shift.

Example 4

Find the possible equations of a cosine function with amplitude 3, period 90°, and phase shift 45°.

The form of the equation will be $y = A \cos(k\theta + c)$. First, find the possible values of A for an amplitude of 3.

$|A| = 3$
$A = 3 \text{ or } -3$

Now find the value of k when the period is 90°.

$\dfrac{360°}{k} = 90°$
$k = 4$

Then find the value of c for a phase shift of 45°.

$-\dfrac{c}{k} = 45°$

$-\dfrac{c}{4} = 45°$
$c = -180°$

The possible equations are $y = 3 \cos(4\theta - 180°)$ or $y = -3 \cos(4\theta - 180°)$.

LESSON 6-2   AMPLITUDE, PERIOD, AND PHASE SHIFT   313

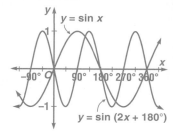

Many real-world situations have cyclical characteristics that can be described with trigonometric functions. When you are writing an equation to describe a situation, remember the characteristics of the sine and cosine graphs. If you know the function value when $x = 0$ and whether the function is increasing or decreasing, you can choose the appropriate trigonometric function to write an equation for the situation.

Function value at $x = 0$	Sign of A	Function
maximum	positive	cosine
minimum	negative	cosine
0, with values increasing	positive	sine
0, with values decreasing	negative	sine

Example 5

The motion of a weight on a certain kind of spring can be described by a modified trigonometric function. At time 0, Carrie pushes the weight upward 3 inches from its equilibrium point and releases it. She finds that the weight returns to the point three inches above the equilibrium point after 2 seconds.

a. Write a function that represents the position of the spring in reference to its equilibrium point, y, in terms of the time, t, in seconds after it was released.

a. At time 0, the weight is 3 inches above the equilibrium point and at its maximum displacement from 0. Since the weight will fall, the values will get smaller. The function will be a cosine function with a positive value of A.

The maximum and minimum points are 3 and –3. Thus, the amplitude is $\left| \dfrac{3 - (-3)}{2} \right|$ or 3. Thus, $A = 3$.

The weight makes a complete cycle in 2 seconds. Thus, the period is 2.

$$\frac{2\pi}{k} = 2 \qquad \textit{Use radians.}$$
$$k = \pi$$

Now write the equation.

$$y = A \cos kt$$
$$y = 3 \cos \pi t \qquad A = 3, k = \pi$$

314   CHAPTER 6   GRAPHS AND INVERSES OF THE TRIGONOMETRIC FUNCTIONS

RETEACHING THE LESSON

Transform $y = \sin x$ into $y = 2 \sin(4x - 360°)$ step by step. Display a sketch of $y = \sin x$. Graph $y = 2 \sin x$, showing that the amplitude has changed to 2. Next, graph $y = 2 \sin 4x$. Show that the period has changed to 90°. Finally, draw $y = 2 \sin(4x - 360°)$. Show that the graph has shifted 90° to the right.

b. What will the position of the weight be after 15.5 seconds?

b. Use a calculator to find y when $t = 15.5$ to find the position of the weight after 15.5 seconds. *Make sure your calculator is in radian mode.*

$$y = 3 \cos \pi (15.5)$$

15.5 ⊠ π = COS ⊠ 3 = *0*

After 15.5 seconds, the weight will be at the equilibrium point.

CHECKING FOR UNDERSTANDING

Communicating Mathematics

Read and study the lesson to answer each question.

1. **Graph** the functions $y = \cos x$ and $y = \sin(x + 90°)$ on a graphing calculator. What is true of these graphs? They coincide.

2. **Explain** what happens to the graph of $y = A \sin \theta$ if A is increased. See margin.

3. **Write** two sentences to describe phase shift to a classmate.
See students' work.

Guided Practice

State the amplitude, period, and phase shift for each function.

4. $y = 4 \sin \theta$ 4, 360°, 0°
5. $y = 2 \sin 5\theta$ 2, 72°, 0°
6. $y = 2 \cos 2\theta$ 2, 180°, 0°
7. $y = \tan(2x - \pi)$ none, $\frac{\pi}{2}$, $\frac{\pi}{2}$
8. $y = 2 \cos 4\theta$ 2, 90°, 0°
9. $y = 3 \cos(\theta - 90°)$ 3, 360°, 90°
10. $y = \tan 2(\theta - 180°)$ none, 90°, 180°
11. $y = 243 \sin(15\theta - 40°)$
    243, 24°, $2\frac{2}{3}$°

Write an equation for each function. 12. $y = \pm 3 \sin\left(\frac{1}{2}\theta + 30°\right)$

12. a sine function with amplitude 3, period 720°, and phase shift 60°

13. a cosine function with amplitude 4, period 4π, and phase shift $\frac{\pi}{2}$

14. a tangent function with period 180° and phase shift 25°
    13. $y = \pm 4 \cos\left(\frac{1}{2}\theta + \frac{\pi}{4}\right)$ 14. $y = \tan(\theta - 25°)$

EXERCISES

Practice

State the amplitude, period, and phase shift for each function.

15. $y = 2 \cos \theta$ 2, 360°, 0°
16. $y = 10 \tan 4\theta$ none, 45°, 0°
17. $y = 110 \sin 20\theta$ 110, 18°, 0°
18. $y = 2 \sin \theta$ 2, 360°, 0°
19. $y = -7 \sin 6\theta$ 7, 60°, 0°
20. $y = 4 \sin \frac{\theta}{2}$ 4, 720°, 0°
21. $y = \frac{1}{4} \cos \frac{\theta}{2}$ $\frac{1}{4}$, 720°, 0°
22. $y = 12 \cos 3\left(x - \frac{\pi}{2}\right)$ 12, $\frac{2\pi}{3}$, $\frac{\pi}{2}$
23. $y = -6 \cos(180° - \theta)$
    6, −360°, 180°
24. $y = 10 \sin\left(\frac{1}{3}\theta - 300°\right)$
    10, 1080°, 900°

Additional Answer

2. The "peaks and valleys" of the graph become taller.

EVALUATING THE LESSON

Checking for Understanding

Exercises 1–14 are designed to help you assess students' understanding through reading, writing, speaking, and modeling. You should work through Exercises 1–3 with your students and then monitor their work on Exercises 4–14.

Closing the Lesson

Speaking Activity Write $y = A \sin(Bx + C)$ on the chalkboard. Tell students the graph of the equation has an amplitude of 5, a period of 60°, and a phase shift to the right of 90°. Ask them to identify A, B, and C. 5; 6; −540°

APPLYING THE LESSON

Homework Exercises

Assignment Guide

Average: 15–41, 46, 47, 50–57
Enriched: 20–46, 48–57

The red A, B, and C flags, printed only in the Teacher's Wraparound Edition, indicate the level of difficulty of the exercises.

Chapter 6, Quiz A, (Lessons 6–1 through 6–2), is available in the *Evaluation Masters*, p. 73.

Write an equation of the sine function with each amplitude, period, and phase shift.

25. amplitude = 5, period = 360°, phase shift = 60° $y = \pm 5 \sin (x - 60°)$

26. amplitude = $\frac{2}{3}$, period = π, phase shift = $\frac{\pi}{4}$ $y = \pm\frac{2}{3} \sin \left(2x - \frac{\pi}{2}\right)$

27. amplitude = 17, period = 45°, phase shift = –60° $y = \pm 17 \sin (8x + 480°)$

28. amplitude = $\frac{1}{2}$, period = $\frac{3\pi}{2}$, phase shift = $-\frac{\pi}{4}$ $y = \pm\frac{1}{2} \sin \left(\frac{4}{3}x + \frac{\pi}{3}\right)$

29. amplitude = 7, period = 225°, phase shift = –90° $y = \pm 7 \sin \left(\frac{8}{5}x + 144°\right)$

Write an equation of the cosine function with each amplitude, period, and phase shift.

30. amplitude = $\frac{1}{3}$, period = 180°, phase shift = 0° $y = \pm\frac{1}{3} \cos 2x$

31. amplitude = 3, period = 180°, phase shift = 120° $y = \pm 3 \cos (2x - 240°)$

32. amplitude = 100, period = 630°, phase shift = –90° $y = \pm 100 \cos \left(\frac{4}{7}x + \frac{360°}{7}\right)$

33. amplitude = $\frac{7}{3}$, period = 150°, phase shift = 270° $y = \pm\frac{7}{3} \cos \left(\frac{12}{5}x - 648°\right)$

34. amplitude = 1, period = $\frac{3\pi}{4}$, phase shift = $-\frac{\pi}{3}$ $y = \pm \cos \left(\frac{8}{3}x + \frac{8\pi}{9}\right)$

Graph each function.   35–42. See margin.

35. $y = \frac{1}{2} \cos \theta$ 36. $y = 3 \sin \theta$ 37. $y = 3 \sec \theta$

38. $y = 4 \sin \frac{\theta}{2}$ 39. $y = \sin (\theta - 45°)$ 40. $y = \cos (\theta + 30°)$

41. $y = -\frac{1}{2} \cos \frac{3}{4}\theta$ 42. $y = -6 \sin \left(2x + \frac{\pi}{4}\right)$

43. The graph of $y = \tan x$ approaches an asymptote at $x = 90°$. What is the first positive value of x for which each of the following has a vertical asymptote?
    a. $y = \tan (x - 45°)$ **b.** $y = \tan 3x$
    c. $y = \tan (2x - 90°)$ **d.** $y = \tan (kx - c)$
    43a. $x = 135°$ 43b. $x = 30°$ 43c. $x = 90°$ 43d. $x = \left(\frac{90 + c}{k}\right)°$

Graphing Calculator

Use a graphing calculator to graph the following functions on the same screen. Then write an equation that relates the sine and cosine functions. 44–45. See margin.

44. $\sin(x + \frac{\pi}{2})$ 45. $\cos x$

Critical Thinking

46. Graph the functions $y = \sin 2x$ and $y = 2 \cos x$ on a graphing calculator. Make a conjecture as to what the graph of $y = \sin 2x + 2 \cos x$ will look like. Then check your results with the graphing calculator. See students' work.

316   CHAPTER 6   GRAPHS AND INVERSES OF THE TRIGONOMETRIC FUNCTIONS

40.

41.

47. Zoology In predator-prey situations, the number of animals in each category tends to vary periodically. A certain region has pumas as predators and deer as prey. The number of pumas varies with time according to the function $P = 500 + 200 \sin 0.4(t - 2)$, and the number of deer varies according to the function $D = 1500 + 400 \sin 0.4t$, with time, t, in years. 47a. 323, 1388

a. How many pumas and deer will there be in the region in 15 years?

b. Graph both of the equations on a graphing calculator. Then sketch the graph on paper. See margin.

c. Write a few sentences to explain how the populations vary. Why do you think they vary as they do? See students' work.

48. Entertainment As you ride a Ferris wheel, the height that you are above the ground varies periodically. Consider the height of the center of the wheel to be the equilibrium point. A particular wheel has a diameter of 38 feet and travels at a rate of 4 revolutions per minute.

a. Write an equation to describe the changes in height, h, of the seat that was filled last before the ride began in terms of time, t, in seconds. *Hint: This seat was at the minimum height at $t = 0$.* $y = -19 \cos\left(\frac{2\pi}{15}t\right) + 19$

b. Find the height of the seat after 22 seconds.

c. If the seats of the Ferris wheel clear the ground by 3 feet, how long after the ride starts will the seat first be 27 feet above the ground? about 4.4 seconds

48b. 18.6 ft above the equilibrium point

49. Hydraulics The branch of physics that involves the behavior of liquids at rest and in motion is called hydraulics. A reservoir is a part of a scientific apparatus in which liquid is held. An important formula in analyzing reservoirs involves the capillary pressure, P. If t is the tension between two fluids, r is the radius of the capillary tube, and θ is the angle between the interface and the capillary wall, then $P = \frac{2t}{r} \cos \theta$. A certain reservoir with an interfacial tension between fluids of 75 d/cm has a capillary tube of radius 0.02 cm.   See margin.

a. Draw a graph of the capillary pressure in the apparatus for $\theta = 0°$ to $90°$.

b. What is the amplitude of this curve? 7500

c. Write a few sentences to explain the meaning of the graph. See students' work.

Mixed Review

50. Graph the inequality $6 < 4x + 2 < 18$. **(Lesson 1-3)** See margin.

51. $\begin{bmatrix} 2 & -1 & 0 \\ 3 & -1 & 1 \\ 2 & 8 & -5 \end{bmatrix}$ **51.** Find the sum of the matrices $\begin{bmatrix} 4 & -3 & 2 \\ 8 & -2 & 0 \\ 9 & 6 & -3 \end{bmatrix}$ and $\begin{bmatrix} -2 & 2 & -2 \\ -5 & 1 & 1 \\ -7 & 2 & -2 \end{bmatrix}$. **(Lesson 2-2)**

LESSON 6-2   AMPLITUDE, PERIOD, AND PHASE SHIFT   317

46.

47b.

49a.

50.

42.

44.–45.

$\sin\left(x + \frac{\pi}{2}\right) = \cos x$

Additional Answers

55. $\sin \alpha = \frac{-3\sqrt{58}}{58}$, $\cos \alpha = \frac{7\sqrt{58}}{58}$,

$\tan \alpha = -\frac{3}{7}$, $\csc \alpha = -\frac{\sqrt{58}}{3}$,

$\sec \alpha = \frac{\sqrt{58}}{7}$, $\cot \alpha = -\frac{7}{3}$

---

52. $x = 0$, maximum; $x = 6$, minimum; $x = -4$, minimum; $x = \frac{2 \pm 2\sqrt{19}}{3}$, points of inflection

52. Find the critical points of the graph of $y = 3x^4 - 8x^3 - 144x^2 + 6$. Then, determine whether each point represents a maximum, a minimum, or a point of inflection. **(Lesson 3-7)**

53. Approximate the real zero(s) of $f(x) = x^5 + 3x^3 - 4$ to the nearest tenth. **(Lesson 4-5)** 1.0

54. Physics A pendulum 20 centimeters long swings 3°30' on each side of its vertical position. Find the length of the arc formed by the tip of the pendulum as it swings. **(Lesson 5-2)** about 2.44 centimeters

55. Find the values of the six trigonometric functions of an angle in standard position if the point at $(7, -3)$ lies on its terminal side. **(Lesson 5-3)** See margin.

56. $x = 180$ or 270°

56. Use a graphing calculator to graph the sine and cosine functions on the same set of axes for $0° \le x \le 360°$. Use the graphs to find the values of x, if any, for which $\sin x + \cos x = -1$. **(Lesson 6-1)** $x = 180°$ or 270°

57. College Entrance Exam Choose the best answer. C
The coordinates of two vertices of an equilateral triangle are $(-6, 0)$ and $(6, 0)$. The coordinates of the third vertex may be

(A) $(0, 3\sqrt{3})$ **(B)** $(6, 6\sqrt{3})$ **(C)** $(0, 6\sqrt{3})$ **(D)** $(6\sqrt{3}, 0)$ **(E)** $(0, 6)$

CASE STUDY FOLLOW-UP

Refer to Case Study 1: *Buying a Home*, on pages 956–958.

Sound waves are *longitudinal* waves because the particles of a sound wave vibrate in the direction of the motion of the wave. The *frequency* of a wave, f, is the number of vibrations occurring in one second. Frequency is measured in hertz. One hertz (Hz) is one vibration per second. The human ear can hear a range of frequencies of sound waves from a low of about 20 Hz to a high of about 20,000 Hz. The relationship between the frequency, wavelength, λ, and speed, v, of a sound wave is given by the formula $v = f\lambda$.

1. A dog that lives next door to the Arlen residence barks constantly at a frequency of 7000 Hz. The speed of sound is 1085 feet/second. Find the wavelength of the dog's bark. 0.155 ft

2. The cost of soundproofing a room, C, depends on the frequency of the sound. One dealer quoted Mrs. Arlen a price, in dollars, of $C = 450 \sin \left[\left(\frac{f}{20,000}\right)90\right]°$ per room. The Arlen house has the same number of rooms as the largest typical American house. How much will it cost the Arlens to soundproof all of the rooms? $1645.87

3. **Research** Find out about the *amplitude* of a sound wave. Research the connection between the frequency and amplitude of a sound wave and the difficulty of soundproofing a room. Write about your findings in a 1-page paper. See students' work.

318 CHAPTER 6 GRAPHS AND INVERSES OF THE TRIGONOMETRIC FUNCTIONS

Enrichment Masters Booklet, p. 37

NAME _____ DATE _____

6-2 **Enrichment Worksheet**

Mass of a Floating Object

An object bobbing up and down in the water exhibits periodic motion. The greater the mass of the object (think of an ocean liner and a buoy), the longer the period of *oscillation* (up and down motion). The greater the horizontal cross-sectional area of the object, the shorter the period. If you know the period and the cross-sectional area, you can find the mass of the object.

Imagine a point on the waterline of a stationary floating object. Let y represent the vertical position of the point above or below the waterline when the object begins to oscillate. ($y = 0$ represents the waterline.) If we neglect air and water resistance, the equation of motion of the object is

$$y = A \sin\left(\sqrt{\frac{9800C}{M}}\, t\right),$$

where A is the amplitude of the oscillation, C is the horizontal cross-sectional area of the object in square meters, M is the mass of the object in kilograms, and t is the elapsed time since the beginning of the oscillation. The argument of the sine is measured in radians and y is measured in meters.

1. A 4-kg log has a cross-sectional area of 0.2 m². A point on the log has a maximum displacement of 0.4 m above or below the water line. Find the vertical position of the point 5 seconds after the log begins to bob.
≈ 0.26 m below the water line

2. Find an expression for the period of an oscillating floating object.
$p = 2\pi\sqrt{\frac{M}{9800C}}$

3. Find the period of the log described in Exercise 1.
≈ 0.28 seconds

4. A buoy bobs up and down with a period of 0.6 seconds. The mean cross-sectional area of the buoy is 1.3 m². Use your expression for the period of an oscillating floating object to find the mass of the buoy.
≈ 116.2 kg

5. Write an equation of motion of the buoy described in Exercise 4. If the amplitude is 0.45 m. $y = 0.45 \sin 10.47t$

T 37
Glencoe Division, Macmillan/McGraw-Hill

EXTENDING THE LESSON

Math Power: Problem Solving

The air flow at a given time in the respiration cycle (one breath in, one breath out) is given by $V = 0.8 \sin \frac{\pi}{3}t$, where V = air flow in L/s and t = time (s). The period of V is the length of one cycle. How many cycles does a person breathe in 1 minute?

$2\pi \div \frac{\pi}{3} = 6$, each cycle = 6s.

$60s \div 6s = 10$ cycles/min

Case Study Follow-Up

This activity provides an opportunity to do research and apply mathematics in solving problems related to issues that may face students in their adult lives. Case Study 1 is located on pages 956–958.

6-3A Graphing Calculators: Graphing Trigonometric Functions

The graphing calculator is a good tool for graphing trigonometric functions. With the calculator, you can see how changing or modifying a trigonometric function alters its graph. The functions can be graphed in degrees or radians; in this lesson we will use degrees. On the TI-81, check to see that you are using degrees by pressing the [MODE] key. If not, use the arrow keys to move to "Deg" and press [ENTER]. On the Casio, press [MODE] 4 [EXE].

Example 1

Graph $y = \cos x$.

The TI-81 graphing calculator does not have any built-in functions, so the viewing window must be set. Set the window to $[-360°, 360°]$ by $[-3, 3]$ with a scale factor of 90° for the x-axis and 1 for the y-axis. You can also obtain this viewing window by pressing [ZOOM] 7; the calculator will set the range values to $[-360°, 360°]$ by $[-3, 3]$ with scale factors of 90° for the x-axis and 0.25 for the y-axis.

TI-81: [Y=] [COS] [X|T] [GRAPH]

The Casio graphing calculator has several built-in functions, and the trigonometric functions of sine, cosine, and tangent are three of them. To use the built-in function, do not press the x key.

Casio: [Graph] [cos] [EXE]

The viewing window is automatically set to $[-360°, 360°]$ by $[-1.6, 1.6]$. The calculator will only set the range for you if you do not use the x key. To graph any trigonometric functions other than the three built-in functions, or for any variations of the functions, you must set the range values manually to change the viewing window.

Notice that the amplitude of the graph in Example 1 is 1. The period of the function is 360°.

Changing a trigonometric equation will also change its graph.

Example 2

Graph $y = 2 \sin \frac{1}{2}x$. Use the viewing window of $[-540°, 540°]$ by $[-3, 3]$ with a scale factor of 90° for the x-axis and 1 for the y-axis. State the amplitude and period of the function.

TI-81: [Y=] 2 [SIN] [(] [X|T] [÷] 2 [)] [GRAPH]

(continued on the next page)

INTRODUCING THE LESSON

Objective   Graph and analyze trigonometric functions on a graphing calculator.

Motivating the Lesson

Remind students of the families of graphs they studied in Chapters 3 and 4. Ask them how the transformations used with these families might affect the graphs of trigonometric functions.

TEACHING THE LESSON

Teaching Tip   Remind students that they can graph the secant, cosecant, and contingent by using the reciprocal of the cosine, sine, and tangent, respectively.

Teaching Tip   Point out that students must often use parentheses to properly enter a trigonometric equation. For example, TAN X/2 means $\frac{\tan x}{2}$.

To enter $\tan \frac{x}{2}$, use TAN (X/2)

More Examples

Graph $y = 3 \sin (2x - 60°)$. State the amplitude, period, and phase shift.   amplitude: 3, period: 180°, phase shift, 30°

Closing the Lesson

Ask students to use the graph in Example 2 to compare the amplitude and period of $y = 2 \sin \frac{1}{2}x$ with the amplitude and period of the parent graph, $y = \sin x$.

APPLYING THE LESSON

Homework Exercises

Assignment Guide

All: 1–12

Additional Answers

	amplitude	period	phase shift
1.	1	360°	0°
2.	none	360°	0°
3.	none	90°	0°
4.	none	360°	0°
5.	none	120°	0°
6.	none	60°	30°
7.	3	360°	−45°
8.	2	120°	−20°
9.	none	180°	0°
10.	none	360°	45°
11.	0.5	180°	45°
12.	none	180°	−90°

For graphs, see Teacher's Answer Key.

Casio: Graph 2 sin ((ALPHA X ÷ 2)) EXE

The amplitude of the function is $\frac{|-2 - 2|}{2} = \frac{4}{2} = 2$. The period of the function is 720°.

You can also graph the other trigonometric functions on the graphing calculator, namely cot x, sec x, and csc x. These functions are also periodic and changing their equations will also change their graphs.

Example 3

Graph $y = \sec x$ and $y = \sec (x + 90°)$ at the same time. Use the viewing window $[-360°, 360°]$ by $[-3, 3]$ with a scale factor of 90° for the x-axis and a scale factor of 1 for the y-axis. State the phase shift of the function.

Recall that $\sec x = \frac{1}{\cos x}$.

TI-81: Y= 1 ÷ COS XIT ENTER
1 ÷ COS ((XIT + 90)) GRAPH

Casio: Graph 1 ÷ cos ALPHA X
: Graph 1 ÷ cos ((ALPHA X + 90)) EXE

Watching the calculator as it graphs shows that the 90° in the second equation moves the graph of $y = \sec x$ 90° to the left. Thus, the phase shift of the function is −90°.

The period of this function is 360°, there is no amplitude, and the phase shift is −90°.

EXERCISES   1–12. See margin.

Graph each equation so that a complete graph is shown. Find the amplitude, period, and phase shift for each function. Then sketch the graph on a piece of paper.

1. $y = \sin x$
2. $y = \csc x$
3. $y = -3 \tan 2x$
4. $y = \cot \frac{1}{2}x$
5. $y = \sec 3x$
6. $y = \tan (3x - 90°)$
7. $y = 3 \sin (x + 45°)$
8. $y = -4 \cos (3x + 60°)$
9. $y = \cot (-x)$
10. $y = \csc (45° - x)$
11. $y = \frac{1}{2} \cos (2x - 90°)$
12. $y = -\sec (2x + 180°) + 1$

6-3 Graphing Trigonometric Functions

Objective 6–3

After studying this lesson, you should be able to:
- graph various trigonometric functions.

Application

The forces due to the gravity of the sun and moon pull upon Earth and cause tides, which are the rise and fall of the ocean waters. In most locations, there are two low tides and two high tides each day, with a period of about 12 hours and 25 minutes. The beaches of the United States have tides that rise and fall between 1 and 20 feet. In the funnel-shaped Bay of Fundy in Nova Scotia, Canada, the tides rise and fall 43 feet or more.

 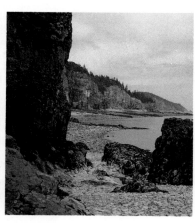

If the rise and fall of the tides is graphed with respect to time, the graph is similar to a sine or cosine graph. On a June day in Daytona, Florida, the high tides occur at 1:04 A.M. and 1:30 P.M., and the low tides occur at 7:15 A.M. and 7:39 P.M. Kelly anchored a stick in the sand and began graphing the distance from the stick to the water at 9:58 P.M. the day before. She marked the stick with a 0 at the level of the water. At this time, the water was midway between high tide and low tide. Her results are shown on the graph below.

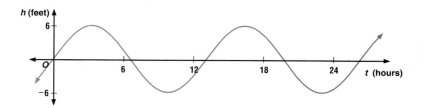

LESSON 6-3 GRAPHING TRIGONOMETRIC FUNCTIONS 321

ALTERNATE TEACHING STRATEGIES

Using Calculators

Have students use graphing calculators to graph each of the following equations on the same set of axes with $y = \sin x$. For each pair of graphs, have them describe how the graphs differ.
1. $y = 2 \sin x$
2. $y = \sin 2x$
3. $y = \sin x + 2$
4. $y = \sin (x + 90°)$

Using Questioning

Ask students to describe how changes in A, B, C, and D affect the graph of the equation $y = A \cos (Bx + C) + D$.
A: changes the amplitude
B: changes the period
C: changes the phase
D: changes the vertical displacement

NCTM Standards: 1–4, 6, 8, 9

Lesson Resources

- Practice Master 6–3
- Enrichment Master 6–3
- Technology Master, p. 11
- Activity Master, p. 16

 Transparency 6–3 contains the 5-Minute Check and a teaching aid for this lesson.

INTRODUCING THE LESSON

5-Minute Check
(over Lesson 6–2)

1. State the amplitude, period, and phase shift for $y = -3 \cos (3x - 180°)$.
   3; 120°; 60° to the right
2. Write an equation of the sine function with amplitude 2, period 90°, and phase shift 45°.
   $y = 2 \sin(4x - 180°)$ **or** $y = -2 \sin(4x - 180°)$
3. Graph the function $y = \sin \frac{1}{2} x$.

Motivating the Lesson

Have students work in groups to graph the equations $y = x$, $y = x + 2$, and $y = x - 2$. Ask them to describe how the graph of $y = x$ is affected by adding 2 to x and by subtracting 2 from x.
Adding 2 raises the graph 2 units. Subtracting 2 lowers it 2 units.

Teaching Tip When discussing methods of graphing trigonometric functions, suggest that students always begin by sketching the basic graph $y = \sin x$, $y = \cos x$, or $y = \tan x$, depending on which function they are dealing with, then altering it as needed to obtain the graph they want to draw.

Chalkboard Example

For Example 1

Graph $y = \sin x$ and $y = \sin x + 3$ on the same set of axes. Then explain the similarities and differences between the graphs.

The graph of $y = \sin x + 3$ is the graph of $y = \sin x$ shifted 3 units up.

Suppose Kelly had measured the distance from the low-tide position of the water instead of from the equilibrium point. The graph would look like the one below.

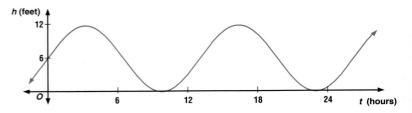

Do you see the similarities between the two graphs? The shapes are the same, but the second graph has been translated vertically. If (t, h) are the coordinates of a point on the first graph, $(t, h + 6)$ are the coordinates of a point on the second graph. So if an equation of the first graph is $h = 6 \sin t$, then an equation of the second graph is $h = 6 \sin t + 6$.

Vertical Displacement	The graph of $y = A \sin (k\theta + c) + h$ is the graph of $y = A \sin (k\theta + c)$ translated h units vertically. If $h > 0$, the graph is moved up, and if $h < 0$, the graph is moved down. This definition applies to all the trigonometric functions.

Example 1

Graph $y = \cos \theta$ and $y = \cos \theta - 1$ on the same set of axes. Then explain the similarities and differences between the graphs.

Generate ordered pairs for the two functions.

θ	0°	45°	90°	135°	180°	225°	270°	315°	360°
$\cos \theta$	1	$\frac{\sqrt{2}}{2}$	0	$-\frac{\sqrt{2}}{2}$	−1	$-\frac{\sqrt{2}}{2}$	0	$\frac{\sqrt{2}}{2}$	1
$\cos \theta - 1$	0	$\frac{\sqrt{2}}{2} - 1$	−1	$-\frac{\sqrt{2}}{2} - 1$	−2	$-\frac{\sqrt{2}}{2} - 1$	−1	$\frac{\sqrt{2}}{2} - 1$	0

Plot the points and draw the curves.

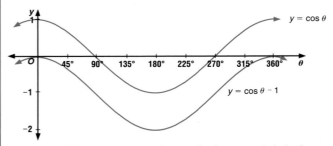

The graph of $y = \cos \theta - 1$ is the graph of $y = \cos \theta$ shifted 1 unit down.

You can graph any trigonometric function by finding its amplitude (if it has an amplitude), its period, and its phase shift and then using your general knowledge of the shape of the trigonometric curves.

Example 2

Graph $y = 4 \sin 2\theta$.

Find the amplitude, period, and phase shift.

amplitude:	*period:*	*phase shift:*
$|A| = 4$	$\dfrac{360°}{k} = \dfrac{360°}{2}$ or $180°$	$-\dfrac{c}{k} = \dfrac{0}{2}$ or 0

The amplitude of 4 tells us that the values of the function vary from –4 to 4. Since the period is 180°, the curve will repeat every 180°. There is no phase shift.

It may be helpful to graph the basic sine curve first, and then graph $y = 4 \sin 2\theta$.

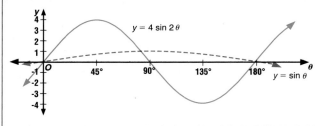

The functions $y = A \cos(k\theta + c)$ and $y = A \tan(k\theta + c)$ can be graphed using the same process.

Example 3

Graph $y = \tan\left(\dfrac{x}{2} - \dfrac{\pi}{6}\right)$.

Find the period. $\qquad \dfrac{\pi}{k} = \dfrac{\pi}{\frac{1}{2}}$ or 2π

Determine the phase shift. $\qquad -\dfrac{c}{k} = -\left(\dfrac{-\frac{\pi}{6}}{\frac{1}{2}}\right)$ or $\dfrac{\pi}{3}$ *Since $c < 0$, the graph is shifted to the right $\dfrac{\pi}{3}$.*

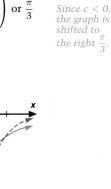

LESSON 6-3   GRAPHING TRIGONOMETRIC FUNCTIONS   323

Compound functions may consist of sums or products of trigonometric functions. For example, $y = \sin x \cdot \cos x$ is a compound function that contains a product of trigonometric functions. Compound functions may also include sums or products of trigonometric functions and other functions. For example, $y = \sin x + x$ is a compound function that is the sum of a trigonometric function and a linear function.

You can graph some compound functions by graphing each function involved separately on the same coordinate axes and then adding the ordinates. After you find a few of the critical points in this way, you can sketch the rest of the curve of the compound function.

Physicists call this method the principle of superposition.

Example 4

Graph $y = \sin x + x$.

First graph $y = x$ and $y = \sin x$ on the same axes. Then add the corresponding ordinates of the functions. Finally, sketch the graph.

x	$\sin x$	$x + \sin x$
0	0	0
$\dfrac{\pi}{2}$	1	$\dfrac{\pi}{2} + 1$ or 2.57
π	0	π or 3.14
$\dfrac{3\pi}{2}$	-1	$\dfrac{3\pi}{2} - 1$ or 3.71
2π	0	2π or 6.28
$\dfrac{5\pi}{2}$	1	$\dfrac{5\pi}{2} + 1$ or 8.85
3π	0	3π or 9.42

Some real-world applications involve finding the result of two influences acting on a system.

Example 5

APPLICATION
Music

A guitar string is fixed at both ends and plucked in the middle. Waves travel down the string toward either end and are reflected. The reflected wave from the right side can be described by the function $y = \sin \pi(x - t)$, and the wave from the right side can be described by $y = \sin 2\pi(x + t)$, where t is time in seconds. Draw a sketch of the wave pattern on the string after 4 seconds.

The equations of the two waves are $y = \sin \pi(x - 4)$ and $y = \sin 2\pi(x + 4)$.

Graph both functions. Then find the sum.

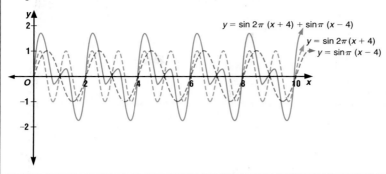

$$y = \sin 2\pi\,(x + 4) + \sin\pi\,(x - 4)$$
$$y = \sin 2\pi\,(x + 4)$$
$$y = \sin\pi\,(x - 4)$$

Example 6 involves the graph of a compound function that is the product of a linear function and a trigonometric function.

Example 6

Graph $y = x\cos x$.

First graph $y = x$ and $y = \cos x$ on the same set of axes. Then find some key points, such as zeros, maxima, and minima.

Since the maximum or minimum points of $y = \cos x$ are ± 1, the corresponding values of $x\cos x$ at these points are $\pm x$. At points where $\cos x = 0$, $x\cos x = 0$. Plot these points and sketch a smooth curve.

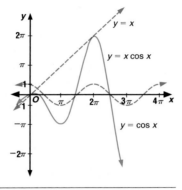

$y = x$

$y = x \cos x$

$y = \cos x$

EVALUATING THE LESSON

Checking for Understanding

Exercises 1–12 are designed to help you assess students' understanding through reading, writing, speaking, and modeling. You should work through Exercises 1–3 with your students and then monitor their work on Exercises 4–12.

Closing the Lesson

Writing Activity   Have each student choose values of *A* and *B* and graph either $y = A\cos Bx$ or $y = A\sin Bx$. Then have students exchange different graphs and graph the other equation, comparing their results with graphs already drawn.

CHECKING FOR UNDERSTANDING

Communicating Mathematics

Read and study the lesson to answer each question.

1. **Analyze** the function $y = A\sin(k\theta + c) + h$. Which variable could you increase or decrease to have each of the following effects on the graph?
   a. stretch the graph vertically increase $|A|$
   b. translate the graph downward vertically decrease h
   c. shrink the graph horizontally increase $|k|$
   d. translate the graph to the left increase c

2. See margin.
2. **Explain** why the method of separately graphing two functions that are being added, then adding their ordinates works for graphing compound functions.

3. **Write** a short paragraph that compares the graphs of $y = 3\sin 2x$ and $y = 3\sin 2x + 4$. See margin.

LESSON 6-3 GRAPHING TRIGONOMETRIC FUNCTIONS 325

RETEACHING THE LESSON

On the chalkboard, draw basic sine or cosine waves altered through various transformations. Have students identify the transformations and tell how they affect the equation $y = \sin x$ or $y = \cos x$. Begin with graphs altered through single transformations and gradually increase the difficulty.

Additional Answers

2. The ordinate of the sum will be the sum of the ordinates.

3. The graph of $y = 3\sin 2x + 4$ is the graph of $y = 3\sin 2x$ shifted 4 units upward.

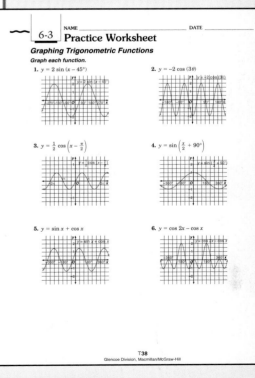

Homework Exercises

Assignment Guide

Average: 13–27, 31, 32, 35–40
Enriched: 16–31, 33–40

The red A, B, and C flags, printed only in the Teacher's Wraparound Edition, indicate the level of difficulty of the exercises.

Exercise Note

In Exercises 15 and 18, the effect of the negative amplitude is to reflect over the *x*-axis the graph of the function drawn as though its amplitude were positive.

Additional Answers

4.

$y = \frac{1}{2}\cos 2\theta$

5.

$y = 6\sin 4\theta$

6.

$y = \tan\left(\frac{x}{2} + \frac{\pi}{2}\right)$

7.

$y = \sec 3\theta$

Guided Practice

Graph each function. 4–12 See margin.

4. $y = \frac{1}{2}\cos 2\theta$
5. $y = 6\sin 4\theta$
6. $y = \tan\left(\frac{x}{2} + \frac{\pi}{2}\right)$
7. $y = \sec 3\theta$
8. $y = -\sin(\theta - 45°)$
9. $y = 5\cos(2\theta + 180°)$
10. $y = x + \cos x$
11. $y = \sin\frac{x}{3} + \frac{x}{3}$
12. $y = \sin x - \cos x$

EXERCISES

Practice **Graph each function.** 13–30. See Teacher's Answer Key.

A 13. $y = \sin(\theta + 90°)$ 14. $y = \sin(\theta - 180°)$

15. $y = -3\sin(\theta - 45°)$ 16. $y = 3\cos(\theta - 90°)$

B 17. $y = \frac{1}{2}\cos\left(\frac{\theta}{2} - 180°\right)$ 18. $y = -\frac{1}{3}\sin(2\theta + 45°)$

19. $y = \tan(\theta + 90°)$ 20. $y = \cot(\theta - 90°)$

21. $\frac{1}{2}y = \sin(3\theta + 180°)$ 22. $2y = 10\sin\left(\frac{\theta}{2} + 90°\right)$

23. $y = \sin x + \sin 2x$ 24. $y = \cos x - \sin x$

25. $y = \cos 2x - \cos 3x$ 26. $y = 2\sin x + 3\cos x$

C 27. $y = \sin x + \sin\left(x + \frac{\pi}{2}\right)$ 28. $y = \frac{1}{2}\sin x - \cos 3x$

29. $y = 2x\sin 2x$ 30. $y = \sin^2 x$

Critical Thinking 31. Graph $y = |\sin 2x|$. See margin.

Applications and Problem Solving

32. **Acoustics** Oscilloscopes are used to observe the behavior of waves. Pure sound waves are translated into electrical signals and displayed on an oscilloscope. They are represented as sine curves. If each square has a vertical measure of 1 and a horizontal measure of 20°, find the amplitude and period of each graph. Write the equations for the graphs.

32a. 2, 160°;
$y = -2\sin\frac{9\theta}{4}$
32b. 2, 80°;
$y = 2\sin\frac{9\theta}{2}$

a.

b.

33. **Electronics** In electrical circuits, the voltage and current can be described by sine or cosine functions. If the graphs of these functions have the same period, but do not pass through their zero points at the same time, they are said to have a *phase difference*. For example, if the voltage is 0 at 90° and the current is 0 for 180°, they are 90° out of phase. Suppose the voltage across an inductor of a circuit is represented by $y = 2\cos 2x$ and the current across the component is represented by $y = \cos(2x - 90°)$. What is the phase relationship between the signals? There is a 45° phase difference.

7.

$y = \sec 3\theta$

8.

$y = -\sin(\theta - 45°)$

9.

$y = 5\cos(2\theta + 180°)$

34. Physics Many natural phenomena, such as the conduction of heat and the weather, can be described using complicated periodic functions. The *sawtooth wave form* is one of the periodic functions that is observed frequently. The French mathematician Joseph Fourier showed that a complex wave can be represented using an infinite series of simple waves like sine or cosine waves.

34a. See margin.

a. The first two terms in the infinite series that generates the sawtooth wave are $-\sin t$ and $-\frac{1}{2}\sin 2t$. Sketch the function $y = -\sin t - \frac{1}{2}\sin 2t$.

b. **Research** Write a one-page paper on Fourier's life and discoveries.
   See students' work.

Mixed Review

35. Solve the following system of equations algebraically. **(Lesson 2-1)**
$$3x + 5y = 4$$
$$14x - 35y = 21 \quad (1.4, -0.04)$$

36. Find the value of k so that $(x^3 - 7x^2 - kx + 6) \div (x - 3)$ results in a remainder of zero. **(Lesson 4-3)** -10

37. Carpentry Carpenters use circular sanders to smooth rough surfaces, such as wood or plaster, before it is finished. The disk of a sander has a radius of 6 inches and is rotating at a speed of 5 revolutions per second. **(Lesson 5-2)**
   a. Find the angular speed of the sander disk in radians per second. 10π radians per second
   b. What is the linear velocity of a point on the edge of the sander disk in feet per second? 15.7 ft/s

38. Utilities A utility pole is braced by a cable attached to it at the top and anchored in a concrete block at ground level, a distance of 4 meters from the base of the pole. If the angle between the cable and the ground is 73°, find the height of the pole and the length of the cable to the nearest tenth of a meter. **(Lesson 5-5)** 13.1 meters; 13.7 meters

39. Write an equation of the cosine function with an amplitude of 4, a period of 180°, and a phase shift of 20°. **(Lesson 6-2)** $y = \pm 4\cos(2x - 40°)$

40. College Entrance Exam Compare quantities A and B below. **C**
   Write A if quantity A is greater.
   Write B if quantity B is greater.
   Write C if the two quantities are equal.
   Write D if there is not enough information to determine the relationship.

$\ell \parallel m$

(A) $x + y$ (B) $x + z$

LESSON 6-3 GRAPHING TRIGONOMETRIC FUNCTIONS 327

EXTENDING THE LESSON

Math Power: Connections

Study the graph of $y = \sin x$. Then determine whether the graph is symmetric with respect to any of the following.
- the x-axis
- the y-axis
- the line $y = x$
- the line $y = -x$
- the origin
It is symmetric only to the origin.

Additional Answer

34a.

Lesson Resources

- Practice Master 6–4
- Enrichment Master 6–4
- Evaluation Master, Quiz B, p. 73
- Activity Master, p. 17

 Transparency 6–4 contains the 5-Minute Check and a teaching aid for this lesson.

INTRODUCING THE LESSON

 5-Minute Check

(over Lesson 6–3)

Tell what you would do to *A*, *k*, *c*, and *h* to bring about each change in the graph of
y = A cos (*kx + c*) + *h*.
1. translate the graph to the right
   decrease c
2. stretch the graph horizontally
   decrease k
3. translate the graph upward
   5 units   **increase h by 5**
4. shrink the graph vertically
   decrease |A|

Prerequisite Skills

Students should be familiar with finding the inverses of functions. Find the inverse of each function.
1. {(0, 1), (5, –3), (–4, 2)}
   {(1, 0), (–3, 5), (2, –4)}
2. *f(x)* = 3*x* – 2
   $f^{-1}(x) = \frac{x+2}{3}$
3. *f(x)* = $\sqrt{x - 5}$
   $f^{-1}(x) = x^2 + 5$

Motivating the Lesson

Have students read the application at the beginning of the lesson. Give the formula $D = 3.5\sqrt{h}$ as a means of approximating the distance in kilometers, *D*, to the horizon from a point *h* meters above sea level. Have students find the distance to the horizon for a pilot 5000 meters above sea level.   **≈ 247 km**

Inverse Trigonometric Functions

Objective
6–4

After studying this lesson, you should be able to:
■ evaluate inverse trigonometric functions.

Application

 FYI...

The Maya were an American Indian people who lived in Central America and southern Mexico from A.D. 250 to 850. They produced exceptional architecture and art sculpture and made notable advancements in math and astronomy.

The Landsat satellites orbit Earth at a height of 920 km. They scan Earth collecting data from reflected sunlight and transmitting it back. The transmissions allow scientists to study the surface features of our planet. The information they have collected has led to the discovery of 112 possible Mayan ruins and 2 confirmed ruins in the Yucatán Peninsula of Mexico.

From a spacecraft in orbit above Earth, like a Landsat satellite, only a portion of the surface of the Earth, called the horizon circle, is visible. Trigonometry can help astronauts determine the size of the horizon circle. Let *h* represent the height of the spacecraft above Earth, *S* is the position of the satellite, *C* is the center of Earth, *H* is the farthest point on Earth's surface that the satellite can see, *r* is the radius of Earth, and *θ* is the angle between $\overline{CH}$ and $\overline{CS}$. Right triangle trigonometry shows us that $\cos \theta = \frac{r}{r+h}$. We can use an inverse trigonometric function to find *θ*, the angular radius of the Landsat satellites. *This problem will be solved in Example 2.*

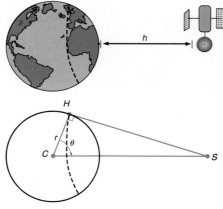

Recall that the inverse of a function may be found by interchanging the coordinates of the ordered pairs of the function. In other words, the domain of the function becomes the range of its inverse, and the range of the function becomes the domain of its inverse. For example, the inverse of *y = 2x + 5* is
x = 2y + 5 or $y = \frac{x-5}{2}$. Also remember that the inverse of a function *may not* be a function.

ALTERNATE TEACHING STRATEGIES

Using Models

Use this demonstration to show that notation for an inverse trigonometric function refers to an *angle*. Display a 30°– 60° right triangle labeled as shown at the right. Point to the 30° angle and ask students to name it in six different ways without using the letter *A*.

arccos $\frac{\sqrt{3}}{2}$, arcsin $\frac{1}{2}$, arctan $\frac{\sqrt{3}}{3}$, arcsec $\frac{2\sqrt{3}}{3}$, arccsc 2, arccot $\sqrt{3}$

The sine function is the set of all ordered pairs $(x, \sin x)$. So the inverse of the sine function, the **arcsine relation**, is the set of all ordered pairs $(\sin x, x)$. The graphs of $y = \sin x$ and $y = \arcsin x$ are shown at the right. The domain of $y = \arcsin x$ is $-1 \le x \le 1$ or $|x| \le 1$, and the range is the set of all real numbers. Notice that the graph of $y = \arcsin x$ fails the vertical line test, so $y = \arcsin x$ is not a function. None of the inverses of the trigonometric functions are functions.

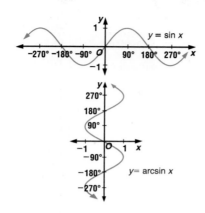

An equation such as $\sin x = 0.3393$ can be written as $x = \arcsin 0.3393$. The latter equation is read "x is an angle whose sine is 0.3393," or "x equals the arcsin of 0.3393." The solution, x, consists of all angles that have 0.3393 as their sine. Infinitely many such angles exist.

Inverses of the Trigonometric Functions	The inverse of $\sin x$ is $\arcsin x$ or $\sin^{-1} x$. The inverse of $\cos x$ is $\arccos x$ or $\cos^{-1} x$. The inverse of $\tan x$ is $\arctan x$ or $\tan^{-1} x$.

The equations in each row of the table below are equivalent. You can use these expressions to rewrite and solve trigonometric equations.

Trigonometric Function	Inverse Trigonometric Function
$y = \sin x$	$x = \sin^{-1} y$ or $x = \arcsin y$
$y = \cos x$	$x = \cos^{-1} y$ or $x = \arccos y$
$y = \tan x$	$x = \tan^{-1} y$ or $x = \arctan y$

Example 1

Find all positive values of x for which $\cos x = \dfrac{\sqrt{3}}{2}$.

If $\cos x = \dfrac{\sqrt{3}}{2}$, then x is an angle or a real number whose cosine is $\dfrac{\sqrt{3}}{2}$.

$x = \arccos \dfrac{\sqrt{3}}{2}$

Therefore, $x = 30°, 330°, 390°, 690°, \cdots$, or $\dfrac{\pi}{6}, \dfrac{11\pi}{6}, \dfrac{13\pi}{6}, \dfrac{23\pi}{6} \cdots$.

Many application problems involve finding the inverse of a trigonometric function.

LESSON 6-4 INVERSE TRIGONOMETRIC FUNCTIONS 329

Teaching Tip When discussing why $y = \arcsin x$ is not a function, remind students that the vertical line test is a method for testing whether a relation is a function. If a vertical line at any point intersects more than one point of the graph of the relation, the relation is not a function.

Chalkboard Example

For Example 1

Find all positive values of x for which $\tan x = 1$.
45°, 225°, ..., 45° + 180k°, for any integer k

Teaching Tip In Example 3, emphasize that arcsin, $\sin^{-1}$, arccos, $\cos^{-1}$, arctan, and $\tan^{-1}$ are symbols for *angles*, just as $\angle$ is a symbol for angle. The symbol $\angle A$ means "the angle whose vertex is point A." Arccos n means "the angle whose cosine is n."

EVALUATING THE LESSON

Checking for Understanding

Exercises 1–14 are designed to help you assess students' understanding through reading, writing, speaking, and modeling. You should work through Exercises 1–2 with your students and then monitor their work on Exercises 3–14.

Additional Answers

1. $y = \sin^{-1} x$ is the inverse relation of $y = \sin x$; $y = (\sin x)^{-1}$ is the function $y = \dfrac{1}{\sin x}$; and $y = \sin (x^{-1})$ is the function $y = \sin \dfrac{1}{x}$

2. Many values of y will be generated for each x value and a function must be one-to-one.

Example 2

Refer to the application at the beginning of the lesson. Find the angular radius of the Landsat satellites if $0° \le \theta \le 90°$. Use 6378 km as the radius of Earth.

We are given that $\cos\theta = \dfrac{r}{r+h}$.

The satellites are 920 km above Earth, so $h = 920$.

$$\cos\theta = \frac{r}{r+h}$$
$$\cos\theta = \frac{6378}{6378+920}$$
$$\theta = \arccos\frac{6378}{6378+920}$$

Landsat satellite photograph

Use a calculator to find θ.

 6378 ÷ ((6378 + 920)) = 2nd COS *29.080456*

The angular radius of the Landsat satellites is about $29°$.

Trigonometric inverses can be used to evaluate expressions.

Example 3

Evaluate each expression. Assume that all angles are in Quadrant I.

a. $\sin(\arcsin 0.4212)$

a. Let $X = \arcsin 0.4212$.
   Then $\sin X = 0.4212$ by the definition of inverse.
   Therefore, by substitution, $\sin (\arcsin 0.4212) = 0.4212$.

b. $\tan\left(\sin^{-1}\dfrac{5}{13}\right)$.

b. Let $A = \sin^{-1}\dfrac{5}{13}$. Then $\sin A = \dfrac{5}{13}$.
   Since $\sin A > 0$, A must be in Quadrant I or II, as shown in the sketch at the right. Assume A is in Quadrant I.

Since $\tan A = \dfrac{\sin A}{\cos A}$, find $\cos A$.

$$x^2 + y^2 = r^2 \qquad \text{\textit{Pythagorean theorem}}$$
$$x^2 + 5^2 = 13^2$$
$$x = 12$$

Therefore, $\cos A = \dfrac{12}{13}$.

Now solve.

$$\tan\left(\sin^{-1}\frac{5}{13}\right) = \tan A$$

$$= \frac{\sin A}{\cos A} \qquad \text{\textit{Definition of tangent ratio}}$$

$$= \frac{\frac{5}{13}}{\frac{12}{13}} \qquad \text{\textit{Substitute } } \frac{5}{13} \text{ \textit{for} } \sin A \text{ \textit{and} } \frac{12}{13} \text{ \textit{for} } \cos A.$$

$$= \frac{5}{12} \qquad \text{\textit{Simplify.}}$$

Therefore, $\tan\left(\sin^{-1}\frac{5}{13}\right) = \frac{5}{12}$

CHECKING FOR UNDERSTANDING

Communicating Mathematics

Read and study the lesson to answer each question. 1–2. See margin.

1. **Compare** $y = \sin^{-1} x$, $y = (\sin x)^{-1}$, and $y = \sin(x^{-1})$.
2. **Explain** why $y = \arctan x$ is not a function.

Guided Practice

Write each equation in the form of an inverse relation.

3. $x = \sin\theta$ $\;\theta = \arcsin x$
4. $\cos\alpha = \frac{1}{3}$ $\;\alpha = \arccos\frac{1}{3}$
5. $\tan y = -3$ $\;y = \arctan -3$
6. $\frac{4}{3} = \tan\theta$ $\;\theta = \arctan\frac{4}{3}$
7. $y = \cos x$ $\;x = \arccos y$
8. $\sin x = 1$ $\;x = \arcsin 1$

Find the values of x in the interval $0° \le x \le 360°$ that satisfy each equation.

9. $x = \arcsin 0$
   $0°, 180°, 360°$
10. $x = \arctan 1$
    $45°, 225°$
11. $x = \arcsin\frac{\sqrt{3}}{2}$
    $60°, 120°$

Evaluate each expression. Assume that all angles are in Quadrant I.

12. $\cos\left(\arccos\frac{4}{5}\right)$ $\;\frac{4}{5}$
13. $\sec(\cos^{-1} 1)$ $\;1$
14. $\tan\left(\cos^{-1}\frac{3}{5}\right)$ $\;\frac{4}{3}$

EXERCISES

Practice

Write each equation in the form of an inverse relation. 17. $\delta = \arctan\frac{3}{2}$

15. $n = \sin\theta$ $\;\theta = \arcsin n$
16. $\cos\beta = \frac{1}{3}$ $\;\beta = \arccos\frac{1}{3}$
17. $\frac{3}{2} = \tan\delta$
18. $\sin\alpha = 1$
    $\alpha = \arcsin 1$
19. $\cos\theta = y$
    $\theta = \arccos y$
20. $\tan A = \sqrt{3}$
    $A = \arctan\sqrt{3}$

Find the values of x in the interval $0° \le x < 360°$ that satisfy each equation.

21. $x = \cos^{-1} 0$ $\;90°, 270°$
22. $x = \sin^{-1}\frac{1}{\sqrt{2}}$ $\;45°, 135°$
23. $x = \arctan\frac{\sqrt{3}}{3}$ $\;30°, 210°$
24. $x = \sec^{-1} 2$ $\;60°, 300°$
25. $\arctan 0 = x$ $\;0°, 180°$
26. $\arcsin\frac{1}{2} = x$ $\;30°, 150°$
27. $\text{arccot } 2.1445 = x$ $\;25°, 205°$
28. $x = \arcsin(-0.5)$ $\;210°, 330°$
29. $\cot^{-1} 0 = x$ $\;90°, 270°$

RETEACHING THE LESSON

Have students draw and label right triangles when they are evaluating expressions involving inverse trigonometric functions.

Example: Find $\cos\left(\tan^{-1}\frac{3}{4}\right)$.

The legs of the right triangle measure 3 and 4. By the Pythagorean theorem, the hypotenuse is 5. The cosine of $\left(\tan^{-1}\frac{3}{4}\right)$, the angle whose tangent is $\frac{3}{4}$, is $\frac{4}{5}$.

Evaluate each expression. Assume that all angles are in Quadrant I.

30. $\sin\left(\sin^{-1}\frac{1}{2}\right)$ $\frac{1}{2}$

31. $\cot\left(\arctan\frac{4}{5}\right)$ $\frac{5}{4}$

32. $\sin\left(\cos^{-1}\frac{\sqrt{3}}{2}\right)$ $\frac{1}{2}$

33. $\sec\left(\cos^{-1}\frac{1}{2}\right)$ 2

34. $\cos\left(\text{arccot}\frac{4}{3}\right)$ $\frac{4}{5}$

35. $\tan\left(\sec^{-1}2\right)$ $\sqrt{3}$

36. $\sin\left(\arctan\sqrt{3} + \text{arccot}\sqrt{3}\right)$ 1

37. $\sin\left(\tan^{-1}1\right) + \cos\left(\cos^{-1}0.5\right)$ $\frac{\sqrt{2}+1}{2}$

38. $\tan\left(\arcsin\frac{\sqrt{2}}{2}\right) - \cot\left(\arccos\frac{\sqrt{2}}{2}\right)$ 0

39. $\tan\left(\sin^{-1}\frac{\sqrt{3}}{2} - \cos^{-1}\frac{\sqrt{3}}{2}\right)$ $\frac{\sqrt{3}}{3}$

Verify each equation. Assume that all angles are in Quadrant I.

40–45. See Teacher's Answer Key.

40. $\sin^{-1}\frac{\sqrt{2}}{2} + \cos^{-1}\frac{\sqrt{2}}{2} = \tan^{-1}\frac{\sqrt{3}}{3} + \tan^{-1}\sqrt{3}$

41. $\arccos\frac{\sqrt{3}}{2} + \arcsin\frac{\sqrt{3}}{2} = \arctan 1 + \text{arccot }1$

42. $\arcsin\frac{2}{5} + \arccos\frac{2}{5} = 90°$

43. $\tan^{-1}\frac{3}{4} + \tan^{-1}\frac{5}{12} = \tan^{-1}\frac{56}{33}$

44. $\tan^{-1}1 + \cos^{-1}\frac{\sqrt{3}}{2} = \sin^{-1}\frac{1}{2} + \sec^{-1}\sqrt{2}$

45. $\arcsin\frac{3}{5} + \arccos\frac{15}{17} = \arctan\frac{77}{36}$

Critical Thinking

46. Explain why the equation $[\cos \circ \cos^{-1}](x) = [\cos^{-1} \circ \cos](x)$ is not always true. Could you restrict the domain and range to make the equations true for an interval? See students' explanations; yes, $0° \leq x \leq 360°$.

Applications and Problem Solving

47. **Navigation** Earth has been charted with vertical and horizontal lines so that points can be named with coordinates. The horizontal lines are called latitude lines. The equator is latitude line 0°. Parallel lines are numbered up to 90° to the north and to the south. The length of any parallel of latitude is equal to the distance around Earth times the cosine of the latitude angle, if we assume a spherical Earth.
    a. If the radius of Earth is about 6400 km, which latitude lines are about 5543 km long? 82°
    b. What is the length of the 90° parallel? Why? 0 km; It is the north or south pole.

48. **Optics** Light travels like waves in many different planes. If light is polarized, all of the waves are traveling in parallel planes. You may have polarized sunglasses that eliminate glare by polarizing the light. Suppose vertically-polarized light with intensity I_o strikes a polarizing filter with its axis at an angle of θ with the vertical. The intensity of the transmitted light, I_t, and θ are related by the equation $\cos\theta = \sqrt{\frac{I_t}{I_o}}$
    a. If one-fourth of the polarized light is transmitted through the lens, at what angle is the lens being held? 60°
    b. At what angle will none of the polarized light be transmitted through the lens? 90°

49. Civil Engineering Highway curves are usually banked, or tilted inward, so that cars can negotiate the curve more safely. The proper banking angle, θ, for a car making a turn of radius r feet at a velocity v feet per second is given by $\tan \theta = \dfrac{v^2}{gr}$ where g is the acceleration due to gravity. Assume that $g = 32 \text{ ft/s}^2$. An engineer is designing a curve with a radius of 1000 feet. If the speed limit on the curve will be 55 mph, at what angle should the curve be banked? about $11.5°$

Mixed Review

50. Geometry The endpoints of $\overline{AB}$ are $A(9,3)$ and $B(-1,1)$. Use the distance formula to show that $P(4, 2)$ is the midpoint of $\overline{AB}$. **(Lesson 1-4)** See margin.

51. Find the value of the determinant $\begin{vmatrix} -2 & 4 & -1 \\ 1 & -1 & 0 \\ -3 & 4 & 5 \end{vmatrix}$. **(Lesson 2-3)** -11

52. Find the inverse of the function $y = \dfrac{3}{2}x - 2$. **(Lesson 3-3)** $y = \dfrac{2}{3}x + \dfrac{4}{3}$

53. Solve $3x^2 - 7x + 2 = 0$ by using the quadratic formula. **(Lesson 4-2)** 2 or $\dfrac{1}{3}$

54. Find the value of $\sin 360°$. **(Lesson 5-4)** 0

55. Angle C of $\triangle ABC$ is a right angle. Solve the triangle if $A = 20°$ and $c = 35$. **(Lesson 5-5)** $a = 11.9, B = 70°, b = 32.9$

56. Which value is greater, $\cos 70°$ or $\cos 170°$? **(Lesson 6-1)** $\cos 70°$

57. Graph $y = 2 \sin x - \dfrac{1}{2}\cos x$. **(Lesson 6-3)** See margin.

58. College Entrance Exam Choose the best answer. B In parallelogram $ABCD$, the ratio of the shaded area to the unshaded area is
(A) 1:2   (B) 1:1
(C) 4:3   (D) 2:1
(E) It cannot be determined from the information given.

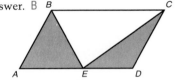

MID-CHAPTER REVIEW

Find the values of θ for which each of the following is true. **(Lesson 6-1)** 1–3. See margin.

1. $\tan \theta = 0$ **2.** $\sec \theta$ is undefined   **3.** $\csc \theta$ 1

State the amplitude, period, and phase shift for each function. Then graph the functions. **(Lesson 6-2 and 6-3)** 4–6. See margin.

4. $y = \sin\left(\theta + \dfrac{\pi}{2}\right)$ **5.** $y = \tan\left(\theta + 60°\right)$ **6.** $y = 5 \sin 2\theta$

Graph each function.   **(Lesson 6-3)** 7–9. See margin.

7. $y = x - \sin x$ **8.** $y = 2 \sin x - \dfrac{1}{2}x$ **9.** $y = 2x + 2 \sin x$

10. Show that $\cos^{-1} \dfrac{\sqrt{2}}{2} = \tan^{-1} 1$. Assume that all angles are in Quadrant I.
(Lesson 6-4) $\cos^{-1} \dfrac{\sqrt{2}}{2} = 45°,\ \tan^{-1} 1 = 45°$; thus, $\cos^{-1}\dfrac{\sqrt{2}}{2} = \tan^{-1} 1$.

LESSON 6-4   INVERSE TRIGONOMETRIC FUNCTIONS   333

EXTENDING THE LESSON

Math Power: Problem Solving

Find an algebraic expression in x that is equivalent to $\sin(\cos^{-1}x)$.

$\sqrt{1 - x^2}$

Mid-Chapter Review

The Mid-Chapter Review provides students with a brief review of the concepts and skills in Lessons 6–1 through 6–4. Lesson numbers are given at the end of problems or instruction lines so students may review concepts not yet mastered.

7.

8.

9.

Enrichment Masters Booklet, p. 39

6-4 Enrichment Worksheet   NAME _____ DATE _____

Algebraic Trigonometric Expressions

In Lesson 6-4, you learned how to use right triangles to find exact values of functions of inverse trigonometric functions. In calculus it is sometimes necessary to convert trigonometric expressions into algebraic ones. You can use the same method to do this.

Example   Write $\sin(\arccos 4x)$ as an algebraic expression in x.

Let $y = \arccos 4x$ and let $z =$ side opposite $\angle y$.

$(4x)^2 + z^2 = 1^2$ *Pythagorean theorem*
$16x^2 + z^2 = 1$
$z^2 = 1 - 16x^2$
$z = \sqrt{1 - 16x^2}$ *Take the square root of each side.*
$\sin y = \dfrac{z}{1}$ *Definition of sine*
$\sin y = \sqrt{1 - 16x^2}$

Therefore, $\sin(\arccos 4x) = \sqrt{1 - 16x^2}$.

Write each of the following as an algebraic expression in x.

1. $\cot(\arccos 4x)$
$\dfrac{4x}{\sqrt{1 - 16x^2}}$

2. $\sin(\arctan x)$
$\dfrac{x}{\sqrt{x^2 + 1}}$

3. $\cos\left(\arctan \dfrac{x}{3}\right)$
$\dfrac{3}{\sqrt{x^2 + 9}}$

4. $\sin[\arccos(x - 2)]$
$\dfrac{\sqrt{x^2 - 4x + 3}}{x - 2}$

5. $\cos\left(\arcsin \dfrac{x - h}{r}\right)$
$\dfrac{\sqrt{r^2 - x^2 + 2xh + h^2}}{r}$

T 39
Glencoe Division, Macmillan/McGraw-Hill

NCTM Standards: 1–4, 6, 9

Lesson Resources

- Practice Master 6–5
- Enrichment Master 6–5
- Transparency 6–5 contains the 5-Minute Check and a teaching aid for this lesson.

INTRODUCING THE LESSON

5-Minute Check

(over Lesson 6–4)

1. Write $2 = \tan x$ in the form of an inverse relation. $x = \arctan 2$

Find all values of x in the interval $0° \leq x \leq 360°$ that satisfy the equation.

2. $x = \cos^{-1} \frac{1}{2}$ 60°, 300°

3. $x = \arctan 1$ 45°, 225°

4. Evaluate $\sin\left(\arccos \frac{2}{3}\right)$.

   Assume that the angle is in Quadrant I. $\frac{\sqrt{5}}{3}$

Motivating the Lesson

Ask these questions about the relation $y = x^2$.
- Is the relation a function?   **yes**
- Give an example to illustrate why the inverse is not a function.
  Sample answer: (2, 4) and (–2, 4) are ordered pairs belonging to the function. Their inverses, (4, 2) and (4, –2), do not belong to a function because the domain member 4 is matched with more than one member of the range.
- How could you restrict $f(x) = x^2$ so that its inverse would be a function?
  Restrict the domain to positive numbers.

6-5 Principal Values of the Inverse Trigonometric Functions

Objective
6–5

After studying this lesson, you should be able to:
- find principal values of inverse trigonometric functions.

Application

The ancient Hindu and Arab peoples had a great interest in astronomy. It was this interest that drove them to master trigonometry. None of the works of the Hindu mathematicians still exist today, but we do know that they made an extensive table of sines using only a few equations. Their work in trigonometry united the fields of algebra, geometry, and arithmetic.

The concept of a function can be applied to the trigonometric ratios and their inverses. Recall that the inverse of a function can be graphed by reflecting the graph of the given function over the line $y = x$. Reflecting the graph of $y = \sin x$ over the line $y = x$ shows that $y = \arcsin x$ does not pass the vertical line test for functions. However, we can limit the domain of the sine function so that its inverse is a function.

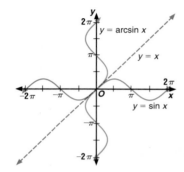

Capital letters are used to distinguish the function with restricted domains from the usual trigonometric functions.

Consider only a part of the domain of the sine function, namely any x such that $-90° \leq x \leq 90°$. The range then contains all of the possible values from –1 to 1. It is possible to define a new function, called Sine, whose inverse is a function.

$$y = \text{Sin } x \text{ if and only if } y = \sin x \text{ and } -90° \leq x \leq 90°$$

The values in the domain of Sine are called **principal values.** Other new functions can be defined as follows.

$$y = \text{Cos } x \text{ if and only if } y = \cos x \text{ and } 0° \leq x \leq 180°$$
$$y = \text{Tan } x \text{ if and only if } y = \tan x \text{ and } -90° < x < 90°$$

You will learn more about the graphs of these functions in Lesson 6-6.

334   CHAPTER 6   GRAPHS AND INVERSES OF THE TRIGONOMETRIC FUNCTIONS

ALTERNATE TEACHING STRATEGIES

Using Graphs

Use this graph of $y = \text{Arcsin } x$ to illustrate how the range of the function is restricted.

Using Logical Reasoning

The function $y = \text{Cos } x$ is defined for $0° \leq x \leq 180°$. Ask students to explain why $y = \text{Sin } x$ is defined for $-90° \leq x \leq 90°$ rather than for the interval in which Cos x is defined.   For each value $y = \sin x$ in the interval $0° \leq x \leq 180°$, there are two values of x. Therefore, the inverse will have two values of the range for each value of the domain, and it cannot be a function.

Note the capital "A" in the name of each inverse function.

The inverses of the Sine, Cosine, and Tangent functions are called Arcsine, Arccosine, and Arctangent, respectively. They are defined as follows.

Arcsine Function	**Given $y = $ Sin x, the inverse Sine function is defined by the equation $y = $ Sin^{-1} x or $y = $ Arcsin x.**
Arccosine Function	**Given $y = $ Cos x, the inverse Cosine function is defined by the equation $y = $ Cos^{-1} x or $y = $ Arccos x.**
Arctangent Function	**Given $y = $ Tan x, the inverse Tangent function is defined by the equation $y = $ Tan^{-1} x or $y = $ Arctan x.**

Example 1

Find each value.

a. Arccos $\dfrac{1}{2}$

a. Let $\theta = $ Arccos $\dfrac{1}{2}$.

$\quad$ Cos $\theta = \dfrac{1}{2}$ $\qquad$ *Definition of Arccos function*

$\quad\quad \theta = 60°$ $\qquad$ *Why is θ not 300°?*

$\quad$ Therefore, Arccos $\dfrac{1}{2} = 60°$.

b. Sin^{-1} $\left(\tan \dfrac{\pi}{4} \right)$

b. Let $x = \tan \dfrac{\pi}{4}$.

$\quad x = 1$

$\quad$ Sin^{-1} $\left(\tan \dfrac{\pi}{4} \right) = $ Sin^{-1} 1 $\qquad$ *Replace $\tan \dfrac{\pi}{4}$ in the original expression with 1.*

$\quad\quad\quad\quad\quad\quad = \dfrac{\pi}{2}$

c. sin $\left($ Sin^{-1} 1 $-$ Cos^{-1} $\dfrac{1}{2} \right)$

c. Let $\alpha = $ Sin^{-1} 1 and $\beta = $ Cos^{-1} $\dfrac{1}{2}$.

$\quad$ Sin $\alpha = 1$ $\qquad$ Cos $\beta = \dfrac{1}{2}$

$\quad\quad \alpha = 90°$ $\qquad\quad \beta = 60°$

$\quad$ sin $\left($ Sin^{-1} 1 $-$ Cos^{-1} $\dfrac{1}{2} \right) = \sin(\alpha - \beta)$

$\quad\quad\quad\quad\quad\quad\quad\quad\quad\quad = \sin(90° - 60°)$ $\qquad \alpha = 90°, \beta = 60°$

$\quad\quad\quad\quad\quad\quad\quad\quad\quad\quad = \sin 30°$

$\quad\quad\quad\quad\quad\quad\quad\quad\quad\quad = \dfrac{1}{2}$

Scientists use trigonometry to describe physical properties. So inverse trigonometric functions are often used to solve scientific problems.

LESSON 6-5 PRINCIPAL VALUES OF THE INVERSE TRIGONOMETRIC FUNCTIONS 335

Teaching Tip When discussing Example 1, point out that Sin x is defined in quadrants I and IV, Cosine x is defined in quadrants I and II, and Tan x is defined in quadrants I and IV.

Chalkboard Example

For Example 1

Find each value.

a. Arcsin $-\dfrac{1}{2}$ $\quad$ −30°

b. Tan^{-1} $\left(\sin \dfrac{\pi}{2} \right)$ $\quad$ 45°

c. cos $\left($ Arctan $\sqrt{3}$ $-$ Arcsin $\dfrac{\sqrt{3}}{2} \right)$
$\quad$ 1

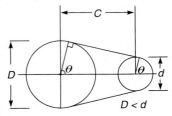

Example 2

APPLICATION

Optics

Photograph taken without polarizing lens

Photograph taken with polarizing lens

Malus' Law describes the amount of light transmitted through two polarizing lenses. If the axes of two lenses are at an angle of θ degrees, the intensity of the light transmitted through them, I, is determined by the equation $I = I_o \cos^2 \theta$, where I_o is the intensity of light that shines on the lenses. At what angle should the axes be held so that one-half of the transmitted light passes through the lenses?

If one-half of the transmitted light passes through the lenses, then $I = \frac{1}{2}I_o$.

$$I = \frac{1}{2}I_o$$

$$I_o \cos^2 \theta = \frac{1}{2}I_o$$

$$\cos^2 \theta = \frac{1}{2} \qquad \textit{Divide each side by } I_o.$$

$$\cos \theta = \frac{\sqrt{2}}{2} \qquad \textit{Take the square root of each side.}$$

$$\theta = \text{Arccos}\frac{\sqrt{2}}{2}$$

$$\theta = 45°$$

The lenses should be held so that their axes are at an angle of $45°$.

You can use a calculator to find inverse trigonometric functions. The calculator will always give the least, or principal, value of the inverse trigonometric function.

Example 3

Find the radian measure of an angle θ in Quadrant I with a tangent of 1.3284.

$\text{Arctan } 1.3284 = \theta \qquad \textit{Make sure your calculator is in radian mode.}$

1.3284 [2nd] [TAN] 0.9255515

The radian measure of θ is about 0.926.

A calculator can also be helpful in finding the value of a complicated trigonometric expression.

Example 4

Find $\sin\left(\text{Arcsin}\dfrac{5}{12} - \text{Arccot}\dfrac{5}{3}\right)$.

5 [÷] 12 [=] [2nd] [SIN] [−] [(] 5 [÷] 3 [)] [1/x]
[2nd] [TAN] [=] [SIN] -0.1104185 $\quad \textit{Arccot } x = \text{Arctan}\frac{1}{x}. \text{ Why?}$

Thus, $\sin\left(\text{Arcsin}\dfrac{5}{12} - \text{Arccot}\dfrac{5}{3}\right) \approx -0.1104$.

RETEACHING THE LESSON

Draw a 30°–60° right triangle on the chalkboard and label the sides 1, $\sqrt{3}$, and 2. If you name an angle, students must respond by giving the sine, cosine, and tangent of the angle. If you name a fraction, students must give an equation involving the fraction and an inverse function.

Example: 60°: $\sin 60° = \dfrac{\sqrt{3}}{2}$, $\cos 60° = \dfrac{1}{2}$, $\tan 60° = \sqrt{3}$;

$\dfrac{1}{2}$: $\cos^{-1}\dfrac{1}{2} = 60°$, $\sin^{-1}\dfrac{1}{2} = 30°$

CHECKING FOR UNDERSTANDING

Communicating Mathematics

1. They are inverse functions.

Read and study the lesson to answer each question. 2–4. See margin.

1. **Describe** the relationship between the functions $y = \text{Sin } x$ and $y = \text{Arcsin } x$.

2. **Explain** why the domains of the trigonometric functions must be restricted in order to ensure that the inverse is a function.

3. How can you tell if the domain of a trigonometric function is restricted?

4. Use your calculator to solve Example 4 by using degrees. Is the result the same? Explain.

Guided Practice

Find each value.

5. $\text{Sin}^{-1}\left(-\dfrac{\sqrt{3}}{2}\right)$ $-60°$

6. $\text{Arctan } 1$ $45°$

7. $\text{Sin}^{-1} 0$ $0°$

8. $\text{Sin}^{-1}\left(-\dfrac{1}{2}\right)$ $-30°$

9. $\text{Tan}^{-1}\left(\dfrac{\sqrt{3}}{3}\right)$ $30°$

10. $\text{Arcsin } 1$ $90°$

11. $\text{Arccos } 0$ $90°$

12. $\cos\left(\text{Cos}^{-1}\dfrac{4}{5}\right)$ $\dfrac{4}{5}$

13. $\tan\left[\text{Cos}^{-1}\left(-\dfrac{3}{5}\right)\right]$ $-\dfrac{4}{3}$

14. $\cos\left(2\,\text{Tan}^{-1}\sqrt{3}\right)$ $-\dfrac{1}{2}$

15. $\sin\left[\text{Arctan}\left(-\dfrac{3}{4}\right) + \text{Arccot}\left(-\dfrac{4}{3}\right)\right]$ $-\dfrac{24}{25}$

EXERCISES

Practice

Find each value.

16. $\text{Arctan } 1$ $45°$

17. $\text{Cos}^{-1}\left(-\dfrac{\sqrt{3}}{2}\right)$ $150°$

18. $\text{Arcsin}\left(-\dfrac{\sqrt{2}}{2}\right)$ $-45°$

19. $\text{Arctan }\dfrac{3}{4}$ $36°52'$

20. $\text{Cos}^{-1}\left(-\dfrac{1}{2}\right)$ $120°$

21. $\text{Arctan }\sqrt{3}$ $60°$

22. $\sin\left(\text{Sin}^{-1}\dfrac{1}{2}\right)$ $\dfrac{1}{2}$

23. $\text{Sin}^{-1}\left(\cos\dfrac{\pi}{2}\right)$ $0°$

24. $\cos\left(\text{Cos}^{-1}\dfrac{1}{2}\right)$ $\dfrac{1}{2}$

25. $\cos\left(\text{Tan}^{-1}\sqrt{3}\right)$ $\dfrac{1}{2}$

26. $\tan\left(\text{Sin}^{-1}\dfrac{5}{13}\right)$ $\dfrac{5}{12}$

27. $\sin\left(\text{Sin}^{-1}\dfrac{\sqrt{3}}{2}\right)$ $\dfrac{\sqrt{3}}{2}$

28. $\sin\left(2\,\text{Cos}^{-1}\dfrac{3}{5}\right)$ $\dfrac{24}{25}$

29. $\cos\left[\text{Arcsin}\left(-\dfrac{1}{2}\right)\right]$ $\dfrac{\sqrt{3}}{2}$

30. $\sin\left(2\,\text{Sin}^{-1}\dfrac{1}{2}\right)$ $\dfrac{\sqrt{3}}{2}$

31. $\sin\left[\text{Arctan}\left(-\sqrt{3}\right)\right]$ $-\dfrac{\sqrt{3}}{2}$

32. $\cos(\text{Tan}^{-1} 1)$ $\dfrac{\sqrt{2}}{2}$

33. $\sin\left(2\,\text{Sin}^{-1}\dfrac{\sqrt{3}}{2}\right)$ $\dfrac{\sqrt{3}}{2}$

34. $\tan\left(\dfrac{1}{2}\text{Sin}^{-1}\dfrac{15}{17}\right)$ $\dfrac{3}{5}$

35. $\sin\left(\dfrac{1}{2}\text{Arctan }\dfrac{3}{5}\right)$ 0.2669

36. $\cos\left(\text{Tan}^{-1}\sqrt{3} - \text{Sin}^{-1}\dfrac{1}{2}\right)$ $\dfrac{\sqrt{3}}{2}$

37. $\cos\left(\text{Cos}^{-1} 0 + \text{Sin}^{-1}\dfrac{1}{2}\right)$ $-\dfrac{1}{2}$

38. $\sin\left(\text{Tan}^{-1} 1 - \text{Sin}^{-1} 1\right)$ $-\dfrac{\sqrt{2}}{2}$

39. $\cos\left[\text{Cos}^{-1}\left(-\dfrac{1}{2}\right) - \text{Sin}^{-1} 2\right]$ not possible

40. $\cos\left[\text{Cos}^{-1}\left(-\dfrac{\sqrt{2}}{2}\right) - \dfrac{\pi}{2}\right]$ $\dfrac{\sqrt{2}}{2}$

41. $\cos\left[\dfrac{4}{3}\pi - \text{Cos}^{-1}\left(-\dfrac{1}{2}\right)\right]$ $-\dfrac{1}{2}$

42. $\sin\left[\dfrac{\pi}{2} - \text{Cos}^{-1}\left(\dfrac{1}{2}\right)\right]$ $\dfrac{1}{2}$

43. $\tan\left(\text{Cos}^{-1}\dfrac{3}{5} - \text{Sin}^{-1}\dfrac{5}{13}\right)$ $\dfrac{33}{56}$

LESSON 6-5 PRINCIPAL VALUES OF THE INVERSE TRIGONOMETRIC FUNCTIONS 337

Additional Answers

2. The trigonometric functions are not one-to-one functions. If the domains were not restricted, the inverses would not be functions.

3. Restricted domains are denoted with a capital letter.

4. yes; The angle is the same if it is measured in degrees or radians.

EVALUATING THE LESSON

Checking for Understanding

Exercises 1–15 are designed to help you assess students' understanding through reading, writing, speaking, and modeling. You should work through Exercises 1–4 with your students and then monitor their work on Exercises 5–15.

Closing the Lesson

Writing Activity Have students write a few sentences explaining why the inverse of the function $f(x) = \sin x$ is not a function. Sample answer: For a given value of the range of f, there are an infinite number of values of the domain. Therefore, each member of the domain of the inverse will be paired with an infinite number of range values, violating the definition of function.

APPLYING THE LESSON

Homework Exercises

Assignment Guide

Average: 16–39, 44, 45, 47–54
Enriched: 21–43, 44–54

The red A, B, and C flags, printed only in the Teacher's Wraparound Edition, indicate the level of difficulty of the exercises.

Critical Thinking

44. Express $\sin(\text{Arcsin } u - \text{Arccos } v)$ in terms of u and v.

$$uv - \sqrt{(1 - v^2)(1 - u^2)}$$

Applications and Problem Solving

45. **Electronics** The average power P of an electrical circuit with alternating current is determined by the equation $P = VI \cos \phi$, where V represents the voltage, I represents the current, and ϕ is the measure of the phase angle. If a certain circuit has a voltage of 120 volts, a current of 0.75 amperes, and produces 7.2 watts of power, what is the measure of the phase angle? about 85.4°

46. **Optics** When you look at an object that is under water, refraction bends the light rays so that the object appears to be closer to the surface than it really is. According to Snell's Law, the angle between a perpendicular to the surface of the water and a beam of light entering the water, I, is related to the angle at which the light travels in the water, r, by the equation $\dfrac{\sin I}{\text{speed of light in air}} = \dfrac{\sin r}{\text{speed of light in water}}$. The speed of light in air is approximately 3.00×10^8 meters per second, and the speed of light in water is approximately 2.00×10^8 meters per second.

   a. Is there any angle at which you could direct a beam of light at the surface of a pool so that the light is not bent? See margin.

   b. Place a pencil in a clear glass jar full of water. Look at it from different angles until you find the one where you can see the whole pencil undistorted. How does the angle at which you are looking at the pencil relate to the angle you found for Exercise 46a? See students' work.

Mixed Review

47. Is the relation $\{(4, 0), (3, 0), (5, -2), (4, -3), (0, -13)\}$ a function? **(Lesson 1-1)** no

48. **Manufacturing** The Eastern Minnesota Paper Company can convert wood pulp to either newsprint or notebook paper. The mill can produce up to 200 units of paper a day, and regular customers require 10 units of notebook paper and 80 units of newsprint per day. If the profit on a unit of notebook paper is $500 and the profit on a unit of newsprint is $350, how much of each should the plant produce? **(Lesson 2-6)** 120 units of notebook and 80 units of newsprint

49. Without graphing, describe the end behavior of the function $y = 4x^5 - 2x^2 + 4$. **(Lesson 3-8)** As $x \to \infty, y \to \infty$; as $x \to -\infty, y \to -\infty$

50. Find all the rational roots of the equation $3x^4 + 20x^3 - 4x^2 + 20x - 7 = 0$. **(Lesson 4-4)** $-7, \dfrac{1}{3}$

51. Determine the number of possible solutions to $\triangle ABC$ if $A = 152°$, $b = 12$, and $a = 10.2$. If a solution exists, solve the triangle. **(Lesson 5-6)** no solution

52. $\sqrt{980} \approx 31.3 \text{ in}^2$ Find the area of a triangle whose sides are 7, 9, and 12 inches long. **(Lesson 5-8)**

53. Find the value of $\sin\left(2 \sin^{-1} \dfrac{1}{2}\right)$. **(Lesson 6-4)** $\dfrac{\sqrt{3}}{2}$

54. **College Entrance Exam** Choose the best answer. A

   Find an expression equivalent to $\left(\dfrac{2x^2}{y}\right)^3$.

   (A) $\dfrac{8x^6}{y^3}$ (B) $\dfrac{64x^6}{y^3}$ (C) $\dfrac{6x^5}{y^3}$ (D) $\dfrac{8x^5}{y^3}$ (E) $\dfrac{2x^5}{y^4}$

338   CHAPTER 6   GRAPHS AND INVERSES OF THE TRIGONOMETRIC FUNCTIONS

EXTENDING THE LESSON

Math Power: Communication

Devise a method to convert decimal angle measures on a calculator to degrees, minutes, and seconds ($1° = 60$ min; 1 min $= 60$ seconds). Write a concise description of your method.   Subtract the measure in degrees and multiply by 60 to find minutes. Subtract the number of minutes and multiply by 60 to find seconds.

6-6A Graphing Calculators: Graphing Inverses of Trigonometric Functions

You can use a graphing calculator to graph inverses of trigonometric functions.

Example 1

Graph $y = $ Arccos x in the viewing window $[-2, 2]$ by $[-360°, 360°]$ with a scale factor of 1 for the x-axis and a scale factor of $90°$ for the y-axis.

You must manually set the range for the graph on the TI-81 graphing calculator. Then enter the equation.

TI-81: Y= | 2nd | COS⁻¹ | X|T | GRAPH

Arcsin, arccos, and arctan are built-in functions on the Casio graphing calculator. For this example, however, we will need to set the viewing window manually and then graph the function.

Casio: Graph | SHIFT | cos⁻¹ | ALPHA | X | EXE

The function is defined on the interval $[-1, 1]$ for x and $[0°, 180°]$ for y.

Example 2

Graph $y = \sin(\text{Tan}^{-1}x)$ in the viewing window $[-5, 5]$ by $[-2, 2]$ with a scale factor of 1 for both axes.

TI-81: Y= | SIN | (| 2nd | TAN⁻¹ | X|T |) | GRAPH

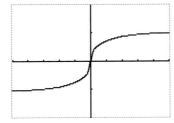

Casio: Graph | sin | (| SHIFT | tan⁻¹ | ALPHA | X |) | EXE

The function is defined on the interval $(-\infty, \infty)$ for x and $(-1, 1)$ for y.

EXERCISES

Graph each equation so that a complete graph is shown. Then sketch the graph on a piece of a paper. 1–6. See Teacher's Answer Key.

1. $y = \text{Arctan } x$

2. $y = \cos(2\text{Sin}^{-1}x)$

3. $y = \cos(\text{Tan}^{-1}x - \text{Cos}^{-1}x)$

4. $y = \sin(\text{Sin}^{-1}x)$

5. $y = \cos(\text{Arctan } 2x)$

6. $y = \sin(\text{Sin}^{-1}x - \text{Cos}^{-1}\frac{x}{2})$

GRAPHING CALCULATORS: GRAPHING INVERSES OF TRIGONOMETRIC FUNCTIONS 339

INTRODUCING THE LESSON

Objective Graph inverses of trigonometric functions on a graphing calculator.

Motivating the Lesson

Ask students to suggest steps for solving the following.

An observer is 1000 feet over level land from a balloon site. A balloon rises at the rate of 7 ft/s. What is the angle of elevation (θ) of the balloon to the observer after t seconds? θ is an angle such that $\tan \theta = \frac{7t}{1000}$.

TEACHING THE LESSON

Teaching Tip Ask students to analyze how the domain and range of an inverse trigonometric function relates to the domain and range of the function itself. How is this similar to polynomial functions?

More Examples

Graph $y = \sin(2 \text{ Cos}^{-1} x)$.

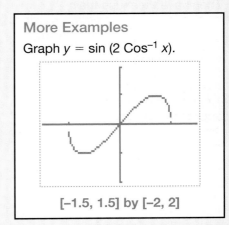

$[-1.5, 1.5]$ by $[-2, 2]$

EVALUATING THE LESSON

Closing the Lesson

Ask students whether the ranges for x and y in Exercise 4 will be real numbers or angle measures. Ask students how they might predict what the graph will look like before using the calculator.

APPLYING THE LESSON

Homework Exercises

Assignment Guide

All: 1–6

NCTM Standards: 1–4, 6, 9

Lesson Resources

- Practice Master 6–6
- Enrichment Master 6–6
- Evaluation Master, Quiz C, p. 754
- Technology Master, p. 12

 Transparency 6–6 contains the 5-Minute Check and a teaching aid for this lesson.

INTRODUCING THE LESSON

 5-Minute Check

(over Lesson 6–5)

Find each value.

1. Arcsin $\frac{\sqrt{2}}{2}$ **45°**

2. $\text{Cos}^{-1}\left(-\frac{1}{2}\right)$ **120°**

3. $\tan\left(\text{Sin}^{-1}\left(-\frac{12}{13}\right)\right)$ $\frac{-12}{5}$

4. Find the radian measure of an angle x in Quadrant I with a tangent of 1.1345.   **≈ 0.8483**

Motivating the Lesson

Have students read the application at the beginning of the lesson. Then have them use their calculators to approximate π using the decimal for $\frac{355}{113}$, discovered by the Chinese mathematician Tsu Ch'ung-chih around A.D. 470. Ask students to compare the first 7 places of the decimal approximation of π with the value given by their calculators. **The difference is 0.0000002.**

6-6 Graphing Inverses of Trigonometric Functions

Objectives   After studying this lesson, you should be able to:

6–6A   ▪ write equations for inverses of trigonometric functions, and

6–6B   ▪ graph inverses of trigonometric functions.

Application   Mathematicians have been trying to calculate the value of the number π accurately for centuries. In 1992, brothers David (*top*) and Gregory (*bottom*) Chudnovsky of Columbia University extended the calculation of the digits of π to 2,160,000,000 places. They performed the calculations using a supercomputer that they assembled from mail-order parts. Their calculation doubled the number of digits previously calculated. The Chudnovsky brothers are studying the digits in hopes of finding patterns within them, but with no results thus far.

One of the methods for approximating π uses inverse trigonometric functions. Gregory's series, named for Scottish mathematician James Gregory, is $\arctan x = x - \frac{x^3}{3} + \frac{x^5}{5} - \frac{x^7}{7} + \cdots$. In 1706, John Machin used Gregory's series to obtain the formula $\frac{\pi}{4} = 4 \arctan\left(\frac{1}{5}\right) - \arctan\left(\frac{1}{239}\right)$. With it, he determined the value of π to 100 decimal places.

Just as the graphs of the sine and arcsine functions are related, the inverse cosine and tangent functions can be graphed using the graphs of the cosine and tangent functions. The values of Arccos x are shown as the colored portion of the curve at the right. There are an unlimited number of values of the arccos x for a given x, but there is only one value of Arccos x for each x. The range of Arccos x is $0° \leq \text{Arccos } x \leq 180°$.

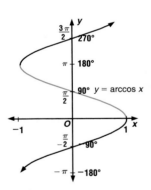

ALTERNATE TEACHING STRATEGIES

Using Models

On an overhead projector, show the graphs of $y = \sin x$ and $y = x$ on the same axes. Reflect the graph of $y = \sin x$ over the graph of $y = x$ to show that the graph of $y = \arcsin x$ is obtained. Repeat with the graphs of the cosine and tangent functions.

Using Charts

Have students complete charts and name ordered pairs (x, y) that illustrate why $y = \arcsin x$ is not a function.
$y = \sin x$
In $y = \arcsin x$, at least two ordered pairs, $\left(\frac{\sqrt{3}}{2}, 60°\right)$ and $\left(\frac{\sqrt{3}}{2}, 120°\right)$, have two different y-values for the same x.

Notice the similarity of the graph of the inverse of the tangent function to the graph of $y = \tan x$ with the axes interchanged. Values of Arctan x are shown as the colored portion of the curve. For each value of x, there is only one value of Arctan x, but infinitely many values for arctan x. The range of Arctan x is $-90° < y < 90°$.

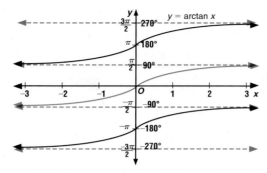

Chalkboard Examples

For Example 1

Find the inverse of the function $y = \csc x$. Then graph both functions.
$y = $ Arccsc x

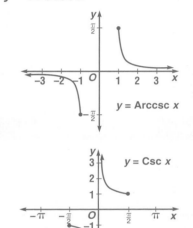

Example 1

You may wish to review finding inverse functions in Lesson 1-2.

Find the inverse of the function $y = \cot x$. Then graph both functions.

To find the inverse of a trigonometric function, exchange x and y.

$y = \cot x$
$x = \cot y$ *Exchange x and y.*
$y = $ Arccot x or $y = \cot^{-1} x$

Now graph the functions.

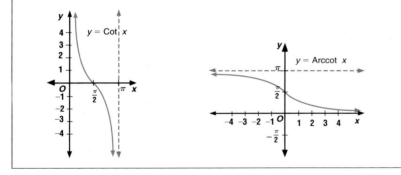

Example 2

Determine if $\cos^{-1}(\cos x) = x$ for all values of x. If false, give a counterexample.

Try several values of x to see if we can find a counterexample.

When $x = 270°$, $\cos^{-1}(\cos x) \ne x$.
So $\cos^{-1}(\cos x) = x$ is not true for all values of x.

x	$\cos x$	$\cos^{-1}(\cos x)$
0°	1	0°
180°	-1	180°
270°	0	90°

For Example 2

Determine if $\sin^{-1}(\sin x) = x$ for all values of x. If false, give a counterexample.
It is false. When $x = 120°$, $\sin x = \dfrac{\sqrt{3}}{2}$. But $\sin^{-1}\left(\dfrac{\sqrt{3}}{2}\right) = 60°$, which does not equal x.

LESSON 6-6 GRAPHING INVERSES OF TRIGONOMETRIC FUNCTIONS 341

Inverse trigonometric functions are used to solve practical problems in many fields.

Example 3

APPLICATION

Medicine

When surgeons join arteries, as when grafting an artery for heart bypass surgery, they must ensure that the friction of the blood passing through the artery at the juncture is minimized. Suppose the angle between the joined arteries measures θ degrees and the radii of the smaller and larger arteries measure r and R millimeters respectively. To minimize the friction, the equation $\operatorname{Cos}\theta = \left(\dfrac{r^4}{R^4}\right)$ must hold. Graph the function for $R = 5$.

If $R = 5$, then $\theta = \operatorname{Cos}^{-1}\left(\dfrac{r^4}{5^4}\right)$ or

$$\theta = \operatorname{Cos}^{-1}\left(\frac{r^4}{625}\right).$$

CHECKING FOR UNDERSTANDING

Communicating Mathematics

Read and study the lesson to answer each question. 1–3. See margin.

1. **Describe** how to draw the graph of an inverse trigonometric function from the graph of the related trigonometric function.

2. **Write** a few sentences describing how to find the equation of the inverse of a trigonometric function.

3. How are the domain and range of a relation related to the domain and range of its inverse?

Guided Practice

State the domain and range of each relation. 4–9. See margin.

4. $y = \sin x$ 5. $y = \tan x$ 6. $y = \operatorname{Cos} x$

7. $y = \arcsin x$ 8. $y = \operatorname{Arccos} x$ 9. $y = \operatorname{Arctan} x$

10. Write the equation for the inverse of the function $y = \cos x$. Then graph the function and its inverse. See margin.

Determine if each of the following is *true* or *false*. If false, give a counterexample.

11. $\tan(\operatorname{Tan}^{-1} x) = x$ for all x
     true

12. $\operatorname{Cot}^{-1}(\cot x) = x$ for all x
     False; answers may vary.

342   CHAPTER 6   GRAPHS AND INVERSES OF THE TRIGONOMETRIC FUNCTIONS

EXERCISES

Practice

State the domain and range of each relation. 13–18. See margin.

13. $y = \cos x$
14. $y = \text{Sin } x$
15. $y = \text{Tan } x$
16. $y = \arccos x$
17. $y = \text{Arcsin } x$
18. $y = \arctan x$

Write the equation for the inverse of each function. Then graph the function and its inverse. 19–24. For graphs, see Teacher's Answer Key.

19. $y = \text{Arctan } x$ $y = \text{Tan } x$
20. $y = \text{Arcsin } x$ $y = \text{Sin } x$
21. $y = \text{Sin } x$ $y = \text{Arcsin } x$
22. $y = \frac{\pi}{2} + \text{Arcsin } x$ $y = \text{Sin } \left(x - \frac{\pi}{2}\right)$
23. $y = \text{Arctan } 2x$ $y = \frac{1}{2} \text{Tan } x$
24. $y = \text{Cos } (x + 90°)$
$\quad y = \text{Cos}^{-1} (x - 90°)$

25–30. Sample counterexamples are given.

Determine if each of the following is *true* or *false*. If false, give a counterexample.

25. $\text{Sin}^{-1} x = -\text{Sin}^{-1} (-x)$, $-1 \le x \le 1$ true
26. $\text{Arccos } x = \text{Arccos } (-x)$, $-1 \le x \le 1$ false, $x = -1$
27. $\text{Cos}^{-1} (-x) = -\text{Cos}^{-1} x$, $-1 \le x \le 1$ false, $x = 1$
28. $\text{Sin}^{-1} x + \text{Cos}^{-1} x = \frac{\pi}{2}$, $-1 \le x \le 1$ true
29. $\text{Cos}^{-1} x = \frac{1}{\text{Cos } x}$ false, $x = \frac{\pi}{2}$
30. $\text{Tan}^{-1} x = \frac{1}{\text{Tan } x}$ false, $x = 0$

Sketch the graph of each equation. 31–32. See Teacher's Answer Key.

31. $y = \tan (\text{Tan}^{-1} x)$
32. $y = \sin (\text{Tan}^{-1} x)$

Critical Thinking

33. Graph $y = \arcsin x$ and $y = \arccos x$ on the same coordinate axes. Give four values of y corresponding to points of intersection of the graphs.
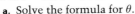
$\frac{\pi}{4} + k\pi$, where k is any integer

Applications and Problem Solving

34. Navigation Navigators aboard ships and airplanes use nautical miles to measure distance. A nautical mile is equal to an arc length of one minute of a degree. The actual length varies slightly since Earth is not a perfect sphere. The formula for the length of a nautical mile in feet, ℓ, on the latitude line θ is $\ell = 6077 - 31 \cos 2\theta$.

34a. $\theta = \frac{1}{2}$ arccos $\left(\frac{6077 - \ell}{31}\right)$

a. Solve the formula for θ.
b. Find the length of a nautical mile on the 40th parallel. $\approx$ 6071.6 ft
c. Where is the length of a nautical mile approximately 6060 feet? 28th parallel

---

Homework Exercises

Assignment Guide

Average: 13–28, 33, 34, 37–42
Enriched: 17–33, 35–42

The red A, B, and C flags, printed only in the Teacher's Wraparound Edition, indicate the level of difficulty of the exercises.

Chapter 6, Quiz C (Lessons 6–5 through 6–6), is available in the *Evaluation Masters*, p. 74.

Additional Answers

13. all real numbers; $-1 \le y \le 1$
14. $-90° \le x \le 90°$; $-1 \le y \le 1$
15. $-90° < x < 90°$; all real numbers
16. $-1 \le x \le 1$; all real numbers
17. $-1 \le x \le 1$; $-90° \le y \le 90°$
18. all real numbers; all real numbers except $90° + 180k°$

Practice Masters Booklet, p. 41

RETEACHING THE LESSON

Have students graph the linear function $f(x) = 2x + 5$ and its inverse $f^{-1}(x) = \frac{x - 5}{2}$ on the same set of axes, together with the line $y = x$. Point out that f and f^{-1} are reflections of each other across the line $y = x$. Have them repeat with a second linear function and its inverse. Show that $y = x$ is a line of reflection for each trigonometric function and its inverse.

35. **Coordinate Geometry**   Suppose ℓ_1 and ℓ_2 are two nonvertical nonperpendicular lines with slopes of m_1 and m_2 respectively. Then the tangent of the angle formed by ℓ_1 and ℓ_2 is given by the formula $\tan \theta = \dfrac{m_2 - m_1}{1 + m_1 m_2}$.

   a. The slope of line a is 2. If lines a and b form an angle of 37°, what is the slope of line b? *Hint: Let a be m_1.*   about −5.43

   b. The slopes of lines s and t are $-\dfrac{1}{2}$ and $\dfrac{3}{4}$, respectively. What is the measure of the angle from s to t? What is the measure of the angle from t to s?
   about 63°; about −63°

36. **History**   Gregory's series is $\arctan x = x - \dfrac{x^3}{3} + \dfrac{x^5}{5} - \dfrac{x^7}{7} + \cdots$. In 1706, John Machin used the Gregory's series to obtain the formula
$$\frac{\pi}{4} = 4 \arctan \left(\frac{1}{5}\right) - \arctan \left(\frac{1}{239}\right).$$

   a. Use the first six terms of Gregory's series and your calculator to approximate $\arctan \left(\dfrac{1}{5}\right)$ and $\arctan \left(\dfrac{1}{239}\right)$.   Answers may vary.
   Sample answers: 0.1973955598; 0.004184076

   b. Use Machin's formula and the values you calculated for Exercise 36a to find an approximation for π. How accurate is your approximation?
   Answers may vary. See students' work.

   c. Research   Write a 1-page paper on approximations of π. Include the methods of approximation other than approximation by Gregory's series and Machin's formula. Find out what method David and Gregory Chudnovsky used with their computer.   See students' work.

Mixed Review

37. Find $[f \circ g](x)$ and $[g \circ f](x)$ if $f(x) = x^3 - 1$ and $g(x) = 3x$.   **(Lesson 1-2)**
$27x^3 - 1; 3x^3 - 3$

38. Write the standard form of the equation of the line that is parallel to the line $2x - 6y = -3$ and passes through the point with coordinates $(9, -4)$.
(Lesson 1-6) $x - 3y - 21 = 0$

39. Solve $\sqrt{2y - 3} - \sqrt{2y + 3} = -1$.   **(Lesson 4-7)** $\dfrac{37}{8}$

40. Find the value of $\cos \alpha$ if $(4, 3)$ lies on the terminal side of the angle in standard position.   **(Lesson 5-3)** $\dfrac{4}{5}$

41. Find $\cos \left(\text{Tan}^{-1} \sqrt{3} - \text{Sin}^{-1} \dfrac{1}{2} \right)$.   **(Lesson 6-5)** $\dfrac{\sqrt{3}}{2}$

42. **College Entrance Exam**   Compare quantities A and B below.   B
Write A if quantity A is greater.
Write B if quantity B is greater.
Write C if the quantities are equal.
Write D if there is not enough information to determine the relationship.

Given: $2 < b < a$

   (A) $\dfrac{120a^5 b^6}{8a^3 b^2}$ **(B)** $\dfrac{120a^4 b^{\frac{13}{2}}}{6a^0 b^{\frac{1}{2}}}$

344   CHAPTER 6   GRAPHS AND INVERSES OF THE TRIGONOMETRIC FUNCTIONS

Enrichment Masters Booklet, p. 41

344   CHAPTER 6   GRAPHS AND INVERSES OF THE TRIGONOMETRIC FUNCTIONS

EXTENDING THE LESSON

Math Power: Problem Solving

By substituting $x = 1$ in Gregory's series, you will obtain the most elegant of all infinite series for generating π:
$$\arctan 1 = 1 - \frac{1^3}{3} + \frac{1^5}{5} - \frac{1^7}{7} + \cdots$$

$$\frac{\pi}{4} = 1 - \frac{1}{3} + \frac{1}{5} - \frac{1}{7} + \cdots$$

Use the first nine terms of the series to approximate π.
3.2523659

6-7 Simple Harmonic Motion

Objective
6-7

After studying this lesson, you should be able to:
- solve problems involving simple harmonic motion.

Application

Buoys are floating markers placed in water to aid in navigation. The centers and sides of navigation channels, wrecks, rocks, and underwater cables are a few of the hazards buoys indicate. Boaters can tell what the buoy indicates by the shape, color, and lights on it. Some buoys also have bells or whistles and are made to reflect radar.

A buoy in a lake channel bobs up and down as the waves move past. Suppose the buoy moves a total of 6 feet from its high point to its low point and returns to its high point every 10 seconds. Assuming that at $t = 0$ the buoy is at its high point, write an equation to describe its motion. *This problem will be solved in Example 1.*

A wide variety of problems involve the rhythmic motion of an object. The motion of a buoy is one example. Other examples of rhythmic motion are the vibrations of a guitar string, the pistons of an engine, and a pendulum moving back and forth. When friction and other factors affecting such motion are ignored, this movement is called **simple harmonic motion.**

The angular velocity of an object that is turning is the number of degrees or radians that a point on the edge of the object moves in a unit of time. Suppose a wheel is turning counterclockwise at a constant angular velocity and P is a point on the rim of the wheel. If the wheel is modeled by a circle with its center at the origin of a rectangular coordinate system, the motion of point P can be described in terms of the coordinates of its position. Since the angular velocity is constant, the measure of angle θ as a function of time is $\theta = kt$, where k is the constant and t represents time. Let A be the measure of the radius of the wheel and substitute kt for θ. Then $\cos \theta$ or $\cos kt = \frac{x}{A}$ and $\sin \theta = \sin kt = \frac{y}{A}$. Solving for x and y produces the following equations for the horizontal and vertical motion of the point P if its initial position was at $(A, 0)$.

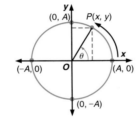

$$x = A \cos kt \qquad\qquad y = A \sin kt$$

ALTERNATE TEACHING STRATEGIES

Using Manipulatives

Have students attach a spring or long elastic band with a weight at the end to a door frame. They should pull and release the spring, measuring the amplitude with a yardstick and the period with a watch. They should take several measurements of each and use the average. Then they should write the equation of motion.

Using Connection

When a pianist plays middle C, the piano string vibrates at a frequency of 264 cycles per second. Ask students to write the equation of simple harmonic motion of the string when $A = 1$ mm. **Sample answer: $y = \sin 528 \pi t$**

NCTM Standards: 1–6, 8, 9

Lesson Resources

- Practice Master 6–7
- Enrichment Master 6–7
- Evaluation Master, Quiz D, p. 74
- Multicultural Activity Master, p. 6

 Transparency 6–7 contains the 5-Minute Check and a teaching aid for this lesson.

INTRODUCING THE LESSON

5-Minute Check

(over Lesson 6–6)

State the domain and range of each relation.
1. $y = \text{Sin } x$.
   $-90° \le x \le 90°$;
   $-1 \le y \le 1$
2. $y = \text{Arctan } x$
   all real numbers;
   $-90° \le y \le 90°$

Write the equation for the inverse of each function.
3. $y = \arccos x$ $y = \cos x$
4. $y = \text{Sin } x$ $y = \text{Arcsin } x$
5. Give an example showing that $\text{Tan}^{-1}(\tan x) \ne x$ if $x < -90°$ or $x > 90°$.
   Answers may vary. If $x = 135°$, $\text{Tan}^{-1}(\tan 135°) = \text{Tan}^{-1}(-1) = -45°$

Motivating the Lesson

Show examples of *simple harmonic motion.* Some possibilities: Hang a weight on a string and swing it to illustrate the harmonic motion of a pendulum; float an object in a container of water and cause the object to bob up and down; hang a weight on a spring and cause the weight to bounce up and down.

Chalkboard Example

For Example 1

A weight on a spring bounces a maximum of 8 inches above and below its equilibrium (zero) point. The time for one complete cycle is 2 seconds.

a. Write two possible equations to describe the motion of the weight.

$x = 8 \cos \pi t$ or

$y = 8 \sin \left(\pi t + \dfrac{\pi}{2} \right)$

b. Draw a graph to show the motion of the weight in 4 seconds.

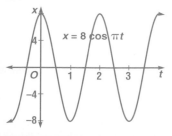

These equations assume that $\theta = 0$ at time $t = 0$. If angle θ measures c radians at time $t = 0$, then $\theta = kt + c$ would express θ as a function of time. Thus, the more general equations for the motion of point P are as follows.

$$x = A \cos (kt + c) \qquad\qquad y = A \sin (kt + c)$$

$-\dfrac{c}{k}$ represents the phase shift in terms of t. The angular phase shift is –c.

You know that the amplitude of each of the functions above is $|A|$, the period is $\dfrac{2\pi}{k}$ (or $\dfrac{360°}{k}$), and the phase shift is $-\dfrac{c}{k}$.

These equations can be used to model problems involving simple harmonic motion. The description of the motion of point P above was with respect to the coordinate system used, rather than the true orientation of the wheel. In an applied problem, the appropriate equation will have to be chosen to conform to the actual physical conditions of the problem. Since sine and cosine curves having the same amplitude and period can be made to coincide by a phase shift, several equations may be used to describe the same simple harmonic motion.

Example 1

APPLICATION

Navigation

Refer to the application problem at the beginning of the lesson.

a. Write two possible equations to describe the motion of the buoy.

a. First, find the amplitude, period, and phase shift of the function.

The amplitude, $|A|$, is $\dfrac{6}{2}$ or 3 feet.

The period is 10 seconds, so $10 = \dfrac{2\pi}{k}$ and $k = \dfrac{\pi}{5}$.

The initial state can be represented by an equation of the form $x = A \cos kt$. Thus, the equation is $x = 3 \cos \dfrac{\pi t}{5}$.

An alternate equation can be written using the sine function. Consider that 2.5 seconds before the cycle begins, or $\dfrac{1}{4}$ of a complete cycle, the buoy is at 0 feet. Thus, the phase shift in terms of time would be –2.5 seconds. Since $-2.5 = -\dfrac{c}{k}$ and $k = \dfrac{\pi}{5}$, $c = \dfrac{\pi}{2}$.

An alternate equation is $y = 3 \sin \left(\dfrac{\pi t}{5} + \dfrac{\pi}{2} \right)$.

Why are the equations equivalent?

b. Draw a graph to show the motion of the buoy in 30 seconds.

b. Graph one of the functions.

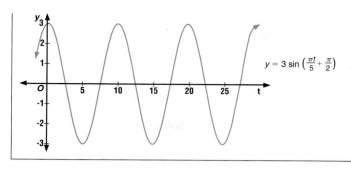

$$y = 3\sin\left(\frac{\pi t}{5} + \frac{\pi}{2}\right)$$

The concept of **frequency** is one that is useful in some applied problems, particularly those involving sound waves or electricity. Frequency is the number of cycles per unit of time and is equal to the reciprocal of the period. For instance, the frequency of the function in Example 1 is $\frac{1}{10}$ or $\frac{1}{10}$ of a cycle per second.

Example 2

APPLICATION

Entertainment

Will Rogers spun a lasso in a vertical circle. The diameter of the loop was 6 feet, and the loop spun 50 times each minute. If the lowest point on the rope was 6 inches above the ground, write an equation to describe the height of this point above the ground after t seconds.

The frequency of the lasso was 50 revolutions per minute, or 50 rpm. At this rate, the lasso made one revolution every $\frac{60}{50}$ or 1.2 seconds. So the period is $1.2 = \frac{2\pi}{k}$ and $k = \frac{5\pi}{3}$ radians/second.

We know that a point on the rope was 6 inches above the ground at time $t = 0$. So let $c = 0$ at $t = 0$. Use the center of the rotation as the origin of a coordinate system. Relative to the center of rotation, the initial position was at $(0, -3)$. *The radius is 3 feet.*

$$h = A\cos(kt + c)$$
$$= -3\cos\left(\frac{5\pi}{3}t + 0\right)$$
$$= -3\cos\frac{5\pi}{3}t$$

This equation gives the position of the point relative to the center of rotation, which was 3 feet 6 inches or 3.5 feet above the ground. Therefore, the equation for the height of the point relative to the ground is $h = -3\cos\frac{5\pi}{3}t + 3.5$.

The study of physics offers many examples of harmonic motion. The movement of a pendulum is one example.

Teaching Tip Many of the students in your class may also be physics students. Have those students comment on the Exploration and add any other information they know about pendulums.

EVALUATING THE LESSON

Checking for Understanding

Exercises 1–13 are designed to help you assess students' understanding through reading, writing, speaking, and modeling. You should work through Exercises 1–3 with your students and then monitor their work on Exercises 4–13.

Closing the Lesson

Speaking Activity Have students give an example of simple harmonic motion. Ask them to specify the amplitude, period, and frequency for their example and to explain the meaning of each.

Practice Masters Booklet, p. 42

EXPLORATION: Physics

Materials: string, small weight like an eraser or washer

Work in groups to complete this exploration. Make a pendulum with a piece of string about 3 feet long and a small weight. Have one group member hold the end of the string or attach it to a door frame so that it can swing freely. Pull the string back and measure the displacement from the equilibrium point. Release the weight and use a stopwatch to time ten full swings of the pendulum. A full swing means that the weight swings over and then back to its starting point. Divide the time for ten swings of the pendulum by 10 to find the time for one full swing. This is the period of the pendulum. 1–4. See margin.

1. Use the distance that you displaced the weight and the time that you measured to write an equation for the position of the weight after t seconds.

2. Use your equation to determine at what time the pendulum will complete two cycles. Then use the stopwatch to measure the time experimentally. Is your equation accurate?

3. Repeat the experiment in Step 1 using a different displacement. How does the equation change?

4. Change the length of the pendulum and repeat the experiment in Step 1 using the same displacement as you did for the first experiment. How does the equation change?

CHECKING FOR UNDERSTANDING

Communicating Mathematics

Read and study the lesson to answer each question. 1. See students' work.

1. **Describe** what it means for an object to be in simple harmonic motion. Give an example of an object that demonstrates this type of motion.

2. **Explain** the relationship between frequency and period. See margin.

3. The frequency of the vibrations of an E string on a guitar is about 330 hertz. How long does it take for the string to make one full vibration? $\frac{1}{330} \approx 0.003$ second

Guided Practice

Find the amplitude, period, frequency, and phase shift.

4. $s = 7 \cos\left(\frac{\pi t}{2} + \frac{\pi}{4}\right)$ $7, 4, \frac{1}{4}, -\frac{1}{2}$

5. $V = -8 \sin(4t - \pi)$ $8, \frac{\pi}{2}, \frac{2}{\pi}, \frac{\pi}{4}$

6. $E = 120 \sin 100\pi t$ $120, \frac{1}{50}, 50, 0$

7. $y = -4 \sin\left(3t + \frac{3\pi}{4}\right)$ $4, \frac{2\pi}{3}, \frac{3}{2\pi}, -\frac{\pi}{4}$

Write an equation with phase shift 0 to represent simple harmonic motion under each set of circumstances.

8. initial position –3, amplitude 3, period 2 $y = -3 \cos \pi t$

9. initial position 0, amplitude 5, period 2 $y = 5 \sin \pi t$

348 CHAPTER 6 GRAPHS AND INVERSES OF THE TRIGONOMETRIC FUNCTIONS

6-7 Practice Worksheet

NAME _____ DATE _____

Simple Harmonic Motion
Find the amplitude, period, frequency, and phase shift.

1. $y = 3 \sin\left(\frac{1}{2}\theta - 90°\right)$
  $3, 720°, \frac{1}{720}, 180°$

2. $y = -\frac{1}{2} \cos\theta$
  $\frac{1}{2}, 360°, \frac{1}{360}, 0°$

3. $y = \sin\left(x + \frac{3\pi}{2}\right)$
  $1, 2\pi, \frac{1}{2\pi}, -\frac{3\pi}{2}$

4. $y = -2 \sin\left(2x - \frac{\pi}{6}\right)$
  $2, \pi, \frac{1}{\pi}, \frac{\pi}{12}$

5. $y = 1.5 \cos\left(\frac{\pi}{6}x + \frac{\pi}{3}\right)$
  $1.5, 12, \frac{1}{12}, -2$

6. $y = 12 \cos\left(2\pi t - \frac{\pi}{6}\right)$
  $12, 1, 1, \frac{1}{12}$

7. $w = -220 \cos 12t$
  $220, 30°, \frac{1}{30}, 0°$

8. $z = -0.3 \sin\left(\frac{3\pi t}{4} - \frac{\pi}{4}\right)$
  $0.3, \frac{8}{3}, \frac{3}{8}, \frac{1}{3}$

Write an equation with phase shift 0 to represent simple harmonic motion under each set of circumstances.

9. initial position 12, amplitude 12, period 8
  $y = 12 \cos \frac{\pi t}{4}$

10. initial position 0, amplitude 2, period 8π
  $y = \pm 2 \sin \frac{t}{4}$

11. initial position –24, amplitude 24, period 6
  $y = -24 \cos \frac{\pi t}{3}$

T42
Glencoe Division, Macmillan/McGraw-Hill

RETEACHING THE LESSON

Give simple examples to help students find A and k in the equation of harmonic motion, $y = A \sin kt$. Remind them that A is the amplitude and k is $\frac{2\pi}{\text{period}}$.

Example: A pendulum makes one complete cycle in 4 seconds, swinging a maximum of 12 cm from its center point. $A = 12$; period = 4; $k = \frac{2\pi}{4} = \frac{\pi}{2}$; equation: $y = 12 \sin \frac{\pi}{2}t$.

Additional Answer

2. They are reciprocals.

348 CHAPTER 6 GRAPHS AND INVERSES OF THE TRIGONOMETRIC FUNCTIONS

10. initial position 0, amplitude 7, period 10 $y = 7 \sin \frac{\pi t}{5}$

11. initial position 7, amplitude 7, period 10 $y = 7 \cos \frac{\pi t}{5}$

12. the y-coordinate of a point P on the rim of a wheel 12 feet in diameter that is turning at 10 rpm; let P be $(6, 0)$ at $t = 0$ seconds $y = 6 \sin \frac{\pi t}{3}$

13. **Navigation**   Ken first observes a buoy at the bottom of a wave bobbing up and down a total distance of 10 feet. The buoy completes a full cycle every 12 seconds.
$y = -5 \cos \frac{\pi t}{6}$

EXERCISES

Practice   **Find the amplitude, period, frequency, and phase shift.**

14. $y = 5 \sin \left(\pi t - \frac{\pi}{2} \right)$ 5, 2, $\frac{1}{2}, \frac{1}{2}$

15. $h = -15 \cos \left(\frac{\pi t}{3} \right) + 21$ 15, 6, $\frac{1}{6}$, 0

16. $y = 10 \sin (2\pi x - \pi)$ 10, 1, 1, $\frac{1}{2}$

17. $E = 150 \cos 80\pi t$ 150, $\frac{1}{40}$, 40, 0

18. $n = -0.1 \sin \left(\frac{\pi t}{4} + \frac{\pi}{4} \right)$ 0.1, 8, $\frac{1}{8}$, -1

19. $W = -25 \cos 8t$ 25, $\frac{\pi}{4}, \frac{4}{\pi}$, 0

Write an equation with phase shift 0 to represent simple harmonic motion under each set of circumstances.

20. initial position -7, amplitude 7, period 4 $y = -7 \cos \frac{\pi t}{2}$

21. initial position 0, amplitude 0.5, period 1 $y = 0.5 \sin 2\pi t$

22. initial position 0, amplitude 22, period 12 $y = 22 \sin \frac{\pi t}{6}$

23. initial position 10, amplitude 10, period $\frac{1}{2}$ $y = 10 \cos 4\pi t$

Critical Thinking

24. **Physics**   A weight in a spring-mass system is oscillating in simple harmonic motion. The amplitude is doubled. How are the period and phase shift affected? They are not affected.

Applications and Problem Solving

25. **Entertainment**   At one time, Cedar Point Amusement Park in Sandusky, Ohio, had a ride called the Rotor in which riders stood against the walls of a spinning cylinder. As the cylinder spun, the riders were held up by friction and the floor of the ride dropped out. The cylinder of the Rotor had a radius of 3.5 meters and rotated counterclockwise at a rate of 14 rpm. Suppose the center of rotation of the Rotor is at the origin of a rectangular coordinate system.

a. What is the period of the function, in terms of t seconds, that represents the position of the door of the ride's cylinder? $\frac{30}{7}$ seconds

25b.
$$\left[3.5\cos\left(\frac{7}{15}\pi t\right),\ 3.5\sin\left(\frac{7}{15}\pi t\right)\right]$$

b. If the initial coordinates of the door of the ride's cylinder are $(3.5, 0)$, what are its coordinates after t seconds?

c. Under the conditions of part b, what are the coordinates of the door's position after 4 seconds? $(3.20, -1.42)$

d. Under the conditions of part b, what are the coordinates of the position of the door after 19.25 seconds? Round to the nearest hundredth. $(-3.50, 0.18)$

e. If the initial coordinates of the position of the door were $(0, 3.5)$, what would the coordinates be after t seconds?

f. If the initial y-coordinate of the position of the door was 2.2, what was the initial x-coordinate? ± 2.72

25e. $\left[3.5\cos\left(\frac{7}{15}\pi t + \frac{\pi}{2}\right), 3.5\sin\left(\frac{7}{15}\pi t + \frac{\pi}{2}\right)\right]$

26. **Automotive Engineering** In a gasoline engine, the explosion of the fuel exerts a thrust of pressure on the pistons which turn the *crankshaft* and power the engine. One thrust of the pistons turns the crankshaft $360°$. As the crankshaft turns, the radius of the throw makes an angle θ with the line from the shaft to the end of the rod. The distance between the end of the rod and the crankshaft center, h, is given by the formula
$h = r\cos\theta + \sqrt{d^2 + r^2(\sin\theta)^2}$,
where r is the measure of the radius of the throw, and d is the measure of the rod. For a certain engine, r is 2.2 inches and d is 5.8 inches.

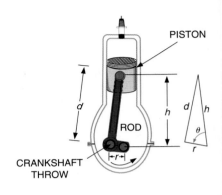

a. Find the distance from the end of the rod to the crankshaft center when $\theta = 30°$. 7.81 in.

b. Graph the distance from the end of the rod to the crankshaft center for values of θ from $0°$ to $360°$ using a graphing calculator. Then sketch the graph.
See margin.

27. **Physics** A weight in a spring-mass system exhibits harmonic motion. The system is in equilibrium when the weight is motionless. If the weight is pulled down or pushed up and released, it would tend to oscillate freely if there were no friction. In a certain spring-mass system, the weight is 5 feet from a 10-foot ceiling when it is at rest. The

motion of the weight can be described by the equation $y = 3\sin\left(\pi t - \frac{\pi}{2}\right)$, where y is the distance from the equilibrium point, and t is measured in seconds.

a. Was the weight pulled down or pushed up before it was released? pulled down

b. How far was the weight from the ceiling when it was released? 8 ft

c. How close will the weight come to the ceiling? 2 ft

d. When does the weight first pass its equilibrium point? $t = \frac{1}{2}$ second

e. What is the greatest distance that the weight will be from the ceiling? 8 ft

f. Find the period of the motion. 2 seconds

g. Find the amplitude of the motion. 3 ft

h. What is the frequency of the motion? $\frac{1}{2}$ cycle/second

i. How far from the ceiling is the weight after 2.5 seconds? 5 ft

28. Zoology The number of predators and the number of prey in a predator-prey system tend to vary periodically. In a certain region with hawks as predators and rodents as prey, the rodent population M varied according to the equation $M = 1200 + 300 \sin \frac{\pi t}{2}$ and the hawk population varied with the equation $H = 250 + 25 \sin \left(\frac{\pi t}{2} - \frac{\pi}{4} \right)$, with t measured in years since January 1, 1970.

a. What was the population of rodents on January 1, 1970? 1200

b. What was the population of hawks on January 1, 1970? 232

c. What are the maximum populations of rodents and hawks? Do these maxima ever occur at the same time? 1500, 275; no

28d. January 1, 1971

d. On what date was the first maximum population of rodents achieved?

e. What is the minimum population of hawks? On what date was the minimum population of hawks first achieved? 225; July 1, 1973

f. Use a graphing calculator to graph both equations on the same set of axes. Write a paragraph to explain why the populations fluctuate in the way that they do. See students' work.

Mixed Review

29. Graph the rational function $y = \frac{-4}{x^2 - 2}$. **(Lesson 3-4)** See margin.

30. Approximate the real zeros of the function $f(x) = 5x^4 - 8x^2 + 2$ to the nearest tenth. **(Lesson 4-5)** −1.1, −0.6, 0.6, 1.1

31. Are the angles −15° and 345° coterminal? **(Lesson 5-1)** yes

32. Geometry A regular hexagon is inscribed in a circle with a radius 6.4 centimeters long. Find the apothem; that is, the distance from the center of the circle to the midpoint of a side. **(Lesson 5-5)** 5.5 cm

33. College Entrance Exam The sum of the reciprocals of a and b is 7 and the difference of the reciprocals of a and b is 3. Find $\frac{1}{a^2} - \frac{1}{b^2}$. 21

EXTENDING THE LESSON

Math Power: Problem Solving

The current, C, in amperes, produced by an alternating current generator is given by $C = 10 \sin (120\pi t - 60\pi)$, where t is the time in seconds. Find the amplitude, frequency, period, and phase shift.
10; 60 cycles/sec; $\frac{1}{60}$ sec; $\frac{1}{2}$

Additional Answer

29.

$y = \frac{-4}{x^2 - 2}$

Enrichment Masters Booklet, p. 42

6-7 | **Enrichment Worksheet**

NAME _____ DATE _____

Trigonometric Functions as Infinite Series

An infinite series is an indicated sum of an an infinite sequence of terms. For example $1 + 3 + 5 + 7 + \cdots$ is an infinite series. A **partial sum** of the series is a sum of the terms up to a designated point. The partial sum of the first three terms of the above series is $1 + 3 + 5$ or 9. For some infinite series, the consecutive partial sums simply grow larger and larger. Such an infinite series is said to **diverge**. The consecutive partial sums of $1 + 3 + 5 + 7 + \cdots$ are 1, 4, 9, 16, $\cdots$ Because they increase without bound, the series $1 + 3 + 5 + 7 + \cdots$ diverges.

For other infinite series, however, the consecutive partial sums approach closer and closer to a specific number. Such a series is said to **converge** to that number. The number is the **sum** of the series.

Consider the infinite series $\frac{1}{2} + \frac{1}{4} + \frac{1}{8} + \frac{1}{16} + \cdots$

1. Write the first five partial sums of the series. $\frac{1}{2}, \frac{3}{4}, \frac{7}{8}, \frac{15}{16}, \frac{31}{32}$

2. The tenth partial sum of the series is $\frac{n}{1024}$. Find n. $n = 1,023$

3. What number appears to be the sum of the series? Why do you think so?1; sample answer: the nth partial sum is $\frac{2^n - 1}{2^n}$. The larger the value of n, the closer the fraction gets to $\frac{2^n}{2^n} = 1$.

Infinite series are used to calculate the values of trigonometric functions. Calculus can be used to establish the infinite series:

$\sin x = x - \frac{x^3}{3!} + \frac{x^5}{5!} - \frac{x^7}{7!} + \cdots$ (3! = 3 · 2 · 1, 5! = 5 · 4 · 3 · 2 · 1, and so on.)

$\cos x = 1 - \frac{x^2}{2!} + \frac{x^4}{4!} - \frac{x^6}{6!} + \cdots$

When x is expressed in radians, these series converge on the values of $\sin x$ and $\cos x$ respectively.

4. $18° = \frac{\pi}{10} \approx 0.3141593$. Store this value in memory in your calculator. Then use it and the first four terms of the infinite series for $\sin x$ to approximate $\sin 18°$. Compare with the value of $\sin 18°$ given by your calculator.
Both give the value 0.309017

5. Use the first four terms of the series for $\cos x$ to approximate $\cos 50°$. Compare with the value of $\cos 50°$ given by your calculator.
series: 0.6427793   calculator: 0.6427876

T42
Glencoe Division, Macmillan/McGraw-Hill

Using the Chapter Summary and Review

The Chapter Summary and Review begins with an alphabetical listing of the new terms that were presented in the chapter. Have students define each term and provide an example of it, if appropriate.

The Skills and Concepts presented in the chapter are reviewed using a side-by-side format. Encourage students to refer to the Objectives and Examples on the left as they complete the review exercises on the right.

The Chapter Summary and Review ends with exercises that review Applications and Problem Solving.

Additional Answers

5.

6.

7.

12.

VOCABULARY

Upon completing this chapter, you should be familiar with the following terms:

amplitude	**309**	**312**	phase shift
arcsine	**329**	**334**	principal values
compound function	**324**	**345**	simple harmonic motion
frequency	**347**	**322**	vertical displacement
period	**311**		

SKILLS AND CONCEPTS

OBJECTIVES AND EXAMPLES	REVIEW EXERCISES

Upon completing this chapter, you should be able to:

Use these exercises to review and prepare for the chapter test.

- graph the trigonometric functions **(Lesson 6-1)**

  Graph $y = \cos x$ on the interval $-90° \le x \le 450°$.

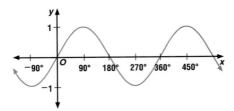

Find each value by referring to the graphs of the trigonometric functions on pages 310–311.

1. $\tan 180°$ 0   **2.** $\sin 450°$ 1

3. $\sec(-270°)$ undefined   **4.** $\cos 540°$ −1

Graph each function on the given interval.

5. $y = \sin x, 90° \le x \le 450°$

6. $y = \tan x, -\pi \le x \le \pi$

7. $y = \cot x, -180° \le x \le 360°$

5–7. See margin.

- find the amplitude, period, and phase shift for a trigonometric function   **(Lesson 6-2)**

  State the amplitude, period, and phase shift for $y = -\sqrt{3}\cos(x - \pi)$.

  amplitude: $|A| = |-\sqrt{3}| = \sqrt{3}$

  period: $\dfrac{360°}{k} = \dfrac{360°}{1} = 360°$

  phase shift: $-\dfrac{c}{k} = -\dfrac{-\pi}{1} = \pi$ or $180°$

State the amplitude (if it exists), period, and phase shift for each function.

8. $y = 4\cos 2x$ 4, 180°, 0°

9. $y = 15\sin\left(\dfrac{3}{2}x + 90°\right)$ 15, 240°, −60°

10. $y = 5\cot\left(\dfrac{x}{2} - 45°\right)$ none, 360°, 90°

11. $y = 2\tan 5x$ none, 36°, 0°

13.

14.

OBJECTIVES AND EXAMPLES	REVIEW EXERCISES

■ graph various trigonometric functions **(Lesson 6-3)**

Graph $y = \sin\left(4x + \frac{\pi}{3}\right)$.

Graph each function.

12. $y = 3\cos\frac{\theta}{2}$

13. $y = 2\tan(3\theta + 90°)$

14. $y = -3\sin(\theta - 45°)$

15. $y = 2\sin x - \cos x$

16. $y = x + 2\sin 2x$

12–16. See margin.

■ evaluate inverse trigonometric functions **(Lesson 6-4)**

Evaluate $y = \sin\left(\arccos\frac{1}{2}\right)$. Assume that the angle is in Quadrant I.

Let $A = \arccos\frac{1}{2}$.

$\cos A = \frac{1}{2}$
$A = 60°$

$\sin\left(\arccos\frac{1}{2}\right) = \sin 60°$

$\qquad = \frac{\sqrt{3}}{2}$

Write each equation in the form of an inverse relation. 17. $\alpha = \arcsin y$ 18. $y = \arctan x$

17. $y = \sin\alpha$ **18.** $\tan y = x$

19. $n = \cos\theta$ **20.** $\sec\theta = y$
19. $\theta = \arccos n$ 20. $\theta = \text{arcsec } y$

Evaluate each expression. Assume that all angles are in Quadrant I.

21. $\cos\left(\arccos\frac{1}{2}\right)$ $\frac{1}{2}$

22. $\tan\left(\text{arccot}\frac{4}{5}\right)$ $\frac{5}{4}$

23. $\sin(\tan^{-1} 1) + \cos(\sin^{-1} 1)$ $\frac{\sqrt{2}}{2}$

24. $\tan\left(\arcsin\frac{\sqrt{3}}{2} + \arccos\frac{\sqrt{3}}{2}\right)$ undefined

---

■ find principal values of inverse trigonometric functions **(Lesson 6-5)**

Find $\cos(\text{Tan}^{-1}1)$.

Let $\theta = \text{Tan}^{-1}1$.

$\text{Tan}\,\theta = 1$

$\qquad \theta = 45°$

So, $\cos 45° = \frac{\sqrt{2}}{2}$.

Find each value.

25. $\cos\left(\text{Sin}^{-1}\frac{1}{2}\right)$ $\frac{\sqrt{3}}{2}$

26. $\sin\left(3\,\text{Sin}^{-1}\frac{\sqrt{3}}{2}\right)$ 0

27. $\sin 2\left(\text{Arcsin}\frac{1}{2}\right)$ $\frac{\sqrt{3}}{2}$

28. $\cos\left(\frac{\pi}{2} - \text{Cos}^{-1}\frac{\sqrt{2}}{2}\right)$ $\frac{\sqrt{2}}{2}$

29. $\cos\left(\text{Arctan}\sqrt{3} + \text{Arcsin}\frac{1}{2}\right)$ 0

For more information on other methods of alternate assessment, you may wish to refer to Glencoe's *Alternate Assessment in the Mathematics Classroom.*

Two multiple-choice tests (Forms 1A and 1B) and two free-response tests (Form 2A and 2B) are provided in the *Evaluation Masters*. Chapter 6 Test, Form 1A is shown below. Chapter 6 Test, Form 2A is shown on the next page.

Evaluation Masters Booklet, pp. 65–66

OBJECTIVES AND EXAMPLES	REVIEW EXERCISES

- graph inverses of trigonometric functions (Lesson 6-6)

  Graph the inverse of $y = \text{Cos } x$.

  The inverse is $y = \text{Arccos } x$.

Write the equation for the inverse of each function. Then graph the function and its inverse.

30. $y = \text{Arcsin } x$ $y = \text{Sin } x$
31. $y = \text{Csc } x$ $y = \text{Arccsc } x$
32. $y = \cot x$ $y = \text{arccot } x$
33. $y = \text{arcsec } x$ $y = \text{sec } x$

30–33. For graphs, see Teacher's Answer Key.

- solve problems involving simple harmonic motion (Lesson 6-7)

  Two equations that describe simple harmonic motion are:

  $x = A \cos (kt + c)$, and
  $y = A \sin (kt + c)$.

  34. $x = 5 \cos 8\pi t$; $y = 5 \sin 8\pi t$
  35. 4 cycles/second
  36. $\left(-\frac{5}{2}, -\frac{5\sqrt{3}}{2}\right)$

The point P is on the circumference of a circle of radius 5 inches that is rotating in a counterclockwise direction at the rate of 4 revolutions per second. Let the initial position of P at $t = 0$ be at $(5, 0)$.

34. Write two equations that describe the position of P after t seconds.

35. What is the frequency of the motion?

36. What are the coordinates of P after $\frac{1}{6}$ second?

APPLICATIONS AND PROBLEM SOLVING

37. **Entertainment** A popular, but dangerous, activity is bungee jumping. A person, whose ankles are attached to a bungee cord, jumps off a ledge and bounces upside-down in mid-air. Suppose a person jumps off the ledge and falls 122 feet before rebounding. Consider the point at which the person rebounds to be $t = 0$. The person then rebounds to a distance of 46 feet from the ledge after 3 seconds. Assume there is no resistance in the bungee cord. **(Lesson 6-2)**

    a. Write a function that represents the person's distance from the equilibrium point as a function of time. $y = -38 \cos \frac{\pi}{3}t$

    b. Write a function that represents the person's vertical distance from the ledge as a function of time. $y = -38 \cos \frac{\pi}{3}t - 84$

    c. What would be the position of the person after 30 seconds? 122 feet below the ledge

38. **Physics** The strength of a magnetic field is called magnetic induction. An equation for magnetic induction is $B = \frac{F}{IL \sin \theta}$, where F is a force on a current I which is moving through a wire of length L at an angle θ to the magnetic field. A wire within a magnetic field is 1 meter long and carries a current of 5.0 A. The force on the wire is 0.2 N and the magnetic induction is 0.04 N/Am. What is the angle of the wire to the magnetic field? **(Lesson 6-5)** $\frac{\pi}{2}$ or 90°

Find the values of x in degrees for which each equation is true. 1–3. k is any integer.

1. $\tan x = 0$ $180k°$

2. $\sin x = -1$ $270° + 360k°$

3. $\cos x = \dfrac{\sqrt{2}}{2}$

     3. $45° + 360k°$ and $315° + 360k°$

Graph each function on the given interval. 4–5. See Teacher's Answer Key.

4. $y = \sin x; -180° \le x \le 180°$

5. $y = \tan x; 0 \le x \le 2\pi$

State the amplitude, period, and phase shift for each function.

6. $y = 3\cos 4\theta$ $3, 90°, 0°$

7. $y = 110\sin(15\theta - 40°)$ $110, 24°, 2\frac{2}{3}°$

8. $y = 10\sin(\pi - x)$ $10, 360°, 180°$

Graph each function. 9–11. See Teacher's Answer Key.

9. $y = 3\cos\dfrac{\theta}{2}$

10. $y = \tan\left(2x - \dfrac{\pi}{4}\right)$

11. $y = 2\cos x - x$

Evaluate each expression. Assume that all angles are in Quadrant I.

12. $\sin\left(\arccos\dfrac{\sqrt{3}}{2}\right)$ $\dfrac{1}{2}$

13. $\tan\left(\cos^{-1}\dfrac{5}{13}\right)$ $\dfrac{12}{5}$

14. $\cos(\arctan\sqrt{3} + \text{arccot}\sqrt{3})$ 0

Find each value.

15. $\sin\left(\text{Arccos}\dfrac{1}{2}\right)$ $\dfrac{\sqrt{3}}{2}$

16. $\cos\left(\dfrac{1}{2}\text{Tan}^{-1}\dfrac{3}{4}\right)$ $\dfrac{3\sqrt{10}}{10}$

17. $\tan\left(\pi + \text{Arcsin}\dfrac{2}{3}\right)$ $\dfrac{2\sqrt{5}}{5}$

Write the equation for the inverse of each function. Then graph the function and its inverse. 18–19. For graphs, see Teacher's Answer Key.

18. $y = \text{Arccsc } x$ $y = \text{Csc } x$

19. $y = \tan x$ $y = \arctan x$

A point P is on the circumference of a circle of radius 10 centimeters with its center at the origin. The circle is rotating in a counterclockwise direction at the rate of 2 radians per second. Let P have coordinates (10, 0) at t = 0.

20. Write an equation that describes the x-coordinate of P after t seconds. $x = 10\cos 2t$

21. Write an equation that describes the y-coordinate of P after t seconds. $y = 10\sin 2t$

22. What is the amplitude of the motion?   10

23. What is the frequency of this motion? $\dfrac{1}{\pi}$

24. Oceanography The tides of the ocean can be described by simple harmonic motion. At midnight and at noon, the high tide rises to the 6-foot mark on a retaining wall. At 6 A.M. and at 6 P.M., the low tide falls to the 2-foot mark. At what mark is the water at 2 P.M.?   3-foot mark

25. Civil Engineering Ms. Jefferson, a civil engineer, is designing a curve for a new highway. She uses the equation, $\tan\theta = \dfrac{v^2}{gr}$, where the radius r will be 1200 feet, the curve will be designed for a maximum velocity of 65 mph, and the acceleration due to gravity is 32 ft/s². At what angle θ should the curve be banked?   13.3°

Bonus
Determine whether the relation $y = x^2 - \cos x$ is *even*, *odd*, or *neither*.   even

This page may be used as a test or as a review. All answers to this test appear in the Selected Answers in the student text.

Standardized Test Practice Questions are also provided in the *Evaluation Masters*.

Evaluation Masters Booklet, pp. 69–70

Test Generator Software is provided in Apple, IBM, and Macintosh versions. You may use this software to create your own tests, based on the needs of your students.

7 TRIGONOMETRIC IDENTITIES AND EQUATIONS

PREVIEWING THE CHAPTER

This chapter begins with an exploration of the basic trigonometric identities. These identities are used to verify other identities and to find numerical values of trigonometric functions. Building on this knowledge, students learn to use the sum and difference identities, as well as the double-angle and half-angle identities for sine, cosine, and tangent functions. Next, students utilize these skills with identities to solve trigonometric equations. In the last two lessons of the chapter, students learn to write linear equations in normal form and to find the distance between parallel lines and the distance from a point to a line by using equations in normal form.

Lesson Objective Chart

Lesson (Pages)		Lesson Objectives	State/Local Objectives
7-1 (358-363)	7-1:	Identify and use reciprocal identities, quotient identities, Pythagorean identities, and symmetry identies.	
7-2 (364-368)	7-2A:	Use the basic trigonometric identities to verify other identities.	
	7-2B:	Find numerical values of trigonometric functions.	
7-3 (371-376)	7-3:	Use the sum and difference identities for sine, cosine, and tangent functions.	
7-4 (377-383)	7-4:	Use the double- and half-angle identities for the sine, cosine, and tangent functions.	
7-5 (387-391)	7-5:	Solve trigonometric equations.	
7-6 (392-397)	7-6:	Write a linear equation in normal form.	
7-7 (398-405)	7-7A:	Find the distance from a point to a line.	
	7-7B:	Find the distance between parallel lines.	
	7-7C:	Write the equations of lines that bisect angles formed by intersecting lines.	

ORGANIZING THE CHAPTER

You may want to refer to the **Course Planning Guide Calendar** on pages T34-T35 for a complete pacing chart.

Lesson Planning Guide

Lesson	Pages	Practice	Enrichment	Evaluation	Graphing Calculator	Computer	Multicultural Activity	Applications	Problem Solving	Case Study Follow-Up	Decision Making	Transparencies
7-1	358-363	p. 43	p. 43						p. 20			7-1
7-2	364-368	p. 44	p. 44	Quiz A, p. 85								7-2
7-3	371-376	p.45	p.45								p. 21	7-3
7-4	377-383	p. 46	p. 46	Quiz B, p. 85 Mid-Chapter Test, p. 87			p. 7					7-4
7-5	387-391	p. 47	p. 47		p. 13							7-5
7-6	392-397	p. 48	p. 44	Quiz C, p. 86		p. 14		p. 19				7-6
7-7	398-405	p. 49	p. 49	Quiz D, p. 86								7-7
Review	406-408	Multiple Choice Tests, Forms 1A and 1B, pp. 77-80 Free Response Tests, Forms 2A and 2B, pp. 81-84 Standardized Test Questions, p. 88										
Test	409											

Blackline Masters Booklets — Technology — Activity Masters

Other Chapter Resources

Student Edition
Case Study Follow-Up, p. 391
Decision Making, p. 397
Technology, p. 384

Other Supplements
Transparency 7-0 for Chapter Opener
Alternate Assessment in the Mathematics Classroom,
    Glencoe Publishing Co., 1993
Cooperative Learning in the Mathematics Classroom,
    Glencoe Publishing Co., 1993

Software
Test and Review Generator Software
    Available for Apple, IBM, and Macintosh
Teacher's Guide for Software Resources

ENHANCING THE CHAPTER

Cooperative Learning

Planning Teaching Materials

When groups have had substantial experience and exhibit reasonable competence in cooperative-learning skills, you may not have to give much special care to how you arrange materials. However, until that time, you should consider how to distribute materials in order to communicate that the activity is to be a group and not an individual activity. One way to do this is to provide only one set of materials or one copy of the worksheet to the group. The members will quickly realize that they have to work together if they are to be successful in achieving the objective and receiving your recognition. A variation on this method is to provide each member of the group with a worksheet but tell the group that you will collect only one of them, chosen at random. This method also encourages members to help one another and to make sure that each member has and understands the correct answer. A third method, appropriate in some activities, is to give each member only part of the materials or resources required to complete the task. Thus, every member must participate if the whole group is to be successful.

For more information on cooperative learning, see pages T20-T21. Additional information on using cooperative groups is available in Glencoe's *Cooperative Learning in the Mathematics Classroom,* ©1993.

Multicultural

Multicultural Activity Masters, p. 7

Activity Masters

Applications, p. 19

Problem Solving, p. 20

Decision Making, p. 21

The Technology feature following Lesson 7-4 provides a computer program written in BASIC computer language that will find the values of cos 2X and sin 2X and the quadrant in which the terminal side of angle X lies. Students are then asked to modify the program and to write a similar program for other trigonometric functions.

In the Exploration in Lesson 7-2, students use a graphing calculator to verify trigonometric identities by using the graphs of the trigonometric functions. Lesson 7-4B instructs students on using the graphing calculator to determine whether or not an equation may be a trigonometric identity. In Lesson 7-5A, students learn two methods for using a graphing calculator to solve trigonometric equations. In the Exploration in Lesson 7-5, students investigate the ways to use the calculator to verify the solution for a trigonometric equation. The graphing calculator program in Lesson 7-7 finds the distance from a point to a line.

Graphing Calculator Exercises, p. 367
Graphing Calculator Program, p. 404

Outside Resources

Books/Periodicals

Miller, Wayne, et al. *Graphing Calculator Activities for Finite Mathematics,* Brooks/Cole Publishing Co, Pacific Grove, CA, 1992.

Hyman, H. *The Mechanical Universe: Trigonometry Primer & Student Study Notes,* Kendall-Hunt, 1986.

Films/Videotapes/Videodiscs

Mathematics: Trigonometry, Great Plains National, University of Nebraska-Lincoln

Modeling the Universe, Pyramid Films

Software

Graphing utilities that include trigonometric functions (see list on page T25)

Technology Masters

Graphing Calculator, p. 13

Computer, p. 14

CHAPTER 7

TRIGONOMETRIC IDENTITIES AND EQUATIONS

HISTORICAL SNAPSHOT

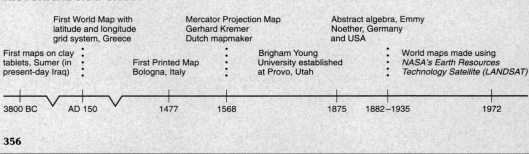

	First World Map with latitude and longitude grid system, Greece		Mercator Projection Map Gerhard Kremer Dutch mapmaker		Abstract algebra, Emmy Noether, Germany and USA	
First maps on clay tablets, Sumer (in present-day Iraq)		First Printed Map Bologna, Italy		Brigham Young University established at Provo, Utah		World maps made using NASA's Earth Resources Technology Satellite (LANDSAT)
3800 BC	AD 150	1477	1568		1875	1882–1935	1972

356

CHAPTER OBJECTIVES

In this chapter, you will:
- Use and verify trigonometric identities.
- Solve trigonometric equations.
- Write the normal form of a linear equation.
- Find the distance from a point to a line and the distance between parallel lines.

CAREER GOAL: Cartography

The political face of the world is constantly changing. Think about the demise of the Soviet Union or the turmoil in Eastern Europe, Western Asia, and Africa. When new political boundaries are formed, cartographers are called upon to make the maps that reflect the changes. Brandon Plewe wants to be a cartographer. He says that "cartography never seems to get stale. It is always new and changing with changes in the world."

Brandon has always had an interest in maps, but never thought it would lead to a career. Instead, he enrolled at BYU in electrical engineering and mathematics. After two years, he decided to take a minor in cartography. "I began to realize that cartography offered new and attractive opportunities for me. Cartography uses computers extensively to draw and analyze maps. It has allowed me to pursue a field in which I have always had an interest, plus allows me to utilize my interest and experience in computers."

Today, cartography involves transforming satellite images into map projections. A satellite image is made up of digital data. Each point, or *pixel*, on this digital image must be converted to its appropriate latitude and longitude. In order to identify the location, each pixel's digital data must be plugged into several different formulas. These cartography formulas often include trigonometry.

Brandon eventually wants to own his own business as a mapmaker, even though he knows that the equipment needed to analyze and produce top quality maps is very expensive. "The world is always changing, so cartographers will always have a job. Making maps is a way to always stay on top of current changes in the world."

READ MORE ABOUT IT

Brown, Lloyd A. *The Story of Maps*. New York: Dover Publications, Inc., 1977.
Jennings, J.H. and S.O. Oduah. *Certificate Map Interpretation*. New York: Cambridge University Press, 1976.
Robinson, Arthur H. and Barbara Bartz Petchenik. *The Nature of Maps*. Chicago: The University of Chicago Press, 1976.

SPOTLIGHT ON...

Brandon Plewe
Age: 23
Class: Senior
School: Brigham Young University, Provo, Utah
Majors: Mathematics and Cartography

"Making maps is a way to always stay on top of current changes in the world."

FOR MORE INFORMATION

If you would like more information about cartography, contact:

American Cartographic Association (ACA)
5410 Grosvenor Lane
Bethesda, MD 20814

Applications

Lesson	Application	Examples	Exercises
7–1	Physics	5	
	Geometry		58
	Language Arts		59
7–2	Optics	2	
	Physics		38
	Civil Engineering		39
7–3	Engineering	2	
	Optics		44
	Geometry		45
7–4	Aeronautics	3	
	Sports		44
	Optics		45
7–5	Optics	4	
	Physics		46
	Optics		47
	Gemology		48
7–6	Manufacturing	2	
	Coordinate Geometry		30
	History		31
7–7	Health	2	
	Entomology		35

Lesson Resources

- Practice Master 7–1
- Enrichment Master 7–1
- Activity Master, p. 20

 Transparency 7–1 contains the 5-Minute Check and a teaching aid for this lesson.

INTRODUCING THE LESSON

 5-Minute Check

(over Chapter 6)

1. Find the values of x for which $\sin x = 0$ is true.
   $180k°$, for any integer k
2. Give the amplitude and period of the function $y = 3 \sin 4\theta$.
   3; 90°
3. Find the value of x in Quadrant I that satisfies $\tan x = \frac{\sqrt{3}}{3}$.
   30°
4. Give the range of Arccos x.
   $0° \leq$ Arccos $x \leq 180°$
5. Find $\sin(\sin^{-1}0.6)$. **0.6**

Motivating the Lesson

Ask students to compare and contrast the following equations:
$x + 3 = 4 \qquad x + 3x = 4x$
Lead them to see that although both statements are equations, the first is true for only one value of the variable, while the second is true for all values. A statement like the second equation is called an *identity*. Have students give some examples of identities.

7-1 Basic Trigonometric Identities

Objective
7–1

After studying this lesson, you should be able to:
- identify and use reciprocal identities, quotient identities, Pythagorean identities, and symmetry identities.

Application

A fly ball soars toward center field as the batter heads toward first base. The ball is an example of a projectile. A formula for the height, h, of a projected object is $h = \frac{v_o^2 \tan^2 \theta}{2g \sec^2 \theta}$, where θ is the measure of the angle of elevation of the initial path of the object, v_o is the initial velocity of the object, and g is the acceleration due to gravity. Is there a simpler way of writing this formula? *This problem will be solved in Example 5.*

In algebra, variables and constants usually represent real numbers. The values of trigonometric functions are also real numbers. Therefore, the language and operations of algebra also apply to trigonometry. Algebraic expressions involve the operations of addition, subtraction, multiplication, division, and exponentiation. These operations are used to form trigonometric expressions. Each expression below is a trigonometric expression.

$$\cos x - x \qquad \sin^2 a + \cos^2 a \qquad \frac{1 - \sec A}{\tan A}$$

Note $\sin^2 A$ and $(\sin A)^2$ are the same, but $\sin A^2$ is not.

A statement of equality between two expressions that is true for *all* values of the variable(s) for which the expressions are defined is called an **identity**. An identity involving trigonometric expressions is a **trigonometric identity**.

Some trigonometric identities were introduced in the discussion of the trigonometric functions. Some of these are reviewed here because they are important in the development of new identities. For example, the definitions of the trigonometric functions are used to derive the **reciprocal identities**.

Reciprocal Identities

The following trigonometric identities hold for all values of A except those for which any function is undefined.

$$\sin A = \frac{1}{\csc A} \qquad \cos A = \frac{1}{\sec A} \qquad \tan A = \frac{1}{\cot A}$$

$$\csc A = \frac{1}{\sin A} \qquad \sec A = \frac{1}{\cos A} \qquad \cot A = \frac{1}{\tan A}$$

You can use the reciprocal identities to find the values of trigonometric functions.

ALTERNATE TEACHING STRATEGIES

Using Cooperative Groups

Have students make a list of trigonometric expressions equal to $\sin x$. For example, $\sin x = \tan x \cos x$. Encourage students to create more involved expressions instead of the simplest expression.

Using Logical Thinking

Have students write an expression that contains all six trigonometric functions and is equal to 3. $\sin^2 x + \cos^2 x + \sec^2 x - \tan^2 x + \csc^2 x - \cot^2 x$

Example 1

If $\tan A = 0.8$, find $\cot A$.

$$\cot A = \frac{1}{\tan A} \qquad \textit{Reciprocal identity}$$

$$= \frac{1}{0.8} \text{ or } 1.25 \qquad \textit{Replace } \tan A \textit{ with } 0.8.$$

The initial definition of the tangent function, $\tan A = \dfrac{\sin A}{\cos A}$, and the reciprocal identities lead us to the **quotient identities**.

Quotient Identities

The following trigonometric identities hold for all values of A, except those for which any function is undefined.

$$\frac{\sin A}{\cos A} = \tan A \quad \longrightarrow \quad \sin A = \cos A \tan A$$

$$\frac{\cos A}{\sin A} = \cot A \quad \longrightarrow \quad \cos A = \sin A \cot A$$

You can use the fact that the graph of $(\cos A, \sin A)$ is a point on the unit circle for all values of A to derive other identities.

$$\sin^2 A + \cos^2 A = 1$$

$$\frac{\sin^2 A}{\cos^2 A} + \frac{\cos^2 A}{\cos^2 A} = \frac{1}{\cos^2 A} \qquad \textit{Divide each side by } \cos^2 A, \textit{ where } \cos^2 A \neq 0.$$

$$\tan^2 A + 1 = \sec^2 A \qquad \textit{Reciprocal identities}$$

The identity $1 + \cot^2 A = \csc^2 A$ can be derived when each side of the equation $\sin^2 A + \cos^2 A = 1$ is divided by $\sin^2 A$. These identities are **Pythagorean identities**.

Pythagorean Identities

The following trigonometric identities hold for all values of A, except those for which any function is undefined.

$$\sin^2 A + \cos^2 A = 1 \qquad \tan^2 A + 1 = \sec^2 A \qquad 1 + \cot^2 A = \csc^2 A$$

Example 2

If $\tan A = \dfrac{2}{5}$, find $\cos A$.

To find $\cos A$, first find $\sec A$.

$$\tan^2 A + 1 = \sec^2 A \qquad \textit{Pythagorean identity}$$

$$\left(\frac{2}{5}\right)^2 + 1 = \sec^2 A \qquad \textit{Replace } \tan A \textit{ with } \frac{2}{5}.$$

$$\frac{29}{25} = \sec^2 A$$

$$\pm\frac{\sqrt{29}}{5} = \sec A$$

Then, find $\cos A$.

$$\cos A = \frac{1}{\sec A} \qquad \textit{Quotient identity}$$

$$= \pm\frac{5}{\sqrt{29}} \text{ or about } \pm 0.93$$

To determine the sign of a function value, you need to know the quadrant in which the angle terminates. The signs of function values in different quadrants are related according to the symmetries of the unit circle. Since we can determine the values of tan A, cot A, sec A, and csc A in terms of sin A and/or cos A with the reciprocal and quotient identities, we only need **symmetry identities** for sin A and cos A.

Symmetry Identities	**The following trigonometric identities hold for any integer k and all values of A.**	
Case 1:	$\sin(A + 360k°) = \sin A$	$\cos(A + 360k°) = \cos A$
Case 2:	$\sin(A + 180°(2k - 1)) = -\sin A$	$\cos(A + 180°(2k - 1)) = -\cos A$
Case 3:	$\sin(360k° - A) = -\sin A$	$\cos(360k° - A) = \cos A$
Case 4:	$\sin(180°(2k - 1) - A) = \sin A$	$\cos(180°(2k - 1) - A) = -\cos A$

An illustration of each case where A is in Quadrant I and $k = 1$ follows.

If A is a quadrantal angle, then neither angle lies within a quadrant. However, the identities still apply.

Case 1: Multiples of 360° are added to A. Since angles measuring A and $A + 360k°$ are coterminal, there is no sign change in the values of sine or cosine.

Case 2: Odd multiples of 180° are added to A and the terminal sides lie in diagonally opposite quadrants. In this case, the signs of both functions change.

Case 3: A is subtracted from multiples of 360° and the terminal sides lie in vertically adjacent quadrants. So only the sign of the sine function is changed.

Case 4: When A is subtracted from odd multiples of 180°, the terminal sides lie in horizontally adjacent quadrants. Only the sign of the cosine function is changed.

To use the symmetry identities with radian measure, replace 180° with π.

Example 3

Express each value as a function of an angle in Quadrant I.

a. **sin 765°**

b. **cos −135°**

a. $765° = 2(360°) + 45°$ *Case 1,*
   $\sin 765° = \sin 45°$ *with $k = 2$*

b. $-135° = 45° + (-180°)$ *Case 2,*
   $\cos -135° = -\cos 45°$ *with $k = 0$*

c. tan 315°

c. $315° = 360° - 45°$ *Case 3, with k = 1*

$$\tan 315° = \frac{\sin 315°}{\cos 315°}$$
$$= \frac{-\sin 45°}{\cos 45°}$$
$$= -\tan 45°$$

The basic trigonometric identities can be used to simplify trigonometric expressions. Simplifying an expression that contains trigonometric functions means that the expression is written as a numerical value or in terms of a single trigonometric function, if possible.

Example 4

Simplify $\sin^2 x + \sin^2 x \tan^2 x$.

$$\sin^2 x + \sin^2 x \tan^2 x = \sin^2 x(1 + \tan^2 x) \quad \textit{Factor.}$$
$$= \sin^2 x \sec^2 x \qquad\qquad \textit{Pythagorean identity}$$
$$= \sin^2 x \cdot \frac{1}{\cos^2 x} \qquad \textit{Reciprocal identity}$$
$$= \tan^2 x \qquad\qquad\qquad \textit{Quotient identity}$$

Now we can solve the application problem presented at the beginning of the lesson.

Example 5

APPLICATION

Physics

Simplify the formula $h = \dfrac{v_o^2 \tan^2 \theta}{2g \sec^2 \theta}$.

$$h = \frac{v_o^2 \tan^2 \theta}{2g \sec^2 \theta}$$

$$= \frac{v_o^2 \left(\dfrac{\sin^2 \theta}{\cos^2 \theta} \right)}{2g \left(\dfrac{1}{\cos^2 \theta} \right)} \qquad tan^2\,\theta = \frac{\sin^2\theta}{\cos^2\theta} \ and \ sec^2\,\theta = \frac{1}{\cos^2\theta}$$

$$= \frac{\dfrac{v_o^2 \sin^2 \theta}{\cos^2\theta}}{\dfrac{2g}{\cos^2\theta}} \qquad \textit{Simplify.}$$

$$= \frac{v_o^2 \sin^2 \theta}{2g} \qquad \text{A simpler formula is } h = \frac{v_o^2 \sin^2 \theta}{2g}.$$

CHECKING FOR UNDERSTANDING

Communicating Mathematics

Read and study the lesson to answer each question. 1–2. See margin.

1. **Describe** what it means to simplify a trigonometric expression.

2. Scientific calculators have keys that will find the sine, cosine, or tangent ratio, but no keys to find the secant, cosecant, or cotangent. Explain why these keys are not necessary.

EVALUATING THE LESSON

Exercises 1–19 are designed to help you assess students' understanding through reading, writing, speaking, and modeling. You should work through Exercises 1–3 with your students and then monitor their work on Exercises 4–19.

Closing the Lesson

Speaking Activity Have students give examples of trigonometric identities and show how each can be used to find the value of one trigonometric function from the value of another.

RETEACHING THE LESSON

Draw a 3-4-5 right triangle on the chalkboard. Have students use the triangle to confirm the reciprocal, quotient, and Pythagorean identities.

Example: $\dfrac{\sin A}{\cos A} = \tan A$

$$\frac{\dfrac{3}{5}}{\dfrac{4}{5}} = \frac{3}{4}$$

$$\frac{3}{4} = \frac{3}{4}$$

Additional Answers

1. Simplifying an expression that contains trigonometric functions means that the expression is written as a numerical value or in terms of a single trigonometric function, if possible.

2. The secant, cosecant, and cotangent can be found by finding the multiplicative inverse of the cosine, sine, or tangent.

Homework Exercises

Assignment Guide

Average: 20–50, 57, 59–69
Enriched: 26–69

The red A, B, and C flags, printed only in the Teacher's Wraparound Edition, indicate the level of difficulty of the exercises.

Additional Answers

3. The identity does not hold true for values of θ for which any of the ratios are undefined.

$\cot \theta = \dfrac{\cos \theta}{\sin \theta}$, is undefined

for $\theta = 0°$ or $180°$.

53. $\pm \sqrt{1 - \sin^2 \theta}$

54. $\pm \dfrac{\sqrt{1 + \cot^2 \theta}}{\cot \theta}$

55. $\pm \dfrac{\sqrt{1 - \cos^2 \theta}}{\cos \theta}$

56. $\pm \dfrac{\sqrt{1 - \cos^2 \theta}}{1 - \cos^2 \theta}$

Practice Masters Booklet, p. 43

---

3. **Explain** why there are some values of θ for which the identity $\cot \theta = \dfrac{\cos \theta}{\sin \theta}$ does not hold and list two specific examples. *See margin.*

Guided Practice

If $\sin A = \dfrac{4}{5}$, and A is in Quadrant I, find each of the following.

4. $\cos A$ $\dfrac{3}{5}$

5. $\tan A$ $\dfrac{4}{3}$

6. $\csc A$ $\dfrac{5}{4}$

Solve for values of θ between and $0°$ and $90°$.

7. If $\tan \theta = 3$, find $\cot \theta$. $\dfrac{1}{3}$

8. If $\sin \theta = \dfrac{5}{13}$, find $\cos \theta$. $\dfrac{12}{13}$

9. If $\cos \theta = \dfrac{2}{3}$, find $\tan \theta$. $\dfrac{\sqrt{5}}{2}$

10. If $\csc \theta = 5$, find $\sec \theta$. $\dfrac{5\sqrt{6}}{12}$

Express each value as a function of an angle in Quadrant I.

11. $\sin 400°$ $\sin 40°$

12. $\tan 475°$ $-\tan 65°$

13. $\cos 220°$ $-\cos 40°$

Simplify.

14. $\csc^2 \theta - \cot^2 \theta$ 1

15. $\dfrac{\sin^2 x + \cos^2 x}{\cos^2 x}$ $\sec^2 x$

16. $\cos y \csc y$ $\cot y$

17. $2\csc^2 \alpha - \csc^4 x + \cot^4 \alpha$ 1

18. $\dfrac{\tan z}{\sin z}$ $\sec z$

19. $\tan A \csc A$ $\sec A$

EXERCISES

Practice

Solve for values of θ between $0°$ and $90°$. 21. undefined

20. If $\cot \theta = 2$, find $\tan \theta$. $\dfrac{1}{2}$

21. If $\sin \theta = 0$, find $\csc \theta$.

22. If $\sec \theta = 4.5$, find $\cos \theta$. $\dfrac{2}{9}$

23. If $\tan \theta = 1$, find $\cot \theta$. 1

24. If $\sin \theta = \dfrac{1}{2}$, find $\cos \theta$. $\dfrac{\sqrt{3}}{2}$

25. If $\tan \theta = \dfrac{\sqrt{3}}{2}$, find $\sec \theta$. $\dfrac{\sqrt{7}}{2}$

26. If $\cot \theta = 0.8$, find $\csc \theta$. $\dfrac{\sqrt{41}}{5}$

27. If $\tan \theta = \dfrac{\sqrt{11}}{2}$, find $\sec \theta$. $\dfrac{\sqrt{15}}{2}$

28. If $\sin \theta = \dfrac{40}{41}$, find $\tan \theta$. $\dfrac{40}{9}$

29. If $\cos \theta = \dfrac{2}{3}$, find $\csc \theta$. $\dfrac{3\sqrt{5}}{5}$

30. If $\cos \theta = \dfrac{3}{5}$, find $\tan \theta$. $\dfrac{4}{3}$

31. If $\tan \theta = \dfrac{7}{2}$, find $\sec \theta$. $\dfrac{\sqrt{53}}{2}$

32. If $\cos \theta = \dfrac{3}{10}$, find $\cot \theta$. $\dfrac{3\sqrt{91}}{91}$

33. If $\tan \theta = \dfrac{1}{2}$, find $\sin \theta$. $\dfrac{\sqrt{5}}{5}$

Express each value as a function of an angle in Quadrant I.

34. $\sin 665°$ $-\sin 55°$

35. $\cos 562°$ $-\cos 22°$

36. $\tan -342°$ $\tan 18°$

37. $\sin (-792°)$ $-\sin 72°$

38. $\csc 850°$ $\csc 50°$

39. $\sec (-210°)$ $-\sec 30°$

Simplify.

40. $\dfrac{\tan x \csc x}{\sec x}$ 1

41. $\dfrac{\cos \theta}{\sec \theta - \tan \theta}$ $1 + \sin \theta$

42. $\tan A \cos^2 A$ $\sin A \cos A$

43. $\sin A \cot A$ $\cos A$

44. $\dfrac{\tan \beta}{\cot \beta}$ $\tan^2 \beta$

45. $\cos x \tan x \csc x$ 1

46. $\dfrac{1}{\sin^2 \theta} - \dfrac{\cos^2 \theta}{\sin^2 \theta}$ 1

47. $\dfrac{\cos^2 A}{1 + \sin A}$ $1 - \sin A$

48. $\dfrac{\csc \beta}{1 + \cot^2 \beta}$ $\sin \beta$

362 CHAPTER 7 TRIGONOMETRIC IDENTITIES AND EQUATIONS

Additional Answer

57. Case 3: $\sin (360k° - A) = -\sin A$ and $\cos (360k° - A) = \cos A$;
Case 4: $\sin ((2k - 1)180° - A) = \sin A$ and
$\cos ((2k - 1)180° - A) = -\cos A$; See students' work for explanations.

49. $\sin^2 A \cos^2 A + \sin^4 A$ $\sin^2 A$

50. $(1 - \sin x)(1 + \sin x)$ $\cos^2 x$

51. $\cos^4 \alpha + 2\cos^2 \alpha \sin^2 \alpha + \sin^4 \alpha$ 1

52. $\sin x + \cos x \tan x$ $2 \sin x$

Write an expression for each of the following in terms of the given function.

53–56. See margin.

53. $\cos \theta$ in terms of $\sin \theta$

54. $\sec \theta$ in terms of $\cot \theta$

55. $\tan \theta$ in terms of $\cos \theta$

56. $\csc \theta$ in terms of $\cos \theta$

Critical Thinking

57. Which of the symmetry identities represents a reflection over the x-axis? over the y-axis? Explain your answer. See margin.

Applications and Problem Solving

58. Geometry The circle at the right is a unit circle with its center at the origin. $\overleftrightarrow{AB}$ and $\overleftrightarrow{CD}$ are tangent to the circle. State which segments represent the ratios $\sin \theta$, $\cos \theta$, $\tan \theta$, $\sec \theta$, $\cot \theta$, and $\csc \theta$. Justify your answers. See margin.

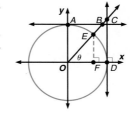

59. Language Arts Look up the word *identity* in a dictionary. Write a few sentences comparing the mathematical meaning and common meanings.
See students' work.

Mixed Review

60. Find the distance between the points at $(2, -5)$ and $(8, -2)$. Then find the slope of the line passing through these points. **(Lesson 1-4)** $3\sqrt{5}, \frac{1}{2}$

61. Is the function $y = 5x^3 - 2x + 5$ odd, even, or neither? **(Lesson 3-1)** neither

62. Without graphing, describe the end behavior of the graph of $y = 2x^2 + 2$.
(Lesson 3-8) As $x \to \infty$, $y \to \infty$; as $x \to -\infty$, $y \to \infty$.

63. State the number of possible positive and negative real zeros of the function $f(x) = x^4 + 2x^3 - 6x - 1$. **(Lesson 4-4)** 1; 3 or 1

64. Change $\frac{15\pi}{16}$ radians to degree measure to the nearest minute. **(Lesson 5-1)** 64. $168°45'$

65. Geometry Each side of a rhombus is 30 units long. One diagonal makes a 25° angle with a side. What is the length of each diagonal to the nearest tenth of a unit? **(Lesson 5-6)** 25.4 units and 54.4 units

66. about 183 miles

66. Navigation A ship at sea is 70 miles from one radio transmitter and 130 miles from another. The angle formed by the rays from the ship to the transmitters measures 130°. How far apart are the transmitters? **(Lesson 5-7)**

67. Find the area of $\triangle ABC$ if $a = 6.2$, $b = 7.5$, and $C = 97°$.
(Lesson 5-8) 23.1 units^2

68. Write an equation with phase shift 0 to represent simple harmonic motion in which the initial position is -6, the amplitude is 6, and the period is 2.
(Lesson 6-7) $y = -6 \cos \pi t$

69. College Entrance Exam Three times the least of three consecutive odd integers is 3 greater than two times the greatest. Find the greatest of the three integers. 15

EXTENDING THE LESSON

Math Power: Problem Solving

Express $\cos x$ in terms of each of the other trigonometric functions. Each expression should contain exactly one function other than the cosine.

Sample answers: $\sqrt{1 - \sin^2 x}$,

$\dfrac{\sqrt{\csc^2 x - 1}}{\csc x}$, $\dfrac{1}{\sec x}$,

$\dfrac{1}{\sqrt{\tan^2 x + 1}}$, $\dfrac{\cot x}{\sqrt{1 + \cot^2 x}}$

Lesson Resources

- Practice Master 7–2
- Enrichment Master 7–2
- Evaluation Master, Quiz A, p. 85

 Transparency 7–2 contains the 5-Minute Check and a teaching aid for this lesson.

INTRODUCING THE LESSON

 5-Minute Check

(over Lesson 7–1)

1. If $\csc x = \frac{8}{5}$, find $\sin x$. $\frac{5}{8}$

2. If $\cot A = \frac{12}{5}$, find $\sin A$. $\pm \frac{5}{13}$

3. Express $\cos 490°$ as a function of an angle in Quadrant I.
   $-\cos 50°$

4. Simplify $\cos^2 x \tan^2 x + \cos^2 x$.
   1

Prerequisite Skills

Students should be familiar with algebraic methods of renaming fractions.

1. Write $\frac{n^2}{3x}$ as a product of two
   fractions. **Sample answer:**
   $\frac{n}{3} \cdot \frac{n}{x}$

2. Find the result of multiplying the numerator and denominator of
   $\dfrac{4\frac{e}{f}}{\frac{1}{f}}$ by f. $4e$

Motivating the Lesson

Have students read the first paragraph of the lesson. Ask them to explain why $\cos \theta$ rather than $\sin \theta$ appears in the first expression for E. Point out that the illumination of the surface will decrease as θ increases. Cos θ, too, decreases as θ increases $(0° < \theta < 90°)$, but $\sin \theta$ increases.

7-2 Verifying Trigonometric Identities

Objectives

After studying this lesson, you should be able to:

7–2A ■ use the basic trigonometric identities to verify other identities, and

7–2B ■ find numerical values of trigonometric functions.

Application

The amount of light that a source provides to a surface is called the illumination. The illumination, E, in footcandles on a surface that is R feet from a source of light with intensity I candelas is $E = \frac{I \cos \theta}{R^2}$, where θ is the measure of the angle between the direction of the light and a line perpendicular to the surface being illuminated. Is the formula $E = \frac{I \cot \theta}{R^2 \csc \theta}$ an equivalent formula? *This problem will be solved in Example 2.*

Verifying trigonometric identities involves transforming one side of the equation into the same form as the other side by using the basic trigonometric identities and the properties of algebra. Either side may be transformed into the form of the other side, or both sides may be transformed separately into other forms that are the same.

Suggestions for Verifying Trigonometric Identities

- **Transform the more complicated side of the equation into the form of the simpler side.**
- **Substitute one or more basic trigonometric identities to simplify the expression.**
- **Factor or multiply to simplify the expression.**
- **Multiply both the numerator and denominator by the same trigonometric expression.**

364 CHAPTER 7 TRIGONOMETRIC IDENTITIES AND EQUATIONS

ALTERNATE TEACHING STRATEGIES

Using Critical Thinking

Use the example below to show why you cannot apply an operation to both sides of an identity to verify it.

Verify that $-2 = 2$.
Solution: Square both sides.
   $4 = 4$
Therefore, $-2 = 2$.

Using Discussion

Have students suggest ways to transform the expression $\sin^2 x - \tan^2 x$ by substitution, factoring, or any other methods they think are appropriate.

Example 1

Remember that you cannot add or subtract quantities from both sides of an identity like we often do with equations.

Verify that $\tan \beta = \dfrac{\cos \beta}{\sin \beta \cot^2 \beta}$ **is an identity.**

Transform the more complicated side of the equation, $\dfrac{\cos \beta}{\sin \beta \cot^2 \beta}$, into the form of the simpler side, $\tan \beta$.

$$\tan \beta \stackrel{?}{=} \frac{\cos \beta}{\sin \beta \cot^2 \beta}$$

$$\tan \beta \stackrel{?}{=} \frac{\cos \beta}{\sin \beta} \cdot \frac{1}{\cot^2 \beta} \qquad \text{\textit{Write as a product of two fractions.}}$$

$$\tan \beta \stackrel{?}{=} \cot \beta \cdot \frac{1}{\cot^2 \beta} \qquad \frac{\cos \beta}{\sin \beta} = \cot \beta$$

$$\tan \beta \stackrel{?}{=} \frac{1}{\cot \beta} \qquad \text{\textit{Multiply.}}$$

$$\tan \beta = \tan \beta \qquad \text{\textit{Reciprocal identity}}$$

The transformation of the right side has produced an expression that is the same as the left side. The identity is verified.

Example 2

APPLICATION

Optics

Refer to the application in the beginning of the lesson. Is the formula $E = \dfrac{I \cos \theta}{R^2}$ **equivalent to the formula** $E = \dfrac{I \cot \theta}{R^2 \csc \theta}$?

$$\frac{I \cos \theta}{R^2} \stackrel{?}{=} \frac{I \cot \theta}{R^2 \csc \theta}$$

$$\frac{I \cos \theta}{R^2} \stackrel{?}{=} \frac{I \dfrac{\cos \theta}{\sin \theta}}{R^2 \dfrac{1}{\sin \theta}} \qquad \cot \theta = \frac{\cos \theta}{\sin \theta}, \csc \theta = \frac{1}{\sin \theta}$$

$$\frac{I \cos \theta}{R^2} \stackrel{?}{=} \frac{I \dfrac{\cos \theta}{\sin \theta}}{R^2 \dfrac{1}{\sin \theta}} \cdot \frac{\sin \theta}{\sin \theta} \qquad \text{\textit{Multiply the numerator and denominator by} } \sin \theta.$$

$$\frac{I \cos \theta}{R^2} = \frac{I \cos \theta}{R^2} \qquad \text{\textit{Simplify.}}$$

Since the expression $\dfrac{I \cot \theta}{R^2 \csc \theta}$ can be transformed into $\dfrac{I \cos \theta}{R^2}$, the two formulas for E are equivalent.

You can use the techniques that you use to verify trigonometric identities to find numerical values of trigonometric functions.

LESSON 7-2   VERIFYING TRIGONOMETRIC IDENTITIES   365

Using Technology

Remind students that by setting each side of the identity equal to *y*, they are creating a system of equations. When the graphs of the system are simultaneous, the system is an identity.

EVALUATING THE LESSON

Exercises 1–12 are designed to help you assess students' understanding through reading, writing, speaking, and modeling. You should work through Exercises 1–2 with your students and then monitor their work on Exercises 3–12.

Practice Masters Booklet, p. 44

Example 3 | Find a numerical value of one trigonometric function of *x* if $\sin x \sec x = 1$.

$\sin x \sec x = 1$

$\sin x \cdot \frac{1}{\cos x} = 1$ $\sec x = \frac{1}{\cos x}$

$\frac{\sin x}{\cos x} = 1$ *Multiply.*

$\tan x = 1$ $\tan x = \frac{\sin x}{\cos x}$

If $\sin x \sec x = 1$, then $\tan x = 1$.

EXPLORATION: Graphing Calculator

You can use a graphing calculator to verify that
$$\csc x = \frac{1 + \sec x}{\sin x + \tan x}$$ is an identity.

1. Use the range values below to set up a viewing window. Mode should be in degrees.
   $-360 \le X \le 360$ $-3 \le Y \le 3$ $XSCL = 90$ $YSCL = 0.25$
2. Let $Y_1 = (1 + 1/\cos x)/(\sin x + \tan x)$ and let $Y_2 = 1/\sin x$.
3. Graph the two functions on the same screen. What do you notice?
   They are the same graph.

CHECKING FOR UNDERSTANDING

Communicating Mathematics

Read and study the lesson to answer each question.

1. **Explain** why you may not use an operation involving both sides of the equation when you are verifying a trigonometric identity. See margin.
2. **Describe** the process you use to verify a trigonometric identity. See students' work.

Guided Practice

Verify that each of the following is an identity. 3–8. See Teacher's Answer Key.

3. $\tan^2 x \cos^2 x = 1 - \cos^2 x$

4. $\csc A \sec A = \cot A + \tan A$

5. $\tan \beta \csc \beta = \sec \beta$

6. $\csc \alpha \cos \alpha \tan \alpha = 1$

7. $\sin \theta \sec \theta \cot \theta = 1$

8. $\sec^2 y - \tan^2 y = \tan y \cot y$

9–12. Sample answers are given.

Find a numerical value of one trigonometric function of each x.

9. $\sin x = \tan x$ $\sec x = 1$

10. $2 \tan x = \cot x$ $\tan x = \pm \frac{\sqrt{2}}{2}$

11. $\sin x = 2 \cos x$ $\tan x = 2$

12. $\tan x \cos x = \frac{1}{2}$ $\sin x = \frac{1}{2}$

366   CHAPTER 7   TRIGONOMETRIC IDENTITIES AND EQUATIONS

RETEACHING THE LESSON

Show how the methods of this lesson can be used to verify simple algebraic identities.

Example 1:
$2m + 6n + 5m - 4n \stackrel{?}{=} 7m + 2n$

$\downarrow$ commutative and
associative properties
$(2m + 5m) + (6n - 4n) \stackrel{?}{=} 7m + 2n$
$\downarrow$
$7m + 2n = 7m + 2n$

Example 2:
Use right triangles to prove identities.

$\tan x \stackrel{?}{=} \frac{\cos x}{\sin x \cot^2 x}$

$\frac{a}{b} \stackrel{?}{=} \frac{b}{c} \div \frac{a}{c} \left(\frac{b}{a}\right)^2$

EXERCISES

Verify that each of the following is an identity. 13–28. See Teacher's Answer Key.

13. $\dfrac{1}{\sec^2 \theta} + \dfrac{1}{\csc^2 \theta} = 1$

14. $\dfrac{\tan x \cos x}{\sin x} = 1$

15. $\dfrac{\sin A}{\csc A} + \dfrac{\cos A}{\sec A} = 1$

16. $\dfrac{1 + \tan^2 \theta}{\csc^2 \theta} = \tan^2 \theta$

17. $\dfrac{1 + \tan \gamma}{1 + \cot \gamma} = \dfrac{\sin \gamma}{\cos \gamma}$

18. $\dfrac{\sec \alpha}{\sin \alpha} - \dfrac{\sin \alpha}{\cos \alpha} = \cot \alpha$

19. $\cos^2 x + \tan^2 x \cos^2 x = 1$

20. $\tan^2 \theta - \sin^2 \theta = \tan^2 \theta \sin^2 \theta$

21. $1 - \cot^4 x = 2 \csc^2 x - \csc^4 x$

22. $\sin \theta + \cos \theta = \dfrac{1 + \tan \theta}{\sec \theta}$

23. $\dfrac{\sec x - 1}{\sec x + 1} + \dfrac{\cos x - 1}{\cos x + 1} = 0$

24. $\sec^4 \alpha - \sec^2 \alpha = \dfrac{1}{\cot^4 \alpha} + \dfrac{1}{\cot^2 \alpha}$

25. $\dfrac{\cos x}{1 + \sin x} + \dfrac{\cos x}{1 - \sin x} = 2 \sec x$

26. $\dfrac{\sec B}{\cos B} - \dfrac{\tan B}{\cot B} = 1$

27. $1 + \sec^2 x \sin^2 x = \sec^2 x$

28. $\dfrac{1 - 2 \cos^2 \theta}{\sin \theta \cos \theta} = \tan \theta - \cot$

29–34. Sample answers are given.
Find a numerical value of one trigonometric function of each x.

29. $2 \sin^2 x = 3 \cos^2 x \;\; \tan x = \pm\dfrac{\sqrt{6}}{2}$

30. $\dfrac{\tan x}{\sin x} = \sqrt{2} \;\; \sec x = \sqrt{2}$

31. $1 - \sin^2 x = \dfrac{1}{9} \;\; \cos x = \pm\dfrac{1}{3}$

32. $\dfrac{\sin x \sec x}{\cot x} = \dfrac{9}{16} \;\; \tan x = \pm\dfrac{3}{4}$

33. $\sec x = \pm 1$ 33. $1 + \tan^2 x = \sin^2 x + \dfrac{1}{\sec^2 x}$

34. $\dfrac{\cos x \tan x}{\csc x} = \dfrac{1}{9} \;\; \sin x = \pm\dfrac{1}{3}$

Graphing Calculator

Use the **SIN**, **COS**, and **TAN** keys on a graphing calculator, together with the basic identities, to find the six trigonometric function values for each degree measure given below. 35–36. See margin.

35. $420°$

36. $-650°$

Critical Thinking

37. Prove each of the following. See margin.
   a. $\sin x + \cos x \geq 1$ if $0° \leq x \leq 90°$

   b. $\tan x + \cot x \geq 2$ if $0° < x < 90°$

Applications and Problem Solving

38. **Physics** A mass weighing w kilograms is at rest on an adjustable plane. The mass begins to slide down the plane when that angle between the plane and the horizontal reaches a certain value θ, known as the angle of repose. The weight of the mass can be expressed in terms of a force parallel to the plane, F_w, and a force perpendicular to the plane, N. Formulas for the magnitudes of F_w and N are $F_w = w \sin \theta$ and $N = w \cos \theta$. Another formula for F_w is $F_w = \mu_s N$, where μ_s is the coefficient of static friction.

   a. Solve $F_w = \mu_s N$ for the coefficient of static friction in terms of θ. $\mu_s = \tan \theta$

   (continued on next page)

LESSON 7-2   VERIFYING TRIGONOMETRIC IDENTITIES   367

Additional Answers

37a. Since $0° \leq x \leq 90°$, then $\sin x \geq 0$ and $\cos x \geq 0$.

Thus, $\sin x \cdot \cos x \geq 0$
$2 \sin x \cdot \cos x \geq 0$
$1 + 2 \sin x \cos x \geq 1$
$\sin^2 x + 2 \sin x \cos x + \cos^2 x \geq 1$
$(\sin x + \cos x)^2 \geq 1$
$\sin x + \cos x \geq 1$

37b. $(\sin x - \cos x)^2 \geq 0$
Thus, $\sin^2 x + \cos^2 x - 2 \sin x \cos x \geq 0$
$\sin^2 x + \cos^2 x \geq 2 \sin x \cos x$
Since $0° < x < 90°$, $\sin x > 0$ and $\cos x > 0$.
Thus $\sin x \cos x > 0$.
Divide by $\sin x \cos x$.

$\dfrac{\sin^2 x}{\sin x \cos x} + \dfrac{\cos^2 x}{\sin x \cos x} \geq 2$

or $\dfrac{\sin x}{\cos x} + \dfrac{\cos x}{\sin x} \geq 2$

and $\tan x + \cot x \geq 2$

---

b. Peg is standing on the wooden plank between the dock and her boat. She is wearing leather-soled shoes, and the plank makes an angle of 24° with the horizontal. What must be the minimum coefficient of static friction of leather on wood? *Hint: Use the formula you found in Exercise 38a.* 0.45

39. Civil Engineering The surface of a section of highway makes an angle of A degrees with the horizontal. An engineer has found that for a particular section, $\dfrac{d^2 - d^2 \cos^2 A}{d^2 - d^2 \sin^2 A} = \dfrac{9}{400}$, where d is the distance along the surface of the road.

a. Make a labeled drawing of the situation. See margin.

b. Find a numerical value for one trigonometric function of A.
$\tan A = \pm\dfrac{3}{20}$

Mixed Review

40. Find $[f \circ g](x)$ and $[g \circ f](x)$ if $f(x) = \dfrac{2}{3}x - 2$ and $g(x) = x^2 - 6x + 9$.
(Lesson 1-2) $\dfrac{2}{3}x^2 - 4x + 4;\ \dfrac{4}{9}x^2 - \dfrac{20}{3}x + 25$

41. Use the remainder theorem to find the remainder for the quotient $(x^4 - 4x^3 - 2x^2 - 1) \div (x - 5)$. Then, state whether the binomial is a factor of the polynomial. **(Lesson 4-3)** 74, no

42. Child Care Melanie King is the manager for the Learning Loft Day Care Center. The center offers all day service for preschool children for $18 per day and after school only service for $6 per day. Fire codes permit only 50 people in the building at one time. State law dictates that a child care worker can be responsible for a maximum of 3 preschool children or 5 school-age children at one time. Ms. King has ten child care workers available to work at the center during the week. How many children of each age group should Ms. King accept to maximize the daily income of the center? **(Lesson 2-6)**

42. 30 preschoolers and 20 school-age

43. A circle has a radius of 12 inches. Find the degree measure of the central angle subtended by an arc 11.5 inches long. **(Lesson 5-2)** 54.9°

44. Simplify $4 \csc \theta \cos \theta \tan \theta$. **(Lesson 7-1)** 4

45. College Entrance Exam Choose the best answer. E
You have added the same positive quantity to the numerator and denominator of a fraction. The result is
(A) greater than the original fraction,
(B) less than the original fraction,
(C) equal to the original fraction,
(D) one-half the original fraction, or
(E) not determinable with the information given.

EXTENDING THE LESSON

Math Power: Connections

Verify that
$$\dfrac{\sin(x+720°)}{1-\cos(x+180°)} = \dfrac{1-\cos(x+360°)}{-\sin(360°-x)}$$

is an identity.

Transform the left side using the symmetry identities.
$$\dfrac{\sin x}{1 - (-\cos x)} =$$

$$\dfrac{1 - \cos x}{1 - \cos x} \cdot \dfrac{\sin x}{1 + \cos x} =$$

$$\dfrac{(1 - \cos x)(\sin x)}{1 - \cos^2 x} =$$

$$\dfrac{(1 - \cos x)(\sin x)}{\sin^2 x} =$$

$$\dfrac{1 - \cos x}{\sin x} =$$

$$\dfrac{1 - \cos x}{-(-\sin x)} =$$

$$\dfrac{1 - \cos(x + 360°)}{-\sin(360° - x)}$$

7-2B Graphing Calculators: Verifying Trigonometric Identities

You can use a graphing calculator to determine whether an equation may be a trigonometric identity by graphing both sides of the equation as two separate functions and then comparing the graphs. If the graphs appear to lay on top of each other, then the equation may be a trigonometric identity. If the graphs do not match, then the equation is not a trigonometric identity. Any equation must be verified algebraically to prove that it is an identity.

Example 1

Use a graphing calculator to determine whether $\tan x + \cot x = \sec x \cdot \csc x$ may be an identity.

Graph the equations $y = \tan x + \cot x$ and $y = \sec x \cdot \csc x$ on the same graph to verify the identity. Use the viewing window $[-360°, 360°]$ by $[-5, 5]$ with a scale of 90° for the x-axis and 1 for the y-axis.

Remember that $\cot x = \dfrac{1}{\tan x}$, $\sec x = \dfrac{1}{\cos x}$, and $\csc x = \dfrac{1}{\sin x}$.

TI-81: [Y=] [TAN] [X|T] [+] [(] 1 [÷] [TAN] [X|T] [)] [ENTER] [(] 1 [÷] [COS] [X|T] [)] [(] 1 [÷] [SIN] [X|T] [)] [GRAPH]

Casio: [Graph] [tan] [ALPHA] [X] [+] [(] 1 [÷] [tan] [ALPHA] [X] [)] [:] [Graph] [(] 1 [÷] [cos] [ALPHA] [X] [)] [(] 1 [÷] [sin] [ALPHA] [X] [)] [EXE]

Since the graphs of the two functions coincide, the equation may be an identity. Verifying algebraically shows that the equation is, in fact, an identity.

The use of parentheses is important when you are graphing complicated fractions or equations involving fractions. Without the parentheses, the calculator may graph something other than the equation you would like it to graph. For example, parentheses must be included when entering the trigonometric function $\tan\left(\dfrac{x}{2}\right)$ or the calculator will graph it as $(\tan x) \div 2$.

Example 2

Use a graphing calculator to determine whether $\cot\left(\dfrac{x}{2}\right) = \dfrac{2\cos x}{1 + 2\sin x}$ may be an identity.

Graph the two equations $y = \cot\left(\dfrac{x}{2}\right)$ and $y = \dfrac{2\cos x}{1 + 2\sin x}$ on the same graph.

(continued on the next page)

GRAPHING CALCULATORS: VERIFYING TRIGONOMETRIC IDENTITIES 369

INTRODUCING THE LESSON

Objective Determine whether an equation may be a trigonometric identity by using a graphing calculator.

Motivating the Lesson

Students may be surprised to find that a graph can be used to help determine whether a statement is provable. Remind them that a solution to an equation can be found by graphing each side of the equation and finding the points of intersection. If an equation is an identity, the graphs of each side of the equation should be identical.

TEACHING THE LESSON

Teaching Tip Ask students what it means for the equation $f(x) = g(x)$ to be an identity. For example, suggest the equation $(x - y)(x + y) = x^2 - y^2$. Ask students what they would do algebraically to show that $f(x) = g(x)$ is *not* an identity.

More Examples

Use a graphing calculator to determine whether each equation may be an identity. Write *yes* or *no*.

a. $\cot x \cdot \cos x = \dfrac{1 - \sin^2 x}{\sin x}$

yes

b. $\cos^4 x - \sin^4 x = (\cos x - \sin x)^4$

no

EVALUATING THE LESSON

Closing the Lesson

Ask students how they might show that $(x + 1)^3 = x^3 + 3x^2 + 3x + 1$ might be an identity.

APPLYING THE LESSON

Homework Exercises

Assignment Guide
All: 1–10

Use the viewing window $[-360°, 360°]$ by $[-3, 3]$ with a scale factor of 90° for the *x*-axis and 1 for the *y*-axis. Remember to use parentheses around the numerator and denominator of the second equation.

TI-81: [Y=] 1 [÷] [TAN] [(] [X|T] [÷]
2 [)] [ENTER] [(] 2 [COS] [X|T]
[)] [÷] [(] 1 [+] 2 [SIN] [X|T] [)]
[GRAPH]

Casio: [Graph] 1 [÷] [tan] [(] [ALPHA]
[X] [÷] 2 [)] [:] [Graph] [(] 2
[cos] [ALPHA] [X] [)] [÷] [(]
1 [+] 2 [sin] [ALPHA] [X] [)]
[EXE]

Since the graphs of the functions do not coincide, the equation is not an identity.

It is important to know that when trying to verify an identity with a squared function, you must first enter the function in parentheses and then square it. For example, to verify $\sin^2 x + \cos^2 x = 1$, you must enter it into your calculator as $(\sin x)^2 + (\cos x)^2$.

EXERCISES

Use a graphing calculator to determine whether each equation *may* be an identity. Write *yes* or *no*.

1. $\cot x - \tan x = 2\cot(2x)$ yes

2. $\tan x \cdot \sin x = \sec x + \cos x$ no

3. $\cos^4 x - \sin^4 x = \cos(2x)$ yes

4. $\dfrac{1 + \cot x}{1 + \tan x} = \dfrac{\sin x}{\cos x}$ no

5. $\cos(x + 90°) = \sin x$ no

6. $\cos(x + 540°) = -\cos x$ yes

7. $\cos^2 x + 1 = 2\cos^2 x + \sin^2 x$ yes

8. $\sec x + \cot x = \dfrac{\sin x + \cos x}{\sin x \cdot \cos x}$ no

9. $2 + \sec^2 x = \tan^2 x$ no

10. $\cot^2 x \cdot \sec^2 x = \csc^2 x$ yes

11. $\cos x = \dfrac{\sin(2x)}{2\sin x}$ yes

12. $\tan\left(\dfrac{x}{2}\right) = \dfrac{\sin x}{1 - \cos x}$ no

13. $\dfrac{1}{\cos x} + \dfrac{1}{\sin x} = 1$ no

14. $\dfrac{\sec^2 x}{1 + \tan^2 x} = \sin^2 x + \cos^2 x$ yes

15. $\sin x(\sin x + \tan x) = 1 + \cos^2 x$ no

16. $\dfrac{\sin x - \cos x}{\cos x} + 1 = \tan x$ yes

17. $\dfrac{\sin x}{\csc x - 1} + \dfrac{\sin x}{\csc x + 1} = 2\tan^2 x$ yes

18. $\csc x + \cot x = \dfrac{\sin x}{1 + \cos x}$ no

7-3 Sum and Difference Identities

Objective
7–3

After studying this lesson, you should be able to:
- use the sum and difference identities for sine, cosine, and tangent functions.

Application

Terri Cox is an electrical engineer designing a three-phase AC-generator. Three-phase generators produce three currents of electricity at one time. They can generate more power for the amount of materials used and lead to better transmission and use of power than single-phase generators can. The three phases of the generator Ms. Cox is making are expressed as $I \cos \theta$, $I \cos (\theta + 120°)$, and $I \cos (\theta + 240°)$. She must show that each phase is equal to the sum of the other two phases but opposite in sign. To do this, she will show that $I \cos \theta + I \cos (\theta + 120°) + I \cos (\theta + 240°) = 0$. *This problem will be solved in Example 2.*

Remember $\overset{\frown}{P_1P_3}$ is the minor arc from P_1 to P_3.

Consider the unit circle on the right. The points P_1, P_2, and P_3 lie on the circle. The measure of $\overset{\frown}{AP_1}$ is s_1. The measure of $\overset{\frown}{P_1P_2}$ and $\overset{\frown}{AP_3}$ is s_2. Therefore, $\overset{\frown}{AP_2}$ is congruent to $\overset{\frown}{P_1P_3}$ since the measure of each is the sum $s_1 + s_2$. Since congruent arcs in the same circle have congruent chords, $\overline{AP_2} \cong \overline{P_1P_3}$.

$$AP_2 = P_1P_3$$
$$\sqrt{(x_2 - 1)^2 + (y_2 - 0)^2} = \sqrt{(x_1 - x_3)^2 + (y_1 - y_3)^2} \quad \textit{Use the distance formula.}$$
$$x_2{}^2 - 2x_2 + 1 + y_2{}^2 = x_1{}^2 - 2x_1x_3 + x_3{}^2 + y_1{}^2 - 2y_1y_3 + y_3{}^2$$
$$(x_2{}^2 + y_2{}^2) - 2x_2 + 1 = (x_1{}^2 + y_1{}^2) + (x_3{}^2 + y_3{}^2) - 2x_1x_3 - 2y_1y_3$$
$$1 - 2x_2 + 1 = \quad 1 \quad + \quad 1 \quad - 2x_1x_3 - 2y_1y_3 \quad \textit{On the unit circle,}$$
$$x_2 = x_1x_3 + y_1y_3 \qquad\qquad\qquad\qquad x^2 + y^2 = 1.$$

FYI...

Generators with more than one phase, called polyphase generators, were developed by Nikola Tesla, a Serbian engineer who immigrated to the United States in 1884. Tesla's invention made it possible to generate current far away from where it was used.

The coordinates of the points on the unit circle allow us to relate s to x and y. Substitute the appropriate functions of s in the equation. Use $x_1 = \cos s_1$, $x_2 = \cos (s_1 + s_2)$, $x_3 = \cos (-s_2)$, $y_1 = \sin s_1$, $y_2 = \sin (s_1 + s_2)$, and $y_3 = \sin(-s_2)$.

$$x_2 = x_1x_3 + y_1y_3$$
$$\cos (s_1 + s_2) = \cos s_1 \cos (-s_2) + \sin s_1 \sin (-s_2) \quad \textit{Substitute.}$$
$$\cos (s_1 + s_2) = \cos s_1 \cos s_2 - \sin s_1 \sin s_2 \quad \textit{cos}(-s_2) = \cos s_2; \sin (-s_2) = -\sin s_2$$

To find an identity for $\cos (s_1 - s_2)$, write $\cos (s_1 - s_2)$ as $\cos [s_1 + (-s_2)]$. Then use the identity above and simplify.

$$\cos [s_1 + (-s_2)] = \cos s_1 \cos (-s_2) - \sin s_1 \sin (-s_2)$$
$$\cos (s_1 - s_2) = \cos s_1 \cos s_2 + \sin s_1 \sin s_2$$

ALTERNATE TEACHING STRATEGIES

Using Patterns

Have students describe the patterns in the signs of the sum and difference identities and suggest methods for remembering the signs.

Using Charts

Have students look at a table of trigonometric functions. Choose two angles (x and y) and have students confirm that $\cos (x + y)$ is not equal to $\cos x + \cos y$, and that $\cos(x - y)$ is not equal to $\cos x - \cos y$.

NCTM Standards: 1–6, 8, 9

Lesson Resources

- Practice Master 7–3
- Enrichment Master 7–3
   Transparency 7–3 contains the 5-Minute Check and a teaching aid for this lesson.

INTRODUCING THE LESSON

 5-Minute Check

(over Lesson 7–2)

Verify that each of the following is an identity. **See Teacher's Wraparound Edition, p. 372.**
1. $\sin x \tan x = \sec x - \cos x$
2. $1 = \tan x \cos x \csc x$
3. $\dfrac{1}{1 - \cos^2 A} = 1 + \cot^2 A$
4. **Find a numerical value of one trigonometric function of x if** $3 \cos x \csc x = 1$.

   $\cot x = \dfrac{1}{3}$ or $\tan x = 3$

Prerequisite Skills

Students should know how to use the distance formula to find the distance between two points in the coordinate plane.
1. Find the distance between the points A (–6,4) and B (6,–1).   **13**
2. Find the distance between the points A (x_1, y_1) and B (x_2, y_2).
   $$\sqrt{(x_2 - x_1)^2 + (y_2 - y_1)^2}$$

Motivating the Lesson

Ask students to use their calculators to check whether the following are true.
$\sin 50° = \sin 40° + \sin 10°$
$\sin 30° = \sin 40° - \sin 10°$
Ask:
- Is $\sin x + \sin y = \sin (x + y)$?
- Is $\sin x - \sin y = \sin (x - y)$?
  no; no

Have students experiment to find out which of these expressions is true:
$\sin(a + b) = \sin a \cos b -$
$\cos a \sin b$
$\sin(a + b) = \sin a \cos b +$
$\cos a \sin b$

Chalkboard Examples

For Example 1

Find cos 75° from values of functions of 30° and 45°.
$\cos 75° = 0.2588$

For Example 2

Use the difference identity for the cosine function to verify the symmetry identity
$\cos(A + 180°) = -\cos A$.

$$\cos(A + 180°) \overset{?}{=} -\cos A$$
$$\cos A \cos 180° -$$
$$\sin A \sin 180° \overset{?}{=} -\cos A$$
$$\cos A\,(-1) - \sin A\,(0) \overset{?}{=} -\cos A$$
$$\cos A = \cos A$$

Teaching Tip Students may question the need for using the difference identity to calculate cos 15° when a calculator does it more simply. Point out that by using the known values for functions of special-triangle angles, an *exact* value can be found for the function of an angle, whereas the calculator gives a decimal approximation.

Replace s_1 with α and s_2 with β so that the cosine of the sum and difference of the measures of two angles are given by the following identities.

Sum and Difference Identities for the Cosine Function	If α and β represent the measures of two angles, then the following identities hold for all values of α and β. $$\cos(\alpha \pm \beta) = \cos \alpha \cos \beta \mp \sin \alpha \sin \beta$$

Note how the addition and subtraction symbols are related in the sum and difference identities.

You can use the sum and difference identities and the values of the trigonometric functions of common angles to find the values of trigonometric functions of other angles. Note that the sum and difference identities may be used if α and β are measured in either degrees or radians. So, α and β may be interpreted as either real numbers or angle measures.

Example 1

Find cos 15° from values of functions of 30° and 45°.

$$\cos 15° = \cos(45° - 30°)$$
$$= \cos 45° \cos 30° + \sin 45° \sin 30°$$
$$= \frac{\sqrt{2}}{2} \cdot \frac{\sqrt{3}}{2} + \frac{\sqrt{2}}{2} \cdot \frac{1}{2}$$
$$= \frac{\sqrt{6} + \sqrt{2}}{4}$$
$$\cos 15° \approx 0.9659$$

We can use the sum identity for the cosine function to solve the application problem from the beginning of the lesson.

Example 2

APPLICATION

Engineering

Show that $I\cos\theta + I\cos(\theta + 120°) + I\cos(\theta + 240°) = 0$.

$$I\cos\theta + I\cos(\theta + 120°) + I\cos(\theta + 240°) \overset{?}{=} 0$$
$$I\cos\theta + I(\cos\theta\cos 120° - \sin\theta\sin 120°) + I(\cos\theta\cos 240° - \sin\theta\sin 240°) \overset{?}{=} 0$$
$$I\cos\theta + I\left(\left(-\frac{1}{2}\right)\cos\theta - \left(\frac{\sqrt{3}}{2}\right)\sin\theta\right) + I\left(\left(-\frac{1}{2}\right)\cos\theta - \left(-\frac{\sqrt{3}}{2}\right)\sin\theta\right) \overset{?}{=} 0$$
$$I\cos\theta - \frac{1}{2}I\cos\theta - \frac{\sqrt{3}}{2}I\sin\theta - \frac{1}{2}I\cos\theta + \frac{\sqrt{3}}{2}I\sin\theta \overset{?}{=} 0$$
$$0 = 0$$

If we replace α with $\frac{\pi}{2}$ and β with s in the identities for $\cos(\alpha \pm \beta)$, the following equations result.

$$\cos\left(\frac{\pi}{2} + s\right) = -\sin s$$
$$\cos\left(\frac{\pi}{2} - s\right) = \sin s$$

Additional Answers

5-Minute Check

1. $$\sin x \tan x \overset{?}{=} \sec x - \cos x$$
    $$\sin x\left(\frac{\sin x}{\cos x}\right) \overset{?}{=} \sec x - \cos x$$
    $$\frac{\sin^2 x}{\cos x} \overset{?}{=} \sec x - \cos x$$
    $$\frac{1 - \cos^2 x}{\cos x} \overset{?}{=} \sec x - \cos x$$
    $$\frac{1}{\cos x} - \frac{\cos^2 x}{\cos x} \overset{?}{=} \sec x - \cos x$$
    $$\sec x - \cos x = \sec x - \cos x$$

2. $$1 \overset{?}{=} \tan x \cos x \csc x$$
    $$1 \overset{?}{=} \frac{\sin x}{\cos x} \cdot \cos x \cdot \frac{1}{\sin x}$$
    $$1 \overset{?}{=} \frac{\sin x}{\sin x} \cdot \frac{\cos x}{\cos x}$$
    $$1 = 1 \cdot 1 \text{ or } 1$$

3. $$\frac{1}{1 - \cos^2 A} \overset{?}{=} 1 + \cot^2 A$$
    $$\frac{1}{1 - \cos^2 A} \overset{?}{=} 1 + \frac{\cos^2 A}{\sin^2 A}$$
    $$\frac{1}{1 - \cos^2 A} \overset{?}{=} \frac{\sin^2 A + \cos^2 A}{\sin^2 A}$$
    $$\frac{1}{1 - \cos^2 A} \overset{?}{=} \frac{1}{\sin^2 A}$$
    $$\frac{1}{1 - \cos^2 A} = \frac{1}{1 - \cos^2 A}$$

Replace s with $\frac{\pi}{2} + s$ in the equation for $\cos\left(\frac{\pi}{2} + s\right)$ and with $\frac{\pi}{2} - s$ in the equation for $\cos\left(\frac{\pi}{2} - s\right)$ to obtain the following equations.

$$\cos s = \sin\left(\frac{\pi}{2} + s\right)$$
$$\cos s = \sin\left(\frac{\pi}{2} - s\right)$$

Replace s with $(\alpha + \beta)$ in the equation for $\cos\left(\frac{\pi}{2} - s\right)$ to derive an identity for the sine of the sum of two real numbers.

$$\cos\left[\frac{\pi}{2} - (\alpha + \beta)\right] = \sin(\alpha + \beta)$$
$$\cos\left[\left(\frac{\pi}{2} - \alpha\right) - \beta\right] = \sin(\alpha + \beta)$$
$$\cos\left(\frac{\pi}{2} - \alpha\right)\cos\beta + \sin\left(\frac{\pi}{2} - \alpha\right)\sin\beta = \sin(\alpha + \beta) \qquad \textit{Use identity for } \cos(\alpha - \beta).$$
$$\sin\alpha\cos\beta + \cos\alpha\sin\beta = \sin(\alpha + \beta) \qquad \textit{Substitute.}$$

Replace β with $(-\beta)$ in the identity for $\sin(\alpha + \beta)$ to derive an identity for the sine of the difference of two real numbers.

$$\sin[\alpha + (-\beta)] = \sin\alpha\cos(-\beta) + \cos\alpha\sin(-\beta)$$
$$\sin(\alpha - \beta) = \sin\alpha\cos\beta - \cos\alpha\sin\beta$$

Sum and Difference Identities for the Sine Function	If α and β represent the measures of two angles, then the following identities hold for all values of α and β. $$\sin(\alpha \pm \beta) = \sin\alpha\cos\beta \pm \cos\alpha\sin\beta$$

Example 3

Find sin 15° from values of functions of 30° and 45°.

$\sin 15° = \sin(45° - 30°)$
$\sin 15° = \sin 45° \cos 30° - \cos 45° \sin 30°$
$$= \frac{\sqrt{2}}{2} \cdot \frac{\sqrt{3}}{2} - \frac{\sqrt{2}}{2} \cdot \frac{1}{2}$$
$$= \frac{\sqrt{6} - \sqrt{2}}{4} \text{ or about } 0.2588$$

We can use the sum and difference identities for the cosine and sine functions to find sum and difference identities for the tangent function.

$$\tan(\alpha + \beta) = \frac{\sin(\alpha + \beta)}{\cos(\alpha + \beta)} \qquad \tan x = \frac{\sin x}{\cos x}$$

$$\tan(\alpha + \beta) = \frac{\sin\alpha\cos\beta + \cos\alpha\sin\beta}{\cos\alpha\cos\beta - \sin\alpha\sin\beta} \qquad \textit{Divide the numerator and denominator by } \cos\alpha\cos\beta.$$

$$\tan(\alpha + \beta) = \frac{\dfrac{\sin\alpha\cos\beta}{\cos\alpha\cos\beta} + \dfrac{\cos\alpha\sin\beta}{\cos\alpha\cos\beta}}{\dfrac{\cos\alpha\cos\beta}{\cos\alpha\cos\beta} - \dfrac{\sin\alpha\sin\beta}{\cos\alpha\cos\beta}} \qquad \textit{Assume } \cos\alpha \neq 0 \textit{ and } \cos\beta \neq 0.$$

$$\tan(\alpha + \beta) = \frac{\tan\alpha + \tan\beta}{1 - \tan\alpha\tan\beta}$$

LESSON 7-3   SUM AND DIFFERENCE IDENTITIES   373

For Example 4

Find tan 15° from values of functions of 45° and 30°.
tan 15° = 0.2679

For Example 5

Verify that tan x = tan $(\pi + x)$ is an identity.

$$\tan x \overset{?}{=} \tan(\pi + x)$$

$$\tan x \overset{?}{=} \frac{\tan \pi + \tan x}{1 - \tan \pi \tan x}$$

$$\tan x \overset{?}{=} \frac{0 + \tan x}{1 - (0)(\tan x)}$$

$$\tan x \overset{?}{=} \tan x$$

EVALUATING THE LESSON

Exercises 1–14 are designed to help you assess students' understanding through reading, writing, speaking, and modeling. You should work through Exercises 1–3 with your students and then monitor their work on Exercises 4–14.

Closing the Lesson

Modeling Activity Label six index cards as follows: sin 30°, sin 45°, cos 30°, cos 45°, +, and −. Have students arrange cards to form the identity for sin 15°, sin 75°, cos 15°, and cos 75°.

Replace β with $-\beta$ to find tan $(\alpha - \beta)$.

$$\tan(\alpha + (-\beta)) = \frac{\tan \alpha + \tan(-\beta)}{1 - \tan \alpha \tan(-\beta)} \qquad \tan(-\beta) = -\tan \beta$$

$$\tan(\alpha - \beta) = \frac{\tan \alpha - \tan \beta}{1 + \tan \alpha \tan \beta}$$

Sum and Difference Identities for the Tangent Function	If α and β represent the measures of two angles, then the following identities hold for all values of α and β. $$\tan(\alpha \pm \beta) = \frac{\tan \alpha \pm \tan \beta}{1 \mp \tan \alpha \tan \beta}$$

Example 4 **Find tan 105° from values of functions of 60° and 45°.**

$$\tan 105° = \tan(60° + 45°)$$
$$= \frac{\tan 60° + \tan 45°}{1 - \tan 60° \tan 45°}$$
$$= \frac{\sqrt{3} + 1}{1 - \sqrt{3} \cdot 1} \qquad \textit{Multiply by } \frac{1 + \sqrt{3}}{1 + \sqrt{3}} \textit{ to simplify.}$$
$$= -2 - \sqrt{3} \text{ or about } -3.7321$$

You can use sum and difference identities to verify other identities.

Example 5 **Verify that cot x = tan $\left(\frac{\pi}{2} - x\right)$ is an identity.**

$$\cot x \overset{?}{=} \tan\left(\frac{\pi}{2} - x\right)$$
$$\cot x \overset{?}{=} \frac{\sin\left(\frac{\pi}{2} - x\right)}{\cos\left(\frac{\pi}{2} - x\right)}$$
$$\cot x \overset{?}{=} \frac{\sin \frac{\pi}{2} \cos x - \cos \frac{\pi}{2} \sin x}{\cos \frac{\pi}{2} \cos x + \sin \frac{\pi}{2} \sin x} \qquad \textit{Use the difference identities.}$$
$$\cot x \overset{?}{=} \frac{1 \cdot \cos x - 0 \cdot \sin x}{0 \cdot \cos x + 1 \cdot \sin x} \qquad \sin \frac{\pi}{2} = 1, \cos \frac{\pi}{2} = 0$$
$$\cot x \overset{?}{=} \frac{\cos x}{\sin x}$$
$$\cot x = \cot x$$

CHECKING FOR UNDERSTANDING

Communicating Mathematics **Read and study the lesson to answer each question.** 1–3. See margin.

1. Is it true that cos $(A + B) = \cos A + \cos B$? Explain your answer.
2. **Describe** a method for finding the exact value of sin 105°. Then find the exact value.
3. **Compare** the identities for cos $(\alpha + \beta)$ and cos $(\alpha - \beta)$. Explain why the signs are different.

RETEACHING THE LESSON

Have students work in pairs to memorize and quiz each other on the sum and difference identities. Then have each student write three problems, one each involving the sine, cosine, and tangent of a sum or difference of two angles, then exchange with another student, and solve.

Additional Answers

1. no; cos $(A + B) = \cos A \cos B - \sin A \sin B$
2. Use the sum identity for the sine function to find sin $(60° + 45°)$. $\frac{\sqrt{6} + \sqrt{2}}{4}$
3. The sign changes because sin $(-\beta) = -\sin \beta$

4–7. See margin.

Guided Practice

Use the sum and difference identities to find the exact value of each function.

4. Find $\cos 105°$ from values of functions of $60°$ and $45°$.
5. Find $\sin 150°$ from values of functions of $120°$ and $30°$.
6. Find $\tan 75°$ from values of functions of $45°$ and $30°$.
7. Find $\cos 150°$ from values of functions of $180°$ and $30°$.

Find the value of each function for $0° < x < 90°$, $0° < y < 90°$, $\sin x = \dfrac{4}{5}$, and $\cos y = \dfrac{3}{5}$.

8. $\sin(x+y)$ $\dfrac{24}{25}$
9. $\cos(x-y)$ 1
10. $\tan(x+y)$ $-\dfrac{24}{7}$

Verify that each of the following is an identity. 11–14. See margin.

11. $\sin(180° - \theta) = \sin\theta$
12. $\cos\left(\dfrac{3\pi}{2} + \theta\right) = \sin\theta$
13. $\tan(270° - x) = \cot x$
14. $\cos(360° - \theta) = \cos\theta$

EXERCISES

Practice

Use the sum and difference identities to find the exact value of each function.

15. $\sin 195°$ $\dfrac{\sqrt{2} - \sqrt{6}}{4}$
16. $\cos 255°$ $\dfrac{\sqrt{2} - \sqrt{6}}{4}$
17. $\tan(-105°)$ $2 + \sqrt{3}$

18. $\sin 75°$
19. $\tan(-195°)$ $\sqrt{3} - 2$
20. $\cos 195°$

18. $\dfrac{\sqrt{6} + \sqrt{2}}{4}$

20. $\dfrac{-\sqrt{6} - \sqrt{2}}{4}$

21. $\tan 165°$ $\sqrt{3} - 2$
22. $\cos 345°$ $\dfrac{\sqrt{6} + \sqrt{2}}{4}$
23. $\sin 285°$ $\dfrac{-\sqrt{6} - \sqrt{2}}{4}$

If α and β are the measures of two first quadrant angles, find the exact value of each function.

24. If $\sin\alpha = \dfrac{5}{13}$ and $\cos\beta = \dfrac{4}{5}$, find $\cos(\alpha + \beta)$. $\dfrac{33}{65}$

25. If $\tan\alpha = \dfrac{4}{3}$ and $\cot\beta = \dfrac{5}{12}$, find $\sin(\alpha - \beta)$. $-\dfrac{16}{65}$

26. If $\cos\alpha = \dfrac{5}{13}$ and $\cos\beta = \dfrac{35}{37}$, find $\tan(\alpha + \beta)$. $\dfrac{480}{31}$

27. If $\sin\alpha = \dfrac{8}{17}$ and $\tan\beta = \dfrac{7}{24}$, find $\cos(\alpha - \beta)$. $\dfrac{416}{425}$

28. If $\csc\alpha = \dfrac{13}{5}$ and $\tan\beta = \dfrac{3}{4}$, find $\tan(\alpha + \beta)$. $\dfrac{56}{33}$

29. If $\cos\alpha = \dfrac{15}{17}$ and $\cot\beta = \dfrac{24}{7}$, find $\sin(\alpha - \beta)$. $\dfrac{87}{425}$

Verify that each of the following is an identity. 30–40. See Teacher's Answer Key.

30. $\sin(270° + x) = -\cos x$
31. $\cos(90° + \theta) = -\sin\theta$
32. $\tan(90° + \theta) = -\cot\theta$
33. $\sin\left(\dfrac{\pi}{2} + x\right) = \cos x$
34. $-\cos\theta = \cos(\pi + \theta)$
35. $\tan(\pi - \theta) = -\tan\theta$
36. $-\sin\theta = \cos\left(\dfrac{\pi}{2} + \theta\right)$
37. $\dfrac{\sin(\beta - \alpha)}{\sin\alpha \sin\beta} = \cot\alpha - \cot\beta$
38. $\sin^2\alpha - \sin^2\beta = \sin(\alpha + \beta)\sin(\alpha - \beta)$
39. $\cos(30° - x) + \cos(30° + x) = \sqrt{3}\cos x$
40. $\cos(\alpha + \beta) + \cos(\alpha - \beta) = 2\cos\alpha\,\cos\beta$

13. $\cot x \overset{?}{=} \tan(270° - x)$

$\cot x \overset{?}{=} \dfrac{\sin(270° - x)}{\cos(270° - x)}$

$\cot x \overset{?}{=} \dfrac{\sin 270° \cos x - \sin x \cos 270°}{\cos 270° \cos x + \sin 270° \sin x}$

$\cot x \overset{?}{=} \dfrac{-1 \cdot \cos x - \sin x \cdot 0}{0 \cdot \cos x + (-1) \sin x}$

$\cot x \overset{?}{=} \dfrac{-\cos x}{-\sin x}$

$\cot x = \cot x$

14. $\cos\theta \overset{?}{=} \cos(360° - \theta)$

$\cos\theta \overset{?}{=} \cos 360° \cos\theta + \sin 360° \sin\theta$

$\cos\theta \overset{?}{=} 1 \cdot \cos\theta + 0 \cdot \sin\theta$

$\cos\theta = \cos\theta$

Enrichment Masters Booklet, p. 45

41–42. See margin.

Derive formulas for each of the following.

41. $\cot(\alpha + \beta)$ in terms of $\cot\alpha$ and $\cot\beta$

42. $\sin(\alpha + \beta + \gamma)$ in terms of functions of α, β, and γ

Critical Thinking

43. Find $\alpha + \beta$ in radians if $\tan\alpha = M$ and $\tan\beta = N$ and $(3M + 3)(2N + 2) = 12$. $\dfrac{\pi}{4} + \pi n$

Applications and Problem Solving

44. Optics   The index of refraction for a medium through which light is passing is the ratio of the velocity of light in free space to the velocity of light in the medium. For light passing symmetrically through a glass prism, the index of refraction, n, is given by the equation $n = \dfrac{\sin\left[\frac{1}{2}(\alpha + \beta)\right]}{\sin\left(\frac{\beta}{2}\right)}$, where α is the deviation angle and β is the angle of the apex of the prism. If $\beta = 60°$, show that $n = \sqrt{3}\sin\left(\frac{\alpha}{2}\right) + \cos\left(\frac{\alpha}{2}\right)$.

44. See Teacher's Answer Key.

45. Geometry   The slope of a line, m, is equal to the tangent of the angle that the line makes with the x-axis. Let θ be the measure of the smaller angle formed by the intersection of the lines ℓ and n. Lines ℓ and n make angles measuring α and β, respectively, with the x-axis. The slopes of lines ℓ and n are m_1 and m_2, respectively. Find an expression for $\tan\theta$ in terms of m_1 and m_2.
$\tan\theta = \dfrac{m_2 - m_1}{1 - m_2 m_1}$

Mixed Review

46. Solve the system algebraically. **(Lesson 2-1)**
$5x - 2y = 9$
$y = 3x - 1$ $(-7, -22)$

47. $y = 2x - 7$

47. Find the equation of the line tangent to the graph of $y = \frac{1}{2}x^2 - 2x + 1$ at $(4, 1)$. Write the equation in slope-intercept form. **(Lesson 3-7)**

48. $x = \dfrac{3 \pm i\sqrt{35}}{4}$

48. Solve the equation $y = 4x^2 - 6x + 11 = 0$ by using the quadratic formula. **(Lesson 4-2)**

49. Find the value of $\csc 270°$ without using a calculator. **(Lesson 5-3)** -1

50. Solve $\triangle ABC$ if $a = 7$, $b = 9$, and $c = 13$. Round angle measures to the nearest minute. **(Lesson 5-6)** $A = 30°48'$, $B = 41°10'$, $C = 108°2'$

51. See Teacher's Answer Key.

51. Verify that $2\sec^2 x = \dfrac{1}{1 + \sin x} + \dfrac{1}{1 - \sin x}$ is an identity. **(Lesson 7-2)**

52. College Entrance Exam   Compare quantities A and B below.   A
Write A if quantity A is greater.
Write B if quantity B is greater.
Write C if the quantities are equal.
Write D if there is not enough information to determine the relationship.

  (A) $7x + 1$ **(B)** $7x - 1$

376   CHAPTER 7   TRIGONOMETRIC IDENTITIES AND EQUATIONS

EXTENDING THE LESSON

Math Power: Problem Solving

Use the identity for $\sin(x + y)$ to derive and simplify an identity for $\sin(x + y + z)$.

$\sin x \cos y \cos z + \cos x \sin y \cos z + \cos x \cos y \sin z - \sin x \sin y \sin z$

7-4 Double-Angle and Half-Angle Identities

Objective
7–4

After studying this lesson, you should be able to:
- use the double- and half-angle identities for the sine, cosine, and tangent functions.

Application

On October 14, 1947, Charles Yeager flew a Bell X-1 rocket airplane to become the first person to fly faster than the speed of sound. The speed of sound is called mach 1. When an airplane exceeds the speed of sound, about 739 mph, a shock wave in the shape of a cone is formed from the nose of the plane. The shock wave produces a sonic boom as it passes. If B is the measure of the angle at the vertex of the cone, and M is the mach number where $M > 1$, the equation $\frac{1}{M} = \sin\left(\frac{B}{2}\right)$ holds. Write this equation in terms of functions of B. Suppose an aircraft forms a cone whose vertex angle measures 45°. What is its speed in relation to the speed of sound; that is, what is its mach number? *This problem will be solved in Example 3.*

As demonstrated in this application, it is sometimes useful to have identities to find the value of a function of twice an angle or half an angle. We can substitute θ for both α and β in $\sin(\alpha + \beta)$ to find an identity for $\sin 2\theta$.

$$\sin 2\theta = \sin(\theta + \theta) \qquad \text{\textit{Substitute } } \theta \text{ \textit{for} } \alpha \text{ \textit{and} } \beta.$$
$$= \sin\theta\cos\theta + \cos\theta\sin\theta$$
$$= 2\sin\theta\cos\theta$$

The same method can be used to find an identity for $\cos 2\theta$.

$$\cos 2\theta = \cos(\theta + \theta)$$
$$= \cos\theta\cos\theta - \sin\theta\sin\theta$$
$$= \cos^2\theta - \sin^2\theta$$

If we substitute $1 - \cos^2\theta$ for $\sin^2\theta$ or $1 - \sin^2\theta$ for $\cos^2\theta$, we will have two alternate identities for $\cos 2\theta$.

$$\cos 2\theta = 2\cos^2\theta - 1$$
$$\cos 2\theta = 1 - 2\sin^2\theta$$

These identities may be used if θ is measured in degrees or radians. So, θ may represent either a degree measure or real number.

LESSON 7-4   DOUBLE-ANGLE AND HALF-ANGLE IDENTITIES   377

ALTERNATE TEACHING STRATEGIES

Using Logical Thinking

To give students practice in deciding which sign to use in half-angle exercises, state the measure of an angle and have students tell the sign of the sine, cosine, and tangent of half the angle.

Using Connections

As an alternative to the method used to derive $\tan 2\theta$ in the lesson, ask students to explain how they could derive the identity using those for $\sin 2\theta$ and $\cos 2\theta$.
$$\tan 2\theta = \frac{\sin 2\theta}{\cos 2\theta}$$

NCTM Standards: 1–6, 9

Lesson Resources

- Practice Master 7–4
- Enrichment Master 7–4
- Evaluation Master, Quiz B, p. 85
- Multicultral Activity, p. 7

 Transparency 7–4 contains the 5-Minute check and a teaching aid for this lesson.

INTRODUCING THE LESSON

5-Minute Check
(over Lesson 7–3)

θ	20°	35°
cos	0.940	0.819
sin	0.342	0.574
tan	0.364	0.700

Use the values in the chart to find the value of each function.
1. cos 55°   **0.574**
2. sin 15°   **0.259**
3. tan 15°   **0.268**
4. Verify that $\cos(90° + x) = -\sin x$ is an identity.

$$\cos(90° + x) \overset{?}{=} -\sin x$$
$$\cos 90° \cos x - $$
$$\sin 90° \sin x \overset{?}{=} -\sin x$$
$$0(\cos x) - 1(\sin x) \overset{?}{=} -\sin x$$
$$-\sin x = -\sin x$$

Motivating the Lesson

Conjecture: If you double the sine of an angle, you obtain the sine of an angle twice the measure of the first. That is, $2\sin x = \sin 2x$.

Ask students to give evidence supporting or contradicting this conjecture.

Teaching Tip When discussing the double-angle and half-angle identities, ask students to explain how they could find similar identities for the cosecant, secant, and cotangent functions. Find and simplify reciprocals of the sine, cosine, and tangent identities, respectively.

The tangent of a double angle can be found by substituting θ for both α and β in $\tan(\alpha+\beta)$.

$$\tan(\theta+\theta) = \frac{\tan\theta + \tan\theta}{1 - \tan\theta\tan\theta}$$
$$= \frac{2\tan\theta}{1 - \tan^2\theta}$$

If θ represents the measure of an angle, then the following identities hold for all values of θ.

Double-Angle Identities

$$\sin 2\theta = 2\sin\theta\cos\theta$$
$$\cos 2\theta = \cos^2\theta - \sin^2\theta$$
$$= 2\cos^2\theta - 1$$
$$= 1 - 2\sin^2\theta$$
$$\tan 2\theta = \frac{2\tan\theta}{1 - \tan^2\theta}$$

Example 1

If $\cos\theta = \dfrac{\sqrt{5}}{5}$ and θ terminates in the first quadrant, find the exact value of each function.

a. $\cos 2\theta$

a. Since we know $\cos\theta$, we will use the identity $\cos 2\theta = 2\cos^2\theta - 1$.

$$\cos 2\theta = 2\cos^2\theta - 1$$
$$= 2\left(\frac{\sqrt{5}}{5}\right)^2 - 1$$
$$= -\frac{3}{5}$$

b. $\sin 2\theta$

b. To use the identity for $\sin 2\theta$, we must first find $\sin\theta$.

$$\sin^2\theta + \cos^2\theta = 1 \qquad\qquad \sin 2\theta = 2\sin\theta\cos\theta$$
$$\sin^2\theta + \left(\frac{\sqrt{5}}{5}\right)^2 = 1 \qquad\qquad = 2\left(\frac{2\sqrt{5}}{5}\right)\left(\frac{\sqrt{5}}{5}\right)$$
$$\sin^2\theta = \frac{4}{5} \qquad\qquad\qquad = \frac{4}{5}$$
$$\sin\theta = \frac{2\sqrt{5}}{5}$$

c. $\tan 2\theta$

c. We must find $\tan\theta$ to use the identity for $\tan 2\theta$.

$$\tan\theta = \frac{\sin\theta}{\cos\theta} \qquad\qquad \tan 2\theta = \frac{2\tan\theta}{1 - \tan^2\theta}$$
$$= \frac{\frac{2\sqrt{5}}{5}}{\frac{\sqrt{5}}{5}} \qquad\qquad\quad = \frac{2(2)}{1 - (2)^2}$$
$$= 2 \qquad\qquad\qquad = -\frac{4}{3}$$

If we solve the two alternate forms of the identity for $\cos 2\theta$ for $\cos \theta$ and $\sin \theta$ respectively, the following equations result.

$$\cos \theta = \pm\sqrt{\frac{1 + \cos 2\theta}{2}}$$

$$\sin \theta = \pm\sqrt{\frac{1 - \cos 2\theta}{2}}$$

Since θ is a real number, 2θ can be replaced with α and θ can be replaced with $\frac{\alpha}{2}$ to derive the identities for half of any angle measure. The identity for the tangent of half of an angle is found by dividing $\sin \frac{\alpha}{2}$ by $\cos \frac{\alpha}{2}$.

$$\tan \frac{\alpha}{2} = \frac{\pm\sqrt{\dfrac{1 - \cos \alpha}{2}}}{\pm\sqrt{\dfrac{1 + \cos \alpha}{2}}}$$

$$= \pm\sqrt{\frac{1 - \cos \alpha}{1 + \cos \alpha}}$$

Half-Angle Identities

If α represents the measure of an angle, then the following identities hold for all values of α.

$$\sin \frac{\alpha}{2} = \pm\sqrt{\frac{1 - \cos \alpha}{2}} \qquad \cos \frac{\alpha}{2} = \pm\sqrt{\frac{1 + \cos \alpha}{2}}$$

$$\tan \frac{\alpha}{2} = \pm\sqrt{\frac{1 - \cos \alpha}{1 + \cos \alpha}} \; (\cos \alpha \neq -1)$$

Example 2

Use a half-angle identity to find the exact value of each function.

a. $\sin 15°$

a. $\sin 15° = \sin \dfrac{30°}{2}$

$$= \pm\sqrt{\frac{1 - \cos 30°}{2}}$$

$$= \pm\sqrt{\frac{1 - \dfrac{\sqrt{3}}{2}}{2}}$$

$$= \pm\frac{\sqrt{2 - \sqrt{3}}}{2}$$

Since $15°$ is a first quadrant angle and sine is positive in the first quadrant, choose the positive value. Thus, $\sin 15° = \dfrac{\sqrt{2 - \sqrt{3}}}{2}$.

(continued on the next page)

LESSON 7-4 DOUBLE-ANGLE AND HALF-ANGLE IDENTITIES   379

Chalkboard Example

For Example 2

Use a half-angle identity to find the exact value of tan 15°.

$2 - \sqrt{3}$

LESSON 7–4   DOUBLE-ANGLE AND HALF-ANGLE IDENTITIES   379

b. **cos 135°**

b. $\cos 135° = \cos \dfrac{270°}{2}$

$= \pm\sqrt{\dfrac{1 + \cos 270°}{2}}$

$= \pm\sqrt{\dfrac{1 + 0}{2}}$

$= \pm\dfrac{\sqrt{2}}{2}$

Since 135° is a second quadrant angle and cosine is negative in the second quadrant, choose the negative value. Thus, $\cos 135° = -\dfrac{\sqrt{2}}{2}$.

We can use the half-angle identity for the sine function to solve the application problem from the beginning of the lesson.

Example 3

APPLICATION

Aeronautics

Write the equation $\dfrac{1}{M} = \sin\left(\dfrac{B}{2}\right)$ in terms of functions of *B*. What is the speed in relation to sound or the mach number of an aircraft that forms a cone whose vertex angle measures 45°?

$\dfrac{1}{M} = \sin\left(\dfrac{B}{2}\right)$

$\dfrac{1}{M} = \pm\sqrt{\dfrac{1 - \cos B}{2}}$

If the angle of the cone measures 45°, $B = 45$.

$\dfrac{1}{M} = \pm\sqrt{\dfrac{1 - \cos 45°}{2}}$

$\dfrac{1}{M} = \sqrt{\dfrac{1 - \frac{\sqrt{2}}{2}}{2}}$ *45° is in Quadrant I, so use the positive value.*

$\dfrac{1}{M} = \dfrac{\sqrt{2 - \sqrt{2}}}{2}$

$M = \dfrac{2}{\sqrt{2 - \sqrt{2}}}$

$M \approx 2.6$

The speed of the aircraft is about mach 2.6. So, the speed of the aircraft is about 2.6 times the speed of sound.

The double- and half-angle identities can also be used to verify other identities.

380   CHAPTER 7   TRIGONOMETRIC IDENTITIES AND EQUATIONS

15. $\sin 2x \overset{?}{=} 2 \cot x \sin^2 x$

$\sin 2x \overset{?}{=} \dfrac{2 \cos x}{\sin x} \cdot \dfrac{\sin^2 x}{1}$

$\sin 2x \overset{?}{=} 2 \cos x \sin x$

$\sin 2x = \sin 2x$

16. $\sin^2 \theta \overset{?}{=} \dfrac{1}{2}(1 - \cos 2\theta)$

$\sin^2 \theta \overset{?}{=} \dfrac{1}{2}(1 - 1 + 2\sin^2 \theta)$

$\sin^2 \theta \overset{?}{=} \dfrac{1}{2}(2 \sin^2 \theta)$

$\sin^2 \theta = \sin^2 \theta$

Example 4

Verify that $\tan \dfrac{x}{2} = \dfrac{1 - \cos x}{\sin x}$ **is an identity for** $0° < x < 90°$.

$$\tan \dfrac{x}{2} \overset{?}{=} \dfrac{1 - \cos x}{\sin x}$$

$$\sqrt{\dfrac{1 - \cos x}{1 + \cos x}} \overset{?}{=} \left(\dfrac{1 - \cos x}{\sin x}\right)\left(\dfrac{1 + \cos x}{1 + \cos x}\right)$$

Use the half-angle identity for tangent. Consider only the positive value since x is in the first quadrant.

$$\left(\sqrt{\dfrac{1 - \cos x}{1 + \cos x}}\right)\left(\sqrt{\dfrac{1 + \cos x}{1 + \cos x}}\right) \overset{?}{=} \dfrac{1 - \cos^2 x}{\sin x\,(1 + \cos x)}$$

$$\sqrt{\dfrac{1 - \cos^2 x}{(1 + \cos x)^2}} \overset{?}{=} \dfrac{\sin^2 x}{\sin x\,(1 + \cos x)}$$

Simplify.

$$\sqrt{\dfrac{\sin^2 x}{(1 + \cos x)^2}} \overset{?}{=} \dfrac{\sin x}{(1 + \cos x)}$$

$$\dfrac{\sin x}{1 + \cos x} = \dfrac{\sin x}{1 + \cos x}$$

Chalkboard Example

For Example 4

Verify that $1 - \cos 2x \sec^2 x = \tan^2 x$ **is an identity.**

$$1 - \cos 2x \sec^2 x \overset{?}{=} \tan^2 x$$

$$1 - \dfrac{1 - 2\sin^2 x}{\cos^2 x} \overset{?}{=} \tan^2 x$$

$$\dfrac{\cos^2 x - (1 - 2\sin^2 x)}{\cos^2 x} \overset{?}{=} \tan^2 x$$

$$\dfrac{(\cos^2 x - 1) + 2\sin^2 x}{\cos^2 x} \overset{?}{=} \tan^2 x$$

$$\dfrac{-\sin^2 x + 2\sin^2 x}{\cos^2 x} \overset{?}{=} \tan^2 x$$

$$\dfrac{\sin^2 x}{\cos^2 x} \overset{?}{=} \tan^2 x$$

$$\tan^2 x = \tan^2 x$$

CHECKING FOR UNDERSTANDING

Communicating Mathematics

Read and study the lesson to answer each question. 1–2. See margin.

1. **Compare** the three identities for $\cos 2\theta$. Under what conditions would you choose to use each one?

2. **Explain** how you determine the sign of a result of a double- or half-angle identity.

3. For each angle in standard position, name the quadrant in which the terminal side lies.
   a. x is a second quadrant angle. In which quadrant does $2x$ lie? III or IV
   b. $\dfrac{x}{2}$ is a first quadrant angle. In which quadrant does x lie? I or II
   c. $2x$ is a second quadrant angle. In which quadrant does $\dfrac{x}{2}$ lie? I, II, III, or IV

Guided Practice

If $\sin A = \dfrac{3}{5}$ **and** A **is in the first quadrant, find each value.**

4. $\cos 2A$ $\dfrac{7}{25}$ 5. $\tan 2A$ $\dfrac{24}{7}$ 6. $\sin 2A$ $\dfrac{24}{25}$

7. $\sin \dfrac{A}{2}$ $\dfrac{\sqrt{10}}{10}$ 8. $\cos \dfrac{A}{2}$ $\dfrac{3\sqrt{10}}{10}$ 9. $\tan \dfrac{A}{2}$ $\dfrac{1}{3}$

Use a half-angle identity to find each value. 10–12. See margin.

10. $\sin 22°30'$ 11. $\cos 22°30'$ 12. $\tan 22°30'$

Verify that each of the following is an identity. 13–16. See margin.

13. $\dfrac{1}{2}\sin 2A = \dfrac{\tan A}{1 + \tan^2 A}$ 14. $\tan 2x \tan x + 2 = \dfrac{\tan 2x}{\tan x}$

15. $\sin 2x = 2 \cot x \sin^2 x$ 16. $\sin^2 \theta = \dfrac{1}{2}(1 - \cos 2\theta)$

LESSON 7-4   DOUBLE-ANGLE AND HALF-ANGLE IDENTITIES   381

EVALUATING THE LESSON

Exercises 1–16 are designed to help you assess students' understanding through reading, writing, speaking, and modeling. You should work through Exercises 1–3 with your students and then monitor their work on Exercises 4–16.

Closing the Lesson

Speaking Activity Ask students the following questions.
- How can you use the sum identities to derive the double-angle identities?
  Substitute θ **for both** α **and** β.
- How can you use the double-angle identities to find the half-angle identities?
  Substitute α **for** 2θ.

RETEACHING THE LESSON

This lesson gives the last of the basic trigonometric identities students will need to know. Have small groups prepare index card pairs for each identity, writing the left side of the identity on one card, the right side on the other. Groups should then shuffle the cards, deal them face down, and play Concentration.

APPLYING THE LESSON

Homework Exercises

Assignment Guide

Average: 17–28, 29–39 odd, 41, 43, 44, 46–52

Enriched: 18–32 even, 33–52

All: Mid-Chapter Review, 1–10

The red A, B, and C flags, printed only in the Teacher's Wraparound Edition, indicate the level of difficulty of the exercises.

Chapter 7, Quiz B, (Lessons 7–3 through 7–4), is available in the *Evaluation Masters*, p. 85.

Additional Answers

23. $\dfrac{\sqrt{2+\sqrt{3}}}{2}$ 24. $-\dfrac{\sqrt{2+\sqrt{3}}}{2}$

25. $2-\sqrt{3}$ 26. $\dfrac{\sqrt{2-\sqrt{3}}}{2}$

27. $\dfrac{\sqrt{2-\sqrt{2}}}{2}$ 28. $2-\sqrt{3}$

41. $\sin 3\alpha = \sin(2\alpha + \alpha)$
$= \sin 2\alpha \cos \alpha + \sin \alpha \cos 2\alpha$
$= (2 \sin \alpha \cos \alpha) \cos \alpha +$
  $\sin \alpha (1 - 2 \sin^2\alpha)$
$= 2 \sin \alpha \cos^2 \alpha + \sin \alpha -$
  $2 \sin^3 \alpha$
$= 2 \sin \alpha (1 - \sin^2 \alpha) + \sin \alpha -$
  $2 \sin^3 \alpha$
$= 2 \sin \alpha - 2 \sin^3\alpha + \sin\alpha -$
  $2 \sin^3 \alpha$
$= 3 \sin \alpha - 4 \sin^3 \alpha$

Practice Masters Booklet, p. 46

Practice   If $\tan y = \dfrac{5}{12}$ and y is in the third quadrant, find each value.

17. $\sin 2y$ $\dfrac{120}{169}$ 18. $\tan 2y$ $\dfrac{120}{119}$ 19. $\sin \dfrac{y}{2}$ $\dfrac{5\sqrt{26}}{26}$

20. $\cos 2y$ $\dfrac{119}{169}$ 21. $\tan \dfrac{y}{2}$ -5 22. $\cos \dfrac{y}{2}$ $-\dfrac{\sqrt{26}}{26}$

Use a half-angle identity to find each value. 23–28. See margin.

23. $\sin 105°$ 24. $\cos \dfrac{13\pi}{12}$ 25. $\tan 195°$

26. $\cos \dfrac{19\pi}{12}$ 27. $\sin \dfrac{7\pi}{8}$ 28. $\tan \dfrac{13\pi}{12}$

Verify that each of the following is an identity. 29–40. See Teacher's Answer Key.

29. $1 + \cos 2A = \dfrac{2}{1 + \tan^2 A}$ 30. $\cos^2 2x + 4 \sin^2 x \cos^2 x = 1$

31. $\csc A \sec A = 2 \csc 2A$ 32. $\dfrac{1 - \tan^2 \theta}{1 + \tan^2 \theta} = \cos 2\theta$

33. $\cot X = \dfrac{\sin 2X}{1 - \cos 2X}$ 34. $\dfrac{1 + \cos x}{\sin x} = \cot \dfrac{x}{2}$

35. $\sin 2B (\cot B + \tan B) = 2$ 36. $1 - \sin A = \left(\sin \dfrac{A}{2} - \cos \dfrac{A}{2}\right)^2$

37. $\cot \dfrac{\alpha}{2} = \dfrac{\sin \alpha}{1 - \cos \alpha}$ 38. $\tan \dfrac{x}{2} = \dfrac{\sin x}{1 + \cos x}$

39. $\dfrac{\cos 2A}{1 + \sin 2A} = \dfrac{\cot A - 1}{\cot A + 1}$ 40. $\dfrac{\sin \alpha + \sin 3\alpha}{\cos \alpha + \cos 3\alpha} = \tan 2\alpha$

Derive a formula for each of the following. 41–42. See margin.

41. $\sin 3\alpha$ in terms of $\sin \alpha$

42. $\cos 3\alpha$ in terms of $\cos \alpha$

Critical Thinking

43. Explain how you would find $\sin A$ if $\sin 4A = \dfrac{2}{3}$ and the terminal side of $4A$ lies in the second quadrant. Then find $\sin A$. See margin.

Applications and Problem Solving

44. **Sports** Betsy King, one of the champions of women's golf, hit a golf ball with an initial velocity of 100 feet per second. The distance that a golf ball travels is found by the formula $d = \dfrac{v_o^2}{g} \sin 2\theta$, where v_o is the initial velocity, g is the acceleration due to gravity, and θ is the measure of the angle that the initial path of the ball makes with the ground. The acceleration due to gravity is 32 ft/s².

382   CHAPTER 7   TRIGONOMETRIC IDENTITIES AND EQUATIONS

---

42. $\cos 3\alpha = \cos(2\alpha + \alpha)$
$= \cos 2\alpha \cos \alpha - \sin 2\alpha \sin \alpha$
$= (2 \cos^2 \alpha - 1) \cos \alpha -$
  $(2 \sin \alpha \cos \alpha) \sin \alpha$
$= 2 \cos^3 \alpha - \cos \alpha -$
  $2 \sin^2 \alpha \cos \alpha$
$= 2 \cos^3 \alpha - \cos \alpha -$
  $2(1 - \cos^2 \alpha) \cos \alpha$
$= 2 \cos^3 \alpha - \cos \alpha - 2 \cos \alpha +$
  $2 \cos^3 \alpha$
$= 4 \cos^3 \alpha - 3 \cos \alpha$

43. See students' work;
$\dfrac{\sqrt{18 - 3\sqrt{18 - 6\sqrt{5}}}}{6}$

44a. $d = \dfrac{2v_o^2}{g} \sin \theta \cos \theta$

44c. 45°; The greatest value of the sine function is 1 and $\sin 2\theta = 1$ when $\theta = 45°$.

7-4
NAME _____ DATE _____

Practice Worksheet

Double-Angle and Half-Angle Identities

If $\sin A = \frac{12}{13}$ and A is in the first quadrant, find each value.

1. $\cos 2A$
$-\dfrac{119}{169}$

2. $\sin 2A$
$\dfrac{120}{169}$

3. $\tan 2A$
$-\dfrac{120}{119}$

4. $\cos \frac{A}{2}$
$\dfrac{3\sqrt{13}}{13}$

5. $\sin \frac{A}{2}$
$\dfrac{2\sqrt{13}}{13}$

6. $\tan \frac{A}{2}$
$\dfrac{2}{3}$

Use a half-angle identity to find each value.

7. $\tan \frac{\pi}{8}$
$\sqrt{\dfrac{2-\sqrt{2}}{2+\sqrt{2}}}$

8. $\cos \frac{5\pi}{8}$
$\dfrac{\sqrt{2}}{2}$

9. $\sin \frac{19\pi}{12}$
$-\dfrac{\sqrt{2+\sqrt{3}}}{2}$

10. $\cos 67\frac{1}{2}°$
$\dfrac{\sqrt{2-\sqrt{2}}}{2}$

Verify that each of the following is an identity.

11. $\tan \frac{A}{2} = \frac{\sin A}{1 + \cos A}$
$\tan \dfrac{A}{2} = \sqrt{\dfrac{1 - \cos A}{1 + \cos A}} \cdot \sqrt{\dfrac{1 + \cos A}{1 + \cos A}}$
$= \sqrt{\dfrac{1 - \cos^2 A}{(1 + \cos A)^2}}$
$= \dfrac{\sin A}{1 + \cos A}$

12. $\tan \frac{A}{2} = \frac{1 - \cos A}{\sin A}$
$\tan \dfrac{A}{2} = \dfrac{\sin A}{1 + \cos A} \cdot \dfrac{1 - \cos A}{1 - \cos A}$
$= \dfrac{\sin A (1 - \cos A)}{1 - \cos^2 A}$
$= \dfrac{\sin A (1 - \cos A)}{\sin^2 A} = \dfrac{1 - \cos A}{\sin A}$

T46
Glencoe Division, Macmillan/McGraw-Hill

a. Write an expression for the distance the ball travels in terms of θ.

b. Use a calculator to find the distance Ms. King's ball traveled if the angle between the initial path of the ball and the ground measured 60°. 270.6 feet

c. At what angle should the ball leave the head of the golf club if Ms. King wants it to travel the maximum distance? Explain. See margin.

45. **Optics** A glass prism has an apex angle of measure α and an angle of deviation of measure β. The index of refraction, n, of the prism is equal to $\dfrac{\sin\left(\dfrac{\alpha+\beta}{2}\right)}{\sin\left(\dfrac{\alpha}{2}\right)}$.

Show that $\sqrt{\dfrac{1-\cos\alpha\cos\beta+\sin\alpha\sin\beta}{1-\cos\alpha}}$ is an equivalent expression for n. Assume that $n > 0$. See margin.

Mixed Review

46. State the domain and range of the relation $\{(3,7),(-1,4),(0,0),(3,-6)\}$. Is the relation a function? **(Lesson 1-1)** See margin.

47. 3x − y − 2 = 0

47. Write the standard form of the equation of the line that is parallel to the line with equation $3x - y = 10$ and passes through $(0,-2)$. **(Lesson 1-6)**

48. Solve the equation $4x^3 + 3x^2 - x = 0$. **(Lesson 4-1)** $0, \dfrac{1}{4}, -1$

49. Does $A = 120°$, $b = 12$, and $a = 4$ determine one triangle, two triangles, or no triangles? **(Lesson 5-5)** no triangle

50. If $\cos\theta = \dfrac{2}{3}$ and $0° \leq \theta \leq 90°$, find $\sin\theta$. **(Lesson 7-1)** $\dfrac{\sqrt{5}}{3}$

51. Find $\tan 150°$ from values of functions of 180° and 30°. **(Lesson 7-3)** $-\dfrac{\sqrt{3}}{3}$

52. **College Entrance Exam** Choose the best answer. B
x is an integer greater than 1. What is the least x for which $a^2 = b^3 = x$ for some integers a and b?

(A) 81   (B) 64   (C) 4   (D) 2   (E) 9

MID-CHAPTER REVIEW

Solve for values between 0° and 90°. (Lesson 7-1)

1. If $\sin\theta = \dfrac{4}{5}$, find $\cos\theta$. $\dfrac{3}{5}$

2. If $\tan\theta = \dfrac{\sqrt{2}}{5}$, find $\cos\theta$. $\dfrac{5\sqrt{3}}{9}$

Simplify. (Lesson 7-1)

3. $\dfrac{1-\sin^2\alpha}{\sin^2\alpha}$ $\cot^2\alpha$

4. $\cos\beta\csc\beta$ $\cot\beta$

5–10. See Teacher's Answer Key.

Verify that each of the following is an identity. (Lessons 7-2, 7-3, 7-4)

5. $\sin\theta\,(1+\cot^2\theta) = \csc\theta$

6. $\cos^2 A = (1-\sin A)(1+\sin A)$

7. $-\cos\theta = \cos(180° - \theta)$

8. $\dfrac{\cos A + \sin A}{\cos A - \sin A} = \dfrac{1+\sin 2A}{\cos 2A}$

9. $\sin^2\theta = \dfrac{1}{2}(1-\cos 2\theta)$

10. $\sin 2x = 2\cot x \sin^2 x$

LESSON 7-4 DOUBLE-ANGLE AND HALF-ANGLE IDENTITIES 383

EXTENDING THE LESSON

Math Power: Problem Solving

Solve the formula $\dfrac{1}{M} = \sqrt{\dfrac{1-\cos B}{2}}$

to find a formula for the cosine of a supersonic plane's cone angle, B, in terms of its speed, M.

$\cos B = \dfrac{M^2 - 2}{M^2}$

Mid-Chapter Review

The Mid-Chapter Review provides students with a brief review of the concepts and skills in Lessons 7–1 through 7–4. Lesson numbers are given at the end of problems or instruction lines so students may review concepts not yet mastered.

Additional Answers

45. $n = \dfrac{\sin\left(\dfrac{\alpha+\beta}{2}\right)}{\sin\left(\dfrac{\alpha}{2}\right)}$

$= \sqrt{\dfrac{\dfrac{1-\cos(\alpha+\beta)}{2}}{\dfrac{1-\cos\alpha}{2}}}$

$= \sqrt{\dfrac{\dfrac{1-(\cos\alpha\cos\beta-\sin\alpha\sin\beta)}{2}}{\dfrac{1-\cos\alpha}{2}}}$

$= \sqrt{\dfrac{\dfrac{1-\cos\alpha\cos\beta+\sin\alpha\sin\beta}{2}}{\dfrac{1-\cos\alpha}{2}}}$

$= \sqrt{\dfrac{1-\cos\alpha\cos\beta+\sin\alpha\sin\beta}{1-\cos\alpha}}$

46. $D = \{-1, 0, 3\}$,
$R = \{-6, 0, 4, 7\}$; no

Enrichment Masters Booklet, p. 46

Technology

Double and Half Angles

The BASIC program below finds the values of cos $2x$ and sin $2x$ given the value of sin x and the quadrant in which x lies.

```
10 INPUT "ENTER THE VALUE OF SIN X: "; S1
20 INPUT "ENTER THE QUADRANT OF ANGLE X: "; Q
30 C1 = SQR (1-S1^2)
40 IF Q = 1 THEN 70
50 IF Q = 4 THEN 70
60 C1 = (-1)*C1
70 PRINT "SIN 2X = ";2*S1*C1
80 PRINT "COS 2X = ";1-2*S1^2
90 END
```

To run the program, type RUN and press the enter key. Enter each value at the colon. This sample is for sin $x = -0.9$, where x is in Quadrant IV.

```
RUN
ENTER THE VALUE OF SIN X: -0.9
ENTER THE QUADRANT OF ANGLE X: 4
SIN 2X = -0.784601809
COS 2X = -0.62
```

EXERCISES

Use the BASIC program to find sin $2x$ and cos $2x$ for each value of sin x in the quadrant given. Round your answers to the nearest thousandth.

2. −0.785, −0.620

1. sin $x = 0.5$, Quadrant I   0.866, 0.5

2. sin $x = 0.9$, Quadrant II

3. sin $x = -0.65$, Quadrant IV   −0.988, 0.155

4. sin $x = -0.01$, Quadrant III   −0.020, 1.000

5. Modify the program to find sin $2x$ and cos $2x$ given the value of cos x and the quadrant in which x lies. See margin.

Use the BASIC program from Exercise 5 to find sin $2x$ and cos $2x$ for each value of cos x in the quadrant given. Round your answers to the nearest thousandth.

6. cos $x = -0.5$, Quadrant II   −0.866, −0.5

7. cos $x = 0.8$, Quadrant IV   −0.96, 0.28

8. Write a BASIC program to find sin $\frac{x}{2}$ and cos $\frac{x}{2}$ given the value of sin x and the quadrant in which x lies. See margin.

384   CHAPTER 7   TRIGONOMETRIC IDENTITIES AND EQUATIONS

7-5A Graphing Calculators: Solving Trigonometric Equations

Solving a trigonometric equation means to find all of the values of x that satisfy the equation, or make its value 0. Setting an equation equal to zero and finding the x-intercepts is one method used to solve an equation. This method was discussed in Lesson 4-5A when we located the zeros of polynomial functions. Another method is to graph each side of the equation as a separate function and find where the graphs intersect. This method was discussed in Lesson 2-1A when we graphed a system of equations and found the point of intersection. The solutions will be the same no matter which method you use.

Example 1

Solve tan $x =$ sin $x \cdot$ cos x if $-360° \leq x \leq 360°$.

First, graph each side of the equation and solve by finding the intersection points. Use the viewing window $[-450°, 450°]$ by $[-3, 3]$ with a scale factor of $90°$ on the x-axis and 1 on the y-axis.

TI-81: Y= TAN X|T ENTER
SIN X|T × COS X|T
GRAPH

Casio: Graph tan ALPHA X :
Graph sin ALPHA X cos
ALPHA X EXE

By tracing and zooming in, the solutions are found to be $-360°, -180°, 0°, 180°$, and $360°$.

Subtracting sin $x \cdot$ cos x from each side of the equation produces the equivalent equation tan $x -$ sin $x \cdot$ cos $x = 0$. Graphing this equation will give you the same solutions, except the solutions are now where the graph crosses the x-axis.

Remember that the solutions will be the same no matter which method you choose, but you need to know what to look for on the graph. If you use the method of graphing two equations, you need to look for the point of intersection because the coordinates of this point satisfy both equations. If you use the method of solving the equation for zero, you need to find the x-intercepts because that is where the equation equals zero.

GRAPHING CALCULATORS: SOLVING TRIGONOMETRIC EQUATIONS   385

INTRODUCING THE LESSON

Objective Solve trigonometric equations on a graphing calculator.

Motivating the Lesson

This lesson provides an excellent opportunity for students to practice their skills of reading and interpreting complicated graphics displays.

TEACHING THE LESSON

Teaching Tip In Example 1, ask students to identify the graph of each side of the equation.

Teaching Tip The graphs in Example 1 seem to coincide at certain intervals of x. Remind students not to assume something without checking their assumption by using the ZOOM feature.

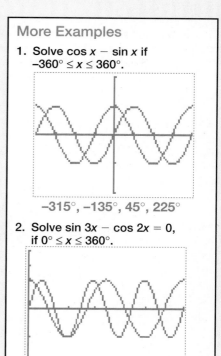

More Examples

1. Solve cos $x -$ sin x if $-360° \leq x \leq 360°$.

   $-315°, -135°, 45°, 225°$

2. Solve sin $3x -$ cos $2x = 0$, if $0° \leq x \leq 360°$.

   $18.91°, 90°, 161.57°$

Example 2 | **Solve 2 cos x − 4 = 0 if $0 \leq x \leq 360°$.**

Since the equation already equals zero, graph $y = 2\cos x - 4$ and find the x-intercepts. Use the viewing window $[-90°, 450°]$ by $[-8, 2]$ with a scale factor of 90° for the x-axis and 1 for the y-axis.

TI-81:   Y= 2 COS X|T − 4 GRAPH

Casio: Graph 2 cos ALPHA X
           − 4 EXE

The graph does not cross the x-axis, so there are no solutions to the equation.

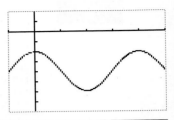

As you have done with other equations, you can use the TRACE and ZOOM features of the calculator to find solutions to trigonometric equations.

Example 3 | **Solve sin $3x$ + cos $2x$ = 1 if $0 \leq x \leq 360°$.**

Let's use the method of solving the equation for zero and finding the x-intercepts. The equation to be graphed then becomes sin $3x$ + cos $2x$ − 1 = 0. Use the viewing window $[-90°, 450°]$ by $[-5, 5]$ with a scale factor of 90° for the x-axis and 1 for the y-axis.

TI-81:   Y= SIN ((3 X|T)) +
           COS ((2 X|T)) − 1
           GRAPH

Casio: Graph sin ((3 ALPHA X
           )) + cos ((2 ALPHA X
           )) − 1 EXE

Now trace and zoom in on the points of intersection to find solutions: 0°, 40.6°, 139.3°, 180°, and 360°.

EXERCISES

Graph each equation so that a complete graph is shown. Then find the solutions to the nearest tenth. 1-10. See margin.

1. tan x = cos $x, 0° \leq x \leq 360°$

2. sin x + cos x = 2, $0° \leq x \leq 360°$

3. 4 sin $2x$ − sin x = 2, $0° \leq x \leq 360°$

4. sin $3x$ = sin x, $-360° \leq x \leq 360°$

5. 2 cos² x = sin² $x, 0° \leq x \leq 360°$

6. 2 cos x = 2 tan x, $-360° \leq x \leq 360°$

7. 3 sin² x + 2 sin x − 4 = 0, $-360° \leq x \leq 360°$

8. sin² x − cos x = 0, $-360° \leq x \leq 360°$

9. sin x · cos x = tan $2x$, $-360° \leq x \leq 360°$

10. 2 sin $2x$ + cos $2x$ + 1 = 0, $0° \leq x \leq 360°$

7-5 Solving Trigonometric Equations

Objective
7-5

After studying this lesson, you should be able to:
- solve trigonometric equations.

Application

FYI...

More than 250 tons of rock are mined for each 1-carat diamond. That is a ratio of 932,500,000 to 1.

The beautiful sparkle of a diamond is created by *refracted* light. Light travels at different speeds in different mediums. When light rays pass from one medium to another in which they travel at a different velocity, the light is bent, or refracted. According to Snell's Law, $n_1 \sin i = n_2 \sin r$, where n_1 is the index of refraction of the medium the light is exiting, n_2 is the index of refraction of the medium it is entering, i is the angle of incidence, and r is the angle of refraction.

The index of refraction of a diamond is 2.42 and the index of refraction of air is 1.00. If a beam of light strikes a diamond at an angle of 35°, what is the angle of refraction? *This problem will be solved in Example 4.*

Trigonometric identities, like all identities, are true for *all* values of the variable for which the expression is defined. However, most **trigonometric equations**, like most algebraic equations, are true for *some* but not *all* values of the variable. Trigonometric equations do not have unique solutions. They have infinitely many solutions, differing by the period of the function, 2π or 360° for the sine and cosine functions, and π or 180° for the tangent function.

If the value of a function is restricted to two adjacent quadrants, a trigonometric equation will have unique solutions. These solutions are called **principal values**. For sin x and tan x, the principal values are in Quadrants I or IV. So x is in the interval $-90° \leq x \leq 90°$. For cos x, the principal values are in Quadrants I or II, so x is in the interval $0° \leq x \leq 180°$.

Example 1

Solve $2\cos^2 x - 5\cos x + 2 = 0$ for principal values of x. Express solutions in degrees.

$$2\cos^2 x - 5\cos x + 2 = 0$$
$$(2\cos x - 1)(\cos x - 2) = 0 \qquad \text{Factor.}$$

$$\begin{array}{lll}
2\cos x - 1 = 0 & \text{or} & \cos x - 2 = 0 \\
2\cos x = 1 & & \cos x = 2 \\
\cos x = \dfrac{1}{2} & & \text{\textit{There is no solution for} } \cos x = 2 \\
x = 60° & & \text{\textit{since} } -1 \leq \cos x \leq 1.
\end{array}$$

The solution is 60°.

When all of the values of x are required, the solution should be represented as $x + 360k°$ for sin x and cos x and $x + 180k°$ for tan x, where k is any integer.

ALTERNATE TEACHING STRATEGIES

Using Models

Borrow a prism and a light source from the physics lab. Use these to show how incident light is refracted by the prism to produce a spectrum.

Using Cooperative Groups

Show how to work backward to create a simple trigonometric equation, beginning with the solution.

$$x = 30° \rightarrow \sin x = \frac{1}{2} \rightarrow 2\sin x = 1$$

Equation: $2\sin x - 1 = 0$

Have groups create trigonometric equations and exchange them with other groups to solve.

NCTM Standards: 1–6, 9

Lesson Resources

- Practice Master 7–5
- Enrichment Master 7–5
- Technology Master, p. 13

Transparency 7–5 contains the 5-Minute Check and a teaching aid for this lesson.

INTRODUCING THE LESSON

5-Minute Check

(over Lesson 7–4)

If $\sin x = \frac{2}{5}$ and x terminates in the first quadrant, find each value.

1. $\cos 2x$ $\frac{17}{25}$

2. $\sin \frac{x}{2}$ $\frac{\sqrt{50 - 10\sqrt{21}}}{10}$

3. Verify that $2\tan x = \frac{\sin 2x}{1 - \sin^2 x}$ is an identity.

$$2\tan x \overset{?}{=} \frac{\sin 2x}{1 - \sin^2 x}$$

$$2\tan x \overset{?}{=} \frac{2\sin x \cos x}{\cos^2}$$

$$2\tan x \overset{?}{=} \frac{2\sin x}{\cos x}$$

$$2\tan x = 2\tan x$$

Prerequisite Skills

Students should know how to use the Zero-Product property to solve equations.
Solve for x.
1. $(x - 3)(x + 2.5) = 0$ 3, –2.5
2. $x^2 - 4x = 0$ 0, 4
3. $x^2 - 5x = -2x + 10$ 5, –2

Motivating the Lesson

Have students use trigonometric tables or calculators to solve the following equations. Values given are correct to four places.
1. $\sin x = 0.4695$ $x = 28°$
2. $\cos x = 0.5736$ $x = 55°$
3. $\tan x = 0.9004$ $x = 42°$

Teaching Tip Before Example 1, discuss how a trigonometric equation can be true for only some values of the variable yet still have an infinite number of solutions. To clarify, give the sample equation $\sin x = \frac{1}{2}$ and list its solutions:

$x = 30°, 390°, 750°, \cdots, 30° + 360k°$

Chalkboard Examples

For Example 1

Solve $2 \sin^2 x + \sin x - 1 = 0$ for principal values of x. $x = 30°$

For Example 2

Solve $4 \cos x \sin x - 2 \sin x - 2\sqrt{3} \cos x + \sqrt{3} = 0$ for all values of x. $60° + 360k°, -60° + 360k°, 120° + 360k°$

For Example 3

Solve $1 - \cos 2x - \sin x = 0$ for principal values of x. $0°, 30°$

For Example 4

A gem has an index of refraction of 1.82. At what incident angle must a beam of light strike the gem to be refracted at an angle of 47°?   about 23.7°

Example 2

Solve $2 \tan x \sin x + 2 \sin x = \tan x + 1$ for all values of x. Express solutions in degrees.

$$2 \tan x \sin x + 2 \sin x = \tan x + 1$$
$$2 \tan x \sin x + 2 \sin x - \tan x - 1 = 0 \quad \textit{Subtract } \tan x + 1 \textit{ from each side.}$$
$$(\tan x + 1)(2 \sin x - 1) = 0 \quad \textit{Factor.}$$

$$\tan x + 1 = 0 \qquad\qquad 2 \sin x - 1 = 0$$
$$\tan x = -1 \qquad\qquad \sin x = \frac{1}{2}$$
$$\text{or}$$
$$x = -45° + 180k° \qquad\qquad x = 30° + 360k°$$
$$\text{or } x = 150° + 360k°$$

The solutions are $-45° + 180k°$, $30° + 360k°$, or $150° + 360k°$.

If an equation cannot be solved easily by factoring, try writing the expressions in terms of only one trigonometric function. Remember to use your knowledge of identities.

Example 3

Solve $\sin^2 x + \cos 2x - \cos x = 0$ for principal values of x.

The first step in solving this equation is to express $\cos 2x$ in terms of $\sin x$.

$$\sin^2 x + \cos 2x - \cos x = 0$$
$$\sin^2 x + (1 - 2 \sin^2 x) - \cos x = 0 \quad \textit{cos } 2x = 1 - 2 \sin^2 x$$
$$1 - \sin^2 x - \cos x = 0$$
$$\cos^2 x - \cos x = 0 \quad \textit{cos}^2 x = 1 - \sin^2 x$$
$$\cos x(\cos x - 1) = 0 \quad \textit{Factor.}$$

$$\cos x = 0 \qquad \text{or} \qquad \cos x - 1 = 0$$
$$x = 90° \qquad\qquad\qquad \cos x = 1$$
$$x = 0°$$

The solutions are $0°$ and $90°$.

Some application problems can be solved by using a calculator to solve a trigonometric equation.

Example 4

APPLICATION

Optics

Refer to the application at the beginning of the lesson. If a beam of light strikes a diamond at an angle of 35°, what is the angle of refraction?

$$n_1 \sin i = n_2 \sin r$$
$$1.00 \sin 35° = 2.42 \sin r \quad \textit{n}_1 = 1.00, n_2 = 2.42, i = 35°$$
$$\sin r = \frac{\sin 35°}{2.42}$$
$$\sin r = 0.2370 \quad \textit{Use a calculator to solve.}$$
$$r = 13.710433$$

The angle of refraction is about $14°$.

It is important to always check your solutions. Some algebraic operations may introduce answers that are *not* solutions to the original equation.

Example 5

Solve $\cos x = 1 + \sin x$ for $0° \le x < 360°$.

$$\cos x = 1 + \sin x$$
$$\cos^2 x = (1 + \sin x)^2 \qquad \text{\textit{Square each side of the equation.}}$$
$$1 - \sin^2 x = 1 + 2\sin x + \sin^2 x \qquad \textit{cos}^2\,x = 1 - \textit{sin}^2\,x$$
$$0 = 2\sin x + 2\sin^2 x$$
$$0 = 2\sin x(1 + \sin x) \qquad \textit{Factor.}$$

$2\sin x = 0$	or $\quad 1 + \sin x = 0$
$\sin x = 0$	$\sin x = -1$
$x = 0°$ or $180°$	$x = 270°$

Check:

$$\cos x = 1 + \sin x \qquad\qquad \cos x = 1 + \sin x \qquad\qquad \cos x = 1 + \sin x$$
$$\cos 0° \stackrel{?}{=} 1 + \sin 0° \qquad \cos 180° \stackrel{?}{=} 1 + \sin 180° \qquad \cos 270° \stackrel{?}{=} 1 + \sin 270°$$
$$1 = 1\ \checkmark \qquad\qquad\qquad -1 \stackrel{?}{=} 1 + 0 \qquad\qquad\qquad 0 \stackrel{?}{=} 1 + (-1)$$
$$\qquad\qquad\qquad\qquad\qquad -1 \ne 1 \qquad\qquad\qquad\qquad\qquad 0 = 0\ \checkmark$$

Based on the check, 180° is not a solution. The solutions are 0° and 270°.

EXPLORATION: Graphing Calculator

You can use a graphing calculator to verify the solution of the equation in Example 5.

1. Use the range values below to set up a viewing window. Mode should be in degrees.

$$0 \le X \le 360 \qquad -3 \le Y \le 3 \qquad XSCL = 90 \qquad YSCL = 0.25$$

2. Let $Y_1 = \cos x$ and let $Y_2 = 1 + \sin x$.
3. Graph the two functions on the same screen.   4. $(0, 1)$ and $(270, 0)$
4. There are two intersection points for the two graphs. Use the TRACE function to find the coordinates of the points of intersection.

CHECKING FOR UNDERSTANDING

Communicating Mathematics

Read and study the lesson to answer each question.

1. **Explain** how solving a trigonometric equation is different from verifying a trigonometric identity. See margin.

2. **State** the number of solutions that each equation has.

    a. $\sin x = 0.5$ **b.** $\cos\theta = -\dfrac{\sqrt{3}}{2}$ if $0° \le \theta \le 180°$ 1   **c.** $\sin 2\alpha = -2$
    infinitely many   none

LESSON 7-5   SOLVING TRIGONOMETRIC EQUATIONS   389

RETEACHING THE LESSON

Give students an opportunity to solve elementary trigonometric equations by inspection.

$$\sin x = \frac{1}{2} \qquad x = 30°$$

Gradually increase the difficulty by showing how the Zero-Product property can be used to solve equations.

Additional Answer

1. Answers may vary. A sample answer is that in solving an equation you may perform the same operation on each side of the equation, but in verifying an identity you may not.

APPLYING THE LESSON

Homework Exercises

Assignment Guide

Average: 17–38, 45,46, 49–56
Enriched: 23–45, 47–56

The red A, B, and C flags, printed only in the Teacher's Wraparound Edition, indicate the level of difficulty of the exercises.

Exercise Note

For the exercises, students should begin by reviewing the values of the trigonometric functions of 0°, 30°, 45°, and 60°.

Additional Answers

11. $0° + 120k°$
12. $0° + 180k°$
13. $0° + 180k°$
14. $45° + 180k°$
15. $90° + 180k°, 120° + 360k°,$
    $240° + 360k°$
16. $0° + 180k°, 60° + 180k°$

37. $45° + 90k°$
38. $90° + 180k°, 30° + 360k°,$
    $150° + 360k°$
39. $270° + 360k°$
40. $120° + 360k°, 240° + 360k°$
41. $0° + 180k°, 90° + 360k°$
42. $0° + 180k°, 90° + 360k°$
43. $60° + 360k°, 300° + 360k°$
44. $0° + 360k°$

46a. 2 inches above the
     equilibrium point

46c.

Guided Practice Solve each equation for principal values of x.

3. $2 \sin x + 1 = 0$ $-30°$
4. $2 \cos x - 1 = 0$ $60°$
5. $\sqrt{2} \sin x - 1 = 0$ $45°$
6. $2 \cos x + 1 = 0$ $120°$
7. $2 \cos x - \sqrt{3} = 0$ $30°$
8. $\sin 2x - 1 = 0$ $45°$
9. $\cos 3x - 0.5 = 0$ $20°, 100°, 140°$
10. $\tan 2x - \sqrt{3} = 0$ $-60°, 30°$

Solve each equation for all values of x. 11–16 See margin.

11. $\cos 2x = \cos x$
12. $\sin x = \tan x$
13. $\sin x + \sin x \cos x = 0$
14. $\sin x = \cos x$
15. $\cos 2x + \cos x + 1 = 0$
16. $\tan^2 x - \sqrt{3} \tan x = 0$

EXERCISES

Practice Solve each equation for $0° \leq x \leq 180°$.

A
17. $4 \sin^2 x - 3 = 0$ $60°, 120°$
18. $2 \sin^2 x + \sin x = 0$ $0° 180°$
19. $\sqrt{3} \tan x + 1 = 0$ $150°$
20. $\sqrt{2} \cos x - 1 = 0$ $45°$
21. $\tan 2x = \cot x$ $30°, 90°, 150°$
22. $2 \cos^2 x = \sin x + 1$ $30°, 150°$
23. $\sin 2x = \cos x$ $30°, 90°, 150°$
24. $\sin^2 x - 3 \sin x + 2 = 0$ $90°$

B
25. $\sin x + \cos x = 0$ $135°$
26. $\cos^2 x - \frac{7}{2} \cos x - 2 = 0$ $120°$
27. $3 \cos 2x - 5 \cos x = 1$ $120°$
28. $\tan^2 x = 3 \tan x$ $0°, 71°34', 180°$
29. $3 \tan^2 x + 4 \sec x = -4$ $180°$
30. $\sin 2x = \cos 3x$ $18°, 90°, 162°$
31. $\sin 2x \sin x + \cos 2x \cos x = 1$ $0°$
32. $3 \sin^2 x - \cos^2 x = 0$ $30°, 150°$
33. $\cos 2x + 3 \cos x - 1 = 0$ $60°$
34. $4 \tan x + \sin 2x = 0$ $0°, 180°$
35. $2 \sin x \cos x + 4 \sin x = \cos x + 2$ $30°, 150°$
36. $\sqrt{3} \cot x \sin x + 2 \cos^2 x = 0$ $90°, 150°$

Solve each equation for all values of x. 37–44. See margin.

C
37. $2 \sin^2 x - 1 = 0$
38. $\cos x - 2 \cos x \sin x = 0$
39. $\sin^2 x - 2 \sin x - 3 = 0$
40. $3 \cos 2x - 5 \cos x = 1$
41. $\cos x \tan x - \sin^2 x = 0$
42. $\sin^2 x - \sin x = 0$
43. $4 \cos^2 x - 4 \cos x + 1 = 0$
44. $\cos x = 3 \cos x - 2$

Critical Thinking

45. Solve $\dfrac{\tan x - \sin x}{\tan x + \sin x} = \dfrac{\sec x - 1}{\sec x + 1}$ for all values of x. all reals except $90k°$, where k is any integer

Applications and Problem Solving

46. **Physics** Ted set up a physics experiment with a weighted spring system. He determined that the motion of the weight can be described by the equation $y = 2 \sin \left(\pi t - \dfrac{\pi}{2} \right)$, where y is the distance in inches from the equilibrium point and t is the time in seconds.

46b. $0.5 + k$ seconds, where k is any integer

a. What is the position of the weight after 3 seconds? See margin.
b. At what times is the weight at the equilibrium point?
c. Graph the motion of the weight for the first 5 seconds. See margin.

390 CHAPTER 7 TRIGONOMETRIC IDENTITIES AND EQUATIONS

47. Optics Lori has placed a small lamp behind her freshwater aquarium. A beam of light strikes the glass of the aquarium at an angle of 10° and passes through the glass and into the water of the aquarium.

    a. Use Snell's Law to find the angle of refraction. Use 1.5 as the index of refraction for glass and 1.0 as the index of refraction for air. ≈ 6.6°

    b. What is the angle of refraction of the beam as it passes from the glass into the water? Use 1.33 as the index of refraction of water. ≈ 7.5°

    c. At what angle will the beam exit through the front of the aquarium? 10°

48. Gemology Explain how a gemologist might use Snell's Law to determine if a diamond is genuine. See margin.

Mixed Review

49. State whether each of the points at $(9, 3)$, $(-1, 2)$, and $(2, -2)$ satisfy the inequality $2x - 4y \leq 7$. **(Lesson 1-3)** yes, yes, no

50. Describe how the graphs of $y = 2x^3$ and $y = 2x^3 + 1$ are related. **(Lesson 3-2)** $y = 2x^3 + 1$ is $y = 2x^3$ shifted 1 unit up

51. Find the critical points of the graph of $y = x^3 - 4x^2 + 4x + 6$. Then determine whether each point is a *minimum*, a *maximum*, or a *point of inflection*. **(Lesson 3-7)** $\left(\frac{2}{3}, 7\frac{5}{27}\right)$ max, $(2, 6)$ min, $\left(\frac{4}{3}, 6\frac{16}{27}\right)$ pt of inf

52. Find the values of the six trigonometric functions of an angle θ in standard position whose terminal side contains the point at $(-3, 2)$. **(Lesson 5-3)** See margin.

53. Evaluate $\sec\left(\cos^{-1}\frac{2}{5}\right)$ if the angle is in Quadrant I. **(Lesson 6-4)** $\frac{5}{2}$

54. If $\csc\theta = 3$ and $0° \leq \theta \leq 90°$, find $\sin\theta$. **(Lesson 7-1)** $\frac{1}{3}$

55. $\dfrac{\sqrt{2 + \sqrt{2 + \sqrt{3}}}}{2}$ **55.** Use a half-angle identity to find the value of $\cos 7°30'$. **(Lesson 7-4)**

56. College Entrance Exam Choose the best answer. A
Let $^*x$ be defined as $^*x = x^3 - x$. What is the value of $^*4 - {}^*(-3)$?

    (A) 84   **(B)** 55   **(C)** −10   **(D)** 22   **(E)** 4

CASE STUDY FOLLOW-UP

Refer to Case Study 4: *The U.S. Economy,* on pages 966–969.

Economic changes often follow cyclical patterns. If there is a reason for a cycle and it is not simply accidental, it can be used to predict future trends. 1, 3. See margin.

1. Describe the apparent cycle in annual percentage changes in the CPI of all items, 1976–1990.

2. If the cycle continues as it has, when will the annual percentage in the CPI next reach +2%? around 1998

3. If $f(x)$ defines the apparent inflation cycle after 1976, where x equals the year, and $f(1983) = 0$, would you write $f(x)$ using the sine or cosine function?

4. Research Find an example of a widely accepted business cycle. In a one-page paper, give evidence to support and deny the existence of the cycle and tell whether you think the cycle exists. See students' work.

EXTENDING THE LESSON

Math Power: Communication

Research the effects of Earth's atmosphere on incident sunlight to find the cause of the blue sky and colorful sunsets. Write a report on your findings.

Case Study Follow-Up

This activity provides an opportunity to do research and apply mathematics in solving problems related to issues that may face students in their adult lives. Case Study 4 is located on pages 966–969.

Additional Answers

48. Measure the angles of refracted light to determine the index of refraction. If the index is 2.42, the diamond is genuine.

52. $\sin\theta = \dfrac{2\sqrt{13}}{13}$, $\cos\theta = \dfrac{-3\sqrt{13}}{13}$,

$\tan\theta = -\dfrac{2}{3}$, $\csc\theta = \dfrac{\sqrt{13}}{2}$,

$\sec\theta = -\dfrac{\sqrt{13}}{3}$, $\cot\theta = -\dfrac{3}{2}$

Case Study Follow-Up

1. The cycle appears to be about 12 years long, ranging between a maximum of about + 12% in 1980 and a minimum of about + 2% in 1986.

3. Answers may vary. A sample answer is the sine function. $f(1983)$ is halfway between the extreme values of the function, as $\sin 0°$ is halfway between the extreme values of the sine function.

Enrichment Masters Booklet, p. 47

~ **7-5** NAME _____ DATE _____
Enrichment Worksheet

The Spectrum

In some ways, light behaves as though it were composed of waves. The wavelength of visible light ranges from about 4×10^{-5} cm for violet light to about 7×10^{-5} cm for red light.

As light passes through a medium, its velocity depends upon the wavelength of the light. The greater the wavelength, the greater the velocity. Since white light, including sunlight, is composed of light of all wavelengths, waves will pass through the medium at an infinite number of different speeds. The index of refraction, n, of the medium is defined by $n = \frac{c}{v}$, where c is the velocity of light in a vacuum (3×10^{10} cm/s), and v is the velocity of light in the medium. As you can see, the index of refraction of a medium is not a constant. It depends on the wavelength and the velocity of light passing through it. (The index of refraction of diamond given in the lesson is an average.)

  1. For all media, $n > 1$. Is the speed of light in a medium greater than or less than c? Explain.
    less than; $v = \frac{c}{n}$. Since $n > 1$, $v < c$.

  2. A beam of violet light travels through water at a speed of 2.234×10^{10} cm/s. Find the index of refraction of water for violet light.
    1.343

The diagram shows why a prism splits white light into a spectrum. Because they travel at different velocities in the prism, waves of light of different colors are refracted different amounts.

  3. Beams of red and violet light strike crown glass at an angle of 20°. Use Snell's Law to find the difference between the angles of refraction of the two beams.
    violet light: $n = 1.531$ red light: $n = 1.513$
    about 0.42°

T47
Glencoe Division, Macmillan/McGraw-Hill

Lesson Resources

- Practice Master 7–6
- Enrichment Master 7–6
- Evaluation Master, Quiz C, p. 86
- Technology Master, p. 14
- Activity Master, p. 19

 Transparency 7–6 contains the 5-Minute Check and a teaching aid for this lesson.

INTRODUCING THE LESSON

 5-Minute Check

(over Lesson 7–5)

Solve each equation for principal values of x.
1. $\tan x - \sqrt{3} = 0$ **60°**
2. $\sin 2x - \sin x = 0$ **0°, 60°**
3. $2\sin^2 x - 5 \sin x + 2 = 0$ **30°**

Prerequisite Skills

Students should know the relationship between the slopes of perpendicular lines.
1. Find the slope of a line perpendicular to the line $3x + 4y - 6 = 0$. $\frac{4}{3}$

2. Find the equation of the line perpendicular to the line $x + 2y + 2 = 0$ and passing through the point (–1, 3).
   $2x - y + 5 = 0$

Motivating the Lesson

Have students read the first three paragraphs of the lesson. Ask them to give everyday examples of normal lines to the following.
1. another line
   adjacent sides of a rectangular wall
2. a circle
   a road and a tire
3. a plane
   a telephone wire entering a house

7-6 Normal Form of a Linear Equation

Objective
7–6

After studying this lesson, you should be able to:
- write a linear equation in normal form.

Application

Don Eger operates a grinding wheel in a large factory. When he uses the grinding wheel to sharpen a dull cutting blade, the sparks fly in a line that is tangent to the wheel. If Mr. Eger holds a blade at a 45° angle to a vertical line and the grinding wheel has a diameter of 8 inches, how far must the lamp be placed above the grinding wheel so that it will not be showered with sparks? *This problem will be solved in Example 2.*

Trigonometric functions sometimes appear in equations whose graphs are not like those of the trigonometric functions themselves. For example, the **normal form** of linear equations can be written in terms of trigonometric functions.

A **normal** is a line that is perpendicular to another line, curve, or surface. The normal form of the equation of a line is written in terms of the length of the normal from the line to the origin. This form uses the trigonometric functions of the positive angle the normal makes with the x-axis.

Suppose ℓ is a line that does not pass through the origin and p units is the length of the normal from the origin. Let C be the point of intersection of the line ℓ with the normal and let ϕ be the positive angle formed by the x-axis and $\overline{OC}$. Draw $\overline{MC}$ perpendicular to the x-axis. Since ϕ is in standard position, $\cos \phi = \frac{OM}{p}$ or $OM = p \cos \phi$ and $\sin \phi = \frac{MC}{p}$ or $MC = p \sin \phi$. So $\frac{p \sin \phi}{p \cos \phi}$ or $\frac{\sin \phi}{\cos \phi}$ is the slope of $\overline{OC}$.

Since ℓ is perpendicular to $\overline{OC}$, its slope is the negative reciprocal of the slope of $\overline{OC}$, or $-\frac{\cos \phi}{\sin \phi}$.

Since ℓ contains C, we can use the point-slope form to write the equation of line ℓ.

$$y - y_1 = m(x - x_1)$$
$$y - p \sin \phi = -\frac{\cos \phi}{\sin \phi}(x - p \cos \phi) \qquad m = -\frac{\cos \phi}{\sin \phi}, (x_1, y_1) = (p \cos \phi, p \sin \phi)$$
$$y \sin \phi - p \sin^2 \phi = -x \cos \phi + p \, \cos^2 \phi \qquad \textit{Multiply each side by } \sin \phi.$$
$$x \cos \phi + y \sin \phi = p(\sin^2 \phi + \cos^2 \phi)$$
$$x \cos \phi + y \sin \phi - p = 0 \qquad \textit{sin}^2 \phi + \cos^2 \phi = 1$$

392 CHAPTER 7 TRIGONOMETRIC IDENTITIES AND EQUATIONS

ALTERNATE TEACHING STRATEGIES

Using Models

Use a straightedge and a wheel or cylindrical can to model the grinding-wheel application. Ask students to estimate the lamp distance. Show how the normal changes as you change the position of the straightedge.

Using Connections

Discuss situations when standard form, y-intercept form, or normal form would be the most appropriate form for a linear equation.

Normal Form

The normal form of a linear equation is
$$x \cos \phi + y \sin \phi - p = 0,$$
where p is the length of the normal from the line to the origin and ϕ is the positive angle formed by the positive x-axis and the normal.

You can write the normal form of a linear equation if you are given the values of ϕ and p.

Example 1

> Write the standard form of the equation of a line for which the length of the normal is 3 units and the normal makes an angle of 60° with the positive x-axis.
>
> $$x \cos \phi + y \sin \phi - p = 0 \qquad \textit{Normal form}$$
> $$x \cos 60° + y \sin 60° - 3 = 0 \qquad \textit{$\phi = 60°$ and $p = 3$}$$
> $$\frac{1}{2}x + \frac{\sqrt{3}}{2}y - 3 = 0$$
> $$x + \sqrt{3}y - 6 = 0 \qquad \textit{Multiply each side by 2.}$$
>
> The equation is $x + \sqrt{3}y - 6 = 0$.

We can use the normal form of a linear equation to solve the application problem presented at the beginning of the lesson.

Example 2

APPLICATION

Manufacturing

> Refer to the application at the beginning of the lesson. How far must the lamp be placed above the grinding wheel so that it will not be showered with sparks?
>
> If we consider the center of the cutting wheel to be the origin, the equation that represents the edge of the cutting wheel is $x^2 + y^2 = 16$. The line of sparks will be at a 45° angle to the vertical. So, in the normal form of the equation, $p = 4$ and $\phi = 90° - 45°$ or 45°.
>
>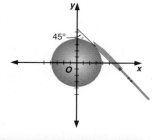
>
> $$x \cos \phi + y \sin \phi - p = 0$$
> $$x \cos 45° + y \sin 45° - 4 = 0$$
> $$\frac{\sqrt{2}}{2}x + \frac{\sqrt{2}}{2}y - 4 = 0$$
> $$x + y - 4\sqrt{2} = 0$$
>
> The line of sparks will cross the y-axis $4\sqrt{2}$ inches above the center of the wheel. Thus, the lamp must be at least $4\sqrt{2} - 4$ or about 1.65 inches above the wheel to avoid being showered with sparks.
>
>

LESSON 7-6 NORMAL FORM OF A LINEAR EQUATION 393

TEACHING THE LESSON

Teaching Tip After discussing the application, stress that the normal form is simply another way of writing the equation of a line. Remind students of the point-slope form and standard form, the two forms with which they are most familiar.

Chalkboard Examples

For Example 1

Write the standard form of the equation of a line for which the length of the normal p is 8 units and the normal makes an angle of 45° with the positive x-axis.
$$\sqrt{2}\,x + \sqrt{2}\,y - 16 = 0$$

For Example 2

A knife is held at a 60° angle to the vertical on a 12-inch diameter cutting wheel. How far above the wheel must the lamp be placed so it will not be showered with sparks? **about 0.93 in.**

1.

Quadrant	I	II	III	IV
coefficient of x ($\cos \phi$)	+	−	−	+
coefficient of y ($\sin \phi$)	+	+	−	−

2. $x \cos \phi + y \sin \phi - p = 0$
Substitute 225° for ϕ and 7 for p.
$x \cos 225° + y \sin 225° - 7 = 0$
Simplify.
$-\frac{\sqrt{2}}{2}x + \left(-\frac{\sqrt{2}}{2}y\right) - 7 = 0$

Multiply each side by $-\sqrt{2}$.
$x + y + 7\sqrt{2} = 0$

3. $x + y - 11\sqrt{2} = 0$

4. $x + \sqrt{3}y - 6 = 0$

5. $x - y = 0$

6. $x + y + 6\sqrt{2} = 0$

7. $\sqrt{3}x + y - 4 = 0$

8. $x - y + \sqrt{2} = 0$

9. $-y - 4 = 0$

10. $-\frac{5x}{\sqrt{26}} + \frac{y}{\sqrt{26}} - \frac{3}{\sqrt{26}} = 0$;

$\frac{3}{\sqrt{26}} \approx 0.6; \approx 169°$

11. $\frac{3x}{\sqrt{10}} - \frac{y}{\sqrt{10}} - \frac{4}{\sqrt{10}} = 0$;

$\frac{4}{\sqrt{10}} \approx 1.3; \approx 342°$

12. $\frac{5x}{\sqrt{26}} + \frac{y}{\sqrt{26}} - \frac{7}{\sqrt{26}} = 0$;

$\frac{7}{\sqrt{26}} \approx 1.4; \approx 11°$

We can transform the standard form of a linear equation, $Ax + By + C = 0$, into normal form if the relationship between the coefficients in the two forms is known. The equations will represent the same line if and only if their corresponding coefficients are proportional. That is, if

$$\frac{A}{\cos \phi} = \frac{B}{\sin \phi} = \frac{C}{-p}, \text{ then } \sin \phi = \frac{-Bp}{C}, \text{ and } \cos \phi = \frac{-Ap}{C}.$$

We can divide $\sin \phi = \frac{-Bp}{C}$ by $\cos \phi = \frac{-Ap}{C}$, where $\cos \phi \neq 0$.

$$\frac{\sin \phi}{\cos \phi} = \frac{-\frac{Bp}{C}}{\frac{Ap}{C}}$$

$$\tan \phi = \frac{B}{A}$$

Refer to the diagram at the right. Consider an angle ϕ in standard position such that $\tan \phi = \frac{B}{A}$. The length of $\overline{OP}$ is $\sqrt{A^2 + B^2}$. Thus, $\sin \phi = \frac{B}{\pm\sqrt{A^2 + B^2}}$ and $\cos \phi = \frac{A}{\pm\sqrt{A^2 + B^2}}$. Since we know that $\frac{B}{\sin \phi} = \frac{C}{-p}$, we can substitute to get the result $\frac{B}{\frac{B}{\pm\sqrt{A^2 + B^2}}} = \frac{C}{-p}$.

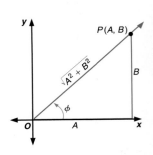

Therefore, $p = \frac{C}{\pm\sqrt{A^2 + B^2}}$.

The $\pm$ sign is used since p is a measure and must be positive in the equation $x \cos \phi + y \sin \phi - p = 0$. Therefore, the sign must be chosen as opposite of the sign of C. That is, if C is positive, use $-\sqrt{A^2 + B^2}$, and, if C is negative, use $\sqrt{A^2 + B^2}$.

If $C = 0$, the sign is chosen so that $\sin \phi$ is positive, that is, the same sign as that of B.

Substitute the values for $\sin \phi$, $\cos \phi$, and p into the normal form.

$$\frac{Ax}{\pm\sqrt{A^2 + B^2}} + \frac{By}{\pm\sqrt{A^2 + B^2}} - \frac{C}{\pm\sqrt{A^2 + B^2}} = 0$$

Notice that the standard form is closely related to the normal form.

Changing the Standard Form to Normal Form	**The standard form of a linear equation, $Ax + By + C = 0$, can be changed to normal form by dividing each term by $\pm\sqrt{A^2 + B^2}$. The sign is chosen opposite the sign of C.**

If the equation of a line is in normal form, you can find the length of the normal, p units, directly from the equation. You can find the angle ϕ by using the relation $\tan \phi = \frac{B}{A}$. However, you must find the quadrant in which the normal lies to find the correct angle for ϕ. When the equation of a line is in normal form, the coefficient of x is equal to $\cos \phi$ and the coefficient of y is equal to $\sin \phi$. Thus, the correct quadrant can be determined by studying the signs of $\cos \phi$ and $\sin \phi$. For example, if $\sin \phi$ is negative and $\cos \phi$ is positive, the normal lies in the fourth quadrant.

Example 3

Write the equation $2x - 5y + 3 = 0$ in normal form. Then, find the length of the normal and the angle it makes with the positive x-axis.

Since C is positive in $2x - 5y + 3 = 0$, use $-\sqrt{A^2 + B^2}$.

$$-\sqrt{A^2 + B^2} = -\sqrt{2^2 + (-5)^2} \text{ or } -\sqrt{29}$$

The normal form is $\dfrac{2x}{-\sqrt{29}} - \dfrac{5y}{-\sqrt{29}} + \dfrac{3}{-\sqrt{29}} = 0$ or $-\dfrac{2x}{\sqrt{29}} + \dfrac{5y}{\sqrt{29}} - \dfrac{3}{\sqrt{29}} = 0.$

Therefore, $\sin\phi = \dfrac{5}{\sqrt{29}}$, $\cos\phi = -\dfrac{2}{\sqrt{29}}$, and $p = \dfrac{3}{\sqrt{29}}$.

$\tan\phi = -\dfrac{5}{2}$ *Why?*

$= -2.5$ *Since $\sin\phi$ is positive and $\cos\phi$ is negative, the*

$\phi \approx 112°$ *terminal side of angle ϕ is in Quadrant II.*

Thus, angle ϕ measures $112°$, and the length of the normal is $\dfrac{3}{\sqrt{29}}$ or about 0.56 units.

CHECKING FOR UNDERSTANDING

Communicating Mathematics

Read and study the lesson to answer each question. 1–2. See margin.

1. **Explain** how you tell in which quadrant the normal to a line lies by examining the x- and y-coefficients of the equation in normal form. Make a table of all of the combinations of signs of x, and y, and the quadrants in which the normal lies.

2. **Describe** how you would write the normal form of the equation of a line for which $p = 7$ and $\phi = 225°$.

Guided Practice

Simplify. 3–6. See margin.

3. $x \cos 45° + y \sin 45° - 11 = 0$

4. $x \cos 60° + y \sin 60° - 3 = 0$

5. $x \cos 135° + y \sin 135° = 0$

6. $x \cos 225° + y \sin 225° - 6 = 0$

7–9. See margin.

Write the standard form of the equation of each line given p, the measure of its normal, and ϕ, the angle the normal makes with the positive x-axis.

7. $p = 2$, $\phi = 30°$

8. $p = 1$, $\phi = 135°$

9. $p = 4$, $\phi = 270°$

Write each equation in normal form. Then find p, the measure of the normal, and ϕ, the angle the normal makes with the positive x-axis. 10–12. See margin.

10. $5x - y + 3 = 0$

11. $3x - y = 4$

12. $5x + y = 7$

APPLYING THE LESSON

Homework Exercises

Chapter 6, Quiz C, (Lessons 7–5 through 7–6), is available in the *Evaluation Masters*, p. 86.

Additional Answers

13. $x + y - 5\sqrt{2} = 0$
14. $x + \sqrt{3}y - 6 = 0$
15. $x + y + 25\sqrt{2} = 0$
16. $\sqrt{3}x - y + 4 = 0$
17. $x + \sqrt{3}y + 16 = 0$
18. $x - \sqrt{3}y + 64 = 0$

19. $-\dfrac{x}{\sqrt{2}} + \dfrac{y}{\sqrt{2}} - \dfrac{6}{\sqrt{2}} = 0$;

$\dfrac{6}{\sqrt{2}} \approx 4.24$; $135°$

20. $\dfrac{2x}{\sqrt{13}} - \dfrac{3y}{\sqrt{13}} - \dfrac{1}{\sqrt{13}} = 0$;

$\dfrac{1}{\sqrt{13}} \approx 0.28$; $-56°19'$

21. $\dfrac{x}{\sqrt{2}} + \dfrac{y}{\sqrt{2}} - \dfrac{8}{\sqrt{2}} = 0$;

$\dfrac{8}{\sqrt{2}} \approx 5.66$; $45°$

22. $\dfrac{3}{5}x + \dfrac{4}{5}y - \dfrac{1}{5} = 0$; $\dfrac{1}{5}$;

$53°8'$

23. $\dfrac{1x}{\sqrt{10}} - \dfrac{3y}{\sqrt{10}} - \dfrac{2}{\sqrt{10}} = 0$;

$\dfrac{2}{\sqrt{10}} \approx 0.63$; $-71°34'$

24. $\dfrac{3}{5}x - \dfrac{4}{5}x - \dfrac{3}{2} = 0$; $\dfrac{3}{2}$;

$-53°8'$

EXERCISES

Practice

13–18. See margin.

Write the standard form of the equation of each line given p, the measure of its normal, and ϕ, the angle the normal makes with the positive x-axis.

13. $p = 5$, $\phi = 45°$ 14. $p = 3$, $\phi = 60°$ 15. $p = 25$, $\phi = 225°$
16. $p = 2$, $\phi = 150°$ 17. $p = 8$, $\phi = 240°$ 18. $p = 32$, $\phi = 120°$

Write each equation in normal form. Then find p, the measure of the normal, and ϕ, the angle that the normal makes with the positive x-axis. 19–24. See margin.

19. $y = x + 6$ 20. $2x - 3y - 1 = 0$ 21. $x + y - 8 = 0$
22. $3x + 4y - 1 = 0$ 23. $x - 3y - 2 = 0$ 24. $6x - 8y - 15 = 0$

25. Write the standard form of the equation of a line if a point on the line nearest to the origin is $(-4, 4)$. $x - y + 8 = 0$

26. The point nearest to the origin on a line is $(3, 3)$. Write the standard form of the equation of the line. $x + y - 6 = 0$

27. $x + \sqrt{3}y + 2 = 0$ and $x + \sqrt{3}y - 2 = 0$

27. Two different lines make an angle of $150°$ with the positive x-axis and are 1 unit from the origin. Write the standard form of the equations of the lines.

28. Write the standard form of the equations of two lines that make an angle of $135°$ with the positive x-axis and are 3 units from the origin.
$x + y + 3\sqrt{2} = 0$ and $x + y - 3\sqrt{2} = 0$

Critical Thinking

29. The point on a line nearest to the origin has coordinates $(4, 3)$. The point on a second line nearest to the origin has coordinates $(-3, 1)$. Where do the two lines intersect? $\left(-\dfrac{5}{13}, \dfrac{115}{13}\right)$

Applications and Problem Solving

30. **Coordinate Geometry** The three sides of a triangle are tangent to a unique circle called the *incircle*. On the coordinate plane, the incircle of $\triangle ABC$ has its center at the origin. The lines whose equations are $x + 4y = 6\sqrt{17}$, $2x + \sqrt{5}y = -18$, and $2\sqrt{2}x = y + 18$ contain the sides of $\triangle ABC$. What is the length of the radius of the incircle? 6 units

31. **History** Ancient slingshots were made from straps of leather that cradled a rock until it was released. One would spin the slingshot in a circle and the initial path of the released rock would be a straight line tangent to the circle at the point of release. The rock will travel the greatest distance if it is released when the angle between the normal to the path and the horizontal is -45°. The center of the circular path is the origin and the radius of the circle measures 1.25 feet.

31b. $x - y - 1.25\sqrt{2} = 0$

a. Draw a labeled diagram of the situation. See margin.
b. Write the equation of the initial path of the rock in standard form.

Mixed Review

32. Write the slope-intercept form of the equation of the line that passes through $(5, 2)$ and $(-4, 4)$. **(Lesson 1-5)** $y = -\frac{2}{9}x + \frac{28}{9}$

33. Are $y = 4x + 4$ and $y = -4x - 4$ inverses of each other? **(Lesson 3-3)** no

34. $3; \frac{1}{2}, \frac{1 \pm i\sqrt{47}}{4}$

34. State the number of roots of the equation $4x^3 - 4x^2 + 13x - 6 = 0$. Then solve the equation. **(Lesson 4-1)**

35. Find a numerical value of one trigonometric function of S if $\tan S \cos S = \frac{1}{2}$. **(Lesson 7-2)** Sample answer: $\sin S = \frac{1}{2}$

36. Solve the equation $\tan x + \cot x = 2$ for principal values of x. **(Lesson 7-5)** $45°$

37. College Entrance Exam Choose the best answer. D

Divide $\frac{a-b}{a+b}$ by $\frac{b-a}{b+a}$.

(A) 1   **(B)** $\frac{(a-b)^2}{(a+b)^2}$ **(C)** $\frac{1}{a^2 - b^2}$ **(D)** -1 **(E)** 0

COOPERATIVE LEARNING

DECISION MAKING

Writing a Budget

The United States has become a nation that operates on credit. In 1990, the federal deficit amounted to about $1000 per citizen, while personal debt averaged more than $3200 per person. One way for individuals to keep control of their finances is to write and stick to a budget. A budget allows you to see where you spend money and readjust your financial priorities when necessary. 1–4. See students' work.

1. Make a list of your basic personal needs like food, clothing, and so on. Then make a second list of things such as rent and utilities that you would have to pay for if you were living by yourself.

2. Research the costs of the items on your lists. Talk to utility companies, read classified ads to learn of apartment rental costs, visit grocery stores to find the cost of food. Then make a realistic estimate of the monthly cost of each item on your lists.

3. Make a reasonable estimate of the amount of money you will need to earn to live within your budget and also be able to save for the future.

4. **Project** Work with your group to complete one of the projects listed at the right based on the information you gathered in Exercises 1–3.

PROJECTS

- Conduct an interview.
- Write a book report.
- Write a proposal.
- Write an article for the school paper.
- Write a report.
- Make a display.
- Make a graph or chart.
- Plan an activity.
- Design a checklist.

LESSON 7-6   NORMAL FORM OF A LINEAR EQUATION   397

EXTENDING THE LESSON

Math Power: Problem Solving

Find the equation in standard form of the normal to the circle $x^2 + y^2 = 25$ at each point where the line with equation $x + 7y - 25 = 0$ intersects the circle.
$3x - 4y + 25 = 0$
$-4x - 3y + 25 = 0$

Decision Making

This activity provides students an opportunity to work together on a given problem. You may wish to refer to pages T20–T21 and page 356c for the various elements of cooperative groups and specific goals and strategies for using them.

Additional Answer

31a.

1.25 ft

Enrichment Masters Booklet, p. 48

NAME _____ DATE _____

7-6 Enrichment Worksheet

Slopes of Perpendicular Lines

The derivation of the normal form of a linear equation uses this familiar theorem, first stated in Lesson 1-6: Two nonvertical lines are perpendicular if and only if the slope of one is the negative reciprocal of the slope of the other.

You can use trigonometric identities to prove that if lines are perpendicular, then their slopes are negative reciprocals of each other.

ℓ_1 and ℓ_2 are perpendicular lines.
α_1 and α_2 are the angles that ℓ_1 and ℓ_2, respectively, make with the horizontal.
Let $m_1 = $ slope of ℓ_1
$m_2 = $ slope of ℓ_2

Complete the following exercises to prove that $m_1 = -\frac{1}{m_2}$.

1. Explain why $m_1 = \tan \alpha_1$ and $m_2 = \tan \alpha_2$.

$\tan \alpha = \frac{\text{change in } y}{\text{change in } x} = m$

2. According to the difference identity for the cosine function, $\cos(\alpha_2 - \alpha_1) = \cos \alpha_2 \cos \alpha_1 + \sin \alpha_2 \sin \alpha_1$. Explain why the left side of the equation is equal to zero.
$\alpha_2 - \alpha_1 = 90°$ and $\cos 90° = 0$.

3. $\cos \alpha_2 \cos \alpha_1 + \sin \alpha_2 \sin \alpha_1 = 0$
$\sin \alpha_2 \sin \alpha_1 = -\cos \alpha_2 \cos \alpha_1$
$\frac{\sin \alpha_1}{\cos \alpha_1} = -\frac{\cos \alpha_2}{\sin \alpha_2}$

Complete using the tangent function. $\tan \alpha_1 = -\frac{1}{\tan \alpha_2}$

Complete, using m_1 and m_2. $m_1 = -\frac{1}{m_2}$

T48
Glencoe Division, Macmillan/McGraw-Hill

NCTM Standards: 1–6, 8, 9

Lesson Resources

- Practice Master 7–7
- Enrichment Master 7–7
- Evaluation Master, Quiz D, p. 86

 Transparency 7–7 contains the 5-Minute Check and a teaching aid for this lesson.

INTRODUCING THE LESSON

 5-Minute Check

(over Lesson 7–6)

1. Write the standard form of the equation of a line for which the length of the normal is 4 and the normal makes an angle of 30° with the positive *x*-axis.
$\sqrt{3}\,x + y - 8 = 0$

2. Write the equation $4x - 3y - 2 = 0$ in normal form.
$\frac{4}{5}x - \frac{3}{5}y - \frac{2}{5} = 0$

Motivating the Lesson

Discuss blood pressure. Blood pressure varies directly with cardiac output, which is the amount of blood ejected from the left ventricle into the aorta each minute. Have students take their pulse rates (1 min) and multiply by 70 mL/s to approximate their cardiac outputs.

7-7 Distance from a Point to a Line

Objectives

After studying this lesson, you should be able to:

- 7-7A ■ find the distance from a point to a line,
- 7-7B ■ find the distance between parallel lines, and
- 7-7C ■ write the equations of lines that bisect angles formed by intersecting lines.

Application

 FYI...

Divide your weight in pounds by 16 to find the approximate number of pints of blood in your body.

Your blood pressure is the pressure that your blood exerts against the walls of your arteries. The pressure depends upon the strength and rate of your heart's contractions, the volume of blood in your circulatory system, and the elasticity of your arteries. Doctors report blood pressures as two measurements, the systolic pressure and the diastolic pressure. The systolic pressure is the pressure of the blood when the heart contracts, and the diastolic pressure is the pressure when the heart is between contractions. As a person ages, his or her arteries tend to lose elasticity, and as a result the blood pressure rises.

In statistics, *prediction equations* are often used to show the relationship between two quantities. A prediction equation relating a person's systolic blood pressure, *y*, to their age, *x*, is $4x - 3y + 228 = 0$. If an actual data point is close to the graph of a prediction equation, the equation gives a good approximation for the coordinates of that point. Linda is 19 years old, and her systolic blood pressure is 112. Her father, who is 45 years old, has a systolic blood pressure of 120. For whom is the given prediction equation a better predictor? *This problem will be solved in Example 2.*

The normal form of a linear equation can be used to find the distance from a point to a line. Let $\overleftrightarrow{RS}$ be a line in the coordinate plane, and let $P(x_1, y_1)$ be a point not on $\overleftrightarrow{RS}$. *P* may lie on the same side of $\overleftrightarrow{RS}$ as the origin does or it may lie on the opposite side. If a line segment joining *P* to the origin does not intersect $\overleftrightarrow{RS}$, point *P* is on the same side of the line as the origin. Construct $\overleftrightarrow{TV}$ parallel to $\overleftrightarrow{RS}$ and passing through *P*. The distance *d* between the parallel lines is the distance from *P* to $\overleftrightarrow{RS}$. We will use a negative distance, *d*, if point *P* and the origin are on the same side of the line.

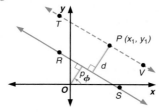

ALTERNATE TEACHING STRATEGIES

Using Connections

Have students use the systolic blood pressure prediction equation and their own ages to find their predicted systolic pressures.

Using Estimation

Before students calculate the distance from a point to a line, they should draw a rough sketch of the graph and estimate the distance to the point, as a check on their calculations.

Let $x \cos \phi + y \sin \phi - p = 0$ be the equation of $\overleftrightarrow{RS}$ in normal form. Since $\overleftrightarrow{TV}$ is parallel to $\overleftrightarrow{RS}$, they have the same slope. The equation for $\overleftrightarrow{TV}$ can be written as $x \cos \phi + y \sin \phi - (p + d) = 0$. Solve this equation for d.

$$d = x \cos \phi + y \sin \phi - p$$

Since $P(x_1, y_1)$ is on $\overleftrightarrow{TV}$, its coordinates satisfy this equation.

$$d = x_1 \cos \phi + y_1 \sin \phi - p$$

We can use an equivalent form of this expression to find d when the equation of a line is in standard form.

Distance from a Point to a Line

The following formula can be used to find the distance from a point (x_1, y_1) to a line with equation $Ax + By + C = 0$.

$$d = \frac{Ax_1 + By_1 + C}{\pm\sqrt{A^2 + B^2}}$$

The sign of the radical is chosen opposite the sign of C.

The distance will be positive if the point and the origin are on opposite sides of the line. The distance will be negative if the origin is on the same side of the line as the point. If you are solving an application problem, the absolute value of d will probably be required.

Example 1

Find the distance between $P(3, -1)$ and the line with equation $2x + 5y - 2 = 0$.

$$d = \frac{Ax_1 + By_1 + C}{\pm\sqrt{A^2 + B^2}}$$

$$= \frac{2(3) + 5(-1) + (-2)}{\pm\sqrt{2^2 + 5^2}} \qquad A = 2, B = 5, C = -2, x_1 = 3, y_1 = -1$$

$$= \frac{-1}{\sqrt{29}} \qquad \text{Since } C \text{ is negative, use } +\sqrt{A^2 + B^2}.$$

$$= -\frac{\sqrt{29}}{29} \text{ or about } -0.19 \qquad |d| = 0.19$$

Therefore, point P is $-\frac{\sqrt{29}}{29}$ or about 0.19 units from the graph of $2x + 5y - 2 = 0$ and is on the same side of the line as the origin.

We can use the formula for the distance between a point and a line to solve the application presented at the beginning of the lesson.

LESSON 7-7 DISTANCE FROM A POINT TO A LINE 399

Teaching Tip Remind students that distance from a point to a line is always measured along a perpendicular.

Chalkboard Example

For Example 1

Find the distance between $P(5, 1)$ and the line with equation $3x + 4y - 4 = 0$.   3 units

Example 2

APPLICATION

Health

Recall that Linda is 19 years old and her father is 45. If Linda's systolic blood pressure is 112 and her father's is 120, for whom is the given prediction equation $4x - 3y + 228 = 0$ a better predictor?

Find the distance between the line and each data point. The prediction equation $4x - 3y + 228 = 0$ is a better predictor for the point that is closer to the line.

Linda:

$P_1 = (19, 112)$

$$d = \frac{Ax_1 + By_1 + C}{\pm\sqrt{A^2 + B^2}}$$

$$= \frac{4(19) + (-3)(112) + 228}{-\sqrt{4^2 + (-3)^2}}$$

$$= \frac{-32}{-5}$$

$$= 6.4$$

Father:

$P_2 = (45, 120)$

$$d = \frac{Ax_1 + By_1 + C}{\pm\sqrt{A^2 + B^2}}$$

$$= \frac{4(45) + (-3)(120) + 228}{-\sqrt{4^2 + (-3)^2}}$$

$$= \frac{48}{-5}$$

$$= -9.6$$

The prediction equation is a better predictor for Linda since her data point, $(19, 112)$ is closer to the graph of the line.

You can use the formula for the distance from a point to a line to find the distance between two parallel lines. To do this, choose a point on one of the lines and use the formula to find the distance from that point to the other line.

Example 3

Find the distance between the lines with equations $3x + 2y = 10$ and $y = -\frac{3}{2}x + 7$.

Since $y = -\frac{3}{2}x + 7$ is in slope-intercept form, we know that $(0, 7)$ are the coordinates of a point on the line, given that 7 is the y-intercept. Use this point to find the distance between the lines.

$$3x + 2y = 10$$
$$3x + 2y - 10 = 0 \qquad \text{\textit{Write the equation in standard form.}}$$

For whom is the prediction equation the best predictor, Linda, her father, or her mother (age 43, systolic pressure 130)?
$d = -2$ for Linda's mother. The equation is the best predictor for the mother.

For Example 3

Find the distance between the lines with equations $3x + 4y - 12 = 0$ and $12x + 16y - 28 = 0$.
1 unit

$$d = \frac{Ax_1 + By_1 + C}{\pm\sqrt{A^2 + B^2}}$$ *Distance from a point to a line*

$$= \frac{3(0) + 2(7) - 10}{\sqrt{3^2 + 2^2}}$$ $A = 3, B = 2, C = -10, x_1 = 0, y_1 = 7$

$$= \frac{4}{\sqrt{13}} \text{ or } \frac{4\sqrt{13}}{13}$$

So, the distance between the lines is $\frac{4\sqrt{13}}{13}$ or about 1.11 units.

An equation of the bisector of an angle formed by two lines in the coordinate plane can also be found using the formula for the distance between a point and a line. The bisector of an angle is the set of all points in the plane equidistant from the sides of the angle. Using this definition, equations of the bisectors of the angles formed by two lines can be found.

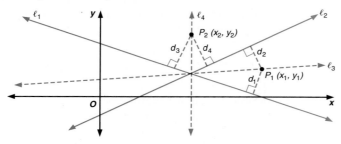

In the figure, ℓ_3 and ℓ_4 are the bisectors of the angles formed by ℓ_1 and ℓ_2. $P_1(x_1, y_1)$ is a point on ℓ_3 and $P_2(x_2, y_2)$ is a point on ℓ_4. Let d_1 be the distance from ℓ_1 to P_1, and let d_2 be the distance from ℓ_2 to P_1.

Notice that P_1 and the origin lie on opposite sides of ℓ_1. So d_1 is positive. Since the origin and P_1 are on opposite sides of ℓ_2, d_2 is also positive. Therefore, for any point $P_1(x_1, y_1)$ on ℓ_3, $d_1 = d_2$. However, d_3 is positive and d_4 is negative. *Why?* Therefore, for any point $P_2(x_2, y_2)$ on ℓ_4, $d_3 = -d_4$.

The origin is in the interior of the angle that is bisected by ℓ_3, but in the exterior of the angle bisected by ℓ_4. So, a good way for you to determine whether to equate distances or to let one distance equal the opposite of the other is to observe the position of the origin.

Relative Position of the Origin

If the origin lies within the angle being bisected, the distances from each line to a point on the bisector have the same sign. If the origin does not lie within the angle being bisected, the distances have opposite signs.

To find the equation of a specific angle bisector, first graph the lines. Then, determine whether to equate the distances or to let one distance equal the opposite of the other.

LESSON 7-7 DISTANCE FROM A POINT TO A LINE 401

Chalkboard Example

For Example 4

Find the equation of the line that bisects the acute angle formed by the graphs of equations $x - 2y + 4 = 0$ and $2x - y - 1 = 0$.

$x - y + 1 = 0$

EVALUATING THE LESSON

Exercises 1–14 are designed to help you assess students' understanding through reading, writing, speaking, and modeling. You should work through Exercises 1–2 with your students and then monitor their work on Exercises 3–14.

Closing the Lesson

Writing Activity Have students choose an arbitrary point and then find the distance from their points to the line with equation $6x + 8y - 5 = 0$.

Practice Masters Booklet, p. 49

Example 4 | **Find an equation of the line that bisects the acute angle formed by the graphs of the equations $3x + y - 9 = 0$ and $2x - 3y + 6 = 0$.**

Graph each equation and sketch the bisector. The origin is in the interior of the acute angle. So $d_1 = d_2$.

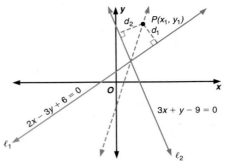

Write expressions for the distances from each line to $P_1(x_1, y_1)$.

$$d_1 = \frac{2x_1 - 3y_1 + 6}{-\sqrt{13}} \qquad \text{Use the formula } \frac{Ax_1 + By_1 + C}{\pm\sqrt{A^2 + B^2}}.$$

$$d_2 = \frac{3x_1 + y_1 - 9}{\sqrt{10}}$$

Since $d_1 = d_2$, use substitution.

$$\frac{2x_1 - 3y_1 + 6}{-\sqrt{13}} = \frac{3x_1 + y_1 - 9}{\sqrt{10}}$$

If we simplify the expressions and drop the subscripts, we find that an equation of the bisector is

$$(2\sqrt{10} + 3\sqrt{13})x + (-3\sqrt{10} + \sqrt{13})y + 6\sqrt{10} - 9\sqrt{13} = 0.$$

CHECKING FOR UNDERSTANDING

Communicating Mathematics

Read and study the lesson to answer each question. 1–2. See margin.

1. **Analyze** the situation where a point lies on a line. Does the equation for the distance between a point and a line give a valid result under these conditions?

2. In Example 2, the distances between the data points and the graph of the prediction equation had opposite signs. Explain what this means for the predictions for these points.

Guided Practice

Find the distance between the point with the given coordinates and line with the given equation. Round to the nearest tenth.

3. $(4, 2)$, $6x - 8y + 1 = 0$ 0.9

4. $(-3, 5)$, $12x + 5y - 3 = 0$ $\frac{14}{13}$

5. $\frac{16\sqrt{58}}{29} \approx 4.2$ 5. $(-1, 4)$, $3x - 7y - 1 = 0$

6. $(-5, 0)$, $x - 3y + 11 = 0$
$\frac{3\sqrt{10}}{5} \approx 1.9$

402   CHAPTER 7   TRIGONOMETRIC IDENTITIES AND EQUATIONS

RETEACHING THE LESSON

Have students work in pairs. One student secretly chooses the equation of a line. The other student chooses a point. Working together, the students graph the point and the line, estimate the distance between the two, and calculate the distance.

Additional Answers

1. yes, $Ax_1 + By_1 + C = 0$ if the point is on the line, so the distance is 0.

2. The prediction for Luisa's systolic blood pressure was too low and the prediction for her father's was too high.

Name the coordinates of one point that satisfy the first equation. Then find the distance from the point to the graph of the second equation. 7–10. See margin.

7. $3x - y + 9 = 0$
   $6x - 2y - 4 = 0$

8. $x + 4 = -2y$
   $2x + 4y - 7 = 0$

9. $\frac{1}{3}x - 4 = y$
   $2x - 6y = 4$

10. $2x - 7y = -9$
    $7y = 2x - 9$

Find an equation of the line that bisects the acute angle formed by the graphs of each pair of equations. 11–14. See margin.

11. $4x - 3y + 12 = 0$
    $5x + 12y - 1 = 0$

12. $9x + 40y = 1$
    $y = -\frac{3}{4}x - 2$

13. $y - 5 = 0$
    $x - y + 2 = 0$

14. $y = x + 3$
    $2x + y - 1 = 0$

EXERCISES

Practice

Solve. 15. $\frac{7\sqrt{2}}{5} \approx 1.98$ 16. $\frac{\sqrt{10}}{10} \approx 0.32$ 18. $\frac{30\sqrt{61}}{61} \approx 3.84$

15. Find the distance from the graph of $x - 7y + 4 = 0$ to the point $C(-4, 2)$.

16. Find the distance from the origin to the graph of $3x - y + 1 = 0$.

17. Find the distance from the point $A(2, -2)$ to a line with equation $2x + 3y + 2 = 0$. Explain what the distance means. 0; the point is on the line

18. Find the distance between the point $B(-3, 2)$ and the graph of $6x - 5y = 2$.

19. The lines whose equations are $3x - 4y - 12 = 0$ and $6x - 8y - 48 = 0$ are parallel. Find the distance between these lines. 2.4

20. $\frac{5\sqrt{2}}{2} \approx 3.54$

21. $\frac{4\sqrt{13}}{13} \approx 1.11$

20. Find the distance between the lines with equations $x + y - 1 = 0$ and $y = -x + 6$.

21. The graphs of $2x - 3y + 1 = 0$ and $3y - 2x = 5$ are parallel lines. Find the distance between the lines.

22. Find the distance between the lines with equations $3x - 5y + 7 = 0$ and $6x - 10y - 2 = 0$. $\frac{4\sqrt{34}}{17} \approx 1.37$

Find the equation of the line that bisects the acute angle formed by the graphs of each pair of equations. 23–26. See margin.

23. $y = 8 - x$
    $2x - y - 4 = 0$

24. $4x + y + 3 = 0$
    $y + x = -2$

25. $x + 4 = y$
    $x + 4y + 6 = 0$

26. $3x + 2y - 2 = 0$
    $2x + 3y + 2 = 0$

Find the equation of the line that bisects the obtuse angle formed by the graphs of each pair of equations. 27–30. See margin.

27. $y = 5 - x$
    $x = 5$

28. $3x + y - 7 = 0$
    $2x + 5y + 3 = 0$

29. $y = 3 - 6x$
    $x + 3y + 1 = 0$

30. $y = 3x - 1$
    $x + y + 2 = 0$

APPLYING THE LESSON

Homework Exercises

Assignment Guide

Average: 15–28, 33–41
Enriched: 18–41

The red A, B, and C flags, printed only in the Teacher's Wraparound Edition, indicate the level of difficulty of the exercises.

Chapter 7, Quiz D, (Lesson 7–7), is available in the *Evaluation Masters*, p. 86

Additional Answers

For Exercises 7–10, answers for points may vary. Sample answers are given.

7. $(0, 9)$; ≈ 3.48

8. $(0, -2)$; $\frac{3\sqrt{5}}{2} \approx 3.35$

9. $(0, -4)$; $\sqrt{10} \approx 3.16$

10. $(-1, 1)$; $\frac{18\sqrt{53}}{53} \approx 2.47$

11. $27x - 99y + 161 = 0$

12. $168x + 364y + 323 = 0$

13. $x - (1 + \sqrt{2})y + 2 + 5\sqrt{2} = 0$

14. $(\sqrt{5} + 2\sqrt{2})x + (\sqrt{2} - \sqrt{5})y + 3\sqrt{5} - \sqrt{2} = 0$

Additional Answers

23. $(2\sqrt{2} + \sqrt{5})x + (\sqrt{5} - \sqrt{2})y - 4\sqrt{2} - 8\sqrt{5} = 0$

24. $(4\sqrt{2} + \sqrt{17})x + (\sqrt{2} + \sqrt{17})y + 3\sqrt{2} + 2\sqrt{17} = 0$

25. $(\sqrt{2} - \sqrt{17})x + (4\sqrt{2} + \sqrt{17})y - 4\sqrt{17} + 6\sqrt{2} = 0$

26. $x + y = 0$

27. $(1 - \sqrt{2})x + y - 5 + 5\sqrt{2} = 0$

28. $(3\sqrt{29} - 2\sqrt{10})x + (\sqrt{29} - 5\sqrt{10})y - 3\sqrt{10} - 7\sqrt{29} = 0$

29. $(6\sqrt{10} - \sqrt{37})x + (\sqrt{10} - 3\sqrt{37})y - 3\sqrt{10} - \sqrt{37} = 0$

30. $(3\sqrt{2} - \sqrt{10})x - (\sqrt{10} + \sqrt{2})y - 2\sqrt{10} - \sqrt{2} = 0$

The program given in Exercise 33 is for use with a TI–81 graphing calculator. For other programmable calculators, have students consult their owner's manual for commands similar to those presented here.

Additional Answers

31. $x - 5y + 10 + 3\sqrt{26} = 0$,
    $x - 5y + 10 - 3\sqrt{26} = 0$

32. $\frac{11\sqrt{2}}{2} \approx 7.78$ units, $\frac{11\sqrt{65}}{13} \approx$

    6.82 units, $\frac{11\sqrt{85}}{17} \approx 5.97$ units

34. radius of $\odot P$
    $= \sqrt{((-5) - (-2))^2 + (6 - 2)^2}$
    $= \sqrt{(-3)^2 + 4^2}$
    $= 5$

    Find the distance between the line and the center of $\odot P$.

    $d = \dfrac{Ax_1 + By_1 + C}{\pm \sqrt{A^2 + B^2}}$

    $= \dfrac{5(-5) + (-12)(6) + 32}{-\sqrt{5^2 + (-12)^2}}$

    $= \dfrac{-65}{-13}$

    $= 5$

    Since the distance from the line to the center of the circle is 5, and the definition of a circle is the set of all points in the plane that are 5 units from the center, the line and the circle have one point in common. Therefore, the line is a tangent by definition.

---

31. Write the equations of the lines that are 3 units from the line with equation $x - 5y + 10 = 0$. See margin.

32. Find the lengths of the three altitudes of a triangle whose vertices are at $(5, 3)$, $(1, -4)$, and $(-4, 1)$. See margin.

Programming

33. The following program will calculate the distance from a point to a line.

```
Prgm 7: PTTOLINE
:ClrHome                              Clears the text screen.
:Disp "AX + BY + C = 0"               Displays the quoted message.
:Disp "A ="
:Input A                              Asks the user to input value A.
:Disp "B ="
:Input B
:Disp "C ="
:Input C
:Disp "X-COORDINATE OF POINT ="
:Input X
:Disp "Y-COORDINATE OF POINT ="
:Input Y
:If C > 0                             If C > 0, the denominator is negative.
:-√(A² + B²)→ D                       Calculates denominator and stores it as D.
:If C ≤ 0                             If C ≤ 0, the denominator is positive.
:√(A² + B²)→ D
:AX + BY + C → N                      Calculates numerator and stores it as N.
:N/D → E                              Calculates distance and stores it as E.
:Disp "DISTANCE ="
:Disp E
```

Use the program to find the distance between the point with the given coordinates and line with the given equation. Round to the nearest tenth.

a. $(8, 5)$; $7x - 2y - 9 = 0$ 5.1 units
b. $(10, 8)$; $6x + y + 12 = 0$ –13.2 units
c. $(-4, 0)$; $y = 9x + 3$ 3.6 units
d. $(-12, 0)$; $y = -0.5x - 6$ 0 units

Critical Thinking

34. Circle P has its center at $(-5, 6)$ and passes through $(-2, 2)$. Show that the line with equation $5x - 12y + 32 = 0$ is tangent to circle P. See margin.

Applications and Problem Solving

35. **Entomology** Jenny is working on an advanced biology project in which she is studying old-fashioned methods used to predict the weather. One of the theories she is investigating is the one that relates the number of times a cricket chirps in a minute to the temperature. She conducted experiments and determined the prediction equation $y = 3x + 28$, where y is the temperature in degrees Fahrenheit and x is the number of times a cricket chirps in a minute. Jenny wished to test her equation with three more data points. They were $(16, 72)$, $(18, 84)$, and $(16, 76)$.

35a. $\frac{2\sqrt{10}}{5} \approx$
1.26 units;
$\frac{\sqrt{10}}{5} \approx$
0.63 units;
0 units

Mixed Review

a. Find the distance between each of the data points and the graph of the prediction equation line.

b. For which data point is Jenny's prediction equation a very good predictor?

c. For which data point is the prediction equation the worst predictor? $(16, 72)$

b. $(16, 76)$

36. Consumer Awareness Bill and Liz are going on a vacation in Jamaica. Bill bought 8 rolls of film and 2 bottles of sunscreen for $35.10. The next day, Liz paid $14.30 for three rolls of film and one bottle of sunscreen. If the price for each bottle of sunscreen and each roll of film are the same, what is the price of a roll of film and a bottle of sunscreen? **(Lesson 2-1)** $3.25, $4.55

37. Create a function in the form $y = f(x)$ that has vertical asymptotes at $x = -2$ and $x = 0$ and a hole at $x = 2$. **(Lesson 3-4)** $y = \dfrac{x-2}{x(x+2)(x-2)}$

38. Determine whether the function $y = \dfrac{4}{x^3} + 1$ is *continuous*, has *infinite discontinuity, jump discontinuity*, or *point discontinuity*. **(Lesson 3-8)** infinite discontinuity

39. Simplify the expression $\dfrac{1 - \sin^2 \alpha}{\sin^2 \alpha}$. **(Lesson 7-1)** $\cot^2 \alpha$

40. $-\dfrac{2x}{\sqrt{29}} +$
$\dfrac{5y}{\sqrt{29}} - \dfrac{3}{\sqrt{29}} = 0;$
$\dfrac{3}{\sqrt{29}} \approx 0.56$ units;
$112°$

40. Change $2x - 5y + 3 = 0$ to normal form. Then find p, the measure of the normal, and ϕ, the angle it makes with the positive x-axis. **(Lesson 7-6)**

41. College Entrance Exam Compare quantities A and B. A

Write A if quantity A is greater.
Write B if quantity B is greater.
Write C if the quantities are equal.
Write D if there is not enough information to determine the relationship.

(A) the area of the shaded region
(B) the area of the small circle

EXTENDING THE LESSON

Math Power: Problem Solving

Find the area of the figure formed by the intersection of the lines with these equations:
$5x - 12y + 31 = 0$
$4x - 3y + 5 = 0$
$5x - 12y - 2 = 0$
$4x - 3y - 28 = 0$
The figure is a parallelogram with area 65 square units.

Enrichment Masters Booklet, p. 49

The Chapter Summary and Review
begins with an alphabetical listing
of the new terms that were
presented in the chapter. Have
students define each term and
provide an example of it, if
appropriate.

The Skills and Concepts
presented in the chapter are
reviewed using a side-by-side
format. Encourage students to
refer to the Objectives and
Examples on the left as they
complete the Review Exercises on
the right.

The Chapter Summary and Review
ends with exercises that review
Applications and Problem Solving.

Additional Answers

5. $\cos^2 x + \tan^2 x \cos^2 x \overset{?}{=} 1$

$\cos^2 x + \dfrac{\sin^2 x}{\cos^2 x} \cos^2 x \overset{?}{=} 1$

$\cos^2 x + \sin^2 x \overset{?}{=} 1$

$1 = 1$

6. $\dfrac{1 - \cos \theta}{1 + \cos \theta} \overset{?}{=} (\csc \theta - \cot \theta)^2$

$\dfrac{1 - \cos \theta}{1 + \cos \theta} \overset{?}{=} \left(\dfrac{1}{\sin \theta} - \dfrac{\cos \theta}{\sin \theta}\right)^2$

$\dfrac{1 - \cos \theta}{1 + \cos \theta} \overset{?}{=} \dfrac{(1 - \cos \theta)^2}{\sin^2 \theta}$

$\dfrac{1 - \cos \theta}{1 + \cos \theta} \overset{?}{=} \dfrac{(1 - \cos \theta)^2}{1 - \cos^2 \theta}$

$\dfrac{1 - \cos \theta}{1 + \cos \theta} \overset{?}{=} \dfrac{(1 - \cos \theta)^2}{(1 - \cos \theta)(1 + \cos \theta)}$

$\dfrac{1 - \cos \theta}{1 + \cos \theta} = \dfrac{1 - \cos \theta}{1 + \cos \theta}$

7. $\dfrac{\sec \theta + 1}{\tan \theta} \overset{?}{=} \dfrac{\tan \theta}{\sec \theta - 1}$

$\dfrac{\sec \theta + 1}{\tan \theta} \overset{?}{=} \dfrac{\tan \theta (\sec \theta + 1)}{\sec^2 \theta - 1}$

$\dfrac{\sec \theta + 1}{\tan \theta} \overset{?}{=} \dfrac{\tan \theta (\sec \theta + 1)}{\tan^2 \theta}$

$\dfrac{\sec \theta + 1}{\tan \theta} = \dfrac{\sec \theta + 1}{\tan \theta}$

8. $\dfrac{\sin^4 x - \cos^4 x}{\sin^2 x} \overset{?}{=} 1 - \cot^2 x$

$\dfrac{(\sin^2 x - \cos^2 x)(\sin^2 x + \cos^2 x)}{\sin^2 x} \overset{?}{=}$

$1 - \cot^2 x$

$\dfrac{\sin^2 x - \cos^2 x}{\sin^2 x} \overset{?}{=} 1 - \cot^2 x$

$1 - \dfrac{\cos^2 x}{\sin^2 x} \overset{?}{=} 1 - \cot^2 x$

$1 - \cot^2 x = 1 - \cot^2 x$

VOCABULARY

Upon completing this chapter, you should be
familiar with the following terms:

double-angle identities **378**		**359**	quotient identities
half-angle identities **379**		**358**	reciprocal identities
identity **358**		**372, 373**	sum and difference identities
normal **392**		**360**	symmetry identities
normal form **392**		**387**	trigonometric equations
principal values **387**		**358**	trigonometric identity
Pythagorean identities **359**			

SKILLS AND CONCEPTS

OBJECTIVES AND EXAMPLES	REVIEW EXERCISES
Upon completing this chapter, you should be able to:	Use these exercises to review and prepare for the chapter test.

■ identify and use identities   **(Lesson 7-1)**

If θ is in Quadrant I and $\cos \theta = \frac{1}{3}$, find $\sin \theta$.

$\sin^2 A + \cos^2 A = 1$

$\sin^2 A + \left(\dfrac{1}{3}\right)^2 = 1$

$\sin^2 A + \dfrac{1}{9} = 1$

$\sin^2 A = \dfrac{8}{9}$

$\sin A = \dfrac{2\sqrt{2}}{3}$

Solve for values of θ between $0°$ and $90°$.

1. If $\sin \theta = \frac{1}{2}$, find $\csc \theta$.   2

2. If $\tan \theta = 4$, find $\sec \theta$. $\sqrt{17}$

3. If $\csc \theta = \frac{5}{3}$, find $\cos \theta$. $\frac{4}{5}$

4. If $\cos \theta = \frac{4}{5}$, find $\tan \theta$. $\frac{3}{4}$

■ use the basic trigonometric identities to verify other identities   **(Lesson 7-2)**

Verify that $\csc x \sec x = \cot x + \tan x$ is an identity.

$\csc x \sec x = \cot x + \tan x$

$\dfrac{1}{\sin x} \cdot \dfrac{1}{\cos x} = \dfrac{\cos x}{\sin x} + \dfrac{\sin x}{\cos x}$

$\dfrac{1}{\sin x \cos x} = \dfrac{\cos^2 x + \sin^2 x}{\sin x \cos x}$

$\dfrac{1}{\sin x \cos x} = \dfrac{1}{\sin x \cos x}$

Verify that each of the following is an identity.

5. $\cos^2 x + \tan^2 x \cos^2 x = 1$

6. $\dfrac{1 - \cos \theta}{1 + \cos \theta} = (\csc \theta - \cot \theta)^2$

7. $\dfrac{\sec \theta + 1}{\tan \theta} = \dfrac{\tan \theta}{\sec \theta - 1}$

8. $\dfrac{\sin^4 x - \cos^4 x}{\sin^2 x} = 1 - \cot^2 x$

5–8. See margin.

13.
$$\cos (90° - \theta) \overset{?}{=} \sin \theta$$
$$\cos 90° \cos \theta + \sin 90° \sin \theta \overset{?}{=} \sin \theta$$
$$(0) \cdot \cos \theta + (1)\sin \theta \overset{?}{=} \sin \theta$$
$$\sin \theta = \sin \theta$$

14.
$$\cos (60° + \theta) + \cos (60° - \theta) \overset{?}{=} \cos \theta$$
$$(\cos 60° \cos \theta - \sin 60° \sin \theta) + (\cos 60° \cos \theta + \sin 60° \sin \theta) \overset{?}{=} \cos \theta$$
$$\dfrac{1}{2} \cos \theta - \dfrac{\sqrt{3}}{2} \sin \theta + \dfrac{1}{2} \cos \theta + \dfrac{\sqrt{3}}{2} \sin \theta \overset{?}{=} \cos \theta$$
$$\cos \theta = \cos \theta$$

- use the sum and difference identities for sine, cosine, and tangent functions (Lesson 7-3)

Find $\sin 105°$.

$$\sin 105° = \sin (60 + 45)°$$
$$= \sin 60° \cos 45° + \cos 60° \sin 45°$$
$$= \frac{\sqrt{3}}{2} \cdot \frac{\sqrt{2}}{2} + \frac{1}{2} \cdot \frac{\sqrt{2}}{2}$$
$$= \frac{\sqrt{6} + \sqrt{2}}{4}$$

Use the sum and difference identities to find the exact value of each function.

9. $\cos 240°$ $-\dfrac{1}{2}$ 10. $\cos 15°$ $\dfrac{\sqrt{2}+\sqrt{6}}{4}$

11. $\sin (-255°)$ $\dfrac{\sqrt{6}+\sqrt{2}}{4}$ 12. $\tan 165°$
                                          $-2+\sqrt{3}$

Verify that each of the following is an identity.

13. $\cos (90° - \theta) = \sin \theta$

14. $\cos (60° + \theta) + \cos (60° - \theta) = \cos \theta$
13–14. See margin.

- use the double- and half-angle identities for the sine, cosine, and tangent functions (Lesson 7-4)

If $\sin x = \dfrac{3}{4}$ and x is in the first quadrant, find $\cos 2x$.

$$\cos 2x = 1 - 2 \sin^2 x$$
$$= 1 - 2 \left(\frac{3}{4}\right)^2$$
$$= -\frac{1}{8}$$

If $\cos \theta = \dfrac{3}{5}$ and θ is in the first quadrant, find each of the following.

15. $\sin 2\theta$ $\dfrac{24}{25}$ 16. $\cos 2\theta$ $-\dfrac{7}{25}$

17. $\sin \dfrac{\theta}{2}$ $\dfrac{\sqrt{5}}{5}$ 18. $\cos \dfrac{\theta}{2}$ $\dfrac{2\sqrt{5}}{5}$

19. $\tan 2\theta$ $-\dfrac{24}{7}$ 20. $\tan \dfrac{\theta}{2}$ $\dfrac{1}{2}$

- solve trigonometric equations (Lesson 7-5)

Solve $2 \cos^2 x - 1 = 0$ for all values of x.

$$2 \cos^2 x - 1 = 0$$
$$\cos^2 x = \frac{1}{2}$$
$$\cos x = \pm \frac{\sqrt{2}}{2}$$
$$x = 45° + 90k°$$

Solve each equation for all values of x.

21. $\tan x + 1 = \sec x$ $360k°$

22. $\sin^2 x + \cos 2x - \cos x = 0$

23. $\sin x \tan x - \tan x = 0$ $180k°$

24. $\cos 2x \sin x = 1$ $270° + 360k°$
22. $90° + 180k°, 360k°$

- write linear equations in normal form (Lesson 7-6)

Write $3x + 2y - 6 = 0$ in normal form.

Since C is negative, use the positive value of $\sqrt{A^2 + B^2} = \sqrt{3^2 + 2^2} = \sqrt{13}$.

The normal form is $\dfrac{3x}{\sqrt{13}} + \dfrac{2y}{\sqrt{13}} - \dfrac{6}{\sqrt{13}} = 0$.

Write each equation in normal form. Then find p, the measure of the normal, and ϕ, the angle the normal makes with the positive x-axis. 25–28. See margin.

25. $7x + 3y - 8 = 0$

26. $6x = 4y - 5$

27. $9x = -5y + 3$

28. $x - 7y = -5$

Alternative Review Strategy

To provide a brief in-class review, you may wish to read the following questions to your students and have them answer verbally.

1. If $\cos x = \dfrac{3}{4}$, find $\sec x$. $\dfrac{4}{3}$

2. If $\tan x = \dfrac{12}{5}$, find $\sin x$. $\dfrac{12}{13}$

3. Simplify $\sec^2 x - 1$. $\tan^2 x$

4. $\cos x \csc x = 0.7$ Find $\cot x$.   0.7

5. Find $\cos 15°$ from values of functions of 30° and 45°.   ≈ 0.9659

6. Find $\tan 75°$ from values of functions of 30° and 45°.   ≈ 3.7321

7. If $\sin x = \dfrac{3}{5}$ and x is in the first quadrant, find $\sin \dfrac{x}{2}$. $\dfrac{\sqrt{10}}{10}$

8. Solve for principal values of x: $2 \cos x = 1$. $x = 60°$

9. Write $4x + 3y - 2 = 0$ in normal form. $\dfrac{4}{5}x + \dfrac{3}{5}y - \dfrac{2}{5} = 0$

10. Find the distance from the point (1, 2) to the line $y = \dfrac{1}{2}x - 5$. $\dfrac{13\sqrt{5}}{5}$

For more information on other methods of alternate assessment, you may wish to refer to Glencoe's *Alternate Assessment in the Mathematics Classroom*.

Additional Answers

25. $\dfrac{7x}{\sqrt{58}} + \dfrac{3y}{\sqrt{58}} - \dfrac{8}{\sqrt{58}} = 0; \dfrac{8}{\sqrt{58}} \approx 1.1; \approx 23°$

26. $-\dfrac{3x}{\sqrt{13}} + \dfrac{2y}{\sqrt{13}} - \dfrac{5}{2\sqrt{13}} = 0 \quad \dfrac{5}{2\sqrt{13}} \approx 0.7; \approx 146°$

27. $\dfrac{9x}{\sqrt{106}} + \dfrac{5y}{\sqrt{106}} - \dfrac{3}{\sqrt{106}} = 0 \quad \dfrac{3}{\sqrt{106}} \approx 0.3; \approx 29°$

28. $-\dfrac{x}{5\sqrt{2}} + \dfrac{7y}{5\sqrt{2}} - \dfrac{1}{\sqrt{2}} = 0; \dfrac{1}{\sqrt{2}} \approx 0.7; \approx 98°$

Two multiple-choice tests (Forms 1A and 1B) and two free-response tests (Form 2A and 2B) are provided in the *Evaluation Masters*. Chapter 7 Test, Form 1A is shown below. Chapter 7 Test, Form 2A is shown on the next page.

Evaluation Masters Booklet, pp. 77–78

■ find the distance from a point to a line **(Lesson 7-7)**

Find the distance between $(-1, 3)$ and the graph of $-3x + 4y = -5$.

$$d = \frac{Ax_1 + By_1 + C}{\pm\sqrt{A^2 + B^2}}$$

$$= \frac{-3x_1 + 4y_1 + 5}{-\sqrt{(-3)^2 + 4^2}}$$

$$= \frac{-3(-1) + 4(3) + 5}{-\sqrt{25}}$$

$$= \frac{20}{-5} \text{ or } -4 \text{ units}$$

Find the distance from the point with the given coordinates to the line with the given equation. Round answers to the nearest tenth.

29. $(5, 6); 2x - 3y + 2 = 0$ 1.7 units
30. $(-3, -4); 2y = -3x + 6$ 6.4 units
31. $(-2, 4); 4y = 3x - 1$ 4.6 units
32. $(21, 20); y = \frac{1}{3}x + 6$ 6.6 units

■ write the equations of lines that bisect angles formed by intersecting lines **(Lesson 7-7)**

Find an equation of the line that bisects the acute angle formed by the lines $-x + 3y - 2 = 0$ and $y = \frac{3}{5}x + 3$.

$$\frac{-x + 3y - 2}{\sqrt{10}} = -\left(\frac{-3x + 5y - 15}{\sqrt{34}}\right)$$

$$-\sqrt{34}x + 3\sqrt{34}y - 2\sqrt{34} = 3\sqrt{10}x - 5\sqrt{10}y + 15\sqrt{10}$$

$$(-\sqrt{34} - 3\sqrt{10})x + (3\sqrt{34} + 5\sqrt{10})y - 2\sqrt{34} - 15\sqrt{10} = 0$$

Find an equation of the line that bisects the acute angle formed by the graphs of each pair of equations.

33. $3x + y - 2 = 0, x + 2y - 3 = 0$
34. $y = \frac{1}{3}x - 6, y = \frac{3}{4}x + 2$
33–34. See margin.

APPLICATIONS AND PROBLEM SOLVING

35. **Physics** While studying two different physics books, Jeremy notices that two different formulas are used to find the height of a projectile. One formula is $h = \frac{v_0^2 \sin^2 \theta}{2g}$; the other is $h = \frac{v_0^2 \tan^2 \theta}{2g \sec^2 \theta}$. Are these two formulas equivalent or is there an error in one of the books? Show your work. **(Lesson 7-2)**
The formulas are equivalent.

36. **Surveying** Talitia Jones is surveying a piece of property. She measures the angle between one side of a rectangular lot and the line from her position to the opposite corner of the lot as 30°. She then measures the angle between that line and the line to a telephone pole on the edge of the property as 45°. If Ms. Jones stands 100 yards from the opposite corner of the property, how far is she from the telephone pole? **(Lesson 7-3)** about 51.76 yards

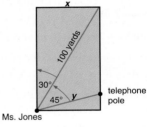

408 CHAPTER 7 TRIGONOMETRIC IDENTITIES AND EQUATIONS

Additional Answers

33. $\left(3\sqrt{5} + \sqrt{10}\right)x + \left(\sqrt{5} + 2\sqrt{10}\right)y - 2\sqrt{5} - 3\sqrt{10} = 0$

34. $\left(5 + 3\sqrt{10}\right)x - \left(15 + 4\sqrt{10}\right)y - 90 + 8\sqrt{10} = 0$

NAME _____ DATE _____

~Chapter 7 Test, Form 1A

Write the letter for the correct answer in the blank at the right of each problem.

1. Solve for the value of tan θ between 0° and 90° if cos $\theta = 0.25$.
   A. 4   B. $\frac{1}{16}$ C. $\sqrt{15}$ D. $\frac{\sqrt{15}}{15}$ 1. __C__

2. If cot $\theta = \frac{5}{12}$, find csc θ for θ between 0° and 90°.
   A. $\frac{12}{13}$ B. $\frac{5}{12}$ C. $\frac{-5}{12}$ D. $\frac{13}{12}$ 2. __D__

3. Express sin 750° as a function of an angle in Quadrant I.
   A. sin 30°   B. –sin 30°   C. sin 15°   D. –sin 15°   3. __A__

4. Simplify $\frac{1 - \cot^2 \sec^2 \theta}{\cot^2 \theta}$.
   A. sec θ B. 1   C. cot θ D. –1   4. __D__

5. Which equation is a trigonometric identity?
   A. tan θ = sin θ sec θ B. sec² θ – csc² θ = 1
   C. tan x sin x = cos x   D. tan² θ = sec² θ + 1   5. __A__

6. Find a numerical value of one trigonometric function if cos x csc x = 2.
   A. sec x = $\frac{1}{2}$ B. sin x = $\frac{1}{2}$ C. tan x = 2   D. cot x = 2   6. __D__

7. Find the value of tan $(x - y)$ for 0° < x < 90° and 0° < y < 90° when sin x = $\frac{15}{17}$ and cos y = $\frac{8}{17}$.
   A. $-\frac{289}{64}$ B. $-\frac{240}{161}$ C. $\frac{240}{161}$ D. 0   7. __D__

8. Use a sum or difference identity to find the exact value of cos 150°.
   A. $\frac{\sqrt{3}}{2}$ B. $-\frac{\sqrt{3}}{2}$ C. $\frac{\sqrt{3} - \sqrt{2}}{2}$ D. $-\frac{\sqrt{2}}{2}$ 8. __B__

9. Which expression is equivalent to cos (90° – θ)?
   A. sin θ B. –sin θ C. cos θ D. –cos θ 9. __A__

10. Use a half-angle identity to find the exact value of cos 67.5°.
    A. $\frac{1}{2}\sqrt{2 - \sqrt{2}}$ B. $-\frac{1}{2}\sqrt{2 - \sqrt{2}}$ C. $-\frac{1}{2}\sqrt{2 + \sqrt{2}}$ D. $\sqrt{3 + 2\sqrt{2}}$ 10. __A__

11. Which expression is *not* equivalent to cos 2θ for all values of θ?
    A. cos² θ – sin² θ B. 2 sin θ cos θ
    C. 1 – 2 sin² θ D. 2 cos² θ – 1   11. __B__

12. If sin $\theta = -\frac{4}{5}$ and θ terminates in Quadrant III, find the exact value of sin 2θ.
    A. $\frac{16}{25}$ B. $-\frac{24}{25}$ C. $\frac{24}{25}$ D. $-\frac{9}{25}$ 12. __C__

T77
Glencoe Division, Macmillan/McGraw-Hill

NAME _____ DATE _____

Chapter 7 Test, Form 1A (continued)

13. Solve 2 sin² x – 3 sin x + 1 = 0 for principal values of x.
    A. 0°, 30°   B. 30°   C. 30°, 90°   D. 0°, 60°   13. __C__

14. Which value is *not* a solution of 2 sin x + 1 = 0?
    A. $\frac{\pi}{6}$ B. $-\frac{\pi}{6}$ C. 210°   D. –30°   14. __A__

15. Write the equation x + y = 5 in normal form to find (cos θ, sin θ).
    A. $\left(\frac{\sqrt{2}}{2}, -\frac{\sqrt{2}}{2}\right)$ B. $\left(\frac{\sqrt{2}}{2}, \frac{\sqrt{2}}{2}\right)$ C. $\left(-\frac{\sqrt{2}}{2}, -\frac{\sqrt{2}}{2}\right)$ D. $\left(-\frac{\sqrt{2}}{2}, -\frac{\sqrt{2}}{2}\right)$ 15. __B__

16. Write the equation 3x + y – 1 = 0 in normal form to find the length, in units, of the normal, p.
    A. $-\frac{\sqrt{10}}{10}$ B. $\frac{\sqrt{10}}{10}$ C. $\frac{\sqrt{2}}{4}$ D. $-\frac{\sqrt{2}}{4}$ 16. __B__

17. Write the equation $\sqrt{3}x + y - 4 = 0$ in normal form to find the angle, ϕ, that the normal to the line makes with the positive x-axis.
    A. 45°   B. 90°   C. 60°   D. 30°   17. __D__

18. Find the distance, in units, between P(–2, 1) and the line with equation 3x – 4y + 1 = 0.
    A. –1.8   B. 1.8   C. 2   D. –2   18. __B__

19. Find the distance, in units, between the lines with equations 2x – 5y = 8 and $y = \frac{2}{5}x - 3$.
    A. $-\frac{23}{29}\sqrt{29}$ B. $\frac{7}{29}\sqrt{29}$ C. $-\frac{7}{29}\sqrt{29}$ D. $\frac{23}{29}\sqrt{29}$ 19. __B__

20. Find the equation of the line that bisects the acute angle formed by the graphs of the equations 6x + 3y – 1 = 0 and 2x + 2y – 3 = 0.
    A. 6$\sqrt{5}$ + 12$\sqrt{2}$ x + 6$\sqrt{5}$ + 6$\sqrt{2}$ y + 9$\sqrt{5}$ + 2$\sqrt{2}$ = 0
    B. 6$\sqrt{5}$ + 12$\sqrt{2}$ x + 6$\sqrt{5}$ + 6$\sqrt{2}$ y – 9$\sqrt{5}$ – 2$\sqrt{2}$ = 0
    C. 6$\sqrt{5}$ – 12$\sqrt{2}$ x + 6$\sqrt{5}$ – 6$\sqrt{2}$ y + 9$\sqrt{5}$ + 2$\sqrt{2}$ = 0
    D. 6$\sqrt{5}$ – 12$\sqrt{2}$ x + 6$\sqrt{5}$ – 6$\sqrt{2}$ y – 9$\sqrt{5}$ – 2$\sqrt{2}$ = 0   20. __B__

Bonus

If –90° < θ < 0° and sin $\theta = -\frac{12}{13}$, find cos 4θ.
A. $\frac{239}{28,561}$ B. $-\frac{239}{28,561}$ C. $\frac{238}{169}$ D. $-\frac{239}{169}$ Bonus: __B__

T78
Glencoe Division, Macmillan/McGraw-Hill

CHAPTER 7 TEST

Solve for values of θ between $0°$ and $90°$.

1. If $\sin\theta = \dfrac{1}{2}$, find $\cos\theta$. $\dfrac{\sqrt{3}}{2}$

2. If $\csc\theta = \dfrac{5}{3}$, find $\cos\theta$. $\dfrac{4}{5}$

3. If $\sec\theta = 3$, find $\tan\theta$. $2\sqrt{2}$

4. If $\sin\theta = \dfrac{4}{5}$, find $\sec\theta$. $\dfrac{5}{3}$

Verify that each of the following is an identity.

5. $\tan\theta(\cot\theta + \tan\theta) = \sec^2\theta$

6. $\sin^2 A\cot^2 A = (1-\sin A)(1+\sin A)$

7. $\dfrac{\sec x}{\sin x} - \dfrac{\sin x}{\cos x} = \cot x$

8. $\dfrac{\cos x}{1+\sin x} + \dfrac{\cos x}{1-\sin x} = 2\sec x$

5–8. See Teacher's Answer Key.

Use the sum and difference identities to find the exact value of each function.

9. $\sin 255°$ $\dfrac{-\sqrt{6}-\sqrt{2}}{4}$

10. $\cos 165°$ $\dfrac{-\sqrt{2}-\sqrt{6}}{4}$

11. $\sin(-195°)$ $\dfrac{\sqrt{6}-\sqrt{2}}{4}$

If $\cos x = \dfrac{3}{4}$ and x is in the fourth quadrant, find each value.

12. $\sin 2x$ $-\dfrac{3\sqrt{7}}{8}$

13. $\cos\dfrac{x}{2}$ $-\dfrac{\sqrt{14}}{4}$

14. $\tan 2x$ $-3\sqrt{7}$

Solve each equation for $0° \le x \le 180°$.

15. $\sin x - \cos x = 0$ $45°$

16. $2\cos^2 x + 3\sin x - 3 = 0$ $30°, 90°, 150°$

17. $\tan^2 x - \sqrt{3}\tan x = 0$ $0°, 60°, 180°$

18. $\tan 2x\cot x - 3 = 0$ $30°, 150°$

Write each equation in normal form. Then find p, the measure of its normal, and ϕ the angle the normal makes with the positive x-axis. 19–21. See margin.

19. $-x + y - 3 = 0$

20. $-3x = 6y - 7$

21. $-10x + 5 = -5y$

Find the distance from the point with the given coordinates to the line with the given equation. Round answers to the nearest tenth.

22. $(-5, 8); 2x + y - 6 = 0$ 3.6 units

23. $(-6, 8); -3x - 4y = 2$ 3.2 units

24. Find the equation of the line that bisects the acute angle formed by the graphs of $7 = 5x + 2y$ and $y = -\dfrac{3}{4}x + 1$. $(25 + 3\sqrt{29})x + (10 + 4\sqrt{29})y - 35 + 4\sqrt{29} = 0$

25. **Physics** The range of a projected object is the distance that it travels from the point where it is released. In the absence of air resistance, a projectile released at an angle of elevation, θ, with an initial velocity of v_0 has a range of $R = \dfrac{v_0^2}{g}\sin 2\theta$, where g is the acceleration due to gravity. Find the range of a projectile with an initial velocity of 88 feet per second if $\sin\theta = \dfrac{3}{5}$ and $\cos\theta = \dfrac{4}{5}$. The acceleration due to gravity is 32 feet per second squared. 232.32 feet

Bonus If $0° < \theta < 90°, x > y > 0$, and $\cot\theta = \dfrac{x^2 - y^2}{2xy}$, find the value of $\sec\theta$. $\dfrac{x^2+y^2}{x^2-y^2}$

CHAPTER 7 TEST 409

This page may be used as a test or as a review. All answers to this test appear in the Selected Answers in the student text.

Standardized Test Practice Questions are also provided in the *Evaluation Masters*.

Evaluation Masters Booklet, pp. 81–82

NAME _____ DATE _____

Chapter 7 Test, Form 2A

1. If $\sin A = -0.6$, find $\csc A$. 1. $-\dfrac{5}{3}$

2. If $\cot A = \dfrac{3}{4}$, find $\sin A$ for A between π and $\dfrac{3\pi}{2}$. 2. $-\dfrac{4}{5}$

3. Express $\sin -750°$ as a function of $30°$. 3. $-\sin 30°$

4. Simplify $\cos\theta\sec\theta\tan^2\theta$. 4. $\tan^2\theta$

5. In which quadrant(s) does $\cos\theta = -\sqrt{1 - \sin^2\theta}$? 5. II, III

6. If $\cot x\sin x = \dfrac{1}{2}$, find the numerical value of $\sec x$. 6. 2

7. Verify that $\tan x\csc x = \sec x$ is an identity. 7. See student's work.

8. Find the exact value of $\sin 165°$. 8. $\dfrac{\sqrt{6}-\sqrt{2}}{4}$

9. If $\sin\alpha = \dfrac{15}{17}$ for $90° < \alpha < 180°$ and $\cos\beta = \dfrac{4}{5}$ for $270° < \beta < 360°$, find $\sin(\alpha + \beta)$. 9. $\dfrac{84}{85}$

10. Use a half-angle identity to find the exact value of $\cos\dfrac{11\pi}{12}$. 10. $-\dfrac{1}{2}\sqrt{2+\sqrt{3}}$

11. If $\cos y = -\dfrac{2}{\sqrt{5}}$ and y is in the second quadrant, find $\cos 2y$. 11. $-\dfrac{17}{25}$

T81
Glencoe Division, Macmillan/McGraw-Hill

NAME _____ DATE _____

Chapter 7 Test, Form 2A (continued)

12. For how many values of θ does $\cos\theta = -\dfrac{1}{2}$? 12. infinitely many

13. Solve $\sin^2 x + 2\sin x - 3 = 0$ for $0 \le x \le 180°$. 13. $90°$

14. Solve $(\tan x - 1)(2\cos x + 1) = 0$ for all values of x. 14. $45° + 180k°, 120° + 360k°, 240° + 360k°$

15. Simplify $x\cos 30° + y\sin 30° + 7 = 0$. 15. $\sqrt{3}x + y + 14 = 0$

16. Write the normal form of $y = 2x + 3$. 16. $\dfrac{-2x}{\sqrt{5}} + \dfrac{y}{\sqrt{5}} - \dfrac{3}{\sqrt{5}} = 0$

17. Find the angle the normal for the equation $4x + 3y - 1 = 0$ makes with the x-axis. 17. $37°$

18. Find the distance between $P(0, 5)$ and the line with equation $-2x + y - 3 = 0$. 18. $\dfrac{2\sqrt{5}}{5}$ or about 0.89 units

19. Find the distance between two parallel lines with equations $2x - 2y = 5$ and $y = x - 1$. 19. $-\dfrac{3\sqrt{2}}{4}$ or about 1.06 units

20. Find the equation of the line that bisects the acute angle formed by the graphs of the equations $3x + y = -6$ and $2x - y = 1$. 20. $(3\sqrt{5} + 2\sqrt{10})x + (\sqrt{5} - \sqrt{10})y + 6\sqrt{5} - \sqrt{10} = 0$

Bonus How are the lines that bisect the angles formed by the equations $3x + y = 6$ and $x - 3y = 1$ related to each other? Bonus: They are perpendicular to each other.

T82
Glencoe Division, Macmillan/McGraw-Hill

Test Generator Software is provided in Apple, IBM, and Macintosh versions. You may use this software to create your own tests, based on the needs of your students.

Additional Answers

19. $-\dfrac{x}{\sqrt{2}} + \dfrac{y}{\sqrt{2}} - \dfrac{3}{\sqrt{2}} = 0$; $\dfrac{3}{\sqrt{2}} \approx 2.1$; $135°$

20. $\dfrac{1}{\sqrt{5}}x + \dfrac{2}{\sqrt{5}}y - \dfrac{7}{3\sqrt{5}} = 0$; $\dfrac{7}{3\sqrt{5}} \approx 1.0$; $\approx 63°$

21. $\dfrac{2}{\sqrt{5}}x - \dfrac{1}{\sqrt{5}}y - \dfrac{1}{\sqrt{5}} = 0$; $\dfrac{1}{\sqrt{5}} \approx 0.4$; $\approx 333°$

CHAPTER TEST 7 409

8 VECTORS AND PARAMETRIC EQUATIONS

PREVIEWING THE CHAPTER

This chapter introduces vectors as directed line segments. Students begin by learning the language of vectors, such as magnitude, amplitude, parallel vectors, and opposites. After students become familiar with the terminology of vectors, they add, subtract, and multiply vectors. They also find ordered pairs that represent vectors, which describe vectors in two-dimensional space. They extend this concept to include ordered triples to describe vectors in three-dimensional space. Next, they solve problems using vectors and right-triangle geometry. Finally, they learn to write and graph parametric equations to model motion and solve problems.

Lesson Objective Chart

Lesson (Pages)	Lesson Objectives		State/Local Objectives
8-1 (412–418)	8-1A:	Find equal, opposite, and parallel vectors.	
	8-1B:	Add and subtract vectors geometrically.	
8-2 (419–424)	8-2A:	Find ordered pairs that represent vectors.	
	8-2B:	Add, subtract, multiply, and find the magnitude of vectors algebraically.	
8-3 (425–429)	8-3A:	Add and subtract vectors in three-dimensional space.	
	8-3B:	Find the magnitude of vectors in three-dimensional space.	
8-4 (430–435)	8-4A:	Find the inner and cross products of two vectors.	
	8-4B:	Determine whether two vectors are perpendicular.	
8-5 (436–441)	8-5:	Solve problems using vectors and right triangle trigonometry.	
8-6 (442–447)	8-6A:	Write vector and parametric equations of lines.	
	8-6B:	Graph parametric equations.	
8-7 (449–455)	8-7A:	Model the motion of a projectile using parametric equations.	
	8-7B:	Solve problems related to the motion of a projectile, its trajectory, and range.	

ORGANIZING THE CHAPTER

You may want to refer to the **Course Planning Guide Calendar** on pages T34-T35 for a complete pacing chart.

Lesson Planning Guide / Blackline Masters Booklets

Lesson	Pages	Practice	Enrichment	Evaluation	Technology: Graphing Calculator	Technology: Computer	Technology: Multicultural Activity	Activity Masters: Applications	Activity Masters: Problem Solving	Activity Masters: Case Study Follow-Up	Activity Masters: Decision Making	Transparencies
8-1	412-418	p. 50	p. 50			p. 16						8-1
8-2	419-424	p. 51	p. 51	Quiz A, p. 97								8-2
8-3	425-429	p. 52	p. 52						p. 23			8-3
8-4	430-435	p. 53	p. 53	Quiz B, p. 97 Mid-Chapter Test, p. 99	p. 15							8-4
8-5	436-441	p. 54	p. 54					p. 22			p. 24	8-5
8-6	442-447	p. 55	p. 55	Quiz C, p. 98								8-6
8-7	449-455	p. 56	p. 56	Quiz D, p. 98			p. 8					8-7
Review	456-458	Multiple Choice Tests, Forms 1A and 1B, pp. 89-92 Free Response Tests, Forms 2A and 2B, pp. 93-96 Standardized Test Questions, p. 100										
Test	459											

Other Chapter Resources

Student Edition

Case Study Follow-Up, p. 441
Decision Making, p. 424
Technology, p. 448
Unit Review, pp. 460-461

Other Supplements

Transparency 8-0 for Chapter Opener
Evaluation Masters, Unit Test, pp. 101-104
Alternate Assessment in the Mathematics Classroom,
    Glencoe Publishing Co., 1993
Cooperative Learning in the Mathematics Classroom,
    Glencoe Publishing Co., 1993

Software

Test and Review Generator Software
    Available for Apple, IBM, and Macintosh
Teacher's Guide for Software Resources

ENHANCING THE CHAPTER

Cooperative Learning

Assigning Roles to Students

Keep in mind that past and current experiences of most students involve competitive rather than cooperative activities. Therefore, remember to be patient as well as persistent in your efforts to develop cooperative interdependence. One way to enhance group skills is to assign each student in the group a specific role. Examples of such roles include a *checker,* who makes sure all members know and can explain the responses, an *encourager,* who motivates silent or reluctant members to participate, a *praiser,* who commends members for good ideas or contributions, a *prober,* who asks questions about or calls for further clarifications of ideas that have been proposed, a *materials handler,* who obtains the necessary items for the activity and then returns them to their proper place, a *recorder,* who writes the group's ideas or answers on paper, and a *help asker,* who requests assistance from the teacher when the group needs it. Other roles may suggest themselves to you to meet certain needs of a particular activity or student. For example, a group member who has difficulty remaining quiet can be assigned the role of *noise monitor,* who uses a non-verbal signal to remind the members to quiet down.

For more information on cooperative learning, see pages T20-T21. Additional information on using cooperative groups is available in Glencoe's *Cooperative Learning in the Mathematics Classroom,* ©1993.

Multicultural

Multicultural Activity Masters, p. 8

NAME _____ DATE _____

8 **Multicultural Activity** (Use after Lesson 8-7)

Maria Gaetana Agnesi

Born in Milan, Italy, Maria Agnesi (1718–1799) was a child prodigy. By the age of thirteen, she spoke fluent Italian, French, Latin, and Greek, and she could read German, Spanish, and Hebrew. From 1738 to 1748, she applied her linguistic abilities to the monumental task of translating and compiling all of the known mathematical works of her time. The resulting text, *Analytical Institutions,* was acclaimed as a masterpiece throughout the world.

One of the many problems discussed in *Analytical Institutions* involves the situation pictured at the right. In the diagram, point A begins at O and travels at a constant rate θ counterclockwise around a circle of radius a. The moving point A determines the location of point P. Agnesi solved the problem of representing P in terms of a and θ by using analytic geometry and parametric equations. In the exercises that follow, you will derive the equations for $P(x, y)$ and sketch the curve known as *the witch of Agnesi.*

1. Refer to the diagram at the right.
   a. Use $\triangle OBT$ to show that $x = 2a \cot \theta$.
   $$\tan \theta = \frac{BT}{OT} = \frac{2a}{x}; \ x = 2a \cot \theta$$
   b. Use $\triangle OAS$ to show that $y = OA \sin \theta$.
   $$\sin \theta = \frac{AS}{OA} = \frac{y}{OA}; \ y = OA \sin \theta$$
   c. Show that $\triangle OAC$ is a right triangle. Since $\angle OAC$ is inscribed in a semicircle, $m\angle OAC = 90°$; thus $\triangle OAC$ is a right triangle.
   d. Use $\triangle OAC$ to show that $y = 2a \sin^2 \theta$.
   $$\sin \theta = \frac{OA}{OC} = \frac{OA}{2a} = \frac{y}{2a \sin \theta}; \ y = 2a \sin^2 \theta$$

2. Use a computer or graphing calculator to graph the curve represented by $x = 2a \cot \theta$ and $y = 2a \sin^2 \theta$, with $a = 1$. Sketch the curve on the grid at the right.

3. **RESEARCH** Find out how the curve you graphed in Exercise 2 came to be known as *the witch of Agnesi.*
   See students' work.

T8
Glencoe Division, Macmillan/McGraw-Hill

Activity Masters

Applications, p. 22

CHAPTER NAME _____ DATE _____

8 **Applications** (Use after Lesson 8-5)

The Angle of Repose

Suppose you place a block of wood on an inclined plane, as shown at the right. If the angle, θ, at which the plane is inclined from the horizontal is very small, the block will not move. If you increase the angle, the block will eventually overcome the force of friction and start to slide down the plane.

At the instant the block begins to slide, the angle formed by the plane is called the *angle of friction,* or the *angle of repose.*

For situations in which the block and plane are smooth but unlubricated, the angle of repose depends *only* on the types of materials in the block and the plane. The angle is independent of the area of contact between the two surfaces and of the weight of the block.

The drawing at the right shows how to use vectors to find a coefficient of friction. This coefficient varies with different materials and is denoted by the Greek letter mu, μ.

$$F = W \sin \theta \quad N = W \cos \theta$$
$$F = \mu N$$
$$\mu = \frac{\sin \theta}{\cos \theta} = \tan \theta$$

Solve. Round your answers to the nearest degree.

1. A wooden chute is built so that wooden crates can slide down into the basement of a store. What angle should the chute make for the crates to slide down at a constant speed?
   27°

2. Will a 100-pound wooden crate slide down a stone ramp that makes an angle of 20° with the horizontal? Explain your answer.
   No, the angle must be at least 27°.

3. If you increase the weight of the crate in Exercise 2 to 300 pounds, does it change your answer?
   No, the weight does not affect the angle.

Material	Coefficient of Friction μ
Wood on wood	0.5
Wood on stone	0.5
Rubber tire on dry concrete	1.0
Rubber tire on wet concrete	0.7

4. A car with rubber tires is driving on dry concrete pavement. If the car tires spin without traction on a hill, how steep is the slant of the street?
   at least 45°

5. For Exercise 4, does it make a difference if it starts to rain? Explain your answer.
   Yes; the street needs to slant only 35° for the car tires to spin.

T22
Glencoe Division, Macmillan/McGraw-Hill

Problem Solving, p. 23

CHAPTER NAME _____ DATE _____

8 **Problem Solving** (Use after Lesson 8-3)

Use Perspective Drawing

Although three-dimensional space cannot physically be reduced to two dimensions for study, it can be modeled by using perspective drawing. A perspective drawing gives an accurate sense of depth, allowing a three-dimensional quantity like a vector to be represented visually.

Example   Sketch the vector from the origin to $P(5, -2, -7)$.

Draw a right prism with sides measuring 5, 2, and 7 units. Begin by sketching mutually perpendicular x-, y-, and z-axes. Locate each coordinate on the correct axis.

Draw parallelograms with pairs of coordinates at opposite vertices.

Complete the prism by drawing the remaining faces. Draw the vector.

$P(5, -2, -7)$

Sketch the vector from the origin to the given point.

1. $A(2, 4, 5)$

2. $B(4, -5, -2)$

3. $C(-3, 1, -3)$

4. $D(-4, -2, -3)$

T23
Glencoe Division, Macmillan/McGraw-Hill

Decision Making, p. 24

CHAPTER NAME _____ DATE _____

8 **Decision Making** (Use after Lesson 8-5)

Choosing Health Insurance

The cost of health care in the United States has skyrocketed in recent years. From 1980 to 1990, medical costs increased 117%. Physicians' fees went up 110%. The price of prescription drugs showed the greatest increase, rising more than 150% during the decade. A prescription that retailed for $10 in 1980 sold for $25 in 1990. In 1980, a typical hospital room cost about $450 per day. By 1990, the daily rate had surpassed $1,000.

With the cost of health care so high, few people can afford to pay for a long hospital stay. Health insurance can pay much of the cost of medical care, but like other medical costs, the price of health insurance has escalated dramatically. It is estimated that 14% of all Americans, some 35 million individuals, cannot afford health insurance.

Answers will vary.

Research the kinds of health insurance that might be suitable for your needs. Use the following questions to guide you.

1. Can you get insurance through an employer? Do you belong to an organization through which you can purchase a group plan?

2. Will you be covered by your parents' health insurance when you go to college? Does the college you are considering offer student health insurance? If so, how much will it cost and what level of coverage will it provide?

3. What is a *deductible?* What are the advantages and disadvantages of various levels of deductibles? If you choose a high deductible, will you be able to afford an expensive illness? At what rate does a policy pay medical expenses after you meet your deductible? Is there a limit to the amount of money you will have to pay out-of-pocket?

4. What is a Health Maintenance Organization (HMO)? Are there any HMOs in your city? Might an HMO offer you a viable option to conventional health insurance?

5. Do you want an insurance plan that allows you to choose your own doctor and hospital, or would you accept a less expensive plan that limited the number of doctors and hospitals you could use?

6. Are you a candidate for the savings that some insurance companies offer to nonsmokers, regular exercisers, and other low-risk customers?

7. What special features should you look for in a policy? Do you have any special health needs? Do you want a policy that covers alternative health care such as chiropractic, acupuncture, or other nontraditional care?

8. After you have completed your research, contact at least three insurance agents and obtain quotes on the cost of the health coverage that you would like to have. Decide on a policy and write a 1-page paper explaining why you chose that policy or explain why you have chosen not to carry health insurance.

T24
Glencoe Division, Macmillan/McGraw-Hill

Technology

The Technology feature following Lesson 8-6 describes how *MET (Mathematics Exploration Toolkit)* can be used to graph parametric equations that solve problems. *MET* is a powerful mathematical manipulation tool from IBM which includes graphing utilities.

In the Exploration in Lesson 8-1, the graphing calculator is used to determine the magnitude of a vector. The graphing calculator program presented in Lesson 8-4 calculates the cross product of two vectors. Another Exploration in Lesson 8-6 uses the graphing calculator to graph parametric equations to simulate an automobile race. Students also learn how to set the ranges for parametric equations in this lesson.

Graphing Calculator Exercises, p. 446

Graphing Calculator Program, p. 434

Outside Resources

Books/Periodicals

Baxandall, Peter and Liebeck, Hans. *Vector Calculus,* Oxford University Press, 1987.

Crowe, Michael J. *A History of Vector Analysis: The Evolution of the Idea of Vectorial System,* Dover, NY., 1985.

Films/Videotapes/Videodiscs

Concepts in Mathematics, Vectors, TV Ontario, The Ontario Educational Communications Authority

Software

IBM Mathematics Exploration Toolkit (MET). IBM

GraphExplorer. Scott Foresman (IBM, Macintosh)

MathTools for Precalculus/Calculus. William K. Bradford Publishing (Macintosh)

Cactusplot. The Cactusplot Company (Apple II, IBM)

Supplementary MathTools. (from MacNumerics by Spring Branch Software, Inc.), William K. Bradford Publishing (Macintosh)

Technology Masters

Graphing Calculator, p. 15

Computer, p. 16

CHAPTER 8

VECTORS AND PARAMETRIC EQUATIONS

HISTORICAL SNAPSHOT

	The Ohio State University established as Ohio Agricultural and Mechanical College		Wright Brother's first flight in *Flyer I* at Kitty Hawk, North Carolina		Neil Alden Armstrong first man on the Moon Apollo 11	
Egyptian engineers scientifically design wood airplane model		*Elements of Vector Analysis*, Josiah Willard Gibbs, Yale College		Launching of Sputnik I (Fellow Traveler)		U.S. Space Station (proposed)
300 BC	AD 1870	1881	1903	1957	1969	1995–2000

410

In this chapter, you will:
- Study about vector notation, magnitude, and amplitude.
- Add, subtract, and multiply vectors.
- Find the inner product and the cross product of vectors.
- Solve and use parametric equations to solve problems.

CAREER GOAL: Aerospace Medicine

At the end of this school year, Regina Brooks will be the first African-American woman to graduate with a degree in aeronautical and astronautical engineering from The Ohio State University. After graduation, Regina is seriously considering going to medical school with a concentration in aerospace medicine. "I hope to be a professional who can bring on and advance space technology." Among other things, a career in aerospace medicine will allow Regina to engage in research on the effects of space on astronauts. "I would love to be part of the space station program or even part of an expedition to Mars," she says.

To prepare herself for college, Regina took courses in algebra, analytic geometry, trigonometry, and precalculus in high school. However, "If I had it to do all over again," says Regina, "I would have taken calculus in high school—it would have made my math courses in college much easier!"

She adds that she has found her mathematics courses to be invaluable in her studies. "When studying actual flight in aeronautics, the use of vectors becomes a very important part of air flow dynamics," Regina explains. "As air flows over each airfoil, the way the air is flowing and its velocity are always identified with vectors."

Regina's major in aeronautical and astronautical engineering has provided her the opportunity to spend summers working for NASA at the Goddard Flight Center in Greenbelt, Maryland, where she helped design the instrument carrier for Spartan 201. She says, "I feel that a part of me is in space aboard the Spartan satellite!"

READ MORE ABOUT IT

Bernards, Neal. *Living in Space.* San Diego: Greenhaven Press, 1990.
Davidson, Frank P. with John Stuart Cox. *MACRO: A Clear Vision of How Science and Technology will Shape Our Future.* New York: William Morrow and Company, 1983.
Taylor, John Jones. *Engineering for You: A Career Guide.* Ames, Iowa: Iowa State University Press, 1991.

SPOTLIGHT ON...

Regina Brooks
Age: 21
Class: Senior
School: The Ohio State University Columbus, Ohio
Major: Aeronautical and Astronautical Engineering

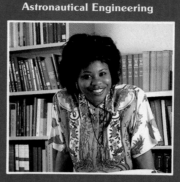

"I hope to be a professional who can bring on and advance space technology."

FOR MORE INFORMATION

If you would like more information about aeronautical and astronautical engineering, contact:

American Institute of Aeronautics and Astronautics (AIAA)
370 L'Enfant Promenade SW
Washington, DC 20024

Applications

Lesson	Application	Examples	Exercises
8–1	Sports Soccer Aviation Physics	3 6	 37 38, 39
8–2	Physics Sports Shipping Recreation	3	 41 42 43
8–3	Physics Electrostatics	3	37 36
8–4	Mechanics Physics	4	 39
8–5	Skiing Physics Aviation Aerospace Transportation Gardening Sports	1 2, 3	 31 25, 30, 32 26 27 28 29
8–6	Language Arts Transporation		32 33
8–7	Soccer Archery Golf Sports Physics	1 2 3	 16, 17, 18, 20 19

NCTM Standards: 1–4, 7

Lesson Resources

- Practice Master 8–1
- Enrichment Master 8–1
- Technology Master, p. 16

Transparency 8–1 contains the 5-Minute Check and a teaching aid for this lesson.

INTRODUCING THE LESSON

 5-Minute Check

(over Chapter 7)

1. Prove that $\frac{\tan^2 x}{1 + \tan^2 x} = \sin^2 x$ is an identity.

$$\frac{\tan^2 x}{1 + \tan^2 x} = \frac{\tan^2 x}{\sec^2 x}$$

$$= \frac{\sin^2 x}{\cos^2 x} \cdot \cos^2 x = \sin^2 x$$

2. Given $\sin \alpha = \frac{1}{2}$ and $\cos \beta = \frac{3}{5}$, find $\sin(\alpha + \beta)$. Assume that α and β are first quadrant angles. $\frac{3 + 4\sqrt{3}}{10}$

3. Find the exact value of $\sin 15°$. $\frac{\sqrt{2 - \sqrt{3}}}{2}$

4. Solve $\sin \theta = 2\sin \theta \cos \theta$ for $0 \le \theta \le 2\pi$. $\frac{\pi}{3}, \frac{5\pi}{3}, 0, \pi, 2\pi$

5. Find the distance from the point at (2, –3) to the line $y = 2x + 4$. $\frac{11\sqrt{5}}{5}$ units

Motivating the Lesson

If a pilot wants to fly a small plane from one city to another, or a boater needs to cross a river, what would happen if each person headed straight for the goal? The wind or current would move the plane or boat off course. For accurate navigation, a person must take into account the direction and magnitude of all external forces acting on the craft. The mathematics involved include trigonometry and vectors.

8-1 Geometric Vectors

Objectives
8–1A
8–1B

After studying this lesson, you should be able to:
- find equal, opposite, and parallel vectors, and
- add and subtract vectors geometrically.

Application

The release of a hot-air balloon begins the annual United States National Hot-Air Balloon Championships. The Championships have been held in Indianola, Iowa, each year since 1963. One year, a balloon rose at a rate of 2 m/s, and it was blown horizontally by a wind of 3 m/s. These velocities can be represented mathematically by **vectors**. A vector is a quantity, or directed distance, that has both magnitude and direction. A vector is represented geometrically by a directed line segment.

A directed line segment with an initial point at O and terminal point at P is shown at the right. The direction of the arrowhead indicates the direction of the vector. The vector at the right can be designated $\vec{v}$ or $\overrightarrow{OP}$. The length of the directed line segment indicates the vector's **magnitude**. The magnitude of $\vec{v}$ is denoted by $|\vec{v}|$.

If a vector has its initial point at the origin, it is in **standard position**. The **amplitude** of the vector is the directed angle between the positive x-axis and the vector. The amplitude of $\vec{u}$, shown above, is 65°.

Example 1

Determine the magnitude (in centimeters) and the amplitude of $\vec{a}$.

Using a ruler and a protractor, sketch the vector in standard position and measure the magnitude and amplitude.

The magnitude is 1.7 cm, and the amplitude is 50°.

ALTERNATE TEACHING STRATEGIES

Using Manipulatives

Students could use geoboards to demonstrate and practice the vector operations presented in this lesson: finding the opposite of a vector, scalar multiplication, addition, and subtraction.

Using Charts

Start with a single vector, $\vec{v}$, having an amplitude of 45° and add it to each of a series of vectors, all of the same magnitude but in the compass directions N, NE, E, and so on. Make a chart of the resultants, noting how the magnitude and amplitude change.

Two vectors are equal if and only if they have the same amplitude, or direction, and the same magnitude. Five vectors are shown at the right. $\vec{a}$ and $\vec{b}$ are equal since they have the same direction and $|\vec{a}| = |\vec{b}|$. $\vec{c}$ and $\vec{d}$ have the same direction but $|\vec{c}| \neq |\vec{d}|$, so $\vec{c} \neq \vec{d}$. Since $\vec{c}$ and $\vec{e}$ have different directions, they are not equal, even though $|\vec{c}| = |\vec{e}|$.

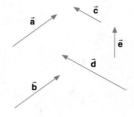

The sum of two or more vectors is called the **resultant** of the vectors. You can find the resultant using either the *parallelogram method* or the *triangle method*. To find the sum of two vectors using the parallelogram method, draw the vectors so that their initial points coincide. Then draw lines to make a complete parallelogram. The diagonal from the initial point to the opposite vertex of the parallelogram is the resultant. *Notice that these methods cannot be used to find the sum of a vector and itself.*

Example 2

Find the sum of $\vec{p}$ and $\vec{q}$ by using the parallelogram method.

Copy $\vec{p}$. Then copy $\vec{q}$, placing the initial point at the initial point of $\vec{p}$.

Form a parallelogram that has $\vec{p}$ and $\vec{q}$ as two of its sides. Draw broken lines to represent the other two sides.

The resultant is the vector from the vertex of $\vec{p}$ and $\vec{q}$ to the opposite vertex of the parallelogram.

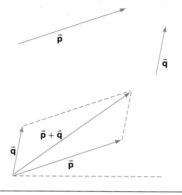

To use the triangle method to find the resultant of two vectors, draw the vectors so that the initial point of the second vector is the terminal point of the first vector. The vector from the initial point of the first vector to the terminal point of the second vector is the resultant.

Example 3

APPLICATION
Sports

At the U.S. National Hot-Air Balloon Championships, a hot-air balloon rose at a rate of 2 m/s, and was blown horizontally by a wind of 3 m/s. Draw a vector representing the resulting velocity of the balloon using the triangle method.

Suppose 1 cm represents 1 m/s. Draw two vectors, $\vec{r}$ and $\vec{w}$, to represent the upward velocity of the balloon and the velocity due to the wind, respectively.

(continued on the next page)

LESSON 8-1 GEOMETRIC VECTORS 413

Chalkboard Examples

For Example 1

Determine the magnitude (in centimeters) and the amplitude of $\vec{v}$. 1.4 cm, 110°

For Example 2

Find the sum of $\vec{u}$ and $\vec{v}$ using the parallelogram method.

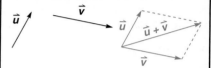

For Example 3

Jan was rowing directly across a river at the rate of 5 mph. The current was flowing at a rate of 3.5 mph. Draw a vector representing the path of the boat.

Teaching Tip After defining the triangle method of vector addition, point out to students that the upper half of the parallelogram used to solve Example 2 is the triangle used in the triangle method.

A scalar possesses only magnitude. Real numbers are scalars.

Copy $\vec{r}$. Then copy $\vec{w}$, placing the initial point of $\vec{w}$ on the terminal point of $\vec{r}$.

The resultant velocity of the balloon is the vector $\vec{p}$ from the initial point of $\vec{r}$ to the terminal point of $\vec{w}$.

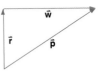

The triangle method is also called the *tip-to-tail method* of adding vectors. You can use this method to add several vectors. Draw the vectors one after another, placing the initial point of each successive vector at the terminal point of the previous one. Then draw the resultant from the initial point of the first vector to the terminal point of the last one.

Two vectors are **opposites** if they have the same magnitude and opposite directions. The opposite of $\vec{b}$ is denoted by $-\vec{b}$. You can use opposite vectors to subtract vectors. To find $\vec{a} - \vec{b}$, find $\vec{a} + (-\vec{b})$.

The product of a scalar k and a vector $\vec{a}$ is a vector with the same direction as $\vec{a}$, if $k > 0$, and a magnitude of $k|\vec{a}|$. If $k < 0$, the vector has the opposite direction. In the figure at the right, $\vec{d} = 3\vec{c}$.

Example 4

Find $2\vec{r} - \vec{s}$.

$2\vec{r} - \vec{s} = 2\vec{r} + (-\vec{s})$.

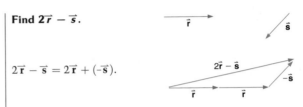

Two vectors are **parallel** if and only if they have the same or opposite directions.

Equal vectors: $\vec{a}$ and $\vec{g}$

Opposite vectors: $\vec{a}$ and $\vec{d}$,
$\quad\quad\quad\quad\quad \vec{c}$ and $\vec{f}$,
$\quad\quad\quad\quad\quad \vec{d}$ and $\vec{g}$

Parallel vectors: $\vec{a}$ and $\vec{d}$, $\vec{a}$ and $\vec{e}$,
$\quad\quad\quad\quad\quad \vec{a}$ and $\vec{g}$, $\vec{b}$ and $\vec{c}$,
$\quad\quad\quad\quad\quad \vec{b}$ and $\vec{f}$, $\vec{c}$ and $\vec{f}$,
$\quad\quad\quad\quad\quad \vec{d}$ and $\vec{e}$, $\vec{d}$ and $\vec{g}$,
$\quad\quad\quad\quad\quad \vec{e}$ and $\vec{g}$

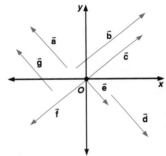

Two or more vectors whose sum is a given vector are called **components** of the given vector. Components can have any direction. Often it is useful to express a vector in terms of two perpendicular components. In the figure at the right, $\vec{y}$ is the vertical component of $\vec{a}$, and $\vec{x}$ is the horizontal component of $\vec{a}$.

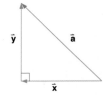

Example 5

$\vec{v}$ **has a magnitude of 2.6 cm and an amplitude of 43°. Find the magnitude of its vertical and horizontal components.**

Draw $\vec{v}$. Then draw a horizontal vector through the initial point and a vertical vector through the terminal point. The vectors will form a right triangle, so we can use the sine and cosine ratios to find the magnitude of the components.

$$\sin 43° = \frac{y}{2.6}$$
$$y \approx 1.8$$

$$\cos 43° = \frac{x}{2.6}$$
$$x \approx 1.9$$

The magnitude of the vertical component is approximately 1.9 cm, and the magnitude of the horizontal component is approximately 1.8 cm.

Vectors are used in physics to represent motion or forces acting upon objects.

Example 6

APPLICATION

Soccer

Two players kick a soccer ball at exactly the same moment. One player's foot exerts a force of 66 N (newtons) north. The other player's foot exerts a force of 88 N east.

a. What is the magnitude of the resulting force upon the ball?

b. What is the direction of the resulting force upon the ball?

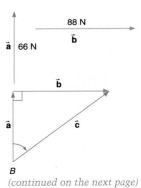

Let $\vec{a}$ represent the force from player 1.
Let $\vec{b}$ represent the force from player 2. Draw the resultant, $\vec{c}$. This represents the force upon the ball. Let B represent the measure of the angle that the resultant makes with $\vec{a}$.

(continued on the next page)

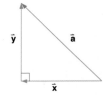

FYI...

A newton (N) is a unit of force used in physics. A force of one newton will accelerate a one-kilogram mass at a rate of one meter per second squared.

a. We can use the Pythagorean theorem to find the magnitude of the resultant.

$$|\vec{c}| = \sqrt{66^2 + 88^2} \quad \textit{Pythagorean theorem}$$
$$= \sqrt{4356 + 7744}$$
$$= \sqrt{12,100} \text{ or } 110$$

The magnitude of $\vec{c}$ is 110 N.

b. The direction of the resultant can be found by using the tangent ratio.

$$\tan B = \frac{\vec{b}}{\vec{a}}$$
$$\tan B = \frac{88}{66}$$
$$B \approx 53°$$

The resultant makes an angle of 53° with $\vec{a}$. The direction of the resulting force is 53° east of north.

EXPLORATION: Graphing Calculator

Determine at what initial velocity a ball must be thrown from the ground at an angle of 30° from the horizontal in order to travel a horizontal distance of 235 feet.

1. The calculator should be in PARAMETRIC mode.

2. Use the range values below to set up a viewing window.

TMIN = 0	XMIN = 0	YMIN = -5
TMAX = 4	XMAX = 250	YMAX = 35
TSTEP = 0.05	XSCL = 30	YSCL = 5

3. Use the equations $X_{1T} = ?$ T cos 30 and $Y_{1T} = ?$ T sin 30 − 16T². Guess replacement values for ? to solve the problem. Check by using the TRACE function. ? = 60

CHECKING FOR UNDERSTANDING

Communicating Mathematics

Read and study the lesson to answer each question. 1–2. See margin.

1. **Compare** a line segment and a vector.

2. **Draw** diagrams illustrating the two methods of adding vectors.

3. Is $\overrightarrow{BA}$ the same as $\overrightarrow{AB}$? Explain. No, they are opposites.

4. **Define** the components of a vector. any two or more vectors whose sum is the given vector

Guided Practice Use a metric ruler and a protractor to draw a vector with the given magnitude and amplitude. 5–10. See margin.

5. 1 cm, 50°   6. 4 cm, 180°   7. 3 cm, 120°
8. 2.5 cm, 270°   9. 18 mm, 45°   10. 35 mm, 65°

Copy each pair of vectors and draw the resultant vector.

11.   12.   13.

14. A vector has a magnitude of 2.2 cm and an amplitude of 30°. Find the magnitude of its vertical and horizontal components. v, 1.1 cm; h, about 1.9 cm

15. A hiker walks 13 km due west, then turns and walks 7 km due north. How far is the hiker from his starting point? about 14.8 km

EXERCISES

Practice

16–28. Answers may vary slightly due to measuring techniques.

Use a metric ruler and a protractor to find each sum or difference. Then, find the magnitude and amplitude of each resultant.

22. ≈ 9.8 cm, ≈ 335°

 16. $\vec{a} + \vec{c}$ ≈ 5.2 cm, ≈ 53°   17. $\vec{a} + \vec{b}$ ≈ 3.4 cm, ≈ 85°   18. $\vec{d} + \vec{b}$ ≈ 2.8 cm, ≈ 142°

19. $\vec{a} + \vec{d}$ ≈ 5 cm, ≈ 3°   20. $2\vec{b}$ ≈ 3 cm, ≈ 135°   21. $3\vec{a}$ ≈ 8.1 cm, ≈ 60°

22. $3\vec{d} + 2\vec{b}$ 23. $\vec{c} - \vec{a}$ ≈ 0.7 cm, ≈ 306° 24. $\vec{a} - \vec{d}$ ≈ 5 cm, ≈ 153°

 25. $3\vec{c} - 2\vec{a}$ ≈ 2.7 cm, ≈ 14°   26. $\vec{a} + \vec{c} + \vec{d}$ ≈ 7.1 cm, ≈ 17°

27. $\vec{b} + \vec{d} - \vec{c}$ ≈ 2.9 cm, ≈ 286°   28. $3\vec{a} + \vec{c} - \vec{d}$ ≈ 11.1 cm, ≈ 79°

Find the magnitude of the vertical and horizontal components of each vector shown for Exercises 16—28.

29. $\vec{a}$ ≈ 2.3 cm,   30. $\vec{b}$ ≈ 1.1 cm,   31. $\vec{c}$ ≈ 1.8 cm,   32. $\vec{d}$ ≈ 2.1 cm,
    ≈ 1.4 cm   ≈ 1.1 cm   ≈ 1.8 cm   ≈ 3.6 cm

33. The magnitude of $\vec{x}$ is 7.3 m, and the magnitude of $\vec{y}$ is 8.8 m. If $\vec{x}$ and $\vec{y}$ are perpendicular, what is the magnitude of their sum? about 11.4 m

34. Is addition of vectors commutative? Justify your answer. *Hint: Find the sum of two vectors, $\vec{r} + \vec{s}$ and $\vec{s} + \vec{r}$, using the triangle method.* Yes; see margin.

LESSON 8-1   GEOMETRIC VECTORS   417

34.

APPLYING THE LESSON

Homework Exercises

Assignment Guide
Average: 16–30, 35–37, 40–45
Enriched: 21–45

The red A, B, and C flags, printed only in the Teacher's Wraparound Edition, indicate the level of difficulty of the exercises.

Additional Answers

6.

7.

8.

9.

10.

35. Sample answer: The other diagonal would be the sum of one of the vectors and the opposite of the other vector, so it is the difference between the original two.

36. yes, if they are opposite vectors; yes, if they form a closed triangle when placed tip-to-tail

37a.

↓5 m/s

100 m/s

39a.

165 N

30° 185 N

300°

195 N

---

35. In the parallelogram drawn for the parallelogram method, what does the diagonal between the two terminal points of the vectors represent? Explain your answer. The difference; see margin.

Critical Thinking

36. Could the sum of two vectors ever be zero? Could the sum of three vectors be zero? Justify your answer and draw a diagram if possible. See margin.

Applications and Problem Solving

37. Aviation An airplane is flying due east at a velocity of 100 m/s. The wind is blowing out of the north at 5 m/s.
  a. Draw a labeled diagram of the situation. See margin.
  b. What is the airplane's resulting velocity? about 100.12 m/s

38. Physics Nina is pushing a lawn mower with a force of 95 N along the handle of the mower.
  a. The handle makes a 60° angle with the horizontal. What are the magnitudes of the horizontal and vertical components of the force? 48 N; 82 N
  b. If Nina lowers the handle so that it makes a 30° angle with the horizontal, what are the magnitudes of the horizontal and vertical components of the force? 82 N; 48 N

39. Physics Shirley, Scott, and Dan are pushing a footlocker across the floor. Shirley is pushing with a force of 185 N at 0°, Scott pushes with a force of 165 N at 30°, and Dan pushes with a force of 195 N at 300°.
  a. Draw a labeled diagram of the situation. See margin.
  b. What are the magnitude and direction of the resulting force on the footlocker? 436.7 N at 193°

Mixed Review

40. Write the standard form of the equation of the line that is parallel to the graph of $y = x - 8$ and passes through $(-3, 1)$. **(Lesson 1-6)** $x - y = -4$

41. Find the equation of the line tangent to the graph of $y = 3x^2$ at $(2, 12)$. **(Lesson 3-6)** $y = 12x - 12$

42. Solve the equation $2x^3 + 5x^2 - 12x = 0$. **(Lesson 4-1)** $0, \frac{3}{2}, -4$

43. Gardening A sprinkler is set to rotate 65° and spray a distance of 6 feet. What is the area of the ground being watered? **(Lesson 5-2)** 20.42 ft²

44. Write an equation with phase shift 0 to represent simple harmonic motion in which the initial position is 0, the amplitude is 3, and the period is 2. **(Lesson 6-7)** $y = 3 \sin \pi t$

45. College Entrance Exam Compare quantities A and B below. D
Write A if quantity A is greater.
Write B if quantity B is greater.
Write C if the two quantities are equal.
Write D if there is not enough information to determine the relationship.
$z = 6y$, where y is a positive integer, and
$z = 2x$, where x is a positive integer
(A) z **(B)** 10

418 CHAPTER 8 VECTORS AND PARAMETRIC EQUATIONS

EXTENDING THE LESSON

Math Power: Connections

Consider the problem presented in Example 6. Ask students how it could be solved if the two forces were not at right angles to one another. How would the law of cosines help?

Construct a triangle having the two original vectors as two of its sides. The third side would be the resultant force on the ball. Its magnitude could be found by applying the law of cosines. Its direction could also be found by the law of cosines, or more easily by the law of sines.

8-2 Algebraic Vectors

Objectives
8–2A
8–2B

After studying this lesson, you should be able to:
- find ordered pairs that represent vectors, and
- add, subtract, multiply, and find the magnitude of vectors algebraically.

Application

The Lynch family is building a log cabin for weekend getaways. Mr. Lynch and his son James have erected a scaffold to stand on while they build the walls of the cabin. They are able to stand on the scaffold and pull up the logs to erect the walls of the cabin. A rope has been attached to a large log. If James pulls with a force of 400 N at an angle of 65° with the horizontal and Mr. Lynch pulls with a force of 600 N at an angle of 110° with the horizontal, what is the net force on the log? *This problem will be solved in Example 3.*

We could draw vectors to represent the forces on the log and then measure to find the magnitude and amplitude of the resultant. However, drawings can be inaccurate and drawings for more complicated systems could be quite confusing. In cases where we want a more precise answer or where the system is more complicated, we can add the vectors algebraically.

Vectors can be represented algebraically using ordered pairs of real numbers. For example, the ordered pair $(1, 2)$ represents the vector from the origin to the point at $(1, 2)$. You can think of this vector as the resultant of a horizontal vector with a magnitude of 1 unit and a vertical vector with a magnitude of 2 units.

Since vectors with the same magnitude and amplitude are equal, many vectors can be represented by an ordered pair. Each vector on the graph at the right can be represented by the ordered pair $(1, 2)$. The initial point of a vector can be any point in the plane.

Assume that P_1 and P_2 are any two distinct points in the coordinate plane. Drawing the horizontal and vertical components of $\overrightarrow{P_1P_2}$ yields a right triangle. So the magnitude of the vector can be found by using the Pythagorean theorem. *Assume that $\overrightarrow{P_1P_2}$ is neither horizontal nor vertical.*

LESSON 8-2   ALGEBRAIC VECTORS   419

ALTERNATE TEACHING STRATEGIES

Using Cooperative Groups

After introducing the concept of vectors represented by ordered pairs, have students work together in small groups, using graph paper to devise rules for the addition, subtraction, and scalar multiplication of vectors.

Using Charts

Have students use a pair of vectors and perform the various vector operations on them, both geometrically and algebraically. They should make a chart showing the work involved for each operation and discuss which method seems easier in each case.

NCTM Standards: 1–4, 8

Lesson Resources

- Practice Masters 8–2
- Enrichment Master 8–2
- Evaluation Master, Quiz A, p. 97

Transparency 8–2 contains the 5-Minute Check and a teaching aid for this lesson.

INTRODUCING THE LESSON

5-Minute Check
(over Lesson 8–1)

1. Use a metric ruler and a protractor to find each sum or difference. Then, find the magnitude and amplitude of each resultant.

a. $\vec{a} + \vec{b}$ 2.82 cm, 74.2°
b. $\vec{b} - 2\vec{a}$ 2.13 cm, 174.7°
c. $-3\vec{a}$ 4.5 cm, 225°

2. Find the magnitude of the vertical and horizontal components of vector $\vec{b}$ above.
1.97 cm, –0.347 cm

Prerequisite Skills

Students need to be familiar with the distance formula.
Find the distance between each pair of points with the given coordinates.
1. (2, 7) and (–3, 19)   13
2. (0, –4) and (8, 2)   10
3. (–4, 9) and (4, –1) $2\sqrt{41}$

Representation of a Vector as an Ordered Pair	Suppose $P_1(x_1, y_1)$ is the initial point of a vector and $P_2(x_2, y_2)$ is the terminal point. The ordered pair that represents $\overrightarrow{P_1P_2}$ is $(x_2 - x_1, y_2 - y_1)$. Its magnitude is given by $\overrightarrow{P_1P_2} = \sqrt{(x_2 - x_1)^2 + (y_2 - y_1)^2}$.

The order of the coordinates representing a vector is important. P_2P_1 is represented by the ordered pair $(x_1 - x_2, y_1 - y_2)$.

Example 1

Find the ordered pair that represents the vector from $A(5, 4)$ to $B(0, -3)$. Then find the magnitude of $\overrightarrow{AB}$.

$$\overrightarrow{AB} = (0 - 5, -3 - 4)$$
$$= (-5, -7)$$

$$|\overrightarrow{AB}| = \sqrt{(0 - 5)^2 + (-3 - 4)^2}$$
$$= \sqrt{5^2 + (-7)^2}$$
$$= \sqrt{74}$$

We can add or subtract vectors, and multiply vectors by a scalar when they are represented as ordered pairs. The rules for these operations on vectors are similar to those for matrices. In fact, vectors in a plane can be represented as row matrices of dimension 1×2.

Vector Operations	The following operations are defined for $\vec{a} = (a_1, a_2)$, $\vec{b} = (b_1, b_2)$, and any real number k.
	Addition: $\vec{a} + \vec{b} = (a_1, a_2) + (b_1, b_2) = (a_1 + b_1, a_2 + b_2)$
	Subtraction: $\vec{a} - \vec{b} = (a_1, a_2) - (b_1, b_2) = (a_1 - b_1, a_2 - b_2)$
	Scalar multiplication: $k\vec{a} = k(a_1, a_2) = (ka_1, ka_2)$

Example 2

If $\vec{q} = (3, 9)$ and $\vec{r} = (-1, 6)$, find each of the following.

a. $\vec{q} + \vec{r}$ b. $\vec{q} - \vec{r}$

a. $\vec{q} + \vec{r} = (3, 9) + (-1, 6)$ b. $\vec{q} - \vec{r} = (3, 9) - (-1, 6)$
      $= (2, 15)$ $= (4, 3)$

c. $5\vec{q}$

c. $5\vec{q} = 5(3, 9)$
    $= (15, 45)$

If we write the vectors described in the application at the beginning of the lesson as ordered pairs, we can find the resultant vector using vector addition.

Example 3

Refer to the application at the beginning of the lesson. If James pulls with a force of 400 N at an angle of 65° with the horizontal and Mr. Lynch pulls with a force of 600 N at an angle of 110° with the horizontal, what is the net force on the log?

Draw a diagram of the situation. Let $\vec{F}_1$ represent the force James exerts, and let $\vec{F}_2$ represent the force that Mr. Lynch exerts.

Write each vector as an ordered pair by finding its horizontal and vertical components. Let $\vec{F}_{1x}$ and $\vec{F}_{1y}$ represent the x- and y-components of $\vec{F}_1$, and let $\vec{F}_{2x}$ and $\vec{F}_{2y}$ represent the x- and y-components of $\vec{F}_2$.

$$\cos 65° = \frac{|\vec{F}_{1x}|}{400}$$
$$|\vec{F}_{1x}| = 400 \cos 65°$$
$$|\vec{F}_{1x}| \approx 169.0$$

$$\cos 70° = \frac{|\vec{F}_{2x}|}{600}$$
$$|\vec{F}_{2x}| = 600 \cos 70°$$
$$|\vec{F}_{2x}| \approx 205.2$$

$$\sin 65° = \frac{|\vec{F}_{1y}|}{400}$$
$$|\vec{F}_{1y}| = 400 \sin 65°$$
$$|\vec{F}_{1y}| \approx 362.5$$

$$\sin 70° = \frac{|\vec{F}_{2y}|}{600}$$
$$|\vec{F}_{2y}| = 600 \sin 70°$$
$$|\vec{F}_{2y}| \approx 563.8$$

$$\vec{F}_1 = (169.0, 362.5)$$

$$\vec{F}_2 = (205.2, 563.8)$$

Find the sum of the vectors.
$$\vec{F}_1 + \vec{F}_2 = (169.0, 362.5) + (205.2, 563.8)$$
$$= (374.2, 926.3)$$

The net force on the log is the magnitude of the sum.

$$|\vec{F}_1 + \vec{F}_2| = \sqrt{(374.2)^2 + (926.3)^2}$$
$$= \sqrt{998,057.33}$$
$$\approx 999.028$$

The net force on the log is about 999 N.

For Example 3

Suppose a force of 6 N at an angle of 70° with the horizontal and a force of 10 N at an angle of 115° with the horizontal are both acting on an object. What is the net force on the object?   **14.9 N**

A vector that is parallel to the x- or y-axis and has a magnitude of one unit is called a **unit vector**. A unit vector in the direction of the positive x-axis is represented by $\vec{i}$, and a unit vector in the direction of the positive y-axis is represented by $\vec{j}$. So $\vec{i} = (1, 0)$ and $\vec{j} = (0, 1)$.

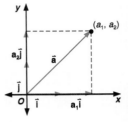

Any vector $\vec{a} = (a_1, a_2)$ can be expressed as $a_1\vec{i} + a_2\vec{j}$.

$$
\begin{aligned}
a_1\vec{i} + a_2\vec{j} &= a_1(1, 0) + a_2(0, 1) &\quad \vec{i} = (1, 0) \text{ and } \vec{j} = (0, 1)\\
&= (a_1, 0) + (0, a_2) &\quad \text{Scalar product}\\
&= (a_1 + 0, 0 + a_2) &\quad \text{Addition of vectors}\\
&= (a_1, a_2)
\end{aligned}
$$

Since $(a_1, a_2) = \vec{a}$, $a_1\vec{i} + a_2\vec{j} = \vec{a}$. Therefore, any vector that is represented by an ordered pair can also be written as the sum of unit vectors.

Example 4

Write $\overrightarrow{CD}$ as the sum of unit vectors for points $C(6, 3)$ and $D(-4, 8)$.

First, write $\overrightarrow{CD}$ as an ordered pair.
$$
\begin{aligned}
\overrightarrow{CD} &= (-4 - 6, 8 - 3)\\
&= (-10, 5)
\end{aligned}
$$

Then, write $\overrightarrow{CD}$ as the sum of unit vectors.
$$
\overrightarrow{CD} = -10\vec{i} + 5\vec{j}
$$

CHECKING FOR UNDERSTANDING

Communicating Mathematics

Read and study the lesson to answer each question. 1–4. See margin.

1. Could the magnitude of a resultant vector ever be less than the magnitude of one of its components? Explain.

2. **Compare and contrast** the vectors $(2, 4)$ and $(4, 2)$.

3. If two vectors have the same magnitude, are the ordered pairs representing them necessarily identical? Explain.

4. If two vectors have the same amplitude, are the ordered pairs representing them necessarily identical? Explain.

Guided Practice

Find the magnitude of each vector and write each vector as the sum of unit vectors.

5. $(4, 3)$
   $5, 4\vec{i} + 3\vec{j}$
6. $(6, 7)$
   $\sqrt{85}, 6\vec{i} + 7\vec{j}$
7. $(-2, -3)$
   $\sqrt{13}, -2\vec{i} - 3\vec{j}$
8. $(-5, 15)$
   $5\sqrt{10}, -5\vec{i} + 15\vec{j}$

Find the ordered pair that represents the vector from A to B. Then find the magnitude of $\overrightarrow{AB}$.

9. $A(4,2), B(2,8)$ $(-2,6), 2\sqrt{10}$

10. $A(0,4), B(3,1)$ $(3,-3), 3\sqrt{2}$

11. $A(-4,0), B(1,9)$ $(5,9), \sqrt{106}$

12. $A(-5,7), B(-1,2)$ $(4,-5), \sqrt{41}$

Find the sum or difference of the given vectors algebraically.

13. $(4,5) + (2,1)$ $(6,6)$

14. $(-1,2) + (3,5)$ $(2,7)$

15. $(-1,6) + (-8,-5)$ $(-9,1)$

16. $(2,4) + (-2,-3)$ $(0,1)$

17. $\vec{i} + \vec{j}$ $(1,1)$

18. $2\vec{i} - \vec{j}$ $(2,-1)$

19. $5\vec{i} + 7\vec{j}$ $(5,7)$

20. $4\vec{i} - \vec{j}$ $(4,-1)$

EXERCISES

Practice   **Find the ordered pair that represents the vector from A to B. Then find the magnitude of $\overrightarrow{AB}$.**

21. $A(7,7), B(-2,-2)$ $(-9,-9), 9\sqrt{2}$

22. $A(-2,5), B(1,3)$ $(3,-2), \sqrt{13}$

23. $A(0,5), B(-5,0)$ $(-5,-5), 5\sqrt{2}$

24. $A(5,0), B(7,6)$ $(2,6), 2\sqrt{10}$

25. $A(4,-5), B(5,-4)$ $(1,1), \sqrt{2}$

26. $A(-9,2), B(-4,-3)$ $(5,-5), 5\sqrt{2}$

27. $A(7,6), B(8,6)$ $(1,0), 1$

28. $A(12,-4), B(19,1)$ $(7,5), \sqrt{74}$

Find an ordered pair to represent $\vec{u}$ in each equation if $\vec{v} = (4,-3)$ and $\vec{w} = (-6,2)$.

29. $\vec{u} = \vec{v} + \vec{w}$ $(-2,-1)$ 30. $\vec{u} = \vec{v} - \vec{w}$ $(10,-5)$ 31. $\vec{u} = 3\vec{v}$ $(12,-9)$

32. $\vec{u} = 4\vec{w}$ $(-24,8)$ 33. $\vec{u} = \vec{w} - 2\vec{v}$ $(-14,8)$ 34. $\vec{u} = \vec{v} - 3\vec{w}$ $(22,-9)$

35. $\vec{u} = 2\vec{v} + 3\vec{w}$ $(-10,0)$ 36. $\vec{u} = 4\vec{w} - 3\vec{v}$ $(-36,17)$ 37. $\vec{u} = 6\vec{w} - 2\vec{v}$

$(-44,18)$

38. Prove that addition of vectors is commutative. See margin.

39. Find the vector that is the additive identity for vectors. By definition, this is the vector that does not alter any vector when added to it. $(0,0)$

Critical Thinking
40a. They are opposites.

40. Suppose the points A, B, C, and D are noncollinear, and $\overrightarrow{AB} + \overrightarrow{CD} = 0$.
   a. What is the relationship between $\overrightarrow{AB}$ and $\overrightarrow{CD}$?
   b. What is true of the quadrilateral with vertices A, B, C, and D? It is a parallelogram.

Applications and Problem Solving
41. 81.7 N, 73.6 N

41. **Sports** In the 1992 Winter Olympic trials, Hershel Walker pushed the *USA I* bobsled with a force of 110 N at an angle of 42° with the horizontal. Find the horizontal and vertical components of the force.

42. **Shipping** Two tugboats are towing a ship into Boston Harbor. Although the tugboats are traveling at the same speed, one tugboat is pulling at an angle of 30°, and the second boat is pulling at an angle of 330°. If each tugboat exerts a force of 6 tons, what is the resultant force on the ship? about 10.4 tons

43. **Recreation** Traci is pulling her sled up the hill with a force of 58 N at an angle
of 50° with the horizontal. If Traci were to pull with the same force and lower the
angle, what effect would this have on the horizontal and vertical components?
The vertical would decrease and the horizontal would increase.

Mixed Review

44. Determine if the graph of $y^2 = 121 - x^2$ is symmetric with respect to the x-axis,
the y-axis, the line $y = x$, the line $y = -x$, or the origin. **(Lesson 3-1)** all

45. Use the quadratic formula to solve $5x^2 - 8x + 12 = 0$. **(Lesson 4-2)** $\frac{4 \pm 2i\sqrt{11}}{5}$

46. Solve $\frac{x+3}{x+2} = 2 - \frac{3}{x^2 + 5x + 6}$. Check the solution. **(Lesson 4-6)** $0, -4$

47. Solve $2\tan x - 4 = 0$ for principal values of x. **(Lesson 7-5)** $63°26'$

48. **Navigation** A boat heads due west across a lake at 8 m/s. If a current of 5 m/s
moves due south, what is the boat's resultant velocity and direction?
(Lesson 8-1) about 9.4 m/s at 58° west of south

49. **College Entrance Exam** Choose the best answer. D
If $a(b + 1) = C$, then $b =$

(A) $C - 1$ (B) $\frac{C-1}{a}$ (C) $C - a + 1$ (D) $\frac{C}{a} - 1$ (E) $C - a$

DECISION MAKING

Choosing a Used Car

Because costs are so high, a new car is out of reach for many
people. But car values depreciate rapidly after two or three
years, making an almost-new car a very economical choice
for a prospective buyer. What factors do you need to take into
consideration when buying a used car?

1. Describe what you would look for in a used car. Include
such factors as the make of the car, its condition, mileage,
and any features or accessories that you feel are important.

2. Outline a plan to make sure that you get the best value for
your money. Talk with mechanics and car owners about
what to look for in a used car. Contact your city or state
consumer protection agency to find out your rights as a
used-car buyer.

3. Research ways to finance the purchase of a used car. Can
you come up with the cash to buy a car outright? Or, will
you need to borrow money from your family or a bank?

4. **Project** Work with your group to complete one of the
projects listed at the right, based on the information you
gathered in Exercises 1–3. 1–4. See students' work.

PROJECTS

- *Conduct an interview.*
- *Write a book report.*
- *Write a proposal.*
- *Write an article for the
  school paper.*
- *Write a report.*
- *Make a display.*
- *Make a graph or chart.*
- *Plan an activity.*
- *Design a checklist.*

424 CHAPTER 8 VECTORS AND PARAMETRIC EQUATIONS

EXTENDING THE LESSON

Math Power: Connections

What is the relationship between the
horizontal and vertical components
of a vector, introduced in Lesson
8–1, and the representation of a
vector as a sum of unit vectors in this
lesson? If $\mathbf{v} = a\mathbf{i} + b\mathbf{j}$, then a is its
horizontal component and b is its
vertical component. Thus, $a = |\mathbf{v}|$
$\cos\theta$ and $b = |\mathbf{v}| \sin\theta$, where θ is
the magnitude of $\mathbf{v}$.

Decision Making

This activity provides students an
opportunity to work together on a
given problem. You may wish to refer
to pages T20–T21 and page 410c for
the various elements of cooperative
groups and specific goals and
strategies for using them.

Enrichment Masters Booklet, p. 51

NAME _____ DATE _____

8-2 **Enrichment Worksheet**

Basis Vectors

The expression $\vec{v} = r\vec{u} + s\vec{w}$, the sum of two vectors each multiplied
by scalars, is called a **linear combination** of the vectors $\vec{u}$ and $\vec{w}$.

Linear Combination Theorem in v_2	Every vector $\vec{v} \in v_2$ can be written as a linear combination of any two nonparallel vectors $\vec{u}$ and $\vec{w}$. The vectors $\vec{u}$ and $\vec{w}$ are said to form a **basis** for the vector space, v_2, which contains all vectors having 1 column and 2 rows.

Example Write the vector $\vec{v} = \begin{pmatrix} -2 \\ 5 \end{pmatrix}$ as a linear combination of

the vectors $\vec{u} = \begin{pmatrix} 2 \\ 3 \end{pmatrix}$ and $\vec{w} = \begin{pmatrix} 1 \\ -4 \end{pmatrix}$.

$\begin{pmatrix} -2 \\ 5 \end{pmatrix} = r\begin{pmatrix} 2 \\ 3 \end{pmatrix} + s\begin{pmatrix} 1 \\ -4 \end{pmatrix} = \begin{pmatrix} 2r + s \\ 3r - 4s \end{pmatrix}$

$-2 = 2r + s$
$5 = 3r - 4s$

Solving the system of equations yields the solution

$r = -\frac{3}{11}$ and $s = -\frac{16}{11}$. So, $\vec{v} = -\frac{3}{11}\vec{u} - \frac{16}{11}\vec{w}$.

Write each vector as a linear combination of the vectors $\vec{u}$ and $\vec{w}$.

1. $\vec{v} = \begin{pmatrix} 1 \\ 5 \end{pmatrix}$, $\vec{u} = \begin{pmatrix} -3 \\ 4 \end{pmatrix}$, $\vec{w} = \begin{pmatrix} 2 \\ -2 \end{pmatrix}$

$\vec{v} = 6\vec{u} + \frac{19}{2}\vec{w}$

2. $\vec{v} = \begin{pmatrix} 1 \\ -1 \end{pmatrix}$, $\vec{u} = \begin{pmatrix} 2 \\ 3 \end{pmatrix}$, $\vec{w} = \begin{pmatrix} 1 \\ 1 \end{pmatrix}$

$\vec{v} = \vec{u} - 4\vec{w}$

3. $\vec{v} = \begin{pmatrix} \frac{1}{2} \\ -1 \end{pmatrix}$, $\vec{u} = \begin{pmatrix} 0 \\ 4 \end{pmatrix}$, $\vec{w} = \begin{pmatrix} \frac{1}{2} \\ 1 \end{pmatrix}$

$\vec{v} = -\frac{1}{2}\vec{u} + \vec{w}$

4. $\vec{v} = \begin{pmatrix} 2 \\ -7 \end{pmatrix}$, $\vec{u} = \begin{pmatrix} -1 \\ -3 \end{pmatrix}$, $\vec{w} = \begin{pmatrix} 4 \\ 2 \end{pmatrix}$

$\vec{v} = \frac{16}{5}\vec{u} + \frac{13}{10}\vec{w}$

8-3 Vectors in Three-Dimensional Space

Objectives
8–3A
8–3B

After studying this lesson, you should be able to:
- add and subtract vectors in three-dimensional space, and
- find the magnitude of vectors in three-dimensional space.

Application

The Sears Tower in Chicago rises an imposing 443 meters above street level. It is the tallest building in the world. Especially in the "Windy City," tall buildings are vulnerable to the force of strong winds. Engineers have designed tuned mass dampers for buildings to help them keep from swaying too much, and possibly tumbling over, when the winds blow. Mass dampers are large blocks of cement or lead which are controlled by computerized hydraulic systems. When the winds blow, the computers move the weights in the direction opposite the force of the wind so that the resultant force reduces the motion of the building. The forces of the winds and the dampers can be represented by vectors in space.

Vectors in three-dimensional space can be described by coordinates in a way similar to the way we describe vectors in a plane. Imagine three real number lines intersecting at the zero point of each so that each line is perpendicular to the plane determined by the other two. To show this arrangement on paper, a figure is used to convey the feeling of depth. The axes are named the x-axis, the y-axis, and the z-axis.

> **FYI...**
>
> The frame of the Sears Tower is made up of vertical tubes that provide the rigidity necessary to limit swaying of the building due to the wind.

Each point in space corresponds to an ordered triple of real numbers. To locate a point P with coordinates (x_1, y_1, z_1), first find x_1 on the x-axis, y_1 on the y-axis, and z_1 on the z-axis. Then imagine a plane perpendicular to the x-axis at x_1 and planes perpendicular to the y- and z-axes at y_1 and z_1, respectively. The three planes will intersect at the point P.

Example 1

Locate the point (3, 5, 4).

Locate 3 on the x-axis, 5 on the y-axis, and 4 on the z-axis.

Now draw broken lines for parallelograms to represent the three planes.

The planes intersect at $(3, 5, 4)$.

LESSON 8-3   VECTORS IN THREE-DIMENSIONAL SPACE   425

8–3 Lesson Notes

NCTM Standards: 1–4, 8

Lesson Resources

- Practice Master 8–3
- Enrichment Master 8–3
- Activity Master, p. 23

 Transparency 8–3 contains the 5-Minute Check and a teaching aid for this lesson.

INTRODUCING THE LESSON

5-Minute Check
(over Lesson 8–2)

1. Find the ordered pair that represents the vector from $A(3, -1)$ to $B(-4, 0)$. Then find the magnitude of $\vec{AB}$. $(-7, 1); 5\sqrt{2}$
2. Find an ordered pair to represent $\vec{u}$ in each equation if $\vec{v} = (-1, -5)$ and $\vec{w} = (6, 4)$.
   a. $\vec{u} = \vec{v} + \vec{w}$ $(5, -1)$
   b. $\vec{u} = 2\vec{v} - \frac{1}{2}\vec{w}$ $(-5, -12)$
   c. $\vec{u} = \vec{w} - \vec{v}$ $(7, 9)$
3. Write $\vec{AB}$ as the sum of unit vectors for points $A(0, 4)$ and $B(-3, 3)$. $-3\vec{i} - \vec{j}$

Motivating the Lesson

Suppose we wish to use vectors to determine the total force acting on an arrow being shot from a bow. In addition to the force applied by the archer, there are the force of gravity and the force of the wind. Two-dimensional vectors are inadequate for the task.

ALTERNATE TEACHING STRATEGIES

Using Logical Reasoning

After introducing the idea of three-dimensional vectors, have students try to come up with some rules for how to perform the various vector operations on them and how to represent them graphically.

Using Models

Have students think of imposing a three-dimensional coordinate system on the classroom. Talk about the various forces acting on objects in the room: the force of air moving through an open window or ventilation duct or the force of gravity. What would be the net force on an object at a particular point?

Teaching Tip   After the application, point out that any two of these planes intersect in a line, so that there is a set of three lines in space intersecting in the single point P.

Teaching Tip   In Example 2, remind students that reversing the order of the coordinates changes the vector from $\overrightarrow{AB}$ to $\overrightarrow{BA}$, which has the same magnitude but opposite direction.

Chalkboard Examples

For Example 1

Locate the point (2, 1, 6).

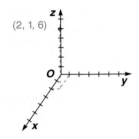

For Example 2

Find the ordered triple that represents the vector from A(–2, –5, 0) to B(3, 1, 8).   (5, 6, 8)

For Example 3

The force of the wind blowing the John Hancock Building at one moment can be expressed as the vector (3120 N, 195 N, 5 N). What is the magnitude of the force?
about 3126 N

Ordered triples, like ordered pairs, can be used to represent vectors. The geometric interpretation is the same for a vector in space as it is for a vector in a plane. A directed line segment from the origin O to $P(x, y, z)$ is called vector $\overrightarrow{OP}$, corresponding to vector (x, y, z).

An extension of the formula for the distance between two points in a plane allows us to find the distance between two points in space. The distance from the origin to a point (x, y, z) is $\sqrt{x^2 + y^2 + z^2}$. So the magnitude of vector (x, y, z) is $\sqrt{x^2 + y^2 + z^2}$.

Representation of a Vector as an Ordered Triple	Suppose $P_1(x_1, y_1, z_1)$ is the initial point of a vector in space and $P_2(x_2, y_2, z_2)$ is the terminal point. The ordered triple that represents $\overrightarrow{P_1P_2}$ is $(x_2 - x_1, y_2 - y_1, z_2 - z_1)$. Its magnitude is given by $$\lvert\overrightarrow{P_1P_2}\rvert = \sqrt{(x_2 - x_1)^2 + (y_2 - y_1)^2 + (z_2 - z_1)^2}.$$

Example 2

Find the ordered triple that represents the vector from $A(3, 7, -1)$ to $B(10, -4, 0)$.

$$\overrightarrow{AB} = (10 - 3, -4 - 7, 0 - (-1))$$
$$= (7, -11, 1)$$

Example 3

APPLICATION
Physics

Refer to the application at the beginning of the lesson. The force of the wind blowing against the Sears Tower at a certain moment can be expressed as the vector (132, 3454, 0), where each measure in the ordered triple represents the force in newtons. What is the magnitude of this force?

$$\text{magnitude} = \sqrt{132^2 + 3454^2 + 0^2}$$
$$= \sqrt{11{,}947{,}540}$$
$$\approx 3456.5$$

The magnitude of the force is about 3457 N.

You can perform operations on vectors represented by ordered triples in the same way that you perform operations on vectors represented by ordered pairs.

Additional Answers

1. First find 3 on the *x*-axis, –1 on the *y*-axis, and 2 on the *z*-axis. Then imagine a plane perpendicular to the *x*-axis at 3 and planes perpendicular to the *y*- and *z*-axes at –1 and 2. The three planes will intersect at (3, –1, 2).
2. The radicand for the magnitude of a vector in space contains another squared term, $(z_2 - z_1)^2$.

Example 4

Find an ordered triple that represents $3\vec{v} - \vec{u}$, if $\vec{v} = (4, -1, 7)$ and $\vec{u} = (9, 11, -3)$.

$$3\vec{v} - \vec{u} = 3(4, -1, 7) - (9, 11, -3)$$
$$= (12, -3, 21) - (9, 11, -3)$$
$$= (3, -14, 24)$$

Three unit vectors are used as components of vectors in space. The unit vectors on the x-, y-, and z-axes are $\vec{i}$, $\vec{j}$, and $\vec{k}$, respectively, where $\vec{i} = (1, 0, 0)$, $\vec{j} = (0, 1, 0)$, and $\vec{k} = (0, 0, 1)$. The unit vectors are shown at the right with a vector $\vec{a} = (a_1, a_2, a_3)$. The component vectors of $\vec{a}$ along the three axes are $a_1\vec{i}$, $a_2\vec{j}$, and $a_3\vec{k}$. $\vec{a}$ can be written as the sum of unit vectors; that is, $\vec{a} = a_1\vec{i} + a_2\vec{j} + a_3\vec{k}$.

Example 5

Write $\overrightarrow{GH}$ as the sum of unit vectors for $G(10, -3, 15)$ and $H(4, 1, -11)$.

First, express $\overrightarrow{GH}$ as an ordered triple. Then write as the sum of unit vectors $\vec{i}$, $\vec{j}$, and $\vec{k}$.

$$\overrightarrow{GH} = (4 - 10, 1 - (-3), -11 - 15)$$
$$= (-6, 4, -26)$$
$$= -6\vec{i} + 4\vec{j} - 26\vec{k}$$

CHECKING FOR UNDERSTANDING

Communicating Mathematics

Read and study the lesson to answer each question.

1. **Describe** the process you would use to locate $(3, -1, 2)$ in space. Then sketch the point on a coordinate system. See margin.

2. **Compare** the formula for the magnitude of a vector in space to the formula for the magnitude of a vector in a plane. See margin.

3. Suppose the unit vectors in a four-dimensional system are $\vec{i}$, $\vec{j}$, $\vec{k}$, and $\vec{\ell}$. Name the coordinates of the terminal points of $\vec{i}$, $\vec{j}$, $\vec{k}$, and $\vec{\ell}$. $\vec{i} = (1, 0, 0, 0)$, $\vec{j} = (0, 1, 0, 0)$, $\vec{k} = (0, 0, 1, 0)$, and $\vec{\ell} = (0, 0, 0, 1)$

Guided Practice

Locate points with the given coordinates. Then find the magnitude of a vector from the origin to each point. 4–9. See Teacher's Answer Key for graphs.

4. $(3, 4, 9)$ $\sqrt{106}$

5. $(-2, 1, 3)$ $\sqrt{14}$

6. $(-1, 0, 4)$ $\sqrt{17}$

7. $(7, 2, 4)$ $\sqrt{69}$

8. $(4, 1, -3)$ $\sqrt{26}$

9. $(-1, -1, 5)$ $3\sqrt{3}$

LESSON 8-3 VECTORS IN THREE-DIMENSIONAL SPACE **427**

RETEACHING THE LESSON

An ordered triple represents a point in three-dimensional space and can also represent the vector whose initial point is the origin and whose terminal point is the given ordered triple. Find a single ordered triple to represent each vector below.

1. $\overrightarrow{AB}$ for $A(0, 0, 5)$ and $B(3, 4, 2)$ $(3, 4, -3)$

2. $\overrightarrow{PQ}$ for $P(-2, 7, -10)$ and $Q(-2, 5, -1)$ $(0, -2, 9)$

3. $\overrightarrow{CD}$ for $C(1, -1, -8)$ and $D(5, -4, 2)$ $(4, -3, 10)$

APPLYING THE LESSON

Homework Exercises

Assignment Guide

Average: 14–25, 26–36 even, 38–44
Enriched: 18–44

The red A, B, and C flags, printed only in
the Teacher's Wraparound Edition, indicate
the level of difficulty of the exercises.

Additional Answers

10. $(1, -4, -4); \vec{i} - 4\vec{j} - 4\vec{k}$
11. $(4, -8, -14); 4\vec{i} - 8\vec{j} - 14\vec{k}$
12. $(11, -6, 15); 11\vec{i} - 6\vec{j} + 15\vec{k}$
13. $(7, 3, -1); 7\vec{i} + 3\vec{j} - \vec{k}$
14. $(-4, -1, 0); \sqrt{17} \approx 4.123$
15. $(2, 0, 3); \sqrt{13} \approx 3.606$
16. $(5, 4, -11); 9\sqrt{2} \approx 12.728$
17. $(-1, 1, -5); 3\sqrt{3} \approx 5.196$
18. $(22, 9, 10); \sqrt{665} \approx 25.788$
19. $(15, -24, 4); \sqrt{817} \approx 28.583$

For each pair of points A and B, find an ordered triple that represents $\overrightarrow{AB}$. Then write $\overrightarrow{AB}$ as the sum of unit vectors. 10–13. See margin.

10. $A(2, 5, 4), B(3, 1, 0)$
11. $A(-1, 3, 10), B(3, -5, -4)$
12. $A(-11, 4, -2), B(0, -2, 13)$
13. $A(-3, 0, 0), B(4, 3, -1)$

EXERCISES

Practice For each pair of points A and B, find an ordered triple that represents $\overrightarrow{AB}$. Then find the magnitude of $\overrightarrow{AB}$. 14–19. See margin.

14. $A(8, 1, 1), B(4, 0, 1)$
15. $A(3, 7, -1), B(5, 7, 2)$
16. $A(-2, 5, 8), B(3, 9, -3)$
17. $A(-2, 4, 7), B(-3, 5, 2)$
18. $A(-2, -4, 1), B(20, 5, 11)$
19. $A(-12, 3, 0), B(3, -21, 4)$

Write each vector as the sum of unit vectors.

20. $(9, 3, -1)$ $9\vec{i} + 3\vec{j} - \vec{k}$
21. $(3, 0, 1)$ $3\vec{i} + \vec{k}$
22. $(0, 2, -2)$ $2\vec{j} - 2\vec{k}$
23. $(-5, -8, 1)$ $-5\vec{i} - 8\vec{j} + \vec{k}$
24. $(-15, 7, 0)$ $-15\vec{i} + 7\vec{j}$
25. $(8, -3, 11)$ $8\vec{i} - 3\vec{j} + 11\vec{k}$

Find an ordered triple to represent $\vec{u}$ in each equation if $\vec{v} = (1, -3, -8)$ and $\vec{w} = (3, 9, -1)$.

26. $\vec{u} = \vec{v} + \vec{w}$ $(4, 6, -9)$
27. $\vec{u} = \vec{w} - \vec{v}$ $(2, 12, 7)$
28. $\vec{u} = 3\vec{v} + \vec{w}$ $(6, 0, -25)$
29. $\vec{u} = \vec{v} - 2\vec{w}$ $(-5, -21, -6)$
30. $\vec{u} = 4\vec{v} - 3\vec{w}$ $(-5, -39, -29)$
31. $\vec{u} = 2\vec{w} - 5\vec{v}$ $(1, 33, 38)$

32. Show that $|\overrightarrow{P_1P_2}| = |\overrightarrow{P_2P_1}|$. See margin.

33. If $\vec{a} = (a_1, a_2, a_3)$, then $-\vec{a}$ is defined to be $(-a_1, -a_2, -a_3)$. Show that $|-\vec{a}| = |\vec{a}|$. See margin.

Critical Thinking Find a unit vector that has the same direction as each given vector.

34. $\vec{a} = \vec{i} + \vec{j} - \vec{k}$
35. $\vec{b} = 4\vec{i} - 3\vec{j} - 12\vec{k}$

34–35. See margin.

Applications and Problem Solving

36. **Electrostatics** Charles Augustin de Coulomb was a French scientist, inventor, and engineer in the late 1700s. He made contributions to the fields of friction, electricity, and magnetism. He also formulated Coulomb's Law, which states that if the electric force F exerted by a charge q_1 at the point Q_1 on a charge q located at point Q is given by the equation $F = \frac{q_1 q}{4\pi\varepsilon_0 r^2}\vec{u}$, where $\vec{u}$ is the unit vector in the direction of $\overrightarrow{Q_1Q}$, r is the distance between the charges, and $\varepsilon_0 = 8.854 \times 10^{-12}$. If the charge of a proton located at $(0, 2 \times 10^{-11}, 0)$ is 1.6×10^{-19} coulombs, find the electric force exerted on an electron of charge -1.6×10^{-19} located at the origin. *Hint: In this case, $\vec{u} = \vec{j}$.* $-5.7522 \times 10^{-7}\,\vec{j}$

428 CHAPTER 8 VECTORS AND PARAMETRIC EQUATIONS

32. $|\overrightarrow{P_1P_2}| = \sqrt{(x_2 - x_1)^2 + (y_2 - y_1)^2 + (z_2 - z_1)^2}$
$= \sqrt{(x_1 - x_2)^2 + (y_1 - y_2)^2 + (z_1 - z_2)^2} = |\overrightarrow{P_2P_1}|$
because $(x - y)^2 = (y - x)^2$ for all real numbers x and y.

33. If $\vec{a} = (a_1, a_2, a_3)$, then $|\vec{a}| = \sqrt{(a_1)^2 + (a_2)^2 + (a_3)^2}$.
If $-\vec{a} = (-a_1, -a_2, -a_3)$, then $|\vec{a}| = \sqrt{(-a_1)^2 + (-a_2)^2 + (-a_3)^2}$.
Since $a_1^2 = (-a_1^2)$, $a_2^2 = (-a_2)^2$, and $a_3^2 = (-a_3)^2$, $|-\vec{a}| = |\vec{a}|$.

34. $\frac{1}{\sqrt{3}}\vec{i} + \frac{1}{\sqrt{3}}\vec{j} - \frac{1}{\sqrt{3}}\vec{k}$

35. $\frac{4}{13}\vec{i} - \frac{3}{13}\vec{j} - \frac{12}{13}\vec{k}$

37. Physics If vectors working on an object are in equilibrium, then their resultant is zero.

   a. Find the vector for the force of the damper that results in equilibrium with the force created by the wind in Example 3. $(-132, -3454, 0)$

   b. Two forces on an object are represented by $(3, -2, 4)$ and $(6, 2, 5)$. Find a third vector that will place the object in equilibrium. $(-9, 0, -9)$

Mixed Review

38. Manufacturing The Simply Sweats Corporation makes high quality sweatpants and sweatshirts. Each garment passes through the cutting and sewing departments of the factory. The cutting and sewing departments have 100 and 180 worker-hours available each week, respectively. The fabric supplier can provide 195 yards of fabric each week. The hours of work and yards of fabric required for each garment are shown in the table below. If the profit from a sweatshirt is $5.50 and the profit from a pair of sweatpants is $4.00, how many of each should the company make for maximum profit? **(Lesson 2-6)** 72 shirts, 0 pants

clothing	cutting	sewing	fabric
shirt	1 h	2.5 h	1.5 yd
pants	1.5 h	2 h	3 yd

39. Determine whether the functions $y = \dfrac{3x}{x+1}$ and $y = \dfrac{x+1}{3x}$ are inverses of one another. **(Lesson 3-3)** no

40. Find the critical points of the graph of $f(x) = \dfrac{1}{2}x^4 + 4x^3 - 7x^2 + 1$. Then determine whether each point represents a maximum, a minimum, or a point of inflection. **(Lesson 3-7)** See margin.

41. Simplify the expression $1 - 2\sin^2 10°$ without using a calculator. **(Lesson 7-4)** $\cos 20°$

42. Write the standard form of the equation of the line that has a normal 3 units long and makes an angle of $60°$ with the positive x-axis. **(Lesson 7-6)** $x + \sqrt{3}y - 6 = 0$

43. Find an ordered pair that represents $\overrightarrow{AB}$ for $A(5, -6)$ and $B(6, -5)$. Then find the magnitude of $\overrightarrow{AB}$. **(Lesson 8-2)** $(1, 1); \sqrt{2} \approx 1.414$

44. College Entrance Exam Compare quantities A and B below. D
   Write A if quantity A is greater.
   Write B if quantity B is greater.
   Write C if the quantities are equal.
   Write D if there is not enough information to determine the relationship.
   Given: $a > 0$
           $b > 0$
           $x > 1$

   (A) $\left(x^a\right)^b$ **(B)** $x^a x^b$

LESSON 8-3   VECTORS IN THREE-DIMENSIONAL SPACE   **429**

EXTENDING THE LESSON

Math Power: Reasoning

a. Have students consider how to define n-dimensional vectors and how to perform addition and scalar multiplication with them. Sample answers: Addition and scalar multiplication would be performed component-wise. Addition would be commutative. The zero vector is the additive identity, and each vector has an additive inverse.

b. What properties would these operations have? Can you think of any uses for n-dimensional vectors where $n > 3$? One could use a fourth component to represent time in addition to the three ordinary spatial dimensions. Vectors with more dimensions could represent responses to a survey with four or more questions.

NCTM Standards: 1–4, 8

Lesson Resources

- Practice Master 8–4
- Enrichment Master 8–4
- Evaluation Master, Quiz B, p. 97
- Technology Master, p. 15

 Transparency 8–4 contains the 5-Minute Check and a teaching aid for this lesson.

INTRODUCING THE LESSON

 5-Minute Check

(over Lesson 8–3)

For Exercises 1–3, use points $C(1, 7, -3)$ and $D(2, -4, 1)$.
1. Find an ordered triple that represents $\overrightarrow{CD}$. $(1, -11, 4)$
2. Find the magnitude of $\overrightarrow{CD}$ $\sqrt{138}$ units
3. Write $\overrightarrow{CD}$ as a sum of unit vectors. $\mathbf{i} - 11\mathbf{j} + 4\mathbf{k}$
4. If $\vec{u} = (3, -3, -2)$ and $\vec{v} = (0, 1, 8)$, find $\vec{w} = 2\vec{u} - \vec{v}$. $(6, -7, -12)$

Prerequisite Skills

Students need to know how to expand a 3×3 determinant by minors. Expand each determinant by minors using its first row.

1. $\begin{vmatrix} 2 & 1 & 0 \\ -4 & 6 & 0 \\ 0 & -3 & 2 \end{vmatrix}$

$2\begin{vmatrix} 6 & 0 \\ -3 & 2 \end{vmatrix} - 1\begin{vmatrix} -4 & 0 \\ 0 & 2 \end{vmatrix} + 0\begin{vmatrix} -4 & 6 \\ 0 & -3 \end{vmatrix}$

2. $\begin{vmatrix} 5 & 0 & -1 \\ 2 & -2 & 3 \\ 0 & 1 & 4 \end{vmatrix}$

$5\begin{vmatrix} -2 & 3 \\ 1 & 4 \end{vmatrix} - 0\begin{vmatrix} 2 & 3 \\ 0 & 4 \end{vmatrix} - 1\begin{vmatrix} 2 & -2 \\ 0 & 1 \end{vmatrix}$

Motivating the Lesson

In the first three lessons of this chapter, students learned to add vectors and multiply them by scalars. How can vectors be multiplied by vectors? Give students a chance to think of some possibilities.

8-4   Perpendicular Vectors

Objectives

After studying this lesson, you should be able to:
8–4A   ■ find the inner and cross products of two vectors, and
8–4B   ■ determine whether two vectors are perpendicular.

Application

Hold a pencil horizontally between two fingers of your left hand and use your right hand to press up on one end of the pencil. The pencil will rotate about the point where your left hand is holding it. In physics, the torque of a force is the measure of the effectiveness of a force in turning an object about a pivot point. We can use perpendicular vectors to find the torque of a force.

Let $\vec{a}$ and $\vec{b}$ be perpendicular vectors, and let $\overrightarrow{BA}$ be a vector between their terminal points as shown. Then the magnitudes of $\vec{a}$, $\vec{b}$, and $\overrightarrow{BA}$ must satisfy the Pythagorean theorem.

$$|\overrightarrow{BA}|^2 = |\vec{a}|^2 + |\vec{b}|^2$$

Use the definition of magnitude of a vector to evaluate $|\overrightarrow{BA}|^2$.

$$|\overrightarrow{BA}|^2 = \left(\sqrt{(a_1 - b_1)^2 + (a_2 - b_2)^2}\right)^2$$
$$= (a_1 - b_1)^2 + (a_2 - b_2)^2$$
$$= a_1^2 - 2a_1b_1 + b_1^2 + a_2^2 - 2a_2b_2 + b_2^2$$
$$= (a_1^2 + a_2^2) + (b_1^2 + b_2^2) - 2(a_1b_1 + a_2b_2)$$
$$= |\vec{a}|^2 + |\vec{b}|^2 - 2(a_1b_1 + a_2b_2) \quad \text{\textit{Compare this equation with the original one.}}$$

Therefore, $|\overrightarrow{BA}|^2 = |\vec{a}|^2 + |\vec{b}|^2$ if and only if $a_1b_1 + a_2b_2 = 0$.

The expression $a_1b_1 + a_2b_2$ is used often in the study of vectors. It is called the **inner product** of $\vec{a}$ and $\vec{b}$.

Inner Product of Vectors in a Plane	If $\vec{a}$ and $\vec{b}$ are two vectors, (a_1, a_2) and (b_1, b_2), the inner product of $\vec{a}$ and $\vec{b}$ is defined as $\vec{a} \cdot \vec{b} = a_1b_1 + a_2b_2$.

$\vec{a} \cdot \vec{b}$ is read "$\vec{a}$ dot $\vec{b}$" and is often called the <u>dot product</u>.

ALTERNATE TEACHING STRATEGIES

Using Critical Thinking

Tell students how the inner product of two vectors is defined and then give students a set of vectors represented by ordered pairs. Have them graph pairs of the vectors, find their inner products, and then formulate a hypothesis about when the inner product is zero.

Using Discussion

Define the cross product of two vectors in three-dimensional space, and ask students if they can discover a geometric relationship between a pair of vectors and their cross product. If a graph does not help students to find a connection, suggest they consider the inner product.

Two vectors are perpendicular if and only if their inner product is zero.

Example 1

Find the inner products of $\vec{a}$ and $\vec{b}$ and of $\vec{a}$ and $\vec{c}$ if $\vec{a} = (3, 12)$, $\vec{b} = (8, -2)$, and $\vec{c} = (3, -2)$. Is either pair of these vectors perpendicular?

$$\vec{a} \cdot \vec{b} = 3(8) + 12(-2)$$
$$= 24 - 24$$
$$= 0$$

$\vec{a}$ and $\vec{b}$ are perpendicular.

$$\vec{a} \cdot \vec{c} = 3(3) + 12(-2)$$
$$= 9 - 24$$
$$= -15$$

$\vec{a}$ and $\vec{c}$ are not perpendicular.

We can also find the inner product of two vectors in space. Two vectors in space are perpendicular if and only if their inner product is zero.

Inner Product of Vectors in Space	If $\vec{a} = (a_1, a_2, a_3)$ and $\vec{b} = (b_1, b_2, b_3)$, then $\vec{a} \cdot \vec{b} = a_1 b_1 + a_2 b_2 + a_3 b_3$.

Example 2

Find the inner product of $\vec{v}$ and $\vec{w}$ if $\vec{v} = (-6, 2, 10)$ and $\vec{w} = (4, 1, 3)$. Are $\vec{v}$ and $\vec{w}$ perpendicular?

$$\vec{v} \cdot \vec{w} = (-6)(4) + 2(1) + 10(3)$$
$$= -24 + 2 + 30$$
$$= 8$$

$\vec{v}$ and $\vec{w}$ are not perpendicular.

Another important product involving vectors in space is the **cross product**. The cross product of two vectors is a vector. This vector does not lie in the plane of the given vectors, but is perpendicular to each of them. Therefore, it is perpendicular to the plane containing the two vectors.

Cross Product of Vectors in Space	If $\vec{a} = (a_1, a_2, a_3)$ and $\vec{b} = (b_1, b_2, b_3)$, then the cross product of $\vec{a}$ and $\vec{b}$ is defined as follows. $$\vec{a} \times \vec{b} = \begin{vmatrix} a_2 & a_3 \\ b_2 & b_3 \end{vmatrix} \vec{i} - \begin{vmatrix} a_1 & a_3 \\ b_1 & b_3 \end{vmatrix} \vec{j} + \begin{vmatrix} a_1 & a_2 \\ b_1 & b_2 \end{vmatrix} \vec{k}$$

An easy way to remember the coefficients of $\vec{i}$, $\vec{j}$, and $\vec{k}$ is to set up a determinant as shown and expand by minors using the first row. *You may want to review expansion by minors in Lesson 2-3.*

$$\begin{vmatrix} \vec{i} & \vec{j} & \vec{k} \\ a_1 & a_2 & a_3 \\ b_1 & b_2 & b_3 \end{vmatrix}$$

LESSON 8-4 PERPENDICULAR VECTORS 431

Chalkboard Examples

For Example 1

Find the inner products of $\vec{a}$ and $\vec{b}$ and of $\vec{a}$ and $\vec{c}$ if $\vec{a} = (2, -5)$, $\vec{b} = (4, 1)$, and $\vec{c} = (10, 4)$. Is either pair of these vectors perpendicular?
3; 0; yes, $\vec{a} \perp \vec{c}$

For Example 2

Find the inner product of $\vec{v}$ and $\vec{w}$ if $\vec{v} = (2, -3, -4)$ and $\vec{w} = (8, 3, 2)$. Are $\vec{v}$ and $\vec{w}$ perpendicular?
-1; no

Teaching Tip Tell students that although the inner product $\vec{a} \cdot \vec{b} = \vec{b} \cdot \vec{a}$, this is not true for the cross product. That is, $\vec{a} \times \vec{b} \neq \vec{b} \times \vec{a}$. These two vectors are parallel, however, since both are perpendicular to the plane containing $\vec{a}$ and $\vec{b}$. Also point out that the dot product of two vectors is a scalar quantity, while the cross product is another vector.

Example 3

Find the cross product of $\vec{a}$ and $\vec{b}$ if $\vec{a} = (5, 2, 3)$ and $\vec{b} = (-2, 5, 0)$. Then verify that the resulting vector is perpendicular to $\vec{a}$ and $\vec{b}$.

$$\vec{a} \times \vec{b} = \begin{vmatrix} \vec{i} & \vec{j} & \vec{k} \\ 5 & 2 & 3 \\ -2 & 5 & 0 \end{vmatrix}$$

$$= \begin{vmatrix} 2 & 3 \\ 5 & 0 \end{vmatrix} \vec{i} - \begin{vmatrix} 5 & 3 \\ -2 & 0 \end{vmatrix} \vec{j} + \begin{vmatrix} 5 & 2 \\ -2 & 5 \end{vmatrix} \vec{k}$$

$$= -15\vec{i} - 6\vec{j} + 29\vec{k} \text{ or } (-15, -6, 29)$$

Find the inner products $(-15, -6, 29) \cdot (5, 2, 3)$ and $(-15, -6, 29) \cdot (-2, 5, 0)$.

$$-15(5) + (-6)(2) + 29(3) = 0 \qquad -15(-2) + (-6)(5) + 29(0) = 0$$

Since the inner products are zero, $(-15, -6, 29)$ is perpendicular to both $(5, 2, 3)$ and $(-2, 5, 0)$.

Example 4

The moment, $\vec{M}$, of a force, $\vec{F}$, at a point Q about another point P is defined by the equation $\vec{M} = \vec{PQ} \times \vec{F}$. The magnitude of $\vec{M}$ represents the torque of the force in pounds per foot. Sumi places a wrench on a nut and is applying a downward force of 32 pounds to tighten the nut. If the center of the nut is at the origin, the force is applied at the point $(0.65, 0, 0.3)$. Find the torque of the force.

First, find $\vec{PQ}$ and $\vec{F}$.

$$\vec{PQ} = (0.65 - 0, 0 - 0, 0.3 - 0)$$
$$\text{or } (0.65, 0, 0.3)$$

$\vec{F}$ is in a downward direction, so
$$\vec{F} = -32\vec{k} \text{ or } (0, 0, -32).$$

32 lb $\vec{F}$

Then, find $\vec{M}$.

$$\vec{M} = \vec{PQ} \times \vec{F}$$

$$= \begin{vmatrix} \vec{i} & \vec{j} & \vec{k} \\ 0.65 & 0 & 0.3 \\ 0 & 0 & -32 \end{vmatrix}$$

$$= \begin{vmatrix} 0 & 0.3 \\ 0 & -32 \end{vmatrix} \vec{i} - \begin{vmatrix} 0.65 & 0.3 \\ 0 & -32 \end{vmatrix} \vec{j} + \begin{vmatrix} 0.65 & 0 \\ 0 & 0 \end{vmatrix} \vec{k}$$

$$= 0\vec{i} + 20.8\vec{j} + 0\vec{k} \text{ or } (0, 20.8, 0)$$

The torque is the magnitude of $\vec{M}$.

$$|\vec{M}| = \sqrt{0^2 + 20.8^2 + 0^2} \text{ or } 20.8$$

The torque of the force is 20.8 lb/ft.

432 CHAPTER 8 VECTORS AND PARAMETRIC EQUATIONS

CHECKING FOR UNDERSTANDING

Communicating Mathematics

Read and study the lesson to answer each question.

1. If the inner product of $\vec{w}$ and $\vec{v}$ is nonzero, what can you say about $\vec{w}$ and $\vec{v}$? They are not perpendicular.

2. Could the inner product of a nonzero vector and itself ever be zero? Explain. No; a vector cannot be perpendicular to itself.

3. **Show** that $\vec{i} \times \vec{j} = \vec{k}$. See margin.

Guided Practice

Find each inner product and state whether the vectors are perpendicular. Write *yes* or *no*.

4. $(3,5) \cdot (4,-2)$ 2, no

5. $(8,4) \cdot (2,4)$ 32, no

6. $(5,-1) \cdot (2,3)$ 7, no

7. $(-6,3) \cdot (1,2)$ 0, yes

8. $(4,2) \cdot (-3,6)$ 0, yes

9. $(11,2) \cdot (-3,16)$ −1, no

10. $(7,-2,4) \cdot (3,8,1)$ 9, no

11. $(-2,4,8) \cdot (16,4,2)$ 0, yes

Find each cross product.

12. $(7,2,1) \times (2,5,3)$ $(1,-19,31)$

13. $(-2,-3,1) \times (2,3,-4)$ $(9,-6,0)$

14. $(1,-3,2) \times (5,1,-2)$ $(4,12,16)$

15. $(-1,0,4) \times (5,2,-1)$ $(-8,19,-2)$

EXERCISES

Practice

Find each inner product and state whether the vectors are perpendicular. Write *yes* or *no*.

16. $(-6,1) \cdot (-1,2)$ 8, no

17. $(2,0) \cdot (0,4)$ 0, yes

18. $(2,-2) \cdot (5,-5)$ 20, no

19. $(2,5) \cdot (0,1)$ 5, no

20. $(5,2) \cdot (-3,7)$ −1, no

21. $(-8,2) \cdot (4.5,18)$ 0, yes

22. $(3,-2,4) \cdot (1,-4,0)$ 11, no

23. $(-4,9,8) \cdot (3,2,-2)$ −10, no

24. $(4,9,-3) \cdot (-6,7,5)$ 24, no

25. $(-6,2,10) \cdot (4,1,9)$ 68, no

Find each cross product. Then verify that the resulting vector is perpendicular to the given vectors.

26. $(1,3,2) \times (2,-1,-1)$ $(-1,5,-7)$, yes

27. $(2,1,2) \times (1,-1,3)$ $(5,-4,-3)$, yes

28. $(1,-3,2) \times (-2,1,-5)$ $(13,1,-5)$, yes

29. $(4,0,-2) \times (-7,1,0)$ $(2,14,4)$, yes

Find a vector perpendicular to the plane containing the given points.

30. $(1,2,3), (-4,2,-1),$ and $(5,-3,0)$ $(-20,-31,25)$

31. $(0,1,2), (-2,2,4),$ and $(-1,-1,-1)$ $(1,-8,5)$
    30–31. Sample answers are given.

LESSON 8-4 PERPENDICULAR VECTORS 433

RETEACHING THE LESSON

Some students may prefer the following method for finding the cross product of two vectors. Write an expanded version of the determinant, as shown below, and then form the sum of the products of each left to right diagonal and the opposites of the products of each right to left diagonal.

$bfi + cdj + aek − bdk − cei − afi$

---

32. Prove that $\vec{a} \cdot \vec{b} = \vec{b} \cdot \vec{a}$ for two-dimensional vectors.

33. Prove that $\vec{a} \cdot \vec{b} = \vec{b} \cdot \vec{a}$ for three-dimensional vectors.

34. Prove that $\vec{a} \times \vec{a} = 0$.

35. Use the definition of cross product to prove that $\vec{a} \times (\vec{b} + \vec{c}) = (\vec{a} \times \vec{b}) + (\vec{a} \times \vec{c})$.

36. Is it true that $\vec{a} \times \vec{b} = \vec{b} \times \vec{a}$? Explain.

Programming

37. The program below calculates the cross product of two vectors.

```
:Prgm8:XPRODUCT
:ClrHome                        Clears the text screen.
:Disp "1ST VECTOR, A1="         Displays the quoted message.
:Input A                        Accepts a value for A.
:Disp "A2="
:Input B
:Disp "A3="
:Input C
:Disp "2ND VECTOR, B1="
:Input D
:Disp "B2="
:Input E
:Disp "B3="
:Input F
:BF-EC→I                        Calculates i coefficient, stores in I.
:DC-AF→J
:AE-BD→K
:Disp "CROSS PRODUCT"
:Disp "COEFF. OF I="
:Disp I                         Displays the value stored in I.
:Disp "COEFF. OF J="
:Disp J
:Disp "COEFF. OF K="
:Disp K
```

Find each cross product.

a. $(1, 3, -2) \times (1, -1, 2)$ $(4, -4, -4)$

b. $(-3, 6, 5) \times (-2, -7, 2)$ $(47, -4, 33)$

Critical Thinking

38. If $\vec{a} \neq 0$, $\vec{a} \cdot \vec{b} = \vec{a} \cdot \vec{c}$, and $\vec{a} \times \vec{b} = \vec{a} \times \vec{c}$, must it be true that $\vec{b} = \vec{c}$? Justify your answer. See Teacher's Answer Key.

Applications and Problem Solving

39. Physics The handle of a jack is at an angle of 30° with the horizontal. A downward force of 55 pounds is applied to the jack at a point 1.5 feet from the point where the handle meets the body of the jack.

  a. Find the moment of the force. $(0, 71.5, 0)$

  b. Find the torque of the force. 71.5 lb/ft

  c. An object tends to rotate around the line that passes through the point P and is parallel to the moment. This line is called the axis of rotation. Find the axis of rotation for the force applied to the jack handle. the y-axis

---

The program given in Exercise 37 is for use with a TI-81 graphing calculator. For other programmable calculators, have students consult their owner's manual for commands similar to those presented here.

Additional Answers

32. $\vec{a} \cdot \vec{b} = (a_1, a_2) \cdot (b_1, b_2)$
$= a_1b_1 + a_2b_2$
$= b_1a_1 + b_2a_2$
$= (b_1, b_2) \cdot (a_1, a_2)$
$= \vec{b} \cdot \vec{a}$

33. $\vec{a} \cdot \vec{b} = (a_1, a_2, a_3) \cdot (b_1, b_2, b_3)$
$= a_1b_1 + a_2b_2 + a_3b_3$
$= b_1a_1 + b_2a_2 + b_3a_3$
$= (b_1, b_2, b_3) \cdot (a_1, a_2, a_3)$
$= \vec{b} \cdot \vec{a}$

36. no; $\vec{a} \times \vec{b}$ and $\vec{b} \times \vec{a}$ have the same magnitude but opposite directions

40. Geometry Find the perimeter of the triangle with vertices at the points $A(2,-1)$, $B(5,3)$, and $C(-3,11)$. **(Lesson 1-4)** 29.31 units

41. Without graphing, determine the end behavior of the graph of the function $y = 11 - 15x - x^3$. **(Lesson 3-8)** See margin.

42. Approximate the real zeros of the function $f(x) = 4x^4 + 5x^3 - x^2 + 1$ to the nearest tenth. **(Lesson 4-5)** $-1.3, -0.6$

43. Find the value of $\cos\left(\text{Tan}^{-1}\dfrac{\sqrt{33}}{4}\right)$. **(Lesson 6-5)** $\dfrac{4}{7}$

44. Find an ordered triple that represents $\overrightarrow{AB}$ for $A(5, 7, -2)$ and $B(0, -11, 8)$. **(Lesson 8-3)** $(-5, -18, 10)$

45. College Entrance Exam Choose the best answer. B
The sum of $\sqrt{12} + \sqrt{27}$ is
(A) $\sqrt{39}$　　(B) $5\sqrt{3}$　　(C) $13\sqrt{3}$　　(D) $7\sqrt{3}$　　(E) $6\sqrt{3}$

MID-CHAPTER REVIEW

Use a metric ruler and a protractor to draw a vector with the given magnitude and amplitude. Then find the magnitude of the horizontal and vertical components of the vector. **(Lesson 8-1)** 1–4. See margin.

1. 1 cm, 65°　　　　**2.** 3.1 cm, 15°　　　　**3.** 0.8 cm, 120°　　　　**4.** 2.2 cm, 160°

Find the ordered pair or ordered triple that represents the vector from A to B. Then find the magnitude of $\overrightarrow{AB}$. **(Lessons 8-2 and 8-3)** 5. $(-8, 1)$; $\sqrt{65} \approx 8.062$　6. $(1, 0)$; 1

5. $A(5, 2), B(-3, 3)$　　　　**6.** $A(-4, 3), B(-3, 3)$　　　　**7.** $A(8, -7), B(-2, 5)$

8. $A(3, 1, -2), B(4, 0, -1)$　　　　**9.** $A(6, 10, -11), B(-2, 4, -12)$
7. $(-10, 12)$; $2\sqrt{61} \approx 15.620$　8. $(1, -1, 1)$; $\sqrt{3} \approx 1.732$　9. $(-8, -6, -1)$; $\sqrt{101} \approx 10.050$

Find an ordered pair or ordered triple to represent $\vec{u}$ in each equation if $\vec{v} = (-2, 7)$, $\vec{w} = (7, -10)$, $\vec{s} = (-2, 1, 3)$ and $\vec{t} = (-1, -1, 5)$. **(Lessons 8-2 and 8-3)**

10. $\vec{u} = \vec{v} + \vec{w}$　$(5, -3)$　　**11.** $\vec{u} = 2\vec{v} - 4\vec{w}$　$(-32, 54)$　　**12.** $\vec{u} = 2\vec{w} - \vec{v}$　$(16, -27)$
13. $\vec{u} = \vec{s} + \vec{t}$　$(-3, 0, 8)$　　**14.** $\vec{u} = \vec{t} - 2\vec{s}$　$(3, -3, -1)$　　**15.** $\vec{u} = 4\vec{t}$　$(-4, -4, 20)$;

Find each inner product and state whether the vectors are perpendicular. **(Lesson 8-4)**

16. $(2, -1) \cdot (3, 4)$　2, no　　**17.** $(-1, 5) \cdot (10, 2)$　0, yes　　**18.** $(9, 2, -4) \cdot (2, -7, 3)$　-8, no

19. Find a vector perpendicular to the plane determined by the points at $(2, -1, 5)$, $(0, 2, 1)$, and $(8, 2, -1)$. **(Lesson 8-4)** Sample answer: $(-6, -36, -24)$

EXTENDING THE LESSON

Math Power: Problem Solving

A pair of nonlinear vectors in three-space defines a plane. Can the fact that the cross product of the vectors is perpendicular to them be used to find an equation for the plane?
Sample answer: If the vectors are (1, 4, −3) and (−2, 5, 5), then an equation for the plane is $35x + y + 13z = 0$.

Mid-Chapter Review

The Mid-Chapter Review provides students with a brief review of the concepts and skills in Lessons 8–1 through 8–4. Lesson numbers are given at the end of problems or instruction lines so students may review concepts not yet mastered.

Additional Answers

Enrichment Masters Booklet, p. 53

8-4 **Enrichment Worksheet**

NAME _____ DATE _____

Vector Equations

Let $\vec{a}$, $\vec{b}$, and $\vec{c}$ be fixed vectors. The equation $f(x) = \vec{a} - 2x\vec{b} + x^2\vec{c}$ defines a vector function of x. For the values of x shown, the assigned vectors are given below.

x	-2	-1	0	1	2
$f(x)$	$\vec{a}+4\vec{b}+4\vec{c}$	$\vec{a}+2\vec{b}+\vec{c}$	$\vec{a}$	$\vec{a}-2\vec{b}+\vec{c}$	$\vec{a}-4\vec{b}+4\vec{c}$

If $\vec{a} = (0, 1)$, $\vec{b} = (1, 1)$, and $\vec{c} = (2, -2)$, the resulting vectors for the values of x are as follows.

x	-2	-1	0	1	2
$f(x)$	$(12,-3)$	$(4, 1)$	$(0, 1)$	$(0,-3)$	$(4,-11)$

For each of the following, complete the table of resulting vectors.

1. $f(x) = x^3\vec{a} - 2x^2\vec{b} + 3x\vec{c}$
$\vec{a} = (1, 1)$　$\vec{b} = (2, 3)$　$\vec{c} = (3, -1)$

x	$f(x)$
-1	$(-14,-4)$
0	$(0, 0)$
1	$(6, -8)$
2	$(10, -22)$

2. $f(x) = 2x^2\vec{a} + 3x\vec{b} - 5\vec{c}$
$\vec{a} = (0, 1, 1)$　$\vec{b} = (1, 0, 1)$　$\vec{c} = (1, 1, 0)$

x	$f(x)$
-2	$(-11, 3, 2)$
-1	$(-8, -3, -1)$
0	$(-5, -5, 0)$
1	$(-2, -3, 5)$

3. $f(x) = x^2\vec{c} + 3x\vec{a} - 4\vec{b}$
$\vec{a} = (1, 1, 1)$　$\vec{b} = (3, 2, 1)$　$\vec{c} = (0, 1, 2)$

x	$f(x)$
0	$(-12, -8, -4)$
1	$(-9, -4, 1)$
2	$(-6, 2, 10)$
3	$(-3, 10, 23)$

4. $f(x) = x^3\vec{a} - x\vec{b} + 3\vec{c}$
$\vec{a} = (0,1,-2)$　$\vec{b} = (1, -2, 0)$　$\vec{c} = (-2, 0, 1)$

x	$f(x)$
-1	$(-5, -3, 5)$
0	$(-6, 0, 3)$
1	$(-7, 3, 1)$
3	$(-9, 33, -51)$

NCTM Standards: 1–4, 8, 9

Lesson Resources

- Practice Master 8–5
- Enrichment Master 8–5
- Activity Masters, pp. 22, 24

 Transparency 8–5 contains the 5-Minute Check and a teaching aid for this lesson.

INTRODUCING THE LESSON

 ### 5-Minute Check

(over Lesson 8–4)

Find each inner product and determine if the vectors are perpendicular.
1. $(-3, 0) \cdot (4, 7)$ **−12; no**
2. $(5, 1, -2) \cdot (2, 0, 5)$ **0; yes**
3. Find the cross product.
   $(3, -2, -1) \times (0, 6, 5)$
   (−4, −15, 18)

Motivating the Lesson

Imagine two people mowing their lawns. One person is six inches taller than the other, and holds the handle of his lawn mower at a steeper angle. Assuming the two people exert equal force, which mower has more force in the horizontal, grass-cutting direction? **The mower held at a steeper angle has a smaller component of its force in the horizontal direction.**

8-5 Applications with Vectors

Objective
8-5

After studying this lesson, you should be able to:
- solve problems using vectors and right triangle trigonometry.

Application

When 1992 Olympic champion Kerrin Lee-Gartner is skiing, the force due to gravity acts vertically. Physicists resolve this force into two perpendicular component vectors. One vector is parallel to the slope of the hill and accelerates Kerrin down the hill, while the other vector is perpendicular to the hill and helps to hold her skis on the surface of the snow.

Vectors can be used to represent any quantity, such as gravity, that has magnitude and direction. Velocity, acceleration, weight, and force are some of the quantities that physicists represent with vectors.

Example 1

APPLICATION

Skiing

Kerrin Lee-Gartner is on a snowy ski slope that makes an angle of 30° with the horizontal.
a. **Draw a labeled diagram that represents the forces at work.**
b. **If she weighs 125 pounds, find the force that propels Kerrin down the slope.**
c. **Use the formulas $W = mg$ and $F = ma$, where W represents weight in pounds, m represents mass in slugs, $g = 32$ ft/s², F represents force in pounds, and a represents acceleration in ft/s², to find Kerrin's acceleration down the slope.**

FYI...

Skis were first used for transport, and are still used for travel in the rural areas of some Scandinavian and Eastern European countries.

a. Let $\vec{F}_1$ represent the force parallel to the slope. This is the force that propels Kerrin down the slope. Let $\vec{F}_2$ represent the force perpendicular to the slope. Kerrin's weight, W, is the resultant of $\vec{F}_1$ and $\vec{F}_2$.

b. Use trigonometry to find $|\vec{F}_1|$.

$$\sin 30° = \frac{125}{|\vec{F}_1|}$$
$$|\vec{F}_1| = \frac{125}{\sin 30°}$$
$$|\vec{F}_1| = 250$$

The force propelling Kerrin down the slope is 250 pounds.

c. To find Kerrin's acceleration, first find her mass.

$$W = mg$$
$$125 = m(32)$$
$$m \approx 3.91$$

Kerrin's mass is 3.91 slugs.
The slug is the gravitational unit of mass.

ALTERNATE TEACHING STRATEGIES

Using Cooperative Groups

Assign each group of students one of the examples in the book and a specific parameter from that example. For instance, think about the weight of the skier or the steepness of the slope from Example 1. Have the group investigate how the solution varies as this parameter varies and give a report to the class.

Using Discussion

Consider a set of vectors representing forces acting simultaneously on an object. Their sum is the net force acting on the object. What does its opposite represent? **the force required to balance the other forces and put the system in equilibrium.**

Then use the formula $F = ma$ to find the acceleration.

$$F = ma$$
$$250 = 3.91a$$
$$a \approx 63.94$$

Kerrin's acceleration is 63.94 feet per second squared.

Example 2

Charlie and Jean Hughes are attempting to haul a large sign to the roof of their antique store. They are standing at the edge of the roof pulling on ropes attached to the sign. The ropes make a 30° angle with each other. If Jean is pulling with a force of 105 N and Charlie is pulling with a force of 110 N, what is the magnitude and direction of the net force on the sign?

Sketch the given vector quantities and the resultant. $\vec{r}$ is the resultant force. θ is the angle that the resultant makes with the 105 N force.

$\angle SJR$ is the supplement of 30°. Since we know two sides and the included angle in $\triangle SJR$, we can use the law of cosines to determine $|\vec{r}|$.

$$|\vec{r}|^2 = 105^2 + 110^2 - 2(105)(110)\cos 150°$$
$$|\vec{r}|^2 = 11{,}025 + 12{,}100 - 23{,}100 \cos 150°$$
$$|\vec{r}| \approx 207.68$$

The magnitude of $\vec{r}$ is about 207.68 N.

Now we can use the law of sines to find the direction of $\vec{r}$.

$$\frac{207.68}{\sin 150°} = \frac{110}{\sin \theta}$$
$$\sin \theta = \frac{110 \sin 150°}{207.68}$$
$$\sin \theta \approx 0.2648$$
$$\theta \approx 15°20' \qquad \textit{Round to the nearest ten minutes.}$$

The force on the sign has a magnitude of about 207.68 N and makes an angle of 15°20' with the 105 N force.

Sometimes there is no motion when several forces are at work on an object. This situation, when the forces balance one another, is called *equilibrium*. If the forces at equilibrium are drawn tip-to-tail, they will form a polygon.

LESSON 8-5   APPLICATIONS WITH VECTORS   437

Chalkboard Examples

For Example 1

A 4-kg mass is sliding down a plane inclined at an angle of 20° with the horizontal.
a. Draw a labeled diagram that represents the forces at work.

b. Find the force that propels the object down the slope, given that $F = mg$, where $g = 9.8$ m/s². **13.4 N**
c. Use the formula $F = ma$, where a represents acceleration in m/s², to find the object's acceleration down the slope. **3.35 m/s²**

For Example 2

A farmer and his son are removing a large boulder from a well. They are pulling on ropes attached to the boulder. The ropes make a 40° angle. If the farmer is pulling with a force of 115 N and his son is pulling with a force of 105 N, what is the magnitude and direction of the net force on the boulder? **206.76 N, at an angle of 21.0° with the 105 N force**

EVALUATING THE LESSON

Checking for Understanding

Exercises 1–9 are designed to help you assess students' understanding through reading, writing, speaking, and modeling. You should work through Exercises 1–2 with your students and then monitor their work on Exercises 3–9.

Closing the Lesson

Modeling Activity Have each student create a problem involving vector quantities, exchange with another student, and solve.

Practice Masters Booklet, p. 54

Example 3
APPLICATION
Physics

A traffic light is supported equally by two cables that make a 160° angle with each other. If the light weighs 1200 pounds, what is the tension of each of the cables?

Draw a sketch of the situation. Then draw the vectors tip-to-tail.

Since the triangle is isosceles, the base angles are congruent. We can use the law of sines to find the tension of the cables.

$$\frac{1200}{\sin 20°} = \frac{x}{\sin 80°}$$
$$x = \frac{1200 \sin 80°}{\sin 20°}$$
$$x \approx 3455.26$$

The tension of each cable is about 3455 pounds.

CHECKING FOR UNDERSTANDING

Communicating Mathematics

Read and study the lesson to answer each question.

1. As you sit still in a chair, the force of gravity pushes you against the chair and the chair pushes back. What can you say about these forces? See margin.

2. If the angle between the cables in Example 3 is increased, will there be more or less tension on the cables? more

Guided Practice

Make a sketch to show the given vectors. 3–5. See margin.

3. a ship traveling at 16 knots at an angle of 25° with the current

4. a force of 35 N acting on an object at an angle of 30° with the level ground

5. a force of 18 N acting on an object while a force of 51 N acts on the same object at an angle of 45° with the first force

Find the magnitude and direction of the resultant vector for each diagram.

6.
45 N
40 N
60.2 N, 48°22′

7.
270°   30 km/h
15 km/h
33.5 km/h, 333°26′

RETEACHING THE LESSON

Present a series of problems to the class involving forces or other vector quantities and work together at drawing a diagram for each. Then decide which strategies for solving triangles will be needed to solve the problems.

8.

23 N 120° 23 N

60°

39.8 N, 90°

9.

250 km/h 25°

110°

45 km/h

220.5 km/h, 16°42′

EXERCISES

Two 10-lb forces act on the same object at the same time. Find the magnitude of their resultant if each of the following is the measurement of the angle between them.

10. 30° 19.3 lb

11. 90° 14.1 lb

12. 120° 10 lb

13. 135° 7.65 lb

14. 170° 1.7 lb

15. 180° 0 lb

16. 111.8 N, 63°26′

16. A 100 N force and a 50 N force act on the same object. The angle between the forces measures 90°. Find the magnitude and direction of the resultant force.

17. Rick and Julie are unloading boxes from a truck. Rick places a box at the top of the loading ramp and lets it slide to the ground. If the ramp makes an angle of 40° with the ground and the box weighs 25 pounds, find the acceleration of the box. Assume that there is no friction. 49.86 ft/s²

18. Denzel pulls a wagon along level ground with a force of 18 N in the handle. If the handle makes an angle of 30° with the horizontal, find the horizontal and vertical components of the force. 15.6 N, 9 N

19. A 33 N force acting at 90° and a 44 N force acting at 60° act concurrently on a point. What is the magnitude and direction of a third force that produces equilibrium at the point? 74 N, 253°

20. A force F_1 of 36 N pulls at an angle of 20° above due east. Pulling in the opposite direction is a force F_2 of 48 N acting at an angle of 42° below due west. Find the magnitude and direction of the resultant force.
19.9 N, 5°22′ west of south

21. A block of ice weighing 300 pounds is held on an ice slide by a rope parallel to the slide. If the slide is inclined at an angle of 22°, find the tension on the rope and the force of the ice perpendicular to the slide. 800.8 lb, 323.5 lb

22. Three forces in a plane act on an object. The forces are 7 N, 11 N, and 15 N. The angle between the 7 N and 11 N forces is 105°, between the 11 N and 15 N forces is 147°, and between the 15 N and 7 N forces is 108°.

11N 105° 7N 147° 108° 15N

a. Are the vectors in equilibrium? no

b. If not, find the magnitude and the direction of the resultant force. 3.7 N, 10°2′ SE

LESSON 8-5 APPLICATIONS WITH VECTORS 439

---

23. Five forces are acting on a point P. They are 60 N at 90°, 40 N at 0°, 80 N at 270°, 40 N at 180°, and 50 N at 60°. What is the magnitude and direction of the vector that would produce equilibrium at point P? 34 N, 223°

24. See margin.

Critical Thinking

24. Jeff is trying to use a long piece of rope to remove a car from some deep mud. Which method should he use to exert more force on the car? Assume that Jeff will exert the same amount of force using either method. Explain your answer.

 a. Tie one end of the rope to the car and pull.

 b. Tie one end to the car and the other end to a nearby tree. Then push on the rope perpendicular to it at a point about halfway between the car and the tree.

Applications and Problem Solving

25. Aviation An airplane flies east for 210 km before turning 70° south and flying for 100 km. Find the distance and direction of the plane from its starting point. 261.7 km, 21°3′ SE

26. Aerospace A descent vehicle landing on the moon is approaching the surface of the moon with a vertical velocity of 35 m/s. The vehicle also has a horizontal velocity of 55 m/s.

 a. What is the speed of the vehicle along its path? 65 m/s
 b. What is the angle of the path with the vertical? 58°

27. Transportation Two riverboat landings are directly across the river from each other. A boat traveling at a speed of 12 mph is attempting to cross directly from one landing to the other. If the current of the river has a speed of 4 mph, at what angle should the skipper head? 19°28′

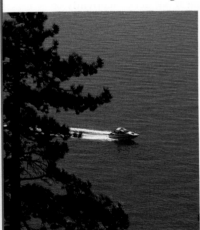

28. Gardening Kristin is exerting a force of 40 pounds along the handle of the lawn mower as she pushes it to cut the grass. The mower handle makes an angle of 30° with the ground. How much force is Kristin exerting forward and downward? 34.6 lb, 20 lb

29. Sports The engine on a boat is propelling it forward with a force of 125 N. The wind is blowing the boat with a force of 85 N at an angle of 72° from the force of the engine. Find the magnitude and direction of the path of the boat. 171.5 N, 28°7′

30. Aviation An airplane is heading due north at 260 mph. A 16-mph wind blows from the east. Find the ground speed and direction of the plane. 260.5 mph, 3°31′ NW

31. Physics Quentin is trying to pull a disabled snowmobile to the lodge. The snowmobile could be pulled with a force of 120 pounds parallel to the ground. If Quentin is pulling at an angle of 25° to the ground, with how much force must he pull? 132.4 lb

32. Aviation An airplane is heading due north at 260 mph. A 16-mph wind blows from the northwest at an angle of 110° clockwise from north. Find the ground speed and direction of the plane. 255.0 mph, 3°23′ NE

Mixed Review

33. Find the value of the determinant $\begin{vmatrix} 2 & 3 & 6 \\ 3 & -1 & -2 \\ 3 & 4 & 2 \end{vmatrix}$ using expansion by minors.
(Lesson 2-3) 66

34. Graph the rational function $y = \dfrac{6}{(x-1)(x+3)}$. **(Lesson 3-4)** See margin.

35. Find all the rational roots of the equation $3x^3 - 4x^2 - 5x + 2 = 0$.
(Lesson 4-4) $2, -1, \dfrac{1}{3}$

36. Use a sum or difference identity to find the exact value of tan (–75°).
(Lesson 7-3) $-2 - \sqrt{3}$

37. Find the inner product of vectors $(4, -1, 8)$ and $(-5, 2, 2)$. Are the vectors perpendicular? **(Lesson 8-4)** –6, no

38. College Entrance Exam Choose the best answer. D
$\overline{AB}$ is a diameter of circle O and $m\angle BOD = 15°$. If $m\angle EOA = 85°$, find $m\angle ECA$.
(A) 85° (B) 50° (C) 70°
(D) 35° (E) 45°

CASE STUDY FOLLOW-UP

Refer to Case Study 2: *Trashing the Planet*, on pages 959–961.

Toxic waste equivalent in weight to the residential and commercial trash thrown out by 10,000 Americans in one day is stored in cylindrical containers in underground storage facilities.

1. Find the weight of the total amount of stored waste. Assume that there are 250 million Americans. 36,000 lb

2. During an earthquake, the containers are toppled against one wall of the facility at a 52° angle. Find the magnitude of the horizontal force pressing against the wall. 22,164 lb

3. The wall is designed to withstand a horizontal force of 32,000 pounds. Find the container angle at which the wall will collapse. about 27°

4. Research Find out about the safety of landfill and hazardous waste sites in your area. Determine if there are any potential dangers to which designers have not, in your opinion, paid adequate attention. Write about your findings in a 1-page paper. See students' work.

LESSON 8-5 APPLICATIONS WITH VECTORS 441

EXTENDING THE LESSON

Math Power: Reasoning

Suppose the traffic light in Example 3 were suspended by three cables, each set at an angle of 120° with the others and at an angle of 10° with the horizontal. The light weighs 1200 pounds. What is the tension of each of the wires? 2303.5 lb

Case Study Follow-Up

This activity provides an opportunity to do research and apply mathematics in solving problems related to issues that may face students in their adult lives. Case Study 2 is located on pages 959–961.

Enrichment Masters Booklet, p. 54

8-5 Enrichment Worksheet

NAME _____ DATE _____

Linearly Dependent Vectors

The **zero vector** is (0, 0) in two dimensions, and (0, 0, 0) in three dimensions.

A set of vectors is called **linearly dependent** if and only if there exist scalars, not all zero, such that a linear combination of the vectors yields a zero vector.

Example Are the vectors $(-1, 2, 1)$, $(1, -1, 2)$, and $(0, -2, -6)$ linearly dependent?

Solve $a(-1, 2, 1) + b(1, -1, 2) + c(0, -2, -6) = (0, 0, 0)$.

$-a + b = 0$
$2a - b - 2c = 0$
$a + 2b - 6c = 0$

The above system does not have a unique solution. Any solution must satisfy the conditions that $a = b = 2c$.

Hence, one solution is $a = 1$, $b = 1$, and $c = \frac{1}{2}$.

$(-1, 2, 1) + (1, -1, 2) + \frac{1}{2}(0, -2, -6) = (0, 0, 0)$, so the three vectors are linearly dependent.

Determine whether the given vectors are linearly dependent. Write yes or no. If the answer is yes, give a linear combination that yields a zero vector.

1. $(-2, 6), (1, -3)$
yes; $(-2, 6) + 2(1, -3) = (0, 0)$

2. $(3, 6), (2, 4)$
yes; $2(3, 6) - 3(2, 4) = (0, 0)$

3. $(1, 1, 1), (-1, 0, 1), (1, -1, -1)$
no

4. $(1, 1, 1), (-1, 0, 1), (-3, -2, -1)$
yes; $2(1, 1, 1) - (-1, 0, 1) + (-3, -2, -1) = (0, 0, 0)$

5. $(2, -4, 6), (3, -1, 2), (-6, 8, 10)$
no

6. $(1, -2, 0), (2, 0, 3), \left(-1, 1, \frac{9}{4}\right)$
no

T54
Glencoe Division, Macmillan/McGraw-Hill

NCTM Standards: 1–4, 6, 8

Lesson Resources

- Practice Master 8–6
- Enrichment Master 8–6
- Evaluation Master, Quiz C, p. 98

 Transparency 8–6 contains the 5-Minute Check and a teaching aid for this lesson.

INTRODUCING THE LESSON

 5-Minute Check
(over Lesson 8–5)

1. Two 15-lb forces are acting on an object, one at 60° above the horizontal, the other at 40° below the horizontal. Find the magnitude and direction of the vector that would produce equilibrium. **19.28 lb at 10° above the horizontal**
2. In still air, an airplane is flying at 250 mph on a heading of 150° from due east. There is a 20-mph wind out of the west. What are the airplane's true course and speed? **232.9 mph on a heading of 147.5°**

Prerequisite Skills

Students should be familiar with the various forms of the equation of a line.
Find an equation for each line described below.
1. connecting the points (–1, 4) and (4, 1) $3x + 5y = 17$
2. with slope 4 and y-intercept –2 $y = 4x - 2$
3. has slope $\frac{2}{3}$ and passes through (–1, –4) $2x - 3y = 10$

Motivating the Lesson

Consider a raindrop that falls from a cloud under the force of gravity and at the same time, is blown horizontally by the wind. How can an equation be written to identify its position at any particular time? Since both its height and horizontal position vary with time, x and y can both be written as functions of time. This idea is introduced in this lesson.

Vectors and Parametric Equations

Objectives After studying this lesson, you should be able to:
8–6A ■ write vector and parametric equations of lines, and
8–6B ■ graph parametric equations.

Application   Davey Allison passed Morgan Shepherd to win the 1992 Daytona 500. Time-lapse photography has allowed us to freeze the positions of their cars as they sped past the finish line. The relative positions of the cars are dependent upon their velocities at a given moment in time and their starting positions. Vector equations and equations known as **parametric equations** allow us to model their movement.

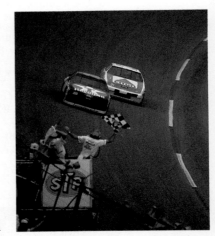

In Lesson 8-2, we described a vector $\overrightarrow{P_1P_2}$ as the ordered pair $(x_2 - x_1, y_2 - y_1)$ for $P_1(x_1, y_1)$ and $P_2(x_2, y_2)$. The slope of a line through P_1 and P_2 is $m = \frac{y_2 - y_1}{x_2 - x_1}$. Since the ordered pair representing a vector is related to slope, we can use vectors to write equations of lines. A vector used to describe the slope of a line is called a **direction vector**.

Example 1   **Write a vector equation describing a line passing through $P_1(-2, -3)$ and parallel to the vector $\vec{a} = (5, 4)$.**

Let ℓ represent the line through $P_1(-2, -3)$ parallel to $\vec{a}$. For any point $P_2(x, y)$ on ℓ, $\overrightarrow{P_1P_2} = (x - (-2), y - (-3))$. Since $\overrightarrow{P_1P_2}$ is on ℓ and is parallel to $\vec{a}$, $\overrightarrow{P_1P_2} = t\vec{a}$, for some value t. By substitution, we have $(x + 2, y + 3) = t(5, 4)$.

Therefore, the equation $(x + 2, y + 3) = t(5, 4)$ is a vector equation describing all of the points (x, y) on ℓ parallel to $\vec{a}$ through $P_1(-2, -3)$.

Using a process similar to the one in Example 1 for any point $P_1(x_1, y_1)$ and vector $\vec{a}$ leads us to the following definition.

ALTERNATE TEACHING STRATEGIES

Using Critical Thinking

Ask students to consider the vector equation $(x - 4, y - 3) = t(5, 1)$. Have the class select different values for t and graph the resulting points (x, y). What sort of function does this vector equation represent? Have the students find an equation in standard form for this line as well.   **a line; $x - 5y = -11$**

Using Problem Solving

Give students a pair of parametric equations and have them make a chart of the values of x and y for a range of t values, and then graph the equation. You may wish to use the equations $y = -16t^2 + 800$ and $x = 22t$ as possible equations, which correlate to *Motivating the Lesson*. Here, x and y are in feet, t in seconds.

Vector Equation of a Line	A line through $P_1(x_1, y_1)$ parallel to the vector $\vec{a} = (a_1, a_2)$ is defined by the set of points $P_2(x, y)$ such that $\overrightarrow{P_1P_2} = t\vec{a}$ for some real number t. Therefore, $(x - x_1, y - y_1) = t(a_1, a_2)$.

The independent variable t in the vector equation of a line is called a **parameter**. We can use vector equations to model physical situations, such as the Daytona 500, where t represents time.

The vector equation $(x - x_1, y - y_1) = t(a_1, a_2)$ can be written as two equations relating the horizontal and vertical components of these two vectors separately.

$$x - x_1 = ta_1 \qquad\qquad y - y_1 = ta_2$$
$$x = x_1 + ta_1 \qquad\qquad y = y_1 + ta_2$$

The resulting equations, $x = x_1 + ta_1$ and $y = y_1 + ta_2$, are known as parametric equations of the line through $P_1(x_1, y_1)$ parallel to $\vec{a} = (a_1, a_2)$.

Parametric Equations of a Line	A line through $P_1(x_1, y_1)$ that is parallel to the vector $\vec{a} = (a_1, a_2)$ has the following parametric equations, where t is any real number. $$x = x_1 + ta_1$$ $$y = y_1 + ta_2$$

If we know the coordinates of a point on a line and its direction vector, we can write its parametric equations.

Example 2

Find the parametric equations for a line parallel to $\vec{b} = (-2, 5)$ and passing through $(3, -5)$. Then make a table of values and graph the line.

Use the general form of the parametric equations of a line with $(a_1, a_2) = (-2, 5)$ and $(x_1, y_1) = (3, -5)$.

$$x = x_1 + ta_1 \qquad\qquad y = y_1 + ta_2$$
$$= 3 + t(-2) \qquad\qquad = -5 + t(5)$$
$$= 3 - 2t \qquad\qquad\quad = -5 + 5t$$

Now make a table of values and graph the line.

t	x	y
-1	5	-10
0	3	-5
1	1	0
2	-1	5

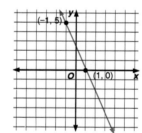

LESSON 8-6   VECTORS AND PARAMETRIC EQUATIONS   443

Teaching Tip In Example 1, it may help to pick a few particular points P_2 on ℓ and show how $\overrightarrow{P_1P_2} = t\vec{a}$ for some specific values of t.

Chalkboard Examples

For Example 1

Write a vector equation describing a line passing through (1, 4) and parallel to the vector $\vec{a} = (-1, 2)$.
$(x - 1, y - 4) = t(-1, 2)$

For Example 2

Find the parametric equations for a line parallel to $\vec{b} = (3, -5)$ and passing through (4, 3). Then make a table of values and graph the line. $x = 4 + 3t, y = 3 - 5t$

Watching a stock car race in which each car circles the track hundreds of times can be confusing. In the same way, the simultaneous variation of x and y with t can also make comparing two systems of parametric equations seem confusing. The graphing calculator can help students see the two systems unfold at the same time.

Teaching Tip   Point out to students that x equals the number of miles a car has traveled, so that when x = 500, that car has finished the race.

Notice in Example 2 that each value of t establishes a point (x, y) on the graph. You can think of these points as representing positions of an object, and of t as representing time in seconds. Evaluating the parametric equations for a value of t gives us the coordinates of the position of the object after t seconds have passed.

FYI...

NASCAR is the National Association for Stock Car Auto Racing. NASCAR races require drivers to use late-model American-made cars. The cars may be altered slightly to increase speed and power.

EXPLORATION: Graphing Calculator

We can simulate a NASCAR race, like the Daytona 500, between two cars by using a graphing calculator and parametric equations. The race is a 500-mile race conducted on a 2-mile oval. One car averages 105 mph. A second car averages 120 mph, but is delayed 30 minutes at the start of the race due to an electrical problem on the pace lap. Which of these two cars will finish before the other, assuming they both finish the race?

First, write a set of parametric equations to represent each car's position at time t hours. Let's simulate the race on two parallel race tracks so that we can make visual comparisons. We will use the formula $d = rt$. *Distance, d, is measured in miles, time, t, is in hours, and the average rate, r, is in miles per hour.*

Car 1 : $x = 105t$ *$d = rt$*
          $y = 1$ *y represents the position of car 1 on track 1.*

Car 2 : $x = 120(t - 0.5)$ *Remember that car 2 started $\frac{1}{2}$ hour late.*
          $y = 2$ *Car 2 is on track 2.*

We must put the graphing calculator in the correct mode for graphing parametric equations. To do this on the TI-81, press the [MODE] button and select the PARAM and SIMUL modes.

Now set your range with the following values:
TMIN = 0, TMAX = 5, TSTEP = 0.01, XMIN = 0, XMAX = 500, XSCL = 10, YMIN = 0, YMAX = 5, and YSCL = 1. Next enter the parametric equations on the Y= menu. Press [GRAPH] to see "the race."

Notice that the line on top reached the edge of the screen first. That line represented the position of the second car, so car 2 finished first. *You can confirm the conclusions using the TRACE function. The car with the lesser t-value when x = 500 is the winner.*

If we are given the equation of a line in slope-intercept form, we can write parametric equations for that line.

Example 3

Write parametric equations for the line $y = 2x - 3$.

In the equation $y = 2x - 3$, x is the independent variable and y is the dependent variable. In parametric equations, t is the independent variable and x and y are both dependent variables. If we set the independent variables x and t equal, we can write two parametric equations in terms of t.

$x = t$
$y = 2t - 3$

Parametric equations for the line are $x = t$ and $y = 2t - 3$.

We can also write the equation of a line in slope-intercept or standard form if we are given the parametric equations of the line.

Example 4

Write an equation of the line in slope-intercept form whose parametric equations are $x = 3 + 2t$ and $y = -1 + 5t$.

Solve each parametric equation for t.

$$x = 3 + 2t \qquad\qquad y = -1 + 5t$$
$$x - 3 = 2t \qquad\qquad y + 1 = 5t$$
$$\frac{x-3}{2} = t \qquad\qquad \frac{y+1}{5} = t$$

Write an equation involving the expressions for t.

$$\frac{x-3}{2} = \frac{y+1}{5}$$
$$5(x - 3) = 2(y + 1)$$
$$5x - 15 = 2y + 2$$
$$y = \frac{5}{2}x - \frac{17}{2}$$

CHECKING FOR UNDERSTANDING

Communicating Mathematics

Read and study the lesson to answer each question.

1. **Explain** how the slope of a line is related to its direction vector.
   See margin.

2. **Confirm** the results of the Exploration by finding the time that each car finished the race. How long after the winning car did the other car finish?
   about 5.4 minutes

3. **Compare** the paths of the cars in the Graphing Calculator Exploration. When did car 2 pass car 1?
   4 hours after the race started

LESSON 8-6   VECTORS AND PARAMETRIC EQUATIONS   445

RETEACHING THE LESSON

Start with a pair of points, and use a chart to examine side by side the different types of equations for the line through the points, including vector and parametric forms, as well as point-slope and general forms.

Additional Answer

1. The direction vector $\overrightarrow{P_1P_2}$ is the ordered pair $(x_2 - x_1, y_2 - y_1)$. The slope of a line through P_1 and P_2 would be $m = \dfrac{y_2 - y_1}{x_2 - x_1}$.

LESSON 8–6   VECTORS AND PARAMETRIC EQUATIONS   445

Writing Activity Give students the equation of a line in standard form and have them write a vector equation and a set of parametric equations for the line.

APPLYING THE LESSON

Homework Exercises

Assignment Guide
Average: 13–19, 20–30 even, 31–39
Enriched: 13–19 odd, 20–39

The red A, B, and C flags, printed only in the Teacher's Wraparound Edition, indicate the level of difficulty of the exercises.

Chapter 8, Quiz C, (Lessons 8–5 through 8–6), is available in the *Evaluation Masters*, p. 98.

Additional Answers

4a. $(x + 5, y - 8) = t(3, 7)$
4b. $x = -5 + 3t, y = 8 + 7t$
4c. $y = \frac{7}{3}x + \frac{59}{3}$

5a. $(x + 1, y + 5) = t(3, 7)$
5b. $x = -1 + 3t, y = -5 + 7t$
5c. $y = \frac{7}{3}x - \frac{8}{3}$

6a. $(x - 6, y - 2) = t(3, 7)$
6b. $x = 6 + 3t, y = 2 + 7t$
6c. $y = \frac{7}{3}x - 12$

7a. $(x - 5, y + 9) = t(3, 7)$
7b. $x = 5 + 3t, y = -9 + 7t$
7c. $y = \frac{7}{3}x - \frac{62}{3}$

8a. $(x + 6, y) = t(3, 7)$
8b. $x = 3t - 6, y = 7t$
8c. $y = \frac{7}{3}x + 14$

9a. $(x - 11, y + 4) = t(3, 7)$
9b. $x = 3t + 11, y = 7t - 4$
9c. $y = \frac{7}{3}x - \frac{89}{3}$

13. $(x + 4, y + 11) = t(-3, 8)$;
$x = -3t - 4, y = 8t - 11$
14. $(x - 1, y - 5) = t(-7, 2)$;
$x = 1 - 7t, y = 5 + 2t$
15. $(x + 1, y) = t(3, 2)$; $x = 3t - 1$,
$y = 2t$
16. $(x + 4, y - 1) = t(-6, 10)$;
$x = -6t - 4, y = 10t + 1$

A line that passes through the point with the given coordinates is parallel to $\vec{a} = (3, 7)$.
a. Write a vector equation for each line.
b. Write parametric equations for each line.
c. Use the parametric equations to write the equation of the line in slope-intercept form. 4–9. See margin.

4. $(-5, 8)$
5. $(-1, -5)$
6. $(6, 2)$
7. $(5, -9)$
8. $(-6, 0)$
9. $(11, -4)$

Write parametric equations for each linear equation.

10. $y = 9x - 1$
$x = t$
$y = 9t - 1$

11. $y = 3x + 11$
$x = t$
$y = 3t + 11$

12. $2x + y - 6 = 0$
$x = t$
$y = 2t + 6$

EXERCISES

13–16. See margin.

Practice Write a vector equation of the line that passes through point P and is parallel to $\vec{a}$. Then write parametric equations for the line.

13. $P(-4, -11), \vec{a} = (-3, 8)$
14. $P(1, 5), \vec{a} = (-7, 2)$
15. $P(-1, 0), \vec{a} = (3, 2)$
16. $P(-4, 1), \vec{a} = (-6, 10)$

Write the equation of each line in parametric form.

17. $y = -2x + 3$
$x = t, y = -2t + 3$

18. $y = 4x - 2$
$x = t, y = -4t - 2$

19. $3x + 2y = 5$
$x = t, y = -\frac{3}{2}t + \frac{5}{2}$

20. $y = -\frac{2}{3}x + \frac{11}{3}$
21. $y = -x + 8$
22. $y = -\frac{5}{4}x + \frac{3}{4}$
23. $y = \frac{1}{4}x + \frac{23}{4}$
24. $y = \frac{4}{9}x + 2$
25. $x = 8$

Write an equation in slope-intercept form of the line with the given parametric equations.

20. $x = 3t - 5$
$y = -2t + 7$

21. $x = -t + 6$
$y = t + 2$

22. $x = -4t + 3$
$y = 5t - 3$

23. $x = 4t - 11$
$y = t + 3$

24. $x = 9t$
$y = 4t + 2$

25. $x = 8$
$y = 2t + 1$

26–28. See margin.

Set up a table of values and then graph each line from its parametric form.

26. $x = 2 + 4t$
$y = -1 + t$

27. $x = -3 + 5t$
$y = 2 - 4t$

28. $x = 1 + t$
$y = 1 - t$

29–30. See margin.

Graphing Calculator
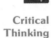
Graph the parametric equations using a graphing calculator. Then sketch the graph.

29. $x = \cos t$
$y = \sin t$

30. $x = 4 \cos t$
$y = 7 \sin t$

Critical Thinking
31. Find parametric equations for the line through $(-4, -3)$ and $(5, 2)$.
Sample answer: $x = t$ and $y = \frac{5}{9}t - \frac{7}{9}$

Applications and Problem Solving
32. **Language Arts** Look up the definition of the word "parameter" in a dictionary. Which definition most closely relates to your mathematical understanding of the word? How do the other definitions relate to the mathematical definition?
See students' work.

446   CHAPTER 8   VECTORS AND PARAMETRIC EQUATIONS

26.

27.

33. Transportation   Two semi-trucks are driving loads from Chicago to Denver, a distance of 1125 miles. The first truck leaves at 8:00 A.M. and averages 50 mph. The second truck leaves at 9:00 A.M. Since it has a lighter load, the second truck averages 54 mph. Set up two sets of parametric equations to model this situation and use a graphing calculator to analyze the model.

   a. How long is it until the second truck overtakes the first truck?   13.5 hours
   b. How far are they from Chicago when the second truck overtakes the first truck?   675 miles
   c. If each of the drivers stops for meals for a total of 3 hours, what time will it be in Chicago when each truck reaches Denver?   9:30 A.M., 8:50 A.M.
   d. How much would the driver of the first truck have to increase her speed in order to arrive in Denver first?   at least 1.53 mph

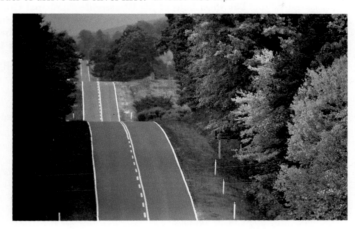

Mixed Review

34. Name all the values of x that are not in the domain of the function $f(x) = \dfrac{x}{|3x| - 12}$.   **(Lesson 1-1)** ± 4

35. $\begin{bmatrix} 28 & 20 \\ 10 & 14 \end{bmatrix}$

35. Find the product of the matrices $\begin{bmatrix} 4 & -1 & 6 \\ 4 & 0 & 2 \end{bmatrix}$ and $\begin{bmatrix} 0 & 3 \\ 2 & -2 \\ 5 & 1 \end{bmatrix}$.   **(Lesson 2-2)**

36. Surveying   A surveyor finds that the angle of elevation from a certain point to the top of a cliff is 60°. From a point 45 feet further away, the angle of elevation to the top of the cliff is 52°. How high is the cliff to the nearest foot? **(Lesson 5-5)**   221 feet

37. State the amplitude, period, and phase shift for the function $y = 8 \cos (\theta - 30°)$.   **(Lesson 7-2)**   8, 360°, 30°

38. A 30-pound force is applied to an object at an angle of 60° with the horizontal. Find the magnitude of the horizontal and vertical components of the force. **(Lesson 8-5)**   15 lb, $15\sqrt{3}$ lb

39. College Entrance Exam   Choose the best answer.   A
   The trinomial $x^2 + x - 20$ is exactly divisible by
   (A) $x - 4$ **(B)** $x + 4$ **(C)** $x + 6$ **(D)** $x - 10$ **(E)** $x - 5$

LESSON 8-6   VECTORS AND PARAMETRIC EQUATIONS   447

EXTENDING THE LESSON

Math Power: Communication

Have students take the ideas of this lesson and extend them to vectors in three-dimensional space. Have them report their results to the class.

Technology

Using Parametric Equations

You can use IBM's *Mathematics Exploration Toolkit* (*MET*) to solve problems involving parametric equations.

Example

The third hole of the Westerville Municipal Golf Course is a 200-yard par three. Ed Gallagher chooses a five iron. His swing launches the ball with an initial velocity of 150 feet per second, and the ball leaves the tee at an initial angle of 25°. How far will the ball travel before it hits the ground?

The parametric equations for the path of the ball are as follows.

$x = t|150| \cos 25°$

$y = t|150| \sin 25° - 16t^2$

Use MET's CALC commands to rewrite the equation.

Enter:		
degrees		*Puts the computer in degree mode.*
lims 0 600 0 100		*Sets viewing window to [0, 600] by [0, 100].*
$x = t150 \cos(25)$		
solvefor t		*Solves the expression for t.*
getright		*Displays the right side of the equation.*
store t		*Stores the current expressions as t.*
$y = t150 \sin(25) - 16t\char`\^2$		
replace		*Replaces t in the expression with stored value of t.*
simplify		*Simplifies the expression.*
graph		*Graphs the equation.*

Pressing ALT and F3 together will allow you to move the cursor around the graphics window and determine the coordinates of different points. Zoom in on the graph where it crosses the x-axis by pressing ALT and F3, then ENTER. Use the arrow keys to box in the area and press ENTER. You can see that the ball will travel about 537 feet.

EXERCISES

1. What is the maximum height of Mr. Gallaghers ball? about 63 feet

2. If Mr. Gallagher hits the ball so that the initial velocity is 160 feet per second and the initial angle is 25°, would his ball travel past the pin? That is, will the ball travel more than 200 yards? yes

Using Parametric Equations to Model Motion

Objectives
8–7A
8–7B

After studying this lesson, you should be able to:
- model the motion of a projectile using parametric equations, and
- solve problems related to the motion of a projectile, its trajectory, and range.

Application

When Jack Nicklaus hits a golf ball, the path of the ball is shaped like a parabola. We can use parametric equations to represent the position of the ball relative to its starting point in terms of the parameter time.

Objects that are launched, like the golf ball, are called projectiles. The path of a projectile is called its trajectory. The horizontal distance that a projectile travels is its range. Physicists describe the motion of a projectile in terms of its position, velocity, and acceleration. These are all vector quantities.

Suppose Nicklaus hits an approach shot with his five-iron. The figure at the right illustrates what happens to the ball after it leaves the head of the club. The magnitude of the initial velocity, $|\vec{v}|$, and direction, θ, of the ball can be described by a vector that can be expressed as the sum of its horizontal and vertical components, $\vec{v}_x$ and $\vec{v}_y$.

As the ball moves, gravity will act on it in the vertical direction. The horizontal component will be unaffected by gravity. So, discounting wind resistance, the horizontal speed is constant throughout the flight of the ball. The vertical speed of the ball is large and positive at the beginning, decreasing to zero at the top of its trajectory, then increasing in the negative direction as it falls. When the ball returns to the ground, its vertical speed is the same as when it left the club head, but in the opposite direction.

LESSON 8-7   USING PARAMETRIC EQUATIONS TO MODEL MOTION   449

ALTERNATE TEACHING STRATEGIES

Using Connections

The flight of a golf ball can be described by a parabola. Thus, it exhibits a certain kind of symmetry. What are the types of symmetry evidenced by its flight? Consider not only the path of the ball, but also the way its height, velocity, and acceleration all change over the time of its flight.

Using Calculators

Gather a variety of projectile problems, such as firing a cannon, hitting a golf ball, baseball, tennis ball, and so on, and have pairs of students investigate these problems, observing the trajectory and range of each projectile, and comparing and contrasting the results in each case.

NCTM Standards: 1–4, 8

Lesson Resources

- Practice Master 8–7
- Enrichment Master 8–7
- Evaluation Master, Quiz D, p. 98
- Multicultural Activity Master, p. 8

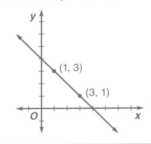
Transparency 8–7 contains the 5-Minute Check and a teaching aid for this lesson.

INTRODUCING THE LESSON

5-Minute Check
(over Lesson 8–6)

1. Write a vector equation of the line that passes through $P(5, -3)$ and is parallel to $\vec{a} = (1, 2)$. Then write parametric equations for the line.
   $(x - 5, y + 3) = t(1, 2)$;
   $x = 5 + t, y = -3 + 2t$

2. Write an equation of the line in slope-intercept form with the given parametric equations.
   $x = -4 + 2t, y = 5 - t$
   $y = -\frac{1}{2}x + 3$

3. Set up a table of values and then graph the line from its parametric form.
   $x = 1 + 2t, y = 3 - 2t$

Motivating the Lesson

Have students take turns throwing a soft Nerf®-type ball at a target or into a basket. Discuss how the angle and the speed with which the ball is thrown help to determine its path. How could speed and angle be measured? Are there equations for the projectile's path in terms of these parameters?

In order to find parametric equations that represent the path of the projectile, we must resolve the initial velocity into its horizontal and vertical components.

$$\cos\theta = \frac{|\vec{v}_x|}{|\vec{v}|} \qquad \sin\theta = \frac{|\vec{v}_y|}{|\vec{v}|}$$
$$|\vec{v}_x| = |\vec{v}|\cos\theta \qquad |\vec{v}_y| = |\vec{v}|\sin\theta$$

Since it is unaffected by gravity, horizontal speed will be the magnitude of the horizontal component of the initial velocity. Therefore, the horizontal position of a projectile after t seconds is given by the following equation.

horizontal distance =   rate   · time
$$x = |\vec{v}|\cos\theta \cdot\ t$$
$$= t|\vec{v}|\cos\theta$$

The vertical distance is the sum of the distance traveled due to the initial velocity and the distance traveled due to gravity. The height of an object affected by gravity is given by the equation $h = \frac{1}{2}gt^2$, where $g = -9.8$ m/s² or -32 ft/s² according to the units of the problem.

vertical distance = distance due to initial velocity + distance due to gravity
$$y = \qquad (|\vec{v}|\sin\theta)t \qquad + \qquad \frac{1}{2}gt^2$$
$$= t|\vec{v}|\sin\theta + \frac{1}{2}gt^2$$

Therefore, the path of a projectile can be expressed in terms of parametric equations.

Parametric Equations for the Path of a Projectile

> **If a projectile is launched at an angle of θ with the horizontal, with an initial velocity of magnitude, $|\vec{v}|$, the path of the projectile may be described by the equations**
> $$x = t|\vec{v}|\cos\theta \text{ and}$$
> $$y = t|\vec{v}|\sin\theta + \frac{1}{2}gt^2,$$
> **where t is time, and g is acceleration due to gravity.**

Example 1

APPLICATION

Soccer

Zoe kicked a soccer ball with an initial velocity of 45 ft/s at an angle of 32° to the horizontal. After 0.6 seconds, how far has the ball traveled horizontally and vertically?

First, write the position of the ball as a pair of parametric equations defining the path of the ball for any time, t, in seconds.

$x = t\lvert\vec{v}\rvert\cos\theta$	$y = t\lvert\vec{v}\rvert\sin\theta + \frac{1}{2}gt^2$
$= t(45)\cos 32°$	$= t(45)\sin 32° + \frac{1}{2}(-32)t^2$ *Let $g = -32$.*
$= 45t\cos 32°$	$= 45t\sin 32° - 16t^2$

Then, find x and y when $t = 0.6$.

$x = 45(0.6) \cos 32°$ $\qquad$ $y = 45(0.6) \sin 32° - 16(0.6)^2$
$\quad \approx 22.9$ $\qquad\qquad\qquad \approx 8.5$

After 0.6 seconds, the ball has traveled 22.9 feet horizontally and 8.5 feet vertically.

The parametric equations describe the path of an object that is launched from ground level. If an object is launched from above ground level, as a baseball would be, you must add the vertical height to the expression for y. This accounts for the fact that at time 0, the object will be above the ground.

Example 2

Denise Parker was a member of the U.S. Olympic Archery Team in 1988 and in 1992. Denise shoots an arrow with an initial velocity of 65 m/s at an angle of 4.5° with the horizontal at a target 70 meters away. If Denise holds the bow 1.5 meters above the ground when she shoots the arrow, how far above the ground will the arrow be when it hits the target?

First, write parametric equations to model the path of the arrow.

$x = t|\vec{\mathbf{v}}| \cos \theta$ $\qquad$ $y = t|\vec{\mathbf{v}}| \sin \theta + \frac{1}{2}gt^2 + h$
$\quad = t(65) \cos 4.5°$ $\qquad$ $= t(65) \sin 4.5° + \frac{1}{2}(\text{-}9.8)t^2 + 1.5$ $\qquad$ *Let g = -9.8.*
$\quad = 65t \cos 4.5°$ $\qquad$ $= 65t \sin 4.5° - 4.9t^2 + 1.5$

Then, find the amount of time that it will take the arrow to travel 70 meters horizontally. This is when it will hit the target.

$70 = 65t \cos 4.5°$

$t = \dfrac{70}{65 \cos 4.5°}$

$t = 1.0802531$ $\qquad$ *Use a calculator.*

The arrow will hit the target in about 1.08 seconds.

To find the vertical position of the arrow at that time, find y when $t = 1.08$.

$y = 65t \sin 4.5° - 4.9t^2 + 1.5$
$\quad = 65(1.08) \sin 4.5° - 4.9(1.08)^2 + 1.5$
$\quad = 1.2924685$ $\qquad$ *Use a calculator.*

The arrow will be about 1.3 meters above the ground when it hits the target.

LESSON 8-7   USING PARAMETRIC EQUATIONS TO MODEL MOTION   451

Chalkboard Example

For Example 3

On the seventh hole, Jack Nicklaus estimates the distance to the pin to be 220 yards. Nicklaus' swing provides an initial velocity of 160 ft/s to the ball at an angle of 28° above the horizontal. Use your graphing calculator to determine if he will hit the pin. (Assume he has directed the ball straight at the pin.) **yes**

EVALUATING THE LESSON

Checking for Understanding

Exercises 1–7 are designed to help you assess students' understanding through reading, writing, speaking, and modeling. You should work through Exercises 1–6 with your students and then monitor their work on Exercise 7.

Closing the Lesson

Speaking Activity   Have students list parametric equations for the path of a projectile given its initial velocity, $\mathbf{v}$, and angle, θ.

Practice Masters Booklet, p. 56

Graphing calculators are helpful when we are using parametric equations to study the paths of projectiles.

Example 3

APPLICATION
Golf

On the sixth hole, Jack Nicklaus selects a five iron. He estimates the distance to the pin to be 200 yards. Nicklaus' swing provides an initial velocity of 150 ft/s to the ball at an angle of 25° above the horizontal. Use a graphing calculator to determine if he will hit the pin. (Assume that he has directed the ball straight at the pin.)

First, write the position of the ball as a pair of parametric equations defining the path of the ball for any time, t, in seconds.

$$x = t|\vec{\mathbf{v}}| \cos \theta$$
$$= t(150) \cos 25°$$
$$= 150t \cos 25°$$

$$y = t|\vec{\mathbf{v}}| \sin \theta + \frac{1}{2}gt^2$$
$$= t(150) \sin 25° + \frac{1}{2}(-32)t^2 \quad \textit{Use -32 for g.}$$
$$= 150t \sin 25° - 16t^2$$

Then, we can use a graphing calculator to see the path of the ball. Use the range values $TMIN = 0$, $TMAX = 5$, $TSTEP = 0.1$, $XMIN = 0$, $XMAX = 600$, $XSCL = 20$, $YMIN = -20$, $YMAX = 50$, and $YSCL = 10$. *Make sure your calculator is in degree mode.*

Graph the equations and estimate the range of the ball. The point where the ball hits the ground is the point where $y = 0$, so use the TRACE function to find the x-coordinate of that point. The ball traveled about 540 feet in the air, so it hits 60 feet short of the pin.

CHECKING FOR UNDERSTANDING   1–3. See margin.

Communicating
Mathematics

Read and study the lesson to answer each question.

1. **Explain** why the vertical spacings between successive positions of the ball are unequal in the photo at the beginning of the lesson.

2. The faces of golf clubs are angled and the angle determines the angle of the initial velocity of the ball. A hockey stick is made with little or no angle to its face. Why?

3. **Analyze** the situation where a projectile is launched at an angle of 90° to the horizontal. How far does the projectile travel horizontally? Can you think of a situation when this happens?

RETEACHING THE LESSON

Have students make a chart with the categories, *angle, velocity, trajectory, range,* and *flight time*. Then taking the basic parametric equations, have them fill in their charts using different values for the parameters $\mathbf{v}$ and θ.

4. What factor affects the vertical velocity of a projectile that does not affect its horizontal velocity? gravity

5. What is the vertical velocity of a golf ball at the highest point in its trajectory? Explain. Zero; for a moment, it is not going up or down.

6. What is the relationship between the vertical velocities of a projectile at its launch and at its landing? equal magnitude with opposite directions

Guided Practice

7. Gretchen Austgen, an outfielder for the West Chicago Wildcats, is 215 feet from home plate after catching a fly ball. The runner tags third and heads for home. Gretchen releases the ball at an initial velocity of 75 ft/s at an angle of 25° with the horizontal. Assume Gretchen releases the ball 5 feet above the ground and aims it directly in line with the plate. 7a. See margin.

   a. Write two parametric equations that represent the path of the ball.

   b. Use a calculator to graph the path of the ball. Sketch the graph shown on the screen. See students' graphs.

   c. How far will the ball travel horizontally before hitting the ground? 145 ft

   d. What is the maximum height of the trajectory? 20.7 ft

   e. The ball will fall short of reaching home plate. Could Gretchen change the initial angle in order for the throw to reach the plate? If so, find the angle she should use. no

EXERCISES

Practice

8. Find the initial vertical velocity of a stone thrown with an initial velocity of 50 ft/s at an angle of 40° with the horizontal. The vertical velocity is the vertical component of the initial velocity vector. 32.14 ft/s

9. Find the initial horizontal velocity of a discus thrown with an initial velocity of 62 ft/s at an angle of 42° with the horizontal. The horizontal velocity is the horizontal component of the initial velocity vector. 46.07 ft/s

10. An airplane flying at an altitude of 3500 feet is dropping supplies to researchers on an island. The path of the plane is parallel to the ground at the time the supplies are released and the plane is traveling at a speed of 300 mph.

10a. See margin.

   a. Write the parametric equations that represent the path of the supplies.

   b. Graph the path of the supplies on your graphing calculator and sketch the graph. See students' graphs.

   c. How long will it take for the supplies to reach the ground? ≈ 14.8 s

   d. How far will the supplies travel horizontally before they land? 6512 feet or 1.23 miles

A projectile is fired from ground level with an initial velocity of 100 feet per second and at an angle of θ° with the horizontal.

11. Find the range and the time in the air of the projectile for each value of θ.

   a. 10° ≈ 107 ft, 1.1 s   **b.** 30° ≈ 270 ft, 3.1 s   **c.** 45° ≈ 313 ft, 4.4 s

   d. 60° ≈ 271 ft, 5.4 s   **e.** 80° ≈ 107 ft, 6.2 s   **f.** 90° ≈ 0 ft, 6.25 s

LESSON 8-7 USING PARAMETRIC EQUATIONS TO MODEL MOTION 453

APPLYING THE LESSON

Homework Exercises

Assignment Guide

Average: 8–13, 15–19, 22–26
Enriched: 9, 11–16, 18–26

The red A, B, and C flags, printed only in the Teacher's Wraparound Edition, indicate the level of difficulty of the exercises.

Chapter 8, Quiz D, (Lesson 8–7), is available in the *Evaluation Masters*, p. 98.

Additional Answers

1. The relative vertical position of the ball varies due to the effects of gravity slowing the vertical velocity on the way up and increasing it on the way down.

2. The hockey players want all of the velocity to be in the horizontal direction to keep the puck on the ice.

3. The projectile is launched straight up; it travels no distance in the horizontal direction; sample answers: toy rockets, a tip-off in a basketball game

7a. $x = 75t \cos 25°$,
$y = 5 + 75t \sin 25° - 16t^2$

10a. Note: The speed must be converted from miles per hour to feet per second.
$x = 440t, y = -16t + 3500$

For Exercise 18, students may find it helpful to refer to Exercise 12.

Additional Answers

13. The range is the same for projectiles fired at angles of $\alpha°$ *and* $(90 - \alpha)°$. But the time in the air is greater when the angle is greater.

14a. They both reach the ground at the same time because their vertical displacements are the same. They are both $850 - 16t^2$.

16b. about 5 inches in front of the Cowboys' goal line

17a. $x = 155t \cos 22°$,
  $y = 155t \sin 22° - 16t^2 + 3$

17b. about 36.12 feet; It will clear the fence.

---

12. At what angle should a projectile be fired in order for it to have maximum range? Explain your answer. 45°; Answers may vary.

13. Use your answers for Exercises 11a-11f to compare the range and time in the air for angles of $\alpha°$ and $(90 - \alpha)°$. What do you notice? See margin.

14. Two stones are launched at the same time from the top of a building 850 feet high. The first stone is simply dropped over the edge, while the second stone is thrown horizontally at 45 ft/s.

    a. Which stone will reach the ground first? Explain your answer. See margin.

    b. About how far apart will the stones be when they land? 328 ft

Critical Thinking

15. If a circle of radius 1 unit is rolled along the x-axis at a rate of 1 unit per second, then the path of a point P on the circle is called a **cycloid**.

    a. Sketch what you think a cycloid must look like. *Hint: Use a coin or some other circular object to simulate the situation.* See students' work.

    b. The parametric equations of a cycloid are $x = t - \sin t$ and $y = 1 - \cos t$ where t is measured in radians. Use a graphing calculator to graph the cycloid. An appropriate range is TMIN = 0, TMAX = 18.8, TSTEP = 0.2, XMIN = -6.5, XMAX = 25.5, XSCL = 2, YMIN = -8.4, YMAX = 12.9, and YSCL = 1. Was your sketch correct? *Make sure your calculator is in radian mode.* See students' work.

Applications and Problem Solving

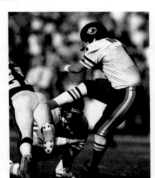

16. **Sports** Kevin Butler, a place kicker for the Chicago Bears, kicks a football in a game with the Dallas Cowboys. The ball leaves the ground with a velocity of 88 ft/s at an angle of 30.0° above the horizontal.

    a. Find the time the ball is in the air.

    b. If the ball is kicked from the Bears' 30 yard line and is aimed straight down the field, where does it land? See margin.

    c. Find the maximum height of the ball.
    16a. 2.75 seconds   16c. 30.24 feet

17. **Sports** Juan Gonzalez, outfielder for the Texas Rangers, comes to bat with the bases loaded and the Rangers down 4 to 1 against the Seattle Mariners. The count on Gonzalez is 3 and 2, and the pitcher throws a smoking fastball about waist high (3 feet above the ground). Gonzalez connects and the ball jumps off the bat with an initial velocity of 155 ft/s at an angle of 22° above the horizontal. As Gonzalez rounds the bases, the ball flies straight at the 420-foot marker in center field where the wall is 15 feet tall. 17a, 17b. See margin.

    a. Write the parametric equations that describe the path of the ball.

    b. Find the height of the ball after it has traveled 420 feet horizontally. Do you think it will clear the fence to be a home run or could the center fielder jump to catch the ball?

    c. How far does the ball travel before it hits the ground? 528.87 feet

18. **Sports** In football, hang time is the time that the ball takes to land after it is kicked. Punters want to give their teammates as much time as possible to get downfield, so they wish to increase the hang time of their punts.

 a. In order for a punter to increase the hang time, should he increase or decrease the angle the ball makes with the horizontal as it leaves his foot? increase

18b. reduce or increase, depending on initial angle and velocity.

 b. Assume the magnitude of the initial velocity of the ball remains constant. How will this affect the range of the ball?

19. **Physics** Erin is performing a physics experiment on projectile motion. She has fired a projectile and measured its range. She hypothesizes that if the magnitude of the initial velocity is doubled and the angle of the velocity remains the same, the projectile will travel twice as far as it did before. Do you agree with her hypothesis? Explain. See margin.

20. **Sports** A sport rifle used for target shooting has a muzzle velocity of 1200 ft/s.

 a. What is the maximum range of the rifle if it is fired about 5 feet above the ground? $\approx$ 45,005 feet or 8.5 miles

 b. How long would a bullet be in the air if it was fired for the maximum range? about 53 seconds

21. **Entertainment** The Fourth of July fireworks at Schrock Park are fired at an angle of 85° with the horizontal. The technicians firing the shells expect them to explode about 250 feet in the air 4 seconds after they are fired.

 a. Find the initial velocity of a shell fired from ground level. 127 ft/s

 b. The technicians will place barriers so that spectators will not be in danger of being showered with debris from the shells. If the barriers will be placed 100 yards from the point directly below the explosion of the shells, how far should the barriers be from the point where the fireworks will be launched? 114.8 yards

Mixed Review

22. Find $[f \circ g](x)$ and $[g \circ f](x)$ for the functions $f(x) = x^2 - 4$ and $g(x) = \frac{1}{2}x + 6$. **(Lesson 1-2)** $\frac{1}{4}x^2 + 6x + 32; \frac{1}{2}x^2 + 4$

23. Graph the inequality $y \le |x + 4|$. **(Lesson 1-3)** See margin.

24. car 1

24. **Statistics** The prediction equation $y = -0.13x + 37.8$ gives the fuel economy, y, for a car with a horsepower of x. Is the equation a better predictor for Car 1, which has a horsepower of 135 and averages 19 miles per gallon, or for Car 2, which has a horsepower of 245 and averages 16 miles per gallon? **(Lesson 7-7)**

25. Write an equation in standard form of the line with the parametric equations $x = 4t + 1$ and $y = 5t - 7$. **(Lesson 8-6)** $5x - 4y - 33 = 0$

26. **College Entrance Exam** Bob Perry invests $2400 in the Fidelity Bank at 5% APR. How much additional money must he invest at 8% so that the total annual income from his investments is 6% per year? $1200

EXTENDING THE LESSON

Math Power: Modeling

A good golfer does take into account the wind speed and direction on the path of the ball. Suppose when Jack Nicklaus steps up to the tee, there is a 15 mph wind blowing at an angle of 110° with the direct-line path toward the pin. How will this affect the flight of the ball? The golf ball will be deflected about 2° from its original course and travel about 574.3 feet before it lands.

Using the Chapter Summary and Review

The Chapter Summary and Review begins with an alphabetical listing of the new terms that were presented in the chapter. Have students define each term and provide an example of it, if appropriate.

The Skills and Concepts presented in the chapter are reviewed using a side-by-side format. Encourage students to refer to the Objectives and Examples on the left as they complete the Review Exercises on the right.

The Chapter Summary and Review ends with exercises that review Applications and Problem Solving.

Additional Answers

15. $(4, -1, -3)$ $4\vec{i} - \vec{j} - 3\vec{k}$
16. $(-10, -3, 6)$ $-10\vec{i} - 3\vec{j} + 6\vec{k}$
17. $(6, 2, 7)$ $6\vec{i} + 2\vec{j} + 7\vec{k}$
18. $(-7, -7, 13)$ $-7\vec{i} - 7\vec{j} + 13\vec{k}$

VOCABULARY

Upon completing this chapter, you should be familiar with the following terms:

amplitude	**412**	**414**	parallel
components	**415**	**443**	parameter
cross product	**431**	**442**	parametric equation
cycloid	**454**	**413**	resultant
direction vector	**442**	**412**	standard position
inner product	**430**	**422**	unit vector
magnitude	**412**	**412**	vector
opposite	**414**		

SKILLS AND CONCEPTS

OBJECTIVES AND EXAMPLES	REVIEW EXERCISES

Upon completing this chapter, you should be able to:

■ add and subtract vectors geometrically **(Lesson 8-1)**

Find the sum of $\vec{a}$ and $\vec{b}$.

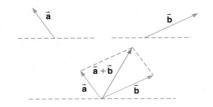

Use these exercises to review and prepare for the chapter test.

Use a metric ruler and a protractor to find each sum or difference. Then, find the magnitude and amplitude of each resultant.
1–4. Answers may vary slightly.

1. $\vec{p} + \vec{q}$ 4.1 cm; 25°   2. $2\vec{p} + \vec{q}$ 5.7 cm; 25°
3. $3\vec{q} - 2\vec{p}$ 4. $4\vec{p} - \vec{q}$ 5 cm; 70°
   5.9 cm; 357°

Find the magnitude of the vertical and horizontal components of each vector above.

5. $\vec{p}$ 1 cm, 0.8 cm   6. $\vec{q}$ 0.5 cm, 2.7 cm

■ find ordered pairs that represent vectors **(Lesson 8-2)**

Find the ordered pair that represents the vector from $M(3, 1)$ to $N(-7, 4)$. Then find the magnitude of $\overrightarrow{MN}$.

$$\overrightarrow{MN} = (-7 - 3, 4 - 1) \text{ or } (-10, 3)$$
$$|\overrightarrow{MN}| = \sqrt{(-7-3)^2 + (4-1)^2} \text{ or } \sqrt{109}$$

Find the ordered pair that represents the vector from C to D. Then find the magnitude of $\overrightarrow{CD}$.

7. $C(2, 3), D(7, 15)$ $(5, 12)$; 13
8. $C(-2, 8), D(4, 12)$ $(6, 4)$; $2\sqrt{13}$
9. $C(2, -3), D(0, 9)$ $(-2, 12)$; $2\sqrt{37}$
10. $C(-6, 4), D(-5, -4)$ $(1, -8)$; $\sqrt{65}$

OBJECTIVES AND EXAMPLES

■ add, subtract, multiply, and find the magnitude of vectors algebraically **(Lesson 8-2)**

Find the ordered pair that represents $\vec{a} + \vec{b}$, if $\vec{a} = (1, -5)$ and $\vec{b} = (-2, 4)$.

$$\vec{a} + \vec{b} = (1, -5) + (-2, 4)$$
$$= (-1, -1)$$

■ add, subtract, and find the magnitude of vectors in 3-dimensional space **(Lesson 8-3)**

Find the ordered triple that represents the vector from $R(-2, 0, 8)$ to $S(5, -4, -1)$. Write it in terms of unit vectors.

$$\vec{RS} = (5 - (-2), -4 - 0, -1 - 8)$$
$$= (7, -4, -9)$$
$$= 7\vec{i} - 4\vec{j} - 9\vec{k}$$

■ find the inner and cross product of two vectors **(Lesson 8-4)**

Find the inner product of $\vec{a}$ and $\vec{b}$ if $\vec{a} = (3, -1, 7)$ and $\vec{b} = (0, -2, -4)$.

$$\vec{a} \cdot \vec{b} = 3(0) + (-1)(-2) + 7(-4)$$
$$= -26$$

■ solve problems using vectors and right triangle trigonometry **(Lesson 8-5)**

Find the magnitude of $\vec{r}$.

210 km/h

θ

45°

$\vec{r}$

42 km/h

Use the law of cosines.

$$|\vec{r}|^2 = 210^2 + 42^2 - 2(210)(42)\cos 45°$$
$$|\vec{r}| \approx 182.7$$

The magnitude is about 182.7 km/h.

REVIEW EXERCISES

Find an ordered pair to represent $\vec{u}$ in each equation if $\vec{v} = (2, -5)$ and $\vec{w} = (3, -1)$.

11. $\vec{u} = \vec{v} + \vec{w}$ (5, -6)
12. $\vec{u} = \vec{v} - \vec{w}$ (-1, -4)
13. $\vec{u} = 3\vec{v} + 2\vec{w}$ (12, -17)
14. $\vec{u} = 3\vec{v} - 2\vec{w}$ (0, -13)

For each pair of points E and F, find an ordered triple that represents $\vec{EF}$. Then write $\vec{EF}$ as the sum of unit vectors.

15. $E(2, -1, 4); F(6, -2, 1)$
16. $E(9, 8, 5); F(-1, 5, 11)$
17. $E(-4, -3, 0); F(2, -1, 7)$
18. $E(3, 7, -8); F(-4, 0, 5)$
15–18. See margin.

Find each inner or cross product.

19. $(5, -1) \cdot (-2, 6)$ -16
20. $(4, 1, -2) \cdot (3, -4, 4)$ 0
21. $(2, -1, 4) \times (6, -2, 1)$ (7, 22, 2)
22. $(5, 2, -1) \times (2, -4, -4)$ (-12, 18, -24)

Find the magnitude and direction of the resultant vector for each diagram.

23.

26 lb

82°

32 lb

43.9 lb; 35°52'

24.

30 m/s

26°

12 m/s

41 m/s; 18°39'

For more information on other methods of alternate assessment, you may wish to refer to Glencoe's *Alternate Assessment in the Mathematics Classroom.*

Alternate Review Strategy

To provide a brief in-class review, you may wish to read the following questions to your students and have them answer verbally.

1. Describe one of the two methods given in the text for adding vectors geometrically. **Answers may vary.**

2. Given the points $C(-3, -6)$ and $D(3, 2)$, find an ordered pair that represents CD and find $|CD|$. **(6, 8), 10**

3. Find the sum of the three-dimensional vectors $(2, -3, 1)$ and $(4, 5, 0)$. **(6, 2, 1)**

4. Describe how to tell whether or not two vectors are perpendicular. **if their inner product is zero**

5. What method could be used to find a vector perpendicular to $(1, 4, 7)$ and $(-2, 3, -2)$? **Find their cross product.**

6. Given two forces acting on an object, how do you find the force that would put the system in equilibrium? **Put the two force vectors tip to tail; the vector connecting the tip of the second to the tail of the last is the balancing force.**

7. Give a set of parametric equations for the line through the point $(4, -3)$ parallel to the vector $\vec{a} = (1, 3)$. **$x = 4 + t, y = -3 + 3t$**

8. A projectile has an initial height of 0 meters. Its horizontal position at time t seconds is given by $x = 20 \cos 15°t$. Give an equation for its vertical position at time t. **$y = 20 \sin 15°t - 4.9t^2$**

Two multiple-choice tests (Forms 1A and 1B) and two free-response tests (Forms 2A and 2B) are provided in the *Evaluation Masters*. Chapter 8 Test, Form 1A is shown below. Chapter 8 Test, Form 2A is shown on the next page.

Evaluation Masters Booklet, pp. 89–90

OBJECTIVES AND EXAMPLES

■ write vector and parametric equations of a line **(Lesson 8-6)**

Find parametric equations for the line parallel to $\vec{c} = (-6, 3)$ and passing through $(1, 4)$.

$x = x_1 + ta_1$ $y = y_1 + ta_2$

$x = 1 + t(-6)$ $y = 4 + t(3)$

$x = 1 - 6t$ $y = 4 + 3t$

■ solve problems related to the motion of a projectile, its trajectory, and range **(Lesson 8-7)**

The parametric equations for the path of a projectile are:

$x = t\,|\vec{v}|\cos\theta$, and

$y = t\,|\vec{v}|\sin\theta + \frac{1}{2}gt^2$.

REVIEW EXERCISES

Write a vector equation of the line that passes through point P and is parallel to $\vec{v}$. Then write parametric equations for the line.

25. $P(3, -5), \vec{v} = (4, 2)$
26. $P(-1, 9), \vec{v} = (-7, -5)$
27. $P(4, 0), \vec{v} = (3, -6)$
28. $P(-2, -7), \vec{v} = (0, 8)$
25–28. See margin.

A soccer ball is kicked with an initial velocity of 30 ft/s at an angle of 28° to the horizontal.

29. Write two parametric equations that represent the path of the ball. See margin.

30. If the ball is not touched before its first bounce, how far will the ball travel horizontally before it hits the ground?
    23.3 ft

APPLICATIONS AND PROBLEM SOLVING

Draw a diagram to help you solve each problem.

31. **Physics**   Karen uses a large wrench to change the tire on her car. If she applies a downward force of 50 pounds at an angle of 60° one foot from the center of the lug nut, find the torque of the force. **(Lesson 8-4)** 25 lb/ft

32. **Physics**   Mike and Marie are moving a stove. They are applying forces of 70 N and 90 N at an angle of 30° to each other. Find the resultant force and the angle it makes with the larger force. **(Lesson 8-5)** 154.6 N, 13°5'

33. **Sports**   José punts a football with an initial velocity of 38 ft/s at an angle of 40° to the horizontal. If the ball is 2 feet above the ground when it is kicked, how high is it after 0.5 seconds? **(Lesson 8-7)** 10.2 feet

Additional Answers

25. $(x - 3, y + 5) = t(4, 2)$;
    $x = 3 + 4t$
    $y = -5 + 2t$

26. $(x + 1, y - 9) = t(-7, -5)$;
    $x = -1 - 7t$
    $y = 9 - 5t$

27. $(x - 4, y) = t(3, -6)$;
    $x = 4 + 3t$
    $y = -6t$

28. $(x + 2, y + 7) = t(0, 8)$;
    $x = -2$
    $y = -7 + 8t$

29. $x = 30t\cos 28°$
    $y = 30t\sin 28° - 16t^2$

CHAPTER 8   TEST

Use a metric ruler, a protractor, and vectors $\vec{a}$ and $\vec{b}$ to solve each problem.

1. Find the magnitude and amplitude of $\vec{a} + \vec{b}$.

2. Find the magnitude and amplitude of $2\vec{a} - 3\vec{b}$.

3. Find the vertical and horizontal components of $\vec{a}$.

4. Find the vertical and horizontal components of $\vec{b}$.

1. ≈ 3.1 cm; $\approx 69°$ 2. ≈ 9.5 cm; $\approx -8°$ 3. ≈ 1.5 cm, ≈ 2.5 cm   4. ≈ 1.4 cm; ≈ 1.4 cm

Find an ordered pair or ordered triple that represents the vector from A to B.

5. $A(3, 6), B(-1, 9)$ $(-4, 3)$

6. $A(-2, 7), B(3, 10)$ $(5, 3)$

7. $A(2, -4, 5), B(9, -3, 7)$ $(7, 1, 2)$

8. $A(-4, -8, -2), B(-8, -10, 2)$ $(-4, -2, 4)$

Let $\vec{r} = (-1, 3, 4)$ and $\vec{s} = (4, 3, -6)$.   14. $-\vec{i} + 3\vec{j} + 4\vec{k}$ 15. $4\vec{i} + 3\vec{j} - 6\vec{k}$

9. Find $\vec{r} - \vec{s}$. $(-5, 0, 10)$

10. Find $3\vec{s} - 2\vec{r}$. $(14, 3, -26)$

11. Find $\vec{r} + 3\vec{s}$. $(11, 12, -14)$

12. Find $|\vec{r}|$. $\sqrt{26}$

13. Find $|\vec{s}|$. $\sqrt{61}$

14. Write $\vec{r}$ as the sum of unit vectors.

15. Write $\vec{s}$ as the sum of unit vectors.

16. Find $\vec{r} \cdot \vec{s}$. -19

17. Find $\vec{r} \times \vec{s}$. $(-30, 10, -15)$

18. Is $\vec{r}$ parallel to $\vec{s}$?   no

Write parametric equations for the line that passes through point P and is parallel to $\vec{a}$.   19–21. See margin.

19. $P(3, 11), \vec{a} = (2, -5)$

20. $P(-2, 0), \vec{a} = (1, 9)$

21. $P(12, -8), \vec{a} = (-4, -7)$

22. Write an equation in slope-intercept form of the line with the parametric equations $x = -2t + 6$ and $y = 9t - 8$. $y = -\dfrac{9}{2}x + 19$

23. **Navigation** A boat that travels at 16 knots in calm water is sailing across a current of 3 knots on a river 250 m wide. The boat makes an angle of 35° with the current heading into the current.
    a. Find the resultant velocity of the boat.   13.7 knots
    b. How far upstream is the boat when it reaches the other shore?   277.7 m

24. **Physics** A downward force of 110 pounds is applied to the end of a 1.5-foot lever. What is the torque of this force about the axle if the angle of the lever to the horizontal is 60°?   82.5 lb/ft

25. **Gardening** Tei uses a sprinkler to water his garden. The sprinkler discharges water with a velocity of 28 feet per second. If the angle of the water with the ground is 35°, how far will the water travel in the horizontal direction?   23 feet

Bonus $90° < \theta < 270°$ or $\cos \theta < 0$
What can you conclude about θ, the angle between two vectors $\vec{u}$ and $\vec{v}$, if $\vec{u} \cdot \vec{v} < 0$?

This page may be used as a test or as a review. All answers to this test appear in the Selected Answers in the student text.

Standardized Test Practice Questions are also provided in the *Evaluation Masters*.

Evaluation Masters Booklet, pp. 93–94

Test Generator Software is provided in Apple, IBM, and Macintosh versions. You may use this software to create your own tests, based on the needs of your students.

Additional Answers

19. $x = 3 + 2t$
    $y = 11 - 5t$
20. $x = -2 + t$
    $y = 9t$
21. $x = 12 - 4t$
    $y = -8 - 7t$

Using the Unit Review

These two pages review the skills and concepts presented in Unit 2. In addition, a four-page unit test, shown below and on the next page, is provided in the *Evaluations Masters Booklet*.

Evaluation Masters Booklet, pp. 101–102

Change each radian measure to degree measure. (Lesson 5-1)

1. $\dfrac{\pi}{2}$ 90°

2. $\dfrac{3\pi}{4}$ 135°

3. $\dfrac{7\pi}{2}$ 630°

4. $-\dfrac{7\pi}{12}$ −105°

Solve. (Lesson 5-2)

5. Find the length of the arc intercepted by a central angle of 60° in a circle of radius 6 inches. 6.28 inches

Find the value of the given trigonometric function of an angle in standard position if a point with the given coordinates lies on its terminal side. (Lesson 5-3)

6. $\cos\theta; (2,3)$ $\dfrac{2\sqrt{13}}{13}$

7. $\tan\theta; (10,2)$ $\dfrac{1}{5}$

8. $\sin\theta; (-4,1)$ $\dfrac{\sqrt{17}}{17}$

9. $\sec\theta; (1,0)$ 1

Find each exact value. Do not use a calculator. (Lesson 5-4)

10. $\sin\pi$ 0

11. $\cot\dfrac{\pi}{3}$ $\dfrac{\sqrt{3}}{3}$

12. $\sec\dfrac{3\pi}{4}$ $-\sqrt{2}$

13. $\csc\left(-\dfrac{2\pi}{3}\right)$ $-\dfrac{2\sqrt{3}}{3}$

Solve each triangle ABC described below. Angle C is the right angle. Round angle measures to the nearest minute and side measures to the nearest tenth. (Lesson 5-5)

14. $A = 25°$, $a = 12.1$

15. $a = 3$, $b = 5$

16. $c = 24$, $B = 63°$
14–16. See margin.

Determine the number of possible solutions. If a solution exists, solve the triangle. Round angle measures to the nearest minute and side measures to the nearest tenth. (Lessons 5-6 and 5-7) 17–19. See margin.

17. $A = 46°$, $a = 86$, $c = 200$

18. $a = 19$, $b = 20$, $A = 65°$

19. $A = 73°$, $B = 65°$, $b = 38$

Find the area of each triangle to the nearest tenth. (Lesson 5-8) All answers are in square units.

20. $a = 5$, $b = 9$, $c = 6$ 14.1

21. $a = 22$, $A = 63°$, $B = 17°$ 78.2

State the amplitude (if it exists), period, and phase shift for each function. (Lesson 6-2)

22. $y = 2\cos 3x$

23. $y = -5\tan 5x$

24. $y = 4\cot\left(\dfrac{x}{2} + 90°\right)$ none, 360°, −180°

22. 2, 120°, 0° 23. none, 36°, 0°

Graph each function. (Lesson 6-3)

25. $y = \dfrac{1}{2}\cos 2x$

26. $y = 3\tan(2x - 90°)$

27. $y = x + 2\sin 3x$
25–27. See Teacher's Answer Key.

Evaluate each expression. Assume that all angles are in Quadrant I. (Lesson 6-4)

28. $\cos\left(\arccos\dfrac{1}{4}\right)$ $\dfrac{1}{4}$

29. $\cot\left(\cos^{-1}\dfrac{2}{3}\right)$ $\dfrac{2\sqrt{5}}{5}$

30. $\cos(\sin^{-1}0) + \sin(\tan^{-1}0)$ 1

Find each value. (Lesson 6-5)

31. $\cos\left(\text{Arccos}\dfrac{1}{2}\right)$ $\dfrac{1}{2}$

32. $\sin(\text{Tan}^{-1}1)$ $\dfrac{\sqrt{2}}{2}$

33. $\cos\left(\dfrac{\pi}{2} - \text{Arccot}\dfrac{\sqrt{3}}{3}\right)$ $\dfrac{\sqrt{3}}{2}$

Write the equation for the inverse of each function. Then graph the function and its inverse. (Lesson 6-6)

34. $y = \arccos x$

35. $y = \cot x$

36. $y = \text{Tan } x$

37. $y = \text{Arcsin } 2x$
34–37. See Teacher's Answer Key.

Solve for values of θ between 0° and 90°. (Lesson 7-1)

38. If $\sec\theta = \dfrac{4}{3}$, find $\cos\theta$. $\dfrac{3}{4}$

39. If $\cos\theta = \dfrac{1}{3}$, find $\sin\theta$. $\dfrac{2\sqrt{2}}{3}$

40. If $\sin\theta = \dfrac{1}{2}$, find $\cot\theta$. $\sqrt{3}$

Additional Answers

14. $B = 65°$, $b = 25.9$, $c = 28.6$

15. $A = 30°58'$, $B = 59°2'$, $c = 5.8$

16. $A = 27°$, $a = 10.9$, $b = 21.4$

17. no solution

18. two; $B = 72°33'$, $c = 14.1$, and $C = 42°27'$, or $B = 107°27'$, $c = 2.8$, and $C = 7°33'$

19. one; $a = 40.1$, $c = 28.1$, $C = 42°$

Verify that each of the following is an identity. (Lesson 7-2)

41. $\tan x + \tan x \cot^2 x = \sec x \csc x$

42. $\sin(180° - \theta) = \tan \theta \cos \theta$
41–42. See Teacher's Answer Key.

Use the sum and difference identities to find the exact value of each function. (Lesson 7-3)

43. $\sin 105°$ $\dfrac{\sqrt{2} + \sqrt{6}}{4}$

44. $\cos 135°$ $-\dfrac{\sqrt{2}}{2}$

45. $\cos 15°$ $\dfrac{\sqrt{2} + \sqrt{6}}{4}$

46. $\sin(-210°)$ $\dfrac{1}{2}$

If $\sin x = \dfrac{2}{5}$ and x is in the first quadrant, find each value. (Lesson 7-4)

47. $\cos 2x$ $\dfrac{17}{25}$

48. $\sin \dfrac{x}{2}$ $\sqrt{\dfrac{5 - \sqrt{21}}{10}}$

49. $\tan \dfrac{x}{2}$ $\sqrt{\dfrac{5 - \sqrt{21}}{5 + \sqrt{21}}}$

50. $\sin 2x$ $\dfrac{4\sqrt{21}}{25}$

Solve each equation for $0° \leq x \leq 180°$. (Lesson 7-5)

51. $\sin^2 x - \sin x = 0$ $0°, 90°, 180°$

52. $\cos 2x = 4 \cos x - 3$ $0°$

53. $5 \cos x + 1 = 3 \cos 2x$ $120°$

Write each equation in normal form. Then find p, the measure of the normal and ϕ, the angle that the normal makes with the positive x-axis. (Lesson 7-6)

54. $2x + 3y - 2 = 0$

55. $5x = -2y + 8$

56. $y = 3x - 7$
54–56. See margin.

Find the distance from the point with the given coordinates to the line with the given equation. Round answers to the nearest tenth. (Lesson 7-7)

57. $(2, 5); 2x - 2y + 3 = 0$ 1.1

58. $(-2, 2); -x + 4y = -6$ −3.9

59. $(1, -3); 4x - y - 1 = 0$ 1.5

Use vectors $\vec{a}$ and $\vec{b}$ for Exercises 60–61.
(Lesson 8-1) 60 – 61. Answers may vary slightly.

60. Find the magnitude (in cm) and amplitude of $\vec{a} + \vec{b}$. 4.5 cm, 94°

61. Find the vertical and horizontal components of $\vec{a}$. 1 cm, 1.8 cm

Find an ordered pair to represent $\vec{u}$ in each equation if $\vec{v} = (1, -3)$ and $\vec{w} = (2, -2)$.
(Lesson 8-2) 62. (3, –5) 63. (1, 1)

62. $\vec{u} = \vec{v} + \vec{w}$

63. $\vec{u} = \vec{w} - \vec{v}$

64. $\vec{u} = 3\vec{v} + 2\vec{w}$ (7, –13)

65. $\vec{u} = -3\vec{v} + \vec{w}$ (–1, 7)

Find an ordered triple to represent $\vec{u}$ in each equation if $\vec{v} = (3, 1, -1)$ and $\vec{w} = (-5, 2, 3)$. Then write $\vec{u}$ as the sum of unit vectors. (Lesson 8-3)

66. $\vec{u} = 2\vec{v} + \vec{w}$

67. $\vec{u} = \vec{v} - 2\vec{w}$

68. $\vec{u} = 3\vec{v} + 3\vec{w}$

69. $\vec{u} = 4\vec{v} - 2\vec{w}$
66–69. See margin.

Find each inner product or cross product. (Lesson 8-4)

70. $(4, -2) \cdot (-2, 3)$ −14

71. $(3, -4, 1) \cdot (4, -2, 2)$ 22

72. $(5, -2, 5) \times (-1, 0, -3)$ (6, 10, –2)

Write a vector equation of the line that passes through point P and is parallel to $\vec{v}$. Then write parametric equations for the line. (Lesson 8-6) 73–74. See margin.

73. $P(0, 5), \vec{v} = (-1, 5)$

74. $P(4, -3), \vec{v} = (-2, -2)$

Evaluation Masters Booklet, pp. 103–104

Additional Answers

54. $\dfrac{2}{\sqrt{13}}x + \dfrac{3}{\sqrt{13}}y - \dfrac{2}{\sqrt{13}} = 0; \dfrac{2}{\sqrt{13}},$
$\approx 56°$

55. $\dfrac{5}{\sqrt{29}}x + \dfrac{2}{\sqrt{29}}y - \dfrac{8}{\sqrt{29}} = 0; \dfrac{8}{\sqrt{29}},$
$\approx 22°$

56. $\dfrac{3}{\sqrt{10}}x - \dfrac{1}{\sqrt{10}}y - \dfrac{7}{\sqrt{10}} = 0; \dfrac{7}{\sqrt{10}}$
$\approx -18°$

66. $(1, 4, 1); \vec{u} = \vec{i} + 4\vec{j} + \vec{k}$

67. $(13, -3, -7); \vec{u} = 13\vec{i} - 3\vec{j} - 7\vec{k}$

68. $(-6, 9, 6); \vec{u} = -6\vec{i} + 9\vec{j} + 6\vec{k}$

69. $(22, 0, -10); \vec{u} = 22\vec{i} - 10\vec{k}$

73. $(x, y - 5) = t(-1, 5); x = -t,$
$y = 5 + 5t$

74. $(x - 4, y + 3) = t(-2, -2);$
$x = 4 - 2t, y = -3 - 2t$

The key theme of Unit 3 is the relationship of different advanced functions and their graphs. The three chapters explore three different topics united by the concept of graphing as a fundamental aspect to their study.

Connections to Other Units

The concepts developed in this unit are related to concepts in Units 1 and 2. The transformations of graphs presented in Units 1 and 2 also apply to the graphs of conic sections, exponential functions, and logarithmic functions. The trigonometric functions presented in Unit 2 are used extensively in the study of complex numbers in polar form.

Multicultural Notes

Greece   Greek philosophers discovered that the pull of the sun and the moon produces a force on Earth that causes it to rotate with a motion somewhat like that of a spinning top. In the rotation, Earth's axis can be imagined to follow a conical path, described as a cone of precision, with a vertex angle of $23\frac{1}{2}°$.

Italy   Significant developments in the science of surveying were made by the Romans who coupled trigonometry and surveying techniques to mark boundaries and make measurements for their extensive construction work. Early Romans developed the *groma* for sighting, the *chorobates* for leveling, and the *libella*, a plumb bob. By the thirteen century, surveying tools included the *quadrans*, with a 90° angle and other scales, and the cross staff, which made it possible to measure distances using proportion and angles. These early instruments have now been replaced by the automatic level and electronic distance measuring equipment, enhanced by cameras and aerial surveying equipment.

UNIT 3

ADVANCED FUNCTIONS AND GRAPHING

Chapter 9	Polar Coordinates and Complex Numbers
Chapter 10	Conics
Chapter 11	Exponential and Logarithmic Functions

You are now ready to apply what you have learned in earlier units to more complex functions. The three chapters in this unit contain very different topics; however, there are some similarities among them. The most striking similarity is that all three chapters require that you have had some experience with graphing.

The chapter on polar coordinates will require you to use your graphing skills on a new set of axes, the polar axes. The graphs that you will construct will not look like the graphs that you have seen thus far; however, you will be able to use the same skills to construct these graphs. In the chapter on conics, you will study the graphs of circles, ellipses, parabolas, and hyperbolas. In this chapter, you will use much of what you have studied about graphing up to this point. Finally, you will examine the exponential and logarithmic functions. These functions are used quite often to model a variety of real-life problems. Examining the graphs of these functions should prove quite illuminating.

As you work through this unit, try to make connections between what you have already studied and what you are currently studying. This will help you to be able to use the skills you have already mastered more effectively in this unit.

462

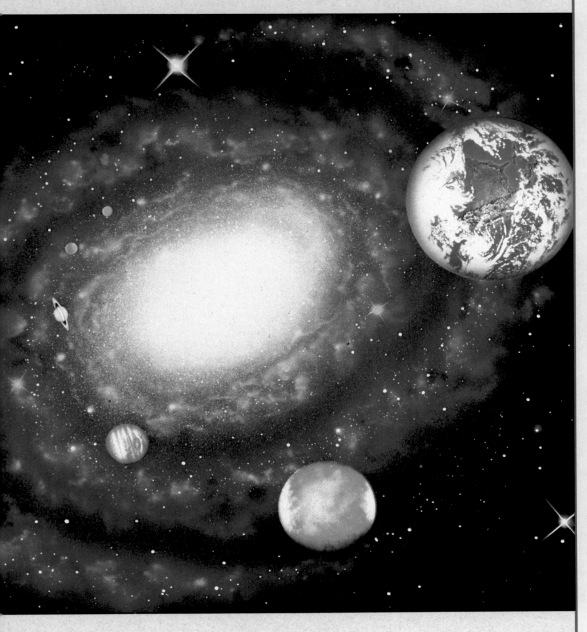

Cooperative Learning

The **Decision Making** activities offer students an opportunity to explore real-world questions while working in cooperative groups. These questions require students to do research and come to a viable conclusion.

Problem Solving

The **Case Study Follow-Ups** provide an arena for problem solving, applying mathematics, and becoming more aware of issues that may face students in their adult lives. These questions require research and applications of the mathematics of the chapter.

Using Technology

Computer and calculator literacy is a growing part of our everyday lives. The features in this unit give students exposure to different technology tools available to facilitate their study of mathematics.

463

CHAPTER 9

POLAR COORDINATES AND COMPLEX NUMBERS

PREVIEWING THE CHAPTER

This chapter extends the concept of coordinates to include graphing on the polar coordinate plane. Students graph polar coordinates and convert between polar and rectangular coordinates. They graph polar equations and polar forms of linear equations. Complex numbers are reviewed, and students learn to add, subtract, multiply, and divide complex numbers in rectangular form. They then write complex coordinates in polar form and find products, quotients, powers, and roots of complex numbers in polar form.

Lesson Objective Chart

Lesson (Pages)	Lesson Objectives		State/Local Objectives
9-1 (466-472)	**9-1:**	Graph polar coordinates and simple polar equations.	
9-2 (475-481)	**9-2:**	Graph polar equations.	
9-3 (483-487)	**9-3:**	Convert from polar coordinates to rectangular coordinates and vice versa.	
9-4 (488-493)	**9-4A:**	Write the polar form of a linear equation.	
	9-4B:	Graph the polar form of a linear equation.	
9-5 (494-500)	**9-5:**	Add, subtract, multiply, and divide complex numbers in rectangular form.	
9-6 (501-505)	**9-6:**	Change complex numbers from rectangular to polar form and vice versa.	
9-7 (506-509)	**9-7:**	Find the product and quotient of complex numbers in polar form.	
9-8 (510-517)	**9-8:**	Find powers and roots of complex numbers in polar form using DeMoivre's theorem.	

ORGANIZING THE CHAPTER

You may want to refer to the **Course Planning Guide Calendar** on pages T34-T35 for a complete pacing chart.

Lesson Planning Guide

Blackline Masters Booklets

Lesson	Pages	Practice	Enrichment	Evaluation	Graphing Calculator	Computer	Multicultural Activity	Applications	Problem Solving	Case Study Follow-Up	Decision Making	Transparencies
9-1	466-472	p. 57	p. 57									9-1
9-2	475-481	p. 58	p. 58	Quiz A, p. 113		p. 18						9-2
9-3	483-487	p. 59	p. 59					p. 25				9-3
9-4	488-493	p. 60	p. 60	Quiz B, p. 113 Mid-Chapter Test, p.115								9-4
9-5	494-500	p. 61	p. 61							p. 27		9-5
9-6	501-505	p. 62	p. 62	Quiz C, p. 114			p. 9					9-6
9-7	506-509	p. 63	p. 63									9-7
9-8	510-517	p. 64	p. 64	Quiz D, p. 114	p. 17				p. 26			9-8
Review	518-520	Multiple Choice Tests, Forms 1A and 1B, pp. 105-108 Free Response Tests, Forms 2A and 2B, pp. 109-112 Standardized Test Questions, p. 116										
Test	521											

Other Chapter Resources

Student Edition
Case Study Follow-Up, p. 481
Decision Making, p. 472
Technology, p. 482

Other Supplements
Transparency 9-0 for Chapter Opener
Alternate Assessment in the Mathematics Classroom,
 Glencoe Publishing Co., 1993
Cooperative Learning in the Mathematics Classroom,
 Glencoe Publishing Co., 1993

Software
Test and Review Generator Software
 Available for Apple, IBM, and Macintosh
Teacher's Guide for Software Resources

ENHANCING THE CHAPTER

Cooperative Learning

Describing the student's Responsibilities to the Group

It is important students understand that they are expected not merely to work in a group but to work *cooperatively* in a group. Each member must accept responsibility for learning the assigned material and for making sure every other member of the group also learns the material. One way to encourage this attitude is to have the group generate a single product, report, or set of answers that each member must sign to indicate agreement with the responses and the ability to justify or explain why the responses are appropriate. Be alert for other ways to encourage group members to rely on one another for help and improvement. For example, when you give a quiz or test, you might inform the group that each member will earn his or her own individual score and can earn bonus points based on how much the group's average score exceeds a preset level of performance.

For more information on cooperative learning, see pages T20-T21. Additional information on using cooperative groups is available in Glencoe's *Cooperative Learning in the Mathematics Classroom*, ©1993.

Multicultural

Multicultural Activity Masters, p. 9

Activity Masters

Applications, p. 25

Problem Solving, p. 26

Decision Making, p. 27

Technology

The Technology feature preceding Lesson 9-3 presents a program written in BASIC computer language that generates ordered pairs for polar equations.

Graphing calculators capable of parametric equations can enhance the instruction in this chapter. In Lesson 9-2A, students learn to graph polar equations. The Graphing Calculator Exploration in Lesson 9-2 investigates graphing parametric equations for polar equations. The Exploration in Lesson 9-8, uses parametric equations on the graphing calculator to find the roots on the rectangular plane, which can be translated into complex numbers. The graphing calculator program presented in this lesson calculates powers of complex numbers.

Graphing Calculator Exercises, pp. 492, 516
Graphing Calculator Program, pp. 516-517

Outside Resources

Books/Periodicals

Kastner, Bernice. *Space Mathematics: A Resource for Secondary School Teachers.* Dale Seymour Publications, Palo Alto, CA, 1988.

Peterson, Ivars. *The Mathematical Tourist,* W.H. Freeman and Co., New York, 1988.

Films/Videotapes/Videodiscs

Mathematics, Trigonometry. Great Plains National, University of Nebraska-Lincoln

Software

MathTools for Precalculus/Calculus. William K. Bradford Publishing (Macintosh)

IBM Mathematics Exploration Toolkit (MET). IBM

GraphExplorer. Scott Foresman (IBM, Macintosh)

Cactusplot. The Cactusplot company (Apple II, IBM)

Pre-Calculus 4.0 with Trigonometry. True BASIC (IBM, Macintosh)

Technology Masters

Graphing Calculator, p. 17

Computer, p. 18

CHAPTER 9

POLAR COORDINATES AND COMPLEX NUMBERS

HISTORICAL SNAPSHOT

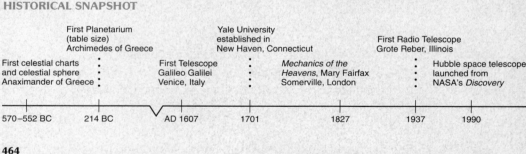

	First Planetarium (table size) Archimedes of Greece		Yale University established in New Haven, Connecticut		First Radio Telescope Grote Reber, Illinois	
First celestial charts and celestial sphere Anaximander of Greece		First Telescope Galileo Galilei Venice, Italy		*Mechanics of the Heavens*, Mary Fairfax Somerville, London		Hubble space telescope launched from NASA's *Discovery*
570–552 BC	214 BC	AD 1607	1701	1827	1937	1990

464

CHAPTER OBJECTIVES

In this chapter, you will:
- Graph polar equations.
- Convert complex numbers from rectangular to polar form and vice versa.
- Perform basic operations on complex numbers in both rectangular and polar form.

CAREER GOAL: Astronomical Research

Some people have a hard time choosing a career, but Greg Howard has always known what he wanted to do with his life. "I've been interested in astronomy for as long as I can remember," he says. "I got a small telescope when I was eight years old, and a larger one when I was fifteen. I spent many hours late at night seeing what I could find. I thought astronomy was beautiful and interesting. I still find it as intriguing as I ever did."

Greg stays busy year-round, always taking the opportunity for summer internships. "Two summers ago," Greg says, "I collected data about *water masers*, using a radio telescope. Water masers are clouds surrounding stars that give off powerful radio energy. Last summer, my advisor and I catalogued a new type of hydrogen cloud. This summer, I'm doing analyses of clusters of galaxies." Greg says that his summer internships were "incredible. I found them to be a good way to apply what I had learned in class to the real world of research."

Greg uses mathematics to find objects in the sky. "Coordinate systems are very important in astronomy," he says. "Finding coordinates is one of the first things that we learn. The *celestial sphere* is an imaginary globe surrounding Earth. We use coordinate systems to locate objects in the sky in terms of their locations on the celestial sphere. Once you define the coordinates for the celestial sphere, and you apply fundamentals about the speed of Earth's rotation and its motion around the sun, then you can determine which parts of the solar system are overhead at any given time, on any given day."

Greg says, "I like being on the edge of new knowledge. There is plenty to be learned. I hope that I will contribute useful research that will enlarge the current knowledge about the universe in which we live."

READ MORE ABOUT IT

Friedman, Herbert. *The Astronomer's Universe*. New York: W.W. Norton & Company, 1990.
Moore, Patrick. *Astronomers' Stars*. New York: W.W. Norton & Company, 1989.
Rukl, Antonin. *Amateur Astronomer*. New York: Gallery Books, 1985.

SPOTLIGHT ON...

Greg Howard
Age: 21
Class: Senior
School: Yale University
    New Haven, Connecticut
Majors: Astronomy and Physics

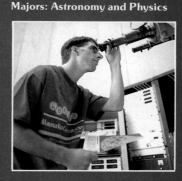

"I hope that I will be able to help enlarge the current knowledge about the universe in which we live."

FOR MORE INFORMATION

If you would like more information about astronomy, contact:

American Astronomical Society (AAS)
2000 Florida Avenue NW, Suite 300
Washington, DC 20009

Applications

Lesson	Application	Examples	Exercises
9–1	Baseball Air Safety	3	39 40
9–2	Toys History		27 28
9–3	Geology Roller Coasters	4	38, 39 40
9–4	Navigation		32
9–5	Electricity Flashlights	6	42–44 41
9–6	Algebra Electricity		34 35
9–7	Algebra Electricity		25 26
9–8	Science		34

Lesson Resources

- Practice Master 9–1
- Enrichment Master 9–1

 Transparency 9–1 contains the 5-Minute Check and a teaching aid for this lesson.

INTRODUCING THE LESSON

 ### 5-Minute Check

(over Chapter 8)

1. A vector has a magnitude of 5.6 cm and an amplitude of 28°. Find the magnitude of its vertical component. **2.6 cm**
2. $\vec{f}$ = (3, 2) and $\vec{w}$ = (–2, 4). Find an ordered pair to represent $\vec{u}$ if $\vec{u} = 2\vec{f} - 3\vec{w}$. **(12, –8)**
3. Find the magnitude of the vector from A (–4, 5) to B (8, 0). **13**
4. Find the inner product of $\vec{c}$ and $\vec{d}$ if $\vec{c}$ = (3, –2) and $\vec{d}$ = (6, 8). **2**
5. In still air, an airplane heads due east at 400 mph. A 40-mph wind blows from the north. Find the ground speed and direction of the plane. **402 mph, 5°43′ SE**

Prerequisite Skills

Students should be able to convert degree measure to radian measure and vice versa.

Write each radian measure in degrees.

1. $\frac{\pi}{4}$ **45°**   2. $\frac{11\pi}{6}$ **330°**

Write each degree measure in radians.

3. 30° $\frac{\pi}{6}$ 4. 450° $\frac{5\pi}{2}$

Motivating the Lesson

Have students graph the point P (1, $\sqrt{3}$) on a coordinate plane and then draw $\overline{OP}$. Ask them to find OP and the angle that $\overline{OP}$ makes with the x-axis. **2; 60°**

9-1   Polar Coordinates

After studying this lesson, you should be able to:
- graph polar coordinates and simple polar equations.

Application

 FYI...

The first cellular telephone service was started in April of 1984 in Washington, D.C., by a subsidiary of AT&T called Advanced Mobile Phone Service, Inc.

In recent years, the portable cellular telephone has gained in popularity, making the office as mobile as a moving vehicle. However, these phones work only if you are in an area serviced by a cellular microwave tower. The Motorola Corporation plans to alleviate this drawback by launching 77 low-orbiting satellites able to relay cellular signals to the entire world. These Iridium satellites, named after the 77 electrons in the iridium atom, are scheduled for launch beginning in 1994. They will circle Earth in seven polar orbits, with each orbit containing 11 satellites.

The map at the right shows an aerial view of the North Pole with latitude and longitude lines. The proposed paths of the seven orbits are shown in red. The latitude lines are concentric circles with the North Pole as their center. The longitude lines intersect the North Pole. These lines are identified by the angles they make with respect to the prime meridian (0° longitude) which goes through Greenwich, England. In mathematics, a coordinate system similar to this one is called a **polar coordinate system**.

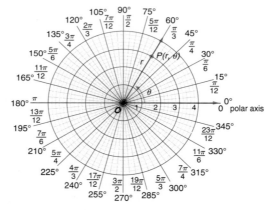

In a polar coordinate system, a fixed point O is called the **pole** or origin. The **polar axis** is usually a horizontal ray directed toward the right from the pole. The location of point P in the polar coordinate system can be identified by polar coordinates in the form (r, θ). If a ray is drawn from the pole through point P, the distance from the pole to point P is $|r|$. The measure of the angle formed by $\overrightarrow{OP}$ and the polar axis is θ. The angle can be measured in degrees or radians. *This grid is sometimes called the polar plane.*

ALTERNATE TEACHING STRATEGIES

Using Cooperative Groups

Have students in each group decide on a method for randomly choosing a point in the polar plane. One student chooses a point and writes its polar coordinates. The other students, in turn, write different pairs of polar coordinates that represent the point.

Using Problem Solving

Point P has polar coordinates (r, θ), where $0° \leq \theta \leq 90°$. Ask students to name three different pairs of polar coordinates that represent P, with the restriction that $-360° \leq \theta \leq 360°$. $(r, \theta - 360°)$, $(-r, \theta + 180°)$, $(-r, \theta - 180°)$

If r is positive, θ is the measure of any angle in standard position that has $\overrightarrow{OP}$ as its terminal side.

If r is negative, θ is the measure of any angle that has the ray opposite $\overrightarrow{OP}$ as its terminal side.

Example 1

Graph each point.
a. $P(3, 120°)$

a. On a polar plane, sketch the terminal side of a 120° angle in standard position.

Since r is positive, find the point along the terminal side 3 units from the pole.

Notice that point P is on the third circle from the pole.

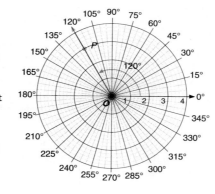

b. $Q\left(-2.5, \dfrac{\pi}{2}\right)$

b. Sketch the terminal side of an angle of $\dfrac{\pi}{2}$ radians in standard position.

Since r is negative, extend the terminal side in the opposite direction. Find the point along this ray 2.5 units from the pole.

Notice that point Q is halfway between the second and third circle from the pole.

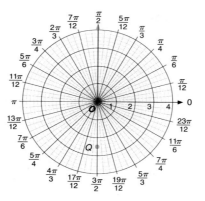

You have seen that r can either be negative or positive. The angle measure θ can also be either negative or positive. If θ is positive, the angle is measured counterclockwise from the polar axis. If θ is negative, the angle is measured clockwise from the polar axis.

LESSON 9-1 POLAR COORDINATES 467

Example 2

Notice that the terminal side of $-\frac{\pi}{3}$ is coincident with that of $\frac{5\pi}{3}$. Also,

$$\left|-\frac{\pi}{3}\right| + \left|\frac{5\pi}{3}\right| = 2\pi.$$

Graph the point P that has polar coordinates $\left(-1, -\frac{\pi}{3}\right)$.

Negative angles are measured counterclockwise. Sketch the terminal side of the angle. Since r is negative, the point $\left(-1, -\frac{\pi}{3}\right)$ is 1 unit from the pole along the ray *opposite* the terminal side of the angle.

Example 3

APPLICATION

Baseball

The figure at the right shows a baseball diamond placed on a rectangular coordinate plane. The coordinates of second base are $(90, 90)$ since the bases are 90 feet apart. Find a pair of polar coordinates for second base if the first-base line is the polar axis and home plate is at the pole?

Since the baselines form a square, a ray from home plate through second base forms a 45° angle with the first-base line. The polar coordinate for θ is 45°.

The value of r can be found by using the Pythagorean theorem.

$$r = \sqrt{90^2 + 90^2}$$
$$r = \sqrt{16,200}$$
$$r \approx 127.28$$

A pair of polar coordinates for second base is $(127.28, 45°)$.

Remember from your study of trigonometry that an angle can be represented in more than one way. For example, a 390° angle is the same as a 30° angle. Likewise on the polar plane, a point can be represented by more than one pair of polar coordinates. Point P is named in six ways below.

For every angle, there are infinitely many representations.

(3, 150°) or (3, –210°)   **(–3, –30°) or (–3, 330°)**

(3, 510°)   **(-3, -390°)**

Multiple Representations of (r, θ)	If P is a point with polar coordinates (r, θ), then P can also be represented by the polar coordinates $(-r, \theta + (2k + 1)\pi)$ or $(r, \theta + 2k\pi)$, where k is any integer.

Example 4

Name four different pairs of polar coordinates that represent point R with the restriction that $-360° \leq \theta \leq 360°$.

Point R can be represented by $(3, 80°)$. Use the formulas for multiple representations of polar coordinates to find three more pairs.

$(-r, \theta + (2k + 1)180°) \rightarrow (-(3), 80° \pm (1)180°)$
$\rightarrow (-3, 260°)$ or $(-3, -100°)$
$(r, \theta + 360k°) \rightarrow (3, 80° + (-1)(360°))$
$\rightarrow (3, -280°)$

An equation that uses polar coordinates is called a **polar equation**. For example, $r = 4\cos\theta$ is a polar equation. A **polar graph** represents the solution set which is the set of points whose coordinates (r, θ) satisfy a given polar equation.

In the Cartesian coordinate system, you studied special types of equations involving constants, such as $y = 3, x = -4, y^2 = 4$, and $x^3 = 27$. The solutions to these equations had a unique representation on the coordinate plane. The same is true for solutions of polar equations.

Example 5

Graph each polar equation.

a. $\theta = \dfrac{\pi}{6}$

a. The solution to this equation consists of all points with coordinates of the form $\left(r, \dfrac{\pi}{6}\right)$. That is, r can have any value as long as θ is $\dfrac{\pi}{6}$. The graphs of these points form a line composed of the ray that forms an angle of $\dfrac{\pi}{6}$ with the polar axis and, to represent negative values of r, the ray opposite that ray.

Checking for Understanding

Exercises 1–9 are designed to help you assess students' understanding through reading, writing, speaking, and modeling. You should work through Exercises 1–3 with your students and then monitor their work on Exercises 4–9.

Closing the Lesson

Writing Activity Have students write a few sentences comparing and contrasting the polar coordinate system and the rectangular coordinate system.

Additional Answers

2. because the graph of reference angles and/or negative radii can result in the same point

4.

(100, –310°), (–100, 230°), (–100, –130°)

5.

$$\left(12.8, \frac{-11\pi}{6}\right), \left(-12.8, \frac{7\pi}{6}\right),$$

$$\left(-12.8, \frac{-5\pi}{6}\right)$$

---

b. $r = 2$

b. The solution to this equation consists of all points with coordinates of the form $(2, \theta)$. That is, θ can have any value as long as r is 2. The graphs of these points form a circle with radius 2.

This circle is also the graph of $r = -2$. Why?

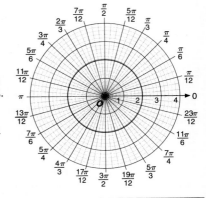

CHECKING FOR UNDERSTANDING

Communicating Mathematics

Read and study the lesson to answer each question.

1. **Determine** which two locations on Earth each of the Iridium satellites will pass over in their orbit. North Pole, South Pole

2. **Explain** why a point in the polar coordinate system cannot be named by a unique ordered pair (r, θ). See margin.

3. **Explain** why the graph in Example 5b is also the graph of $r = -2$. The points 2 units from the origin in the opposite direction are on the circle where $r = 2$.

Guided Practice

Graph the point represented by the given polar coordinates. Then name three other pairs of polar coordinates that represent the same point with $-360° \le \theta \le 360°$.
4–6. See margin.

4. $(100, 50°)$

5. $\left(12.8, \frac{\pi}{6}\right)$

6. $(1.2, 70°)$

Graph each polar equation. 7–9. See Teacher's Answer Key.

7. $r = 3$

8. $\theta = 10°$

9. $\theta = \frac{\pi}{2}$

EXERCISES

10–21. See Teacher's Answer Key.

Practice

Graph the point that has the given polar coordinates.

A

10. $(3, 0)$

11. $\left(2, \frac{\pi}{4}\right)$

12. $\left(\frac{1}{4}, \frac{2\pi}{3}\right)$

13. $\left(\frac{1}{2}, \frac{-3\pi}{2}\right)$

14. $\left(-2, \frac{5\pi}{6}\right)$

15. $\left(-3, \frac{\pi}{3}\right)$

16. $(0.5, 1)$

17. $(4, -3)$

18. $(6, -45°)$

19. $(8, 585°)$

20. $(-4, 135°)$

21. $(2, -30°)$

470   CHAPTER 9   POLAR COORDINATES AND COMPLEX NUMBERS

6.

(1.2, –290°), (–1.2, 250°), (–1.2, –110°)

Name four different pairs of polar coordinates that represent point A.

22.

23.

24.

22–24. Answers will vary.
For sample answers, see margin.

Graph each polar equation. 25–36. See Teacher's Answer Key.

25. $r = 6$ **26.** $r = \sqrt{3}$ **27.** $r = (2)^3$

28. $\theta = \dfrac{\pi}{4}$ **29.** $\theta = -\pi$ **30.** $r = 1.27$

31. $\theta = 145°$ **32.** $\theta = -\dfrac{5\pi}{6}$ **33.** $\theta = -220°$

34. $r = -4$ **35.** $r = 1.5$ **36.** $\theta = 360°$

37. Find an ordered pair of polar coordinates to represent the point whose rectangular coordinates are $(-3, 4)$. Sample answer: $(5, 127°)$

Critical Thinking

38. Three circles are externally tangent to each other. If each circle has a radius of 4 units and each side of the triangle is tangent to two of the circles, find the area of the triangle. $64\sqrt{3} + 96$ sq units

Applications and Problem Solving

39b. $(60.5, 45°)$

39. Baseball Refer to Example 3. Sample answers are given.
  a. What are the polar coordinates for first and third bases? $(90, 0°)$, $(90, 90°)$
  b. What are the polar coordinates for the pitcher's mound if the pitcher's mound is located 60.5 feet from home plate on a line from home plate to second base?

40. Air Safety The largest airport in the world is the King Khalid International Airport outside Riyadh, Saudi Arabia. It covers 86 square miles. It also has the largest control tower, which is 243 feet high. The radar at the control tower is at the center of a large polar coordinate system that monitors flights in and out of the airport. The polar axis is due east and r is measured in miles.

  a. If an airplane is on its final approach and is at a point with coordinates $(5, 270°)$, which direction is the airplane heading as it lands? due north

  b. How far is the airplane from the control tower? 5 miles

RETEACHING THE LESSON

Give the polar coordinates of a point. Have students answer these questions.
- How far is the point from the pole?
- What is the measure of the angle formed by the polar axis and the ray from the pole through the point?

Have students describe where the point is located on the polar plane and then graph it.

APPLYING THE LESSON

Homework Exercises

Assignment Guide

Average: 11–37 odd, 38, 39, 41–46
Enriched: 10–36 even, 37–46

The red A, B, and C flags, printed only in the Teacher's Wraparound Edition, indicate the level of difficulty of the exercises.

Additional Answers

22. $\left(2, \dfrac{\pi}{6}\right)$, $\left(2, \dfrac{-11\pi}{6}\right)$, $\left(-2, \dfrac{-5\pi}{6}\right)$, $\left(-2, \dfrac{7\pi}{6}\right)$

23. $\left(2, \dfrac{2\pi}{3}\right)$, $\left(2, \dfrac{-4\pi}{3}\right)$, $\left(-2, \dfrac{-\pi}{3}\right)$, $\left(-2, \dfrac{5\pi}{3}\right)$

24. $(100, 208°)$, $(100, -152°)$, $(-100, 28°)$, $(-100, -332°)$

Practice Masters Booklet, p. 57

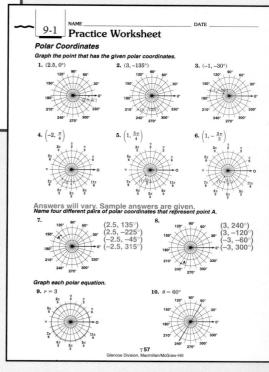

41. Solve $4x^2 - 9x + 5 = 0$ by using the quadratic formula. **(Lesson 4-2)** 1.25, 1

42. Change $\frac{3\pi}{8}$ radians to degree measure to the nearest minute. **(Lesson 5-1)** 67°30′

43. cos 20° + sin 50°

43. State which is greater, $\cos 20° + \sin 50°$ or $\cos 80° + \sin 40°$. **(Lesson 6-1)**

44. For $0° < \theta < 90°$, find $\cot\theta$ if $\tan\theta = \frac{\sqrt{2}}{5}$. **(Lesson 7-1)** $\frac{5\sqrt{2}}{2}$

45. 15 feet horizontally, 22 feet vertically

45. Jessie kicked a football with an initial velocity of 60 ft/s at an angle of 60° to the horizontal. After 0.5 seconds, how far has the ball traveled horizontally and vertically? *Use* $x = t|\overline{v}|\cos\theta, y = t|\overline{v}|\sin\theta + \frac{1}{2}gt^2$, *and* $g = 32\ ft/s^2$. **(Lesson 8-7)**

46. College Entrance Exam Choose the best answer. A
The number of degrees through which the hour hand of a clock moves in 2 hours 12 minutes is

(A) 66°   **(B)** 72°   **(C)** 126°   **(D)** 732°   **(E)** 792°

COOPERATIVE LEARNING

DECISION MAKING

The Budget Deficit

Each year the federal government spends several hundred billion dollars more than it takes in, falling further and further into debt. Because all possible solutions to the problem are politically unpopular, Congress and the President have been slow to address the problem. What do you think should be done to get the budget under control? Since belt-tightening will require sacrifice on everyone's part, how would you convince people that such sacrifices are necessary? What can you do to raise public and congressional awareness of the problem and help in the search for a solution? 1–4. See students' work.

1. Research causes and effects of the federal deficit. How long has it been a problem? Why have legislators been negligent in coming to grips with the deficit? How does the deficit affect the country?

2. Describe steps that could be taken to reduce the budget deficit. If you were a legislator, what would you do to help get the deficit under control?

3. Describe what you can do to help find a solution to the problem. Would it help to write a letter to your congressional representative? Could you work to raise public consciousness about the dangers of the deficit through a publicity campaign?

4. Project Work with your group to complete one of the projects listed at the right based on the information you gathered in Exercises 1–3.

PROJECTS

- *Conduct an interview.*
- *Write a book report.*
- *Write a proposal.*
- *Write an article for the school paper.*
- *Write a report.*
- *Make a display.*
- *Make a graph or chart.*
- *Plan an activity.*
- *Design a checklist.*

EXTENDING THE LESSON

Math Power: Problem Solving

At the North Pole, if you walk 1 mile south, 1 mile east (along a line of latitude), and 1 mile north, you end up back at the pole. There are an infinite number of points near the South Pole such that if you walk 1 mile east, 1 mile south, and 1 mile north, you arrive at your starting point. Where are they?

$1 + \dfrac{1}{2\pi}$ miles from the South Pole

Decision Making

This activity provides students an opportunity to work together on a given problem. You may wish to refer to pages T20–T21 and page 464c for the various elements of cooperative groups and specific goals and strategies for using them.

Enrichment Masters Booklet, p. 57

9-1
NAME _____ DATE _____
Enrichment Worksheet

Distance on the Earth's Surface

As you learned in Lesson 9-1, lines of longitude on Earth's surface intersect at the North and South Poles. A line of longitude that passes completely around Earth is called a **great circle**. All great circles have the same circumference, found by calculating the circumference of a circle with Earth's radius, 3963.2 miles. (Since Earth is slightly flattened at the poles, it is not precisely spherical. The difference is so small, however, that for most purposes it can be ignored.)

1. Find the circumference of a great circle.
24,901.5 miles
On a great circle, position is measured in degrees north or south of the equator. Pittsburgh's position of 40° 26′ N means that radii from Earth's center to Pittsburgh and to the point of intersection of the equator and Pittsburgh's longitude line form an angle of 40° 26′. (See the figure above.)

2. Find the length of one degree of arc on a longitude line.
69.2 miles
3. Charleston, South Carolina (32° 46′ N), and Guayaquil, Ecuador (2° 9′ S), both lie on Pittsburgh's longitude line. Find the distance from Pittsburgh to each of the other cities.
530.3 miles; 2945.5 miles
Because circles of latitude are drawn parallel to the equator, their radii and circumferences grow steadily shorter as they approach the poles. The length of one degree of arc on a circle of latitude depends on how far north or south of the equator the circle is located. The figure at the right shows a circle of latitude of radius r located θ degrees north of the equator. Because the radii of the equator and the circle of latitude are parallel, $m\angle NEO = \theta$. Therefore, $\cos\theta = \frac{r}{R}$, which gives $r = R\cos\theta$, where R represents the radius of Earth.

4. Find the radius and circumference of a circle of latitude located 70° north of the equator. **1355.5 miles; 8516.9 miles**
5. Find the length of one degree of arc on the circle described in Exercise 4. **23.7 miles**
6. Bangor, Maine, and Salem, Oregon, are both located at latitude 44° 50′ N. Their respective longitudes are 68° 46′ and 123° 2′ west of Greenwich. Find the distance from Bangor to Salem.
2662.0 miles

T 57
Glencoe Division, Macmillan/McGraw-Hill

9-2A Graphing Calculators: Graphing Polar Equations

You can graph polar equations and read polar coordinates on a TI-81 graphing calculator by changing the MODE settings. To begin, press [MODE] and select parametric graphing by using the arrow keys to move to the word "Param" and pressing [ENTER] when it is blinking. Also, be sure the calculator is in radian mode. Then press [CLEAR] to exit the mode screen.

Before entering polar equations into a graphing calculator, you must first convert them into parametric form by using the equations $x = r \cos \theta$ and $y = r \sin \theta$. Then enter the equations into the calculator by using the [XIT] key for θ.

Check the [RANGE]. Make sure you have selected an appropriate viewing window. Also, make sure that the calculator will plot enough points to draw a complete graph by checking the Tmin, Tmax, and Tstep values of the range. Tmin is the minimum value for T (or θ) to be plotted, Tmax is the maximum value for T (or θ) to be plotted, and Tstep is the increase in T (or θ) for each point plotted. The period of the polar equation being graphed is a sufficient range for Tmin and Tmax values.

Example 1

Graph the polar equation $r = 2 \cos \theta$ in the viewing window $[-5, 5]$ by $[-3, 3]$ with a scale factor of 1 for both axes and Tmin $= 0$, Tmax $= 3.1416$, and Tstep $= 0.05$.

We can convert the polar equation into parametric form by substituting $2 \cos \theta$ for r in the equations $x = r \cos \theta$ and $y = r \sin \theta$. This produces the equations $x = (2 \cos \theta) \cos \theta$ and $y = (2 \cos \theta) \sin \theta$, which we can enter into the graphing calculator.

TI-81: [Y=] [(] 2 [COS] [XIT] [)] [COS]
[XIT] [ENTER] [(] 2 [COS]
[XIT] [)] [SIN] [XIT] [GRAPH]

The graph appears to be an ellipse, but pressing [ZOOM] 5 to graph the equation squarely shows that it is actually a circle with radius 2 and center at (1, 0).

You can also read both the rectangular and polar coordinates of a graph by using the [MODE] key and the arrow keys to highlight "Rect" to read the rectangular coordinates, and "Polar" to read the polar coordinates. Pressing the [TRACE] key to trace along a graph will tell you which coordinates are currently being read.

INTRODUCING THE LESSON

Objective Graph polar equations and read polar coordinates on a TI-81 graphing calculator.

Motivating the Lesson

This lesson provides students with the opportunity to see how important the equations that transform polar coordinates into rectangular coordinate are. A polar graph cannot be obtained until you make the transformation of coordinates.

TEACHING THE LESSON

Teaching Tip Not all graphing calculators (for example, Casio *fx*-7000) have the ability to graph parametric equations. If students do not have a TI-81 calculator, have them check their owner's manuals to see if their calculator has parametric capabilities. The Casio *fx*-7700 does not require parametrics to graph polar equations.

More Examples

Graph r = 2 cos 3θ.

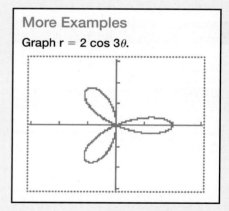

Teaching Tip The selection of Tmax will take some thought. Ask students to graph the equation in Example 1 with Tmax $= 5\pi$, Tmax $= \pi$, and Tmax $= 2\pi$. Ask them to describe the graphs they obtain with each setting.

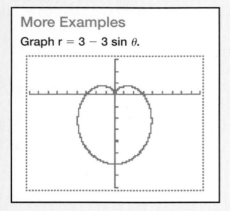
Example 2

Graph the polar equation $r = \dfrac{3}{\sin \theta}$ in the viewing window $[-5, 5]$ by $[-5, 5]$ with scale factors of 1 for both axes and Tmin = 0, Tmax = 2π, and Tstep = 0.05.

Converting into parametric form produces the equations $x = \dfrac{3 \cos \theta}{\sin \theta}$ and $y = 3$.

TI-81: Y= 3 COS X|T ÷ SIN
X|T ENTER 3 GRAPH

Graphing the equation shows that the graph is a line.

There are several different types of curves that can be formed by graphing polar equations.

Example 3

Graph the polar equation $r = 8 \cos 4\theta$ in the standard viewing window with scale factors of 1 for both axes and Tmin = 0, Tmax = 6.2832, and Tstep = 0.05.

Converting the equations into parametric form produces the equations $x = (8 \cos 4\theta) \cos \theta$ and $y = (8 \cos 4\theta) \sin \theta$.

TI-81: Y= ((8 COS 4 X|T))
COS X|T ENTER ((8
COS 4 X|T)) SIN X|T
GRAPH

The graph is an eight-petaled rose with its center at the origin.

You can experiment with Tmin, Tmax, and Tstep values to get an idea as to how they affect the graph of a polar equation. For instance, in Example 3, changing Tmax to π will only produce half of the rose, and changing Tstep to 1 will completely distort the graph because only 7 points will be plotted, namely $t = 0, 1, 2, 3, 4, 5,$ and 6.

EXERCISES   1–8. See margin.

Convert each equation into its equivalent parametric form and graph each equation on a TI-81 graphing calculator. Then sketch the graph on a piece of paper.

1. $r = 0.50\theta, 0 \leq \theta \leq 8\pi$
2. $r = 3\sqrt{\cos 2\theta}, 0 \leq \theta \leq 2\pi$
3. $r = 6 + 6 \sin \theta, 0 \leq \theta \leq 2\pi$
4. $r = 7 + 4 \cos \theta, 0 \leq \theta \leq 2\pi$
5. $r = 8 \sin 4\theta, 0 \leq \theta \leq 2\pi$
6. $r = 4\sqrt{\sin 2\theta}, 0 \leq \theta \leq 2\pi$
7. $r = 1 + 2 \sin \theta, 0 \leq \theta \leq 2\pi$
8. $r = 10 + 10 \cos \theta, 0 \leq \theta \leq 2\pi$

Graphs of Polar Equations

NCTM Standards: 1–6, 8

Objective
9–2

After studying this lesson, you should be able to:
- graph polar equations.

Application

A nautilus is a mollusk native to the southern Pacific and Indian Oceans. Inside its shell are spiraling chambers that appear to be lined with a pearl-like substance. The chambers are connected by a tube that absorbs gases from the chambers allowing the shell to act as a float.

Curves like the one suggested in this shell are called **classical curves** and can be graphed using polar coordinates.

Polar graphs can be classified in families. The graphs below show the parent graphs of $r = \sin\theta$ and $r = \cos\theta$.

$r = \sin\theta$

$r = \cos\theta$

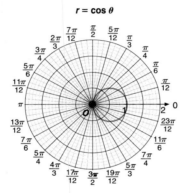

Notice that both of these parent graphs are circles with a diameter of 1 unit. Both pass through the origin. As with the families of graphs you studied in Chapter 3, you can alter the position and shape of the graph by multiplying the function by a number or by adding to it. You can also multiply θ by a number or add a number to it in order to alter the graph. However, the changes in the graphs of polar equations can be quite different from those you studied in Chapter 3.

Lesson Resources

- Practice Master 9–2
- Enrichment Master 9–2
- Evaluation Master, Quiz A, p. 113
- Technology Master, p. 18

 Transparency 9–2 contains the 5-Minute Check and a teaching aid for this lesson.

INTRODUCING THE LESSON

5-Minute Check

(over Lesson 9–1)

For Exercises 1–3, see graph below.

1. Graph the points $A\left(3, \frac{\pi}{4}\right)$ and $B\,(-4, -60°)$.
2. Graph $\theta = -210°$.
3. Graph $r = 2$.

2–3.

4. Point P has polar coordinates (3, 60°). Name three other pairs of polar coordinates that represent P. Suppose $-360° \le \theta \le 360°$.
(3, –300°), (–3, 240°), (–3, –120°)

Motivating the Lesson

Have students work in cooperative groups. Have them use their calculators to make a table of values for the equation $r = \sin\theta$, plot the ordered pairs (r, θ) on the polar plane, and describe the graph.
The graph is a circle of diameter 1 with center at (0.5, 90°).

ALTERNATE TEACHING STRATEGIES

Using Discussion

The entire graph $r = \sin\theta$ can be drawn easily, but the graph $r = \theta$ spirals outward without bound, so only a portion of it can be drawn. Ask students to explain the distinction between the equations that leads to this difference in the graphs. As θ increases, $r = \theta$ increases. Sin θ, however, is never greater than 1 or less than –1, so $r = \sin\theta$ will never exceed those limits.

Using Critical Thinking

In rectangular coordinates, if a vertical line intersects a graph in more than one point, the graph is not the graph of a function. Ask students to give a counterexample showing that the vertical line test is not valid in polar coordinates. The sine is a function but since the graph of $r = \sin\theta$ is a circle, a vertical line will intersect the graph in two points.

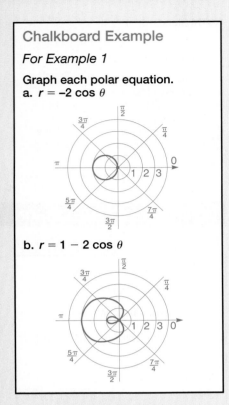
Teaching Tip After Example 1a, point out that the coefficient A in $r = A \sin \theta$ or $r = A \cos \theta$ has the effect of expanding (or contracting, if $A < 1$) the sine or cosine circle by a factor of A.

Example 1

Graph each polar equation.
a. $r = 6 \sin \theta$

a. Make a table of values. Round the values of r to the nearest tenth. Graph the ordered pairs and connect them with a smooth curve.

θ	$\sin \theta$	$6 \sin \theta$	(r, θ)
0°	0	0	(0, 0°)
30°	0.5	3	(3, 30°)
60°	0.9	5.4	(5.4, 60°)
90°	1	6	(6, 90°)
120°	0.9	5.4	(5.4, 120°)
150°	0.5	3	(3, 150°)
180°	0	0	(0, 180°)
210°	−0.5	−3	(−3, 210°)
240°	−0.9	−5.4	(−5.4, 240°)
270°	−1	−6	(−6, 270°)
300°	−0.9	−5.4	(−5.4, 300°)
330°	−0.5	−3	(−3, 330°)
360°	0	0	(0, 360°)

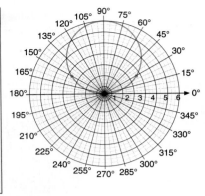

The complete graph is determined by values for θ between 0° and 180°. The graph of $r = 6 \cos \theta$ looks like the parent graph of $r = \sin \theta$, but has a diameter 6 times that of the parent.

b. $r = 2 + 3 \cos \theta$

b.

θ	$2 + 3 \cos \theta$	(r, θ)
0	5	(5, 0)
$\frac{\pi}{6}$	4.6	$(4.6, \frac{\pi}{6})$
$\frac{\pi}{3}$	3.5	$(3.5, \frac{\pi}{3})$
$\frac{\pi}{2}$	2	$(2, \frac{\pi}{2})$
$\frac{2\pi}{3}$	0.5	$(0.5, \frac{2\pi}{3})$
$\frac{5\pi}{6}$	−0.6	$(-0.6, \frac{5\pi}{6})$
π	−1	$(-1, \pi)$
$\frac{7\pi}{6}$	−0.6	$(-0.6, \frac{7\pi}{6})$
$\frac{4\pi}{3}$	0.5	$(0.5, \frac{4\pi}{3})$
$\frac{3\pi}{2}$	2	$(2, \frac{3\pi}{2})$
$\frac{5\pi}{3}$	3.5	$(3.5, \frac{5\pi}{3})$
$\frac{11\pi}{6}$	4.6	$(4.6, \frac{11\pi}{6})$
2π	5	$(5, 2\pi)$

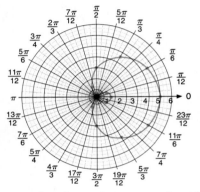

Notice that the graph is symmetric with respect to the polar axis, as is its parent graph. However, the appearance of a small loop inside the outside graph, which is not a circle, does not resemble the parent graph. This graph is called a limaçon.

In Lesson 9-1, you studied two types of polar equations involving constants, for example, $r = 6$ and $\theta = \frac{\pi}{3}$. Another polar equation of this type is $r = n\theta$, where n is a real number and θ is expressed in terms of radians. *In order to determine the exact shape of the graph of a polar equation, you may need to graph many polar coordinates.*

Chalkboard Example

For Example 2

Graph $r = -\theta$.

Example 2

Graph $r = 2\theta$.

θ	2θ	(r, θ)
$\frac{\pi}{6}$	$\frac{\pi}{3}$	$\left(1, \frac{\pi}{6}\right)$
$\frac{\pi}{3}$	$\frac{2\pi}{3}$	$\left(2.1, \frac{\pi}{3}\right)$
$\frac{\pi}{2}$	π	$\left(3.1, \frac{\pi}{2}\right)$
$\frac{2\pi}{3}$	$\frac{4\pi}{3}$	$\left(4.2, \frac{2\pi}{3}\right)$
$\frac{5\pi}{6}$	$\frac{5\pi}{3}$	$\left(5.2, \frac{5\pi}{6}\right)$
π	2π	$(6.3, \pi)$
$\frac{7\pi}{6}$	$\frac{7\pi}{3}$	$\left(7.3, \frac{7\pi}{6}\right)$
$\frac{4\pi}{3}$	$\frac{8\pi}{3}$	$\left(8.4, \frac{4\pi}{3}\right)$
$\frac{3\pi}{2}$	3π	$\left(9.4, \frac{3\pi}{2}\right)$
$\frac{5\pi}{3}$	$\frac{10\pi}{3}$	$\left(10.5, \frac{5\pi}{3}\right)$
$\frac{11\pi}{6}$	$\frac{11\pi}{3}$	$\left(11.5, \frac{11\pi}{6}\right)$
2π	4π	$(12.6, 2\pi)$

In this example, θ must be expressed in radians since r is a real number.

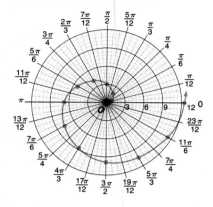

This type of graph is called the spiral of Archimedes, named after the Greek mathematician who discovered it.

The limaçon in Example 1b and the *spiral of Archimedes* in Example 2 are two of the classical curves, which can be formed by graphing polar equations. The equations that distinguish these and other classical curves are listed in the chart below.

Classical Curves		
Curve Name	**Polar Equation**	**General Graph**
rose	$r = a \cos n\theta$ $r = a \sin n\theta$ *n is a positive integer.*	

LESSON 9-2   GRAPHS OF POLAR EQUATIONS   477

lemniscate *(pronounced lehm NIHS kuht)*	$r^2 = a^2 \cos 2\theta$ $r^2 = a^2 \sin 2\theta$	
limaçon *(pronounced lee muh SOHN)*	$r = a + b\cos\theta$ $r = a + b\sin\theta$	
cardioid *(pronounced KARD ee oyd)*	$r = a + a\cos\theta$ $r = a + a\sin\theta$	
spiral of Archimedes *(pronounced ar kih MEED eez)*	$r = a\theta$	

As with the equations you have graphed in a rectangular coordinate system, you can graph more than one polar equation on the same polar coordinate system. However, the points where the graphs intersect do not always represent common solutions to equations, since each point can be represented by infinitely many polar coordinates.

Example 3

Graph the system of polar equations below.

$r = 3\cos 2\theta$

$r = -3$

Then solve the system and compare the common solutions to the points of intersection of the polar graphs.

Graph each of the polar equations. The graphs intersect at the points with coordinates $(3, 0°), (3, 90°), (3, 180°)$, and $(3, 270°)$.

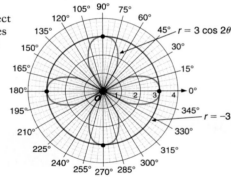

To solve the system of equations, substitute -3 for r in the first equation and solve for θ.

$3\cos 2\theta = -3$

$\cos 2\theta = -1$

$2\theta = \text{Arccos}(-1)$

$2\theta = 180° \text{ or } -180°$

$\theta = 90° \text{ or } -90°$

Thus, the common solutions are $(-3, 90°)$ and $(-3, -90°)$.

Now compare the common solutions to the coordinates of the points of intersection of the graphs.

The point represented by $(3, 90°)$ is the same point represented by $(-3, -90°)$. The point at $(3, 270°)$ is the same as the point at $(-3, 90°)$. So the other two points of intersection do not represent common solutions to the polar equations.

Polar equations can be written in parametric form and graphed on a graphing calculator. The parametric equations for a polar equation $r = f(\theta)$ are $x = f(t) \cos t$ and $y = f(t) \sin t$. For example, the parametric equations for $r = 3 \cos 2\theta$ are $x = 3 \cos 2t \cos t$ and $y = 3 \cos 2t \sin t$.

EXPLORATION: Graphing Calculator

Graph $r = 2 + 2 \sin \theta$ and $r = 2 \sin 2\theta$ on a graphing calculator and determine the common solutions.

1. Set the mode and the viewing window by using the settings below.

RAD MODE	PARAM MODE	POLAR MODE
TMIN: 0	TMAX: 7	TSCL: 0.05
XMIN: -4	XMAX: 5	XSCL: 1
YMIN: -2	YMAX: 5	YSCL: 1

2. Write the polar equations in parametric form. The parametric equations for $r = 2 + 2 \sin \theta$ are $x = (2 + 2 \sin t) \cos t$ and $y = (2 + 2 \sin t) \sin t$ and the parametric equations for $r = 2 \sin 2\theta$ are $x = 2 \sin 2t \cos t$ and $y = 2 \sin 2t \sin t$. Press the $\boxed{Y=}$ key and enter the equations.

3. Press $\boxed{\text{GRAPH}}$.

4. Press $\boxed{\text{TRACE}}$ and position the cursor over each point of intersection. The up and down arrows will allow us to move back and forth between the two graphs. If the r- and θ-coordinates of the points of intersection are the same for both graphs, then the point is a common solution to the system of equations. What is the common solution to this system of equations? $(1.3, -2.8)$

CHECKING FOR UNDERSTANDING

Communicating Mathematics

Read and study the lesson to answer each question.

1. **Determine** which of the classical polar curves best represents the shape of the chambered nautilus. the spiral of Archimedes

2. **Explain** why you cannot use a polar coordinate plane scaled in degrees in order to graph $r = a\theta$. r must be a real number, thus requiring the use of radians, which are real numbers.

LESSON 9-2   GRAPHS OF POLAR EQUATIONS   479

RETEACHING THE LESSON

If students have difficulty drawing polar graphs by using tables of values, suggest that they use the "wheel-and-spoke" graphing method. Have them begin at 0° and work their way counterclockwise around the circle. At each spoke (multiples of 30° or 45°), have them find the value of r and plot the point (r, θ).

Using Technology

Ask students to graph $r = \sin \theta$ using parametric equations, to confirm the method for changing polar equations to parametric equations. Enter the equations $x = \sin t \cos t$ and $y = \sin^2 t$.

EVALUATING THE LESSON

Checking for Understanding

Exercises 1–5 are designed to help you assess students' understanding through reading, writing, speaking, and modeling. You should work through Exercises 1–2 with your students and then monitor their work on Exercises 3–5.

Closing the Lesson

Modeling Activity   Have students identify the curves represented by the following equations, explaining their method. Then have them sketch the curves.
$r = 2 + 3 \cos \theta$ limaçon
$r = 4\theta$ spiral
$r = 5 + 5 \sin \theta$ cardioid
$r = 3 \sin 2\theta$ rose
$r^2 = 4 \cos 2\theta$ lemniscate

Practice Masters Booklet, p. 58

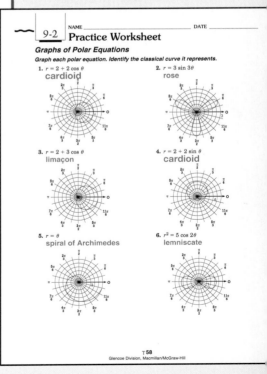

Homework Exercises

Assignment Guide

Average: 6–18, 21, 24, 27, 30–34
Enriched: 9–17 odd, 19–34

The red A, B, and C flags, printed only in the Teacher's Wraparound Edition, indicate the level of difficulty of the exercises.

Chapter 9, Quiz A (Lessons 9–1 through 9–2) is available in the *Evaluation Masters*, p. 113.

Exercise Note

In Exercises 18–20, point out that points of intersection of two graphs do not necessarily represent common solutions. Intersection points must be checked in the equations to see if they satisfy them.

Using Technology

Exercises 21–23 require the use of graphing calculators to estimate the solutions for each system of equations. Have students experiment with different ranges and with the ZOOM feature to find the best estimates.

Additional Answers

3.

4.

3–4. See margin for graphs.

Guided Practice

Copy and complete the table for each polar equation. Then graph the equation.

3. $r = 8 \cos \theta$

θ	$\cos \theta$	$8 \cos \theta$	(r, θ)
0°	1	8	$(8, 0°)$
30°	0.9	6.9	$(6.9, 30°)$
60°	0.5	4	$(4, 30°)$
90°	0	0	$(0, 90°)$
120°	−0.5	−4	$(−4, 120°)$
150°	−0.9	−6.9	$(−6.9, 150°)$
180°	−1	−8	$(−8, 180°)$
210°	−0.9	−6.9	$(−6.9, 210°)$
240°	−0.5	−4	$(−4, 240°)$
270°	0	0	$(0, 270°)$
300°	0.5	4	$(4, 300°)$
330°	0.9	6.9	$(6.9, 330°)$

4. $r = 2 + 2 \sin \theta$

θ	$\sin \theta$	$2 + 2 \sin \theta$	(r, θ)
0°	0	2	$(2, 0°)$
30°	0.5	3	$(3, 30°)$
60°	0.9	3.7	$(3.7, 60°)$
90°	1	4	$(4, 90°)$
120°	0.9	3.7	$(3.7, 120°)$
150°	0.5	3	$(3, 150°)$
180°	0	2	$(2, 180°)$
210°	−0.5	1	$(1, 210°)$
240°	−0.9	0.3	$(0.3, 240°)$
270°	−1	0	$(0, 270°)$
300°	−0.9	0.3	$(03, 300°)$
330°	−0.5	1	$(1, 330°)$

5. Identify the classical curve that the graph of $r = 2 + 2 \sin \theta$ represents. cardioid

6–23. For graphs, see Teacher's Answer Key.

EXERCISES

Practice

Graph each polar equation. Identify the classical curve it represents.

6. $r = 6\theta$ spiral of Archimedes **7.** $r = \dfrac{\theta}{2}$ spiral of Archimedes **8.** $r = 5 + 2 \cos \theta$ limaçon

9. $r = 5 \sin 5\theta$ rose **10.** $r = 3 + 3 \sin \theta$ cardioid **11.** $r = 4 + 6 \cos \theta$ limaçon

12. $r = 5 \cos 2\theta$ rose **13.** $r^2 = 16 \cos 2\theta$ lemniscate **14.** $r^2 = 4 \sin 2\theta$ lemniscate

15. $r = 4 + 4 \sin \theta$ cardioid **16.** $r = 6 \cos 3\theta$ rose **17.** $r = 3 \cos 3\theta$ rose

Graph each system of equations. Solve the system and compare the common solutions to the points of intersection of the polar graphs. Assume $-2\pi \leq \theta \leq 2\pi$.

18. $\left(\dfrac{1}{2}, 30°\right)$, $\left(\dfrac{1}{2}, 150°\right)$

18. $r = \sin \theta$
$r = 1 - \sin \theta$

19. $r = 2\sqrt{3} \cos \theta$
$r = 2 \sin \theta$
$(\sqrt{3}, 60°), (-\sqrt{3}, 240°)$

20. $r = 4 \cos \theta$
$r = 2 \sin 90°$
$(2, 60°), (2, -60°)$

Graphing Calculator

Graph each system of equations using a graphing calculator. Then determine the common solutions. Round your answers to the nearest tenth. 21. (2.1, 0.8)

21. $r = 3 \sin \theta$
$r = 3 \cos \theta$

22. $r = 3 \sin \theta$
$r = 3 \sin 3\theta$

23. $r = 3 \cos \theta - 1$
$r = 3 \sin 2\theta$

22. $(0, 0), (2.0, 0.8), (2.1, 2.3)$ 23. $(3.0, -0.9), (1.8, 0.3), (3.0, 0.9), (2.2, -1.2)$

Critical Thinking

24. If the polar equation of a four-petaled rose can be generalized as $r = a \cos 2\theta$ or $r = a \sin 2\theta$, make a conjecture about the relationship between the value of a and the graph. length of petal = $|a|$ units

25. If the polar equation of a rose can be generalized as $r = a \cos n\theta$ or $r = a \sin n\theta$, make a conjecture about the relationship between the value of n and the graph.

26. What effect does replacing the cosine function by the sine function have on the graph of a polar rose such as $r = a \cos n\theta$? 25–26. See margin.

480   CHAPTER 9   POLAR COORDINATES AND COMPLEX NUMBERS

---

25. If *n* is odd, the rose has *n* petals, each of which is traced twice from 0 to 2π.
If *n* is even, the rose has 2*n* petals, each of which is traced once from 0 to 2π.

26. The graph is the same as that of the sine but rotated counterclockwise.

Applications and Problem Solving

27. Toys In the 1960s, the Kenner Toy Company introduced an art toy, called a Spirograph®, in which a child guided a notched circle inside a notched circular frame to create designs. The type of design created depended on the size of the circle chosen and the size of the frame. One of the designs you could create can also be generated by graphing $r^2 = \sin 10\theta$. Graph the design. Then describe the shape of the graph. *See margin.*

28. History In addition to his other mathematical accomplishments, the French mathematician Pierre de Fermat (1601–1665) is credited with discovering a spiral defined by the equation $r^2 = \theta$. Graph Fermat's spiral. *See margin.*

29. Research Use a dictionary or encyclopedia to investigate the origin of the terms *lemniscate, limaçon,* and *cardioid.* In your own words, explain why you think these names were chosen for the classical curves. *See students' work.*

Mixed Review

30. Surveying To find the height of a mountain peak, points A and B were located on a plain in line with the peak and the angle of elevation was measured from each point. The angle at A was $36°40'$, and the angle at B was $21°10'$. The distance from A to B was 570 feet. How high is the peak above the level of the plain? **(Lesson 5-5)**

≈ 460 ft

31. $\dfrac{-\sqrt{6} - \sqrt{2}}{4}$

31. Use the sum and difference identities to find the exact value of $\sin 255°$. **(Lesson 7-3)**

32. Find the inner product $(3, -2, 4) \cdot (1, -4, 0)$. Then state whether the vectors are perpendicular. Write *yes* or *no*. **(Lesson 8-4)** *11, no*

33. Name three other pairs of polar coordinates that represent the point at $(10, -20°)$. Suppose $-360° \le \theta \le 360°$. **(Lesson 9-1)** *$(10, 340°), (-10, -200°), (-10, 160°)$*

34. College Entrance Exam What is the least positive number greater than 2 that has a remainder of 2 when it is divided by 3, 4, or 5? *62*

CASE STUDY FOLLOW-UP

Refer to Case Study 2: *Trashing the Planet*, on pages 959–961.
4. See students' work.

Use tracing paper to transfer the photographs of the holes in the ozone layer onto polar graph paper. *2. 1989: a lemniscate and two cardioids; 1991: a limaçon*

1. Use polar coordinates to describe changes in the hole from 1989 to 1991. Estimate the increases in the radius and the area of the hole. *20%; 80%*
2. Describe the shapes of the holes in terms of classical curves.
3. How many more deaths due to skin cancer can be expected in the next 50 years as a result of the depletion of the ozone layer? *about 5.2 million*
4. **Research** Find out about changes in the ozone layer since the photos were taken. In a 1-page paper, describe the changes and current efforts to solve the problem.

EXTENDING THE LESSON

Math Power: Communication

Write a paragraph explaining why the point of intersection of two polar equations may not represent a common solution of the equations. Each point in the polar plane has infinitely many representations. Since a point of intersection represents two different equations, it may have two different representations, neither of which satisfies the other equation.

Case Study Follow-Up

This activity provides an opportunity to do research and apply mathematics in solving problems related to issues that may face students in their adult lives. Case Study 2 is located on pages 959-961.

Additional Answers

27.

a rose with 10 petals

28.

Enrichment Masters Booklet, p. 58

9-2 Enrichment Worksheet

Symmetry in Graphs of Polar Equations

It is sometimes helpful to analyze polar equations for certain properties that predict symmetry in the graph of the equation. The following rules guarantee the existence of symmetry in the graph. However, the graphs of some polar equations exhibit symmetry even though the rules do not predict it.

1. If replacing θ by $-\theta$ yields the same equation, then the graph of the equation is symmetric with respect to the line containing the polar axis (the x-axis in the rectangular coordinate system).
2. If replacing θ by $\pi - \theta$ yields the same equation, then the graph of the equation is symmetric with respect to the line $\theta = \frac{\pi}{2}$ (the y-axis in the rectangular coordinate system).
3. If replacing r by $-r$ yields the same equation, then the graph of the equation is symmetric with respect to the pole.

Example Identify the symmetry of and graph $r = 3 + 3 \sin \theta$. Since $\sin (\pi - \theta) = \sin \theta$, by rule 2 the graph is symmetric to the line $\theta = \frac{\pi}{2}$. Therefore, it is only necessary to plot points in the first and fourth quadrants.

θ	$3 + 3 \sin \theta$	r, θ
$-\frac{\pi}{2}$	0	$\left(-\frac{\pi}{2}, 0\right)$
$-\frac{\pi}{3}$	0.4	$\left(-\frac{\pi}{3}, 0.4\right)$
$-\frac{\pi}{6}$	1.5	$\left(-\frac{\pi}{6}, 1.5\right)$
0	3.0	$(0, 3.0)$
$\frac{\pi}{6}$	4.5	$\left(\frac{\pi}{6}, 4.5\right)$
$\frac{\pi}{3}$	5.6	$\left(\frac{\pi}{3}, 5.6\right)$
$\frac{\pi}{2}$	6.0	$\left(\frac{\pi}{2}, 6.0\right)$

The points in the second and third quadrants are found by using symmetry.
See students' graphs.

Identify the symmetry of and graph each polar equation on polar grid paper.

1. $r = 2 + 3 \cos \theta$ Symmetric with respect to polar axis
2. $r^2 = 4 \sin 2\theta$ Symmetric with respect to the pole

T58
Glencoe Division, Macmillan/McGraw-Hill

Objective This optional page shows how a computer BASIC program can be used to generate ordered pairs for a polar equation.

Teaching Suggestions

This program generates polar coordinates which can then be graphed by hand on polar graph paper. Point out that the program generates the second coordinate (the polar angle) in increments of $\frac{\pi}{12}$. The first coordinate r comes from substituting the value of the polar angle into the polar equation. To generate coordinates with increments smaller or larger than $\frac{\pi}{12}$ for the angle, change line 170.

For example, for increments of $\frac{\pi}{6}$, change line 170 to read

170 THETA = N/6*3.1415926.

Change line 180 to change the polar equation.

1.

2.

3.

Technology

► **BASIC**
Spreadsheets
Software

Graphing Polar Equations

Polar equations are often used to represent complex graphs, such as roses and spirals. Some computer-generated animations use these graphs to create visual effects.

The BASIC program shown at the right will generate twenty-five ordered pairs for the polar equation $r = 2 \cos\theta + 3 \sin\theta$. You can plot the points and connect them with a smooth curve to graph the equation.

```
120  PRINT "PLOT POINTS, THEN CONNECT"
130  PRINT "THEM IN THE ORDER SHOWN."
140  PRINT "R", "THETA"
150  PRINT "-------", "-------"
160  FOR N=0 TO 24
170  THETA=N/12*3.1415926
180  R=2*COS(THETA)+3*SIN(THETA)
190  PRINT R, N; "PI/12"
200  IF N<>12 THEN GOTO 230
210  PRINT "PRESS [ENTER] FOR MORE...";
220  INPUT A$
230  NEXT N
240  END
```

```
PLOT POINTS, THEN CONNECT
THEM IN THE ORDER SHOWN.
R                    THETA
-------              -------
2                    0 PI/12
2.708309             1 PI/12
3.232051             2 PI/12
3.535534             3 PI/12
3.598076             4 PI/12
3.415416             5 PI/12
3                    6 PI/12
2.38014              7 PI/12
1.598076             8 PI/12
.7071068             9 PI/12
-.2320506            10 PI/12
-1.155394            11 PI/12
-2                   12 PI/12
PRESS [ENTER] FOR MORE...
-2.708309            13 PI/12
-3.232051            14 PI/12
```

To execute the program, type RUN and then press [Enter]. Part of the program output is shown at the left. You can change line 180 of the program to generate ordered pairs for any polar equation of the form $r = f(\theta)$. The graph of $r = 2 \cos\theta + 3 \sin\theta$ is shown below.

EXERCISES   1–4. See margin.

Use the program to generate ordered pairs for each equation. Then sketch the graph.

1. $r = \cos\theta - 2 \sin\theta$

2. $r = 4 - 3 \sin\theta$

3. $r = \cos\left(2\theta + \frac{\pi}{3}\right)$

4. $r = 0.75\theta$

4.

482   CHAPTER 9   POLAR COORDINATES AND COMPLEX NUMBERS

Polar and Rectangular Coordinates

Objective
9–3

After studying this lesson, you should be able to:
■ convert from polar coordinates to rectangular coordinates and vice versa.

NCTM Standards: 1–6, 8

Lesson Resources

- Practice Master 9–3
- Enrichment Master 9–3
- Activity Master, p. 25

 Transparency 9–3 contains the 5-Minute Check and a teaching aid for this lesson.

Application

In Lesson 9-1, we talked about longitude lines and latitude lines forming a polar coordinate system. However, when was the last time you saw a map of the world done on a polar plane? Instead, you have probably seen the land masses and waterways of the world portrayed on a rectangular system. On maps of this type, the actual shapes of Earth's features are distorted to fit the rectangular system.

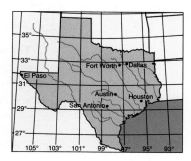

While some real-world phenomena cannot be modeled easily using a rectangular coordinate system, it is possible to write polar coordinates as rectangular coordinates and vice versa.

INTRODUCING THE LESSON

5-Minute Check
(over Lesson 9–2)

Identify the classical curve represented by each equation.
1. $r = 2\theta$ spiral
2. $r = 2 \sin 3\theta$ rose
3. $r = 4 + 4 \cos \theta$ cardioid
4. Graph $r = 2 \sin \theta$

Suppose a rectangular coordinate system is superimposed on a polar coordinate system so that the origins coincide and the x-axis aligns with the polar axis. Let P be any point in the plane. In polar coordinates, P is identified by (r, θ). In rectangular coordinates, P is identified by (x, y). Trigonometric functions can be used to find the rectangular coordinates if you know the polar coordinates. *You will develop this formula in Exercise 37.*

Conversion from Polar Coordinates to Rectangular Coordinates

The rectangular coordinates (x, y) of a point named by the polar coordinates (r, θ) can be found by using the following formulas.

$$x = r \cos \theta$$
$$y = r \sin \theta$$

LESSON 9-3 POLAR AND RECTANGULAR COORDINATES 483

Motivating the Lesson

Sketch a 30°–60° right triangle on the chalkboard. Ask students to evaluate each expression.

a. $2 \cos 30°$ $\sqrt{3}$
b. $2 \sin 30°$ 1

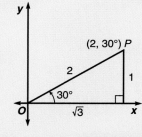

Ask students to relate the values of the expressions to the rectangular coordinates of P. They are the x- and y-coordinates of the point.

ALTERNATE TEACHING STRATEGIES

Using Cooperative Groups

Have each student give the polar coordinates of a point to another student. The second student converts the coordinates to rectangular form and passes them to a third student, who converts them back to polar form. Students should now compare the two polar forms and, if they are not equal, find where the error occurred. Repeat beginning with rectangular coordinates.

Using Models

The orbit of the planet Mercury can be modeled by the polar equation $r = \dfrac{3.4 \times 10^7}{1 - 0.2 \cos \theta}$, where r is Mercury's distance from the sun in miles. Ask students to find Mercury's greatest and least distances from the sun.
4.3×10^7 miles; 2.8×10^7 miles

Example 1

Find the rectangular coordinates of each point.

a. $A\left(-2, \dfrac{3\pi}{4}\right)$

a. For $\left(-2, \dfrac{3\pi}{4}\right)$, $r = -2$ and $\theta = \dfrac{3\pi}{4}$.

$$x = r\cos\theta \qquad\qquad y = r\sin\theta$$
$$= -2\cos\left(\frac{3\pi}{4}\right) \qquad = -2\sin\left(\frac{3\pi}{4}\right)$$
$$= -2\left(-\frac{\sqrt{2}}{2}\right) \qquad = -2\left(\frac{\sqrt{2}}{2}\right)$$
$$= \sqrt{2} \qquad\qquad\quad = -\sqrt{2}$$

The rectangular coordinates of A are $(\sqrt{2}, -\sqrt{2})$ or about $(1.41, -1.41)$.

b. $B(6, -50°)$

b. $x = r\cos\theta \qquad\qquad\qquad y = r\sin\theta$
    $= 6\cos(-50°) \qquad\qquad\quad = 6\sin(-50°)$
    $= 6\cos 50° \quad cos\,(-50°) = \cos 50° \qquad = 6(-\sin 50°) \quad sin(-50°) = -\sin 50°$
    $\approx 6(0.64279) \qquad\qquad\qquad \approx 6(-0.76604)$
    $\approx 3.86 \qquad\qquad\qquad\qquad \approx -4.60$

The rectangular coordinates of B are about $(3.86, -4.60)$.

If a point is named by the rectangular coordinates (x, y), you can find the corresponding polar coordinates by using the Pythagorean theorem and the Arctangent function. Since the Arctangent function only determines angles in the first or fourth quadrants, you must add π radians to the value of θ for points with coordinates (x, y) that lie in the second or third quadrants.

When x is zero, $\theta = \pm\dfrac{\pi}{2}$. Why?

When $x > 0$, $\theta = $ Arctan $\dfrac{y}{x}$.

When $x < 0$, $\theta = $ Arctan $\dfrac{y}{x} + \pi$.

Conversion from Rectangular Coordinates to Polar Coordinates

The polar coordinates (r, θ) of a point named by the rectangular coordinates (x, y) can be found by the following formulas.

$$r = \sqrt{x^2 + y^2}$$
$$\theta = \text{Arctan }\frac{y}{x}, \text{ when } x > 0$$
$$\theta = \text{Arctan }\frac{y}{x} + \pi, \text{ when } x < 0$$

In this formula, θ is expressed in radians.

484 CHAPTER 9 POLAR COORDINATES AND COMPLEX NUMBERS

Example 2

You can review the inverse trigonometric functions in Lesson 6-4.

Find the polar coordinates of $C(-3, 5)$.

$$r = \sqrt{x^2 + y^2} \qquad \theta = \text{Arctan}\,\frac{y}{x} + \pi \quad (x < 0)$$

$$= \sqrt{(-3)^2 + 5^2} \qquad = \text{Arctan}\left(\frac{5}{-3}\right) + \pi$$

$$= \sqrt{34} \qquad\qquad \approx 2.11$$

$$\approx 5.83$$

The polar coordinates of C are $(5.83, 2.11)$.

Other polar coordinates can also represent this point.

Equations expressed in rectangular form can also be written as polar equations and vice versa.

Example 3

Write the rectangular equation $x^2 + y^2 = 25$ in polar form.

$$x^2 + y^2 = 25$$
$$(r\cos\theta)^2 + (r\sin\theta)^2 = 25 \qquad x = r\cos\theta, y = r\sin\theta$$
$$r^2(\cos^2\theta + \sin^2\theta) = 25$$
$$r^2 = 25 \qquad \cos^2\theta + \sin^2\theta = 1$$
$$r = \pm 5$$

The polar equation is $r = 5$ or $r = -5$.

Polar equations are excellent models for natural phenomena.

Example 4

APPLICATION

Geology

A drumlin is an elliptical, streamlined hill composed of till deposited beneath glacial ice. In 1959, Richard J. Chorley concluded that the shape of a drumlin could best be modeled by the petal of a rose curve. The equation for a drumlin can be expressed as $r = \ell \cos k\theta$ for $\frac{-\pi}{2k} \leq \theta \leq \frac{\pi}{2k}$, where ℓ is the length of the drumlin and $k > 1$ is a parameter that is the ratio of the length to the width. Chorley's analysis revealed that the area covered by a drumlin was approximated by $A = \frac{\ell^2\pi}{4k}$. Find the area in square meters of a drumlin modeled by the equation $r = 420\cos 3\theta$.

In the equation $r = 420\cos 3\theta$, $\ell = 420$ and $k = 3$. $\quad r = \ell \cos k\theta$

$$A = \frac{\ell^2\pi}{4k}$$

$$= \frac{420^2\pi}{4(3)}$$

$$= 46{,}181.41201$$

The area of this drumlin is about $46{,}181.4$ square meters.

LESSON 9-3   POLAR AND RECTANGULAR COORDINATES   485

EVALUATING THE LESSON

Checking for Understanding

Exercises 1–13 are designed to help you assess students' understanding through reading, writing, speaking, and modeling. You should work through Exercises 1–2 with your students and then monitor their work on Exercises 3–13.

Closing the Lesson

Writing Activity   Have each student write the polar coordinates of one point and the rectangular coordinates of another on a sheet of paper. Students exchange papers and convert the coordinates of each point into the opposite coordinate system.

APPLYING THE LESSON

Homework Exercises

Assignment Guide

Average: 14–34, 36, 38, 41–46
Enriched: 17–33, 35, 37, 39–46

The red A, B, and C flags, printed only in the Teacher's Wraparound Edition, indicate the level of difficulty of the exercises.

Practice Masters Booklet, p. 59

NAME _____   DATE _____

9-3 Practice Worksheet

Polar and Rectangular Coordinates

Find the polar coordinates of each point with the given rectangular coordinates.
1. $(0, 4)$ 2. $\left(\frac{1}{2}, -\frac{\sqrt{3}}{2}\right)$ 3. $\left(-\frac{\sqrt{3}}{2}, \frac{1}{2}\right)$
$\left(4, \frac{\pi}{2}\right)$ $\left(1, -\frac{\pi}{3}\right)$ $\left(1, \frac{5\pi}{6}\right)$

4. $(4, 0)$ 5. $(-1, -\sqrt{3})$ 6. $(2, 2)$
$(4, 0)$ $\left(2, \frac{4\pi}{3}\right)$ $\left(2\sqrt{2}, \frac{\pi}{4}\right)$

Find the rectangular coordinates of each point with the given polar coordinates.
7. $(6, 120°)$ 8. $(-4, 45°)$ 9. $(3, 300°)$
$(-3, 3\sqrt{3})$ $(-2\sqrt{2}, -2\sqrt{2})$ $\left(\frac{3}{2}, -\frac{3\sqrt{3}}{2}\right)$

10. $\left(4, \frac{\pi}{6}\right)$ 11. $\left(0, \frac{13\pi}{3}\right)$ 12. $\left(3, -\frac{3\pi}{4}\right)$
$(2\sqrt{3}, 2)$ $(0, 0)$ $\left(-\frac{3\sqrt{2}}{2}, -\frac{3\sqrt{2}}{2}\right)$

Write each rectangular equation in polar form.
13. $x^2 + y^2 = 9$ 14. $y = 3$
$r = \pm 3$ $r \sin\theta = 3$ or $r = 3 \csc\theta$

15. $x^2 - y^2 = 1$ 16. $x^2 + y^2 - 2y = 0$
$r^2 = \frac{1}{\cos 2\theta} = \sec 2\theta$ $r = 2\sin\theta$

Write each polar equation in rectangular form.
17. $r = 4$ 18. $\theta = -\frac{\pi}{3}$
$x^2 + y^2 = 16$ $y = -\sqrt{3}x$

19. $r\cos\theta = 5$ 20. $r = -3\sec\theta$
$x = 5$ $x = -3$

T59
Glencoe Division, Macmillan/McGraw-Hill

CHECKING FOR UNDERSTANDING

Communicating Mathematics

Read and study the lesson to answer each question. 2. Add π to the value of θ.

1. **Describe** any differences that appear in the graphs of the two polar equations found in Example 3. Since $r = \pm 5$, they are both circles of radius 5.

2. **Explain** how you compensate for an angle whose terminal side lies in the second or third quadrant when using the Arctan function to change from rectangular to polar coordinates.

Guided Practice

Find each value. Express θ in radians to the nearest hundredth.
3. Arctan 1 0.79 4. Arctan 4.5 1.35 5. Arctan $\sqrt{6}$ 1.18

Find the polar coordinates of each point with the given rectangular coordinates.
6. $(5, 12)$ $(13, 1.18)$ 7. $(-2, -2)$ $(2\sqrt{2}, 3.93)$ 8. $(-1, -3)$ $(\sqrt{10}, 4.39)$

Find the rectangular coordinates of each point with the given polar coordinates.
9. $\left(3, \frac{\pi}{2}\right)$ $(0, 3)$ 10. $\left(-2, \frac{\pi}{4}\right)$ $(-\sqrt{2}, -\sqrt{2})$ 11. $(2.5, 2)$ $(-1.04, 2.27)$

12. Write $x^2 + y^2 = 9$ in polar form. $r = 3$ or $r = -3$
13. Write $r = 7$ in rectangular form. $x^2 + y^2 = 49$

EXERCISES

Practice

Find the polar coordinates of each point with the given rectangular coordinates.

A
14. $(0, 1.5)$ $\left(1.5, \frac{\pi}{2}\right)$ 15. $(0, 3)$ $\left(3, \frac{\pi}{2}\right)$ 16. $\left(\frac{\sqrt{3}}{2}, \frac{1}{2}\right)$ $\left(1, \frac{\pi}{6}\right)$
17. $(2, 0)$ $(2, 0)$ 18. $(-0.25, 0)$ $(0.25, \pi)$ 19. $(-\sqrt{2}, -\sqrt{2})$ $\left(2, \frac{5\pi}{4}\right)$

Find the rectangular coordinates of each point with the given polar coordinates.
20. $(\sqrt{2}, 45°)$ $(1, 1)$ 21. $(5, 0.93)$ $(2.99, 4.01)$ 22. $(\sqrt{29}, -1.19)$ $(2, -5)$
23. $(\sqrt{2}, 4.39)$ $(-0.45, -1.34)$ 24. $(\sqrt{13}, -0.59)$ $(3.00, -2.01)$ 25. $(3.464, 2.09)$ $(-1.72, 3.01)$

Write each rectangular equation in polar form.
26. $y = -5$ $r\sin\theta = -5, r = -5\csc\theta$ 27. $x = 10$ $r\cos\theta = 10, r = 10\sec\theta$

B
28. $x^2 + y^2 = 7$ $r = \sqrt{7}, r = -\sqrt{7}$ 29. $2x^2 + 2y^2 = 5y$ $r = \frac{5}{2}\sin\theta$

Write each polar equation in rectangular form.
30. $r = 12$ $x^2 + y^2 = 144$ 31. $\theta = -45°$ $y = -x$
32. $r\sin\theta = 4$ $y = 4$ 33. $r = -2\sec\theta$ $x = -2$

C
34. Write $x = y$ in polar form. $\theta = 45°$
35. Write $r = \cos\theta + \sin\theta$ in rectangular form. $x^2 + y^2 = x + y$

486   CHAPTER 9   POLAR COORDINATES AND COMPLEX NUMBERS

RETEACHING THE LESSON

Use the figures to clarify the relationships between polar and rectangular representations of the coordinates of a point.

Critical Thinking

36. Find the equation in rectangular form that has the same graph as the polar equation $r = \dfrac{5}{3 \cos \theta + 8 \sin \theta}$. Write the equation in standard form.
$3x + 8y - 5 = 0$

37. Write a convincing argument to prove that when converting polar coordinates to rectangular coordinates, the formulas $x = r \cos \theta$ and $y = r \sin \theta$ hold true. Include a labeled drawing in your answer. See margin.

Applications and Problem Solving

38. **Geology** Refer to Example 4. The area of a drumlin formed near Salamander Glacier in Glacier National Park in Montana is 4380 square yards. It has a length of 132 yards. Find its polar equation. $r = 132 \cos 3.124\theta$

39. **Geology** If a drumlin is modeled by the equation $r = \ell \cos 5\theta$ and has an area of 7542 square meters, find its length. about 219 meters

40. **Roller Coasters** The thrill of riding a roller coaster down a hill comes from the feeling that the rider and the train are indeed falling together. The seat force is all that riders feel as they sit in the car of the coaster. For example, a seat force of 1.00 means that a person feels 100% of their body weight resting on the seat. A seat force of 0.70W means that the person feels only 70% of their body weight, giving the sensation that they are coming out of their seat. The seat force down a slope can be described as $F = W \cos \theta$, where W is the person's weight and θ is the angle of the downslope. The maximum downslope being used to construct roller coasters today is 60°.

W cosine θ

a. Find the seat force for a hill with this downslope. $0.5W$

b. Describe what this seat force means and the effect the rider feels. The rider feels only half his or her weight and the rider comes out of his or her seat.

Mixed Review

41. Create a function of the form $y = f(x)$ whose graph resembles $y = x^3$, but has holes at $x = -2$ and $x = 0$. **(Lesson 3-4)**

41. $y = \dfrac{x^4(x + 2)}{x(x + 2)}$

42. Find the equation of the line that bisects the acute angle formed by the lines $x - y + 2 = 0$ and $y - 5 = 0$. **(Lesson 7-7)** $x - (1 + \sqrt{2})y + 2 + 5\sqrt{2} = 0$

43. State whether $\overrightarrow{AB}$ and $\overrightarrow{CD}$ are *equal, opposite, parallel,* or *none* of these for $A(-2, 5)$, $B(3, -1)$, $C(2, 6)$, and $D(7, 0)$. **(Lesson 8-1)** equal

44. Name three different pairs of polar coordinates that represent point R. Suppose $-360° \le \theta \le 360°$. **(Lesson 9-1)** $(90, 208°), (90, -152°), (-90, 28°)$

45. Graph $r = 12 \cos 2\theta$. **(Lesson 9-2)** See margin.

46. **College Entrance Exam** Compare quantities A and B. A
Write A if quantity A is greater.
Write B if quantity B is greater.
Write C if the quantities are equal.
Write D if there is not enough information to determine the relationship.

(A) $\dfrac{\frac{1}{8} + \frac{6}{4}}{\frac{3}{16}}$

(B) $\dfrac{\frac{2}{12} + \frac{1}{3}}{\frac{12}{16}}$

LESSON 9-3 POLAR AND RECTANGULAR COORDINATES 487

EXTENDING THE LESSON

Math Power: Problem Solving

Write the rectangular equation $\dfrac{x^2}{16} + \dfrac{y^2}{25} = 1$ in polar form.

$r = \sqrt{\dfrac{400}{9 \cos^2 \theta + 16}}$

Exercise Note

In Exercises 14–25, remind students that they can check their answers by converting them back into the original coordinate system and comparing the result with the coordinates of the point with which they began.

Additional Answer

37. Let the coordinates of $P(r, \theta)$ be (x, y).

$\sin \theta = \dfrac{y}{r}$, so $y = r \sin \theta$

$\cos \theta = \dfrac{x}{r}$, so $x = r \cos \theta$

45.

Enrichment Masters Booklet, p. 59

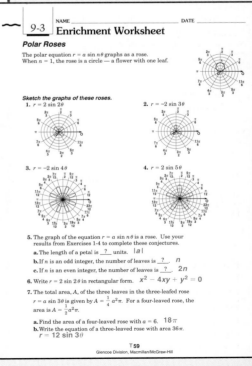

NAME _____ DATE _____

9-3 Enrichment Worksheet

Polar Roses

The polar equation $r = a \sin n\theta$ graphs as a rose. When $n = 1$, the rose is a circle — a flower with one leaf.

Sketch the graphs of these roses.
1. $r = 2 \sin 2\theta$ 2. $r = -2 \sin 3\theta$
3. $r = -2 \sin 4\theta$ 4. $r = 2 \sin 5\theta$

5. The graph of the equation $r = a \sin n\theta$ is a rose. Use your results from Exercises 1-4 to complete these conjectures.
a. The length of a petal is __?__ units. $|a|$
b. If n is an odd integer, the number of leaves is __?__. n
c. If n is an even integer, the number of leaves is __?__. $2n$
6. Write $r = 2 \sin 2\theta$ in rectangular form. $x^2 - 4xy + y^2 = 0$
7. The total area, A, of the three leaves in the three-leafed rose $r = a \sin 3\theta$ is given by $A = \frac{1}{4}a^2\pi$. For a four-leaved rose, the area is $A = \frac{1}{2}a^2\pi$.
a. Find the area of a four-leaved rose with $a = 6$. 18π
b. Write the equation of a three-leaved rose with area 36π. $r = 12 \sin 3\theta$

T 59
Glencoe Division, Macmillan/McGraw-Hill

LESSON 9–3 POLAR AND RECTANGULAR COORDINATES 487

NCTM Standards: 1–6, 8

Lesson Resources

- Practice Master 9–4
- Enrichment Master 9–4
- Evaluation Master, Quiz B, p. 113

 Transparency 9–4 contains the 5-Minute Check and a teaching aid for this lesson.

INTRODUCING THE LESSON

 5-Minute Check

(over Lesson 9–3)

1. Find the rectangular coordinates of $A\left(3, \frac{\pi}{4}\right)$.
$\left(\frac{3\sqrt{2}}{2}, \frac{3\sqrt{2}}{2}\right)$

2. Find the polar coordinates of $B(-2, 5)$. $(\sqrt{29}, 1.95)$

3. Write the rectangular equation $x^2 + y^2 = 100$ in polar form.
$r = \pm 10$

4. Write the polar equation $r \sin \theta = 5$ in rectangular form.
$y = 5$

Prerequisite Skills

Students should be familiar with the normal form of a linear equation.

1. Write the equation of a line in standard form for which the normal of length 3 makes an angle of 60° with the *x*-axis.
$x + \sqrt{3}y - 6 = 0$

2. Change $3x + 4y - 5 = 0$ to normal form. $\frac{3}{5}x + \frac{4}{5}y - 1 = 0$

Motivating the Lesson

Ask students to give the polar form of these linear equations.
a. $y = 0$ $\theta = 0$
b. $x = 0$ $\theta = \frac{\pi}{2}$

c. $y = x$ $\theta = \frac{\pi}{4}$

Point out that, in rectangular form, the above equations can be converted to polar form relatively easily. For most equations, the conversion is more difficult. This lesson will explain how to make the conversion.

9-4 Polar Form of a Linear Function

Objectives
After studying this lesson, you should be able to:
9–4A ▪ write the polar form of a linear equation, and
9–4B ▪ graph the polar form of a linear equation.

Application

In 1691, Jakob Bernouilli introduced the polar coordinate system. However, Isaac Newton was actually the first to think of using polar coordinates. In a paper entitled *Method of Fluxions*, written about 1671, he showed ten types of coordinate systems that could be used to graph equations. One of these systems was the polar coordinate system. The reason that Newton is usually not credited with the first published use of the coordinate system is that his paper was not published until 1736, nine years after his death.

Newton suggested that different coordinate systems were necessary to graph different types of equations. While using different coordinate systems may make graphing easier, it is also convenient to be able to graph equations of different forms on the same coordinate system.

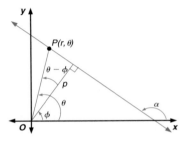

The polar form of the equation for line ℓ is closely related to the normal form, which is $x \cos \phi + y \sin \phi - p = 0$. But we have learned that $x = r \cos \theta$ and $y = r \sin \theta$. The polar form of the equation of line ℓ can be obtained by substituting these values into the normal form.

$$x \cos \phi + y \, \sin \, \phi - p = 0$$
$$(r \cos \theta) \cos \phi + (r \sin \theta) \sin \phi - p = 0$$
$$r(\cos \theta \cos \phi + \sin \theta \sin \phi) = p$$
$$r \cos(\theta - \phi) = p$$

$$\cos \theta \cos \phi + \sin \theta \sin \phi = \cos(\theta - \phi)$$

Polar Form of a Linear Equation

The polar form of a linear equation, where p is the length of the normal and ϕ is the positive angle between the positive *x*-axis and the normal, is
$$p = r \, \cos(\theta - \phi).$$

You can review the normal form of a linear equation in Lesson 7-6.

In the polar form of a linear equation, θ and r are variables, and p and ϕ are constants. Values for p and ϕ can be obtained from the normal form of the standard equation of a line. Remember to choose the value for ϕ according to the quadrant in which the normal lies.

488   CHAPTER 9   POLAR COORDINATES AND COMPLEX NUMBERS

ALTERNATE TEACHING STRATEGIES

Using Connections

Have students find p and θ for the equation $Ax + By + C = 0$ and then use them to write the polar form of the equation. They can use this as a formula for writing the polar form of the standard equation of a line.
$$\frac{C}{\sqrt{A^2 + B^2}} = r \cos \left(\theta - \arctan \frac{B}{A}\right)$$

Using Problem Solving

Ask students to write sec $\theta = r$ in rectangular form.
$$\sec \theta = r$$
$$\frac{1}{\cos \theta} = r$$
$$1 = r \cos \theta$$
$$1 = x$$

Example 1

Write each equation in polar form.
a. $2x + 3y - 1 = 0$

a. Write the equation in normal form.

$$\frac{Ax}{\pm\sqrt{A^2 + B^2}} + \frac{By}{\pm\sqrt{A^2 + B^2}} + \frac{C}{\pm\sqrt{A^2 + B^2}} = 0$$ *Normal form of the standard form, $Ax + By + C = 0$.*

We need to find the value of $\pm\sqrt{A^2 + B^2}$.

$\pm\sqrt{A^2 + B^2} = \pm\sqrt{2^2 + 3^2}$ or $\pm\sqrt{13}$ *Since C is negative, use $\sqrt{13}$.*

The normal form is $x\left(\dfrac{2}{\sqrt{13}}\right) + y\left(\dfrac{3}{\sqrt{13}}\right) - \dfrac{1}{\sqrt{13}} = 0$.

The general equation for the normal form is $x\cos\phi + y\sin\phi - p = 0$.

So, $\cos\phi = \dfrac{2}{\sqrt{13}}$, $\sin\phi = \dfrac{3}{\sqrt{13}}$, and $p = \dfrac{1}{\sqrt{13}}$ or $\dfrac{\sqrt{13}}{13}$.

Since $\cos\phi$ and $\sin\phi$ are positive, the normal is in the first quadrant. You can use a calculator to find ϕ.

$\phi = \arctan\dfrac{B}{A}$

$\quad = \arctan\dfrac{3}{2}$

$\quad = 56.30993247$ or about $56°$ *Round to the nearest degree.*

Substitute values for p and ϕ into the polar form.

$p = r\cos(\theta - \phi)$

$\dfrac{\sqrt{13}}{13} = r\cos(\theta - 56°)$

The polar form of $2x + 3y - 1 = 0$ is $\dfrac{\sqrt{13}}{13} = r\cos(\theta - 56°)$.

b. $3x - 4y + 5 = 0$

b. Write the equation in normal form.

$$\frac{3x}{-\sqrt{3^2 + (-4)^2}} + \frac{-4y}{-\sqrt{3^2 + (-4)^2}} + \frac{5}{-\sqrt{3^2 + (-4)^2}} = 0$$ *Since C is positive, use $-\sqrt{A^2 + B^2}$.*

The normal form is $-\dfrac{3}{5}x + \dfrac{4}{5}y - 1 = 0$. So, $\cos\phi = -\dfrac{3}{5}$, $\sin\phi = \dfrac{4}{5}$, and $p = 1$.

Since $\sin\phi$ is positive and $\cos\phi$ is negative, the normal is in the second quadrant.

$\phi = \arctan\dfrac{-4}{3}$

$\quad \approx -53°$ *Round to the nearest degree.*

To find the angle in the second quadrant, add $180°$ to ϕ.
$-53° + 180° = 127°$

Substitute the values for p and ϕ into the polar form.
$p = r\cos(\theta - \phi)$
$1 = r\cos(\theta - 127°)$

The polar form of $3x - 4y + 5 = 0$ is $1 = r\cos(\theta - 127°)$.

LESSON 9-4   POLAR FORM OF A LINEAR FUNCTION   489

Chalkboard Example

For Example 1

Write each equation in polar form.
a. $12x - 5y + 13 = 0$
$\quad 1 = r\cos(\theta - 157°)$
b. $x + 2y - 3 = 0$
$\quad \dfrac{3\sqrt{5}}{5} = r\cos(\theta - 63°)$

Teaching Tip   After Example 1, remind students of the slope-intercept form of a linear equation and ask them to give the slope and y-intercept of the equations in the example.

$-\dfrac{2}{3}, \dfrac{1}{3}; \dfrac{3}{4}, \dfrac{5}{4}$

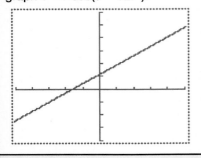
The polar form of a linear equation can be written as an equation in rectangular form.

Example 2

Write $1 = r \cos (\theta + 30°)$ in rectangular form.

$1 = r \cos (\theta + 30°)$

$1 = r(\cos \theta \cos 30° - \sin \theta \sin 30°)$ *Double-angle identity*

$1 = r \left(\dfrac{\sqrt{3}}{2} \cos \theta - \dfrac{1}{2} \sin \theta \right)$ $\cos 30° = \dfrac{\sqrt{3}}{2}$ and $\sin 30° = \dfrac{1}{2}$

$1 = \dfrac{\sqrt{3}}{2} \cdot r \cos \theta - \dfrac{1}{2} \cdot r \sin \theta$ *Multiply.*

$1 = \dfrac{\sqrt{3}}{2} x - \dfrac{1}{2} y$ $r \cos \theta = x$ and $r \sin \theta = y$

$2 = \sqrt{3} x - y$ *Multiply each side by 2.*

$0 = \sqrt{3} x - y - 2$

The rectangular form of $1 = r \cos (\theta + 30°)$ is $0 = \sqrt{3} x - y - 2$.

The polar form of a linear equation can be graphed by preparing a table of coordinates and then graphing the ordered pairs on the polar system.   *If the graphs of the ordered pairs do not lie in a straight line, then an error has occurred.*

Example 3

Graph the equation $3 = r \cos (\theta + 15°)$.

Write the equation in the form $r = \dfrac{3}{\cos(\theta + 15°)}$. Use your calculator to make a table of values. Graph the ordered pairs on a polar plane.

θ	0°	30°	60°	90°	120°	150°	180°
r	3.1	4.24	11.59	-11.59	-4.24	-3.1	-3.1

Additional Answers

7.

8.

Example 4

Use a graphing calculator to graph $3 = r\cos(\theta - 135°)$.

Write the equation in the form $r = \dfrac{3}{\cos(\theta - 135°)}$.

Convert the polar equation to its equivalent parametric form.

$$x = \frac{3}{\cos(t - 135°)} \cdot \cos t$$

$$y = \frac{3}{\cos(t - 135°)} \cdot \sin t$$

Before plotting these parametric equations, be sure to check your MODE and RANGE settings.

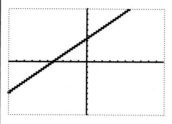

CHECKING FOR UNDERSTANDING

Communicating Mathematics

Read and study the lesson to answer each question.

1. **Explain** how you determine which value of ϕ you use when converting the polar form of an equation to rectangular form. See margin.

2. **Explain** why only values of θ from 0° through 180° were used for calculating values of r in Example 3. Because all possible values of $\cos\theta$ are contained in that range.

Guided Practice

Write the normal form of each linear equation. 5. $\dfrac{2\sqrt{10}}{5} = r\cos(\theta + 72°)$

3. $2x + 3y - 5 = 0$ $\dfrac{2x}{\sqrt{13}} + \dfrac{3y}{\sqrt{13}} - \dfrac{5}{\sqrt{13}} = 0$ 4. $2x - y = -6$ $\dfrac{-2x}{\sqrt{5}} + \dfrac{y}{\sqrt{5}} - \dfrac{6}{\sqrt{5}} = 0$

5. Write $x - 3y - 4 = 0$ in polar form. Round ϕ to the nearest degree.

6. Write $2 = r\cos\left(\theta - \dfrac{\pi}{4}\right)$ in rectangular form. $x + y - 2\sqrt{2} = 0$

7–8. For graphs, see margin.

Complete the table for each equation. Then graph the equation.

7. $r\cos(\theta + 10°) = 2$

θ	20°	25°	50°	60°
r	2.31	2.44	4	5.85

8. $r\cos(\theta + 20°) = 3$

θ	10°	25°	40°	60°
r	3.46	4.24	6	17.3

LESSON 9-4 POLAR FORM OF A LINEAR FUNCTION 491

Practice Masters Booklet, p. 60

Homework Exercises

Assignment Guide

Average: 9–23, 27, 30, 31, 33–37
Enriched: 13–26, 28–30, 32–37
All: Mid-Chapter Review, 1–6

The red A, B, and C flags, printed only in the Teacher's Wraparound Edition, indicate the level of difficulty of the exercises.

Chapter 9, Quiz B, (Lessons 9–3 through 9–4) is available in the *Evaluation Masters*, p. 113.

Exercise Note

In Exercises 23–26, students should find the rectangular form of the equation of each line using the methods of Chapter 1, then convert to polar form.

Using Technology

For Exercise 27, point out that students can use the guess-and-check strategy to find appropriate range settings. Begin with a wide general range, check the results, and gradually focus in on the desired settings.

Additional Answers

27. The MODE settings should be the standard default settings except for **DEGREE** and **PARAM.** The RANGE settings will vary. Suggested settings are: Tmin: 0, Tmax: 360, Tstep: 5; Xmin: –6, Xmax: 6; Xscl: 1, Ymin: –4, Ymax: 4, Yscl: 1

28. $x = \dfrac{2}{\cos(t + 20°)} \cdot \cos t$

$y = \dfrac{2}{\cos(t + 20°)} \cdot \sin t$

29.

EXERCISES

Practice   **Graph each polar equation.** 9–14. See Teacher's Answer Key.

 A

9. $2 = r\cos(\theta + 20°)$ 10. $5 = r\cos\left(\theta + \dfrac{\pi}{4}\right)$

11. $1.5 = r\cos(\theta - 10°)$ 12. $1.6 = r\cos(\theta - 15°)$

13. $r = \dfrac{2.5}{\cos\left(\theta - \dfrac{\pi}{2}\right)}$ 14. $r = \dfrac{2.4}{\cos(\theta + 60°)}$

Write each equation in polar form. Round ϕ to the nearest degree.

15. $x = 12$ $12 = r\cos\theta$ 16. $y - x = 0$ $0 = r\cos(\theta - 135°)$

 B

17. $y = 3x + 4$ $\dfrac{2\sqrt{10}}{5} = r\cos(\theta - 162°)$ 18. $5 = y + 2x$ $\sqrt{5} = r\cos(\theta - 27°)$

Write each equation in rectangular form.

19. $r\cos\left(\theta + \dfrac{\pi}{2}\right) = 0$ $y = 0$ 20. $r = \dfrac{1}{\cos\theta}$ $x = 1$

21. $r\cos\theta - 3 = 0$ $x = 3$ 22. $r\cos\left(\theta - \dfrac{\pi}{3}\right) - 4 = 0$
     $x + \sqrt{3}y - 8 = 0$

Find the polar form of the equation of a line that passes through the pair of points with the given coordinates.

 C

23. $(2, -4)$ and $(1, 3)$ 24. $(4, 2)$ and the origin
     $\sqrt{2} = r\cos(\theta - 8°)$ $0 = r\cos(\theta + 63°)$

Find the polar form of the equation of a line for each situation.

25. has a slope of 0.6 and a y-intercept of 4 $\dfrac{10\sqrt{34}}{17} = r\cos(\theta - 121°)$

26. passes through $(3, -2)$ and has a slope of $-\dfrac{1}{2}$ $\dfrac{\sqrt{5}}{5} = r\cos(\theta - 243°)$

27–29. See margin.

Graphing Calculator

27. Describe the appropriate mode and range settings for Example 5.

28. If you were to graph the equation $2 = r\cos(\theta + 20°)$ on a graphing calculator, what parametric equations would you use?

29. Graph $2 = r\cos\left(\theta - \dfrac{\pi}{4}\right)$ on a graphing calculator. Sketch the graph on a piece of paper.

Critical Thinking

30. Describe how you would modify the polar equation in Example 4 to create a new linear polar equation whose graph intersects the given line at an angle of 90°. Sketch the graph of both lines. See margin.

Applications and Problem Solving

31. **Research** In 1729, Jacob Hermann proclaimed that polar coordinates were just as efficient as Cartesian coordinates for studying geometric loci. However, Hermann was not a well-known mathematician, and, as a result, few people paid attention to his theories. Twenty years later, a famous Swiss mathematician made the polar coordinate system more popular. Who was that mathematician? Leonhard Euler

32. Navigation A ship is being tracked by the sonar of a submerged submarine. The sonar screen is a polar system in which the submarine is the origin. The submarine pilot records the path of the ship as $8 = 13r \cos(\theta - 67°)$. Find the linear equation of the path of the ship. $5x + 12y - 8 = 0$

Mixed Review

33. Find $\cos\left(\arcsin \dfrac{\sqrt{3}}{2}\right)$. Assume the angles are in Quadrant I. **(Lesson 6-4)** 0.5

34. Engineering A wheel in a motor is turning counterclockwise at 2 radians per second. There is a small hole in the wheel 3 centimeters from its center. Suppose a model of the wheel is drawn on a rectangular coordinate system with the wheel centered at the origin. If the hole has initial coordinates $(3, 0)$, what are its coordinates after t seconds? **(Lesson 8-5)** $(3 \cos 2t, 3 \sin 2t)$

35. Graph $r = 6 \cos 3\theta$. **(Lesson 9-2)** See margin.

36. Write the polar equation $r = 6$ in rectangular form. **(Lesson 9-3)** $x^2 + y^2 = 36$

37. College Entrance Exam Choose the best answer. B
A typist uses a sheet of paper that is 9 inches wide by 12 inches long. He leaves a 1-inch margin on each side and a 1.5-inch margin on top and bottom. What part of the page is used for typing?

(A) $\dfrac{5}{12}$ (B) $\dfrac{7}{12}$ (C) $\dfrac{5}{9}$ (D) $\dfrac{3}{4}$ (E) none of these

---

MID-CHAPTER REVIEW

1–3. For graphs, see Teacher's Answer Key.
1. Graph point $P(-6, -45°)$ on a polar plane. Name three other pairs of polar coordinates that represent the same point. **(Lesson 9-1)** $(6, 135°), (6, -225°), (-6, 315°)$

2. Graph $r = 3\theta$. **(Lesson 9-2)**

3. Graph $r = 6 + 6 \sin \theta$. Identify the classical curve it represents. **(Lesson 9-2)** cardioid

4. Find the rectangular coordinates of $D(\sqrt{2}, 135°)$. **(Lesson 9-3)** $(-1, 1)$

5. Find the polar coordinates of $E(1, \sqrt{3})$. **(Lesson 9-3)** $(2, 60°)$ or $\left(2, \dfrac{\pi}{3}\right)$

6. Write $x + y - 6 = 0$ in polar form. **(Lesson 9-4)** $3\sqrt{2} = r \cos\left(\theta - \dfrac{\pi}{4}\right)$

EXTENDING THE LESSON

Math Power: Communication

In this lesson you learned that Isaac Newton wrote about ten types of coordinate systems. Create a coordinate system different from the rectangular and the polar coordinate systems. Write a paper describing your system. Explain how a point is graphed and describe any advantages or disadvantages your system may have.

Mid-Chapter Review

The Mid-Chapter Review provides students with a brief review of the concepts and skills in Lessons 9–1 through 9–4. Lesson numbers are given at the end of problems or instruction lines so students may review concepts not yet mastered.

Additional Answers

30. Since the angle the normal makes with the line dictates the slope of the line, a normal at 135° provides a line that makes an angle of 45° with the positive direction of the polar axis. In order to have a line at a 90° angle with the given line, it must have its normal at an angle of 90° with the normal of the first line. One such equation might be $3 = r \cos(\theta - 45°)$. For graphs, see student's work.

35.

Enrichment Masters Booklet, p. 60

NCTM Standards: 1–6, 14

Lesson Resources

- Practice Master 9–5
- Enrichment Master 9–5
- Activity Master, p. 27

 Transparency 9–5 contains the 5-Minute Check and a teaching aid for this lesson.

INTRODUCING THE LESSON

 5-Minute Check

(over Lesson 9–4)

1. **Graph the equation**
   $2 = r \cos (\theta - 30°)$.

2. **Write $3x + 4y - 2 = 0$ in polar form.**
   $\frac{2}{5} = r \cos (\theta - 53°)$

3. **Write $2 = r \cos (\theta - 45°)$ in rectangular form.**
   $\sqrt{2}x + \sqrt{2}y - 4 = 0$

Prerequisite Skills

Students should be able to find the product of two binomials.

Find the product.
1. $(x - 4)(x + 5)$ $x^2 + x - 20$
2. $(2n - 3)(-4n + 1)$
   $-8n^2 + 14n - 3$
3. $(k - 3)(k + 3)$ $k^2 - 9$

9-5 Simplifying Complex Numbers

Objective
9–5

After studying this lesson, you should be able to:
■ add, subtract, multiply, and divide complex numbers in rectangular form.

Application

You will learn more about fractals in Chapter 13.

The computer-generated image shown above is known as the M-set Rug. It is a magnified portion of the boundary of a fractal known as the Mandelbrot set. It is formed by repeated evaluation of complex numbers through the function $f(z) = z^2 + c$. Generating images such as this requires multiplication and addition of complex numbers.

Recall that complex numbers are numbers in the form $a + bi$, where a and b are real numbers and i, the imaginary unit, is defined by $i^2 = -1$. Various powers of i are shown below.

$$i^1 = i \qquad i^2 = -1 \qquad i^3 = i^2 \cdot i = -i \qquad i^4 = (i^2)^2 = 1$$
$$i^5 = i^4 \cdot i = i \qquad i^6 = i^4 \cdot i^2 = -1 \qquad i^7 = i^4 \cdot i^3 = -i \qquad i^8 = (i^2)^4 = 1$$

Notice the repeating pattern of the powers of i.

$$i, -1, -i, 1, i, -1, -i, 1$$

In general, the value of i^n, where n is a whole number, can be found by dividing n by 4 and examining the remainder.

To find the value of i^n, let R = the remainder when n is divided by 4.	
if R = 0	$i^n = 1$
if R = 1	$i^n = i$
if R = 2	$i^n = -1$
if R = 3	$i^n = -i$

ALTERNATE TEACHING STRATEGIES

Using Models

Use a Venn diagram to show how the sets of numbers relate.

Using Problem Solving

Have students solve equations that require practice with operations on complex numbers.
- Solve $(3 + 4i) + x = -2 + 7i$. $-5 + 3i$
- Solve $\frac{n}{-2 + i} = 3 - i$. $-5 + 5i$

You can also find the value of any power of i by rewriting the power in terms of a power of a power. For example, $i^{35} = i^{4(8)+3}$ or $(i^4)^8 \cdot i^3$.

Example 1

Find i^{27}.

Method 1

$27 \div 4 = 6 \text{ R } 3$
If $R = 3, i^n = -i$.
$i^{27} = -i$

Method 2

$i^{27} = (i^2)^{13} \cdot i$
$\phantom{i^{27}} = (-1)^{13} \cdot i$
$\phantom{i^{27}} = -i$

You have learned that a complex number is composed of a real part a and an imaginary part bi. When $b = 0$, the complex number is a real number. When $b \neq 0$, as in $6 + 5i$, the complex number is an *imaginary number*. When $b \neq 0$ and $a = 0$, as in $-8i$, the imaginary number becomes a

Complex Numbers ($a + bi$)

Reals ($b = 0$)	Imaginary ($b \neq 0$)
	Pure Imaginary ($a = 0$)

pure imaginary number. Complex numbers can be added and subtracted by combining their real parts and their imaginary parts.

Example 2

Simplify each expression.
a. $(2 + 5i) + (-8 - i)$

a. $(2 + 5i) + (-8 - i) = [2 + (-8)] + [5i + (-i)]$
$ = -6 + 4i$

b. $(9 + 6i) - (i + 5)$

b. $(9 + 6i) - (i + 5) = 9 + 6i - i - 5$
$ = (9 - 5) + (6i - i)$
$ = 4 + 5i$

The product of two or more complex numbers can be found by using the same procedures you use when multiplying binomials.

Example 3

Simplify $(1 + 3i)(2 + 4i)$.

$(1 + 3i)(2 + 4i) = 1(2 + 4i) + 3i(2 + 4i)$
$ = 1(2) + 1(4i) + 3i(2) + 3i(4i)$

(continued on the next page)

LESSON 9-5 SIMPLIFYING COMPLEX NUMBERS 495

Ask students to explain why the equation $x^2 = 4$ has a real-number solution, but the equation $x^2 = -4$ does not. If $x^2 = -4$ has a solution, $x < 0$, $x = 0$, or $x > 0$. Since $0^2 = 0$, $x \neq 0$. If $x < 0$ or $x > 0$, then x^2 is a positive number and cannot equal -4. Therefore, $x^2 = -4$ has no real-number solution.

TEACHING THE LESSON

Teaching Tip Before Example 1, point out that the sum, difference, product, or quotient of two complex numbers is also a complex number and should be expressed in the form $a + bi$.

Chalkboard Examples

For Example 1

Find i^{35}. $-i$

For Example 2

Simplify each expression.
a. $(-3 + 4i) + (4 - 5i)$ $1 - i$
b. $(5 + 8i) - (-3 + i)$ $8 + 7i$

For Example 3

Simplify $(-2 + 4i)(-2 + 4i)$.
$-12 - 16i$

Teaching Tip Before Example 3, remind students of the FOIL method for multiplying binomials: multiply *first* terms, *outer* terms, *inner* terms, and *last* terms.

$$= 2 + 4i + 6i + 12i^2$$
$$= 2 + 10i + 12(-1) \qquad i^2 = -1$$
$$= -10 + 10i$$

In Chapter 4, you learned that the solution to a quadratic equation sometimes involves an imaginary number. Remember that when this happens, there are always two imaginary solutions. Pairs of imaginary solutions in the form $a + bi$ and $a - bi$ are called **conjugates**. The product of two conjugates is always a real number.

Example 4

Solve $x^2 - 7x + 15 = 0$. Check your solution.

Use the quadratic formula.

$$x = \frac{-(-7) \pm \sqrt{(-7)^2 - 4(1)(15)}}{2(1)}$$

$$= \frac{7 \pm \sqrt{-11}}{2} \text{ or } \frac{7 \pm i\sqrt{11}}{2}$$

Check: $x = \dfrac{7 + i\sqrt{11}}{2}$

$$\left(\frac{7 + i\sqrt{11}}{2}\right)^2 - 7\left(\frac{7 + i\sqrt{11}}{2}\right) + 15 \stackrel{?}{=} 0 \quad x = \frac{7 + i\sqrt{11}}{2}$$

$$\frac{49 + 14i\sqrt{11} + (-11)}{4} - \frac{49 + 7i\sqrt{11}}{2} + 15 \stackrel{?}{=} 0 \quad \textit{Expand.}$$

$$49 + 14i\sqrt{11} - 11 - 98 - 14i\sqrt{11} + 60 \stackrel{?}{=} 0 \quad \textit{Multiply each side by 4.}$$

$$0 = 0 \quad \checkmark$$

$$x = \frac{7 - i\sqrt{11}}{2}$$

$$\left(\frac{7 - i\sqrt{11}}{2}\right)^2 - 7\left(\frac{7 - i\sqrt{11}}{2}\right) + 15 \stackrel{?}{=} 0 \quad x = \frac{7 - i\sqrt{11}}{2}$$

$$\frac{49 - 14i\sqrt{11} + (-11)}{4} - \frac{49 - 7i\sqrt{11}}{2} + 15 \stackrel{?}{=} 0 \quad \textit{Expand.}$$

$$49 - 14i\sqrt{11} - 11 - 98 + 14i\sqrt{11} + 60 \stackrel{?}{=} 0 \quad \textit{Multiply each side by 4.}$$

$$0 = 0 \quad \checkmark$$

Whenever a fraction has a radical expression in the denominator, the denominator is usually rationalized. For example, $\dfrac{1}{3 + \sqrt{2}}$ becomes $\dfrac{1}{3 + \sqrt{2}} \cdot \dfrac{3 - \sqrt{2}}{3 - \sqrt{2}}$ or $\dfrac{3 - \sqrt{2}}{7}$. A similar process is used to rationalize the denominators of fractions that contain imaginary numbers.

Example 5

Simplify $\dfrac{4-3i}{2+i}$.

$\dfrac{4-3i}{2+i} = \left(\dfrac{4-3i}{2+i}\right)\left(\dfrac{2-i}{2-i}\right)$ *Multiply the numerator and denominator by the conjugate of the denominator.*

$= \dfrac{8-4i-6i+3i^2}{4-i^2}$

$= \dfrac{8-10i+3(-1)}{4-(-1)}$

$= \dfrac{5-10i}{5}$

$= 1-2i$

Chalkboard Example

For Example 5

Simplify $\dfrac{-3+i}{4-3i}$. $-\dfrac{3}{5} - \dfrac{1}{5}i$

The list below summarizes the operations with imaginary numbers presented in this lesson.

Operations with Complex Numbers

> **For any complex numbers $a + bi$ and $c + di$, the following is true.**
> $(a + bi) + (c + di) = (a + c) + (b + d)i$
> $(a + bi) - (c + di) = (a - c) + (b - d)i$
> $(a + bi)(c + di) = (ac - bd) + (ad + bc)i$
> $\dfrac{a + bi}{c + di} = \dfrac{(ac + bd) + (bc - ad)i}{c^2 + d^2}$

Complex numbers are often used in the study of electricity, specifically alternating current (AC) electricity. In a simplified electrical circuit, there are three basic components to be considered:

- the flow of electrical **current**, I,
- the resistance to that flow, Z, called **impedance**, and
- the electromotive force, E, called **voltage**.

Impedance is the result of having resistors, coils, and capacitors in a circuit, and is measured in ohms. Voltage refers to the electrical potential in a circuit and is measured in volts. Current is measured in amperes (amps). The formula $E = I \cdot Z$ illustrates the relationship among these components.

Current, impedance, and voltage are often expressed as complex numbers. Electrical engineers use j instead of i to represent the imaginary unit. For electrical engineers, $j = \sqrt{-1}$ and $j^2 = -1$. When they write a complex number, they use the form $a + bj$.

FYI...

Henry Cavendish (1731–1810), an English physicist and chemist, discovered many of the basic laws of electricity. Since he had no instruments to measure the strength of an electric current, he shocked himself with the current and then estimated the current in terms of his pain.

LESSON 9-5 SIMPLIFYING COMPLEX NUMBERS   497

For the total impedance, $a + bj$, the real part a represents the opposition to current flow due to resistors, and the imaginary part bj represents the opposition due to coils and capacitors. If two circuits are connected so that the current flows through them one after the other, the circuits are said to be connected in series. The total voltage and total impedance of circuits in series are found by adding the voltages and adding the impedances of the two circuits, respectively.

Example 6

APPLICATION

Electricity

Two AC circuits are connected in series, one with an impedance of $3 + 5j$ ohms and the other with an impedance of $2 - 4j$ ohms.
a. **Find the total impedance.**
b. **Then find the current if the total voltage is 110 volts.**

a. The total impedance is the sum of the individual impedances.
   $(3 + 5j) + (2 - 4j) = 5 + j$
   The total impedance is $5 + j$ ohms.

b. Substitute the total impedance and the total voltage into the formula $E = I \cdot Z$.

$$E = I \cdot Z$$
$$110 = I \cdot (5 + j) \qquad E = 110 \text{ volts and } Z = 5 + j \text{ ohms}$$
$$\frac{110}{5 + j} = I \qquad \text{Solve for I.}$$
$$\left(\frac{110}{5 + j}\right)\left(\frac{5 - j}{5 - j}\right) = I \qquad \text{Rationalize the denominator.}$$
$$\frac{550 - 110j}{26} = I$$
$$21.15 - 4.23j = I \qquad \text{The current is } 21.15 - 4.23j \text{ amperes.}$$

CHECKING FOR UNDERSTANDING

Communicating Mathematics

Read and study the lesson to answer each question. 2–3. See margin.

1. **Write** a few sentences to show how operations with imaginary numbers are similar to operations with binomials. See students' work.

2. **Explain** how the set of real numbers is related to the set of complex numbers.

3. What units are used to measure current, impedance, and voltage?

Guided Practice

Simplify.

4. $i^{15} + i^{28}$ $1 - i$

5. $(4 + 5i) + (3 + 2i)$ $7 + 7i$

6. $(8 + 3i) - (1 - 6i)$ $7 + 9i$

7. $(4 + 3i)(2 - i)$ $11 + 2i$

8. $(i - 6)^2$ $35 - 12i$

9. $\frac{1 + i}{3 + 2i}$ $\frac{5 + i}{13}$

10. $\frac{2}{12 + i}$ $\frac{24 - 2i}{145}$

11. $\frac{7i}{-5i}$ $-\frac{7}{5}$

EXERCISES

APPLYING THE LESSON

Practice

Simplify.

12. $i^{24} + i^{61}$ $1 + i$

13. $i^4(7 + 2i)$ $7 + 2i$

14. $(7 - 6i) + (9 + 11i)$ $16 + 5i$

15. $(-5 + 2i\sqrt{7}) - (2 - 7i\sqrt{7})$ $-7 + 9i\sqrt{7}$

16. $(-3 - 10i) - (-5 - 4i)$ $2 - 6i$

17. $-6(2 - 8i) + 3(5 + 7i)$ $3 + 69i$

18. $4(7 - i) - 5(2 - 6i)$ $18 + 26i$

19. $(3 + 5i)(4 - i)$ $17 + 17i$

20. $(4 - 2i\sqrt{3})(1 + 5i\sqrt{3})$ $34 + 18i\sqrt{3}$

21. $(3 - 4i)^2$ $-7 - 24i$

B

25. $-8 + 6i\sqrt{2}$

22. $(\sqrt{5} + 2i)^2$ $1 + 4i\sqrt{5}$

23. $(8 - \sqrt{-11})(8 + \sqrt{-11})$ 75

24. $(6 - 4i)(6 + 4i)$ 52

25. $(5 + \sqrt{-8}) + (-13 + 4\sqrt{-2})$

26. $\dfrac{2 - 4i}{1 + 3i}$ $-1 - i$

27. $\dfrac{3 - i}{2 - i}$ $\dfrac{7 + i}{5}$

Solve each equation. Check the solution.

28. $x^2 - x + 1 = 0$ $\dfrac{1 \pm i\sqrt{3}}{2}$

29. $x^2 + 4x + 29 = 0$ $-2 \pm 5i$

Find values for x and y that make each sentence true.

C

30. $3x - 5yi = 15 - 20i$ $x = 5, y = 4$

31. $\sqrt{3}x + 7yi = 6 - 2i$ $x = 2\sqrt{3}, y = -\dfrac{2}{7}$

32. $(x - y) + (2x + y)i = -3 + 9i$
    $x = 2, y = 5$

33. $(2x - y) + (x + y)i = -4 - 5i$
    $x = -3, y = -2$

Simplify.

34. $(3 - i)(1 + 2i)(2 + 3i)$ $-5 + 25i$

35. $(4 + 3i)(2 - 5i)(4 - 3i)$ $50 - 125i$

36. $\dfrac{3}{\sqrt{2} - 5i}$ $\dfrac{\sqrt{2} + 5i}{9}$

37. $\dfrac{2 + i\sqrt{3}}{12 + i\sqrt{3}}$ $\dfrac{27 + 10i\sqrt{3}}{147}$

38. $\dfrac{(1 - 2i)^2}{(2 - i)^2}$ $\dfrac{7 - 24i}{25}$

39. $\dfrac{2 + i}{(1 - i)^2}$ $\dfrac{-1 + 2i}{2}$

Critical Thinking

40. Write a paragraph comparing the addition of vectors to addition of complex numbers. See margin.

Applications and Problem Solving

41. **Flashlights** In a two-battery flashlight, the positive terminal of the first battery touches the negative terminal of the second. The positive terminal of the second battery touches the center terminal of the light bulb. A metal strip connects the bulb to the switch which is connected to the negative terminal of the first battery. When you turn the flashlight on, the switch completes the circuit, and the bulb lights up. Each of the batteries are 1.5-volt batteries, and the current is $(1 + j\sqrt{3})$ amps.

    a. What is the total electromotive force of the two batteries? 3 volts

    b. What is the total impedance of the circuit in the flashlight? $0.75(1 - j\sqrt{3})$ ohms

---

Homework Exercises

Assignment Guide

Average: 12–35, 40, 41, 45–53
Enriched: 20–53

The red A, B, and C flags, printed only in the Teacher's Wraparound Edition, indicate the level of difficulty of the exercises.

Additional Answer

40. The addition of vectors, when expressed in terms of their unit vector components, behave exactly like the addition of imaginary numbers. When adding vectors you add the horizontal components together and then the vertical components. This parallels adding the real parts and then the imaginary parts.

Additional Answers

48.

52.

Enrichment Masters Booklet, p. 61

NAME _____ DATE _____

9-5 Enrichment Worksheet

Spherical Coordinates

There are many coordinate systems for locating a point in the two-dimensional plane. You have studied the two most common systems, rectangular coordinates and polar coordinates.

The most commonly used three-dimensional coordinate systems are the extended rectangular system, with an added z-axis, and the *spherical coordinate* system, a modification of polar coordinates. Point $P(d, \theta, \phi)$ in three-dimensional space is located using three spherical coordinates:

d = distance from origin
θ = angle relative to x-axis
ϕ = angle relative to y-axis

The figure at the right shows point Q with rectangular coordinates (2, 5, 6).

1. Find OA and AB.
   2; 6
2. Find OB by using the Pythagorean theorem.
   $2\sqrt{10}$
3. Find QB.
   5
4. Find d.
   $\sqrt{65}$
5. Use inverse trigonometric functions to find θ and ϕ to the nearest degree. Write the spherical coordinates of Q.
   $(\sqrt{65}, 72°, 52°)$

Find the spherical coordinates of the point with the given rectangular coordinates. Round distances to the nearest tenth and angles to the nearest degree.

6. (4, 12, 3)
   (13, 37°, 23°)
7. (−2, −3, −1)
   (3.7, −27°, 143°)
8. (a, b, c)
   $\left(\sqrt{a^2 + b^2 + c^2}, \arctan\left(\frac{c}{a}\right), \arccos\left(\frac{b}{\sqrt{a^2 + b^2 + c^2}}\right)\right)$

T61
Glencoe Division, Macmillan/McGraw-Hill

---

42. Electricity A circuit has a current of $(6 - 8j)$ amps and an impedance of $(14 + 8j)$ ohms. Find the voltage of this circuit. $148 - 64j$ volts

43. Electricity Find the current of a circuit of $(70 + 226j)$ volts with an impedance of $(6 + 8j)$ ohms. $22.28 + 7.96j$ amps

44. Electricity What is the impedance of a circuit whose current is $(-6 - 2j)$ amps and whose electromotive force is $(-50 + 100j)$ volts? $2.5 - 17.5j$ ohms

Mixed Review

45. Write the equation $2x + 5y - 10 = 0$ in slope-intercept form. Then name the slope and y-intercept. **(Lesson 1-5)** $y = -\frac{2}{5}x + 2, m = -\frac{2}{5}$, y-intercept $= 2$

46. Solve the system below by using matrices. **(Lesson 2-4)**
$a + b + c = 6$
$2a - 3b + 4c = 3$
$4a - 8b + 4c = 12$ $(7, 1, -2)$

47. Education The semester test in your English class consists of short answer and essay questions. Each short answer question is worth 5 points and each essay question is worth 15 points. You may choose up to 20 questions of any type to answer. It takes 2 minutes to answer each short answer question and 12 minutes to answer each essay question. **(Lesson 2-6)**

   a. You have one hour to complete the test. Assuming that you answer all of the questions that you attempt correctly, how many of each type should you answer to earn the highest score? 18 SA, 2 essay for a score of 120

   b. You have two hours to complete the test. Assuming that you answer all of the questions that you attempt correctly, how many of each type should you answer to earn the highest score? 12 SA, 8 essay for a score of 180 points

48. Write the equation for the inverse of $y = \cos x$. Then graph the function and its inverse. **(Lesson 6-6)** $y = \arccos x$; For graphs, see margin.

49. See Teacher's Answer Key.

49. Verify that $\sin^4 A + \cos^2 A = \cos^4 A + \sin^2 A$ is an identity. **(Lesson 7-2)**

50. Find the sum of the vectors $(3, 5)$ and $(-1, 2)$ algebraically. **(Lesson 8-2)** $(2, 7)$

51. Write $x^2 + y^2 = 25$ in polar form. **(Lesson 9-3)** $r = 5$ or $r = -5$

52. Graph $r = \dfrac{1}{\cos(\theta + 15°)}$. **(Lesson 9-4)** See margin.

53. College Entrance Exam Compare quantities A and B. B
Write A if quantity A is greater.
Write B if quantity B is greater.
Write C if the quantities are equal.
Write D if there is not enough information to determine the relationship.

Given: $m\angle K = 60°$

(A) the area of the smaller triangle
(B) the area of the shaded region

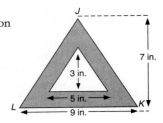

500   CHAPTER 9   POLAR COORDINATES AND COMPLEX NUMBERS

EXTENDING THE LESSON

Math Power: Problem Solving

Explain the fallacy in this proof.

$$i = i$$
$$\sqrt{-1} = \sqrt{-1}$$
$$\sqrt{\frac{1}{-1}} = \sqrt{\frac{-1}{1}}$$
$$\frac{\sqrt{1}}{\sqrt{-1}} = \frac{\sqrt{-1}}{\sqrt{1}}$$
$$\sqrt{1}\sqrt{1} = \sqrt{-1}\sqrt{-1}$$
$$1 = -1$$

$\sqrt{\dfrac{a}{b}} = \dfrac{\sqrt{a}}{\sqrt{b}}$ only for $a \geq 0$ and $b > 0$.

Polar Form of Complex Numbers

Objective
9–6

After studying this lesson, you should be able to:
■ change complex numbers from rectangular to polar form and vice versa.

Application

In 1833, at the Royal Irish Academy in Dublin, Ireland, William Rowan Hamilton presented the concept that complex numbers could be expressed in the form $a + bi$. He further put forth the idea that if a were represented on the x-axis and b were represented on the y-axis, each complex number $a + bi$ could be graphed on this rectangular plane. His proposals are still being followed today.

This coordinate system is also called the complex plane.

When complex numbers are expressed in the form $x + yi$, where x is the real part and yi is the imaginary part, the complex number is said to be in **rectangular form**. Sometimes the rectangular form is written as an ordered pair (x, y).

To graph a complex number in rectangular form, the horizontal axis is the real axis and the vertical axis is the imaginary axis. Point P on the graph at the left is the graph of the complex number $3 + 4i$.

The angle θ is called the **amplitude**, and r, the length of the hypotenuse, is called the **modulus**. Two complex numbers are equal if and only if their moduli are equal and their amplitudes differ by integral multiples of 2π radians. This means that θ can be replaced by $\theta + 2k\pi$ for any integer k.

EXPLORATION: Modeling

1. Graph points A and B on the complex plane so that A is the graph of $6 + 7i$ and B is the graph of $-2 + 3i$. Label the origin O.
2. Draw a line through B that is parallel to $\overrightarrow{OA}$.
3. Draw a line through A that is parallel to $\overrightarrow{OB}$.
4. Label the point where the two lines intersect as point C.
5. What are the coordinates of C and what imaginary number does $\overrightarrow{OC}$ represent? $(4, 10), 4 + 10i$
6. How does this number compare with the sum of the complex numbers originally graphed? They are the same.   7. See margin.
7. What conjecture might you make based on this information?
8. Test your conjecture by graphing several other pairs of complex numbers and following the steps given above. See students' work.

ALTERNATE TEACHING STRATEGIES

Using Connections

Students may be uneasy about the idea of breaking a sum like $3 + 4i$ into two parts and graphing it as though it were the ordered pair $(3, 4i)$. Remind them that vectors were similarly broken down and graphed according to magnitude and direction. The process is common in mathematics because it allows abstract quantities to be represented graphically.

Using Graphs

Refer students to the graph on the first page of the lesson. Remind them that they can always convert between rectangular and polar forms of a complex number by sketching a right triangle, writing the two parts of the triangle represented by the coordinates of the number, and finding either x and y or r and θ, as needed.

9–6   Lesson Notes

NCTM Standards: 1–6, 8, 14

Lesson Resources

- Practice Master 9–6
- Enrichment Master 9–6
- Evaluation Master, Quiz C, p. 114
- Multicultural Activity Master, p. 9

 Transparency 9–6 contains the 5-Minute Check and a teaching aid for this lesson.

INTRODUCING THE LESSON

🕐 **5-Minute Check**

(over Lesson 9–5)

Simplify.
1. i^{39} $-i$
2. $(3 - 6i) - (-2 + 2i)$ $5 - 8i$
3. $(2 + 4i)(3 - 5i)$ $26 + 2i$
4. $\frac{-5 + 9i}{1 - i}$ $-7 + 2i$
5. Solve $x^2 + x + 1 = 0$.
   $-\frac{1}{2} \pm i \frac{\sqrt{3}}{2}$

Motivating the Lesson

Have students read the application at the beginning of the lesson. Stress the power of Hamilton's idea; it permits complex numbers to be represented and manipulated graphically. Ask students to name and give examples of other two-component mathematical quantities that could be graphed on the plane. Sample answer: binomials, $2x + 3y$

Additional Answers

Exploration
7. The sum of the complex numbers is represented by the diagonal of the parallelogram containing the segments representing the two original complex numbers.

Chalkboard Example

For Example 1

Graph each complex number. Then express it in polar form.
a. $1 - 4i$
   $\sqrt{17}(\cos 4.96 + i\sin 4.96)$
b. $-3 - 2i$
   $\sqrt{13}(\cos 3.73 + i\sin 3.73)$

Recall that $x = r\cos\theta$ and $y = r\sin\theta$. As with other rectangular coordinates, complex coordinates can be written in polar form by substituting these values for x and y. This form of a complex number is often called the **polar** or **trigonometric form**.

Polar Form of a Complex Number (Trigonometric Form)	The polar form or trigonometric form of a complex number is $$x + yi = r(\cos\theta + i\sin\theta).$$

$r(\cos\theta + i\sin\theta)$ is often abbreviated as r cis θ.

Values for r and θ can be found by using the same process used when you changed other rectangular coordinates to polar coordinates. For $x + yi$,

$r = \sqrt{x^2 + y^2}$ and $\theta = \text{Arctan}\,\dfrac{y}{x}$ if $x > 0$ or $\theta = \text{Arctan}\left(\dfrac{y}{x} + \pi\right)$ if $x < 0$.

The amplitude θ is usually expressed in radian measure, and the angle is in standard position along the polar axis.

Example 1

Graph each complex number. Then express it in polar form.

a. $-2 + i$

a. Graph the complex number on the complex plane.

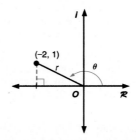

Since the point lies in the second quadrant, the value of θ should be greater than $\dfrac{\pi}{2}$ and less than π radians.

Find values for r and θ.

$r = \sqrt{x^2 + y^2}$

$\quad = \sqrt{(-2)^2 + 1^2}$

$\quad = \sqrt{5}$

$\theta = \text{Arctan}\,\dfrac{y}{x} + \pi \qquad$ *Notice that $x < 0$.*

$\quad = \text{Arctan}\,\dfrac{1}{-2} + \pi \qquad$ *Notice that $\dfrac{\pi}{2} < 2.68 < \pi$.*

$\quad \approx 2.68 \qquad\qquad$ *Use your calculator.*

Therefore, $-2 + i \approx \sqrt{5}\,(\cos 2.68 + i\sin 2.68)$.

b. 1 + i

b. Graph $1 + i$
on the complex plane.
$0 < \theta < \frac{\pi}{2}$

Find values for r and θ.

$r = \sqrt{1^2 + 1^2}$
$\quad = \sqrt{2}$

$\theta = \text{Arctan } \frac{1}{1}$ *Notice that x > 0.*

$\quad = \frac{\pi}{4}$

Therefore, $1 + i = \sqrt{2}\left(\cos\frac{\pi}{4} + i\sin\frac{\pi}{4}\right)$.

If you know the values of r and θ, you can write a complex number in the
form $x + yi$.

Example 2

Graph $8\left(\cos\frac{7\pi}{6} + i\sin\frac{7\pi}{6}\right)$. Then express it in rectangular form.

Graph the complex number on the
complex plane.
The value of θ is $\frac{7\pi}{6}$, and the value
of r is 8.

The terminal side is in the third
quadrant. So, the values x and y
should both be negative.

Find values for x and y.

$x = r\cos\theta$ $y = r\sin\theta$

$\quad = 8\cos\frac{7\pi}{6}$ $\quad = 8\sin\frac{7\pi}{6}$

$\quad = -8\cos\frac{\pi}{6}$ $\quad = -8\sin\frac{\pi}{6}$

$\quad = -8\left(\frac{\sqrt{3}}{2}\right)$ $\quad = -8\left(\frac{1}{2}\right)$

$\quad = -4\sqrt{3}$ $\quad = -4$

Therefore, $8\left(\cos\frac{7\pi}{6} + i\sin\frac{7\pi}{6}\right) = -4\sqrt{3} - 4i$.

LESSON 9-6   POLAR FORM OF COMPLEX NUMBERS   503

Checking for Understanding

Exercises 1–14 are designed to help you assess students' understanding through reading, writing, speaking, and modeling. You should work through Exercises 1–4 with your students and then monitor their work on Exercises 5–14.

Closing the Lesson

Speaking Activity   Ask students to explain how they would convert the coordinates of P to rectangular form and the coordinates of Q to polar form. Then have them give the answer.

P: (–3, 1); Q: (2, 60°)

Practice Masters Booklet, p. 62

CHECKING FOR UNDERSTANDING

Communicating Mathematics

Read and study the lesson to answer each question. 1–4. See margin.

1. **Define** the term *modulus* when referring to complex numbers.
2. **Describe** the amplitude of a complex number.
3. **Make a conjecture** about why mathematicians use the form r cis θ for a complex number in polar form.
4. **Describe** the relationship between α and β if r cis α and r cis β both represent the same complex number.

5–10. See Teacher's Answer Key.

Guided Practice

Graph each complex number. Then express the number in polar form.

5. $-1 + i$
6. $-2(1 - i)$
7. $0 + 70i$
8. $-6 + 0i$
9. $3 - i\sqrt{3}$
10. $2(1 - i\sqrt{3})$

11–14. For graphs, see Teacher's Answer Key.

Graph each complex number. Then express the number in rectangular form.

11. $4(\cos 0 + i \sin 0)$ 4
12. $3(\cos \pi + i \sin \pi)$ –3
13. $3 \cos \frac{\pi}{2} + 3i \sin \frac{\pi}{2}$ $3i$
14. $0.5\left(\cos \frac{5\pi}{6} + i \sin \frac{5\pi}{6}\right)$ $-\frac{\sqrt{3}}{4} + \frac{1}{4}i$

EXERCISES

Practice

Express each complex number in polar form.   15–23. See Teacher's Answer Key.

Ⓐ
15. $-1 - i$
16. $6i$
17. $10i$
18. $-5 - i$
19. $4 + 3i$
20. $2\sqrt{3} - 3i$
21. $1 + i\sqrt{3}$
22. $-4i$
23. -5

Express each complex number in rectangular form.

24. $6\left(\cos \frac{3\pi}{2} + i \sin \frac{3\pi}{2}\right)$ $-6i$
25. $24\left(\cos \frac{5\pi}{3} + i \sin \frac{5\pi}{3}\right)$ $12 - 12i\sqrt{3}$

Ⓑ
26. $\sqrt{2}\left(\cos \frac{5\pi}{4} + i \sin \frac{5\pi}{4}\right)$ $-1 - i$
27. $3(\cos 2 + i \sin 2)$ $\approx -1.25 + 2.73i$
28. $4(\cos 3 + i \sin 3)$ $\approx -3.96 + 0.56i$
29. $2\left(\cos \frac{\pi}{6} + i \sin \frac{\pi}{6}\right)$ $\sqrt{3} + i$

Ⓒ
30. $\sqrt{2}\, i \sin\left(\frac{-\pi}{2}\right) + \sqrt{2} \cos\left(\frac{-\pi}{2}\right)$ $-i\sqrt{2}$
31. $5\left(\cos \frac{17\pi}{6} + i \sin \frac{17\pi}{6}\right)$ $\frac{-5\sqrt{3}}{2} + \frac{5}{2}i$

Critical Thinking

32. Let C represent a complex number. If $C = x + yi$ is a real number, show why its modulus is equal to its absolute value. If C is a real number, then $y = 0$, $|C| = |x|$, and $r = \sqrt{x^2}$ or $|x|$.
33. Refer to the Exploration on page 501. Make a general conjecture about how to find the sum of two complex numbers graphically. See margin.

Applications and Problem Solving

34. **Algebra**   Find the zeros of $f(x) = x^2 - 4x + 8$. Graph them on the complex plane. $2 \pm 2i$; For graph, see Teacher's Answer Key.

504   CHAPTER 9   POLAR COORDINATES AND COMPLEX NUMBERS

RETEACHING THE LESSON

Have students work in groups of three. Each student writes the rectangular form of a complex number and passes it to the right. The student on the right converts the number to polar form and passes it to the right. The next student converts the number back to rectangular form, compares the results with the original number, and, if necessary, finds where errors occurred.

Additional Answers

1. Modulus is the length of the radius vector for the polar form of a complex number. The modulus is equal to $\sqrt{x^2 + y^2}$ for $x + yi$.
2. angle formed by the polar axis and the radius vector
3. Answers may vary. Sample answer: It is easier to write and it is shorter.
4. Their measures will differ by some multiple of 2π.

35. Electricity Find the current of an electrical circuit whose voltage is $(70 + 226j)$ volts and impedance is $(6 + 8j)$ ohms. Then write the three complex numbers in this problem in polar form. Round values to the nearest tenth. *The relationship among current (I), voltage (E), and impedance (Z) is $E = I \cdot Z$.* See margin.

Mixed Review

36. Hobbies Sara likes bird watching. She wishes to build a rectangular bird feeder that is 6 inches tall and has a volume of 192 cubic inches. The material for the front and back costs 5¢ per square inch, the materials for the sides cost 10¢ per square inch, and the material for the bottom costs 20¢ per square inch. Find the dimensions of the bird feeder that will be the most economical to build. **(Lesson 3-7)** 4 in. by 8 in. by 6 in.

37. Air Traffic Safety The traffic pattern for airplanes into San Diego's airport is over the heart of downtown. Therefore, there are restrictions on the heights of new construction. The owner of an office building wishes to erect a microwave tower on top of the building. According to the architect's design, the angle of elevation from a point on the ground to the top of the 40-foot tower is 56°. The angle of elevation from the ground point to the top of the building is 42°. The maximum allowed height of any structure is 100 feet. Will the city allow the building of this tower? Explain.
(Lesson 5-6) See margin.

38. Solve $\sin 2x + 2\sin x = 0$ for $0° \le x \le 360°$.
(Lesson 7-5) $0°, 180°, 360°$

39. Find an ordered triple to represent $\vec{u}$ if $\vec{u} = \vec{v} + \vec{w}$, $\vec{v} = (2, -5, -3)$, and $\vec{w} = (-3, 4, -7)$. Then write $\vec{u}$ as the sum of unit vectors. **(Lesson 8-3)**
$$\vec{u} = (-1, -1, -10) = -\vec{i} - \vec{j} - 10\vec{k}$$

40. Graph $3 = r\cos\left(\theta - \dfrac{\pi}{3}\right)$. **(Lesson 9-4)** See Teacher's Answer Key.

41. Electricity The reactance of an electrical circuit is found by the formula $X = X_L - X_C$, where X_L represents the reactance from the inductions and X_C represents the reactance from all capacitors. Suppose a circuit has a total reactance of $8i$ ohms. If the reactance of the capacitors is $7i$ ohms, find the reactance of the inductions. **(Lesson 9-5)** $15i$ ohms

42. College Entrance Exam Choose the best answer. D
A pulley having a 9-inch diameter is belted to a pulley having a 6-inch diameter, as shown in the figure. If the large pulley runs at 120 rpm (revolutions per minute), how fast does the small pulley run?

(A) 80 rpm
(B) 100 rpm
(C) 160 rpm
(D) 180 rpm
(E) 240 rpm

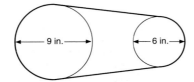

9 in. — 6 in.

LESSON 9-6 POLAR FORM OF COMPLEX NUMBERS 505

EXTENDING THE LESSON

Math Power: Problem Solving

Express $a + bi$ in polar form $(a > 0)$.
$$\sqrt{a^2 + b^2}\left(\frac{a}{\sqrt{a^2 + b^2}} + i\,\frac{b}{\sqrt{a^2 + b^2}}\right)$$

Additional Answer

37. No, the height of the building is approximately 61.9 feet, making a total of 101.9 feet with the tower, which is over the city's limit.

NCTM Standards: 1–6, 14

Lesson Resources

- Practice Master 9–7
- Enrichment Master 9–7

 Transparency 9–7 contains the 5-Minute Check and a teaching aid for this lesson.

INTRODUCING THE LESSON

 5-Minute Check

(over Lesson 9–6)

Express in polar form.

1. $4 + 3i$
   $5(\cos 0.64 + i \sin 0.64)$
2. $-1 - i$
   $\sqrt{2}\left(\cos \frac{5\pi}{4} + i \sin \frac{5\pi}{4}\right)$

Express in rectangular form.

3. $6(\cos \frac{\pi}{6} + i \sin \frac{\pi}{6})$

   $3\sqrt{3} + 3i$
4. $5(\cos \pi + i \sin \pi)$ -5

Motivating the Lesson

State that advances in mathematics often simplify previously complex or tedious tasks. Multiplication, for example, greatly simplifies the process of repeated addition. Ask students to give further examples.
Sample answer: Rules of exponents simplify multiplication. $(5^4)^6 = 5^{24}$.
State that this lesson will introduce a simplified method for multiplying complex numbers in polar form.

9-7 Products and Quotients of Complex Numbers in Polar Form

Objective 9-7

After studying this lesson, you should be able to:
- find the product and quotient of complex numbers in polar form.

Application

The image of the M-set Rug, shown below and in Lesson 9-5, was created by Dr. Richard F. Voss. Dr. Voss has been a Research Staff Member at the IBM Thomas J. Watson Research Laboratory in Yorktown Heights, New York, since 1975. His research has focused on condensed matter physics. The M-set Rug is now shown at a magnification of 10^{23}. At this magnification, the entire Mandelbrot set would be approximately 1,000,000 light years across.

Without the ability to multiply and add complex numbers rapidly on a computer, images like the one above would be impossible to create. When two complex numbers are written in polar form, their product or quotient can easily be computed.

 FYI...

Fractal geometry was used to create a landscape that was used in the Death Star sequence of the movie *Star Wars*.

Let $r_1(\cos \theta_1 + i \sin \theta_1)$ and $r_2(\cos \theta_2 + i \sin \theta_2)$ represent two complex numbers. A formula for the product of the two numbers can be obtained by multiplying the two numbers directly and then simplifying the result.

$r_1(\cos \theta_1 + i \sin \theta_1) \cdot r_2(\cos \theta_2 + i \sin \theta_2)$

$= r_1 r_2 (\cos \theta_1 \cos \theta_2 + i \cos \theta_1 \sin \theta_2 + i \sin \theta_1 \cos \theta_2 + i^2 \sin \theta_1 \sin \theta_2)$

$= r_1 r_2 [(\cos \theta_1 \cos \theta_2 - \sin \theta_1 \sin \theta_2) + i(\sin \theta_1 \cos \theta_2 + \cos \theta_1 \sin \theta_2)]$

$= r_1 r_2 [\cos(\theta_1 + \theta_2) + i \sin(\theta_1 + \theta_2)]$

Product of Complex Numbers in Polar Form	The product of two complex numbers can be found as follows. $r_1(\cos \theta_1 + i \sin \theta_1) \cdot r_2(\cos \theta_2 + i \sin \theta_2) = r_1 r_2[\cos(\theta_1 + \theta_2) + i \sin(\theta_1 + \theta_2)]$

Notice that the modulus $(r_1 r_2)$ of the product of the two complex numbers is the product of their moduli. The amplitude of the product $(\theta_1 + \theta_2)$ is the sum of the amplitudes.

ALTERNATE TEACHING STRATEGIES

Using Connections

Have students study the derivation of the rule for finding the product of two complex numbers on the first page of the lesson. Ask them to explain how the final step in the derivation follows from the previous step.
The sum identities for the sine and cosine are applied.

Using Discussion

Use the abbreviation for the polar form of a complex number and these examples to stimulate discussion and clarify the rules for multiplication and division.
(8 cis 50°)(2 cis 10°) = 16 cis 60°
(8 cis 50°) ÷ (2 cis 10°) = 4 cis 40°

Example 1 | **Find the product** $8\left(\cos\dfrac{3\pi}{4}+i\sin\dfrac{3\pi}{4}\right)\cdot 2\left(\cos\dfrac{5\pi}{4}+i\sin\dfrac{5\pi}{4}\right)$. **Then express the product in rectangular form.**

Find the modulus and amplitude of the product.

$$r = r_1 r_2$$
$$= 8(2)$$
$$= 16$$

$$\theta = \theta_1 + \theta_2$$
$$= \frac{3\pi}{4} + \frac{5\pi}{4}$$
$$= 2\pi$$

The product is $16(\cos 2\pi + i\sin 2\pi)$.

Now find the rectangular form of the product.

$$8\left(\cos\frac{3\pi}{4}+i\sin\frac{3\pi}{4}\right)\cdot 2\left(\cos\frac{5\pi}{4}+i\sin\frac{5\pi}{4}\right) = 16(\cos 2\pi + i\sin 2\pi)$$
$$= 16(1 + i\cdot 0) \text{ or } 16$$

The rectangular form of this product is 16.

Suppose the quotient of two complex numbers is expressed as a fraction. A formula for this quotient can be found by rationalizing the denominator.

$$\frac{r_1(\cos\theta_1 + i\sin\theta_1)}{r_2(\cos\theta_2 + i\sin\theta_2)}$$

$$= \frac{r_1(\cos\theta_1 + i\sin\theta_1)}{r_2(\cos\theta_2 + i\sin\theta_2)}\cdot\frac{(\cos\theta_2 - i\sin\theta_2)}{(\cos\theta_2 - i\sin\theta_2)}$$

$$= \frac{r_1}{r_2}\cdot\frac{(\cos\theta_1\cos\theta_2 + \sin\theta_1\sin\theta_2) + i(\sin\theta_1\cos\theta_2 - \cos\theta_1\sin\theta_2)}{\cos^2\theta_2 + \sin^2\theta_2}$$

$$= \frac{r_1}{r_2}[\cos(\theta_1 - \theta_2) + i\sin(\theta_1 - \theta_2)] \qquad \textit{sin}^2\,\theta + \cos^2\theta = 1$$

Quotient of Complex Numbers in Polar Form	**The quotient of two complex numbers can be found as follows.** $\dfrac{r_1(\cos\theta_1 + i\sin\theta_1)}{r_2(\cos\theta_2 + i\sin\theta_2)} = \dfrac{r_1}{r_2}[\cos(\theta_1 - \theta_2) + i\sin(\theta_1 - \theta_2)]$

Notice the modulus $\left(\dfrac{r_1}{r_2}\right)$ of the quotient of two complex numbers is the quotient of their moduli. The amplitude $(\theta_1 - \theta_2)$ of the quotient is the difference of the amplitudes.

LESSON 9-7 PRODUCTS AND QUOTIENTS OF COMPLEX NUMBERS IN POLAR FORM 507

EVALUATING THE LESSON

Checking for Understanding

Exercises 1–6 are designed to help you assess students' understanding through reading, writing, speaking, and modeling. You should work through Exercises 1–2 with your students and then monitor their work on Exercises 3–6.

Closing the Lesson

Speaking Activity Have students explain in their own words how they would find the product and quotient of the complex numbers r_1 cis θ_1 and r_2 cis θ_2.

Example 2 Find the quotient $2\left(\cos \frac{\pi}{6} + i \sin \frac{\pi}{6}\right) \div \left(\cos \frac{\pi}{3} + i \sin \frac{\pi}{3}\right)$. Then express the quotient in rectangular form.

Find the modulus and the amplitude.

$$r = \frac{r_1}{r_2} \qquad \theta = \theta_1 - \theta_2$$
$$= \frac{2}{1} \qquad = \frac{\pi}{6} - \frac{\pi}{3}$$
$$= 2 \qquad = -\frac{\pi}{6}$$

Now find the rectangular form of the quotient, $2\left(\cos\left(-\frac{\pi}{6}\right) + i \sin\left(-\frac{\pi}{6}\right)\right)$.

$$2\left(\cos \frac{\pi}{6} + i \sin \frac{\pi}{6}\right) \div \left(\cos \frac{\pi}{3} + i \sin \frac{\pi}{3}\right) = 2\left[\cos\left(-\frac{\pi}{6}\right) + i \sin\left(-\frac{\pi}{6}\right)\right]$$
$$= 2\left[\frac{\sqrt{3}}{2} + \left(-\frac{1}{2}i\right)\right] \text{ or } \sqrt{3} - i$$

The rectangular form is $\sqrt{3} - i$.

CHECKING FOR UNDERSTANDING

Communicating Mathematics

Read and study the lesson to answer each question. 1–2. See margin.

1. **Rewrite** the polar form of the product in Example 1 using r cis θ notation.

2. **Describe** the process you would use to find $(r \text{ cis } \theta)^2$ and the results obtained.
   4. $24\left(\cos \frac{5\pi}{4} + i \sin \frac{5\pi}{4}\right)$, $-12\sqrt{2} - 12i\sqrt{2}$ or $-17.0 - 17.0i$

Guided Practice

Find each product or quotient. Then write the result in rectangular form.

3. $5(\cos \pi + i \sin \pi) \cdot 6(\cos 2\pi + i \sin 2\pi)$ $30(\cos 3\pi + i \sin 3\pi)$, -30

4. $3\left(\cos \frac{3\pi}{4} + i \sin \frac{3\pi}{4}\right) \cdot 8\left(\cos \frac{\pi}{2} + i \sin \frac{\pi}{2}\right)$

5. $15(\cos 2\pi + i \sin 2\pi) \div 5(\cos \pi + i \sin \pi)$ $3(\cos \pi + i \sin \pi)$, -3

6. $6\left(\cos \frac{\pi}{6} + i \sin \frac{\pi}{6}\right) \div 2\left(\cos \frac{2\pi}{3} + i \sin \frac{2\pi}{3}\right)$ $3\left(\cos \frac{3\pi}{2} + i \sin \frac{3\pi}{2}\right)$, $-3i$

EXERCISES

Practice **Find each product or quotient.**

7. $(-1 - i)(1 + i)$ $-2i$

8. $(-4 - 4i\sqrt{3}) \div 2i$ $-2\sqrt{3} + 2i$

9. $(3 + 3i) \div (-2 + 2i)$ $-\frac{3}{2}i$

10. $(-2 + 2i)(\sqrt{3} + i)$
    $-2(1 + \sqrt{3}) - 2i(1 - \sqrt{3})$ or $-5.46 + 1.46i$

Find each product or quotient. Then write the result in rectangular form.

11. $3(\cos 30° + i \sin 30°) \cdot 2(\cos 60° + i \sin 60°)$ $6(\cos 90° + i \sin 90°)$, $6i$

12. $2\left(\cos \frac{2\pi}{3} + i \sin \frac{2\pi}{3}\right) \cdot 3\left(\cos \frac{7\pi}{6} + i \sin \frac{7\pi}{6}\right)$ $6\left(\cos \frac{11\pi}{6} + i \sin \frac{11\pi}{6}\right)$, $3\sqrt{3} - 3i$
    or $5.2 - 3i$

13. $4\left(\cos \frac{3\pi}{4} + i \sin \frac{3\pi}{4}\right) \div \sqrt{2}\left(\cos \frac{2\pi}{3} + i \sin \frac{2\pi}{3}\right)$

    13. $2\sqrt{2}\left(\cos \frac{\pi}{12} + i \sin \frac{\pi}{12}\right)$, $\approx 2.7 + 0.7i$

RETEACHING THE LESSON

Have students find the product of two complex numbers in polar form by first converting the numbers to rectangular form and then multiplying. Have them check their answers using the simplified method of this lesson. Repeat, finding the quotient of two complex numbers in polar form.

Additional Answers

1. Find the product of
   $8 \text{ cis } \frac{3\pi}{4} \cdot 2 \text{ cis } \frac{5\pi}{4}$.

   $16 \text{ cis } \left(\frac{3\pi}{4} + \frac{5\pi}{4}\right)$ $16 \text{ cis } 2\pi$

2. Square its modulus and double its amplitude.
   $(r \text{ cis } \theta)^2 = r^2 \text{ cis } 2\theta$

14. $6\left(\cos\frac{\pi}{6}+i\sin\frac{\pi}{6}\right)\cdot 2\left(\cos\frac{2\pi}{3}+i\sin\frac{2\pi}{3}\right)$ $12\left(\cos\frac{5\pi}{6}+i\sin\frac{5\pi}{6}\right),$ $-6\sqrt{3}+6i$ or $-10.4+6i$

B

15. $3\left(\cos\frac{7\pi}{6}+i\sin\frac{7\pi}{6}\right)\cdot 6\left(\cos\frac{\pi}{6}+i\sin\frac{\pi}{6}\right)$ $18\left(\cos\frac{4\pi}{3}+i\sin\frac{4\pi}{3}\right),-9-9i\sqrt{3}$

16. $3\sqrt{2}\left(\cos\frac{\pi}{4}+i\sin\frac{\pi}{4}\right)\div\sqrt{2}\left(\cos\frac{\pi}{6}+i\sin\frac{\pi}{6}\right)$ $3\left(\cos\frac{\pi}{12}+i\sin\frac{\pi}{12}\right),2.90+0.78i$

17. $2\left(\cos\frac{\pi}{4}+i\sin\frac{\pi}{4}\right)\cdot 3\left(\cos\frac{\pi}{2}+i\sin\frac{\pi}{2}\right)$ $6\left(\cos\frac{3\pi}{4}+i\sin\frac{3\pi}{4}\right),-3\sqrt{2}+3i\sqrt{2}$

18. $12(\cos\pi+i\sin\pi)\div 4\left(\cos\frac{\pi}{6}+i\sin\frac{\pi}{6}\right)$ $3\left(\cos\frac{5\pi}{6}+i\sin\frac{5\pi}{6}\right),\frac{-3\sqrt{3}}{2}+\frac{3}{2}i$

20. $6.4(\cos 2.3+$ $i\sin 2.3),\approx$ $-4.26+4.77i$

19. $9.24(\cos 1.8+i\sin 1.8)\div 3.1(\cos 0.7+i\sin 0.7)$ $2.98(\cos 1.1+i\sin 1.1),$ $\approx 1.35+2.66i$

20. $2(\cos 0.8+i\sin 0.8)\cdot 3.2(\cos 1.5+i\sin 1.5)$

C

21. $\frac{1}{3}\left(\cos\frac{7\pi}{8}+i\sin\frac{7\pi}{8}\right)\cdot 3\sqrt{3}\left[\cos\left(-\frac{\pi}{4}\right)+i\sin\left(-\frac{\pi}{4}\right)\right]$ $\sqrt{3}\left(\cos\frac{5\pi}{8}+i\sin\frac{5\pi}{8}\right),$ $\approx -0.66+1.6i$

22. $6\sqrt{3}\left(\cos\frac{5\pi}{4}+i\sin\frac{5\pi}{4}\right)\div\sqrt{3}\left(\cos\frac{\pi}{6}+i\sin\frac{\pi}{6}\right)$

23. $8\left(\cos\frac{3\pi}{2}+i\sin\frac{3\pi}{2}\right)\div\frac{4}{5}\left(\cos\frac{\pi}{2}+i\sin\frac{\pi}{2}\right)$ $10(\cos\pi+i\sin\pi),-10$

22. $6\left(\cos\frac{13\pi}{12}+i\sin\frac{13\pi}{12}\right),\approx -5.8-1.55i$

Critical Thinking

24. Suppose $a+bi$ is multiplied by $1+i\sqrt{3}$. By how many degrees must the radius from the origin to (a, b) be rotated to coincide with the radius from the pole to the graph of the product? **60°**

Applications and Problem Solving

25. See margin.

25. **Algebra** If s_1 and s_2 are roots of a quadratic equation $ax^2+bx+c=0$, then $s_1+s_2=\frac{-b}{a}$ and $s_1\cdot s_2=\frac{c}{a}$. Verify that $4\sqrt{2}\left(\cos\frac{\pi}{4}+i\sin\frac{\pi}{4}\right)$ and $4\sqrt{2}\left[\cos\left(-\frac{\pi}{4}\right)+i\sin\left(-\frac{\pi}{4}\right)\right]$ are the polar forms of the roots of $x^2-8x+32=0$.

26. **Electricity** The polar form of the voltage of a circuit is $161(\cos 337°+i\sin 337°)$ volts. The polar form of the impedance is $32(\cos 300°+i\sin 300°)$ ohms. Find the polar form of the current. *Use $E=I\cdot Z$.* $\approx 5(\cos 37°+i\sin 37°)$ amps

Mixed Review

27. **Geometry** Two sides of a triangle are 400 feet and 600 feet long, and the included angle measures 46°20′. Find the perimeter and area of the triangle. **(Lesson 5-8)** ≈ 1434 ft, $\approx 86,751$ ft^2

28. Graph $y=\cos 3\theta$ on a rectangular coordinate plane. **(Lesson 6-3)** See margin.

29. Simplify $2(4-3i)(7-2i)$. **(Lesson 9-5)** $44-58i$

30. Express $5\left(\cos\frac{5\pi}{6}+i\sin\frac{5\pi}{6}\right)$ in rectangular form. **(Lesson 9-6)** $\frac{-5\sqrt{3}}{2}+\frac{5}{2}i$

31. **College Entrance Exam** Choose the best answer. **A**
Six quarts of a 20% solution of alcohol in water are mixed with 4 quarts of a 60% solution of alcohol in water. The alcoholic strength of the mixture is

(A) 36% **(B)** 40% **(C)** 48% **(D)** 60% **(E)** 80%

LESSON 9-7 PRODUCTS AND QUOTIENTS OF COMPLEX NUMBERS IN POLAR FORM 509

EXTENDING THE LESSON

Math Power: Problem Solving

Find $\sqrt[3]{8\left(\cos\frac{\pi}{3}+i\sin\frac{\pi}{3}\right)}$.

$2\left(\cos\frac{\pi}{9}+i\sin\frac{\pi}{9}\right)$

Additional Answer

28.

NCTM Standards: 1–6, 8, 14

Lesson Resources

- Practice Master 9–8
- Enrichment Master 9–8
- Evaluation Master, Quiz D, p. 114
- Technology Master, p. 17
- Activity Master, p. 26

Transparency 9–8 contains the 5-Minute Check and a teaching aid for this lesson.

INTRODUCING THE LESSON

5-Minute Check

(over Lesson 9–7)

1. Express the product
   6(cos 60° + *i* sin 60°)
   2(cos 30° + *i* sin 30°) in polar form.
   12(cos 90° + *i* sin 90°)
2. Express the product in Exercise 1 in rectangular form.
   12*i*
3. Express the quotient
   $20\left(\cos \frac{\pi}{2} + i \sin \frac{\pi}{2}\right) \div$
   $5\left(\cos \frac{\pi}{3} + i \sin \frac{\pi}{3}\right)$ in polar form.
   $4\left(\cos \frac{\pi}{6} + i \sin \frac{\pi}{6}\right)$
4. Express the quotient in Exercise 3 in rectangular form.
   $2\sqrt{3} + 2i$

Motivating the Lesson

Tell students to imagine that a new type of number has been defined and that a method for finding the product of two such numbers has been worked out. Let *A**B represent the operation of multiplying *A* by *B*. Ask students to explain how to represent A^2, A^3, and A^n.
$A^2 = A*A$; $A^3 = A*A*A$;
$A^n = A*A*A*\cdots*A$ (*n* times)

9-8 Powers and Roots of Complex Numbers

Objective
9–8

After studying this lesson, you should be able to:
- find powers and roots of complex numbers in polar form using De Moivre's theorem.

Application

Abraham De Moivre (1667–1754) began his work in mathematics with his study of probability. He published his first work, entitled *Doctrine of Chances*, in 1718. He also worked extensively in number theory and in 1730, presented a theorem for finding the power of a complex number written in polar form. You will learn about this theorem, which bears his name, in this lesson.

You can use the formula for the product of complex numbers to find the square of a complex number.

$$[r(\cos \theta + i \sin \theta)]^2 = [r(\cos \theta + i \sin \theta)] \cdot [r(\cos \theta + i \sin \theta)]$$
$$= r^2[\cos(\theta + \theta) + i \sin (\theta + \theta)]$$
$$= r^2(\cos 2\theta + i \sin 2\theta)$$

Other powers of complex numbers can be found by using the theorem developed by Abraham De Moivre.

De Moivre's Theorem	$[r(\cos \theta + i \sin \theta)]^n = r^n(\cos n\theta + i \sin n\theta)$

Mathematical induction will be formally introduced in Chapter 12.

A method of proof called **mathematical induction** can be used to prove that De Moivre's theorem is valid for any positive integer *n*. The theorem has been shown to be valid when $n = 1$ and $n = 2$. Assume the theorem is valid for $n = k$. That is, assume that

$$[r(\cos \theta + i \sin \theta)]^k = r^k(\cos k\theta + i \sin k\theta).$$

ALTERNATE TEACHING STRATEGIES

Using Connections

Summarize mathematical induction. Induction is used to prove that a proposition is true for an infinite sequence of integers. First it is shown that, for every integer *k* for which the proposition is true, it is also true for *k* + 1. Then the proposition is shown to be true for a specific integer *n*. Conclusion: the proposition is true for *n* + 1, (*n* + 1) + 1, and all integers > *n*.

Using Discussion

Use the abbreviation for the polar form of a complex number and these examples to stimulate discussion and clarify the rules for finding powers and roots of complex numbers.
(2 cis 20°)^5 = 2^5 cis 5 · 20°
   = 32 cis 100°
(27 cis 45°)$^{\frac{1}{3}}$ = $27^{\frac{1}{3}}$ cis $\frac{45°}{3}$
   = 3 cis 15°

Multiply each side of the equation by $r(\cos\theta + i\sin\theta)$.

$[r(\cos\theta + i\sin\theta)]^{k+1}$

$\quad = [r^k(\cos\ k\theta + i\sin k\theta)] \cdot [r(\cos\theta + i\sin\theta)]$

$\quad = r^{k+1}(\cos\ k\theta\cos\theta + (\cos k\theta)(i\sin\theta) + i\sin k\theta\cos\theta + i^2\sin k\theta\sin\theta)$

$\quad = r^{k+1}[(\cos\ k\theta\cos\theta - \sin k\theta\sin\theta) + i(\sin k\theta\cos\theta + \cos k\theta\sin\theta)]$

$\quad = r^{k+1}[\cos\ (k\theta + \theta) + i\sin\ (k\theta + \theta)]$ *Sum identities for sine and cosine*

$\quad = r^{k+1}[\cos\ (k+1)\theta + i\sin\ (k+1)\theta]$

Since the right side of the last equation gives the same result as can be obtained directly by substituting $k + 1$ for n, the formula is valid for all positive integral values of n.

Example 1

Find $(1 - i)^8$.

Write $1 - i$ in polar form. Find r and θ.

$r = \sqrt{1^2 + (-1)^2}$
$\quad = \sqrt{2}$

$\theta = \text{Arctan}\ \dfrac{-1}{1}$ $\theta = \text{Arctan}\ \dfrac{v}{x}$ *if x > 0*

$\quad = -\dfrac{\pi}{4}$ or $\dfrac{7\pi}{4}$

$1 - i = \sqrt{2}\left(\cos\dfrac{7\pi}{4} + i\sin\dfrac{7\pi}{4}\right)$

Use De Moivre's theorem to find the 8th power of the complex number in polar form.

$(1 - i)^8 = \left[\sqrt{2}\left(\cos\dfrac{7\pi}{4} + i\sin\dfrac{7\pi}{4}\right)\right]^8$

$\quad = (\sqrt{2})^8\left[\cos 8\left(\dfrac{7\pi}{4}\right) + i\sin 8\left(\dfrac{7\pi}{4}\right)\right]$

$\quad = 16(\cos 14\pi + i\sin 14\pi)$

Write the result in rectangular form.

$16(\cos 14\pi + i\sin 14\pi) = 16[1 + i(0)]$
$\qquad\qquad\qquad\qquad\quad = 16$

Thus, $(1 - i)^8 = 16$.

It can be proven that De Moivre's theorem is also valid when n is a rational number. Therefore, the roots of complex numbers can be found by letting $n = \dfrac{1}{2}, \dfrac{1}{3}, \dfrac{1}{4}, \ldots$. In general, the pth principle root of a complex number can be found as follows.

Chalkboard Example

For Example 1

Find $(1 + i)^5$. $-4 - 4i$

$$(x + yi)^{\frac{1}{p}} = [r(\cos\theta + i\sin\theta)]^{\frac{1}{p}}$$

$$= r^{\frac{1}{p}}\left(\cos\frac{\theta}{p} + i\sin\frac{\theta}{p}\right)$$

Example 2

Find $\sqrt{i}$.

$\sqrt{i} = i^{\frac{1}{2}}$

$\qquad = (0 + i)^{\frac{1}{2}}$

$\qquad = \left[1\left(\cos\dfrac{\pi}{2} + i\sin\dfrac{\pi}{2}\right)\right]^{\frac{1}{2}}$

$x = 0$ *and* $y = 1$
$r = \sqrt{0^2 + 1^2}$ *or* 1
$\theta = Arctan\,\dfrac{1}{0}$ *or* $\dfrac{\pi}{2}$

$\qquad = 1^{\frac{1}{2}}\left[\cos\left(\dfrac{1}{2}\right)\left(\dfrac{\pi}{2}\right) + i\sin\left(\dfrac{1}{2}\right)\left(\dfrac{\pi}{2}\right)\right]$ *De Moivre's theorem*

$\qquad = 1\left(\cos\dfrac{\pi}{4} + i\sin\dfrac{\pi}{4}\right)$

$\qquad = \dfrac{\sqrt{2}}{2} + \dfrac{i\sqrt{2}}{2}$

Thus, $\sqrt{i} = \dfrac{\sqrt{2}}{2} + \dfrac{\sqrt{2}}{2}i$. *This is the principal root of* i.

Example 3

Find $(1 + i)^{\frac{1}{3}}$. Express the answer in the form $a + bi$ with a and b to the nearest hundredth.

In this complex number, $x = 1$ and $y = 1$.

$(1 + i)^{\frac{1}{3}} = \left[\sqrt{2}\left(\cos\dfrac{\pi}{4} + i\sin\dfrac{\pi}{4}\right)\right]^{\frac{1}{3}}$ $r = \sqrt{1^2 + 1^2}$ *or* $\sqrt{2}$
$\theta = Arctan\,\dfrac{1}{1}$ *or* $\dfrac{\pi}{4}$

$\qquad = 2^{\frac{1}{2}\cdot\frac{1}{3}}\left(\cos\dfrac{1}{3}\cdot\dfrac{\pi}{4} + i\sin\dfrac{1}{3}\cdot\dfrac{\pi}{4}\right)$ $\sqrt{2} = 2^{\frac{1}{2}}$

$\qquad = \sqrt[6]{2}\left(\cos\dfrac{\pi}{12} + i\sin\dfrac{\pi}{12}\right)$

$\qquad = 1.084215081 + 0.290514555i$ *Use a calculator.*

The cube root of $(1 + i)^{\frac{1}{3}}$ is about $1.08 + 0.29i$.

It can be proven that any complex number has p distinct pth roots. That is, it has two square roots, three cube roots, four fourth roots, five fifth roots, and so on. Since $\cos\theta = \cos(\theta + 2n\pi)$ and $\sin\theta = \sin(\theta + 2n\pi)$, when $n = 1, 2, 3,...,$ a more general formula for finding pth roots of complex numbers can be written in the following way.

512   CHAPTER 9   POLAR COORDINATES AND COMPLEX NUMBERS

The p distinct pth roots of $x + yi$ can be found by replacing n with 0, 1, 2, ..., $p - 1$, successively, in the following equation.

$$(x + yi)^{\frac{1}{p}} = (r[\cos(\theta + 2n\pi) + i\sin(\theta + 2n\pi)])^{\frac{1}{p}}$$

$$= r^{\frac{1}{p}}\left(\cos\frac{\theta + 2n\pi}{p} + i\sin\frac{\theta + 2n\pi}{p}\right)$$

Example 4

Find three cube roots of -8.

In rectangular form, $-8 = -8 + 0i$. Write the polar form of $-8 + 0i$.

$-8 + 0i = 8[\cos(\pi + 2n\pi) + i\sin(\pi + 2n\pi)]$ $r = \sqrt{8^2 + 0^2}$ or 8

$\theta = \text{Arctan}\,\dfrac{0}{8} + \pi$ or π

Now write an expression for the cube roots of $-8 + 0i$.

$$(-8 + 0i)^{\frac{1}{3}} = (8[\cos(\pi + 2n\pi) + i\sin(\pi + 2n\pi)])^{\frac{1}{3}}$$

$$= 2\left(\cos\frac{\pi + 2n\pi}{3} + i\sin\frac{\pi + 2n\pi}{3}\right)$$

Let $n = 0, 1$, and 2 successively to find the three cube roots.

Let n = 0. $2\left[\cos\left(\dfrac{\pi + 2(0)\pi}{3}\right) + i\sin\left(\dfrac{\pi + 2(0)\pi}{3}\right)\right] = 2\left(\cos\dfrac{\pi}{3} + i\sin\dfrac{\pi}{3}\right)$

$$= 2\left(\frac{1}{2} + i\frac{\sqrt{3}}{2}\right)$$

$$= 1 + i\sqrt{3}$$

Let n = 1. $2\left[\cos\left(\dfrac{\pi + 2(1)\pi}{3}\right) + i\sin\left(\dfrac{\pi + 2(1)\pi}{3}\right)\right] = 2(\cos\pi + i\sin\pi)$

$$= 2(-1) + i(0)$$

$$= -2$$

Let n = 2. $2\left[\cos\left(\dfrac{\pi + 2(2)\pi}{3}\right) + i\sin\left(\dfrac{\pi + 2(2)\pi}{3}\right)\right] = 2\left(\cos\dfrac{5\pi}{3} + i\sin\dfrac{5\pi}{3}\right)$

$$= 2\left[\frac{1}{2} + i\left(\frac{-\sqrt{3}}{2}\right)\right]$$

$$= 1 - i\sqrt{3}$$

The three cube roots of -8 are -2, $1 + i\sqrt{3}$, and $1 - i\sqrt{3}$.
These roots can be checked by multiplication.

You can also determine the nth roots of a number on a graphing calculator.

LESSON 9-8 POWERS AND ROOTS OF COMPLEX NUMBERS   513

After discussing the Graphing Calculator Exploration, have students find the three cube roots of –1 by solving the equation $x^3 + 1 = 0$, using this factorization: $x^3 + 1 = (x + 1)(x^2 - x + 1)$.

$-1, \frac{1}{2} + \frac{\sqrt{3}}{2}i, \frac{1}{2} - \frac{\sqrt{3}}{2}i$

Chalkboard Example

For Example 5

Solve $x^3 + 27 = 0$.

$-3, \frac{3}{2} + \frac{3\sqrt{3}}{2}i, \frac{3}{2} - \frac{3\sqrt{3}}{2}i$

Teaching Tip After Example 5, ask students to explain a simple method for solving the equation $x^4 - 1 = 0$.

$(x^2 + 1)(x^2 - 1) = 0$
$x^2 = -1 \text{ or } x^2 = 1$
$x = i, -i, 1, -1$

Chalkboard Example

For Example 6

Graph the four fourth roots of i.

EXPLORATION: Graphing Calculators

Find the three cube roots of 1.

1. Select the DEG and PARAM modes.
2. Set the parametric range parameters to: *TMIN: 0, TMAX: 360*, and *TSTEP: 120*.
3. Set the viewing window parameters to: *XMIN: –2, XMAX: 2, XSCL: 1, YMIN: –2, YMAX: 2,* and *YSCL: 1.*
4. Enter the parametric equations $x_{1T} = \cos T$ and $y_{1T} = \sin T$.
5. Graph the equations.
6. The vertices of the figure represent the cube roots of 1. Use the TRACE function to find all three cube roots. $-0.5 \pm 0.8660254i, 1$

Find the three cube roots of –1. 8. $0.5 \pm 0.8660254i, -1$

1. Use the same parametric range parameters as above.
2. Enter $x_{1T} = -\cos T$ and $y_{2T} = -\sin T$. Then TRACE.
3. How does the graph of the cube roots of –1 compare with the graph of the cube roots of 1? They are reflections over the y-axis.

You can solve some polynomial equations by using De Moivre's theorem.

Example 5

Solve $x^4 + 1 = 0$.

$$x^4 + 1 = 0$$
$$x^4 = -1$$
$$x^4 = -1 + 0i$$

Write $-1 + 0i$ in polar form.

$-1 + 0i = \cos \pi + i \sin \pi$ $r = \sqrt{1^2 + 0^2}$ or $1, \theta = \text{Arctan} \frac{0}{-1} + \pi$ or π

Then write an expression for the fourth roots of $-1 + 0i$.

$$(-1 + 0i)^{\frac{1}{4}} = [\cos (\pi + 2n\pi) + i \sin (\pi + 2n\pi)]^{\frac{1}{4}}$$
$$= \cos \frac{\pi + 2n\pi}{4} + i \sin \frac{\pi + 2n\pi}{4}$$

Let $n = 0, 1, 2,$ and 3 successively to find the fourth roots, $x_1, x_2, x_3,$ and x_4.

Let $n = 0$. $x_1 = \cos \frac{\pi}{4} + i \sin \frac{\pi}{4} = \frac{\sqrt{2}}{2} + \frac{\sqrt{2}}{2}i$

Let $n = 1$. $x_2 = \cos \frac{3\pi}{4} + i \sin \frac{3\pi}{4} = -\frac{\sqrt{2}}{2} + \frac{\sqrt{2}}{2}i$

Let $n = 2$. $x_3 = \cos \frac{5\pi}{4} + i \sin \frac{5\pi}{4} = -\frac{\sqrt{2}}{2} - \frac{\sqrt{2}}{2}i$

Let $n = 3$. $x_4 = \cos \frac{7\pi}{4} + i \sin \frac{7\pi}{4} = \frac{\sqrt{2}}{2} - \frac{\sqrt{2}}{2}i$

The roots of $x^4 + 1 = 0$ are $\frac{\sqrt{2}}{2} \pm \frac{\sqrt{2}}{2}i$ and $-\frac{\sqrt{2}}{2} \pm \frac{\sqrt{2}}{2}i$.

514   CHAPTER 9   POLAR COORDINATES AND COMPLEX NUMBERS

The roots of a complex number are cyclical in nature. That means, when the roots are graphed on the complex plane, the roots are equally spaced around a circle. The graphs below show the cube roots of 1 and the fourth roots of –1.

Compare the graph of the fourth roots of –1 with the results from Example 5.

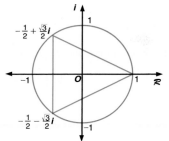

The cube roots of 1 form the vertices of an equilateral triangle.

The fourth roots of –1 form the vertices of a square.

If one pth root of a complex number is known, all the pth roots can be graphed on the complex plane.

Example 6

Graph the three cube roots of 27.

The modulus of $27 + 0i$ is 27, and $27^{\frac{1}{3}} = 3$. Graph $r = 3$ on the complex plane.

One of the cube roots is $(3 + 0i)$. Graph this point.

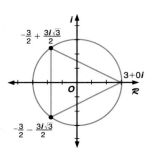

Since the roots are cyclic, they will occur at equal intervals. To find these intervals, divide 360° by 3. Each interval is 120°. Graph $(3, 120°)$ and $(3, 240°)$.

You can solve the equation $x^3 - 27 = 0$ to find the exact roots.

The three roots are $3 + 0i$, $-\frac{3}{2} + \frac{3i\sqrt{3}}{2}$, and $-\frac{3}{2} - \frac{3i\sqrt{3}}{2}$.

CHECKING FOR UNDERSTANDING

Communicating Mathematics

Read and study the lesson to answer each question.

1. **Find** the product $(1 + i)(1 + i)(1 + i)(1 + i)(1 + i)$ by traditional multiplication. Compare the results with the results using De Moivre's theorem on $(1 + i)^5$. Which method do you prefer? Same results, $-4 - 4i$; answers may vary.

2. **Describe** the geometric figures formed by the graphs of the roots of each of the following.

   a. $x^{\frac{1}{3}}$ equilateral triangle   **b.** $x^{\frac{1}{4}}$ square   **c.** $x^{\frac{1}{6}}$ regular hexagon

3. **Determine** which degree intervals you would use to graph the 6th roots of 64. What is the principal 6th root? 360° ÷ 6 = 60° intervals; 2

LESSON 9-8   POWERS AND ROOTS OF COMPLEX NUMBERS   515

Homework Exercises

The red A, B, and C flags, printed only in the Teacher's Wraparound Edition, indicate the level of difficulty of the exercises.

Chapter 9, Quiz D, (Lessons 9–7 through 9–8) is available in the *Evaluation Masters*, p. 114.

Using Technology

In Exercises 28–30, students can check their answers by solving the related equation such as $x^6 - 1 = 0$ for Exercise 29, using difference of two squares and difference of two cubes factorizations.

Using Technology

The program given in Exercise 31 is for use with a TI-81 graphing calculator. For other programmable calculators, have students consult their owner's manual for commands similar to those presented here.

Additional Answers

22. $\frac{1}{2} \pm \frac{\sqrt{3}}{2}i, -1$

23. $1, 0.31 \pm 0.95i, -0.81 \pm 0.59i$

24. $2, -1 \pm i\sqrt{3}$

25. $\pm i, \frac{\sqrt{3}}{2} \pm \frac{1}{2}i, \frac{-\sqrt{3}}{2} \pm \frac{1}{2}i$

26. $\pm 1, \pm i$

27. $0.81 \pm 0.59i, -1, -0.31 \pm 0.95i$

Guided Practice **Find each power. Express the result in rectangular form.**

4. $\left(\cos \frac{\pi}{6} + i \sin \frac{\pi}{6}\right)^4$ $-\frac{1}{2} + \frac{\sqrt{3}}{2}i$

5. $\left[3 \left(\cos \frac{\pi}{3} + i \sin \frac{\pi}{3}\right)\right]^2$ $-\frac{9}{2} + \frac{9\sqrt{3}}{2}i$

6. $(\sqrt{2} + i\sqrt{2})^5$ $-16\sqrt{2} - 16i\sqrt{2}$

7. $\left(-\frac{\sqrt{3}}{2} - \frac{i}{2}\right)^3$ $-i$

Find each root. Express the result in rectangular form.

8. $(4i)^{\frac{1}{2}}$ $\sqrt{2} + i\sqrt{2}$

9. $[-1(\cos \pi + i \sin \pi)]^{\frac{1}{3}}$ $-\frac{1}{2} - \frac{\sqrt{3}}{2}i$

EXERCISES

Practice **Find each power. Express the result in rectangular form.**

10. $(1 - i)^5$ $-4 + 4i$

11. $(3 + 4i)^4$ $-527 - 336i$

12. $[-3(1 - i)]^3$ $54 + 54i$

13. $(1 + i)^{20}$ -1024

14. $(-2 + 2i\sqrt{3})^4$ $-128 + 128i\sqrt{3}$

15. $(12i - 5)^2$ $-119 - 120i$

Find each root. Express the result in the form $a + bi$, with a and b to the nearest hundredth.

16. $(0 + 8i)^{\frac{1}{3}}$ $1.73 + i$

17. $[-2(1 + i)]^{\frac{1}{4}}$ $0.72 + 1.08i$

18. $\sqrt[10]{-4i}$ $1.02 + 0.52i$

19. $(0 + 1i)^{\frac{1}{3}}$ $\frac{\sqrt{3}}{2} + \frac{1}{2}i$ or $0.87 + 0.5i$

20. $(-1)^{\frac{1}{5}}$ $0.81 + 0.59i$

21. $\sqrt[4]{-2 + 2i\sqrt{3}}$ $1.22 + 0.71i$

22–27. See margin. For graphs, see Teacher's Answer Key.
Solve each equation. Then graph the roots on the complex plane.

22. $x^3 + 1 = 0$

23. $x^5 = 1$

24. $x^3 - 8 = 0$

25. $x^6 = -1$

26. $x^4 + 1 = 2$

27. $x^5 - 6 = -7$

Graphing Calculator

Use a graphing calculator and parametric equations to find the roots.

28. $\sqrt[4]{1}$ $-1, 1, -i, i$

29. $\sqrt[6]{1}$

30. $\sqrt[5]{1}$

29. $\pm 1 + 0i, -0.5 \pm 0.87i, 0.5 \pm 0.87i$ 30. $1 + 0i, 0.31 \pm 0.95i, -0.81 \pm 0.59i$

Programming

31. The following program will calculate powers of complex numbers.

```
Prgm 9: CMPLXPWR
:ClrHome                          Clears the text screen
:Disp "ENTER A IN A + BI."        Displays message.
:Input A                          Accepts a value of a.
:Disp "ENTER B IN A + BI."
:Input B
:Disp "ENTER POWER."
:Input P
:R ▶ P(A, B)                      Converts rectangular coordinates to polar.
:R^Pcos Pθ→X                      Calculates real part of power.
:R^Psin Pθ→Y                      Calculates imaginary part of power.
```

```
:Disp "REAL PART = "
:Disp X
:Disp "IMAGINARY PART = "
:Disp Y
```

31a. $2 + 11i$
31b. $-7 + 24i$
31d. See margin.

Use the program to find each power.

a. $(2 + i)^3$ **b.** $(1 - 2i)^4$ **c.** $(0 - 3i)^8$ 6561

d. Write a similar program to find the roots of a complex number.

Critical Thinking

32. How many distinct integral divisors exist for 42^3, excluding 1 and 42^3? Explain how you arrived at your solution. Explanations will vary, 62.

33. Refer to the Graphing Calculator Exploration on page 514.

a. What Tstep values should be set in order to find the nth roots of 1? $\dfrac{360°}{n}$

b. What would you see after graphing the parametric equations associated with this process? a regular n-gon with one vertex at (1, 0)

Applications and Problem Solving

34. Science A buzzard will soar for hours circling its prospective meal. Buzzards actually circle in a pattern that can be modeled by successive powers of z^n, where $z = 1.1(\cos \dfrac{\pi}{3} + i \sin \dfrac{\pi}{3})$. Graph the course of the buzzard for $n = 8, 7, 6, \cdots, 2, 1, \dfrac{1}{2}, \dfrac{1}{3}, \dfrac{1}{4}, \dfrac{1}{5}$. See margin.

Mixed Review

35. Find the slope of the line tangent to the graph of $y = -2x^2 + 3x + 1$ at $(1, 2)$. **(Lesson 3-6)** -1

36. Travel Martina went to Acapulco, Mexico, on a vacation with her parents. One of the sights they visited was a cliff-diving exhibition into the waters of the Gulf of Mexico. Martina stood at a lookout site on top of a 200-foot cliff. A team of medical experts were in a boat below in case of an accident. The angle of depression to the boat was 21°. How far is the boat from the base of the cliff? **(Lesson 5-5)** about 521 feet

37. Food Industry Fishmongers will often place ice over freshly-caught fish that are to be shipped to preserve the freshness without freezing. Suppose a block of ice weighing 300 kilograms is held on an ice slide by a rope parallel to the slide. The slide is inclined at an angle of 22°. **(Lesson 8-5)**

a. What is the pull on the rope? 800.8 kg

b. What is the force on the slide? 278.2 kg

38. Express $\sqrt{2}\left(\cos \dfrac{-\pi}{2} + i \sin \dfrac{-\pi}{2}\right)$ in rectangular form. **(Lesson 9-6)** $0 - i\sqrt{2}$

39. Find the product $5\left(\cos \dfrac{3\pi}{4} + i \sin \dfrac{3\pi}{4}\right) \cdot 2(\cos \dfrac{2\pi}{3} + i \sin \dfrac{2\pi}{3})$. Then express it in rectangular form. **(Lesson 9-7)** $10\left(\cos \dfrac{17\pi}{12} + i \sin \dfrac{17\pi}{12}\right)$, $-2.59 - 9.66i$

40. College Entrance Exam Choose the best answer. C
$\star x$ is defined such that $\star x = x^2 - 2x$. The value of $\star 2 - \star 1$ is

(A) -1 **(B)** 0   **(C)** 1   **(D)** 2   **(E)** 4

LESSON 9-8 POWERS AND ROOTS OF COMPLEX NUMBERS 517

EXTENDING THE LESSON

Math Power: Reasoning

When they are graphed on the complex plane, the pth roots of a complex number are spaced at intervals of $\dfrac{\pi}{9}$ around a circle.

Find p.   18

Additional Answer

34.

Using the Chapter Summary and Review

The Chapter Summary and Review begins with an alphabetical listing of the new terms that were presented in the chapter. Have students define each term and provide an example of it, if appropriate.

The Skills and Concepts presented in the chapter are reviewed using a side-by-side format. Encourage students to refer to the Objectives and Examples on the left as they complete the review exercises on the right.

The Chapter Summary and Review ends with exercises that review Applications and Problem Solving.

Additional Answers

9.

10.

11.

12.

VOCABULARY

Upon completing this chapter, you should be familiar with the following terms:

501 amplitude	**466** polar axis	**469** polar graph
475 classical curve	**466** polar coordinate system	**466** pole
496 conjugate	**469** polar equation	**501** rectangular form
501 modulus	**502** polar form	**502** trigonometric form

SKILLS AND CONCEPTS

OBJECTIVES AND EXAMPLES	REVIEW EXERCISES
Upon completing this chapter, you should be able to:	Use these exercises to review and prepare for the chapter test.

■ graph polar coordinates and simple polar equations **(Lesson 9-1)**

Graph point P that has polar coordinates $\left(-2, \dfrac{5\pi}{6}\right)$.

Graph the point that has the given polar coordinates. Then, name three other pairs of polar coordinates for each point.

1. $(-3, 50°)$ **2.** $(1.5, -110°)$

3. $\left(2, \dfrac{\pi}{4}\right)$ **4.** $\left(-3, -\dfrac{\pi}{2}\right)$

Graph each polar equation.

5. $r = \sqrt{7}$ **6.** $r = -2$

7. $\theta = -80°$ **8.** $\theta = \dfrac{3\pi}{4}$

1–8. See Teacher's Answer Key.

■ graph polar equations **(Lesson 9-2)**

Graph $r = 3 + 3 \sin \theta$.

This graph is a cardioid.

Graph each polar equation. Identify the classical curve it represents.

9. $r = 7 \cos \theta$ rose

10. $r = 2 + 4 \cos \theta$ limaçon

11. $r = 3\theta$ spiral of Archimedes

12. $r = 6 \sin 2\theta$ rose
9–12. See margin for graphs.

OBJECTIVES AND EXAMPLES

■ change from polar coordinates to rectangular coordinates and vice versa
(Lesson 9-3)

Find the rectangular coordinates of $C(-3, 0.8)$.

$x = r \cos \theta \qquad y = r \sin \theta$
$\quad = -3 \cos (0.8) \quad = -3 \sin (0.8)$
$\quad = -2.09 \qquad\quad = -2.15$

The rectangular coordinates of C are $(-2.09, -2.15)$.

■ write the polar form of a linear equation
(Lesson 9-4)

Write $\sqrt{2}x - \sqrt{2}y - 6 = 0$ in polar form.

The normal form is $\dfrac{\sqrt{2}}{2}x - \dfrac{\sqrt{2}}{2}y - 3 = 0$.

So, $\cos \phi = \dfrac{\sqrt{2}}{2}$, $\sin \phi = -\dfrac{\sqrt{2}}{2}$, and $p = 3$. Thus, $\phi = -45°$ or $315°$.

The polar form is $3 = r \cos (\theta - 315°)$.

■ add subtract, multiply, and divide complex numbers in rectangular form.
(Lesson 9-5)

Simplify $(2 - 4i) - (5 + 2i)$.
$(2 - 4i) - (5 + 2i) = 2 - 4i - 5 - 2i$
$\qquad\qquad = (2 - 5) + (-4i - 2i)$
$\qquad\qquad = -3 - 6i$

■ convert complex numbers from rectangular to polar form and vice versa
(Lesson 9-6)

Express $4 - 3i$ in polar form.

$r = \sqrt{4^2 + (-3)^2} \qquad \theta = \text{Arctan } \dfrac{y}{x} + \pi$

$\quad = 5 \qquad\qquad\qquad = \text{Arctan } \dfrac{-3}{4} + \pi$

$\qquad\qquad\qquad\qquad\quad = 2.50$

The polar form is $(5, 2.5)$.

REVIEW EXERCISES

Find the rectangular coordinates of each point with the given polar coordinates.

13. $\left(6, \dfrac{\pi}{4}\right)$ $(3\sqrt{2}, 3\sqrt{2})$ **14.** $\left(2, -\dfrac{\pi}{6}\right)$ $(\sqrt{3}, -1)$

15. $(-2, 2.3)$ $\quad\quad$ **16.** $(-1, -4.5)$
$\quad (1.33, -1.49) \qquad\qquad (0.21, -0.98)$

Find the polar coordinates of each point with the given rectangular coordinates.

17. $(-\sqrt{3}, -3)$ $\left(2\sqrt{3}, \dfrac{4\pi}{3}\right)$ **18.** $(5, 5)$ $\left(5\sqrt{2}, \dfrac{\pi}{4}\right)$

19. $(3, -2)$ $(3.61, -0.59)$ **20.** $(-4, 2)$ $(4.47, 2.68)$

Write each equation in polar form. Round θ to the nearest degree.

21. $2x + y = -3$ $\dfrac{3\sqrt{5}}{5} = r \cos (\theta - 207°)$

22. $y = -3x - 4$ $\dfrac{2\sqrt{10}}{5} = r \cos (\theta - 198°)$

Write each equation in rectangular form.

23. $3 = r \cos \left(\theta - \dfrac{\pi}{3}\right)$ $x + \sqrt{3}y - 6 = 0$

24. $4 = r \cos \left(\theta + \dfrac{\pi}{2}\right)$ $y + 4 = 0$

Simplify.

25. $(2 + 3i) + (4 - 4i)$ $6 - i$

26. $(-3 - i) - (2 + 7i)$ $-5 - 8i$

27. $i^{10} \cdot i^{25}$ $-i$ $\qquad\qquad$ **28.** $i^3(4 - 3i)$ $-3 - 4i$

29. $(-i - 7)(i - 7)$ 50 $\quad$ **30.** $\dfrac{4 + i}{5 - 2i}$ $\dfrac{18 + 13i}{29}$

31. $\dfrac{5}{\sqrt{2} - 4i}$ $\dfrac{5\sqrt{2} + 20i}{18}$ **32.** $\dfrac{8 - i}{2 + 3i}$ $1 - 2i$

Express each complex number in polar form.

33. $-2 + 2i\sqrt{3}$ $\qquad\qquad$ **34.** $6 - 8i$
33–34. See margin.

Express each complex number in rectangular form.

35. $4\left(\cos \dfrac{5\pi}{6} + i \sin \dfrac{5\pi}{6}\right)$ $-2\sqrt{3} + 2i$

36. $8\left(\cos \dfrac{7\pi}{4} + i \sin \dfrac{7\pi}{4}\right)$ $4\sqrt{2} - 4i\sqrt{2}$

Alternate Review Strategy

To provide a brief in-class review, you may wish to read the following questions to your students and have them answer verbally.

1. Name three different pairs of polar coordinates that represent point A (2, 20°).
   (2, –340°), (–2, 200°), (–2, –160°)
2. Describe the graph $r = 2$.
   a circle of radius 2 with center at the origin
3. Identify the classical curve that the graph of $r = 2 \cos 3\theta$ represents. **rose**
4. Find the rectangular coordinates of the point (4, 30°). **$(2\sqrt{3}, 2)$**
5. Give the equation $r = 3$ in rectangular form.
   $x^2 + y^2 = 9$
6. Give the polar form of a linear equation 8 units from the origin if the normal makes a 75° angle with the positive x-axis. **$8 = r \cos (\theta - 75°)$**
7. Simplify $(3 - i)(-4 + 2i)$.
   $-10 + 10i$
8. Express $4 + 3i$ in polar form.
   $5(\cos 0.64 + i \sin 0.64)$
9. Find the product $(2 \text{ cis } 20°) \cdot (4 \text{ cis } 50°)$. **8 cis 70°**
10. Find $(2 \text{ cis } 12°)^5$. **32 cis 60°**

For more information on other methods of alternate assessment, you may wish to refer to Glencoe's *Alternate Assessment in the Mathematics Classroom.*

Additional Answers

33. $4\left(\cos \dfrac{2\pi}{3} + i \sin \dfrac{2\pi}{3}\right)$

34. $10(\cos (-0.93) + i \sin (-0.93))$

Two multiple-choice tests (Forms 1A and 1B) and two free-response tests (Form 2A and 2B) are provided in the *Evaluation Masters*. Chapter 9 Test, Form 1A is shown below. Chapter 9 Test, Form 2A is shown on the next page.

Evaluation Masters Booklet, pp. 105–106

- find the product and quotient of complex numbers in polar form **(Lesson 9-7)**

Find the product
$$3\left(\cos\frac{\pi}{2}+i\sin\frac{\pi}{2}\right)\cdot 2\left(\cos\frac{3\pi}{4}+i\sin\frac{3\pi}{4}\right).$$
Then express in rectangular form.

$$r = r_1 r_2 \qquad \theta = \theta_1 + \theta_2$$
$$= 3(2) \qquad = \frac{\pi}{2}+\frac{3\pi}{4}$$
$$= 6 \qquad = \frac{5\pi}{4}$$

The product is $6\left(\cos\frac{5\pi}{4}+i\sin\frac{5\pi}{4}\right)$ or $-3\sqrt{2}+3\sqrt{2}i$, in rectangular form.

- find powers and roots of complex numbers in polar form using De Moivre's theorem **(Lesson 9-8)**

Find $(3-3i)^{\frac{1}{2}}$.

$$(-3+3i)^{\frac{1}{2}} = \left[3\sqrt{2}\left(\cos\frac{3\pi}{4}+i\sin\frac{3\pi}{4}\right)\right]^{\frac{1}{2}}$$
$$= (3\sqrt{2})^{\frac{1}{2}}\left(\cos\frac{3\pi}{8}+i\sin\frac{3\pi}{8}\right)$$
$$= 2.06(0.38+0.92i)$$
$$= 0.78+1.90i$$

Find each product or quotient. Then write the result in rectangular form. 37–41. See margin.

37. $2\left(\cos\frac{\pi}{3}+i\sin\frac{\pi}{3}\right)\cdot 4\left(\cos\frac{\pi}{3}+i\sin\frac{\pi}{3}\right)$

38. $1.9(\cos 2.1 + i\sin 2.1)\cdot 3(\cos 0.8 + i\sin 0.8)$

39. $8\left(\cos\frac{7\pi}{6}+i\sin\frac{7\pi}{6}\right)\div 2\left(\cos\frac{5\pi}{3}+i\sin\frac{5\pi}{3}\right)$

40. $6\left(\cos\frac{\pi}{2}+i\sin\frac{\pi}{2}\right)\div 4\left(\cos\frac{\pi}{6}+i\sin\frac{\pi}{6}\right)$

41. $2.2(\cos 1.5 + i\sin 1.5)\div 4.4(\cos 0.6 + i\sin 0.6)$

Find each power. Express the result in rectangular form. 42–47. See margin.

42. $(2+2i)^8$ 43. $(\sqrt{3}-i)^7$
44. $(-1+i)^4$ 45. $(-2-2i\sqrt{3})^3$

Find each root. Express the result in the form $a+bi$, with a and b to the nearest hundredth.

46. $\sqrt[4]{i}$ 47. $(\sqrt{3}+i)^{\frac{1}{3}}$
48–49. See Teacher's Answer Key.

Solve each equation. Then graph the roots.

48. $x^5 - 32 = 0$ 49. $x^6 - 1 = 0$

APPLICATIONS AND PROBLEM SOLVING

50. **Chemistry** An electron moves about the nucleus of an atom at such a high speed that if it were visible to the eye, it would appear as a cloud. Identify the classical curve represented by the electron cloud at the right. **(Lesson 9-2)**
lemniscate

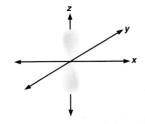

51. **Electricity** Find the current of a circuit of $(50+180j)$ volts with an impedance of $(4+5j)$ ohms. *Use $E = I \cdot Z$.* **(Lesson 9-5)** $(22.44 + 16.95j)$ amps

520 CHAPTER 9 POLAR COORDINATES AND COMPLEX NUMBERS

Additional Answers

37. $8\left(\cos\frac{2\pi}{3}+i\sin\frac{2\pi}{3}\right)$;

$-4+4i\sqrt{3}$

38. $5.7(\cos 2.9 + i\sin 2.9)$; $-5.53 + 1.36i$

39. $4\left[\cos\left(\frac{-\pi}{2}\right)+i\sin\left(\frac{-\pi}{2}\right)\right]$; $-4i$

40. $\frac{3}{2}\left(\cos\frac{\pi}{3}+i\sin\frac{\pi}{3}\right)$;

$\frac{3}{4}+\frac{3\sqrt{3}}{4}i$

41. $0.5(\cos 0.9 + i\sin 0.9)$
0.31 + 0.39i

42. 4096

43. $-64\sqrt{3}+64i$

44. -4

45. 64

46. $0.92 + 0.38i$

47. $1.24 + 0.22i$

Graph the point that has the given polar coordinates. Then, name three other pairs of polar coordinates for each point. 1–4. See Teacher's Answer Key.

1. $\left(-2, \dfrac{5\pi}{4}\right)$ 2. $\left(3, -\dfrac{\pi}{6}\right)$ 3. $(2.5, 140°)$ 4. $(-1.7, 25°)$

Graph each polar equation. 5–10. See Teacher's Answer Key.

5. $r = -4$ 6. $\theta = \dfrac{3\pi}{2}$ 7. $r = 8 \sin \theta$

8. $r = 10 \sin 2\theta$ 9. $r = 6 \cos 3\theta$ 10. $r = 6 + \sin \theta$

Find the rectangular coordinates of each point with the given polar coordinates.

11. $\left(3, -\dfrac{5\pi}{4}\right)$ $\left(-\dfrac{3\sqrt{2}}{2}, \dfrac{3\sqrt{2}}{2}\right)$ 12. $(-4, 1.4)$ $(-0.68, -3.94)$ 13. $\left(2\sqrt{2}, \dfrac{\pi}{4}\right)$ $(2, 2)$

Write each equation in polar form. Round ϕ to the nearest degree. 14–16. See margin.

14. $5x + 6y = -3$ 15. $2x - 4y = 1$ 16. $y = -\dfrac{1}{3}x + 2$

Simplify.

17. i^{93} i 18. $(2 - 5i) + (-2 + 4i)$ $-i$ 19. $(-4 + i) - (4 - 2i)$ $-8 + 3i$

20. $(3 + 5i)(3 - 2i)$ $19 + 9i$ 21. $(7 + i)^2$ $48 + 14i$ 22. $\dfrac{6 - 2i}{2 + i}$ $2 - 2i$

Express each complex number in polar form. 23–25. See margin.

23. $-4 + 4i$ 24. -5 25. $6 - 6i\sqrt{3}$

Find each product or quotient. Then write the result in rectangular form.

26. $4\left(\cos \dfrac{3\pi}{2} + i \sin \dfrac{3\pi}{2}\right) \cdot 3\left(\cos \dfrac{\pi}{4} + i \sin \dfrac{\pi}{4}\right)$ $12\left(\cos \dfrac{7\pi}{4} + i \sin \dfrac{7\pi}{4}\right)$; $6\sqrt{2} - 6i\sqrt{2}$

27. $(\sqrt{3} - 3i)(\sqrt{3} + i)$ $6 - 2i\sqrt{3}$

28. $2\sqrt{3}\left(\cos \dfrac{2\pi}{3} + i \sin \dfrac{2\pi}{3}\right) \div \sqrt{3}\left(\cos \dfrac{\pi}{6} + i \sin \dfrac{\pi}{6}\right)$ $2\left(\cos \dfrac{\pi}{2} + i \sin \dfrac{\pi}{2}\right)$; $2i$

29. Find $(1 - i)^8$.   16
30. Find $\sqrt[3]{-8i}$. $-\sqrt{3} - i$ or $-1.73 - i$
31. Find all roots of $x^8 - 1 = 0$. $1, \dfrac{\sqrt{2}}{2} + \dfrac{\sqrt{2}}{2}i, i, -\dfrac{\sqrt{2}}{2} + \dfrac{\sqrt{2}}{2}i, -1, -\dfrac{\sqrt{2}}{2} - \dfrac{\sqrt{2}}{2}i, -i, \dfrac{\sqrt{2}}{2} - \dfrac{\sqrt{2}}{2}i$

32. **Electricity** The polar form of the current of a circuit is $8(\cos 307° + j \sin 307°)$. The polar form of the impedance is $20(\cos 115° + j \sin 115°)$. Find the polar form of the voltage of this circuit. *Use $E = I \cdot Z$.* $160(\cos 62° + j \sin 62°)$

33. **Number Theory** Find the zeros of $f(x) = 3x^2 + 6x + 7$. Graph them on the complex plane. $-1 \pm \dfrac{2i\sqrt{3}}{3}$; For graph, see Teacher's Answer Key.

Bonus   Graph $r = 3 \tan \theta$.   See Teacher's Answer Key.

Test Generator Software is provided in Apple, IBM, and Macintosh versions. You may use this software to create your own tests, based on the needs of your students.

This page may be used as a test or as a review. All answers to this test appear in the Selected Answers in the student text.

Standardized Test Questions are also provided in the *Evaluation Masters*.

Evaluation Masters Booklet, pp. 109–110

Additional Answers

14. $\dfrac{3}{\sqrt{61}} = r \cos (\theta - 230°)$

15. $\dfrac{1}{2\sqrt{5}} = r \cos (\theta + 63°)$

16. $\dfrac{6}{\sqrt{10}} = r \cos (\theta - 72°)$

23. $4\sqrt{2}\left(\cos \dfrac{3\pi}{4} + i \sin \dfrac{3\pi}{4}\right)$

24. $5(\cos \pi + i \sin \pi)$

25. $12\left[\cos\left(-\dfrac{\pi}{3}\right) + i \sin \left(-\dfrac{\pi}{3}\right)\right]$

PREVIEWING THE CHAPTER

This chapter explores the characteristics of the conic sections, their graphs, and how they are interrelated in the general form. First students review the equation and graph of a circle. They learn to translate the graph to different center points. Building on these skills, students learn the standard and general forms of the equations for parabolas, ellipses, and hyperbolas. They also graph these equations. Students learn to recognize the conic sections by their equation and find the eccentricity of the graphs. Graphs of the conic sections are translated and rotated using matrices. Students also learn to write equations of the tangents and the normals to conic section curves.

Lesson Objective Chart

Lesson (Pages)	Lesson Objectives	State/Local Objectives
10-1 (524-532)	**10-1A:** Use the standard and general forms of the equation of a circle.	
	10-1B: Graph circles.	
10-2 (534-541)	**10-2A:** Use the standard and general forms of the equation of a parabola.	
	10-2B: Graph parabolas.	
10-3 (542-550)	**10-3A:** Use the standard and general forms of the equation of an ellipse.	
	10-3B: Graph ellipses.	
10-4 (551-559)	**10-4A:** Use the standard and general forms of the equation of a hyperbola.	
	10-4B: Graph hyperbolas.	
10-5 (561-567)	**10-5A:** Recognize conic sections by their equations.	
	10-5B: Find the eccentricity of conic sections.	
10-6 (570-576)	**10-6A:** Find the equations of conic sections that have been translated or rotated.	
	10-6B: Find the angle of rotation for a given equation and sketch its graph.	
10-7 (579-584)	**10-7:** Graph and solve systems of second-degree equations and inequalities.	
10-8 (585-591)	**10-8A:** Write equations of tangents and normals to conic sections.	
	10-8B: Find the length of a segment tangent to a circle.	

ORGANIZING THE CHAPTER

You may want to refer to the **Course Planning Guide Calendar** on pages T34-T35 for a complete pacing chart.

Lesson Planning Guide

Lesson	Pages	Practice	Enrichment	Evaluation	Graphing Calculator	Computer	Multicultural Activity	Applications	Problem Solving	Case Study Follow-Up	Decision Making	Transparencies
					Technology			Activity Masters				
10-1	524-532	p. 65	p. 65							p. 30		10-1
10-2	534-541	p. 66	p. 66	Quiz A, p. 125								10-2
10-3	542-550	p. 67	p. 67									10-3
10-4	551-559	p. 68	p. 68	Quiz B, p. 125 Mid-Chapter Test, p.127	p. 19			p. 28				10-4
10-5	561-567	p. 69	p. 69			p. 20			p. 29			10-5
10-6	570-576	p. 70	p. 70	Quiz C, p. 126								10-6
10-7	579-584	p. 71	p. 71				p. 10					10-7
10-8	585-591	p. 72	p. 72	Quiz D, p. 126								10-8
Review	592-594	Multiple Choice Tests, Forms 1A and 1B, pp. 117-120 Free Response Tests, Forms 2A and 2B, pp. 121-124 Standardized Test Questions, p. 128										
Test	595											

Other Chapter Resources

Student Edition
Case Study Follow-Up, p. 550
Decision Making, p. 532
Technology, p. 560

Other Supplements
Transparency 10-0 for Chapter Opener
Alternate Assessment in the Mathematics Classroom,
    Glencoe Publishing Co., 1993
Cooperative Learning in the Mathematics Classroom,
    Glencoe Publishing Co., 1993

Software
Test and Review Generator Software
    Available for Apple, IBM, and Macintosh
Teacher's Guide for Software Resources

ENHANCING THE CHAPTER

Cooperative Learning

Explaining the Task

To make sure that students focus on the relevant concepts and skills throughout the session, it is important that you provide them with a clear understanding of the academic task that they are to complete. Be sure to explain clearly the objectives that are to be achieved and the procedures that students are expected to follow. Review and define pertinent concepts and, when possible, connect the task and objectives to students' previously-acquired knowledge and experience. Then, provide examples to help students comprehend what it is they are to do and to learn. Finally, ask the class specific questions about the assignment to make sure all students understand what the assignment is and how they are to proceed. Although students in a cooperative-learning group can ask one another about that which they do not understand, you can help make sure that such questions are appropriately and productively related to the new content by beginning every session with a clear definition of the task and procedures.

For more information on cooperative learning, see pages T20-T21. Additional information on using cooperative groups is available in Glencoe's *Cooperative Learning in the Mathematics Classroom*, ©1993.

Multicultural

Multicultural Activity Masters, p. 10

> **10** NAME _____ DATE _____
> **Multicultural Activity** (Use after Lesson 10-7)
>
> **Ancient Problems: Duplication of the Cube**
>
> One of the problems that attracted the interest of the early Greek mathematicians was the duplication of the cube. In this case, "duplication" does not mean making an exact copy. The problem is to find the side of a cube whose volume is double that of a given cube.
>
> Geometric construction, using only a compass and a straightedge, was the only method the Greeks had to solve the problem. It turns out that, under these restrictions, there is no way to solve the problem. However, it can be solved by using conic sections. The duplication of the cube can be written algebraically as $x^3 = 2a^3$, where a is the length of a side of the given cube.
>
> **Solve each problem.**
>
> 1. The first mathematician to make some progress on the duplication of the cube was Hippocrates of Chios, who lived around 420 B.C. He transformed the problem into a three-part proportion, $a:x = x:y = y:2a$. Use the proportion to write a system of two quadratic equations. Then show that the system is equivalent to the algebraic statement of the problem given above.
> $ay = x^2$ and $2ax = y^2$; $y = \frac{x^2}{a}$, $2ax = \frac{x^4}{a^2}$, so $2a^3 = x^3$
>
> 2. About 340 B.C. Menaechmus found that the solution is the intersection of the parabolas $y^2 = 2ax$ and $x^2 = ay$. Graph the parabolas and estimate the solution if a equals 5 units. $x \approx 6.5$
>
>
>
> 3. In the 1600s, Descartes pointed out a slightly different solution. He used the system below.
> $x^2 = ay$
> $x^2 + y^2 = ay + bx$
>   In Descartes' solution, $b = 2a$. Graph the system and estimate the solution if a equals 4 units. $x \approx 5$
>
> T 10
> Glencoe Division, Macmillan/McGraw-Hill

Activity Masters

Applications, p. 28

> **10** NAME _____ DATE _____
> **Applications** (Use after Lesson 10-6)
>
> **Planetary Orbits**
>
> The orbit of a planet around the sun is an ellipse with the sun at one focus. Let the pole of a polar coordinate system be that focus and the polar axis passes through the other focus. The polar equation of an ellipse is $r = \frac{2ep}{1 - e\cos\theta}$. Since $2p = \frac{b^2}{c}$ and
>
> $b^2 = a^2 - c^2$, $2p = \frac{a^2 - c^2}{c} = \frac{a^2}{c}\left(1 - \frac{c^2}{a^2}\right)$.
>
> Because $e = \frac{c}{a}$, $2p = a\left(\frac{a}{c}\right)\left(1 - \left(\frac{c}{a}\right)^2\right) = a\left(\frac{1}{e}\right)(1 - e^2)$.
>
>
>
> Therefore, $2ep = a(1 - e^2)$. Substituting into the polar equation of an ellipse yields an equation that is useful for finding distances from the planet to the sun.
>
> $r = \frac{a(1 - e^2)}{1 - e\cos\theta}$
>
> Note that e is the eccentricity of the orbit and a is the length of the semi-major axis of the ellipse. Also, a is the mean distance of the planet from the sun.
>
> **Example** The mean distance of Venus from the sun is 6.724×10^7 miles, and the eccentricity of its orbit is 0.006788. Find the minimum and maximum distances of Venus from the sun.
> The minimum distance occurs when $\theta = \pi$.
> $r = \frac{6.724 \times 10^7(1 - 0.006788^2)}{1 - 0.006788\cos\pi} = 6.678 \times 10^7$ miles
> The maximum distance occurs when $\theta = 0$.
> $r = \frac{6.724 \times 10^7(1 - 0.006788^2)}{1 - 0.006788\cos 0} = 6.770 \times 10^7$ miles
>
> **Complete.**
>
> 1. The mean distance of Mars from the sun is 1.4164×10^8 miles, and the eccentricity of its orbit is 0.093382. Find the minimum and maximum distances of Mars from the sun.
>   minimum distance $= 1.284 \times 10^8$ miles
>   maximum distance $= 1.548 \times 10^8$ miles
> 2. The minimum distance of Earth from the sun is 9.1445×10^7 miles, and the eccentricity of its orbit is 0.016734. Find the mean and maximum distances of Earth from the sun.
>   mean distance $= 9.300 \times 10^7$ miles
>   maximum distance $= 94.56 \times 10^6$ miles
>
> T 28
> Glencoe Division, Macmillan/McGraw-Hill

Problem Solving, p. 29

> CHAPTER **10** NAME _____ DATE _____
> **Problem Solving** (Use after Lesson 10-5)
>
> **Working Backward**
>
> If you know the coordinates of enough points, you can find the equation of a conic section containing those points. The number of points required depends on the conic section. In general, you will need as many points as there are coefficients in the general form of the equation of the conic. To find the equation of a parabola with directrix parallel to the x-axis, for example, you will need three points, since there are three coefficients, D, E, and F, in the general equation $x^2 + Dx + Ey + F = 0$. To find the desired equation, begin with the solution, the general equation for the conic. Work backward to the coefficients by substituting the coordinates of the points in the general equation and solving the resulting system of equations.
>
> **Example** A parabola with directrix parallel to the x-axis contains points at (3, 7), (1, 3), and (-2, 12). Find the equation of the parabola.
>
> Substitute the coordinates in the general equation $x^2 + Dx + Ey + F = 0$.
> (1) $\quad 9 + 3D + 7E + F = 0$
> (2) $\quad 1 + D + 3E + F = 0$
> (3) $\quad 4 - 2D + 12E + F = 0$
>
> (1) - (2): $8 + 2D + 4E + 0 = 0 \quad \rightarrow \quad 72 + 18D + 36E = 0$ *Multipy by 9.*
> (2) - (3): $-3 + 3D - 9E + 0 = 0 \quad \rightarrow \quad \underline{-12 + 12D - 36E = 0}$ *Multiply by 4.*
> $\qquad\qquad\qquad\qquad\qquad\qquad\qquad 60 + 30D \qquad = 0$ *Add.*
> $\qquad\qquad\qquad\qquad\qquad\qquad\qquad\qquad\qquad D = -2$
> Substitution of $D = -2$ in other equations yields $E = -1$ and $F = 4$.
> The equation is $x^2 - 2x - y + 4 = 0$.
>
> **Solve.**
>
> 1. A parabola with directrix parallel to the y-axis contains points at (0, -1), (4, 1) and (4, -3). Find the equation of the parabola.
> $y^2 - x + 2y + 1 = 0$
> 2. A circle contains points at (-3, 4), (5, 0), and (1, -2√6). Find the equation of the circle.
> $x^2 + y^2 - 25 = 0$
> 3. An ellipse contains points at (0, 2), $\left(1, \frac{4\sqrt{2}}{3}\right)$, $\left(-2, \frac{2\sqrt{5}}{3}\right)$, (-3, 0), and (0, -2). Find the equation of the ellipse.
> $4x^2 + 9y^2 - 36 = 0$
>
> T 29
> Glencoe Division, Macmillan/McGraw-Hill

Case Study Follow-Up, p. 30

> CHAPTER **10** NAME _____ DATE _____
> **Case Study Follow-Up** (Use after Lesson 10-1)
>
> **Landfill National Park**
>
> Refer to Case Study 2: *Trashing the Planet*, on pages 959-961 in your textbook.
>
> Suppose that in order to demonstrate his commitment to cleaning up the planet, a presidential candidate announced that if he were elected, his first act would be to create a national park out of trash. For a period of one year, all residential and commercial trash normally sent to landfills in the United States would be trucked to a suitable spot and spread out in an ever-widening circle to a thickness of 3 feet. The latest scientific methods would be applied to convert the trash to playgrounds, picnic areas, and amber waves of grain. The candidate promises that he would reside at the center of the park and each week draw a graph of the park for the American people.
>
> The candidate's environmental policy committee produced the following data.
> a. Sixty percent of American trash is residential. Forty percent is commercial.
> b. Residential trash averages 425 lb/yd³. Commercial trash averages 375 lb/yd³.
>
> Using miles as units, sketch Landfill National Park after one year and write the equation of the park's border. Assume that the candidate's home is at the origin. $x^2 + y^2 = (8.2)^2$
>
>
>
> T 30
> Glencoe Division, Macmillan/McGraw-Hill

Technology

The Technology feature preceding Lesson 10-5 uses IBM's *MET (Mathematics Exploration Toolkit)* to investigate the shape of the graph of a hyperbola as c approaches 0 in the equation $\frac{x^2}{d^2} - \frac{y^2}{b^2} = c$.

The graphing calculator is used frequently throughout the chapter. The Exploration in Lesson 10-1 uses the calculator to verify conjectures about graphs of circles. The graphing calculator program in that lesson will determine the radius and coordinates of the center of a circle from an equation. Lesson 10-2A demonstrates how to use the TRACE function to find the vertex of a parabola. The Exploration in Lesson 10-2 investigates the behavior of the graph of a parabola for different ranges. The behavior of the graph of an ellipse is investigated in the Exploration in Lesson 10-3. Lesson 10-6A gives instruction on graphing all of the conic sections, and Lesson 10-7A instructs students in solving quadratic equations and inequalities by graphing.

Graphing Calculator Exercises, pp. 530, 540, 549, 558, 575

Graphing Calculator Program, pp. 530–531

Technology Masters

Graphing Calculator, p. 19

Computer, p. 20

Outside Resources

Books/Periodicals

Akheizer. *Elements of the Theory of Elliptic Functions,* American Mathematical Society, Providence, RI, 1990.

Salmon, George. *Conic Sections,* 6th edition, Chelsea Publishing Co.

Films/Videotapes/Videodiscs

Concepts in Mathematics, Conic Sections, TV Ontario, The Ontario Educational Communications Authority

Conic Sections, Pheonix/BFA Films and Video, Inc.

Mathematical Curves, Churchill Films

Software

Graphing utilities that include conics *(see list on page T25)*

The Geometer's Sketchpad. Key Curriculum Press (Macintosh)

Geometric Connectors: Transformations. Sunburst (Apple II, IBM)

CHAPTER 10

CONICS

HISTORICAL SNAPSHOT

	First Barometer ('Torricelli Tube') Florence, Italy		Celsius temperature scale developed in Uppsala, Sweden		University of North Carolina established at Asheville	
Conic Sections Apollonius (The "Great Geometer"), Alexandria		Fahrenheit temperature scale developed in Holland		Beaufort Wind Scale developed in England		First Weather Satellite NASA's *TIROS-I*, USA
262–190 BC	AD 1644		1714 1742	1806		1955 1960

522

CHAPTER OBJECTIVES

In this chapter, you will:
- Write equations of circles, parabolas, ellipses, and hyperbolas.
- Graph circles, parabolas, ellipses, and hyperbolas.
- Recognize conic sections by their equations.
- Write equations of tangents and normals to conic sections.

CAREER GOAL: Meteorology

James Martin was born with spinal muscular atrophy, a disorder in which there is a bad connection between the nerves and muscles in his legs and arms. He credits his family with being his inspiration. "My mom and dad put me in public school and always encouraged me to pursue my dreams."

James hasn't wasted any time pursuing his dreams. He works part-time as a computer specialist at the National Climatic Center in Asheville, part of the National Oceanic and Atmospheric Administration. At the the University of North Carolina, James majors in computer sciences and atmospheric sciences "so that I can become more familiar with the climate that I work with every day." James hopes that with a bachelor's degree, he will achieve a higher grade in civil service, with supervisory responsibilities. Having the title of meteorologist will also lead to more career opportunities.

Meteorologists use conics and vectors, especially in the study of the cone-shaped hurricane. If you cut horizontally across a hurricane, you would find a circle. A velocity vector drawn tangent to this circle represents the circulation speed of the hurricane. James says that the algebra, geometry, and trigonometry courses he took in high school prepared him well for his college mathematics courses.

From James' perspective, both computer science and atmospheric science offer opportunities for the physically challenged. "I hope that I can encourage other people who are physically challenged to be active in society. I also want to show society that we who are physically challenged don't have to be pushed back into a corner. We have a lot to offer if just given the opportunity."

READ MORE ABOUT IT

Bohren, Craig F. *What Light Through Yonder Window Breaks? More Experiments in Atmospheric Physics.* New York: John Wiley & Sons, 1991.

Carpenter, Clive. *The Changing World of Weather.* New York: Facts on File, 1991.

Spiegel, Herbert J. and Arnold Gruber. *From Weather Vanes to Satellites.* New York: John Wiley & Sons, 1991.

SPOTLIGHT ON...

James Martin
Age: 31
Class: Senior
School: University of North Carolina
  Asheville, North Carolina
Majors: Computer Science and Atmospheric Sciences

"I hope that I can encourage other people who are physically challenged to be active in society."

FOR MORE INFORMATION

If you would like more information about meteorology, contact:

American Meteorological
  Society (AMS)
45 Beacon Street
Boston, MA 02108

Applications

Lesson	Application	Examples	Exercises
10–1	Communications Spacecraft	5	46 47
10–2	Communications Entertainment Baseball	3 5	38 39 40
10–3	Space Travel Astronomy	1	43, 44
10–4	Chemistry Analytical Geometry Space Travel	5	53 54 55
10–5	Astronomy Construction	3	41 42
10–6	Manufacturing Sports		39 40
10–7	Manufacturing Agriculture Space Science	2	37 38
10–8	Geography Design Communications	1	40 41

Lesson Resources

- Practice Master 10–1
- Enrichment Master 10–1
- Activity Master, p. 30

 Transparency 10–1 contains the 5-Minute Check and a teaching aid for this lesson.

INTRODUCING THE LESSON

🕐 5-Minute Check
(over Chapter 9)

1. Find the polar coordinates of the point with rectangular coordinates $(\sqrt{3}, 1)$. **(2, 30°)**
2. Identify the curve represented by $r = \sin \theta$. **circle**
3. Write $x^2 + y^2 = 25$ in polar form. **$r = \pm 5$**
4. Simplify $(2 - i)(-3 + 4i)$. **$-2 + 11i$**
5. Find $6(\cos 20° + i \sin 20°) \cdot 2(\cos 30° + i \sin 30°)$ **$12(\cos 50° + i \sin 50°)$**

Prerequisite Skills

Students should know how to complete the square.

Find the value of *n* that makes each trinomial a perfect square.
1. $x^2 + 12x + n$ **36**
2. $y^2 - nx + 100$ **20**
3. $k^2 - 5k + n$ **$\frac{25}{4}$**

4. Solve $x^2 + 2x = 48$ by completing the square. **6, –8**

Motivating the Lesson

Have students read the application at the beginning of the lesson. Ask them to imagine that the epicenter of the quake is the origin of a polar coordinate system and ask them to find the polar equation of the circle that passes through San Francisco. *r* = **56 miles**

10-1 The Circle

Objectives
10–1A
10–1B

After studying this lesson, you should be able to:
- use the standard and general forms of the equation of a circle, and
- graph circles.

Application

The third game of the 1989 World Series between the San Francisco Giants and the Oakland Athletics was about to begin on Tuesday, October 17, when the Loma Prieta earthquake struck, registering 7.1 on the Richter Scale. The epicenter of the quake was in the Santa Cruz Mountains, approximately 56 miles south of San Francisco. The seismic waves traveled outward from the epicenter.

A **locus** is a set of points (and only those points) that satisfy a given set of conditions. A **circle** is the locus of all points in a plane at a given distance from a fixed point on the plane called the **center**. The distance from the center to any point on the circle is called the **radius** of the circle. In the map at the left, each circle has the same center, but a different radius. Seismologists use these circles to determine the strength of the quake as you get farther away from its epicenter.

Each successive circle on the map is 10 miles farther from the epicenter, and each circle is centered at the epicenter. Circles that have the same center, but not necessarily the same radius, are called **concentric circles**. The equations for some of this family of circles are given below.

$x^2 + y^2 = 10^2$ *includes the immediate area around the epicenter*
$x^2 + y^2 = 30^2$ *includes the area out to San Jose*
$x^2 + y^2 = 60^2$ *includes the area out to San Francisco and Oakland*

ALTERNATE TEACHING STRATEGIES

Using Connections

In polar coordinates, a circle of radius 5 has the equation $r = 5$.
Show that by substituting $r = \sqrt{x^2 + y^2}$, the equation can be transformed into rectangular coordinates.
$$\sqrt{x^2 + y^2} = 5$$
$$x^2 + y^2 = 25$$

Using Discussion

Help students to see the meaning of the terms $x - h$ and $y - k$, which appear throughout this chapter. These terms indicate that the point (x, y) has been shifted horizontally by *h* and vertically by *k*. Illustrate by having students graph $(4, 6)$ and $(4 - 5, 6 - (-3))$ to see that $(4, 6)$ is shifted left 5 and up 3.

EXPLORATION: Modeling

Materials: graph paper, corrugated cardboard, 10-centimeter piece of string, thumb tack

1. Tape a piece of centimeter graph paper onto a large piece of corrugated cardboard.
2. Draw the x-axis and y-axis. Plot the point $C(-2, 3)$.
3. Attach one end of the string to the thumb tack. Press the tack into the corrugated cardboard at point C.
4. Tie the string around your pencil.
5. Move your pencil around the tack, keeping the string taut.

In the Exploration above, the length of string from the thumbtack to the pencil acted as a radius from point C. This activity models the set of all points that are at a fixed distance from a given point, in other words, a circle.

The word radius can refer to the distance from the center of a circle to a point on the circle, or to the segment that connects those two points.

In the figure at the right, the center of the circle is at the origin. By drawing a perpendicular from any point $P(x, y)$ on the circle but not on an axis, you form a right triangle. The Pythagorean theorem can be used to write an equation that describes every point on a circle whose center is located at the origin.

$$x^2 + y^2 = r^2$$

This is the equation of the parent graph of all circles.

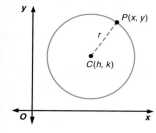

Suppose $C(h, k)$ is the center of a circle, $P(x, y)$ is any point on the circle, and r is the radius of the circle. You can use the distance formula to write an equation for the circle.

$$d = \sqrt{(x_2 - x_1)^2 + (y_2 - y_1)^2}$$
$$r = \sqrt{(x - h)^2 + (y - k)^2}$$ *$(x_2, y_2) = (x, y), (x_1, y_1) = (h, k),$ and $d = r$*
$$r^2 = (x - h)^2 + (y - k)^2$$

This is known as the standard form of the equation of a circle.

Standard Form of the Equation of a Circle	The standard form of the equation of a circle with radius r and center at (h, k) is $$(x - h)^2 + (y - k)^2 = r^2.$$

TEACHING THE LESSON

Teaching Tip In the Exploration, point out that the pencil on the end of the string is a primitive version of a compass.

Teaching Tip After discussing the standard form of the equation of a circle, point out that the signs in the equation will be opposite the signs of h and k.

center: $(-2, 3)$

$$\begin{array}{cc} -2 & +3 \\ \downarrow & \downarrow \end{array}$$

equation: $(x + 2)^2 + (y - 3)^2 = r^2$

Point out that the concept of a center at (h, k) will be used throughout this chapter.

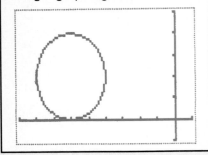
Example 1

Write the equation of a circle that is tangent to the *y*-axis and has its center at (−5, 6). Then graph the equation.

Since the circle is tangent to the *y*-axis, the distance from the center to the *y*-axis is the radius. Since the center is 5 units left of the *y*-axis, the radius is 5.

The equation of the circle can be found by substituting 5 for r, −5 for h, and 6 for k.

The equation is $(x − (−5))^2 + (y − 6)^2 = (5)^2$ or $(x + 5)^2 + (y − 6)^2 = 25$.

You can graph an equation for a circle by using a graphing calculator.

Example 2

Graph $(x − 4)^2 + (y + 5)^2 = 16$ by using a graphing calculator.

Solve the equation for *y*.

$$(x − 4)^2 + (y + 5)^2 = 16$$
$$(y + 5)^2 = 16 − (x − 4)^2$$
$$y + 5 = \pm\sqrt{16 − (x − 4)^2} \qquad \textit{Take the square root of each side.}$$
$$y = \pm\sqrt{16 − (x − 4)^2} − 5$$

Select a standard range on the calculator. Input the parts of the radical equation as separate equations.

$$Y_1 = \sqrt{16 − (x − 4)^2} − 5$$
$$Y_2 = -\sqrt{16 − (x − 4)^2} − 5$$

Note that the display does not look like a circle. On the TI-81, you can make it look like a circle by pressing ZOOM and 5. On Casio calculators, you must alter your range and scale values to achieve a circular appearance.

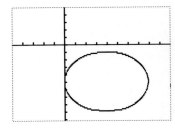

The standard form of the equation of a circle can be expanded to obtain a general form of the equation.

If r = 0, the circle is a point. If r < 0, a real circle does not exist.

$$(x − h)^2 + (y − k)^2 = r^2$$
$$(x^2 − 2hx + h^2) + (y^2 − 2ky + k^2) = r^2$$
$$x^2 + y^2 + (−2h)x + (−2k)y + (h^2 + k^2) = r^2$$

Since h, k, and r are constants, $−2h, −2k, (h^2 + k^2)$, and r^2 are also constants. The equation can be written as $x^2 + y^2 + Dx + Ey + F = 0$. This is called the general form of the equation of a circle.

General Form of the Equation of a Circle

The general form of the equation of a circle is
$$x^2 + y^2 + Dx + Ey + F = 0,$$
where D, E, and F are constants.

Notice that the coefficients of x^2 and y^2 in the general form must be 1. If those coefficients are not 1, the equation can be transformed by division so that they are 1. Also notice that there is no term containing the product of the variables, xy.

When the equation of a circle is given in general form, it can be rewritten in standard form by completing the square for the terms in x and the terms in y.

Example 3

The equation of a circle is $x^2 + y^2 - 10x + 4y + 17 = 0$. Find the radius and the coordinates of the center. Then graph the equation.

You can review completing the square in Lesson 4-2.

$$x^2 + y^2 - 10x + 4y + 17 = 0$$
$$(x^2 - 10x + \ ?) + (y^2 + 4y + \ ?) = -17 \qquad \textit{Complete the squares.}$$
$$(x^2 - 10x + 25) + (y^2 + 4y + 4) = -17 + 25 + 4$$
$$(x - 5)^2 + (y + 2)^2 = 12$$
$$(x - 5)^2 + (y + 2)^2 = \left(\sqrt{12}\right)^2$$

The center of the circle is located at $(5, -2)$, and the radius is $\sqrt{12}$ or $2\sqrt{3}$ units.

Notice that this is the result of translating the parent graph with radius $\sqrt{12}$ 5 units right and 2 units down.

You know that any two points in the coordinate plane determine a unique line. Any three noncollinear points in the coordinate plane determine a unique circle. An equation of the circle passing through three such points can be found by substituting the coordinates of each point into the general form of the equation. This will produce a system of three equations in three variables (D, E, and F). By solving this system of equations, the general form of the equation of the circle that passes through the three given points can be found.

Example 4

Find the equation of the circle that passes through $(-2, 3)$, $(6, -5)$, and $(0, 7)$. Then identify the center and radius of the circle.

Substitute each ordered pair for (x, y) in $x^2 + y^2 + Dx + Ey + F = 0$.

$$(-2)^2 + (3)^2 + D(-2) + E(3) + F = 0 \qquad (x, y) = (-2, 3)$$
$$(6)^2 + (-5)^2 + D(6) + E(-5) + F = 0 \qquad (x, y) = (6, -5)$$
$$(0)^2 + (7)^2 + D(0) + E(7) + F = 0 \qquad (x, y) = (0, 7)$$

(continued on the next page)

You can also solve this system by using matrices.

Simplify the system of equations.

$$-2D + 3E + F + 13 = 0$$
$$6D - 5E + F + 61 = 0$$
$$7E + F + 49 = 0$$

The solution to the system is $D = -10$, $E = -4$, and $F = -21$.

The equation of the circle is $x^2 + y^2 - 10x - 4y - 21 = 0$ or $(x - 5)^2 + (y - 2)^2 = 50$, after completing the square. Its center is at $(5, 2)$, and its radius is $\sqrt{50}$ units.

Satellites often orbit in circles around Earth. The radius of the orbit determines where the satellite is in relation to a fixed point on Earth. Satellites such as *Syncom*, *Early Bird*, *Intelsat*, and *ATS* are placed in geosynchronous orbits about the equator. This means that, since they complete one orbit in 24 hours, each satellite is above the same spot on Earth at all times. When the satellites are "parked" in this orbit, antennas can be pointed at a fixed point on Earth, making it possible to process directional signals very rapidly.

Example 5

APPLICATION

Communications

The distance that a satellite in geosynchronous orbit is above the equator can be found by subtracting the radius of Earth (6400 km) from the distance, r, that the satellite is from the center of Earth. The formula for the distance is $r = \sqrt[3]{\dfrac{GM_e t^2}{4\pi^2}}$, where

G = the universal constant (6.67×10^{-11} newtons m²/kg²),

M_e = the mass of Earth (5.98×10^{24} kg), and

t = period of one orbit (86,400 seconds).

Find the distance a satellite in geosynchronous orbit is above the equator.

$$r = \sqrt[3]{\frac{GM_e t^2}{4\pi^2}}$$

$$= \sqrt[3]{\frac{(6.67 \times 10^{-11} \text{ newton m}^2/\text{kg}^2)(5.98 \times 10^{24} \text{ kg})(86,400 \text{ s})^2}{4\pi^2}}$$ *1 newton = 1 kg · m/s²*

$$= \sqrt[3]{7.542143065 \times 10^{22}} \text{ m} \quad \text{Use a calculator.}$$

$$\approx 42,250,474.3 \text{ m}$$

$$\approx 42,250.5 \text{ km}$$

To find the distance above the equator, subtract the radius of Earth from r.

$$d = r - r_E$$
$$= 42,250.5 - 6400$$
$$= 35,850.5$$

The satellite is 35,850.5 kilometers above the equator.

8.

EXPLORATION: Graphing Calculator

1. Graph $y_1 = (25 - x^2)^{\frac{1}{2}}$ and $y_2 = -(25 - x^2)^{\frac{1}{2}}$.

Remember to use ZOOM and 5 on the TI-81 to achieve a circular appearance.

2. For each situation, make a conjecture about the behavior of the graph. Then verify by graphing.
   a. x is replaced with $(x - 2)$.
   b. x is replaced with $(x + 2)$.
   c. y is replaced with $(y - 2)$. Center is at $(0, 2)$.
   d. y is replaced with $(y + 2)$. Center is at $(0, -2)$.
   e. 25 is replaced with 16. The radius is 4 units.

a. Center is at $(2, 0)$.
b. Center is at $(-2, 0)$.

CHECKING FOR UNDERSTANDING

Communicating Mathematics

Read and study the lesson to answer each question. 1, 3, 4. See margin.

1. **Write** the equations of a family of five concentric circles whose center is at $(-2, 6)$.

2. **Describe** the coefficients of the x^2 and y^2 terms in the equation of a circle written in standard form. Both are 1.

3. **Explain** the process for rewriting an equation of a circle in standard form as an equation in general form.

4. **Define** the term *geosynchronous* and tell how it relates to concentric circles.

Guided Practice

Write the standard form of the equation of a circle with the given center coordinates and radius. Then graph the equation. 5–8. For graphs, see margin.

5. $(0, 0), 9$ $x^2 + y^2 = 81$

6. $(0, 0), \sqrt{6}$ $x^2 + y^2 = 6$

7. $(2, -7), 10$ $(x - 2)^2 + (y + 7)^2 = 100$

8. $(3, -2), 7$ $(x - 3)^2 + (y + 2)^2 = 49$

Find the radius and the coordinates of the center of the circle for each equation. Then graph the equation. 9–12. For graphs, see Teacher's Answer Key.

9. $(x - 4)^2 + (y - 3)^2 = 9$ $3, (4, 3)$

10. $(x + 4)^2 + (y - 7)^2 = 7$ $\sqrt{7}, (-4, 7)$

11. $4(x - 3)^2 + 4(y - 2)^2 = 10$ $\frac{\sqrt{10}}{2}, (3, 2)$

12. $9(x + 5)^2 = 4 - 9(y + 3)^2$ $\frac{2}{3}, (-5, -3)$

13. Write the standard form of the equation of the circle that passes through the origin, $(2.8, 0)$, and $(5, 2)$. $(x - 1.4)^2 + (y - 3.75)^2 = 16.02$

LESSON 10-1   THE CIRCLE   529

RETEACHING THE LESSON

Carefully review the process of completing the square. Remind students that to complete the square of a quadratic expression in *x*, they should divide the coefficient of *x* by 2 and then square it. Give mental math exercises for practice.
Example: What should you add to $x^2 + 8x$ to make a perfect square?
16

APPLYING THE LESSON

Homework Exercises

The red A, B, and C flags, printed only in the Teacher's Wraparound Edition, indicate the level of difficulty of the exercises.

Exercise Note

Before completing the square in Exercises 14–25, students should check to see that the coefficients of x^2 and y^2 are 1. If they are not, students should factor out the coefficients so that they can complete the square on x^2 and y^2.

Using Technology

In Exercises 38–41, encourage students to estimate the radius and center of each circle before beginning and then to check their calculator results against their estimates.

Using Technology

The program given in Exercise 42 is for use with a TI–81 graphing calculator. For other programmable calculators, have students consult their owner's manual for commands similar to those presented here.

Additional Answers

14. $(x + 3)^2 + (y + 5)^2 = 16$
15. $(x - 7)^2 + (y - 4)^2 = 5$
16. $x^2 + y^2 = 64$
17. $(x + \frac{1}{2})^2 + y^2 = 1$

18. $(x - 2)^2 + (y + 3)^2 = 25$
19. $x^2 + y^2 = 9$
20. $(x + 4)^2 + (y + 1)^2 = 25$
21. $(x + 0.25)^2 + (y - 1)^2 = 9$
22. $(x - 1)^2 + (y + 3)^2 = 16$
23. $(x - \frac{3}{2})^2 + (y + \frac{1}{4})^2 = 7$

24. $(x - 2)^2 + (y - 6)^2 = 10$
25. $(x + 7)^2 + (y + 12)^2 = 36$

Practice

14–25. See margin. For graphs, see Teacher's Answer Key.

Write the standard form of each equation. Then graph the equation.

A

14. center at $(-3, -5)$, radius 4
15. center at $(7, 4)$, radius $\sqrt{5}$
16. $x^2 = 64 - y^2$
17. $x^2 + y^2 + x = \dfrac{3}{4}$
18. $x^2 + y^2 - 4x + 6y - 12 = 0$
19. $3x^2 + 3y^2 - 27 = 0$
20. $x^2 + y^2 + 8x + 2y - 8 = 0$
21. $16x^2 + 16y^2 + 8x - 32y = 127$
22. $6x^2 - 12x + 6y^2 + 36y = 36$
23. $16x^2 - 48x - 75 + 16y^2 + 8y = 0$
24. $x^2 + y^2 - 4x - 12y + 30 = 0$
25. $x^2 + y^2 + 14x + 24y + 157 = 0$

Write the standard form of the equation of the circle that passes through the points with the given coordinates. Then identify the center and the radius of the circle.

26–31. See margin.

B

26. $(7, -1), (11, -5), (3, -5)$
27. $(1, 3), (5, 5), (5, 3)$
28. $(5, 3), (-2, 2), (-1, -5)$
29. $(7, -1), (7, 5), (1, -1)$
30. $(-10, -5), (-2, 7), (-9, 0)$
31. $(2, -1), (-3, 0), (1, 4)$

32–37. See margin.

Write the equation of the circle that satisfies each set of conditions.

32. The circle passes through $(7, -1)$ and has its center at $(-2, 4)$.
33. The circle passes through the origin and has its center at $(-3, 4)$.

C

34. The endpoints of a diameter are at $(-2, -3)$ and at $(4, 5)$.
35. The endpoints of a diameter are at $(-3, 4)$ and at $(2, 1)$.
36. The center of the circle is on the x-axis, its radius is 1, and it passes through $\left(\dfrac{\sqrt{2}}{2}, \dfrac{\sqrt{2}}{2}\right)$.
37. The circle is tangent to the line $2x - y = -3$ and has its center at $(5, 12)$.

Graphing Calculator

Use a graphing calculator to graph each equation. 38–41. See margin.

38. $(x - 4)^2 + (y - 1)^2 = 25$
39. $(x + 3)^2 + (y + 5)^2 = 16$
40. $4x^2 + 4y^2 = 49$
41. $x^2 + 14x + y^2 + 6y + 50 = 0$

Programming

42. The following program will determine the radius and the coordinates of the center of a circle from an equation written in general form.

```
Prgm 10: CIRCL.EQ
:ClrHome
:Disp "X² + Y² + DX + EY + F = 0"
:Disp "D ="
:Input D
:Disp "E ="
:Input E
:Disp "F ="
:Input F
:-D/2 → H          Calculates x-coordinate of vertex, stores in H.
:-E/2 → K          Calculates y-coordinate of vertex, stores in K.
:-F + D²/4 + E²/4 → R   Calculates square of radius value, stores in R.
```

38.

39.

```
:If R < 0
:Goto 1
:√R → R
:Disp "H ="
:Disp H
:Disp "K ="
:Disp K
:Disp "R ="
:Disp R
:Goto 2
:Lbl 1
:Disp "NO CIRCLE"
:Lbl 2
```

If the value of R is negative, no circle exists.

Calculates radius, stores in R.

For each equation, use the program shown above to find the radius of the circle and coordinates of its center.

a. $x^2 + y^2 - 6y - 16 = 0$ 5, (0, 3) **b.** $x^2 + y^2 + 2x - 10 = 0$ 3.3166, (-1, 0)

43. $r = 0, C(1, -2)$; It is a point.

Critical Thinking

43. Find the radius and the coordinates of the center of a circle defined by the equation $x^2 + y^2 - 2x + 4y + 5 = 0$. Describe the graph of this circle.

44. Write the equation of the family of circles in which $h = k$ and the radius is 8. Let k be any real number. Describe this family of circles. See margin.

45. If the equation of a circle is written in standard form and $h^2 + k^2 - r^2 = 0$, what is true of the graph of that equation? It passes through the origin; the center is at (h, k) and the radius is $\sqrt{h^2 + k^2}$.

Applications and Problem Solving

46. Communications Refer to Example 5. Determine the velocity (v) in meters/second of a communication satellite in a geosynchronous circular orbit if $v = \sqrt{\dfrac{GM}{r}}$, where r = the distance from the center of Earth to the satellite, G = the universal constant, and M = the mass of Earth. 3.07×10^3 m/s

47. Spacecraft The formula for determining the velocity of a craft in a parked position above Earth, presented in Exercise 46, can also be used for a craft parked above any other planet or moon. In NASA's history, there were six Apollo spacecraft from 1969–1972 that had to maintain a parked position above the LEM landing craft on the lunar surface. Determine the velocity of the Apollo spacecraft necessary to be parked above the moon's surface at an altitude of 110 kilometers. The mass of the moon is 0.012 times the mass of Earth, and the radius of the moon is 1740 kilometers. 1608.5 m/s

LESSON 10-1   THE CIRCLE   531

48. Technology Diego has a computer program that will graph all of the trigonometric functions. However, it only accepts angle measures in terms of radians. Find the radian measure (to the nearest thousandth) equivalent to each degree measure he needs to input in the software. **(Lesson 5-1)**
   a. 60° 1.047   **b.** −105° −1.833   **c.** 1000° 17.46   **d.** −90° −1.571

49. State which value is greater, sin 10° or sin 100°. **(Lesson 6-1)** sin 100°

50. Find tan θ if sec θ = $\frac{5}{3}$ and 0° ≤ θ ≤ 90°. **(Lesson 7-1)** $\frac{4}{3}$

51. Find the coordinates of point D such that $\overrightarrow{AB}$ and $\overrightarrow{CD}$ are equal vectors for points $A(5, 2)$, $B(-3, 3)$, and $C(0, 0)$. **(Lesson 8-1)** $D(-8, 1)$

52. Simplify $(\sqrt{2} + i)(4\sqrt{2} + i)$. **(Lesson 9-5)** $7 + 5i\sqrt{2}$

53. Find $(2\sqrt{3} + 2i)^{\frac{1}{5}}$. Express the answer in the form $a + bi$ with a and b to the nearest hundredth. **(Lesson 9-8)** $1.31 + 0.14i$

54. College Entrance Exam Compare quantities A and B below. A
Write A if quantity A is greater.
Write B if quantity B is greater.
Write C if the two quantities are equal.
Write D if there is not enough information to determine the relationship.
Eight separate cubes, each with an edge of 1 inch, are positioned together to create a large cube.

(A) surface area of one small cube   **(B)** $\frac{\text{surface area of the large cube}}{8}$

DECISION MAKING

Choosing a Home Computer

Since the introduction of the personal computer, millions of Americans have purchased computers for home use. Many buyers have been happy with their purchases, but others have discovered that they bought too much or too little, or worse yet, that they didn't need a computer at all.

1. Describe the features you would look for in a home computer. Include such factors as capacity, capabilities, programs you want to run, type of printer, and any other features you feel are important.

2. Research computers and costs. Talk to computer owners and retailers, read articles and ads, and contact computer manufacturers. Then make a list of three computers that would adequately meet your needs.

3. Outline a plan for financing the cost of each computer on your list.

4. Project Work with your group to complete one of the projects listed at the right based on the information you gathered in Exercises 1–3. 1–4. See students' work.

PROJECTS

- *Conduct an interview.*
- *Write a book report.*
- *Write a proposal.*
- *Write an article for the school paper.*
- *Write a report.*
- *Make a display.*
- *Make a graph or chart.*
- *Plan an activity.*
- *Design a checklist.*

532   CHAPTER 10   CONICS

EXTENDING THE LESSON

Math Power: Problem Solving
Find the area of the circle with the equation $x^2 + y^2 - 14x + 4y - 11 = 0$. 64π square units

Decision Making
This activity provides students an opportunity to work together on a given problem. You may wish to refer to pages T20–T21 and page 522c for the various elements of cooperative groups and specific goals and strategies for using them.

Enrichment Masters Booklet, p. 65

10-1 Enrichment Worksheet

Spheres

The set of all points in three-dimensional space that are a fixed distance, r (the **radius**) from a fixed point, C (the **center**) is called a **sphere**. The equation below is an algebraic representation of the sphere shown at the right.
$(x - h)^2 + (y - k)^2 + (z - l)^2 = r^2$

A line segment containing the center of a sphere and having its endpoints on the sphere is called a **diameter** of the sphere. The endpoints of a diameter are called **poles** of the sphere. A **great circle** of a sphere is the intersection of the sphere and a plane containing the center of the sphere.

1. If $x^2 + y^2 - 4y + z^2 + 2z - 4 = 0$ is an equation of a sphere and $(1, 4, -3)$ is one pole of the sphere, find the coordinates of the opposite pole.
(−1, 0, 1)

2. a. On the coordinate system at the right, sketch the sphere described by the equation $x^2 + y^2 + z^2 = 9$.

b. Is $P(2, -2, -2)$ inside, outside, or on the sphere? outside

c. Describe a way to tell if a point with coordinates $P(a, b, c)$ is inside, outside, or on the sphere with equation $x^2 + y^2 + z^2 = r^2$.
$a^2 + b^2 + c^2 < r^2$: inside the sphere
$a^2 + b^2 + c^2 = r^2$: on the sphere
$a^2 + b^2 + c^2 > r^2$: outside the sphere

3. If $x^2 + y^2 + z^2 - 4x + 6y - 2z - 2 = 0$ is an equation of a sphere, find the circumference of a great circle, and the surface area and volume of the sphere.
8π units; 64π square units; $\frac{256\pi}{3}$ cubic units

4. The equation $x^2 + y^2 = 4$ represents a set of points in three-dimensional space. Describe that set of points in your own words. Illustrate with a sketch on the coordinate system at the right.
a cylinder

T 65
Glencoe Division, Macmillan/McGraw-Hill

10-2A Graphing Calculators: Locating the Vertex of a Parabola

You can use a graphing calculator to find the coordinates of the vertex of a parabola by using the TRACE and ZOOM functions.

Example

Graph the equation $y = (x + 4)^2 - 2$ and determine the coordinates of the vertex of the parabola.

First, graph the parabola in the standard viewing window.

TI-81: $\boxed{Y=}$ $\boxed{(}$ $\boxed{X|T}$ $\boxed{+}$ 4 $\boxed{)}$ $\boxed{x^2}$ $\boxed{-}$ 2 $\boxed{GRAPH}$

Casio: $\boxed{Graph}$ $\boxed{(}$ $\boxed{ALPHA}$ $\boxed{X}$ $\boxed{+}$ 4 $\boxed{)}$ $\boxed{x^2}$ $\boxed{-}$ 2 $\boxed{EXE}$

Tracing and zooming in shows the coordinates of the vertex to be $(-4, -2)$.

You may notice that as you zoom in on the vertex of the parabola, the function begins to look more and more like a straight line, and it becomes more and more difficult to find the high or low point. This is one instance when it is better to use the $\boxed{ZOOM}$ "Box" command or $\boxed{ZOOM}$ 1 command if you are using a TI-81 graphing calculator. You can keep the "cup" shape of the graph by enclosing the vertex in a short, fat box. This way, the graph of the function will still look like a parabola in the new viewing window and it is easier to find the coordinates of the vertex.

To zoom in using the box, first press $\boxed{ZOOM}$ 1. Then use the arrow keys to move the blinking dot to where you want one of the corners of your box to be. Press $\boxed{ENTER}$. Now use the arrow keys to move the blinking dot to the opposite corner of the box. Press $\boxed{ENTER}$ again. The calculator will redraw the graph with your box being the new viewing window.

EXERCISES

Graph each equation so that a complete graph is shown. Then find the coordinates of the vertex to the nearest tenth.

1. $(-2, -10)$
           1. $y = x^2 + 4x - 6$
     2. $y = (x - 3)^2 + 7$ $(3, 7)$
     3. $y = 3(x + 1)^2 - 4$ $(-1, -4)$

           4. $y = 6x^2 + 10x + 12$
     5. $y = 9x^2 + 66x - 120$
     6. $y = 0.5x^2 - 11x + 289$
           $(-0.8, 7.8)$
         $(-3.7, -240.9)$
        $(11.0, 228.5)$

CHAPTER 10   GRAPHING CALCULATORS: LOCATING THE VERTEX OF A PARABOLA   533

INTRODUCING THE LESSON

Objective   Locate the vertex of a parabola on a graphing calculator.

Motivating the Lesson

Write the following quadratic equations on the chalkboard. Ask students which parabola has the minimum vertex.
$y = (x - 2)^2 + 2$
$y = (x - 2)^2 - 1$
$y = (x + 3)^2 + 2$
$y = (x - 5)^2 - 4$

TEACHING THE LESSON

Teaching Tip   Remind students that the vertex of a parabola is also the minimum (or maximum) of the quadratic function.

More Examples

Graph $y = 3x^2 - 4x - 2$ and determine the coordinates of the vertex of the parabola.

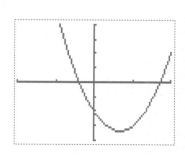

$(0.67, -3.33)$

APPLYING THE LESSON

Homework Exercises

Assignment Guide
All: 1–8

EVALUATING THE LESSON

Closing the Lesson

Ask students to discuss the statement: *The vertex of any equation of the form $y = ax^2 + c$ lies along the y-axis.* Ask students to give examples to verify their conclusions.

NCTM Standards: 1–6, 8

Lesson Resources

- Practice Master 10–2
- Enrichment Master 10–2
- Evaluation Master, Quiz A, p. 125

Transparency 10–2 contains the 5-Minute Check and a teaching aid for this lesson.

INTRODUCING THE LESSON

5-Minute Check

(over Lesson 10–1)

1. Write the equation of a circle with center at (5, –7) and radius of 9 units.
   $(x - 5)^2 + (y + 7)^2 = 81$
2. Find the center and radius of the circle with equation $x^2 + y^2 + 8x - 2y + 15 = 0$.
   center: (–4, 1)
   radius: $\sqrt{2}$ **units**

Motivating the Lesson

Have students draw a line and a point near the line on a sheet of paper. Ask them to find points that appear to be equidistant from the point and the line, to connect them, and to describe the resulting curve.
Answers may vary. The curve is a parabola, a curve that looks like a length of rope dangling between two supports.

10-2 The Parabola

Objectives
10–2A
10–2B

Application

After studying this lesson, you should be able to:
- use the standard and general forms of the equation of a parabola, and
- graph parabolas.

FYI...

A communications satellite in geosynchronous orbit above Earth's equator remains at a fixed point above Earth because it moves at the same speed as Earth.

To facilitate worldwide communications, satellites are placed in geosynchronous orbits approximately 22,400 miles above Earth's surface over the equator. The satellites act as space bridges that receive signals from a ground-based parabolic dish antenna and then retransmit them at a lower frequency to a parabolic dish located in another geographic region. In a parabolic reception dish, all of the rays are directed to a feedhorn, located at the focal point of the parabola.

In previous chapters, you have seen that the graphs of quadratic equations like $y = x^2$ are called **parabolas**. A parabola is defined as the locus of all points in a given plane that are the same distance from a given point, called the **focus**, and a given line, called the **directrix**. *Remember that the distance from a point to a line is the length of the segment from the point perpendicular to the line.*

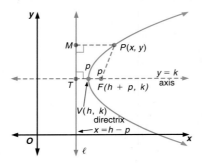

In the figure at the left, F is the focus of the parabola, and ℓ is the directrix. This parabola is symmetric with respect to the line $y = k$, which passes through the focus. This line is called the **axis of symmetry**, or, more simply, the **axis**, of the parabola. The point at which the axis intersects the parabola is called the **vertex**. Suppose the vertex V has coordinates (h, k). Let p be the distance from the focus to the vertex, FV. By the definition of a parabola, the distance from any point on the parabola to the focus must equal the distance from that point to the directrix. So, if $FV = p$, then $VT = p$. The coordinates of F are $(h + p, k)$ and the equation of the directrix is $x = h - p$.

ALTERNATE TEACHING STRATEGIES

Using Applications

Mention some applications of parabolas. A car headlight reflector has a parabolic cross section; the light appears at the focus. Comets that make a single visit to the sun have parabolic orbits. (Comets that return again and again travel in elliptical orbits.) Suspension bridge cables form catenaries, which are parabolic-like curves.

Using Connections

Remind students that they have already seen parabolas in connection with quadratic equations. The graph of a quadratic equation is a parabola. Have students make a table of values for the quadratic equation $y = x^2$ and graph the parabola.

Now suppose $P(x, y)$ is any other point on the parabola. From the definition of parabola, you know that $PF = PM$. Since M lies on the directrix, the coordinates of M are $(h - p, y)$. You can use the distance formula to determine an equation for the parabola.

$$PF = PM$$
$$\sqrt{[x - (h + p)]^2 + (y - k)^2} = \sqrt{[x - (h - p)]^2 + (y - y)^2}$$
$$[x - (h + p)]^2 + (y - k)^2 = [x - (h - p)]^2$$
$$x^2 - 2x(h + p) + (h + p)^2 + (y - k)^2 = x^2 - 2x(h - p) + (h - p)^2$$

This equation can be simplified to obtain the equation
$$(y - k)^2 = 4p(x - h).$$

When p is positive, the parabola opens to the right.
When p is negative, the parabola opens to the left.

Unlike the equation of a circle, the equation of a parabola has only one squared term.

This is the equation of a parabola whose directrix is parallel to the y-axis. The equation of a parabola whose directrix is parallel to the x-axis can be obtained by switching the terms in the parentheses of the previous equation.
$$(x - h)^2 = 4p(y - k)$$

When p is positive, the parabola opens upward.
When p is negative, the parabola opens downward.

Standard Form of the Equation of a Parabola

The standard form of the equation of a parabola with vertex at (h, k) and directrix parallel to the y-axis is
$$(y - k)^2 = 4p(x - h),$$
where p is the distance from the vertex to the focus.

The standard form of the equation of a parabola with vertex at (h, k) and directrix parallel to the x-axis is
$$(x - h)^2 = 4p(y - k),$$
where p is the distance from the vertex to the focus.

Example 1

Find the coordinates of the focus and the vertex and the equations of the directrix and the axis of symmetry for the parabola with equation $x^2 - 12y = 0$. Then graph the equation.

First write the equation in the form $(x - h)^2 = 4p(y - k)$.
$$(x - 0)^2 = 4(3)(y - 0) \qquad 4p = 12, \text{ so } p = 3$$

Since $(h, k) = (0, 0)$, the vertex is at the origin. Since x is squared, the directrix of the parabola is parallel to the x-axis. Since p is positive, the parabola opens upward. The distance from the vertex to the focus is 3 units. So, the coordinates of the focus are $(0, 0 + 3)$ or $(0, 3)$.

The axis of symmetry contains the vertex and the focus. The axis of symmetry is the line $x = 0$, or the y-axis.

Since the directrix is 3 units below the vertex, the equation of the directrix is $y = -3$.

(continued on the next page)

Chalkboard Example

For Example 1

Find the coordinates of the focus and the vertex and the equations of the directrix and the axis of symmetry for the parabola with equation $y^2 + 2x = 0$. Then graph the equation.

focus: $(-\frac{1}{2}, 0)$; vertex: $(0, 0)$;

directrix: $x = \frac{1}{2}$; axis of

symmetry: $y = 0$

Teaching Tip   After Example 1, have students find the equation of the graph with the same shape and orientation as the graph in Example 1 but with vertex at $(-2, 5)$. $(x + 2)^2 - 12(y - 5) = 0$

Graph the directrix, the vertex, and the focus.
To determine the shape of the parabola, graph
several other ordered pairs that satisfy the
equation and connect them with a smooth
curve.

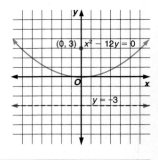

You can also graph a parabola by using a graphing calculator.

Example 2

Use a graphing calculator to graph $(x + 7) = (y - 2)^2$.

Solve for y.

$$x + 7 = (y - 2)^2$$
$$\pm\sqrt{x + 7} = y - 2$$
$$\pm\sqrt{x + 7} + 2 = y$$

Select an appropriate range. As with
circles, you need to graph both
equations to complete the parabola.

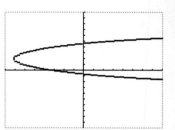

In Example 2, notice that the graph of $(x + 7) = (y - 2)^2$ has the same shape
as the graph of $x = y^2$, but it is translated 7 units left and 2 units up. The values
of h and k in the standard form of the equation of a parabola will tell you how
many units to translate the parent graphs $y^2 = 4px$ and $x^2 = 4py$.

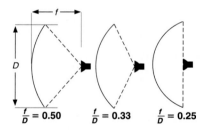

Parabolic satellite dishes are categorized as
deep, average, or shallow by using the ratio of
the focal length (f) to the diameter (D) of the
dish at its widest part. If $\frac{f}{D} < 0.3$, the dish is
categorized as deep. If $\frac{f}{D} > 0.45$, the dish is
categorized as shallow. If $0.3 \leq \frac{f}{D} \leq 0.45$, the
dish is categorized as average. Deeper dishes
are preferred because they are less susceptible
to interference from environmental noise.

Example 3

APPLICATION

Communications

The Winegard Company produces the QuadStar Perforated Antenna, which is a satellite dish made from aluminum with 2-millimeter perforations. The diameter of the satellite dish is 3 meters, and it has a $\dfrac{f}{D}$ ratio of 0.278. Write an equation that models the shape of this dish. Assume that the vertex is at the origin and the parabola opens to the right.

Find the value of f, which is also the value of p.

$$\frac{f}{D} = 0.278$$

$$\frac{p}{3} = 0.278 \qquad f = p \text{ and } D = 3$$

$$p = 0.834$$

Since the parabola opens to the right, the directrix is parallel to the y-axis.

$$(y - k)^2 = 4p(x - h)$$
$$(y - 0)^2 = 4(0.834)(x - 0) \qquad (h, k) = (0, 0), \text{ and } p = 0.834$$
$$y^2 = 3.336x$$

The equation that models the shape of the satellite dish is $y^2 = 3.336x$.

Chalkboard Example

For Example 3

A gardener sprays water from a hose at a tomato plant 40 feet away. The water flows in a parabolic arc 15 feet high in the center. At what height above the ground is the width of the arc 20 feet? $11\frac{1}{4}$ ft

You can use the same process you used with circles to rewrite the standard form of the equation of a parabola as the general form of the equation of a parabola.

$$(y - k)^2 = 4p(x - h)$$
$$y^2 - 2ky + k^2 = 4px - 4ph$$
$$y^2 - 4px - 2ky + k^2 + 4ph = 0 \qquad h, k, \text{ and } p \text{ are constants.}$$
$$y^2 + Dx + Ey + F = 0 \qquad\qquad D = -4p, E = -2k, F = k^2 + 4ph$$

$$(x - h)^2 = 4p(y - k)$$
$$x^2 - 2hx + h^2 = 4py - 4pk$$
$$x^2 - 2hx - 4py + h^2 + 4pk = 0 \qquad h, k, \text{ and } p \text{ are constants.}$$
$$x^2 + Dx + Ey + F = 0 \qquad\qquad D = -2h, E = -4p, F = h^2 + 4pk$$

General Form for the Equation of a Parabola	**The general form of the equation of a parabola is** $y^2 + Dx + Ey + F = 0$, **when the directrix is parallel to the y-axis, or** $x^2 + Dx + Ey + F = 0$, **when the directrix is parallel to the x-axis.**

An equation in general form can be rewritten in standard form to determine the coordinates of the vertex, (h, k), and the distance from the vertex to the focus, p.

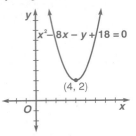
Example 4

Write the standard form of $y^2 - 4x + 2y + 5 = 0$. Then graph the equation.

Since y is squared, the directrix of the graph of this parabola is parallel to the y-axis.

$$y^2 - 4x + 2y + 5 = 0$$
$$y^2 + 2y = 4x - 5$$
$$y^2 + 2y + 1 = 4x - 5 + 1 \qquad \textit{Complete the square.}$$
$$y^2 + 2y + 1 = 4x - 4 \qquad \textit{Simplify.}$$
$$(y + 1)^2 = 4(x - 1) \qquad \textit{Factor.}$$

The standard form of the equation is $(y + 1)^2 = 4(x - 1)$.

The vertex of the parabola is at $(1, -1)$. The distance from the vertex to the focus is 1.

Sketch the parabola.

$y^2 - 4x + 2y + 5 = 0$

$(1, -1)$

EXPLORATION: Graphing Calculator

1. Graph $y_1 = x^2$.

2. For each situation, make a conjecture about the location of the vertex. Then verify by graphing.
   a. x is replaced with $(x - 2)$. Vertex is at $(2, 0)$.
   b. x is replaced with $(x + 2)$. Vertex is at $(-2, 0)$.
   c. y is replaced with $(y - 2)$. Vertex is at $(0, 2)$.
   d. y is replaced with $(y + 2)$. Vertex is at $(0, -2)$.

Parabolas are often used to demonstrate maximum or minimum points in real-world situations.

Example 5

APPLICATION

Entertainment

The amusement park has been charging \$12 per person for admission and averaging 1000 patrons per day. The directors of the park are considering a \$2 increase in the price for next season. They have calculated that for each \$2 increase they propose, they will probably lose 100 patrons per day. What should be the ideal admission fee for the greatest income on an average day?

Let y = the income from admissions.
Let x = the number of \$2 price increases.

$$\text{Income} = (\text{number of customers}) \cdot (\text{cost of a ticket})$$
$$y = (1000 - 100x) \cdot (12 + 2x)$$
$$y = 12{,}000 + 2000x - 1200x - 200x^2$$
$$y = -200(x^2 - 4x) + 12{,}000$$
$$y - 12{,}000 = -200(x^2 - 4x)$$
$$y - 12{,}000 + (-800) = -200(x^2 - 4x + 4) \quad \textit{Complete the square.}$$
$$y - 12{,}800 = -200(x - 2)^2$$
$$\frac{-1}{200}(y - 12{,}800) = (x - 2)^2$$

The vertex of the parabola is at $(2, 12{,}800)$, and because p is negative, it opens downward.

Remember that the vertex is the maximum or minimum point of a parabola. Since the parabola opens downward, the vertex is the maximum.

The x-coordinate of the vertex, 2, represents two increases of \$2. The y-coordinate, 12,800, represents a maximum income of \$12,800.

Maximum income will occur with an admission fee of $12 + 2(\$2)$ or \$16.

EVALUATING THE LESSON

Checking for Understanding

Exercises 1–12 are designed to help you assess students' understanding through reading, writing, speaking, and modeling. You should work through Exercises 1–3 with your students and then monitor their work on Exercises 4–12.

Closing the Lesson

Modeling Activity Have students sketch a line, a point not on the line, and the parabola determined by the two. Have them identify the focus, the directrix, the vertex, and the axis of symmetry.

CHECKING FOR UNDERSTANDING

Communicating Mathematics

Read and study the lesson to answer each question. 1–2. See margin.

1. **Describe** how you can determine from the equation of a parabola in what direction the parabola opens.

2. **Describe** how you can determine from the equation of a parabola which axis the directrix is parallel to.

3. **Explain** how you might distinguish an equation for a parabola from an equation for a circle. An equation for a parabola only has one squared term.

Guided Practice

Find the coordinates of the vertex and the value of p for the equation of each parabola. State the direction in which the parabola opens. 5. $(9, -12)$, 5, right

4. $16(y - 4) = x^2$ $(0, 4)$, 4, up
5. $20(x - 9) = (y + 12)^2$
6. $(x - 3)^2 = -8(y + 4)$ $(3, -4)$, -2, down
7. $2(y + 8) = (x - 6)^2$ $(6, -8)$, 0.5, up

Name the coordinates of the vertex and focus, and the equation of the directrix of the parabola defined by each equation. Then graph the equation.

8. $x^2 - 8y = 0$
9. $(x - 2)^2 = 8(y + 1)$
10. $(y + 2)^2 = -16(x - 3)$

8–10. See margin. For graphs, see Teacher's Answer Key.

Write the standard form of each equation.

11. $y^2 - 6y - 4x = -9$ $(y - 3)^2 = 4x$
12. $y^2 + 12y - 16x - 12 = 0$ $(y + 6)^2 = 16(x + 3)$

RETEACHING THE LESSON

If students have difficulty drawing the graphs of parabolas, remind them of the value of the basic technique of plotting points. With only the vertex and two points, one on either side of the axis of symmetry, students can see the general shape of the parabola and graph it with a certain degree of accuracy.

Practice Masters Booklet, p. 66

10-2 **Practice Worksheet**

NAME _____ DATE _____

The Parabola

For each equation,
a. write the standard form,
b. find the coordinates of the focus and vertex, and the equation of the directrix and axis of symmetry, and
c. graph the equation.

1. $x^2 - 2x + 1 = 8y - 16$
2. $y^2 + 6y + 9 = 16 - 16x$

$(x - 1)^2 = 8(y - 2)$;
focus: $(1, 4)$; vertex: $(1, 2)$;
directrix: $y = 0$;
axis of symmetry: $x = 1$

$(y + 3)^2 = -16(x - 1)$;
focus: $(-3, -3)$; vertex: $(1, -3)$;
directrix: $x = 5$;
axis of symmetry: $y = 3$

Write the equation of the parabola that meets each set of conditions. Then graph the equation.

3. The parabola has its focus at $(1, 3)$ and the vertex at $(1, 2)$.
4. The focus is at $(2, 1)$, and the equation of the directrix is $x = -2$.

$(x - 1)^2 = 4(y - 2)$
$(y - 1)^2 = 8x$

T66
Glencoe Division, Macmillan/McGraw-Hill

Homework Exercises

Assignment Guide

Average: 13–29, 36, 38, 41–46
Enriched: 19–37, 39–46

The red A, B, and C flags, printed only in the Teacher's Wraparound Edition, indicate the level of difficulty of the exercises.

Chapter 10, Quiz A, (Lessons 10–1 through 10–2) is available in the *Evaluation Masters*, p. 125.

Using Technology

In Exercises 32–35, students can use the vertical-line test to decide whether a graph is the graph of a function. They should see that the graphs of equations that are parabolas with directrices parallel to the *x*-axis are functions, while those with directrices parallel to the *y*-axis are not.

Additional Answers

13a. $(y - 2)^2 = x - 7$
13b. vertex: (7, 2); focus: (7.25, 2); directrix: $x = 6.75$; axis: $y = 2$
14a. $(y + 5)^2 = -4(x - 1)$
14b. vertex: (1, −5); focus: (0, −5); directrix: $x = 2$; axis: $y = -5$
15a. $(x + 4)^2 = -4(y - 2)$
15b. vertex: (−4, 2); focus: (−4, 1); directrix: $y = 3$; axis: $x = -4$
16a. $(x - 1)^2 = 12(y - 1)$
16b. vertex: (1, 1); focus: (1, 4); directrix: $y = -2$; axis: $x = 1$
17a. $y^2 = -2x$

17b. vertex: (0, 0); focus: $\left(-\frac{1}{2}, 0\right)$;

directrix: $x = \frac{1}{2}$; axis: $y = 0$

18a. $x^2 = \frac{19}{3}y$

18b. vertex: (0, 0); focus: $\left(0, \frac{19}{12}\right)$;

directrix: $y = -\frac{19}{12}$; axis: $x = 0$

19a. $(x - 3)^2 = 10(y + 1)$

19b. vertex: (3, −1); focus: $\left(3, \frac{3}{2}\right)$;

directrix: $y = -\frac{7}{2}$; axis: $x = 3$

EXERCISES

Practice

For each equation, 13–22. See margin. For graphs, see Teacher's Answer Key.
a. **write the standard form,**
b. **find the coordinates of the focus and vertex, and the equation of the directrix and axis of symmetry, and**
c. **graph the equation.**

13. $y^2 - 4y + 4 = x - 7$ 14. $-4x + 4 = y^2 + 10y + 25$
15. $x^2 + 8x + 4y + 8 = 0$ 16. $x^2 - 2x - 12y + 13 = 0$
17. $y^2 + 2x = 0$ 18. $3x^2 - 19y = 0$
19. $4x^2 - 40y - 24x - 4 = 0$ 20. $x^2 + 4x + 2y + 10 = 0$
21. $y^2 + 3x = 6y$ 22. $2x^2 - 16x + 16y + 64 = 0$

Write the equation of the parabola that meets each set of conditions. Then graph the equation. 23–30. See margin. For graphs, see Teacher's Answer Key.

23. The vertex is at the origin, and the focus is at (−3, 0).

24. The focus is at (2, 5), and the equation of directrix is $x = 4$.

25. The parabola passes through (5, 2), has a vertical axis, and has a maximum at (4, 3).

26. The parabola passes through (2, −1), has its vertex at (−7, −5), and opens to the right.

27. The equation of axis is $x = 2$, the focus is at (2, −6), and $p = -2$.

28. The focus is at (3, 0), the length from the focus to the vertex is 2 units, and the parabola has a minimum.

29. The parabola has a horizontal axis and passes through the origin, (3, −2), and (−1, 2).

30. The parabola has a vertical axis and passes through the origin, (3, −2), and (−2, 2).

31. Consider the standard form of the equation of a parabola in which the vertex is known but the value of p is not known.
    a. As the value of $|p|$ becomes increasingly great, what happens to the shape of the parabola? The opening becomes narrower.
    b. As the value of $|p|$ becomes increasingly small, what happens to the shape of the parabola? The opening becomes wider.

Graphing Calculator

Graph each parabola. Then state the coordinates of the vertex and tell whether the graph is the graph of a function. Write *yes* or *no*.

32. $x^2 - 4x - 4y - 12 = 0$ (2, −4), yes   33. $x^2 + 2x + 2y - 5 = 0$ (−1, 3) yes
34. $y^2 + 2y - x + 6 = 0$ (5, −1), no   35. $y^2 + 6y - 8x + 65 = 0$ (7, −3), no
32–35. For graphs, see Teacher's Answer Key.

Critical Thinking

The *latus rectum* of a parabola is the line segment through the focus that is perpendicular to the axis and has endpoints on the parabola. The length of the latus rectum is $|4p|$ units, where p is the distance from the vertex to the focus.

37. $(x - 4)^2 + (y - 3)^2 = 16$

Applications and Problem Solving

36. Write the equation of the parabola with vertex at $(-2, 1)$, axis $y = 1$, and latus rectum 4 units long. $(y - 1)^2 = 4(x + 2)$

37. The latus rectum of the parabola with equation $(x - 4)^2 = 8(y - 1)$ coincides with the diameter of a circle. Write the equation of the circle.

38. **Communications** If a parabolic satellite dish is 10 feet in diameter, determine the range of focal distances for each type of dish.
    a. a shallow dish $f > 4.5$ feet
    b. an average dish $3 \le f \le 4.5$ feet
    c. a deep dish $f < 3$ feet

39. **Entertainment** The local theater guild puts on plays during the summer at the outdoor amphitheater at a cost of $4 per person. The average attendance at each performance is 500 people. Next summer, they would like to increase the cost of the tickets, but they also want to maximize their profits to keep their program alive. The director estimates that for every $1 increase in admission cost, the attendance at each performance will decrease by 50.
    a. What price should the director propose to maximize their income? $7
    b. What is the maximum income that might be expected? $2450

40. **Baseball** Juan Gonzalez of the Texas Rangers was the 1992 major league home run champion. One day, Mr. Gonzalez popped up a baseball at an initial velocity, v_0, of 64 feet/second. Its distance, s, above the ground after t seconds is described by $s = v_0 t - 16t^2$. 40a. See Teacher's Answer Key.
    a. Graph the function $s = v_0 t - 16t^2$.
    b. Name the coordinates of the vertex. $(2, 64)$
    c. What does the value of s at the vertex represent? the maximum height
    d. How many seconds is the ball in the air? 4 seconds

Mixed Review

41. Graph $y = \sin 4\theta$. **(Lesson 6-2)** See Teacher's Answer Key.

42. Verify that $\csc \theta \cos \theta \tan \theta = 1$ is an identity. **(Lesson 7-2)** See margin.

43. Find an ordered pair to represent $\vec{u}$ if $\vec{u} = \vec{v} + \vec{w}$, if $\vec{v} = (3, -5)$ and $\vec{w} = (-4, 2)$. **(Lesson 8-2)** $(-1, -3)$

44. Find $\frac{1}{3}\left(\cos \frac{7\pi}{8} + i \sin \frac{7\pi}{8}\right) \cdot 3\sqrt{3}\left[\cos\left(-\frac{\pi}{4}\right) + i \sin\left(-\frac{\pi}{4}\right)\right]$. Then express the product in rectangular form with a and b to the nearest hundredth. **(Lesson 9-7)** $\sqrt{3}\left(\cos \frac{5\pi}{8} + i \sin \frac{5\pi}{8}\right)$; $-0.66 + 1.60i$

45. Write the standard form of the equation of a circle with a center at $(7, 4)$ and a radius of $\sqrt{2}$ units. **(Lesson 10-1)** $(x - 7)^2 + (y - 4)^2 = 2$

46. **College Entrance Exam** Choose the best answer. B
    A swimming pool is 75 feet long and 42 feet wide. If 7.48 gallons equals 1 cubic foot, how many gallons of water are needed to raise the level of the water 4 inches?
    (A) 140   **(B)** 7854   **(C)** 31,500   **(D)** 94,500   **(E)** 727,650

EXTENDING THE LESSON

Math Power: Problem Solving

A parabola with directrix parallel to the x-axis passes through the points $(1, 2)$, $(-2, 14)$, and $(3, 4)$. Find the equation of the parabola.
$y = x^2 - 3x + 4$

Additional Answers

20a. $(x + 2)^2 = -2(y + 3)$
20b. vertex: $(-2, -3)$; focus: $(-2, -3.5)$; directrix: $y = -2.5$; axis: $x = -2$
21a. $(y - 3)^2 = -3(x - 3)$
21b. vertex: $(3, 3)$; focus: $\left(\frac{9}{4}, 3\right)$; directrix: $x = \frac{15}{4}$; axis: $y = 3$
22a. $(x - 4)^2 = -8(y + 2)$
22b. vertex: $(4, -2)$; focus: $(4, -4)$; directrix: $y = 0$; axis: $x = 4$
23. $y^2 = -12x$
24. $(y - 5)^2 = -4(x - 3)$
25. $(x - 4)^2 = -1(y - 3)$
26. $(y + 5)^2 = \frac{16}{9}(x + 7)$
27. $(x - 2)^2 = -8(y + 4)$
28. $(x - 3)^2 = 8(y + 2)$
29. $(y - 2)^2 = 4(x + 1)$
30. $\left(x - \frac{13}{2}\right)^2 = 15\left(y + \frac{169}{60}\right)$
42. $\csc \theta \cos \theta \tan \theta$
$$= \frac{1}{\sin \theta} \cdot \cos \theta \cdot \frac{\sin \theta}{\cos \theta}$$
$$= \frac{\sin \theta}{\sin \theta} \cdot \frac{\cos \theta}{\cos \theta}$$
$$= 1$$

Enrichment Masters Booklet, p. 66

NAME _____ DATE _____
10-2 Enrichment Worksheet

Tilted Parabolas

The diagram at the right shows a fixed point $F(1, 1)$ and a line d whose equation is $y = -x - 2$. If $P(x, y)$ satisfies the condition that $PD = PF$, then P is on a parabola. Our objective is to find an equation for the tilted parabola; which is the locus of all points that are the same distance from $(1,1)$ and the line $y = -x - 2$.

To do this, first find an equation for the line m through $P(x, y)$ and perpendicular to line d at $D(a, b)$. Using this equation and the equation for line d, find the coordinates (a, b) of point D in terms of x and y. Then use $(PD)^2 = (PF)^2$ to find an equation for the parabola.

Refer to the discussion above.

1. Find an equation for line m.
   $x - y + (b - a) = 0$

2. Use the equations for lines m and d to show that the coordinates of point D are $D(a, b) = D\left(\frac{x - y - 2}{2}, \frac{y - x - 2}{2}\right)$.
   From the equation for line m,
   $-a + b = -x + y$. From the equation for line d,
   $a + b = -z$. Subtract to get $a = \frac{x - y - 2}{2}$.
   Add to get $b = \frac{y - x - 2}{2}$.

3. Use the coordinates o D, along with $(PD)^2 = (PF)^2$ to find an equation of the parabola with focus F and directrix d.
   $x^2 - 2xy + y^2 - 8x - 8y = 0$

4. a. Every parabola has an axis of symmetry. Find an equation for the axis of symmetry of the parabola described above. Justify your answer.
   $y = x$, since $y = x$ contains $F(1,1)$ and is perpendicular to d.
   b. Use your answer from part a to find the coordinates of the vertex of the parabola. Justify your answer.
   $(0,0)$, since $(0,0)$ is midway between point F and line d.

T 66
Glencoe Division, Macmillan/McGraw-Hill

NCTM Standards: 1–6, 8

Lesson Resources

- Practice Master 10–3
- Enrichment Master 10–3

 Transparency 10–3 contains the 5-Minute Check and a teaching aid for this lesson.

INTRODUCING THE LESSON

5-Minute Check

(over Lesson 10–2)

Find each of the following for the parabola with equation
$y^2 - 6y - 4x + 17 = 0$.
1. standard form of the equation
   $(y - 3)^2 = 4(x - 2)$
2. coordinates of the focus
   (3, 3)
3. coordinates of the vertex
   (2, 3)
4. equation of the directrix $x = 1$
5. equation of the axis of symmetry $y = 3$

Motivating the Lesson

Have students read the application at the beginning of the lesson. Tell them that a circle is a special form of ellipse. Ask them to speculate about the location of the foci in a circle. **They become a single focus, the center of the circle.**

10-3   The Ellipse

Objectives

After studying this lesson, you should ·be able to:

10–3A
- use the standard and general forms of the equation of an ellipse, and

10–3B
- graph ellipses.

Application

Satellites, including spacecraft, travel around planets and their moons in an elliptical orbit with the center of the planet as one of the two foci. The point at which the satellite is closest to a planet is the perihelion, and the point at which it is farthest is the aphelion.

An **ellipse** is the locus of all points in a plane such that the sum of the distances from two given points in the plane, called foci, is constant. In the figure at the right, F_1 and F_2 are the foci of the ellipse. P and Q are any two points on the ellipse. By definition, $PF_1 + PF_2 = QF_1 + QF_2$.

Foci is the plural of focus.

EXPLORATION: Modeling

Materials: 2 pushpins, corrugated cardboard, paper, 10-inch piece of string, pencil

1. Attach a piece of graph paper to the corrugated cardboard. Draw two points on the paper approximately 4 inches apart.

2. Insert one pushpin at each point.

3. Tie the ends of the string together and loop it around the pins.

4. Insert your pencil and pull outward until the string is taut. Move the pencil around the pins, keeping the string taut.

   See students' work.

5. Write a paragraph telling why this is a model of an ellipse.

ALTERNATE TEACHING STRATEGIES

Using Logical Reasoning

After students complete the Exploration, ask them to explain how the activity demonstrates that an ellipse is the locus of all points such that the sum of the distances from two given points is constant. **The circumference of the loop and the distance between the pins are constants. Therefore, their difference—the sum of the pencil's distances from the pins—is constant.**

Using Models

Have students cut a circle from paper and mark a point in the interior that is not the center. Have them fold a point of the circumference onto the marked point and crease the paper, then repeat for a succession of other points around the circumference. The creases will create the shape of an ellipse around the marked point.

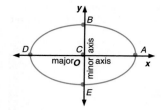

The parent graph of an ellipse is shown at the left. An ellipse has two axes of symmetry, in this case, the x-axis and the y-axis. The point where these axes meet is called the center of the ellipse. The center of the parent graph of an ellipse is the origin.

Notice that the ellipse intersects each axis of symmetry two times. The longer line segment, $\overline{AD}$, which contains the foci, is called the **major axis**. The shorter segment, $\overline{BE}$, is called the **minor axis**. The endpoints of each axis are the vertices of the ellipse.

The center separates each axis into two congruent segments. Suppose we let b represent the length of the **semi-minor axis** $\overline{BC}$ and a represent the length of the **semi-major axis** $\overline{CA}$. The foci are located along the major axis, c units from the center. There is a special relationship among the values a, b, and c.

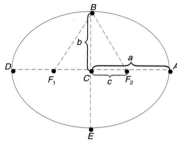

Suppose you draw $\overline{BF_1}$ and $\overline{BF_2}$. The lengths of these segments are equal. Since B and A are two points on the ellipse, you can use the definition of an ellipse to find the length of $\overline{BF_2}$.

$$BF_1 + BF_2 = AF_1 + AF_2 \qquad \textit{Definition of ellipse}$$
$$BF_1 + BF_2 = AF_1 + DF_1 \qquad AF_2 = DF_1$$
$$BF_1 + BF_2 = AD$$
$$BF_1 + BF_2 = 2a$$
$$2(BF_2) = 2a \qquad BF_1 = BF_2$$
$$BF_2 = a$$

Since $BF_2 = a$ and $\triangle BCF_2$ is a right triangle, $b^2 + c^2 = a^2$, by the Pythagorean theorem.

Example 1

APPLICATION

Space Travel

The graph below models the elliptical path of a space probe around two moons of a planet. The foci of the path are the centers of the moons. Find the coordinates of the foci.

The center of the ellipse is the origin.

$a = \frac{1}{2}(314)$ or 157

$b = \frac{1}{2}(110)$ or 55

The distance from the origin to the foci is c km.

$$c^2 + b^2 = a^2$$
$$c^2 + (55)^2 = (157)^2$$
$$c \approx 147$$

The foci are at $(147, 0)$ and $(-147, 0)$.

The standard form of the equation of an ellipse can be derived from the definition and the distance formula. Consider the special case when the center is at the origin.

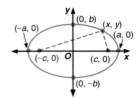

Suppose the foci are at $(c, 0)$ and $(-c, 0)$, and (x, y) are the coordinates of any point on the ellipse. By definition, the sum of the distances from (x, y) to the foci is a constant. Let $2a$ represent this constant. Using the distance formula, $2a = \sqrt{(x + c)^2 + y^2} + \sqrt{(x - c)^2 + y^2}$. Now simplify to find an expression that does not contain radicals.

$$\sqrt{(x + c)^2 + y^2} = 2a - \sqrt{(x - c)^2 + y^2} \qquad \text{Isolate a radical.}$$

$$(x + c)^2 + y^2 = 4a^2 + (x - c)^2 + y^2 - 4a\sqrt{(x - c)^2 + y^2} \qquad \text{Square each side.}$$

$$a^2 - xc = a\sqrt{(x - c)^2 + y^2} \qquad \text{Simplify.}$$

$$a^4 - 2a^2xc + x^2c^2 = a^2[(x - c)^2 + y^2] \qquad \text{Square each side.}$$

$$x^2(a^2 - c^2) + a^2y^2 = a^2(a^2 - c^2) \qquad \text{Simplify.}$$

$$\frac{x^2}{a^2} + \frac{y^2}{a^2 - c^2} = 1 \qquad \begin{array}{l}\text{Divide each side}\\ \text{by } a^2(a^2 - c^2).\end{array}$$

$$\frac{x^2}{a^2} + \frac{y^2}{b^2} = 1 \qquad b^2 = a^2 - c^2$$

This is the equation of an ellipse whose center is the origin and whose foci are on the x-axis. When the foci are on the y-axis, the equation is of the form

$$\frac{y^2}{a^2} + \frac{x^2}{b^2} = 1.$$

The standard form of the equation of an ellipse with a center other than the origin is a translation of the parent graph to a center at (h, k). The standard form of the equation of ellipses and their graphs are given below.

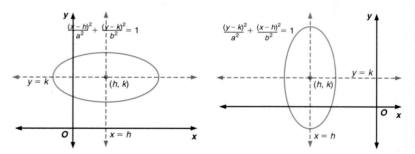

Standard Form of the Equation of an Ellipse

The standard form of the equation of an ellipse with center at (h, k) and major axis of length $2a$ units, where $b^2 = a^2 - c^2$, is as follows.

$$\frac{(x-h)^2}{a^2} + \frac{(y-k)^2}{b^2} = 1, \text{ when the major axis is parallel to the } x\text{-axis,}$$

or

$$\frac{(y-k)^2}{a^2} + \frac{(x-h)^2}{b^2} = 1, \text{ when the major axis is parallel to the } y\text{-axis.}$$

Teaching Tip Compare the equations of an ellipse centered at the origin with an ellipse centered at (h, k). Ask students how this relates to what they learned about parabolas in Lesson 10–2.

In all ellipses, $a^2 > b^2$. You can use this information to determine the orientation of the major axis from the values given in the equation. If a^2 is the denominator of the x terms, the major axis is parallel to the x-axis. If a^2 is the denominator of the y terms, the major axis is parallel to the y-axis.

Chalkboard Example

For Example 2

Graph $\frac{(y+2)^2}{25} + \frac{(x-3)^2}{16} = 1$.

Example 2

Graph $\dfrac{(x-4)^2}{121} + \dfrac{(y+5)^2}{64} = 1$.

Determine the values of $a, b, c, h,$ and k.

$a = \sqrt{121}$ or 11 $\qquad b = \sqrt{64}$ or 8 $\qquad c = \sqrt{a^2 - b^2}$
$$= \sqrt{57} \text{ or about } 7.55$$

$h = 4$ $\qquad\qquad k = -5$

If the center of the ellipse were the origin, the vertices of the major axis would be at $(11, 0)$ and $(-11, 0)$, the vertices of the minor axis would be at $(0, 8)$ and $(0, -8)$, and the foci would be at $(7.55, 0)$ and $(-7.55, 0)$. However, the center is at $(4, -5)$, which indicates that each of these vertices is translated 4 units to the right and 5 units down.

$$
\begin{aligned}
(0, 0) &\rightarrow (0 + 4, 0 - 5) \text{ or } (4, -5) \\
(11, 0) &\rightarrow (11 + 4, 0 - 5) \text{ or } (15, -5) \\
(-11, 0) &\rightarrow (-11 + 4, 0 - 5) \text{ or } (-7, -5) \\
(0, 8) &\rightarrow (0 + 4, 8 - 5) \text{ or } (4, 3) \\
(0, -8) &\rightarrow (0 + 4, -8 - 5) \text{ or } (4, -13) \\
(7.55, 0) &\rightarrow (7.55 + 4, 0 - 5) \text{ or } (11.55, -5) \\
(-7.55, 0) &\rightarrow (-7.55 + 4, 0 - 5) \text{ or } (-3.55, -5)
\end{aligned}
$$

Graph these translated points. Other points on the ellipse can be found by substituting values for x and y. Complete the ellipse.

Chalkboard Examples

For Example 3

Use a graphing calculator to graph $\frac{(y+4)^2}{9} + \frac{(x+5)^2}{4} = 1$.

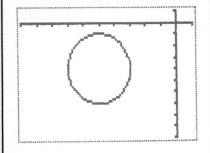

For Example 4

Find the coordinates of the center, the foci, and the vertices of the ellipse with the equation $4x^2 + 9y^2 - 8x - 54y + 49 = 0$. Then graph the equation.

center: (1, 3)
foci: $(1 + \sqrt{5}, 3)$, $(1 - \sqrt{5}, 3)$
vertices: (–2, 3), (4, 3), (1, 5), (1, 1)

You can also use a graphing calculator to graph an ellipse.

Example 3

Use a graphing calculator to graph $\dfrac{(x+2)^2}{16} + \dfrac{(y-3)^2}{49} = 1$.

First solve the equation for y.

$$\frac{(x+2)^2}{16} + \frac{(y-3)^2}{49} = 1$$

$49(x+2)^2 + 16(y-3)^2 = 784$ *Multiply by the least common denominator, 784.*

$$(y-3)^2 = \frac{784 - 49(x+2)^2}{16}$$ *Isolate the y term.*

$$y - 3 = \pm\frac{\sqrt{784 - 49(x+2)^2}}{4}$$ *Take the square root of each side.*

$$y = \pm\frac{\sqrt{784 - 49(x+2)^2}}{4} + 3$$

The last step represents two equations. Graph both equations on the same screen. Our viewing window goes from –7 to 3 on the x-axis and –6 to 12 on the y-axis.

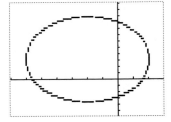

As with circles and parabolas, the standard form of the equation of an ellipse can be expanded to obtain the general form. The result is a second-degree equation of the form $Ax^2 + Cy^2 + Dx + Ey + F = 0$, where $A \neq 0$ and $C \neq 0$, and A and C have the same sign. An equation in general form can be rewritten in standard form to determine the center at (h, k), the length of the semi-major axis (a), and the length of the semi-minor axis (b).

Example 4

Find the coordinates of the center, the foci, and the vertices of the ellipse with the equation $4x^2 + y^2 - 8x + 6y + 9 = 0$. Then graph the equation.

First write the equation in standard form.

$$4x^2 + y^2 - 8x + 6y + 9 = 0$$
$$4(x^2 - 2x + \text{?}) + (y^2 + 6y + \text{?}) = -9 + \text{?} + \text{?}$$
$$4(x^2 - 2x + 1) + (y^2 + 6y + 9) = -9 + 4(1) + 9$$ *Complete the square.*
$$4(x-1)^2 + (y+3)^2 = 4$$ *Factor.*
$$\frac{(x-1)^2}{1} + \frac{(y+3)^2}{4} = 1$$ *Divide each side by 4.*

The center is at $(1,-3)$. Since $a^2 > b^2$, $a^2 = 4$ and $b^2 = 1$. Thus, the major axis is parallel to the y-axis. Since $c^2 = a^2 - b^2$, $c = \sqrt{3}$.

If the center of the ellipse were the origin, the foci would be at $(0, \sqrt{3})$ and $(0, -\sqrt{3})$. The vertices would be at $(1, 0), (-1, 0), (0, 2)$, and $(0, -2)$. However, the center is at $(1, -3)$, so translate each point 1 unit right and 3 units down.

center: $(1, -3)$

foci: $(1, \sqrt{3} - 3), (1, -\sqrt{3} - 3)$

vertices: $(2, -3), (0, -3),$
$\qquad\qquad (1, -1), (1, -5)$

Sketch the ellipse.

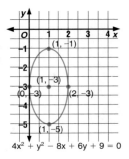

$4x^2 + y^2 - 8x + 6y + 9 = 0$

EXPLORATION: Graphing Calculator

1. Graph $y_1 = \left(16 - \frac{16}{9}x^2\right)^{\frac{1}{2}}$ and $y_2 = -\left(16 - \frac{16}{9}x^2\right)^{\frac{1}{2}}$.

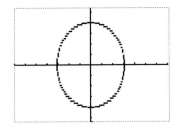

2. For each situation, make a conjecture about the behavior of the graph. Then verify by graphing.
   a. x is replaced with $(x - 2)$. The ellipse is moved 2 units right.
   b. x is replaced with $(x + 2)$. The ellipse is moved 2 units left.
   c. y is replaced with $(y - 2)$. The ellipse is moved 2 units down.
   d. y is replaced with $(y + 2)$. The ellipse is moved 2 units up.
   e. 9 is switched with 16. The ellipse is rotated $90°$.

CHECKING FOR UNDERSTANDING

Communicating Mathematics

Read and study the lesson to answer each question.

1. **Explain** how you can determine whether the major axis of an ellipse is parallel to the x-axis or the y-axis. See margin.

RETEACHING THE LESSON

Use the equation below to illustrate the relationship between an ellipse and its equation.

$$\frac{(x - 3)^2}{10^2} + \frac{(y - 2)^2}{8^2} = 1$$

- The center is at $(3, 2)$.
- The semi-major axis measures 10.
- The semi-minor axis measures 8.
- The distance from the center to each focus is $\sqrt{10^2 - 8^2} = 6$.

Additional Answer

1. If the a^2 is the denominator of the x terms, the major axis is parallel to the x-axis. If it is the denominator of the y terms, the major axis is parallel to the y-axis.

After students complete the Exploration, ask them to name the equations they would graph on their calculators to obtain an ellipse with center at $(4, -1)$, a major axis of 10 parallel to the x-axis, and a minor axis of 4. Have them verify their conjectures by graphing.

$$y_1 = \left(4 - \frac{4}{25}(x - 4)^2\right)^{\frac{1}{2}} - 1$$

$$y_2 = -\left(4 - \frac{4}{25}(x - 4)^2\right)^{\frac{1}{2}} - 1$$

EVALUATING THE LESSON

Checking for Understanding

Exercises 1–14 are designed to help you assess students' understanding through reading, writing, speaking, and modeling. You should work through Exercises 1–4 with your students and then monitor their work on Exercises 5–14.

$$\frac{(x + 5)^2}{36} + \frac{(y - 7)^2}{16} = 1 \text{ and}$$

$$\frac{(y - 7)^2}{36} + \frac{(x + 5)^2}{16} = 1$$

Practice Masters Booklet, p. 67

10-3 | **Practice Worksheet**

NAME _____ DATE _____

The Ellipse

For each equation, find the coordinates of the center, foci, and vertices of the ellipse. Then graph the equation.

1. $4x^2 + y^2 - 32x + 4y + 64 = 0$

center: $(4, -2)$;
foci: $(4, -2 \pm \sqrt{3})$;
vertices: $(4, 0), (4, -4), (3, -2),$
$(5, -2)$

2. $4x^2 + 9y^2 - 8x - 36y + 4 = 0$

center: $(1, 2)$;
foci: $(1 \pm \sqrt{5}, 2)$;
vertices: $(-2, 2), (1, 4),$
$(4, 2), (1, 0)$

Write the equation of the ellipse that meets each set of conditions.

3. The foci are at $(-2, 1)$ and $(-2, -7)$, and $a = 5$.

$\frac{(y + 3)^2}{25} + \frac{(x + 2)^2}{9} = 1$

4. The length of the semi-major axis is 6 units, and the foci are at $(0,2)$ and $(8, 2)$.

$\frac{(x - 4)^2}{36} + \frac{(y - 2)^2}{20} = 1$

5. The center is at $(1, 3)$, one vertex is at $(1, 8)$, and $\frac{c}{a} = \frac{4}{5}$.

$\frac{(y - 3)^2}{25} + \frac{(x - 1)^2}{9} = 1$

State whether the graph of each equation is a circle, parabola, or ellipse. Justify your answer.

6. $x^2 + 4y^2 - 2x - 16y + 1 = 0$

ellipse; $\frac{(x - 1)^2}{16} + \frac{(y - 2)^2}{4} = 1$

7. $x^2 + 4y - 16 = 0$

parabola; $x^2 = 4(-1)(y - 4)$

8. $x^2 + y^2 + 6x + 2y + 7 = 0$

circle; $(x + 3)^2 + (y + 1)^2 = 3$

9. $4x^2 + 4y^2 - 20x - 24 = 0$

circle; $\left(x - \frac{5}{2}\right)^2 + y^2 = \frac{49}{4}$

T 67
Glencoe Division, Macmillan/McGraw-Hill

Closing the Lesson

Writing Activity Ask students to write the equations of two ellipses, each with a center at (–5, 7), a semi-major axis measuring 6, and a semi-minor axis measuring 4.

APPLYING THE LESSON

Homework Exercises

Assignment Guide

Average: 15–35, 42, 43, 45–51
Enriched: 23–51

The red A, B, and C flags, printed only in the Teacher's Wraparound Edition, indicate the level of difficulty of the exercises.

Additional Answers

2. Solve the equation for *y*. This will result in two equations. Graph both equations on the same screen.

5. center: (0, 0), foci: (0, ±√5), vertices: (0, ±3), (±2, 0)

6. center: (4, –6), foci: (4 ± √7, –6), vertices: (0, –6), (8, –6), (4, –3), (4, –9)

7. center: (–2, 0), foci: (–2 ± 4√2, 0), vertices: (–11, 0), (7, 0), (–2, 7), (–2, –7)

8. center: (6, 7), foci: (6, 7 ± √21), vertices: (–4, 7), (16, 7), (6, 18), (6, –4)

9. center: (0, –9), foci: (0, –9 ± 4√3), vertices: (0, –1), (0, –17), (–4, –9), (4, –9)

10. center: (–10, 9), foci: (–10 ± √161, 9), vertices: (–25, 9), (5, 9), (–10, 17), (–10, 1)

15. center: (3, 4), foci: (6, 4), (0, 4), vertices: (8, 4), (–2, 4), (3, 0), (3, 8)

16. center: (–2, 1), foci: (–2, 1 ±√21), vertices: (0, 1), (–4, 1), (–2, –4), (–2, 6)

17. center: (0, 0), foci: (±√5, 0), vertices: (–3, 0), (3, 0), (0, –2), (0, 2)

18. center: (1, –2), foci: (1, –2 ± √5), vertices: (1, –5), (1, 1), (–1, –2), (3, –2)

---

2. **Explain** how you would graph an ellipse on a graphing calculator. See margin.

3. **Describe** the shape of an ellipse in which *a* equals *b*. a circle

4. What is the relationship among *a*, *b*, and *c* in reference to an ellipse?
$$a^2 = b^2 + c^2$$

Guided Practice For each equation, find the coordinates of the center, foci, and vertices of the ellipse. Then graph the equation. 5–10. See margin. For graphs, see Teacher's Answer Key.

5. $\dfrac{x^2}{4} + \dfrac{y^2}{9} = 1$

6. $\dfrac{(x-4)^2}{16} + \dfrac{(y+6)^2}{9} = 1$

7. $\dfrac{(x+2)^2}{81} + \dfrac{y^2}{49} = 1$

8. $\dfrac{(x-6)^2}{100} + \dfrac{(y-7)^2}{121} = 1$

9. $\dfrac{x^2}{16} + \dfrac{(y+9)^2}{64} = 1$

10. $\dfrac{(x+10)^2}{225} + \dfrac{(y-9)^2}{64} = 1$

Write the standard equation of each ellipse.

11.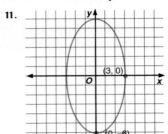
$$\dfrac{x^2}{9} + \dfrac{y^2}{36} = 1$$

12.
$$\dfrac{(x+2)^2}{16} + \dfrac{y^2}{4} = 1$$

13.
$$\dfrac{x^2}{49} + \dfrac{(y+5)^2}{25} = 1$$

14.
$$\dfrac{(x+3)^2}{25} + \dfrac{(y-4)^2}{64} = 1$$

EXERCISES   15–22. See margin. For graphs, see Teacher's Answer Key.

Practice For each equation, find the coordinates of the center, foci, and vertices of the ellipse. Then graph the equation.

15. $\dfrac{(x-3)^2}{25} + \dfrac{(y-4)^2}{16} = 1$

16. $\dfrac{(x+2)^2}{4} + \dfrac{(y-1)^2}{25} = 1$

17. $4x^2 + 9y^2 = 36$

18. $9x^2 + 4y^2 - 18x + 16y = 11$

548   CHAPTER 10   CONICS

19. $4y^2 - 8y + 9x^2 - 54x + 49 = 0$

20. $x^2 - 2x + y^2 - 2y - 6 = 0$

21. $9y^2 + 108y + 4x^2 - 56x = -484$

22. $18x^2 + 12y^2 - 144x - 48y = -120$

Write the equation of the ellipse that meets each set of conditions. 23. $\dfrac{y^2}{64} + \dfrac{x^2}{36} = 1$

23. The center is the origin, $a = 8$, $b = 6$, and the major axis is parallel to y-axis.

24. The center is at $(-3, -1)$, the length of the horizontal semi-major axis is 7 units, and the length of semi-minor axis is 5 units. $\dfrac{(x+3)^2}{49} + \dfrac{(y+1)^2}{25} = 1$

25. The length of the semi-minor axis is $\dfrac{2}{3}$ the length of the horizontal semi-major axis, the center is the origin, and $a = 6$. $\dfrac{x^2}{36} + \dfrac{y^2}{16} = 1$

26. The center is the origin, $\dfrac{1}{2} = \dfrac{c}{a}$, and the length of the horizontal semi-major axis is 10 units. $\dfrac{x^2}{100} + \dfrac{y^2}{75} = 1$

27. The foci are at $(-2, 0)$ and $(2, 0)$, and $a = 7$. $\dfrac{x^2}{49} + \dfrac{y^2}{45} = 1$

28. The semi-major axis has length 4 units, and foci are at $(2, 3)$ and $(2, -3)$. $\dfrac{y^2}{16} + \dfrac{(x-2)^2}{7} = 1$

State whether the graph of each equation is a circle, parabola, or ellipse. Justify your answer. 29–34. For justifications, see margin.

29. $x^2 + 3y^2 + 2x - 5y = 129$ ellipse

30. $x^2 + y + 4x - 2 = 0$ parabola

31. $2x^2 - 5x + y - 19 = 0$ parabola

32. $y^2 + 2y = x - x^2 + 12$ circle

33. $5x^2 - 2x + 2y^2 - 9y = 22$ ellipse

34. $12x^2 + 24x + 12y^2 + 72y = 124$ circle

35. Write the equation of the ellipse that passes through $(4, 2)$ and has foci at $(1, -1)$ and $(1, 5)$. $\dfrac{(y-2)^2}{18} + \dfrac{(x-1)^2}{9} = 1$

36. An ellipse has values a and b such that $b^2 = a^2(1 - 0.7^2)$ and the length of the vertical major axis is 20 units. Write the equation of the ellipse if its center is at $(3, 0)$. $\dfrac{y^2}{100} + \dfrac{(x-3)^2}{51} = 1$

37. Draw an ellipse that is tangent to the x- and y-axes and has its center at $(-3, 7)$. Then write the equation of the ellipse in general form.
$49x^2 + 9y^2 + 294x - 126y + 441 = 0$ For graph, see Teacher's Answer Key.

38. $(-1, -1)$, $(5, -1)$, $(2, -3)$, $(2, 1)$ 39. $(5, -3)$, $(1, -3)$, $(3, -2)$, $(3, -4)$

Graph each equation. Then use the TRACE function to approximate the coordinates of the vertices to the nearest integer. 38–41. For graphs, see Teacher's Answer Key.

38. $4x^2 + 9y^2 - 16x + 18y = 11$

39. $x^2 + 4y^2 - 6x + 24y = -41$

40. $16x^2 + 25y^2 + 32x - 150y = 159$
$(4, 3)$, $(-6, 3)$, $(-1, 7)$, $(-1, -1)$

41. $4x^2 + y^2 - 8x - 2y = 1$
$(0, 1)$, $(2, 1)$, $(1, -1)$, $(1, 3)$

Critical Thinking

42. One circle is internally tangent to an ellipse with equation $4x^2 + 9y^2 = 36$. Another circle is externally tangent to the same ellipse. Write the equations of the two circles if all three graphs have the same center.
$x^2 + y^2 = 4$, $x^2 + y^2 = 9$

Using Technology

In Exercises 38–41, remind students that they can use the guess-and-check strategy to find an appropriate range. Guess a range, check it, and adjust depending on the results. Continue, fine tuning with each new guess.

Additional Answers

19. center: $(3, 1)$, foci: $(3, 1 \pm \sqrt{5})$, vertices: $(3, 4)$, $(3, -2)$, $(1, 1)$, $(5, 1)$

20. center: $(1, 1)$, circle of radius $\sqrt{8}$ units

21. center: $(7, -6)$, foci: $(7 \pm \sqrt{5}, -6)$, vertices: $(10, -6)$, $(4, -6)$, $(7, -4)$, $(7, -8)$

22. center: $(4, 2)$, foci: $(4, 2 \pm \sqrt{6})$, vertices: $(4, 2 \pm 3\sqrt{2})$, $(4 \pm 2\sqrt{3}, 2)$

29. two squared terms, $A \neq C$

30. one squared term

31. one squared term

32. two squared terms, $A = C$

33. two squared terms, $A \neq C$

34. two squared terms, $A = C$

43. Astronomy   All of the planets in our solar system have elliptical orbits with the sun as one focal point. If the orbit of Mercury is about 46 million kilometers from the sun at its closest point and 70 million kilometers from the sun at its farthest point, what is the length of the major axis?   116 million km

44. Astronomy   The orbit of Earth is about 9.1×10^7 miles from the sun at its closest point and 9.3×10^7 miles from the sun at its farthest point.
   a. What is the length of the major axis? 1.84×10^8 miles
   b. What is the distance from the sun to the other focus? 2.0×10^6 miles

Mixed Review

45. Graph $y = \csc (\theta + 60°)$.   **(Lesson 6-2)**   See margin.

46. Find $\cos (A + B)$ if $\cos A = \frac{5}{13}$ and $\cos B = \frac{35}{37}$ and A and B are first quadrant angles.   **(Lesson 7-3)** $\frac{31}{481}$

47. Aviation   An airplane flies at an air speed of 425 mph on a heading due south. It flies against a headwind of 110 mph from a direction 30° east of south. Find the airplane's ground speed and direction.   **(Lesson 8-5)**   334.3 mph, 9°28′ SW

48. Express $-5 - i$ in polar form.   **(Lesson 9-6)** $\sqrt{26}(\cos 3.34 + i \sin 3.34)$

49. Write the standard form of the equation of the circle that passes through $(0, -9)$, $(7, -2)$, and $(-5, -10)$.   **(Lesson 10-1)** $(x + 5)^2 + (y - 3)^2 = 169$

50. Find the coordinates of the vertex and focus and the equation of the directrix of the parabola whose equation is $(x + 5)^2 = 12y$.   **(Lesson 10-2)**

51. College Entrance Exam   If the base of a rectangle is increased by 30% and the altitude of the rectangle is decreased by 20%, by what percent is the area increased?   4

50. $(-5, 0)$, $(-5, 3)$, $y = -3$

CASE STUDY FOLLOW-UP

Refer to Case Study 3: *The Legal System,* on pages 962–965.

An elliptical rotunda on the north side of the building that symbolizes the American legal system is a "whispering gallery." The major axis of the rotunda measures 44.4 feet. The minor axis measures 35.6 feet.

1. Where is the rotunda?   in the U.S. Capitol in Washington, D.C.

2. Two people standing at the two foci can easily hear each other whispering, even if there is other noise in the room. How far apart are the whisperers standing?   26.6 ft

3. **Research**   Find out about the size and shape of the dome of the U.S. Capitol. Can the dome be described in terms of conic sections? Write about your findings in a 1-page paper.   See students' work.

EXTENDING THE LESSON

Math Power: Problem Solving

The great Indian mathematician Srinivasa Ramanujan discovered an excellent approximation for the circumference of an ellipse, using the formula $C = \pi[3(a + b) - \sqrt{(a + 3b)(3a + b)}]$. Approximate the circumference of an ellipse with $a = 5$ and $b = 3$ (to six decimal places).
25.526986

Case Study Follow-Up

This activity provides an opportunity to do research and apply mathematics in solving problems related to issues that may face students in their adult lives. Case Study 3 is located on pages 962–965.

10-4 The Hyperbola

Objectives
10–4A
10–4B

After studying this lesson, you should be able to:
- use the standard and general forms of the equation of a hyperbola, and
- graph hyperbolas.

Application

Cassegrain antenna satellite dishes are used in extremely hot climates, because the feedhorn is behind the antenna, protected from direct exposure to solar energy. The Cassegrain antenna satellite dish has two different reflectors. A parabolic surface redirects the rays to a second reflective hyperbolic surface, which directs the rays to the feedhorn.

A **hyperbola** is the locus of all points in the plane such that the absolute value of the differences of the distance from two given points in the plane, called **foci**, is constant. That is, if F_1 and F_2 are the foci of a hyperbola and P and Q are any two points on the hyperbola, $|PF_1 - PF_2| = |QF_1 - QF_2|$.

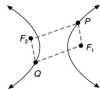

The center of a hyperbola is the midpoint of the segment whose endpoints are the foci. The point on each branch of the hyperbola nearest the center is called a vertex. The **asymptotes** of a hyperbola are lines that the curve approaches as it recedes from the center. As you move farther out along the branches, the distance between points on the hyperbola and the asymptotes approaches zero. The distance from the center to a vertex is a units, and the distance from the center to a focus is c units.

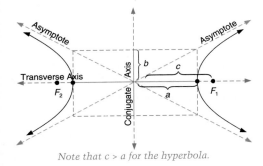

Note that c > a for the hyperbola.

A hyperbola has two axes of symmetry. The line segment that has its endpoints at the vertices is called the **transverse axis** and has a length of $2a$ units. The segment perpendicular to the transverse axis through the center is called the **conjugate axis** and has length $2b$ units. For a hyperbola, the relationship among $a, b,$ and c is represented by $a^2 + b^2 = c^2$. The asymptotes contain the diagonals of the rectangle that is $2a$ units by $2b$ units. The point at which the diagonals meet coincides with the center of the hyperbola.

LESSON 10-4 THE HYPERBOLA 551

NCTM Standards: 1–6, 8

Lesson Resources

- Practice Master 10–4
- Enrichment Master 10–4
- Evaluation Master, Quiz B, p. 125
- Technology Master, p. 19
- Activity Master, p. 28

Transparency 10–4 contains the 5-Minute Check and a teaching aid for this lesson.

INTRODUCING THE LESSON

5-Minute Check
(over Lesson 10–3)

Find each of the following for the ellipse with equation
$3x^2 + 4y^2 - 6x + 16y + 7 = 0$.

1. equation in standard form
   $$\frac{(x-1)^2}{4} + \frac{(y+2)^2}{3} = 1$$

2. coordinates of the center
   $(1, -2)$

3. coordinates of the foci
   $(2, -2), (0, -2)$

4. coordinates of the vertices
   $(-1, -2), (3, -2), (1, -2 + \sqrt{3}),$
   $(1, -2 - \sqrt{3})$

Motivating the Lesson

Draw a set of coordinate axes on the chalkboard. Ask students to name ordered pairs satisfying the equation $xy = 16$. Plot the points and show the two branches of the hyperbola $xy = 16$ in the first and third quadrants.

ALTERNATE TEACHING STRATEGIES

Using Connections

Point out the significance of the rectangle in the graph at the bottom of this page. If a plus sign appears in the standard form of the equation of the graph, the rectangle is used to draw an ellipse. If a minus sign appears, the diagonals of the rectangle and the ends of the transverse axis are used to draw a hyperbola.

Using Applications

Hyperbolas with equations of the form $xy = c$, where c is a constant, suggest inverse variation. As one variable increases, the other must decrease in order for their product to remain constant. An example is a group of runners running a distance, d. Since $d = rt$, the set of ordered pairs (r, t) for all the runners will form a hyperbola.

The standard form of the equation of a hyperbola with the origin as its center can be derived from the definition and the distance formula. Suppose the foci are on the x-axis at $(c, 0)$ and $(-c, 0)$, and (x, y) are the coordinates of any point on the hyperbola. Let $2a$ represent the common difference.

$$\sqrt{(x-c)^2 + y^2} - \sqrt{(x+c)^2 + y^2} = 2a \qquad \textit{Apply the distance formula.}$$

$$\sqrt{(x-c)^2 + y^2} = 2a + \sqrt{(x+c)^2 + y^2} \qquad \textit{Rearrange terms.}$$

$$(x-c)^2 + y^2 = 4a^2 + 4a\sqrt{(x+c)^2 + y^2} + (x+c)^2 + y^2 \quad \textit{Square each side.}$$

$$-4xc - 4a^2 = 4a\sqrt{(x+c)^2 + y^2} \qquad \textit{Simplify.}$$

$$xc + a^2 = -a\sqrt{(x+c)^2 + y^2}$$

$$x^2c^2 + 2a^2xc + a^4 = a^2x^2 + 2a^2xc + a^2c^2 + a^2y^2 \qquad \textit{Square each side.}$$

$$(c^2 - a^2)x^2 - a^2y^2 = a^2(c^2 - a^2) \qquad \textit{Simplify.}$$

$$\frac{x^2}{a^2} - \frac{y^2}{c^2 - a^2} = 1 \qquad \textit{Divide by } a^2(c^2 - a^2).$$

$$\frac{x^2}{a^2} - \frac{y^2}{b^2} = 1 \qquad \textit{By the Pythagorean theorem, } c^2 - a^2 = b^2.$$

If the foci are on the y-axis, the equation is $\dfrac{y^2}{a^2} - \dfrac{x^2}{b^2} = 1$.

As with the other graphs we have studied in this chapter, the standard form of the equation of a hyperbola with center other than the origin is a translation of the parent graph to a center at (h, k).

Notice that a^2 is always the denominator of the first term.

Standard Form of the Equation of a Hyperbola

The standard form of the equation of a hyperbola with center at (h, k) and transverse axis of length $2a$ units, where $b^2 = c^2 - a^2$, is as follows.

$\dfrac{(x-h)^2}{a^2} - \dfrac{(y-k)^2}{b^2} = 1$, when the transverse axis is parallel to the x-axis, or

$\dfrac{(y-k)^2}{a^2} - \dfrac{(x-h)^2}{b^2} = 1$, when the transverse axis is parallel to the y-axis.

Example 1 | **Find the equation of a hyperbola if the foci are at (2, 5) and (–4, 5) and the transverse axis is 4 units long.**

A sketch of the graph is helpful. Let F_1 and F_2 be the foci, let V_1 and V_2 be the vertices, and let C be the center.

Find the center.

The center is the midpoint of F_1F_2.

The center is at $\left(\dfrac{-4+2}{2}, \dfrac{5+5}{2}\right)$ or $(-1, 5)$.

Thus, $h = -1$ and $k = 5$.

Find c, a^2, and b^2.

$c = CF_1$	$2a = V_1V_2$	$b^2 = c^2 - a^2$
$c = 3$	$2a = 4$	$b^2 = 9 - 4$
	$a = 2$	$b^2 = 5$
	$a^2 = 4$	

Use the standard form when the transverse axis is parallel to the x-axis.

$$\frac{(x-h)^2}{a^2} - \frac{(y-k)^2}{b^2} = 1$$

$$\frac{(x+1)^2}{4} - \frac{(y-5)^2}{5} = 1$$

Before graphing a hyperbola, it is often helpful to graph the asymptotes. As noted in the beginning of the lesson, the asymptotes contain the diagonals of the rectangle defined by the transverse and conjugate axes. Suppose the center of a hyperbola is the origin and the transverse axis lies along the x-axis. Study the figure below.

Notice that the x-coordinates of the vertices correspond to the x-coordinates of the endpoints of the transverse axis. The y-coordinates correspond to the y-coordinates of the endpoints of the conjugate axis.

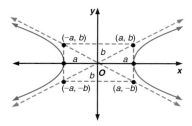

The endpoints of the transverse and conjugate axes are also the midpoints of the sides of the rectangle.

LESSON 10-4   THE HYPERBOLA   553

When the transverse axis lies along the x-axis, the slopes of the asymptotes are $\frac{b}{a}$ and $-\frac{b}{a}$. Both of the x-intercepts are 0. The equations of the asymptotes are $y = \frac{b}{a}x$ and $y = -\frac{b}{a}x$. If the transverse axis of a hyperbola is along the y-axis, the slopes of the asymptotes are $\pm\frac{a}{b}$. Thus, the equations of the asymptotes would be $y = -\frac{a}{b}x$ and $y = \frac{a}{b}x$.

The equations of the asymptotes of any hyperbola can be determined by a translation of the graph to a center at (h, k).

Equations of the Asymptotes of a Hyperbola	**The equations of the asymptotes of a hyperbola are** $y - k = \pm\frac{b}{a}(x - h)$, for a horizontal transverse axis, or $y - k = \pm\frac{a}{b}(x - h)$, for a vertical transverse axis.

Example 2

Find the coordinates of the center, foci, and vertices, and the equations of the asymptotes of the graph of $\frac{(y-3)^2}{25} - \frac{(x-2)^2}{16} = 1$. Then graph the equation.

Since the y terms are in the first expression, the hyperbola has a vertical transverse axis.

The center is at $(2, 3)$, $a = 5$, and $b = 4$.

The equations of the asymptotes are $y - 3 = \pm\frac{5}{4}(x - 2)$.

The vertices are at $(2, 8)$ and $(2, -2)$.

Since $c^2 = a^2 + b^2$, $c = \sqrt{41}$. Thus, the foci are at $(2, 3 + \sqrt{41})$ and $(2, 3 - \sqrt{41})$. $\sqrt{41} \approx 6.4$

Graph the vertices and the asymptotes. Then sketch the hyperbola.

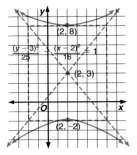

You can graph a hyperbola on a graphing calculator. First solve for y. Then graph the two resulting equations on the same screen.

By expanding the standard form for a hyperbola, you can find the general form, $Ax^2 + Cy^2 + Dx + Ey + F = 0$, where $A \neq 0$, $C \neq 0$, and A and C have different signs. As with the other general forms we have studied, the general form of a hyperbola can be rewritten in standard form. This is helpful since the standard form of the equation of a hyperbola contains important information about the hyperbola and thus, is easier to graph.

Example 3

Find the coordinates of the center, foci, and vertices, and the equations of the asymptotes of the graph of $25y^2 - 9x^2 - 100y - 72x - 269 = 0$. Then graph the equation.

Write the equation in standard form. Use the same process you used with ellipses.

$$25y^2 - 9x^2 - 100y - 72x - 269 = 0$$
$$(25y^2 - 100y + \ ?) - (9x^2 + 72x + \ ?) = 269$$
$$25(y^2 - 4y + 4) - 9(x^2 + 8x + 16) = 269 + 25(4) - 9(16)$$
$$25(y - 2)^2 - 9(x + 4)^2 = 225$$
$$\frac{(y - 2)^2}{9} - \frac{(x + 4)^2}{25} = 1$$

The center is at $(-4, 2)$. Since the y terms are in the first expression, the transverse axis is vertical.

$a = 3, b = 5$, and $c = \sqrt{34}$

The foci are at $(-4, 2 + \sqrt{34})$ and $(-4, 2 - \sqrt{34})$.

The vertices are at $(-4, -1)$ and $(-4, 5)$.

The asymptotes are the lines
$y - 2 = \pm\frac{3}{5}(x + 4)$.

Graph the vertices and asymptotes. Then sketch the hyperbola.

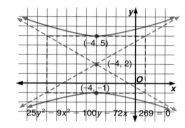

In the standard form of a hyperbola, if $a = b$ the hyperbola is an **equilateral hyperbola**. The asymptotes of an equilateral hyperbola are perpendicular. A special case of the equilateral hyperbola is when the coordinate axes are the asymptotes. The general equation of such a hyperbola is $xy = c$, where c is a nonzero constant. The branches of the equilateral hyperbola lie in the first and third quadrants if c is positive and in the second and fourth quadrants if c is negative.

Example 4

Graph $xy = -25$.

Since c is negative, the hyperbola lies in the second and fourth quadrants.

The transverse axis is along the line $y = -x$.

The coordinates of the vertices must satisfy the equation of the hyperbola and also be points on the transverse axis. Thus, the vertices are at $(5, -5)$ and $(-5, 5)$.

LESSON 10-4   THE HYPERBOLA   555

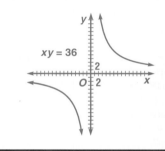

The graphs of functions that vary inversely are hyperbolas with equations of the form $xy = c$. By definition, x varies inversely as y if there is some constant c such that $xy = c$. Boyle's Law in chemistry is an example of a function that varies inversely.

Example 5

APPLICATION

Chemistry

Boyle's Law states that the pressure (P) exerted by a gas varies inversely as the volume (V) of a gas if the temperature remains constant. A specific gas is collected in a 242-cm³ container. The pressure is measured and is found to be 87.6 kilopascals. Use the formula $PV = c$ to find c.

$$c = PV$$
$$= (87.6)(242)$$
$$= 21,299.2 \qquad \text{The value of } c \text{ is } 21,299.2.$$

CHECKING FOR UNDERSTANDING

Communicating Mathematics

Read and study the lesson to answer each question. 1–2. See margin.

1. **Describe** how you can determine whether the transverse axis of a hyperbola is horizontal or vertical.

2. **Give an example** of the equation of an equilateral hyperbola whose axes are the coordinate axes. Tell how its graph differs from other hyperbolas in this lesson.

3. Refer to Example 5.
    a. If the pressure is increased, what happens to the volume? It decreases.
    b. If the pressure is decreased, what happens to the volume? It increases.
4–9. See Teacher's Answer Key.

Guided Practice

Find the coordinates of the center, the foci, and the vertices and the equations of the asymptotes of the graph of each equation. Then graph the equation.

4. $\dfrac{y^2}{36} - \dfrac{x^2}{49} = 1$

5. $\dfrac{(x+3)^2}{25} - \dfrac{(y-4)^2}{49} = 1$

6. $\dfrac{x^2}{16} - \dfrac{(y-5)^2}{81} = 1$

7. $\dfrac{(y-5)^2}{4} - \dfrac{(x-8)^2}{100} = 1$

8. $\dfrac{y^2}{169} - \dfrac{(x+12)^2}{289} = 1$

9. $\dfrac{(x+11)^2}{144} - \dfrac{(y+7)^2}{36} = 1$

Write the equation of each hyperbola.

10. $\dfrac{x^2}{25} - \dfrac{(y-5)^2}{9} = 1$

11. $\dfrac{(y-3)^2}{16} - \dfrac{(x-4)^2}{9} = 1$

10.

11.

12.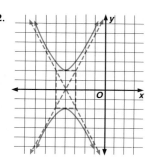

$\dfrac{y^2}{4} - \dfrac{(x+4)^2}{1} = 1$

13.

$\dfrac{x^2}{9} - \dfrac{y^2}{9} = 1$

14. Graph $xy = 81$. See Teacher's Answer Key.

EXERCISES   15–22. See margin.

Practice

Find the coordinates of the center, the foci, and the vertices, and equations of the asymptotes of the graph of each equation. Then graph the equation.

A

15. $\dfrac{x^2}{25} - \dfrac{y^2}{16} = 1$

16. $\dfrac{(y-3)^2}{16} - \dfrac{(x-2)^2}{25} = 1$

17. $81x^2 - 36y^2 = 2916$

18. $(x+6)^2 - 4(y+3)^2 = 36$

19. $9x^2 - 4y^2 - 54x - 40y - 55 = 0$

20. $y^2 - 5x^2 + 20x = 50$

21. $-4y^2 + 9x^2 - 90x - 24y = -153$

22. $49x^2 - 25y^2 + 294x + 200y = 1184$

State whether the graph of each equation is a circle, ellipse, parabola, or hyperbola.

23. $x^2 + 4y^2 + 5x - 2y = 144$ ellipse

24. $x^2 = y^2 + 8x + 12$ hyperbola

25. $2x^2 + 4x + 2y^2 + 6y = 66$ circle

26. $4y^2 + 6x - 3y = 33$ parabola

27. $4y^2 - 3x + 7x^2 - 7y = 18$ ellipse

28. $y^2 + 9y = 7x + 3x^2 + 52$ hyperbola

Graph each equation. 29–35. See Teacher's Answer Key.

B

29. $xy = 9$

30. $xy = -16$

31. $4xy = -9$

32. $9xy = 25$

33. $\dfrac{(x+1)^2}{4} - \dfrac{(y-4)^2}{16} = 1$

34. $\dfrac{y^2}{16} - \dfrac{x^2}{9} = 1$

35. $\dfrac{(y-2)^2}{4} - \dfrac{(x-3)^2}{9} = 1$

36–39. See margin.

Write an equation of the hyperbola that meets each set of conditions.

36. The center is at $(-1, 4)$, $a = 2$, $b = 3$; it has a horizontal transverse axis.

37. The length of the transverse axis is 8 units; the foci are at $(0, -5)$ and $(0, 5)$.

38. The length of the conjugate axis is 6 units; the vertices are at $(3, 4)$ and $(3, 0)$.

39. The vertices are at $(6, 3)$ and $(0, 3)$, and a focus is at $(8, 3)$.

C

40. The hyperbola is equilateral and has foci at $(8, 0)$ and $(-8, 0)$. $\dfrac{x^2}{32} - \dfrac{y^2}{32} = 1$

41. The hyperbola is equilateral and has foci at $(0, 5)$ and $(0, -5)$. $41.\ \dfrac{2y^2}{25} - \dfrac{2x^2}{25} = 1$

42. The equation of one asymptote is $2x - 9 = 3y$. The hyperbola has its center at $(3, -1)$ and a vertex at $(6, -1)$. $\dfrac{(x-3)^2}{9} - \dfrac{(y+1)^2}{4} = 1$

LESSON 10-4   THE HYPERBOLA   557

Additional Answers

36. $\dfrac{(x+1)^2}{4} - \dfrac{(y-4)^2}{4} = 1$

37. $\dfrac{y^2}{16} - \dfrac{x^2}{9} = 1$

38. $\dfrac{(y-2)^2}{4} - \dfrac{(x-3)^2}{9} = 1$

39. $\dfrac{(x-3)^2}{9} - \dfrac{(y-3)^2}{16} = 1$

APPLYING THE LESSON

Homework Exercises

Assignment Guide

Average: 15–40, 46, 50, 53, 56–63
Enriched: 27–63
All: Mid-Chapter Review, 1–10

The red A, B, and C flags, printed only in the Teacher's Wraparound Edition, indicate the level of difficulty of the exercises.

Chapter 10, Quiz B (Lessons 10–3 through 10–4) is available in the *Evaluation Masters*, p. 125.

Exercise Note

For Exercises 23–28, suggest that students draw up a list of characteristics of equations of the conic sections that they can use to distinguish one conic section from another.

Addtional Answers

15–22. For graphs, see Teacher's Answer Key.

15. center: $(0, 0)$, foci: $(\pm\sqrt{41}, 0)$, vertices: $(5, 0)$, $(-5, 0)$, asymptotes: $y = \pm\dfrac{4}{4}x$

16. center: $(2, 3)$, foci: $(2, 3 \pm \sqrt{41})$, vertices: $(2, -1)$, $(2, 7)$, asymptotes: $y - 3 = \pm\dfrac{4}{5}(x - 2)$

17. center: $(0, 0)$, foci: $(\pm\sqrt{117}, 0)$, vertices: $(6, 0)$, $(-6, 0)$, asymptotes: $y = \pm\dfrac{3}{2}x$

18. center: $(-6, -3)$, foci: $(-6 \pm 3\sqrt{5}, -3)$, vertices: $(0, -3)$, $(-12, -3)$, asymptotes: $y + 3 = \pm0.5(x + 6)$

19. center: $(3, -5)$, foci: $(3 \pm \sqrt{13}, -5)$, vertices: $(5, -5)$, $(1, -5)$, asymptotes: $y + 5 = \pm\dfrac{3}{2}(x - 3)$

20. center: $(2, 0)$, foci: $(2, 6)$, $(2, -6)$, vertices: $(2, \pm\sqrt{30})$, asymptotes: $y = \pm\sqrt{5}(x - 2)$

21. center: $(5, -3)$, foci: $(5 \pm \sqrt{13}, -3)$, vertices: $(7, -3)$, $(3, -3)$, asymptotes: $y + 3 = \pm\dfrac{4}{3}(x - 5)$

22. center: $(-3, 4)$, foci: $(-3 \pm \sqrt{74}, 4)$, vertices: $(2, 4)$, $(-8, 4)$, asymptotes: $y - 4 = \pm\dfrac{7}{5}(x + 3)$

LESSON 10–4   THE HYPERBOLA   557

Additional Answers

46.

47.

48.

49.

Graphing Calculator

44. $\dfrac{17(x-1)^2}{9} - \dfrac{17y^2}{144} = 1$

Critical Thinking

Applications and Problem Solving

43. The vertex is at $(4,5)$, the center is at $(4,2)$, and an equation of one asymptote is $4y + 4 = 3x$. $\quad \dfrac{(y-2)^2}{9} - \dfrac{(x-4)^2}{16} = 1$

44. The slopes of the asymptotes are ± 4, and the foci are at $(4,0)$ and $(-2,0)$.

45. The foci are at $(1,5)$ and $(1,-3)$, and the slopes of the asymptotes are ± 2.
$\dfrac{5(y-1)^2}{64} - \dfrac{5(x-1)^2}{16} = 1$

46–49. For graphs, see margin.

Graph each equation. Then state whether the graph is a hyperbola or an ellipse.

46. $16x^2 - y^2 + 96x + 8y = -112$ 47. $7x^2 + 3y^2 - 28x - 12y = -19$

48. $y^2 - 4x^2 - 2y - 16x + 1 = 0$ 49. $x^2 - 3y^2 + 6y + 6x = 18$
46. hyperbola   47. ellipse   48. hyperbola   49. hyperbola

50. Determine the equations of the asymptotes of an equilateral hyperbola whose transverse axis is on the x-axis and center is the origin. $\quad y = \pm x$

51. Write an equation of the hyperbola that passes through $(2,0)$ and has asymptotes with equations $x - 2y = 0$ and $x + 2y = 0$. $\quad \dfrac{x^2}{4} - y^2 = 1$

52. Write an equation of the hyperbola that passes through $(4,2)$ and has asymptotes with equations $y = 2x$ and $y = -2x + 4$. $\quad \dfrac{(x-1)^2}{9} - \dfrac{(y-2)^2}{36} = 1$

53. **Chemistry** According to Boyle's law, the pressure, P, (in kilopascals) exerted by a gas varies inversely as the volume, V, (in cubic centimeters) of a gas if the temperature remains constant. That is, $PV = c$. Suppose the constant for neon gas is 10,440.
   a. Graph the function $PV = c$, for $c = 10,440$. See margin.
   b. Determine the volume of neon if the pressure is 90 kilopascals. $116\ cm^3$
   c. Determine the volume of neon if the pressure is 180 kilopascals. $58\ cm^3$
   d. Study your results for parts b and c. If the pressure is doubled, make a conjecture about the effect on the volume of the gas. $V = 0.5$ (original V)

54. **Analytical Geometry** Two hyperbolas in which the transverse axis of one is the conjugate axis of the other are called *conjugate hyperbolas*. In equations of conjugate hyperbolas, the x^2 and y^2 terms are reversed. For example, $\dfrac{x^2}{9} - \dfrac{y^2}{4} = 1$ and $\dfrac{y^2}{4} - \dfrac{x^2}{9} = 1$ are equations of conjugate hyperbolas. 54a–d. See margin.
   a. Graph $\dfrac{x^2}{9} - \dfrac{y^2}{4} = 1$ and $\dfrac{y^2}{4} - \dfrac{x^2}{9} = 1$ on the same coordinate plane.
   b. What is true of the asymptotes of conjugate hyperbolas?
   c. Write the equation of the conjugate hyperbola for $\dfrac{(y-5)^2}{25} - \dfrac{(x-3)^2}{9} = 1$.
   d. Graph the conjugate hyperbolas in part c.

55. **Space Travel** On March 2, 1972, the *Pioneer 10* space probe was launched from Cape Canaveral. It became the first spacecraft to travel beyond all the planets in our solar system. The rate the spacecraft travels, r, varies inversely as the time spent in traveling, t, if the distance, d, remains constant.
   a. How long did it take *Pioneer 10* to travel from Earth to Pluto, a distance of 4.58×10^9 kilometers, if the average speed was 4.69×10^4 km/h?
   b. In approximately what month and year did it pass by Pluto?
55. a. 9.77×10^4 hours or 4070 days   55. b. May, 1983 (actual: June 13, 1983)

53a.

54a.

54d.

54b. They are the same lines.

54c. $\dfrac{(x-3)^2}{9} - \dfrac{(y-5)^2}{25} = 1$

Mixed Review

56. Find $\sin(\arctan\sqrt{3})$. Assume the angle is in Quadrant I. **(Lesson 6-4)** $0.5\sqrt{3}$

57. Verify that $\cot X = (\sin 2X) \div (1 - \cos 2X)$ is an identity. **(Lesson 7-4)**

57. See margin.

58. Use determinants to show how to find the cross product of the vectors $(5, 2, 3)$ and $(-2, 5, 0)$. Do not evaluate. **(Lesson 8-4)** See margin.

59. Write $x = y$ in polar form. **(Lesson 9-3)** $0 = r\cos(\theta - 135°)$

60. Write the normal form of $x - y + 4 = 0$. **(Lesson 7-6)** $-\dfrac{x}{\sqrt{2}} + \dfrac{y}{\sqrt{2}} - \dfrac{4}{\sqrt{2}} = 0$

61. $(y+1)^2 = 4(x-1)$

61. Write the standard form of $y^2 - 4x + 2y + 5 = 0$. **(Lesson 10-2)**

62. Find the coordinates of the center and vertices of the ellipse whose equation is $4x^2 + 25y^2 + 250y + 525 = 0$. **(Lesson 10-3)** $(0,-5), (\pm5,-5), (0,-3), (0,-7)$

63. College Entrance Exam Choose the best answer. C

Let $^*x^*$ be defined such that $^*x^* = x + \dfrac{1}{x}$. Find the value of $^*6^* + {}^*4^* + {}^*2^*$.

(A) 12 (B) $12\dfrac{7}{12}$ (C) $12\dfrac{11}{12}$ (D) $13\dfrac{1}{12}$ (E) $13\dfrac{5}{12}$

MID-CHAPTER REVIEW

2, 4, 6, 9, 10. See Teacher's Answer Key.

1. Write the standard form of the equation of a circle with center at $(2,-7)$ and radius of 9 units. **(Lesson 10-1)** $(x - 2)^2 + (y + 7)^2 = 81$

2. Graph the circle whose equation is $x^2 + y^2 - 6x + 4y - 3 = 0$. **(Lesson 10-1)**

3. Find the coordinates of the vertex and the focus, and equation of the directrix of the parabola whose equation is $(y - 3)^2 - 4x = 0$. **(Lesson 10-2)** $V: (0,3), F: (1,3), D: x = -1$

4. Graph the parabola whose equation is $y - (x - 3)^2 = 0$. **(Lesson 10-2)**

5. Find the coordinates of the center and the foci, the length of the major axis, and the length of the minor axis for the graph of $x^2 + 16y^2 - 6x - 64y + 57 = 0$. **(Lesson 10-3)** $(3,2), (3\pm\sqrt{15},2), 8, 2$

6. Graph the ellipse described in Exercise 5. **(Lesson 10-3)**

7. Space Travel A space module is in an elliptical orbit around a planet. The maximum distance from the center of the planet to the module is 300 kilometers, and the minimum distance is 200 kilometers. If a model of this orbit is graphed with the center of the ellipse at the origin, write the equation that represents the path of the space module. **(Lesson 10-3)** $40{,}000x^2 + 90{,}000y^2 = 3{,}600{,}000{,}000$

8. Write $3y^2 + 24y - x^2 - 2x + 41 = 0$ in standard form and identify the shape of its graph. **(Lesson 10-4)** $\dfrac{(y+4)^2}{2} - \dfrac{(x+1)^2}{6} = 1$, hyperbola

9. Graph the equation in Exercise 8. **(Lesson 10-4)**

10. Graph $xy = -100$. **(Lesson 10-4)**

LESSON 10-4 THE HYPERBOLA 559

EXTENDING THE LESSON

Math Power: Problem Solving

Find the center of the conic section represented by the equation $Ax^2 + Cy^2 + Dx + Ey + F = 0$.

$\left(-\dfrac{D}{2A}, -\dfrac{E}{2C}\right)$

Mid-Chapter Review

The Mid-Chapter Review provides students with a brief review of the concepts and skills in Lessons 10–1 through 10–4. Lesson numbers are given at the end of problems or instruction lines so students may review concepts not yet mastered.

Enrichment Masters Booklet, p. 68

Using Technology

Objective This optional page shows how graphing software can be used to explore the graphs of a family of hyperbolas.

Teaching Suggestions

Have students predict the asymptotes for Exercises 1 through 3 before graphing the family of hyperbolas. Then verify the asymptotes by graphing. In Exercise 4, have them predict the effect of shifting the center of the hyperbola 4 units up along the y-axis on the equations of the asymptotes. Verify by graphing.

Additional Answers

1. $y = \pm \frac{4}{7}x$

2. $y = \pm \frac{2}{3}x$

3. $y = \pm \frac{7}{4}x$

4. $y = 4 \pm \frac{1}{3}x$

Technology

Asymptotes of a Hyperbola

IBM's *Mathematics Exploration Toolkit (MET)* software allows you to graph hyperbolas written in the form $\frac{(x-0)^2}{a^2} - \frac{(y-0)^2}{b^2} = c$. You can use MET to explore a family of hyperbolas with centers at $(0,0)$. To do this, replace c in the equation above by $1, 0.5, 0.1,$ and 0. Observe what happens to the shape of the graph as c gets closer to 0. Use the following steps.

Enter	Result
hyper 0 0 4 5	*Displays $\frac{(x-0)^2}{4^2} - \frac{(y-0)^2}{5^2} = 1$.*
scale 10	*Sets the scale from –10 to 10.*
graph	*Graphs the hyperbola.*
substitute 0.5 1	*Replaces 1 with 0.5.*
graph	
substitute 0.1 0.5	*Replaces 0.5 with 0.1.*
graph	
color 2	
substitute 0 0.1	*Changes color of graph to red.*
graph	*Replaces 0.1 with 0.*

Notice that as the values move from 1 toward 0, the hyperbolas seem to be straightening. Finally, when the constant term is 0, the result is the asymptote lines. Solve to find the the equations of the asymptotes.

$$\frac{x^2}{4^2} - \frac{y^2}{5^2} = 0$$

$$\frac{y^2}{5^2} = \frac{x^2}{4^2}$$

$$y^2 = \frac{5^2 x^2}{4^2}$$

$$y = \pm \frac{5x}{4} \qquad \text{Thus, the equations of the asymptotes are } y = \pm \frac{xb}{a}.$$

EXERCISES

Use *MET* to graph each hyperbola for $c = 1, 0.5, 0.1,$ and 0. Then sketch the graph and find the equations for the asymptotes. 1–4. See margin.

1. $\frac{(x-0)^2}{7^2} - \frac{(y-0)^2}{4^2} = 1$ **2.** $\frac{(x-0)^2}{3^2} - \frac{(y-0)^2}{2^2} = 1$

3. $\frac{(x-0)^2}{4^2} - \frac{(y-0)^2}{7^2} = 1$ **4.** $\frac{(x-0)^2}{6^2} - \frac{(y-4)^2}{2^2} = 1$

560   CHAPTER 10   CONICS

10-5 Conic Sections

Objectives
10–5A
10–5B

After studying this lesson, you should be able to:
- recognize conic sections by their equations, and
- find the eccentricity of conic sections.

Application

The words *ellipse, hyperbola,* and *parabola* were first used by members of the Pythagorean society in ancient Greece around 540 B.C. These terms were used in connection with regions instead of curves as we refer to them today. Menaechmus (350 B.C.) is credited with the first treatment of the terms as curves generated by sections of geometric solids. However, it was Apollonius of Perga (about 225 B.C.), an astronomer of some fame in Greece, who wrote an eight-book essay entitled *Conic Sections*. His work differed from others in that he obtained all of the **conic sections** from one double right cone intersected by a plane. Apollonius stated that all variations in the shape of a conic section could be obtained by varying the slope of the plane intersecting the conical surface, as shown in the figures below.

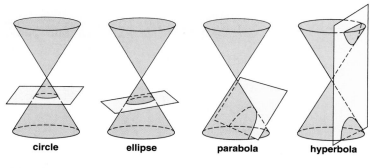

| circle | ellipse | parabola | hyperbola |

If the plane passes through the vertex of the conical surface, as illustrated below, the intersection is a **degenerate case**. The degenerate cases are a point, a line, and two intersecting lines.

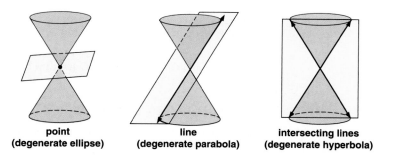

| point
(degenerate ellipse) | line
(degenerate parabola) | intersecting lines
(degenerate hyperbola) |

LESSON 10-5   CONIC SECTIONS   561

NCTM Standards: 1–6, 8

Lesson Resources

- Practice Master 10–5
- Enrichment Master 10–5
- Technology Master, p. 20
- Activity Master, p. 29

 Transparency 10–5 contains the 5-Minute Check and a teaching aid for this lesson.

INTRODUCING THE LESSON

 5-Minute Check
(over Lesson 10–4)

Find each of the following for the hyperbola with equation
$$\frac{(x+2)^2}{64} - \frac{(y-3)^2}{36} = 1.$$

1. **coordinates of the center**
   (–2, 3)
2. **coordinates of the foci**
   (–12, 3), (8, 3)
3. **coordinates of the vertices**
   (–10, 3), (6, 3)
4. **equations of the asymptotes**
   $y - 3 = \pm\frac{3}{4}(x + 2)$

Motivating the Lesson

Write the equations of an ellipse and a hyperbola in standard form on the chalkboard. Have students rewrite each as a polynomial without fractions equal to zero. Ask them to imagine they had been told that one polynomial represented an ellipse and one a hyperbola. Ask them to explain how they could tell which was which.
For the ellipse, the signs of x^2 and y^2 would be the same. For the hyperbola, they would be different.

ALTERNATE TEACHING STRATEGIES

Using Models

Block the spout in a large funnel and fill the funnel about one-third full of liquid. Cover the open end with clear plastic. Begin with the funnel held upright. Show the circular surface of the liquid. Tilt the funnel at greater and greater angles, showing the surface progressively as an ellipse, a parabola, and, at a 90° angle, half of a hyperbola.

Using Logical Reasoning

Ask students to explain how the general equation for conic sections can represent a point (a degenerate ellipse) and a line (a degenerate parabola).
point: $F = 0$
line: $Dx + Ey + F = 0$

Chalkboard Example

For Example 1

Identify the conic represented by each equation.
a. $3x^2 - 2y^2 - 4x + 5y = -3$
   hyperbola
b. $-4x^2 - 4y^2 + 6x + y = -5$
   circle
c. $8x^2 + y^2 + 3x - 7y = 0$
   ellipse
d. $y^2 - x + 3y - 9 = 0$
   parabola

A general equation for each of the conic sections we have studied has been determined. All of these equations are forms of the general equation for conic sections.

General Equation for Conic Sections	**The equation of a conic section can be written in the form $Ax^2 + Bxy + Cy^2 + Dx + Ey + F = 0$, where $A, B,$ and C are not all zero.**

The graph of a second-degree equation in two variables always represents a conic or a degenerate case, unless the equation has no graph at all in the real number plane. Most of the conic sections that we have studied have axes that are parallel to the coordinate axes. The general equations of these conics have no xy term; thus, $B = 0$. The hyperbola whose equation is $xy = k$ does not have axes parallel to the coordinate axes. In its equation, $B \neq 0$.

To identify the conic section represented by a given equation, it is helpful to write the equation in standard form. However, you can also identify the conic section by how the equation compares to the general equation. The table below summarizes the standard forms and differences among the general forms.

Conic Section	Standard Form of Equation	Variation of General Form of Conic Equations
circle	$(x - h)^2 + (y - k)^2 = r^2$	$A = C$
parabola	$(y - k)^2 = 4p(x - h)$ or $(x - h)^2 = 4p(y - k)$	Either A or C is zero.
ellipse	$\dfrac{(x - h)^2}{a^2} + \dfrac{(y - k)^2}{b^2} = 1$ or $\dfrac{(y - k)^2}{a^2} + \dfrac{(x - h)^2}{b^2} = 1$	A and C have the same sign, and $A \neq C$.
hyperbola	$\dfrac{(x - h)^2}{a^2} - \dfrac{(y - k)^2}{b^2} = 1$ $\dfrac{(y - k)^2}{a^2} - \dfrac{(x - h)^2}{b^2} = 1$ or $xy = k$	A and C have opposite signs.

The circle is actually a special form of the ellipse, $a^2 = b^2 = r^2$.

Example 1 **Identify the conic section represented by each equation.**
a. $5y^2 - 3x^2 + 4x - 3y - 100 = 0$

a. $A = -3$ and $C = 5$. Since $A \neq C$ and they have different signs, the conic is a hyperbola.

b. $2x^2 + 4y^2 - 8x - 8y + 36 = 0$

b. $A = 2$ and $C = 4$. Since A and C have the same sign and are not equal, the conic is an ellipse.

c. $2x^2 + 2y^2 - 9x + 3y - 100 = 0$

c. $A = 2$ and $C = 2$. Since $A = C$, the conic is a circle.

d. $7x^2 + 3x - 8y - 25 = 0$

d. $A = 7$ and $C = 0$. Since $C = 0$, the conic is a parabola.

Another way to define conics is by using eccentricity. A conic section is defined to be the locus of points such that, for any point P in the locus, the ratio of the distance between that point and a fixed point to the distance between that point and a fixed line ℓ is constant. That ratio is the **eccentricity** of the curve, denoted by e.

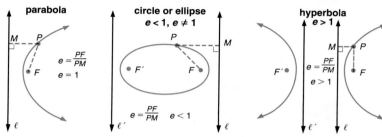

When e = 0, the ellipse is a circle.

The eccentricity for ellipses can also be defined as $e = \dfrac{c}{a}$, where c is the distance from the center to the focus and a is the distance from the center to the vertex. Since $0 < c < a$, you can divide by a to show that $0 < e < 1$. If e is closer to zero, the two foci are near the center of the ellipse. In the figure at the right, when $e = \dfrac{1}{5}$, the ellipse looks more like a circle. When e is closer to 1, the ellipse is elongated as in the graph where $e = \dfrac{5}{6}$.

Sometimes, you may need to find the value of b when you know the values of a and e. In an ellipse, $b^2 = a^2 - c^2$ and $\dfrac{c}{a} = e$. By using the two equations, it can be shown that $b^2 = a^2(1 - e^2)$.

$\dfrac{c}{a} = e$

$c = ae$ *Multiply each side by a.*

$c^2 = a^2e^2$ *Square each side.*

$b^2 = a^2 - c^2$

$b^2 = a^2 - a^2e^2$ $c^2 = a^2e^2$

$b^2 = a^2(1 - e^2)$

LESSON 10-5 CONIC SECTIONS 563

Example 2

Write the equation of the ellipse with center at $(-2, 3)$, $a = 7$, and $e = 0.5$. The major axis is horizontal.

Find b^2.

$b^2 = a^2(1 - e^2)$
$\quad = 49(1 - 0.25)$ $a = 7$ and $e = 0.5$
$\quad = 36.75$

Since the major axis is horizontal, use the form $\frac{(x - h)^2}{a^2} + \frac{(y - k)^2}{b^2} = 1$.

$\frac{(x - (-2))^2}{7^2} + \frac{(y - 3)^2}{36.75} = 1$ $h = -2, k = 3, a = 7, b^2 = 36.75$

The equation of the ellipse is $\frac{(x + 2)^2}{49} + \frac{(y - 3)^2}{36.75} = 1$.

The orbits of astronomical bodies are often described by their eccentricity.

Example 3

APPLICATION

Astronomy

Halley's comet last passed near Earth in April of 1986. Its next appearance is expected in the year 2061. The comet has an elliptical orbit with the sun as one of its foci. Astronomers have determined that the orbit is about 0.5871045 AU (astronomical units) at its closest point (perihelion) to the sun. The eccentricity of the orbit is 0.9672759 and the length of the semi-major axis is 17.94104 AU. *1 AU = the average distance between the sun and Earth, about 9.3×10^7 miles.*

a. **Sketch the orbit of Halley's comet showing the sun in its respective position.**

b. **Find the length of the semi-minor axis of the orbit.**

c. **Find the distance of the comet from the sun at its farthest point (aphelion).**

a. The sketch at the right shows the sun as a focus for the elliptical orbit.

b. b is the length of the semi-minor axis.
$b^2 + a^2(1 - e^2)$
$b = \sqrt{a^2(1 - e^2)}$
$b = \sqrt{(17.94104)^2(1 - 0.9672759^2)}$
Use your calculator.

$b = 4.552124232$ AU

c. *aphelion* $=$ *length of major axis* $-$ *perihelion*
$\quad SA = 2(17.94104) - 0.5871045$
$\quad SA = 35.2949755$ *Use your calculator.*

The aphelion is about 35 AU.

11. parabola,
$(y + \frac{1}{2})^2 = -2(x - 2)$

12. hyperbola,
$\frac{(y + 4)^2}{2} - \frac{(x + 1)^2}{6} = 1$

The eccentricity for a hyperbola can also be defined as $e = \dfrac{c}{a}$. However, in a hyperbola, $0 < a < c$. So, $0 < 1 < e$ or $e > 1$. Since $c^2 = a^2 + b^2$ in hyperbolas, it can be shown that $b^2 = a^2(e^2 - 1)$. *You will derive this formula in Exercise 4.*

Example 4

Write the equation of the hyperbola with center at $(-3, 1)$, a focus at $(2, 1)$, and eccentricity $\dfrac{5}{4}$.

A general sketch using the points given is often helpful.

Since the center and focus have the same y-coordinate, the transverse axis is horizontal. Use the form
$$\frac{(x - h)^2}{a^2} - \frac{(y - k)^2}{b^2} = 1.$$

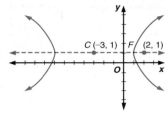

The focus is 5 units to the right of the center, so $c = 5$. Now use the eccentricity to find the value of a and b^2.

$$e = \frac{c}{a} \qquad\qquad b^2 = a^2(e^2 - 1)$$
$$\frac{5}{4} = \frac{5}{a} \quad c = 5 \text{ and } e = \frac{5}{4} \qquad b^2 = 16\left(\frac{25}{16} - \frac{16}{16}\right)$$
$$4 = a \qquad\qquad b^2 = 9$$
$$16 = a^2$$

The equation is $\dfrac{(x + 3)^2}{16} - \dfrac{(y - 1)^2}{9} = 1$.

CHECKING FOR UNDERSTANDING

Communicating Mathematics

Read and study the lesson to answer each question. 1–4. See margin.

1. **Explain** in your own words what a conic section is.

2. **Tell** how the general form of the equation of a conic section is modified for each of the following.
   a. ellipse **b.** hyperbola **c.** circle **d.** parabola

3. **Describe** a circle in terms of the equation of an ellipse.

4. **Derive** the equation $b^2 = a^2(e^2 - 1)$ for a hyperbola.

Guided Practice

Identify the conic section represented by each equation.

5. $x^2 - 6x - 4y + 9 = 0$ parabola
6. $x^2 + y^2 + 6y - 8x + 24 = 0$ circle
7. $x^2 - 4y^2 + 10x - 16y + 5 = 0$ hyperbola
8. $9y^2 + 27x^2 - 6y - 108x + 82 = 0$ ellipse

Identify the conic section represented by each equation and write the equation in standard form. Then graph the equation. 9–12. See margin.

9. $x^2 - 8x + 11 = -y^2$
10. $9x^2 + 25y^2 - 54x - 50y - 119 = 0$
11. $4y^2 + 4y + 8x = 15$
12. $x^2 - 3y^2 + 2x - 24y = 41$

LESSON 10-5 CONIC SECTIONS 565

Homework Exercises

Assignment Guide

Average: 14–37, 40, 41, 43–48
Enriched: 18–48

The red A, B, and C flags, printed only in the Teacher's Wraparound Edition, indicate the level of difficulty of the exercises.

Exercise Note

In Exercises 14–19, students must identify the conic before they can determine how to find the value of c to use in the expression for eccentricity.

Additional Answers

20. parabola, $y^2 = 8(x-1)$
21. hyperbola, $xy = \frac{4}{9}$
22. point, (0, 0)
23. parabola, $x^2 = 4(y+7)$
24. circle, $(x-3)^2 + (y-6)^2 = 4$
25. hyperbola,
$\frac{(x-2)^2}{5} - \frac{(y+2)^2}{5} = 1$

26. ellipse,
$\frac{(x+1)^2}{9} + (y-6)^2 = 1$

27. parabola, $(x-4)^2 = y$
28. intersecting lines, $y = \pm 3x$
29. point, (2, 3)

35. $\frac{y^2}{100} + \frac{(x-3)^2}{51} = 1$

36. $\frac{(y+1)^2}{4} - \frac{(x-3)^2}{5} = 1$

---

13. Write the equation of the ellipse whose center is the origin, $a = 2$, $e = \frac{3}{4}$, and the major axis is parallel to the y-axis. $\frac{y^2}{4} + \frac{x^2}{1.75} = 1$

EXERCISES

Practice

Determine the eccentricity of the conic section represented by each equation.

14. $(y-5)^2 = 4(x-5)$ 1

15. $4y^2 - 8y + 9x^2 - 54x + 49 = 0$ $\frac{\sqrt{5}}{3}$

16. $5x^2 - 9y^2 = 45$ $\frac{\sqrt{14}}{3}$

17. $(x+5)^2 + (y-1)^2 = 100$ 0

18. $25x^2 + y^2 - 100x + 6y + 84 = 0$ $\frac{2\sqrt{6}}{5}$

19. $x^2 - y^2 + 2y - 5 = 0$ $\sqrt{2}$

20–29. See margin. For graphs, see Teacher's Answer Key.

B

Identify the conic section represented by each equation. Write the equation in standard form and graph the equation.

20. $y^2 - 8x = -8$

21. $9xy = 4$

22. $2x^2 + 5y^2 = 0$

23. $x^2 - 4y - 28 = 0$

24. $x^2 - 6x + y^2 - 12y + 41 = 0$

25. $x^2 - 4x - y^2 - 5 - 4y = 0$

26. $(x+1)^2 + 9(y-6)^2 = 9$

27. $x^2 = y + 8x - 16$

28. $y^2 = 9x^2$

29. $(x-2)^2 + (y-3)^2 = 0$

Write the equation of the conic that meets each set of conditions.

30. an ellipse with center at $(3, 1)$, a vertical semi-major axis 6 units long, and $e = \frac{1}{3}$ $\frac{(y-1)^2}{36} + \frac{(x-3)^2}{32} = 1$

31. an ellipse with eccentricity 0.25, foci at $(3, 5)$ and $(1, 5)$ $\frac{(x-2)^2}{16} + \frac{(y-5)^2}{15} = 1$

32. a hyperbola with foci at $(5, 0)$ and $(-5, 0)$ and eccentricity $\frac{5}{3}$ $\frac{x^2}{9} - \frac{y^2}{16} = 1$

33. a hyperbola with foci at $(0, 8)$ and $(0, -8)$ and eccentricity $\frac{4}{3}$ $\frac{y^2}{36} - \frac{x^2}{28} = 1$

34. a hyperbola with eccentricity $\frac{5}{4}$, foci at $(0, 9)$ and $(0, -1)$ $\frac{(y-4)^2}{16} - \frac{x^2}{9} = 1$

35. an ellipse with a vertical major axis 20 units long, center at $(3, 0)$, and $e = \frac{7}{10}$

36. a hyperbola with center at $(3, -1)$, a focus at $(3, -4)$, and $e = 1.5$

C

37. ellipse passing through $(4, 2)$ with foci at $(1, -1)$ and $(1, 5)$ $\frac{(y-2)^2}{18} + \frac{(x-1)^2}{9} = 1$

38. Find the eccentricity of the hyperbola that has foci at $(1, -4)$ and $(1, 6)$ and passes through $(1, 4)$. $\frac{5}{3}$

39. Find the eccentricity of the hyperbola that passes through $(0, 2)$ and has foci at $(0, 3)$ and $(0, -3)$. 1.5

Critical Thinking

40. Identify the conic section represented by $x^2 - 2xy + 3y^2 = 1$. Discuss how this conic section differs from others presented in this lesson. Ellipse; axes are not parallel to coordinate axes.

Applications and Problem Solving

41b.
$$\frac{x^2}{27,248,400} + \frac{y^2}{26,550,840.96} = 1$$

41. Astronomy A satellite orbiting Earth follows an elliptical path with the center of Earth as one focus. The eccentricity of the orbit is 0.16, and the major axis is 10,440 miles long.

  a. If the mean diameter of Earth is 7920 miles, find the greatest and least distance of the satellite from the surface of Earth. 2095.2 miles, 424.8 miles

  b. Assuming that the center of the ellipse is the origin and the foci lie on the x-axis, write the equation of the orbit of the satellite.

42. Construction The 50-foot tall arch of a bridge over a small stream is shaped like half an ellipse. The span of the bridge is 120 feet. a. $\dfrac{x^2}{3600} + \dfrac{y^2}{2500} = 1$

  a. Suppose a model of this bridge is drawn on a coordinate plane with the origin located on the bridge midway between the ends of the bridge. Draw the model and write the equation of the ellipse representing this model.

  b. Suppose a model of this bridge is drawn on a coordinate plane with one end of the bridge at the origin. Draw the model and write the equation of the ellipse representing this model.
  $$\frac{(x - 60)^2}{3600} + \frac{y^2}{2500} = 1 \text{ or } \frac{(x + 60)^2}{3600} + \frac{y^2}{2500} = 1,$$
  depending on which end is used

Mixed Review

43. Engineering A metallic ring used in a sprinkler system has a diameter of 13.4 cm. Find the length of the metallic cross brace if it subtends a central angle of $26°20'$. **(Lesson 5-6)** 3.05 cm

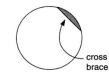

cross brace

44. Find Arccos $\dfrac{\sqrt{3}}{2}$. **(Lesson 6-5)** 30°

45. Solve $\sin^2 A = \cos A - 1$ for principal values of A. **(Lesson 7-5)** 0°

46. Graph $r = 5 \cos 2\theta$. **(Lesson 9-2)** See margin.

47. Write the equation of a hyperbola with center at $(3, -1)$, a focus at $(3, -4)$ and eccentricity 1.5. **(Lesson 10-4)** $\dfrac{(y + 1)^2}{4} - \dfrac{(x - 3)^2}{5} = 1$

48. College Entrance Exam Choose the best answer. E
If one half of the female students in a certain school eat in the cafeteria and one third of the male students eat there, what fractional part of the student body eats in the cafeteria?

(A) $\dfrac{5}{12}$ (B) $\dfrac{2}{5}$ (C) $\dfrac{3}{4}$ (D) $\dfrac{5}{6}$ (E) not enough information given

LESSON 10-5   CONIC SECTIONS   567

EXTENDING THE LESSON

Math Power: Communication

Although a parabola seems to be half of a hyperbola, it cannot be represented by the equation of a hyperbola. Explain how the standard forms of the equations of a parabola and a hyperbola can be used to show this. Both A and C appear in the standard form of the equation of a hyperbola, but A or C equals zero in the equation of a parabola.

INTRODUCING THE LESSON

Objective   Graph conic sections on a graphing calculator.

Motivating the Lesson

Show students a large rubber band lying on a flat surface such that the rubber band models an ellipse. Ask students how they could transform the rubber band into a circle. Encourage students to see the relationship between circles and ellipses.

TEACHING THE LESSON

Teaching Tip   You may wich to review completing the square. This skill is needed in this lesson as well as in Lesson 10–6.

More Examples

1. Graph the hyperbola whose equation is $x^2 - y^2 = 9$.

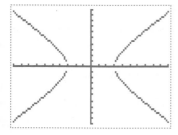

2. Graph the ellipse $9x^2 + 4y^2 + 16y = 20$.

10-6A   Graphing Calculators: Conic Sections

The parabola, circle, ellipse, and hyperbola are all types of conic sections. You can use a graphing calculator to graph them; however, some algebra is often required before you can enter the equations into the graphing calculator. This is because most of the conic sections are relations, but not functions.

Since a graphing calculator will only plot functions, we must first manipulate the equations before entering them into the calculator to be graphed. For example, the equation of the circle, $x^2 + y^2 = 9$, cannot be entered directly since the equation must be in a "$y =$" format. We must solve the equation for y and then enter each equation into the calculator as a function.

Example 1

Graph the circle whose equation is $x^2 + y^2 = 16$.

First, solve the equation for y.

$$x^2 + y^2 = 16$$
$$y^2 = 16 - x^2$$
$$y = \pm\sqrt{16 - x^2}$$

Now enter two equations into the calculator: $y = \sqrt{16 - x^2}$ and $y = -\sqrt{16 - x^2}$. Since both of these equations are functions, they can be graphed by the calculator.

TI–81: [Y=] [2nd] [√] [(] 16 [−] [X|T]
[x²] [)] [ENTER] [(−)] [2nd] [√]
[(] 16 [−] [X|T] [x²] [)]
[GRAPH]

Casio: [Graph] [√] [(] 16 [−] [ALPHA]
[X] [x²] [)] [:] [Graph] [(−)] [√]
[(] 16 [−] [ALPHA] [X] [x²] [)]
[EXE]

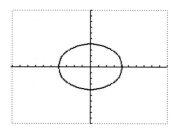

The graph appears to be an ellipse even though it is actually a circle. The viewing window is distorted and must be adjusted so that the scale of the x- and y-axes are equal in length.

You can make the graph square on the TI–81 by pressing [ZOOM] 5. On the Casio, you can make the graph square by pressing [RANGE] [SHIFT] [Mcl]

RANGE EXE . However, this range does not show a complete graph for this example, so we must use a multiple of this "default" range to view a complete graph. Use $[-9.4, 9.4]$ by $[-6.2, 6.2]$ with a scale factor of 1 for both axes. This viewing window gives a complete graph of the conic section and the graph now appears as a circle.

Other types of conic sections that are relations can be graphed on a graphing calculator by solving the equations for y and graphing two separate equations that are functions.

Example 2

Graph the hyperbola $x^2 - y^2 + 8x + 4y + 9 = 0$.

Solve the equation for y by completing the square.

$$y^2 - 4y = x^2 + 8x + 9$$
$$(y^2 - 4y + 4) + 16 = (x^2 + 8x + 16) + 9 + 4 \qquad \textit{Complete the squares.}$$
$$(y - 2)^2 + 16 = (x + 4)^2 + 13$$
$$(y - 2)^2 = (x + 4)^2 - 3$$
$$y - 2 = \pm\sqrt{(x + 4)^2 - 3}$$
$$y = 2 \pm \sqrt{(x + 4)^2 - 3}.$$

Now enter the two equations to graph the relation.

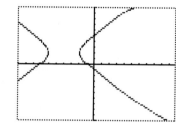

TI–81: Y= 2 + 2nd √ (((
XT + 4) x² − 3)
ENTER 2 − 2nd √ ((
((XT + 4) x² − 3)
GRAPH

Casio: Graph 2 + √ ((((ALPHA X + 4) x² − 3)) :
Graph 2 − √ ((((ALPHA X + 4) x² − 3)

EXERCISES

Solve each equation so that it can be entered into a graphing calculator. Then graph each conic section and sketch the graph on a piece of paper. 1–6. See margin.

1. $x = y^2 + 5y + 22$
2. $x^2 + (y - 3)^2 = 4$
3. $5x^2 + 10y^2 = 150$
4. $12x^2 + 4y^2 - 2x = 44$
5. $4x^2 - y^2 + 24x - 8y + 12 = 0$
6. $4x^2 - 9y^2 - 16x + 144y - 540 = 0$

GRAPHING CALCULATORS: CONIC SECTIONS   569

Teaching Tip Remind students that they cannot always identify the graph of an equation by its shape on the calculator's screen. Depending on the range values chosen, a circle can appear as an ellipse and vice versa.

EVALUATING THE LESSON

Closing the Lesson

Ask students what they would include when writing a section for a graphing calculator manual on graphing conic sections.

APPLYING THE LESSON

Homework Exercises

Assignment Guide
All: 1–6

Additional Answers

1. $y = -2.5 \pm \sqrt{x - 15.75}$
2. $y = 3 \pm \sqrt{4 - x^2}$
3. $y = \pm \sqrt{15 - 0.5x^2}$
4. $y = \pm \sqrt{11 + 0.5x - 3x^2}$
5. $y = -4 \pm \sqrt{(2x + 6)^2 - 8}$
6. $y = 8 \pm \dfrac{\sqrt{(2x - 4)^2 + 20}}{3}$

For graphs, see Teacher's Answer Key.

Lesson Resources

- Practice Master 10–6
- Enrichment Master 10–6
- Evaluation Master, Quiz C, p. 126

 Transparency 10–6 contains the 5-Minute Check and a teaching aid for this lesson.

INTRODUCING THE LESSON

5-Minute Check
(over Lesson 10–5)

Identify the conic section represented by each equation.
1. $3x^2 - 2y^2 - 5x + 8y = 0$
   hyperbola
2. $2x^2 + 3x + 5y - 7 = 0$
   parabola
3. $-4x^2 - 4y^2 + 2x + y = 0$
   circle
4. $8x^2 + 5y^2 - x + 6y = 0$
   ellipse
5. Find the eccentricity of the ellipse with equation.
   $\frac{x^2}{169} + \frac{y^2}{144} = 1$ $\frac{5}{13}$

Prerequisite Skills

Students should be familiar with matrix addition and multiplication.
Let $A = \begin{bmatrix} 1 & 2 \\ 4 & 3 \end{bmatrix}$ and

let $B = \begin{bmatrix} -3 & 5 \\ 2 & -1 \end{bmatrix}$.

1. Find $A + B$. $\begin{bmatrix} -2 & 7 \\ 6 & 2 \end{bmatrix}$

2. Find AB. $\begin{bmatrix} 1 & 3 \\ -6 & 17 \end{bmatrix}$

Motivating the Lesson

Ask students to find the equation of the ellipse that is the result of rotating the ellipse $\frac{x^2}{36} + \frac{y^2}{25} = 1$ 90° about the origin.
$\frac{x^2}{25} + \frac{y^2}{36} = 1$

10-6 Transformations of Conics

Objectives

After studying this lesson, you should be able to:

10–6A ■ find the equations of conic sections that have been translated or rotated, and

10–6B ■ find the angle of rotation for a given equation and sketch its graph.

Application

A cam is a rotating piece of machinery that gives motion to another piece of machinery. Commonly, a cam is used to convert circular motion into back-and-forth motion. In a sewing machine, cams convert the rotary motion of the motor into the up-and-down motion of the needle. The camshaft in an automobile engine converts the rotary motion of the engine into the up-and-down motion of the pistons.

In a punch press, the cam is elliptical with the camshaft passing through one of the foci. The simplified drawing at the right shows that when the elongated part of the cam is up, the punch is up. As the cam rotates, it moves the press stem in a smooth downward motion.

Thus far, we have used a transformation called a translation to show how the parent graph of each of the conic sections is translated to a center other than the origin. For example, the equation of the parabola $y = 4px^2$ became $y - k = 4p(x - h)^2$ for a center at (h, k). You can also translate points of a figure by using a **translation matrix**. The coordinates of the points you want to translate are placed in a matrix with the first row containing the x-coordinates and the second row containing the y-coordinates. The translation matrix has the same number of rows and columns as the matrix containing the coordinates of the points. If the points are to be translated in relation to a point at (h, k), all elements of the first row of the translation matrix equal h and all elements of the second row equal k.

A translation of a set of points with respect to (h, k) is often written $T_{(h, k)}$.

ALTERNATE TEACHING STRATEGIES

Using Critical Thinking

Ask students to explain why a 50° rotation about the origin of the graph of $\frac{x^2}{16} + \frac{y^2}{16} = 1$ does not change the graph.
The equation represents a circle, which is unchanged by any rotation about its center.

Using Problem Solving

Write the equation $Ax^2 + 8xy + 4y^2 = 0$ on the chalkboard. Ask students to find values of A that will produce equations that represent circles, ellipses, hyperbolas, and parabolas.

Example 1

Use a translation matrix to find the coordinates of the vertices of the ellipse with equation $\frac{x^2}{25} + \frac{y^2}{9} = 1$, with respect to $T_{(-8,\,3)}$.

The original equation is an ellipse whose center is the origin. Its vertices are at $(-5, 0)$, $(5, 0)$, $(0, 3)$, and $(0, -3)$. Write these ordered pairs as a matrix and add the translation matrix for $T_{(-8,\,3)}$.

$$\begin{bmatrix} -5 & 5 & 0 & 0 \\ 0 & 0 & 3 & -3 \end{bmatrix} + \begin{bmatrix} -8 & -8 & -8 & -8 \\ 3 & 3 & 3 & 3 \end{bmatrix} = \begin{bmatrix} -13 & -13 & -8 & -8 \\ 3 & 3 & 6 & 0 \end{bmatrix}$$

The vertices of the translated ellipse are at $(-13, 3)$, $(-3, 3)$, $(-8, 6)$, and $(-8, 0)$.

The graph shows the ellipse and its translation.

The equation of the translated ellipse is $\frac{(x+8)^2}{25} + \frac{(y-3)^2}{9} = 1$.

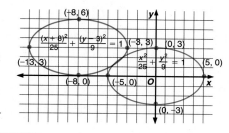

Except for hyperbolas whose equations are of the form $xy = k$, all of the conic sections we have studied thus far have been oriented with their axes parallel to the coordinate axes. In the general form of these conics, $B = 0$. Whenever $B \neq 0$, the axes of the conic section are not parallel to the coordinate axes. That is, the graph is rotated.

The figures below show a hyperbola whose center is the origin and its rotation. Notice that the angle of rotation has the same measure as the angles formed by the positive x-axis and the transverse axis and the positive y-axis and the conjugate axis.

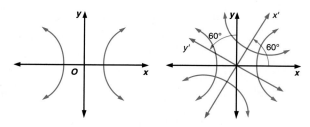

The coordinates of the points of a rotated figure can be found by using a rotation matrix.

Rotation Matrix

A rotation of θ about the origin can be described by the matrix

$$\begin{bmatrix} \cos\theta & -\sin\theta \\ \sin\theta & \cos\theta \end{bmatrix}.$$

Chalkboard Example

For Example 2

Find an equation of a 45° rotation about the origin of the graph of $\frac{x^2}{16} - \frac{y^2}{4} = 1$. Then sketch the graph and its rotation.

$-3x^2 + 10xy - 3y^2 = 32$

A positive value of θ indicates a counterclockwise rotation. A negative value of θ indicates a clockwise rotation.

You may wish to review matrix multiplication in Lesson 2–2.

Suppose $P(x, y)$ is a point on the graph of a conic section and $P'(x', y')$ is its image after a counterclockwise rotation of θ. The values of x' and y' can be found by matrix multiplication.

$$\begin{bmatrix} x' \\ y' \end{bmatrix} = \begin{bmatrix} \cos\theta & -\sin\theta \\ \sin\theta & \cos\theta \end{bmatrix} \cdot \begin{bmatrix} x \\ y \end{bmatrix}$$

The inverse of the rotation matrix represents a rotation of $-\theta$. Multiply each side of the equation by the inverse rotation matrix to solve for x and y.

$$\begin{bmatrix} \cos\theta & \sin\theta \\ -\sin\theta & \cos\theta \end{bmatrix} \cdot \begin{bmatrix} x' \\ y' \end{bmatrix} = \begin{bmatrix} \cos\theta & \sin\theta \\ -\sin\theta & \cos\theta \end{bmatrix} \cdot \begin{bmatrix} \cos\theta & -\sin\theta \\ \sin\theta & \cos\theta \end{bmatrix} \cdot \begin{bmatrix} x \\ y \end{bmatrix}$$

$$\begin{bmatrix} x'\cos\theta + y'\sin\theta \\ -x'\sin\theta + y'\cos\theta \end{bmatrix} = \begin{bmatrix} 1 & 0 \\ 0 & 1 \end{bmatrix} \cdot \begin{bmatrix} x \\ y \end{bmatrix}$$

$$\begin{bmatrix} x'\cos\theta + y'\sin\theta \\ -x'\sin\theta + y'\cos\theta \end{bmatrix} = \begin{bmatrix} x \\ y \end{bmatrix}$$

The result is the following two equations.

$$x = x'\cos\theta + y'\sin\theta$$
$$y = -x'\sin\theta + y'\cos\theta$$

This means that to find the equation of a conic section with respect to a rotation of θ, you can replace x with $x\cos\theta + y\sin\theta$ and replace y with $-x\sin\theta + y\cos\theta$.

Example 2

Find an equation of a 60° rotation about the origin of the graph of $\frac{x^2}{25} + \frac{y^2}{9} = 1$. Then sketch the graph and its rotation.

The graph of this equation is an ellipse.
Find the expressions to replace x and y.

Replace x with $x\cos 60° + y\sin 60°$ or $\frac{1}{2}x + \frac{\sqrt{3}}{2}y$.

Replace y with $-x\sin 60° + y\cos 60°$ or $-\frac{\sqrt{3}}{2}x + \frac{1}{2}y$.

Computation is often easier if the equation is rewritten as an equation with denominators of 1.

$$\frac{x^2}{25} + \frac{y^2}{9} = 1$$

$$9x^2 + 25y^2 = 225 \qquad \textit{Multiply each side by 225.}$$

$$9\left(\frac{1}{2}x + \frac{\sqrt{3}}{2}y\right)^2 + 25\left(-\frac{\sqrt{3}}{2}x + \frac{\sqrt{1}}{2}y\right)^2 = 225 \qquad \textit{Replace x and y.}$$

$$\frac{9}{4}(x^2 + 2\sqrt{3}xy + 3y^2) + \frac{25}{4}(3x^2 - 2\sqrt{3}xy + y^2) = 225 \qquad \textit{Expand the binomial.}$$

$$84x^2 - 32\sqrt{3}xy + 52y^2 = 900 \qquad \textit{Simplify.}$$

$$21x^2 - 8\sqrt{3}xy + 13y^2 = 225 \qquad \textit{Divide each side by 4.}$$

The equation of the ellipse after the 60° rotation is
$21x^2 - 8\sqrt{3}xy + 13y^2 = 225$.

The graph below shows the ellipse and its rotation.

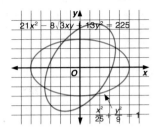

$21x^2 - 8\sqrt{3}xy + 13y^2 = 225$

$\dfrac{x^2}{25} + \dfrac{y^2}{9} = 1$

The discriminant of a second-degree equation is defined as $B^2 - 4AC$ for the general equation $Ax^2 + Bxy + Cy^2 + Dx + Ey + F = 0$. The discriminant remains unchanged under any rotation. That is, $B^2 - 4AC = (B')^2 - 4A'C'$. In Lesson 10–5, you learned to identify a conic from its general form. You can also use the discriminant to identify a conic section from its equation.

Identifying Conics By Using the Discriminant

For the general equation $Ax^2 + Bxy + Cy^2 + Dx + Ey + F = 0$:
- **if $B^2 - 4AC < 0$, the graph is a circle ($A = C$) or an ellipse ($A \neq C$);**
- **if $B^2 - 4AC > 0$, the graph is a hyperbola;**
- **if $B^2 - 4AC = 0$, the graph is a parabola.**

Remember that the graphs can also be degenerate cases.

Example 3

Identify the graph of the equation $4x^2 - 5xy + 16y^2 = 32$.

Find the discriminant.
$B^2 - 4AC = (-5)^2 - 4(4)(16)$ or -231

Since $B^2 - 4AC < 0$ and $A \neq C$, the graph of the equation is an ellipse.

You can also use values from the general form to find the angle of rotation about the origin.

Angle of Rotation About the Origin

For the general equation $Ax^2 + Bxy + Cy^2 + Dx + Ey + F = 0$, the angle of rotation θ about the origin can be found by

$$\theta = \frac{\pi}{4}, \text{ if } A = C, \text{ or}$$

$$\tan 2\theta = \frac{B}{A - C}, \text{ if } A \neq C \text{ and } 0 < 2\theta < \pi.$$

LESSON 10-6   TRANSFORMATIONS OF CONICS   573

Chalkboard Example

For Example 4

Identify the graph of the equation $7x^2 - 6\sqrt{3}xy + 13y^2 = 16$. Then find θ and use a graphing calculator to draw the graph.
ellipse; $30°$

EVALUATING THE LESSON

Checking for Understanding

Exercises 1–12 are designed to help you assess students' understanding through reading, writing, speaking, and modeling. You should work through Exercises 1–3 with your students and then monitor their work on Exercises 4–12.

Practice Masters Booklet, p. 70

NAME _____ DATE _____

10-6 **Practice Worksheet**

Transformations of Conics

Identify the graph of each equation. Write the equation of the translated graph in general form. Then draw the graph.

1. $x^2 + y^2 = 9$ for $T_{(-2, 1)}$

2. $2x^2 - 4x + 3 - y = 0$ for $T_{(1, -1)}$

circle; $(x + 2)^2 + (y - 1)^2 = 9$

parabola; $(x - 2)^2 = 4\left(\frac{1}{8}\right)(y - 0)$

Suppose the graph of each equation is rotated about the origin for the given angle. Find an equation of the rotated graph.

3. $x^2 - y^2 = 16$, $\theta = 45°$

$xy = 8$

4. $21x^2 - 10\sqrt{3}xy + 31y^2 = 144$, $\theta = 30°$

$\dfrac{x^2}{9} + \dfrac{y^2}{4} = 1$

Identify the graph of each equation. Then find θ to the nearest degree.

5. $2x^2 - 4xy + y^2 + 3 = 0$
ellipse; $38°$

6. $x^2 + 3xy + 3y^2 = 3$
hyperbola; $45°$

7. $3x^2 + 4\sqrt{3}xy - y^2 = 15$
hyperbola; $30°$

T70
Glencoe Division, Macmillan/McGraw-Hill

Example 4 | **Identify the graph of the equation $16x^2 - 24xy + 9y^2 - 30x - 40y = 0$. Then find θ and use a graphing calculator to draw the graph.**

$B^2 - 4AC = (-24)^2 - 4(16)(9)$ *A = 16, B = -24, and C = 9*
$= 0$

The graph is a parabola.

$\tan 2\theta = \dfrac{B}{A - C}$ $A \neq C$

$= \dfrac{-24}{16 - 9}$ or $\dfrac{-24}{7}$

$\tan 2\theta = \dfrac{-24}{7}$ or -3.428571429

$2\theta = -74°$ *Round to the nearest degree.*

$\theta = -37°$

To graph the equation, you must solve for y. Rewrite the equation in quadratic form, $ay^2 + by + c = 0$.

$$\underset{\downarrow}{a} \qquad \underset{\downarrow}{b} \qquad \underset{\downarrow}{c}$$

$$9y^2 + (-24x - 40)y + (16x^2 - 30x) = 0$$

Now use the quadratic formula to solve for y.

$$y = \frac{-(-24x - 40) \pm \sqrt{(-24x - 40)^2 - 4(9)(16x^2 - 30x)}}{2(9)}$$

$$= \frac{24x + 40 \pm \sqrt{(24x + 40)^2 - 576x^2 + 1080x}}{18}$$

Enter each equation and graph.

CHECKING FOR UNDERSTANDING

Communicating Mathematics   **Read and study the lesson to answer each question.** 1–3. See margin.

1. **Write** the matrix for $T_{(-4, 4)}$ used to translate six points of a hyperbola.

2. **Sketch** an ellipse with a vertical major axis. Then sketch the ellipse rotated 90°.

3. **Explain** how you can use the quadratic formula to graph the equation $8x^2 + 4xy + 5y^2 = 40$.

RETEACHING THE LESSON

To avoid mistakes in identifying conics by using the discriminant, students should be deliberate in evaluating the discriminant. Encourage them first to identify and write down the values of *A*, *B*, and *C*. Then have them evaluate B^2 and $4AC$, subtract the latter from the former, and compare the result with 0.

Additional Answers

1. $\begin{bmatrix} -4 & -4 & -4 & -4 & -4 & -4 \\ 4 & 4 & 4 & 4 & 4 & 4 \end{bmatrix}$

2.

Identify the graph of each equation. Write the equation of the translated graph for $T_{(-5, 6)}$ in general form. Then draw the graph. 4–7. See margin.

4. $4x^2 + 5y^2 = 20$

5. $3x^2 - 16 = -3y^2$

6. $3y^2 - 7x^2 = 21$

7. $(x + 3)^2 = 4y$

Suppose the graph of each equation is rotated about the origin for the given angle. Find an equation of the rotated graph. 8–11. See margin.

8. $x^2 - 8y = 0, \theta = 90°$

9. $6x^2 + 5y^2 = 30, \theta = 60°$

10. $49x^2 - 16y^2 = 784, \theta = \dfrac{\pi}{4}$

11. $y^2 + 8x = 0, \theta = \dfrac{\pi}{6}$

12. Identify the graph of the equation $5y^2 + 4xy + 8x^2 - 40 = 0$. Then find θ.
ellipse, $\theta \approx 26.6°$

EXERCISES

Identify the graph of each equation. Write the equation of the translated graph in general form. Then draw the graph. 13–16. See margin.

13. $x^2 + y^2 = 6$ for $T_{(2, 3)}$

14. $9x^2 - 25y^2 = 225$ for $T_{(0, -5)}$

15. $y = 2x^2 - 7x + 5$ for $T_{(-3, -4)}$

16. $3x^2 + y^2 = 9$ for $T_{(-1, 2)}$

Suppose the graph of each equation is rotated about the origin for the given angle. Find an equation of the rotated graph. 17–20. See margin.

17. $x^2 - y^2 = 9, \theta = 45°$

18. $x^2 - 5x + y^2 = 3, \theta = \dfrac{\pi}{4}$

19. $xy = -6, \theta = \dfrac{\pi}{4}$

20. $7x^2 - 6\sqrt{3}xy + 13y^2 = 16, \theta = 30°$

Identify the graph of each equation. Then find θ to the nearest degree.

21. $8x^2 + 5xy - 4y^2 + 2 = 0$ hyperbola, 11°

22. $9x^2 + 4xy + 6y^2 = 20$ ellipse, 27°

23. $2x^2 + 9xy + 14y^2 - 5 = 0$ ellipse, –37°

24. $x^2 - 2xy + y^2 - 5x - 5y = 0$ parabola, 45°

25. $2x^2 + 4\sqrt{3}xy + 6y^2 + \sqrt{3}x - y = 0$ parabola, –30°

26. $2x^2 + 4xy + 2y^2 + 2\sqrt{2}x - 2\sqrt{2}y + 12 = 0$ parabola, 45°

The graph of each equation is a degenerate case. Identify the graph and then draw it. 27–30. For graphs, see Teacher's Answer Key.

27. $3(x - 1)^2 + 4(y + 4)^2 = 0$ point

28. $xy - y^2 + 2x^2 = 0$ intersecting lines

29. $(x - 3)^2 - (x + 4)^2 = -4(y - 1)$ line

30. $(x + 3)^2 + (y + 3)^2 - 6(x + y) = 18$ point

Use the quadratic formula to solve each equation for y. Then use a graphing calculator to draw the graph. 31–36. See Teacher's Answer Key.

31. $8x^2 + 5xy - 4y^2 = -2$

32. $9x^2 + 4xy + 6y^2 - 20 = 0$

33. $2x^2 + 9xy + 14y^2 = 5$

34. $x^2 - 2xy + y^2 - 5x - 5y = 0$

35. $2x^2 + 4\sqrt{3}xy + 6y^2 + \sqrt{3}x = y$

36. $2x^2 + 4xy + 2y^2 + 2\sqrt{2}x - 2\sqrt{2}y = -12$

Additional Answers

13-16. For graphs, see Teacher's Answer Key.

13. circle, $x^2 + y^2 - 4x - 6y + 7 = 0$

14. hyperbola, $9x^2 - 25y^2 - 250y - 850 = 0$

15. parabola, $2x^2 + 5x - y - 2 = 0$

16. ellipse, $3x^2 + y^2 + 6x - 4y - 2 = 0$

17. $2xy = 9$

18. $2x^2 - 5\sqrt{2}x - 5\sqrt{2}y + 2y^2 = 6$

19. $x^2 - y^2 = 12$

20. $13x^2 - 6\sqrt{3}xy + 7y^2 = 16$

Writing Activity   Have students write four general equations for conics, one representing a circle, one representing an ellipse, one representing a hyperbola, and one representing a parabola.

APPLYING THE LESSON

Homework Exercises

Assignment Guide

Average: 13–28, 37, 39, 41–46
Enriched: 19–36, 38, 40–46

The red A, B, and C flags, printed only in the Teacher's Wraparound Edition, indicate the level of difficulty of the exercises.

Chapter 10, Quiz C, (Lessons 10–5 through 10–6) is available in the *Evaluation Masters*, p. 126.

Using Technology

After students complete Exercises 31–36, encourage them to experiment to see how slight changes in the value of *A, B,* or *C* affect the graphs of the equations.

Additional Answers

3. Write the equation in terms of $ay^2 + by + c = 0$.
$5y^2 + (4x)y + (8x^2 - 40) = 0$
Then use $a = 5$, $b = 4x$, and $c = 8x^2 - 40$ in the quadratic formula. $y =$
$$\dfrac{-4x \pm \sqrt{(4x)^2 - 4(5)(8x^2 - 40)}}{2(5)}.$$
Graph the two equations on the same screen.

4–7. For graphs, see Teacher's Answer Key.

4. ellipse, $4x^2 + 5y^2 + 40x - 60y + 260 = 0$

5. circle, $3x^2 + 3y^2 + 30x - 36y + 167 = 0$

6. hyperbola, $7x^2 - 3y^2 + 70x - 36y + 88 = 0$

7. parabola, $x^2 + 16x - 4y + 88 = 0$

8. $y^2 + 8x = 0$

9. $21x^2 + 2\sqrt{3}xy + 23y^2 = 120$

10. $33x^2 + 130xy + 33y^2 = 1568$

11. $x^2 + 16\sqrt{3}x - 2\sqrt{3}xy + 16y + 3y^2 = 0$

Critical Thinking

37. Determine the rotation and/or translation needed to transform the graph of $5x^2 + 4xy + 8y^2 - 36 = 0$ to a graph whose center is the origin and whose axes are on the x- and y-axes. rotation of about 26°30′

38. Determine the minimum angle of rotation for the graphs of each equation so that the rotated graph coincides with the original graph. Sketch the graph.
  a. $6x^2 + 8y^2 = 24$ 180°   **b.** $5y^2 - x^2 = 25$ 180°
  c. $12x^2 + 12y^2 = 108$ any degree   **d.** $y = (x+3)^2$ 360°
  38. See Teacher's Answer Key for graphs.

Applications and Problem Solving

39. Manufacturing A cam in a punch press is shaped like an ellipse with the equation $\dfrac{x^2}{169} + \dfrac{y^2}{25} = 1$. The camshaft goes through the focus on the positive axis.
  a. Graph a model of the cam. 39a–c. See margin.
  b. Find an equation that translates the model so that the camshaft is at the origin.
  c. Find the equation of the model in part b when the cam is rotated to an upright position.

40. Sports A football is a model of an *ellipsoid*. An ellipsoid is formed when an ellipse centered at the origin is rotated in space around the x- or y-axis. The figure at the right shows an ellipsoid rotated about the y-axis. Suppose the equation of the ellipsoid that models a football is $\dfrac{y^2}{30.25} + \dfrac{x^2}{11.56} + \dfrac{z^2}{11.56} = 1$. Find the equation of the circle that intersects the x- and z-axes. $x^2 + z^2 = 11.56$

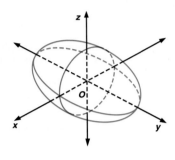

Mixed Review

41. Given $A = 43°, b = 20$, and $a = 11$, do these measurements determine one triangle, two triangles, or no triangle? **(Lesson 5-6)** no triangle

42. $y = 3 \sin \pi t$

42. Physics Write an equation with phase shift 0 to represent simple harmonic motion for an initial position of 0, amplitude 3, and period 2. **(Lesson 6-7)**

43. Graph $3r = 12$ on a polar plane. **(Lesson 9-1)** See margin.

44. Find $(-5 + 12i)^2$. **(Lesson 9-8)** $-119 - 120i$

45. Write the standard form of $x^2 - 8x + y^2 = -11$ and identify the conic section it represents. **(Lesson 10-5)** $(x-4)^2 + y^2 = 5$, circle

46. College Entrance Exam Compare quantity A and quantity B below. D
  Write A if quantity A is greater than quantity B.
  Write B if quantity B is greater than quantity A.
  Write C if the two quantities are equal.
  Write D if there is not enough information to determine the relationship.

  (A) $(\sqrt{x})^2$ **(B)** $\dfrac{1}{x^2}$

576 CHAPTER 10 CONICS

EXTENDING THE LESSON

Math Power: Problem Solving

The angle of rotation about the origin of the graph of $2x^2 + 4xy + Cy^2 + 3x - 2y = 0$ is 30°. Find C.

$\dfrac{6 - 4\sqrt{3}}{3}$

10-7A Graphing Calculators: Solving Quadratic Systems

As we have seen, the graphing calculator is a good tool for solving systems of equations, including those involving quadratic equations. By using the techniques used to graph conic sections in Lesson 10-6A, we can graph and solve systems involving quadratics.

Example 1

Graph the system of equations below and find its solution to two decimal places.

$$4y^2 + 2x = 5$$
$$4x^2 + 6y^2 = 12$$

First, solve each equation for y.

$$4y^2 = 5 - 2x \qquad\qquad 6y^2 = 12 - 4x^2$$

$$y^2 = \frac{1}{4}(5 - 2x) \qquad\qquad y^2 = 2 - \frac{2}{3}x^2$$

$$y = \pm\frac{1}{2}\sqrt{5 - 2x} \qquad\qquad y = \pm\sqrt{2 - \frac{2}{3}x^2}$$

Then, graph the equations using the viewing window $[-4.5, 4.5]$ by $[-3, 3]$ for the TI-81 and $[-4.7, 4.7]$ by $[-3.1, 3.1]$ for the Casio. Use a scale factor of 1 for all axes.

The solutions are $(-0.75, -1.27)$, $(-0.75, 1.27)$, $(1.5, -0.71)$, and $(1.5, 0.71)$, accurate to two decimal places. Notice the symmetry of the points and the symmetry of the graph.

You can find the solutions to any combination of equations in a system involving quadratics using a graphing calculator. The solutions to the equations of two conic sections or the solutions to one conic section and a line can be found.

GRAPHING CALCULATORS: SOLVING QUADRATIC SYSTEMS 577

INTRODUCING THE LESSON

Objective Graph and solve systems of quadratic equations.

Motivating the Lesson
Ask students to sketch all possible situations in which a parabola might intersect an ellipse. Then ask them to tell how many intersection points are possible in each situation.

TEACHING THE LESSON

Teaching Tip Remind students that they used graphing to solve systems of equations in Chapter 2. The same premise applies to systems involving quadratics.

More Examples

Graph each system of equations below and find its solutions to two decimal places.

1. $9x^2 + 4y^2 = 36$
   $9x^2 - 4y^2 = 36$

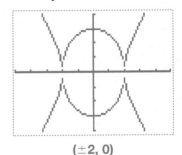

$(\pm 2, 0)$

2. $x + y = 2.82$
   $x^2 + y^2 = 4$

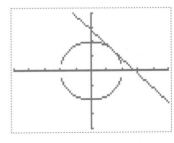

$(1.30, 1.52), (1.52, 1.30)$

Additional Answers

Exercises (p. 578)

1.

2.

Example 2

Graph the system of equations below and find its solution to two decimal places.

$$x^2 = 7 - y^2$$
$$y^2 + y - 4x^2 = 10$$

First, solve both equations for y.

$$-y^2 = x^2 - 7 \qquad\qquad y^2 + y = 10 + 4x^2$$
$$y^2 = 7 - x^2 \qquad\qquad y^2 + y + \frac{1}{4} = 10 + 4x^2 + \frac{1}{4}$$
$$y = \pm\sqrt{7 - x^2} \qquad\qquad \left(y + \frac{1}{2}\right)^2 = \frac{41}{4} + 4x^2$$
$$y + \frac{1}{2} = \pm\sqrt{\frac{41}{4} + 4x^2}$$
$$y = -\frac{1}{2} \pm \sqrt{\frac{41}{4} + 4x^2}$$

Then enter the equations into a graphing calculator. Use the viewing window $[-8, 8]$ by $[-5, 5]$ with a scale factor of 1 for all axes.

TI-81:

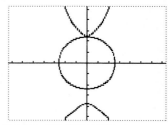

Casio:

Although it appears that the graphs intersect, using zoom-in shows that there are no solutions to this system because the two graphs do not intersect.

EXERCISES

Use a graphing calculator to graph each system of equations and find the solutions to two decimal places.

1. $x^2 + y^2 = 6$ $(\pm 2.31, 0.82),$
   $2x^2 - 4y^2 = 8$ $(\pm 2.31, -0.82)$

2. $2x^2 = 3 - y$ $(0, 3)$
   $x^2 + \frac{y^2}{9} = 1$

3. $y^2 = 4 - x$ $(1.57, \pm 1.56),$
   $3x^2 - y^2 = 5$ $(-1.91, \pm 2.43)$

4. $(x - 3)^2 + (y - 1)^2 = 4$ no
   $(2x + 1)^2 + (4y - 1)^2 = 4$ solution

5. $4x^2 - 9y^2 = -36$
   $4x^2 + 9y^2 = 36$ $(0, \pm 2)$

6. $x^2 = 10 - y^2$
   $y^2 = 0.2x - 0.6$ $(3.16, \pm 0.18)$

578 CHAPTER 10 CONICS

5.

6.

3. **Explain** why the negative values of w^2 and w were not used in finding the solution to the problem in Example 2.

4. **Describe** how you solve a system of inequalities by graphing.

Guided Practice

Use the graphs to determine the number of solutions for each system of equations.

5. 4

6. 2

7. 3

8. none

9. 1

10. 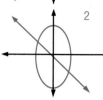 2

Graph each system of equations. Then solve. Round the coordinates of the solutions to the nearest tenth. 11–13. For graphs, see Teacher's Answer Key.

11. $x^2 + y^2 = 16$
$x^2 + y^2 = 9$
no solution

12. $x^2 + y^2 = 49$
$x + 1 = 0$ $(-1, \pm 6.9)$

13. $2y - x + 3 = 0$
$x^2 = 16 - y^2$
$(4.0, 0.5), (-2.8, -2.9)$

Graph each system of inequalities. 14–15. See margin.

14. $y + x^2 < 0$
$x^2 + y^2 < 9$

15. $x^2 - 16y^2 \geq 16$
$x^2 + y^2 \geq 49$

EXERCISES

Practice

Graph each system of equations. Then solve. Round the coordinates of the solutions to the nearest tenth. 16–27. For graphs, see Teacher's Answer Key.

A

16. $y^2 = 100 - x^2$ $(8, 6)$,
$x - y = 2$ $(-6, -8)$

17. $y = 7 - x$ no solution
$y^2 + x^2 = 9$

18. $y^2 - x^2 = 4$
$y - 5 = 0$ $(\pm 4.6, 5)$

19. $x - y = 0$ $(3, 3), (-1, -1)$
$\frac{(x-1)^2}{20} + \frac{(y-1)^2}{5} = 1$

20. $xy = 2$
$x^2 = 3 + y^2$ $(2, 1), (-2, -1)$

21. $x^2 + 2y^2 = 10$ $(\pm 2, 1.7)$
$3x^2 - y^2 = 9$ $(\pm 2, -1.7)$

22. $\frac{(x-2)^2}{36} - \frac{(y+3)^2}{4} = 1$
$x - y = 0$ no solution

23. $5x^2 + y^2 = 30$ $(\pm 1, 5)$,
$9x^2 - y^2 + 16 = 0$ $(\pm 1, -5)$

B

24. $x^2 + y^2 = 64$
$x^2 + 64y^2 = 64$ $(\pm 8, 0)$

25. $9x^2 + 4y^2 = 36$
$9x^2 - 4y^2 = 36$ $(\pm 2, 0)$

26. $(y - 1)^2 = x + 4$
$y + 1 = -x$ $(0, -1), (-3, 2)$

27. $xy = -4$ $(3, -\frac{4}{3}), (4, -1)$,
$x^2 + 9y^2 = 25$ $(-3, \frac{4}{3}), (-4, 1)$

LESSON 10-7 SYSTEMS OF SECOND-DEGREE EQUATIONS AND INEQUALITIES 583

14.

15.

Closing the Lesson

Modeling Activity Two different conics can intersect in 1 point, 2 points, 3 points, or 4 points. Have students draw sketches illustrating each possibility.

APPLYING THE LESSON

Homework Exercises

Assignment Guide

Average: 16–32, 36, 37, 39–44
Enriched: 22–44

The red A, B, and C flags, printed only in the Teacher's Wraparound Edition, indicate the level of difficulty of the exercises.

Additional Answers

1.

2.

3. Negative values for width are not appropriate for this application.

4. Graph each inequality. The region in which the graphs overlap represents the solution to the system.

Graph each system of inequalities. 28–35. See Teacher's Answer Key.

28. $10 \geq (x - 5)^2 + 2y$
$y \geq -2x + 9$

29. $(x + 1)^2 + (y + 1)^2 > 16$
$9x^2 + y^2 < 81$

30. $x^2 + y^2 \geq 25$
$x^2 + y^2 \leq 100$

31. $(x + 3)^2 + (y + 2)^2 \leq 36$
$y + 4 = 0$

 32. $16x^2 - 25y^2 \geq 400$
$xy \geq 2$

33. $x^2 - 16 < 4y^2$
$x - (y - 1)^2 > 0$

34. $x^2 + y^2 \geq 16$
$x + y = 2$

35. $9x^2 + 4y^2 \leq 36$
$4x^2 + 9y^2 \geq 36$

Critical Thinking

36. Solve the system of equations below.
$x^2 + y^2 = 1$
$y = 3x + 1$
$x^2 + (y + 1)^2 = 4$ (0, 1)

Applications and Problem Solving

37. Agriculture Mr. Wise owns a dairy farm in Plains, Georgia. He wishes to section off a small portion of a field to contain newly weaned calves. He has 56 feet of fencing and a 4-foot gate. He would like to enclose an area of 216 square feet. Use a system of equations to find the dimensions of the fenced area. 12 ft by 18 ft

38. Space Science A satellite is placed in a geosynchronous orbit at a height of 35,800 kilometers above the equator. The radius of Earth is about 6400 kilometers. Another satellite is placed in an elliptical orbit such that its closest point to Earth is 10,000 kilometers.

a. Draw a model of this situation. See margin.

b. Determine the possible number of times that these two satellites might collide. 2 times

c. How do you think these types of collisions are prevented? See students' work.

Mixed Review

39. Surveying A surveying crew is studying a housing project for possible relocation for the airport expansion. They are located on the ground, level with the houses. If the distance to one of the houses is 253 meters and the distance to the other is 319 meters, what is the distance between the houses if the angle subtended by them at the point of observation is $42°12'$? **(Lesson 5-7)** 214.9 meters

40. Write the equation for the inverse of $y = \cos x$. **(Lesson 6-6)** $y = \arccos x$

41. Given points $A(3, 3, -1)$ and $B(5, 3, 2)$, find an ordered triple that represents $\overrightarrow{AB}$. **(Lesson 8-3)** (2, 0, 3)

42. Find $6 \left(\cos \frac{5\pi}{8} + i \sin \frac{5\pi}{8} \right) \div 12 \left(\cos \frac{\pi}{2} + i \sin \frac{\pi}{2} \right)$. Then express the quotient in rectangular form. **(Lesson 9-7)** $0.5 \left(\cos \frac{\pi}{8} + i \sin \frac{\pi}{8} \right)$, $0.46 + 0.10i$

43. Find the coordinates of the vertex of a parabola whose equation is $y - 3 = (x + 4)^2$ with respect to $T_{(-3,5)}$. **(Lesson 10-6)** (−7, 8)

44. College Entrance Exam The average of 8 numbers is 6. The average of 6 other numbers is 8. What is the average of all 14 numbers? 6.86

EXTENDING THE LESSON

Math Power: Communication

Two points located 14 units apart on the x-axis are the centers of circles the sum of whose radii is 28. The circles intersect at (5, 12) and (5, −12). Find the equations of the circles.
$x^2 + y^2 = 169$ and
$(x - 14)^2 + y^2 = 225$

10-8 Tangents and Normals to the Conic Sections

Objectives
10–8A
10–8B

After studying this lesson, you should be able to:
- write equations of tangents and normals to conic sections, and
- find the length of a segment tangent to a circle.

Application

On April 25, 1990, the Hubble Space Telescope was deployed from the cargo bay of the space shuttle *Discovery*. When the first pictures were sent back to Earth, the stars had diffused halos of light around them. Such fuzzy images are caused when light from the inner and outer edges of the primary mirror are not brought to the same focal plane. Scientists have now concluded that the center of the primary mirror has the correct curvature, but the overall shape is more hyperbolic than it should be. At the edge of the mirror, the deviation from a parabolic curvature to a circular is serious enough to cause the halo effect. One solution to this problem is the installation of new optical instruments that compensate for the error in curvature.

Some of the rays of light that skim the surfaces of the mirrors of the Hubble Telescope can be modeled by lines that are tangent to the curves of the surface. Remember that a tangent to a curve intersects the curve in one point. The slope of the curve at a given point is also the slope of the tangent at that point.

Perpendicular lines have slopes that are negative reciprocals.

A line tangent to a circle is perpendicular to the radius at the point of tangency. Since the slope of the radius to $P(x_1, y_1)$ on a circle with center at the origin is $\frac{y_1}{x_1}$, the slope of the tangent is $-\frac{x_1}{y_1}$. You can write the point-slope form of the equation of the tangent using the coordinate of the point of tangency $P(x_1, y_1)$.

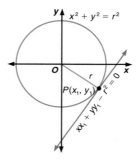

$$m = \frac{y - y_1}{x - x_1}$$

$$-\frac{x_1}{y_1} = \frac{y - y_1}{x - x_1} \qquad m = -\frac{x_1}{y_1}$$

$$xx_1 - x_1^2 = -yy_1 + y_1^2$$

$$xx_1 + yy_1 = x_1^2 + y_1^2 \qquad \text{Since } (x_1, y_1) \text{ is on the}$$

$$xx_1 + yy_1 = r^2 \qquad \text{circle, } (x_1)^2 + (y_1)^2 = r^2.$$

Equation of the Tangent to a Circle

The equation of the line tangent to the circle $x^2 + y^2 = r^2$ at (x_1, y_1) is $xx_1 + yy_1 - r^2 = 0$.

ALTERNATE TEACHING STRATEGIES

Using Cooperative Groups

Have students work in groups of four. In a group, students should divide the four conic sections among themselves, one student to a section. Each student writes the standard form of an equation of his or her conic section, chooses a point of tangency, and exchanges with another student. Students find the slope of the tangent at the given point of tangency.

Using Models

Have students graph a circle with its center at the origin. Tell them to choose a point on the circle, write its coordinates, and draw the radius from the point to the center. Then have them draw the tangent to the circle at the chosen point. Have students count squares to find the slope of the tangent and the slope of the particular radius.

10–8 Lesson Notes

NCTM Standards: 1–6, 8

Lesson Resources

- Practice Master 10–8
- Enrichment Master 10–8
- Evaluation Master, Quiz D, p. 126
   Transparency 10–8 contains the 5-Minute Check and a teaching aid for this lesson.

INTRODUCING THE LESSON

 5-Minute Check

(over Lesson 10–7)

1. Find the number of possible points in which a circle and a parabola can intersect.
   0, 1, 2, 3, or 4
2. Solve algebraically.
   $x + y = 7$
   $x^2 + y^2 = 25$
   (3, 4), (4, 3)
3. Graph the solution for the system of inequalities below.
   $x^2 + y^2 \le 25$
   $y + 1 > (x - 2)^2$

Motivating the Lesson

Ask students to explain why the tangent, $\overline{AB}$, is perpendicular to the radius, $\overline{OA}$, at the point of tangency A.

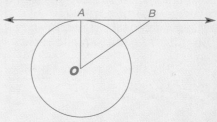

Any other point B on the tangent is outside the circle, so $BO > AO$. Therefore, AO is the shortest distance from the tangent to O, and $\overline{AB} \perp \overline{OA}$.

Chalkboard Example

For Example 1

A goat, tied to a circular corn bin, stretches the rope tight so that it is tangent to the bin at a point 6 feet north and 4 feet east of the center. If the center is at (0, 0), determine the equation of the line representing the rope.
$2x + 3y = 26$

Teaching Tip When discussing the tangent-slope chart, point out the patterns in the formulas for the slopes of tangents to ellipses and hyperbolas. For either conic, the two formulas are reciprocals of each other. For the two conics, the analogous formulas differ only in sign.

Example 1

APPLICATION

Geography

At the base of volcanic Mount Shasta is the small town of Mount Shasta, California. The town is 10 miles south and 7 miles west of the center of the volcano. A road that is tangent to the base of the volcano runs through the center of town. If the center of the volcano is at $(0, 0)$, determine the equation of the line representing the road.

The center of the circle is at $(0, 0)$ so the equation of the circle is $x^2 + y^2 = r^2$.
The point on the circle representing the town of Mount Shasta is at $(-7, -10)$.
The radius of the circle is $\sqrt{(-10)^2 + (-7)^2}$ or $\sqrt{149}$.

Substitute the values for x_1, y_1, and r into the equation for the line tangent to a circle.

$$xx_1 + yy_1 - r^2 = 0$$
$$x(-7) + y(-10) - (\sqrt{149})^2 = 0$$
$$-7x - 10y - 149 = 0$$
$$7x + 10y + 149 = 0$$

The equation of the line representing the road is $7x + 10y = -149$.

Equations for lines tangent to other conic sections, including circles whose centers are not the origin, can be found. The chart below lists formulas for the slopes of lines tangent to the graphs of given equations.

You can review another method for finding the equation of the line tangent to a parabola in Lesson 3-6.

Conic Section	Standard Form of Equation	Slope of Tangent at (x, y)
circle	$(x-h)^2 + (y-k)^2 = r^2$	$-\dfrac{(x-h)}{(y-k)}$
parabola	$(y-k)^2 = 4p(x-h)$	$\dfrac{2p}{y-k}$
	$(x-h)^2 = 4p(y-k)$	$\dfrac{x-h}{2p}$
ellipse	$\dfrac{(x-h)^2}{a^2} + \dfrac{(y-k)^2}{b^2} = 1$	$-\dfrac{b^2(x-h)}{a^2(y-k)}$
	$\dfrac{(y-k)^2}{a^2} + \dfrac{(x-h)^2}{b^2} = 1$	$-\dfrac{a^2(x-h)}{b^2(y-k)}$
hyperbola	$\dfrac{(x-h)^2}{a^2} - \dfrac{(y-k)^2}{b^2} = 1$	$\dfrac{b^2(x-h)}{a^2(y-k)}$
	$\dfrac{(y-k)^2}{a^2} - \dfrac{(x-h)^2}{b^2} = 1$	$\dfrac{a^2(x-h)}{b^2(y-k)}$

When you have found the slope, you can then use the slope-intercept form to write the equation of the slope of the tangent.

Example 2

Find the equation of the line tangent to the graph of $\dfrac{x^2}{16} - \dfrac{y^2}{4} = 1$ at (5, 1.5).

The equation represents a hyperbola with a horizontal transverse axis. Thus, use $\dfrac{b^2(x - h)}{a^2(y - k)}$ for the slope of the tangent. In this case, $a^2 = 16$, $b^2 = 4$, $h = 0$, $k = 0$, $x_1 = 5$, and $y_1 = 1.5$.

Find the slope.

$$m = \dfrac{b^2(x - h)}{a^2(y - k)}$$

$$= \dfrac{4(5 - 0)}{16(1.5 - 0)} \text{ or } \dfrac{5}{6}$$

Use the point-slope form.

$$y - y_1 = m(x - x_1)$$

$$y - \dfrac{3}{2} = \dfrac{5}{6}(x - 5)$$

The equation of the line tangent to the hyperbola at (5, 1.5) is

$$y - \dfrac{3}{2} = \dfrac{5}{6}(x - 5) \text{ or } 5x - 6y - 16 = 0.$$

You can also determine which members of a family of lines are tangent to a given conic.

Example 3

A family of lines with slope 4 can be represented by the equation $y = 4x + k$, where k is a constant. Find which member(s) of this family of lines is tangent to the circle with equation $x^2 + y^2 = 153$.

The slope of the line is 4. The slope of the tangent to a circle is $-\dfrac{x - h}{y - k}$. Find the relationship of x and y at the point of tangency.

$$m = -\dfrac{x - h}{y - k}$$

$$4 = -\dfrac{x - 0}{y - 0} \qquad m = 4, (h, k) = (0, 0)$$

$$-4y = x$$

family of lines represented by $y = 4x + k$

A point of tangency for a line in this family is a point on the circle for which $x = -4y$. Substitute $-4y$ for x in the equation of the circle.

$$x^2 + y^2 = 153$$
$$(-4y)^2 + y^2 = 153$$
$$17y^2 = 153$$
$$y = \pm 3$$

If you substitute these values for y into the equation for the circle, you find there are four resulting ordered pairs: $(12, 3), (-12, 3), (12, -3),$ and $(-12, -3)$.

(continued on the next page)

LESSON 10-8   TANGENTS AND NORMALS TO THE CONIC SECTIONS   587

However, since $-\dfrac{x}{y} = 4$, you can eliminate $(12, 3)$ and $(-12, -3)$. *Why?*

$(-12, 3)$ and $(12, -3)$ are the points of tangency.

You can use these points and the given slope to find the equations of the tangent lines.

$y - 3 = 4(x - (-12))$ or $y = 4x + 51$
$y + 3 = 4(x - 12)$ or $y = 4x - 51$

If $P(x_1, y_1)$ is a point in the plane of the circle with equation $(x - h)^2 + (y - k)^2 = r^2$, then P lies outside the circle if and only if $(x_1 - h)^2 + (y_1 - k)^2 > r^2$. This indicates that there are two lines from point P tangent to the circle. Sometimes it is necessary to find the length of the segment from that point to the point of tangency.

The length of the tangent segment PT can be found by using the Pythagorean theorem. Let $C(h, k)$ represent the center of the circle, $P(x_1, y_1)$ represent a point outside the circle, and $T(x_2, y_2)$ represent one of the points of tangency. Let $TP = t$, $CT = r$, and $CP = d$. Thus, $t = \sqrt{d^2 - r^2}$.

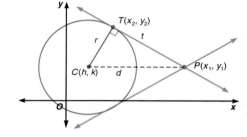

The distance formula can be used to find that $d^2 = (x_1 - h)^2 + (y_1 - k)^2$. You can substitute this value of d^2 into $t = \sqrt{d^2 - r^2}$ to obtain a formula for the length of a segment tangent to a circle.

Length of a Segment Tangent to a Circle	The length t of a tangent segment from (x_1, y_1) to the circle with equation $(x - h)^2 + (y - k)^2 = r^2$ can be found by using the formula $$t = \sqrt{(x_1 - h)^2 + (y_1 - k)^2 - r^2}.$$

Example 4

Find the length of the tangent segment from $(-4, 7)$ to the circle with equation $x^2 + y^2 = 10$.

$t = \sqrt{(x_1 - h)^2 + (y_1 - k)^2 - r^2}$
$ = \sqrt{(-4 - 0)^2 + (7 - 0)^2 - 10}$
$ = \sqrt{55}$

The length of the tangent segment is $\sqrt{55}$ or about 7.42 units.

The **normal** to a curve at any point on the curve is the line perpendicular to the tangent at that point. The slope of the normal is the negative reciprocal of the slope of the tangent.

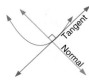

Example 5

Find the equations of the tangent and the normal to the graph of
$$\frac{y^2}{64} + \frac{x^2}{49} = 1 \text{ at } \left(\frac{7\sqrt{3}}{2}, 4 \right).$$

The graph is an ellipse with a horizontal major axis. Use $-\frac{b^2(x-h)}{a^2(y-k)}$ for the slope of the tangent.

The slope of the tangent is $\dfrac{-64\left(\frac{7\sqrt{3}}{2}\right)}{49(4)}$ or $-\dfrac{8\sqrt{3}}{7}$. The equation of the tangent is $y - 4 = -\dfrac{8\sqrt{3}}{7}\left(x - \dfrac{7\sqrt{3}}{2}\right)$ or $8\sqrt{3}x + 7y - 112 = 0$.

The slope of the normal is $\dfrac{7}{8\sqrt{3}}$. The equation of the normal is $y - 4 = \dfrac{7}{8\sqrt{3}}\left(x - \dfrac{7\sqrt{3}}{2}\right)$ or $14x - 16\sqrt{3}y + 15\sqrt{3} = 0$.

EVALUATING THE LESSON

Checking for Understanding

Exercises 1–12 are designed to help you assess students' understanding through reading, writing, speaking, and modeling. You should work through Exercises 1–2 with your students and then monitor their work on Exercises 3–12.

Closing the Lesson

Speaking Activity A circle, a parabola, an ellipse, and a hyperbola all have their centers at (0, 0) and all contain the point at (3, 4). Have students use the chart on page 586 to state the slope of the tangents to each of the conic sections.

CHECKING FOR UNDERSTANDING

Communicating Mathematics

Read and study the lesson to answer each question.

1. **Illustrate** how there can be two lines tangent to a hyperbola from a given point outside the hyperbola. See margin.

2. **Explain** how you can determine which line in a family of lines is tangent to a circle. You use the slope of the tangent to determine the coordinates of the point of tangency. Then substitute that value into the equation of the circle.

Guided Practice

Find the slopes of the tangent and the normal to the graph of each equation at the given point. 5. 0, undefined   6. 0, undefined

3. $(x+4)^2 - 8(y+3) = 0, (0, -1)$ 1, -1

4. $\dfrac{(x-2)^2}{10} + \dfrac{(y-3)^2}{10} = 1, (-1, 2)$ $-3, \frac{1}{3}$

5. $25(x-3)^2 + 4(y-1)^2 = 100, (3, -4)$

6. $(x+2)^2 + 4(y-3)^2 = 36, (-2, 6)$

7. $\dfrac{(y+2)^2}{8} = x - 3, (5, 2)$ 1, -1

8. $9x^2 = 8y^2 + 72, (-4, -3)$ $\frac{3}{2}, -\frac{2}{3}$

LESSON 10-8   TANGENTS AND NORMALS TO THE CONIC SECTIONS   589

RETEACHING THE LESSON

Write the equation of a conic section in standard form on the chalkboard. Have students identify h, k, r, p, a, and/or b, the variables that appear in standard forms of the equations. Give the coordinates of a point on the conic section and have the students use the tangent-slope chart to find the slope at the given point.

Additional Answer

1.

Homework Exercises

Assignment Guide

Average: 13–33, 37, 40, 42–48
Enriched: 19–48

The red A, B, and C flags, printed only in the Teacher's Wraparound Edition, indicate the level of difficulty of the exercises.

Chapter 10, Quiz D, (Lessons 10–7 through 10–8) is available in the *Evaluation Masters*, p. 126.

Exercise Note

For Exercises 13–28, encourage students to draw a quick sketch of each curve and the tangent or normal at the specified point, and to estimate the equation or length, as required.

Additional Answers

9. $9x - 8y - 145 = 0$,
$9y + 8x = 0$
10. $4x - y + 1 = 0$,
$x + 4y - 4 = 0$
11. $4x + 5y - 25 = 0$,
$25x - 20y - 64 = 0$
12. $x - 2 = 0, y = 0$
13. $2x + \sqrt{21}y - 25 = 0$,
$y - \frac{\sqrt{21}}{2}x = 0$
14. $\sqrt{13}x + 6y - 49 = 0$,
$13y - 6\sqrt{13}x = 0$
15. $10x + 4y + 116 = 0$,
$5y - 2x = 0$
16. $3x + \sqrt{6}y - 5 = 0$,
$\sqrt{6}x - 3y = 0$
17. $x + 5y + 14 = 0$,
$5x - y - 8 = 0$
18. $3\sqrt{3}x + y - 15 = 0$,
$x - 3\sqrt{3}y + 17\sqrt{3} = 0$
19. $2x - \sqrt{5}y + 13 = 0$,
$\sqrt{5}x + 2y + 2\sqrt{5} = 0$
20. $11x - 5y + 13 = 0$,
$5x + 11y + \frac{3}{5} = 0$
21. $x + y - 8 = 0$,
$x - y - 6 = 0$
22. $x = 8, y = 3$
23. $x = -4, y = -3$
24. $8x - 3y + 11 = 0$,
$3x + 8y + 68 = 0$
33. $y = -\frac{3}{4}x + 10$,

$y = -\frac{3}{4}x - 10$

Find the equations of the tangent and the normal to the graphs of each equation at the given point. Write the equations in standard form. 9–12. See margin.

9. $x^2 + y^2 = 145, (9, -8)$
10. $x^2 + 4x - y + 1 = 0, (0, 1)$
11. $\frac{x^2}{25} + \frac{y^2}{9} = 1, (4, 1.8)$
12. $\frac{x^2}{4} - y^2 = 1, (2, 0)$

EXERCISES

Practice Find the equations of the tangent and the normal to the graphs of each equation at the point with the given coordinates. Write the equations in standard form.
13–24. See margin.

13. $x^2 + y^2 = 25, (2, \sqrt{21})$
14. $\frac{x^2}{49} + \frac{y^2}{49} = 1, (\sqrt{13}, 6)$
15. $x^2 - 6 = 110 - y^2, (-10, -4)$
16. $3x^2 + 3y^2 = 5, \left(1, \frac{\sqrt{6}}{3}\right)$
17. $y(y + 1) - x = 5, (1, -3)$
18. $(y - 3)^2 + 9x^2 = 36, (\sqrt{3}, 6)$
19. $y^2 + (x + 2)^2 = 9, (-4, \sqrt{5})$
20. $2x^2 - 7x + 5y = 11, \left(-1, \frac{2}{5}\right)$
21. $(x - 4)^2 + 3y^2 = 12, (7, 1)$
22. $(x - 4)^2 + (y - 3)^2 = 16, (8, 3)$

23. $9(x - 1)^2 - 25(y + 3)^2 = 225, (-4, -3)$
24. $32(x - 2)^2 - 9(y - 1)^2 = 576, (-4, -7)$

Find the length of the tangent segment from each point to the graph of the given circle.

25. $(6, 2), x^2 + y^2 = 37$ $\sqrt{3}$ or 1.73
26. $(4, -1), (x + 3)^2 + y^2 = 4$ $\sqrt{46}$ or 6.78
27. $\sqrt{33}$ or 5.74
27. $(10, 1), x(x - 6) + y(y - 8) = 0$
28. $(-7, 2), 4(x + 3)^2 + 4(y - 2)^2 = 16$
$2\sqrt{3}$ or 3.46
29. Find the equations of the horizontal lines tangent to the graph of circle $x^2 + y^2 = 25$. $y = \pm 5$
30. $x = \pm 7$
30. Find the equations of the vertical lines tangent to the graph of circle $x^2 + y^2 = 49$.
31. Find the equations of the tangents if the lines tangent to the graph of $\frac{x^2}{25} + \frac{y^2}{64} = 1$ are horizontal. $y = \pm 8$
32. Find the equations of the normals if the lines tangent to the graph of $x^2 + 4y^2 = 16$ are vertical. $y = 0$
33. The graph of $x^2 + y^2 = 64$ has two tangents that belong to the family of lines $y = -\frac{3}{4}x + k$. Find the equations of the tangents. See margin.
34. A line passes through the origin and $(2, 16)$. It is also tangent to the graph of $y = (x + 2)^2$.
 a. Name the family of lines to which this line belongs. $y = 8x + b$
 b. Write the equation of the tangent. $y = 8x$
35. If the line $6x - 2y = 5$ is parallel to the line tangent to the graph of $4y = x^2 + 4x - 16$ at a, find the value of a. $a = 4$
36. The line $y = 2x$ is tangent to the graph of $y = x^2 + ax + b$ at $(2, 4)$. Find the values of a and b. $a = -2, b = 4$

40a.

40b. ± 0.84

40c. $y = -0.84x + 4.5$,
$y = 0.84x + 4.5$,
$y = 0.84x - 4.5$,
$y = -0.84x - 4.5$

Critical Thinking

37. Find the point on the parabola $x^2 - 6x - 2y + 1 = 0$ at which the tangent line makes a $45°$ angle with the positive x-axis. $(4, -3.5)$

38. Determine the positive value of k such that the line $x + y = 4$ is tangent to an equilateral hyperbola $xy = k$. $k = 4$

39. $\overline{CD}$ is tangent to circle A at D and $\overline{BC}$ intersects circle A at E. If $AB = 4$, $CE = EB = 6$, and $CD = 2\sqrt{30}$, find the radius of circle A. 8 units

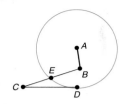

Applications and Problem Solving

40. Design For the cover design of a mathematics textbook, artist Cathy Watterson decides to make one of the shapes an ellipse with a horizontal major axis 8 centimeters long and a minor axis 6 centimeters long. She would like to place tangents at four different points around the ellipse so that the ellipse is enclosed in a parallelogram. The distance from each point of tangency to the major axis is 2 centimeters. 40a–c. See margin.

a. Make a sketch of this design.
b. Find the slope of each tangent.
c. Write the equations of the four tangents.

41. Communications A microwave signal from a television tower is tangent to the parabolic curve of a reflector at a point 2 meters right and 3 meters up from the vertex of the parabola. If a model of this reflector and signal were drawn on a coordinate plane, the parabola would have its vertex at $(0, 0)$, open to the right, and the distance from the vertex to the focus would be $\dfrac{9}{8}$ units.

a. Make a sketch of the model. See margin.
b. Determine the equation of the tangent at the given point. $4y - 3x - 6 = 0$

Mixed Review

42. The area of a triangle is 24 cm². One side is 6 cm long and another side is 10 cm long. Find the measure of the included angle of those two sides. **(Lesson 5-8)** $53°8'$

43. Graph $y = \cos\left(x - \dfrac{\pi}{6}\right)$. **(Lesson 6-1)** See margin.

44. Find the equation of the line that bisects the obtuse angle formed by the graphs of $2x - 3y + 9 = 0$ and $x + 4y + 4 = 0$. **(Lesson 7-7)** See margin.

45. Simplify $(3i + 5)^2$. **(Lesson 9-5)** $16 + 30i$

46. Express $5\left(\cos\dfrac{\pi}{6} + i\sin\dfrac{\pi}{6}\right)$ in rectangular form. **(Lesson 9-6)** $\dfrac{-5\sqrt{3}}{2} + \dfrac{5}{2}i$

47. Graph the system of inequalities below. **(Lesson 10-7)**
$xy \geq 2$
$x - 3y = 2$ See margin.

48. College Entrance Exam Choose the best answer. B
The area of a square is $49x^2$ in². What is the length of the diagonal of the square?

(A) $7x$ in. **(B)** $7x\sqrt{2}$ in. **(C)** $14x$ in. **(D)** $7x^2$ in. **(E)** $\dfrac{7x}{\sqrt{2}}$ in.

LESSON 10-8 TANGENTS AND NORMALS TO THE CONIC SECTIONS 591

EXTENDING THE LESSON

Math Power: Problem Solving

Find the points of tangency and the equations of the tangents from $\left(0, \dfrac{13}{3}\right)$ to the circle $x^2 + y^2 = 13$.

points of tangency: (2, 3), (–2, 3)

equations: $y = -\dfrac{2}{3}x + \dfrac{13}{3}$

$y = \dfrac{2}{3}x + \dfrac{13}{3}$

Additional Answer

47.

Additional Answers

41a.

43.

44. $(2\sqrt{17} + \sqrt{13})x + (4\sqrt{13} - 3\sqrt{17})y + 9\sqrt{17} + 4\sqrt{13} = 0$

Enrichment Masters Booklet, p. 72

NAME _____ DATE _____

10-8 Enrichment Worksheet

Discriminants and Tangents

The diagram at the right shows that through a point P outside of a circle C, there are lines that do not intersect the circle, lines that intersect the circle in one point (tangents), and lines that intersect the circle in two points (secants).

Given the coordinates for P and an equation for the circle C, how can we find the equation of a line tangent to C that passes through P?

Suppose P has coordinates $P(0, 0)$ and $\odot C$ has equation $(x - 4)^2 + y^2 = 4$. Then a line tangent through P has equation $y = mx$ for some real number m.

Thus, if $T(r, s)$ is a point of tangency, then
$s = mr$ and $(r - 4)^2 + s^2 = 4$.
Therefore, $(r - 4)^2 + (mr)^2 = 4$.
$r^2 - 8r + 16 + m^2r^2 = 4$
$(1 + m^2)r^2 - 8r + 16 = 4$
$(1 + m^2)r^2 - 8r + 12 = 0$

The equation above has exactly one real solution for r if the discriminant is 0, that is, when $(-8)^2 - 4(1 + m^2)(12) = 0$. Solve this equation for m and you will find the slopes of the lines through P that are tangent to circle C.

1. a. Refer to the discussion above. Solve $(-8)^2 - 4(1 + m^2)(12) = 0$ to find the slopes of the two lines tangent to circle C through point P.
$\pm\dfrac{\sqrt{3}}{3}$

b. Use the values of m from part **a** to find the coordinates of the two points of tangency.
$(3, \pm\sqrt{3})$

2. Suppose P has coordinates $(0, 0)$ and circle C has equation $(x + 9)^2 + y^2 = 9$. Let m be the slope of the tangent line to C through P.

a. Find the equations for the lines tangent to circle C through point P.
$y = \pm\dfrac{\sqrt{2}}{4}x$

b. Find the coordinates of the points of tangency.
$(-8, \pm2\sqrt{2})$

T 72
Glencoe Division, Macmillan/McGraw-Hill

Using the Chapter Summary and Review

The Chapter Summary and Review begins with an alphabetical listing of the new terms that were presented in the chapter. Have students define each term and provide an example of it, if appropriate.

The Skills and Concepts presented in the chapter are reviewed using a side-by-side format. Encourage students to refer to the Objectives and Examples on the left as they complete the review exercises on the right.

The Chapter Summary and Review ends with exercises that review Applications and Problem Solving.

Additional Answers

21.

22.

23.

24.

VOCABULARY

Upon completing this chapter, you should be familiar with the following terms:

asymptote **551**	**534** focus
axis **534**	**551** hyperbola
axis of symmetry **534**	**524** locus
center **524**	**543** major axis
circle **524**	**543** minor axis
concentric circles **524**	**589** normal
conic sections **561**	**534** parabola
conjugate axis **551**	**524** radius
degenerate case **561**	**543** semi-major axis
directrix **534**	**543** semi-minor axis
eccentricity **563**	**570** translation matrix
ellipse **542**	**551** transverse axis
equilateral hyperbola **555**	**534** vertex

SKILLS AND CONCEPTS

OBJECTIVES AND EXAMPLES	REVIEW EXERCISES

Upon completing this chapter, you should be able to:

■ graph circles **(Lesson 10-1)**

Graph $(x - 2)^2 + (y + 1)^2 = 8$.

center: $(2, -1)$

radius: $\sqrt{8}$ or $2\sqrt{2}$ units

Use these exercises to review and prepare for the chapter test.

Write the standard form of each equation. Then graph the equation. 1–4. See Teacher's Answer Key for graphs.

1. $3x^2 = 81 - 3y^2$ $x^2 + y^2 = 27$
2. $x^2 = 6y - y^2$ $x^2 + (y - 3)^2 = 9$
3. $x^2 + y + y^2 = 12 - 3x$ $(x + \frac{3}{2})^2 + (y + \frac{1}{2})^2$
4. $x^2 + 14x + y^2 + 6y = 23$ $= \frac{29}{2}$
   4. $(x + 7)^2 + (y + 3)^2 = 81$

■ graph parabolas **(Lesson 10-2)**

Graph $(x + 1)^2 = 2(y - 3)$.

vertex: $(-1, 3)$

focus: $(-1, \frac{7}{2})$

directrix: $y = \frac{5}{2}$

Find the coordinates of the focus and vertex and the equation of the directrix of each parabola whose equation is given. Then graph the equation. 5–8. See Teacher's Answer Key.

5. $(x - 7)^2 = 8(y - 3)$
6. $(y + 4)^2 = -16(x - 1)$
7. $y^2 + 6y - 4x + 25 = 0$
8. $x^2 + 4x - y + 8 = 0$

OBJECTIVES AND EXAMPLES

- graph ellipses **(Lesson 10-3)**

Graph $\dfrac{(x+1)^2}{16} + \dfrac{(y-3)^2}{4} = 1$.

center: $(-1, 3)$

foci:
$(-1 + 2\sqrt{3}, 3)$,
$(-1 + 2\sqrt{3}, 3)$

vertices:
$(3, 3), (-5, 3)$,
$(-1, 5), (-1, 1)$

- graph hyperbolas **(Lesson 10-4)**

Graph $\dfrac{(y-2)^2}{4} - (x-5)^2 = 1$.

center: $(5, 2)$

foci:
$(5, 2 + \sqrt{5})$
$(5, 2 - \sqrt{5})$

vertices:
$(5, 4)$,
$(5, 0)$

asymptotes: $y - 2 = \pm\dfrac{1}{2}(x - 5)$

- recognize conic sections by their equations **(Lesson 10-5)**

Identify the conic section represented by $3x^2 - 5x - y + 1 = 0$.

There is only one squared term. The conic is a parabola.

For equations and graphs for Exercises 17–20, see Teacher's Answer Key.

- find the equations of conic sections that have been translated or rotated **(Lesson 10-6)** 21–24. See margin for graphs.

Write the equation of the parabola $y = 2(x - 1)^2$ for $T_{(-2, 4)}$.

The vertex of $y = 2(x - 1)^2$ is at $(1, 0)$.

$$\begin{bmatrix} 1 \\ 0 \end{bmatrix} + \begin{bmatrix} -2 \\ 4 \end{bmatrix} = \begin{bmatrix} -1 \\ 4 \end{bmatrix}$$

The vertex of the translated parabola is at $(-1, 4)$. The equation of the translated parabola is $(y - 4) = 2(x + 1)^2$.

REVIEW EXERCISES

For each equation, find the coordinates of the center, foci, and vertices of the ellipse. Then graph the equation.

9. $\dfrac{(x-3)^2}{25} + \dfrac{(y+1)^2}{4} = 1$

10. $\dfrac{(x-5)^2}{16} + \dfrac{(y-2)^2}{36} = 1$

11. $(x-4)^2 + 4(y-6)^2 = 36$

12. $3(x+3)^2 + 2(y-4)^2 = 12$

9–12. See Teacher's Answer Key.

Find the coordinates of the center, foci, and vertices and the equations of the asymptotes of the graph of each equation. Then graph the equation.

13. $x^2 - \dfrac{y^2}{2} = 4$

14. $2(x+5)^2 - (y-1)^2 = 8$

15. $y^2 - 5x^2 + 20x = 50$

16. $9x^2 - 16y^2 - 36x + 96y + 36 = 0$

13–16. See Teacher's Answer Key.

Identify the conic section represented by each equation. Write the equation in standard form and graph the equation.

17. $4x^2 - 8x + y^2 = 12$ ellipse

18. $xy = 0$ degenerate hyperbola

19. $2(x-4)^2 = -2(y-1)^2 + 8$ circle

20. $x^2 - 6y - 8x + 16 = 0$ parabola

Write the equation of each translated or rotated graph below. Then graph the equation. 21. $(x+3)^2 + (y-2)^2 = 3$

21. $x^2 + y^2 = 3$ for $T_{(-3,2)}$

22. $4x^2 - 16(y-1)^2 = 64$ for $T_{(1,-2)}$

23. $4x^2 + 9y^2 = 36$, $\theta = \dfrac{\pi}{6}$

24. $y^2 - 4x = 0$, $\theta = 45°$

22. $(x-1)^2 - 4(y+1)^2 = 16$

23. $21x^2 - 10\sqrt{3}xy + 31y^2 = 144$

24. $\dfrac{1}{2}x^2 - xy + \dfrac{1}{2}y^2 - 3\sqrt{2}x - \sqrt{2}y + 7 = 0$

Alternative Review Strategy

To provide a brief in-class review, you may wish to read the following questions to your students and have them answer verbally.

1. State the center and radius of the circle with equation $(x - 2)^2 + (y + 5)^2 = 4$.
   (2, –5); 2 units

2. Find the vertex and focus of the parabola with equation $y^2 - 4x - 4y - 8 = 0$.
   (–3, 2); (–2, 2)

3. Find the lengths of the major and minor axes of the ellipse with equation $\dfrac{(x-3)^2}{25} + \dfrac{(y+4)^2}{16} = 1$.
   10; 8

4. Find the center of the ellipse with equation $4x^2 + 9y^2 + 16x - 18y - 11 = 0$.
   (–2, 1)

5. In which quadrant(s) does the graph of $xy = -16$ lie? **II and IV**

6. Find the equations of the asymptotes of the hyperbola with equation $\dfrac{x^2}{64} - \dfrac{y^2}{25} = 1$.
   $y = \pm\dfrac{5}{8}x$

7. Identify the conic section with an eccentricity of 1.
   parabola

8. Identify the graph of the equation $5x^2 + 6xy + y^2 - 3x + y + 2 = 0$.
   hyperbola

9. Find the angle of rotation about the origin for the graph in Exercise 8.
   about 28°

10. Solve the system of equations.
    $x + y^2 = 4$
    $x^2 - y^2 = 16$
    (4, 0), (–5, –3), (–5, 3)

For more information on other methods of alternate assessment, you may wish to refer to Glencoe's *Alternate Assessment in the Mathematics Classroom*.

Two multiple-choice tests (Forms 1A and 1B) and two free-response tests (Forms 2A and 2B) are provided in the *Evaluation Masters*. Chapter 10 Test, Form 1A is shown below. Chapter 10 Test, Form 2A is shown on the next page.

Evaluation Masters Booklet, pp. 117–118

OBJECTIVES AND EXAMPLES	REVIEW EXERCISES

- graph and solve systems of second-degree equations and inequalities   **(Lesson 10-7)**

Graph the system of equations. Then solve.

$y = x^2 + 1$
$3y^2 = x^2 + 11$

$$
\begin{array}{r}
x^2 \quad\;\; - y \; + 1 = 0 \\
-x^2 + 3y^2 \quad\;\; - 11 = 0 \\
\hline
3y^2 - y - 10 = 0
\end{array}
$$

So, $y = -\dfrac{5}{3}$ or $y = 2$.

Substituting the values for y in one of the original equations, the solutions are $(1, 2)$ and $(-1, 2)$.

Graph each system of equations. Then solve.

25. $(x - 1)^2 + 4(y - 1)^2 = 20$
    $x = y$ $(3, 3), (-1, -1)$

26. $x^2 - 4x - 4y - 4 = 0$
    $(x - 2)^2 = -4y$ $(0, -1), (4, -1)$

Graph each system of inequalities.

27. $y \geq x^2 + 4$
    $x^2 + y^2 < 49$

28. $x^2 + (y - 2)^2 \geq 0$
    $x^2 + 9(y - 2)^2 \leq 9$

For graphs for Exercises 25–28, see Teacher's Answer Key.

- write equations of tangents and normals to conic sections   **(Lesson 10-8)**

Find the equation of the line tangent to the graph of $4x^2 + y^2 = 4$ at $(0.5, 2)$.

$$m = \frac{-b^2(x - h)}{a^2(y - k)}$$

$$= \frac{-4(0.5 - 0)}{1(2 - 0)} \text{ or } -1$$

The equation of the tangent line is

$y - 2 = -1\left(x - \dfrac{1}{2}\right)$ or $2x + 2y - 5 = 0$.

Find the equations of the tangent and the normal to the graphs of each equation at the given point. Write the equations in standard form.   29. $x = 1, y = 1$

29. $x^2 - 4y^2 + 2x + 8y - 7 = 0, (1, 1)$

30. $4x^2 - 9y^2 = 36, (6, 2\sqrt{3})$

31. $y = -4(x + 1)^2, (-2, -4)$

32. $9x^2 + 25y^2 = 225, \left(4, \dfrac{9}{5}\right)$

30. $4x - 3\sqrt{3}y - 6 = 0, 9x + 4\sqrt{3}y - 78 = 0$
31. $8x - y + 12 = 0, x + 8y + 34 = 0$
32. $4x + 5y - 25 = 0, 25x - 20y - 64 = 0$

34. $\dfrac{x^2}{36,000,000} + \dfrac{y^2}{34,560,000} = 1$

APPLICATIONS AND PROBLEM SOLVING

33. **Construction** Ms. Lopez, a construction worker, is building a bay window in the shape of a semi-ellipse for a new home. The width of the window is to be 5 feet and its depth is to be 2 feet. To sketch the arch of the bay window, Ms. Lopez uses a 5-foot string attached to two thumbtacks. Where should the thumbtacks be placed? *Hint: The thumbtacks are at the foci.* **(Lesson 10-3)** 1.5 feet from the center

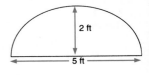

34. **Astronomy** A satellite orbiting Earth follows an elliptical path with Earth at its center. The eccentricity of the orbit is 0.2, and the major axis is 12,000 miles long. Assuming that the center of the ellipse is the origin and the foci lie on the x-axis, write the equation of the orbit of the satellite. **(Lesson 10-5)**

Identify the conic section represented by each equation. Write the equation in standard form and graph the equation. For equations and graphs for Exercises 1–8, see Teacher's Answer Key.

1. $(x+3)^2 = 8(y+2)$ parabola

2. $4x^2 - y^2 = 0$ degenerate hyperbola

3. $2x^2 - 13y^2 + 5 = 0$ hyperbola

4. $16(x-3)^2 + 81(y+4)^2 = 1296$ ellipse

5. $y^2 - 2x + 10y + 27 = 0$ parabola

6. $(x-4)^2 - 9(y-5)^2 = 36$ hyperbola

7. $x^2 + 2y^2 + 2x - 12y + 11 = 0$ ellipse

8. $x^2 + 4x = -(y^2 - 6)$ circle
   9. $(x+8)^2 + (y-3)^2 = 53$

9. Write the equation of the circle with center at (-8, 3) that passes through (-6, -4).

10. Write the equation of the parabola that has a focus at (3, -5) and whose equation of directrix is $y = -2$. $(x-3)^2 = -6\left(y + \frac{7}{2}\right)$

11. Write the equation of an ellipse centered at the origin that has a horizontal major axis, $e = \frac{1}{2}$, and $2c = 1$. $x^2 + \frac{4y^2}{3} = 1$

12. Write the equation of the hyperbola that has eccentricity $\frac{3}{2}$ and foci at (-5, -2) and (-5, 4). $\frac{(y-1)^2}{4} - \frac{(x+5)^2}{5} = 1$

Write the equation of each translated or rotated graph below. Then graph the equation. For graphs for Exercises 13–14, see Teacher's Answer Key.

13. $4(x+1)^2 + (y-3)^2 = 36$ for $T_{(3,-5)}$
    $4(x-2)^2 + (y+2)^2 = 36$

14. $2x^2 - y^2 = 8, \theta = 60°$
    $-x^2 + 6\sqrt{3}xy + 5y^2 = 32$

15. Graph the system of equations. Then solve.
    $x^2 + 4y^2 = 4$
    $(x-1)^2 + y^2 = 1$ $(2, 0), \left(\frac{2}{3}, \frac{2\sqrt{2}}{3}\right), \left(\frac{2}{3}, -\frac{2\sqrt{2}}{3}\right)$

16. Graph the system of inequalities. For graphs for Exercises 15–16, see Teacher's Answer Key.
    $x^2 + y^2 - 2x - 4y + 1 \geq 0$
    $x^2 - 4y - 2x + 5 \geq 0$

Find the equations of the tangent and the normal to the graphs of each equation at the given point. Write the equations in standard form.

17. $x^2 + y^2 + 6x - 10y = 0, (2, 1)$
    $4y - 5x + 6 = 0, 5y + 4x - 13 = 0$

18. $16x^2 - y^2 - 4y - 20 = 0, (\sqrt{2}, 2)$
    $4\sqrt{2}x - y - 6 = 0, \sqrt{2}x + 8y - 18 = 0$

19. **Geometry** The diameter of a circle has endpoints at (-2, 3) and (4, 5). Find the equation for the circle. $(x-1)^2 + (y-4)^2 = 10$

20. **Technology** Mr. Wilson bought a motion detector light and installed it in the center of his backyard. It can detect motion within a circle defined by the equation $x^2 + y^2 = 90$. If a person walks northeast through the backyard along a line defined by the equation $y = 2x - 3$, at what point will the motion detector light turn on? $(-3, -9)$

Bonus
If the graph of the circle $x^2 + y^2 = k$ is tangent to the graph of the line $x + y = 2k$ where k is positive, find the value of k. $\frac{1}{2}$

This page may be used as a test or as a review. All answers to this test appear in the Selected Answers in the student text.

Standardized Test Questions are also provided in the *Evaluation Masters.*

Evaluation Masters Booklet, pp. 121–122

Test Generator Software is provided in Apple, IBM, and Macintosh versions. You may use this software to create your own tests, based on the needs of your students.

CHAPTER 11 EXPONENTIAL AND LOGARITHMIC FUNCTIONS

PREVIEWING THE CHAPTER

This chapter reviews the properties of integral exponents and extends them to rational and irrational exponents. Students graph exponential functions and inequalities and learn to use the exponential function $y = e^x$. The properties of logarithms are deduced using the properties of exponents. After graphing logarithmic functions and inequalities, students find common logarithms and antilogarithms of numbers. They also use common logarithms to compute powers and roots. Students solve exponential and logarithmic equations and inequalities. Finally, they find natural logarithms of numbers and solve equations involving natural logarithms.

Lesson Objective Chart

Lesson (Pages)	Lesson Objectives	State/Local Objectives
11-1 (598-604)	**11-1A:** Use the properties of exponents.	
	11-1B: Evaluate and simplify expressions containing rational exponents.	
11-2 (606-613)	**11-2A:** Evaluate expressions with irrational exponents.	
	11-2B: Graph exponential functions.	
	11-2C: Graph exponential inequalities.	
11-3 (614-619)	**11-3:** Use the exponential function $y = e^x$.	
11-4 (622-628)	**11-4A:** Evaluate expressions involving logarithms.	
	11-4B: Solve equations involving logarithms.	
	11-4C: Graph logarithmic functions and inequalities.	
11-5 (629-633)	**11-5A:** Find common logarithms and antilogarithms of numbers.	
	11-5B: Use common logarithms to compute powers and roots.	
11-6 (636-640)	**11-6A:** Solve exponential and logarithmic equations.	
	11-6B: Solve exponential and logarithmic inequalities.	
11-7 (641-645)	**11-7A:** Find natural logarithms of numbers.	
	11-7B: Solve equations using natural logarithms.	

ORGANIZING THE CHAPTER

You may want to refer to the **Course Planning Guide Calendar** on pages T34-T35 for a complete pacing chart.

Lesson Planning Guide / Blackline Masters Booklets

Lesson	Pages	Practice	Enrichment	Evaluation	Graphing Calculator	Computer	Multicultural Activity	Applications	Problem Solving	Case Study Follow-Up	Decision Making	Transparencies
11-1	598-604	p. 73.	p. 73					p. 31				11-1
11-2	606-613	p. 74	p. 74	Quiz A, p. 137		p. 22						11-2
11-3	614-619	p. 75	p. 75									11-3
11-4	622-628	p. 76	p. 76	Quiz B, p. 137 Mid-Chapter Test, p.139	p. 21							11-4
11-5	629-633	p. 77	p. 77						p. 32			11-5
11-6	636-640	p. 78	p. 78	Quiz C, p. 138		p. 11						11-6
11-7	641-645	p. 79	p. 79	Quiz D, p. 138						p. 33		11-7
Review	646-648	Multiple Choice Tests, Forms 1A and 1B, pp. 129-132										
Test	649	Free Response Tests, Forms 2A and 2B, pp. 133-136 Standardized Test Questions, p. 140										

Other Chapter Resources

Student Edition

Case Study Follow-Up, p. 619
Decision Making, p. 604
Technology, p. 620
Unit Review, pp. 650-651

Other Supplements

Transparency 11-0 for Chapter Opener
Evaluation Masters, Unit Test, pp. 141-144
Alternate Assessment in the Mathematics Classroom,
    Glencoe Publishing Co., 1993
Cooperative Learning in the Mathematics Classroom,
    Glencoe Publishing Co., 1993

Software

Test and Review Generator Software
Available for Apple, IBM, and Macintosh
Teacher's Guide for Software Resources

ENHANCING THE CHAPTER

Cooperative Learning

Establishing Individual Accountability

It is important for the success of a cooperative-learning session that students recognize their individual responsibility to the whole group. Not only is it unfair when only a few members of the group do all the work, it is contrary to the purpose of a cooperative-learning group; that is, to enhance the learning of each and every member. One way to encourage every-member participation is to make positive and rewarding comments about the members' contributions to the group. Another way is to evaluate the performance of each member of the group. Some tactics that can be used are to ask a reluctant participant to paraphrase what another member has just said, to ask a member if they agree with a statement just made by another member, and to say at the outset that you will randomly select a member from the group to explain the group's answers. Since the members of a group quickly observe who is a participant and who is not, another successful tactic is to assign the role of *encourager* to one of the members of the group. This student's main responsibility is to encourage each and every member of the group to participate.

For more information on cooperative learning, see pages T20-T21. Additional information on using cooperative groups is available in Glencoe's *Cooperative Learning in the Mathematics Classroom*, ©1993.

Multicultural

Multicultural Activity Masters, p. 11

NAME _____ DATE _____

11 Multicultural Activity (Use after Lesson 11-6)

Radioactive Decay

Marie Skłodowska was a Polish-born chemist who married French chemist Pierre Curie in 1895. She became interested in measuring and analyzing the radiation given off by uranium during the course of some of his experiments. Marie and Pierre Curie collaborated in the investigation of radioactivity for the next decade. They received a Nobel Prize for their work in 1903. After Pierre's death, Marie Curie continued her research of polonium (named after her native Poland) and radium.

Radioactive materials contain unstable isotopes that emit rays and particles in the process of radioactive decay. The amount of time it takes for the unstable isotopes to change to more stable forms is measured in terms of **half-lifes**. The half-life of a radioactive isotope is the amount of time required for one half of any initial quantity to decay.

1. The hydrogen isotope tritium is radioactive, with a half-life of 12.5 years. How much of a 1-gram sample of this isotope remains after 25 years?
   0.25 gram

2. It takes 45 hours for $\frac{7}{8}$ of a highly radioactive sodium isotope to decay. What is the half-life of this isotope?
   15 hours

3. Radiocarbon has a half-life of 5600 years. If a piece of excavated wood has $\frac{1}{4}$ the relative radiocarbon as a newly-cut piece of the same kind of wood, how old is the excavated wood?
   11,200 years

4. Suppose that the radiocarbon found in a fossil bone is $\frac{1}{16}$ of that found in living bone tissue. How old is the fossil bone?
   22,400 years

5. **Research** Look up Marie and Pierre Curie in a reference work and write a report on one or both of them.
   See students' reports.

T11
Glencoe Division, Macmillan/McGraw-Hill

Activity Masters

Applications, p. 31

CHAPTER NAME _____ DATE _____

11 Applications (Use after Lesson 11-1)

Doubling

According to an article by Thomas H. McMahon in the July 1975 issue of *Scientific American*, the height of a tree varies directly with the $\frac{2}{3}$ power of the radius of the trunk at its base ($h = kr^{\frac{2}{3}}$ where k is a constant). Suppose you own a stand of trees that can be used for making paper. The amount of wood pulp and, therefore, the value of the trees should be proportional to the volume of the trees. If we approximate a tree without its branches as a right circular cone, the formula for the volume of the tree is $\frac{1}{3}\pi r^2 h = \frac{1}{3}\pi r^2(kr^{\frac{2}{3}})$ or $\frac{1}{3}\pi kr^{\frac{8}{3}}$.

If the trees on your land have radii of 3 inches and increase in radius one-fourth inch per year, it is possible to find the number of years it would take for the value of the trees to double.

volume of one tree now $= \frac{1}{3}\pi k(3)^{\frac{8}{3}} = \frac{1}{3}\pi k\left(3 + \frac{1}{4} \cdot 0\right)^{\frac{8}{3}}$

volume of one tree after 1 year $= \frac{1}{3}\pi k\left(3 + \frac{1}{4} \cdot 1\right)^{\frac{8}{3}}$

volume of one tree after y years $= \frac{1}{3}\pi k\left(3 + \frac{1}{4} \cdot y\right)^{\frac{8}{3}}$

We want the volume to double: 2(present volume) $= 2 \cdot \frac{1}{3}\pi k \cdot 3^{\frac{8}{3}}$.

Therefore, we are looking for the value of y that makes the following equation true.
$2 \cdot \frac{1}{3}\pi k \cdot 3^{\frac{8}{3}} = \frac{1}{3}\pi k\left(3 + \frac{1}{4}y\right)^{\frac{8}{3}}$ or $2 \cdot \frac{1}{3}\pi k \cdot \sqrt[3]{3^8} = \frac{1}{3}\pi k\sqrt[3]{\left(3 + \frac{1}{4}y\right)^8}$

Solve.

1. Solve this equation for y, showing all work. Give a decimal approximation to the nearest tenth of a year. $y = 3.6$.

2. According to the Rule of 72, an investment at $p\%$ takes about $\frac{72}{p}$ years to double. In Exercise 1, what percent are you making on your investment? $3.6 = \frac{72}{p}$; 20%

3. Generalize the situation in Exercise 1. Let:
   $m = $ the number of times you want the value to increase (in Exercise 1, $m = 2$),
   $r = $ the initial radius in inches (in Exercise 1, $r = 3$), and
   $n = $ the number of inches the radius increases per year $\left(\text{in Exercise 1, } n = \frac{1}{4}\right)$.
   Derive the following formula: $y = \frac{r}{n}(m^{\frac{3}{8}} - 1)$.
   $m \cdot \frac{1}{3}\pi k \cdot r^{\frac{8}{3}} = \frac{1}{3}\pi k(r + ny)^{\frac{8}{3}}$; $mr^{\frac{8}{3}} = (r + ny)^{\frac{8}{3}}$;
   $\left[mr^{\frac{8}{3}}\right]^{\frac{3}{8}} = \left[(r + ny)^{\frac{8}{3}}\right]^{\frac{3}{8}}$; $m^{\frac{3}{8}}r = r + ny$; $\frac{r}{n}(m^{\frac{3}{8}} - 1) = y$

T31
Glencoe Division, Macmillan/McGraw-Hill

Problem Solving, p. 32

CHAPTER NAME _____ DATE _____

11 Problem Solving (Use after Lesson 11-4)

Working Backward

Often you can evaluate logarithmic and exponential expressions by assuming that you know their values, then working backward to find them.

Example Evaluate $\log_{\frac{8}{27}} \frac{81}{16}$.

Assume that the expression is equal to x. $\log_{\frac{8}{27}} \frac{81}{16} = x$

Rewrite the expression in exponential form. $\left(\frac{8}{27}\right)^x = \frac{81}{16}$

Express both sides of the equation using equal bases. $\left(\left[\frac{2}{3}\right]^3\right)^x = \left(\frac{2}{3}\right)^4$

Solve using the property of equality for exponential functions. $3x = -4$

$x = -\frac{4}{3}$

Evaluate each expression.

1. $\log_2 64$ **6**

2. $\log_{81} 27$ $\frac{3}{4}$

3. $\log_{\frac{9}{4}} \frac{2}{3}$ $\frac{1}{2}$

4. $\log_{\frac{25}{4}} \frac{16}{625}$ -2

5. $10^{\log_{10} 7}$ **7**

6. $\log_{10} \sqrt{0.01}$ $-\frac{2}{3}$

7. $\log_3 \frac{1}{27}$ -3

8. $4^{5\log_4 2}$ **32**

T32
Glencoe Division, Macmillan/McGraw-Hill

Case Study Follow-Up, p. 33

CHAPTER NAME _____ DATE _____

11 Case Study Follow-Up (Use after Lesson 11-7)

Growth in Crime

Refer to Case Study 3: *The Legal System*, on pages 962-965 in your textbook.

In order to use the formula $y = ne^{kt}$ to find the size of a population after t years, you must know y, the final population, and n, the initial population. Suppose you do not know the initial population but that you know p, the percent increase in population n that led to final population y. Statistics are often given in this way. Case Study 3, for example, states that the number of forcible rapes in the United States increased 24.3% from 1981 to 1990, and that 102,560 forcible rapes were committed in 1990. In order to calculate the number of forcible rapes that might be committed in some future year, you could find the number committed in 1981 and use the population-growth formula unchanged. But a slight adaptation of the formula may make your work easier.

initial population $= n$
final population $= y$
percent increase in population: $p = 100\left(\frac{y - n}{n}\right)$

$\frac{p}{100} = \frac{y}{n} - 1$

$\frac{p}{100} + 1 = \frac{y}{n}$

$y = ne^{kt}$

$\frac{y}{n} = e^{kt}$

$\frac{p}{100} + 1 = e^{kt}$

This formula allows you to calculate k using p, the percent increase in a population over a period of time t.

1. Assume that crime growth can be modeled using an exponential equation. Round answers to the nearest 10,000.
   a. The population of the United States was 248.7 million in 1990. Find the number of prisoners in the United States in 1990. **1,060,000**
   b. Between 1980 and 1990, the prison population of the United States increased 134%. In what year would you expect the number of prisoners to surpass 2 million? **1997**
   c. Find the expected prison population in 2010. **5,800,000**

2. Find the number of violent crimes that can be expected in 2000.
   2,510,000

T33
Glencoe Division, Macmillan/McGraw-Hill

Technology

The Technology feature preceding Lesson 11-3 demonstrates how to use a spreadsheet to calculate compound interest and account balance. Throughout this chapter, a scientific calculator is used for computations with exponents and logarithms.

Lesson 11-2A introduces graphing exponential functions. The Exploration in Lesson 11-2 uses the TRACE function to locate the coordinates of specific points on the graph of an exponential function. The graphing calculator program in this lesson calculates loan payments. Lesson 11-4A introduces students to graphing logarithmic functions on the graphing calculator. Lesson 11-6A demonstrates how to solve exponential and logarithmic equations and inequalities with a graphing calculator. These skills are used in Lesson 11-6 to check the accuracy of students' solutions.

Graphing Calculator Exercises, pp. 617, 639
Graphing Calculator Program, p. 612

Outside Resources

Books/Periodicals

Klopfenstein, Kenneth F. *Exponential and Logarithmic Functions,* Davies and Associates, Aurora, CO, 1991.

Barrett, Gloria, and John Goebbel. "The Impact of Graphing Calculators on the Teaching and Learning of Mathematics," *1990 NCTM Yearbook: Teaching and Learning Mathematics in the 1990's.* NCTM, Reston, VA, 1990, pp. 205-211.

Films/Videotapes/Videodiscs

Mathematics and Music, Public Television Library

Powers and Roots, TPC Training Systems

Software

Graphing utilities *(see list on page T25)*

Technology Masters

Graphing Calculator, p. 21

Computer, p. 22

CHAPTER 11

EXPONENTIAL AND LOGARITHMIC FUNCTIONS

HISTORICAL SNAPSHOT

	The sandwich John Montagu, 4th Earl of Sandwich, England		Canned food Bryan Donkin United Kingdom		McDonald's Hamburgers founded in Pasadena, California	
Logarithms John Napier Scotland		Number theory Sophie Germain Paris, France		Frozen food Clarence Birdseye Massachusetts		Established Dept. of Food Science and Technology Colorado State University
AD 1614	1762	1801	1812	1923	1948	1985

596

two liquids at a time, the students should try to discover a rule or rules for what the pH of a mixture will be. They should try to discover a rule that works for combinations of a particular pair of liquids. Each group should report its results to the class.

CHAPTER OBJECTIVES

In this chapter, you will:

- Use the properties of exponents and logarithms.
- Solve equations by using the properties of exponents and logarithms.
- Graph exponential and logarithmic functions.

CAREER GOAL: Food Management

Sometimes inspiration can come from unexpected places. Hernan Rodriguez-Palacios's brother is a chef who has studied in Paris. As a result, he has always had an interest in food. His career goal, however, is much different from that of his brother. Hernan would like to own and operate a brewery some day.

Hernan's interest may seem narrow, but his training is preparing him for a number of different careers. "Food science and technology includes a broad spectrum of career opportunities," Hernan says. "These include food production, handling, processing, distribution, marketing, preservation, and consumption." Hernan's main interest is fermentation. He says, "The process of fermentation is involved in a wide spectrum of foods as well as in the production of antibiotics and alcohol fuels."

Food scientists use logarithms to determine the *pH balance* of foods. The pH balance is a measure of the basicity or acidity of a solution. A pH value of 7 is considered to be neutral, while a pH value below 7 indicates an acid and a pH value above 7 indicates a base. Each pH unit represents a factor of 10. So lemon juice, which has a pH balance of 2, is 10^{4-2}, or 100, times more acidic than tomato juice, which has a pH balance of 4.

While food has been around a long time, Hernan says, "Food science and technology is a very young field of study. A person has the opportunity to select from so many unanswered questions and investigate one or more that are of special interest. There are still many unsolved questions to explore."

READ MORE ABOUT IT

Ammerman, Gale R. *Your Future in Food Technology Careers.* New York: Richards Rosen Press, Inc., 1975.

Birch, G.G. *Food for the Nineties.* New York: Elsevier Science Publishing Co. Inc., 1990.

Van Den Brul, Caroline and Susan Spindler. *Tomorrow's World: Food.* New York: Parkwest Publications, Inc., 1986.

SPOTLIGHT ON...

Hernan Rodriguez-Palacios
Age: 26
Class: Junior
School: Colorado State University
Fort Collins, Colorado
Major: Food Technology

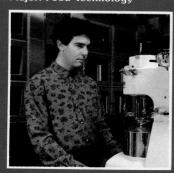

"Food science and technology is a very young field of study—there are still many unsolved questions to explore."

FOR MORE INFORMATION

If you would like more information about food science and technology, contact:

Institute of Food Technologists
221 North LaSalle Street
Chicago, IL 60601

Applications

Lesson	Application	Examples	Exercises
11-1	Anatomy	1	
	Architecture		54
	Aerospace		55
	Chemistry		56
11-2	Finance	4, 5	
	Banking		39, 41
	Entertainment		40
	Financial		
	Planning		42
	Construction		43
11-3	Physics	2	
	Psychology	3	
	Engineering		29
	Chemistry		30
	Finance		31
	Forestry		32
	Political		
	Science		33
	Medicine		34
	Biology		35
	Banking		36
11-4	Biology	3	62, 63
11-5	Psychology	2	
	Chemistry	3	
	Astronomy		40
	Geology		41
11-6	Archeology	2	
	Biology	3	
	Accounting		42
	Chemistry		43
	Sales		44
11-7	Demographics	1	
	Linguistics	2	
	Chemistry		31
	Banking		32
	Ecology		33
	Sales		34
	Finance		35
	Meteorology		36
	Business		37
	Sociology		38
	Medicine		39

NCTM Standards: 1–5, 14

Lesson Resources

- Practice Master 11–1
- Enrichment Master 11–1
- Activity Master, p. 31

  Transparency 11–1 contains the 5-Minute Check and a teaching aid for this lesson.

INTRODUCING THE LESSON

5-Minute Check

(over Chapter 10)

1. Write the equation for the ellipse having its center at (–2, 3), a major axis of length 10, and a minor axis of length 8, if its major axis is parallel to the y-axis.
$$\frac{(x+2)^2}{16} + \frac{(y-3)^2}{25} = 1$$

Identify the conic section represented by each equation. Write the equation in standard form and graph the equation.

2. $x^2 + y^2 - 2x - 8 = 0$
circle; $(x-1)^2 + y^2 = 9$

3. $9x^2 - 4y^2 + 36x + 8y - 4 = 0$
hyperbola; $\frac{(x+2)^2}{4} - \frac{(y-1)^2}{9} = 1$

4. Find the points of intersection of the circle $x^2 + y^2 = 25$ and the parabola $y = x^2 - 5$.
(0, –5), (3, 4), (–3, 4)

11-1 Rational Exponents

Objectives

After studying this lesson, you should be able to:

11–1A ■ use the properties of exponents, and

11–1B ■ evaluate and simplify expressions containing rational exponents.

Application

In your studies of biology, chemistry, and physics, you sometimes have to use very large numbers like Avogadro's number, 602,205,000,000,000,000,000,000, or the mass of Earth, 5,980,000,000,000,000,000,000,000 kg. Other times you must use very small numbers like Newton's universal gravitational constant, 0.0000000000667, or the diameter of a red blood cell, 0.000000775 m. Working with these numbers is a problem if your calculator displays less than ten digits. Expressing these numbers in **scientific notation** allows you to work with them more easily. A number is in scientific notation when it is in the form $a \times 10^n$, where $1 \le a < 10$ and n is an integer. Written in scientific notation, Avogadro's number is 6.02205×10^{23} and Newton's constant is 6.67×10^{-11}.

Working with numbers in scientific notation requires a knowledge of the definitions and properties of integral exponents. For any real number x and a positive integer n, the following definitions hold.

Definition	**Example**
If $n = 1$, $x^n = x$.	$5^1 = 5$
If $n > 1$, $x^n = \overbrace{x \cdot x \cdot x \cdots x}^{n \text{ factors}}$.	$3^3 = 3 \cdot 3 \cdot 3$ or 27
If $x \ne 0$, $x^0 = 1$.	$6^0 = 1$
If $x \ne 0$, $x^{-n} = \frac{1}{x^n}$.	$2^{-4} = \frac{1}{2^4}$ or $\frac{1}{16}$

These definitions can be used to verify the properties of exponents for positive integers m and n and real numbers a and b.

Properties of Exponents

Suppose m and n are positive integers, and a and b are real numbers. Then the following properties hold.

Product property:	$a^m a^n = a^{m+n}$
Power of a power property:	$(a^m)^n = a^{mn}$
Power of a quotient property:	$\left(\frac{a}{b}\right)^m = \frac{a^m}{b^m}$, where $b \ne 0$
Power of a product property:	$(ab)^m = a^m b^m$
Quotient property:	$\frac{a^m}{a^n} = a^{m-n}$, where $a \ne 0$

ALTERNATE TEACHING STRATEGIES

Using Logical Reasoning

Challenge students to use the properties of exponents to find a number x such that $2^x \cdot 2^x = 2$. Next, have them find a number y such that $3^y \cdot 3^y \cdot 3^y = 3$. After a few more such examples, they should recognize the general rule,
$$a^{\frac{1}{n}} = \sqrt[n]{a}.$$

Using Cooperative Groups

Assign each group of students one of the properties of exponents and have them first show two or three specific examples of how it is used and then show how the property can be derived from the definitions of exponents.

Example 1

APPLICATION

Anatomy

FYI...

Red blood cells make up 44% of your blood. They are produced at the rate of 2.3 million per second by the red bone marrow of your long bones.

Red blood cells are circular-shaped cells that carry oxygen through your bloodstream. The diameter of a red blood cell is about 7.75×10^{-7} m. Find the area of one of these cells. Express your answer in scientific notation.

The radius of a circle is one-half its diameter. Thus, $r = \dfrac{7.75 \times 10^{-7}}{2}$ or 3.875×10^{-7} m.

$$A = \pi r^2 \qquad \textit{Formula for the area of a circle}$$
$$= \pi(3.875 \times 10^{-7})^2 \qquad r = 3.875 \times 10^{-7}$$
$$= \pi(3.875)^2(10^{-7})^2 \qquad \textit{Properties of exponents}$$
$$= \pi(3.875)^2(10^{-14})$$

Use a calculator to evaluate. The calculator will give the solution in scientific notation if the number has more than eight digits.

[2nd] [π] [$\times$] 3.875 [x²] [$\times$] 10 [yˣ] 14 [+/-] [=] ᴴ.ᴵ˥²ᑫ˥˥ᑫ − ᴵᴈ

The area of the blood cell is about 4.72×10^{-13} m².

Expressions with rational exponents can be defined so that the properties of integral exponents are still valid. Consider the expressions $2^{\frac{1}{2}}$ and $9^{\frac{1}{3}}$. Extending the laws for integral exponents gives us the following equations.

$$2^{\frac{1}{2}} \cdot 2^{\frac{1}{2}} = 2^{\frac{1}{2} + \frac{1}{2}}$$
$$= 2^1 \text{ or } 2$$

We know that, by definition, $\sqrt{2} \cdot \sqrt{2} = 2$. Therefore, it makes sense to define $2^{\frac{1}{2}}$ as $\sqrt{2}$.

$$9^{\frac{1}{3}} \cdot 9^{\frac{1}{3}} \cdot 9^{\frac{1}{3}} = 9^{\frac{1}{3} + \frac{1}{3} + \frac{1}{3}}$$
$$= 9^1 \text{ or } 9$$

But $\sqrt[3]{9} \cdot \sqrt[3]{9} \cdot \sqrt[3]{9} = 9$. So, it makes sense to define $9^{\frac{1}{3}}$ as $\sqrt[3]{9}$.

In general, let $y = b^{\frac{1}{n}}$ for a real number b and a positive integer n. Then, $y^n = (b^{\frac{1}{n}})^n = b^{\frac{n}{n}}$ or b. But $y^n = b$ if and only if $y = \sqrt[n]{b}$. Therefore, we can define $b^{\frac{1}{n}}$ as follows.

Definition of $b^{\frac{1}{n}}$

For any real number $b \geq 0$ and any integer $n > 1$,
$$b^{\frac{1}{n}} = \sqrt[n]{b}.$$
This also holds when $b < 0$ and n is odd.

Why is this definition not valid if $b < 0$ and n is even?

LESSON 11-1 RATIONAL EXPONENTS 599

Prerequisite Skills

Some students may benefit from a quick review of scientific notation.

Write the following expressions in scientific notation.
1. 93,000,000 9.3×10^7
2. 0.0000000305 3.05×10^{-8}

Write each expression below in decimal notation.
3. 1.3×10^5 130,000
4. 9.908×10^{-6} 0.000009908

Motivating the Lesson

There is a famous story about a man offered any reward he wished to name by his king. The reward he requested was one grain of wheat for the first square on a chess board, two grains of wheat for the second square, four for the third square, and so on. How many grains of wheat would he have received if the king met his request? Collect answers from students. They will involve the use of scientific notation. The answer is more wheat than existed in the whole kingdom, $2^{64} - 1$, about 1.845×10^{19} grains.

APPLYING THE LESSON

Teaching Tip   When introducing the properties of exponents, point out the distinction between the first, which is the product of m factors of a with n factors of a, and the second, which is the product of n groups of m factors of a each.

Chalkboard Example

For Example 1

The diameter of the planet Jupiter is 1.427×10^5 km. What is its volume? Recall that the volume of a sphere with radius r is given by $V = \frac{4}{3}\pi r^3$. 1.521×10^{15} km³

The properties of integral exponents given on page 598 can be extended to rational exponents.

Example 2   **Evaluate.**

a. $256^{\frac{1}{4}}$

a. $256^{\frac{1}{4}} = \left(4^4\right)^{\frac{1}{4}}$ *Rewrite 256 as 4^4.*

  $= 4^{\frac{4}{4}}$ $(a^m)^n = a^{mn}$

  $= 4^1$ or 4

b. $5^{\frac{1}{2}} \cdot 15^{\frac{1}{2}}$

b. $5^{\frac{1}{2}} \cdot 15^{\frac{1}{2}} = 5^{\frac{1}{2}} \cdot 5^{\frac{1}{2}} \cdot 3^{\frac{1}{2}}$ $(ab)^m = a^m b^m$

  $= 5^{\frac{1}{2} + \frac{1}{2}} \cdot 3^{\frac{1}{2}}$ $a^m a^n = a^{m+n}$

  $= 5^1 \cdot 3^{\frac{1}{2}}$ $b^{\frac{1}{n}} = \sqrt[n]{b}$

  $= 5\sqrt{3}$

How can you evaluate an expression with a rational exponent in which the numerator is not 1? Study the two methods for evaluating $7^{\frac{2}{3}}$ shown below.

Method 1	*Method 2*
$7^{\frac{2}{3}} = \left(7^{\frac{1}{3}}\right)^2$	$7^{\frac{2}{3}} = \left(7^2\right)^{\frac{1}{3}}$
$= \left(\sqrt[3]{7}\right)^2$	$= \sqrt[3]{7^2}$

Therefore, $\left(\sqrt[3]{7}\right)^2$ and $\sqrt[3]{7^2}$ both equal $7^{\frac{2}{3}}$. In general, we define $b^{\frac{m}{n}}$ as $(b^{\frac{1}{n}})^m$ or $(b^m)^{\frac{1}{n}}$. Now apply the definition of $b^{\frac{1}{n}}$ to $(b^{\frac{1}{n}})^m$ and $(b^m)^{\frac{1}{n}}$.

$$(b^{\frac{1}{n}})^m = (\sqrt[n]{b})^m \qquad\qquad (b^m)^{\frac{1}{n}} = \sqrt[n]{b^m}$$

Thus, $b^{\frac{m}{n}}$ is defined as $(\sqrt[n]{b})^m$ or $\sqrt[n]{b^m}$.

Definition of Rational Exponents

For any nonzero number b, and any integers m and n with $n > 1$,
$$b^{\frac{m}{n}} = \sqrt[n]{b^m} = (\sqrt[n]{b})^m$$
except when $\sqrt[n]{b}$ is not a real number.

600   CHAPTER 11   EXPONENTIAL AND LOGARITHMIC FUNCTIONS

Example 3

Evaluate $64^{\frac{5}{6}}$.

$64^{\frac{5}{6}} = \left(2^6\right)^{\frac{5}{6}}$ *Rewrite 64 as 2^6.*

$\phantom{64^{\frac{5}{6}}} = 2^5$ *$(a^m)^n = a^{mn}$*

$\phantom{64^{\frac{5}{6}}} = 32$

You can rewrite an expression containing radicals with rational exponents or vice versa.

Example 4

Express $\sqrt[4]{8x^2y^8}$ using rational exponents.

$\sqrt[4]{8x^2y^8} = (8x^2y^8)^{\frac{1}{4}}$ *$b^{\frac{1}{n}} = \sqrt[n]{b}$*

$\phantom{\sqrt[4]{8x^2y^8}} = 8^{\frac{1}{4}}x^{\frac{2}{4}}y^{\frac{8}{4}}$ *$(ab)^m = a^m b^m$*

$\phantom{\sqrt[4]{8x^2y^8}} = 8^{\frac{1}{4}}x^{\frac{1}{2}}y^2$

Example 5

Express $(7a)^{\frac{5}{8}}b^{\frac{3}{8}}$ using radicals.

$(7a)^{\frac{5}{8}}b^{\frac{3}{8}} = ((7a)^5 b^3)^{\frac{1}{8}}$ *$a^{mn} = (a^m)^n$*

$\phantom{(7a)^{\frac{5}{8}}b^{\frac{3}{8}}} = (7^5 a^5 b^3)^{\frac{1}{8}}$ *$(ab)^m = a^m b^m$*

$\phantom{(7a)^{\frac{5}{8}}b^{\frac{3}{8}}} = \sqrt[8]{7^5 a^5 b^3}$ *$b^{\frac{1}{n}} = \sqrt[n]{b}$*

To simplify a radical, use the product property to factor out the *n*th roots and use the smallest index possible for the radical.

Example 6

Simplify $\sqrt{x^3 y^9}$.

$\sqrt{x^3 y^9} = (x^3 y^9)^{\frac{1}{2}}$ *$b^{\frac{1}{n}} = \sqrt[n]{b}$*

$\phantom{\sqrt{x^3 y^9}} = x^{\frac{3}{2}}y^{\frac{9}{2}}$ *$(ab)^m = a^m b^m$*

$\phantom{\sqrt{x^3 y^9}} = x^{\frac{2}{2}}x^{\frac{1}{2}}y^{\frac{8}{2}}y^{\frac{1}{2}}$

$\phantom{\sqrt{x^3 y^9}} = |x|y^4\sqrt{xy}$ *Use $|x|$ to denote the principal root for $x^{\frac{2}{2}}$ since x may be negative.*

CHECKING FOR UNDERSTANDING

Communicating Mathematics

Read and study the lesson to answer each question.

1. **Explain** why rational exponents are not defined when the denominator of the exponent is even and the base is negative. See margin.

2. **Write** an expression that is equivalent to $\sqrt[3]{46}$. $46^{\frac{1}{3}}$

LESSON 11-1   RATIONAL EXPONENTS   601

RETEACHING THE LESSON

Have students write each property of exponents for a concrete numerical example, and then write a similar expanded form for the general case as well. For example, the product of powers property may look like $2^3 \cdot 2^4 = (2 \cdot 2 \cdot 2)(2 \cdot 2 \cdot 2 \cdot 2) = 2^7$ for a concrete example, and $a^m \cdot a^n = (a \cdot a \cdot \cdots a)(a \cdot a \cdot \cdots a) = a^{m+n}$ for the general case.

Additional Answer

1. If the base were negative and the denominator were even, then we would be taking an even root of a negative number, which is undefined.

EVALUATING THE LESSON

Checking for Understanding

Exercises 1–13 are designed to help you assess students' understanding through reading, writing, speaking, and modeling. You should work through Exercises 1–4 with your students and then monitor their work on Exercises 5–13.

Closing the Lesson

Speaking Activity   Have each student recite one of the properties of exponents and demonstrate it with an example.

Practice Masters Booklet, p. 73

Homework Exercises

Assignment Guide

Average: 14–29, 30–50 even, 53–66
Enriched: 18–30 even, 31–66

The red A, B, and C flags, printed only in the Teacher's Wraparound Edition, indicate the level of difficulty of the exercises.

Additional Answer

3. No; for a number to be in scientific notation, the exponent on 10 must be an integer.

---

3. Is $6.03 \times 10^{0.4}$ written in scientific notation? Explain. See margin.

4. When you are multiplying two expressions with like bases raised to different powers, you maintain the bases and __?__ the exponents. When you are dividing two expressions with like bases and different exponents, you maintain the bases and __?__ the exponents. add; subtract

Guided Practice

Evaluate.

5. $81^{\frac{1}{2}}$ 9

6. $27^{-\frac{2}{3}}$ $\frac{1}{9}$

7. $7^{\frac{1}{4}} \cdot 7^{\frac{7}{4}}$ 49

Express using rational exponents.

8. $\sqrt[4]{a}$ $a^{\frac{1}{4}}$

9. $\sqrt{xy^3}$ $x^{\frac{1}{2}}y^{\frac{3}{2}}$

10. $\sqrt[3]{8x^3y^6}$ $2xy^2$

Express using radicals.

11. $15^{\frac{1}{5}}$ $\sqrt[5]{15}$

12. $25^{\frac{1}{3}}$ $\sqrt[3]{25}$

13. $a^{\frac{3}{4}}y^{\frac{1}{4}}$ $\sqrt[4]{a^3y}$

EXERCISES

Practice

Evaluate.

14. $\sqrt[3]{125}$ 5

15. $3^{-4} \cdot 3^8$ 81

16. $\sqrt[4]{16^2}$ 4

17. $(5^{\frac{3}{4}})^4$ 125

18. $(169^{\frac{1}{2}})^0$ 1

19. $(8^{-\frac{1}{2}})^{-\frac{2}{3}}$ 2

20. $(\sqrt[3]{216})^2$ 36

21. $(3^{-1} + 3^{-2})^{-1}$ $\frac{9}{4}$

22. $81^{\frac{1}{2}} - 81^{-\frac{1}{2}}$ $8\frac{8}{9}$

23. $\dfrac{16^{\frac{3}{4}}}{16^{\frac{1}{4}}}$ 4

24. $(\sqrt[3]{343})^{-2}$ $\frac{1}{49}$

25. $\dfrac{27}{27^{\frac{2}{3}}}$ 3

Express using rational exponents.

B

26. $\sqrt{a^6b^3}$ $a^3b^{\frac{3}{2}}$

27. $\sqrt[6]{b^3}$ $b^{\frac{1}{2}}$

28. $\sqrt{25a^4b^{10}}$ $5a^2b^5$

29. $\sqrt[3]{125a^2b^3}$ $5a^{\frac{2}{3}}b$

30. $\sqrt[3]{64s^9t^{15}}$ $4s^3t^5$

31. $\sqrt[4]{24a^{12}b^{16}}$ $24^{\frac{1}{4}}a^3b^4$

32. $\sqrt{169x^5}$ $13x^{\frac{5}{2}}$

33. $\sqrt[5]{32x^5y^8}$ $2xy^{\frac{8}{5}}$

34. $\sqrt[5]{15x^3y^{15}}$ $15^{\frac{1}{5}}x^{\frac{3}{5}}y^3$

Express using radicals.

35. $64^{\frac{1}{6}}$ $\sqrt[6]{64}$ or 2

36. $x^{\frac{2}{3}}$ $\sqrt[3]{x^2}$

37. $4^{\frac{1}{3}}a^{\frac{2}{3}}y^{\frac{4}{3}}$ $y\sqrt[3]{4a^2y}$

38. $x^{\frac{4}{7}}y^{\frac{3}{7}}$ $\sqrt[7]{x^4y^3}$

39. $(rt^2)^{\frac{1}{5}}v^{\frac{3}{5}}$ $\sqrt[5]{rt^2v^3}$

40. $a^{\frac{1}{6}}b^{\frac{4}{6}}c^{\frac{3}{6}}$ $\sqrt[6]{ab^4c^3}$

41. $\dfrac{x^{\frac{2}{3}}}{x^{\frac{1}{3}}}$ $\sqrt[3]{x}$

42. $15x^{\frac{1}{3}}y^{\frac{1}{5}}$ $15\sqrt[15]{x^5y^3}$

43. $(x^{10}y^2)^{\frac{1}{5}}a^{\frac{2}{5}}$ $x^2\sqrt[5]{y^2a^2}$

Simplify. 48. $2^{-8}x^{-8}$ or $\dfrac{1}{256x^8}$ 50. $a^{\frac{7}{2}}b^{\frac{7}{2}}$ or $a^3b^3\sqrt{ab}$ 51. $a^{-2}b^8c^{-5}$ or $\dfrac{b^8}{a^2c^5}$

44. $4x^2(4x)^{-2}$ $\dfrac{1}{4}$

45. $x^6 \cdot x^{-3} \cdot x^2$ x^5

46. $(y^{-2})^4 \cdot y^8$ 1

47. $(5x^{\frac{1}{3}})^3$ $125x$

48. $((2x)^4)^{-2}$

49. $(4y^4)^{\frac{3}{2}}$ $8y^6$

50. $\sqrt{a^3b^2} \cdot \sqrt{a^4b^5}$

51. $(a^{\frac{1}{2}}b^{-2}c^{\frac{5}{4}})^{-4}$

52. $(5ac)^{\frac{1}{3}}(a^2c^3)^{\frac{1}{3}}$
$ac\sqrt[3]{5c}$ or $5^{\frac{1}{3}}ac^{\frac{4}{3}}$

Critical Thinking

53. Find the simplest expression for $\dfrac{3^{60}}{9^{30}}$. 1

Applications and Problem Solving

54. Architecture Mathematicians have shown that a soap bubble will enclose a maximum space with a minimum amount of material. Architects have used this property to create buildings that enclose a great amount of space while using a small amount of building material. If a soap bubble has a surface area of A, then its volume, V, is given by the equation $V = 0.094\sqrt{A^3}$. Find the surface area of a bubble with a volume of 7.5 cm³. ≈ 18.53 cm²

55. Aerospace The typical period of the orbit of a space shuttle around Earth is approximately 90 minutes. The radius of Earth is approximately 6400 km. Use the formula $r = \sqrt[3]{\dfrac{GM_e t^2}{4\pi^2}}$, where r represents the distance in meters from the center of Earth to the satellite, $G = 6.67 \times 10^{-11}$, t represents the time in seconds, and M_e represents the mass of Earth, which is 5.98×10^{24} kg, to determine how far the space shuttle is above Earth. 254 km

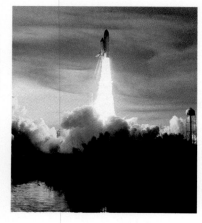

56. Chemistry All matter is composed of atoms. The nucleus of an atom is the center portion of the atom that contains most of the mass of the atom. A theoretical formula for the radius, r, of the nucleus of an atom is $r = (1.3 \times 10^{-15})A^{\frac{1}{3}}$ meters, where A is the mass number of the nucleus. Find the radius of the nucleus, if the mass number of an isotope of carbon is 12. 2.98×10^{-15} m

Mixed Review

57. Graph $y > |x| - 2$. **(Lesson 3-5)** See margin.

58. Solve the equation $27x^2 + 15x - 8 = 0$. **(Lesson 4-1)** $\dfrac{1}{3}, -\dfrac{8}{9}$

59. Find all rational roots of the equation $2x^3 + x^2 - 8x - 4 = 0$. **(Lesson 4-4)** $-2, -\dfrac{1}{2}, 2$

60. Change $\dfrac{\pi}{24}$ to degree measure. **(Lesson 5-1)** $7.5°$

61. Aviation An airplane flying at an altitude of 9000 meters passes directly overhead. Fifteen seconds later, the angle of elevation to the plane is 60°. How fast is the airplane flying? **(Lesson 5-5)** about 346 m/s

62. Graph the polar equation $r = -3$. **(Lesson 9-1)** See margin.

LESSON 11-1 RATIONAL EXPONENTS 603

63. $28 - 96i$

63. Find $(-3 + i)^4$. Express the result in rectangular form. **(Lesson 9-8)**

64. Name the coordinates of the center, foci, and vertices, and the equations of the asymptotes of the hyperbola that has the equation $x^2 - 4y^2 - 12x - 16y = -16$. **(Lesson 10-4)** See margin.

65. Find the length of the tangent segment from $(-1, -1)$ to the circle with equation $(x - 5)^2 + (y + 1)^2 = 4$. **(Lesson 10-8)** $4\sqrt{2}$ units

66. College Entrance Exam Compare quantities A and B below. C
Write A if quantity A is greater.
Write B if quantity B is greater.
Write C if the quantities are equal.
Write D if there is not enough information to determine the relationship.

(A) the sum of the measures of the angles in a scalene triangle

(B) the sum of the measures of the angles in an equilateral triangle

DECISION MAKING

Homelessness

America has always had homeless people, but in recent years, with the country experiencing a sluggish economy and rising unemployment, the number of homeless people has risen alarmingly. Exact figures are impossible to determine, but most authorities estimate that there are at least a million homeless Americans. Is there anything you can do to help alleviate the problem?

1. Research the extent of homelessness in your community. Are there shelters for the homeless? Are city or state funds allocated to provide for the needs of people without permanent shelter?

2. What are the causes of homelessness? What are the responsibilities of Americans who have homes toward those who do not? Talk to people who are involved in trying to solve the problem to learn their views on these questions.

3. What, if anything, can you do to help alleviate the problems of the homeless? Make a list of three viable options.

4. **Project** Work with your group to complete one of the projects listed at the right based on the information you gathered for Exercises 1–3. 1–4. See students' work.

PROJECTS

- *Conduct an interview.*
- *Write a book report.*
- *Write a proposal.*
- *Write an article for the school paper.*
- *Write a report.*
- *Make a display.*
- *Make a graph or chart.*
- *Plan an activity.*
- *Design a checklist.*

604 CHAPTER 11 EXPONENTIAL AND LOGARITHMIC FUNCTIONS

EXTENDING THE LESSON

Math Power: Reasoning

What is meant by an expression of the form a^{b^c}? For example, is $\left(2^2\right)^3$ the same as $2^{\left(2^3\right)}$?

$2^{2^3} = 2^8 = 256$. It is not the same as $(2^2)^3 = 4^3 = 64$.

Decision Making

This activity provides students an opportunity to work together on a given problem. You may wish to refer to pages T20–T21 and page 596c for the various elements of cooperative groups and specific goals and strategies for using them.

11-2A   Graphing Calculators: Graphing Exponential Functions

In our society today, there are many applications that involve exponential functions. Exponential functions are functions of the form $y = a^x$, where $a > 0$ and $a \neq 1$. You can use a graphing calculator to draw all types of exponential functions, even those that would be extremely difficult to draw by hand.

Example 1

Graph $y = 3^x$ and $y = \left(\dfrac{1}{3}\right)^x$ on the same set of axes. Use the viewing window $[-5, 5]$ by $[-1, 9]$.

Enter the equations and graph.

TI-81: [Y=] 3 [^] [X|T] [ENTER] [(]
1 [÷] 3 [)] [^] [X|T] [GRAPH]

Casio: [Graph] 3 [xʸ] [ALPHA] [X] [:]
[Graph] [(] 1 [÷] 3 [)] [xʸ]
[ALPHA] [X] [EXE]

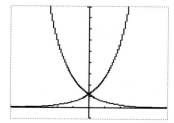

The intersection point is $(0, 1)$.

Example 2

Graph $y = 9^{2+x}$. Use the viewing window $[-7, 1]$ by $[-1, 9]$.

Enter the equations and graph.

TI-81: [Y=] 9 [^] [(] 2 [+] [X|T] [)]
[GRAPH]

Casio: [Graph] 9 [xʸ] [(] 2 [+] [ALPHA]
[X] [)] [EXE]

When entering this equation into your calculator, remember to use parentheses around the exponent. If you do not use parentheses, the calculator will graph the equation $y = 9^2 + x$.

EXERCISES

Graph each equation so that a complete graph is shown. Then sketch the graph on a piece of paper. 1–9. See Teacher's Answer Key.

1. $y = 0.01^x$
2. $y = 5^x$
3. $y = -5^x$
4. $y = 5^{-x}$
5. $y = -5^{-x}$
6. $y = 0.5^{x-3}$
7. $y = -4^{x+6}$
8. $y = -\left(\dfrac{1}{2}\right)^{3-2x}$
9. $y = 7^{1-x}$

GRAPHING CALCULATORS: GRAPHING EXPONENTIAL FUNCTIONS   605

INTRODUCING THE LESSON

Objective   Graph exponential functions on a graphing calculator.

Motivating the Lesson

Ask students to sketch the graph of the following situation.
   In the first week of the new year, Marcella put away 1¢ in savings. Each week thereafter, she put away double the previous week's amount.

TEACHING THE LESSON

Teaching Tip   Ask students to use their calculators to find ordered pairs representing $(x, 3^x)$ for $x = -1, -2, -3, -4,$ and -5. Have them sketch these points. Point out that even though the values of 3^x decrease, they still remain positive. Thus, the graph of $y = 3^x$ approaches but does not intersect the x-axis.

More Examples

Graph $y = 2^{2x-1} - 1$.

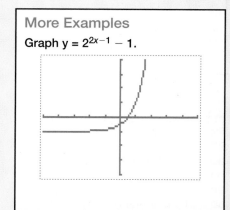

APPLYING THE LESSON

Homework Exercises

Assignment Guide

All: 1–10

TEACHING THE LESSON

Closing the Lesson

Ask students to graph $y = 2^x$ and discuss the statement, "Every positive real number can be expressed as some power of 2."

Lesson Resources

- Practice Master 11-2
- Enrichment Master 11-2
- Evaluation Master, Quiz A, p. 137
- Technology Master, p. 22

 Transparency 11-2 contains the 5-Minute Check and a teaching aid for this lesson.

INTRODUCING THE LESSON

 5-Minute Check

(over Lesson 11–1)

Evaluate.

1. $125^{\frac{2}{3}}$ **25**

2. $(3^0 - 3^2)^{\frac{1}{3}}$ **−2**

3. Express $\sqrt[3]{81a^4b^3}$ using rational exponents.
   $81^{\frac{1}{3}}a^{\frac{4}{3}}b$

4. Express $25^{\frac{1}{2}}x^{\frac{5}{4}}y^{\frac{1}{4}}$ using radicals.
   $5\sqrt[4]{x^5y}$

5. Simplify $\sqrt{a^3b} \cdot \sqrt{8ab^2}$.
   $2a^2b\sqrt{2b}$ or $2^{\frac{3}{2}}a^2b^{\frac{3}{2}}$

Motivating the Lesson

In Lesson 11–1, expressions of the form a^x were defined for $a > 0$ and x a rational number. So given the appropriate formula, we could calculate how much money is in an interest-bearing account after so many months or how large a bacteria colony is after so many hours of growth. But simple calculation is not our goal. We want the capability of modeling such situations for ourselves and answering important questions such as when our bank account will double or when the bacteria colony will reach a certain critical size. This requires a study of the exponential functions, $y = a^x$.

11-2 Exponential Functions

Objectives

After studying this lesson, you should be able to:

11–2A ■ evaluate expressions with irrational exponents,

11–2B ■ graph exponential functions, and

11–2C ■ graph exponential inequalities.

Application

FYI...

Laws requiring drivers and/or passengers to wear seat belts are on the books in 41 states.

In the United States, automobile accidents cause about 1.6 million injuries each year. It is estimated that the number of injuries could be cut in half if everyone wore seat belts whenever they are in a moving vehicle. However, less than 20% of drivers and passengers wear seat belts.

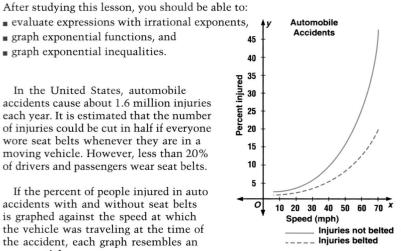

If the percent of people injured in auto accidents with and without seat belts is graphed against the speed at which the vehicle was traveling at the time of the accident, each graph resembles an **exponential curve**.

An exponential curve is the graph of a function of the form $y = a^x$. In the previous lesson, the expression a^x was defined for integral and rational exponents. The next step is to define a^x when x is an irrational number so that the properties of exponents remain valid.

Consider the graph of $y = 2^x$, where x is an integer. This is a function since there is a unique y-value for each x-value.

x	−4	−3	−2	−1	0	1	2	3	4	5
2^x	$\frac{1}{16}$	$\frac{1}{8}$	$\frac{1}{4}$	$\frac{1}{2}$	1	2	4	8	16	32

The graph shows that the function is increasing. That is, for any values x_1 and x_2, if $x_1 < x_2$, then $2^{x_1} < 2^{x_2}$.

Suppose the domain of $y = 2^x$ is expanded to include all rational numbers. The additional points graphed seem to "fill in" the graph of $y = 2^x$. That is, if k is between x_1 and x_2, then 2^k is between 2^{x_1} and 2^{x_2}. The graph of $y = 2^x$, when x is a rational number, is indicated by the broken line on the graph at the top of the next page.

Notice that the vertical scale is condensed.

606   CHAPTER 11   EXPONENTIAL AND LOGARITHMIC FUNCTIONS

ALTERNATE TEACHING STRATEGIES

Using Graphing Calculators

Have students graph $y = 2^x$ and discuss some of the basic features of the graph, for example, its continuity, intercepts, domain and range, and that it is an increasing function. Then graph $y = \left(\frac{1}{2}\right)^x$ and $y = 3^x$ and talk about how they are related to the first graph.

Using Charts

Start with the exponential functions $y = \frac{1}{2}^x$, $y = 2^x$, $y = 3^x$, and $y = -2^x$. Make a chart of the function values for each integer value from $x = -3$ to $x = 3$. Then graph each function and compare and contrast the graphs.

x	2^x
-3.5	0.09
-2.5	0.18
-1.5	0.35
-0.5	0.71
0.5	1.41
1.5	2.83
2.5	5.66
3.5	11.31
4.5	22.63

Values given in the table are approximate.

Since a^x has not been defined for irrational numbers, there are still "holes" in the graph of $y = 2^x$. How could we expand the domain of $y = 2^x$ to include both rational and irrational numbers? Consider a possible meaning for an expression such as $2^{\sqrt{3}}$. Since $1.7 < \sqrt{3} < 1.8$, it follows that $2^{1.7} < 2^{\sqrt{3}} < 2^{1.8}$. Closer and closer approximations for $\sqrt{3}$ allow us to find closer approximations for $2^{\sqrt{3}}$.

Therefore, we can now define a value for a^x when x is an irrational number.

Definition of Irrational Exponents	If x is an irrational number and $a > 0$, then a^x is the real number between a^{x_1} and a^{x_2} for all possible choices of rational numbers x_1 and x_2, such that $x_1 < x < x_2$.

You can use a calculator to find an approximate value of a^x for real values of x.

Example 1

Use a calculator to evaluate each expression to the nearest ten thousandth.

a. $3^{\sqrt{3}}$

a. 3 [y^x] 3 [2nd] [$\sqrt{x}$] [=] 6.7049919

$3^{\sqrt{3}} \approx 6.7050$

b. 5^{π}

b. 5 [y^x] [2nd] [π] [=] 156.99255

$5^{\pi} \approx 156.9926$

LESSON 11-2 EXPONENTIAL FUNCTIONS 607

Teaching Tip The definition of irrational exponents assures that the function $y = a^x$ is continuous for all real values of x. Using the idea of limit that was presented in Lesson 3–6, this definition is written $a^x = \lim_{r \to x} a^r$, where r represents a rational number.

Chalkboard Example

For Example 1

Use a calculator to evaluate each expression to the nearest ten thousandth.
a. $5^{\sqrt{2}}$ 9.7385
b. 0.4^{π} 0.0562

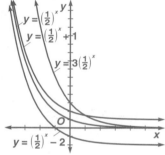
An **exponential function** has the form $y = a^x$, where *a* is a positive real number. The figure at the right shows the graphs of several exponential functions. Notice that the point with coordinates (0, 1) is common to each function. Compare the graph of $y = 2^x$ to the graph of $y = \left(\frac{1}{2}\right)^x$. What do you notice? When $a > 1$ and *x* is increasing, is the graph of $y = a^x$ increasing or decreasing? When $a < 1$ and *x* is increasing, is the graph increasing or decreasing?

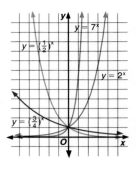

Example 2

Discuss the behavior of the graphs of $y = 2^x$ and $y = 3^x$. Compare the values of 2^x and 3^x on the intervals $-10 \le x < 0$ and $0 < x \le 10$.

Both graphs have *y*-intercepts at (0, 1). In the interval $-10 \le x < 0$, $2^x > 3^x$ and both graphs approach the *x*-axis as *x* approaches –10.

In the interval $0 < x \le 10$, $3^x > 2^x$.

The graphs of exponential functions can be transformed in the same way as the graphs of other functions.

Example 3

Graph the functions $y = 3^x$, $y = 3^x + 2$, $y = 3^x - 1$, and $y = 8(3^x)$ on the same set of axes. Then describe the transformations of the parent graph $y = 3^x$ that have taken place to form each of the other graphs.

The horizontal asymptote of the graph of $y = 3^x + 2$ is the line $y = 2$ instead of $y = 0$, as for the graph of $y = 3^x$. The graph of $y = 3^x$ has been translated 2 units up.

The horizontal asymptote of the graph of $y = 3^x - 1$ is the line $y = -1$. The *y*-intercept is 0. The graph of $y = 3^x$ has been translated 1 unit down.

The horizontal asymptote of the graph of $y = 8(3^x)$ is the line $y = 0$ and the *y*-intercept is 8. The graph is much steeper than the parent graph.

In this lesson, we will only consider annuities where the payments are made at the end of each payment period.

Bankers call a series of payments made at equal intervals of time an **annuity**. The **present value of an annuity**, P_n, is the sum of the present values of all the periodic payments P. So an annuity of P dollars per period for n periods is worth P_n dollars now. In other words, a lump-sum investment of P_n dollars now will provide payments of P dollars per period for the next n periods. An example of this type of annuity is a retirement plan in which an employee saves money in an account that will provide monthly income after he or she retires.

The formula below can be used to find the present value of an annuity, P_n, if a series of n payments of P dollars each are made.

$$P_n = P \left[\frac{1 - (1 + i)^{-n}}{i} \right]$$

The **future value of an annuity**, F_n, is the sum of all of the annuity payments plus any accumulated interest. The formula below can be used to find the future value of an annuity, F_n, if a series of n payments of P dollars each are made.

$$F_n = P \left[\frac{(1 + i)^n - 1}{i} \right]$$

In both formulas, the variable i represents the interest rate per payment interval. Banks usually state interest rates as **annual percentage rates** or **APRs**. The interest rate per payment interval is equal to the APR divided by the number of payment intervals per year.

Example 4

A monthly mortgage payment consists of an amount paid toward the principal and the interest on the loan. It may also contain an amount for the property taxes that the mortgage holder will pay from an escrow and an amount for insurance that protects the mortgage holder in case of default on the loan. The Wimberlys have taken a 30-year mortgage for $100,000, with an interest rate of 9.0%, on their new home.
a. **What will the monthly payment for the principal and interest be?**
b. **How much will the Wimberlys pay in interest over the life of the loan?**

a. Use the formula for the present value of an annuity to find the monthly payment. The APR is 9.0%, so the interest rate is $\frac{9.0\%}{12}$ or 0.75% per month. In the formula, $i = 0.0075$. *Why?*

The Wimberlys will make 12×30 or 360 payments on the loan. So the value of n in the formula is 360.

$$P_n = P \left[\frac{1 - (1 + i)^{-n}}{i} \right]$$

$$100{,}000 = P \left[\frac{1 - (1 + 0.0075)^{-360}}{0.0075} \right] \qquad P_n = 100{,}000,\ i = 0.0075,\ \text{and } n = 360$$

$$\frac{750}{1 - (1.0075)^{-360}} = P$$

$$804.62262 = P \qquad \text{Use a calculator to evaluate.}$$

The monthly payment will be $804.62.   *(continued on the next page)*

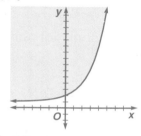
b. The Wimberlys will pay 360×804.62 or \$289,663.20 for the principal and interest on the loan. So, they will pay $289,663.20 - 100,000$ or \$189,663.20 in interest over the 30-year period.

As you can see in Example 4, a surprisingly large amount of interest is usually paid in a mortgage. Likewise, in an IRA, a large amount of interest can be earned.

Example 5

APPLICATION

Finance

When Jim Baldini started his first job after he finished college, he opened an individual retirement account (IRA). He plans to contribute \$2500 per year for 38 years until he reaches age 62. He hopes to earn an average APR of 8% over the 38-year period.
a. If Mr. Baldini contributes to his IRA at the rate that he plans, how much will his account be worth when he is 62 years old?
b. How much interest will be earned on the account?

a. Use the formula for the future value of an annuity.

$$F_n = P\left[\frac{(1+i)^n - 1}{i}\right]$$

$$= 2500\left[\frac{(1+0.08)^{38} - 1}{0.08}\right] \qquad i = 0.08, n = 38, P = 2500$$

$$= 2500\left[\frac{(1.08)^{38} - 1}{0.08}\right]$$

$$= 550,789.86 \qquad\qquad \textit{Use a calculator to evaluate.}$$

The value of Mr. Baldini's account will be \$550,789.86.

b. Mr. Baldini will pay 2500×38 or \$95,000 into his IRA. So, the account will earn $550,789.86 - 95,000$ or \$455,789.86 in interest.

EXPLORATION: Graphing Calculator

The approximate world population, y, can be expressed as a function of the year, x, in the equation $y = 10^{0.00389x + 2}$.

1. Use the settings below to set up a viewing window.

XMIN = 1800   YMIN = 0
XMAX = 2180   YMAX = 7000000000
XSCL = 50   YSCL = 1000000000

2. Press $\boxed{Y=}$ and enter the equation.

3. Use the TRACE function to determine the population growth from 1800 to the year 2000. According to the graph, what can we expect the population to be in the year 2000? 6.0256×10^9

Graphing exponential inequalities is similar to graphing other inequalities.

Example 6 | **Graph $y < 2^x - 4$.**

First, graph $y = 2^x - 4$. Since the points on this curve are not in the solution of the inequality, the graph of $y = 2^x - 4$ is shown as a dashed curve.

Then, use $(0, 0)$ as a test point to determine which area to shade.

$0 < 2^0 - 4$
$0 < 1 - 4$
$0 \not< -3$

Since $(0, 0)$ does not satisfy the inequality, the region that does not contain the origin should be shaded.

CHECKING FOR UNDERSTANDING

Communicating Mathematics

Read and study the lesson to answer each question. 1–3. See margin.

1. **Compare and contrast** the graphs of $y = 4^x$ and $y = 4^x - 3$.

2. **Compare and contrast** the graphs of $y = a^x$ and $y = \left(\frac{1}{a}\right)^x$, where a is an integer greater than 1.

3. **Describe** an annuity. Give examples of different types of annuities.

4. **Choose** the correct term.
   a. If $0 < a < 1$, a^x (decreases, increases) as x increases. decreases
   b. If $a > 1$, a^x (decreases, increases) as x increases. increases

Guided Practice

Use a calculator to evaluate each expression to the nearest ten thousandth.

5. $2^{\sqrt{6}}$ 5.4622
6. $5^{\sqrt{2}}$ 9.7385
7. $\left(\frac{1}{3}\right)^{\pi}$ 0.0317

Graph each equation. 8–12. See Teacher's Answer Key.

8. $y = 2^x$
9. $y = -2^x$
10. $y = 2^{-x}$

11. Compare the graphs for Exercises 8, 9, and 10. What do you notice?

12. Graph $y < 2^x + 1$.

13. **Finance** What is the present value of an annuity that pays $1000 every six months for nine years if the APR is 10%? $11,689.59

EXERCISES

Practice

Use a calculator to evaluate each expression to the nearest ten thousandth.

14. $7^{\sqrt{5}}$ 77.5705
15. $8^{\sqrt{3}}$ 36.6604
16. $5^{\sqrt{10}}$ 162.3070

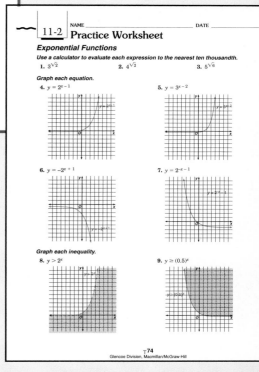

RETEACHING THE LESSON

The definition for $y = a^x$ when x is irrational may seem hard to understand. Have students use their calculators to write out the successive approximations for a specific case. For example, to define $2^{\sqrt{3}}$ we might consider the following sequence:

$3.24901 \approx 2^{1.7} < 2^{\sqrt{3}} < 2^{1.8} \approx 3.482202$
$3.31728 \approx 2^{1.73} < 2^{\sqrt{3}} < 2^{1.74} \approx 3.34035$ and so on.

Additional Answers

1. The graph $y = 4^x - 3$ is the graph of $y = 4^x$ shifted 3 units downward.

2. The graphs of $y = a^x$ and $y = \left(\frac{1}{a}\right)^x$ are reflections of each other across the y-axis.

3. An annuity is a series of equal payments made at equal intervals of time. Some examples are retirement plans, Christmas club accounts, mortgages, and car loans.

Using Technology

The program given in Exercise 37 is for use with a TI-81 graphing calculator. For other programmable calculators, have students consult their owner's manual for commands similar to those presented here.

Exercise Notes

For Exercise 38, students may wish to graph the function by first graphing both $y = -x$ and $y = 2^x$ on the same set of axes, and then visually adding the y-values of these two graphs at each x to plot points on the graph of $y = 2^x - x$.

Additional Answers

26. They are reflections of each other across the y-axis.
27. They have similar shape, but the graph of Exercise 19 is steeper.
28. The graph of Exercise 24 is the graph of Exercise 23 reflected across the x-axis. The graph of Exercise 25 is the graph of Exercise 24 shifted 6 places to the right.

29.

30.

Graph each equation. 17–25. See Teacher's Answer Key.

17. $y = 3^x$
18. $y = \left(\frac{1}{3}\right)^x$
19. $y = 5^{-x}$
20. $y = 3^{-x}$
21. $y = -3^x$
22. $y = \left(\frac{1}{5}\right)^x$
23. $y = 2^{x+3}$
24. $y = -2^{x+3}$
25. $y = -2^{x-3}$

26–28. See margin.
26. Compare and contrast the graphs for Exercises 17 and 18.
27. Compare and contrast the graphs for Exercises 19 and 20.
28. Compare and contrast the graphs for Exercises 23, 24, and 25.

Graph each inequality. 29–36. See margin.

29. $y < 5^x$
30. $y > -4^x$
31. $y \leq \left(\frac{1}{2}\right)^x$
32. $y < 2^{x-4}$
33. $y \geq 3^x - 4$
34. $y \leq -4^x$

35. Without graphing, describe how the graphs of $y = -3^x$ and $y = 3^x$ are related.
36. Without graphing, describe how the graphs of $y = 5^x$ and $y = 5^{-x}$ are related.

Programming

37. The program below will calculate loan payments. You must input the amount of the loan, the annual percentage rate, the number of payments per year, and the number of years in the life of the loan.

```
Prgm 11:LOANPYMT
:ClrHome                              Clears the text screen.
:Disp "LOAN AMOUNT = "                Displays the quoted message.
:Input A                              Accepts a value for A.
:Disp "APR (AS A DECIMAL) = "
:Input R
:Disp "NO. OF PAYMENTS"
:Disp "PER YEAR = "
:Input N
:Disp "NO. OF YEARS = "
:Input Y
:A(R/N)/(1-(1+R/N)^(-NY))→ P         Calculates the payment, stores it in P.
:Disp "PAYMENT = "
:Disp P                              Displays the value stored in P.
```

Use the program above to find the monthly payment for each loan described below.

Exercise	Amt. of Loan (A)	Annual Percentage Rate (R)	No. of Payments per Year (N)	No. of Years (Y)
a.	$1500	18%	12	3
b.	$20,000	11%	12	5
c.	$125,000	9%	12	30

$54.23 (a.)
$434.85 (b.)
$1005.78 (c.)

Critical Thinking

38. Graph the function $y = 2^x - x$. See margin.

31.

32.

33.

34.

Applications and Problem Solving

39. Banking What is the future value of an annuity if $1000 is deposited into an account paying 6% every six months for 12 years? $34,426.47

40. Entertainment The state of Ohio offers its lottery winners a choice of prizes, with the jackpot amount paid in equal annual payments over 26 years or the present value of the annuity in one lump sum. If Mr. Arthur won a $4.5 million jackpot, how much would his lump-sum payment be? The interest rate used to find the present value is the yearly rate of inflation; assume this rate to be 5%. $2,488,012.84

41. over 30 years, #2 is better; over 5 years, #1 is better

41. Banking Ms. Bailey is considering two different investment structures for her IRA. One structure has her pay $500 each month into an account with an APR of 7.2%. The second structure has her pay $1500 every quarter into an account with an APR of 7.3%. Which structure will give Ms. Bailey a better return on her investment in thirty years? in five years?

42. Financial Planning The Sungs are saving for their daughter's college education. If they want to add $20,000 to her college fund at the end of five years, how much should they deposit each month into an account with an APR of 6.12%? $285.77

43. Construction A sinking fund is a fund to which regular payments are made in order to pay off a debt when it is due. The Gallway Construction Company foresees the need to buy a new cement truck in four years. At that time, the truck will probably cost $120,000. The firm sets up a sinking fund in order to accumulate the money. How much should the firm's semiannual payments to the fund be if the fund earns an APR of 7%? $13,257.20

Mixed Review

44. State the domain and range of the relation $\{(0,2),(4,-2),(9,-3),(-7,11),(-2,0)\}$. Is the relation a function? **(Lesson 1-1)** See margin.

45. Find the value of $\begin{vmatrix} 7 & -3 & 5 \\ 4 & 0 & -1 \\ 8 & 2 & 0 \end{vmatrix}$. **(Lesson 2-3)** 78

46. max at $\left(\frac{2}{3}, \frac{14}{27}\right)$; min at $(4,-18)$; inf at $\left(\frac{7}{3}, -\frac{236}{27}\right)$

46. Find the critical points of the function $y = x^3 - 7x^2 + 8x - 2$. Then, determine whether each point represents a maximum, a minimum, or a point of inflection. **(Lesson 3-7)**

47. If $\sin\theta = \frac{7}{8}$ and the terminal side of θ is in the first quadrant, find $\cos 2\theta$. **(Lesson 7-4)** $-\frac{17}{32}$

48. Find an ordered pair that represents $\overrightarrow{AB}$ for $A(8,3)$ and $B(0,-2)$. Then, find the magnitude of $\overrightarrow{AB}$. **(Lesson 8-2)** $(-8,-5)$; $\sqrt{89}$

49. Express $-6 + 6i$ in polar form. **(Lesson 9-6)** See margin.

50. Express $\sqrt{20a^4b^{12}}$ using rational exponents. **(Lesson 11-1)** $20^{\frac{1}{2}}a^2b^6$

51. College Entrance Exam Choose the best answer. C
A carpenter divides a board that is 7 feet 9 inches long into three equal parts. What is the length of each part?

(A) 2 ft $6\frac{1}{3}$ in.　(B) 2 ft $8\frac{1}{3}$ in.　(C) 2 ft 7 in.　(D) 2 ft 8 in.　(E) 2 ft 9 in.

LESSON 11-2 EXPONENTIAL FUNCTIONS 613

EXTENDING THE LESSON

Math Power: Problem Solving

In this lesson, it was noted that $y = 3^x$ "grows faster" than $y = 2^x$. Thus, if $x > 0$, $3^x > 2^x$, how does the rate of growth of a polynomial function like $y = x^2$ or $y = x^5$ compare with the rate of growth of $y = 2^x$? $y = 2^x$ grows faster than any polynomial.

---

35. They are reflections over the x-axis.

36. They are reflections over the y-axis.

38.

$x = 2^x - x$

44. domain: $\{-7, -2, 0, 4, 9\}$; range $\{-3, -2, 0, 2, 11\}$; yes

49. $6\sqrt{2}\left(\cos\frac{3\pi}{4} + i\sin\frac{3\pi}{4}\right)$

Enrichment Masters Booklet, p. 74

NAME _____ DATE _____

11-2 Enrichment Worksheet

Finding Solutions of $x^y = y^x$

Perhaps you have noticed that if x and y are interchanged in equations such as $x = y$ and $xy = 1$, the resulting equation is equivalent to the original equation. The same is true of the equation $x^y = y^x$. However, finding solutions of $x^y = y^x$ and drawing its graph is not a simple process.

Solve each problem. Assume that x and y are positive real numbers

1. If $a > 0$, will (a, a) be a solution of $x^y = y^x$? Justify your answer.
Yes, since $a^a = a^a$ must be true by the reflexive prop. of equality.
2. If $c > 0$, $d > 0$, and (c, d) is a solution of $x^y = y^x$, will (d, c) also be a solution? Justify your answer.
Yes; replacing x with d, y with c gives $d^c = c^d$; but if (c, d) is a solution, $c^d = d^c$. So, by the symmetric property of equality, $d^c = c^d$ is true.
3. Use 2 as a value for y in $x^y = y^x$. The equation becomes $x^2 = 2^x$.
a. Find equations for two functions, $f(x)$ and $g(x)$ that you could graph to find the solutions of $x^2 = 2^x$. Then graph the functions on a separate sheet of graph paper.
$f(x) = x^2$, $g(x) = 2^x$ See students' graphs.
b. Use the graph you drew for part a to state two solutions for $x^2 = 2^x$. Then use these solutions to state two solutions for $x^y = y^x$.
$(2, 4)$; $(2, 2)$, $(4, 2)$
4. In this exercise, a graphing calculator will be very helpful. Use the technique from Exercise 3 to complete the tables below. Then graph $x^y = y^x$ for positive values of x and y. If there are asymptotes, show them in your diagram using dotted lines. Note that in the table, some values of y call for one value of x, others call for two.

x	y
$\frac{1}{2}$	$\frac{1}{4}$
$\frac{3}{4}$	$\frac{3}{4}$
1	1
2	2
4	2
3	3
2.5	3

x	y
4	4
2	4
5	5
1.8	5
8	8
1.5	8

T 74
Glencoe Division, Macmillan/McGraw-Hill

LESSON 11-2 EXPONENTIAL FUNCTIONS 613

NCTM Standards: 1–4, 6

Lesson Resources

- Practice Master 11-3
- Enrichment Master 11-3

 Transparency 11-3 contains the 5-Minute Check and a teaching aid for this lesson.

INTRODUCING THE LESSON

 5-Minute Check

(over Lesson 11–2)

1. Evaluate $4^{\sqrt{6}}$ to the nearest ten thousandth.   **29.8359**

Graph each equation or inequality.
2. $y = 0.8^x$

3. $y < 3^x + 1$

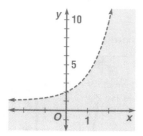

4. Name a function whose graph is the same as $y = 2^x$ reflected over the y-axis.
$y = \left(\dfrac{1}{2}\right)^x$ or $y = 2^{-x}$

11-3   The Number *e*

Objective
11-3

After studying this lesson, you should be able to:
- use the exponential function $y = e^x$.

Application

Byron received a total of $700 in cash gifts for his high school graduation. He is going to invest his money in a savings account so that he can buy a car after he graduates from college. The Brentwood Savings and Loan offers a statement savings account that pays 4.5% APR compounded quarterly. At this rate, what would the balance of Byron's savings account be after four years?

Advertisements for savings accounts offer **compound interest**. When interest is compounded, it is added to the beginning principal at a specified time, thus forming the new principal. Suppose the beginning principal is P, the annual interest rate is r, interest is compounded n times per year, and A is the account balance after t years. Then the compound interest formula is $A = P\left(1 + \dfrac{r}{n}\right)^{nt}$.

Byron can find the amount that will be in his account after four years by applying the compound interest formula. Since Byron's account is compounded quarterly, $n = 4$.

$$A = P\left(1 + \frac{r}{n}\right)^{nt}$$
$$= 700\left(1 + \frac{0.045}{4}\right)^{(4\cdot4)} \qquad P = 700, r = 0.045, n = 4, \text{ and } t = 4$$
$$= 700(1 + 0.01125)^{16}$$
$$= \$837.21$$

If Byron invests his money in the account that offers 4.5% interest compounded quarterly, his account will have a balance of $837.21 after four years.

Another bank in Byron's community offers an account with 4.4% APR with the interest compounded continuously. If interest is compounded continuously, the formula $A = Pe^{rt}$ can be used to find the amount in the account. The variables P, r, and t represent the principal, the annual interest rate, and the time in years, respectively. The number e is a special irrational number. This number is the sum of the infinite series shown below.

$$e = 1 + \frac{1}{1} + \frac{1}{1\cdot2} + \frac{1}{1\cdot2\cdot3} + \frac{1}{1\cdot2\cdot3\cdot4} + \cdots + \frac{1}{1\cdot2\cdot3\cdot\ \cdots\ \cdot n} + \cdots$$

614   CHAPTER 11   EXPONENTIAL AND LOGARITHMIC FUNCTIONS

ALTERNATE TEACHING STRATEGIES

Using Cooperative Groups

Present the formula for compound interest and have groups of students calculate the value of an account with a principal of $1000 after three years at 6% interest compounded annually, quarterly, monthly, daily, and hourly. Note how the sequence of values appears to converge to a limit. This limiting value is Pe^{rt}. In this example, $Pe^{rt} = \$1197.22$.

Using Critical Thinking

After introducing the number e and its value, have students find the value of $\left(1 + \dfrac{1}{n}\right)^n$ for n = 1, 10, 100, ... What is the limit of this sequence? It is the number e. Now have students explore the value of $\lim\limits_{n\to\infty}\left(1 + \dfrac{x}{n}\right)^n$ for some number x. This limit is e^x. This definition of e is the one used to derive the formula $A = Pe^{rt}$.

The following computation for e is correct to three decimal places.

$$e = 1 + 1 + \frac{1}{1 \cdot 2} + \frac{1}{1 \cdot 2 \cdot 3} + \frac{1}{1 \cdot 2 \cdot 3 \cdot 4} + \frac{1}{1 \cdot 2 \cdot 3 \cdot 4 \cdot 5} +$$
$$\frac{1}{1 \cdot 2 \cdot 3 \cdot 4 \cdot 5 \cdot 6} + \frac{1}{1 \cdot 2 \cdot 3 \cdot 4 \cdot 5 \cdot 6 \cdot 7}$$
$$= 1 + 1 + \frac{1}{2} + \frac{1}{6} + \frac{1}{24} + \frac{1}{120} + \frac{1}{720} + \frac{1}{5040}$$
$$= 1 + 1 + 0.5 + 0.16667 + 0.04167 + 0.00833 + 0.00139 + 0.000198$$
$$= 2.718$$

One of the most important exponential functions is $y = e^x$. A graph of $y = e^x$ is shown at the right.

You can use a calculator to find values of $y = e^x$.

Example 1

Find the value of $e^{4.243}$ to the nearest ten thousandth.

4.243 [2nd] [LN] *69.616388*   *The meaning of the term ln x will be discussed in the next lesson.*

Therefore, $e^{4.243} \approx 69.6164$.

You can check the solution by evaluating $2.718^{4.243}$ on your calculator.

Now we can use the formula for continuously compounded interest to find the amount in Byron's bank account after four years.

$A = Pe^{rt}$
$\quad = 700e^{(0.044 \cdot 4)}$ *$P = 700, r = 0.044,$ and $t = 4$*
$\quad = 700e^{0.176}$
$\quad = 834.70664$ *Use a calculator to evaluate.*

If Byron chooses the account with 4.4% APR with interest compounded continuously, the balance in his account will be $834.71 after four years.

There are many applications for the number e. Newton's Law of Cooling expresses the relationship between the temperature (in °F)of a cooling object, y, and the time elapsed since cooling began, t in minutes. This relationship is given by the following equation.

$$y = ae^{-kt} + c$$

In this equation, c represents the temperature of the medium surrounding the cooling object, and a and k represent constants related to the cooling object itself.

LESSON 11-3   THE NUMBER e 615

Motivating the Lesson

Under ideal conditions, the rate of growth of a population would be directly proportional to the size of the population. This situation gives rise to the differential equation $\frac{dP}{dt} = kP$. The solution of this equation is $P = Ce^{kt}$, where P is the final population, C is the initial size of the population, k is a constant and t is the time (in years). The number e, which comes up in many interesting mathematical problems like this one, is the topic of this lesson.

TEACHING THE LESSON

Teaching Tip The number e, like π, is *transcendental*. That is, it cannot occur as a root of any polynomial function with rational coefficients.

Chalkboard Example

For Example 1

Find the value of $e^{-1.27}$ to the nearest ten thousandth.   0.2808

Example 2

APPLICATION

Physics

Janet heated vegetable soup to 210°F in the microwave at school. If the room temperature is 70°, what will the temperature of the soup be after 10 minutes? Assume that $a = 140$ and $k = 0.01$.

$$y = ae^{-kt} + c$$
$$= 140e^{-0.01(10)} + 70 \qquad a = 140, k = 0.01, t = 10, \text{ and } c = 70$$
$$= 140e^{-0.1} + 70$$
$$\approx 196.67724 \qquad \text{Use a calculator to evaluate.}$$

The soup will be about 197°F after 10 minutes.

Another application involving e has to do with the amount of knowledge that a person retains after a certain amount of time has passed.

Example 3

APPLICATION

Psychology

The *Ebbinghaus Model* for human memory gives the percent, p, of acquired knowledge that a person retains after an amount of time. The formula is $p = (100 - a)e^{-bt} + a$, where t is the time in weeks, and a and b vary from one person to another. If $a = 18$ and $b = 0.6$ for a certain student, how much information will the student retain two weeks after learning a new topic?

$$p = (100 - a)e^{-bt} + a$$
$$= (100 - 18)e^{-(0.6 \cdot 2)} + 18 \qquad a = 18, b = 0.6, \text{ and } t = 2$$
$$= 82e^{-1.2} + 18$$
$$\approx 42.7 \qquad \text{Use a calculator to evaluate.}$$

The student will retain about 43% of the information after two weeks.

CHECKING FOR UNDERSTANDING

Communicating Mathematics

Read and study the lesson to answer each question.

1. **Explain** how interest compounded monthly and interest compounded continuously are different. See students' work.

2. The function $y = e^x$ is an exponential function. How do you expect that the graphs of $y = e^x$ and $y = e^{-x}$ would be related? See margin.

3. If the interest rates are the same, would you choose a savings account that compounded interest monthly or continuously? Why? Continuously; interest compounds faster, so it has a higher yield.

616 CHAPTER 11 EXPONENTIAL AND LOGARITHMIC FUNCTIONS

RETEACHING THE LESSON

Guided Practice

Use a calculator to evaluate each expression to the nearest tenth.

4. $e^{2.1}$ 8.2

5. $e^{3.3}$ 27.1

6. $e^{0.4}$ 1.5

7. $\sqrt{e}$ 1.6

8. $e^{-5.1} - 1$ –1.0

9. $(2e)^{2.8}$ 114.5

10. Use a graphing calculator to graph the equation $y = e^{2x}$. Over which intervals is the function increasing or decreasing? See margin.

11. **Banking**   If interest is compounded semiannually, find the future value of $1200 invested for $4\frac{1}{2}$ years at 7.5% per year. $1671.38

EXERCISES

Practice

Use a calculator to evaluate each expression to the nearest ten thousandth.

12. $e^{1.6}$ 4.9530

13. $e^{4.3}$ 73.6998

14. $\sqrt[3]{e}$ 1.3956

15. $2\sqrt[4]{e^3}$ 4.2340

16. $4\sqrt[3]{e^2}$ 7.7909

17. e^0 1.0000

Graphing Calculator

Use a graphing calculator to graph each equation. Then determine the interval in which each function is increasing or decreasing. 18–23. See margin.

18. $y = xe^x$

19. $y = 2e^x$

20. $y = \left(\frac{1}{4}\right)e^x$

21. $y = 5e^{x-3}$

22. $y = -0.1e^x$

23. $y = e^{x^2}$

24. **Statistics**   The graph of $y = e^{-x^2}$ approximates a *normal curve*. The normal curve is a bell-shaped curve that is often used to represent the distribution of a particular trait in a normal population. Graph the given function on a graphing calculator and sketch the curve on paper. See margin.

Given the original principal, the annual interest rate, the amount of time for each investment, and the type of compounded interest, find the amount at the end of the investment.

25. $P = \$1000$, $r = 10\%$, $t = 4$ years, monthly $1489.35

26. $P = \$3200$, $r = 6\%$, $t = 5$ years 6 months, quarterly $4440.20

27. $P = \$750$, $r = 5.5\%$, $t = 3$ years 2 months, continuously $892.69

28. $P = \$45,000$, $r = 7.2\%$, $t = 30$ years, daily $390,118.09

Applications and Problem Solving

29. **Engineering**   A flexible cable suspended between two points, such as a suspension bridge cable, forms a catenary curve. Graph the catenary $y = \dfrac{e^x + e^{-x}}{2}$ on a graphing calculator and sketch the curve on paper. See margin.

30. **Chemistry**   A beaker of water has been heated to 200°F in a room that is 72°F. If $k = 0.01$ and $a = 128$, use Newton's Law of Cooling to find the temperature of the water after 3 hours. about 93 F

24.

29.

Checking for Understanding

Exercises 1–11 are designed to help you assess students' understanding through reading, writing, speaking, and modeling. You should work through Exercises 1–3 with your students and then monitor their work on Exercises 4–11.

Closing the Lesson

Speaking Activity   Have students describe one of the applications of the exponential function $y = e^x$ illustrated in this lesson.

APPLYING THE LESSON

Homework Exercises

Assignment Guide

Average: 12–28, 29–35 odd, 37–44
Enriched: 16–44

The red A, B, and C flags, printed only in the Teacher's Wraparound Edition, indicate the level of difficulty of the exercises.

Using Technology

In Exercises 18–23, point out that the function $y = e^x$, like any exponential function, has a y-intercept of 1 and, since $e > 1$, it is increasing for all real values of x. Have students use graphing calculators to verify this.

Additional Answers

10. increasing from $-\infty$ to ∞
18. decreasing from $-\infty$ to -1; increasing from -1 to ∞
19. increasing from $-\infty$ to ∞
20. increasing from $-\infty$ to ∞
21. increasing from $-\infty$ to ∞
22. decreasing from $-\infty$ to ∞
23. decreasing from $-\infty$ to 0, increasing from 0 to ∞

31. **Finance** The interest rate offered on a passbook savings account is 3.78% APR compounded continuously. Another account compounds interest monthly. What should the interest rate of the second account be so that the interest earned over one year is the same as the interest earned for the first account? ≈ 3.786%

32. **Forestry** The yield, y, in millions of cubic feet of trees per acre for a forest stand that is t years old is given by $y = 6.7e^{\frac{-48.1}{t}}$.
   a. Find the yield after 15 years. 271,292 ft³
   b. Find the yield after 50 years. 2,560,257 ft³
   c. Graph the yield per year on a graphing calculator for 150 years. Does the yield ever decrease? If so, when? no

33. **Political Science** One model used by political scientists to predict the number of legislators in the U.S. House of Representatives that will serve continuously is given by the exponential function $y = 434e^{-\frac{2t}{25}}$, where y is the number of legislators and t is the number of years since 1965.
   a. According to this model, how many of the legislators from 1965 were still in office in 1980? 131
   b. Predict the number of legislators from 1965 still in office in 1995. 39
   c. Graph the number of legislators from 1965 in office in the years 1965 to 2060 on a graphing calculator. When does the model predict that all of the members of the 1965 House will be out of office? Does this seem realistic? *Hint: Take the year that the predicted number of legislators becomes less that 0.5 to be the year that the last member of the 1965 House leaves office.* See margin.

34. **Medicine** Physicians measure the cardiac output, the amount of blood that a heart can pump in an amount of time, in order to determine how healthy the heart is. In the dye-dilution procedure for determining cardiac output, the amount of dye, D, in milligrams in the heart t minutes after injection is given by $D = de^{\frac{-rt}{V}}$, where d is the number of milligrams of dye injected, r is a constant representing the outflow of blood in liters per minute, and V is the volume of the heart in liters. Find the amount of dye in the heart after 30 seconds if $V = 0.4$ L, $r = 1.3$ liters per minute, and $d = 2.2$ mg. 0.4332 mg

35. **Biology** It has been observed that the rate of growth of a population of organisms will increase until the population is half of its maximum and then the rate will decrease. If m is the maximum population and b and c are constants determined by the type of organism, the population, n, after t years is given by $n = \dfrac{M}{1 + be^{-ct}}$. A certain organism yields the values of $M = 200$, $b = 20$, and $c = 0.35$. What is the shape of this curve? See margin.

36. **Banking** If your bank account earns interest that is compounded more than one time per year, the effective annual yield of the account, E, is the interest rate that would give the same amount of interest earnings if the interest were compounded once per year. If P dollars are invested, the value of the investment is $A = P(1 + E)$.

36a. $E = \left(1 + \frac{r}{n}\right)^n - 1$

   a. Find a formula for the effective annual yield for an account with interest compounded n times per year.

   b. Find a formula for the effective annual yield for an account with interest compounded continuously. $E = e^r - 1$

   c. What is the effective annual yield of an account bearing 5.6% interest compounded monthly? What is the effective annual yield of an account with the same rate of interest compounded continuously? 5.75%, 5.76%

Critical Thinking

37. The expression $\left(1 + \frac{1}{n}\right)^n$ can be used to approximate e. Greater values of n give closer approximations for e. Find the value of the expression for $n = 5, 100, 500,$ and 10,000. 2.48832; 2.704813829; 2.715568521; 2.718145927

Mixed Review

38. Write the standard form of the equation of the line that is parallel to $y = 4x - 8$ and passes through $(-2, 1)$. **(Lesson 1-6)** $4x - y + 9 = 0$

39. Transportation A boat trailer has wheels with a diameter of 14 inches. If the trailer is being pulled by a car going 45 miles per hour, what is the angular velocity of the wheels in revolutions per second? **(Lesson 5-2)** 18 rps

40. 3.53 units

41. $15 = r \sin \theta$

40. Find the distance from the line $y = 9x - 3$ to the point at $(-3, 2)$. **(Lesson 7-7)**

41. Write the rectangular equation $y = 15$ in polar form. **(Lesson 9-4)**

42. Write the standard form of the equation $x^2 - 4x + y^2 - 6y - 3 = 0$. Then, graph the equation. **(Lesson 10-1)** See margin.

43. Finance What is the monthly principal and interest payment on a home mortgage of $90,000 for 30 years at 11.5%? **(Lesson 11-2)** $891.26

44. College Entrance Exam If $c + d = 12$ and $c^2 - d^2 = 48$, then what is the value of $(c - d)$? 4

CASE STUDY FOLLOW-UP

Refer to Case Study 4: *The U.S. Economy*, on pages 966–969.

Suppose the friendly and very wealthy foreign nation of Biparmala agreed to help the United States pay off its national debt. Also suppose that the terms of the agreement were as follows: first, the U.S. has to cut its annual budget deficit to zero immediately, preventing any further rise in the debt. Then, individual Americans would be asked to invest their shares of the national debt in Biparmala. In return, Biparmala would pay 20% interest on these investments, compounded continuously, for ten years. 1. $96,000

1. About how much would each investor's investment be worth in ten years?

2. About how many Americans would need to become investors in order for the plan to succeed? about 31 million

3. Research Read about the growth of the national debt and the many plans to reduce it. Choose the plan that seems most feasible to you and write about it in a 1-page paper. See students' work.

LESSON 11-3 THE NUMBER e 619

EXTENDING THE LESSON

Math Power: Connections

Given the identity $\cos\theta + i \sin\theta = e^{i\theta}$, and assuming that the properties of exponents hold for imaginary numbers as well, show that
$(r \text{ cis } \alpha)(s \text{ cis } \beta) = rs \text{ cis }(\alpha + \beta)$.

$(r \text{ cis } \alpha)(s \text{ cis } \beta) = (r\, ei^{\alpha})(s\, ei^{\beta})$

$= rs\, ei^{\alpha} \cdot ei^{\beta}$

$= rs\, ei^{(\alpha + \beta)}$

$= rs \text{ cis }(\alpha + \beta)$.

Case Study Follow-Up

This activity provides an opportunity to do research and apply mathematics in solving problems related to issues that may face students in their adult lives. Case Study 4 is located on pages 966–969.

Additional Answer

42.

$(x - 2)^2 + (y - 3)^2 = 16$

Enrichment Masters Booklet, p. 75

NAME _____ DATE _____

11-3 Enrichment Worksheet

Approximations for π and e

The following expression can be used to approximate e. If greater and greater values of n are used, the value of the expression approximates e more and more closely.

$$\left(1 + \frac{1}{n}\right)^n$$

Another way to approximate e is to use this infinite sum. The greater the value of n, the closer the approximation.

$$e = 1 + 1 + \frac{1}{2} + \frac{1}{2 \cdot 3} + \frac{1}{2 \cdot 3 \cdot 4} + \dots + \frac{1}{2 \cdot 3 \cdot 4 \cdot \dots \cdot n} + \dots$$

In a similar manner, π can be approximated using an infinite product discovered by the English mathematician John Wallis (1616-1703).

$$\frac{\pi}{2} = \frac{2}{1} \cdot \frac{2}{3} \cdot \frac{4}{3} \cdot \frac{4}{5} \cdot \frac{6}{5} \cdot \frac{6}{7} \cdots \frac{2n}{2n-1} \cdot \frac{2n}{2n+1} \cdots$$

Solve each problem.

1. Use a calculator with an e^x key to find e to 7 decimal places.
2.7182818

2. Use the expression $\left(1 + \frac{1}{n}\right)^n$ to approximate e to 3 decimal places. Use 5, 100, 500, and 7000 as values of n.
2.488, 2.705, 2.716, 2.718

3. Use the infinite sum to approximate e to 3 decimal places. Use the whole numbers from 3 through 6 as values of n.
2.667, 2.708, 2.717, 2.718

4. Which approximation method approaches the value of e more quickly?
the infinite sum

5. Use a calculator with a π key to find π to 7 decimal places.
3.1415927

6. Use the infinite product to approximate π to 3 decimal places. Use the whole numbers from 3 through 6 as values of n.
2.926, 2.972, 3.002, 3.023

7. Does the infinite product give good approximations for π quickly?
no

8. Show that $\pi^4 + \pi^5$ is equal to e^6 to 4 decimal places.
To 4 decimal places, they both equal 403.4288.

9. Which is larger, e^π or π^e?
$e^\pi > \pi^e$

10. The expression $x^{\frac{1}{x}}$ reaches a maximum value at $x = e$. Use this fact to prove the inequality you found in Exercise 9.
$e^{\frac{1}{e}} > \pi^{\frac{1}{\pi}}$; $\left(e^{\frac{1}{e}}\right)^{\pi e} > \left(\pi^{\frac{1}{\pi}}\right)^{\pi e}$; $e^\pi > \pi^e$

T 75
Glencoe Division, Macmillan/McGraw-Hill

LESSON 11-3 THE NUMBER e 619

Objective This optional page shows how a spreadsheet can be used to calculate the value of an investment after a specified number of years.

Teaching Suggestions

Encourage students to use the *replicate* feature of a spreadsheet when entering the compound interest formulas into cells B5 through B24. The references to A cells are relative and change in successive lines. The references to B cells are absolute and stay the same. Point out that you can also generate the same values in cells B6 through B24 by recursion. You may want to have students work in groups to determine how to change the spreadsheet so that it generates the same values by recursion.

Additional Answers

1. Expand the spreadsheet to contain 50 rows instead of 24.
2. You could add a column to give the amounts for a second rate and then add another column subtracting one amount from the other.

Technology

BASIC
▶ **Spreadsheets**
Software

Compound Interest

You can use a spreadsheet to calculate how funds increase due to compound interest. Use the formula $A = P\left(1 + \frac{r}{n}\right)^{nt}$, where A is the amount in the account after t years, with an initial investment of P dollars at an annual interest rate r, if the interest is compounded n times per year. The spreadsheet below is set up to find the value of an investment after 1 to 20 years. The principal is entered in cell B1, the number of times that the interest is compounded per year is entered in cell B2, and the rate is entered in B3. Cells B5 to B24 contain a variation of the compound interest formula that will compute the balance in the account after successive years.

	COMPOUND INTEREST	
	A	B
1	PRINCIPAL	
2	TIMES COMPOUNDED	
3	RATE	
4	YEAR	BALANCE
5	1	B1*(1 + B3/ B2) ∧ (B2 * A5)
6	2	B1*(1 + B3/ B2) ∧ (B2 * A6)
24	20	B1*(1 + B3/B2) ∧ (B2 * A24)

```
= = = = = = = = = = = = = = = = =
          COMPOUND INTEREST
= = = = = = = = = = = = = = = = =
1      PRINCIPAL           9500
2      TIMES COMPOUNDED    12
3      RATE                0.055
4      YEAR                BALANCE
5      1                   10035.87
6      2                   10601.98
```

At the left is a partial printout from the spreadsheet. It shows the amount accumulated in an account that bears 5.5% interest compounded monthly if the principal is $9500.

EXERCISES

1. Describe how you could modify the spreadsheet program to print 50 years of account balances. See margin.

2. Describe how you could modify the spreadsheet program to print comparisons of the amount accumulated in accounts with two different interest rates. See margin.

11-4A Graphing Calculators: Graphing Logarithmic Functions

You can use a graphing calculator to graph logarithmic functions. A logarithmic function is a function of the form $x = a^y$, where $a > 0$ and $a \neq 1$. This function can also be written as $y = \log_a x$, and it is the inverse of an exponential function $y = a^x$.

Example 1

Graph $y = \log_4 x$. State the domain and range of the function.

To graph logarithmic functions with bases other than 10, you must first change the equation by using the change of base formula, $\log_a x = \dfrac{\log x}{\log a}$. In this example, $\log_4 x = \dfrac{\log x}{\log 4}$. Use the viewing window $[-1, 5]$ by $[-3, 3]$.

TI-81: [Y=] [LOG] [X|T] [÷] [LOG] 4
        [GRAPH]

Casio: [Graph] [log] [ALPHA] [X] [÷]
        [log] 4 [EXE]

The graph of the equation has a vertical asymptote at $x = 0$. The domain is $x > 0$, and the range is the set of real numbers.

Example 2

Graph $y = \log (x + 6)$. State the domain and range of the function.

Use the viewing window $[-10, 10]$ by $[-2, 2]$.

TI-81: [Y=] [LOG] [(] [X|T] [+] 6 [)]
        [GRAPH]

Casio: [Graph] [log] [(] [ALPHA] [X]
        [+] 6 [)] [EXE]

The graph of the equation has a vertical asymptote at $x = -6$. It may appear as though the graph starts at $x = -6$, but actually, the calculator cannot graph enough values to show the true behavior of the graph. In this case, it is important to know how to interpret the graph that the calculator draws. The domain is $x > -6$, and the range is the set of real numbers.

EXERCISES

1–8. See Teacher's Answer Key.

Graph each equation so that a complete graph is shown. Then sketch the graph on a piece of paper and state the domain and range of each function.

1. $y = \log_6 x$
2. $y = \log(x + 2)$
3. $y = \log_5(-x)$
4. $y = \log_x 5$
5. $y = \log_3(x + 4)$
6. $y = \log_6(3 - x)$
7. $y = \log_{10}(x^2)$
8. $y = \log_{-4} x$

GRAPHING CALCULATORS: GRAPHING LOGARITHMIC FUNCTIONS 621

APPLYING THE LESSON

Homework Exercises

Assignment Guide

All: 1–10

INTRODUCING THE LESSON

Objective Graph logarithmic functions a on graphing calculator.

Motivating the Lesson

Ask students to recall how the graph of the inverse of a polynomial function relates to the graph of the function. Ask students to sketch how the inverse of a given exponential function might look.

TEACHING THE LESSON

Teaching Tip Remind students that logarithms with a base other than 10 must be rewritten as a quotient.

More Examples

Graph $y = -\log_4 (x - 2)$. State the domain and the range of the function.

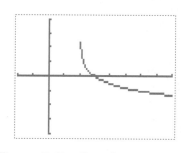

D: $x > 2$, R: all reals

EVALUATING THE LESSON

Closing the Lesson

Ask students to graph $y = \log x$ and $y = -\log_4(x - 2)$ on the same screen. Have students tell how the second graph is related to the first.

NCTM Standards: 1–4, 6

Lesson Resources

- Practice Master 11–4
- Enrichment Master 11–4
- Evaluation Master, Quiz B, p. 137
- Technology Master, p. 21

 Transparency 11–4 contains the 5-Minute Check and a teaching aid for this lesson.

INTRODUCING THE LESSON

 5-Minute Check

(over Lesson 11–3)

Use a calculator to evaluate each expression to the nearest ten thousandth.
1. $e^{2.1}$ **8.1662**
2. $\sqrt[3]{e^2}$ **1.9477**
3. Find the value of the investment after five years if $5000 is invested at 6.5% compounded quarterly. **$6902.10**
4. A colony of bacteria has 5000 members at noon. Its population t hours later is given by the equation $P = 5000\,e^{0.02t}$. How many bacteria are present at 4:30 P.M.? **about 5471**

Motivating the Lesson

To solve $\sqrt{x+5} = \sqrt{x-1}$, we would square each side of the equation. To find the angle A such that $\frac{\sin A}{4} = \frac{\sin 25°}{5}$, we would use the inverse sine function. In the same way, if we want to solve equations involving exponential functions we need to know what the inverse of such a function is. The inverse of an exponential function is a logarithmic function.

11-4 Logarithmic Functions

Objectives
After studying this lesson, you should be able to:
- **11–4A** ▪ evaluate expressions involving logarithms,
- **11–4B** ▪ solve equations involving logarithms, and
- **11–4C** ▪ graph logarithmic functions and inequalities.

Application

When bacteria cells are placed in a medium that provides all of the nutrients needed for growth, the population increases according to a pattern called the bacterial growth curve. The growth occurs in four stages called the lag phase, the log phase, the stationary phase, and the decline phase. During the log phase, bacteria multiply almost exponentially.

Bacteria multiply by mitosis; that is, one cell divides into two new cells. This division process can take minutes or hours depending on the type of bacteria and the conditions of the medium. *Escherichia coli*, or *E. coli*, is one of the fastest growing bacteria. It can reproduce itself by mitosis in 15 minutes.

Suppose a petri dish contains 100 *E. coli*. The formula $b = 100(2^t)$ can be used to find the number of bacteria, b, in the dish after t fifteen-minute periods. If you wanted to know when there would be 12,800 bacteria in the dish, you would have to use an inverse function to find the value of t when $b = 12,800$. *This problem will be solved in Example 3.*

The exponential function $y = a^x$ increases for $a > 1$ and decreases for $0 < a < 1$. Since the function is one-to-one, its inverse is also a function. The inverse of $y = a^x$ is $x = a^y$. In the function $x = a^y$, y is called the **logarithm** of x. It is usually written as $y = \log_a x$ and is read *y equals the log, base a, of x*. The function $y = \log_a x$ is called a **logarithmic function**. Notice that since $y = a^x$ and $x = a^y$ are inverses, their graphs are reflections of each other over the line $y = x$.

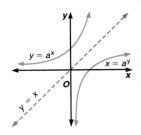

Definition of Logarithmic Function	The logarithmic function $y = \log_a x$, where $a > 0$ and $a \neq 1$, is the inverse of the exponential function $y = a^x$. Therefore, $y = \log_a x$ if and only if $x = a^y$.

Each logarithmic equation corresponds to an exponential equation. For example, the equation $y = \log_2 16$ can be written as $2^y = 16$. Since $2^4 = 16$, $\log_2 16 = 4$.

622   CHAPTER 11   EXPONENTIAL AND LOGARITHMIC FUNCTIONS

ALTERNATE TEACHING STRATEGIES

Using Manipulatives

Have students graph the function $y = 2^x$ and the line $y = x$ on the same set of axes. Use string to reflect each point of the graph of $y = 2^x$ across the line $y = x$. The segment of string connecting the point $(x, 2^x)$ to the point $(2^x, x)$ will be perpendicular to the line $y = x$, and the points will be equidistant from the line. Plot a series of points and then draw the curve $y = \log_2 x$.

Using Connections

Have students write the list of the properties of exponents, given on page 598. Have them translate each one into the corresponding property for logarithms. For example, $a^m a^n = a^{m+n}$ corresponds to $\log_b mn = \log_b m + \log_b n$.

Example 1

> **Write $\log_{10} 0.01 = -2$ in exponential form.**
>
> The base is 10 and the exponent is –2.
> $0.01 = 10^{-2}$

Example 2

> **Evaluate the expression $\log_8 64$.**
>
> Let $x = \log_8 64$.
>
> $\begin{aligned} x &= \log_8 64 \\ 8^x &= 64 \qquad && \textit{Definition of logarithm} \\ 8^x &= 8^2 \\ x &= 2 \qquad && \textit{Property of equality for exponential functions} \end{aligned}$

Logarithms can help us solve the application problem from the beginning of the lesson.

Example 3

APPLICATION
Biology

> **If the population of 100 bacteria doubles every fifteen minutes, how long will it take for the population to reach 12,800?**
>
> $\begin{aligned} b &= 100(2^t) \\ 12{,}800 &= 100(2^t) \qquad && b = 12{,}800 \\ 128 &= 2^t \qquad && \textit{Divide each side by 100.} \\ \log_2 128 &= t \qquad && \textit{Write the problem in logarithmic form.} \\ \log_2 2^7 &= t \qquad && 128 = 2^7 \\ 7 &= t \qquad && \textit{Definition of logarithm} \end{aligned}$
>
> The population will be 12,800 in 7 time periods, that is, in 105 minutes or 1 hour 45 minutes.

Since the logarithmic function and the exponential function are inverses of each other, both of their compositions yield the identity function.

$\begin{aligned} y &= a^x \\ &= a^{\log_a x} \qquad && \textit{Let } x = \log_a x. \\ &= x \end{aligned}$

$\begin{aligned} y &= \log_a x \\ &= \log_a a^x \qquad && \textit{Let } x = a^x. \\ &= x \end{aligned}$

Since logarithms are exponents, the properties of logarithms can be derived from the properties of exponents.

Properties of Logarithms

> Suppose m and n are positive numbers, b is a positive number other than 1, and p is any real number. Then the following properties hold.
>
> | | |
> |---|---|
> | Product property: | $\log_b mn = \log_b m + \log_b n$ |
> | Quotient property: | $\log_b \dfrac{m}{n} = \log_b m - \log_b n$ |
> | Power property: | $\log_b m^p = p \cdot \log_b m$ |
> | Property of equality: | If $\log_b m = \log_b n$, then $m = n$. |

LESSON 11-4   LOGARITHMIC FUNCTIONS   623

TEACHING THE LESSON

Teaching Tip   Since the logarithmic function $y = \log_a x$ is the inverse of the exponential function $y = a^x$, its domain is the set of positive real numbers and its range is the set of all real numbers.

Chalkboard Examples

For Example 1

Write $\log_8 2 = \frac{1}{3}$ in exponential form. $8^{\frac{1}{3}} = 2$

For Example 2

Evaluate the expression $\log_3 27$.
3

For Example 3

If a bacteria colony doubles every twenty minutes and there are 500 bacteria at noon, when will the population reach 16,000?
1:40 P.M.

Example 4

Use the properties of exponents to show that the quotient property of logarithms is valid.

Let $\log_b m = x$ and let $\log_b n = y$.
Then $b^x = m$ and $b^y = n$.   *Write each equation in exponential form.*

$$\frac{m}{n} = \frac{b^x}{b^y} \qquad\qquad \textit{Find the quotient of m and n.}$$

$$\frac{m}{n} = b^{x-y} \qquad\qquad \frac{a^m}{a^n} = a^{m-n}$$

$$\log_b \frac{m}{n} = \log_b b^{x-y} \qquad \textit{Take the logarithm of each side.}$$

$$\log_b \frac{m}{n} = x - y \qquad\qquad \log_a a^x = x$$

$$\log_b \frac{m}{n} = \log_b m - \log_b n \qquad \textit{Substitute for x and y.}$$

Therefore, $\log_b \dfrac{m}{n} = \log_b m - \log_b n$.

Equations can be written involving logarithms. Use the properties of logarithms and the definition of a logarithm to solve these equations.

Example 5

Solve each equation.

a. $\log_b \sqrt{3} = \dfrac{1}{4}$

a. $\log_b \sqrt{3} = \dfrac{1}{4}$

$$b^{\frac{1}{4}} = \sqrt{3} \qquad \textit{Definition of logarithm}$$

$$\sqrt[4]{b} = \sqrt{3} \qquad \textit{Definition of } b^{\frac{1}{n}}$$

$$b = (\sqrt{3})^4 \qquad \textit{Raise each side to the fourth power.}$$

$$b = 9$$

b. $\log_8 (5x + 3) = \log_8 (45 - 2x)$

b. $\log_8 (5x + 3) = \log_8 (45 - 2x)$

$$5x + 3 = 45 - 2x \qquad \textit{Property of Equality}$$

$$7x = 42$$

$$x = 6$$

c. $\log_2 (4x + 10) - \log_2 (x + 1) = 3$

c. $\log_2 (4x + 10) - \log_2 (x + 1) = 3$

$$\log_2 \frac{4x + 10}{x + 1} = 3 \qquad \textit{Quotient property of logarithms}$$

$$\frac{4x + 10}{x + 1} = 2^3 \qquad \textit{Definition of logarithm}$$

$$4x + 10 = 8(x + 1)$$

$$4x = 2$$

$$x = \frac{1}{2}$$

624   CHAPTER 11   EXPONENTIAL AND LOGARITHMIC FUNCTIONS

You can graph a logarithmic function by rewriting the logarithmic function as an exponential function and constructing a table of values.

Example 6

Graph $y = \log_2 (x - 2)$.

The equation $y = \log_2(x - 2)$ can be written as $2^y = x - 2$.

x	$x - 2$	y
2.125	0.125	−3
2.25	0.25	−2
2.5	0.5	−1
3	1	0
4	2	1
6	4	2
10	8	3

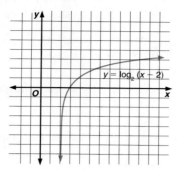

$y = \log_2 (x - 2)$

EXPLORATION: Graphing Calculator

In the Graphing Calculator Exploration in Lesson 11-2, an equation representing population growth was given as $y = 10^{0.00389x+2}$. Since the logarithmic function is the inverse of the exponential function, population growth can also be modeled with the logarithmic function $x = \dfrac{\log y - 2}{0.00389}$.

1. Use the settings below to set up a viewing window.

XMIN=0   YMIN=1800
XMAX=12000000000   YMAX=2180
XSCL=1000000000   YSCL=25

2. Since graphing calculators graph y as a function of x, the equation will need to be rewritten as follows: $y = \dfrac{\log x - 2}{0.00389}$. Press $\boxed{Y =}$ and enter the equation.

3. Use the TRACE function to determine the population growth from 1800 to the year 2000. According to the graph, when can we expect the world population to be double the population in 1960? 2038

You can graph logarithmic inequalities using the same graphing techniques, as shown in Example 6. Choose a test point to determine which region to shade.

LESSON 11-4 LOGARITHMIC FUNCTIONS 625

Checking for Understanding

Exercises 1–18 are designed to help you assess students' understanding through reading, writing, speaking, and modeling. You should work through Exercises 1–3 with your students and then monitor their work on Exercises 4–18.

Closing the Lesson

Writing Activity Have students write an equation in exponential form. Then have them exchange papers, and rewrite the equation they have in logarithmic form.

Homework Exercises

Assignment Guide

Average: 19–39, 40–60 even, 61–75
Enriched: 19–39 odd, 40–75
All: Mid-Chapter Review, 1–12

The red A, B, and C flags, printed only in the Teacher's Wraparound Edition, indicate the level of difficulty of the exercises.

Chapter 11, Quiz B, Lessons 11–3 through 11–4), is available in the *Evaluation Masters*, p. 137.

Additional Answers

1. In the equation $y = a^x$, x is the logarithm.

3. Let $b^x = m$, then $\log_b m = x$.
$$(b^x)^p = m^p$$
$$b^{xp} = m^p$$
$$\log_b b^{xp} = \log_b m^p$$
$$xp = \log_b m^p$$
$$p \log_b m = \log_b m^p$$

4. $\log_4 64 = 3$

5. $\log_6 \left(\frac{1}{36}\right) = -2$

6. $\log_{49} 7 = \frac{1}{2}$

7. $27^{\frac{1}{3}} = 3$

8. $16^{\frac{1}{2}} = 4$

9. $9^{\frac{3}{2}} = 27$

CHECKING FOR UNDERSTANDING

Communicating Mathematics

Read and study the lesson to answer each question.

1. **Explain** how logarithms are related to exponents. See margin.
2. Why do you think that the second phase of growth for a colony of bacteria is called the log phase? See students' work.
3. **Show** that the power property of logarithms is valid. See margin.

Guided Practice

Write each equation in logarithmic form. 4–6. See margin.

4. $4^3 = 64$ 5. $6^{-2} = \frac{1}{36}$ 6. $49^{\frac{1}{2}} = 7$

Write each equation in exponential form. 7–9. See margin.

7. $\log_{27} 3 = \frac{1}{3}$ 8. $\log_{16} 4 = \frac{1}{2}$ 9. $\log_9 27 = \frac{3}{2}$

Evaluate each expression.

10. $\log_2 32$ 5   11. $\log_{10} 1000$ 3   12. $\log_7 \frac{1}{343}$ -3

Solve each equation.

13. $\log_6 x + \log_6 9 = \log_6 54$ 6   14. $\log_7 n = \frac{2}{3} \log_7 8$ 4

15. $4 \log_2 x + \log_2 5 = \log_2 405$ 3   16. $\log_8 48 - \log_8 w = \log_8 4$ 12

17. Graph $y = \log_3(x + 1)$. See margin.   18. Graph $y < \log_2 x$. See margin.

EXERCISES

Practice

Write each equation in logarithmic form. 19–24. See margin.

19. $2^4 = 16$ 20. $5^{-2} = \frac{1}{25}$ 21. $3^{-3} = \frac{1}{27}$

22. $10^6 = 1,000,000$ 23. $8^{-\frac{2}{3}} = \frac{1}{4}$ 24. $4^0 = 1$

Write each equation in exponential form. 25–30. See margin.

25. $\log_2 8 = 3$ 26. $\log_5 125 = 3$ 27. $\log_{10} 10,000 = 4$

28. $\log_7 \frac{1}{2401} = -4$ 29. $\log_8 2 = \frac{1}{3}$ 30. $\log_{\sqrt{6}} 36 = 4$

Evaluate each expression.

31. $\log_9 9^6$ 6   32. $\log_{10} 0.01$ -2   33. $12^{\log_{12} 5}$ 5

34. $\log_2 \frac{1}{16}$ -4   35. $\log_6 6^5$ 5   36. $\log_8 16$ $\frac{4}{3}$

37. $\log_a a^{10}$ 10   38. $\log_{11} 11$ 1   39. $10^{4 \log_{10} 2}$ 16

Solve each equation.

40. $\log_x 49 = 2$ 7   41. $\log_5 0.04 = x$ -2

42. $\log_6(4x + 4) = \log_6 64$ 15   43. $\log_3(3x) = \log_3 36$ 12

17.
$y = \log_3(x + 1)$

18.
$y < \log_2 x$

44. $\log_x 16 = -4$ $\frac{1}{2}$

46. $\log_{10} \sqrt[3]{10} = x$ $\frac{1}{3}$

48. $2\log_6 4 - \frac{1}{4}\log_6 16 = \log_6 x$ 8

50. $3\log_7 4 + 4\log_7 3 = \log_7 x$ 5184

52. $\log_6 x = \frac{1}{2}\log_6 9 + \frac{1}{3}\log_6 27$ 9

54. $\log_{10} x + \log_{10} x + \log_{10} x = \log_{10} 8$ 2

45. $\log_6 216 = x$ 3

47. $\log_2 4 + \log_2 6 = \log_2 x$ 24

49. $\log_3 12 - \log_3 x = \log_3 3$ 4

51. $\log_4(x-3) + \log_4(x+3) = 2$ 5

53. $\log_9 5x = \log_9 6 + \log_9(x-2)$ 12

Graph each equation or inequality. 55–60. See Teacher's Answer Key.

55. $y = \log_4 x$

56. $y = \log_{10} x$

57. $y = \log_{\frac{1}{2}} x$

58. $y = \log_2 (x-1)$

59. $y \le \log_6 x$

60. $y > \log_{10} (x+1)$

Critical Thinking

61. Explain why 1 is excluded from the possible values of the base of the logarithmic function. All powers of 1 are 1, so the inverse is not a function.

Applications and Problem Solving

62. Biology The generation time for bacteria is the time that it takes for the population to double. The generation time, G, can be found using experimental data and the formula $G = \dfrac{t}{3.3 \log_{10}\frac{b}{f}}$, where t is the time period, b is the number of bacteria at the beginning of the experiment, and f is the number of bacteria at the end of the experiment. The generation time for mycobacterium tuberculosis is 16 hours. How long will it take for two of these bacteria to multiply into 256 bacteria? 422.4 hours or 17 days 14 hours 24 minutes

63. Biology Atlantic salmon swim up to 2000 miles upstream to spawn each year. Scientists who study salmon have found that the oxygen consumption of a yearling salmon, O, is given by the function $O = 100(3^{\frac{3s}{5}})$, where s is the speed that the fish is traveling in feet per second.

   a. Find the oxygen consumption of a fish that is not moving. 100 units

   b. How fast is a fish swimming when its oxygen consumption is 2700 units? 5 ft/s

Mixed Review

64. Write the slope-intercept form of the equation of the line through the points with coordinates $(8, 5)$ and $(-6, 0)$. **(Lesson 1-5)** $y = \frac{5}{14}x + \frac{15}{7}$

65. Business Pristine Pipes Inc. produces plastic pipe for use in newly-built homes. Two of the basic types of pipe have different diameters, wall thicknesses, and strengths. The strength of a pipe is increased by mixing a special additive into the plastic before it is molded. The table below shows the resources needed to produce 100 feet of each type of pipe and the amount of the resource available each week.

Resource	Pipe A	Pipe B	Resource Availability
Extrusion Dept.	4 hours	6 hours	48 hours
Packaging Dept.	2 hours	2 hours	18 hours
Strengthening additive	2 pounds	1 pound	16 pounds

If the profit on 100 feet of type A pipe is $34 and on type B pipe is $40, how much of each should be produced? **(Lesson 2-6)** 300 ft of A, 600 ft of B

LESSON 11-4 LOGARITHMIC FUNCTIONS   627

RETEACHING THE LESSON

Have students list the properties of logarithms across the top of a piece of paper, and then do the following exercises, listing each one and its answer in the appropriate column. Given $\log_b x = 3$, and $\log_b y = -2$, find the value of each expression.

1. $\log_b xy$ 1   2. $\log_b \frac{x}{y}$ 5

3. $\log_b \frac{y}{x}$ –5   4. $\log_b x^2$ 6

5. $\log_b \sqrt{y}$ –1   6. $\log_b \sqrt[3]{xy}$ $\frac{1}{3}$

Additional Answers

19. $\log_2 16 = 4$

20. $\log_5 \frac{1}{25} = -2$

21. $\log_3 \left(\frac{1}{27}\right) = -3$

22. $\log_{10} 1{,}000{,}000 = 6$

23. $\log_8 \frac{1}{4} = -\frac{2}{3}$

24. $\log_4 1 = 0$

25. $2^3 = 8$

26. $5^3 = 125$

27. $10^4 = 10{,}000$

28. $7^{-4} = \frac{1}{2401}$

29. $8^{\frac{1}{3}} = 2$

30. $(\sqrt{6})^4 = 36$

Practice Masters Booklet, p. 76

4.

$y = 0.1^x$

66. $y = \pm\sqrt{\dfrac{7-x}{8}}$ **66.** Find the inverse of $y = 7 - 8x^2$. **(Lesson 3-3)**

67. Find the equation of the line tangent to the graph of $y = x^2 - 6x + 4$ at $(-1, 11)$. Write the equation in slope-intercept form. **(Lesson 3-6)** $y = -8x + 3$

68. Solve $\dfrac{-4}{x-1} = \dfrac{7}{2-x} + \dfrac{3}{x+1}$. **(Lesson 4-6)** $\dfrac{5}{13}$

69. Find $\cos 90°$ without using a calculator. **(Lesson 5-4)** 0

70. Solve $\cos 2x + \sin x = 1$ for principal values of x. **(Lesson 7-5)** $0°, 30°$

71. Find the inner product of $\vec{u}$ and $\vec{v}$ if $\vec{u} = (9, 5, 3)$ and $\vec{v} = (-3, 2, 5)$. Are the vectors perpendicular? **(Lesson 8-4)** -2, no

72. Find $(8 - 2i)(2 + 6i)$. **(Lesson 9-5)** $28 + 44i$

73. Write the standard form of the equation $x^2 - 4x - 4y^2 = 0$. Then identify the conic section. **(Lesson 10-5)** $\dfrac{(x-2)^2}{4} - \dfrac{y^2}{1} = 1$; hyperbola

74. Banking Find the amount accumulated if $600 is invested at 6% for 15 years and interest is compounded continuously. **(Lesson 11-3)** $1475.76

75. College Entrance Exam Choose the best answer. D
Divide $6\sqrt{45}$ by $3\sqrt{5}$.
   (A) 9   **(B)** 4   **(C)** 15   **(D)** 6   **(E)** 54

MID-CHAPTER REVIEW

Evaluate. **(Lesson 11-1)**

1. $81^{\frac{3}{4}}$ 27

2. $\dfrac{25^{\frac{3}{4}}}{25^{\frac{1}{4}}}$ 5

3. $\sqrt[3]{\sqrt{27}}$ $\sqrt{3}$

4. Graph the equation $y = 0.1^x$. **(Lesson 11-2)** See margin.

5. Financial Planning Teresa Slane plans to contribute $2500 annually to a Keogh retirement account with an APR of 9%. Assuming the APR remains the same, what will the value of the account be in 25 years? **(Lesson 11-2)** $211,752.24

Evaluate each expression to the nearest ten thousandth. **(Lesson 11-3)**

6. $e^{3.8}$ 44.7012

7. $5\sqrt{3e}$ 14.2783

8. $e^{\frac{2}{5}}$ 1.4918

9. Meteorology The atmospheric pressure, p, varies with the altitude, a, above Earth. For altitudes up to about 10 km, the pressure in millimeters of mercury is given by $p = 760e^{-0.125a}$ when a is measured in kilometers. Find the atmospheric pressure 4.3 km above Earth. **(Lesson 11-3)** about 444 mm of mercury

Solve each equation. **(Lesson 11-4)**

10. $\log_x 512 = 3$ 8

11. $\log_{\sqrt{5}} 5 = x$ 2

12. $\log_5 (x^2 - 30) = \log_5 6$ ± 6

EXTENDING THE LESSON

Math Power: Reasoning

If $\log_{10} x$ is an integer, x is a power of 10. If $\log_{10} x$ is a rational number other than an integer, can x itself be rational? no

Mid-Chapter Review

The Mid-Chapter Review provides students with a brief review of the concepts and skills in Lessons 11–1 through 11–4. Lesson numbers are given at the end of problems or instruction lines so students may review concepts not yet mastered.

11-5 Common Logarithms

Objectives
11–5A
11–5B

After studying this lesson, you should be able to:
- find common logarithms and antilogarithms of numbers, and
- use common logarithms to compute powers and roots.

Application

As people gain experience in performing a task, the time required for them to perform the task is reduced until they reach a standard minimum time. For businesses, this means that as a worker gains experience at his or her job, the amount of money spent on labor per item is reduced. This effect can be represented by a learning curve.

FYI...

The learning curve allows manufacturers to position themselves well in a competitive market. Companies with more experienced workers spend less on labor, so they can keep their prices low.

The learning curve was first developed in the aircraft industry before World War II. A survey of major airplane manufacturers showed that while the time required to build different types of airframes was very different, the rates at which workers increased their productivity was strikingly similar. They found that labor time for the eighth unit was 80% of the labor time for the fourth unit, and time for the twelfth unit was 80% of the labor for the sixth unit. Each time the number of airplanes produced was doubled, the time required was reduced by 20%. So the rate of learning for aircraft construction was 80%. While the rate of learning may be different for another product, the pattern of learning is the same.

The formula for a learning curve is $u_n = kn^b$, where u_n is the number of hours of labor for the nth product, k is the number of hours of labor for the first product, n is the number of products made, and $b = \dfrac{\log r}{\log 2}$, where r is the learning rate. Notice that no base is indicated for the logarithms in the expression for b. When no base is indicated, the base is assumed to be 10. So, $\log r$ means $\log_{10} r$. Logarithms with base 10 are called **common logarithms**.

You can find the common logarithms of integral powers of 10 easily.

$\log 1000 = 3$	since	$1000 = 10^3$
$\log 100 = 2$	since	$100 = 10^2$
$\log 10 = 1$	since	$10 = 10^1$
$\log 1 = 0$	since	$1 = 10^0$
$\log 0.1 = -1$	since	$0.1 = 10^{-1}$
$\log 0.01 = -2$	since	$0.01 = 10^{-2}$

LESSON 11-5   COMMON LOGARITHMS   629

NCTM Standards: 1–4, 6

Lesson Resources

- Practice Master 11–5
- Enrichment Master 11–5
- Activity Master, p. 32

 Transparency 11–5 contains the 5-Minute Check and a teaching aid for this lesson.

INTRODUCING THE LESSON

 5-Minute Check
(over Lesson 11–4)

1. Write $2^{-3} = \frac{1}{8}$ in logarithmic form.
   $\log_2 \frac{1}{8} = -3$

2. Write $\log_9 27 = \frac{3}{2}$ in exponential form.
   $9^{\frac{3}{2}} = 27$

3. Evaluate $\log_5 \frac{1}{5^2}$. -2

Solve each equation.
4. $\log_4 2 + \log_4 x = 1$ 2
5. $\log_6 x + \log_6 2x = 2$ $3\sqrt{2}$

Motivating the Lesson

Have students look at their calculators. Then ask students which button(s) can be used to find logarithms. Answers should include those that are marked "log" or "ln." What are the bases for these logarithmic functions? Why are they included on a calculator rather than some other logarithms? These questions will be addressed in the remainder of Chapter 11.

ALTERNATE TEACHING STRATEGIES

Using Critical Thinking

What is $\sqrt[3]{-125}$? It is –5. What answer does your calculator give for this question? Many calculators will give an error message. The reason is that a calculator or computer uses logarithms to do many computations, and the logarithm of a negative number is not real. Work together on some examples of how logarithms can simplify computation.

Using Computers

Have students write a flowchart of the steps involved in using logarithms to calculate a value as in Example 4. It may be best to first do the chart for a specific problem and then generalize it.

Teaching Tip Since the characteristic is the exponent of ten needed when the number is written in scientific notation, another method of finding the logarithm is as follows:

log 40,000 = log 4.0 × 10⁴
= 4 + log 4.0
≈ 4.6021.

Chalkboard Examples

For Example 1

Given that log 3 ≈ 0.4771, evaluate each logarithm.
a. log 0.0003   ≈ −3.5229
b. log 3000   ≈ 3.4771

For Example 2

Use the equation of a learning curve given in the application at the start of the lesson.
a. The Lewis Engine Works produces gasoline engines for lawn mowers. Find the number of hours required to build the thirtieth gasoline engine, assuming that the learning rate is 82% and it took 510 hours to build the first one.
   192.6 hours
b. The Lewis Engine Works pays the workers who make its gasoline engines an average of $11.85 per hour. How much less will the labor on the thirtieth engine cost than the labor for the first engine?
   $3761.19

The common logarithms of numbers that differ by integral powers of ten are closely related.

Example 1

> **Given that log 4 ≈ 0.6021, evaluate each logarithm.**
> **a. log 40,000**   **b. log 0.004**
>
> **a.** $\log 40{,}000 = \log (10{,}000 \cdot 4)$ **b.** $\log 0.004 = \log \left(\dfrac{4}{1000}\right)$
> $= \log 10{,}000 + \log 4$ $= \log 4 - \log 1000$
> $\approx 4 + 0.6021$ $\approx 0.6021 - 3$
> ≈ 4.6021 ≈ -2.3979

Look closely at the results of Example 1. Each of the common logarithms is made up of two parts, the **characteristic** and the **mantissa**. The mantissa is the logarithm of a number between 1 and 10. Thus, mantissas are greater than 0 and less than 1. In Example 1, the mantissa is log 4 or 0.6021. The characteristic is the exponent of ten that is used to write the number in scientific notation. In Example 1, the characteristic of 10,000 is 4, and the characteristic of $\dfrac{1}{1000}$ is −3. Traditionally, a logarithm is expressed as the indicated sum of the mantissa and the characteristic.

You can use a scientific calculator to solve equations containing common logarithms.

Example 2

APPLICATION

Psychology

> **Refer to the application presented at the beginning of the lesson for the equation of a learning curve.**
> **a. The Carter Truck Company produces diesel engines for trucks. Find the number of hours required to build the forty-fifth engine, assuming that the learning rate is 75% and it took 48,000 hours to build the first one.**
> **b. The company pays its workers an average of $11.50 per hour. How much less will the labor on the forty-fifth engine cost than the labor for the first engine?**
>
> **a.** $u_n = kn^b$
>
> $u_{45} = 48{,}000(45)^{\frac{\log 0.75}{\log 2}}$ $n = 45, k = 45{,}000, \text{ and } b = \dfrac{\log 0.75}{\log 2}$
>
> Evaluate with a calculator.
>
> 48000 45 $\boxed{y^x}$ $\boxed{(}$ 0.75 $\boxed{\text{LOG}}$ $\boxed{\div}$ 2 $\boxed{\text{LOG}}$ $\boxed{)}$ $\boxed{=}$ *9887.7175*
>
> The forty-fifth engine will take about 9888 hours to complete.
>
> **b.** The first engine took 48,000 − 9888 or 38,112 hours longer to make. This would save the company an additional $11.50 × 38,112 or $438,288.

630   CHAPTER 11   EXPONENTIAL AND LOGARITHMIC FUNCTIONS

Sometimes the logarithm of x is known to have a value of a, but x is not known. Then x is called the **antilogarithm** of a, written *antilog a*. If $\log x = a$, then $x = $ antilog a. *Remember that the inverse of a logarithmic function is an exponential function.*

Teaching Tip In Example 3, point out that $\log \frac{1}{H^+} = \log 1 - \log H^+ = -\log H^+$, so $\log H^+ = -pH$.

Example 3

The pH of a solution is a measure of its acidity. A low pH indicates an acidic solution, and a high pH indicates a basic solution. Neutral water has a pH of 7. The pH of a solution is related to the concentration of hydrogen ions it contains by the formula $pH = \log \frac{1}{H^+}$, where H^+ is the number of gram atoms of hydrogen ions per liter. If the pH of tomato juice is 4.1, what is the concentration of hydrogen ions?

$$pH = \log \frac{1}{H^+}$$

$$4.1 = \log \frac{1}{H^+} \qquad pH = 4.1$$

antilog $4.1 = \dfrac{1}{H^+}$ *Take the antilogarithm of each side.*

$$H^+ = \frac{1}{\text{antilog } 4.1}$$

Evaluate with a calculator.

$1 \div 4.1 \boxed{\text{2nd}} \boxed{\text{LOG}} \boxed{=} \; 0.0000794$

The concentration of hydrogen ions is about 7.94×10^{-5} gram atoms per liter.

Logarithms can be used to solve problems involving powers and roots. Before scientific calculators were invented, this was the most efficient method available.

Example 4

Use logarithms to evaluate $\dfrac{24.8\sqrt{451}}{(39.6)^3}$.

Let $A = \dfrac{24.8\sqrt{451}}{(39.6)^3}$. Then $\log A = \log\left[\dfrac{24.8\sqrt{451}}{(39.6)^3}\right]$.

$$\log A = \log\left[\frac{24.8\sqrt{451}}{(39.6)^3}\right]$$

$$= \log 24.8 + \frac{1}{2}\log 451 - 3\log 39.6 \qquad \textit{What properties are used?}$$

$$\approx 1.3945 + \frac{1}{2}(2.6542) - 3(1.5977)$$

$$\approx -2.0715$$

$A \approx$ antilog -2.0715

$\quad \approx 0.00848$

The value of the expression is approximately 0.00848.
Check the result with your calculator.

LESSON 11-5 COMMON LOGARITHMS 631

Chalkboard Examples

For Example 3

The pH of a solution is related to the concentration of hydrogen ions it contains by the formula $pH = \log \frac{1}{H^+}$, where H^+ is the number of gram atoms of hydrogen ions per liter. If the pH of ocean water is 8.8, what is the concentration of hydrogen ions? 1.58×10^{-9}

For Example 4

Use logarithms to evaluate $\dfrac{16(4.9)^3}{\sqrt[3]{596}}$. ≈ 223.7

CHECKING FOR UNDERSTANDING

Communicating Mathematics

Read and study the lesson to answer each question.   1. They are the same.

1. **Explain** the relationship between the characteristic of a common logarithm and the exponent of 10 for a number expressed in scientific notation.

2. What kind of function are you using when you take the antilogarithm of a number? exponential

3. If the characteristic for $\log x$ is 3, then $\underline{\ ?\ } \leq x < \underline{\ ?\ }$. 1000, 10,000

Guided Practice

Use a calculator to find the common logarithm of each number to the nearest ten thousandth.

4. 98.2 1.9921
5. 424 2.6274
6. 2.43 0.3856

Use a calculator to find the antilogarithm of each number to the nearest hundredth.

7. 2.5499 354.73
8. 0.4398 2.75
9. –1.8989 0.01

Between which two integral powers of ten is each number?

10. antilog 2.3456
    100 and 1000
11. antilog 4.8740
    10,000 and 100,000
12. antilog –2.5232
    0.001 and 0.01

Evaluate each expression by using logarithms. Round to the nearest tenth. Check your work with a calculator.

13. $784 \times 47.9 \times 0.0748$ 2809.0

14. $\dfrac{6.39 \times 1.54}{3.78}$ 2.6

15. $(1.69)^4 \times 221$ 1802.8

16. $7.32 \div \sqrt[4]{0.0743}$ 14.0

EXERCISES

Practice

Use a calculator to find the common logarithm of each number to the nearest ten thousandth.

A

17. 894.3 2.9515
18. 0.7849 –0.1052
19. 0.0054 –2.2676
20. 0.871 –0.0600
21. 22,892 4.3597
22. 4.4×10^7 7.6435

Use a calculator to find the antilogarithm of each number to the nearest hundredth.

B

23. 0.2586 1.81
24. –0.2586 0.55
25. –1.9725 0.01
26. 2.2675 – 3 0.19
27. 4.9243 84,004.01
28. 0.01 1.02

Evaluate each expression by using logarithms. Round to the nearest tenth. Check your work with a calculator.

29. $754 \times 24.5 \times 0.0128$ 236.5

30. $\dfrac{5.43 \times 7.12}{2.28}$ 17.0

31. $642 \times (2.01)^3$ 5213.4

32. $\sqrt{5.81 \times 71.1}$ 20.3

33. $\sqrt[3]{(3.05)(730)}$ 13.1

34. $8.83 \div \sqrt[5]{0.4218}$ 10.5

C

35. $\left(\dfrac{1}{0.7891}\right)^4$ 2.6

36. $\sqrt[6]{82.9}$ 2.1

37. $\sqrt{\dfrac{8.4}{0.31}}$ 5.2

38. $\dfrac{37.9\sqrt{488}}{(1.28)^3}$ 399.2

RETEACHING THE LESSON

Have students make a chart to aid in their understanding of common logarithms.
Write the integers 1, 2, 3, 4, and 5 across the top, and ×1, ×10, ×10² down the side. Then have students fill in the value of the common logarithm for each entry in the table to four decimal places. Next, add rows for ×10⁻¹, ×10⁻².

39. Find the value of x in $(3x)^{\log 3} - (5x)^{\log 5} = 0$ if $x > 0$. $\frac{1}{15}$

40. Astronomy The parallax of a star is the difference in direction of the star as seen from two widely separated points. Astronomers use the parallax of a star to determine its distance from Earth. The apparent magnitude of a star is its brightness as observed from Earth. Astronomers use parsecs to measure interstellar space. One parsec is about 3.26 light years or 19.2 trillion miles. The absolute magnitude is the magnitude a star would have if it were 10 parsecs from Earth. The greater the magnitude of a star the fainter the star appears. For stars more than 30 parsecs, or 576 trillion miles from Earth, the formula relating the parallax, p, the absolute magnitude, M, and the apparent magnitude, m, is $M = m + 5 + 5 \log p$.

a. The star M35 in the constellation Gemini has an apparent magnitude of 5.3 and a parallax of about 0.018. Find the absolute magnitude of this star. 1.58

b. Stars with apparent magnitudes greater than 5 can be seen only with a telescope. If a star has an apparent magnitude of 8.6 and an absolute magnitude of 5.3, find its parallax to four decimal places. 0.0219

41. Geology The intensity of an earthquake is described by a number on the Richter scale. The Richter scale number, R, of an earthquake is given by the formula $R = \log\left(\frac{a}{T}\right) + B$, where a is the amplitude of the vertical ground motion in microns, T is the period of the seismic wave in seconds, and B is a factor that accounts for the weakening of seismic waves.

a. Find the intensity of an earthquake to the nearest tenth if a recording station measured the magnitude as 200 microns and the period as 1.6 seconds, and $B = 4.2$. 6.3

b. How much more intense is an earthquake of magnitude 5 on the Richter scale than an earthquake that measures 4 on the Richter scale? 10 times

42. $10\sqrt{5}, -\frac{1}{2}$

**Mixed
Review**

42. Find the distance between the points with coordinates $(-9, 6)$ and $(11, -4)$. Then, find the slope of the line passing through the points. **(Lesson 1-4)**

43. $\begin{bmatrix} 8 & 8 & -1 \\ 2 & -8 & -3 \end{bmatrix}$

43. Find $A + B$ if $A = \begin{bmatrix} 8 & 5 & -1 \\ 0 & -6 & -3 \end{bmatrix}$ and $B = \begin{bmatrix} 0 & 3 & 0 \\ 2 & -2 & 0 \end{bmatrix}$. **(Lesson 2-2)**

44. about
101.1 cm and
76.9 cm

44. Geometry The sides of a parallelogram are 55 cm and 71 cm long. Find the length of each diagonal if the larger angle measures $106°$. **(Lesson 5-7)**

45. Verify that $\dfrac{\sin^2 x}{\cos^4 x + \cos^2 x \sin^2 x} = \tan^2 x$ is an identity. **(Lesson 7-2)** See margin.

46. If $A = (12, -5, 18)$ and $B = (0, -11, 21)$, find an ordered triple that represents $\overrightarrow{AB}$. **(Lesson 8-3)** $(-12, -6, 3)$

47. $\dfrac{(x-2)^2}{4} + \dfrac{(y-6)^2}{3} = 1$

47. Write the equation of the ellipse with foci at $(3, 6)$ and $(1, 6)$ that passes through $(0, 6)$. **(Lesson 10-3)**

48. Solve $\log_5(7x) = \log_5(5x + 16)$. **(Lesson 11-4)** 8

49. College Entrance Exam Choose the best answer. B
Fisher's Farm Market sells onions by the pound. The price of 3 pounds of onions is d dollars. At this rate, how many pounds of onions could you buy for 80 cents?

(A) $2.4d$ **(B)** $\dfrac{2.4}{d}$ **(C)** $\dfrac{3d}{8}$ **(D)** $\dfrac{8d}{3}$ **(E)** $0.8d$

EXTENDING THE LESSON

Math Power: Problem Solving

Write the numbers 7, 49 and 343 in base 7, then next to each, write its base 7 logarithm. What similarities can you see between base 7 and base 10? Given that $\log_7 2 = 0.3562$, what do you expect the $\log_7 14$ to be? the $\log_7 \dfrac{2}{343}$? $1 + 0.3562$

or 1.3562; $0.3562 - 3 = -2.6438$

Enrichment Masters Booklet, p. 77

NAME _____ DATE _____

11-5 Enrichment Worksheet

The Slide Rule

Before the invention of electronic calculators, computations were often performed on a slide rule. A slide rule is based on the idea of logarithms. It has two movable rods labeled with C and D scales. Each of the scales is logarithmic.

To multiply 2×3 on a slide rule, move the C rod to the right as shown below. You can find 2×3 by adding log 2 to log 3, and the slide rule adds the lengths for you. The distance you get is 0.778, or the logarithm of 6.

1-2 See students' work.
Follow the steps to make a slide rule.

1. Use graph paper that has small squares, such as 10 squares to the inch. Using the scales shown at the right, plot the curve $y = \log x$ for $x = 1, 1.5,$ and the whole numbers from 2 through 10. Make an obvious heavy dot for each point plotted.

2. You will need two strips of cardboard. A 5-by-7 index card, cut in half the long way, will work fine. Turn the graph you made in Exercise 1 sideways and use it to mark a logarithmic scale on each of the two strips. The figure shows the mark for 2 being drawn.

3. Explain how to use a slide rule to divide 8 by 2. Line up the 2 on the C scale with the 8 on the D scale. The quotient is the number on the D scale below the 1 on the C scale.

T77
Glencoe Division, Macmillan/McGraw-Hill

Objective   Solve exponential and logarithmic equations and inequalities.

Motivating the Lesson

Ask students to recall how they could solve the equation $x + 2 = 3x^2 - 4$ by using graphs. Point out that there are two methods that can be used. These same two techniques can be used to solve logarithmic and exponential equations.

INTRODUCING THE LESSON

Teaching Tip   You may wish to have students solve the equations in Examples 1 and 2 using the first method to confirm the solutions.

More Examples

1. Solve $3^{4x-2} = (0.2)^{3x-1}$ to the nearest hundredth. Use the viewing window $[-1, 1]$ by $[-2, 6]$.

0.42

11-6A   Graphing Calculators: Exponential and Logarithmic Equations and Inequalities

You can use a graphing calculator to solve equations involving logarithms and exponents, just as you have used it to solve other types of equations. Once again, there are two methods that you can use to find the solution to an equation. The first method is to graph both equations and find the x-coordinate of the point of intersection. The second method is to transform the equation so that one side equals zero and find the x-intercept of the graph. For exponential and logarithmic equations, the second method is often easier because it is easier to see where the graph crosses the x-axis than to see the point of intersection. Often the point of intersection is near an asymptote and the gradual decrease or increase can make the point of intersection difficult to find.

Example 1

Solve $\left(\dfrac{1}{4}\right)^{3x} = 6^{x-2}$. Use the viewing window $[-2, 4]$ by $[-3, 3]$.

Let's use the second method to solve the equation. Transforming the original equation to get zero on one side yields $\left(\dfrac{1}{4}\right)^{3x} - 6^{x-2} = 0$. Transforming the equation so that either side is zero will produce the same solution.

TI-81: `Y=` `.25` `∧` `(` `(` `3` `X|T` `)` `)` `−` `6`
`∧` `(` `(` `X|T` `−` `2` `)` `)` `GRAPH`

Casio: `Graph` `.25` `xʸ` `(` `(` `3` `ALPHA`
`X` `)` `)` `−` `6` `xʸ` `(` `(` `ALPHA`
`X` `−` `2` `)` `)` `EXE`

Using the TRACE and ZOOM functions on the calculator shows that the solution is about 0.6022.

To solve logarithmic equations, use the same steps you used to solve exponential equations.

Example 2

Solve $\log(x + 3) = \log(7 - 4x)$. Use the viewing window $[-5, 5]$ by $[-3, 3]$.

Transform the equation so that $\log(x + 3) - \log(7 - 4x) = 0$. Graph this equation and look for the x-intercepts.

TI-81: `Y=` `LOG` `(` `(` `X|T` `+` `3` `)` `)` `−`
`LOG` `(` `(` `7` `−` `4` `X|T` `)` `)` `GRAPH`

Casio: `Graph` `log` `(` `(` `ALPHA` `X`
`+` `3` `)` `)` `−` `log` `(` `(` `7` `−` `4`
`ALPHA` `X` `)` `)` `EXE`

Using the TRACE and ZOOM functions on the calculator shows that the solution is 0.8.

You can also use a TI-81 graphing calculator to solve inequalities involving exponents and logarithms. The "Shade(" command can be used to graph inequalities and indicate areas that are solutions. The "Shade(" command can be found under the DRAW menu of the calculator.

Example 3

Solve the inequality $7^{x+4} \leq 0.1^{2x+8}$. Use the viewing window $[-10, 1]$ by $[-1, 3]$.

Decide which side of the inequality must be the upper bound and which side must be the lower bound. In this case, 7^{x+4} is the lower bound because it is less than or equal to 0.1^{2x+8}. Thus, 0.1^{2x+8} is the upper bound.

Next, clear all equations from the Y= list and clear the graphics screen by pressing [2nd] [DRAW] 1 [ENTER]. This must be done before graphing any other inequalities using the "Shade(" command.

Now, graph the inequality.

TI-81: [2nd] [DRAW] 7

7 [^] [(] [(] [X|T] [+] 4 [)] [ALPHA]

[,] .1 [^] [(] [(] 2 [X|T] [+] 8 [)] [)] [)]

[ENTER]

You can use the arrow keys and the ZOOM function of the calculator to find the solution. The graph shows this inequality is true for $x \leq -4.00$.

EXERCISES

Solve each equation to the nearest hundredth by using a graphing calculator.

1. $2^x = 95$ 6.57
2. $4^x = x^4$ −0.77, 2, 4
3. $5^x = 4^{x+3}$ 18.64
4. $4 \log (x + 3) = 9$ 174.83
5. $\log (2x + 3) = -\log(3 - x)$ −1.39, 2.89
6. $0.16^{4+3x} = 0.3^{8-x}$ 0.34
7. $3 \log (x^3) = \log(x - 1)$ no solution
8. $12^{0.5x} = 8^{0.1x-4}$ −8.04

Solve each inequality by using a TI-81 graphing calculator.   12. $3.5 < x < 4$

9. $4^{2x-5} \leq -3^{x-3}$ no solution
10. $0.5^{2x} - 4 \leq 0.1^{5-x}$ $x \geq -1$
11. $\log (5x) > \log(x + 2)$ $x > \frac{1}{2}$
12. $\log_4 (x - 3) > \log_5 (2x - 7)$
13. $\log (3x - 1) \leq 2^{x-7}$
   $x \leq 0.68, x \geq 7.41$
14. $5^x > \log_5 x$ all real numbers

GRAPHING CALCULATORS: EXPONENTIAL AND LOGARITHMIC EQUATIONS AND INEQUALITIES   635

NCTM Standards: 1–4, 6

Lesson Resources

- Practice Master 11–6
- Enrichment Master 11–6
- Evaluation Master, Quiz C, p. 138
- Multicultural Activity Master, p. 11

 Transparency 11–6 contains the 5-Minute Check and a teaching aid for this lesson.

INTRODUCING THE LESSON

 5-Minute Check

(over Lesson 11–5)

Use a calculator to find the common logarithm of each number to the nearest ten thousandth.
1. 902.5 **2.9554**
2. 0.0034 **−2.4685**

Use a calculator to find the antilogarithm of each number to the nearest hundredth.
3. 1.3424 **22.00**
4. −1.7447 **0.02**
5. Evaluate $\frac{\sqrt{209}}{(5.1)^3}$ using

logarithms. **≈ 0.109**

Motivating the Lesson

Show some photographs of different kinds of fossils, perhaps a dinosaur skeleton, some seashells in rock, petrified wood, and so on, and ask students to guess the age of each one. Then inquire as to how scientists studying such fossils can date them with any degree of accuracy. Finding the age of a fossil is just one example of using logarithms to solve an exponential equation.

11-6 Exponential and Logarithmic Equations

Objectives
11–6A
11–6B

Application

After studying this lesson, you should be able to:
- solve exponential and logarithmic equations, and
- solve exponential and logarithmic inequalities.

The ages of fossils were first estimated by their relative positions in layers of rock. While excavating for a canal, surveyor William Smith (1769–1839)observed that fossils occurred in layers. He reasoned that because rock forms in layers with younger rock forming on older rock, the fossils in lower layers must be older than fossils in upper layers.

Modern methods of estimating the age of a fossil or rock use the presence of naturally-occurring radioactive atoms. Radioactivity was discovered by Henri Becquerel in the late 1890s. Radioactive substances decay into more stable substances over time. The time it takes for one-half of a quantity of a radioactive element to decay is called the half-life of the element.

The element used most often in determining age is carbon-14, which is present in all living organisms. Radioactive carbon-14 decays, at a predictable rate, into the more stable carbon-12. In 1947, William Libby became the first person to use carbon-14 to date plant and animal remains. Since carbon dating is thought to be accurate only for fossils less than 50,000 years old, potassium-40 or rubidium-87 is used for fossils thought to be older than 50,000 years.

The formula $y = y_o \cdot c^{\frac{t}{T}}$ can be used to describe growth and decay in nature. The final amount is y, the initial amount is y_o, c is the constant of proportionality, t is time, and T is the time per cycle of c. When you use the growth and decay formula to solve a problem involving half-life, you will use $c = \frac{1}{2}$ and T is the half-life.

When finding the age of a fossil, you must find the value of t in the exponent. Logarithms can be used to solve equations in which variables appear as exponents. Such equations are called **exponential equations**. Solutions to equations involving exponential expressions are based on the fact that if $a^{x_1} = a^{x_2}$ for some base a and real numbers x_1 and x_2, then $x_1 = x_2$.

Example 1

Solve the equation $6.7^{x-2} = 42$.

$$6.7^{x-2} = 42$$
$$\log 6.7^{x-2} = \log 42 \qquad \textit{Take the logarithm of each side.}$$
$$(x-2)\log 6.7 = \log 42 \qquad \textit{Power property}$$
$$x = \frac{\log 42}{\log 6.7} + 2$$
$$x \approx 3.965$$

The solution is approximately 3.965.

ALTERNATE TEACHING STRATEGIES

Using Questioning

Have the class solve $0.52^{x-4} = 11$. Discuss the actual steps taken in the solution. Why did you take the logarithm of each side of the equation? Why did you use logarithms to base 10? Suppose you had taken the logarithm of each side to base 0.52. How would this change the solution? The idea behind this line of questioning is the change of base formula.

Using Applications

Refer to Lesson 11–3. The application at the beginning of the lesson and Example 2 both contain exponential functions. Have students consider questions such as "When will the value of Byron's investment grow to $4000?" and "When will the soup be 140°F?" Solve these problems. **about 39 years; about 69 minutes**

Example 2

APPLICATION

Archaeology

Stonehenge is an ancient megalithic site in southern England. Some believe it was designed to make astronomical observations, but archaeologists cannot agree on the reason that Stonehenge was constructed. Charcoal samples taken from a series of holes at Stonehenge have about 0.63 pounds of carbon-14 in a one-pound sample. Estimate the age of the charcoal pits at Stonehenge. Assume that the half-life of carbon-14 is 5730 years.

$$y = y_o \cdot c^{\frac{t}{T}}$$

$$0.63 = 1 \cdot (0.5)^{\frac{t}{5730}}$$ $y = 0.63, y_o = 1, c = 0.5, T = 5730$

$$\log 0.63 = \log(0.5)^{\frac{t}{5730}}$$ *Take the logarithm of each side.*

$$\log 0.63 = \frac{t}{5730} \log 0.5$$ *Power property*

$$t = \frac{5730 \log 0.63}{\log 0.5}$$ *Solve for t.*

$$t \approx 3819.4820$$ *Evaluate with a calculator.*

The charcoal pits at Stonehenge are estimated to be 3819 years old.

The formula for growth and decay can also be used to describe the growth of a population. Choose the constant of proportionality as the ratio between the ending and beginning populations. For example, if you wish to know the time that it takes for a population to double, use $c = 2$ in the equation $y = y_o \cdot c^{\frac{t}{T}}$.

Example 3

APPLICATION

Biology

Under ideal conditions, the population of single-celled organisms in a pond will double in 5 days. How much time will it take for the original population to increase seven times?

At the ending time, there would be 7 organisms for every 1 organism at the starting time. So we can use $y = 7$ and $y_o = 1$.

$$y = y_o \cdot c^{\frac{t}{T}}$$

$$7 = 1 \cdot (2)^{\frac{t}{5}}$$ $c = 2$ and $T = 5$

$$\log 7 = \log(2)^{\frac{t}{5}}$$ *Take the logarithm of each side.*

$$\log 7 = \frac{t}{5} \log 2$$ *Power property*

$$t = \frac{5 \log 7}{\log 2}$$

$$t \approx 14.04$$

The organisms will reach 7 times their original population in about 14 days.

Graphing is an alternate way of solving exponential or logarithmic equations. To do this, graph each side of the equation as a function and find the coordinates of the intersection of the graphs.

LESSON 11-6 EXPONENTIAL AND LOGARITHMIC EQUATIONS 637

Teaching Tip In the formula for growth and decay, if $0 < c < 1$, the population decays over time, whereas if $c > 1$, the population grows.

Teaching Tip In Example 1, note how the power property of logarithms allows us to transform the original equation into a linear equation in x.

Chalkboard Examples

For Example 1

Solve the equation $3.9^{x+1} = 28$. ≈ 1.448

For Example 2

Phosphorus-32 is a radioactive substance with a half-life of 14.3 days. How long would it take to reduce a 100-gram sample of P-32 to 15 grams? **about 39 days**

For Example 3

Under ideal conditions, the population of a certain bacterial colony will double in 45 minutes. How much time will it take for the population to increase five-fold? **about 1.74 hours**

Teaching Tip In Example 5, students should check the sign of any quantity such as $(1 - \log 5)$ before multiplying or dividing by it. If it is negative, the inequality will be reversed by this operation.

EVALUATING THE LESSON

Checking for Understanding

Exercises 1–15 are designed to help you assess students' understanding through reading, writing, speaking, and modeling. You should work through Exercises 1–3 with your students and then monitor their work on Exercises 4–15.

Additional Answers

1. If $a^{x_1} = a^{x_2}$ and $a \neq 1$, then $x_1 = x_2$.
2. The constant of proportionality will be positive when the formula describes growth and negative when it describes decay.

Example 4

Solve $5^x = 12^{3-x}$ by graphing.

Graph $y = 5^x$ and $y = 12^{3-x}$ on the same set of axes.

The graphs appear to intersect at about $(1.8, 18.1)$.

Therefore, $5^x = 12^{3-x}$ when $x \approx 1.8$.

Check the solution by graphing with a graphing calculator and using the TRACE function to find the intersection point.

You can use the techniques for solving logarithmic or exponential equations to solve exponential and logarithmic inequalities.

Example 5

Solve $5^{x+3} > 10^{x-6}$.

$$5^{x+3} > 10^{x-6}$$
$$\log 5^{x+3} > \log 10^{x-6}$$
$(x+3)\log 5 > (x-6)\log 10$ *Power property*
$x\log 5 + 3\log 5 > x - 6$ *$\log 10 = 1$*
$6 + 3\log 5 > x - x\log 5$
$6 + 3\log 5 > x(1 - \log 5)$
$\dfrac{6 + 3\log 5}{1 - \log 5} > x$ *Solve for x.*
$26.90 > x$ *Evaluate with a calculator.*

Sometimes you want to find the logarithm of a number to a base other than 10. These problems can be solved with common logarithms and a calculator.

Example 6

Express $\log_8 92$ in terms of common logarithms. Then find its value.

Let $x = \log_8 92$.
$8^x = 92$ *Write the equation in exponential form.*
$\log 8^x = \log 92$ *Take the logarithm of each side.*
$x\log 8 = \log 92$ *Power property*
$x = \dfrac{\log 92}{\log 8}$ *Solve for x.*

The value of the logarithm is $\dfrac{\log 92}{\log 8}$ or about 2.1745. Thus, $8^{2.1745} \approx 92$.

Any logarithm can be expressed in terms of a different base. However, the base is usually changed to base 10 or base e so that they may be evaluated with a calculator. *We will discuss logarithms to base e in the next lesson.*

Change of Base Formula

Suppose a, b, and n are positive numbers, and neither a nor b is 1. Then, the following equation is true. $\log_a n = \dfrac{\log_b n}{\log_b a}$

---

3. an equation involving a variable as a exponent; no

4. $x = \dfrac{\log 72}{\log 3}$; 3.89

5. $x = \dfrac{\log 98}{\log 7}$; 2.36

6. $x = \dfrac{\log 63}{2\log 6}$; 1.16

7. $x = \dfrac{\log 121}{\log 5}$; 2.98

8. $x = -\dfrac{\log 10}{\log 2}$; -3.32

9. $x = \dfrac{\log 16}{\log 3}$; 2.52

10. $x = \dfrac{\log 128}{3\log 5}$; 1.00

11. $x = -\dfrac{\log 18}{\log 3}$; -2.63

12. $x = \dfrac{\log 3\sqrt{2}}{\log 3}$; 1.32

13. $x > 3.807$
14. $x \leq 1.766$
15. $x \geq 4.716$

Example 7 | Find the value of $\log_3 14$ using the change of base formula.

$$\log_a n = \frac{\log_b n}{\log_b a}$$

$$\log_3 14 = \frac{\log 14}{\log 3} \qquad a = 3, b = 10, n = 14$$

$$\approx \frac{1.1461}{0.4771}$$

$$\approx 2.4022 \qquad \text{The value of } \log_3 14 \text{ is about } 2.4022.$$

CHECKING FOR UNDERSTANDING

Communicating Mathematics

Read and study the lesson to answer each question. 1–3. See margin.

1. **Explain** why we can use logarithms to solve equations involving variables that are exponents.

2. When will the constant of proportionality in the growth and decay formula be positive and when will it be negative?

3. **Define** exponential equations. Is $x^6 = 248$ an exponential equation?

Guided Practice

State x in terms of common logarithms. Then find the value of x to the nearest hundredth. 4–12. See margin.

4. $3^x = 72$
5. $7^x = 98$
6. $6^{2x} = 63$

7. $x = \log_5 121$
8. $2^{-x} = 10$
9. $x = \log_3 16$

10. $5^{3x} = 128$
11. $3^{-x} = 18$
12. $3^x = 3\sqrt{2}$

Solve each inequality by using logarithms. 13–15. See margin.

13. $2^x > 14$
14. $5^x \leq 7\sqrt{6}$
15. $10^{x-3} \geq 52$

EXERCISES

Practice

Solve each equation or inequality by using logarithms. Round solutions to the nearest hundredth.

16. $6^x = 72$ 2.39
17. $2^x = 27$ 4.75
18. $4.3^x < 76.2$ $x < 2.97$

19. $2.2^{x-5} = 9.32$ 7.83
20. $9^{x-4} = 7.13$ 4.89
21. $6^{3x} = 81$ 0.82

22. $x < \log_3 52.7$ $x < 3.61$
23. $x = \log_4 19.5$ 2.14
24. $x^{\frac{2}{3}} \geq 27.6$ $x \geq 145$

25. $x^{\frac{2}{5}} = 17.3$ 1244.84
26. $5^{x-1} = 2^x$ 1.76
27. $3^{2x} = 7^{x-1}$ −7.74

28. $6^{x-2} = 4^x$ 8.84
29. $12^{x-4} = 3^{x-2}$ 5.58
30. $\log_2 x = -3$ 0.13

31. $\log_x 6 > 1$ $1 < x < 6$
32. $\log_{27} \frac{1}{3} = x$ −0.33
33. $2^x > \sqrt{3^{x-2}}$ −7.64

34. $6^{x^2-2} < 48$ −2.04 < x < 2.04
35. $\log_3 \sqrt[4]{5} = x$ 0.37
36. $\sqrt[3]{4^{x-1}} = 6^{x-2}$ 2.35

Graphing Calculator

Use a graphing calculator to solve each equation or inequality by graphing. Round solutions to the nearest hundredth.

37. $6^{x+2} = 14^{x-3}$ 13.57
38. $x^{\frac{2}{5}} = 2$ 5.66
39. $12^{x-4} > 4^x$ $x > 9.05$

40. Graph $y = \log_2 x$ on a graphing calculator. How does the graph differ from $y = \log_{10} x$? It is steeper.

LESSON 11-6   EXPONENTIAL AND LOGARITHMIC EQUATIONS   **639**

RETEACHING THE LESSON

Solve these equations by first taking the logarithm of each side and then applying the product rule of logarithms to transform the exponential equation into one that is linear.

1. $500 = 50 \cdot 2^{\frac{t}{2}}$ 66.439

2. $5 = 28\left(\frac{1}{2}\right)^{\frac{t}{14.3}}$ 35.542

3. $0.32^{x-1} = 7$ −0.708
4. $9^{x+2} = 4^{2x}$ 7.638

Closing the Lesson

Modeling Activity   Have students give an example of an exponential equation that models population growth.

APPLYING THE LESSON

Homework Exercises

Assignment Guide
Average: 16–28, 29–39 odd, 41–52
Enriched: 16–26 even, 27–52

The red A, B, and C flags, printed only in the Teacher's Wraparound Edition, indicate the level of difficulty of the exercises.

Chapter 11, Quiz C, (Lessons 11–5 through 11–6), is available in the *Evaluation Masters*, p. 138.

Using Technology

In Exercises 37–39, note that the range of each exponential function is the set of positive real numbers, while the domain is the set of all real numbers. The reverse is true for the logarithmic functions in Exercise 40.

Practice Masters Booklet, p. 78

11-6   NAME _____ DATE _____

Practice Worksheet

Exponential and Logarithmic Equations

Solve each equation or inequality by using logarithms.

1. $8^x = 10$ 1.1073
2. $12^x = 18$ 1.1632

3. $2.4^x \leq 20$ $x \leq 3.4219$
4. $1.8^{x-5} = 19.8$ 10.0795

5. $4^{2x+1} = 15.2$ 0.4815
6. $3^{5x} = 85$ 0.8088

7. $x < \log_2 15$ $x < 3.9069$
8. $x \geq \log_3 12.3$ $x \geq 2.2843$

9. $x^{\frac{2}{3}} > 25.3$ $x \geq 127.2567$
10. $x^{0.4} = 18.9$ 1552.9394

11. $3^{2x-2} = 2x$ 1.4608
12. $4^{1-2x} = 3^{2x}$ 0.2789

T78
Glencoe Division, Macmillan/McGraw-Hill

Additional Answers

45.

$x + 4y < 9$

47. $y = \pm 17 \sin (8x + 480°)$
50. $x^2 = -12y$;

$x^2 = -12y$

$(0, -3)$

Enrichment Masters Booklet, p. 78

Critical Thinking

41. Solve the equation $2^{2a+3} - 2^{a+3} - 2^a + 1 = 0.$ −3 or 0

Applications and Problem Solving

42. Accounting   Assets such as houses, cars, business equipment, and art appreciate or depreciate with time. The formula we used to compute compound interest can be used to find the future value of these assets. Depreciation or appreciation is given in terms of one year, so $n = 1$ in the formula $A = P\left(1 + \frac{r}{n}\right)^{nt}$. This makes the formula for the future value of an object $A = P(1 + r)^t$, where P is the initial value, r is the rate of appreciation or depreciation, and t is the time in years. If the object is appreciating, then $r > 0$. If the object is depreciating, then $r < 0$.

a. You are considering buying a new car that has a list price of $12,000. A book that gives comparisons of different cars says that in past years this model has depreciated at a rate of 15% per year. If you are planning on keeping the car for five years, how much would you expect the car to be worth when you are ready to sell it? $5324.46

b. Homes in the Sunbury area appreciate at a rate of about 4% per year. If a home sold for $89,000 this year, after how many years would you expect the home to be worth $124,000? 8.5 years or 8 yrs 6 months

c. Inflation causes prices to rise over time. The rate of inflation in each country fluctuates in reaction to various economic conditions. Suppose the rate of inflation in the United States averages 3.5%. If a school lunch costs $1.85 today and a friend says he paid $1.35 for the same type of lunch some time ago, how long ago do you think he bought his lunch? 9.2 years or 9 years 2 months

43. Chemistry   After 13 years, 2.1 pounds of radioactive material remain from a 7-pound sample. What is the half-life of this material? 7.48 yr

44. Sales   After t years, the annual sales in hundreds of thousands of units of a product, q, is given by $q = \left(\frac{1}{2}\right)^{0.8^t}$. This equation is a Gompertz equation that describes growth in many areas of study.

a. Find the annual sales of the product after 7 years. 86,471 units

b. After how many years will the annual sales be about 64,171 units? 2 yr

Mixed Review

45. Graph $x + 4y < 9$.   **(Lesson 1-3)** See margin.

46. Solve $2x^2 + 7x - 4 = 0$ by completing the square.   **(Lesson 4-2)** −4, 0.5

47. Write an equation of the sine function that has an amplitude of 17, a period of 45, and a phase shift of −60°.   **(Lesson 6-2)** See margin.

48. Simplify $\frac{\tan^2 t}{1 - \sec^2 t}$.   **(Lesson 7-1)** −1

49. Find the rectangular coordinates of the point with polar coordinates $(0.25, \pi)$.   **(Lesson 9-3)** $(-0.25, 0)$

50. Write the equation of the parabola with vertex at $(0, 0)$ and focus at $(0, -3)$. Then, draw the graph.   **(Lesson 10-2)** See margin.

51. Use logarithms to evaluate $\left(\frac{1}{0.381}\right)^2$.   **(Lesson 11-5)** 6.89

52. College Entrance Exam   Choose the best answer. B
Which is equivalent to 6.02×10^3?
(A) 602   **(B)** 6020   **(C)** 0.00602   **(D)** 0.0602   **(E)** none of these

---

EXTENDING THE LESSON

Math Power: Reasoning

Prove $(\log_a b)(\log_b c) = \log_a c$.
By the change of base formula,
$\log_b c = \frac{\log_a c}{\log_a b}$. Multiplying by
$\log_a b$, we get $(\log_a b)(\log_b c) = \log_a c$.

11-7 Natural Logarithms

NCTM Standards: 1–4, 6

Objectives
11–7A
11–7B

After studying this lesson, you should be able to:
- find natural logarithms of numbers, and
- solve equations using natural logarithms.

Application

The city planners of Bakersfield, California, are studying the current and future needs of the city. The sewage system they have in place now can support 250,000 residents. The current population of the city is 175,000, up from 106,000 ten years ago. Assuming that the population will continue to grow at this rate, when will the sewage system need to be updated? How many people will the new system have to accommodate for the system to last 15 years before needing to be updated again? *This problem will be solved in Example 1.*

The growth or decay of a population can be modeled by using an exponential equation. A general formula for growth and decay is $y = ne^{kt}$, where y is the final amount, n is the initial amount, k is a constant, and t is time. If a population is growing, $k > 0$; if a population is decaying, $k < 0$.

Often when you solve problems involving the number e, it is best to use logarithms to the base e. These are called **natural logarithms** and are usually denoted **ln x**. The key marked LN on your calculator will display the natural logarithm of a number. Since e is a positive number between 2 and 3, all of the properties of logarithms also hold for natural logarithms. Note that if $\log_e e = x$ and $e^x = e$, then $x = 1$. Thus, $\ln e = 1$.

Example 1

Demographics

Refer to the application above.
a. **When will the sewage system need to be updated?**
b. **How many people will the new system have to accommodate for the upgraded system to last 15 years before needing to be updated again?**

a. First, we must find the value of the constant k in the exponential growth formula. To do this, use the two known population values.

$$y = ne^{kt}$$
$$175,000 = 106,000e^{10k} \qquad \text{\textit{y = 175,000, n = 106,000, and t = 10}}$$
$$1.6509 \approx e^{10k}$$
$$\ln 1.6509 \approx \ln e^{10k} \qquad \text{\textit{Take the natural logarithm of each side.}}$$
$$\ln 1.6509 \approx 10k \ln e \qquad \text{\textit{Power property}}$$
$$0.5013 \approx 10k \qquad \text{\textit{ln e = 1}}$$
$$0.05013 \approx k$$

The value of k is about 0.05013.   *(continued on the next page)*

Lesson Resources

- Practice Master 11–7
- Enrichment Master 11–7
- Evaluation Master, Quiz D, p. 138
- Activity Master, p. 33

 Transparency 11–7 contains the 5-Minute Check and a teaching aid for this lesson.

INTRODUCING THE LESSON

5-Minute Check
(over Lesson 11–6)

Solve each equation or inequality by using logarithms. Give each answer to the nearest ten thousandth.
1. $4^{-x} = 15$ –1.9534
2. $x > \log_2 6.5$ $x > 2.7004$
3. $5^{x-1} = 2^{x+1}$ 2.5129
4. The half-life of Phosphorus-33 is about 25 days. When will a 20-gram sample of P-33 be reduced to 8 grams?
   about 33 days

Motivating the Lesson

We saw in Lesson 11–3 that the equation $A = Pe^{rt}$ is used to model continuous compounding of interest. It would be natural to ask questions such as, "When will my bank account double in value or reach a certain savings goal?" The most direct method for solving such an equation is to use logarithms to base e.

ALTERNATE TEACHING STRATEGIES

Using Discussion

Find the doubling time of $4000 invested at 4.5% compounded continuously, first using common logarithms and then base e logarithms. Discuss which method seems easier.

Why don't we use base $\frac{1}{2}$ for a problem concerning half-life or base $\left(1 + \frac{r}{n}\right)$ for compounding interest?

Using Modeling

Have students work in small groups. Give each group a pair of population figures for your city, county, state, the U.S., and so on. Have each group find the doubling time for their problem, then compare the value of k and the doubling time for each population as a class.

Teaching Tip The model $y = ne^{kt}$ assumes that the population grows at a rate of $100k\%$ with continuous compounding, just as in the case of a bank account with continuously compounded interest. Even though each birth itself is a discrete event, the aggregate behavior of a large population can often be well described in this way.

Then, we can find the time when the population will be 250,000.

$$y = ne^{kt}$$
$$250{,}000 \approx 175{,}000e^{0.05013t}$$
$$1.4286 \approx e^{0.05013t}$$
$$\ln 1.4286 \approx 0.05013t \ \ln e$$
$$t \approx 7.11$$

The current system must be updated in about 7 years.

b. We need to find the number of people that will live in Bakersfield 15 years after the system is updated. The population will be 250,000 when it is updated, so $n = 250{,}000$.

$$y = ne^{kt}$$
$$= 250{,}000e^{(0.05013)(15)}$$
$$= 530{,}283$$

To last 15 years, the updated system should be designed to accommodate about 530,300 people.

Sometimes you know the natural logarithm of a number x and must find x. The antilogarithm of a natural logarithm is written **antiln x**. If $\ln x = a$, then $x = $ antiln a. Use the INV or 2nd and LN keys of your calculator to evaluate the antilogarithm of a natural logarithm.

Example 2

FYI...

The romance languages are all derived from Latin. The major romance languages that are in use today are French, Italian, Portuguese, Romanian, and Spanish.

If two languages have evolved separately from a common ancestral language, the number of years since the split, $n(r)$, is given by the formula $n(r) = -5000 \ln r$, where r is the percent of the words from the ancestral language that are common to both languages now. If two languages split off from a common ancestral language about 2000 years ago, what portion of the words from the ancestral language would you expect to find in each language today?

$$n(r) = -5000 \ln r$$
$$2000 = -5000 \ln r$$
$$-0.4 = \ln r$$
$$\text{antiln } -0.4 = r$$
$$0.67 \approx r \qquad \textit{Use a calculator to evaluate.}$$

One would expect about 67% of the words from the ancestral language to be common to both languages today.

CHECKING FOR UNDERSTANDING

Communicating Mathematics

Read and study the lesson to answer each question.

1. If the population of a city decreases over an amount of time, would you expect the value of k in $y = ne^{kt}$ to be positive or negative? Explain. See margin.

2. **Compare** the formula for growth and decay, $y = ne^{kt}$, to the formula for the balance of an account with interest compounded continuously, $A = Pe^{rt}$. How are the formulas related? See margin.

Guided Practice

Use a calculator to find each value to the nearest ten thousandth.

3. ln 9.32 2.2322

4. ln 4.01 1.3888

5. ln 0.21 −1.5606

6. antiln 2.84 17.1158

7. antiln 0.7831 2.1882

8. antiln −3.874 0.0208

Solve each equation.

9. $9 = e^x$ 2.1972

10. $18 = e^{3x}$ 0.9635

11. $65 = e^{6x}$ 0.6957

12. **Biology** Kim is studying bacteria in her advanced biology class. She has calculated that $k = 0.658$ for a certain type of bacteria when t is measured in hours. How long would it take for 15 of these bacteria to multiply into 250 bacteria? 4.28 hours

EXERCISES

Practice

Use a calculator to find each value to the nearest ten thousandth.

13. ln 56.8 4.0395

14. ln 0.0198 −3.9221

15. ln 980 6.8876

16. ln 0.0089 −4.7217

17. ln 1 0

18. $\ln\left(\dfrac{1}{0.32}\right)$ 1.1394

19. antiln 4.987 146.4963

20. antiln 2.94 18.9158

21. antiln 0.62 1.8589

22. antiln −0.053 0.9484

23. antiln 0 1

24. antiln −2.81 0.0602

Solve each equation. Round solutions to the nearest hundredth.

25. $1600 = 4e^{0.045t}$ 133.14

26. $10 = 5e^{5k}$ 0.14

27. $\ln 4.5 = \ln e^{0.031t}$ 48.52

28. $25 = e^{0.075y}$ 42.92

29. $\ln 40.5 = \ln e^{0.21t}$ 17.63

30. $\ln 60.3 = \ln e^{0.21t}$ 19.52

Applications and Problem Solving

31. **Chemistry** Radium 226, which used to be used for cancer treatment and as an ingredient in fluorescent paint, decomposes radioactively. Its half-life is 1800 years. Find the constant k you would use in the decay formula for radium. Use 1 gram as the original amount. −0.000385

32. **Banking** Mr. Cuthbert invested a sum of money in a certificate of deposit that pays 8% interest compounded continuously. Recall that the formula for the amount in an account earning interest compounded continuously is $A = Pe^{rt}$. If Mr. Cuthbert made the investment on January 1, 1986 and the account is worth $10,000 on January 1, 2005, what was the original amount in the account? $2187.12

LESSON 11-7 NATURAL LOGARITHMS 643

RETEACHING THE LESSON

Since the natural logarithm function is available on a scientific calculator, it can be easily used in solving exponential equations. Have students work several problems from Lesson 11-6, Exercises 16-36, using natural logarithms. This should help students become more familiar with their use and application.

EVALUATING THE LESSON

Checking for Understanding

Exercises 1–12 are designed to help you assess students' understanding through reading, writing, speaking, and modeling. You should work through Exercises 1–2 with your students and then monitor their work on Exercises 3–12.

Closing the Lesson

Speaking Activity   Compare and contrast the common and natural logarithmic functions, and give examples of applications of each.

APPLYING THE LESSON

Homework Exercises

Assignment Guide

Average: 13–24, 25-39 odd, 41–49
Enriched: 13–23 odd, 25–49

The red A, B, and C flags, printed only in the Teacher's Wraparound Edition, indicate the level of difficulty of the exercises.

Chapter 11, Quiz D, (Lesson 11–7), is available in the *Evaluation Masters*, p. 138.

Practice Masters Booklet, p. 79

NAME _____ DATE _____

11-7 Practice Worksheet

Natural Logarithms

Use a calculator to find each value to the nearest ten thousandth.

1. ln 43.2 3.7658

2. ln 0.0217 −3.8304

3. ln 985 6.8926

4. ln 0.0076 −4.8796

5. ln 10 2.3026

6. $\ln \frac{1}{0.6}$ 0.5108

7. antiln (−0.256) 0.7741

8. antiln 4.62 101.4940

9. antiln (−1.62) 0.1979

Solve each equation.

10. $1500 = 6e^{0.043t}$ 128.41

11. $1249 = 175e^{-0.04t}$ −49.13

12. $\ln 6.7 = \ln (e^{0.21t})$ 9.06

13. $\ln 724.6 = \ln (e^{6.3t})$ 1.05

14. **Banking** Ms. Cubbatz invested a sum of money in a certificate of deposit that pays 8% interest compounded continuously. Recall that the formula for the amount in an account earning interest compounded continuously is $A = Pe^{rt}$. If Ms. Cubbatz made the investment on January 1, 1989 and the account is worth $12,000 on January 1, 1993, what was the original amount in the account? $8713.79

T79
Glencoe Division, Macmillan/McGraw-Hill

33. Ecology DDT is an insecticide that has been used by farmers. It decays slowly and is sometimes absorbed by plants that animals and humans eat. DDT absorbed in the mud at the bottom of a lake is degraded into harmless products by bacterial action. Experimental data shows that 10% of the initial amount is eliminated in 5 years.

   a. Find the value of k in the decay formula. −0.0211

   b. How much of the original amount of DDT is left after 10 years? 81%

   c. The U.S. Environmental Protection Agency banned almost all use of DDT in the U.S. in 1972. If none has been used near the lake since then, in what year will the concentration of DDT fall below 25%? 2037

34. Sales Sales of a product under relatively stable market conditions tend to decline at a constant annual rate in the absence of promotional activities. This sales decline can be expressed by the exponential function of the form $s = s_o e^{-at}$, where s is the sales at time t, t is time in years, s_o is the sales at time $t = 0$, and a is the sales decay constant. Suppose sales of On-Time Watches were 45,000 the first year and 37,000 the second year.

   a. Find the value of a in the equation for this sales decline. 0.196

   b. Find the projected sales for three years from now. 24,995

   c. If the trend continues, when would you expect sales to be 15,000 units? 5.6 years

35. Finance Mike Kallenberg deposited some money in a bank account that earns 5.6% interest compounded continuously.

   a. How long would it take to double the amount of money in Mr. Kallenberg's account? about 12.4 years

   b. The Rule of 72 says that if you divide 72 by the interest rate of an account that compounds interest continuously, the result is the approximate number of years that it will take for the money in the account to double. Do you think that the rule of 72 is accurate? Explain. Answers may vary.

36. Meteorology The atmospheric pressure varies with the altitude above the surface of Earth. Meteorologists have determined that for altitudes up to 10 km, the pressure p in millimeters of mercury is given by $p = 760e^{-0.125a}$, where a is the altitude in kilometers.

   a. What is the atmospheric pressure at an altitude of 3.3 km? 503.1 mm

   b. At what altitude will the atmospheric pressure be 450 mm of mercury? 4.2 km

37. Business Have you ever wondered how long it will probably take for you to receive service when you are standing in a line? The probability that a customer will receive service after waiting T time periods can be described by an exponential function. If μ is the average number of customers serviced in a time period, then the probability p that a customer will be serviced in T time periods is given by $p = 1 - e^{-\mu T}$.

   a. The admissions clerk at Grady Memorial Hospital can service an average of 3 patients per hour. What is the probability that a customer will be serviced within 25 minutes? 0.713

   b. After how long is the probability that a patient in the admissions office will be serviced greater than 90%? about 46 minutes

38. Sociology Rumors seem to spread like wild fire. Sociologists study the behavior of organized groups of people. A sociologist has shown that the fraction of people in a group, p, who have heard a rumor after t days can be approximated by $p = \dfrac{p_o e^{kt}}{1 - p_o(1 - e^{kt})}$, where p_o is the fraction of people who had heard the rumor at time $t = 0$, and k is a constant.

a. Suppose $k = 0.1$ and $p_o = \dfrac{1}{15}$. Find the fraction of the people who have heard the rumor after two weeks. 0.225

b. At time $t = 0$, 15% of the people in a group had heard a certain rumor. If after 2 days 20% of the people had heard the rumor, what is the value of k in the equation? 0.174

39. Medicine Patients are often given glucose intravenously during surgery. When glucose is injected into the bloodstream at a constant rate of c grams per minute, the body converts the glucose and removes it from the bloodstream at a rate proportional to the amount present. The amount of glucose in the bloodstream at time t in minutes is given by $g(t) = \dfrac{c}{a} + \left(g_o - \dfrac{c}{a}\right) e^{-at}$, where a is a constant.

a. Suppose at time $t = 0$, there are 0.07 grams of glucose in the bloodstream and glucose is being administered at a rate of 0.1 gram per minute. If $a = 1.25$, what is the amount of glucose in the bloodstream after 15 minutes? 0.08 g

b. For a certain patient, there are 0.08 grams of glucose in the bloodstream at $t = 0$. After 2 minutes, the amount of glucose in the bloodstream is 0.046 grams. If the value of a in the equation is 1.28, how many grams of glucose are being administered each minute? 0.055 g

Critical Thinking Solve for x. Round solutions to the nearest hundredth.

40. $e^{2x} - 2e^x + 1 = 0$ 0

41. $e^{-2x} - 4e^{-x} + 3 = 0$ 0 or –1.10

Mixed Review

42. Find $[f \circ g](x)$ and $[g \circ f](x)$ for $f(x) = 8x$ and $g(x) = 2 - x^2$. **(Lesson 1-2)**

42. $16 - 8x^2$; $2 - 64x^2$

43. Find the coordinates of P' if $P(4, 9)$ and P' are symmetric with respect to $M(-2, 9)$. **(Lesson 3-1)** $(-8, 9)$

44. Geometry The length of the sides of a rhombus is 10 centimeters, and one diagonal is 12 centimeters long. Find the area of the rhombus. **(Lesson 5-8)** 96 cm²

45. Write an equation with phase shift 0 to represent simple harmonic motion if the initial position is 0, the amplitude is 12, and the period is 2. **(Lesson 6-7)**

45. Sample answer: $y = 12 \sin \pi t$

46. Write an equation of the line with parametric equations $x = 11 - t$ and $y = 8 - 6t$ in slope-intercept form. **(Lesson 8-6)** $y = 6x - 58$

47. Graph $r = 2 + 2\cos\Theta$. **(Lesson 9-2)** See margin.

48. Solve $3.6^x = 58.9$ by using logarithms. **(Lesson 11-6)** 3.182

49. College Entrance Exam Choose the best answer. Simplify $\dfrac{\frac{1}{x} + \frac{1}{y}}{3}$. D

(A) $\dfrac{3x + 3y}{xy}$ (B) $\dfrac{3xy}{x + y}$ (C) $\dfrac{xy}{3}$ (D) $\dfrac{x + y}{3xy}$ (E) none of these

EXTENDING THE LESSON

Math Power: Connections

It can be shown that $e^{i\theta} = \text{cis } \theta$. We could use this equation to define natural logarithms for negative numbers. What would be the value of ln –1, ln –e, and ln –5? Note: θ should be in radians.

$i\pi$, $1 + i\pi$, $\ln 5 + i\pi$

Additional Answer

47.

Enrichment Masters Booklet, p. 79

NAME _____ DATE _____

11-7 Enrichment Worksheet

Hyperbolic Functions

The *hyperbolic functions* are a family of functions of great importance in calculus and higher-level mathematics. Because they are defined in terms of the hyperbola, their name is derived from that word. These functions have an interesting relationship to the number e and to the trigonometric functions, uniting those seemingly unrelated subjects with the conic sections.

The hyperbolic functions can be written in terms of e.

Hyperbolic sine of x: $\sinh x = \dfrac{e^x - e^{-x}}{2}$

Hyperbolic cosine of x: $\cosh x = \dfrac{e^x + e^{-x}}{2}$

Hyperbolic tangent of x: $\tanh x = \dfrac{\sinh x}{\cosh x} = \dfrac{e^x - e^{-x}}{e^x + e^{-x}}$

Identities involving hyperbolic functions exhibit strong resemblances to trigonometric identities.

Example Show that $\sinh 2x = 2 \sinh x \cosh x$.

$\sinh 2x = \dfrac{e^{2x} - e^{-2x}}{2}$ ← Replace x in the definition above by $2x$.

$= 2\left(\dfrac{e^{2x} - e^{-2x}}{4}\right)$

$= 2\left(\dfrac{(e^x)^2 - (e^{-x})^2}{4}\right)$ ← difference of two squares

$= 2\left(\dfrac{e^x - e^{-x}}{2}\right)\left(\dfrac{e^x + e^{-x}}{2}\right)$

$= 2 \sinh x \cosh x$

1. Find $\cosh^2 x - \sinh^2 x$. 1

Prove each identity.

2. $\sinh(-x) = -\sinh x$

$\sinh(-x) = \dfrac{e^{-x} - e^x}{2} = \dfrac{-(e^x - e^{-x})}{2} = -\left(\dfrac{e^x - e^{-x}}{2}\right) = -\sinh x$

3. $\sinh(x + y) = \sinh x \cosh y + \cosh x \sinh y$

$\sinh(x + y) = \dfrac{e^{x+y} - e^{-(x+y)}}{2}$

$= \dfrac{e^{x+y} - e^{-(x+y)}}{4} + \dfrac{e^{x+y} - e^{-(x+y)}}{4}$

$= \dfrac{e^{x+y} - e^{-x}}{2} \cdot \dfrac{e^y + e^{-y}}{2} + \dfrac{e^x + e^{-x}}{2} \cdot \dfrac{e^y - e^{-y}}{2}$

$= \sinh x \cosh y + \cosh x \sinh y$

T79
Glencoe Division, Macmillan/McGraw-Hill

Using the Chapter Summary and Review

The Chapter Summary and Review begins with an alphabetical listing of the new terms that were presented in the chapter. Have students define each term and provide an example of it, if appropriate.

The Skills and Concepts presented in the chapter are reviewed using a side-by-side format. Encourage students to refer to the Objectives and Examples on the left as they complete the Review Exercises on the right.

The Chapter Summary and Review ends with exercises that review Applications and Problem Solving.

Additional Answers

9.

10.

11.

12.

VOCABULARY

Upon completing this chapter, you should be familiar with the following terms:

annual percentage rates, APRs **609**
annuity **609**
antilogarithm **631**
characteristic **630**
common logarithms **629**
compound interest **614**
exponential curve **606**
exponential equations **636**

608 exponential function
609 future value of an annuity
622 logarithm
622 logarithmic function
630 mantissa
641 natural logarithms, ln x
609 present value of an annuity
598 scientific notation

SKILLS AND CONCEPTS

OBJECTIVES AND EXAMPLES	REVIEW EXERCISES

Upon completing this chapter, you should be able to:

Use these exercises to review and prepare for the chapter test.

- evaluate and simplify expressions containing rational exponents
(Lesson 11-1)

Simplify $(6c^4d)^2(3c)^{-2}$.

$$(6c^4d)^2(3c)^{-2} = \frac{36c^8d^2}{9c^2}$$
$$= 4c^6d^2$$

Evaluate.

1. $\left(\frac{1}{64}\right)^{\frac{1}{6}}$ $\frac{1}{2}$

2. $27^{\frac{4}{3}}$ 81

3. $(9^{\frac{3}{4}})^{\frac{2}{3}}$ 3

4. $\left(\frac{216}{729}\right)^{\frac{2}{3}}$ $\frac{4}{9}$

Simplify.

5. $3x^2(3x)^{-2}$ $\frac{1}{3}$

6. $(6a^{\frac{1}{3}})^3$ $216a$

7. $\left(\frac{1}{2}x^4\right)^3$ $\frac{1}{8}x^{12}$

8. $(2a)^{\frac{1}{3}}(a^2b)^{\frac{1}{3}}$ $2^{\frac{1}{3}}ab^{\frac{1}{3}}$

- graph exponential functions
(Lesson 11-2)

Graph $y = \left(\frac{1}{2}\right)^{x-1}$

Graph each equation. 9–12. See margin.

9. $y = 3^{-x}$

10. $y = \left(\frac{1}{2}\right)^x$

11. $y = 2^{x-1}$

12. $y = -4^{-x}$

646 CHAPTER 11 EXPONENTIAL AND LOGARITHMIC FUNCTIONS

OBJECTIVES AND EXAMPLES	REVIEW EXERCISES

OBJECTIVES AND EXAMPLES

■ use the exponential function $y = e^x$
(**Lesson 11-3**)

Evaluate $\sqrt{e^3}$: $\sqrt{e^3} = (e^3)^{\frac{1}{2}}$ or $e^{1.5}$

1.5 [2nd] [LN] 4.4816891

REVIEW EXERCISES

Use a calculator to evaluate each expression to the nearest ten thousandth.

13. $e^{2.34}$ 10.3812   **14.** $\sqrt[5]{e}$ 1.2214

15. $3\sqrt[4]{e^3}$ 6.3510   **16.** $\frac{1}{4}\sqrt{e^5}$ 3.0456

■ solve equations and evaluate expressions involving logarithms   (**Lesson 11-4**)

Solve $\log_5 4 + \log_5 x = \log_5 36$.

$\log_5 4 + \log_5 x = \log_5 36$
$\qquad \log_5 4x = \log_5 36$
$\qquad\qquad 4x = 36$
$\qquad\qquad\quad x = 9$

Solve each equation.

17. $\log_x 81 = 4$ 3   **18.** $\log_{\frac{1}{2}} x = -4$ 16

19. $\log_3 3 + \log_3 x = \log_3 45$ 15

20. $2\log_6 4 - \frac{1}{3}\log_6 8 = \log_6 x$ 8

21. $\log_2 x = \frac{1}{3}\log_2 27$ 3

■ find common logarithms and antilogarithms of numbers   (**Lesson 11-5**)

Find the antilog of -1.3719.

1.3719 [+/-] [2nd] [LOG] 0.0424717

Use a calculator to find the common logarithm of each number to the nearest ten thousandth.

22. 0.0459   -1.3382   **23.** 42.8   1.6314

Use a calculator to find the antilogarithm of each number to the nearest hundredth.

24. 1.6314   42.80   **25.** -0.1555   0.70

■ use common logarithms to compute powers and roots   (**Lesson 11-5**)

Use logarithms to evaluate $\sqrt{\frac{5.1^3}{4.3}}$.

Let $A = \sqrt{\frac{5.1^3}{4.3}}$.

$\log A = \log \sqrt{\frac{5.1^3}{4.3}}$

$\log A = \frac{1}{2}(3\log 5.1 - \log 4.3)$

$\log A \approx 0.7446$

$\qquad A \approx 5.5542$

Evaluate each expression using logarithms. Round answers to the nearest hundredth.

26. $(4.22)^3 \times 0.629$ 47.27

27. $\sqrt{9.12^2 \times 5.51}$ 21.41

28. $\left(\frac{6.32}{8.67}\right)^3$ 0.39

29. $\frac{43.9\sqrt{54.8}}{(1.29)^4}$ 117.35

■ solve exponential and logarithmic equations   (**Lesson 11-6**)

Solve $7^{x+1} = 18.6$.

$7^{x+1} = 18.6$
$\log 7^{x+1} = \log 18.6$
$(x+1)\log 7 = \log 18.6$
$\qquad\quad x = \frac{\log 18.6}{\log 7} - 1$ or 0.5022

Solve each equation using logarithms. Round answers to the nearest hundredth.

30. $2.5^x = 65.7$ 4.57   **31.** $x = \log_3 8.9$ 1.99

32. $4^{y+3} = 28.4$ -0.59   **33.** $7^{x-2} = 5^{3-x}$ 2.45

34. $2.3^{x^2} = 66.6$ ±2.25   **35.** $\sqrt{3^x} = 2^{x+1}$ -4.82

Alternate Review Strategy

To provide a brief in-class review, you may wish to read the following questions to the class and have them answer verbally.

1. Give the value of each expression.
   a. $\left(\frac{1}{2}\right)^{-3}$ 8

   b. $\left(\sqrt{81}\right)^{\frac{3}{2}}$ 27

2. Describe how the graphs of $y = 2^x$ and $y = 3^x$ are related. Both have (0, 1) as their y-intercept, and both are increasing for all x. 2^x is greater for $x < 0$, while 3^x is greater for $x > 0$.

3. What equation is used to find the value of a bank account when interest is compounded continuously? $A = Pe^{rt}$

4. If $\log_b 3 = m$, what is $\log_b 27$? $3m$

5. What are the domain and range of the function $y = \log_7 x$? D: the set of positive reals R: the set of all real numbers

6. If $\log 1.4 \approx 0.1461$, what is $\log 140{,}000$? ≈ 5.1461

7. Use your calculator to find the antilog of 2.3054.   202

8. Given the equation $5^{3-x} = 14$, what equation results when you take the log of each side and apply the power rule? $(3 - x)\log 5 = \log 14$

9. What is $\ln 34.9$? ≈ 3.5525

For more information on other methods of alternate assessment, you may wish to refer to Glencoe's *Alternate Assessment in the Mathematics Classroom*.

Two multiple-choice tests (Forms 1A and 1B) and two free-response tests (Forms 2A and 2B) are provided in the *Evaluation Masters*. Chapter 11 Test, Form 1A is shown below. Chapter 11 Test, Form 2A is shown on the next page.

Evaluation Masters Booklet, pp. 129–130

OBJECTIVES AND EXAMPLES	REVIEW EXERCISES
■ find natural logarithms of numbers (Lesson 11-7)	Use a calculator to find each value to the nearest ten thousandth.

Find ln 9.65.

9.65 [LN] *2.2669579*

36. ln 8.63 2.1552   **37.** ln 403 5.9989
38. antiln 3.7015   **39.** antiln 7.1121
     40.5080   1226.7210

■ use natural logarithms to solve problems (Lesson 11-7)

Solve $400 = 2e^{0.032t}$.
$$400 = 2e^{0.032t}$$
$$200 = e^{0.032t}$$
$$\ln 200 = \ln e^{0.032t}$$
$$\ln 200 = 0.032t \ln e$$
$$5.2983 = 0.032t$$
$$165.6 = t$$

Solve each equation. Round solutions to the nearest hundredth.

40. $4500 = 3e^{0.061t}$ 119.89
41. $16 = 5e^{0.4k}$ 2.91
42. $\ln 19.8 = \ln e^{0.083t}$ 35.97
43. $\ln 6.2 = \ln e^{0.55t}$ 3.32
44. $6.6 = 1.5\, e^{210k}$ 0.01

APPLICATIONS AND PROBLEM SOLVING

45. Keyboarding The keyboarding teacher, Mr. Eckert, found that the average number of words per minute, N, input by his students after t weeks was $N = 65 - 30e^{-0.20t}$. **(Lessons 11-3, 11-7)**
 a. What was the average number of words per minute after 2 weeks? 45 words per minute
 b. What was the average number of words per minute at the end of the semester, 15 weeks? 64 words per minute
 c. When will the average student in the class input 50 words per minute? at 3.5 weeks

46. Sound The decibel, db, is the unit of measure for the intensity of sound. The equation to determine the decibel rating of a sound is $\beta = 10 \cdot \log \frac{I}{I_0}$, where $I_0 = 10^{-12}$ W/m², the reference intensity of the faintest audible sound. **(Lesson 11-5)**
 a. Find the decibel rating, in db, of a whisper that has an intensity of 1.15×10^{-10} W/m². 20.6 db
 b. Find the decibel rating of a teacher's voice in front of a classroom that has an intensity of 9×10^{-9} W/m². 39.5 db
 c. Find the decibel rating of a rock concert that has an intensity of 8.95×10^{-3} W/m². 99.5 db

47. Archaeology Carbon-14 tests are often performed to determine the age of an organism that died a long time ago. Carbon-14 has a half-life of 5730 years. If a turtle shell is found and tested to have 65% of its original carbon-14, how old is it? **(Lesson 11-6)** 3561 years old

48. Population A certain city has a population of $P = 142{,}000e^{0.014t}$ where t is the time in years and $t = 0$ is the year 1970. In what year will the city have a population of 200,000? **(Lesson 11-7)** 1994

648 CHAPTER 11 EXPONENTIAL AND LOGARITHMIC FUNCTIONS

Addtional Answers
Chapter Test

7.

8.

CHAPTER 11 TEST

Evaluate.

1. $343^{\frac{2}{3}}$ 49

2. $(0.064)^{-\frac{1}{3}}$ 2.5

3. $49^{\frac{3}{2}} + 49^{-\frac{1}{2}}$ $343\frac{1}{7}$

Simplify.

4. $((2a)^3)^{-2}$ $\frac{1}{64a^6}$

5. $(x^{\frac{3}{2}}y^2a^{\frac{5}{4}})^4$ $x^6y^8a^5$

6. $\sqrt{a^2b} \cdot \sqrt{a^3b^5}$ $a^{\frac{5}{2}}b^3$

Graph each equation. 7–8. See margin.

7. $y = \left(\frac{1}{3}\right)^{x-2}$

8. $y = 5^{x+1}$

Solve each equation.

9. $\log_x \sqrt[3]{8} = \frac{1}{3}$ 8

10. $\log_5(2x) = \log_5(3x - 4)$ 4

11. $\frac{1}{2}\log_3 64 - \log_3 x = \log_3 4$ 2

12. $3.6^x = 72.4$ 3.34

13. $4^{x+3} = 25.8$ –0.66

14. $6^{x-1} = 8^{2-x}$ 1.54

Find each value to the nearest ten thousandth.

15. $\frac{e^2}{5}$ 1.4778

16. $\frac{1}{2}\sqrt[5]{e^2}$ 0.7459

17. log 542 2.7340

18. ln 0.248 –1.3943

19. antiln 1.1217 3.0701

20. antilog –1.9101 0.0123

Find the present value of each investment.

21. $3000 for 6 years at 8% compounded quarterly $4825.31

22. $6000 for 2 years at 12% compounded continuously $7627.49

23. Traffic Engineering The Ohio Department of Engineering is studying the traffic flow on State Route 23. They have found that you can predict the daily number of gaps in traffic greater than some time t by using the equation $n = 208(1.9)^{-0.11t}$, where t is measured in seconds. Find the number of gaps between vehicles that are greater than 3 seconds on any given day. 168 gaps

24. Biology A certain bacteria will triple in 6 hours. If the final count is 8 times the original, how much time has passed? 11 hours, 21 minutes

25. Optics The zoo has a large aquarium with several different types of fish and plants. One of the plants requires light at an intensity of 4.5 units in order to grow. The equation for the intensity of light passing through water is $I = 10e^{-0.3x}$, where x is the depth in meters. Use this equation to find the maximum depth of water at which the plant can grow. 2.66 meters

Bonus

Find the value of x for $a > 1$ such that $\log_2(\log_3(\log_a x)) = 1$. a^9

This page may be used as a test or as a review. All answers to this test appear in the Selected Answers in the student text.

Standardized Test Questions are also provided in the *Evaluation Masters*.

Evaluation Masters Booklet, pp. 133–134

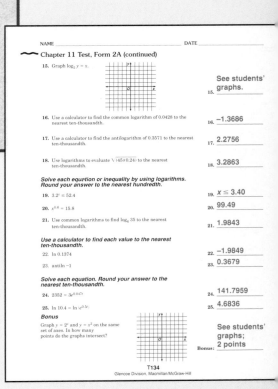

Test Generator Software is provided in Apple, IBM, and Macintosh versions. You may use this software to create your own tests, based on the needs of your students.

3 UNIT REVIEW

Graph the point that has the given polar coordinates. Then, name three other pairs of polar coordinates for each point. (Lesson 9-1)

1. $(2, 60°)$
2. $(-4, 45°)$
3. $(1.5, \frac{\pi}{6})$
4. $(-2, \frac{-2\pi}{3})$

1–4. See Teacher's Answer Key.

Graph each polar equation. (Lessons 9-1 and 9-2) 5–8. See Teacher's Answer Key.

5. $r = \sqrt{5}$
6. $\theta = 60°$
7. $r = 3\cos\theta$
8. $r = 2 + 2\sin\theta$

Find the polar coordinates of each point with the given rectangular coordinates. (Lesson 9-3)

9. $(-2, -2)$ $(2.83, 3.93)$
10. $(2, 2)$ $(2.83, 0.79)$
11. $(2, -3)$ $(3.61, -0.98)$
12. $(-3, 1)$ $(3.16, 2.82)$

Write each polar equation in rectangular form. (Lesson 9-4)

13. $2 = r\cos\left(\theta - \frac{\pi}{2}\right)$ $y = 2$
14. $4 = r\cos\left(\theta + \frac{\pi}{3}\right)$ $x - \sqrt{3}y - 8 = 0$

Simplify. (Lesson 9-5)

15. i^{45} i
16. $(3 + 2i) + (3 - 3i)$ $6 - i$
17. $i^4(3 + 3i)$ $3 + 3i$
18. $(-i - 5)(i - 5)$ 26
19. $\frac{2 + i}{2 - 3i}$ $\frac{1 + 8i}{13}$
20. $\frac{3}{\sqrt{2} - 2i}$ $\frac{\sqrt{2} + 2i}{2}$

Express each complex number in polar form. (Lesson 9-6) 21–24. See margin.

21. $-3i$
22. $3 + 3i$
23. $-1 + 2i$
24. $4 - 5i$

Find each product. Then write the result in rectangular form. (Lesson 9-7)

25. $2\left(\cos\frac{\pi}{2} + i\sin\frac{\pi}{2}\right) \cdot 4\left(\cos\frac{\pi}{2} + i\sin\frac{\pi}{2}\right)$ -8
26. $1.5(\cos 3.1 + i\sin 3.1) \cdot 2(\cos 0.5 + i\sin 0.5)$ $-2.69 - 1.33i$

Solve. (Lesson 9-8) 27. $8 - 8i$

27. Find $(1 + i)^7$ by DeMoivre's Theorem. Express the result in rectangular form.
28. Solve the equation $x^5 - 1 = 0$ for all roots. See margin.

Find the coordinates of the center and the length of the radius of each circle whose equation is given. (Lesson 10-1)

29. $4x^2 + 4y^2 = 49$ $(0, 0); \frac{7}{2}$
30. $x^2 + 10x + y^2 + 8y = 20$ $(-5, -4); \sqrt{61}$
31. $x^2 + y^2 + 9x - 8y + 4 = 0$ $(-\frac{9}{2}, 4), \frac{\sqrt{129}}{2}$

Find the coordinates of the focus and vertex and the equation of the directrix and the axis of symmetry of each parabola whose equation is given. Then graph the equation. (Lesson 10-2)

32. $(x - 2)^2 = 2(y - 4)$
33. $y^2 + 2y - 5x + 18 = 0$

32–33. See Teacher's Answer Key.

Find the coordinates of the center, foci, and vertices of each ellipse whose equation is given. Then graph the equation. (Lesson 10-3) 34–35. See Teacher's Answer Key.

34. $(x - 1)^2 + 2(y - 3)^2 = 25$
35. $4(x + 2)^2 + 25(y - 2)^2 = 100$

Additional Answers

21. $3\left(\cos\frac{3\pi}{2} + i\sin\frac{3\pi}{2}\right)$
22. $3\sqrt{2}\left(\cos\frac{\pi}{4} + i\sin\frac{\pi}{4}\right)$
23. $\sqrt{5}(\cos 2.03 + i\sin 2.03)$
24. $\sqrt{41}(\cos(-0.9) + i\sin(-0.9))$
28. $1, 0.31 + 0.95i, -0.81 + 0.59i, -0.81 - 0.59i, 0.31 - 0.95i$

Find the coordinates of the center, foci, and vertices and the equations of the asymptotes of each hyperbola whose equation is given. Then graph the equation.   (Lesson 10-4)

36. $4x^2 - y^2 = 27$

37. $\dfrac{(x+1)^2}{4} - \dfrac{(y+3)^2}{9} = 1$

36–37. See Teacher's Answer Key.

Identify the conic section represented by each equation. Write the equation in standard form and graph the equation. (Lesson 10-5)

38. $12y - 3x + 2x^2 + 1 = 0$ parabola

39. $4(x-1)^2 = 25(y+3)^2 + 100$ hyperbola

40. $x^2 + 4x + y^2 - 12y + 4 = 0$ circle

38–40. For equations and graphs, see Teacher's Answer Key.

Write the equation of each translated or rotated graph below. Then draw the graph. (Lesson 10-6)

41. $x = 3(y+2)^2 + 1$ for $T_{(1,\,-5)}$

42. $x^2 - \dfrac{y^2}{16} = 1,\, \theta = \dfrac{\pi}{3}$

41–42. See Teacher's Answer Key.

Graph each system of equations. Then solve. (Lesson 10-7)

43. $x^2 - 2x - 2y - 2 = 0$
     $(x-4)^2 = -8y$

44. $x^2 - (y-1)^2 \geq 0$
     $x^2 + 2(y-3)^2 \leq 9$

43–44. See Teacher's Answer Key.

Find the equations of the tangent and the normal to the graphs of each equation at the given point. Write the equations in standard form.   (Lesson 10-8) 45–47. See margin.

45. $(x-1)^2 + (y+2)^2 = 2,\, (2,-1)$

46. $(y-4)^2 = 2(x+3),\, (5,0)$

47. $\dfrac{(y-3)^2}{25} - \dfrac{(x-2)^2}{16} = 1,\, (2,8)$

Simplify.   (Lesson 11-1)

48. $\sqrt{16x^2y^7}$ $4\,|x|\,y^3\sqrt{y}$

49. $\sqrt[3]{54a^4b^3c^8}$ $3abc^2\sqrt[3]{2ac^2}$

50. $(3^2c^3d^5)^{\frac{1}{5}}$ $d\sqrt[5]{9c^3}$

51. $(3x)^2(3x^2)^{-2}$ $\dfrac{1}{x^2}$

Graph each equation.   (Lesson 11-2)

52. $y = 2^{-x}$

53. $y = 2^{x+2}$

52–53. See Teacher's Answer Key.

Use a calculator to evaluate each expression to the nearest ten thousandth. (Lesson 11-3)

54. $e^{2.3}$ 9.9742

55. $\sqrt[3]{8e}$ 2.7912

56. $\dfrac{e^3}{4}$ 5.0214

57. $e^{-4.7}$ 0.0091

Solve each equation.   (Lesson 11-4)

58. $\log_x 36 = 2$ 6

59. $\log_2(2x) = \log_2 27$ $\dfrac{27}{2}$

60. $\log_5 x = \dfrac{1}{3}\log_5 64 + 2\log_5 3$ 36

Evaluate each expression using logarithms. (Lesson 11-5)

61. $(4.32)^2 \times (8.13)^3$ 10,028.573

62. $\sqrt{(6.1)^3(10.3)}$ 48.352

63. $\dfrac{5.4\sqrt{7.8}}{(1.4)^3}$ 5.496

Solve each equation using logarithms. (Lesson 11-6)

64. $2.3^x = 23.4$ 3.79

65. $x = \log_4 16$ 2

66. $5^{x-2} = 2^x$ 3.51

Solve each equation.   (Lesson 11-7)

67. $46 = e^x$ 3.83

68. $18 = e^{4k}$ 0.72

69. $519 = 3e^{0.035t}$ 147.24

UNIT 3 REVIEW   651

Evaluation Masters Booklet, pp. 143–144

DISCRETE MATHEMATICS

Discrete mathematics is a branch of mathematics that deals with finite or discontinuous quantities. The distinction between continuous and discrete quantities is one that you have encountered throughout your life. For example, think of a staircase. You can slide your hand up the banister, but you have to climb the stairs one by one. The banister represents a continuous quantity, like a line graph. The stairs represent discrete quantities, like the points on a scatter plot. You will learn to use the skills you will acquire in this unit to solve problems that involve both discrete and continuous quantities.

Usually discrete mathematics is defined in terms of its key topics. These include graphs, certain functions, logic, combinatorics, sequences, iteration, algorithms, recursion, matrices, and induction. Some of these topics have already been introduced in this book. For example, linear functions are continuous, while step functions, which you examined in Chapter 3, are discrete.

In this unit, you will construct models, discover and use algorithms, and examine exciting new concepts as you solve real-world problems. It is our hope that you will greatly increase your understanding of this branch of mathematics and its limitations and advantages as a way of looking at the world.

652

Unit 4 Focus

The theme of Unit 4 is discrete mathematics, with emphasis on sequences, iteration, combinatorics, statistics, and graph theory.

Connections to Other Units

The concepts developed in this unit are related to concepts in Units 1 and 5. Step functions presented in Unit 1 are examples of discrete functions. The concept of limits applied to sequences and series in this unit is extended to functions in Unit 5.

Multicultural Notes

Japan Capsule architecture is a building form which was developed in Japan. Prefabricated framing-units are assembled to create a structure's skeleton. Prefabricated capsule rooms are then inserted into the framework. In the perfect framework, the strength of the structural elements is sufficient without being redundant, which is an application of graph theory. These elements are often made of steel because of its high strength-to-weight ratio. The Takara Beautillion in Osaka and the Nakagin Capsule Tower are examples of capsule architecture.

Africa About 1650 B.C., a scribe named A'h-mosè lived in Egypt. This scribe wrote and also embellished older works of mathematics. Modern scholars refer to this scribe as Ahmes. The Ahmes Papyrus is one of the oldest mathematical documents in existence. Among other mathematical topics, it contains the first references to arithmetic series. The papyrus was purchased in Egypt by English Egyptologist A. Henry Rhind in the mid-19th century. Some scholars today refer to this historical artifact as the Rhind Papyrus. It was later acquired by the British Museum.

653

PREVIEWING THE CHAPTER

This chapter reviews arithmetic and geometric sequences and series and introduces infinite series and sequences. Students learn to evaluate limits and find the sum of a series. They determine whether a series is convergent or divergent and express a series using sigma notation. Pascal's triangle is reviewed and applied to the expansion of binomial expressions. The binomial theorem is then introduced. Students examine the work of Fibonacci and Euler to learn about special series and sequences such as the exponential series, the trigonometric series, and the series for e. Finally, they use mathematical induction to prove the validity formulas.

Lesson Objective Chart

Lesson (Pages)	Lesson Objectives	State/Local Objectives
12-1 (656-662)	**12-1A:** Find the nth term and arithmetic means of an arithmetic sequence.	
	12-1B: Fine the sum of n terms of an arithmetic series.	
12-2 (663-669)	**12-2A:** Fine the nth term and geometric means of a geometric sequence.	
	12-2B: Find the sum of n terms of a geometric series.	
12-3 (671-678)	**12-3A:** Find the limit of the terms of an infinite sequence.	
	12-3B: Find the sum of an infinite geometric series.	
12-4 (679-684)	**12-4:** Determine whether a series is convergent or divergent.	
12-5 (685-690)	**12-5:** Use sigma notation.	
12-6 (691-695)	**12-6:** Use the binomial theorem to expand binomials.	
12-7 (696-701)	**12-7A:** Evaluate e^x by using the exponential series.	
	12-7B: Use Euler's formula to write the exponential form of a complex number.	
	12-7C: Evaluate the logarithms of negative numbers.	
12-8 (702-705)	**12-8:** Use mathematical induction to prove the validity of formulas.	

ORGANIZING THE CHAPTER

You may want to refer to the **Course Planning Guide Calendar** on pages T34-T35 for a complete pacing chart.

| | | | | **Blackline Masters Booklets** | | | | | | | | |
| | | | | | | **Technology** | | | **Activity Masters** | | | |
Lesson	**Pages**	Practice	Enrichment	Evaluation	Graphing Calculator	Computer	Multicultural Activity	Applications	Problem Solving	Case Study Follow-Up	Decision Making	Transparencies
12-1	656-662	p. 80	p. 80				p. 12					12-1
12-2	663-669	p. 81	p. 81	Quiz A, p. 153	p. 23					p. 36		12-2
12-3	671-678	p. 82	p. 82									12-3
12-4	679-684	p. 83	p. 83	Quiz B, p. 153 Mid-Chapter Test, p.155								12-4
12-5	685-690	p. 84	p.84						p. 35			12-5
12-6	691-695	p. 85	p. 85	Quiz C, p. 154		p. 24						12-6
12-7	696-701	p. 86	p. 86									12-7
12-8	702-705	p. 87	p. 87	Quiz D, p. 154				p. 34				12-8
Review	706-708	Multiple Choice Tests, Forms 1A and 1B, pp. 145-148 Free Response Tests, Forms 2A and 2B, pp. 149-152 Standardized Test Questions, p. 156										
Test	709											

Other Chapter Resources

Student Edition
Case Study Follow-Up, p. 662
Decision Making, p. 678
Technology, p. 670

Other Supplements
Transparency 12-0 for Chapter Opener
Alternate Assessment in the Mathematics Classroom,
    Glencoe Publishing Co., 1993
Cooperative Learning in the Mathematics Classroom,
    Glencoe Publishing Co., 1993

Software
Test and Review Generator Software
    Available for Apple, IBM, and Macintosh
Teacher's Guide for Software Resources

ENHANCING THE CHAPTER

Cooperative Learning

Explaining the Criteria for Success

In addition to clearly explaining the specific tasks to be performed before the group begins its work, you should also clearly explain the criteria by which the final work will be evaluated. These criteria should be structured so that they can be achieved without one student in the group penalizing another. The criteria also should be fashioned to be realistic but challenging for each and every member of the group. For some types of activities, the criteria can be as straight forward as answering a certain number of problems correctly. For other types of activities, just completing the assignment or simply doing better this time than last time may be sufficient criteria for success. Although some teachers are successful in maintaining group interdependence when establishing different criteria for different members during a group-learning session, others find it better to reserve such differing criteria for whole-class activities, such as during the administration of a quiz or chapter test.

For more information on cooperative learning, see pages T20-T21. Additional information on using cooperative groups is available in Glencoe's *Cooperative Learning in the Mathematics Classroom*, ©1993.

Multicultural

Multicultural Activity Masters, p. 12

Activity Masters

Applications, p. 34

Problem Solving, p. 35

Case Study Follow-Up, p. 36

Technology

The technology feature preceding Lesson 12-3 illustrates how a spreadsheet program may be used to construct an amortization schedule. Some scientific calculators may have a feature for finding the sum of a given set of numbers. Have students refer to their manuals to determine if their calculator has this feature.

In the Exploration in Lesson 12-2, students learn how to use the graph of a exponential function to determine the sum in a geometric series. The graphing calculator program in Lesson 12-5 evaluates a sum given in summation notation. Students use the program to find the sum of a series.

Graphing Calculator Exercises, p. 689

Outside Resources

Books/Periodicals

Finkbeiner, Daniel T., II, and Wendell D. Lindstrom. *A Primer of Discrete Mathematics,* W.H. Freeman, New York, 1987.

Capocelli, R.M., editor. *Sequences,* Springer-Verlag New York, Inc., 1989.

Films/Videotapes/Videodiscs

Sequences and Series, Massachusetts Institute of Technology

Dimension, AIMS Instructional Media

Technology Masters

Graphing Calculator, p. 23

Computer, p. 24

CHAPTER 12

SEQUENCES AND SERIES

HISTORICAL SNAPSHOT

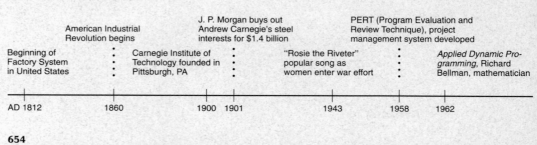

			J. P. Morgan buys out Andrew Carnegie's steel interests for $1.4 billion		PERT (Program Evaluation and Review Technique), project management system developed	
	American Industrial Revolution begins					
Beginning of Factory System in United States		Carnegie Institute of Technology founded in Pittsburgh, PA		"Rosie the Riveter" popular song as women enter war effort		*Applied Dynamic Programming*, Richard Bellman, mathematician
AD 1812	1860		1900 1901	1943	1958	1962

654

predict the limit before creating the spreadsheet. Have them also use a spreadsheet to verify the formula for the sum of an infinite geometric series. Finally, have them generalize their results, prepare a report, and present it to the class.

CHAPTER OBJECTIVES

In this chapter, you will:
- Identify arithmetic, geometric, and infinite sequences.
- Find sums of arithmetic, geometric, and infinite series.
- Expand binomials.
- Use mathematical induction to prove the validity of formulas.

CAREER GOAL: Operations Research

What do a dairy farm, an aluminum foundry, and an international bank have in common? These are all places where Michael Gallmeyer has worked. Michael grew up on a dairy farm. He says, "In farming you are exposed to many things. For instance, when something breaks, you fix it. You get to see more in the way of technology, mechanics, and animal science." Michael originally considered a career in electrical engineering, but decided that it was too restrictive for him. He wanted a career that would allow him to enter several different areas. Industrial management has offered him that opportunity.

In industrial management, companies often have to make decisions about their investment in energy conservation. Suppose ABC, Inc. has $10,000 to invest. One option is to put it in a savings account at 6% per year for ten years. The *future value* of that investment is $17,910. Another option is to use that $10,000 to install solar energy panels. This option promises a $1000 per year savings in energy costs. Let's say they invest this $1000 savings in a savings account at 6%. The future value of that investment is $13,181. So far, it appears that it is more profitable to take the first option. However, without the conversion to solar energy, ABC would be paying $1000 more for energy each year. When you deduct the *present value* of this $1000 annual expenditure, their $17,910 return becomes only $17,910 − $7360 or $10,550. Therefore, ABC will have saved money by converting to solar energy.

Industrial management has provided Michael with some very marketable skills. In the summer of 1992, he interned with the Advanced Technology Group of J.P. Morgan, an international corporate bank. About this experience, he says, "I'm beginning to realize just how quantitative business has become and how important mathematics is to acquiring the toolkit of skills that the business world needs."

READ MORE ABOUT IT

Conley, William C. *Computer Optimization Techniques.* New York: Petrocelli Books, Inc., 1984.
Finlay, Paul N. *Mathematical Modelling in Business Decision-Making,* New York: St. Martin's Press, 1985.
Hoyt, Douglas B. *Opportunities in Information Systems Careers.* Lincolnwood, IL: VGM Career Horizons, 1991.

SPOTLIGHT ON...

Michael Gallmeyer
Age: 21
Class: Junior
School: Carnegie Mellon
   University
   Pittsburgh, Pennsylvania
Major: Industrial Management

"You need mathematics to acquire the tool kit of skills that the business world needs."

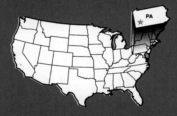

FOR MORE INFORMATION

If you would like more information about industrial management, contact:

Society for Industrial and
   Applied Mathematics (SIAM)
3600 University City Science
   Center
Philadelphia, PA 19104-2688

Applications

Lesson	Application	Examples	Exercises
12–1	Savings	6	
	Geometry		39
	Employment		41
	Number		
	Theory		42
	Food		43
	Banking		44
12–2	Biology	3	31
	Investment		29
	Finance	6	30, 32
	Number		
	Theory		33
12–3	Physics	5	40
	Chemistry		39
	Coordinate		
	Geometry		41
12–4	Employment		28
	Physics		29
12–5	Finance		59
	Ballooning		60
12–6	Family	2	27
	Coins		28
	Chemistry		29
12–7	Biology		42
	Number		
	Theory		43
12–8	Time		21
	Economics		22
	Family		23

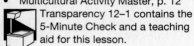

Lesson Resources

- Practice Master 12–1
- Enrichment Master 12–1
- Multicultural Activity Master, p. 12
  Transparency 12–1 contains the 5-Minute Check and a teaching aid for this lesson.

INTRODUCING THE LESSON

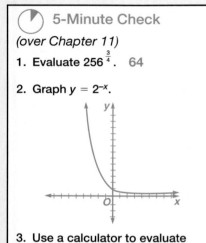

5-Minute Check

(over Chapter 11)

1. Evaluate $256^{\frac{3}{4}}$.   **64**

2. Graph $y = 2^{-x}$.

3. Use a calculator to evaluate $e^{3.54}$ to the nearest ten thousandth.   **34.4669**
4. Solve $\log_x 243 = 5$.   **3**
5. Solve $3.4^x = 82.3$ using logarithms.   **3.6039**

Motivating the Lesson

Have students try to guess how much money they would have after a month if you gave them a nickel the first day, two nickels the second day, three nickels the third day, and so on.   **In 31 days, they would have 496 nickels or $24.80.**

12-1 Arithmetic Sequences and Series

Objectives

12–1A
12–1B

After studying this lesson, you should be able to:
- find the nth term and arithmetic means of an arithmetic sequence, and
- find the sum of n terms of an arithmetic series.

Application

Jason's younger brother, Jeffrey, is very interested in collecting basketball cards. Jason has quite a few basketball cards that he has collected over the years. As a birthday gift to Jeffrey, Jason has decided to give Jeffrey 3 basketball cards today, 6 basketball cards tomorrow, 9 basketball cards the next day, and so on each day for 14 days. How many cards will Jason give Jeffrey on the 14th day?

The chart below shows the number of Jason's cards that Jeffrey will receive each day.

Day	1	2	3	4	5	6	7	8	9	10	11	12	13	14
Number of Cards	3	6	9	12	15	18	21	24	27	30	33	36	39	42

Thus, Jeffrey will receive 42 of Jason's cards on the 14th day.

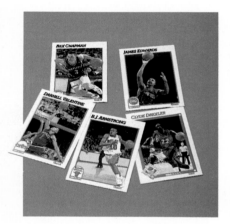

The set of numbers representing the number of Jason's cards that Jeffrey would receive each day is an example of a **sequence**. A sequence is a set of numbers in a specific order. The **terms** of a sequence are the numbers in it. The first term of a sequence is denoted a_1, or a, the second term is a_2, and so on up to the nth term, a_n.

Symbol	a_1	a_2	a_3	a_4	a_5	a_6
Term	13	21.5	30	38.5	47	55.5

In this sequence, how might a_7 be determined?

The sequences given in the tables above are both examples of **arithmetic sequences**. The difference between successive terms of an arithmetic sequence is a constant called the **common difference**, denoted d.

Arithmetic Sequence

> An arithmetic sequence is a sequence in which each term after the first, a_1, is equal to the sum of the preceding term and the common difference, d. The terms of the sequence can be represented as follows.
>
> $$a_1, a_1 + d, a_1 + 2d, \cdots$$

656 CHAPTER 12 SEQUENCES AND SERIES

ALTERNATE TEACHING STRATEGIES

Using Cooperative Groups

Have students work in groups to make a list of sequences they already know, such as sequences of positive even integers, powers of two, and so on. Also list applications of sequences. Have them present their list to the class for comparison.

Using Calculators

Have students enter the difference for an arithmetic sequence into the memory of a calculator. Then give them the first term of the sequence and have them add the difference repeatedly. Pause after each addition to record the value of the next term.

To find the next term in an arithmetic sequence, first find the common difference by subtracting any term from its succeeding term. Then add the common difference to the last term to find the next term in the sequence.

Example 1

Find the next three terms in each sequence.

a. $-5, 7, 19, \cdots$

a. First, find the common difference.
$$7 - (-5) = 12 \qquad\qquad 19 - 7 = 12$$
The common difference is 12.

Then, add 12 to the third term to get the fourth term, and so on.
$$19 + 12 = 31 \qquad 31 + 12 = 43 \qquad 43 + 12 = 55$$
The next three terms are 31, 43, and 55.

b. $r + 15, r + 8, r + 1, \cdots$

b. First, find the common difference.
$$(r + 8) - (r + 15) = -7 \qquad\qquad (r + 1) - (r + 8) = -7$$
The common difference is -7.

Then, add -7 to the third term to get the fourth term, and so on.
$$r + 1 + (-7) = r - 6 \qquad r - 6 + (-7) = r - 13 \qquad r - 13 + (-7) = r - 20$$
The next three terms are $r - 6$, $r - 13$, and $r - 20$.

The nth term of an arithmetic sequence can be found by using a formula if the first term and the common difference are known. This type of formula is called a **recursive** formula. This means that each succeeding term is formulated from one or more previous terms. Consider an arithmetic sequence in which $a = -11$ and $d = 4$. Notice the pattern in the way the terms are formed.

first term	a_1	a	-11
second term	a_2	$a + d$	$-11 + 1(4) = -7$
third term	a_3	$a + 2d$	$-11 + 2(4) = -3$
fourth term	a_4	$a + 3d$	$-11 + 3(4) = 1$
fifth term	a_5	$a + 4d$	$-11 + 4(4) = 5$
$\vdots$	$\vdots$	$\vdots$	$\vdots$
nth term	a_n	$a + (n - 1)d$	$-11 + (n - 1)4$

The nth Term of an Arithmetic Sequence

The nth term of an arithmetic sequence with first term a_1 and common difference d is given by the following formula.

$$a_n = a_1 + (n - 1)d$$

Notice that the preceding formula has four variables: $a_n, a_1, n,$ and d. If any three of these are known, the fourth can be found. By definition, the nth term is also equal to $a_{n-1} + d$, where a_{n-1} is the $(n - 1)$th term. That is, $a_n = a_{n-1} + d$.

LESSON 12-1 ARITHMETIC SEQUENCES AND SERIES 657

TEACHING THE LESSON

Teaching Tip After defining *common difference*, emphasize that the difference between any two terms must be the same for the sequence to be arithmetic. Also point out that there are sequences that are not arithmetic. For example, 100, 50, 25 is a sequence that is not arithmetic.

Chalkboard Example

For Example 1

Find the next three terms in each sequence.
a. $-12, -1, 10, \cdots$. 21, 32, 43
b. $r - 4, r - 1, r + 2, \cdots$. $r + 5$, $r + 8$, $r + 11$

Example 2

Find the 68th term in the sequence 16, 7, -2, $\cdots$.

First, find the common difference.
$$7 - 16 = -9 \qquad -2 - 7 = -9$$
The common difference is -9.

Then, use the formula for the nth term of an arithmetic sequence.
$$a_n = a_1 + (n - 1)d$$
$$a_{68} = 16 + (68 - 1)(-9) \qquad n = 68, a_1 = 16, \text{ and } d = -9$$
$$= -587$$

Example 3

Find the first term in the sequence for which $a_{31} = 197$ and $d = 10$.

$$a_n = a_1 + (n - 1)d$$
$$a_{31} = a_1 + (31 - 1)d \qquad n = 31 \text{ and } d = 10$$
$$197 = a_1 + 30(10) \qquad a_{31} = 197$$
$$a_1 = -103$$

Sometimes you may know two terms of an arithmetic sequence that are not in consecutive order. The terms between any two nonconsecutive terms of an arithmetic sequence are called **arithmetic means**. In the sequence below, 76 and 85 are the arithmetic means between 67 and 94.
$$49, 58, 67, 76, 85, 94$$

Example 4

Form an arithmetic sequence that has five arithmetic means between -11 and 19.

This sequence will have the form $-11, \underline{\ ?\ }, \underline{\ ?\ }, \underline{\ ?\ }, \underline{\ ?\ }, \underline{\ ?\ }, 19$.

First, find the common difference.
$$a_n = a_1 + (n - 1)d \qquad n = 7$$
$$19 = -11 + (7 - 1)d \qquad a_7 = 19 \text{ and } a_1 = -11$$
$$19 = -11 + 6d$$
$$d = 5$$

Then, determine the arithmetic means.
$$-11 + 5 = -6 \qquad -6 + 5 = -1 \qquad -1 + 5 = 4 \qquad 4 + 5 = 9 \qquad 9 + 5 = 14$$

The sequence is $-11, -6, -1, 4, 9, 14, 19$.

An indicated sum is $1 + 2 + 3 + 4$. The sum of $1 + 2 + 3 + 4$ is 10.

An **arithmetic series** is the indicated sum of the terms of an arithmetic sequence. The lists below show some examples of arithmetic sequences and their corresponding arithmetic series.

Arithmetic Sequence	Arithmetic Series
3, 8, 13, 18, 23	$3 + 8 + 13 + 18 + 23$
$\frac{1}{2}, \frac{1}{4}, 0, -\frac{1}{4}, -\frac{1}{2}$	$\frac{1}{2} + \frac{1}{4} + 0 + \left(-\frac{1}{4}\right) + \left(-\frac{1}{2}\right)$
$a_1, a_2, a_3, a_4, \cdots, a_n$	$a_1 + a_2 + a_3 + a_4 + \cdots + a_n$

The symbol S_n is used to represent the sum of the first n terms of a series. To develop a formula for S_n for an arithmetic series, a series can be written in two ways and added term by term, as shown below. The second equation for S_n given below is obtained by reversing the order of the terms in the series.

$$S_n = a_1 + (a_1 + d) + (a_1 + 2d) + \cdots + (a_n - 2d) + (a_n - d) + a_n$$
$$+ S_n = a_n + (a_n - d) + (a_n - 2d) + \cdots + (a_1 + 2d) + (a_1 + d) + a_1$$
$$2S_n = (a_1 + a_n) + (a_1 + a_n) + (a_1 + a_n) + \cdots + (a_1 + a_n) + (a_1 + a_n) + (a_1 + a_n)$$
$$2S_n = n(a_1 + a_n) \quad \textit{There are n terms in the series, all of which are } (a_1 + a_n).$$

Therefore, $S_n = \dfrac{n(a_1 + a_n)}{2}$.

Sum of an Arithmetic Series	The sum of the first n terms of an arithmetic series is given by the following formula. $$S_n = \frac{n}{2}(a_1 + a_n)$$

Example 5

Find the sum of the 27 terms in the series $-14 - 8 - 2 - \cdots + 142$.

$$S_n = \frac{n}{2}(a_1 + a_n)$$
$$S_{27} = \frac{27}{2}(-14 + 142) \qquad n = 27, a_1 = -14, \text{ and } a_{27} = 142$$
$$= 1728$$

When the value of the last term, a_n, is not known, you can still determine the sum of the series. Using the formula for an arithmetic sequence, you can derive another formula for the sum of an arithmetic series.

$$S_n = \frac{n}{2}(a_1 + a_n)$$
$$S_n = \frac{n}{2}[a_1 + (a_1 + (n-1)d)] \qquad a_n = a_1 + (n-1)d$$
$$S_n = \frac{n}{2}[2a_1 + (n-1)d]$$

Example 6

APPLICATION

Savings

Celeste Bay will be a freshman at The University of Kentucky in the fall. Starting one month from today, she plans to withdraw $10 from her savings account, and then increase her withdrawal by $10 each week so that she can purchase items for college. If her account has a balance of $1200 today, how long will it take her to empty her savings account?

Let S_n = the amount of money that is currently in the savings account, $1200.
Let a_1 = the first withdrawal of $10. In this example, $d = 10$.
We want to find n, the number of weeks that it will take to empty the savings account.

(continued on the next page)

Exercises 1–18 are designed to help you assess students' understanding through reading, writing, speaking, and modeling. You should work through Exercises 1–4 with your students and then monitor their work on Exercises 5–18.

Closing the Lesson

Speaking Activity Have each student make up an arithmetic sequence, give the first term, the difference, and the next five terms in the sequence.

Practice Masters Booklet, p. 80

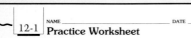

NAME _____ DATE _____

12-1 Practice Worksheet

Arithmetic Sequences and Series

Solve.

1. Find the 24th term in the sequence for which $a = -27$ and $d = 3$.
   42

2. Find n for the sequence for which $a_n = 27$, $a = -12$, and $d = 3$.
   14

3. Find d for the sequence for which $a = -12$ and $a_{23} = 32$.
   2

4. Find the first term in the sequence for which $d = -3$ and $a_6 = 5$.
   20

5. Find the first term in the sequence for which $a_4 = -21$ and $a_7 = -3$.
   −39

6. Find the sixth term in the sequence $-3 + \sqrt{2}, 0, 3 - \sqrt{2}, \cdots$.
   $12 - 4\sqrt{2}$

7. Find the 45th term in the sequence $-17, -11, -5, \cdots$.
   247

8. Form a sequence that has one arithmetic mean between 35 and 45.
   5, 10, 15, ···

9. Find the sum of the first 13 terms in the series $-5 + 1 + 7 + \cdots + 43$.
   403

T80
Glencoe Division, Macmillan/McGraw-Hill

$$S_n = \frac{n}{2}[2a_1 + (n-1)d]$$

$1200 = \frac{n}{2}[2(10) + (n-1)(10)]$ *$S_n = 1200$, $a_1 = 10$, and $d = 10$*

$2400 = n[20 + (n-1)(10)]$ *Multiply each side by 2.*

$2400 = n(20 + 10n - 10)$ *Simplify.*

$2400 = n(10 + 10n)$

$0 = 10n^2 + 10n - 2400$

$0 = n^2 + n - 240$ *Divide each side by 10.*

$0 = (n-15)(n+16)$ *Factor.*

$n - 15 = 0$ or $n + 16 = 0$

$n = 15$ $n = -16$ *–16 is not a possible answer.*

Thus, it would take Celeste 15 weeks to empty her account.

CHECKING FOR UNDERSTANDING

Communicating Mathematics

Read and study the lesson to answer each question.

1. Refer to the application at the beginning of the lesson.
   a. What formula would you use to determine how many of Jason's cards Jeffrey will have at the end of 14 days? $S_n = \frac{n}{2}[2a_1 + (n-1)d]$
   b. How many of Jason's cards will Jeffrey have at the end of 14 days? 315
   c. Graph the numbers in the first table. Let days be the x-coordinate and let number of cards be the y-coordinate, and connect the points. Describe the graph. a linear function

2. Choose the correct term: If the numbers in a sequence are decreasing, then the common difference is (positive, negative). negative

3. In Example 4, why does n equal 7? There will be 7 terms in all.

4. Refer to Example 6.
   a. If Celeste begins to withdraw the money from her savings account on March 1, will the account be empty by the end of August? yes
   b. Why is –16 *not* a possible answer? The number of weeks cannot be negative.

Guided Practice

Find the next five terms in each arithmetic sequence.

5. $5, 9, 13, \cdots$ 17, 21, 25, 29, 33

6. $-9, -2, 5, \cdots$ 12, 19, 26, 33, 40

7. $5, -1, -7, \cdots$ −13, −19, −25, −31, −37

8. $0, 7, 14, \cdots$ 21, 28, 35, 42, 49

9. $1.5, 3, 4.5, \cdots$ 6, 7.5, 9, 10.5, 12

10. $a, a+3, a+6, \cdots$ $a+9$, $a+12$, $a+15$, $a+18$, $a+21$

11. $-n, 0, n, \cdots$ 2n, 3n, 4n, 5n, 6n

12. $x, 2x, 3x, \cdots$ 4x, 5x, 6x, 7x, 8x

13. $b, -b, -3b, \cdots$ −5b, −7b, −9b, −11b, −13b

14. $5k, -k, \cdots$ −7k, −13k, −19k, −25k, −31k

15. Find the 79th term in the sequence $-7, -4, -1, \cdots$. 227

16. Find the first term in the sequence for which $a_{15} = 38$ and $d = -3$. 80

17. Form an arithmetic sequence that has one arithmetic mean between 12 and 21. 12, 16.5, 21

18. Find the sum of the first 63 terms in the series $-19 - 13 - 7 - \cdots$. 10,521

RETEACHING THE LESSON

Have students use counters, base-ten unit blocks, or other objects to model a sequence. Have them write the first 20 terms of the sequence being modeled. Then have them use the model to find the sum of the first 20 terms.

EXERCISES

Practice

A ▶

Solve. Assume that each sequence is an arithmetic sequence.

19. Find the 19th term in the sequence for which $a_1 = 11$ and $d = -2$. –25

20. Find the 16th term in the sequence for which $a_1 = 1.5$ and $d = 0.5$. 9

21. Find n for the sequence for which $a_n = 37, a_1 = -13$, and $d = 5$. 11

22. Find n for the sequence for which $a_n = 633, a_1 = 9$, and $d = 24$. 27

23. Find the first term in the sequence for which $d = -2$ and $a_7 = 3$. 15

24. Find the first term in the sequence for which $d = \frac{2}{3}$ and $a_8 = 15$. $10\frac{1}{3}$

25. Find d for the sequence for which $a_1 = 4$ and $a_{11} = 64$. 6

26. Find d for the sequence for which $a_1 = -6$ and $a_{29} = 20$. $\frac{13}{14}$

B ▶

27. Find the sixth term in the sequence $-2 + \sqrt{3}, -1, -\sqrt{3}, \cdots$. $3 - 4\sqrt{3}$

28. Find the seventh term in the sequence $1 + i, 2 - i, 3 - 3i, \cdots$. $7 - 11i$

29. Find the 43rd term in the sequence $-19, -15, -11, \cdots$. 149

30. Find the 58th term in the sequence $10, 4, -2, \cdots$. –332

31. Form a sequence that has one arithmetic mean between 36 and 48. 36, 42, 48

32. Form a sequence that has two arithmetic means between –4 and 5. –4, –1, 2, 5

33. $\sqrt{2}, \dfrac{10 + 2\sqrt{2}}{3},$

$\dfrac{20 + \sqrt{2}}{3}, 10$

33. Form a sequence that has two arithmetic means between $\sqrt{2}$ and 10.

34. Form a sequence that has three arithmetic means between 1 and 4.

C ▶

34. 1, 1.75,
2.5, 3.25, 4

35. Find the sum of the first 11 terms in the series $-3 - 1 + 1 + 3 + \cdots$. 77

36. Find the sum of the first 32 terms in the series $0.5 + 0.75 + 1 + \cdots$. 140

37. Find n for a series for which $a_1 = -7, d = 1.5$, and $S_n = -14$. 8

38. Find n for a series for which $a_1 = 5, d = 3$, and $S_n = 440$. 16

Critical! Thinking

39. Geometry The measures of the angles of a convex polygon form an arithmetic sequence. The least measurement in the sequence is 129°. The greatest measurement is 159°. Find the number of sides in this polygon. 10

40. Find the sum of the first 102 terms in the sequence $5, 7, 2, \cdots$, where $a_n = a_{n-1} - a_{n-2}$ for all $n > 2$. 0

Applications and Problem Solving

41. Employment Terri works after school at the Fine Foods Supermarket. One day, Terri had to stack cans of soup in a grocery display in the form of a triangle. On the top row, there was only one can. Each row below it contained one more can than the one above it. On the bottom row, there were 21 cans. If all of the cans were the same size, how many cans were in the display? 231 cans

42. Number Theory Find the sum of the first 100 positive even integers and the first 100 positive odd integers. Are the sums the same? If not, by how much do they differ? Explain your findings. No; 100; see margin.

43. Food Michael is a chocoholic. On New Year's Day, he ate one piece of chocolate. On the next day, he ate 2 pieces. On each subsequent day, he ate one additional piece of candy.

  a. How many pieces of candy did he eat on the last day of January? 31

  b. How many pieces did he eat during the month of January?

43b. 496

LESSON 12-1 ARITHMETIC SEQUENCES AND SERIES 661

APPLYING THE LESSON

Homework Exercises

Assignment Guide

Average: 19–28, 29–43 odd, 45–51
Enriched: 20–30 even, 31–51

The red A, B, and C flags, printed only in the Teacher's Wraparound Edition, indicate the level of difficulty of the exercises.

Additional Answer

42. Each of the first 100 even integers is 1 greater than each of the first 100 odd integers.

44. **Banking**   Juan García has $650 in a checking account, and he is closing out the account by writing one check against it each week. The first check is for $20, the second is for $25, and so on. Each check exceeds the previous one by $5. In how many weeks will the balance in Juan's account be $0 if there is no service charge?   13 weeks

Mixed Review

45. 1, 3
45. Find $[f \circ g](4)$ and $[g \circ f](4)$ if $f(x) = x^2 - 4x + 5$ and $g(x) = x - 2$.   **(Lesson 1-2)**

46. 10 cases of drug A, 5 cases of drug B
46. **Business**   A pharmaceutical company manufactures two drugs. Each case of drug A requires 3 hours of processing time and 1 hour of curing time per week. Each case of drug B requires 5 hours of processing time and 5 hours of curing time per week. The schedule allows 55 hours of processing time and 45 hours of curing time weekly. The company must produce no more than 10 cases of drug A and no more than 9 cases of drug B. If the company makes a profit of $320 on each case of drug A and $500 on each case of drug B, how many cases of each drug should be produced in order to maximize profit?   **(Lesson 2-6)**

47. **Geometry**   Find the area of a regular pentagon that is inscribed in a circle with a diameter of 7.3 cm.   **(Lesson 5-5)**   31.68 cm^2

48. Simplify $\dfrac{\tan^2 \theta - \sin^2 \theta}{\tan^2 \theta \sin^2 \theta}$.   **(Lesson 7-1)**   1

49. Simplify $(2 + i)(3 - 4i)(1 + 2i)$.   **(Lesson 9-5)**   20 + 15i

50. Solve $45.9 = e^{0.075t}$.   **(Lesson 11-7)**   51.02

51. **College Entrance Exam**   Choose the best answer.   D
    If $\dfrac{x}{y}$ is a fraction greater than 1, which of the following must be less than 1?

    (A) $\dfrac{2y}{x}$ (B) $\dfrac{x}{2y}$ (C) $\sqrt{\dfrac{x}{y}}$ (D) $\dfrac{y}{x}$ (E) $\left(\dfrac{x}{y}\right)^2$

CASE STUDY FOLLOW-UP

Refer to Case Study 1, *Buying a Home*, on pages 956–958.

Rebecca and Tom Payton decide to buy a $200,000 home. They put 20% down and apply for a 15-year, 9% FRM to finance the balance. The Paytons have a combined gross annual income of $70,000.   1–2. See margin.   3. See students' work.

1. Do the Paytons meet the 28% debt requirement? Explain.

2. Use an arithmetic series to find the total amount the Paytons will repay the mortgage lender during the life of the loan. Identify the first term, the common difference, and the number of terms.

3. **Research** current mortgage rates and the types of mortgages currently available in your city. Then choose a mortgage lender for a $150,000 mortgage. Write about your findings in a 1-page paper. Explain why you chose that particular lender.

662   CHAPTER 12   SEQUENCES AND SERIES

662   CHAPTER 12   SEQUENCES AND SERIES

EXTENDING THE LESSON

Math Power: Problem Solving
Give an example of an arithmetic sequence whose terms are all multiples of 3 and 5, but not multiples of 4 or 6.
Sample answer: 15, 45, 75, 105, ⋯

Case Study Follow-Up
This activity provides an opportunity to do research and apply mathematics in solving problems related to issues that may face students in their adult lives. Case Study 1 is located on pages 956–958.

12-2 Geometric Sequences and Series

Objectives
12–2A
12–2B

After studying this lesson, you should be able to:
- find the nth term and geometric means of a geometric sequence, and
- find the sum of n terms of a geometric series.

Application

For his science experiment, Adam exposed the plants he was growing to a grow light for 20 hours each day. During the course of the school year, he found that the plants grew 7% each month. When he began his experiment, the plants were 3 inches tall. Predict how tall they will be at the beginning of the ninth month. *This problem will be solved in Example 3.*

The following sequence is an example of a **geometric sequence**.

$$1,\ 0.5,\ 0.25,\ 0.125, \cdots$$ *Can you find the next term?*

The ratio of successive terms in a geometric sequence is a constant called the **common ratio**, denoted r.

Geometric Sequence

A geometric sequence is a sequence in which each term after the first, a_1, is the product of the preceding term and the common ratio, r. The terms of the sequence can be represented as follows, where a_1 is nonzero and r is not equal to 1 or 0.

$$a_1, a_1r, a_1r^2, \cdots.$$

The common ratio of a geometric sequence can be found by dividing any term by the preceding term. Then multiply the last term by the common ratio to find the next term in the sequence.

Example 1

Find the next three terms in the geometric sequence 27, 135, 675, $\cdots$.

First, find the common ratio.
$135 \div 27 = 5$ $675 \div 135 = 5$
The common ratio is 5.

Then, multiply the third term by 5 to get the fourth term, and so on.
$675 \cdot 5 = 3375$ $3375 \cdot 5 = 16{,}875$ $16{,}875 \cdot 5 = 84{,}375$
The next three terms are 3375, 16,875, and 84,375.

LESSON 12-2   GEOMETRIC SEQUENCES AND SERIES   663

ALTERNATE TEACHING STRATEGIES

Using Charts

Use charts to show the recursive nature of geometric sequences. Express the terms after the first as the product of the power of the common ratio and the first term of the sequence.

Using Applications

Have students work in groups to make a list of applications of geometric sequences. Compare lists with other groups. Some examples include compound interest, growth and decay problems, and depreciation.

12–2   Lesson Notes

NCTM Standards: 1-4, 12

Lesson Resources

- Practice Master 12–2
- Enrichment Master 12–2
- Evaluation Master, Quiz A, p. 153
- Technology Master, p. 23
- Activity Master, p. 36

 Transparency 12–2 contains the 5-Minute Check and a teaching aid for this lesson.

INTRODUCING THE LESSON

5-Minute Check

(over Lesson 12–1)

1. Find the next five terms in the sequence 6, –2, –10, $\cdots$. –18, –26, –34, –42, –50
2. Find the 12th term in the sequence for which $a_1 = -2$ and $d = -3$.   –35
3. Find n for the sequence for which $a_n = 28$, $a_1 = -12$, and $d = 4$.   11
4. Find d for the sequence for which $a_1 = -6$ and $a_{14} = -97$. –7
5. Find the 34th term in the sequence 8, –2, –12, $\cdots$.   –322
6. Find the sum of the first 25 terms of the sequence $-12 - 8 - 4 + 0 \cdots$.   900

Motivating the Lesson

Tear a square piece of paper with an area of one in half. Then tear it in half again. Ask students to predict the area of one of the resulting rectangles after 5 tears.

As with arithmetic sequences, geometric sequences are also recursive. Successive terms of a geometric sequence can be expressed as the product of the common ratio and the previous term. Thus, it follows that each term can be expressed as the product of a_1 and a power of r. The terms of a geometric sequence for which $a_1 = 3$ and $r = 4$ can be represented as follows.

first term	a_1	a_1	3
second term	a_2	$a_1 r$	$3 \cdot 4^1 = 12$
third term	a_3	$a_1 r^2$	$3 \cdot 4^2 = 48$
fourth term	a_4	$a_1 r^3$	$3 \cdot 4^3 = 192$
fifth term	a_5	$a_1 r^4$	$3 \cdot 4^4 = 768$
⋮	⋮	⋮	⋮
nth term	a_n	$a_1 r^{n-1}$	$3 \cdot 4^{n-1}$

The *n*th Term of a Geometric Sequence

The *n*th term of a geometric sequence with first term a_1 and common ratio r is given by the following formula.
$$a_n = a_1 r^{n-1}$$

By definition, the *n*th term is also equal to $a_{n-1} r$, where a_{n-1} is the $(n-1)$th term. That is, $a_n = a_{n-1} r$.

Example 2

Find the 14th term in the sequence 1, $\frac{1}{3}$, $\frac{1}{9}$, ⋯ .

First, find the common ratio.

$$\frac{1}{3} \div 1 = \frac{1}{3} \qquad\qquad \frac{1}{9} \div \frac{1}{3} = \frac{1}{3}$$

The common ratio is $\frac{1}{3}$.

Then, use the formula for the *n*th term of a geometric sequence.

$$a_n = a_1 r^{n-1}$$

$$a_{14} = 1 \left(\frac{1}{3}\right)^{14-1} \qquad n = 14, a_1 = 1, \text{ and } r = \frac{1}{3}$$

$$= \left(\frac{1}{3}\right)^{13}$$

$$= \frac{1}{3^{13}} \text{ or } \frac{1}{1,594,323} \qquad \textit{Use a calculator.}$$

Geometric sequences can represent growth and decay. For a common ratio greater than 1, a sequence denotes growth. Examples are compound interest, appreciation of personal property, and population. Sequences that represent decay have a common ratio that is less than 1. Examples include depreciation and radioactive behavior.

Example 3

APPLICATION

Biology

Refer to the application at the beginning of the lesson. Predict how tall the plants will be at the beginning of the ninth month.

At the beginning of the first month, the plants were 3 inches tall. At the beginning of the second month, the plants will be $3 + 3(0.07)$ or 3.21 inches tall. At the beginning of the third month, the plants will be $3.21 + 3.21(0.07)$ or 3.4347 inches tall. The sequence of heights at the beginning of the month may be generated by using the formula for the nth term of a geometric series.

$$a_n = a_1 r^{n-1}$$
$$a_9 = 3(1.07)^{9-1} \qquad n = 9, a_1 = 3, \text{ and } r = 1.07$$
$$= 5.15$$

Thus, the plants will be 5.15 inches tall at the beginning of the ninth month.

The terms between any two nonconsecutive terms of a geometric sequence are called **geometric means**.

Example 4

Form a sequence that has two geometric means between 136 and 459.

This sequence will have the form $136, \underline{}, \underline{}, 459$.

First, find the common ratio.

$$a_n = a_1 r^{n-1}$$
$$a_4 = a_1 r^3 \qquad \text{Since there will be 4 terms in the sequence, } n = 4.$$
$$459 = 136 r^3 \qquad a_4 = 459 \text{ and } a_1 = 136$$
$$r^3 = \frac{459}{136} \text{ or } \frac{27}{8}$$
$$r = \frac{3}{2} \qquad \text{Take the cube root of each side.}$$

Then, determine the geometric means.

$$136 \cdot \frac{3}{2} = 204 \qquad\qquad 204 \cdot \frac{3}{2} = 306$$

The sequence is 136, 204, 306, 459.

A **geometric series** is the indicated sum of the terms of a geometric sequence. The lists below show some examples of geometric sequences and their corresponding geometric series.

Geometric Sequence	**Geometric Series**
$1, 4, 16, 64, 256$	$1 + 4 + 16 + 64 + 256$
$2, 1, \frac{1}{2}, \frac{1}{4}, \frac{1}{8}$	$2 + 1 + \frac{1}{2} + \frac{1}{4} + \frac{1}{8}$
$a_1, a_2, a_3, a_4, \cdots, a_n$	$a_1 + a_2 + a_3 + a_4 + \cdots + a_n$

LESSON 12-2   GEOMETRIC SEQUENCES AND SERIES   665

Chalkboard Examples

For Example 3

A certain chemical decays at the rate of one-half its weight every 6 months. If 100 grams is the initial weight of the chemical, how much remains after 4 years?   about 0.39 g

For Example 4

Form a sequence that has two geometric means between 128 and 54.   128, 96, 72, 54

To develop a formula for the sum of a series, S_n, write an expression for S_n and for rS_n, as shown below. Then subtract rS_n from S_n and solve for S_n.

$$S_n = a_1 + a_1r + a_1r^2 + \cdots + a_1r^{n-2} + a_1r^{n-1}$$
$$\underline{-(rS_n = \qquad a_1r + a_1r^2 + \cdots + a_1r^{n-2} + a_1r^{n-1} + a_1r^n)}$$
$$S_n - rS_n = a_1 \qquad\qquad\qquad\qquad\qquad\qquad - a_1r^n$$

$$S_n(1-r) = a_1 - a_1r^n \qquad \textit{Factor.}$$

$$S_n = \frac{a_1 - a_1r^n}{1-r} \qquad \textit{Divide each side by } 1-r, r \neq 1.$$

Sum of a Geometric Series	**The sum of the first n terms of a geometric series is given by the following formula.** $$S_n = \frac{a_1 - a_1r^n}{1-r}, r \neq 1$$

Example 5

Find the sum of the first eight terms of the series $3 - 6 + 12 + \cdots$.

First, find the common ratio.
$-6 \div 3 = -2 \qquad\qquad 12 \div (-6) = -2$
The common ratio is –2.

Then, find the sum.

$$S_n = \frac{a_1 - a_1r^n}{1-r}$$

$$S_8 = \frac{3 - 3(-2)^8}{1-(-2)} \qquad n = 8, a_1 = 3, \text{ and } r = -2$$

$$= \frac{3 - 3(256)}{3}$$

$$= -255$$

Thus, the sum of the first eight terms is –255.

In Chapter 11, you studied annuities and present and future value. Recall that the future value of an annuity is the sum of all payments plus the interest earned on each payment. Suppose an annuity pays an APR of 6% and you make 4 semiannual payments of $1000 into the account. The equation below gives the future value, F_n, of the account after the fourth payment.

The semiannual percentage rate is 3% since the APR is 6%.

$$F_n = 1000 + 1000(1.03)^1 + 1000(1.03)^2 + 1000(1.03)^3 = \$4183.63$$

As you learned in Chapter 11, this type of annuity can be represented by the formula $F_n = P\frac{(1+i)^n - 1}{i}$. However, this expression is also a geometric series with $a_1 = \$1000$, $r = 1.03$, and $n = 4$.

Example 6

APPLICATION

Finance

Phillip Morrow is investing $500 quarterly (January 1, April 1, July 1, and October 1) in a retirement account that pays an APR of 12%, compounded quarterly. Interest for each quarter is posted on the first day of the following quarter. Determine the value of the investment at the end of the year.

Since the interest is compounded quarterly, the interest rate per quarter is 12% ÷ 4 or 3%. The value of the common ratio, r, for each term in the series is $1 + 0.03$ or 1.03.

$$S_n = \frac{a_1 - a_1 r^n}{1 - r}$$

$$S_4 = \frac{500 - 500(1.03)^4}{1 - 1.03} \qquad a_1 = 500, r = 1.03, \text{ and } n = 4$$

$$= \frac{500 - 500(1.1255088)}{-0.03} \qquad \textit{Use a calculator to evaluate.}$$

$$= 2091.81$$

The value of the retirement account at the end of the year will be $2091.81.

EXPLORATION: Graphing Calculator

You can use a graphing calculator to examine the growth of Mr. Morrow's investment over a 2-year period.

1. Use the range values below to set up a viewing window.

XMIN = 0   YMIN = 500
XMAX = 9.5   YMAX = 5000
XSCL = 1   YSCL = 500

2. Let $Y_1 = \dfrac{500 - 500(1.03)^x}{1 - 1.03}$, where x represents the quarters that have passed.

3. Graph the equation.

4. What would be the value of Mr. Morrow's investment after 2 years? Use the TRACE function. $4446.17

CHECKING FOR UNDERSTANDING

Communicating Mathematics

Read and study the lesson to answer each question. 1–3. See margin.

1. **Explain** why the common ratio is considered to be unequal to 1 or 0.
2. **Explain** why the first term in a geometric sequence must be nonzero.
3. **Explain** why arithmetic and geometric sequences are recursive.

RETEACHING THE LESSON

Use cooperative groups to give students practice in determining the terms of a geometric sequence. Have one student give the first term of a geometric sequence. Then have the second student in the group give a second term. The third student then has to determine the common ratio and give the third term, and so on. Continue this pattern for a given number of times.

Additional Answers

2. If the first term in a geometric sequence were zero, then finding the common ratio would mean dividing by zero. Division by zero is undefined.
3. Arithmetic and geometric sequences are recursive because if you know the previous terms, you can find the next term.

EVALUATING THE LESSON

Checking for Understanding

Exercises 1–15 are designed to help you assess students' understanding through reading, writing, speaking, and modeling. You should work through Exercises 1–5 with your students and then monitor their work on Exercises 6–14.

Closing the Lesson

Writing Activity Describe how to determine the value of an account at the end of one year if equal deposits are made quarterly and the account pays an APR of 10%.

Additional Answer

1. If the common ratio were equal to 1, the sequence would be of the form $x, x, x, \cdots$, which would be a sequence of the same number. A common ratio of 0 is impossible.

Practice Masters Booklet, p. 81

Homework Exercises

Assignment Guide

Average: 16–29, 31, 34–38
Enriched: 16–24 even, 25–38

The red A, B, and C flags, printed only in the Teacher's Wraparound Edition, indicate the level of difficulty of the exercises.

Chapter 12, Quiz A, (Lessons 12–1 through 12–2), is available in the *Evaluation Masters*, p. 153.

Additional Answers

4a.

Beginning of Month	Height
1	3
2	3.21
3	3.43
4	3.68
5	3.93
6	4.21
7	4.50
8	4.82
9	5.15

5. $S_n = \dfrac{a_1 - a_1 r^n}{1 - r}$

$F_n = \dfrac{P - P r^n}{1 - r}$ *Substitute the principal P for a_1 and the future value F_n for S_n.*

$F_n = \dfrac{P r^n - P}{r - 1}$ *Factor out –1.*

$F_n = \dfrac{P(r^n - 1)}{r - 1}$ *Factor out P.*

$F_n = P\dfrac{[(1 + i)^n - 1]}{(1 + i) - 1}$ *Substitute $1 + i$ for r.*

$F_n = P\dfrac{(1 + i)^n - 1}{i}$ *Simplify.*

---

4. Refer to Example 3.   4b. an exponential function

  a. Make a table to represent the situation. In the first row, put the number of months, and in the second row, put the height of the plants. See margin.

  b. Graph the numbers in the table. Let months be the *x*-coordinate and let height of the plants be the *y*-coordinate, and connect the points. Describe the graph.

5. Show how the formula for the future value of an annuity can be derived from the formula for the sum of a geometric series. See margin.

Guided Practice

Find the next four terms of each geometric sequence.

6. 2, 3, ···

7. 7, 3.5, ···

8. 1.2, 3.6, ···

6. $\dfrac{9}{2}, \dfrac{27}{4}, \dfrac{81}{8}, \dfrac{243}{16}$
7. 1.75, 0.875, 0.4375, 0.21875
8. 10.8, 32.4, 97.2, 291.6

Determine whether the given terms form a geometric sequence. Write *yes* or *no*.

9. $\sqrt{2}, 2, \sqrt{8}, \cdots$ yes

10. $\sqrt[3]{3^2}, 3, 3\sqrt[3]{3}, \cdots$ yes

11. $t^{-2}, t^{-1}, 1, \cdots$ yes

12. The first term of a geometric sequence is $\dfrac{1}{2}$, and the common ratio is $\dfrac{2}{3}$. Find the ninth term of the sequence. $\dfrac{128}{6561}$

13. If $r = 2$ and $a_5 = 24$, find the first term of the geometric sequence. $\dfrac{3}{2}$

14. Form a sequence that has two geometric means between –2 and 54. $-2, 6, -18, 54$

15. Find the sum of the first five terms of the series $\dfrac{5}{3} + 5 + 15 + \cdots$. $201\dfrac{2}{3}$

EXERCISES

Practice

Solve.

16. The first term of a geometric sequence is –3, and the common ratio is $\dfrac{2}{3}$. Find the next four terms. $-2, -1\dfrac{1}{3}, -\dfrac{8}{9}, -\dfrac{16}{27}$

17. The first term of a geometric sequence is 8, and the common ratio is $\dfrac{3}{2}$. Find the next three terms. 12, 18, 27

18. Find the ninth term of the geometric sequence $\sqrt{2}, 2, 2\sqrt{2}, \cdots$. $16\sqrt{2}$

19. Find the sixth term of the geometric sequence 10, 0.1, 0.001, ···. 10^{-9}

20. Find the first four terms of the geometric sequence for which $a_5 = 32\sqrt{2}$ and $r = -\sqrt{2}$. $8\sqrt{2}, -16, 16\sqrt{2}, -32$

21. Find the first three terms of the geometric sequence for which $a_4 = 2.5$ and $r = 2$. 0.3125, 0.625, 1.25

22. $\dfrac{1}{4}, \pm 1, 4$

22. Form a sequence that has one geometric mean between $\dfrac{1}{4}$ and 4.

23. Form a sequence that has two geometric means between 1 and 27. 1, 3, 9, 27

24. Find the sum of the first seven terms of the series $\dfrac{1}{2} + \dfrac{1}{4} + \dfrac{1}{8} + \cdots$. $\dfrac{127}{128}$

25. Find the sum of the first six terms of the series $2 + 3 + 4.5 + \cdots$. 41.5625

26. Find the sum of the first nine terms of the series $0.5 + 1 + 2 + \cdots$. 255.5

27. $31(1 + \sqrt{2})$

27. Find the sum of the first ten terms of the series $1 + \sqrt{2} + 2 + 2\sqrt{2} + \cdots$.

Critical Thinking

28. The sum of the first six terms in a geometric sequence of real numbers is 252. Find the sum of the first four terms when the sum of the first two terms is 12. 60

668 CHAPTER 12 SEQUENCES AND SERIES

29. **Investment** The Landbury Museum has been investing in paintings for many years. Twenty years ago, the museum purchased a painting by one of the French impressionist painters for $180,000. The value of the painting has appreciated at a rate of 14% per year. Find the value of the painting after 10, 20, 30, 40, and 50 years, assuming that the rate of appreciation remains constant.

30. **Finance** Eric Scheidt is purchasing a new car that costs $13,500. He estimates that the value of the car will depreciate at a rate of 18% per year. Determine the value of the car when he plans to trade it in 5 years.

31. **Biology** The population of a certain bacteria doubles every 30 minutes. The initial population is 150. Determine the number of organisms that would exist after 12 hours and after 24 hours. 1.258×10^9, 2.111×10^{16}

32. **Finance** Mr. Leshnock invests $5000 annually in an insurance annuity for twenty years. What will the annuity be worth if it has an APR of 9.5%?

33. **Number Theory** If you tear a piece of paper that is 0.005 centimeters thick in half, and place the two pieces on top of each other, the height of the pile of paper is 0.010 centimeters. Let's call this the second pile. If you tear these two pieces of paper in half, the third pile will have four pieces of paper in it.
    a. How high is the third pile? the fourth pile? 0.020 cm, 0.040 cm
    b. Write a formula to determine how high the nth pile is. $0.005(2)^{n-1}$
    c. Use the formula to determine in theory how high the 10th pile would be and how high the 100th pile would be. 2.56 cm, 3.169×10^{27} cm

Mixed Review

34. **Geometry** The vertices of a parallelogram are at $(2,4)$, $(5,9)$, $(14,9)$, and $(11,4)$. Find the lengths of the diagonals. **(Lesson 1-4)** 7.8 units, 13 units

35. Graph $y = \dfrac{2}{3} \cos \theta$. **(Lesson 6-2)** See margin.

36. Write the standard form of the equation of the circle that passes through the points with coordinates $(5,0)$, $(1,-2)$, and $(4,-3)$. **(Lesson 10-1)**

37. **Physical Science** The adiabatic process is the cooling of air as it moves upward into the atmosphere. Dry air expands as it moves upward into the atmosphere. For each 1000 feet that it moves upward, the air cools 5°F. Suppose the temperature at ground level is 80°F. **(Lesson 12-1)** 37a. 80, 75, 70, $\cdots$
    a. Write a sequence representing the temperature decrease per 1000 feet.
    b. If n is the height of the air in thousands of feet, write a formula for the temperature T in terms of n. $T = 80 - 5n$
    c. What is the ground level temperature if the air at 40,000 feet is –125°F? 75°F

38. **College Entrance Exam** Choose the best answer. A
$$\frac{1}{2} \cdot \frac{2}{3} \cdot \frac{3}{4} \cdot \frac{4}{5} \cdot \frac{5}{6} \cdot \frac{6}{7} =$$
    (A) $\dfrac{1}{7}$ (B) $\dfrac{3}{7}$ (C) $\dfrac{21}{27}$ (D) $\dfrac{6}{7}$ (E) $\dfrac{7}{8}$

EXTENDING THE LESSON

Math Power: Reasoning

Find a and b if $3b$, $3ab$, 3, $\dfrac{ab}{3}$, $\cdots$ are consecutive terms of a geometric sequence.
$a = \pm\dfrac{1}{3}$, $b = 9$

Objective This optional page shows how a spreadsheet can be used to calculate the payments on a consumer loan.

Teaching Suggestions

Encourage students to use a *formatting* feature of the spreadsheet to fix the number of decimal places at 2 so that values in columns B, C, and D can represent money. The spreadsheet will then automatically round the amount in the cell to the nearest cent. Some spreadsheets also add a *$* if formatted to do so. Emphasize that the required payment made each month is the same even though the interest paid each month goes down and the principal paid each month goes up.

Technology

Amortization

Most consumer loans, like mortgages for homes, are paid in a series of equal payments made over a period of time. This is called **amortization**. The money from each payment includes an interest payment and a principal payment. The interest due for the period since the last payment was made is paid first, and then the remaining money from the payment goes toward reducing the principal. The spreadsheet program below constructs an amortization schedule for a two-year loan.

AMORTIZATION SCHEDULE			
	A	B	C	D
1		LOAN AMOUNT	PAYMENT	INTEREST RATE
2				
3	PAYMENT	INTEREST PAID	PRINCIPAL PAID	BALANCE DUE
4	0	0	0	B2
5	1	D2/12*D4	C2-B5	D4-C5
6	2	D2/12*D5	C2-B6	D5-C6
28	24	D2/12*D27	D27	0

Lee is taking out a two-year loan to buy a computer for college. The loan amount is $1600, the monthly payment is $75.32, and the interest rate is 12.0%. A portion of the amoritization table for Lee's loan is shown below.

```
= = = = = = = = = = = = = = = = = = = = = = = = = = = = = = = = = = = = =
                          AMORTIZATION SCHEDULE
= = = = = = = = = = = = = = = = = = = = = = = = = = = = = = = = = = = = =
1                    LOAN AMOUNT       PAYMENT          INTEREST RATE
2                    1600              75.32            0.120
3      PAYMENT       INTEREST PAID     PRINCIPAL PAID   BALANCE DUE
4      0             0                 0                1600.00
5      1             16.00             59.32            1540.68
6      2             15.41             59.91            1480.77
```

EXERCISES

1. See margin.

1. Explain why the amount of interest paid per month grows smaller.
2. Suppose Lee sends in $10 extra with his payment each month. Use the spreadsheet program to determine how much faster his loan will be paid. 3 months early

Additional Answer

1. The principal is less each month. Therefore, the amount of interest due on the principal is less.

12-3 Infinite Sequences and Series

Objectives
12–3A
12–3B

After studying this lesson, you should be able to:
- find the limit of the terms of an infinite sequence, and
- find the sum of an infinite geometric series.

Application

A vacuum pump removes 25% of the air from a sealed jar on each stroke of its piston. The jar contains 1 liter of air before the pump starts. Write a sequence to represent the amount of air remaining inside the jar after each stroke of the piston. Will there ever be no air inside the jar?

If 25% of the air is removed from the jar after each stroke, then 75% of the air remains in the jar. We can write a geometric sequence to represent the situation, with $a = 1$ and $r = 0.75$.

Stroke	Air Remaining	Terms of Sequence
1	$1(0.75)^1$	0.75
2	$1(0.75)^2$	0.5625
3	$1(0.75)^3$	0.4219
4	$1(0.75)^4$	0.3164
5	$1(0.75)^5$	0.2373
⋮	⋮	⋮
10	$1(0.75)^{10}$	0.0563
⋮	⋮	⋮
100	$1(0.75)^{100}$	3.2×10^{-13}
⋮	⋮	⋮
500	$1(0.75)^{500}$	3.4×10^{-63}
⋮	⋮	⋮
n	$1(0.75)^n$	ar^n

FYI...

The Thermos™ is actually the trade name for a vacuum flask in which the air between two bottles, one inside the other, has been drawn out by a vacuum pump.

In theory, the sequence above can have infinitely many terms. Thus, it is called an **infinite sequence**. As n increases, the terms of the sequence decrease and get closer and closer to zero. The amount of air in the sealed jar will never actually be zero; however, the amount of air approaches zero as n increases without bound.

Consider the infinite sequence $1, \frac{1}{2}, \frac{1}{3}, \frac{1}{4}, \frac{1}{5}, \cdots$, whose nth term is $\frac{1}{n}$. Several terms of this sequence are graphed below.

LESSON 12-3 INFINITE SEQUENCES AND SERIES 671

NCTM Standards: 1-4, 12, 13

Lesson Resources

- Practice Master 12–3
- Enrichment Master 12–3

 Transparency 12–3 contains the 5-Minute Check and a teaching aid for this lesson.

INTRODUCING THE LESSON

 5-Minute Check

(over Lesson 12-2)

1. Find the next four terms of the geometric sequence 4, 12, ⋯ .
   36, 108, 324, 972
2. The first term of a geometric sequence is –4, and the common ratio is 1.5. Find the next four terms.
   –6, –9, –13.5, –20.25
3. Find the tenth term of the geometric sequence $\sqrt{3}, 3, 3\sqrt{3}, \cdots$. **243**
4. Form a sequence that has one geometric mean between $\frac{1}{2}$ and 2. $\frac{1}{2}, \pm 1, 2$
5. Find the sum of the first six terms of the series $2 - 8 + 32 - \cdots$. **–1638**

Prerequisite Skills

Students should be familiar with finding the power of a fraction.
1. Find $\left(\frac{1}{2}\right)^{50}$.

   $\left(\frac{1}{2^{50}}\right)$ or about 8.9×10^{-16}

2. Find $\frac{10^4 + 5(10)}{4(10)^3}$. **2.5125**

ALTERNATE TEACHING STRATEGIES

Using Manipulatives

Use paper-folding to demonstrate the limit of the sequence $1, \frac{1}{2}, \frac{1}{4}, \frac{1}{8} \cdots$.

Using Mini-Math Labs

Give groups of students a tennis ball and a meter stick. Have them drop a tennis ball from a given height and record the vertical distances it reaches before coming to rest. Discuss the series formed by the path of the ball.

The goal of the Booster Club is to raise $4000 during a telethon to build a concession stand for the football field. If they raise $\frac{1}{2}$ of the amount the first hour and $\frac{1}{2}$ of the remaining amount each hour after that, how long should it take to reach its goal? Can it ever reach its goal?

It can never reach its goal because it takes an infinite amount of time. After about 16 hours, however, it will be very close to the goal.

TEACHING THE LESSON

Teaching Tip After graphing the sequence given on page 671, encourage students to graph several terms of an infinite sequence before trying to determine its limit.

Chalkboard Examples

For Example 1

Find the limit of each sequence.

a. $3, \frac{3}{4}, \frac{3}{16}, \dots$. **0**

b. $\frac{3}{2}, \frac{12}{16}, \frac{33}{54} \dots$. $\frac{1}{2}$

For Example 2

Evaluate each expression.

a. $\lim\limits_{n\to\infty} \frac{3n+6}{n}$ **3**

b. $\lim\limits_{n\to\infty} \frac{n^2-3n+4}{n^2-1}$ **1**

Notice that the terms approach 0 as n increases. Zero is called the *limit* of the terms in this sequence. This can be expressed as follows.

$$\lim_{n\to\infty} \frac{1}{n} = 0 \qquad \text{\small ∞ is the symbol for infinity.}$$

This is read "the limit of 1 over n, as n approaches infinity, equals zero."

If a general expression for the nth term of a sequence is known, the limit can usually be found by substituting large values for n. Consider the following examples.

Example 1

Find the limit of each infinite sequence.

a. $2, \dfrac{2}{5}, \dfrac{2}{25}, \dfrac{2}{125}, \cdots, \dfrac{2}{5^{n-1}}, \cdots$.

a. The 50th term is $\dfrac{2}{5^{49}}$, or about 1.13×10^{-34}. The 100th term is $\dfrac{2}{5^{99}}$, or about 1.27×10^{-69}. Notice that the values appear to approach 0.
Therefore, $\lim\limits_{n\to\infty} \dfrac{2}{5^{n-1}} = 0$.

b. $\dfrac{7}{3}, \dfrac{20}{24}, \dfrac{45}{81}, \cdots, \dfrac{n^3+6n}{3n^3}, \cdots$.

b. The 50th term is $\dfrac{(50)^3 + 6(50)}{3(50)^3}$ or 0.3341. The 100th term is $\dfrac{(100)^3 + 6(100)}{3(100)^3}$ or 0.3335. The 500th term is $\dfrac{(500)^3 + 6(500)}{3(500)^3}$ or 0.3333.
Notice that the values appear to approach $\dfrac{1}{3}$.
Therefore, $\lim\limits_{n\to\infty} \dfrac{n^3+6n}{3n^3} = \dfrac{1}{3}$.

The form of the expression for the nth term of a sequence can often be altered to make the limit easier to find.

Example 2

Evaluate each expression.

a. $\lim\limits_{n\to\infty} \dfrac{4n+2}{n}$

a. $\lim\limits_{n\to\infty} \dfrac{4n+2}{n} = \lim\limits_{n\to\infty} \left(4 + \dfrac{2}{n}\right)$ *Simplify.*

$\qquad = \lim\limits_{n\to\infty} 4 + \lim\limits_{n\to\infty} \dfrac{2}{n}$ *The limit of a sum equals the sum of the limits.*

But $\lim\limits_{n\to\infty} \dfrac{2}{n} = 0$. Therefore, $\lim\limits_{n\to\infty} 4 + \lim\limits_{n\to\infty} \dfrac{2}{n} = 4 + 0$ or 4.
Thus, the limit is 4.

b. $\lim\limits_{n\to\infty} \dfrac{n^2 + 2n - 5}{n^2 - 1}$

b. Divide the numerator and denominator by the highest power of n that occurs in either the numerator or the denominator, in this case, n^2.

$$\lim_{n\to\infty} \frac{n^2 + 2n - 5}{n^2 - 1} = \lim_{n\to\infty} \frac{\dfrac{n^2}{n^2} + \dfrac{2n}{n^2} - \dfrac{5}{n^2}}{\dfrac{n^2}{n^2} - \dfrac{1}{n^2}}$$

$$= \lim_{n\to\infty} \frac{1 + \dfrac{2}{n} - \dfrac{5}{n^2}}{1 - \dfrac{1}{n^2}} \qquad \textit{Simplify.}$$

$$= \frac{1 + 0 - 0}{1 - 0} \text{ or } 1 \quad \textit{lim} \frac{2}{n} = 0, \textit{lim} \frac{5}{n^2} = 0, \textit{lim} \frac{1}{n^2} = 0$$
$\quad\quad\quad\quad\quad\quad\quad\quad\quad\quad\quad\quad\quad _{n\to\infty}\quad\quad _{n\to\infty}\quad\quad _{n\to\infty}$

Thus, the limit is 1.

Limits do not exist for all sequences. If the absolute value of the terms of a sequence becomes arbitrarily great or if the terms do not approach a value, the sequence has no limit. Example 3 illustrates both of these cases.

Example 3

Evaluate each expression.

a. $\lim\limits_{n\to\infty} \dfrac{3n^2 + 4}{2n}$

a. $\lim\limits_{n\to\infty} \dfrac{3n^2 + 4}{2n} = \lim\limits_{n\to\infty} \left(\dfrac{3}{2}n + \dfrac{2}{n} \right)$

$$= \lim_{n\to\infty} \frac{3}{2}n + \lim_{n\to\infty} \frac{2}{n}$$

$$= \lim_{n\to\infty} \frac{3}{2}n$$

Since $\dfrac{3}{2}n$ becomes increasingly large as n approaches infinity, the sequence has no limit.

b. $\lim\limits_{n\to\infty} \dfrac{(-1)^n n^3}{3n^3 + 4n}$

b. $\lim\limits_{n\to\infty} \dfrac{(-1)^n n^3}{3n^3 + 4n} = \lim\limits_{n\to\infty} (-1)^n \left(\dfrac{1}{3 + \dfrac{4}{n^2}} \right)$ *Divide the numerator and denominator by n^3.*

$$= \lim_{n\to\infty} (-1)^n \cdot \frac{1}{3} \qquad \lim_{n\to\infty} \left(\frac{1}{3 + \frac{4}{n^2}} \right) = \frac{1}{3}$$

When n is even, $(-1)^n = 1$. When n is odd, $(-1)^n = -1$. Thus, the odd-numbered terms approach $-\dfrac{1}{3}$, and the even-numbered terms approach $\dfrac{1}{3}$. Therefore, the sequence has no limit.

An **infinite series** is the indicated sum of the terms of an infinite sequence. Consider the series $\frac{1}{2} + \frac{1}{4} + \frac{1}{8} + \frac{1}{16} + \cdots$. Since this is a geometric series, you can find the sum of the first 100 terms by using the formula $S_n = \frac{a_1 - a_1 r^n}{1 - r}$, where $r = \frac{1}{2}$.

$$S_{100} = \frac{\frac{1}{2} - \frac{1}{2}\left(\frac{1}{2}\right)^{100}}{1 - \frac{1}{2}} = \frac{\frac{1}{2} - \left(\frac{1}{2}\right)^{101}}{\frac{1}{2}} = 1 - \left(\frac{1}{2}\right)^{100}$$

Since $\left(\frac{1}{2}\right)^{100}$ is very close to 0, S_{100} is nearly equal to 1. No matter how many terms are added, the sum of the infinite series will never exceed 1. Thus, 1 is the sum of the infinite series.

Sum of an Infinite Series	If S_n is the sum of n terms of a series, and S is a number such that $S > S_n$ for all n, and $S - S_n$ approaches zero as n increases without limit, then the sum of the infinite series is S. $$\lim_{n \to \infty} S_n = S$$

If an infinite series has a limit, and thus, has a sum, the nth term of the series, a_n, must approach 0 as $n \to \infty$. Thus, if $\lim_{n \to \infty} a_n \neq 0$, the series has no sum. If $\lim_{n \to \infty} a_n = 0$, the series may or may not have a sum.

The formula for the sum of the first n terms of a geometric series can be written as follows.

$$S_n = \frac{a_1(1 - r^n)}{1 - r}, r \neq 1$$

Suppose $n \to \infty$; that is, the number of terms increases without limit. If $|r| > 1, r^n$ increases without limit as $n \to \infty$. However, when $|r| < 1$, r^n approaches 0 as $n \to \infty$. Then, S_n approaches the value $\frac{a_1}{1 - r}$.

Sum of an Infinite Geometric Series	The sum, S, of an infinite geometric series for which $|r| < 1$ is given by the following formula. $$S_n = \frac{a_1}{1 - r}$$

Example 4

Find the sum of the series $\frac{1}{25} + \frac{1}{250} + \frac{1}{2500} + \cdots$.

In this series, $a_1 = \frac{1}{25}$ and $r = \frac{1}{10}$. Since $|r| < 1, S_n = \frac{a_1}{1 - r}$.

$$S_n = \frac{a_1}{1 - r}$$

$$= \frac{\frac{1}{25}}{1 - \frac{1}{10}}$$

$$= \frac{2}{45}$$

The sum of the series is $\frac{2}{45}$.

Chalkboard Examples

For Example 4

Find the sum of the series
$\frac{1}{15} + \frac{1}{150} + \frac{1}{1500} + \cdots$.

$\frac{2}{27}$

For Example 5

A tennis ball dropped from a height of 24 feet bounces 50% of the height from which it fell on each bounce. What is the vertical distance it travels before coming to rest? **72 ft**

Example 5

A tennis ball dropped from a height of 30 feet bounces 40% of the height from which it fell on each bounce. What is the vertical distance it travels before coming to rest?

The distance traveled is the actual path of the ball.

The distance is given by the following series.

$30 + 12 + 12 + 4.8 + 4.8 + 1.92 + 1.92 + \cdots$

Notice that in this series, each term after the first term is repeated. This series can be rewritten as the sum of two infinite geometric series as follows.

$$30 + 12 + 4.8 + 1.92 + \cdots$$
$$+ \qquad 12 + 4.8 + 1.92 + \cdots$$

For both series, $r = 0.4$, but $a_1 = 30$ in the first series and $a_1 = 12$ in the second series.

First Series

$S_n = \frac{30}{1 - 0.4}$ or 50

Second Series

$S_n = \frac{12}{1 - 0.4}$ or 20

Therefore, the ball travels $50 + 20$ or 70 feet before coming to rest.

You can use what you now know about infinite series to write repeating decimals as fractions. The first step is to write the repeating decimal as an infinite geometric series.

Chalkboard Example

For Example 6

Write $0.110110\cdots$ as a fraction.

$\dfrac{110}{999}$

Example 6 | Write $0.123123\cdots$ as a fraction.

$$0.\overline{123} = \frac{123}{1000} + \frac{123}{1,000,000} + \frac{123}{1,000,000,000} + \cdots$$

$$S_n = \frac{a_1}{1-r}$$

$$= \frac{\dfrac{123}{1000}}{1 - \dfrac{1}{1000}} \qquad a_1 = \frac{123}{1000} \text{ and } r = \frac{1}{1000}$$

$$= \frac{123}{999} \text{ or } \frac{41}{333}$$

Thus, $0.123123\cdots = \dfrac{41}{333}$.

EVALUATING THE LESSON

Checking for Understanding

Exercises 1–16 are designed to help you assess students' understanding through reading, writing, speaking, and modeling. You should work through Exercises 1–4 with your students and then monitor their work on Exercises 5–16.

Closing the Lesson

Modeling Activity Have students make a number line model of an infinite sequence.

CHECKING FOR UNDERSTANDING

Communicating Mathematics

Read and study the lesson to answer each question. 1, 4. See margin.

1. **Explain** why 0 is the limit of any geometric sequence for which $|r| < 1$.

2. A sequence has a limit if $|r|$ is   b
   a. greater than 1.   b. less than 1.

3. Choose the correct terms to make two true sentences. When determining the limit of a rational expression, if the highest power of the variable that appears in the numerator is (greater than, less than) the highest power of the variable that appears in the denominator, the limit (does, does not) exist. Use examples to explain your answer. greater than, does not; less than, does

4. Do infinite arithmetic series have limits? Explain your answer.

Guided Practice

Write an expression for the nth term of each sequence.

5. $1, 2, 4, 8, \cdots$ 2^{n-1}

6. $5, 7, 9, 11, \cdots$ $2n+3$

7. $3, 2, \dfrac{4}{3}, \dfrac{8}{9}, \cdots$ $3 \cdot \left(\dfrac{2}{3}\right)^{n-1}$

8. $3, \dfrac{5}{2}, \dfrac{7}{3}, \dfrac{9}{4}, \cdots$ $\dfrac{2n+1}{n}$

Evaluate each limit, or state that the limit does not exist.

9. $\displaystyle\lim_{n\to\infty} \frac{1-2n}{5n}$ $-\dfrac{2}{5}$

10. $\displaystyle\lim_{n\to\infty} \frac{n+1}{n}$ 1

11. $\displaystyle\lim_{n\to\infty} \frac{3n-5}{n}$ 3

Find the sum of each infinite series, or state that the sum does not exist.

12. $2\sqrt{2} + 8 + 16\sqrt{2} + \cdots$ does not exist

13. $\dfrac{1}{20} + \dfrac{1}{40} + \dfrac{1}{80} + \cdots$ $\dfrac{1}{10}$

Write each repeating decimal as a fraction.

14. $0.454545\cdots$ $\dfrac{5}{11}$

15. $0.888\cdots$ $\dfrac{8}{9}$

16. $7.259259\cdots$ $7\dfrac{7}{27}$

Additional Answers

1. Each succeeding term is smaller than the one preceding it since the succeeding terms are equal to the preceding term multiplied by a number that is less than 1. Therefore, the terms of the sequence are getting smaller and smaller, and thus, approach 0.

4. Since the terms of an arithmetic series do not approach zero as $n \to \infty$, infinite arithmetic series do not have limits.

EXERCISES

Practice **Evaluate each limit, or state that the limit does not exist.**

17. $\lim\limits_{n\to\infty}\dfrac{1}{3^n}$ 0

18. $\lim\limits_{n\to\infty}\dfrac{2n^2-6n}{5n^2}$ $\dfrac{2}{5}$

19. $\lim\limits_{n\to\infty}\dfrac{n^2-4}{2n}$ does not exist

20. $\lim\limits_{n\to\infty}\dfrac{(n+2)(2n-1)}{n^2}$ 2

21. $\lim\limits_{n\to\infty}\dfrac{n^2+n-3}{n^2}$ 1

22. $\lim\limits_{n\to\infty}\dfrac{3n+1}{n-3}$ 3

23. $\lim\limits_{n\to\infty}\dfrac{4n^2+5}{3n^2+2n}$ $\dfrac{4}{3}$

24. $\lim\limits_{n\to\infty}\dfrac{2n^3}{n^2+4n}$ does not exist

25. $\lim\limits_{n\to\infty}\dfrac{2n+(-1)^n}{n^2}$ 0

 Write each repeating decimal as a fraction.

26. $0.555\cdots$ $\dfrac{5}{9}$

27. $0.2727\cdots$ $\dfrac{3}{11}$

28. $0.370370\cdots$ $\dfrac{10}{27}$

29. $0.3181818\cdots$ $\dfrac{7}{22}$

30. $3.242424\cdots$ $3\dfrac{8}{33}$

31. $2.205205\cdots$ $2\dfrac{205}{999}$

 Find the sum of each infinite series, or state that the sum does not exist.

32. $\dfrac{2}{3}+\dfrac{1}{3}+\dfrac{1}{6}+\dfrac{1}{12}+\cdots$ $1\dfrac{1}{3}$

33. $\sqrt{3}+1+\dfrac{\sqrt{3}}{3}+\cdots$ $\dfrac{3}{2}\left(\sqrt{3}+1\right)$

34. $\dfrac{2}{7}+\dfrac{4}{7}+\dfrac{8}{7}+\cdots$ does not exist

35. $0.2+0.02+0.002+\cdots$ $\dfrac{2}{9}$

36. $10+5+2.5+\cdots$ 20

37. $2+3+\dfrac{9}{2}+\cdots$ does not exist

Critical Thinking

38. Evaluate $\lim\limits_{n\to\infty}\dfrac{\sqrt{n}}{\sqrt{n}+1}$. 1

Applications and Problem Solving

39. Chemistry A vacuum pump removes 20% of the air in a sealed jar on each stroke of its piston. The jar contains 21 liters of air before the pump starts. After how many strokes will only 42% of the air remain? 4 strokes

40. Physics A tennis ball dropped from a height of 12 feet bounces 70% of the height from which it fell on each bounce. What is the vertical distance it travels before coming to rest? 68 feet

41. Coordinate Geometry Two bugs start at the origin, one traveling along the positive half of the x-axis and the other traveling along the positive half of the y-axis. Each bug moves 1 unit on the first move, $\dfrac{1}{2}$ unit on the second move, and so on, where on any subsequent move the bug moves only half as far as the preceding move. The bugs always move at exactly the same time. How far apart will the bugs be after infinitely many moves? $2\sqrt{2}$ units

Mixed Review

42. Find the product $\dfrac{1}{2}\begin{bmatrix} 9 & -3 \\ -6 & 6 \end{bmatrix}$. **(Lesson 2-2)** $\begin{bmatrix} \frac{9}{2} & -\frac{3}{2} \\ -3 & 3 \end{bmatrix}$

43. Solve the equation $3k^2+3k+2=0$ by using the quadratic formula. **(Lesson 4-2)** $k=\dfrac{-3\pm i\sqrt{15}}{6}$

Assignment Guide

Average: 17–31, 32–40 even, 42–47
Enriched: 17–25 odd, 26–47

The red A, B, and C flags, printed only in the Teacher's Wraparound Edition, indicate the level of difficulty of the exercises.

Practice Masters Booklet, p. 82

12-3 **Practice Worksheet**

NAME _____ DATE _____

Infinite Sequences and Series

Evaluate each limit, or state that the limit does not exist.

1. $\lim\limits_{n\to\infty}\dfrac{n^2-1}{n^2+1}$ 1

2. $\lim\limits_{n\to\infty}\dfrac{4n^2-5n}{3n^2+4}$ $\dfrac{4}{3}$

3. $\lim\limits_{n\to\infty}\dfrac{5n^2+1}{6n}$ does not exist

4. $\lim\limits_{n\to\infty}\dfrac{(n-1)(3n+1)}{5n^2}$ $\dfrac{3}{5}$

5. $\lim\limits_{n\to\infty}\dfrac{5n^3+1}{3n^2+1}$ does not exist

6. $\lim\limits_{n\to\infty}\dfrac{3n-(-1)^n}{4n^2}$ 0

Write each repeating decimal as a fraction.

7. $0.49999\cdots$ $\dfrac{1}{2}$

8. $1.999\cdots$ 2

9. $2.242424\cdots$ $2\dfrac{8}{33}$

10. $0.127127\cdots$ $\dfrac{127}{999}$

11. $1.164164\cdots$ $1\dfrac{164}{999}$

12. $0.6414141\cdots$ $\dfrac{127}{198}$

Find the sum of each infinite series, or state that the sum does not exist.

13. $\dfrac{2}{5}+\dfrac{6}{25}+\dfrac{18}{125}+\cdots$ 1

14. $\dfrac{3}{4}+\dfrac{15}{8}+\dfrac{75}{16}+\cdots$ does not exist

---

RETEACHING THE LESSON

Give students examples of different ratios r and ask them to tell whether a geometric series with each of the given ratios has a limit. Have students explain their answers. For example, give students the ratio $\dfrac{1}{4}$. Have them use $\dfrac{1}{4}$ to write a geometric series. Then they should decide if this geometric series has a limit.

44. Aviation An airplane flies at 150 km/h and heads 30° south of east. A 50-km/h wind blows in the direction 25° west of south. Find the ground speed and direction of the plane. **(Lesson 8-5)** 162.2 km/h, 47°53' SE

45. Find S_{14} for the arithmetic series for which $a_1 = 3.2$ and $d = 1.5$. **(Lesson 12-1)** 181.3

46. Form a sequence that has three geometric means between 2 and $\frac{1}{8}$. **(Lesson 12-2)** $2, \pm 1, \frac{1}{2}, \pm \frac{1}{4}, \frac{1}{8}$

47. College Entrance Exam Compare quantities A and B below. C
Write A if quantity A is greater.
Write B if quantity B is greater.
Write C if the two quantities are equal.
Write D if there is not enough information to determine the relationship.

(A) the number of positive odd integer factors of 26

(B) the number of positive even integer factors of 26

DECISION MAKING

Finding Money for College

How much will it cost you to go to college? If you can get into the college of your choice, will you be able to afford to attend? The cost of going to college has skyrocketed in recent years, with expenses at a few schools topping $20,000 per year. Nevertheless, through smart planning and diligent searching for financial aid, you may be able to afford the school of your choice. 1–4. See students' work.

1. Use the list of colleges you compiled for the Decision Making feature in Chapter 2. Find the estimated annual cost of attending each school.

2. Research the financial aid that is available to students attending the schools on your list. What scholarships does the college offer? Will the school help you find a job? Can you get a loan from the college, the federal government, or some other agency? How much money can you earn on a part-time job?

3. Draw up a financial plan for meeting the expenses of the colleges on your list.

4. **Project** Work with your group to complete one of the projects listed at the right based on the information you gathered in Exercises 1–3.

PROJECTS

- *Conduct an interview.*
- *Write a book report.*
- *Write a proposal.*
- *Write an article for the school paper.*
- *Write a report.*
- *Make a display.*
- *Make a graph or chart.*
- *Plan an activity.*
- *Design a checklist.*

Enrichment Masters Booklet, p. 82

678 CHAPTER 12 SEQUENCES AND SERIES

EXTENDING THE LESSON

Math Power: Communication

Have groups of students discuss the concept of *infinity*. Have them give examples to support their statements. Then have a class discussion about *infinity*.

Decision Making

This activity provides students an opportunity to work together on a given problem. You may wish to refer to pages T20–T21 and page 654c for the various elements of cooperative groups and specific goals and strategies for using them.

12-4 Convergent and Divergent Series

Objective
12-4

After studying this lesson, you should be able to:
- determine whether a series is convergent or divergent.

Application

To plan for his retirement, Al Early has been placing $1200 each year in an annuity that offers a 12% annual percentage rate. The table below shows the value of Mr. Early's annuity at the end of selected years.

Number of Years	Value of First $1200	Value of Annuity
1	$1200.00	$1200.00
2	$1200(1.12)^1 = \$1344.00$	$2544.00
3	$1200(1.12)^2 = \$1505.28$	$4049.28
4	$1200(1.12)^3 = \$1685.91$	$5735.19
5	$1200(1.12)^4 = \$1888.22$	$7623.42
⋮	⋮	⋮
10	$1200(1.12)^9 = \$3327.69$	$21,058.48
⋮	⋮	⋮
15	$1200(1.12)^{14} = \$5864.53$	$44,735.66
⋮	⋮	⋮
n	$1200(1.12)^{n-1}$	$1200\dfrac{(1.12)^n - 1}{0.12}$

The value of the annuity at the end of each year is a partial sum of the series that represents the value of the annuity. These partial sums form a sequence. As the number of terms used for the partial sums increases without bound, the value of the partial sums increases without bound. This result is to be expected, since the common ratio, r, of this sequence is 1.12 and $|r| > 1$. Since the sequence of partial sums does not approach a limit, the infinite series is said to **diverge**. If a sequence has a limit, then the related infinite series is said to **converge**.

Convergent and Divergent Series	If an infinite series has a sum, or limit, the series is convergent. If a series is not convergent, it is divergent.

Example 1

Determine whether each series is convergent or divergent.

a. $\dfrac{2}{3} + \dfrac{1}{3} + \dfrac{1}{6} + \cdots$

a. This is a geometric series, with $r = \dfrac{1}{2}$. Since $|r| < 1$, the series has a limit. Therefore, the series is convergent.

(continued on the next page)

LESSON 12-4   CONVERGENT AND DIVERGENT SERIES   679

12-4   Lesson Notes

NCTM Standards: 1-4, 12, 13

Lesson Resources

- Practice Master 12-4
- Enrichment Master 12-4
- Evaluation Master, Quiz B, p. 153

 Transparency 12-4 contains the 5-Minute Check and a teaching aid for this lesson.

INTRODUCING THE LESSON

 5-Minute Check
(over Lesson 12–3)

1. Write an expression for the nth term of the sequence $1, \dfrac{1}{3}, \dfrac{1}{9}, \dfrac{1}{27}, \cdots$. $\left(\dfrac{1}{3}\right)^{n-1}$

2. Evaluate $\lim\limits_{n \to \infty} \dfrac{2 - 2n}{6n}$. $-\dfrac{1}{3}$

3. Evaluate $\lim\limits_{n \to \infty} \dfrac{1}{4^n}$. 0

4. Find the sum of the infinite series $\dfrac{1}{10} + \dfrac{1}{20} + \dfrac{1}{40} + \cdots$. $\dfrac{1}{5}$

5. Write the repeating decimal $0.4545\cdots$ as a fraction. $\dfrac{5}{11}$

Motivating the Lesson

Discuss the following paradox: A horse in a race can never finish the race because he first travels half the distance around the track, then he travels half of the remaining distance, then he travels half of the remaining distance, and so on.

ALTERNATE TEACHING STRATEGIES

Using Manipulatives

Have students cut string with lengths 1 unit, $\dfrac{1}{2}$ unit, $\dfrac{1}{4}$ unit, and so on. Line them up end to end to show that the pieces add up to 2.

Using Computers

Have students use a spreadsheet to verify if Exercises 13–22 on page 683 converge to a limit.

Teaching Tip Before discussing Example 1, stress that for $|r| > 1$, an infinite series grows without bound and is therefore divergent.

Chalkboard Examples

For Example 1

Determine whether each series is convergent or divergent.

a. $\frac{1}{4} + \frac{1}{12} + \frac{1}{36} + \cdots$

   convergent

b. $-8 - 2 + 4 + \cdots$ divergent

c. $1 + 5 + 25 + \cdots$ divergent

For Example 2

Use the ratio test to determine whether the following series are convergent or divergent.

a. $2 + \frac{3}{2} + \frac{4}{3} + \frac{5}{4} + \cdots$

   convergent

b. $3 - \frac{9}{2} + \frac{27}{4} - \frac{81}{8} + \cdots$

   divergent

---

b. $-4 - 2 - 0 + 2 + \cdots$

b. This is an arithmetic series with $d = 2$. Since arithmetic series have no limits, the series is divergent.

c. $1 + 3 + 9 + 27 + \cdots$

c. This is a geometric series with $r = 3$. Since $|r| > 1$, the series has no limit. Therefore, the series is divergent.

When a series is neither arithmetic nor geometric, it is more difficult to determine whether the series is convergent or divergent. Several different techniques can be used. One test for convergence is the **ratio test**. This test can *only* be used when all terms of a series are positive. The test depends upon the ratio of consecutive terms of a series, which must be expressed in general form.

Ratio Test *for Convergence* *of a Series*	Let a_n and a_{n+1} represent two consecutive terms of a series of positive terms. Suppose $\lim\limits_{n\to\infty} \frac{a_{n+1}}{a_n}$ exists and that $r = \lim\limits_{n\to\infty} \frac{a_{n+1}}{a_n}$. The series is convergent if $r < 1$ and divergent if $r > 1$. If $r = 1$, the test provides no information.

Example 2   Use the ratio test to determine whether the following series are convergent or divergent.

a. $1 + \frac{1}{1 \cdot 2} + \frac{1}{1 \cdot 2 \cdot 3} + \frac{1}{1 \cdot 2 \cdot 3 \cdot 4} + \cdots$

a. First, find the nth term. Then, use the ratio test.

$$a_n = \frac{1}{1 \cdot 2 \cdots n}, \; a_{n+1} = \frac{1}{1 \cdot 2 \cdots (n+1)}$$

$$r = \lim_{n\to\infty} \frac{a_{n+1}}{a_n}$$

$$= \lim_{n\to\infty} \frac{\frac{1}{1 \cdot 2 \cdots (n+1)}}{\frac{1}{1 \cdot 2 \cdots n}}$$

$$= \lim_{n\to\infty} \frac{1 \cdot 2 \cdots n}{1 \cdot 2 \cdots (n+1)} \quad \text{\textit{Note that} } 1 \cdot 2 \cdots (n+1) = 1 \cdot 2 \cdots n \cdot (n+1).$$

$$= \lim_{n\to\infty} \frac{1}{n+1} \text{ or } 0$$

Since $r < 1$, the series is convergent.

b. $\dfrac{3}{4} + \dfrac{7}{8} + \dfrac{11}{12} + \dfrac{15}{16} + \cdots$

b. $a_n = \dfrac{4n-1}{4n}, a_{n+1} = \dfrac{4(n+1)-1}{4(n+1)}$ or $\dfrac{4n+3}{4n+4}$

$r = \lim\limits_{n\to\infty} \dfrac{\dfrac{4n+3}{4n+4}}{\dfrac{4n-1}{4n}}$

$= \lim\limits_{n\to\infty} \dfrac{4n(4n+3)}{(4n+4)(4n-1)}$

$= \lim\limits_{n\to\infty} \dfrac{16n^2 + 12n}{16n^2 + 12n - 4}$

$= \lim\limits_{n\to\infty} \dfrac{16 + \dfrac{12}{n}}{16 + \dfrac{12}{n} - \dfrac{4}{n^2}}$ *Divide by the highest power of n.*

$= \dfrac{16+0}{16+0-0}$ or 1 Since $r = 1$, the test fails.

When the ratio test does not determine if a series is convergent or divergent, other methods must be used.

Example 3

Determine whether the following series is convergent or divergent.

$$1 + \dfrac{1}{2} + \dfrac{1}{3} + \dfrac{1}{4} + \cdots$$

The series in this example is known as the harmonic series.

Suppose the terms are grouped as follows. Beginning after the second term, the number of terms in each successive group is doubled.

$$(1) + \left(\dfrac{1}{2}\right) + \left(\dfrac{1}{3} + \dfrac{1}{4}\right) + \left(\dfrac{1}{5} + \dfrac{1}{6} + \dfrac{1}{7} + \dfrac{1}{8}\right) + \left(\dfrac{1}{9} + \cdots + \dfrac{1}{16}\right) + \cdots$$

Notice that the first enclosed expression is greater than $\dfrac{1}{2}$, and the second is equal to $\dfrac{1}{2}$. Beginning with the third expression, each sum of enclosed terms is greater than $\dfrac{1}{2}$. Since there are an unlimited number of such expressions, the sum of the series is unlimited. Thus, the series is divergent.

A series can be compared to other series that are known to be convergent or divergent. The following list of series can be used for reference.

Summary of Series for Reference

1. Convergent: $a_1 + a_1 r + a_1 r^2 + \cdots + a_1 r^{n-1} + \cdots, |r| < 1$
2. Divergent: $a_1 + a_1 r + a_1 r^2 + \cdots + a_1 r^{n-1} + \cdots, |r| > 1$
3. Divergent: $a_1 + (a_1 + d) + (a_1 + 2d) + (a_1 + 3d) + \cdots$
4. Divergent: $1 + \dfrac{1}{2} + \dfrac{1}{3} + \dfrac{1}{4} + \dfrac{1}{5} + \cdots + \dfrac{1}{n} + \cdots$
5. Convergent: $1 + \dfrac{1}{2^p} + \dfrac{1}{3^p} + \cdots + \dfrac{1}{n^p} + \cdots, p > 1$

LESSON 12-4   CONVERGENT AND DIVERGENT SERIES   681

Chalkboard Example

For Example 3

Determine whether the following series is convergent or divergent.

$\dfrac{1}{1} + \dfrac{2}{3} + \dfrac{3}{5} + \dfrac{4}{7} + \cdots$

cannot determine since limit = 1

EVALUATING THE LESSON

Checking for Understanding

Exercises 1–12 are designed to help you assess students' understanding through reading, writing, speaking, and modeling. You should work through Exercises 1–3 with your students and then monitor their work on Exercises 4–12.

Closing the Lesson

Speaking Activity   Ask students to summarize the different tests to determine when a series is convergent or when a series is divergent.

Practice Masters Booklet, p. 83

If a series has all positive terms, the **comparison test** can be used to determine whether the series is convergent or divergent.

Comparison Test	**A series of positive terms is convergent if each term of the series is equal to or less than the value of the corresponding term of some convergent series of positive terms. The series is divergent if each term is equal to or greater than the corresponding term of some divergent series of positive terms.**

Example 4

Use the comparison test to determine whether the following series are convergent or divergent.

a. $\frac{3}{4} + \frac{3}{5} + \frac{3}{6} + \frac{3}{7} + \cdots$

   a. The general term of this series is $\frac{3}{n+3}$. The general term of the divergent series $1 + \frac{1}{2} + \frac{1}{3} + \frac{1}{4} + \frac{1}{5} + \cdots$ is $\frac{1}{n}$. Since $\frac{3}{n+3} > \frac{1}{n}$ for all $n > 1$, the series $\frac{3}{4} + \frac{3}{5} + \frac{3}{6} + \frac{3}{7} + \cdots$ is also divergent.

b. $\frac{1}{2 + 1^2} + \frac{1}{2 + 2^2} + \frac{1}{2 + 3^2} + \cdots$

   b. The general term of this series is $\frac{1}{2 + n^2}$. The general term of the convergent series $1 + \frac{1}{2^2} + \frac{1}{3^2} + \frac{1}{4^2} + \cdots$ is $\frac{1}{n^2}$. Since $\frac{1}{2 + n^2} < \frac{1}{n^2}$ for all n, the series $\frac{1}{2 + 1^2} + \frac{1}{2 + 2^2} + \frac{1}{2 + 3^2} + \cdots$ is also convergent.

CHECKING FOR UNDERSTANDING

Communicating Mathematics

1a–c. See students' work.

2a–c. See students' work.

Read and study the lesson to answer each question.

1. a. **Make up** your own infinite arithmetic series.
   b. **State** the 50th and 100th terms of your series.
   c. **State** the sum of the first 50 terms and the sum of the first 100 terms of your series.
   d. Why do infinite arithmetic series not converge? See margin.

2. a. **Make up** an infinite geometric series in which $|r| > 1$.
   b. **State** the 50th and 100th terms of your series.
   c. **State** the sum of the first 50 terms and the sum of the first 100 terms of your series.
   d. Why does this type of infinite geometric series not converge? See margin.

3. Which test might you use if the ratio test finds the limit of the ratio of the $(n + 1)$th term to the nth term is 1? Sample answer: comparison test

RETEACHING THE LESSON

Use calculators to compute the partial sums for the series $\frac{1}{2} + \frac{1}{4} + \frac{1}{8} + \cdots$. Some students may first need to write the terms of the series on paper before using the calculator to add them. Remind them to add the next term of the series to the previous sum. Add the partial sums until it is apparent that the limit of the series is 1.

Additional Answers

1d. Infinite arithmetic series do not converge because they do not approach zero as $n \to \infty$.

2d. In a geometric series where $|r| > 1$, each succeeding term is larger than the one preceding it. Therefore, the series approaches ∞ and thus, does not converge.

State whether each series is *arithmetic, geometric,* or *neither.* Then determine whether the series is *convergent* or *divergent.*

4. $1 + 3 + 5 + \cdots$ A, D

5. $\frac{1}{4} + \frac{3}{8} + \frac{5}{16} + \frac{7}{32} + \cdots$ N, C

6. $\frac{1}{2} + \frac{1}{8} + \frac{1}{32} + \cdots$ G, C

7. $\frac{1}{4} + \frac{5}{16} + \frac{3}{8} + \frac{7}{16} + \cdots$ A, D

8. $\frac{8}{3} + \frac{32}{9} + \frac{128}{27} + \cdots$ G, D

9. $64 + 32 + 16 + \cdots$ G, C

Use the ratio test to determine whether each series is *convergent* or *divergent.*

10. $1 + \frac{1}{2^2} + \frac{1}{3^3} + \frac{1}{4^4} + \cdots$ C

11. $1 + \frac{1}{2!} + \frac{1}{3!} + \cdots$ C

12. Use the comparison test to determine whether the series $\frac{2}{1} + \frac{3}{2} + \frac{4}{3} + \cdots$ is *convergent* or *divergent.* D

APPLYING THE LESSON

Homework Exercises

Assignment Guide

Average: 13–21, 23, 24, 27–31
Enriched: 14–22 even, 24–31
All: Mid-Chapter Review, 1–9

The red A, B, and C flags, printed only in the Teacher's Wraparound Edition, indicate the level of difficulty of the exercises.

Chapter 12, Quiz B, (Lessons 12–3 through 12–4) is available in the *Evaluation Masters*, p. 153.

EXERCISES

Practice

Use the ratio test to determine whether each series is *convergent* or *divergent.*

13. $\frac{1}{2} + \frac{2}{2^2} + \frac{3}{2^3} + \cdots$ C

14. $\frac{1}{1 \cdot 2} + \frac{1}{2 \cdot 2^2} + \frac{1}{3 \cdot 2^3} + \cdots$ C

15. $\frac{1}{1 \cdot 2} + \frac{1}{3 \cdot 4} + \frac{1}{5 \cdot 6} + \cdots$ cannot tell

16. $10 + \frac{10^2}{1 \cdot 2} + \frac{10^3}{1 \cdot 2 \cdot 3} + \cdots$ C

17. $1 + \frac{2}{1 \cdot 2 \cdot 3} + \frac{3}{1 \cdot 2 \cdot 3 \cdot 4 \cdot 5} + \cdots$ C

18. $\frac{1}{1 \cdot 2} + \frac{1}{1 \cdot 2 \cdot 3 \cdot 4} + \frac{1}{1 \cdot 2 \cdot 3 \cdot 4 \cdot 5 \cdot 6} + \cdots$ C

Use the comparison test to determine whether each series is *convergent* or *divergent.*

19. $\frac{1}{1^2} + \frac{1}{3^2} + \frac{1}{5^2} + \cdots$ C

20. $\frac{1}{2 \cdot 1} + \frac{1}{2 \cdot 2} + \frac{1}{2 \cdot 3} + \cdots$ D

21. $\frac{1}{2} + \frac{2}{3} + \frac{3}{4} + \cdots$ D

22. $\frac{2}{1} + \frac{3}{2} + \frac{4}{3} + \cdots$ D

Determine whether each series is *convergent* or *divergent.* Use the appropriate test.

23. $4 + 3 + \frac{9}{4} + \cdots$ C

24. $\frac{6}{5} + \frac{2}{5} + \frac{2}{15} + \cdots$ C

25. $\frac{1}{3 + 1^2} + \frac{1}{3 + 2^2} + \frac{1}{3 + 3^2} + \cdots$ C

26. $1 + \frac{1}{1 \cdot 2 \cdot 3} + \frac{1}{1 \cdot 2 \cdot 3 \cdot 4 \cdot 5} + \cdots$ C

Critical
Thinking

27. Find the least positive number n such that the product of the first n terms exceeds 390,625 when given the sequence $5^{\frac{1}{7}}, 5^{\frac{2}{7}}, 5^{\frac{3}{7}}, \cdots, 5^{\frac{n}{7}}$. 11

Applications and Problem Solving

28. **Employment** Matthew Stern and Beth Adams begin work and receive $2000 each the first month. Mr. Stern will receive a raise of $120 each month thereafter. Ms. Adams will receive a 5% raise each month thereafter.
    a. At the end of 12 months, how much are Mr. Stern and Ms. Adams making per month? Who has the higher monthly income? S, $3320, A, $3420.68; A
    b. How much did Mr. Stern and Ms. Adams make during the 12-month period? Who has the higher yearly income? S, $31,920, A, $31,834.25; S

29. **Physics** Kenneth drops a Super★Bouncer ball from his balcony. The balcony is 20 feet above the ground. If the ball rebounds 90% of the height from which it fell on each bounce, find the vertical distance that the ball travels before coming to rest. 380 feet

Mixed Review

30. Determine whether the graph of $x^2 + y^2 = 16$ is symmetric with respect to the origin, the x-axis, the y-axis, the line $y = x$, or the line $y = -x$. **(Lesson 3-1)** all

31. **Surveying** A building 60 feet tall is on top of a hill. A surveyor is at a point on the hill and observes that the angle of elevation to the top of the building measures 42° and the angle of elevation to the bottom measures 18°. How far is the surveyor from the bottom of the building? **(Lesson 5-6)** 109.63 ft

32. Complete the table below for the equation $r = \dfrac{2}{\cos(\theta + 30°)}$. **(Lesson 9-4)**

θ	0°	15°	30°	70°
r	2.31	2.83	4	−11.52

33. Evaluate $\lim\limits_{n \to \infty} \dfrac{n-1}{n}$, or state that the limit does not exist. **(Lesson 12-3)** 1

34. **College Entrance Exam** Simplify the expression $\dfrac{0.25 + 0.25 + 0.25 + 0.25}{4}$. 0.25

MID-CHAPTER REVIEW

1. Form an arithmetic sequence that has seven arithmetic means between 5 and 17.
   (Lesson 12-1) $5, 6\frac{1}{2}, 8, 9\frac{1}{2}, 11, 12\frac{1}{2}, 14, 15\frac{1}{2}, 17$

2. Find S_{23} for the arithmetic series for which $a_1 = -3$ and $d = 6$. **(Lesson 12-1)** 1449

3. Form a geometric sequence that has three geometric means between 2 and $\frac{1}{8}$.
   (Lesson 12-2) $2, \pm1, \frac{1}{2}, \pm\frac{1}{4}, \frac{1}{8}$

4. Find the sum of the first nine terms of the series $\frac{2}{3} + \frac{1}{3} + \frac{1}{6} + \cdots$. **(Lesson 12-2)** $\frac{511}{384}$

5. Evaluate $\lim\limits_{n \to \infty} \dfrac{3n^2 + 4}{2n}$, or state that the limit does not exist. **(Lesson 12-3)** DNE

6. Find the sum of the series $1 + \frac{2}{5} + \frac{4}{25} + \cdots$. **(Lesson 12-4)** $1\frac{2}{3}$

7. Write $0.3636\cdots$ as a fraction. **(Lesson 12-3)** $\frac{4}{11}$

8. Determine if the series $1 + \frac{1}{5} + \frac{1}{25} \cdots$ is *convergent* or *divergent*. **(Lesson 12-4)** C

9. **Finance** Carmella Jackson invests $2000 annually in an insurance annuity for 42 years. What will the annuity be worth if it has an APR of 8%? **(Lesson 12-2)** $608,487.05

EXTENDING THE LESSON

Math Power: Problem Solving

Suppose an infinite geometric series with positive terms converges to a sum. What is the sum of the even-numbered terms in terms of r, the common ratio? $\dfrac{r}{1 + r}$

Mid-Chapter Review

The Mid-Chapter Review provides students with a brief review of the concepts and skills in Lessons 12–1 through 12–4. Lesson numbers are given at the end of problems or instruction lines so students may review concepts not yet mastered.

Enrichment Masters Booklet, p. 83

12-4 Enrichment Worksheet

NAME _____ DATE _____

Alternating Series

The series below is called an alternating series.
$$1 - 1 + 1 - 1 + \cdots$$
The reason is that the signs of the terms alternate. An interesting question is whether the series converges. In the exercises, you will have an opportunity to explore this series and others like it.

1. Consider $1 - 1 + 1 - 1 + \cdots$.
   a. Write an argument that suggests that the sum is 1.
   $1 - 1 + 1 - 1 + \cdots = 1 + (-1 + 1) + (-1 + 1) + \cdots$
   $= 1 + 0 + 0 + \cdots$
   $= 1$
   b. Write an argument that suggests that the sum is 0.
   $1 - 1 + 1 - 1 + \cdots = (1 - 1) + (1 - 1) + (1 - 1) + \cdots$
   $= 0 + 0 + 0 + \cdots$
   $= 0$
   c. Write an argument that suggests that there is no sum.
   (*Hint:* Consider the sequence of partial sums.)
   Let S_n be the nth partial sum. Then
   $S_n = \begin{cases} 1 \text{ if } n \text{ is odd.} \\ 0 \text{ if } n \text{ is even.} \end{cases}$
   Since 1, 0, 1, 0, ... has no limit, the original series has no sum.

2. Make up an alternating series, other than a geometric series with negative common ratio, that has a sum. Justify your answer. Sample answer:
   $\frac{1}{1} - \frac{1}{4} + \frac{1}{9} - \frac{1}{16} + \cdots$ is convergent because each term is less than or equal to the corresponding term in a p-series with $p = 2$.

3. Make up an alternating series, other than a geometric series with negative common ratio, that does not have a sum. Justify your response. Sample answer:
   $-\frac{2}{1} + \frac{4}{2} - \frac{8}{3} + \frac{16}{4} - \frac{32}{5} + \cdots + \frac{(-2)^{n+1}}{n} + \cdots$
   diverges, since the terms continue to increase in absolute value.

T83
Glencoe Division, Macmillan/McGraw-Hill

12-5 Sigma Notation and the *n*th Term

Objective 12–5

After studying this lesson, you should be able to:
- use sigma notation.

Application

Stephanie Seim is responsible for purchasing the cushioned seats for the Theater in the Round. In the first row, there will be 10 seats. In each additional row, two more seats will be added. How many seats will there be in the 15th row? How many seats will there be in the *n*th row? How many seats does Ms. Seim need to order for the 15 rows that the theater has?

Since this sequence is arithmetic, we can use the formula for the *n*th term of an arithmetic sequence to find the number of seats in the 15th row.

$$a_n = a + (n-1)d$$
$$a_{15} = 10 + (15-1)2 \qquad a = 10, n = 15, \text{ and } d = 2$$
$$= 38 \qquad \text{There are 38 seats in the 15th row.}$$

To determine the number of seats in the *n*th row, we can use the same formula.

$$a_n = a + (n-1)d$$
$$= 10 + (n-1)2 \qquad a = 10 \text{ and } d = 2$$
$$= 10 + 2n - 2$$
$$= 2n + 8 \qquad \text{There are } 2n + 8 \text{ seats in the } n\text{th row.}$$

To determine the total number of seats in the theater, we can use the formula for the sum of an arithmetic series.

$$S_n = \frac{n}{2}(a + a_n)$$
$$= \frac{15}{2}(10 + 38) \qquad n = 15, a = 10, \text{ and } a_n = 38$$
$$= 360 \qquad \text{Ms. Seim should order 360 seats for the theater.}$$

$\sum_{n=1}^{15}(2n + 8)$ *is read "the summation from n = 1 to 15 of 2 times n plus 8."*

The series $10 + 12 + 14 + \cdots + 38$ represents the number of seats in the 15 rows of the theater. In mathematics, the Greek letter sigma, Σ, is often used to indicate a sum or series. The series above can be written as $\sum_{n=1}^{15}(2n + 8)$. This represents a series of terms that are obtained by multiplying 2 by *n* and adding 8, first for $n = 1$, then for $n = 2$, and so on to $n = 15$.

$$\sum_{n=1}^{15}(2n + 8) = [2(1) + 8] + [2(2) + 8] + [2(3) + 8] + \cdots + [2(15) + 8]$$
$$= 10 + 12 + 14 + \cdots + 38 \text{ or } 360$$

LESSON 12-5   SIGMA NOTATION AND THE *n*TH TERM   685

12–5 Lesson Notes

NCTM Standards: 1-4, 12, 13

Lesson Resources

- Practice Master 12–5
- Enrichment Master 12–5
- Activity Master, p. 35

 Transparency 12–5 contains the 5-Minute Check and a teaching aid for this lesson.

INTRODUCING THE LESSON

 5-Minute Check

(over Lesson 12-4)

1. State whether the series is arithmetic, geometric, or neither. Then determine whether the series $75 + 15 + 3 + \cdots$ is convergent or divergent.
   geometric, convergent
2. Use the ratio test to determine whether the series $\frac{1}{2} + \frac{1}{4} + \frac{1}{8} + \frac{1}{16} + \cdots$ is convergent or divergent. **convergent**
3. Use the comparison test to determine whether the series $\frac{1}{2} + \frac{2}{3} + \frac{3}{4} + \cdots$ is convergent or divergent. **divergent**

Motivating the Lesson

Have students write an expression representing the sum of the first twenty odd numbers. Explain that they will learn a shorter notation in this lesson.

ALTERNATE TEACHING STRATEGIES

Using Communication

Have students read expressions aloud using sigma notation. Have them tell the index of summation and the number of terms in the series.

Using Cooperative Groups

Have students use groups to write sample series in expanded form and in sigma notation. Have them give examples of series that cannot be expressed in sigma notation.

Teaching Tip Before discussing sigma notation, explain that $\sum$, the Greek capital sigma, is used like the English S and may be the reason why it was chosen to represent a series.

Teaching Tip Before discussing the examples, point out that the number of terms is the maximum value of the index of summation minus the minimum value of the index plus one.

Chalkboard Examples

For Example 1

Write each of the following in expanded form and find the sum.

a. $\sum_{b=4}^{7} (3^b + 1)$ 3244

b. $\sum_{n=1}^{\infty} 2\left(\frac{1}{3}\right)^n$ 1

For Example 2

Express the series $16 + 19 + 22 + 25 + 28$ using sigma notation.

$$\sum_{n=5}^{9} (3n + 1)$$

The variable used with the summation symbol is called the **index of summation**. In the previous example, the index of summation is n. The number above the sigma is the maximum value of the index of summation.

Example 1

Write each of the following in expanded form and find the sum.

a. $\displaystyle\sum_{b=3}^{5} (2^b - b)$

a. $\displaystyle\sum_{b=3}^{5} (2^b - b) = (2^3 - 3) + (2^4 - 4) + (2^5 - 5)$

$\qquad\qquad\qquad\quad = \quad 5 \quad + \quad 12 \quad + \quad 27$

$\qquad\qquad\qquad\quad = \quad 44$

b. $\displaystyle\sum_{n=1}^{\infty} 3\left(\frac{1}{2}\right)^{n+1}$

b. $\displaystyle\sum_{n=1}^{\infty} 3\left(\frac{1}{2}\right)^{n+1} = 3\left(\frac{1}{2}\right)^{1+1} + 3\left(\frac{1}{2}\right)^{2+1} + 3\left(\frac{1}{2}\right)^{3+1} + 3\left(\frac{1}{2}\right)^{4+1} + \cdots$

$\qquad\qquad\qquad\qquad = \quad \frac{3}{4} \quad + \quad \frac{3}{8} \quad + \quad \frac{3}{16} \quad + \quad \frac{3}{32} \quad + \cdots$

This is an infinite series. Use the formula $S_n = \dfrac{a}{1-r}$.

$S_n = \dfrac{a}{1-r}$

$\quad = \dfrac{\frac{3}{4}}{1 - \frac{1}{2}} \qquad a = \dfrac{3}{4} \text{ and } r = \dfrac{1}{2}$

$\quad = \dfrac{3}{2}$

Therefore, $\displaystyle\sum_{n=1}^{\infty} 3\left(\frac{1}{2}\right)^{n+1} = \frac{3}{2}$.

A series in expanded form can be written using sigma notation if a general formula can be written for the nth term of the series.

Example 2

Express the series $10 + 17 + 26 + 37 + \cdots + 122$ using sigma notation.

Notice that each term is 1 more than a perfect square. Thus, the nth term of the series is $n^2 + 1$. Since $10 = 3^2 + 1$ and $122 = 11^2 + 1$, the index of summation goes from $n = 3$ to $n = 11$.

Therefore, $10 + 17 + 26 + 37 + \cdots + 122 = \displaystyle\sum_{n=3}^{11} (n^2 + 1)$.

Not all sequences are arithmetic or geometric. Some important sequences are generated by products of consecutive integers. The product $n(n-1)(n-2)\cdots 3 \cdot 2 \cdot 1$ is called **n factorial** and is symbolized $n!$.

Definition of n Factorial	The expression $n!$ (**n factorial**) is defined as follows for n, an integer greater than zero. $$n! = n(n-1)(n-2)\cdots 1$$ <div align="center">*By definition, $0! = 1! = 1$.*</div>

Example 3

Evaluate each expression.

a. **6!**

b. $\dfrac{9!}{5!3!}$

a. $6! = 6 \cdot 5 \cdot 4 \cdot 3 \cdot 2 \cdot 1$
  $= 720$

b. $\dfrac{9!}{5!3!} = \dfrac{9 \cdot 8 \cdot 7 \cdot 6 \cdot 5!}{5!3!}$
  $= 504$

Example 4

Express the series $-\dfrac{3}{1} + \dfrac{9}{2} - \dfrac{27}{6} + \dfrac{81}{24}$ using sigma notation.

The sequence representing the numerators is 3, 9, 27, 81. This is a geometric sequence with a common ratio of 3. Thus, the nth term can be represented by 3^n.

Because the series has alternating signs, one factor for the general term of the series is $(-1)^n$. Thus, when n is odd, the terms are negative, and when n is even, the terms are positive.

The sequence representing the denominators is 1, 2, 6, 24. This sequence is generated by factorials.

$1! = 1$
$2! = 1 \cdot 2$ or 2
$3! = 1 \cdot 2 \cdot 3$ or 6
$4! = 1 \cdot 2 \cdot 3 \cdot 4$ or 24

Therefore, $-\dfrac{3}{1} + \dfrac{9}{2} - \dfrac{27}{6} + \dfrac{81}{24} = \displaystyle\sum_{n=1}^{4} \dfrac{(-1)^n 3^n}{n!}$.

You can check this answer by substituting values of n into the general term.

CHECKING FOR UNDERSTANDING

Communicating Mathematics

Read and study the lesson to answer each question.

1. In the application at the beginning of the lesson, we wrote the series
$10 + 12 + 14 + \cdots + 38$ as $\displaystyle\sum_{n=1}^{15}(2n+8)$. Could $\displaystyle\sum_{n=0}^{14}(2n+10)$ represent the same series? Why or why not? See margin.

LESSON 12-5 SIGMA NOTATION AND THE nTH TERM 687

RETEACHING THE LESSON

Have groups of students make up a geometric series expressed in sigma notation. Then exchange series with other groups and have them rewrite the series in expanded form.

Additional Answer

1. Yes; $\displaystyle\sum_{n=0}^{14}(2n+10)$ also represents the series $10 + 12 + 14 + \cdots + 38$.

Homework Exercises

Assignment Guide

Average: 17–22, 23–49 odd, 52, 53,
58, 60–69

Enriched: 22–48 even, 49–69

The red A, B, and C flags, printed only in the Teacher's Wraparound Edition, indicate the level of difficulty of the exercises.

Additional Answers

23. $-2 + (-1) + 0$

24. $15 + 18 + 21 + 24$

25. $-4 + (-6) + (-8) + (-10) +$
    (-12)

26. $9 + 8 + 7 + 6 + 5 + 4 + 3 + 2$
    $+ 1$

27. $6 + 12 + 20 + 30$

28. $1 + (-1) + (-3) + (-5) + (-7) +$
    (-9)

29. $28 + 82 + 244 + 730$

30. $4 + 16 + 64 + 256$

31. $1\frac{1}{2} + 3\frac{1}{2} + 9\frac{1}{2} + 27\frac{1}{2}$

32. $5 + 1 + 0.2 + 0.04 + \cdots$

33. $2 + 1 + \frac{1}{2} + \frac{1}{4} + \cdots$

34. $5 + \frac{15}{4} + \frac{45}{16} + \cdots$

---

2. **State** the number of terms in each series.

   a. $\sum\limits_{n=0}^{5} 5n - 12$ 6

   b. $\sum\limits_{k=25}^{125} 425(2)^{k-1}$ 101

   c. $\sum\limits_{j=-4}^{4} \left(\frac{3}{4}\right)^{j}$ 9

3. If the index of summation begins with 1, what does the number above the sigma represent? the number of terms in the series

4. Given the series $\sum\limits_{k=1}^{6} (4k + 3)$, identify two other series expressed in sigma notation that would generate the same terms. Sample answers: $\sum\limits_{k=0}^{5} (4k + 7)$, $\sum\limits_{k=2}^{7} (4k - 1)$

5–9. See margin for expanded form.

Guided Practice

Write each expression in expanded form and find the sum.

5. $\sum\limits_{j=1}^{4} (j + 2)$ 18

6. $\sum\limits_{a=4}^{7} 2a$ 44

7. $\sum\limits_{p=5}^{7} (3p + 2)$ 60

8. $\sum\limits_{a=0}^{4} (0.5 + 2^{a})$ 33.5

9. $\sum\limits_{b=0}^{\infty} 6\left(\frac{2}{3}\right)^{b}$ 18

Express each series using sigma notation. Sample answers are given.

10. $3 + 6 + 9 + 12$ $\sum\limits_{n=1}^{4} 3n$

11. $16 + 8 + 4 + 2 + 1$ $\sum\limits_{n=1}^{5} \frac{32}{2^{n}}$

12. $19 + 18 + 16 + 12 + 4$ $\sum\limits_{n=0}^{4} (20 - 2^{n})$

13. $\frac{2}{5} + \frac{3}{5} + \frac{4}{5} + \cdots$ $\sum\limits_{n=2}^{\infty} \frac{n}{5}$

Evaluate each expression.

14. $7!$ 5040

15. $3(6!)$ 2160

16. $\frac{12!}{10!}$ 132

EXERCISES

Practice

Evaluate each expression.

17. $9!$ 362,880

18. $2(5!)$ 240

19. $3!4!$ 144

20. $5!3!$ 720

21. $\frac{10!}{8!}$ 90

22. $\frac{6!}{4!3!}$ 5

23–34. See margin for expanded form.

Write each expression in expanded form and find the sum.

23. $\sum\limits_{r=1}^{3} (r - 3)$ −3

24. $\sum\limits_{k=5}^{8} 3k$ 78

25. $\sum\limits_{b=4}^{8} (4 - 2b)$ −40

26. $\sum\limits_{z=1}^{9} (10 - z)$ 45

27. $\sum\limits_{b=2}^{5} (b^{2} + b)$ 68

28. $\sum\limits_{k=2}^{7} (5 - 2k)$ −24

29. $\sum\limits_{n=3}^{6} (3^{n} + 1)$ 1084

30. $\sum\limits_{m=1}^{4} 4^{m}$ 340

31. $\sum\limits_{p=1}^{4} \left(3^{p-1} + \frac{1}{2}\right)$ 42

32. $\sum\limits_{r=0}^{\infty} 5(0.2)^{r}$ 6.25

33. $\sum\limits_{k=1}^{\infty} 4\left(\frac{1}{2}\right)^{k}$ 4

34. $\sum\limits_{j=0}^{\infty} 5\left(\frac{3}{4}\right)^{j}$ 20

Additional Answers

5. $(1 + 2) + (2 + 2) + (3 + 2) + (4 + 2)$ or $3 + 4 + 5 + 6$

6. $2(4) + 2(5) + 2(6) + 2(7)$ or $8 + 10 + 12 + 14$

7. $[3(5) + 2] + [3(6) + 2] + [3(7) + 2]$ or $17 + 20 + 23$

8. $(0.5 + 2^{0}) + (0.5 + 2^{1}) + (0.5 + 2^{2}) + (0.5 + 2^{3}) + (0.5 + 2^{4})$ or
   $1.5 + 2.5 + 4.5 + 8.5 + 16.5$

9. $6\left(\frac{2}{3}\right)^{0} + 6\left(\frac{2}{3}\right)^{1} + 6\left(\frac{2}{3}\right)^{2} + 6\left(\frac{2}{3}\right)^{3} + \cdots + 6\left(\frac{2}{3}\right)^{\infty}$ or $6 + 4 + \frac{8}{3} + \frac{16}{9} + \cdots + 6\left(\frac{2}{3}\right)^{\infty}$

Express each series using sigma notation. 35–48. See margin.

35. $10 + 20 + 30 + 40 + 50$

36. $2 + 4 + 8 + \cdots + 64$

37. $3 + 6 + 12 + \cdots + 48$

38. $3 + 30 + 300 + 3000$

39. $\dfrac{1}{2} + \dfrac{1}{3} + \dfrac{1}{4} + \cdots + \dfrac{1}{10}$

40. $\dfrac{1}{2} + \dfrac{1}{4} + \dfrac{1}{6} + \cdots + \dfrac{1}{14}$

41. $11 + 9 + 7 + 5$

42. $-8 + 4 - 2 + 1$

43. $2 + 4 + 6 + \cdots$

44. $4 + 9 + 14 + \cdots$

45. $\dfrac{2}{3} + \dfrac{2}{4} + \dfrac{2}{5} + \cdots$

46. $5 + 25 + 125 + \cdots$

47. $1 + \dfrac{1}{2} + \dfrac{2}{3} + \dfrac{6}{4} + \dfrac{24}{5}$

48. $\dfrac{2 \cdot 4}{3} + \dfrac{6 \cdot 8}{8} + \dfrac{24 \cdot 16}{15} + \cdots$

Simplify as far as possible. Assume that x and y are positive integers, $x > y$, and $x > 2$.

49. $\dfrac{x!}{(x-2)!}$ $\quad x(x-1)$

50. $\dfrac{(x+1)!}{(x-1)!}$ $\quad x(x+1)$

51. $\dfrac{(x-y)!}{(x-y-1)!}$ $\quad x - y$

Programming

52. The program below will evaluate a sum given in summation notation. The formula for the nth term must be stored in Y_1. You must input values for the lower and upper bounds of summation.

```
Prgm12:SIGMASUM
:ClrHome            Clears the text screen.
:Disp "NTH TERM MUST"   Displays the quoted message.
:Disp "BE IN Y₁"
:Disp "LOWER BOUND ="
:Input L            Accepts a value for L.
:Disp "UPPER BOUND ="
:Input U
:0 → S              Sets the initial value of the sum to 0.
:L → X              Stores the lower bound in X.
:Lbl 1              Sets a marker at position 1.
:S + Y₁ → S         Adds the value of Y₁ to previous sum value.
:X + 1 → X          Increases X by 1.
:If X = U + 1       Checks if upper bound has been reached.
:Goto 2             Program execution goes to line ``Lbl 2."
:Goto 1
:Lbl 2              Sets a marker at position 2.
:Disp "SUM ="
:Disp S             Displays the value stored in S.
```

Use the program to find the sum of each sequence.

a. $\displaystyle\sum_{x=3}^{6}(x+2)$ $\quad 26$

b. $\displaystyle\sum_{x=3}^{7}(2x-1)$ $\quad 45$

c. $\displaystyle\sum_{x=3}^{5}(2^x - x)$ $\quad 44$

LESSON 12–5   SIGMA NOTATION AND THE nTH TERM   689

Using Technology

The program given in Exercise 52 is for use with a TI-81 graphing calculator. For other programmable calculators, have students consult their owner's manual for commands similar to those presented here.

Additional Answers

35. $\displaystyle\sum_{k=1}^{5} 10k$

36. $\displaystyle\sum_{k=1}^{6} 2^k$

37. $\displaystyle\sum_{k=0}^{4} 3 \cdot 2^k$

38. $\displaystyle\sum_{k=0}^{3} 3 \cdot 10^k$

39. $\displaystyle\sum_{k=2}^{10} \dfrac{1}{k}$

40. $\displaystyle\sum_{k=1}^{7} \dfrac{1}{2k}$

41. $\displaystyle\sum_{k=0}^{3} (11 - 2k)$

42. $\displaystyle\sum_{k=1}^{3} (-2)^{3-k}$

43. $\displaystyle\sum_{k=1}^{\infty} 2k$

44. $\displaystyle\sum_{k=1}^{\infty} (5k - 1)$

45. $\displaystyle\sum_{k=3}^{\infty} \dfrac{2}{k}$

46. $\displaystyle\sum_{k=1}^{\infty} 5^k$

47. $\displaystyle\sum_{k=0}^{\infty} \dfrac{k!}{k+1}$

48. $\displaystyle\sum_{k=2}^{\infty} \dfrac{k!2^k}{k^2 - 1}$

Critical Thinking

Determine whether each equation is *true* or *false*. Explain your answer.

53. $\sum_{k=0}^{5} a^k + \sum_{n=6}^{10} a^n = \sum_{b=0}^{10} a^b$ true

54. $\sum_{r=3}^{7} 3^r + \sum_{a=7}^{9} 3^a = \sum_{j=3}^{9} 3^j$ false

55. $\sum_{n=1}^{10} (5+n) = \sum_{m=0}^{9} (4+m)$ false

56. $\sum_{r=2}^{8} (2r-3) = \sum_{s=3}^{9} (2s-5)$ true

57. $2\sum_{k=3}^{7} k^2 = \sum_{k=3}^{7} 2k^2$ true

58. $3\sum_{n=1}^{5} (n+3) = \sum_{n=1}^{15} (n+3)$ false

Applications and Problem Solving

59. **Finance** Suppose Dr. Cynthia Morgan invests $1500 in an annuity every six months for 30 years. What will the annuity be worth if it has an APR of 8% and is compounded annually? $360,110.31

60. **Ballooning** After one minute, a hot air balloon rose 90 feet. After that time, each succeeding minute the balloon rose 70% as far as it did the previous minute.
   a. How far above Earth was the balloon after 8 minutes? 282.71 feet
   b. What was the maximum height of the balloon? 300 feet

Mixed Review

61. **Agriculture** If Ms. Huffman harvests her apple crop now, the yield will average 120 pounds per tree. Also, she will be able to sell the apples for $0.48 per pound. However, she knows that if she waits, her yield will increase by about 10 pounds per week, while the selling price will decrease by $0.03 per pound per week. **(Lesson 3-7)**
   a. How many weeks should Ms. Huffman wait in order to maximize profit? 2 weeks
   b. What is the maximum profit? $58.80 per tree

62. Find the value of k in $(x^2 + 8x + k) \div (x - 2)$ so that the remainder is zero. **(Lesson 4-3)** –20

63. Find the value of $\sin (\text{Tan}^{-1} 1 - \text{Sin}^{-1} 1)$. **(Lesson 6-5)** $-\dfrac{\sqrt{2}}{2}$

64. Find the inner product $(1,3) \cdot (3,-2)$ and state whether the vectors are perpendicular. Write *yes* or *no*. **(Lesson 8-4)** –3, no

65. Write the equation of the parabola with vertex at $(6,-1)$ and focus at $(3,-1)$. **(Lesson 10-2)** $(y+1)^2 = -12(x-6)$

66. Express $\sqrt[6]{64a^6 b^{-2}}$ using rational exponents. **(Lesson 11-1)** $2ab^{-\frac{1}{3}}$

67. Write $0.222\cdots$ as a fraction. **(Lesson 12-3)** $\dfrac{2}{9}$

68. Determine whether the series $\dfrac{1}{9} + \dfrac{1}{27} + \dfrac{1}{81} + \cdots$ is *convergent* or *divergent*. **(Lesson 12-5)** C

69. **College Entrance Exam** Choose the best answer. Which of the following equations are equivalent? A
   I. $2x + 4y = 8$ II. $3x + 6y = 12$
   III. $4x + 8y = 8$ IV. $6x + 12 = 16$
   (A) I and II only   (B) I and IV only   (C) II and IV only
   (D) III and IV only   (E) I, II, and III

690   CHAPTER 12   SEQUENCES AND SERIES

EXTENDING THE LESSON

Math Power: Reasoning

Use sigma notation to express the total number of unit cubes needed to form a cube that is n units on each edge.

$\sum_{b=1}^{n} b^3$

Enrichment Masters Booklet, p. 84

12-6 The Binomial Theorem

Objective
12-6

After studying this lesson, you should be able to:
■ use the binomial theorem to expand binomials.

Application

Blaise Pascal (1623–1662) was a French mathematician who was considered by many to be a true genius. At the age of 12, he discovered many of the theorems of elementary geometry without any assistance. By age 14, he was participating in weekly gatherings with a group of noted French mathematicians. At 18, he invented the first computing machine. Throughout his life, he made contributions to probability, calculus, and geometry.

In this lesson, you will learn about a sequence of numbers called **Pascal's triangle**. Pascal first used this triangle to answer a question posed to him by a gambler about how to divide the stakes when a dice game is interrupted. However, this triangle had appeared in China as early as A.D. 1303, when it was published in Chu Shih-chieh's *Precious Mirror of the Four Elements*. It is also believed that Omar Khayyam, a Persian mathematician who lived about A.D. 1100, had some knowledge of the coefficients of the triangle. In addition, Niccolo Tartaglia of Italy claimed the triangle as his own invention in 1556.

As you examine the triangle, note that if two consecutive numbers in any row are added, the sum is a number in the following row. The three numbers form a triangle, as shown below.

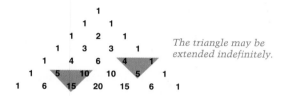

The triangle may be extended indefinitely.

One of the applications of Pascal's triangle is the expansion of binomial expressions of the form $(x + y)^n$. In the first row, $n = 0$. In any row, the second number indicates the power to which the binomial is raised. In the expansion process, the coefficients of the terms, written in decreasing order of x or y, are the same as the numbers in the triangle.

1	$(x + y)^0 =$	1
1 1	$(x + y)^1 =$	$1x + 1y$
1 2 1	$(x + y)^2 =$	$1x^2 + 2xy + 1y^2$
1 3 3 1	$(x + y)^3 =$	$1x^3 + 3x^2y + 3xy^2 + 1y^3$
1 4 6 4 1	$(x + y)^4 =$	$1x^4 + 4x^3y + 6x^2y^2 + 4xy^3 + 1y^4$
1 5 10 10 5 1	$(x + y)^5 =$	$1x^5 + 5x^4y + 10x^3y^2 + 10x^2y^3 + 5xy^4 + 1y^5$

LESSON 12-6 THE BINOMIAL THEOREM 691

ALTERNATE TEACHING STRATEGIES

Using Discussion

Make sure students understand the pattern in Pascal's triangle. Have them list the first ten rows of the triangle. Discuss the relationship between the rows of the triangle and the binomial theorem.

Using Calculators

Use a calculator to find $(1 + 0.05)^6$. Compare this to the expansion of $(1 + 0.05)^6$ found by using the binomial theorem.

NCTM Standards: 1-4, 12, 13

Lesson Resources

- Practice Master 12–6
- Enrichment Master 12–6
- Evaluation Master, Quiz C, p. 154
- Technology Master, p. 24

 Transparency 12–6 contains the 5-Minute Check and a teaching aid for this lesson.

INTRODUCING THE LESSON

5-Minute Check

(over Lesson 12–5)

1. Evaluate the expression $\frac{9!}{3!4!}$. **2520**

2. Write the expression $\sum\limits_{j=1}^{5} (2j - 1)$ in expanded form and find the sum. **$1 + 3 + 5 + 7 + 9$; 25**

3. Write $\sum\limits_{n=5}^{9} (2^n - 1)$ in expanded form and find the sum. **$31 + 63 + 127 + 255 + 511$; 987**

4. Express the series $5 + 7 + 9 + 11 + 13$ using sigma notation. $\sum\limits_{j=1}^{5} (2j + 3)$

5. Express the series $-4 - 7 - 10 - 13 - 16 - 19$ using sigma notation. $\sum\limits_{j=1}^{6} (-3j - 1)$

Prerequisite Skills

Students should be familiar with finding the square of a binomial.
1. Find $(x - 3)^2$. **$x^2 - 6x + 9$**
2. Find $(3x - y)^2$. **$9x^2 - 6xy + y^2$**

Motivating the Lesson

Have students expand the product $(3x - y)(3x - y)(3x - y)(3x - y)$ by hand. Point out that a shorter method will be learned in this chapter.

The following patterns are seen in the expansions.

1. The expansion of $(x + y)^n$ has $n + 1$ terms.
2. The first term is x^n and the last term is y^n.
3. In successive terms, the exponent of x decreases by 1, and the exponent of y increases by 1.
4. The degree of each term is n.
5. In any term, if the coefficient is multiplied by the exponent of x and the product is divided by the number of that term, the result is the coefficient of the following term.
6. The coefficients are symmetric. That is, the first term and the last term have the same coefficient. The second term and the second from the last term have the same coefficient, and so on.

Example 1

Use Pascal's triangle to expand each binomial.
a. $(x + y)^6$

a. First, write the series without the coefficients. Recall that the expansion should have $6 + 1$ or 7 terms, with the first term being x^6 and the last term being y^6. Also note that the exponents of x should decrease from 6 to 0 while the exponents of y should increase from 0 to 6, while the degree of each term is 6.

$$x^6 + x^5y + x^4y^2 + x^3y^3 + x^2y^4 + xy^5 + y^6 \qquad y^0 = 1, x^0 = 1$$

Then, use the numbers in the seventh row of Pascal's triangle as the coefficients of the terms.

$$\begin{array}{ccccccc} 1 & 6 & 15 & 20 & 15 & 6 & 1 \end{array}$$
$$(x + y)^6 = x^6 + 6x^5y + 15x^4y^2 + 20x^3y^3 + 15x^2y^4 + 6xy^5 + y^6$$

b. $(2x + y)^7$

b. Extend Pascal's triangle to the eighth row.

$$\begin{array}{cccccccc} 1 & 7 & 21 & 35 & 35 & 21 & 7 & 1 \end{array}$$

Then, write the expansion and simplify each term. Replace each x with $2x$.

$$(2x + y)^7 = (2x)^7 + 7(2x)^6y + 21(2x)^5y^2 + 35(2x)^4y^3 + 35(2x)^3y^4 +$$
$$21(2x)^2y^5 + 7(2x)y^6 + y^7$$
$$= 128x^7 + 448x^6y + 672x^5y^2 + 560x^4y^3 + 280x^3y^4 +$$
$$84x^2y^5 + 14xy^6 + y^7$$

You can use Pascal's triangle to solve real-world problems in which there are only two outcomes for each event. For example, to determine the distribution of answers on true-false tests, to determine the combinations of heads and tails when tossing a coin, or to determine the possible sequences of boys and girls in a family.

Example 2

APPLICATION

Family

There are seven children in the Jones family. Of these seven children, there are at least four girls. How many of the possible groups of boys and girls have at least four girls?

To find the number of possible groups, expand $(g + b)^7$. Use the eighth row of Pascal's triangle for the expansion.

$$g^7 + 7g^6b + 21g^5b^2 + 35g^4b^3 + 35g^3b^4 + 21g^2b^5 + 7gb^6 + b^7$$

To have at least four girls means that there could be 4, 5, 6, or 7 girls in the family. The total number of ways to have at least four girls is the same as the sum of the coefficients of g^7, g^6b, g^5b^2, and g^4b^3. This sum is $1 + 7 + 21 + 35$ or 64.

Thus, there are 64 possible groups of boys and girls in which there are at least four girls.

The general form of the expansion of $(x + y)^n$ can also be determined by the **binomial theorem**.

The Binomial Theorem

If *n* is a positive integer, then the following is true.

$$(x + y)^n = x^n + nx^{n-1}y + \frac{n(n-1)}{1 \cdot 2}x^{n-2}y^2 +$$
$$\frac{n(n-1)(n-2)}{1 \cdot 2 \cdot 3}x^{n-3}y^3 + \cdots + y^n$$

Example 3

Use the binomial theorem to expand $(x - 2y)^4$.

$$(x - 2y)^4 = x^4 + 4x^3(-2y) + \frac{4 \cdot 3x^2(-2y)^2}{1 \cdot 2} + \frac{4 \cdot 3 \cdot 2x(-2y)^3}{1 \cdot 2 \cdot 3} + \frac{4 \cdot 3 \cdot 2(-2y)^4}{1 \cdot 2 \cdot 3 \cdot 4}$$
$$= x^4 - 8x^3y + 24x^2y^2 - 32xy^3 + 16y^4$$

An equivalent form of the binomial theorem uses both sigma and factorial notation. It is written as follows, where *n* is a positive integer and *r* is a positive integer or zero.

$$(x + y)^n = \sum_{r=0}^{n} \frac{n!}{r!(n-r)!}x^{n-r}y^r$$

You can use this form of the binomial theorem to find individual terms of an expansion.

LESSON 12-6   THE BINOMIAL THEOREM   693

Chalkboard Examples

For Example 2

There are six children in the Patel family. Of these six children, there are at least three boys. How many of the possible groups of boys and girls have at least three boys?
42

For Example 3

Use the binomial theorem to expand $(3x - y)^6$. $729x^6 - 1458x^5y + 1215x^4y^2 - 540x^3y^3 + 135x^2y^4 - 18xy^5 + y^6$

EVALUATING THE LESSON

Checking for Understanding

Exercises 1–10 are designed to help you assess students' understanding through reading, writing, speaking, and modeling. You should work through Exercises 1–4 with your students and then monitor their work on Exercises 5–10.

Closing the Lesson

Writing Activity Write a paragraph describing all of the patterns in Pascal's triangle.

Practice Masters Booklet, p. 85

Example 4 | Find the third term of $(x - 3y)^5$.

$$(x - 3y)^5 = \sum_{r=0}^{5} \frac{5!}{r!(5 - r)!} x^{5-r}(-3y)^r$$

Since r increases from 0 to n, r is one less than the number of the term.

To find the third term, evaluate the general term for $r = 2$.

$$\frac{5!}{2!(5 - 2)!}x^{5-2}(-3y)^2 = \frac{5 \cdot 4 \cdot 3!}{2!3!}x^3(-3y)^2$$
$$= 90x^3y^2$$

The third term of $(x - 3y)^5$ is $90x^3y^2$.

CHECKING FOR UNDERSTANDING

Communicating Mathematics

Read and study the lesson to answer each question. 2–3. See margin.

1. **Research** Pascal. Then write a one-page paper about his contributions to the field of mathematics. See students' work.

2. **Write** the terms of the ninth and tenth rows of Pascal's triangle.

3. **Write** an expression to represent the sum of the terms in each row of Pascal's triangle.

4. The number of terms in the expansion of $(a + b)^n$ is __?__, and the degree of each term is __?__. $n + 1, n$

Guided Practice

5. Use Pascal's triangle to expand $(a + b)^7$. See margin.

Use the binomial theorem to expand each binomial. 6–8. See margin.

6. $(n + 2)^7$
7. $(4 - b)^4$
8. $(2x - 3y)^3$

Find the designated term of each binomial expansion.

9. 4th term of $(a + b)^7$ $35a^4b^3$
10. 4th term of $(a - \sqrt{2})^8$ $-112\sqrt{2}\,a^5$

EXERCISES

11–20. See margin.

Practice

 Use Pascal's triangle to expand each binomial.

11. $(x + y)^5$
12. $(r - s)^6$
13. $(x - 2)^7$
14. $(2a + b)^7$

 Use the binomial theorem to expand each binomial.

15. $(x + 3)^6$
16. $(2 + d)^4$
17. $(2x + y)^6$
18. $(3x - y)^5$
19. $(2x + \sqrt{3})^4$
20. $(3a^2 - 2b)^4$

 Find the designated term of each binomial expansion.

21. 5th term of $(2x - y)^9$ $4032x^5y^4$
22. 5th term of $(2a - 3b)^8$ $90,720a^4b^4$

RETEACHING THE LESSON

Ask groups of students to find the third term of $(x - 2y)^5$, $(x - 2y)^6$, and $(x - 2y)^7$. Discuss how Pascal's triangle can be used to find the third terms.
$40x^3y^2$, $60x^4y^2$, $84x^5y^2$; Answers will vary.

Additional Answers

2. 9: 1 8 28 56 70 56 28 8 1
   10: 1 9 36 84 126 126 84 36 9 1
3. 2^{n-1}
5. $a^7 + 7a^6b + 21a^5b^2 + 35a^4b^3 + 35a^3b^4 + 21a^2b^5 + 7ab^6 + b^7$
6. $n^7 + 14n^6 + 84n^5 + 280n^4 + 560n^3 + 672n^2 + 448n + 128$
7. $256 - 256b + 96b^2 - 16b^3 + b^4$
8. $8x^3 - 36x^2y + 54xy^2 - 27y^3$

23. 7th term of $\left(x - \frac{1}{2}y\right)^{10}$ $\frac{105}{32}x^4y^6$ **24.** 6th term of $(3x - 2y)^{11}$

$$-10{,}777{,}536x^6y^5$$

25. Find the sum of the coefficients for the variables in the expansion of $(4x - 1)^{16}$.

$$43{,}046{,}721$$

Critical Thinking

26. Assume that the binomial theorem is true for all rational values of n. Find an approximate value of $\sqrt{6}$ by applying the binomial theorem to the equivalent form of $\sqrt{6}$ derived below.   2.45

$$\sqrt{6} = \sqrt{4 + 2} = 2\sqrt{1 + \frac{2}{4}} = 2\left(1 + \frac{1}{2}\right)^{\frac{1}{2}}$$

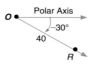

Applications and Problem Solving

27. Family If six children are born into the same family, how many of the possible groups of boys and girls have at least two boys?   57

28. Coins A coin is flipped four times. How many of the possible sets of heads and tails have:
- **a.** 0 tails   1
- **b.** 1 tail   4
- **c.** 2 tails   6
- **d.** 3 tails   4

29. 50%, 25%, 1.56%, $100[1 - (0.5)^d]\%$

29. Chemistry If the half-life of Polonium-210 is 138 days, what percent of the element remains after 138 days, 276 days, 828 days, and d days?

Mixed Review

30. Given $f(x) = 4 + 6x - x^3$, find $f(9)$. **(Lesson 1-1)**   −671

31. Find the value of csc 180° without using a calculator. **(Lesson 5-4)**   undefined

32. Name four different pairs of polar coordinates that represent point R. **(Lesson 9-1)**
$(40, -30°), (40, 330°), (-40, -210°), (-40, 150°)$

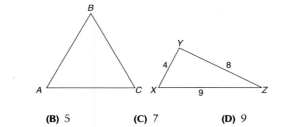

33. Write $\displaystyle\sum_{n=1}^{\infty} 3\left(\frac{1}{2}\right)^{n+1}$ in expanded form and find the sum. **(Lesson 12-5)**   1.5

34. College Entrance Exam Choose the best answer.   C
For the triangles shown below, the perimeter of $\triangle ABC$ equals the perimeter of $\triangle XYZ$. If $\triangle ABC$ is equilateral, what is the length of side AB?

(A) 4   **(B)** 5   **(C)** 7   **(D)** 9   **(E)** 15

LESSON 12-6   THE BINOMIAL THEOREM   695

EXTENDING THE LESSON

Math Power: Connections

Find the value of $(0.99)^6$ by expanding $(1 - 0.01)^6$. Round the nearest hundredth.   0.94

Additional Answers

18. $243x^5 - 405x^4y + 270x^3y^2 - 90x^2y^3 + 15xy^4 - y^5$

19. $16x^4 + 32\sqrt{3}x^3 + 72x^2 + 24\sqrt{3}x + 9$

20. $81a^8 - 216a^6b + 216a^4b^2 - 96a^2b^3 + 16b^4$

NCTM Standards: 1-4, 12, 13

Lesson Resources

- Practice Master 12-7
- Enrichment Master 12-7

 Transparency 12-7 contains the 5-Minute Check and a teaching aid for this lesson.

INTRODUCING THE LESSON

5-Minute Check

(over Lesson 12–6)

1. Use Pascal's triangle to expand $(a + b)^5$.
   $a^5 + 5a^4b + 10a^3b^2 + 10a^2b^3 + 5ab^4 + b^5$
2. Use the binomial theorem to expand $(n + 3)^5$.
   $n^5 + 15n^4 + 90n^3 + 270n^2 + 405n + 243$
3. Find the third term of $(2x + y)^6$.
   $240x^4y^2$
4. Find the fourth term of $(x - 4y)^6$.
   $-1280x^3y^3$

Prerequisite Skills

Students should be familiar with finding the value of a trigonometric function of an angle measured in radians.

1. Find $\sin\left(\frac{\pi}{4}\right)$ and $\sin\left(\frac{\pi}{8}\right)$.

   0.7071, 0.3827
2. Find $\cos\left(\frac{\pi}{4}\right)$ and $\cos\left(\frac{\pi}{8}\right)$.

   0.7071, 0.9239

Motivating the Lesson

Have students make a collage of examples of the Fibonacci sequence found in nature. Some examples are in leaf-growth patterns, spirals in pineapples, and the population growth of some animals.

12-7 Special Sequences and Series

Objectives
12–7A
12–7B
12–7C

After studying this lesson, you should be able to:
- evaluate e^x by using the exponential series,
- use Euler's formula to write the exponential form of a complex number, and
- evaluate the logarithms of negative numbers.

Application

FYI...

It is ironic that the sequence for which Fibonacci is famous is from one obscure problem in his book, *Liber Abaci*. This book is more well known for its role in introducing Hindu-Arabic numerals to Europeans.

The **Fibonacci sequence** describes patterns of numbers found in nature. This sequence was presented by an Italian mathematician named Leonardo de Pisa, also known as Fibonacci, in 1201. The first two numbers in the sequence are 1; that is, $a_1 = 1$ and $a_2 = 1$. Each additional term in the sequence is generated by adding the two previous terms. The first seven terms of the sequence are 1, 1, 2, 3, 5, 8, and 13.

In nature, plants with spiral leaf-growth patterns have spiral ratios that are adjacent terms in the Fibonacci sequence. In a daisy, for example, the ratio is 21 to 34, in a pine cone, the ratio is 5 to 8, and in a pineapple, the ratio is 8 to 13. Numbers in this sequence also describe other patterns in nature, such as spiral galaxies and the population growth of rabbits.

Another important series is the series that is used to define the irrational number e. In 1748, Leonhard Euler (pronounced OY ler), a Swiss mathematician, published a work in which he developed this irrational number. In his honor, the number is called e, the Euler number. The number is the sum of the following infinite series.

$$e = 1 + \frac{1}{1!} + \frac{1}{2!} + \frac{1}{3!} + \frac{1}{4!} + \frac{1}{5!} + \cdots + \frac{1}{n!} + \cdots$$

The binomial theorem can be used to derive the series for e, as follows. Let v be any number and apply the binomial theorem to $(1 + v)^n$.

$$(1 + v)^n = 1 + nv + \frac{n(n - 1)}{2!}v^2 + \frac{n(n - 1)(n - 2)}{3!}v^3 + \cdots$$

Now let k be a variable such that $v = \frac{1}{k}$ and let x be a variable such that $kx = n$. Then, substitute these values for v and n.

$$\left(1 + \frac{1}{k}\right)^{kx} = 1 + kx\left(\frac{1}{k}\right) + \frac{kx(kx - 1)}{2!}\left(\frac{1}{k}\right)^2 + \frac{kx(kx - 1)(kx - 2)}{3!}\left(\frac{1}{k}\right)^3 + \cdots$$

$$= 1 + x + \frac{x\left(x - \frac{1}{k}\right)}{2!} + \frac{x\left(x - \frac{1}{k}\right)\left(x - \frac{2}{k}\right)}{3!} + \cdots$$

ALTERNATE TEACHING STRATEGIES

Using Discussion

Have students discuss the definitions of the exponential series and the trigonometric series. Make sure they understand that these series are convergent for all values of the variable used in the series and that they can be used to find an approximation to any degree of accuracy.

Using Computers

Use spreadsheets to approximate the limit of $\left(1 + \frac{1}{k}\right)^k$ as k goes to infinity and the value of $1 + 1 + \frac{1}{2!} + \frac{1}{3!} + \cdots$ as the number of terms increases without bound. Have students compare the values of each.

Then, find the limit of $\left(1 + \dfrac{1}{k}\right)^{kx}$ as k increases without bound.

Recall that $\lim\limits_{k \to \infty} \dfrac{1}{k} = 0$.

$$\lim_{k \to \infty}\left(1 + \dfrac{1}{k}\right)^{kx} = 1 + x + \dfrac{x^2}{2!} + \dfrac{x^3}{3!} + \dfrac{x^4}{4!} + \dfrac{x^5}{5!} + \cdots$$

Let $x = 1$.

$$\lim_{k \to \infty}\left(1 + \dfrac{1}{k}\right)^{k} = 1 + 1 + \dfrac{1}{2!} + \dfrac{1}{3!} + \dfrac{1}{4!} + \cdots$$

Thus, e can be defined as follows.

Definition of e	$e = \lim\limits_{k \to \infty}\left(1 + \dfrac{1}{k}\right)^{k} = 1 + 1 + \dfrac{1}{2!} + \dfrac{1}{3!} + \dfrac{1}{4!} + \cdots$

e^x can be approximated by using the following series. This series is often called the **exponential series.**

$$e^x = 1 + x + \dfrac{x^2}{2!} + \dfrac{x^3}{3!} + \dfrac{x^4}{4!} + \dfrac{x^5}{5!} + \cdots$$

Euler's name is associated with a number of important mathematical relationships. Among these is the relationship between the exponential series and a series called the **trigonometric series.** The trigonometric series for $\cos x$ and $\sin x$ are given below.

$$\cos x = 1 - \dfrac{x^2}{2!} + \dfrac{x^4}{4!} - \dfrac{x^6}{6!} + \dfrac{x^8}{8!} - \cdots$$

$$\sin x = x - \dfrac{x^3}{3!} + \dfrac{x^5}{5!} - \dfrac{x^7}{7!} + \dfrac{x^9}{9!} - \cdots$$

These two series are convergent for all values of x. By replacing x with any angle measure expressed in radians and carrying out the computations, approximate values of the trigonometric functions can be found to any desired degree of accuracy.

Example 1

Use the first five terms of the trigonometric series to find the value of $\sin \dfrac{\pi}{4}$ to four decimal places.

$\dfrac{\pi}{4} \approx 0.7854$

$$\sin x \approx x - \dfrac{x^3}{3!} + \dfrac{x^5}{5!} - \dfrac{x^7}{7!} + \dfrac{x^9}{9!}$$

$$\sin (0.7854) \approx 0.7854 - \dfrac{(0.7854)^3}{3!} + \dfrac{(0.7854)^5}{5!} - \dfrac{(0.7854)^7}{7!} + \dfrac{(0.7854)^9}{9!}$$

$$\approx 0.7854 - \dfrac{0.4845}{6} + \dfrac{0.2989}{120} - \dfrac{0.1843}{5040} + \dfrac{0.1137}{362,880}$$

$$\approx 0.7071 \quad \textit{Compare this result to the actual value.}$$

Chalkboard Example

For Example 1

Use the first five terms of the trigonometric series to find the value of $\cos\left(\dfrac{\pi}{4}\right)$ to four decimal places.   0.7071

LESSON 12-7   SPECIAL SEQUENCES AND SERIES   697

Another very important formula is derived by replacing x by $i\alpha$ in the exponential series, where i is the imaginary unit and α is the measure of an angle in radians.

$$e^{i\alpha} = 1 + i\alpha + \frac{(i\alpha)^2}{2!} + \frac{(i\alpha)^3}{3!} + \frac{(i\alpha)^4}{4!} + \cdots$$

$$= 1 + i\alpha - \frac{\alpha^2}{2!} - i\frac{\alpha^3}{3!} + \frac{\alpha^4}{4!} + \cdots$$

Group the terms according to whether or not they contain the factor i.

$$e^{i\alpha} = \left(1 - \frac{\alpha^2}{2!} + \frac{\alpha^4}{4!} - \frac{\alpha^6}{6!} + \cdots\right) + i\left(\alpha - \frac{\alpha^3}{3!} + \frac{\alpha^5}{5!} - \frac{\alpha^7}{7!} + \cdots\right)$$

Notice that the real part is exactly $\cos \alpha$ and the coefficient of i in the imaginary part is exactly $\sin \alpha$. This relationship is called **Euler's formula.**

Euler's Formula	$e^{i\alpha} = \cos \alpha + i \sin \alpha$

If $-i\alpha$ had been substituted for x rather than $i\alpha$, the result would have been $e^{-i\alpha} = \cos \alpha - i \sin \alpha$.

Euler's formula can be used to write the exponential form of a complex number, $x + yi$, where θ is expressed in radians.

$$x + yi = r(\cos \theta + i \sin \theta)$$
$$= re^{i\theta}$$

Example 2

You may wish to review the polar form of complex numbers in Lesson 9-6.

Write $\sqrt{3} + i$ in exponential form.

Write the polar form of $\sqrt{3} + i$. Recall that $x + yi = r(\cos \theta + i \sin \theta)$, where $r = \sqrt{x^2 + y^2}$ and $\theta = \text{Arctan} \frac{y}{x}$ when $x > 0$.

$r = \sqrt{(\sqrt{3})^2 + 1^2}$ or 2 and $\theta = \text{Arctan} \frac{1}{\sqrt{3}}$ or $\frac{\pi}{6}$ $x = \sqrt{3}$ and $y = 1$

$$\sqrt{3} + i = 2\left(\cos \frac{\pi}{6} + i \sin \frac{\pi}{6}\right)$$

$$= 2e^{i\frac{\pi}{6}}$$

Thus, the exponential form of $\sqrt{3} + i$ is $2e^{i\frac{\pi}{6}}$.

The equations for $e^{i\alpha}$ and $e^{-i\alpha}$ can be used to derive the exponential values of $\sin \alpha$ and $\cos \alpha$.

$$e^{i\alpha} - e^{-i\alpha} = (\cos \alpha + i \sin \alpha) - (\cos \alpha - i \sin \alpha)$$

$$e^{i\alpha} - e^{-i\alpha} = 2i \sin \alpha$$

$$\sin \alpha = \frac{e^{i\alpha} - e^{-i\alpha}}{2i}$$

Additional Answers

2. $a_{n+1} = a_n + a_{n-1}$ for $n \geq 2$

3. the trigonometric series and the exponential series

6. 1, 1, 2, 3, 5, 8, 13, 21, 34, 55, 89, 144, 233, 377, 610, 987, 1597, 2584, 4181, 6765

7. $\frac{1}{1} = 1$, $\frac{2}{1} = 2$, $\frac{3}{2} = 1.5$, $\frac{5}{3} = 1.667$, $\frac{8}{5} = 1.6$, $\frac{13}{8} = 1.625$, $\frac{21}{13} = 1.615$, $\frac{34}{21} = 1.619$,

$\frac{55}{34} = 1.618$; They approach 1.618.

$$e^{i\alpha} + e^{-i\alpha} = (\cos \alpha + i \sin \alpha) + (\cos \alpha - i \sin \alpha)$$
$$e^{i\alpha} + e^{-i\alpha} = 2 \cos \alpha$$
$$\cos \alpha = \frac{e^{i\alpha} + e^{-i\alpha}}{2}$$

From your study of logarithms, you know that there is no real number that is the logarithm of a negative number. However, you can use a special case of Euler's formula to find a complex number that is the natural logarithm of a negative number.

$$e^{i\alpha} = \cos \alpha + i \sin \alpha$$
$$e^{i\pi} = \cos \pi + i \sin \pi \qquad \textit{Let } \alpha = \pi.$$
$$e^{i\pi} = -1 + i(0)$$
$$e^{i\pi} = -1 \qquad\qquad \textit{So, } e^{i\pi} + 1 = 0.$$

This equation has been called the most beautiful relationship in mathematics because it relates three of the most important numbers, e, π, and i.

If you take the natural logarithm of both sides of $e^{i\pi} = -1$, you will obtain a value for ln (-1).

$$\ln e^{i\pi} = \ln (-1)$$
$$i\pi = \ln (-1)$$

Thus, the natural logarithm of a negative number $-k$ exists since $\ln (-k) = \ln (-1)k = \ln (-1) + \ln k$, a complex number.

Example 3

Evaluate ln (-540).

$$\ln (-540) = \ln (-1) + \ln 540$$
$$\approx i\pi + 6.2916$$
Thus, $\ln (-540) \approx i\pi + 6.2916$.   *The logarithm is a complex number.*

CHECKING FOR UNDERSTANDING

Communicating Mathematics

Read and study the lesson to answer each question. 2–3. See margin.

1. **Research** other examples, besides the ones given at the beginning of the lesson, of the Fibonacci sequence in nature. See students' work.

2. **Write** a recursive formula for the terms of the Fibonacci sequence.

3. Euler's formula represents a relationship between what two series?

4. **State** the equation that relates e, π, and i. $e^{i\pi} = \cos \pi + i \sin \pi$

5. **Research** the meaning of the term *transcendental number*. See students' work.

Guided Practice

Answer each question about the Fibonacci sequence. 6–7. See margin.

6. List the first 20 terms of the Fibonacci sequence.

7. Find the following quotients to the nearest thousandth.
$$\frac{2\text{nd term}}{1\text{st term}}, \frac{3\text{rd term}}{2\text{nd term}}, \frac{4\text{th term}}{3\text{rd term}}, \cdots, \frac{10\text{th term}}{9\text{th term}}$$
What do you notice?

LESSON 12-7 SPECIAL SEQUENCES AND SERIES **699**

RETEACHING THE LESSON

Use cooperative groups to verify the derivations of the exponential series and the trigonometric series. Have each group discuss the convergence of each series and use the series to approximate values of e^x, $\sin x$, or $\cos x$. Encourage students to use calculators in the discovery process.

EVALUATING THE LESSON

Checking for Understanding

Exercises 1–19 are designed to help you assess students' understanding through reading, writing, speaking, and modeling. You should work through Exercises 1–5 with your students and then monitor their work on Exercises 6–19.

Closing the Lesson

Writing Activity Have students write a paragraph explaining how they would approximate a trigonometric value by using the trigonometric series.

Practice Masters Booklet, p. 86

Homework Exercises

Assignment Guide

Average: 20–28 even, 29–36, 38, 39,
41, 42, 44–49
Enriched: 21–39 odd, 38, 40–49

The red A, B, and C flags, printed only in the Teacher's Wraparound Edition, indicate the level of difficulty of the exercises.

8. Although the Fibonacci sequence is not a geometric sequence, the farther it is extended, the more closely it approximates a geometric series. What is the common ratio of this series? about 1.618

Use the first five terms of the exponential series $e^x = 1 + x + \dfrac{x^2}{2!} + \dfrac{x^3}{3!} + \dfrac{x^4}{4!} + \cdots$ and a calculator to approximate each value to the nearest hundredth.

9. $e^{1.1}$ 2.99

10. $e^{-0.5}$ 0.61

11. $e^{0.95}$ 2.58

Write each expression or complex number in exponential form.

12. $2\left(\cos \dfrac{\pi}{3} + i \sin \dfrac{\pi}{3}\right)$ $2e^{j\frac{\pi}{3}}$

13. $5\left(\cos \dfrac{5\pi}{3} + i \sin \dfrac{5\pi}{3}\right)$ $5e^{j\frac{5\pi}{3}}$

14. $\sqrt{2}\left(\cos \dfrac{5\pi}{4} + i \sin \dfrac{5\pi}{4}\right)$ $\sqrt{2}e^{j\frac{5\pi}{4}}$

15. $12\left(\cos \dfrac{\pi}{6} + i \sin \dfrac{\pi}{6}\right)$ $12e^{j\frac{\pi}{6}}$

16. i $e^{j\frac{\pi}{2}}$

17. $6i$ $6e^{j\frac{\pi}{2}}$

Find each value.

18. $\ln (-4)$ $i\pi + 1.3863$

19. $\ln (-0.0082)$ $i\pi - 4.8036$

EXERCISES

Practice

Use the first five terms of the exponential series $e^x = 1 + x + \dfrac{x^2}{2!} + \dfrac{x^3}{3!} + \dfrac{x^4}{4!} + \cdots$ and a calculator to approximate each value to the nearest hundredth.

20. $e^{1.5}$ 4.40

21. $e^{0.45}$ 1.57

22. $e^{4.6}$ 51.06

23. $e^{2.3}$ 9.14

24. $e^{0.8}$ 2.22

25. $e^{1.9}$ 6.39

Use the first five terms of the appropriate trigonometric series to approximate the value of each function to four decimal places. Then, compare the approximation to the actual value.

26. $\sin \pi$ 0.0069; 0

27. $\cos \pi$ −0.9760; −1

28. $\cos \dfrac{\pi}{4}$ 0.7071, 0.7071

Write each expression or complex number in exponential form.

29. $1\left(\cos \dfrac{\pi}{4} + i \sin \dfrac{\pi}{4}\right)$ $e^{j\frac{\pi}{4}}$

30. $3\left(\cos \dfrac{3\pi}{4} + i \sin \dfrac{3\pi}{4}\right)$ $3e^{j\frac{3\pi}{4}}$

31. $4 - 4i$ $4\sqrt{2}e^{j\frac{7\pi}{4}}$

32. $-1 + i\sqrt{3}$ $2e^{j\frac{2\pi}{3}}$

33. $3 + 3i\sqrt{3}$ $6e^{j\frac{\pi}{3}}$

34. $-2\sqrt{3} - 2i$ $4e^{j\frac{7\pi}{6}}$

Find each value.

35. $\ln (-7)$ $i\pi + 1.9459$

36. $\ln (-6.2)$ $i\pi + 1.8245$

37. $\ln (-5.23)$ $i\pi + 1.6544$

38. $\ln (-48.2)$ $i\pi + 3.8754$

39. $\ln (-0.036)$ $i\pi - 3.3242$

40. $\ln (-4320)$ $i\pi + 8.3710$

41. Examine Pascal's triangle. What relationship can you find between Pascal's triangle and the Fibonacci sequence? See margin.

42. Biology A famous problem posed by Fibonacci concerned the breeding patterns of rabbits. He made the following assumptions: (1) newborn rabbits become adults in one month; (2) each pair of adult rabbits produces one pair of newborn rabbits each month; (3) no rabbits die; (4) there are an equal number of male and female rabbits.

42a. 13 pairs, 55 pairs, 233 pairs

a. Starting with a single pair of newborn rabbits, how many pairs of rabbits are there at the end of 6 months? 9 months? 12 months?

b. How does this relate to the Fibonacci sequence? Use a table to show your answer. See Teacher's Answer Key.

43. Number Theory The ancient Greeks were very interested in number patterns. Triangular numbers are numbers that can be represented by a triangular array of dots, with n dots on each side. The first five triangular numbers are 1, 3, 6, 10, and 15.

a. Is this sequence an arithmetic or geometric sequence, or neither? neither
b. What are the next five terms in this sequence? 21, 28, 36, 45, 55
c. Write the general formula for the nth term. $\dfrac{n(n+1)}{2}$
d. What is the 50th term in the sequence? 1275

44. $y = \dfrac{x^4(x+2)}{x(x+2)}$

Mixed
Review

44. Create a function of the form $y = f(x)$ whose graph has holes at $x = -2$ and 0, and resembles the graph of $y = x^3$. **(Lesson 3-4)**

45. Solve $\sin^2 x = \cos x - 1$ for principal values of x. **(Lesson 7-5)** $0°$

46. Boating A boat heads due west across a lake at 8 m/s. If a current of 5 m/s moves due south, what is the boat's resultant velocity? **(Lesson 8-1)** about 9.4 m/s

47. Finance Glen Scott invests $100 at 7% compounded continuously, how much will he have at the end of 15 years? **(Lesson 11-3)** $285.77

48. Find the third term of $(x - 3y)^5$. **(Lesson 12-6)** $90x^3y^2$

49. College Entrance Exam Choose the best answer.
$\sqrt{2}\%$ of $3\sqrt{2}$ is A

(A) 0.06   (B) 0.3   (C) $\dfrac{1}{3}$ (D) 6   (E) $33\dfrac{1}{3}$

EXTENDING THE LESSON

Math Power: Reasoning

Verify $\lim\limits_{R \to \infty} \left(1 + \dfrac{2}{k}\right)^k = e^2.$

$\left(1 + \dfrac{2}{k}\right)^k = \left(1 + \dfrac{1}{\frac{k}{2}}\right)^k = \left[\left(1 + \dfrac{1}{\frac{k}{2}}\right)^{\frac{k}{2}}\right]^2 = e^2$

41. If you add the numbers on the diagonal lines as shown, the sums are the terms of the Fibonacci sequence.

Enrichment Masters Booklet, p. 86

NAME _____ DATE _____
12-7 Enrichment Worksheet

Power Series

A **power series** is a series of the form
$$a_0 + a_1x + a_2x^2 + a_3x^3 + \cdots$$
where each a_i is a real number. Many functions can be represented by power series. For instance, the function $f(x) = e^x$ can be represented by the series
$$e^x = 1 + x + \dfrac{x^2}{2!} + \dfrac{x^3}{3!} + \cdots.$$

Check students' graphs.
Use a graphing calculator or computer to graph the functions in Exercises 1-4.

1. $f_2(x) = 1 + x$ **2.** $f_3(x) = 1 + x + \dfrac{x^2}{2!}$

3. $f_4(x) = 1 + x + \dfrac{x^2}{2!} + \dfrac{x^3}{3!}$ **4.** $f_5(x) = 1 + x + \dfrac{x^2}{2!} + \dfrac{x^3}{3!} + \dfrac{x^4}{4!}$

5. Write a statement that relates the sequence of graphs suggested by Exercises 1-4 and the function $y = e^x$.
The functions defined by the partial sums converge to $y = e^x$. That is, as n increases, the graphs of f_n come into closer coincidence with the graph of $y = e^x$ for more and more values of x.

6. The series $1 + x^2 + x^4 + x^6 + \cdots$ is a power series for which each $a_i = 1$. The series is also a geometric series with first term 1 and common ratio x^2.
a. Find the function that this power series represents. $y = \dfrac{1}{1 - x^2}$
b. For what values of x does the series give the values of the function in part a? $-1 < x < 1$

7. Find a power series representation for the function $f(x) = \dfrac{3}{1 + x^2}$.
$3 - 3x^2 + 3x^4 - 3x^6 + \cdots$

NCTM Standards: 1-4, 12, 13

Lesson Resources

- Practice Master 12–8
- Enrichment Master 12–8
- Evaluation Master, Quiz D, p. 154
- Activity Master, p. 34

 Transparency 12–8 contains the 5-Minute Check and a teaching aid for this lesson.

INTRODUCING THE LESSON

 5-Minute Check

(over Lesson 12–7)

1. Find the approximate value of $e^{2.4}$. **11.02**
2. Write $3(\cos \frac{\pi}{4} + i \sin \frac{\pi}{4})$ in exponential form.

   $3e^{i\frac{\pi}{4}}$

3. Find ln(–3). $i\pi + 1.0986$
4. Write –4 –4i in exponential form.

   $4\sqrt{2}e^{i\frac{5\pi}{4}}$

5. Use the first five terms of the trigonometric series for sin x to approximate the value of $\sin \frac{\pi}{2}$ to four decimal places. Then compare the approximation to the actual value. **1.0000, 1**

Motivating the Lesson

Line up a row of dominoes on end in such a way that if the first one falls, all of them will fall. Explain that if the first one falls, so will the second one fall; if the second one falls, so will the third one fall, and so on. Relate this to the concept of a mathematical induction.

12-8 Mathematical Induction

Objective 12–8

After studying this lesson, you should be able to:
- use mathematical induction to prove the validity of formulas.

Application

Consider the series $1 + 3 + 5 + 7 + \cdots$. What is the first term? What is the sum of the first two terms? the first three terms? the first four terms? Look for a pattern by finding the first five partial sums.

$$
\begin{aligned}
1 &= 1 &= 1^2 \\
1 + 3 &= 4 &= 2^2 \\
1 + 3 + 5 &= 9 &= 3^2 \\
1 + 3 + 5 + 7 &= 16 &= 4^2 \\
1 + 3 + 5 + 7 + 9 &= 25 &= 5^2
\end{aligned}
$$

Notice that each partial sum is the square of the number of terms being added, or n^2. Even though we know that this rule is true for the first five partial sums, we do not know if this rule will be true for a partial sum having 1,000,000 odd numbers or n odd numbers.

A method of proof called **mathematical induction** can be used to prove certain formulas or conjectures. Mathematical induction depends on a recursive process that is much like climbing a ladder. First, you must climb onto the first step. Then, you must be able to climb from one step to the next. Thus, if you can get onto the first step, you can certainly climb to the second. If you are on the second step, you can climb to the third. If you are on the third step, you can climb to the fourth, and so on indefinitely, for all steps.

In general, the following steps are used to prove a result by mathematical induction.

Proof by Mathematical Induction

1. **First, verify that S_n is valid for the first possible case, usually $n = 1$.**
2. **Then, assume that S_n is valid for $n = k$ and prove that it is also valid for $n = k + 1$.**

Thus, since S_n is valid for $n = 1$ (or any other first case), it is valid for $n = 2$. Since it is valid for $n = 2$, it is valid for $n = 3$, and so on, indefinitely.

Let's use mathematical induction to prove the conjecture that was made at the beginning of the lesson. Notice that this sequence of numbers is arithmetic with a common difference of 2. The general formula for the nth term is $2n - 1$.

$S_n: 1 + 3 + 5 + 7 + \cdots + (2n - 1) = n^2$

1. First, verify that S_n is valid for the first possible case, $n = 1$.

   If $n = 1$, then S_1 is 1. The sum is 1 and $1^2 = 1$, so the formula, S_n, is valid for the first case.

ALTERNATE TEACHING STRATEGIES

Using Communication

Have students discuss the process of proving a statement by mathematical induction. Be sure they understand the importance of verifying the first possible case.

Using Critical Thinking

Give an example of a real-life situation that depends on a recursive process much like mathematical induction.
Sample answer: Using an elevator to reach a floor of a hotel depends on first reaching the floor below the floor you want, and so on, down to the first floor.

2. Then, assume that S_n is valid for $n = k$ and prove that it is also valid for $n = k + 1$.

It must be proven that if S_k: $1 + 3 + 5 + 7 + \cdots = k^2$, then S_{k+1}: $1 + 3 + 5 + 7 + \cdots = (k + 1)^2$ is also valid.

The $(k + 1)$th term is $2k + 1$.

The kth term of the series S_k is $2k - 1$. Substitute $k + 1$ for k. Then $2(k + 1) - 1 = 2k + 1$. You can write a formula for S_{k+1} by adding the next term, $2k + 1$, to each side.

S_k: $1 + 3 + 5 + 7 + \cdots + (2k - 1) = k^2$

S_{k+1}: $1 + 3 + 5 + 7 + \cdots + (2k - 1) + (2k + 1) = k^2 + (2k + 1)$
$$= (k + 1)^2$$

Since the formula for the sum for $n = k + 1$ produces the same result as the direct computation of the sum of the series, the formula is valid for $n = k + 1$ if it is valid for $n = k$. Thus, it can be concluded that since the formula is valid for $n = 1$, it is also valid for $n = 2$. Since it is valid for $n = 2$, it is valid for $n = 3$, and so on, indefinitely. Therefore, the following formula is valid for any positive integer n.

S_n: $1 + 3 + 5 + 7 + \cdots + (2n - 1) = n^2$

Example

Prove S_n: $1 + 4 + 7 + \cdots + (3n - 2) = \dfrac{n(3n - 1)}{2}$.

1. First, verify that S_n is valid for $n = 1$.

Since $S_1 = 1$ and $\dfrac{1[3(1) - 1]}{2} = 1$, the formula is valid for $n = 1$.

2. Then, assume that S_n is valid for $n = k$ and prove that it is also valid for $n = k + 1$.

S_k: $1 + 4 + 7 + \cdots + (3k - 2) = \dfrac{k(3k - 1)}{2}$ $3(k + 1) - 2 = 3k + 1$

S_{k+1}: $1 + 4 + 7 + \cdots + (3k - 2) + (3k + 1) = \dfrac{k(3k - 1)}{2} + (3k + 1)$

$$= \dfrac{k(3k - 1)}{2} + \dfrac{2(3k + 1)}{2}$$

$$= \dfrac{3k^2 - k + 6k + 2}{2}$$

$$= \dfrac{3k^2 + 5k + 2}{2}$$

$$= \dfrac{(k + 1)(3k + 2)}{2}$$

If $k + 1$ is substituted into the original formula, the same result is obtained.

$S_{k+1} = \dfrac{(k + 1)[3(k + 1) - 1]}{2}$ or $\dfrac{(k + 1)(3k + 2)}{2}$

Thus, if the formula is valid for $n = k$, it is also valid for $n = k + 1$. Since S_n is valid for $n = 1$, it is also valid for $n = 2$, $n = 3$, and so on.

LESSON 12-8 MATHEMATICAL INDUCTION 703

Teaching Tip Before discussing the Example, show S_n in table form and ask students if they can determine a pattern in the numbers.

Chalkboard Example

For the Example

**Prove S_n: $2 + 6 + 10 + \cdots + (4n - 2) = 2n^2$. Since $S_1 = 2$ and $2(1)^2 = 2$, the formula is valid for $n = 1$.
Assume S_n is valid for $n = k$.
$S_k = 2 + 6 + 10 + \cdots + (4k - 2) = 2k^2$.
$S_{k+1} = 2 + 6 + 10 + \cdots + (4k - 2) + (4(k+1) - 2)$
$= 2k^2 + (4(k+1) - 2)$
$= 2k^2 + 4k + 2$
$= 2(k^2 + 2k + 1)$
$= 2(k + 1)^2$**

If $k + 1$ is substituted in the original formula, the same result is obtained. $S_{k+1} = 2(k + 1)^2$. Thus, if the formula is valid for $n = k$, it is also valid for $n = k + 1$. Since S_n is valid for $n = 1$, it is also valid for $n = 2$, $n = 3$, and so on.

Checking for Understanding

Exercises 1–11 are designed to help you assess students' understanding through reading, writing, speaking, and modeling. You should work through Exercises 1–4 with your students and then monitor their work on Exercises 5–11.

Closing the Lesson

Modeling Activity Describe how the BASIC program below is a model of mathematical induction.

```
10    INPUT N
20    PRINT N
30    LET N = N + 1
40    GOTO 20
50    END
```

Sample answer: S_1 is the input, which is printed in line 20. Since it is printed, S_1 is true. The value of the output of line 20 is incremented by one and becomes the new output. This forms an arithmetic sequence. You can assume that S_k is true, namely that the program will output the first k values of the arithmetic sequence. If S_k is printed, then S_{k+1} is printed.

Practice Masters Booklet, p. 87

CHECKING FOR UNDERSTANDING

Communicating Mathematics

Read and study the lesson to answer each question.

1. **Determine** the general formula for the sum of n terms of the series $2 + 4 + 6 + \cdots + 2n$. $n(n+1)$

2. **Describe** the initial step that you must perform when verifying a formula by mathematical induction. Verify S_n is valid for $n = 1$.

3. In the second step of the mathematical induction process, you must assume that S_n is true for __?__ and prove that it is also valid for __?__. $n = k, n = k + 1$

4. **State** the formula for the sum of the first n positive integers. $\frac{n(n+1)}{2}$

Guided Practice

Find the sum of each series.

5. $1 + 4 + 7 + \cdots + 148$ 3725

6. the even integers between 29 and 51 440

7. the first nine terms of the series $1^2 + 3^2 + 5^2 + \cdots$ 969

8. the first six terms of the series $2^5 + 2^6 + 2^7 + \cdots$ 2016

Use mathematical induction to prove that each formula is valid for all positive integral values of n. 9–11. See Teacher's Answer Key.

9. $2 + 4 + 6 + \cdots + 2n = n(n+1)$

10. $1 + 3 + 6 + \cdots + \frac{n(n+1)}{2} = \frac{n(n+1)(n+2)}{6}$

11. $\frac{1}{2} + \frac{1}{2^2} + \frac{1}{2^3} + \cdots + \frac{1}{2^n} = 1 - \frac{1}{2^n}$

EXERCISES

Practice

Use mathematical induction to prove that each formula is valid for all positive integral values of n. 12–19. See Teacher's Answer Key.

 12. $1^2 + 2^2 + 3^2 + \cdots + n^2 = \frac{n(n+1)(2n+1)}{6}$

13. $1^3 + 2^3 + 3^3 + \cdots + n^3 = \frac{n^2(n+1)^2}{4}$

 14. $1^2 + 3^2 + 5^2 + \cdots + (2n-1)^2 = \frac{n(2n-1)(2n+1)}{3}$

15. $1 + 2 + 4 + \cdots + 2^{n-1} = 2^n - 1$

16. $-\frac{1}{2} - \frac{1}{4} - \frac{1}{8} - \cdots - \frac{1}{2^n} = \frac{1}{2^n} - 1$

17. $1^4 + 2^4 + 3^4 + \cdots + n^4 = \frac{6n^5 + 15n^4 + 10n^3 - n}{30}$

 18. $a + (a+d) + (a+2d) + \cdots + [a + (n-1)d] = \frac{n}{2}[2a + (n-1)d]$

19. $\frac{1}{1 \cdot 2} + \frac{1}{2 \cdot 3} + \frac{1}{3 \cdot 4} + \cdots + \frac{1}{n(n+1)} = \frac{n}{n+1}$

Critical Thinking

20. Use mathematical induction to prove that the binomial theorem is valid for all positive integral values of n. See Teacher's Answer Key.

RETEACHING THE LESSON

Have students discuss how to prove that $1 + 4 + 9 + \cdots + n^2 = \frac{n(n+1)(2n+1)}{6}$ for all integers $n \geq 1$.

First they should verify the formula for the $n = 1$ case. Then they should assume the k th case is true and use it to show that the kth case leads to the $(k+1)$st case.

21. Time The Johnson family's grandfather clock strikes only on the hour.
 a. Can this situation be modeled by an arithmetic, geometric, or infinite sequence? arithmetic
 b. If it strikes once at 1:00, twice at 2:00, and so on, how many times will it strike in a 24-hour period? 156 times

22. Economics Each time you buy something, it affects the nation's economy. The store from which the purchase is made now has money to spend. This trend continues and forms a sequence that is described in the multiplier doctrine of economics.
 a. Can this situation be modeled by an arithmetic, geometric, or infinite sequence? infinite
 b. Suppose you receive a $600 refund on your income taxes and that you spend 70% of this refund. Also suppose that the people who receive your money spend 70% of what they receive, and so on indefinitely. How much money will eventually be spent? $2000

23. Geneology The number of direct ancestors that you have had is given by the series $2 + 2^2 + 2^3 + 2^4 + \cdots + 2^n$, where n is the number of generations. Assume that you were not related to any of your ancestors in more than one way.
 a. Can this situation be modeled by an arithmetic, geometric, or infinite sequence? geometric
 b. How many direct ancestors have you had since the year A.D. 1000? (Assume that a generation is 30 years.) 1.718×10^{10}

Mixed Review

24. Find the value of the determinant $\begin{vmatrix} -1 & -2 \\ 3 & -6 \end{vmatrix}$. **(Lesson 2-3)** 12

25. Solve $\dfrac{2}{x+2} = \dfrac{x}{2-x} + \dfrac{x^2+4}{x^2-4}$. **(Lesson 4-6)** no solution

26. Graph $y = -3\sin(\theta - 45°)$. **(Lesson 6-3)** See margin.

27. Name the coordinates of the center, foci, and vertices of the ellipse with equation $\dfrac{(y-3)^2}{16} + \dfrac{x^2}{9} = 1$. **(Lesson 10-3)** $(0,3); (0, 3+\sqrt{7}), (0, 3-\sqrt{7}); (0,7), (0,-1), (3,3), (-3,3)$

28. Write $-1 + i$ in exponential form. **(Lesson 12-7)** $\sqrt{2}e^{i\frac{3\pi}{4}}$

29. College Entrance Exam Compare quantities A and B below. A
Write A if quantity A is greater.
Write B if quantity B is greater.
Write C if the two quantities are equal.
Write D if there is not enough information to determine the relationship.

Year	Cars Sold by Bob's Buicks
1992	
1993	

In 1992, Bob's Buicks sold 270 more cars than in 1993.

(A) the number of cars each represents   **(B)** 100

LESSON 12-8 MATHEMATICAL INDUCTION 705

EXTENDING THE LESSON

Math Power: Problem Solving

Give an example of a statement that is true for all positive integers $n \geq 2$, but is not true for $n = 1$.
Sample answer: $2^n > 2^{n-1} + 1$

Additional Answer

26.

$y = -3\sin(\theta - 45°)$

APPLYING THE LESSON

Homework Exercises

Assignment Guide

Average: 12–15, 17, 18, 20, 21, 24–29
Enriched: 12–16 even, 17–29

The red A, B, and C flags printed only in the Teacher's Wraparound Edition, indicate the level of difficulty of the exercises.

Chapter 12, Quiz D, (Lessons 12–7 through 12–8) is available in the *Evaluation Masters*, p. 154.

Exercise Notes

For Exercises 22 and 23, encourage students to make a chart of the terms of the series involved.

Enrichment Masters Booklet, p. 87

Using the Chapter Summary and Review

The Chapter Summary and Review begins with an alphabetical listing of the new terms that were presented in the chapter. Have students define each term and provide an example of it, if appropriate.

The Skills and Concepts presented in the chapter are reviewed using a side-by-side format. Encourage students to refer to the Objectives and Examples on the left as they complete the Review Exercises on the right.

The Chapter Summary and Review ends with exercises that review Applications and Problem Solving.

Additional Answers

14. $(2(5) - 4) + (2(6) - 4) + (2(7) - 4) + (2(8) - 4) + (2(9) - 4) + (2(10) - 4) + (2(11) - 4); 84$

15. $(0.4)^1 + (0.4)^2 + (0.4)^3 + \cdots + (0.4)^\infty ; \frac{2}{3}$

18. $a^6 - 6a^5x + 15a^4x^2 - 20a^3x^3 + 15a^2x^4 - 6ax^5 + x^6$

19. $16r^4 + 96r^3s + 216r^2s^2 + 216rs^3 + 81s^4$

VOCABULARY

Upon completing this chapter, you should be familiar with the following terms:

658 arithmetic mean	698 Euler's formula	702 mathematical induction
656 arithmetic sequence	697 exponential series	687 n factorial, $n!$
658 arithmetic series	696 Fibonacci sequence	691 Pascal's triangle
693 binomial theorem	665 geometric mean	680 ratio test
656 common difference	663 geometric sequence	657 recursive
663 common ratio	665 geometric series	656 sequence
682 comparison test	686 index of summation	656 term
679 converge	671 infinite sequence	697 trigonometric series
679 diverge	674 infinite series	

SKILLS AND CONCEPTS

OBJECTIVES AND EXAMPLES	REVIEW EXERCISES
Upon completing this chapter, you should be able to:	Use these exercises to review and prepare for the chapter test.

- find the nth term and arithmetic means of an arithmetic sequence **(Lesson 12-1)**

Find the 35th term in the sequence $-5, -1, 3, \cdots$.

$d = -1 - (-5)$ or 4
$a_n = a + (n-1)d$
$a_{35} = -5 + (35-1)(4)$
$\quad = 131$

1. Find the next five terms of the sequence $3, 4.3, 5.6, \cdots$. $6.9, 8.2, 9.5, 10.8, 12.1$

2. Find the 20th term of the arithmetic sequence for which $a_1 = 7$ and $d = -4$. -69

3. Form a sequence that has three arithmetic means between 6 and -4. $6, 3.5, 1, -1.5, -4$

- find the nth term and geometric means of a geometric sequence **(Lesson 12-2)**

Find the 9th term of the sequence $-8, 4, -2, 1, \cdots$.

$r = \frac{4}{-8}$ or $-\frac{1}{2}$
$a_n = ar^{n-1}$
$a_9 = -8\left(-\frac{1}{2}\right)^{9-1}$
$\quad = -\frac{1}{64}$

4. Find the next four terms of the sequence $343, 49, 7, \cdots$. $1, \frac{1}{7}, \frac{1}{49}, \frac{1}{343}$

5. Find the 7th term of the geometric sequence for which $a_1 = 2.2$ and $r = 2$. 140.8

6. Form a sequence that has three geometric means between 0.2 and 125. Sample answer: $0.2, 1, 5, 25, 125$

OBJECTIVES AND EXAMPLES	REVIEW EXERCISES

■ find the limit of the terms of an infinite sequence **(Lesson 12-3)**

Evaluate $\lim\limits_{n\to\infty}\dfrac{n^2+3}{2n}$.

$\lim\limits_{n\to\infty}\dfrac{n^2+3}{2n}=\lim\limits_{n\to\infty}\left(\dfrac{n}{2}+\dfrac{3}{2n}\right)$

$\qquad = \lim\limits_{n\to\infty}\dfrac{n}{2}+\lim\limits_{n\to\infty}\dfrac{3}{2n}$

$\qquad = \lim\limits_{n\to\infty}\dfrac{n}{2}+0$

Since $\dfrac{n}{2}$ becomes infinitely large as n approaches infinity, the sequence has no limit.

Evaluate each limit, or state that the limit does not exist.

7. $\lim\limits_{n\to\infty}\dfrac{2n}{5n+1}$ $\dfrac{2}{5}$

8. $\lim\limits_{n\to\infty}\dfrac{4n+1}{n}$ 4

9. $\lim\limits_{n\to\infty}\dfrac{(-1)^n n^2}{5n^2}$ does not exist

10. $\lim\limits_{n\to\infty}\dfrac{4n^3-3n}{n^4-4n^3}$ 0

■ determine whether a series is convergent or divergent **(Lesson 12-4)**

Determine whether $\dfrac{1}{2^2}+\dfrac{1}{4^2}+\dfrac{1}{6^2}+\cdots$ is convergent or divergent.

The general term of this series is $\dfrac{1}{(2n)^2}$.

Compare with $\dfrac{1}{n^2}$, the general term of a convergent series. Since $\dfrac{1}{(2n)^2}<\dfrac{1}{n^2}$, the series is convergent.

Use the comparison test to determine whether each series is *convergent* or *divergent*.

11. $\dfrac{6}{1}+\dfrac{7}{2}+\dfrac{8}{3}+\cdots$ divergent

12. $\dfrac{1}{1^3}+\dfrac{1}{2^3}+\dfrac{1}{3^3}+\cdots$ convergent

13. $2+1+\dfrac{2}{3}+\dfrac{1}{2}+\dfrac{2}{5}+\dfrac{1}{3}+\dfrac{2}{7}+\cdots$ divergent

---

■ use sigma notation **(Lesson 12-5)**

Write $\sum\limits_{n=1}^{3}(n^3-2)$ in expanded form and find the sum.

$\sum\limits_{n=1}^{3}(n^3-2)=(1^3-2)+(2^3-2)+(3^3-2)$

$\qquad = -1+6+25$

$\qquad = 30$

Write each expression in expanded form and find the sum. 14–15. See margin.

14. $\sum\limits_{a=5}^{11}(2a-4)$

15. $\sum\limits_{k=1}^{\infty}(0.4)^k$

Express each series using sigma notation.

16. $-1+1+3+5+\cdots$ $\sum\limits_{n=0}^{9}(2n-1)$

17. $2+5+10+17+\cdots+82$ $\sum\limits_{n=1}^{9}(n^2+1)$

■ use the binomial theorem to expand binomials **(Lesson 12-6)**

Find the 4th term of $(2x+y)^7$.

$(2x+y)^7=\sum\limits_{r=0}^{7}\dfrac{7!}{r!(7-r)!}(2x)^{7-r}y^r$

The fourth term, $\dfrac{7!}{3!(7-3)!}(2x)^{7-3}y^3$, is

$\dfrac{7\cdot6\cdot5\cdot4!}{3!4!}(2x)^4y^3$, or $560x^4y^3$.

Use the binomial theorem to expand each binomial. 18–19. See margin.

18. $(a-x)^6$

19. $(2r+3s)^4$

Find the designated term of each binomial expansion.

20. 5th term of $(x-1)^{15}$ $1365x^{11}$

21. 8th term of $(x+3y)^{10}$ $262{,}440x^3y^7$

For more information on other methods of alternate assessment, you may wish to refer to Glencoe's *Alternate Assessment in the Mathematics Classroom.*

Alternate Review Strategy

To provide a brief in-class review, you may wish to read the following questions to your students and have them answer verbally.

1. Find the next three terms of the sequence $-8, 2, 12, \cdots$. **22, 32, 42**
2. Find the 20th term in the sequence $-3, -12, -21, \cdots$. **-174**
3. Find the sum of the first 18 terms in the series $2+13+24+\cdots$. **1719**
4. Find the 7th term in the sequence $1, 5, 25, \cdots$. **15,625**
5. Find the sum of the first eight terms of the series $-2+4-8+16-\cdots$. **170**
6. Find the limit of the sequence $\dfrac{5}{3}, \dfrac{12}{12}, \dfrac{21}{27}, \cdots$, with nth term equal to $\dfrac{n^2+4n}{3n^2}$. **$\dfrac{1}{3}$**
7. Find the sum of the series $\dfrac{5}{9}+\dfrac{5}{90}+\dfrac{5}{900}+\cdots$. **$\dfrac{50}{81}$**
8. Determine whether the series $4+2+1+\dfrac{1}{2}+\cdots$ is convergent or divergent. **convergent**
9. Find $\sum\limits_{n=1}^{5}(2n-5)$. **5**
10. Find $(a+b)^7$. **$a^7+7a^6b+21a^5b^2+35a^4b^3+35a^3b^4+21a^2b^5+7ab^6+b^7$**
11. Evaluate $\ln(-280)$. **$i\pi\;+5.63$**
12. Use mathematical induction to prove that $2+8+14+\cdots+(6n-4)=n(3n-1)$ for all $n\geq1$. Since $S_1=2$ and $1(3\cdot1-1)=2$, the formula is valid for $n=1$.
 Assume S_n is valid for $n=k$.
 $S_k=2+8+14+\cdots+(6k-4)$
 $\quad=k(3k-1)$.
 $S_k+1=2+8+14+\cdots+(6k-4)+(6(k+1)-4)$
 $\quad=k(3k-1)+(6(k+1)-4)$
 $\quad=3k^2+5k+2$
 $\quad=(k+1)(3k+2)$
 $\quad=(k+1)((3(k+1)-1)$
 If $k+1$ is substituted in the original formula, the same result is obtained.
 $S_k+1=(k+1((3(k+1)-1)$.
 Thus, if the formula is valid for $n=k$, it is also valid for $n=k+1$. Since S_n is valid for $n=1$, it is also valid for $n=2$, $n=3$, and so on.

Two multiple-choice tests (Forms 1A and 1B) and two free-response tests (Forms 2A and 2B) are provided in the *Evaluation Masters*. Chapter 12 Test, Form 1A is shown below. Chapter 12 Test, Form 2A is shown on the next page.

Evaluation Masters Booklet, pp. 145–146

NAME _____ DATE _____

Chapter 12 Test, Form 1A

Write the letter for the correct answer in the blank at the right of each problem.

1. Find the eighth term of the geometric sequence $-\sqrt{7}, 7, -7\sqrt{7}, \cdots$.
   A. 2401   B. -2401   C. 16,807   D. $240\sqrt{7}$ **1. A**

Evaluate each limit, or state that the limit does not exist.

2. $\lim_{n\to\infty} \frac{5n^3 + 2n^2}{11n^3 - 7n^2 + 3}$
   A. does not exist   B. 0   C. $\frac{11}{5}$ D. $\frac{5}{11}$ **2. D**

3. $\lim_{n\to\infty} \frac{12n^4 - 5n}{9n^3 + n^2}$
   A. $\frac{4}{3}$ B. does not exist   C. 0   D. $\frac{7}{10}$ **3. B**

4. Write $0.476476476\cdots$ as a fraction.
   A. $\frac{476}{999}$ B. $\frac{476}{99}$ C. $\frac{476}{9999}$ D. $\frac{999}{476}$ **4. A**

5. Express $0.9 + 0.009 + 0.00009 + \cdots$ using sigma notation.
   A. $\sum_{k=1}^{\infty} (0.9)10^{k-1}$ B. $\sum_{k=1}^{\infty} (9)10^{1-k}$
   C. $\sum_{k=1}^{\infty} (9)10^{1-2k}$ D. $\sum_{k=1}^{\infty} (0.9)10^{-k}$ **5. C**

Find the sum of each infinite series, or state that the sum does not exist.

6. $\frac{1}{7} + \frac{5}{14} + \frac{25}{28} + \cdots$
   A. does not exist   B. $\frac{5}{21}$ C. $\frac{5}{12}$ D. $\frac{1}{6}$ **6. A**

7. $\frac{11}{5} - \frac{33}{35} + \frac{99}{245} - \cdots$
   A. does not exist   B. $\frac{77}{50}$ C. $\frac{22}{7}$ D. $-\frac{77}{50}$ **7. B**

8. Find the seventh term in the sequence $-6 - \sqrt{6}, 0, 6 + \sqrt{6}, \cdots$.
   A. $42 + 7\sqrt{6}$ B. $24 + 4\sqrt{6}$ C. $36 + 6\sqrt{6}$ D. $30 + 5\sqrt{6}$ **8. D**

9. Find the sum of the first five terms of the series $2 + \frac{4}{3} + \frac{8}{9} + \cdots$.
   A. $\frac{422}{81}$ B. $\frac{81}{422}$ C. $\frac{260}{81}$ D. $\frac{130}{27}$ **9. A**

10. Find the sum of the first 20 terms of the series $11 + 3 - 5 - \cdots$.
   A. -149   B. 1300   C. -141   D. -1300   **10. D**

11. Find the eighth term of $(3x - y)^{11}$.
   A. $-26,730x^4y^7$ B. $26,730x^4y^7$ C. $26,730x^7y^4$ D. $-26,730x^7y^4$ **11. A**

NAME _____ DATE _____

Chapter 12 Test, Form 1A (continued)

12. Use the first five terms of the exponential series
   $e^x = 1 + x + \frac{x^2}{2!} + \frac{x^3}{3!} + \frac{x^4}{4!} + \cdots$ to approximate $e^{0.7}$.
   A. 1.0123   B. 2.0037   C. 2.0123   D. 2.1194   **12. C**

13. Write $\sum_{k=1}^{3} 4\left(\frac{2}{3}\right)^k$ in expanded form and find the sum.
   A. $4\left(\frac{2}{3}\right)^2 + \left(\frac{2}{3}\right)^2 + \left(\frac{2}{3}\right)^2$ B. $\left(\frac{4\cdot2}{3}\right)^2 + \left(\frac{4\cdot2}{3}\right)^3 + \left(\frac{4\cdot2}{3}\right)^4; \frac{4672}{9}$
   C. $4\left(\frac{2}{3}\right) + 4\left(\frac{2}{3}\right)^2 + 4\left(\frac{2}{3}\right)^3; \frac{76}{9}$ D. $4\left(\frac{2}{3}\right) + 4\left(\frac{2}{3}\right)^2 + 4\left(\frac{2}{3}\right)^3; \frac{152}{27}$ **13. D**

14. Use the binomial theorem to expand $(x - 3\sqrt{2}x)^4$.
   A. $x^4 - 216\sqrt{2}x^3 + 108x^2 - 216\sqrt{2}x + 324$
   B. $-x^4 + 12\sqrt{2}x^3 - 108x^2 + 216\sqrt{2}x - 324$
   C. $x^4 + 12\sqrt{2}x^3 + 108x^2 + 216\sqrt{2}x + 324$
   D. $x^4 - 12\sqrt{2}x^3 + 108x^2 - 216\sqrt{2}x + 324$ **14. D**

15. Which of the following series is convergent?
   A. $1.5 + 3 + 4.5 + \cdots$ B. $1.5 - 3 + 4.5 - \cdots$
   C. $7.5 + 1.5 + 0.3 + \cdots$ D. $-7.5 + 7.5 - 7.5 + \cdots$ **15. C**

16. Evaluate $\frac{7!}{2!3!}$.
   A. 840   B. 5040   C. 7   D. 420   **16. D**

17. Express $1 + 1\cdot2 + 1\cdot2\cdot3 + \cdots + 1\cdot2\cdot3\cdots10$ using sigma notation.
   A. $\sum_{k=1}^{10} k!$ B. $\sum_{k=0}^{10} k!$ C. $\sum_{k=1}^{10} (k-1)!$ D. $\sum_{k=0}^{10} (k-1!)$ **17. A**

18. Find $\ln(-25)$.
   A. 3.2189   B. $i\pi + 3.2189$ C. $i\pi - 3.2189$ D. -3.2189   **18. B**

19. Write $6\sqrt{3} - 6i$ in exponential form.
   A. $12e^{\frac{5\pi i}{6}}$ B. $12e^{\frac{11\pi i}{6}}$ C. $12e^{\frac{7\pi i}{6}}$ D. $6e^{\frac{11\pi i}{6}}$ **19. B**

20. Which step do you take first in proving a statement is true by mathematical induction?
   A. Show that the statement is true for the kth term.
   B. Show that the statement is true for the $(k+1)$st term.
   C. Show that the statement is true for the first term.
   D. Assume that the statement is true for the kth term.   **20. C**

Bonus
Evaluate $\sum_{k=1}^{10}(2k+1) - \sum_{k=1}^{10} 2k$.
   A. -10   B. -1   C. 10   D. 11   **Bonus: C**

OBJECTIVES AND EXAMPLES

■ use Euler's formula to write the exponential form of a complex number **(Lesson 12-7)**

Write $\sqrt{3} - i$ in exponential form.

$r = \sqrt{(\sqrt{3})^2 + (-1)^2}$ or 2

$\theta = \text{Arctan } \frac{-1}{\sqrt{3}}$ or $\frac{5\pi}{6}$

$\sqrt{3} - i = 2\left(\cos\frac{5\pi}{6} + i\sin\frac{5\pi}{6}\right) = 2e^{i\frac{5\pi}{6}}$

■ use mathematical induction to prove the validity of formulas **(Lesson 12-8)**

Proof by mathematical induction:

1. First, verify that S_n is valid for the first possible case, usually $n = 1$.

2. Then, assume that S_n is valid for $n = k$ and prove that it is also valid for $n = k + 1$.

REVIEW EXERCISES

Write each complex number in exponential form.

22. $4i$ $4e^{i\frac{\pi}{2}}$ **23.** $2 - 2i$ $2\sqrt{2}e^{i\frac{7\pi}{4}}$

24. $-5 - 5i\sqrt{3}$ $10e^{i\frac{4\pi}{3}}$ **25.** $3\sqrt{3} + 3i$ $6e^{i\frac{\pi}{6}}$

Use mathematical induction to prove that each formula is valid for all positive integral values of *n*. 26–27. See Teacher's Answer Key.

26. $1 + 2 + 3 + \cdots + n = \dfrac{n(n+1)}{2}$

27. $3 + 8 + 15 + \cdots + n(n+2)$
   $= \dfrac{n(n+1)(2n+7)}{6}$

APPLICATIONS AND PROBLEM SOLVING

28. Budgets   The United States Department of Defense plans to cut the budget on one of its projects by 12 percent each year. If the current budget is $150 million, what will the budget be in 6 years?   **(Lesson 12-2)** $79,159,787.52

29. Ballooning   One minute after it is released, a gas-filled balloon rises 100 feet. In each succeeding minute, the balloon rises only 50% as far as it rose in the previous minute. How far will the balloon rise in 5 minutes?   **(Lesson 12-5)**   193.75 feet

1. Find the next five terms of the sequence $3, 4.5, 6, \cdots$. 7.5, 9, 10.5, 12, 13.5

2. Find the next four terms of the sequence $\dfrac{1}{4}, \dfrac{1}{10}, \dfrac{1}{25}, \dfrac{2}{125}, \cdots$. $\dfrac{4}{625}, \dfrac{8}{3125}, \dfrac{16}{15{,}625}, \dfrac{32}{78{,}125}$

3. Form a sequence that has three arithmetic means between –4 and 8. –4, –1, 2, 5, 8

4. Form a sequence that has three geometric means between 16 and 1. Sample answer: 16, 8, 4, 2, 1

5. Find the 24th term of the sequence $-6, -1, 4, \cdots$. 109

6. Find the eighth term of the sequence $\dfrac{1}{2}, \dfrac{3}{4}, \dfrac{9}{8}, \dfrac{27}{16}, \cdots$. $\dfrac{2187}{256}$

7. Find n for an arithmetic sequence for which $S_n = 345$, $a = 12$, and $d = 5$. 10

8. Find the sum of the first 10 terms of the geometric series $\dfrac{5}{2} + 5 + 10 + \cdots$. $2557\dfrac{1}{2}$

Evaluate each limit, or state that the limit does not exist.

9. $\displaystyle\lim_{n\to\infty}\dfrac{n^3 + 3}{3n^2 + 1}$ does not exist

10. $\displaystyle\lim_{n\to\infty}\dfrac{n^3 + 4}{2n^3 + 3n}$ $\dfrac{1}{2}$

Determine whether each series is *convergent* or *divergent*.

11. $\dfrac{1}{3\cdot 1^2} + \dfrac{1}{3\cdot 2^2} + \dfrac{1}{3\cdot 3^2} + \cdots$ convergent

12. $\dfrac{1}{6} + \dfrac{1}{3} + \dfrac{1}{2} + \dfrac{2}{3} + \cdots$ divergent

Write each series using sigma notation. Sample answers are given.

13. $5 + 10 + 15 + \cdots + 95$ $\displaystyle\sum_{k=1}^{19} 5k$

14. $7 + 9 + 11 + 13 + \cdots$ $\displaystyle\sum_{k=4}^{\infty} (2k - 1)$

Find the designated term of each binomial expansion.

15. sixth term of $(a + 2)^{10}$ $8064a^5$

16. fifth term of $(3x - y)^8$ $5670x^4y^4$

17. Write $-2 + 2i$ in exponential form. $2\sqrt{2}\,e^{i\frac{3\pi}{4}}$

18. Use mathematical induction to prove that the following formula is valid for all positive integral values of n. See Teacher's Answer Key.
$$2\cdot 3 + 4\cdot 5 + 6\cdot 7 + \cdots + 2n(2n + 1) = \dfrac{n(n + 1)(4n + 5)}{3}$$

19. **Finance** Ms. Jackson deposits $200 into an annuity every 3 months. The annuity pays an APR of 8% and interest is compounded quarterly. What will be the total value of the annuity at the end of 10 years? $12,080.40

20. **Geneology** Using sigma notation, write a formula to find the number of direct ancestors you have had in the past 6 generations. Then, find this number.

grand-parents

parents

generation

$\displaystyle\sum_{n=1}^{6} 2^n$; 126 ancestors

Bonus
Geometry If the area of $\triangle ABC$ is 80 square units and the geometric mean between the lengths of sides $\overline{AB}$ and $\overline{AC}$ is 16 units, find sin A. 0.625

This page may be used as a test or as a review. All answers to this test appear in the Selected Answers in the student text.

Standardized Test Questions are also provided in the *Evaluation Masters*.

Evaluation Masters Booklet, pp. 149–150

NAME _____ DATE _____

Chapter 12 Test, Form 2A

Sequences and Series

1. Find the eighth term of the geometric sequence $\sqrt{3}, -3, 3\sqrt{3}\cdots$. 1. **–81**

Evaluate each limit, or state that the limit does not exist.

2. $\displaystyle\lim_{n\to\infty}\dfrac{3n^3 - 2n^2}{9n^3 - 5n^2 + 4}$ 2. $\dfrac{1}{3}$

3. $\displaystyle\lim_{n\to\infty}\dfrac{13n^4 + 5n^2}{9n^3 - 5n^2 + 4}$ 3. **does not exist**

4. Write $0.373737\cdots$ as a fraction. 4. $\dfrac{37}{99}$

5. Express $0.2 + 0.002 + 0.00002 + \cdots$ using sigma notation. 5. Sample answer: $\displaystyle\sum_{k=1}^{\infty} 2\cdot 10^{1-2k}$

Find the sum of each infinite series, or state that the sum does not exist.

6. $\dfrac{2}{7} + \dfrac{6}{14} + \dfrac{18}{28} + \cdots$ 6. **does not exist**

7. $\dfrac{11}{5} - \dfrac{22}{15} + \dfrac{44}{45} - \cdots$ 7. $\dfrac{33}{25}$

8. Find the sixth term in the sequence $-3 - \sqrt{3}, -3, -3 + \sqrt{3}, \cdots$. 8. $-3 + 4\sqrt{3}$

9. Find the sum of the first five terms of the series $\dfrac{2}{3} + \dfrac{4}{9} + \dfrac{8}{27} + \cdots$. 9. $\dfrac{422}{243}$

10. Find the sum of the first 12 terms of the series $-11 - 3 + 5 + \cdots$. 10. **396**

T149
Glencoe Division, Macmillan/McGraw-Hill

NAME _____ DATE _____

Chapter 12 Test, Form 2A (continued)

11. Find the sum of the first 12 terms in the series $-12 + 6 - 3 + \cdots$. 11. $-7\dfrac{31}{32}$

12. Use the first five terms of the exponential series $e^x = 1 + x + \dfrac{x^2}{2!} + \dfrac{x^3}{3!} + \dfrac{x^4}{4!} + \cdots$ to approximate $e^{2.7}$. 12. **12.84**

13. Write $\displaystyle\sum_{k=0}^{2} 5\left(\dfrac{2}{7}\right)^k$ in expanded form and find the sum. 13. $5 + \dfrac{10}{7} + \dfrac{20}{49}; \dfrac{335}{49}$

14. Use the binomial theorem to expand $(2x - \sqrt{2})^4$. 14. $16x^4 - 32\sqrt{2}x^3 + 48x^2 - 16\sqrt{2}x + 4$

15. Prove $1 + 5 + 9 + \cdots + 4n - 3 = n(2n - 1)$ by using mathematical induction. Write your proof on a separate piece of paper. 15. See students' work.

Determine whether each series is convergent or divergent. Use the ratio test or the comparison test.

16. $\dfrac{2}{1^3} + \dfrac{2}{2^3} + \dfrac{2}{3^3} + \cdots$ 16. **convergent**

17. $\dfrac{2^1}{1} + \dfrac{2^2}{2} + \dfrac{2^3}{3} + \cdots$ 17. **divergent**

18. Express $\dfrac{1\cdot 3}{2} + \dfrac{2\cdot 4}{3} + \dfrac{3\cdot 5}{4} + \cdots + \dfrac{9\cdot 11}{10}$ using sigma notation. 18. $\displaystyle\sum_{k=2}^{10} \dfrac{k^2 - 1}{k}$

19. Find $\ln(-12.7)$. 19. $l\pi + 2.5416$

20. Write $\sqrt{3} - i$ in exponential form. 20. $2e^{-\frac{11\pi}{6}i}$

Bonus
Find the sum of the coefficients of the expansion of $(x + y)^6$. Bonus: **64**

T150
Glencoe Division, Macmillan/McGraw-Hill

Test Generator Software is provided in Apple, IBM, and Macintosh versions. You may use this software to create your own tests, based on the needs of your students.

CHAPTER 13 ITERATION AND FRACTALS

PREVIEWING THE CHAPTER

This chapter introduces iteration and identifies the basic paths produced when a linear function is iterated. Students learn to find the fixed point for a linear function and to determine if it is a repeller or an attractor. They then perform graphical iteration on a logistic function and determine if the behavior of the function is predictable or unpredictable. Next, the iteration of complex numbers is presented and students plot the orbit of complex numbers on the complex plane. Finally, fractal geometry, the Julia set, and the Mandelbrot set are introduced.

Lesson Objective Chart

Lesson (Pages)	Lesson Objectives		State/Local Objectives
13-1 (712-716)	**13-1:**	Iterate functions using real numbers.	
13-2 (717-721)	**13-2A:**	Perform graphical iteration on a linear function.	
	13-2B:	Identify a fixed point as an attractor or a repeller.	
13-3 (722-728)	**13-3A:**	Perform graphical iteration on the logistic function.	
	13-3B:	Determine if the behavior of a function is predictable or unpredictable.	
13-4 (730-733)	**13-4A:**	Iterate complex numbers.	
	13-4B:	Plot the orbit of a complex number under iteration in the complex plane.	
13-5 (734-739)	**13-5A:**	Determine if a point escapes or is a prisoner under iteration.	
	13-5B:	Determine if a Julia set is connected or is a dust of points.	
13-6 (740-745)	**13-6A:**	Determine if a complex number is inside the Mandelbrot set.	
	13-6B:	Determine the color of a point outside the Mandelbrot set.	

ORGANIZING THE CHAPTER

You may want to refer to the **Course Planning Guide Calendar** on pages T34-T35 for a complete pacing chart.

Lesson Planning Guide

Lesson	Pages	Practice	Enrichment	Evaluation	Graphing Calculator	Computer	Multicultural Activity	Applications	Problem Solving	Case Study Follow-Up	Decision Making	Transparencies
				Blackline Masters Booklets								
					Technology				**Activity Masters**			
13-1	712-716	p. 88	p. 88		p. 25			p. 37				13-1
13-2	717-721	p. 89	p. 89	Quiz A, p. 165					p. 38			13-2
13-3	722-728	p. 90	p. 90	Quiz B, p. 165 Mid Chapter Test, p. 167		p. 26						13-3
13-4	730-733	p. 91	p. 91	Quiz C, p. 166								13-4
13-5	734-739	p. 92	p. 92								p. 39	13-5
13-6	740-745	p. 93	p. 93	Quiz D, p. 166		p. 13						13-6
Review	746-748	Multiple Choice Tests, Forms 1A and 1B, pp. 157-160										
Test	749	Free Response Tests, Forms 2A and 2B, pp. 161-164 Standardized Test Questions, p. 168										

Other Chapter Resources

Student Edition
Case Study Follow-Up, p. 745
Decision Making, p. 733
Technology, p. 729

Other Supplements
Transparency 13-0 for Chapter Opener
Alternate Assessment in the Mathematics Classroom,
    Glencoe Publishing Co., 1993
Cooperative Learning in the Mathematics Classroom,
    Glencoe Publishing Co., 1993

Software
Test and Review Generator Software
    Available for Apple, IBM, and Macintosh
Teacher's Guide for Software Resources

ENHANCING THE CHAPTER

Cooperative Learning

Monitoring Students' Behavior

Group-learning sessions are not opportunities for the teacher to relax and, in fact, often require more diligence and self-control of the teacher than other modes of instruction. The teacher should spend the time observing the groups as they work to identify problems they are having with the assignment and in working cooperatively. Keeping a written record of the observations made can provide the teacher with a useful guide for planning future activities, for assigning roles to different students, for defining additional goals to be achieved, and for conducting conferences with individual students or their parents. It is not necessary that the teacher be quiet during these observations. However, any intervention should not disrupt but enhance the groups' efforts. For example, praising positive group behavior, encouraging reluctant members to participate, and skillfully asking questions to advance the group when they seem to be at a deadend will go far in assuring successful and satisfying cooperative-learning sessions.

For more information on cooperative learning, see pages T20-T21. Additional information on using cooperative groups is available in Glencoe's *Cooperative Learning in the Mathematics Classroom,* ©1993.

Multicultural

Multicultural Activity Masters, p. 13

CHAPTER **13** NAME _____ DATE _____
Multicultural Activity (Use after Lesson 13-6)

Fractals

Dr. Benoit Mandelbrot was born in Poland in 1924. He was educated in France and now works as a research fellow for IBM in the United States. He is best known for his work with fractals. Fractals can be informally defined as figures that have the property of self-similarity. Such figures are usually highly complex, with their parts having the same form as the entire figure. The study of fractals is related to powers of complex numbers and to the process of function iteration. Fractals have applications in many fields; examples include describing stock-market behavior, fluctions in heart rhythms, turbulence in weather, and irregular coastlines and cloud formations.

An earlier mathematical curve, now classified as a fractal, was the Koch "snowflake" curve. This curve was created in 1904 by the Swedish mathematician Helge von Koch. To create a snowflake curve, a process of iteration is applied to an equilateral triangle. The curve has many properties that intrigue mathematicians.

You can use the following steps to create a Koch snowflake curve.
For Exercise 1-4, see students' work.
1. Draw a large equilateral triangle.

2. On each side of your triangle, draw an equilateral triangle with sides $\frac{1}{3}$ as long as the sides of the original triangle. Center these triangles on each side.

3. On the sides of the figure you constructed for Exercise 2, append triangles, again $\frac{1}{3}$ the size of the segments to which they are appended.

4. Repeat the process to produce a snowflake curve. This process could be carried on indefinitely.

5. **Research** Read about Mandelbrot or Koch and write a report about either of their careers. See students' reports.

T **13**
Glencoe Division, Macmillan/McGraw-Hill

Activity Masters

Applications, p. 37

CHAPTER **13** NAME _____ DATE _____
Applications (Use after Lesson 13-1)

Fibonacci Iteration

A new interest in iteration has led to some of the most important and exciting developments in modern mathematics. But iteration is not new. In fact, one of the most interesting and most studied applications of iteration, the Fibonacci sequence, dates back to the beginning of the thirteenth century and to mathematician Leonardo of Pisa, who introduced algebra to Western Europe in 1202.

The nth iterate of the Fibonacci sequence, F_n, is found by adding together the previous two iterates.

$$F_n = F_{n-1} + F_{n-2}$$

As with any iteration, there is no direct method for finding desired iterates. You must choose an initial value and then generate iterates one by one. Since the definition does not allow calculation of the first two Fibonacci iterates, they are defined to be 1 and 1.

1. Find the first twelve iterates of the Fibonacci sequence.
1, 1, 2, 3, 5, 8, 13, 21, 34, 55, 89, 144

Much of the interest in Fibonacci iterates arises in their appearance in seemingly unrelated areas of study. One such appearance occurs in the study of *golden rectangles.* A golden rectangle is a rectangle the ratio of whose length and width is $\frac{1+\sqrt{5}}{2}$. This ratio is generally designated by the Greek letter *phi*, ϕ, and is approximately equal to 1.618034.

2. Complete.

ϕ = 1.618034			
ϕ^2 =	2.618034	$= \phi +$	1
ϕ^3 =	4.236068	$= 2\phi +$	1
ϕ^4 =	6.854102	$= 3\phi +$	2
ϕ^5 =	11.09017	$= 5\phi +$	3
ϕ^6 =	17.944272	$= 8\phi +$	5

3. Describe the patterns in the table. The coefficients of ϕ and the addends form the Fibonacci iterates.

4. a. Find $\frac{F_n}{F_{n-1}}$ for the second through twelfth Fibonacci iterates.
1; 2; 1.5; 1.6; 1.6; 1.625; 1.6153846; 1.6190476; 1.617647; 1.618; 1.6179775
b. What number do the iterates appear to be approaching? ϕ

T **37**
Glencoe Division, Macmillan/McGraw-Hill

Problem Solving, p. 38

CHAPTER **13** NAME _____ DATE _____
Problem Solving (Use after Lesson 13-2)

Using Estimation

By analyzing the relationship between the slope of a given linear function and the slope of $f(x) = x$, you can estimate the type of path that graphical iterations of the given function will take.

Example Estimate the type of path iterations of $f(x) = 2x - 3$ will take.

The slope of $f(x) = 2x - 3$ is steeper than that of $f(x) = x$. Notice how this affects iteration paths. Successive segments increase in length. The path remains within the angle formed by the intersecting graphs. Therefore, the iteration path staircases out.

Estimate the type of path iterations of each function will take. Explain how the slope of the given function affects the iteration path.

1. $f(x) = \frac{1}{2}x + 1$
Each path remains within the angle formed by the line and $f(x) = x$, but successive segments decrease in length. This causes the path to staircase in.

2. $f(x) = -2x + 1$
The first segment lies within the angle formed by the line and $f(x) = x$. In order for the second segment to return to $f(x) = x$, however, it cannot stay within the angle. Instead, it traverses an angle adjacent to the first angle. This leads to a spiral path, outward, since successive segments increase in length.

3. $f(x) = -\frac{1}{2}x + 1$
As with the line in Exercise 2, successive segments here move from angle to adjacent angle, producing a spiral. The segments decrease in length, so the spiral is inward.

T **38**
Glencoe Division, Macmillan/McGraw-Hill

Decision Making, p. 39

CHAPTER **13** NAME _____ DATE _____
Decision Making (Use after Lesson 13-5)

What Will You Eat?

Americans may be the most food-conscious people on earth. The list of best-selling books often features several diet books. Faddish diets become popular, then disappear overnight, to be replaced immediately by new ones. Nutrition experts become celebrities and appear regularly on TV talk shows. Millions of people invest in weight-loss programs, spending more than $15 billion on such programs during one recent year.

The results of this interest have been mixed. On the positive side, increased demand for natural foods has improved the overall quality of food in many areas. It has reduced the use of additives, pesticides, and other chemicals and has opened a new market for companies looking to capitalize on the new interest in organic foods.

At the same time, there is evidence that neither the health nor the eating habits of most Americans have changed appreciably, despite all of the talk about food. More than half of all Americans have dieted or are dieting, yet 62 percent remain overweight and 44 million people are clinically obese, that is, more than 20 pounds overweight. One survey reports that more than half of all high school girls are unsatisfied with their appearance. This dissatisfaction is at least partially responsible for an epidemic of eating disorders, particularly bulemia and anorexia nervosa.

What is a healthy diet? How can you balance important nutritional needs against the need to enjoy yourself and maintain a sensible attitude toward food? Research diet and nutrition. Use the following questions to guide you. Answers will vary.

1. What simple and straightforward guidelines about food and nutrition do most nutritionists agree on?
2. Should you be concerned about the number of calories you eat each day? If so, how do you determine the number of calories that is right for you?
3. Of what importance are carbohydrates, fats, and proteins? Should you be concerned about the relative proportion of these that you consume?
4. What is the importance, if any, of supplemental vitamins and minerals? If you eat a balanced diet, do you need a supplement?
5. How important is one's cholesterol reading? Is a low reading desirable or is the concern over cholesterol exaggerated?
6. Is there a connection between a healthy diet and a healthy overall lifestyle? Can you have one without the other?
7. Can exercise counteract the effects of an unhealthy diet?
8. After you have completed your research, decide on what you consider to be a healthy diet. Write a 1-page paper describing your conclusions and explain the reasons behind your decision.

T **39**
Glencoe Division, Macmillan/McGraw-Hill

Technology

The Technology feature preceding Lesson 13-4 illustrates how to use a defer sequence, defined on IBM's *MET (Mathematics Exploration Toolkit),* to perform graphical iteration on a given function. The new field of fractal geometry relies heavily upon technology and, specifically in this chapter, the TI-81 graphing calculator. The Exploration in Lesson 13-3 presents a program that performs graphical iteration of a logistic function on the graphing calculator. The Exploration in Lesson 13-5 lists another program that can be used to determine if an initial point is in the escape set or in the prisoner set of a function. It can also be used to determine if a Julia set is connected or disconnected. Another Exploration in Lesson 13-6 presents a program that performs iteration to determine if a point is in the Mandelbrot set. The graphing calculator program in this lesson will draw a rough picture of the Mandelbrot set.

Graphing Calculator Exercises, pp. 726, 744

Graphing Calculator Programs, pp. 724-725, 737-738, 742, 744

Outside Resources

Books/Periodicals

Barnsley, Michael. *Fractals Everywhere,* San Diego: Academic Press, 1988.

Wegner, T. and Peterson, M. *Fractal Creations,* Waite Group Press, Mill Valley, CA, 1991.

Films/Videotapes/Videodiscs

For All Practical Purposes: Introduction to Contemporary Mathematics, The Annenberg/CPB Project, Washington, DC

Focus on Fractals, Art Matrix, Ithaca, NY

Software

The Desktop Fractal Design System. Academic Press (IBM, Macintosh)

Fractal Attraction. Academic Press (Macintosh)

TIMS Math Series. William K. Bradford Publishing (Apple II, IBM, Macintosh)

Technology Masters

Graphing Calculator, p. 25

Computer, p. 26

CHAPTER 13

ITERATION AND FRACTALS

HISTORICAL SNAPSHOT

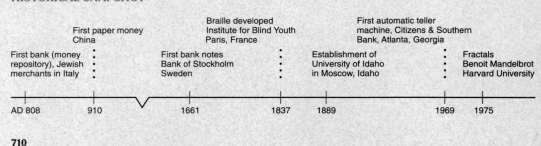

	First bank notes Bank of Stockholm Sweden		First automatic teller machine, Citizens & Southern Bank, Atlanta, Georgia	
First bank (money repository), Jewish merchants in Italy	First paper money China	Braille developed Institute for Blind Youth Paris, France	Establishment of University of Idaho in Moscow, Idaho	Fractals Benoit Mandelbrot Harvard University
AD 808	910	1661 1837	1889	1969 1975

710

CHAPTER OBJECTIVES

In this chapter, you will:
- Iterate functions numerically.
- Perform graphical iteration on both linear and quadratic functions.
- Develop an understanding of chaotic long-term behavior for some functions.
- Explore and examine fractals.

CAREER GOAL: Government Finance

In a recent evening news broadcast, the anchorman said, "The Dow Jones Industrial Average is up and stock prices are down in light trading." Did you ever wonder what this means for the nation's economy? J. Richard Rock became interested in finance from watching the news. "Finance opens a lot of doors; it is one area where you can quickly see the fruits of your labor."

Richard would like to work in the public sector. "I would especially like to work in the treasurer's office for the state of Idaho, or in the state budget office." These offices serve the state in different ways. "All of the state's funds are invested by the treasurer, so they grow continually at minimum risk," Richard says. "The budget office, on the other hand, determines what the demand for the state's products and services will be in the future, and then structures the state budget accordingly."

"Mathematics plays a significant role in investment banking," Richard says. "The mathematical model used to determine the appropriate return on an investment is the *capital asset pricing model* (CAPM), $R_f + \beta (R_m - R_f)$. In this model, R_f represents the risk-free rate, β is the expression of risk, and R_m is the average market rate. A β of 0 means that the investment carries little or no risk, while a β greater than 1 represents a riskier investment. Suppose the risk-free rate on investments is currently 8%, the average market return is 12%, and a stock has been assigned a β of 1.5. Using the CAPM, the appropriate return that the company should offer its investors is 14%."

Richard has a genetic disease called retinitus pigmentosas and is legally blind. "As a blind person," he says, "I've had a lot of opportunities. I want to give back more than I've been given."

READ MORE ABOUT IT

Baxter, Neale. *Opportunities in State and Local Government Careers*. Lincolnwood, Illinois: VGM Career Horizons, 1985.

Dalton, John M. *How the Stock Market Works*. New York: New York Institute of Finance, 1988.

Sumichrast, Michael and Dean A. Christ. *Opportunities in Financial Careers*. Lincolnwood, Illinois: VGM Career Horizons, 1985.

SPOTLIGHT ON...

J. Richard Rock
Age: 20
Class: Senior
School: University of Idaho
  Moscow, Idaho
Major: Finance

"As a blind person, I've had a lot of opportunities—I want to give back more than I've been given."

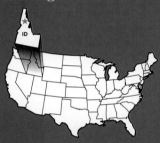

FOR MORE INFORMATION

If you would like more information about finance, contact:

American Finance Association (AFA)
New York University
Graduate School of Business Administration
100 Trinity Place
New York, NY 10006

Applications

Lesson	Application	Examples	Exercises
13–1	Finance	2	
	Banking		28
	Biology		29
13–2	Finance		32
	Banking		33
13–3	Biology		29
	Research		30
13–4	Research		32
13–5	Language Arts		31
	Medicine		32
13–6	Geology		29
	Botany		30

NCTM Standards: 1-4, 6

Lesson Resources

- Practice Master 13–1
- Enrichment Master 13–1
- Technology Master, p. 25
- Activity Master, p. 37

 Transparency 13–1 contains the 5-Minute Check and a teaching aid for this lesson.

INTRODUCING THE LESSON

5-Minute Check

(over Chapter 12)

Identify each series as geometric, arithmetic, or neither, and give a formula for the *n*th term.

1. 10, 6, 2, –2, ...
   arith.; $a_n = 14 - 4n$
2. 10, 6, 0, –8, –18, ...
   neither; $a_n = 12 - n(n + 1)$
3. 10, 6, 3.6, 2.16, ...
   geo.; $a_n = 10(0.6)^n$

Evaluate.

4. $\sum_{n=1}^{10} (n - 5)$ 5

5. $\sum_{n=0}^{\infty} 4\left(\frac{2}{3}\right)^n$ 12

Prerequisite Skills

Some students may find a brief review of the composition of functions helpful.

Given the functions $f(x) = x^2 + 1$, $g(x) = 2 - x$, and $h(x) = \sqrt{x}$, find each composition below.
1. $f \circ g$ $x^2 - 4x + 5$
2. $g \circ f$ $1 - x^2$
3. $f \circ h$ $x + 1$
4. $h \circ g$ $\sqrt{2 - x}$

Motivating the Lesson

Christmas Clubs, offered by some banks, are a popular way to save extra money for the holidays. How much money would accumulate by the end of 52 weeks if $15 is deposited each week at an annual interest rate of 3.9% compounded weekly?   **$795.70**
This question can be addressed through the topic of iterated functions.

13-1 Iterating Functions with Real Numbers

Objective
13–1

After studying this lesson, you should be able to:
- iterate functions using real numbers.

Application

FYI...

Pierre François Verhulst was a Belgian mathematician. He is credited with developing this dynamics model in 1845.

The population of a species in a defined area changes over time. Changes in the availability of food, good or bad weather conditions, the amount of hunting allowed, disease, and the presence or absence of predators can all affect the population of a species. We can use a mathematical equation to model the changes in a population.

The Verhulst population model is one tool used to represent the changes in the population of a species. The model uses the recursive formula $p_{n+1} = p_n + rp_n(1 - p_n)$, where n represents the number of time periods that have passed, p_n represents the percentage of the maximum sustainable population that exists at time n, and r represents the growth rate.

The table and graph on the next page show the changes that the Verhulst model generates for the population of elk on the Bridger Range in the Rocky Mountains of western Montana. We assumed that the population in 1984 was 10% of the maximum population sustainable and that the growth rate was 2.5. A growth rate of 2.5 means that if there were no restrictions on the growth of the population, it would grow 2.5% each year. The method used to find the first few iterates is shown.

You may wish to review the composition of functions in Lesson 1-2.

$p_{n+1} = p_n + rp_n(1 - p_n)$
$p_{1985} = 0.1000 + (2.5)(0.1000)(1 - 0.1000)$ $p_{1984} = 10\%$ or $0.1000, r = 2.5$
$= 0.3250$

$p_{1986} = 0.3250 + (2.5)(0.3250)(1 - 0.3250)$
≈ 0.8734

$p_{1987} = 0.8734 + (2.5)(0.8734)(1 - 0.8734)$
≈ 1.1498

ALTERNATE TEACHING STRATEGIES

Using Calculators

Suggest a function f for the class to work with, and have students use their calculators to find successive iterates for a given value of x_0, listing the pairs n, $f^n(x_0)$ on paper. A calculator will retain many decimal places and allow good accuracy over many iterations.

Using Connections

Consider the function $f(x) = \frac{1}{2}\left(\frac{k}{x} + x\right)$, where k is some constant.
What happens to the values of this function under successive iterations?
Try $k = 65$, $x_0 = 7$ and $k = 4$, $x_0 = -1$. What does this iterated function find?
finds square root of the k value by the "guess, divide, and average" technique

Year	P_n	Year	P_n
1984	0.1000	1990	0.5383
1985	0.3250	1991	1.1596
1986	0.8734	1992	0.6969
1987	1.1498	1993	1.2250
1988	0.7192	1994	0.5359
1989	1.2241	1995	1.1577

Elk Population Bridger Range

$$p_{n+1} = p_n + r p_n (1 - p_n)$$

Notice that to determine the percentage of the maximum sustainable population for a year, you must use the percentage from the previous year. This process of composing a function with itself repeatedly is called **iteration**. Each output is called an **iterate**. To iterate a function $f(x)$, find the function value, $f(x_0)$, of the initial value x_0. The second iterate is the value of the function performed on the output, that is $f(f(x_0))$. A shorthand notation for iterates is $x_0, f(x_0), f^2(x_0), f^3(x_0), \cdots, f^n(x_0)$. Be sure not to confuse this type of notation with exponents.

Example 1

Find the first three iterates, $x_1, x_2,$ and x_3, of the function $f(x) = 2x + 1$ for an initial value of $x_0 = 1$.

To obtain the first iterate, find the value of the function for $x_0 = 1$.

$f(x_0) = f(1)$
$\quad = 2(1) + 1$ or 3   So, $x_1 = 3$.

To obtain the second iterate, x_2, substitute the function value for the first iterate, x_1, for x.

$f(x_1) = f(3)$
$\quad = 2(3) + 1$ or 7   So, $x_2 = 7$.

Now find the third iterate, x_3, by substituting x_2 for x.

$f(x_2) = f(7)$
$\quad = 2(7) + 1$ or 15   So, $x_3 = 15$.

Therefore, the first three iterates of the function $f(x) = 2x + 1$ for an initial value of $x_0 = 1$ are 3, 7, and 15.

Iteration sequences may represent a wide variety of real-world situations. One use of iteration is amortization. Amortization is the process of repaying a loan by paying a series of equal payments over time. Home mortgages and some consumer loans are amortized. In an amortized loan, the money from each payment consists of an interest payment and a principal payment. After the necessary interest is paid, the rest of the payment goes toward reducing the principal.

LESSON 13-1   ITERATING FUNCTIONS WITH REAL NUMBERS   713

Example 2

APPLICATION

Finance

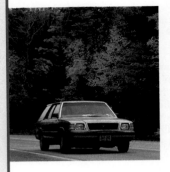

Interest amounts were rounded to the nearest cent.

Charlotte is taking out a two-year, simple-interest loan for a used car. The loan amount is $2500 with a monthly payment of $115.94. The interest rate on the loan is 10.5%.

a. **Derive an equation for the balance of the loan after n payments.**

b. **Find the balance of Charlotte's loan after each of the first five payments.**

a. Let b_n represent the balance after the nth payment. So $b_0 = 2500$. The simple interest for a payment is found by multiplying the balance of the loan after the $(n-1)$st payment by the monthly interest rate, which is $\frac{10.5\%}{12}$ or 0.00875. Thus, if i_n represents the interest payment for the nth month, then $i_n = 0.00875(b_{n-1})$.

The principal portion of each month's payment is the monthly payment minus the interest portion of the payment. So, if p_n is the principal portion of the payment for the nth month, $p_n = 115.94 - i_n$.

The balance of the loan after a monthly payment is the previous month's balance minus the principal portion of the payment. Thus, $b_n = b_{n-1} - p_n$.

Now we can write the equation.

$b_n = b_{n-1} - p_n$ *balance = previous balance − principal payment*
$b_n = b_{n-1} - (115.94 - i_n)$ *principal payment = payment − interest*
$b_n = b_{n-1} - (115.94 - 0.00875(b_{n-1}))$ *interest = rate · previous balance*
$b_n = b_{n-1} - 115.94 + 0.00875(b_{n-1})$ *Simplify.*
$b_n = 1.00875(b_{n-1}) - 115.94$

b. Use the formula to find the balance after each of the first five payments.

$b_1 = 1.00875(2500.00) - 115.94$ or $2405.93
$b_2 = 1.00875(2405.93) - 115.94$ or $2311.04
$b_3 = 1.00875(2311.04) - 115.94$ or $2215.32
$b_4 = 1.00875(2215.32) - 115.94$ or $2118.76
$b_5 = 1.00875(2118.76) - 115.94$ or $2021.36

CHECKING FOR UNDERSTANDING

Communicating Mathematics

Read and study the lesson to answer each question. 1–4. See margin.

1. **Define** and give an example of iteration.

2. **Explain** how iteration and composition of functions are related.

3. Refer to the application at the beginning of the lesson.

   a. The years when the percentage of the maximum sustainable population is greater than 1 are years in which the maximum sustainable population is exceeded. Explain what this means for the population and how the next year's population number will be affected.

Additional Answers

1. Iteration is the process of repeatedly passing the output from one application of a function back through the same function. An example of iteration is an amortized loan.

2. Iteration is the repeated composition of a function upon itself.

3a. There are more animals than the environment can sustain. The population will decrease.

3b. Less than 1; see students' explanations.

4. The principal payment increases. It is the payment minus the interest and the balance on which the interest is computed is getting smaller.

b. Do you think that the percentage of the maximum population in 1996 will be greater than 1 or less than 1? Explain.

4. Does the principal portion of an amortized loan payment increase or decrease as more payments are made? Explain.

Guided Practice

Find the first three iterates of each function using the given initial value.

5. $f(x) = 2x + 1; x_0 = 2$ 5, 11, 23
6. $f(x) = 3x - 7; x_0 = 4$ 5, 8, 17
7. $f(x) = x^2 - 1; x_0 = -1$ 0, -1, 0
8. $f(x) = (x - 5)^2; x_0 = 6$ 1, 16, 121
9. $f(x) = -2x^3 + 5x - 4; x_0 = 1$ -1, -7, 647
10–12. See margin.

Find the first ten iterates for $f(x) = 3x - 5$ for each initial value.

10. $x_0 = 2.2$
11. $x_0 = -1$
12. $x_0 = 4.9$

EXERCISES

Practice

Find the first three iterates of each function using the given initial value. If necessary, round your answers to the nearest hundredth. 13–16. See margin.

13. $f(x) = x^2; x_0 = -1$
14. $f(x) = x^2; x_0 = -2$
15. $f(x) = x^3 + 1; x_0 = 1.1$
16. $f(x) = x(3 - x); x_0 = 2.1$

Find the first ten iterates for $f(x) = 2.8x(1 - x)$ for each initial value. If necessary, round your answers to the nearest hundredth. 17–20. See margin.

17. $x_0 = 0.2$
18. $x_0 = 0.5$
19. $x_0 = 0.9$
20. $x_0 = 0.01$

Find the first ten iterates for $f(x) = 3.1x(1 - x)$ for each initial value. If necessary, round your answers to the nearest hundredth. 21–24. See margin.

21. $x_0 = 0.2$
22. $x_0 = 0.45$
23. $x_0 = 0.9$
24. $x_0 = 1$

25. Suppose $t_{n+1} = \dfrac{2}{t_n}$. Find the first ten iterates for each initial value. See margin.

   a. $t_0 = 1$
   b. $t_0 = 4$
   c. $t_0 = a$
   d. What do you observe about the iterates of this function?
   e. Is there any initial value you could use so that all of the iterates of this function are the same?

26. If the iterates of a function become the same value after many iterations, that value is called an *attractor*. A *period-2 attractor* emerges when the iterates begin to repeat a sequence of two values after some iterations. If no pattern emerges after thousands of iterations, the results are *chaotic*.

   a. What is the attractor for the function $f(x) = 2.8x(1 - x)$, if x_0 is any value between 0 and 1? *Hint: Find at least thirty iterates.* 0.64

26b. period-2 attractor

   b. Does the function $f(x) = 3.1x(1 - x)$ have an attractor or a period-2 attractor, or is it chaotic when it is iterated for an initial value between 0 and 1?

   c. Find the first thirty iterates of the function $f(x) = 4x(1 - x)$ for an initial value between 0 and 1. Do the iterates seem to have an attractor, a period-2 attractor, or do they appear to be chaotic? chaotic unless $x_0 = 0.25, 0.5,$ or 0.75

LESSON 13-1   ITERATING FUNCTIONS WITH REAL NUMBERS   715

RETEACHING THE LESSON

The new terminology introduced in this lesson may make the procedure difficult to follow. A diagram like the following will make it clearer.

Given: $f(x) = 3x + 2$ $x_0 = -2$

$x_1 = f(x_0) = 3(-2) + 2 = -4$

$x_2 = f(x_1) = 3(-4) + 2 = -10$

$x_3 = f(x_2) = 3(-10) + 2 = -28$

$x_4 = f(x_3) = 3(-28) + 2 = -82$

Additional Answers

21. 0.50, 0.78, 0.53, 0.77, 0.55, 0.77, 0.55, 0.77, 0.55, 0.77
22. 0.77, 0.55, 0.77, 0.55, 0.77, 0.55, 0.77, 0.55, 0.77, 0.55
23. 0.28, 0.62, 0.73, 0.61, 0.74, 0.60, 0.74, 0.60, 0.74, 0.60
24. 0, 0, 0, 0, 0, 0, 0, 0, 0, 0
25a. 2, 1, 2, 1, 2, 1, 2, 1, 2, 1
25b. $\dfrac{1}{2}, 4, \dfrac{1}{2}, 4, \dfrac{1}{2}, 4, \dfrac{1}{2}, 4, \dfrac{1}{2}, 4$
25c. $\dfrac{2}{a}, a, \dfrac{2}{a}, a, \dfrac{2}{a}, a, \dfrac{2}{a}, a, \dfrac{2}{a}, a$
25d. They repeat in pairs.
25e. yes, $\pm \sqrt{2}$

27. 0.66, 0.666, 0.6666, ... The values approach $\frac{2}{3}$.

29a. $p_{n+1} = p_n + 1.75p_n (1 - p_n)$

29b. 458, 525, 479, 514, 489, 508, 494, 505, 496, 503, 498, 501, 499, 501, 499

29c.

Enrichment Masters Booklet, p. 88

NAME _____ DATE _____

13-1 **Enrichment Worksheet**

Depreciation

To run a business, a company purchases assets such as equipment or buildings. For tax purposes, the company distributes the cost of these assets as a business expense over the course of a number of years. Since assets depreciate (lose some of their market value) as they get older, companies must be able to figure the depreciation expense they are allowed to take when they file their income taxes.

Depreciation expense is a function of these three values:
1. **asset cost**, or the amount the company paid for the asset;
2. **estimated useful life**, or the number of years the company can expect to use the asset;
3. **residual or trade-in value**, or the expected cash value of the asset at the end of its useful life.

In any given year, the **book value** of an asset is equal to the asset cost minus the accumulated depreciation. This value represents the unused amount of asset cost that the company may depreciate in future years. The useful life of the asset is over once its book value is equal to its residual value.

There are several methods of determining the amount of depreciation in a given year. In the **declining-balance method**, the depreciation expense allowed each year is equal to the book value of the asset at the beginning of the year times the depreciation rate. Since the depreciation expense for any year is dependent upon the depreciation expense for the previous year, the process of determining the depreciation expense for a year is an iteration.

The table below shows the first two iterates of the depreciation schedule for a $2500 computer with a residual value of $500 if the depreciation rate is 40%.

End of Year	Asset Cost	Depreciation Expense	Book Value at End of Year
1	$2500	$1000 (40% of $2500)	$1500 ($2500 - $1000)
2	$2500	$600 (40% of $1500)	$900 ($1500 - $600)

1. Find the next two iterates for the depreciation expense function.
   $360; $40 (only $40 remains of the asset cost before the residual value is reached)
2. Find the next two iterates for the end-of-year book value function.
   $540; $500
3. Explain the depreciation expense for year 5.
   There is no depreciation expense because the book value equals the residual value.

T 88
Glencoe Division, Macmillan/McGraw-Hill

Critical Thinking

27. Iterate the function $f(x) = 0.1x + 0.6$ several times with the initial value of $x_0 = 0.6$. Describe the pattern that emerges. *See margin.*

Applications and Problem Solving

28. **Banking** The balance of a savings account using simple interest compounded at the end of a period of time can be found by iterating the function $p_{n+1} = p_n + rp_n$, where p_n is the principal after n periods of time and r is the interest rate for a period of time.

28a. $4475.23, $4757.17, $5056.87

a. John Thomas has a savings account that has an annual yield of 6.3%. Find the balance of the account after each of the first three years if his initial balance is $4210.

b. Find the balance in Mr. Thomas' account for the first three years using the formula $A = P(1 + r)^t$, where A is the final account balance, P is the principal, r is the annual interest rate, and t is the time in years. Are the results the same as the results of the iterated function?
   $4475.23, $4757.17, $5056.87; yes

29. **Biology** The population of grizzly bears on the high Rocky Mountain Front near Choteau, Montana, has a growth rate of 1.75. The maximum population of bears that can be sustained in the area is 500 bears, and the current population is 240 bears.

a. Write the Verhulst model equation for the population.

b. Find the population of bears at the end of each of the first fifteen years. *Hint: Remember that p_n represents the percentage of the maximum sustainable population at time n.*

c. Graph the bear population for the first fifteen years.

d. Describe the changes in the population of bears. Explain why these changes occur. *Answers may vary.*
   29a–c. See margin.

Mixed Review

30. Find the area of triangle ABC if $a = 9.2$, $b = 12.5$, and $C = 98°$. Round your answer to the nearest tenth. **(Lesson 5-8)** 56.9 sq units

31. Find $(2 - i)^4$. Express the result in rectangular form. **(Lesson 9-8)** $-7 - 24i$

32. Write the standard form of the equation of the circle that passes through $(0, 9)$, $(-7, 2)$, and $(0, -5)$. **(Lesson 10-1)** $x^2 + (y - 2)^2 = 49$

33. 0.6, 0, -0.6, -1.2, -1.8

33. Find the next five terms of the sequence 3, 2.4, 1.8, 1.2, $\cdots$. **(Lesson 12-1)**

34. Prove that the sum of the cubes of three consecutive positive integers is divisible by 9 using mathematical induction. **(Lesson 12-8)** See Teacher's Answer Key.

35. **College Entrance Exam** Choose the best answer. Simplify $\dfrac{1 + \dfrac{1}{x}}{\dfrac{y}{x}}$. A

(A) $\dfrac{x + 1}{y}$ (B) $\dfrac{x^2 + 1}{xy}$ (C) $\dfrac{x + 1}{xy}$ (D) $\dfrac{x + 1}{x}$ (E) none of these

EXTENDING THE LESSON

Math Power: Reasoning

A continued fraction, such as

$1 + \dfrac{1}{1 + \dfrac{1}{1 + \dfrac{1}{1 + \dots}}}$ can be represented as

an iterated function. Challenge students to write this fraction as an iterated function and evaluate it.

$\dfrac{1 + \sqrt{5}}{2}$

13-2 Graphical Iteration of Linear Functions

Objectives
13–2A
13–2B

After studying this lesson, you should be able to:
- perform graphical iteration on a linear function, and
- identify a fixed point as an attractor or a repeller.

Application

Astronomers believe that when a large star collapses from its own weight, it becomes a black hole. Black holes are invisible stars that have such a strong gravitational pull that nothing, not even light, can escape their influence. Objects that pass near a black hole are pulled in closer and closer to the hole. An **attractor** in an iteration behaves in much the same way.

Graphing the iterations of a function can help us understand the process of iteration better. To do this, graph a function $g(x)$ and the line $f(x) = x$ on the same set of axes. Choose an initial value, x_0, and locate the point $(x_0, 0)$. Draw a vertical line from $(x_0, 0)$ to the graph of $g(x)$. This will be the segment from the point $(x_0, 0)$ to $(x_0, g(x_0))$. Now draw a horizontal segment from this point to the graph of the line $f(x) = x$. This will be the segment from $(x_0, g(x_0))$ to $(g(x_0), g(x_0))$. Repeat the process for many iterations. This process is called **graphical iteration**.

You can think of the line $f(x) = x$ as a mirror that reflects each function value to become the input for the next iteration of the function. The points where the graph of the function $g(x)$ intersects the graph of the line $f(x) = x$ are called **fixed points**. There is one fixed point for a linear function like the one illustrated above. If you try to iterate the initial value that corresponds to the x-coordinate of a fixed point, the iterates will all be the same.

Graphical iteration can generate many different paths for the points being iterated. Four basic paths are possible when a linear function is iterated. Two of the paths look like staircases and two look like spirals.

LESSON 13-2 GRAPHICAL ITERATION OF LINEAR FUNCTIONS **717**

Teaching Tip When considering graphs like those shown at the beginning of the lesson, students may think that the "staircase" will reach the fixed point of the iteration. This is not the case; in fact, the staircase has infinite length. When performing iteration on a linear function, the type of path is determined by the line itself, independent of the initial point chosen.

Chalkboard Example

For Example 1

Perform graphical iteration on the function $f(x) = \frac{1}{2}x$ for the first

three iterates if the initial value is $x_0 = 3$. Which of the four types of paths does the iteration take?
staircase inward

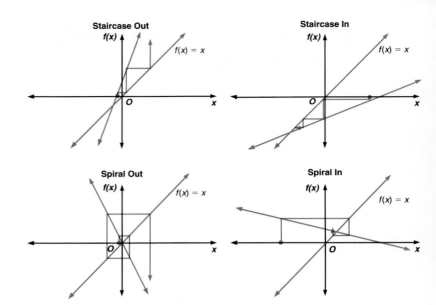

If a path staircases or spirals out from a fixed point, the x-coordinate of the fixed point is called a **repeller**. You can think of a repeller as a point that pushes everything away from itself. If a path staircases or spirals in to a fixed point, the x-coordinate of the point is an **attractor**. Attractors act like the black holes, pulling everything near them in. The graphs on the left above illustrate repellers, while the graphs on the right illustrate attractors.

Example 1

Perform graphical iteration on the function $g(x) = 3x$ for the first three iterates if the initial value is $x_0 = 0.2$. Which of the four types of paths does the iteration take?

To do the graphical iteration, first graph the functions $f(x) = x$ and $g(x) = 3x$.

Start at the point $(0.2, 0)$ and draw a vertical line to the graph of $g(x) = 3x$. From that point, draw a horizontal line to the graph of $f(x) = x$.

Repeat the process from the point on $f(x) = x$. Then repeat again.

The path of the iterations is a staircase out. So, the x-coordinate of the fixed point, 0, is a repeller.

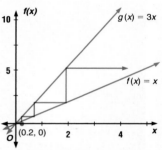

Notice that the scales on the axes are different.

718   CHAPTER 13   ITERATION AND FRACTALS

Sometimes when you are analyzing the long-term behavior of the iterations of a function, it is helpful to know the fixed points. Since the fixed points occur where the graphs of the function and $f(x) = x$ intersect, you can find the fixed points by solving a system of equations.

Example 2

Find the fixed point for the function $g(x) = -0.5x + 6$. Then iterate the function graphically for $x_0 = -4$. Is the x-coordinate of the fixed point a repeller or an attractor?

We can find the coordinates of the fixed point by solving the following system of equations.

$$g(x) = -0.5x + 6$$
$$f(x) = x$$

Solve by substitution.
$$x = -0.5x + 6$$
$$1.5x = 6$$
$$x = 4$$

The coordinates of the fixed point are $(4, 4)$.

Now iterate the function graphically. Begin at the initial value of $x_0 = -4$. Draw a vertical line to the graph of $g(x) = -0.5x + 6$. From that point, draw a horizontal line to the graph of $f(x) = x$. Repeat the process from this point until the pattern becomes clear.

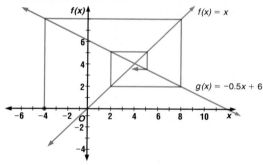

The graph is a spiral in toward $(4, 4)$, so the x-coordinate of the fixed point, 4, is an attractor. This means that the long-term behavior of iterating $g(x) = -0.5x + 6$ for any initial point is predictable. The iterates will become 4 as the number of iterations increases without bound.

CHECKING FOR UNDERSTANDING

Communicating Mathematics

Read and study the lesson to answer each question.

1. **Define** a fixed point. How can you identify a fixed point? See margin.

RETEACHING THE LESSON

Present a linear function and an initial point. Then perform the iteration by direct computation, as was done in Lesson 13–1, and, at the same time, show each corresponding step of the graphical iteration technique introduced in this lesson. In this way, students can compare the two methods and see how each one is done.

Additional Answers

1. A fixed point is a point that represents an initial value whose iterates for the function are constant. The fixed points are the points where the graphs of the function and $f(x) = x$ intersect.

Homework Exercises

The red A, B, and C flags, printed only in the Teacher's Wraparound Edition, indicate the level of difficulty of the exercises.

Chapter 13, Quiz A, (Lessons 13–1 through 13–2), is available in the *Evaluation Masters*, p. 165.

Exercise Note

In Exercises 9–18, 4 or 5 iterations should be sufficient to complete each problem.

---

2. **Explain** what the presence of a spiral in or staircase in path tells us about the fixed point. It is an attractor.

Guided Practice

Copy the graphs shown and perform graphical iteration for the first three iterates of the initial point shown.

3.

4.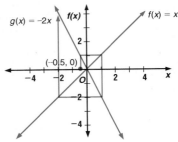

Find the fixed point for each function. Then perform graphical iteration for $x_0 = 2$. Is the x-coordinate of the fixed point a repeller or an attractor?

5. $f(x) = 6x + 2$
$-\frac{2}{5}$ is a repeller

6. $f(x) = 0.2x - 1$ -1.25 is an attractor

EXERCISES

Practice

Copy the graphs shown and perform graphical iteration for the first four iterates of the initial point shown.

7.

8.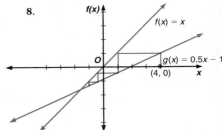

Graph each function and the function $f(x) = x$ on the same set of axes. Then perform graphical iteration for $x_0 = 1$. State the slope of the linear function and the type of path that the graphical iteration forms.

9. $g(x) = 4x + 2$ 4, staircase out

10. $g(x) = 10x - 6$ 10, staircase out

11. $g(x) = -2x$ -2, spiral out

12. $g(x) = 0.5x + 3$ 0.5, staircase in

13. $g(x) = -0.75x + 4$ -0.75, spiral in

14. $g(x) = -0.6x$ -0.6, spiral in

15. $g(x) = -6x - 1$ -6, spiral out

16. $g(x) = \frac{2}{3}x + 2$ $\frac{2}{3}$, staircase in

17. $g(x) = 10x - 5$ 10, staircase out

18. $g(x) = -\frac{1}{4}x - \frac{1}{4}$, spiral in

Study your answers for Exercises 9—18. Describe the slopes of functions that have the following iteration paths.

19. spiral in $-1 < m < 0$

20. spiral out $m < -1$

21. staircase in $0 < m < 1$

22. staircase out $m > 1$

Find the coordinates of the fixed point for each function. Is the *x*-coordinate of the fixed point a repeller or an attractor? 23–26. See margin.

23. $f(x) = 2.5x + 4$

24. $f(x) = -3x + 2$

25. $f(x) = 0.75x - 5$

26. $f(x) = -0.8x - 18$

27–30. See margin.

27. Which functions in Exercises 23–26 have paths with a spiraling behavior?

28. Find a linear function that has an attractor of $\frac{7}{9}$ under iteration.

29. The value 0.4 is a repeller for iterations of a certain linear function. Find a possible equation for this function.

30. Find a linear function that has -2 as a repeller under iteration.

Critical Thinking

31. What linear function has all real numbers as attractors? $f(x) = x$

Applications and Problem Solving

32. Finance The function $p_{n+1} = p_n + rp_n$ gives the balance of a bank account after n time periods.
  a. Find the coordinates of the fixed point for the iteration of the function. Assume that $r > 0$. $(0, 0)$
  b. Is the *x*-coordinate of the fixed point a repeller or an attractor? repeller

33. Banking The function $b_n = \left(1 + \frac{r}{12}\right) b_{n-1} - p$ gives the balance due on a student loan after n payments if r is the annual interest rate and p is the payment amount. *Hint: Solve a system of equations.*
  a. Find the coordinates of the fixed point for the iteration of the function. Assume that $r > 0$ and $p > 0$. Explain what is happening to the relationship between the interest and the payment at this point. See margin.
  b. Is the *x*-coordinate of the fixed point a repeller or an attractor? repeller

Mixed Review

34. Find the product $-2 \begin{bmatrix} 6 & -2 \\ 0 & -1 \end{bmatrix}$. **(Lesson 2-2)** $\begin{bmatrix} -12 & 4 \\ 0 & 2 \end{bmatrix}$

35. Find all rational roots of the equation $12x^4 - 11x^3 - 54x^2 - 18x + 8 = 0$. **(Lesson 4-4)** $\frac{1}{4}, -\frac{4}{3}$

36. Entertainment Ryan observes that the angle of elevation to the top of the Sky Needle, a ride at Magic Planet Amusement Park, is 81° when he stands 50 feet from its base. If Ryan is 6 feet tall, about how tall is the Sky Needle? **(Lesson 5-5)** 322 feet

37. Find the sum of the first six terms of the series $8 + 6 + 4.5 + \cdots$. **(Lesson 12-2)** $26\frac{39}{128}$

38. Find the first four iterates for $f(x) = 6.5x(1 - x)$ for $x_0 = 0.7$. If necessary, round your answers to the nearest hundredth. **(Lesson 13-1)** See margin.

39. College Entrance Exam In Captain Harper's battalion, 30% of the enlistees are from Texas, and 10% of these are from Dallas. What percent of the enlistees in the battalion are from Dallas? 3%

EXTENDING THE LESSON

Math Power: Problem Solving

Consider the function given in Example 1. What is the length of the stair step path from the point (0.2, 0.2) on the line $y = x$ up to the third time the path returns to this line?

10.4

What pattern do you notice in the path itself? Each successive tread of the stair case is 3 times as long as the one before it.

NCTM Standards: 1-4, 6

Lesson Resources

- Practice Master 13–3
- Enrichment Master 13–3
- Evaluation Master, Quiz B, p. 165
- Technology Master, p. 26

 Transparency 13–3 contains the 5-Minute Check and a teaching aid for this lesson.

INTRODUCING THE LESSON

 5-Minute Check

(over Lesson 13–2)

1. Perform graphical iteration on the function $f(x) = 0.2x - 1$ for the first four iterates of the initial point $x_0 = 5$.

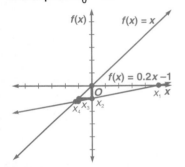

State the type of path formed by graphical iteration of each function.
2. $f(x) = 3x - 2$ **staircase out**
3. $f(x) = 2 - 0.5x$ **spiral in**
4. Find the coordinates of the fixed point for $f(x) = 1.2x + 6$. Is this fixed point a repeller or an attractor? **(–30, –30); repeller**

Motivating the Lesson

What is the major difference in the iterative behavior of the functions $f(x) = 0.99x + 5$ and $g(x) = 1.01x + 5$? A very small difference in the value of the slope causes the fixed point in one case to be an attractor while in the other case it is a repeller. In this lesson, we will see even more dramatic changes in iterative behavior caused by a tiny change in the value of a single parameter.

13-3 Graphical Iteration of the Logistic Function

Objectives
After studying this lesson, you should be able to:
13–3A ■ perform graphical iteration on the logistic function, and
13–3B ■ determine if the behavior of a function is predictable or unpredictable.

Application

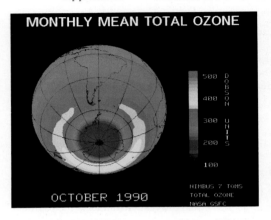

MONTHLY MEAN TOTAL OZONE

OCTOBER 1990

NIMBUS 7 TOMS
TOTAL OZONE
NASA GSFC

The state of the environment has become a hotly debated topic in the 1990s. Scientists and citizens' groups are all pressing for more action from governments concerning issues such as global warming and the deterioration of the ozone layer. Changes in industries and political policies are aimed at cleaning up the environment and restoring habitat for wildlife. However, the suggested changes may not have the effect that is anticipated.

FYI...

Overproduction of the greenhouse gases causes the heating of Earth's surface that is called global warming. Greenhouse gases are produced by termites, wetlands, coal mining, the burning of fossil fuels, and cud-chewing animals.

Up until this point, we have studied the behavior of linear functions under iteration. The work of researchers such as Edward N. Lorenz and Mitchel Feigenbaum has shown that most natural phenomena, like global weather, river currents, and population growth, are described most effectively by nonlinear functions. When these functions are iterated, their behavior may or may not be predictable. Very slight changes in the parameter values of a function can cause the iterated functions to change from stable and predictable behavior to unpredictable behavior which is known as **chaos**. This means that seemingly slight changes in the world's environment may have unpredictable results.

One of the nonlinear functions used to describe natural phenomena is the **logistic function**, $f(x) = ax(1 - x)$. The graph of the logistic function is a parabola with x-intercepts at 0 and 1, as shown at the right. These will be the x-intercepts regardless of the value of a. The vertex of the graph of the logistic function is always the point with coordinates $\left(\frac{1}{2}, \frac{a}{4}\right)$.

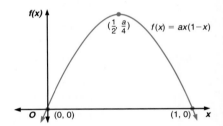

$\left(\frac{1}{2}, \frac{a}{4}\right)$ $f(x) = ax(1-x)$

(0, 0)   (1, 0)

ALTERNATE TEACHING STRATEGIES

Using Problem Solving

Draw a graph of the logistic function $f(x) = 3.2x(1 - x)$ on the chalkboard along with the line $y = x$. Have students find the fixed points and consider the iterative behavior of the initial point 0.5. Within just a few iterations, students will begin to see a period-2 attractor at work.

Using Charts

Have each student work with a set of three logistic functions, having values of 1.0, 2.8, and 3.2. Students can examine the iterative behavior of each for a few values of x_0, perhaps 0.3 and 0.9, and then make a chart showing their results.

Example 1

> **Without graphing, find the vertex of the graph of $y = 6x(1 - x)$.**
>
> In this function, $a = 6$ and the vertex of every logistic function is $\left(\frac{1}{2}, \frac{a}{4}\right)$.
>
> Therefore, the vertex is at $\left(\frac{1}{2}, \frac{6}{4}\right)$ or $(0.5, 1.5)$.

The behavior of the logistic function under iteration varies greatly as the parameter value of a changes. Let's look closely at the behavior of this function if $0 < a \leq 4$ and the initial value is between 0 and 1.

The graphical iterations for an initial value of 0.1 and three different values of a are shown below. For $a = 1.5$, the graphical iteration is a staircase that converges on a fixed point attractor. For $a = 2.6$, the iteration pattern ends in a spiral that converges on a fixed point attractor. The iteration pattern for $a = 3.3$ moves away from a fixed point repeller and settles into a cyclical pattern. A cyclical pattern is one where the iterates begin to repeat in a predictable pattern over time. Even though the three patterns are very different, all three have predictable long-term behavior.

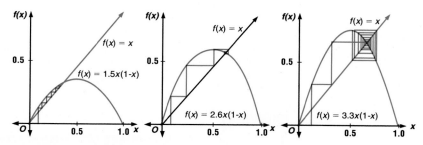

If $a = 4$ in the logistic function, the iteration pattern is quite different. The graphs below show the graphical iteration for the initial value $x_0 = 0.24$ after 10, 40, and 100 iterations.

The behavior of the iteration pattern never seems to converge on one point or pattern. The third graph shows the iteration pattern filling the entire interval from 0 to 1 on the x-axis. This visual filling outcome is called **mixing**. Mixing is a good indicator that a system is unstable.

LESSON 13-3   GRAPHICAL ITERATION OF THE LOGISTIC FUNCTION   723

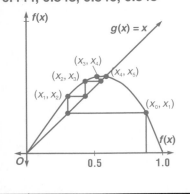
Example 2

Find the coordinates of the fixed points for the function $f(x) = 1.5x(1 - x)$. From the graph on the previous page, which point appears to be an attractor?

Like linear functions, the coordinates of the fixed points of a nonlinear iteration can be found by solving a system of equations.

$$f(x) = x$$
$$f(x) = 1.5x(1 - x)$$

Substitute.

$$x = 1.5x(1 - x)$$
$$x = 1.5x - 1.5x^2$$
$$0 = 0.5x - 1.5x^2$$
$$0 = 0.5x(1 - 3x)$$
$$0 = 0.5x \quad \text{or} \quad 0 = 1 - 3x$$
$$x = 0 \quad \text{or} \quad x = \frac{1}{3}$$

The fixed points are at $(0, 0)$ and $\left(\frac{1}{3}, \frac{1}{3}\right)$. By observing the graph, it appears that $\frac{1}{3}$ is an attractor.

Observing the long-term behavior of iteration requires performing many steps of graphical iteration. Performing these iterations by hand is very time consuming and tedious. Technology can help us perform these steps to observe their behavior.

EXPLORATION: Graphing Calculator

The program below will perform graphical iteration of a logistic function on a TI-81 graphing calculator. To enter the program into the program memory, select the EDIT option in the program menu. Refer to the TI-81 manual for menus to locate unfamiliar keystrokes.

```
Line 1   :ClrDraw
Line 2   :Fix 3
Line 3   :0→Xmin
Line 4   :1→Xmax
Line 5   :0.1→Xscl
Line 6   :0→Ymin
Line 7   :1→Ymax
Line 8   :0.1→Yscl
Line 9   :Disp "A ="
Line 10  :Input A
Line 11  :Disp "I ="
Line 12  :Input I
Line 13  :DrawF AX(1 - X)
Line 14  :DrawF X
Line 15  :0→M
Line 16  :0→C
Line 17  :If C = 0
Line 18  :Goto 2
Line 19  :Lbl 1
Line 20  :AI - AII→I
Line 21  :M + 1→M
Line 22  :If M < C
Line 23  :Goto 1
Line 24  :Goto 3
Line 25  :Lbl 2
Line 26  :Line(I,0,I,I)
```

```
Line 27  :Lbl 3        Line 33  :Pause
Line 28  :AI — AII → J  Line 34  :J→I
Line 29  :Line (I,I,I,J) Line 35  :M + 1→M
Line 30  :Line (I,J,J,J) Line 36  :If M < C + 15
Line 31  :Pause         Line 37  :Goto 3
Line 32  :Disp J        Line 38  :End
```

Use the program to perform the first five steps of iteration of the function $f(x) = 2.5x(1 - x)$ for an initial value of 0.250.

1. Enter $a = 2.5$ and $i = 0.250$.

2. The first three iterates are as follows, to the nearest thousandth. *Press* ENTER *to display the iterates.*

   $x_0 = i = 0.250$
   $x_1 = 0.469$
   $x_2 = 0.623$

3. Find the next three iterates.
   $x_3 = 0.587$
   $x_4 = 0.606$
   $x_5 = 0.597$

The program given in the Exploration can be used to examine the long-term iterative behavior of a function. To do this, replace Line 16 with "100 → C". This modification will make the calculator begin graphing and displaying values at the 100th iterate. If the graph is approaching an attractor, the values of the iterates will all be getting closer to it. Some forms of stable long-term behavior cause the iterates to repeat in a pattern. If the iterates repeat every n steps, the function is said to have a **period-n attractor** and the fixed point is a repeller. For example, if the iterates eventually settle into the pattern $0.12, 0.45, 1.23, 0.12, 0.45, 1.23, \cdots$, this function has a period-3 attractor.

Example 3

Modify the program in the Graphing Calculator Exploration so that the iterates will begin printing at the 100th iterate. Use the modified graphical iteration program to determine the long-term iterative behavior of the function $f(x) = 3.1x(1 - x)$ for any initial value in the interval 0 to 1.

The iterates form the pattern $0.765, 0.558, 0.765, 0.558, \ldots$. So the function has a period-2 attractor, 0.558 and 0.765.

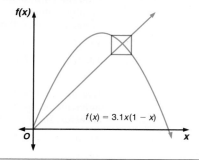

LESSON 13-3   GRAPHICAL ITERATION OF THE LOGISTIC FUNCTION   725

Chalkboard Example

For Example 3

Use the modified iterative behavior program given in Example 3 in the Student Edition to determine the long-term iterative behavior of the function $f(x) = 3.3x(1 - x)$ for any initial value in the interval 0 to 1. The pattern is 0.479, 0.824, 0.479, 0.824, ... The function has a period-2 attractor.

Exercises 1–12 are designed to help you assess students' understanding through reading, writing, speaking, and modeling. You should work through Exercises 1–3 with your students and then monitor their work on Exercises 4–12.

Closing the Lesson

Writing Activity Have students write down a logistic function and an initial point between 0 and 1, exchange papers, and find the first four iterates using graphical iteration.

APPLYING THE LESSON

Homework Exercises

Assignment Guide

Average: 13–24, 28–36
Enriched: 16–36
All: Mid-Chapter Review, 1–9

The red A, B, and C flags, printed only in the Teacher's Wraparound Edition, indicate the level of difficulty of the exercises.
**Chapter 13, Quiz B,
(Lesson 11–3)**, is available in the *Evaluation Masters*, p. 165.

Using Technology

In Exercises 21–26, remind students to set the value of C equal to 100 at line 16 of the program to examine the long-term behavior of each function.

CHECKING FOR UNDERSTANDING

Communicating Mathematics

Read and study the lesson to answer each question. 1–3. See margin.

1. Can the long-term iterative behavior of the logistic function be predicted if the parameter value *a* is changed? Why or why not?
2. **Explain** how you can find the coordinates of the fixed points of a logistic function.
3. **Describe** the long-term iterative behavior of a function with a period-4 attractor.

Guided Practice

Find the coordinates of the vertex of the graph of each logistic function.

4. $f(x) = 2x(1 - x)$
   $(0.5, 0.5)$
5. $f(x) = 3x(1 - x)$
   $(0.5, 0.75)$
6. $f(x) = 1.2x(1 - x)$
   $(0.5, 0.3)$

Find the coordinates of the fixed points for each function. Use the graphical iteration program to graph the function and determine if the *x*-coordinate of each nonzero fixed point is a repeller or an attractor. 7–10. See margin.

7. $f(x) = 2x(1 - x)$
8. $f(x) = 3x(1 - x)$
9. $f(x) = 1.2x(1 - x)$
10. $f(x) = x(1 - x)$

Use the modified graphical iteration program to determine the long-term iterative behavior of the function $f(x) = ax(1 - x)$ for each value of *a*. Write *period-n attractor*, *fixed point attractor*, or *chaos*.

11. $a = 2.95$ fixed point attractor
12. $a = 3.05$ period-2 attractor

EXERCISES

Practice

Find the coordinates of the vertex of the graph of each logistic function.

13. $f(x) = 2.4x(1 - x)$ $(0.5, 0.6)$
14. $f(x) = 0.4x(1 - x)$ $(0.5, 0.1)$
15. $f(x) = 4x(1 - x)$
    $(0.5, 1)$
16. $f(x) = 0.64x(1 - x)$
    $(0.5, 0.16)$

Find the coordinates of the fixed points for each of the following functions. Use the graphical iteration program to graph the function and determine if the *x*-coordinate of each nonzero fixed point is a repeller or an attractor. 17–20. See margin.

17. $f(x) = 1.6x(1 - x)$
18. $f(x) = 2.9x(1 - x)$
19. $f(x) = 3.2x(1 - x)$
20. $f(x) = 3.4x(1 - x)$

21. period-2 attractor
22. period-4 attractor

Use the modified graphical iteration program to determine the long-term iterative behavior of the function $f(x) = ax(1 - x)$ for each value of *a*. Write *period-n attractor*, *fixed point attractor*, or *chaos*.

21. $a = 3.24$
22. $a = 3.50$
23. $a = 3.68$ chaos
24. $a = 2.2$
    fixed pt attractor
25. $a = 3.74$
    period-5 attractor
26. $a = 3.8$
    chaos

27. The long-term iterative behavior of the logistic function forms patterns according to the value of a. That is, if a is in a certain range, the long-term behavior is a fixed point attractor. The next range shows that the long-term behavior is a period-2 attractor. The values of a that are the transition points between one range and the next are called *bifurcation points*, and the phenomenon is called *period doubling*.

    a. Find the value of a for which the long-term iterative behavior of $f(x) = ax(1 - x)$ makes a transition from a fixed point attractor to a period-2 attractor. $a \approx 3$

    b. Find the value of a for which the long-term iterative behavior of $f(x) = ax(1 - x)$ makes a transition from a period-2 attractor to a period-4 attractor. $a \approx 3.4495$

    c. What is the value of a for which the long-term iterative behavior of $f(x) = ax(1 - x)$ makes a transition from a period-4 attractor to a period-8 attractor? $a \approx 3.5441$

    d. Describe the long-term iterative behavior of the logistic function as the value of a increases just past 3.569946. chaos

Critical Thinking

28. Dynamic systems like those found in nature are very sensitive to initial conditions. MIT meteorologist Edward N. Lorenz discussed this dependence in his paper "The Butterfly Effect," which asked the question, "Can the flap of a butterfly's wings in Brazil cause a tornado in Texas?"

    a. Find the first ten iterates of the function $f(x) = 4x(1 - x)$ for both of the initial values $x_0 = 0.200$ and 0.201. Compare the tenth iterates. Did the change in initial value change the iterates greatly? 0.962, 0.449; yes

    b. Explain why you think this is called the Butterfly Effect. See students' work.

Applications and Problem Solving

29. Biology The Verhulst population model describing the population of antelope in an area is $p_{n+1} = p_n + 1.75p_n(1 - p_n)$. The maximum population sustainable in the area is 40 and the current population is 24.

29a–b. See margin.

    a. Find the population of antelope after each of the first ten years.

    b. Determine the long-term behavior of the population.

    c. Suppose the food supply has changed so that the growth rate for antelope has increased to 2.6 instead of 1.75. What will the long-term behavior of the population be? period-4 attractor

30. Research Find articles on the Butterfly Effect in periodicals like *Discover*, *Omni*, or *Scientific American*. Write a one-page paper on the research that lead to the discovery of the Butterfly Effect. In what fields have scientists found applications for these discoveries? See students' work.

LESSON 13-3 GRAPHICAL ITERATION OF THE LOGISTIC FUNCTION 727

Enrichment Masters Booklet, p. 90

Mixed Review

31. Solve $\dfrac{x}{x-5} + \dfrac{17}{25-x^2} = \dfrac{1}{x+5}$. **(Lesson 4-6)** −6, 2

32. **Geometry** The sides of a parallelogram are 20 cm and 32 cm long. If the longer diagonal measures 40 cm, find the measures of the angles of the parallelogram. Round measures to the nearest minute. **(Lesson 5-7)** $97°54', 82°6'$

33. Write the standard form of the equation $25x^2 + 4y^2 - 100x - 40y + 100 = 0$. Then identify the conic section. **(Lesson 10-5)** See margin.

34. Find the sum of the infinite series $\dfrac{1}{16} + \dfrac{1}{8} + \dfrac{1}{4} + \cdots$, if it exists. **(Lesson 12-3)** does not exist

35. Find the coordinates of the fixed point for the function $f(x) = 1.36x + 2$. Is the x-coordinate of the fixed point a repeller or an attractor?
   (Lesson 13-2) $\left(-\dfrac{50}{9}, -\dfrac{50}{9}\right)$; repeller

36. **College Entrance Exam** Compare quantities A and B below. A
   Write A if quantity A is greater.
   Write B if quantity B is greater.
   Write C if the two quantities are equal.
   Write D if there is not enough information to determine the relationship.

   Given: $x = 1,\quad 1 > y > 0$

   (A) $\dfrac{1}{y}$ (B) x

MID-CHAPTER REVIEW

Find the first three iterates of each function using the given initial value. If necessary, round your answers to the nearest hundredth. (Lesson 13-1) 1-4. See margin.

1. $f(x) = 5x - 3; x_0 = 8$
2. $f(x) = x^3; x_0 = 0.9$
3. $f(x) = x^2 - 4x + 2; x_0 = 2$
4. $f(x) = x^2(1 - 2x); x_0 = 0.6$

Graph each function and the function $f(x) = x$ on the same set of axes. Then perform graphical iteration for $x_0 = 2$. State the type of path that the iteration forms. (Lesson 13-2) 5-7. See margin.

5. $f(x) = 2x - 4$
6. $f(x) = 6 - \dfrac{x}{2}$
7. $f(x) = 8 - 3x$

8. Is the fixed point for the function $f(x) = -5x + 9$ an attractor or a repeller? **(Lesson 13-2)** repeller

9. Use the modified graphical iteration program to determine the long-term iterative behavior of the function $f(x) = 0.5x(1 - x)$ for each value of a. Write *period-n attractor, fixed point attractor,* or *chaos.* **(Lesson 13-3)** fixed point attractor

728   CHAPTER 13   ITERATION AND FRACTALS

EXTENDING THE LESSON

Math Power: Problem Solving

Investigate the iterative behavior of the non-logistic parabola, $f(x) = 0.5x^2 - 1$. Where are the fixed points, and are they attractors or repellers?

$1 \pm \sqrt{3}$ are fixed points, and since $f(x) = f(-x)$, $-1 \pm \sqrt{3}$ become fixed after a single iteration. If $|x| < 1 + \sqrt{3}$, its iterates will converge toward $1 - \sqrt{3}$, the only attractor. For other values of x, they diverge.

Mid-Chapter Review

The Mid-Chapter Review provides students with a brief review of the concepts and skills in Lessons 13–1 through 13–3. Lesson numbers are given at the end of problems or instruction lines so students may review concepts not yet mastered.

Technology

Graphical Iteration

BASIC
Spreadsheets
► **Software**

IBM's *Mathematics Exploration Toolkit (MET)* allows you to define a sequence of commands and expressions to be stored and used as often as you like. These sequences are called *defer sequences*. Use the commands listed below to define a defer sequence to perform graphical iteration on the function $f(x) = 3.3x(1 - x)$.

Enter	Result
lims 0 1 0 1	*Sets the range of viewing window.*
color 3	*Sets the color to white.*
$y = 3.3x(1 - x)$	*Creates the function to be iterated.*
store q	*Stores the function as q.*
graph	*Graphs the function.*
$y = x$	
graph	*Graphs y = x.*
0.1	*Sets the starting point to 0.1.*
defer iterate	*Creates a defer sequence called "iterate."*
store x	*Stores the current value, now 0.1, as x.*
q	*Retrieves the function stored as q.*
replace	*Replaces x in the function with 0.1.*
getright	*Retrieves the right side of the equation.*
value	*Finds the value of the expression.*
store y	*Stores the values as y.*
color 2	*Changes the color to red.*
segment x x x y	*Draws a segment from (x, x) to (x, y).*
segment x y y y	*Draws a segment from (x, y) to (y, y).*
y	*Retrieves the value of y.*
replace	*Makes the value of y active.*
stop	*Ends the defer sequence.*

The graphics screen shows one iteration of the function. Type **repeat iterate 30 [Enter]** to perform 30 more iterates. Notice the pattern of iterates. The function $f(x) = 3.3x(1 - x)$ has a period-2 attractor.

EXERCISES

Use a defer sequence to perform graphical iteration on each function. Then describe the long-term iterative behavior of the function. Write *period-n attractor*, *fixed point attractor*, *fixed point repeller*, or *chaos*.

1. $f(x) = 3x + 2$ fixed point repeller
2. $f(x) = -0.3x + 1$ fixed point attractor
3. $f(x) = 0.4x - 5$ fixed point attractor
4. $f(x) = 3.4x(1 - x)$ period-2 attractor
5. $f(x) = 3.9x(1 - x)$ chaos
6. $f(x) = 3.5x(1 - x)$ period-4 attractor
7. $f(x) = 2.75x(1 - x)$
8. $f(x) = 4.0x(1 - x)$ chaos

7. fixed point attractor

LESSON 13-3 GRAPHICAL ITERATION OF THE LOGISTIC FUNCTION 729

Using Technology

Objective This optional page shows how graphing software can be used to perform graphical iteration on a function.

Teaching Suggestions

Encourage students to predict the long-term iterative behavior of each function before having the computer repeat the iterations. Then use the computer to verify their predictions. Also have them determine how many iterations it takes before they see the pattern that occurs.

NCTM Standards: 1-4, 5, 6

Lesson Resources

- Practice Master 13–4
- Enrichment Master 13–4
- Evaluation Master, Quiz C, p. 166

 Transparency 13–4 contains the 5-Minute Check and a teaching aid for this lesson.

INTRODUCING THE LESSON

🕐 5-Minute Check

(over Lesson 13–3)

1. Find the coordinates of the vertex of the graph of $f(x) = 3x(1 - x)$.   **(0.5, 0.75)**
2. Find the coordinates of the fixed points of $f(x) = 2x(1 - x)$. Graph the function and find the first three iterates for $x_0 = 0.25$.   **(0, 0) and (0.5, 0.5); 0.375, 0.469, 0.498**
3. Use the modified iterate behavior program to determine the long-term iterative behavior of $f(x) = 2.4x(1 - x)$. Write *period-n attractor, fixed point attractor*, or *chaos*.   **fixed point attractor**

Prerequisite Skills

Students should be able to find the square of a complex number.

Find the square of each number z.
1. $z = -3i$ **−9**
2. $z = -1 - 2i$ **−3 + 4*i***
3. $z = 5 - 4i$ **9 − 40*i***
4. $z = 2 + 3i$ **−5 + 12*i***

Motivating the Lesson

We are now familiar with the technique of iterating functions, both graphically and by direct calculation. Consider a function $f(z)$, which maps each complex number z to some new point in the complex plane. What sort of path would be traced by iterating such a function for a particular initial point z_0?

13-4 Complex Numbers and Iteration

Objectives

After studying this lesson, you should be able to:
- 13–4A   ▪ iterate complex numbers, and
- 13–4B   ▪ plot the orbit of a complex number under iteration in the complex plane.

Application

One of the most exciting areas of modern mathematics is fractal geometry. This area of study was virtually unknown until Benoit B. Mandelbrot of the Physics Department at IBM's T.J. Watson Research Center made a mathematical breakthrough in 1980. Mandelbrot discovered the complex geometric structure that is called the Mandelbrot set. The Mandelbrot set and other fractal pictures are the result of iterating complex numbers through a quadratic equation.

You may wish to review complex numbers in Lesson 9-5.

As you know from your previous studies of complex numbers, every complex number has a real part and an imaginary part. At the right, the complex number $a + bi$ has been graphed on the complex plane. The horizontal axis of the complex plane represents the real part of the number, and the vertical axis represents the imaginary part.

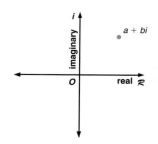

Functions can be iterated over the complex numbers.

Example 1

f(z) is used to denote a function on the complex number plane.

Find the first four iterates of the function $f(z) = 0.5z + 1$, if the initial value is $18 + 16i$.

$z_0 = 18 + 16i$
$z_1 = 0.5(18 + 16i) + 1$ or $10 + 8i$
$z_2 = 0.5(10 + 8i) + 1$ or $6 + 4i$
$z_3 = 0.5(6 + 4i) + 1$ or $4 + 2i$
$z_4 = 0.5(4 + 2i) + 1$ or $3 + i$

ALTERNATE TEACHING STRATEGIES

Using Critical Thinking

Have students calculate the value of the function $f(z) = 0.4z - 1$ for $z = 2 - 2i$. What happens if we calculate $f(z)$ for this new value? Have students go on to calculate a few more iterates. What appears to be happening to the values of the iterates?
values converge to −1.67 + 0*i*

Using Connections

In Lesson 9–8, we discussed finding the *n*th roots of unity in the complex plane. For a given value of *n*, we found these roots to be *n* points evenly spaced around the unit circle. What would happen if we used one of these points as the initial point for the iteration of the function $f(z) = z^2$?
Iterates are all points on unit circle.

Just as we can represent the iteration of a real number through a function by graphing, we can graph the iteration sequence of complex numbers on the complex plane. The graph at the right shows the **orbit**, or sequence of successive iterates, of the initial value of $z_0 = 18 + 16i$ from Example 1.

The function $f(z) = z^2 + c$, where c and z are complex numbers is central to the study of fractal geometry.

Example 2

Consider the function $f(z) = z^2 + c$.
a. Find the first six iterates of the function for $z_0 = 1 + i$ and $c = -i$.
b. Plot the orbit of the initial point at $1 + i$ under iteration of the function $f(z) = z^2 - i$ for six iterations.
c. Describe the long-term behavior of the function under iteration.

a. $z_1 = (1 + i)^2 - i$ or i
   $z_2 = (i)^2 - i$ or $-1 - i$
   $z_3 = (-1 - i)^2 - i$ or i
   $z_4 = (i)^2 - i$ or $-1 - i$
   $z_5 = (-1 - i)^2 - i$ or i
   $z_6 = (i)^2 - i$ or $-1 - i$

b.

c. The iterates repeat after some time. This is a period-2 attractor.

CHECKING FOR UNDERSTANDING

Communicating Mathematics

Read and study the lesson to answer each question. 1, 3. See margin.

1. **Define** the orbit of a complex number under iteration.

2. Is the set of complex numbers closed to squaring? That is, will the square of a complex number always be a complex number? yes

3. **Compare** the method of graphing the orbit of a function $f(z) = z^2 + c$ for a complex number with the method of graphing orbits of the logistic function for some real number.

4–6. See margin.

Guided Practice

Find the first three iterates of the function $f(z) = 0.6z + 2i$ for each initial value.

4. $z_0 = 25 + 40i$ 5. $z_0 = 5 - 10i$ 6. $z_0 = 6i$

7–9. See margin.

Find the first three iterates of the function $f(z) = z^2 - 3i$ for each initial value.

7. $z_0 = 2i$ 8. $z_0 = 1 - i$ 9. $z_0 = 1$

Closing the Lesson

Speaking Activity Have students compare and contrast the techniques used to iterate functions evaluated only for real numbers and functions evaluated for complex numbers.

10. Plot the orbit of the initial value $z_0 = 0 - i$ under iteration for the function $f(z) = z^2 - 1$ for four iterations. See Teacher's Answer Key.

EXERCISES

Practice

A

Find the first three iterates of the function $f(z) = 2z + i$ for each initial value.
11–16. See margin.

11. $z_0 = 1 + 2i$
12. $z_0 = 5i$
13. $z_0 = 3$

14. $z_0 = 4 - i$
15. $z_0 = \frac{1}{2} - \frac{1}{4}i$
16. $z_0 = 0.1i$

Find the first three iterates of the function $f(z) = 3z + (2 - 3i)$ for each initial value. 17–22. See margin.

B

17. $z_0 = 1 + 2i$
18. $z_0 = -2 + 3i$
19. $z_0 = 4 + i$

20. $z_0 = -1 + 2i$
21. $z_0 = 0.5 - i$
22. $z_0 = \frac{1}{3} + \frac{2}{3}i$

Find the first four iterates of the function $f(z) = z^2 + c$ for each given value of c and each initial value. 23–26. See margin.

23. $c = 1 + 2i$; $z_0 = 0$
24. $c = 0$; $z_0 = \frac{\sqrt{2}}{2} - \frac{\sqrt{2}}{2}i$

25. $c = 2 - 3i$; $z_0 = 1 + 2i$
26. $c = 5 + 3i$; $z_0 = i$

Plot the orbit of each initial value for four iterations of the function $f(z) = z^2 + (1 - i)$. 27–30. See margin.

C

27. $z_0 = 1 + i$
28. $z_0 = 0$

29. $z_0 = i$
30. $z_0 = -2$

Critical Thinking

31. If $f(z) = z^2 + c$ is iterated with an initial value of $z_0 = 2 + 3i$ and $z_1 = -1 + 15i$, find c. $4 + 3i$

Applications and Problem Solving

32. **Research** Use a book or periodicals from a local library to research the work of Benoit Mandelbrot. Are there any new discoveries being made in the field of fractal geometry? Write a one-page paper about your findings. See students' work.

Mixed Review

33. Find the value of $\begin{vmatrix} 5 & 3 & -2 \\ 0 & 2 & -2 \\ -3 & 0 & -1 \end{vmatrix}$. **(Lesson 2-3)** -4

34. **Security** A motion-detector light in the Gallagher's yard turns on when it senses motion within 25 feet of the light. The side boundaries of the monitored area form an angle of 135°. What is the area of the portion of the yard that is within the range of the motion sensor? Round to the nearest square foot. **(Lesson 5-2)** 736 ft²

25 ft

Monitored Area

135°

732 CHAPTER 13 ITERATION AND FRACTALS

35. Express $\sqrt[4]{81x^4yz}$ using rational exponents. **(Lesson 11-1)** $3xy^{\frac{1}{4}}z^{\frac{1}{4}}$

36. See margin.

36. Write the series $1 + 5 + 25 + 125 + \cdots$ using sigma notation. **(Lesson 12-5)**

37. Use the modified graphical iteration program to determine the long-term iterative behavior of the function $f(x) = 1.6x(1 - x)$. Write *period-n attractor, fixed point attractor*, or *chaos*. **(Lesson 13-3)** fixed point attractor

38. College Entrance Exam Choose the best answer. C
Layne answered all of the questions on a 25-question test. The test is scored by adding 4 points for each correct answer and subtracting 1 point for each incorrect answer. If Layne scored 70 on the test, how many questions did she answer correctly?

(A) 17   **(B)** 18   **(C)** 19   **(D)** 20   **(E)** 22

DECISION MAKING

Crime

The number of crimes committed in the United States increased by an average of more than 100,000 annually during the 1980s. The nation's prison population increased 134% during that decade. How should a citizen respond to the huge increase in crime we are witnessing? Does the answer lie in tougher laws and stricter punishment? Or should we concentrate on eliminating poverty, providing more job opportunities, increasing funding for education, and attacking other social problems that may lead to future crime?

1–4. See students' work.

1. Research the extent of the crime problem in your community. How big is the problem? What is being done to reduce the amount of crime?

2. Describe what you think should be done to attack the problem of crime in your area. Contact law enforcement officers, attorneys, people in social service agencies, and others who deal with the problem locally to learn their views and to find out how citizens can become involved. Investigate any neighborhood crime watch program in your area. Are there experts who could come to your school to discuss crime prevention?

3. Draw up a list of three ways you can help to lower the crime rate in your community.

4. Project Work with your group to complete one of the projects listed at the right based on the information you gathered in Exercises 1–3.

PROJECTS

- *Conduct an interview.*
- *Write a book report.*
- *Write a proposal.*
- *Write an article for the school paper.*
- *Write a report.*
- *Make a display.*
- *Make a graph or chart.*
- *Plan an activity.*
- *Design a checklist.*

LESSON 13-4 COMPLEX NUMBERS AND ITERATION 733

EXTENDING THE LESSON

Math Power: Problem Solving

The linear function $f(x) = 0.8x + 1$ has a fixed point attractor at $(5, 5)$. Does the function $f(z) = 0.8z + 1$, which is to be evaluated for complex values, have a fixed point attractor as well?
yes, $5 + 0i$

Decision Making

This activity provides students an opportunity to work together on a given problem. You may wish to refer to pages T20–T21 and page 710c for the various elements of cooperative groups and specific goals and strategies for using them.

Additional Answers

28.

29.

30.

36. Answers may vary. A sample answer is $\displaystyle\sum_{x=0}^{\infty} 5^x$.

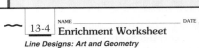

Enrichment Masters Booklet, p. 91

LESSON 13-4 COMPLEX NUMBERS AND ITERATION 733

NCTM Standards: 1-6

Lesson Resources

- Practice Master 13–5
- Enrichment Master 13–5
- Activity Master, p. 39

Transparency 13–5 contains the 5-Minute Check and a teaching aid for this lesson.

INTRODUCING THE LESSON

5-Minute Check

(over Lesson 13–4)

Find the first three iterates of the function $f(z) = 3z - 2i$ for each initial value.

1. $z_0 = 4 + i$
   $12 + i, 36 + i, 108 + i$
2. $z_0 = 0.3 + 0.7i$
   $0.9 + 0.1i, 2.7 - 1.7i, 8.1 - 7.1i$
3. Plot the orbit of the initial point $z_0 = 0.3 + 0.4i$ under iteration of the function $f(z) = z^2 + (0.5 - 0.5i)$ for six iterations. $0.43 - 0.26i, 0.6173 - 0.7236i, 0.3575 - 1.3934i, -1.3137 - 1.4961i, -0.0127 + 3.4309i, -11.2707 - 0.5874i$

Motivating the Lesson

Prepare slips of paper with phrases such as "a mountain range," "a craggy mountain," "a rough stretch of mountain side," "a large, rough boulder," and so on, written on them. Ask each student to select a slip of paper and draw an outline of the object on the chalkboard. Discuss how similar the drawings are, even though the scale repeatedly gets smaller. This is an example of a fractal, one of the topics discussed in this lesson.

13-5 Escape Points, Prisoner Points, and Julia Sets

Objectives
13–5A
13–5B

After studying this lesson, you should be able to:
- determine if a point escapes or is a prisoner under iteration, and
- determine if a Julia set is connected or is a dust of points.

Application

For many centuries, people have used science and mathematics to better understand the world. However, Euclidean geometry, the geometry of points, lines, and planes that you have probably already studied, is not adequate to describe the natural world. Things like coastlines, clouds, and mountain ranges require a new type of geometry. This type of geometry is called **fractal geometry**.

Richard Voss, a physicist at the IBM T.J. Watson Research Center, created the image of the mountain range shown at the right using fractal geometry. Dr. Voss has found that he can use fractal geometry to simulate some of the beauty of natural forms. This relationship to nature has enabled scientists to use fractal geometry to study natural phenomena that had seemed out of reach. Currently, Dr. Voss is studying how fractal geometry can be used to date Chinese art and to help doctors diagnose breast cancer from mammograms.

FYI...

Gaston Julia was severely wounded while serving in the French Army in World War I. He lost his nose and required several surgeries. He conducted much of his mathematical research in a hospital between these operations.

At the heart of fractal geometry are the Julia sets. Named for mathematician Gaston Julia, Julia sets involve graphing the behavior of a function that is iterated in the complex plane. As a function is iterated, the iterates either escape or are held prisoner. If the iterates of a function approach infinity for some initial value, the initial point is called an escaping point. If the iterates do not approach infinity for some initial value, that point is called a prisoner point. Suppose the function $f(z) = z^2 + c$ is iterated for two different initial values. If the first one is an escaping point and the second one is a prisoner point, the graphs of the orbits may look like those shown on the next page.

734   CHAPTER 13   ITERATION AND FRACTALS

ALTERNATE TEACHING STRATEGIES

Using Cooperative Groups

Organize students into small groups and assign each group a function of the form $f(z) = z^2 + c$. Ask each group to investigate the iterative behavior of its function for a few values of z_0, determining which points are prisoner points and which ones escape.

Using Computers

Have students write a flowchart for finding the iterates of a complex-valued function $f(z) = z^2 + c$ when z_0 and c are input. The program should include a loop to count the number of iterations and perhaps a test for overflow.

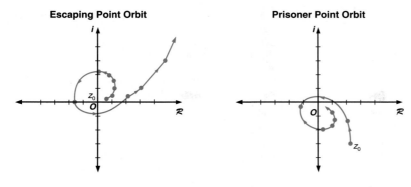

Escaping Point Orbit

Prisoner Point Orbit

Some initial points will neither escape nor be held prisoner. These points will orbit about in a cyclical pattern.

Example 1

Recall from Chapter 9 that the modulus of a complex number is the distance that the graph of the complex number is from the origin. So $|a + bi| = \sqrt{a^2 + b^2}$.

Find the first four iterates of the function $f(z) = z^2 + c$ where $c = 0 + 0i$ for initial values whose moduli are in the regions $|z_0| < 1, |z_0| = 1$, and $|z_0| > 1$. Graph the orbits and describe the results.

Choose an initial value in each of the intervals. For $|z_0| < 1$, we will use $z_0 = 0.5 + 0.5i$, for $|z_0| = 1, 0.5 + 0.5\sqrt{3}i$, and for $|z_0| > 1, 0.75 + 0.75i$.

$|z_0| < 1$ $|z_0| = 1$ $|z_0| > 1$

$z_0 = 0.5 + 0.5i$ $z_0 = 0.5 + 0.5\sqrt{3}i$ $z_0 = 0.75 + 0.75i$

$z_1 = (0.5 + 0.5i)^2$ $z_1 = -0.5 + 0.5\sqrt{3}i$ $z_1 = 1.125i$

     or $0.5i$ $z_2 = -0.5 - 0.5\sqrt{3}i$ $z_2 = -1.265$

$z_2 = (0.5i)^2$ or -0.25 $z_3 = -0.5 + 0.5\sqrt{3}i$ $z_3 = 1.602$

$z_3 = (-0.25)^2$ or 0.0625 $z_4 = -0.5 - 0.5\sqrt{3}i$ $z_4 = 2.565$

$z_4 = 0.0625^2$ or 0.0039

In the first case, where $|z_0| < 1$, the iterates will approach 0, since each successive square will be smaller than the one before. Thus, the orbit in this case approaches 0, a fixed point. In the second case, where $|z_0| = 1$, the iterates are orbiting around on the unit circle. When $|z_0| > 1$, the iterates approach infinity, since each square will be greater than the one before.

LESSON 13-5   ESCAPE POINTS, PRISONER POINTS, AND JULIA SETS   735

The orbits in Example 1 demonstrate that the iterative behavior of various initial values in different regions behave in different ways. An initial value whose graph is inside the unit circle is a prisoner point. A point chosen on the unit circle stays on the unit circle, and a point outside of the unit circle escapes. Other functions of the form $f(z) = z^2 + c$ when iterated over the complex plane also have regions in which the points behave this way; however, they are usually not circles.

All of the initial points for a function on the complex plane are split into three sets, those that escape, called the **escape set E**, and those that do not escape, called the **prisoner set P**. The boundary between the escape set and the prisoner set is called the **Julia set**. The escape set, the prisoner set, and the Julia set for the function in Example 1 are graphed at the right. The Julia set in Example 1 is the unit circle.

The Julia set for $f(z) = z^2$ is unusual since it is not a **fractal**. One of the characteristics of a fractal is that it exhibits **self-similarity**. Self-similar objects are those in which we can find replicas of the entire shape or object imbedded over and over again inside the object in different sizes. For example, if you look at the branch of a tree, it resembles the entire tree, only smaller. The broccoli shown at the left is one plant that exhibits fractal self-similarity.

Julia sets can be divided into two groups: those that are connected, like the unit circle, and those that are disconnected. Examples of the graphs of connected and disconnected Julia sets are shown below.

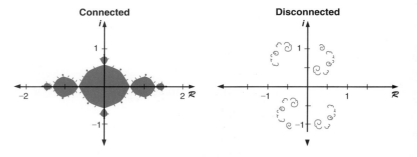

Julia sets like these can be generated by using powerful computers. You can determine if a Julia set for a function is connected or disconnected by applying the following test.

Test for Connectedness of a Prisoner Set

If the initial point $0 + 0i$ escapes to infinity under iteration in some function $f(z) = z^2 + c$, where c is a complex number, then the prisoner set of that function is disconnected. If $0 + 0i$ does not escape to infinity, the prisoner set is connected.

$0 + 0i$ is known as the <u>critical point</u>.

Example 2

Determine if the prisoner set for the function $f(z) = z^2 + 1 - i$ is connected or disconnected.

Test the initial value $0 + 0i$. Find the first five iterates and the distance from each iterate to the origin to determine if the value is escaping.

$z_0 = 0 + 0i$	$\|z_0\| = \sqrt{0^2 + 0^2}$ or 0
$z_1 = 1 - i$	$\|z_1\| = \sqrt{(1)^2 + (-1)^2} \approx 1.414$
$z_2 = 1 - 3i$	$\|z_2\| = \sqrt{(1)^2 + (-3)^2} \approx 3.162$
$z_3 = -7 - 7i$	$\|z_3\| = \sqrt{(-7)^2 + (-7)^2} \approx 9.899$
$z_4 = 1 + 97i$	$\|z_4\| = \sqrt{(1)^2 + (97)^2} \approx 97.005$
$z_5 = -9407 + 193i$	$\|z_5\| = \sqrt{(-9407)^2 + (193)^2} \approx 9408.980$

Since the iterates are getting farther away from the origin, the critical point will escape to infinity. Therefore, the Julia set for the function $f(z) = z^2 + 1 - i$ is disconnected.

Since the Julia set of a function is the set of points that lie on the boundary between the prisoner set and the escape set, the Julia set for a function with a connected prisoner set is the boundary of the prisoner set. If the prisoner set for a function is disconnected, the Julia set is disconnected and is the prisoner set itself. Disconnected Julia sets are called **dust** since they look like a dusting of points scattered in a fractal pattern on the plane.

The graphing calculator program listed below can be used to help you test to see if an initial point is in the escape set or the prisoner set of some function. It will display the sequence of iterates for a given initial point. You can also use this program to determine if a Julia set is connected or disconnected by using the critical point as your initial point.

EXPLORATION: Graphing Calculator

1. Enter the program below into the program memory of a TI-81 graphing calculator.

```
Line 1 :ClrHome          Line 3 :Input A
Line 2 :Disp "A IN C =    Line 4 :Disp "B IN C
        A + BI"                   = A + BI"
```

(continued on the next page)

Line 5   : Input B
Line 6   : Disp " "
Line 7   : Disp "X IN THE INITIAL
           POINT"
Line 8   : Input X
Line 9   : Disp "Y IN THE INITIAL
           POINT"
Line 10 : Input Y
Line 11 : 0→M
Line 12 : Lbl 1
Line 13 : Disp " "
Line 14 : X→R
Line 15 : Y→S
Line 16 : R² − S² + A→X
Line 17 : 2RS + B→Y
Line 18 : Disp X
Line 19 : Disp Y
Line 20 : Pause
Line 21 : M + 1→M
Line 22 : If M < 15
Line 23 : Goto 1
Line 24 : End

2. Use the program to iterate the function $f(z) = z^2 + (-1 + 0i)$ for the initial value $1 + 0.5i$.

3. Observe the iterates. $(1 + 0.5i)$ is in the escape set for the function since its iterates escape to infinity.

EVALUATING THE LESSON

Checking for Understanding

Exercises 1–10 are designed to help you assess students' understanding through reading, writing, speaking, and modeling. You should work through Exercises 1–3 with your students and then monitor their work on Exercises 4–10.

Closing the Lesson

Modeling Activity   Have each student name a natural phenomenon that exhibits fractal geometry and tell how this relates to the iteration of complex-valued functions.

APPLYING THE LESSON

Homework Exercises

Assignment Guide
Average: 11–23, 24–28 even, 30–38
Enriched: 15–38

The red A, B, and C flags, printed only in the Teacher's Wraparound Edition, indicate the level of difficulty of the exercises.

Practice Masters Booklet, p. 92

CHECKING FOR UNDERSTANDING

Communicating Mathematics

Read and study the lesson to answer each question. 1–3. See margin.

1. **Define** the prisoner set of a function.

2. **Describe** how the Julia set of a function is related to the prisoner set of the function.

3. **Explain** how you can determine if the Julia set of a function is connected or disconnected.

Guided Practice

Determine whether the graph of each value is in the prisoner set, the escape set, or the Julia set of the function $f(z) = z^2$.

4. $0.5 - 0.5i$ prisoner set   5. $1 + 2i$ escape set

6. $-0.25 - 0.2i$ prisoner set

7. $0.5 - 0.5\sqrt{3}i$ Julia set   8. $-1.5 + 0i$ escape set

9. $\frac{2\sqrt{2}}{3} + \frac{1}{3}i$ Julia set

10. Is the Julia set for the function $f(z) = z^2 + 2 + 2i$ connected or disconnected? disconnected

EXERCISES

Practice

Determine whether the graph of each value is in the prisoner set or the escape set for the function $f(z) = z^2 + (-5 + 0i)$.

11. $1 + 2i$ escape set   12. $4 - 2i$ escape set

13. $\frac{1 + \sqrt{21}}{2} + 0i$ prisoner set

Determine whether the graph of each value is in the prisoner set or the escape set for the function $f(z) = z^2 + (-1 + 0i)$.

14. $1 + 1i$ escape set   15. $1 - 2i$ escape set   16. $0.5 + 0i$ prisoner set

738   CHAPTER 13   ITERATION AND FRACTALS

RETEACHING THE LESSON

Give students a list of points, such as i, $1 - i$, $0.3 + 0.3i$, $0.8 + 0.8i$, -1, and $1 - 0.2i$. Have them organize the points on a chart according to whether the modulus is less than, equal to, or greater than 1. Then have students describe the iterative behavior of each point for the function $f(z) = z^2$.

Additional Answers

1. The prisoner set of a function is the set of all the points which do not approach infinity when iterated under the function.

2. If the prisoner set is connected, then the Julia set is the boundary between the prisoner set and the escape set. If the prisoner set is disconnected, then the Julia set is the prisoner set.

Determine whether the Julia set for each function is connected or disconnected.

B

17. $f(z) = z^2 + (-1 + 0i)$

18. $f(z) = z^2 + (-0.3 + 0.7i)$

19. $f(z) = z^2 + (-1.25 + 0i)$

20. $f(z) = z^2 + (-0.3 - 0.3i)$

21. $f(z) = z^2 + (-1 + 0.5i)$

22. $f(z) = z^2 + (0.11 - 0.7i)$

23. $f(z) = z^2 + (-1.2 + 0i)$

24. $f(z) = z^2 + (0.4 + 0.5i)$

25. $f(z) = z^2 + (4 - 0.5i)$

26. $f(z) = z^2 + (0.31 + 0.04i)$

Find one value whose graph is in the prisoner set and one value whose graph is in the escape set of each function. 27–29. Answers will vary.

C

27. $f(z) = z^2 + (-0.2 + 0i)$

28. $f(z) = z^2 + (-0.75 + 0.25i)$

29. $f(z) = z^2 + (0.02 + 0.25i)$

30. $z_0 = \dfrac{1 \pm \sqrt{13}}{2}$

Critical Thinking

30. As you know, a fixed point is mapped to itself under a function. Since fixed points do not escape to infinity, they must be in the prisoner set of the function. Find a fixed point for the function $f(z) = z^2 + (-3 + 0i)$. *Hint: $f(z) = z$ for a fixed point.*

Applications and Problem Solving

31. Language Arts The book *Jurassic Park* by Michael Crichton involves a mathematician who uses the principles of fractal geometry to describe why a park of dinosaurs would not work. Find a copy of the book or a book review and describe the role that fractal geometry plays in the book. See students' work.

32. Medicine Investigate the use of fractal geometry to diagnose breast cancer that Dr. Voss is studying. Is the technique in use today? How accurate are the results? See students' work.

Mixed Review

33. Graph the rational function $y = \dfrac{2}{x - 4}$. **(Lesson 3-4)** See margin.

34. Find values of x in the interval $0° \le x \le 360°$ such that $x = \cos^{-1} -\dfrac{1}{\sqrt{2}}$. **(Lesson 6-4)** $135°, 225°$

35. If $\sin r = \dfrac{3}{5}$ and r is in the first quadrant, find $\cos 2r$. **(Lesson 7-4)** $\dfrac{7}{25}$

36. Use the binomial theorem to expand $(n + 2)^4$. **(Lesson 12-6)** See margin.

37. Find the first four iterates of the function $f(z) = z^2 + (1 - 3i)$ for $z_0 = 0$. **(Lesson 13-4)** See margin.

38. College Entrance Exam Choose the best answer.

If $\dfrac{a}{b} = \dfrac{4}{5}$, what is the value of $2a + b$? E

(A) 3

(B) 13

(C) 14

(D) 26

(E) cannot be determined from given information

EXTENDING THE LESSON

Math Power: Reasoning

An important result having to do with the iterative behavior of a function $f(z) = z^2 + c$ is the escaping theorem: If $|f^n(z_0)| > 2$ for some integer $n \ge 0$, then the orbit of z_0 escapes to infinity. What variation of this theorem holds in the special case $c = 0 + 0i$? How could you use this theorem to speed up a program for testing iterative behavior?

Lesson Resources

- Practice Master 13–6
- Enrichment Master 13–6
- Evaluation Master, Quiz D, p. 166
- Multicultural Activity Master, p. 13

Transparency 13-6 contains the 5-Minute Check and a teaching aid for this lesson.

INTRODUCING THE LESSON

 5-Minute Check

(over Lesson 13–5)

Determine whether each point is in the prisoner set or the escape set for the function $f(z) = z^2 + 0.5i$.
1. i prisoner
2. $1 - i$ escape

Determine whether the Julia set for each function is connected or disconnected.
3. $f(z) = z^2 + (1 - i)$
   disconnected
4. $f(z) = z^2 + 0.2$ **connected**
5. Find a point in the prisoner set of the function $f(z) = z^2$.
   Sample answer: $0.6 + 0.8i$

Motivating the Lesson

The previous lesson involved studying the iterative behavior of a particular function, $f(z) = z^2 + c$ for different initial values z_0. What would happen if we shifted the focus and kept $z_0 = 0 + 0i$ while c is allowed to vary? The result is the intricate fractal known as the Mandelbrot set.

13-6 The Mandelbrot Set

Objectives
13–6A
13–6B

Application

After studying this lesson, you should be able to:
- determine if a complex number is inside the Mandelbrot set, and
- determine the color of a point outside the Mandelbrot set.

Gaston Julia was a world-famous mathematician in the 1920s, but his work was all but forgotten until Benoit Mandelbrot brought it back to light in the late 1970s. Mandelbrot was first introduced to Julia's work by his uncle Szolem Mandelbrojt, who was a mathematics professor at the prestigious Collège de France in Paris. But Mandelbrot didn't like Julia's work and chose another area of study, which eventually led him back to Julia's work. Mandelbrot's study of Julia's work led him to discover the **Mandelbrot set** and to invent fractal geometry. The Mandelbrot set is a complex mathematical picture. The set of pictures below shows successive zoom-ins on the Mandelbrot set. The rectangular window in each figure shows the region in the next zoom-in.

ALTERNATE TEACHING STRATEGIES

Using Connections

In Exercises 17–26 from Lesson 13–5, a number of Julia sets were determined to be connected or disconnected. Have students list the functions in a chart, with the column headings "connected" and "disconnected." Then, use this information to make a new chart with headings "in the Mandelbrot set" and "not in the Mandelbrot set."

Using Discussion

Show students a color picture of the Mandelbrot set. Tell them that the points in black are the points of the Mandelbrot set itself. Ask what they think the colors show. When they arrive at the idea of rate of escape, discuss how you might make such a graph.

Both the Julia sets and the Mandelbrot set are created by iterating the function $f(z) = z^2 + c$ with z and c representing complex numbers. To define a Julia set, the parameter c is fixed and the initial value, z_0, is allowed to vary. The Mandelbrot set is defined by fixing $z_0 = 0 + 0i$ and allowing c to vary. If the iterations of the function $f(z) = z^2 + c$ do not approach infinity for some value of c, then the point c is in the Mandelbrot set. That is, if the Julia set for the function $f(z) = z^2 + c_1$ is connected, then c_1 is in the Mandelbrot set.

Test for Points in the Mandelbrot Set	A point c_1 lies in the Mandelbrot set if the Julia set associated with that point is connected. That is, if the iterates of $f(z) = z^2 + c_1$ do not escape to infinity, then the point c_1 is in the Mandelbrot set.

The figure below shows the Mandelbrot set and the Julia sets that are related to some of the points inside and outside of the Mandelbrot set. Notice that the Julia sets related to points inside of the Mandelbrot set are connected and the sets related to points outside of the Mandelbrot set are disconnected.

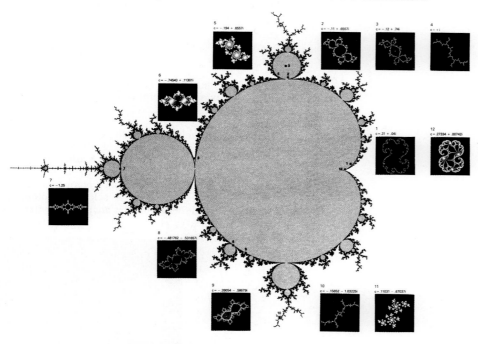

Performing the iterations to determine if a point is in the Mandelbrot set can be tedious. The program shown on page 742 can be used with a TI-81 graphing calculator to perform these iterations. The program displays each iterate and checks its distance from the origin. If the iterates from the critical point do not travel at least 80 units from the origin in 20 iterations, the critical point is assumed to be a prisoner point. If the point does escape, the number of iterations that it took to travel 80 units from the origin is displayed.

LESSON 13-6   THE MANDELBROT SET   741

Teaching Tip   Point out that the Mandelbrot set is symmetric with respect to the x-axis, so that if z is a member of the set, so is its complex conjugate.

Using Technology

Refer to the program in the Exploration. Since c is the value of $z_1 = (0 + 0i)^2 + c$, then $z_2 = c^2 + c$. This is the iterate calculated on the first pass at lines 11 and 12, and displayed at lines 13 and 14. Thus, z_0 and z_1 are never displayed at all, but students know their values are 0 and c, respectively.

Teaching Tip By the way the sets of points of each color are distributed throughout the complex plane, we can see that the rate at which a point escapes to infinity is related to how close it is to the Mandelbrot set.

Additional Answers

1. If the iterations of the function $f(z) = z^2 + c$ for the initial point $z_0 = 0 + 0i$ do not escape to infinity, then the point c is in the Mandelbrot set.
2. A point is in the Mandelbrot set if its associated Julia set is connected.
3. If a point is in the Mandelbrot set, it is colored black. If a point escapes to infinity, then the color represents the number of iterations it takes to escape past a certain point.
4. The use of color in each case allows us to visualize the differences in areas of the land or the set.

5. a. disconnected
   b. outside
   c. orange
6. a. connected
   b. inside
   c. black
7. a. disconnected
   b. outside
   c. light blue

8. a. disconnected
   b. outside
   c. orange
9. a. disconnected
   b. outside
   c. light blue
10. a. connected
    b. inside
    c. black

EXPLORATION: Graphing Calculator

Use the program below to determine if the point $-0.5 + i$ is in the Mandelbrot set.

We assume that if a point does not move at least 80 units from the origin in less than 20 iterations the point is a prisoner point.

```
Line 1   :ClrHome
Line 2   :Disp "A IN
              C = A + BI"
Line 3   :Input A
Line 4   :Disp "B IN
              C = A + BI"
Line 5   :Input B
Line 6   :Disp" "
Line 7   :A→R
Line 8   :B→S
Line 9   :1→M
Line 10  :Lbl 1
Line 11  :R² - S² + A → X
Line 12  :2RS + B→S
Line 13  :X→R
Line 14  :Disp R

Line 15  :Disp S
Line 16  :Pause
Line 17  :Disp " "
Line 18  :M + 1→M
Line 19  :If M > 20
Line 20  :Goto 2
Line 21  :If (R² + S²) < 6400
Line 22  :Goto 1
Line 23  :Disp " "
Line 24  :Disp "THE ESCAPING
              ITERATION COUNT IS "
Line 25  :Disp M
Line 26  :End
Line 27  :Lbl 2
Line 28  :Disp " "
Line 29  :Disp "C IS A
              PRISONER POINT"
```

The result of running the program for $-0.5 + i$ is that the point escapes after 6 iterations. Therefore, the point is outside of the Mandelbrot set.

Mapmakers use colors to help distinguish between areas with different characteristics. For example, some maps use blue to denote water, white to denote land, and yellow for metropolitan areas. Mathematicians use colors to describe different areas of fractal pictures as well. The different colors are used to represent the different speeds at which a point iterates to infinity. In the picture of a portion of the Mandelbrot set below, the points colored black are in the Mandelbrot set and the points that are not black iterate to infinity.

742   CHAPTER 13   ITERATION AND FRACTALS

The following coloring scheme was used to color the Mandelbrot set picture.

Color a point:	If:
Black	Its iterates fail to escape to infinity.
Dark blue	Iterates are 80 units from origin in 1 to 3 iterations.
Orange	Iterates are 80 units from origin in 4 to 6 iterations.
Light blue	Iterates are 80 units from origin in 7 to 9 iterations.
Red	Iterates are 80 units from origin in 10 to 12 iterations.
Yellow	Iterates are 80 units from origin in 13 to 15 iterations.
Purple	Iterates are 80 units from origin in 16 or more iterations.

Example

For each value of c given, complete the following.
a. **Determine whether the Julia set associated with each value of c is connected or disconnected.**
b. **Determine if the point is inside or outside of the Mandelbrot set.**
c. **Use the color scheme given above to assign a color to the point.**

1. $c = 0.8 + 0.1i$ 2. $c = -1.5 + 0.01i$ 3. $c = 0.1 + 0.05i$

1. The point escapes after 5 iterations. Since it is an escaping point, the associated Julia set is disconnected. The point is outside of the Mandelbrot set. According to the color scheme, it should be orange.

2. The point escapes after 16 iterations, so the associated Julia set is disconnected. The point is outside of the Mandelbrot set and should be colored purple.

3. The point $0.1 + 0.05i$ is a prisoner point. Its associated Julia set is connected. Thus, the point is inside of the Mandelbrot set and should be colored black.

CHECKING FOR UNDERSTANDING

Communicating Mathematics

Read and study the lesson to answer each question. 1–4. See margin.

1. **Describe** how you determine if a point is in the Mandelbrot set.

2. **Explain** how the Julia sets and the Mandelbrot set are related.

3. What is the significance of the colors in the Mandelbrot set?

4. **Compare** the use of color on the Mandelbrot set to the color used on a map.
5–10. See margin.

Guided Practice

For each value of c, complete the following.
a. **Determine whether the Julia set associated with each value of c is connected or disconnected.**
b. **Determine if the point is inside or outside of the Mandelbrot set.**
c. **Use the color scheme given in the lesson to assign a color to the point.**

5. $c = 1 + i$

6. $c = -1 + 0i$

7. $c = -1 - 0.65i$

8. $c = -1 + i$

9. $c = 0.57 + 0.25i$

10. $c = -1 + 0.25i$

RETEACHING THE LESSON

Lessons 13–5 and 13–6 use the same technique to different ends. In both cases, the function $f(z) = z^2 + c$ is iterated, and in both cases the point $0 + 0i$ plays a crucial role. Have students discuss what the role of $0 + 0i$ is in each case and what information its iteration reveals.

Chalkboard Example

For the Example

Use the graphing calculator program and coloring scheme to determine the color that should be assigned to each point.
a. $0.4 - 0.2i$ black
b. $-1 - i$ dark blue
c. $0.4 + 0.5i$ light blue

EVALUATING THE LESSON

Checking for Understanding

Exercises 1–10 are designed to help you assess students' understanding through reading, writing, speaking, and modeling. You should work through Exercises 1–4 with your students and then monitor their work on Exercises 5–10.

Closing the Lesson

Speaking Activity   Have students compare and contrast the techniques used to construct the Mandelbrot set and a Julia set.

Practice Masters Booklet, p. 93

NAME _____   DATE _____
13-6 **Practice Worksheet**

The Mandelbrot Set
For each value of c given, complete the following.
a. Determine whether the Julia set associated with each value of c is connected or disconnected.
b. Determine if the point is inside or outside of the Mandelbrot set.
c. Use the color scheme given on page 743 in the lesson to assign a color to the point.

1. $c = -1$
connected,
inside,
black

2. $c = -i$
connected,
inside,
black

3. $c = -0.8 + 0.5i$
disconnected,
outside,
yellow

4. $c = 2 + i$
disconnected,
outside,
dark blue

5. $c = -0.4 - 0.6i$
connected,
inside,
black

6. $c = -0.3 + i$
disconnected,
outside,
orange

T93
Glencoe Division, Macmillan/McGraw-Hill

Homework Exercises

Assignment Guide

Average: 11–18, 19–25 odd, 28–36
Enriched: 16–36

The red A, B, and C flags, printed only in the Teacher's Wraparound Edition, indicate the level of difficulty of the exercises.

Chapter 13, Quiz D, (Lessons 13–5 through 13–6), is available in the *Evaluation Masters*, p. 166.

Exercise Note

Exercises 11–24 require the use of the graphing calculator program given in this lesson. Note that parts **a** and **b** are just different ways of asking the same question.

Using Technology

The program in Exercise 27 begins with setting up a window at lines 3 through 5 that will display all of the Mandelbrot set. Lines 10 through 17 create a grid of points, each of which is tested for membership in the Mandelbrot set. Lines 21 through 30 do the iterations that check whether or not a particular point escapes. If the point does not escape, it and its complex conjugate are both plotted as members of the Mandelbrot set.

Additional Answers

11. a. disconnected
    b. outside
    c. light blue
12. a. connected
    b. inside
    c. black
13. a. connected
    b. inside
    c. black
14. a. disconnected
    b. outside
    c. orange
15. a. connected
    b. inside
    c. black
16. a. disconnected
    b. outside
    c. light blue

17. a. disconnected
    b. outside
    c. light blue
18. a. disconnected
    b. outside
    c. orange
19. a. disconnected
    b. outside
    c. purple
20. a. disconnected
    b. outside
    c. red

21. a. disconnected
    b. outside
    c. light blue
22. a. disconnected
    b. outside
    c. orange
23. a. disconnected
    b. outside
    c. light blue
24. a. disconnected
    b. outside
    c. light blue

EXERCISES

Practice   For each value of *c* given, complete the following. 11–24. See margin.
a. Determine whether the Julia set associated with each value of *c* is connected or disconnected.
b. Determine if the point is inside or outside of the Mandelbrot set.
c. Use the color scheme given in the lesson to assign a color to the point.

11. $c = -1.25 + 0.5i$ 12. $c = -0.6 - 0.05i$
13. $c = -1 + 0i$ 14. $c = 2 + 0i$

15. $c = -0.5 + 0.5i$ 16. $c = -2.01 + 0i$
17. $c = -0.75 + 0.5i$ 18. $c = -1 + 0.75i$
19. $c = -1.3 + 0.1i$ 20. $c = -1.3 + 0.3i$
21. $c = -0.8 + 0.5i$ 22. $c = 0.6 - 1.8i$
23. $c = 0.5 + 0.5i$ 24. $c = 0.5 + 0.6i$

25. A function of the form $f(z) = z^2 + c$ has a disconnected prisoner set. Where is *c* located in relation to the Mandelbrot set? outside the set

26. See students' work.

26. One of the most interesting characteristics of fractals is that they are *self-similar*. That is, small replicas of the image are repeated again and again in a fractal. Describe some of the self-similarity you see in the Mandelbrot set.

Programming

27. Use the following program to draw a rough picture of the Mandelbrot set on a TI-81 graphing calculator. *Note: This program will take approximately 20 minutes to run.* See students' work.

```
Line 1   :All-off
Line 2   :ClrDraw
Line 3   :-2.6→Xmin
Line 4   :1.0→Xmax
Line 5   :0.5→Xscl
Line 6   :-1.2→Ymin
Line 7   :1.2→Ymax
Line 8   :0.5→Yscl
Line 9   :DispGraph
Line 10  :0.0379→C
Line 11  :0.0381→D
Line 12  :0→J
Line 13  :Lbl J
Line 14  :-1.2 + JD→B
Line 15  :0→I
Line 16  :Lbl I
Line 17  :-2.6 + IC→A
Line 18  :A→X
Line 19  :B→Y

Line 20  :1→K
Line 21  :Lbl 1
Line 22  :X²→U
Line 23  :Y²→V
Line 24  :2XY + B→Y
Line 25  :U - V + A→X
Line 26  :K + 1→K
Line 27  :If U + V > 100
Line 28  :Goto 2
Line 29  :If K < 15
Line 30  :Goto 1
Line 31  :PT-On(A,B)
Line 32  :PT-On(A,-B)
Line 33  :Lbl 2
Line 34  :IS>(I,95)
Line 35  :Goto I
Line 36  :IS>(J,31)
Line 37  :Goto J
Line 38  :End
```

Critical Thinking

28. Based on the graphing calculator graph of the Mandelbrot set, what are the dimensions of the smallest rectangle that would enclose the Mandelbrot set?
−2 to 1 on the real axis and −1 to 1 on the imaginary axis

Applications and Problem Solving

29. **Geology** The Landsat-1 satellite took the photograph of the foothills of the Himalayas shown at the right on December 14, 1972. Describe the fractal self-similarity of the foothills. See students' work.

30. **Botany** Botanists have found that the angle between the main branches of a tree and its trunk remains constant in each species. How is this finding related to fractal geometry? See margin.

Mixed Review

31. (−3, 2)

31. Find an ordered pair that represents $\overrightarrow{AB}$ for $A(8, -3)$ and $B(5, -1)$. **(Lesson 8-2)**

32. **Physics** Don and Joyce are standing on a cliff that is 150 feet high. At the same time, Joyce drops a stone and Don throws a stone horizontally at a velocity of 35 ft/s. About how far apart will the stones be when they land? **(Lesson 8-7)**
107 ft

33. Solve the equation $\log_{\frac{1}{3}} x = -3$. **(Lesson 11-4)** 27

34. Use the ratio test to determine if the series $\frac{1}{3} + \frac{2}{3^2} + \frac{3}{3^3} + \cdots + \frac{n}{3^n} + \cdots$ is convergent or divergent. **(Lesson 12-4)** convergent

35. Determine whether the point at $2 + 4i$ is in the prisoner set or the escape set for the function $f(z) = z^2 + (0 - i)$. **(Lesson 13-5)** escape set

36. **College Entrance Exam** Choose the best answer. B
The sum of three consecutive odd integers is always divisible by

(A) 2　　　　(B) 3　　　　(C) 5　　　　(D) 6　　　　(E) 2 and 3

CASE STUDY FOLLOW-UP

Refer to Case Study 2: *Trashing the Planet* on pages 959–961.

Suppose you have three maps of Saudi Arabia that have the following scales.
A: 1 inch = 200 miles　　　B: 1 inch = 50 miles　　　C: 1 inch = 15 miles
The length of the oil spill created during the Gulf War along the Persian Gulf coastline of Saudi Arabia is measured on each map. The measurements on maps A, B, and C were 1.8 inches, 7.3 inches and 26.7 inches, respectively. 2–3. See students' work.

1. Use the measurement from each map to find the length of the oil spill on the coastline. Are the lengths you found all the same? 360 m, 365 m, 400.5 m; no

2. Mathematician Benoit B. Mandelbrot discovered that the smaller the scale of a map, the greater the measurement of the length of a feature on the map. Use the measures of the length of the oil spill found in Exercise 1 to estimate the scale of the map of Saudi Arabia in the case study.

3. **Research** Read about Dr. Mandelbrot's study of the coastline of Britain. Summarize your findings in a 1–page paper.

EXTENDING THE LESSON

Math Power: Connections

How might different colors be used to enhance the graph of a connected Julia set for some function $f(z) = z^2 + c$?　A color scheme similar to that given in the text for the Mandelbrot set could be used. For example, all prisoner points could be colored black, and other points colored according to how many iterations it takes for their modulus to exceed some value.

Case Study Follow-Up

This activity provides an opportunity to do research and apply mathematics in solving problems related to issues that may face students in their adult lives. Case Study 2 is located on pages 959–961.

Using the Chapter Summary and Review

The Chapter Summary and Review begins with an alphabetical listing of the new terms that were presented in the chapter. Have students define each item and provide an example of it, if appropriate.

The Skills and Concepts presented in the chapter are reviewed using a side-by-side format. Encourage students to refer to the Objectives and Examples on the left as they complete the Review Exercises on the right.

The Chapter Summary and Review ends with exercises that review Applications and Problem Solving.

VOCABULARY

Upon completing this chapter, you should be familiar with the following terms:

attractor **718**	**736** Julia set
dust **737**	**722** logistic function
escape set **736**	**740** Mandelbrot set
fixed points **717**	**723** mixing
fractal **736**	**731** orbit
fractal geometry **734**	**725** period-n attractor
graphical iteration **717**	**736** prisoner set
iterate **713**	**718** repeller
iteration **713**	**736** self-similarity

SKILLS AND CONCEPTS

OBJECTIVES AND EXAMPLES	REVIEW EXERCISES

Upon completing this chapter, you should be able to:

■ iterate functions using real numbers **(Lesson 13-1)**

Find the first three iterates of $f(x) = (x + 1)^2$ for an initial value of $x_0 = -1$.

$f(x_0) = f(-1) = (-1 + 1)^2 = 0$
$f(x_1) = f(0) = (0 + 1)^2 = 1$
$f(x_2) = f(1) = (1 + 1)^2 = 4$

Use these exercises to review and prepare for the chapter test.

Find the first three iterates of each function using the given initial value. If necessary, round your answers to the nearest hundredth. 3. 0.34, 12.81, 3248.37

1. $f(x) = 5 - 2x, x_0 = 3$ -1, 7, -9
2. $f(x) = x^2 + 3, x_0 = 0$ 3, 12, 147
3. $f(x) = (x + 2)^3, x_0 = -1.3$
4. $f(x) = x^2 + x - 6, x_0 = 2.5$ 2.75, 4.31, 16.89

■ identify a fixed point as an attractor or a repeller **(Lesson 13-2)**

Find the x-coordinate of the fixed point for $f(x) = 3 - 2x$. Is it a repeller or an attractor?

1 is a repeller.

Find the x-coordinate of the fixed point for each function. Is it a repeller or an attractor?

5. $f(x) = 3x + 1$ $-\frac{1}{2}$ is a repeller
6. $f(x) = 0.5x - 3$ -6 is an attractor
7. $f(x) = -6x + 5$ $\frac{5}{7}$ is a repeller
8. $f(x) = -2x + 0.3$ 0.1 is a repeller

746 CHAPTER 13 ITERATION AND FRACTALS

OBJECTIVES AND EXAMPLES	REVIEW EXERCISES

OBJECTIVES AND EXAMPLES

■ perform graphical iteration on the logistic function (Lesson 13-3)

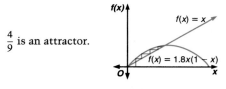

$\frac{4}{9}$ is an attractor.

■ determine if the behavior of a function is predictable or unpredictable (Lesson 13-3)

Describe the long-term iterative behavior of the function $f(x) = 3.49x(1-x)$.

The iterates form the repeating pattern 0.829, 0.494, 0.872, 0.389. So the function has a period-4 attractor.

■ iterate complex numbers (Lesson 13-4)

Find the first three iterates of the function $f(z) = 2z - (4 + i)$ if the initial value is $3 - i$.

$z_1 = 2(3-i) - (4+i)$ or $2 - 3i$
$z_2 = 2(2-3i) - (4+i)$ or $-7i$
$z_3 = 2(-7i) - (4+i)$ or $-4 - 15i$

■ determine if a point escapes or is a prisoner under iteration (Lesson 13-5)

Is the point $1 - 2i$ in the prisoner set or the escape set for the function $f(z) = z^2 + (3 + 0i)$?

$z_0 = 1 - 2i$ $z_3 = 172$
$z_1 = -4i$ $z_4 = 29,587$
$z_2 = -13$

The sequence of iterates approaches infinity, so $1 - 2i$ is in the escape set.

REVIEW EXERCISES

Find the coordinates of the fixed points for each of the following functions. Use the graphical iteration program on pages 724–725 to graph the function and determine if the x-coordinate of a non-zero fixed point is a repeller or an attractor. 9–12. See margin.

9. $f(x) = 2.7x(1-x)$
10. $f(x) = 1.9x(1-x)$
11. $f(x) = 3.19x(1-x)$
12. $f(x) = 3.35x(1-x)$

Describe the long-term iterative behavior of the function $f(x) = ax(1-x)$ for each value of a.

13. $a = 3.33$ period-2 attractor
14. $a = 2.0$ fixed point attractor
15. $a = 3.52$ period-4 attractor
16. $a = 3.78$ chaos

Find the first three iterates of the function $f(z) = 0.5z + (4 - 2i)$ for each initial value.

17. $z_0 = 4i$ $4, 6 - 2i, 7 - 3i$
18. $z_0 = -8$ $-2i, 4 - 3i, 6 - 3.5i$
19. $z_0 = -4 + 6i$ $2 + i, 5 - 1.5i, 6.5 - 2.75i$
20. $z_0 = 12 - 8i$ $10 - 6i, 9 - 5i, 8.5 - 4.5i$

Is each point in the prisoner set or the escape set for the function $f(z) = z^2 + (-1 + 0i)$?

21. $0 + 2i$ escape
22. $0 + 0.7i$ prisoner
23. $1.628 + 0i$ escape
24. $0.5 - 0.5i$ escape

Alternate Review Strategy

To provide a brief in-class review, you may wish to read the following questions to the class and have them answer verbally.
1. List the first three iterates of $f(x) = x^2 - 1$ given $x_0 = -1$.
   0, –1, 0
2. What types of paths are exhibited under graphical iteration of a function with a fixed-point attractor?
   staircase in and spiral in
3. What special role does the line $y = x$ play in graphical iteration?
   It acts as a mirror, reflecting each function value to become input for the next iteration.
4. Give an example of a logistic function having a fixed point attractor. Sample answer: $f(x) = 1.2x(1-x)$
5. List the first three iterates of $f(z) = 0.5z + i$ given $z_0 = 4$.
   $2 + i, 1 + 1.5i, 0.5 + 1.75i$
6. Beginning with $z_0 = 0 + 0i$, after several iterations the modulus is found to be greater than 100. What does this tell us about the iterative behavior of the function $f(z)$? It has a disconnected Julia set.
7. How do you find the color of a point that escapes the Mandelbrot set? See how many iterations it takes for it to escape.

For more information on other methods of alternate assessment, you may wish to refer to Glencoe's *Alternate Assessment in the Mathematics Classroom*.

Additional Answers

9. (0, 0), (0.630, 0.630); attractor
10. (0, 0), (0.474, 0.474); attractor
11. (0, 0), (0.687, 0.687); repeller
12. (0, 0), (0.701, 0.701); repeller

Two multiple-choice tests (Forms 1A and 1B) and two free-response tests (Forms 2A and 2B) are provided in the *Evaluation Masters*. Chapter 13 Test, Form 1A is shown below. Chapter 13 Test, Form 2A is shown on the next page.

Evaluation Masters Booklet, pp. 157–158

■ determine if a Julia set is connected or is a dust of points   **(Lesson 13-5)**

Determine if the Julia set for the function $f(z) = z^2 + (-1 + 0.2i)$ is connected or disconnected. Use the initial value $0 + 0i$.

$z_0 = 0 + 0i$ | $|z_0| = 0$
$z_1 = -0.04 - 0.2i$ | $|z_2| \approx 0.204$
$z_2 = -1.038 - 0.216i$ | $|z_3| \approx 1.060$
$z_3 = 0.032 - 0.249i$ | $|z_4| \approx 0.251$

Since the iterates do not escape to infinity, the Julia set is connected.

Determine whether the Julia set for each function is connected or disconnected.

25. $f(z) = z^2 + (-1 - 1i)$ disconnected
26. $f(z) = z^2 + (0.2 + 0.2i)$ connected
27. $f(z) = z^2 + (0.5 + 0.1i)$ disconnected
28. $f(z) = z^2 + (-0.3 - 0.2)$ connected

■ determine the color of a point outside the Mandelbrot set   **(Lesson 13-6)**

Determine the color that should be assigned to the point $0.2 - 1.4i$.

The point escapes after 5 iterations, so it should be colored orange.

Use the program on page 742 and the color scheme on page 743 to assign a color to each point.

29. $c = 0.5 + 0.8i$ orange
30. $c = 0.6 - 0.3i$ light blue
31. $c = -0.7 + 0.5i$ red
32. $c = 0.12 - 0.3i$ black

APPLICATIONS AND PROBLEM SOLVING

33a. $b_n = 1.00792b_{n-1} - 714.73$ 33b. $84,958.48; $84,916.63; $84,874.45; $84,831.94

33. **Banking**   Marcos and Carla Rodriguez have a 30-year mortgage of $85,000 on their home. The interest rate is 9.5% and the monthly principal and interest payment is $714.73.   **(Lesson 13-1)**

   a. Derive an equation for the balance of the mortgage after n payments.

   b. Find the balance of the mortgage after each of the first 4 payments.

34. **Biology**   The Verhulst population model equation that describes the population of otters in a certain area is $p_{n+1} = p_n + 1.9p_n(1 - p_n)$. The maximum population sustainable in the area is 72, and the current population is 54. **(Lesson 13-3)** 34a. 80, 64, 78, 66, 76, 67, 76, 68, 75, 69

   a. Find the population of otters at the end of each of the first ten years.

   b. Determine the long-term iterative behavior. fixed point attractor

748   CHAPTER 13   ITERATION AND FRACTALS

Find the first three iterates of each function using the given initial value. If necessary, round your answers to the nearest hundredth.

1. $f(x) = 4x - 5, x_0 = 2$
   3, 7, 23

2. $f(x) = (x - 2)^2, x_0 = 1.1$
   0.81, 1.42, 0.34

3. $f(x) = x^3 + 7, x_0 = -2$
   -1, 6, 223

Find the x-coordinate of the fixed point for each function. Is it a repeller or an attractor?

4. $f(x) = 2x - 5$
   (5, 5); repeller

5. $f(x) = 0.2x - 2$
   (-2.5, -2.5); attractor

6. $f(x) = -2x + 0.4$
   (0.133, 0.133); repeller

7. Describe the slope of the graph of a function whose iterations spiral inward. $-1 < m < 0$

Find the coordinates of the vertex and the fixed points for the graph of each logistic function. Then, use a graphing calculator to describe the long-term iterative behavior of the function. 8–10. See margin.

8. $f(x) = 1.6x(1 - x)$

9. $f(x) = 3.48x(1 - x)$

10. $f(x) = 3.88x(1 - x)$

Find the first three iterates of the function $f(z) = 2z + (3 - i)$ for each initial value.

11. $z_0 = 2i$
    $3 + 3i, 9 + 5i, 21 + 9i$

12. $z_0 = -1 + 2i$
    $1 + 3i, 5 + 5i, 13 + 9i$

13. $z_0 = 0.5 + i$
    $4 + i, 11 + i, 25 + i$

Is each point in the prisoner set or the escape set for the function $f(z) = z^2 + (-2 + 0i)$?

14. $1 + i$ escape

15. $0.8 + 0i$ prisoner

16. $0.5 - 0.5i$ escape

Determine whether the Julia set for each function is connected or disconnected.

17. $f(z) = z^2 + (-1 + 1i)$
    disconnected

18. $f(z) = z^2 + (0.2 - 0.2i)$
    connected

19. $f(z) = z^2 + (-0.6 + 0.4i)$
    connected

Use a graphing calculator to determine if each point is inside or outside of the Mandelbrot set. If the point is outside, state the number of iterations it takes for the iterations to exceed 80.

20. $c = -0.6 + 0.5i$
    outside; 15

21. $c = 0.4 + 0.1i$
    outside; 11

22. $c = -0.7 + 0.8$
    outside; 7

23. $c = 0.5 + 0.7i$
    outside; 6

24. If a function of the form $f(z) = z^2 + c$ has a connected prisoner set, where is c located in relation to the Mandelbrot set? inside the Mandelbrot set

25. **Biology** The Verhulst population model equation that describes the population of bald eagles in an area is $p_{n+1} = p_n + 2.1p_n(1 - p_n)$. The maximum population sustainable in the area is 120 and the current population is 90. Find the population of bald eagles after each of the first 5 years. 137, 96, 136, 97, 136

Bonus If $f(z) = z^2 + (2 + 2i)$ is iterated for some z_0 and $z_1 = 7 - 10i$, find z_0. $3 - 2i$

Test Generator Software is provided in Apple, IBM, and Macintosh versions. You may use this software to create your own tests, based on the needs of your students.

Additional Answers

8. (0.5, 0.4); (0, 0), (0.375, 0.375); fixed point attractor

9. (0.5, 0.87); (0, 0), (0.713, 0.713); period-4 attractor

10. (0.5, 0.97); (0, 0), (0.742, 0.742); chaos

This page may be used as a test or as a review. All answers to this test appear in the Selected Answers in the student text.

Standardized Test Questions are also provided in the *Evaluation Masters*.

Evaluation Masters Booklet, pp. 161–162

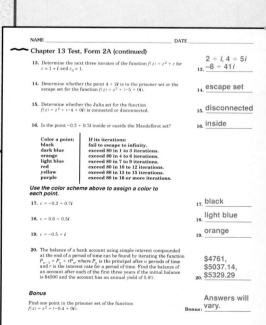

NAME _____ DATE _____

Chapter 13 Test, Form 2A

1. Find the first three iterates of the function $f(x) = -x^2$ using $x_0 = -\frac{1}{3}$.
   1. $-\frac{1}{9}, -\frac{1}{81}, -\frac{1}{6561}$

2. Determine, to the nearest hundredth, the tenth iterate for $f(x) = 1.2x(x - 1)$ using $x_0 = 0.9$.
   2. 0.42

Graph each function and the function $f(x) = x$ on the same set of axes. Then perform graphical iteration for the first four iterates for the given value of x_0.

3. $f(x) = -1.5x - 2$; $x_0 = 1$
   3. See students' graphs.

4. $f(x) = 2x$; $x_0 = 0.5$
   4. See students' graphs.

5. Determine the slope of the linear function $f(x) = 0.3x - 7$ and the type of path that the iteration forms.
   5. $m = 0.3$; staircase in

6. Find the coordinates of the fixed point for the function $f(x) = -1.2x - 11$.
   6. (-5, -5)

Determine whether the x-coordinate of the fixed point for each function is an attractor or a repeller.

7. $f(x) = -0.2x + 5$
   7. attractor

8. $f(x) = 0.2x - 1$
   8. attractor

9. Find the coordinates of the vertex of the graph of the logistic function $f(x) = 1.2x(1 - x)$.
   9. (0.5, 0.3)

10. One of the two fixed points for the function $f(x) = 0.5x(1 - x)$ is at (0, 0). Find the other fixed point.
    10. (-1, -1)

11. The iterates of a given function form the pattern 1.215, 3.177, 1.215, 3.177, … Describe the long-term iterative behavior of the function. Write *period-n attractor*, *fixed-point attractor*, or *chaos*.
    11. period -2 attractor

12. Let $f(z) = 3z + 1$ and $z_0 = 2 + i$. Determine $z_1, z_2,$ and z_3.
    12. $z_1 = 7 + 3i$, $z_2 = 22 + 9i$, $z_3 = 67 + 27i$

T 161
Glencoe Division, Macmillan/McGraw-Hill

NAME _____ DATE _____

Chapter 13 Test, Form 2A (continued)

13. Determine the next three iterates of the function $f(z) = z^2 + c$ for $c = 1 + i$ and $z_0 = 1$.
    13. $2 + i, 4 + 5i, -8 + 41i$

14. Determine whether the point $4 + 2i$ is in the prisoner set or the escape set for the function $f(z) = z^2 + (-5 + 0i)$.
    14. escape set

15. Determine whether the Julia set for the function $f(z) = z^2 + (-4 + 0i)$ is connected or disconnected.
    15. disconnected

16. Is the point $-0.3 + 0.7i$ inside or ouside the Mandelbrot set?
    16. inside

Color a point:	If its iterations:
black	fail to escape to infinity.
dark blue	exceed 80 in 1 to 3 iterations.
orange	exceed 80 in 4 to 6 iterations.
light blue	exceed 80 in 7 to 9 iterations.
red	exceed 80 in 10 to 12 iterations.
yellow	exceed 80 in 13 to 15 iterations.
purple	exceed 80 in 16 or more iterations.

Use the color scheme above to assign a color to each point.

17. $c = -0.3 + 0.7i$
    17. black

18. $c = 0.6 + 0.5i$
    18. light blue

19. $c = -0.5 + i$
    19. orange

20. The balance of a bank account using simple interest compounded at the end of a period of time can be found by iterating the function $P_{n+1} = P_n + rP_n$, where P_n is the principal after n periods of time and r is the interest rate for a period of time. Find the balance of an account after each of the first three years if the initial balance is $4500 and the account has an annual yield of 5.8%.
    20. $4761, $5037.14, $5329.29

Bonus

Find one point in the prisoner set of the function $f(z) = z^2 + (-0.4 + 0i)$.
Bonus: Answers will vary.

T 162
Glencoe Division, Macmillan/McGraw-Hill

14 COMBINATORICS AND PROBABILITY

PREVIEWING THE CHAPTER

This chapter reviews the basic counting principle, dependent and independent events, permutations and combinations, and probability. Students may or may not be familiar with topics such as circular permutations, reflective arrangements, and using complements in probability. In addition to finding simple probability, students find the probability of mutually exclusive events, inclusive events, and events dependent on a preceding event (conditional probability of an event). Finally, students learn to find the probability of an event by using the binomial theorem.

Lesson Objective Chart

Lesson (Pages)	Lesson Objectives	State/Local Objectives
14-1 (752-757)	**14-1A:** Solve problems related to the basic counting principle.	
	14-1B: Distinguish between dependent and independent events.	
14-2 (758-763)	**14-2A:** Solve problems involving permutations with repetitions.	
	14-2B: Solve problems involving circular permutations.	
14-3 (764-767)	**14-3:** Solve problems involving combinations.	
14-4 (768-773)	**14-4A:** Find the probability of an event.	
	14-4B: Find the odds for the success and failure of an event.	
14-5 (774-778)	**14-5:** Find the probability of independent and dependent events.	
14-6 (779-783)	**14-6A:** Identify mutually exclusive events.	
	14-6B: Find the probability of mutually exclusive and inclusive events.	
14-7 (784-789)	**14-7:** Find the probability of an event given the occurrence of another event.	
14-8 (790-794)	**14-8:** Find the probability of an event by using the binomial theorem.	

ORGANIZING THE CHAPTER

You may want to refer to the **Course Planning Guide Calendar** on pages T34-T35 for a complete pacing chart.

| Lesson Planning Guide | | | | Blackline Masters Booklets | | | | | | | | | |
| | | | | | | Technology | | | | Activity Masters | | | |
Lesson	Pages	Practice	Enrichment	Evaluation	Graphing Calculator	Computer	Multicultural Activity	Applications	Problem Solving	Case Study Follow-Up	Decision Making	Transparencies
14-1	752-757	p. 94	p. 94						p. 41			14-1
14-2	758-763	p. 95	p. 95	Quiz A, p. 177								14-2
14-3	764-767	p. 96	p. 96		p. 27		p. 14					14-3
14-4	768-773	p. 97	p. 97	Quiz B, p. 177 Mid-Chapter Test, p.179								14-4
14-5	774-778	p. 98	p. 98							p. 42		14-5
14-6	779-783	p. 99	p. 99	Quiz C, p. 178				p. 40				14-6
14-7	784-789	p. 100	p. 100									14-7
14-8	790-794	p. 101	p. 101	Quiz D, p. 178		p. 28						14-8
Review	796-798	Multiple Choice Tests, Forms 1A and 1B, pp. 169-172 Free Response Tests, Forms 2A and 2B, pp. 173-176										
Test	799	Standardized Test Questions, p. 180										

Other Chapter Resources

Student Edition
Case Study Follow-Up, p. 773
Decision Making, p. 757
Technology, p. 795

Other Supplements
Transparency 14-0 for Chapter Opener
Alternate Assessment in the Mathematics Classroom,
    Glencoe Publishing Co., 1993
Cooperative Learning in the Mathematics Classroom,
    Glencoe Publishing Co., 1993

Software
Test and Review Generator Software
    Available for Apple, IBM, and Macintosh
Teacher's Guide for Software Resources

ENHANCING THE CHAPTER

Cooperative Learning

Providing Task Assistance

When monitoring cooperative-learning groups as they do their work, you should resist temptation to intervene any more often than is absolutely necessary. Even when intervening, your role should be more that of an enhancer than of an answerer. For example, when a group appears to be stuck, say something such as, "Let's do a little brainstorming about ..." or "What do you think would happen if you tried ..." and give a hint to get them moving again. Even when it is necessary to clarify instructions or review procedures and strategies, encourage the group to work their way through the problem by recalling a specific instruction you gave before the session began and then ask, "Now who remembers what we said you should do next?" When students themselves seek assistance, they should first discuss among themselves and agree on the question that they want answered. The member whose role is *asker* should then address the question to you. You should respond only to the specific question, using terms relevant to the task, and then have one or more other members of the group paraphrase your answer to make sure that it is understood.

For more information on cooperative learning, see pages T20-T21. Additional information on using cooperative groups is available in Glencoe's *Cooperative Learning in the Mathematics Classroom,* ©1993.

Multicultural

Multicultural Activity Masters, p. 14

14	NAME _____ DATE _____

Multicultural Activity (Use after Lesson 14-3)

Srinivasa Ramanujan

Srinivasa Ramanujan (1887-1920) was considered by many to be India's greatest mathematician. He made an astonishing number of contributions to mathematics in his brief lifetime. The notebooks that he left behind are crammed with more than 4000 results, primarily in the field of number theory. His achievements are even more remarkable in view of the fact that the mathematics he knew was largely self-taught.

One of Ramanujan's many accomplishments was the in-depth study of the partitions of a natural number. A **partition** of a natural number *n* is a set of natural numbers the sum of whose elements is *n*. For example, these are some of the partitions of the natural number 11.

$$\{11\} \quad \{2, 9\} \quad \{1, 7, 3\} \quad \{1, 5, 5\} \quad \{1, 1, 1, 3, 4\}$$

Each of these partitions suggests additional partitions. For instance, $\{1, 7, 3\}$ gives rise to $\{1, 1, 6, 3\}$ and $\{1, 3, 4, 3\}$ by partitioning the element 7. In all, there are 56 ways to write 11 as a sum of natural numbers. That is, there are 56 partitions of 11.

1. List all the partitions of 5.
   $\{5\}, \{1, 4\}, \{2, 3\}, \{1, 1, 3\}, \{1, 2, 2\},$
   $\{1, 1, 1, 2\}, \{1, 1, 1, 1, 1\}$
2. List all the partitions of 6 that consist of either two elements or three elements.
   $\{1, 5\}, \{2, 4\}, \{3, 3\}, \{1, 1, 4\}, \{1, 2, 3\}, \{2, 2, 2\}$
3. List all the partitions of 7 that consist of four elements.
   $\{1, 1, 1, 4\}, \{1, 1, 2, 3\}, \{1, 2, 2, 2\},$
4. How many partitions of 9 have only the numbers 1 or 2 as elements? List them.
   five; $\{1, 1, 1, 1, 1, 1, 1, 1, 1\}, \{1, 1, 1, 1, 1, 1, 1, 2\}$
   $\{1, 1, 1, 1, 1, 2, 2\}, \{1, 1, 1, 2, 2, 2\}, \{1, 2, 2, 2, 2\}$
5. List all the partitions of 11 that consist of distinct (unrepeated) elements. (*Hint:* There are 12 such partitions.)
   $\{11\}, \{1, 10\}, \{2, 9\}, \{3, 8\}, \{4, 7\}, \{5, 6\}, \{1, 2, 8\}$
   $\{1, 3, 7\}, \{1, 4, 6\}, \{2, 3, 6\}, \{2, 4, 5\}, \{1, 2, 3, 5\}$

T 14

Glencoe Division, Macmillan/McGraw-Hill

Activity Masters

Applications, p. 40

CHAPTER 14	NAME _____ DATE _____

Applications (Use after Lesson 14-6)

Probability in Genetics

Genes are the units that transmit hereditary traits. The possible forms that a gene may take, **dominant** and **recessive**, are called **alleles**. A particular trait is determined by two alleles, one from the female parent and one from the male parent. If an organism displays the trait that is dominant, it may have either two dominant alleles or one dominant and one recessive allele. If the organism displays the trait that is recessive, it must have two recessive alleles.

Example Consider a plant in which tall stems, T, are dominant to short stems, t. What is the probability of obtaining a long-stemmed plant if two long-stemmed plants both with the genetic formula Tt are crossed?

	T	t
T	TT	Tt
t	Tt	tt

A *Punnett square* is a chart used to determine the possible combinations of characteristics among offspring.

3 tall-stemmed
+ 1 short-stemmed
4 total
Thus, the probability is $\frac{3}{4}$.

In a certain plant, red flowers, R, are dominant to white flowers, r. If a white-flowered plant, rr is crossed with a red-flowered plant, Rr, find the probability of each of the following.

1. white-flowered plant $\frac{1}{2}$
2. red-flowered plant $\frac{1}{2}$

In a certain plant, tall, T, is dominant to short, t. Green pods, G, are dominant to yellow pods, g. Plants with the genetic formulas TtGg and TTGg are crossed. Find the probability of each of the following.

3. tall plant with green pods $\frac{3}{4}$
4. tall plant with yellow pods $\frac{1}{4}$

T 40

Glencoe Division, Macmillan/McGraw-Hill

Problem Solving, p. 41

CHAPTER 14	NAME _____ DATE _____

Problem Solving (Use after Lesson 14-1)

Modeling

A permutation problem can often be visualized and then solved through the use of a simple model or sketch. Refer to Example 4 of Lesson 14-1 in your textbook. Instead of resorting to the formula for evaluating permutations, model the four chosen runners standing in position at the beginning of the race.

Although we don't know who is in position 1, we know that six runners were qualified to run there.

Since one runner of the six qualified has moved into position 1, only five remain to fill position 2.

Similarly, four runners remain to fill position 3 and three runners remain to fill position 2.

By the basic counting principle, the number of different possible line-ups is $6 \cdot 5 \cdot 4 \cdot 3 = 360$.

Draw a sketch to model each problem. Then solve.

1. In how many ways can the letters (*a, b, c, d, e, f, g, h*) be arranged to form 3-letter codes? No letter may be repeated.
   $\boxed{8}\ \boxed{7}\ \boxed{6}$
   $8 \cdot 7 \cdot 6 = 336$
2. In how many ways can five suspected burglars be arranged in a police line-up?
   $\boxed{5}\ \boxed{4}\ \boxed{3}\ \boxed{2}\ \boxed{1}$
   $5 \cdot 4 \cdot 3 \cdot 2 \cdot 1 = 120$
3. How many different four-card hands can be dealt from a standard deck of 52 cards?
   $\boxed{52}\ \boxed{51}\ \boxed{50}\ \boxed{49}$
   $52 \cdot 51 \cdot 50 \cdot 49 = 6,497,400$
4. How many different six-question tests can be written from a pool of 15 questions?
   $\boxed{15}\ \boxed{14}\ \boxed{13}\ \boxed{12}\ \boxed{11}\ \boxed{10}$
   $15 \cdot 14 \cdot 13 \cdot 12 \cdot 11 \cdot 10 = 3,603,600$

T 41

Glencoe Division, Macmillan/McGraw-Hill

Case Study Follow-Up, p. 42

CHAPTER 14	NAME _____ DATE _____

Case Study Follow-Up (Use after Lesson 14-5)

Probability and Home Buying

Refer to Case Study 1: *Buying a Home*, on pages 956-958 in your textbook.

Solve. Assume that the statistics cited in the Case Study apply equally to all buyers and to all homes during a stated time period.

1. Find the probability that a new home purchased in the United States in 1970 had central air-conditioning.
   0.34
2. What are the odds that a home owner in 1990, chosen at random, was Hispanic? $\frac{1}{24}$
3. There are 5600 homes in Centerville. Assume that the homes in Centerville are representative of those in the United States.
   a. About how many of the homes would you expect to be 70 or more years old?
   560
   b. What is the probability that a Centerville home is 70 years of age or older? $\frac{1}{10}$
   c. What are the odds that a home in Centerville is less than 70 years of age?
   9 to 1
4. What is the probability that a randomly chosen house in the United States is a single-unit structure with eight or more rooms?
   0.084
5. Find the probability that a couple searching for a new home in 1990 chose a house with one or more fireplaces, less than eight rooms, and that the couple's mortgage application was approved.
   0.494
6. Find the probability that a new house built in 1990 had central air-conditioning, less than two bathrooms, and was heated by electricity.
   0.02
7. What is the probability that a home purchased in 1990 was heated by a fuel other than gas and that the purchaser was African-American?
   0.033

T 42

Glencoe Division, Macmillan/McGraw-Hill

The Technology feature following Lesson 14-8 presents a computer program written in BASIC computer language. The program simulates the rolling of two dice for a given number of rolls. The program then prints the number of times each sum from 2 to 12 was rolled, the experimental probability, and the theoretical probability.

Students may find that their scientific calculators have keys that will find the number of permutations or combination for a given number of items taken n at a time. They may want to consult their owner's manuals to find out what combinatoric or probability related features their calculators possess. A graphing calculator program is presented in Lesson 14-4 that will generate random numbers between two given values.

Graphing Calculator Program, p. 772

Outside Resources

Books/Periodicals

Holroyd, F.C. and R.J. Wilson, editors. *Geometrical Combinatorics,* Pitman, 1984.

American Mathematical Society Editors. *Probabilistic Problems of Discrete Mathematics,* American Mathematical Society, 1989.

Films/Videotapes/Videodiscs

Mathematics, Probability, and Statistics, Great Plains National, University of Nebraska-Lincoln

Probability, Agency of Instructional Technology, Bloomington, IN

Software

Probability Theory. True BASIC (IBM, Macintosh)

Permutations and Combinations. Courses By Computers, INC., William K. Bradford Publishing (Apple II, IBM)

A Chance Look. Sunburst (Apple II)

Probability Lab. MECC (Apple II)

Technology Masters

Graphing Calculator, p. 27

Computer, p. 28

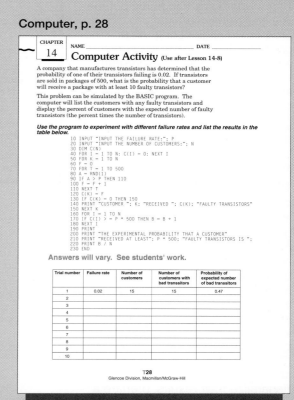

CHAPTER 14

COMBINATORICS AND PROBABILITY

HISTORICAL SNAPSHOT

	Benjamin Bannecker, black mathematician, saves design of Washington, D.C.		Establishment of Howard University Washington, D.C.		Chernobyl nuclear disaster Ukraine, USSR	
Ars Conjectandi, on probability, Jakob Bernoulli, Switzerland		William Nylander makes connection between lichens and air quality		Establishment of Environmental Protection Agency (EPA)		*Exxon Valdez* oil spill, Alaska
AD 1713	1790	1866	1867	1970	1986	1989

750

CHAPTER OBJECTIVES

In this chapter, you will:
- Solve problems involving combinations and permutations.
- Distinguish between dependent or independent and mutually exclusive or inclusive events.
- Find probabilities.
- Find odds for the success or failure of an event.

CAREER GOAL: Special Education with Math and Science

With majors in environmental science and special education, and minors in civil engineering and allied science, Heather Katz stays pretty busy. Though her interests are varied, her goal remains clear. "I want to teach mathematics and science to students with disabilities." Eventually, Heather wants to earn a PhD in special education and help develop and implement programs for students with disabilities.

Heather was recently diagnosed with a mild reading comprehension disability. "If I'd been diagnosed in elementary school," Heather says, "I probably would have received the help that I needed. But when I got to high school, a teacher told me that I would never get through college math courses." Heather remained firm. "If I had listened to that teacher, I wouldn't be where I am today."

Today, Heather uses mathematics in many ways. "In environmental science, we use probability to analyze underground storage tanks. We want to examine the danger that gasoline or other chemicals will leak into the groundwater. This type of analysis begins by designating a *plume*. This is an area of land within which several underground storage tanks are located. To determine the probability of chemicals getting into the groundwater, wells are drilled within the plume, samples are taken of the groundwater, and then the levels of contamination in the samples are measured. The levels of contamination of the sample wells will help you to then calculate the probability that your plume is contaminated."

Heather says, "Special education can be very frustrating. But I want to teach disabled children that they can succeed in spite of their disabilities, and that they shouldn't let their disabilities stop them from achieving their goals."

READ MORE ABOUT IT

Ehrlich, Paul R. and Anne H. *Healing the Planet*. New York: Addison-Wesley Publishing Company, Inc., 1991.

Shore, Kenneth. *The Special Education Handbook: A Comprehensive Guide for Parents and Educators*. New York: Teachers College Press, 1986.

Zipko, Stephen J. *Toxic Threat*. Englewood Cliffs, New Jersey: Julian Messner, 1990.

SPOTLIGHT ON...

Heather Katz
Age: 24
Class: Senior
School: Howard University
    Washington, D.C.
Majors: Environmental Science
    and Special Education

"I want to teach children that they can succeed in spite of their disabilities."

FOR MORE INFORMATION

If you would like more information about environmental science or special education, contact:

Institute of Environmental
    Sciences (IES)
940 E. Northwest Highway
Mt. Prospect, IL 60056

Council for Exceptional
    Children (CEC)
1920 Association Drive
Reston, VA 22091

Applications

Lesson	Application	Examples	Exercises
14–1	Sports	4	46
	Finance		47
14–2	Food	3	
	Communi-cation		
	cation		37
	Entertainment		38
14–3	Business	2	
	Geometry		36
	Sports		37
14–4	Quality Control	3	
	Weather	4	
	Finance		34
	Education		35
14–5	School	2	
	Business		33
	Political		
	Science		34
14–6	Fund-Raising	2	
	Education	3	
	Business		7
	Sports		34
	Medicine		35
14–7	Business		37
	Medicine		38
	Money		39
14–8	Sports	1	
	School	2	
	Cooking		33
	Skeet		
	Shooting		34
	Finance		35

Lesson Resources

- Practice Master 14–1
- Enrichment Master 14–1
- Activity Master, p. 41

 Transparency 14–1 contains the 5-Minute Check and a teaching aid for this lesson.

INTRODUCING THE LESSON

 5-Minute Check

(over Chapter 13)

1. Find the first three iterates of $f(x) = 3x - 1$ for an initial value $x_0 = -2$. **−7, −22, −67**
2. Without graphing, find the vertex of the graph of $y = 4x(1 - x)$.
   $\left(\frac{1}{2}, 1\right)$
3. Find the first two iterates of the function $f(z) = 0.5z + 2$, if the initial point is $12 + 14i$.
   $z_1 = 8 + 7i$; $z_2 = 6 + 3.5i$
4. Determine whether $0.2 + 0.2i$ is in the prisoner set or the escape set of $f(z) = z^2$.
   prisoner set
5. Determine whether the point $-0.5 + 0.5i$ is inside or outside the Mandelbrot set. **inside**

Prerequisite Skills

Students should be familiar with evaluating factorials.
Evaluate.
1. 5! **120**
2. 6!8! **29,030,400**
3. $\frac{9!4!}{5!}$ **72,576**

Motivating the Lesson

Have students guess how many different five-digit numbers can begin with the numeral 9. **10,000**

14-1 Permutations

Objectives
14–1A
14–1B

After studying this lesson, you should be able to:
- solve problems related to the basic counting principle, and
- distinguish between dependent and independent events.

Application

There are two tunnels under the Hudson River by which you can enter the borough of Manhattan in New York City from the west, and three bridges and one tunnel by which you can leave Manhattan to go south to Brooklyn. After entering Manhattan by the first tunnel, you have the choice of going south to Brooklyn by four exits. So there are four exits by way of the first tunnel. Likewise, there are four exits by way of the second tunnel. Altogether, there are 2×4 or 8 possible routes through Manhattan from west to south.

The choice of ways to enter Manhattan does *not* affect the choice of ways to exit to Brooklyn. Thus, these two choices are called **independent events**. Events that do affect each other are called **dependent events**.

The investigation of the different possibilities for the arrangement of objects is called **combinatorics**. This example of choosing possible routes illustrates a rule of combinatorics known as the **basic counting principle**.

Basic Counting Principle	**Suppose one event can be chosen in p different ways, and another independent event can be chosen in q different ways. Then the two events can be chosen successively in $p \cdot q$ ways.**

This principle can be extended to any number of independent events.

752   CHAPTER 14   COMBINATORICS AND PROBABILITY

ALTERNATE TEACHING STRATEGIES

Using Cooperative Groups

Have students work in groups to gather the data and create a tree diagram of all of the choices of yogurt flavors with toppings at a local frozen-yogurt shop.

Using Calculators

Have students use the permutation function of a calculator to find the number of permutations of n objects taken r at a time. Point out that the symbolism used for permutations may vary depending on the type of calculator; for example, $_nP_r$ and $P(n, r)$.

Example 1

How many seven-digit phone numbers can begin with the prefix 827?

Since the phone numbers all begin with 827, there is only one choice for each of the first three digits. There are 10 choices for each of the last four digits.

digit in phone number:	1st	2nd	3rd	4th	5th	6th	7th
ways to choose:	1	1	1	10	10	10	10

Thus, there are $1 \cdot 1 \cdot 1 \cdot 10 \cdot 10 \cdot 10 \cdot 10$ or 10,000 numbers.

A **tree diagram** is often used to show all of the choices.

Example 2

Mrs. Wilson has decided to buy a Chevrolet Caprice or a Buick Roadmaster. She has narrowed down the choices of exterior colors to silver metallic, white, or dark cherry metallic, and interior colors to grey or red. How many different selections of these models and colors are possible?

There are $2 \cdot 3 \cdot 2$ or 12 different selections possible. The possible selections are shown in the tree diagram below.

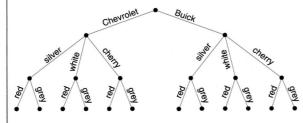

Notice that there are 12 choices, each of which differs from the others in some way.

Suppose Maria, Chiyo, and Wayne have been selected to debate another team at the annual debate contest. In how many different orders can they debate? If Maria goes first, then either Chiyo or Wayne can go second, and the other will go third. The possible arrangements of debates are listed below.

1st	Maria	Maria	Chiyo	Chiyo	Wayne	Wayne
2nd	Chiyo	Wayne	Maria	Wayne	Maria	Chiyo
3rd	Wayne	Chiyo	Wayne	Maria	Chiyo	Maria

There are six distinct orders in which the debates can be scheduled.

The arrangement of objects in a certain order is called a **permutation.** In a permutation, the order of the objects is very important.

LESSON 14-1   PERMUTATIONS   753

Teaching Tip   After defining dependent events and independent events, have students give their own examples of each kind of event.

Chalkboard Examples

For Example 1

How many seven-digit phone numbers can begin with 28? **100,000**

For Example 2

Mr. Casey has decided to buy a new suit, either one made of wool or one made of rayon. He has narrowed down the choices of colors to gray, blue, black, or tan, and the matching tie to a floral, a stripe, or a geometric pattern. How many different selections of his suit and tie are possible?   **24**

EVALUATING THE LESSON

Checking for Understanding

Exercises 1–15 are designed to help you assess students' understanding through reading, writing, speaking, and modeling. You should work through Exercises 1–4 with your students and then monitor their work on Exercises 5–15.

Closing the Lesson

Speaking Activity   Have students describe how to make a tree diagram to determine the number of physical appearances possible for characteristics such as hair color, eye color, gender, right-handed or left-handed, and so on.

APPLYING THE LESSON

Homework Exercises

The red A, B, and C flags, printed only in the Teacher's Wraparound Edition, indicate the level of difficulty of the exercises.

Suppose there is time for only two debates at the contest. How many ways can the debates be scheduled if two of the three team members are asked to debate? There are three persons who can be scheduled to debate first, and then either of two persons can be scheduled to debate second. Therefore, there are six ways to schedule the three team members taken two at a time, as can be verified by the basic counting principle. The possible arrangements, or permutations, are listed below.

1st	Maria	Maria	Chiyo	Chiyo	Wayne	Wayne
2nd	Chiyo	Wayne	Maria	Wayne	Maria	Chiyo

The symbol $P(n, n)$ denotes the number of permutations of n objects taken all at once. The symbol $P(n, r)$ denotes the number of permutations of n objects taken r at a time.

Definition of $P(n, n)$ and $P(n, r)$

The number of permutations of n objects, taken n at a time, is defined as
$$P(n, n) = n!.$$

The number of permutations of n objects, taken r at a time, is defined as
$$P(n, r) = \frac{n!}{(n-r)!}.$$

Recall that $n! = n(n-1)(n-2)\ldots(1)$.

Example 3

How many ways can eight different cans of soup be displayed in a row on a shelf?

Since order is important, this situation is a permutation.

$$P(8, 8) = 8!$$
$$= 8 \cdot 7 \cdot 6 \cdot 5 \cdot 4 \cdot 3 \cdot 2 \cdot 1 \text{ or } 40{,}320$$

There are 40,320 ways that the cans can be displayed.

Example 4

At the 1992 United States Olympic Track and Field Trials, Mark Witherspoon, Leroy Burrell, Dennis Mitchell, Mike Marsh, James Jett, and Carl Lewis qualified to run in the 4 × 100 meter relay. Only four of them were allowed to run in the race. How many different line-ups were possible from these qualifiers?

$$P(6, 4) = \frac{6!}{(6-4)!}$$
$$= \frac{6 \cdot 5 \cdot 4 \cdot 3 \cdot 2 \cdot 1}{2 \cdot 1} \text{ or } 360$$

There were 360 ways that the coach could have arranged the runners.

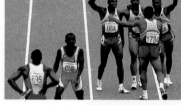

CHECKING FOR UNDERSTANDING

Communicating Mathematics

Read and study the lesson to answer each question. 1–2. See margin.

1. **Describe** the conditions under which two given events are considered to be independent of each other.

2. **Explain** how the basic counting principle works. Use an example in your answer.

3. What is a permutation? an arrangement in which order is important

4. **Write** an expression for the number of ways 5 books can be stacked from a group of 11 different books. Sample answer: $P(11, 5)$ or 55,440

Guided Practice

State whether the events are _independent_ or _dependent_. 5. independent 6. dependent

5. tossing 3 coins one at a time

6. choosing 5 numbers in a bingo game

7. choosing color and size when ordering an item of clothing
independent

8. choosing a president, secretary, and treasurer for a club See margin.

State whether each statement is _true_ or _false_.

9. $6! - 3! = 3!$ false

10. $5 \cdot 4! = 5!$ true

11. $\dfrac{8!}{4!} = 2!$ false

12. $(5 - 3)! = 5! - 3!$ false

Find each value.

13. $P(4, 2)$ 12

14. $P(9, 1)$ 9

15. $P(6, 3)$ 120

EXERCISES

Practice

Find each value.

16. $P(5, 3)$ 60

17. $P(5, 5)$ 120

18. $P(7, 4)$ 840

19. $P(11, 10)$ 39,916,800

20. $\dfrac{P(6, 4)}{P(5, 3)}$ 6

21. $\dfrac{P(6, 3) \cdot P(4, 2)}{P(5, 2)}$ 72

22. How many ways can 7 different books be stacked on a shelf? 5040

23. A penny, a nickel, and a dime are tossed simultaneously. How many different ways can the coins land? 8

24. There are four roads from Erie to Mead, three from Mead to Titus, and four from Titus to Corry. How many different routes are there from Erie to Corry? 48

25. Regular license plates in Ohio have three letters followed by three digits. How many possible plates are there? 17,576,000

26. There are 10 students in a class that meets in a room that has 12 chairs arranged in a row. How many ways is it possible for the students to be seated? 239,500,800

Cup A contains two yellow counters, cup B contains one yellow and one red counter, and cup C contains two yellow counters and one red counter. A die is thrown. If a 1 or 2 shows, a counter is drawn from cup A. If a 3 or 4 shows, a counter is drawn from cup B. If a 5 or 6 shows, a counter is drawn from cup C. An outcome is a combination of a number on a die and a color of a counter, where counters of the same color are distinguishable.

27. How many possible outcomes are there? 14

28. Make a tree diagram to show all possible outcomes. See margin.

29. In how many of the possible outcomes is a red counter drawn? 4

30. In how many of the possible outcomes is a yellow counter drawn? 10

LESSON 14-1 PERMUTATIONS 755

RETEACHING THE LESSON

Have students work in pairs to arrange colored tiles or number cards in a tree diagram to make a model of possible permutations of a given situation. Have students record each possibility. Encourage them to continue modeling until all of the possibilities are found.

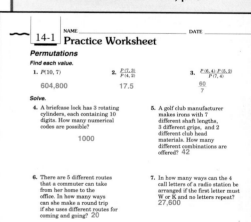

Additional Answers

45b. $\dfrac{736+763+367+376+637+673}{6} =$

$592 = 37(7 + 3 + 6)$
The pattern holds for all triples. Let h, t, **and** u **be the digits.**

$100h + 10t + u$
$100h + 10u + t$
$100t + 10h + u$
$100t + 10u + h$
$100u + 10t + h$
$+ \; 100u + 10h + t$

$200(h + t + u) +$
$20(h + t + u) +$
$2(h + t + u) = 222(h + t + u)$
$\dfrac{222(h + t + u)}{6} = 37(h + t + u)$

Find the number of different ways the letters of the word *pairs* can be arranged given the following.

31. The first letter must be p. 24

32. The first letter must be a vowel. 48

33. The first letter cannot be a vowel. 72

34. The letter r must be in the middle place. 24

35. Using the letters from the word *equation*, how many five-letter patterns can be formed in which q is followed immediately by u? 480

36. How many five-digit whole numbers between and including 56,000 and 59,999 can be formed if no digit is repeated? 1344

Truck license plate numbers in a certain state consist of five digits followed by two letters. Find the number of possible license plates for each situation.

37. The letters O and I cannot be used.

38. The letters must be different.

39. The letter O cannot be used.

40. The five digits cannot be 00000.

37. 57,600,000   38. 65,000,000   39. 62,500,000   40. 67,599,999

Find the value of *n* in each equation.

41. $n[P(5,3)] = P(7,5)$ 42

42. $P(n,4) = 3[P(n,3)]$ 6

43. $7[P(n,5)] = P(n,3) \cdot P(9,3)$ 12

44. $P(n,4) = 40[P(n-1,2)]$ 8

Critical Thinking

45. The digits 2, 5, and 8 can be arranged in six ways:

258   285   528   582   825   852

The average of these six numbers is $\dfrac{3330}{6} = 555 = 37(2 + 5 + 8)$.

If the digits are 1, 4, and 5, then the average of the six arrangements is

$\dfrac{2220}{6} = 370 = 37(1 + 4 + 5)$.

a. Use this pattern to find the average of the six arrangements of 7, 3, and 6. 592

b. Will this pattern hold for all triples of digits? If so, prove it. See margin.

Applications and Problem Solving

46. Sports The eight finalists in the men's 100-meter breaststroke at the 1992 Summer Olympics were Nick Gillingham of Great Britain, Vassili Iranov of the Unified Team, Phillip Rogers of Australia, Nelson Diebel of the United States, Norbert Rozsa of Hungary, Akira Hayashi of Japan, Dmitri Volkov of the Unified Team, and Adrian Moorehouse of Great Britain. Medals were given to the first three swimmers to finish the race.

a. How many ways could the medals be awarded in such a race? 336

b. If all eight swimmers finished the race, how many different orders of finish were possible? 40,320

47. Finance The state of Ohio has a Super Lotto drawing twice a week in which 6 numbers (1 through 46) are drawn at random. The proceeds from the lottery help to finance education in the state. How many ways can 6 numbers be drawn? 6,744,109,680

48. Line ℓ_1 has a slope of $\frac{1}{4}$, and line ℓ_2 has a slope of 4. Are the lines parallel, perpendicular, or neither? **(Lesson 1-6)** neither

49. Find the slope of the line tangent to the graph of $y = 2x^2$ at $(-1, 2)$. **(Lesson 3-6)** 49. -4

50. Evaluate $\tan(\cos^{-1}\frac{3}{5})$. **(Lesson 6-5)** $\frac{4}{3}$

51. Simplify $(4 - 3i)(-4 + 3i)$. **(Lesson 9-5)** $-7 + 24i$

52. **Finance** Jill wants to invest a sum of money at 9% interest compounded continuously. How much must she invest now to have a total of $25,000 in 5 years? **(Lesson 11-7)** $15,940.70

53. disconnected; outside
53. Determine whether the Julia set associated with $C = 1 - 0.5i$ is connected or disconnected. Is the point in the Mandelbrot set? **(Lesson 13-6)**

54. **College Entrance Exam** If $x^2 + y^2 = 16$ and $xy = 8$, what is $(x + y)^2$? 32

DECISION MAKING

Choosing Car Insurance

More than 46,000 people were killed in car accidents in 1990. Nearly 150,000 suffered permanent disabilities. Medical expenses resulting from car accidents amounted to more than $6 billion. What kinds of insurance should you purchase to protect yourself against theft, medical costs, and damage your car might sustain in an accident? How can you choose the right insurance company? How can you be sure you are buying the right level of protection without overinsuring yourself? 1–4. See students' work.

1. Describe the insurance protection you think you should have as a driver. If you are unsure of terminology or the kinds of insurance that are available, talk to an insurance agent or read a consumer article on car insurance.

2. Find out how you can choose the right insurance company. Talk to car owners about their experiences, good and bad, with insurers. Learn about how insurers are rated by consumer groups and state insurance commissions.

3. Make a list of three companies and get a quote from each for the type of car insurance you think you should have.

4. **Project** Work with your group to complete one of the projects listed at the right based on the information you gathered in Exercises 1–3.

PROJECTS

- *Conduct an interview.*
- *Write a book report.*
- *Write a proposal.*
- *Write an article for the school paper.*
- *Write a report.*
- *Make a display.*
- *Make a graph or chart.*
- *Plan an activity.*
- *Design a checklist.*

LESSON 14-1 PERMUTATIONS 757

EXTENDING THE LESSON

Math Power: Connections

How many different segments can be drawn connecting any two of six points arranged in a hexagonal pattern? 15

Decision Making

This activity provides students an opportunity to work together on a given problem. You may wish to refer to pages T20–T21 and page 750c for the various elements of cooperative groups and specific goals and strategies for using them.

Enrichment Masters Booklet, p. 94

14-1 Enrichment Worksheet
NAME _____ DATE _____

Approximating Factorials

James Stirling (1692-1770) was a teacher, a friend of Sir Isaac Newton, and a mathematician who made important contributions to calculus. Today he is best remembered as the creator of a formula for approximating factorials.

Stirling's Formula

$n! \approx \sqrt{2n\pi}\left(\frac{n}{e}\right)^n$, where e is the irrational number 2.7182818....

1. Stirling proved that the error using his formula, $\frac{n!}{\sqrt{2n\pi}\left(\frac{n}{e}\right)^n}$, is less than $\frac{12n}{12n-1}$.

As n increases, will the approximations obtained using Stirling's formula become more accurate or less accurate? Explain.

More accurate; the fraction $\frac{12n}{12n-1}$ is always greater than 1. As n grows larger, however, $12n$ gets closer to $12n-1$. The fractional error $\frac{12n}{12n-1}$ gets smaller and closer to 1.

2. Complete the chart. Use 2.718 for e.

n	$n!$	$\sqrt{2n\pi}\left(\frac{n}{e}\right)^n$	$\frac{n!}{\sqrt{2n\pi}\left(\frac{n}{e}\right)^n}$
10	3.6288×10^6	3.5987×10^6	1.008
20	2.4329×10^{18}	2.4228×10^{18}	1.004
30	2.6525×10^{32}	2.6452×10^{32}	1.003
40	8.1592×10^{47}	8.1422×10^{47}	1.002
50	3.0414×10^{64}	3.0363×10^{64}	1.002
60	8.3210×10^{81}	8.3094×10^{81}	1.001

T 94
Glencoe Division, Macmillan/McGraw-Hill

NCTM Standards: 1–4, 12

Lesson Resources

- Practice Master 14–2
- Enrichment Master 14–2
- Evaluation Master, Quiz A, p. 177

 Transparency 14–2 contains the 5-Minute Check and a teaching aid for this lesson.

INTRODUCING THE LESSON

 5-Minute Check

(over Lesson 14–1)

1. Find $P(6, 2)$.   **30**
2. Find $P(9, 7) \cdot P(8, 7)$.
   7,315,660,800
3. Find $\dfrac{P(7, 3) \cdot P(6, 4)}{P(5, 2)}$.   **3780**
4. How many ways can six different compact discs be stacked vertically?   **720**
5. There are eight children in a room with a row of 10 chairs. How many ways is it possible for the children to be seated?   **1,814,400**

Motivating the Lesson

Have students list all the possible four-letter patterns with the letters *eebm*.   **24**   How many of the patterns have the same appearance?   **12**

14-2   Permutations with Repetitions and Circular Permutations

Objectives
14–2A
14–2B

After studying this lesson, you should be able to:
- solve problems involving permutations with repetitions, and
- solve problems involving circular permutations.

Application

Spell-checking software is designed to check the spelling in a document as well as to look for double words, words with numbers and some types of capitalization errors. Other software options include looking up words phonetically, counting words, and displaying all the words in the dictionary that match a pattern.

Suppose you meant to type the word *tooth* in a health report but accidentally entered *tootj*. How many different patterns could spell-checking software check using the five letters of *tootj*?   *This problem will be solved in Example 1.*

In a simpler case, how many permutations of the letters of the word *too* are there? By tagging the o's as o_1 and o_2, the following arrangements are possible.

$$
\begin{array}{ccc}
to_1o_2 & o_1to_2 & o_1o_2t \\
to_2o_1 & o_2to_1 & o_2o_1t
\end{array}
$$

There are six arrangements when subscripts are taken into account, but only three arrangements without subscripts, too, oto, and oot.

When some objects are alike, use the following rule to find the number of permutations of those objects.

Permutations with Repetitions	The number of permutations of n objects of which p are alike and q are alike is $$\frac{n!}{p!q!}.$$

Example 1

How many five-letter patterns can be formed from the letters of the word *tootj*?

The five letters can be arranged in $P(5, 5)$ or $5!$ ways. However, several of these 120 arrangements have the same appearance since there are two o's and two t's. The arrangements are exactly the same unless the o's and t's are "tagged."

Find the number of permutations of 5 objects of which 2 are t's and 2 are o's.

ALTERNATE TEACHING STRATEGIES

Using Charts

Use charts to help organize all the eight-letter patterns that can be formed from the letters in *football*.

Using Applications

Use supermarket advertisements to find examples of circular party trays made up of various food items. Have students find the different number of arrangements of the items on the trays.

$$\frac{5!}{2!2!} = \frac{5 \cdot 4 \cdot 3 \cdot 2 \cdot 1}{2 \cdot 1 \cdot 2 \cdot 1}$$

$$= 30$$

The spell-checking software would have to check 30 five-letter patterns.

Example 2

How many nine-letter patterns can be formed from the letters of the word *Tennessee*?

$$\frac{9!}{4!2!2!} = \frac{9 \cdot 8 \cdot 7 \cdot 6 \cdot 5 \cdot 4 \cdot 3 \cdot 2 \cdot 1}{4 \cdot 3 \cdot 2 \cdot 1 \cdot 2 \cdot 1 \cdot 2 \cdot 1}$$ *There are 4 e's, 2 n's, and 2 s's in Tennessee.*

$$= 3780$$

There are 3780 nine-letter patterns.

TEACHING THE LESSON

Chalkboard Examples

For Example 1

How many six-letter patterns can be formed from the letters in *iihaaw*?   180

For Example 2

How many different eleven-letter patterns can be formed from the letters of the word *Mississippi*? 34,650

Teaching Tip   After discussing Example 2, have students formulate their own examples using words with repeated letters and give the number of letter patterns that are possible for those words.

So far, you have been studying arrangements of objects that are in a line. Consider the problem of making distinct arrangements of five people eating at a round table. How many seating arrangements are possible?

Let the letters A, B, C, D, and E represent the five people. Three possible arrangements are shown below.

Sometimes it is helpful to treat a circular permutation as though it were a linear permutation. Then, think of the linear permutation as being wrapped around a circle like a string around a tree trunk.

  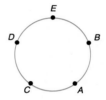

How does the first arrangement change if each person moves two places to the left? How do the arrangements differ?

When objects are arranged in a circle, some of the arrangements are alike. In the seating situation above, these arrangements fall into groups of five, each of which can be found by rotating the circle $\frac{1}{5}$ of a revolution. Thus, the number of distinct arrangements around the table is $\frac{1}{5}$ of the total number of arrangements in a line.

$$\frac{1}{5} \cdot 5! = \frac{5 \cdot 4 \cdot 3 \cdot 2 \cdot 1}{5}$$

$$= 4 \cdot 3 \cdot 2 \cdot 1$$

$$= 4! \text{ or } (5-1)!$$

Thus, there are $(5-1)!$ arrangements of 5 objects around a circle.

Circular Permutations

If n objects are arranged in a circle, then there are $\dfrac{n!}{n}$ or $(n-1)!$ permutations of the n objects around the circle.

Example 3

APPLICATION

Food

An ice cream parlor has 8 different toppings from which to choose. This week, you can create your own sundae. The eight toppings are placed on a revolving tray. How many ways can the toppings be arranged?

$$(8-1)! = 7!$$
$$= 7 \cdot 6 \cdot 5 \cdot 4 \cdot 3 \cdot 2 \cdot 1 \text{ or } 5040$$

There are 5040 ways in which the toppings can be arranged on the tray.

Circular arrangements with fixed points of reference are treated as linear permutations.

Suppose five people are to be seated at a round table where one person is seated next to the door. Let each circle below represent a table and the labeled points represent the people at that table. Let the arrow represent the seat next to the door.

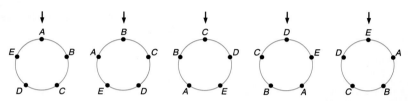

These arrangements are different. In each one, a different person sits closest to the door. Thus, there are $P(5, 5)$ or $5!$ arrangements relative to the door.

If n objects on a circle are arranged in relation to a fixed point, then there are $n!$ permutations.

Suppose three charms are placed on a bracelet that has no clasp. It appears that there are at most $(3-1)!$ or 2 different arrangements of charms on the bracelet.

760   CHAPTER 14   COMBINATORICS AND PROBABILITY

What happens if the bracelet with the first arrangement is turned over? The second arrangement appears. Thus, there is really only one arrangement of the three charms. These two arrangements are reflections of each other. There are only half as many arrangements when reflections are possible.

$$\frac{(3-1)!}{2} = \frac{2}{2} \text{ or } 1$$

Example 4

Six charms are to be placed on a bracelet.

a. How many ways can they be placed if the bracelet has no clasp?

a. This is a circular permutation. Because the bracelet can be turned over, the arrangement is also reflective.

$$\frac{(6-1)!}{2} = \frac{5 \cdot 4 \cdot 3 \cdot 2 \cdot 1}{2} \text{ or } 60$$

There are 60 ways to arrange the charms.

b. How many ways can they be placed if the bracelet has a clasp?

b. This is no longer a circular permutation since objects are arranged with respect to a fixed point, the clasp. However, it is still reflective.

$$\frac{6!}{2} = \frac{6 \cdot 5 \cdot 4 \cdot 3 \cdot 2 \cdot 1}{2} \text{ or } 360$$

There are 360 ways to arrange the charms.

CHECKING FOR UNDERSTANDING

Communicating Mathematics

Read and study the lesson to answer each question. 1–4. See margin.

1. **Explain** what a permutation with repetitions is.

2. **Describe** the difference between a linear permutation and a circular permutation.

3. **Explain** how to determine whether circular arrangements are alike.

4. **Explain** how to determine if a reflection is possible for an arrangement.

5. Under what conditions is a circular arrangement treated as a linear permutation?
when there is a fixed reference point

Guided Practice

Determine whether each arrangement of objects is *linear* or *circular*. Then state whether it is *reflective* and find the number of arrangements.

6. a football huddle of 11 players circular, not reflective, 3,628,800

7. 6 chairs arranged in a circle circular, not reflective, 120

8. 8 beads on a necklace with no clasp circular, reflective, 2520

9. 10 chairs arranged in a row linear, not reflective, 3,628,800

LESSON 14-2   PERMUTATIONS WITH REPETITIONS AND CIRCULAR PERMUTATIONS   761

RETEACHING THE LESSON

Form groups of four students to give students practice in arranging themselves in different circular arrangements, including an arrangement with a fixed point (a student). Have them count the number of arrangements they determine and compare the number to the actual number of permutations possible.

Homework Exercises

Assignment Guide

Average: 10–15, 16–24 even, 19,
25–35 odd, 36, 37, 39–45
Enriched: 10–30 even, 17, 21, 23,
31–45

The red A, B, and C flags, printed only in the Teacher's Wraparound Edition, indicate the level of difficulty of the exercises.

Chapter 14, Quiz A, (Lessons 14–1 through 14–2), is available in the *Evaluation Masters*, p. 177.

Exercise Notes

For Exercises 31–35, encourage students to make diagrams to help them decide which arrangements are appropriate.

EXERCISES

Practice **Determine whether each arrangement of objects is *linear* or *circular*. Then state whether it is *reflective*.** 10. circular, not reflective   11. linear, not reflective

10. people seated around a square table relative to each other

11. people seated around a square table relative to one chair

12. a list of students in a given class
    linear, not reflective

13. placing coins in a circle on a desk
    circular, not reflective

How many different ways can the letters of each word be arranged?

14. FLOWER 720
15. ALGEBRA 2520
16. PARALLEL 3360
17. CANDIDATE 90,720
18. ARREARS 420
19. MONOPOLY 6720
20. QUADRATIC 181,440
21. BASKETBALL 453,600
22. CLOCKMAKER 907,200

23. How many ways can 7 keys be arranged on a key ring? 360

24. How many ways can 7 people be seated around a campfire? 720

25. How many ways can 8 charms be arranged on a bracelet that has no clasp? 2520

26. How many ways can 4 congressmen and 4 congresswomen be seated alternately at a round table? 144

27. How many different arrangements can be made with ten pieces of silverware laid in a row if three are identical spoons, four are identical forks, and three are identical knives? 4200

28. How many different six-digit license plates of the same state can have the digits 3, 5, 5, 6, 2, and 6? 180

29. Five algebra books and four geometry books are to be placed on a shelf. How many ways can they be arranged if all of the algebra books must be together? 14,400

30. How many ways can 6 points be labeled U through Z on the circle at the right, relative to the y-intercept? 720

31. How many ways can 5 people be seated around a circular table if 2 of the people must be seated next to each other? 12

32. Twenty beads are strung on a necklace with no clasp. Fourteen are natural wood and 6 are red. How many ways can the beads be strung on the necklace? 969

Three men and three women are to be seated in a row containing six chairs. Find the number of seating arrangements for each situation.

33. The men and the women are to sit in alternate chairs. 72

34. The men are to sit in three adjoining chairs. 144

35. The men are to sit in three adjoining chairs and the women are to sit in three adjoining chairs. 72

36. To win a math contest, Joyce must determine how many marbles are in a box. She is told that there are 3 identical red marbles and some number of identical white marbles in the box. She is also told that there are 35 linear permutations of the marbles. What number should Joyce choose? 7

37. Communication Morse code is a system of dots, dashes, and spaces that telegraphers in the United States and Canada once used to send messages by wire. How many different arrangements are there of 4 dots and 2 dashes? 15

38. Entertainment A Sony® CD changer holds 5 CDs on a circular platter. How many different ways can 5 CDs be arranged on the changer? 24

39. Food Processing A meat packer makes a kind of sausage using beef, pork, cereal, fat, water, and spices. The minimum cereal content is 12%, the minimum fat content is 15%, the minimum water content is 6.5%, and the spices are 0.5%. The remaining ingredients are beef and pork. There must be at least 30% beef for flavor and at least 20% pork for texture. The beef content must equal or exceed the pork content. The cost of all of the ingredients except beef and pork is $32 per 100 pounds. Beef can be purchased for $140 per 100 pounds and pork for $90 per 100 pounds. Find the combination of beef and pork for the minimum cost. What is the minimum cost per 100 pounds? **(Lesson 2-6)** 30% beef, 20% pork; $76

40. Carpentry A cross brace is installed as a gate, as shown in the diagram at the right.
  a. Find the measure of the angle that the cross brace makes with the rail. 61.4°
  b. How many inches long is the brace? **(Lesson 5-5)** 50.1 inches

44 in.   rails
   a
24 in.

41. $c = 9.5$, $A = 38°20'$, $B = 36°22'$

41. Solve $\triangle ABC$ if $C = 105°18'$, $a = 6.11$, and $b = 5.84$. **(Lesson 5-7)**

42. Solve $\cos 2x + \sin x = 1$ for principal values of x. **(Lesson 7-5)** $0°, 30°$

43. Write the equation of the hyperbola with center at $(3,-1)$, focus at $(3,-4)$, and eccentricity $\frac{3}{2}$. **(Lesson 10-4)** $\dfrac{(y+1)^2}{4} - \dfrac{(x-3)^2}{5} = 1$

44. Akiko took 6 dresses, 5 pairs of shoes, and 2 coats on a trip. How many different outfits consisting of these items of clothing are possible? **(Lesson 14-1)** 60

45. College Entrance Exam Compare quantities A and B below. B
Write A if quantity A is greater.
Write B if quantity B is greater.
Write C if the two quantities are equal.
Write D if there is not enough information to determine the relationship.
  (A) $\sqrt{0.4}$ **(B)** $(0.4)2$

EXTENDING THE LESSON

Math Power: Reasoning

Suppose a teacher posts her grades in the following way:
4 As, 3 Bs, 8 Cs, 2 Ds, and 1 F.
How many different ways can these grades be randomly assigned to her 18 students? 551,350,800

Enrichment Masters Booklet, p. 95

NAME _____ DATE _____

14-2 Enrichment Worksheet

Street Networks: Finding All Possible Routes

A section of a city is laid out in square blocks. Going north from the intersection of 1st Avenue and 1st Street, the avenues are 1st, 2nd, 3rd, and so on. Going east, the streets are numbered in the same way.

6th Ave.
5th Ave.
4th Ave.
3rd Ave.
2nd Ave.
1st Ave.
1st St. 2nd St. 3rd St. 4th St. 5th St. 6th St.

Factorials can be used to find the number, $r(e, n)$, of different routes between two intersections. The formula is shown at the right. The number of streets going east is e; the number of avenues going north is n.
$$r(e, n) = \frac{[(e-1) + (n-1)]!}{(e-1)!\,(n-1)!}$$

The following problems examine the possible routes from one location to another. Assume that you never use a route that is unnecessarily long. Assume that $e \geq 1$ and $n \geq 1$.

Solve each problem.

1. List all the possible routes from 1st Street and 1st Avenue to 4th Street and 3rd Avenue. Use ordered pairs to show the routes, with street numbers first and avenue numbers second. Each route must start at (1, 1) and end at (4, 3).

$(1, 1) \rightarrow (2, 1) \rightarrow (3, 1) \rightarrow (4, 1) \rightarrow (4, 2) \rightarrow (4, 3)$
$(1, 1) \rightarrow (2, 1) \rightarrow (3, 1) \rightarrow (3, 2) \rightarrow (4, 2) \rightarrow (4, 3)$
$(1, 1) \rightarrow (2, 1) \rightarrow (3, 1) \rightarrow (3, 2) \rightarrow (3, 3) \rightarrow (4, 3)$
$(1, 1) \rightarrow (2, 1) \rightarrow (2, 2) \rightarrow (3, 2) \rightarrow (4, 2) \rightarrow (4, 3)$
$(1, 1) \rightarrow (2, 1) \rightarrow (2, 2) \rightarrow (3, 2) \rightarrow (3, 3) \rightarrow (4, 3)$
$(1, 1) \rightarrow (2, 1) \rightarrow (2, 2) \rightarrow (2, 3) \rightarrow (3, 3) \rightarrow (4, 3)$
$(1, 1) \rightarrow (1, 2) \rightarrow (2, 2) \rightarrow (3, 2) \rightarrow (4, 2) \rightarrow (4, 3)$
$(1, 1) \rightarrow (1, 2) \rightarrow (2, 2) \rightarrow (3, 2) \rightarrow (3, 3) \rightarrow (4, 3)$
$(1, 1) \rightarrow (1, 2) \rightarrow (2, 2) \rightarrow (2, 3) \rightarrow (3, 3) \rightarrow (4, 3)$
$(1, 1) \rightarrow (1, 2) \rightarrow (1, 3) \rightarrow (2, 3) \rightarrow (3, 3) \rightarrow (4, 3)$

2. Use the formula to compute the number of routes from (1, 1) to (4, 3). There are 4 streets going east and 3 avenues going north.

3. Find the number of routes from 1st Street and 1st Avenue to 7th Street and 6th Avenue.

2. $\dfrac{(3+2)!}{3!2!} = 10$ **3.** $\dfrac{(6+5)!}{6!5!} = 462$

T 95
Glencoe Division, Macmillan/McGraw-Hill

NCTM Standards: 1–4, 12

Lesson Resources

- Practice Master 14–3
- Enrichment Master 14–3
- Multicultural Activity Master, p. 14
- Technology Master, p. 27

 Transparency 14–3 contains the 5-Minute Check and a teaching aid for this lesson.

INTRODUCING THE LESSON

 5-Minute Check

(over Lesson 14–2)

1. There are 8 chairs arranged in a row.
   a. Determine whether the arrangement is linear or circular. **linear**
   b. Determine whether the arrangement is reflective. **no**
   c. Find the number of arrangements. **40,320**
2. How many different ways can the letters of the word *Canada* be arranged? **120**
3. How many ways can you seat 11 persons around a round table? **3,628,800**

Motivating the Lesson

Have students guess how many different lottery tickets can be chosen if there are 54 numbers possible and six numbers chosen. **25,827,165**

14-3 Combinations

Objective 14–3

After studying this lesson, you should be able to:
- solve problems involving combinations.

Application

Three students are chosen from the 5 juniors on the Student Council to study recycling opportunities in the high school. The first student can be selected in five ways, the second student in four ways, and the third student in three ways, for a total of $5 \cdot 4 \cdot 3$ or 60 ways. But consider the following six possible selections: (Andy, Bev, Cita), (Andy, Cita, Bev), (Bev, Cita, Andy), (Bev, Andy, Cita), (Cita, Andy, Bev), and (Cita, Bev, Andy). All these are considered the same. For each group of three people, there are 3! or 6 ways that they can be arranged in order. Thus, if order is disregarded, there are $\frac{60}{3!}$ or 10 different groups of three that can be selected from the five students. In this situation, the order in which the people are chosen is *not* a consideration.

The selection above is called a **combination** of five things taken three at a time. It is denoted by $C(5, 3)$. Evaluate $C(5, 3)$ as follows.

$$C(5, 3) = \frac{5!}{2!3!}$$
$$= \frac{5 \cdot 4 \cdot 3 \cdot 2 \cdot 1}{2 \cdot 1 \cdot 3 \cdot 2 \cdot 1} \text{ or } 10$$

Definition of $C(n, r)$

The number of combinations of n objects, taken r at a time, is written $C(n, r)$.

$$C(n, r) = \frac{n!}{(n - r)!r!}$$

The main difference between a permutation and a combination is whether order is considered (as in permutation) or not (as in combination).

Example 1

From a list of 10 different books, how many groups of 5 books can be selected?

Since order is not important, this selection is a combination of 10 things taken 5 at a time.

$$C(10, 5) = \frac{10!}{(10 - 5)!5!}$$
$$= \frac{10!}{5!5!}$$
$$= \frac{10 \cdot 9 \cdot 8 \cdot 7 \cdot 6 \cdot \cancel{5!}}{\cancel{5!}5!}$$
$$= \frac{10 \cdot 9 \cdot 8 \cdot 7 \cdot 6}{5 \cdot 4 \cdot 3 \cdot 2 \cdot 1} \text{ or } 252$$

There are 252 groups.

ALTERNATE TEACHING STRATEGIES

Using Models

Have students model the way selections can be made from a given group. Have one student stand. How many groups of 1 can be formed? Have two students stand. How many groups of 1 can be formed? How many groups of 2? Have three students stand, and so on. Record the possibilities.

Using Manipulatives

Give groups of students different sets of manipulatives like algebra tiles, cards, coins, and so on. Have each group write a problem involving combinations of its set of manipulatives and then present the problem to the class.

Example 2

APPLICATION

Business

A pizza delivery shop has 12 different toppings from which to choose. This week, if you buy a 2-topping pizza, you get 2 more toppings free. How many different ways can the special 4-topping pizza be made?

$$C(12,4) = \frac{12!}{(12-4)!4!}$$

$$= \frac{12!}{8!4!}$$

$$= \frac{12 \cdot 11 \cdot 10 \cdot 9}{4 \cdot 3 \cdot 2 \cdot 1} \text{ or } 495$$

There are 495 ways the special pizza can be made.

Example 3

From a group of 4 men and 5 women, how many committees of 3 men and 2 women can be formed?

Order is not important. There are two questions to consider.
• How many ways can 3 men be chosen from 4?
• How many ways can 2 women be chosen from 5?

The answer is the product of two combinations, $C(4,3)$ and $C(5,2)$.

$$C(4,3) \cdot C(5,2) = \frac{4!}{(4-3)!3!} \cdot \frac{5!}{(5-2)!2!}$$

The combinations are multiplied to use the basic counting principle.

$$= \frac{4!}{1!3!} \cdot \frac{5!}{3!2!}$$

$$= 4 \cdot 10 \text{ or } 40$$

There are 40 possible committees.

Example 4

A bag contains 3 red, 5 white, and 8 blue marbles. How many ways can 2 red, 1 white, and 2 blue marbles be chosen?

$C(3,2)$ Two of 3 red marbles will be chosen.
$C(5,1)$ One of 5 white marbles will be chosen.
$C(8,2)$ Two of 8 blue marbles will be chosen.

$$C(3,2) \cdot C(5,1) \cdot C(8,2) = \frac{3}{1} \cdot \frac{5}{1} \cdot \frac{8 \cdot 7}{2 \cdot 1} \text{ or } 420$$

There are 420 different ways.

LESSON 14-3   COMBINATIONS   765

TEACHING THE LESSON

Teaching Tip   After discussing Example 1, discuss the difference between an permutation of ten books taken five at a time and a combination of ten books taken five at a time.

Chalkboard Examples

For Example 1

From a row of eight different varieties of soup on a shelf, how many groups of five cans can be selected?   **56**

For Example 2

An ice cream shop has eight different toppings from which to choose. This week, if you buy three toppings for your sundae, you get another topping free. How many different ways can the sundae be made?   **70**

For Example 3

From a group of 6 men and 4 women, how many committees of 2 men and 2 women can be formed?   **90**

For Example 4

A bag contains 4 green, 3 yellow, and 6 white marbles. How many ways can 2 green, 1 yellow, and 4 blue marbles be chosen?   **270**

Checking for Understanding

Exercises 1–11 are designed to help you assess students' understanding through reading, writing, speaking, and modeling. You should work through Exercises 1–3 with your students and then monitor their work on Exercises 4–11.

Closing the Lesson

Modeling Activity Have students make a table of all the combinations of six books selected four at a time. Have them actually use books to verify their answer. **15**

Homework Exercises

Assignment Guide

Average: 12–15, 16–36 even, 38–42
Enriched: 15–25 odd, 27–42
All: Mid-Chapter Review, 1–5

The red A, B, and C flags, printed only in the Teacher's Wraparound Edition, indicate the level of difficulty of the exercises.

Practice Masters Booklet, p. 96

NAME _____ DATE _____
14-3 Practice Worksheet

Combinations
Evaluate each expression.

1. $C(7, 2)$
21

2. $C(10, 4)$
210

3. $C(8, 8)$
1

4. $C(10, 4) \cdot C(5, 3)$
2100

5. $C(12, 4) \cdot C(8, 3)$
27,720

6. $P(4, 3) \cdot C(8, 6)$
672

7. $P(12, 3) \cdot C(2, 1) \cdot C(6, 5)$
15,840

8. $P(8, 3) \cdot C(9, 6) \cdot C(8, 2)$
790,272

Solve.

9. Sally has 7 candles, each a different color. How many ways can she arrange the candles in a candelabra that holds 3 candles? 210

10. In how many ways can a student choose 4 books from 2 geometry, 4 geography, 5 history, and 2 physics books? 1001

11. Eight toppings for pizza are available. In how many ways can Jim choose 3 of the toppings? 56

12. From a list of 12 books, how many groups of 5 books can be selected? 792

13. How many committees of 5 students can be selected from class of 25? 53,130

14. Leroy can afford to buy 2 of the 6 CDs he wants. How many possible combinations could he buy? 15

15. A box contains 12 black and 8 green marbles. In how many ways can 3 black and 2 green marbles be chosen? 6160

16. A box contains 12 black and 8 green marbles. In how many ways can 5 marbles be chosen? 15,504

T96
Glencoe Division, Macmillan/McGraw-Hill

CHECKING FOR UNDERSTANDING

Communicating Mathematics

Read and study the lesson to answer each question.

1. **Describe** the difference between a permutation and a combination. See margin.
2. **Write** an expression to represent the number of different groups of 5 basketball players that could be formed from a team of 9 players. $C(9, 5)$
3. **Explain** how you would find how many bouquets of 2 red carnations and 3 white daisies can be formed from a group of 8 red carnations and 9 white daisies.
See margin.

Guided Practice

State whether each arrangement represents a *permutation* or a *combination*.

4. 10 books on a shelf permutation
5. a subset of 12 elements contained in a set of 26 combination
6. a hand of 7 cards from a deck of 52 cards combination
7. 8 people seated around a circular table permutation

Evaluate each expression.

8. $C(4, 2)$ 6
9. $C(12, 7)$ 792
10. $C(6, 6)$ 1
11. $C(3, 2) \cdot C(8, 3)$
168

EXERCISES

Practice

A **B**

Evaluate each expression.

12. $C(20, 15)$ 15,504
13. $C(8, 5) \cdot C(7, 3)$ 1960
14. $C(8, 2) \cdot C(5, 1) \cdot C(4, 2)$ 840
15. $P(4, 2) \cdot C(13, 3) \cdot C(13, 2)$ 267,696

16. From a list of 10 books, how many groups of 4 books can be selected? 210
17. There are 85 telephones in the editorial department of Glencoe Publishing Company. How many 2-way connections can be made among the office phones?
18. How many baseball teams of 9 members can be formed from 14 players? 2002
19. The cast of a school play requires 4 girls and 3 boys. They will be selected from 7 eligible girls and 9 eligible boys. How many ways can the cast be selected?
20. Suppose there are 8 points in a plane, no 3 of which are collinear. How many distinct triangles could be formed with these points as vertices? 56
21. Consider a deck of 52 cards.
    a. How many different 5-card hands can have 5 cards of the same suit? 5148
    b. How many different 4-card hands can have each card from a different suit?
17. 3570   19. 2940   28,561

Find the value of *n* in each equation.

22. $C(n, 12) = C(30, 18)$ 30
23. $C(14, 3) = C(n, 11)$ 14
24. $C(11, 8) = C(11, n)$ 3
25. $C(n, 5) = C(n, 7)$ 12

A bag contains 4 red, 6 white, and 9 blue marbles. How many ways can 5 marbles be selected to meet each condition?

C

26. all white 6
27. all blue 126
28. exactly 2 are blue 4320
29. 2 one color, 3 another color 2808

RETEACHING THE LESSON

Give students examples of different combinations such as $C(5, 3)$ and ask them to make up problems that can be solved with the combinations and then solve the problems.

Additional Answers

1. A permutation is an arrangement in which the order is important. A combination is an arrangement where order is not important.
3. Find the product of these two combinations, $C(8, 2)$ and $C(9, 3)$.

From a group of **8 juniors** and **10 seniors**, a committee of 5 is to be formed to discuss plans for the prom. How many committees can be formed given each condition?

30. all juniors 56   **31.** 3 juniors, 2 seniors

32. 1 junior, 4 seniors **33.** all seniors 252
31. 2520   32. 1680

Critical Thinking

35. See margin.

34. Prove $C(n, r) = \frac{P(n, r)}{r!}$. See margin.

35. Describe the pattern of outcome values produced when you find each number of combinations of n objects taken r at a time, $C(n, r)$, as r goes from 0 to n.

Applications and Problem Solving

36. Geometry A decagon is a polygon with 10 vertices and 10 sides. A diagonal is a segment that connects any two nonconsecutive vertices of a polygon. Find the total number of diagonals that can be drawn in a decagon. 35

37. Sports How many different baseball teams of nine players can Defiance High School put on the field if they have 2 players that can only play catcher, 6 players that can only be pitchers, and 17 that can play any of the other seven positions?
233,376

Mixed Review

38. Solve $18x^3 - 34x^2 + 16x = 0$. **(Lesson 4-1)** $0, \frac{8}{9}, 1$

39. Find an ordered triple that represents $\vec{AB}$, if $\vec{A} = (-2, 5, 8)$ and $\vec{B} = (3, 9, -3)$. **(Lesson 8-3)** $(5, 4, -11)$

40. Write an expression for the nth term of the sequence $\frac{4}{2}, \frac{9}{4}, \frac{14}{6}, \frac{19}{8}, \cdots$. **(Lesson 12-3)** $\frac{5n-1}{2n}$

41. A food vending machine has 6 different items on a revolving tray. How many ways can the items be arranged on the tray? **(Lesson 14-2)** 120

42. College Entrance Exam Choose the best answer. A

If k is any odd integer and $x = 6k$, then $\frac{x}{2}$ will always be

(A) odd   **(B)** even   **(C)** positive   **(D)** negative   **(E)** zero

---

MID-CHAPTER REVIEW

1. At the Burger Hut, you can order your hamburger with or without cheese, with or without onions or pickles, and either rare, medium, or well-done. How many different hamburgers are possible? **(Lesson 14-1)** 24

2. How many 7-letter patterns can be formed from the letters of *benzene*? **(Lesson 14-2)** 420

3. How many ways can 5 people be seated at a round table relative to each other? **(Lesson 14-2)** 24

4. How many ways can a club of 13 members choose 4 different officers? **(Lesson 14-3)** 17,160

5. How many ways can a club of 13 members choose a 4-person committee? **(Lesson 14-3)** 715

EXTENDING THE LESSON

Math Power: Connections

List two more rows in the array below. Find the elements in the array. Find any patterns in the array.

$C(1, 0)$ $C(1, 1)$
$C(2, 0)$ $C(2, 1)$ $C(2, 2)$
$C(3, 0)$ $C(3, 1)$ $C(3, 2)$ $C(3, 3)$
$C(4, 0)$ $C(4, 1)$ $C(4, 2)$ $C(4, 3)$ $C(4, 4)$
$C(5, 0)$ $C(5, 1)$ $C(5, 2)$ $C(5, 3)$ $C(5, 4)$ $C(5, 5)$

Sample Answer: Each entry is the sum of the two entries above it. One is the first entry in each row.

Mid-Chapter Review

The Mid-Chapter Review provides students with a brief review of the concepts and skills in Lessons 14–1 through 14–3. Lesson numbers are given at the end of problems or instruction lines so students may review concepts not yet mastered.

Lesson Resources

- Practice Master 14–4
- Enrichment Master 14–4
- Evaluation Master, Quiz B, p. 177

 Transparency 14–4 contains the 5-Minute Check and a teaching aid for this lesson.

INTRODUCING THE LESSON

 5-Minute Check

(over Lesson 14–3)

1. Evaluate $C(6, 2)$. **15**
2. Evaluate $C(8, 4) \cdot C(6, 5)$. **420**
3. From a list of 6 books, how many groups of 3 books can be selected? **20**
4. Find the value of n in the equation $C(n, 8) = C(12, 4)$. **12**
5. A bag contains 5 red and 7 blue marbles. How many ways can 2 red and 3 blue marbles be chosen? **350**

Motivating the Lesson

Write 100 numbers on slips of paper and choose one winning number. Have each student draw a number and predict the probability that it is the winning number. Repeat the experiment several times, each time decreasing the number of slips of paper.

14-4 Probability and Odds

Objectives
14–4A
14–4B

After studying this lesson, you should be able to:
- find the probability of an event, and
- find the odds for the success and failure of an event.

Application

The cover story in the October 19, 1992 issue of *USA Today* reported that if you were a registered voter, there was a 1 in 1140 chance that a national political pollster would call you before Election Day. After reading this, few registered voters would linger by the phone from 6 to 9 every night waiting to be part of the next day's political headlines. When we are uncertain about the occurrence of an event, we can measure the chances of its happening with **probability**.

When you roll a die, there are six possible outcomes. The die will show either 1, 2, 3, 4, 5, or 6. A desired outcome is called a **success**. Any other outcome is called a **failure**.

Probability of Success and of Failure

If an event can succeed in s ways and fail in f ways, then the probability of success $P(s)$ and the probability of failure $P(f)$ are as follows.

$$P(s) = \frac{s}{s+f} \qquad P(f) = \frac{f}{s+f}$$

 FYI...

A description of probability was first presented by the French mathematician Pierre-Simon Laplace in 1795.

An event that cannot fail has a probability of 1. An event that cannot succeed has a probability of 0. Thus, the probability of success, $P(s)$, is always between 0 and 1 inclusive.

The sum of the probability of success and the probability of failure for any event is always equal to 1.

$$P(s) + P(f) = \frac{s}{s+f} + \frac{f}{s+f}$$
$$= \frac{s+f}{s+f} \text{ or } 1$$

This property is often used in finding the probability of events. For example, if $P(s) = \frac{1}{4}$, then the $P(f) = 1 - \frac{1}{4}$ or $\frac{3}{4}$. Because their sum is 1, $P(s)$ and $P(f)$ are called **complements**.

Example 1

The term at random means that an outcome is chosen without any preference.

A box contains 3 baseballs, 7 softballs, and 11 tennis balls. What is the probability that a ball selected at random will be a tennis ball?

The probability of selecting a tennis ball is written $P(\text{tennis ball})$.

768 CHAPTER 14 COMBINATORICS AND PROBABILITY

ALTERNATE TEACHING STRATEGIES

Using Charts

Have students make a chart of the possibilities of rolling two dice. Then list the possible outcomes such as $P(\text{sum is 7})$ and give their probabilities.

Using Critical Thinking

Explain why the theoretical probability of an event may not match the experimental probability for that event. How does the number of experiments affect how close the experimental probability is to the theoretical probability?

There are 11 ways to select a tennis ball from the box and $3 + 7$ or 10 ways not to select a tennis ball from the box. So, $s = 11$ and $f = 10$.

$$P(\text{tennis ball}) = \frac{s}{s+f}$$

$$= \frac{11}{11 + (3 + 7)} \text{ or } \frac{11}{21}$$

The probability of selecting a tennis ball is $\frac{11}{21}$.

The counting methods you used for permutations and combinations are often used in determining probability.

Example 2

Two cards are drawn at random from a standard deck of 52 cards. What is the probability that both are hearts?

$$P(\text{two hearts}) = \frac{C(13, 2)}{C(52, 2)} \qquad \begin{array}{l}\textit{There are } C(13, 2) \textit{ ways to select 2 of 13 hearts.}\\ \textit{There are } C(52, 2) \textit{ ways to select 2 of 52 cards.}\end{array}$$

$$= \frac{\frac{13!}{11!2!}}{\frac{52!}{50!2!}}$$

$$= \frac{78}{1326} \text{ or } \frac{1}{17}$$

The probability of selecting two hearts is $\frac{1}{17}$.

FYI...

Playing cards are often used in probability and combinatorics. There are 52 playing cards in a standard deck, 13 in each of the four suits: hearts, diamonds, spades, and clubs. There are 3 face cards in each suit: the jack, the queen, and the king.

Some probability applications are more easily solved by using complements.

Example 3

APPLICATION

Quality Control

A collection of 15 transistors contains 3 that are defective. If 2 transistors are selected at random, what is the probability that at least one of them is good?

The complement of selecting at least 1 good transistor is selecting 2 defective transistors.

$$P(\text{2 defective transistors}) = \frac{C(3, 2)}{C(15, 2)}$$

$$= \frac{3}{105} \text{ or } \frac{1}{35}$$

Thus, the probability of selecting at least one good transistor is $1 - \frac{1}{35}$ or $\frac{34}{35}$.

Another way to measure the chance of an event occurring is with **odds**. The probability of the success of an event and its complement are used when computing the odds of an event.

Chalkboard Examples

For Example 1

A box contains 4 basketballs, 3 footballs, and 15 volleyballs. What is the probability that a ball selected at random will be a volleyball?

$\frac{15}{22}$

For Example 2

Three cards are drawn at random from a standard deck of 52 cards. What is the probability that all three are clubs?

$\frac{11}{850}$

For Example 3

A collection of 38 computer disks contains four that are defective. If two are selected at random, what is the probability that at least one of them is good?

$\frac{697}{703}$

Teaching Tip Before discussing Example 3, stress that the probability of getting a good transistor must be the complement of the probability of getting a transistor that is not good.

LESSON 14-4 PROBABILITY AND ODDS 769

For Example 4

The probability of an accident on a construction site is 8%. Find the odds that there will be not be an accident.
$$\frac{23}{2}$$

For Example 5

A box contains 13 red, 13 blue, 13 green, and 13 white marbles. Six marbles are drawn at random. What are the odds that the first 5 marbles will be the same color and the last marble will be another color?
$$\frac{50,193}{5,039,437} \text{ or about } \frac{1}{100}$$

EVALUATING THE LESSON

Checking for Understanding

Exercises 1–15 are designed to help you assess students' understanding through reading, writing, speaking, and modeling. You should work through Exercises 1–4 with your students and then monitor their work on Exercises 5–15.

Closing the Lesson

Speaking Activity Ask students to explain how to find the odds that an event will occur.

Definition of Odds

The odds of the successful outcome of an event is the ratio of the probability of its success to the probability of its failure.

$$\text{Odds} = \frac{P(s)}{P(f)}$$

Example 4

APPLICATION

Weather

The Channel 11 weather forecaster announces that the probability of rain tomorrow is 60%. Find the odds that it will *not* rain tomorrow.

The probability of rain tomorrow is 60% or $\frac{3}{5}$.

$$P(f) = \frac{3}{5} \qquad P(s) = 1 - \frac{3}{5} \text{ or } \frac{2}{5}$$

$$\text{Odds} = \frac{P(s)}{P(f)}$$

$$= \frac{\frac{2}{5}}{\frac{3}{5}} \text{ or } \frac{2}{3}$$

The odds that it will not rain is $\frac{2}{3}$.   *This is read "two to three."*

Sometimes when computing odds, you must find the total number of possible outcomes. This can involve finding permutations or combinations.

Example 5

Suppose Judi draws 5 cards from a standard deck of 52 cards. What are the odds that 4 cards will be of one suit and the other card will be of another suit?

First, find how many 5-card hands meet these conditions.

$P(4, 2)$ Select 2 suits among 4. Order is important since different numbers of cards are to come from each suit.

$C(13, 4)$ Select 4 cards from a suit containing 13 cards.

$C(13, 1)$ Select 1 card from the other suit.

Then, use the basic counting principle.

$$P(4, 2) \cdot C(13, 4) \cdot C(13, 1) = \frac{4!}{2!} \cdot \frac{13!}{9!4!} \cdot \frac{13!}{12!1!} \text{ or } 111,540$$

The number of successes is 111,540.

Find the total number of 5-card hands.

$$C(52, 5) = \frac{52!}{47!5!} \text{ or } 2,598,960$$

The number of 5-card hands that do not meet the conditions is 2,598,960 − 111,540 or 2,487,420.

Finally, find the odds.

$$P(s) = \frac{111{,}540}{2{,}598{,}960} \qquad P(f) = \frac{2{,}487{,}420}{2{,}598{,}960}$$

$$\text{Odds} = \frac{\dfrac{111{,}540}{2{,}598{,}960}}{\dfrac{2{,}487{,}420}{2{,}598{,}960}} \text{ or } \frac{143}{3189}$$

Thus, the odds are $\frac{143}{3189}$ or about $\frac{1}{22}$.

CHECKING FOR UNDERSTANDING

Communicating Mathematics

Read and study the lesson to answer each question. 1–4. See margin.

1. **Explain** what is meant by probability.
2. **Describe** the relationship between the probability of success and the probability of failure for any event.
3. **Write** an example of an outcome with a probability of 0.
4. **Describe** the difference between the probability of the successful outcome of an event and the odds of the successful outcome of an event.

Guided Practice

State the odds of an event occurring given the probability of the event.

5. $\frac{1}{2}$ $\frac{1}{1}$
6. $\frac{3}{4}$ $\frac{3}{1}$
7. $\frac{7}{15}$ $\frac{7}{8}$
8. $\frac{3}{20}$ $\frac{3}{17}$

State the probability of an event occurring given the odds of the event.

9. $\frac{3}{4}$ $\frac{3}{7}$
10. $\frac{6}{5}$ $\frac{6}{11}$
11. $\frac{4}{9}$ $\frac{4}{13}$
12. $\frac{1}{1}$ $\frac{1}{2}$

Suppose you select 2 letters at random from the word *algebra*. Find each probability.

13. $P2$ (consonants) $\frac{2}{7}$
14. $P(2 \text{ vowels})$ $\frac{1}{7}$
15. $P(1 \text{ vowel and 1 consonant})$ $\frac{4}{7}$

EXERCISES

16. The odds are 7 to 5 that the Boston Celtics win in the conference championship game on Saturday night. What is the probability that they will win? $\frac{7}{12}$

17. The probability of Jason getting accepted at the University of Michigan is $\frac{3}{4}$. What are the odds that he will *not* get accepted? $\frac{1}{3}$

John has the following variety of CDs, in no particular order, in a carrying case: 5 rap CDs, 9 rock CDs, 4 country CDs, and 2 top 40 CDs. Two are selected at random. Find each probability.

18. $P(2 \text{ rap })$ $\frac{1}{19}$
19. $P(2 \text{ rock })$ $\frac{18}{95}$
20. $P(2 \text{ country })$ $\frac{3}{95}$
21. $P(1 \text{ rap and 1 rock })$ $\frac{9}{38}$

LESSON 14-4   PROBABILITY AND ODDS   771

RETEACHING THE LESSON

Have students do a survey of the class to gather the following data: how many students walk to school, how many drive to school, and how many take the bus. Then have them find the probabilities that correspond to each mode of transportation to school.

Additional Answer

4. Sample answer: The probability of the successful outcome of an event is the ratio of the number of successful outcomes to the total number of outcomes possible. The odds of the successful outcome of an event is the ratio of the probability of its success to the probability of its failure.

Using Technology

The program given in Exercise 32 is for use with a TI-81 graphing calculator. For other programmable calculators, have students consult their owner's manual for commands similar to those presented here.

A die is thrown two times. What are the odds of each event occurring?

22. no fives $\frac{25}{11}$

23. at least one five $\frac{11}{25}$

24. both fives $\frac{1}{35}$

Of seventeen students in a class, five have blue eyes. Two students are chosen at random. Find the probability of each selection. Then find the odds of that selection.

25. P(both have blue eyes) $\frac{5}{68}, \frac{5}{63}$

26. P(neither has blue eyes) $\frac{33}{68}, \frac{33}{35}$

27. P(at least one has blue eyes) $\frac{35}{68}, \frac{35}{33}$

From a deck of 52 playing cards, 7 cards are dealt. What are the odds of each event occurring?

28. all kings 0

29. all face cards $\frac{99}{16,722,971}$

30. all from one suit $\frac{33}{643,162}$

31. 4 from one suit and 3 from another $\frac{4719}{9,000,011}$

Programming

32. The following program will generate random numbers between two values. You input a seed number, which determines the way in which the numbers are generated. Note that the program will not eliminate duplicate numbers, and the factory set seed number is 0.

```
Prgm 14: RAND.NUM
:ClrHome
:Disp "LEAST INTEGER"
:Input S
:Disp "GREATEST INTEGER"
:Input L
:Disp "SEED NUMBER"
:Input N
:Disp "NUMBER OF VALUES TO GENERATE"
:Input A
:0 → B
:N → Rand        Sets a starting point in the random number table.
:Lbl 1
:B+1 → B
:Int ((L−S+1)Rand + S) → R    Calculates value of desired random
:Disp R                       number, and stores in R.
:Pause                        Waits until user presses ENTER.
:If A ≠ B
:Goto 1
```

Run each program. See students' work.

a. Let $S = 1$ and $L = 6$ to simulate rolls of a die.

b. Let $S = 1$ and $L = 2$ to simulate a coin toss.

c. Let $S = 1$ and $L = 54$ to simulate a lottery with 54 numbers.

Critical Thinking

33. A magician cuts a rope in two pieces at a point selected at random. What is the probability that the length of the longer rope is at least 8 times the length of the shorter rope? $\frac{2}{9}$

Applications and Problem Solving

34. **Finance** The state of Pennsylvania has a Wild Card Lotto drawing twice a week in which 6 numbers out of 48 are drawn at random. The proceeds from the lottery help to finance programs for senior citizens in the state. What is the probability of winning one of the weekly Lotto drawings if you buy one ticket? $\frac{1}{12,271,512}$

35. **Education** The table on the next page gives the status of employment of 500 students at Hawkins College.

Employment Status	Class				
	Freshman	Sophomore	Junior	Senior	Totals
Unemployed	75	56	35	18	184
Part-time	55	46	45	45	191
Full-time	30	28	30	37	125
Totals	160	130	110	100	500

a. If a student is selected at random, find the probability that the student is unemployed. $\frac{46}{125}$

b. If a student is selected at random, find the probability that the student is a freshman employed part-time. $\frac{11}{100}$

c. Find the probability that an unemployed student selected at random is a senior. $\frac{9}{92}$

Mixed Review

36. Write an equation of the sine function with an amplitude 2, period 180°, and phase shift 45°. **(Lesson 6-2)** $y = \pm 2\sin(2x - 90°)$

37. If α and β are measures of two first quadrant angles, find $\cos(\alpha + \beta)$ if $\tan\alpha = \frac{4}{3}$ and $\cot\beta = \frac{5}{12}$. **(Lesson 7-3)** $-\frac{33}{65}$

38. See margin.

38. Suppose the function $f(x) = x^2 - 1$ is to be iterated to produce a fractal. Find the first four iterates of the function if the initial value of x is $(1 + i)$. **(Lesson 13-4)**

39. Suppose there are 9 points on a circle. How many 4-sided closed figures can be formed by joining any 4 of these points? **(Lesson 14-3)** 126

40. **College Entrance Exam** Choose the best answer. C
    If $a + b = 8$ and $3b - 4 = -13a$, then what is the value of a?

    (A) $\frac{-13}{3}$ **(B)** -3 **(C)** -2 **(D)** 10 **(E)** 2

CASE STUDY FOLLOW-UP

Refer to Case Study 3: *The Legal System*, on pages 962–965.

While walking one evening, Detective Odds heard a scream and looked up to see a thief running by. The thief was carrying something, but it was too dark for Odds to tell if the object was a car stereo or a purse. "It's got to be a stereo," said Odds. Three suspects were rounded up: Pilfer, whose 29 previous arrests included 8 for stereo theft; Filch, who had 15 stereo thefts among his 55 arrests; and Plunder, who had been nabbed 81 times, 22 on a stereo rap. "It's Pilfer," said Odds.

1. Explain Detective Odds' reasoning. See margin.
2. **Research** Talk to a police detective or district attorney to find out how probability and statistics are used in crime detection. Write about your findings in a 1-page paper. See students' work.

LESSON 14-4 PROBABILITY AND ODDS 773

EXTENDING THE LESSON

Math Power: Connections

Draw a tree diagram to illustrate the probability of getting two tails if you toss a coin three times.

$\frac{3}{8}$

Case Study Follow-Up

This activity provides an opportunity to do research and apply mathematics in solving problems related to issues that may face students in their adult lives. Case Study 3 is located on pages 962–965.

Additional Answers

38. $(1 + i, -1 + 2i),$
    $(-1 + 2i, -4 - 4i),$
    $(-4 - 4i, -1 + 32i),$
    $(-1 + 32i, -1024 - 64i)$

Case Study Follow-Up

1. According to figures cited in Case Study 3, thefts of motor vehicle accessories occur 15 times more often than purse thefts. Since the probability of Pilfer stealing a stereo is greater than either Filch or Pluder, it must be Pilfer.

Enrichment Masters Booklet, p. 97

14-4 **Enrichment Worksheet**
NAME _____ DATE _____

Geometric Probability

If a dart, thrown at random, hits the triangular board shown at the right, what is the change that is will hit the shaded region? This chance, also called a probability, can be determined by comparing the area of the board. This ratio indicates what fraction of the tosses should hit in the shaded region.

$$\frac{\text{area of shaded region}}{\text{area of triangular board}} = \frac{\frac{1}{2}(4)(6)}{\frac{1}{2}(8)(6)}$$

$$= \frac{12}{24} \text{ or } \frac{1}{2}$$

In general, if S is a subregion of some region R, then the probability, $P(S)$, that a point, chosen at random, belongs to subregion S is given by the following.

$$P(S) = \frac{\text{area of subregion } S}{\text{area of region } R}$$

Find the probability that a point, chosen at random, belongs to the shaded subregions of the following regions.

 1. $\frac{1}{2}$ 2. $\frac{5}{9}$ 3. $\frac{\pi}{4}$

The dart board shown at the right has 5 concentric circles whose centers are also the center of the square board. Each side of the board is 38 cm, and the radii of the circles are 2 cm, 5 cm, 8 cm, 11 cm, and 14 cm. A dart hitting within one of the circular regions scores the number of points indicated on the board, while a hit anywhere else scores 0 points. If a dart, thrown at random, hits the board, find the probability of scoring the indicated number of points. Write your answer in terms of π.

4. 0 points $\frac{361 - 49\pi}{361}$ 5. 1 point $\frac{75\pi}{1444}$ 6. 2 points $\frac{57\pi}{1444}$

7. 3 points $\frac{39\pi}{1444}$ 8. 4 points $\frac{21\pi}{1444}$ 9. 5 points $\frac{\pi}{361}$

T 97
Glencoe Division, Macmillan/McGraw-Hill

NCTM Standards: 1–4, 11, 12

Lesson Resources

- Practice Master 14–5
- Enrichment Master 14–5
- Activity Master, p. 42

 Transparency 14–5 contains the 5-Minute Check and a teaching aid for this lesson.

INTRODUCING THE LESSON

 5-Minute Check

(over Lesson 14–4)

1. State the odds of an event if the probability of the event is $\frac{5}{8}$. $\frac{5}{3}$

2. Two cards are drawn at random from a standard deck of 52 cards. What is the probability that both are spades? $\frac{1}{17}$

3. A collection of 18 fuses contains two that are defective. If one is selected at random, what is the probability that it is good? $\frac{8}{9}$

4. Chrissy draws four cards from a standard deck of 52 cards. What are the odds that the three cards will be spades and the other card will be of another suit? $\frac{44,616}{226,109}$ or about $\frac{1}{5}$

Motivating the Lesson

Suppose a student in class is chosen at random. What is the probability that the student is a girl, the student has curly hair, and the student wears glasses?

14-5 Probability of Independent and Dependent Events

Objective
14–5

After studying this lesson, you should be able to:
- find the probability of independent and dependent events.

Application

As you made your course selections for this current school year, you could select certain courses only if certain other courses had been taken previously; that is, if you satisfied the prerequisite requirements. However, you could select other courses regardless of the courses previously taken. Thus, the selection of a specific course may or may not be dependent upon the selection of another. The idea that some events are independent and others are dependent on other events is an important one in the study of probability.

Suppose a die is tossed twice. The probability that the first toss shows a 5 is $\frac{1}{6}$. The probability that the second toss shows a 5 is $\frac{1}{6}$. By using the basic counting principle, the probability that both tosses show 5s is $\frac{1}{6} \cdot \frac{1}{6}$ or $\frac{1}{36}$. Since the outcome of the first toss does not affect the outcome of the second toss, the events are independent.

Probability of Two Independent Events	If two events, A and B, are independent, then the probability of both events occurring is the product of each individual probability. $$P(A \text{ and } B) = P(A) \cdot P(B)$$

Example 1

Find the probability of getting a sum of 7 on the first toss of two dice and a sum of 4 on the second toss.

Let A be a sum of 7 on the first toss. Let B be a sum of 4 on the second toss.

$$P(A) = \frac{6}{36} \qquad P(B) = \frac{3}{36} \qquad \textit{Why?}$$

The two tosses are independent.

$$P(A \text{ and } B) = P(A) \cdot P(B)$$
$$= \frac{6}{36} \cdot \frac{3}{36} \text{ or } \frac{1}{72}$$

The probability of a 7 on the first toss and a 4 on the second toss is $\frac{1}{72}$.

ALTERNATE TEACHING STRATEGIES

Using Manipulatives

Have students use colored marbles or colored candies to model probability experiments. Have them choose the items from a bag, both with replacement and without replacement. Discuss the probabilities involved.

Using Cooperative Groups

Have students use groups to write sample events that are independent or dependent. Then find the probabilities of each event. Present the samples to the class.

Example 2

APPLICATION

School

Students in Mr. Meyer's physics lab often refer to the *CRC Handbook of Chemistry and Physics*. Even though they contain the same information, 4 of the handbooks have brown covers, and 3 have red. One student selects a handbook at random from the shelf, looks up the heat of combustion for an organic compound, and places the book back on the shelf. A second student does the same thing. What is the probability that both students looked at a brown handbook?

The events are independent since the first handbook is placed back on the shelf. The outcome of the second selection is not affected by the results of the first selection.

$$P(\text{both brown}) = P(\text{brown}) \cdot P(\text{brown})$$
$$= \frac{4}{7} \cdot \frac{4}{7} \text{ or } \frac{16}{49}$$

The probability that both students selected a brown handbook is $\frac{16}{49}$ or about $\frac{1}{3}$.

In the example above, what is the probability of both students selecting a brown handbook if the first selection is not put back on the shelf? These events are dependent because the outcome of the first event affects the second selection. Suppose the first selection is brown.

first selection   *second selection*

$P(\text{brown}) = \frac{4}{7}$ $P(\text{brown}) = \frac{3}{6}$ *Notice that when the brown book is removed, there is not only one less brown book but also one less book on the shelf.*

$$P(\text{both brown}) = P(\text{brown}) \cdot P(\text{brown})$$
$$= \frac{4}{7} \cdot \frac{3}{6} \text{ or } \frac{2}{7}$$

The probability that both students selected a brown handbook is $\frac{2}{7}$.

Probability of Two Dependent Events

If two events, *A* and *B*, are dependent, then the probability of both events occurring is found as follows.

$$P(A \text{ and } B) = P(A) \cdot P(B \text{ following } A)$$

Example 3

Kwag has 4 navy socks and 6 black socks in a drawer. One dark morning he randomly pulls out 2 socks. What is the probability that he will select a pair of navy socks?

(continued on the next page)

LESSON 14-5   PROBABILITY OF INDEPENDENT AND DEPENDENT EVENTS   775

TEACHING THE LESSON

Teaching Tip   Before discussing the probability of two independent events, have students give examples of independent and dependent events.

Chalkboard Examples

For Example 1

Find the probability of getting a sum of 5 on the first toss of two dice and a sum of 3 on the second toss.

$\frac{1}{162}$

For Example 2

Adam goes to the grocery store to buy cereal. The shelves contain 9 boxes of Brand A and 6 boxes of Brand B. He selects one brand at random and then puts it back. Another person does the same thing. What is the probability that both persons selected Brand A?

$\frac{9}{25}$

For Example 3

Huy has a bag that contains 4 red, 6 green, and 3 brown candies. He randomly chooses 3 candies from the bag. What is the probability that he will choose all brown candies?

$\frac{1}{286}$

EVALUATING THE LESSON

Checking for Understanding

Exercises 1–7 are designed to help you assess students' understanding through reading, writing, speaking, and modeling. You should work through Exercises 1–3 with your students and then monitor their work on Exercises 4–7.

Closing the Lesson

Writing Activity Have students write a paragraph explaining the difference between independent and dependent events. Give an example.

APPLYING THE LESSON

Homework Exercises

Assignment Guide
Average: 8–19, 21, 23, 26, 29, 31, 33, 35–39
Enriched: 8–22 even, 23–39

The red A, B, and C flags, printed only in the Teacher's Wraparound Edition, indicate the level of difficulty of the exercises.

Practice Masters Booklet, p. 98

14-5 Practice Worksheet

NAME _____ DATE _____

Probability of Independent and Dependent Events

There are 3 nickels, 2 dimes, and 5 quarters in a purse. Three coins are selected in succession at random.

1. Find the probability of selecting 1 nickel, 1 dime, and 1 quarter in that order without replacement. $\frac{1}{24}$

2. Find the probability of selecting 1 nickel, 1 dime, and 1 quarter in that order with replacement. $\frac{3}{100}$

3. Find the probability of selecting 1 nickel, 1 dime, and 1 quarter in any order with replacement. $\frac{9}{50}$

4. Find the probability of selecting 1 nickel, 1 dime, and 1 quarter in any order without replacement. $\frac{1}{4}$

A red, a green, and a yellow die are tossed. What is the probability that the following occurs?

5. All 3 dice show a 4. $\frac{1}{216}$

6. None of the 3 dice shows a 4. $\frac{125}{216}$

7. The red die shows an even number, and the other 2 show different odd numbers. $\frac{1}{12}$

8. All 3 dice show the same number. $\frac{1}{36}$

From a standard deck of 52 cards, 2 cards are selected. What is the probability that the following occurs?

9. 2 black cards selected without replacement $\frac{25}{102}$

10. 2 black cards selected with replacement $\frac{1}{4}$

11. 1 red card and 1 spade in any order selected without replacement $\frac{13}{51}$

12. 1 red card and 1 spade in that order selected without replacement $\frac{13}{102}$

T98
Glencoe Division, Macmillan/McGraw-Hill

This situation is equivalent to pulling out 1 sock, not replacing it, then pulling out another.

$$P(\text{navy, navy}) = P(\text{navy}) \cdot P(\text{navy following navy})$$
$$= \frac{4}{10} \cdot \frac{3}{9} \text{ or } \frac{2}{15}$$

The probability that Kwag will select a pair of navy socks is $\frac{2}{15}$.

CHECKING FOR UNDERSTANDING

Communicating Mathematics

Read and study the lesson to answer each question. 1–2. See margin.

1. **Write** an example of two independent events.

2. **Describe** what is meant by dependent events.

3. **Explain** how to find the probability of two dependent events. Multiply the probability of the first times the probability of the second.
4. dependent, $\frac{2}{5}$

Guided Practice

Determine if each event is *independent* or *dependent*. Then find the probability.

4. There are 2 glasses of root beer and 4 glasses of cola on the counter. Dave drinks two of them at random. What is the probability that he drank 2 glasses of cola?

5. A bowl contains 5 oranges and 4 tangerines. Noelle randomly selects one, puts it back, and then selects another. What is the probability that both selections were oranges? independent, $\frac{25}{81}$

6. A green die and a red die are tossed. What is the probability that a 4 shows on the green die and a 5 shows on the red die? independent, $\frac{1}{36}$

7. A bag contains 4 red, 4 green, and 7 blue marbles. Three are selected in sequence without replacement. What is the probability of selecting a red, a green, and a blue marble in that order? dependent, $\frac{8}{195}$

EXERCISES

Practice

A

Determine if each event is *independent* or *dependent*. Then find the probability.

8. When Luis plays José on his video game, the odds are 4 to 3 that Luis will win. What is the probability that he will win the next four games? independent, $\frac{256}{2401}$

9. There are two traffic lights along the route that Laura rides from home to school. One traffic light is red 50% of the time. The next traffic light is red 60% of the time. The lights operate on separate timers. Find the probability that these lights will both be red on Laura's way home from school. independent, $\frac{3}{10}$

There are 5 pennies, 7 nickels, and 9 dimes in an antique coin collection. Suppose two coins are to be selected at random from the collection. Find each probability.

10. $P(\text{selecting 2 pennies})$, if no replacement occurs $\frac{1}{21}$

11. $P(\text{selecting 2 pennies})$, if replacement occurs $\frac{25}{441}$

12. $P(\text{selecting the same coin twice})$, if no replacement occurs 0

RETEACHING THE LESSON

Ask students to find the probability of choosing a green ball from a box containing 3 white balls, 4 yellow balls, and 5 green balls. Then have them calculate the probability of choosing two green balls, both with replacement and without replacement.

Additional Answers

1. Sample answer: Select one card from a deck of cards, replace it, and then select another card.

2. The outcome of one event does affect the outcome of the other.

Michael's family is preparing to move to a new home. Michael is helping his mother do some packing. There are 5 clocks, 5 candles, and 6 picture frames randomly placed on a table waiting to be boxed. Michael accidentally knocks two items off the table and breaks them. Find each probability.

13. P(breaking 2 picture frames) $\frac{1}{8}$

14. P(breaking 2 clocks) $\frac{1}{12}$

15. P(breaking a clock, then a candle) $\frac{5}{48}$

16. P(breaking a clock and a candle) $\frac{5}{24}$

Two dice are tossed. Find each probability.

17. P(no 2s) $\frac{25}{36}$

18. P(two numbers alike) $\frac{1}{6}$

19. P(two different numbers) $\frac{5}{6}$

20. P(2 and any other number) $\frac{5}{36}$

21. A box contains 5 red markers, 4 black markers, and 7 blue markers. Three are selected, one after the other. Find the probability that all three are different colors if:

   a. no replacement occurs. $\frac{1}{24}$ b. replacement occurs each time. $\frac{35}{1024}$

22. Brian's wallet contains four $1 bills, three $5 bills, and two $10 bills. If 3 bills are selected in succession, find the probability of selecting one of each if:

   a. each bill is replaced. $\frac{8}{243}$ b. no bills are replaced. $\frac{1}{21}$

For a bingo game, wooden balls numbered consecutively from 1 to 75 are placed in a box. Five balls are drawn at random. Find each probability.

23. P(selecting 5 even numbers), if replacement occurs $\frac{69{,}343{,}957}{2{,}373{,}046{,}875} \approx 0.029$

24. P(selecting 5 even numbers), if no replacement occurs $\frac{52{,}307{,}640}{2{,}071{,}126{,}800} \approx 0.025$

25. P(selecting 5 consecutive numbers), if no replacement occurs $\frac{1}{29{,}170{,}800}$

A standard deck of 52 cards contains 4 suits of 13 cards each. Find each probability if 13 cards are drawn and no replacement occurs.

26. P(all diamonds) $\frac{1}{635{,}013{,}559{,}600}$

27. P(all one suit) $\frac{4}{635{,}013{,}559{,}600}$

28. P(all red cards) $\frac{19}{1{,}160{,}054}$

29. P(all face cards) 0

30. For two events, X and Y, $P(X) = \frac{3}{10}$ and $P(Y) = \frac{1}{2}$. Are X and Y independent or dependent events, if $P(X \text{ and } Y) = \frac{1}{5}$? Explain. Dependent; if X and Y are independent, $P(X \text{ and } Y) = \frac{3}{20}$.

31. A group of people was asked to choose a letter from the alphabet. How many people would have to respond in order for the probability of two persons choosing the same letter to be greater than $\frac{1}{2}$? **7**

32. A room full of people are surveyed to determine their birthday (day and month only). How many people would have to respond for the probability of any two of them having the same birthday to be greater than $\frac{1}{2}$? Assume 366 different birthdays are possible. **23**

33. Business A furniture buyer has ordered 100 grandfather clocks from an overseas manufacturer. Four clocks are damaged in shipment, but the packaging shows no indication of such damage. If a dealer buys 6 clocks without examining the contents, what is the probability that she does not have a damaged clock?

33. $\frac{435,643}{560,175}$

34. Glenn, $\frac{851}{721}$

34. Political Science A 1992 poll based on returns from 2,035 registered Ohioans who intended to vote found that 37% were Republican, 40% were Democrat, and 21% were independent. Mike DeWine, a Republican, and John Glenn, a Democrat, were senatorial candidates. In the poll, 77% of the Republicans and 83% of the Democrats said they would vote for their party's candidate, while 41% of the independents said they would vote Democratic and 33% said they would vote Republican. If these people are representative of the entire state, which candidate had the better chance of winning Ohio's senate race, and by what odds?

35. Determine whether the graph of $f(x) = -\frac{1}{2}x^3$ is symmetric with respect to the x-axis, the y-axis, the line $y = x$, the line $y = -x$, or the origin. **(Lesson 3-1)**

35. origin

36. Write the polar equation $r \sin \theta = 2$ in rectangular form. **(Lesson 9-3)** $y = 2$

37. Write the series $3 + 9 + 27 + \cdots$ using sigma notation. **(Lesson 12-5)** $\sum\limits_{k=1}^{\infty} 3^k$

38. Two dice are tossed and their sum is 6. Find the probability that each die shows a 3. **(Lesson 14-4)** $\frac{1}{5}$

39. College Entrance Exam Choose the best answer. **B**
The length of a rectangle is 1 unit and the width is w units. If the width is increased by 3 units, by how many units will the perimeter be increased?

(A) 4 **(B)** 6 **(C)** 12 **(D)** $2w + 3$ **(E)** $2w + 6$

EXTENDING THE LESSON

Math Power: Reasoning

Suppose you are in a room with 24 other people. What is the probability that there will be two people in the room with the same birthday? Assume that there are 365 possible birthdays. **0.57**

Enrichment Masters Booklet, p. 98

14-6 Probability of Mutually Exclusive or Inclusive Events

Objectives
14–6A
14–6B

After studying this lesson, you should be able to:
- identify mutually exclusive events, and
- find the probability of mutually exclusive and inclusive events.

Application

In August, 1992, Hurricane Andrew caused billions of dollars of damage to south Florida and Louisiana. After a relief effort, 200 people in one community were surveyed to determine whether they donated food or money. Of the sample, 65 people said they donated food and 50 people said they donated money. Of these people, 30 people said they donated both. If a member of the community were selected at random, what is the probability that he or she donated food *or* money? *This problem will be solved in Example 2.*

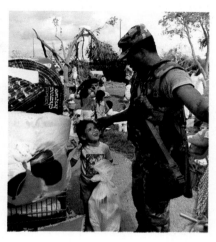

Mutually exclusive events <u>cannot</u> occur simultaneously.

When tossing a die, what is the probability of tossing a 3 or a 4? In this case, both events cannot happen at the same time. That is, the events are **mutually exclusive**. The probability of tossing a 3 or a 4 is $\frac{1}{6} + \frac{1}{6}$ or $\frac{2}{6}$.

Probability of Mutually Exclusive Events

If two events, A and B, are mutually exclusive, then the probability that either A or B occurs is the sum of their probabilities.

$$P(A \text{ or } B) = P(A) + P(B)$$

Inclusive events <u>can</u> occur simultaneously.

What is the probability of drawing a king or a black card from a deck of cards? It is possible to draw a card that is both a king and a black card. Therefore, these events are *not* mutually exclusive. They are called **inclusive** events. In this case, you must adjust the formula for mutually exclusive events much like you did to account for duplication in some permutations.

$P(\text{king})$	$P(\text{black card})$	$P(\text{black king})$
$\frac{4}{52}$	$\frac{26}{52}$	$\frac{2}{52}$
1 king in each suit	*clubs and spades*	*king of clubs and king of spades*

LESSON 14-6 PROBABILITY OF MUTUALLY EXCLUSIVE OR INCLUSIVE EVENTS 779

14–6 Lesson Notes

NCTM Standards: 1–4, 11, 12

Lesson Resources

- Practice Master 14–6
- Enrichment Master 14–6
- Evaluation Master, Quiz C, p. 178
- Activity Master, p. 40

 Transparency 14–6 contains the 5-Minute Check and a teaching aid for this lesson.

INTRODUCING THE LESSON

 5-Minute Check

(over Lesson 14–5)

1. Find the probability of getting a sum of 6 on the first toss of two dice and a sum of 5 on the second toss.
$\frac{5}{324}$

2. A bowl contains 4 apples and 3 oranges. Jason selects a piece of fruit at random, puts it back, and then selects another one at random. What is the probability that both selections were apples?
$\frac{16}{49}$

3. A box contains 6 red markers, 3 green markers, and 4 blue markers. Three are selected at random, one after the other. Find the probability of selecting 3 red markers if:
a. no replacement occurs.
$\frac{10}{143}$

b. replacement occurs each time.
$\frac{216}{2197}$

Motivating the Lesson

Ask students what is wrong with the statement, "Ryan's golf score was 84 and 78." Use student responses to start a discussion of mutually exclusive events.

ALTERNATE TEACHING STRATEGIES

Using Models

Use Venn diagrams to illustrate the probability of inclusive events.

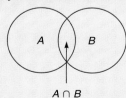

$A \cap B$

Using Charts

Suppose a commuter must drive through three stop lights in order to get to work. If a light is green, she is happy. If a light is red, she is angry. If more than one light is red, she is late for work. Make a chart of the eight possible combinations of green or red lights. Use the chart to find the probability that she will be late for work. $\frac{3}{8}$

Teaching Tip After discussing mutually exclusive events and inclusive events, ask students to give their own examples.

Chalkboard Examples

For Example 1

Gina has 6 pennies, 4 nickels, and 5 dimes in her change purse. She takes one coin from the purse at random. What is the probability that it is a nickel or dime?

$\frac{3}{5}$

For Example 2

Out of a group of 48 patients, a hospital has determined that 18 have high blood pressure, 20 have arteriosclerosis (clogged arteries), and 12 have both. What is the probability that a patient in this group has either high blood pressure or arteriosclerosis?

$\frac{13}{24}$

For Example 3

There are 6 children in the Patel family, 4 girls and 2 boys. Four children are chosen to model for the fashion show. What is the probability that at least three girls are chosen?

$\frac{3}{5}$

The probability of drawing a black king is counted twice, once for a king and once for a black card. To find the correct probability you must subtract P(black king) from the sum of P(king) and P(black card).

$$P(\text{king or black card}) = \frac{4}{52} + \frac{26}{52} - \frac{2}{52} \text{ or } \frac{7}{13}$$

The probability of drawing a king or a black card is $\frac{7}{13}$.

Probability of Inclusive Events	If two events, A and B, are inclusive, then the probability that either A or B occurs is the sum of their probabilities decreased by the probability of both occurring. $$P(A \text{ or } B) = P(A) + P(B) - P(A \text{ and } B)$$

Example 1

Leroy has 4 pennies, 3 nickels, and 6 dimes in his pocket. He takes one coin from his pocket at random. What is the probability that it is a penny or a dime?

These are mutually exclusive events since a coin cannot be a penny *and* a dime. Find the sum of the individual probabilities.

$$P(\text{penny}) = \frac{4}{13} \qquad P(\text{dime}) = \frac{6}{13}$$

$$P(\text{penny or dime}) = \frac{4}{13} + \frac{6}{13} \text{ or } \frac{10}{13}$$

The probability of selecting a penny or a dime is $\frac{10}{13}$.

Example 2

APPLICATION

Fund-Raising

In the application at the beginning of the lesson, determine the probability that a member of the community chosen at random donated food or money for the victims of Hurricane Andrew.

Since it is possible to donate both food and money, these events are inclusive.

$$P(\text{donate food}) = \frac{65}{200}$$

$$P(\text{donate money}) = \frac{50}{200}$$

$$P(\text{donate both}) = \frac{30}{200}$$

$$P(\text{donate food or money}) = \frac{65}{200} + \frac{50}{200} - \frac{30}{200} \text{ or } \frac{85}{200}$$

The probability that someone donated food or money is $\frac{85}{200}$ or $\frac{17}{40}$.

Example 3

APPLICATION

Education

There are 5 men and 4 women on the school board for the Titusville Area School District. A committee of 5 members is being selected at random to study the feasibility of building a new elementary school. What is the probability that the committee will have at least 3 men?

At least 3 men means that the committee may have 3, 4, or 5 men. It is not possible to select a group of 3 men, a group of 4 men, and a group of 5 men all in the same 5-member committee. Thus, the events are mutually exclusive.

$$P(\text{at least 3 men}) = P(\text{3 men}) + P(\text{4 men}) + P(\text{5 men})$$

$$= \frac{C(5,3) \cdot C(4,2)}{C(9,5)} + \frac{C(5,4) \cdot C(4,1)}{C(9,5)} + \frac{C(5,5) \cdot C(4,0)}{C(9,5)}$$

$$= \frac{60}{126} + \frac{20}{126} + \frac{1}{126} \text{ or } \frac{9}{14}$$

The probability of at least 3 men on the committee is $\frac{9}{14}$.

CHECKING FOR UNDERSTANDING

Communicating Mathematics

Read and study the lesson to answer each question. 1–4. See margin.

1. **Describe** the difference between mutually exclusive and inclusive events.

2. **Write** an example of two mutually exclusive events in your own life.

3. **Write** an example of two events in your life that are not mutually exclusive.

4. **Draw** a Venn diagram to illustrate the events in the application at the beginning of the lesson.

Guided Practice

Determine if each event is *mutually exclusive* or *inclusive*. Then find the probability.

5. Two dice are tossed.
   a. $P(\text{sum is 6 or sum is 9})$
   b. $P(\text{only one die shows a 2})$

5a. exclusive, $\frac{1}{4}$

5b. inclusive, $\frac{11}{36}$

6. A card is drawn from a standard deck of cards.
   a. $P(\text{drawing an ace or a red card})$
   b. $P(\text{drawing a king or a queen})$

6a. inclusive, $\frac{7}{13}$

6b. exclusive, $\frac{2}{13}$

7. **Business** An auto club's emergency service team knows from experience that when a member calls to report that their car won't start, the probability that the engine is flooded is $\frac{1}{2}$, the probability that the battery is dead is $\frac{2}{5}$, and the probability that both the engine is flooded and the battery is dead is $\frac{1}{10}$. What is the probability that the next member to report that their car won't start has a flooded engine or a dead battery?

7. inclusive, $\frac{4}{5}$

LESSON 14-6 PROBABILITY OF MUTUALLY EXCLUSIVE OR INCLUSIVE EVENTS 781

Additional Answer

4.

Donated Food   Both   Donated Money

35   30   20

No Donation 115

Practice Masters Booklet, p. 99

14-6 **Practice Worksheet**

NAME _____ DATE _____

Probability of Mutually Exclusive or Inclusive Events

An urn contains 7 white marbles and 5 blue marbles. Four marbles are selected without replacement. What is the probability that each occurs?

1. all white or all blue
   $\frac{8}{99}$
2. exactly 3 white
   $\frac{35}{99}$
3. at least 3 white
   $\frac{14}{33}$
4. exactly 3 white or exactly 3 blue
   $\frac{49}{99}$

Two cards are drawn from a standard deck of 52 cards. What is the probability that each occurs?

5. 2 spades
   $\frac{1}{17}$
6. 2 spades or 2 red cards
   $\frac{31}{102}$
7. 2 red cards or 2 jacks
   $\frac{55}{221}$
8. 2 spades or 2 face cards
   $\frac{47}{442}$

Three dice are tossed. What is the probability that each occurs?

9. exactly two 5s
   $\frac{5}{72}$
10. at least two 5s
    $\frac{2}{27}$
11. three 5s
    $\frac{1}{216}$
12. no 5s
    $\frac{125}{216}$

T99
Glencoe Division, Macmillan/McGraw-Hill

Homework Exercises

Assignment Guide

Average: 8–12, 13-27 odd, 30, 33, 34,
36–40
Enriched: 10–12, 14-28 even, 29–40

The red A, B, and C flags, printed only in the Teacher's Wraparound Edition, indicate the level of difficulty of the exercises.

Chapter 14, Quiz C, (Lessons 14–5 through 14–6), is available in the *Evaluation Masters*, p. 178.

EXERCISES

Practice

A

Determine if each event is *mutually exclusive* or *inclusive*. Then find the probability.

8. Five coins are dropped onto the floor. What is the probability that at least three of them land tails-up? exclusive, $\frac{1}{2}$

9. In homeroom, 5 of the 12 girls have blonde hair and 6 of the 15 boys have blonde hair. What is the probability of randomly selecting a boy or a blonde-haired person as homeroom representative to the student council? inclusive, $\frac{20}{27}$

10. A card is drawn from a deck of cards. What is the probability that it is a red card or a face card? inclusive, $\frac{8}{13}$

Two faces of a die are red, two are blue, and two are white. The die is tossed. Find each probability.

11. $P(\text{shows either red or blue})$ $\frac{2}{3}$

12. $P(\text{does not show red})$ $\frac{2}{3}$

Kevin has 11 CDs in the glove compartment of his car. Six are rock and 5 are rap. He selects three at random to take to a party. Find each probability.

B

13. $P(\text{all 3 rock or all 3 rap})$ $\frac{2}{11}$

14. $P(\text{exactly 2 rap})$ $\frac{4}{11}$

15. $P(\text{at least 2 rap})$ $\frac{14}{33}$

16. $P(\text{at least 2 rock})$ $\frac{19}{33}$

Two cards are drawn from a standard deck of cards. Find each probability.

17. $P(\text{both aces or both face cards})$ $\frac{12}{221}$

18. $P(\text{both aces or both black})$ $\frac{55}{221}$

19. $P(\text{both black or both face cards})$ $\frac{188}{663}$

20. $P(\text{both either red or an ace})$ $\frac{63}{221}$

The athletic director is counting the ticket money after the basketball game on Tuesday. Six coins fall from her desk to the floor. Find each probability.

21. $P(\text{landing 3 heads or 2 tails})$ $\frac{35}{64}$

22. $P(\text{landing at least 4 tails})$ $\frac{11}{32}$

23. $P(\text{landing 4 heads or 1 tail})$ $\frac{21}{64}$

24. $P(\text{landing all heads or all tails})$ $\frac{1}{32}$

There are 7 men and 7 women on the city council. A committee of 6 members is to be selected at random to attend a state convention. Find the probability of each group being selected.

25. $P(\text{all men or all women})$ $\frac{2}{429}$

26. $P(\text{5 men or 5 women})$ $\frac{14}{143}$

27. $P(\text{3 men and 3 women})$ $\frac{175}{429}$

28. $P(\text{at least 4 women})$ $\frac{127}{429}$

The numbers 1 through 25 are written on Ping-Pong® balls and placed in a wire cage. The numbers 20 through 40 are written on Ping-Pong® balls and placed in a different wire cage. One ball is chosen at random from each spinning cage. Find each probability.

29. P(each is a 22) $\frac{1}{525}$

30. P(neither is a 25) $\frac{32}{35}$

31. P(at least one is a 23) $\frac{3}{35}$

32. P(each is greater than 10) $\frac{3}{5}$

Critical Thinking

33. A bag contains 15 billiard balls, numbered consecutively from 1 to 15. Six balls are selected at random. What is the probability that the sum of the numbers on the billiard balls will be odd? $\frac{72}{143}$

Applications and Problem Solving

34. Sports The Texas Ranger pitching staff has 5 left-handers and 8 right-handers. If 2 pitchers are selected at random to warm up, what is the probability that at least one of them is a right-hander? $\frac{34}{39}$

35. Medicine Mrs. Sopher visits two doctors, Dr. Briggs and Dr. Villa, for a diagnosis. The probability that Dr. Briggs correctly diagnoses a disease is $\frac{93}{100}$, and the probability that Dr. Villa correctly diagnoses a disease is $\frac{97}{100}$. What is the probability that at least one of the two doctors makes the correct diagnosis? $\frac{9979}{10,000}$

Mixed Review

36. Construction A highway curve, in the shape of an arc of a circle, is 0.25 miles. The direction of the highway changes 45° from one end of the curve to the other. Find the radius of the circle in feet that the curve follows. **(Lesson 5-2)** 1681 feet

37. Write the equation of the ellipse with center at $(3, 1)$, semi-major axis of length 6 units, and eccentricity $\frac{1}{3}$. The major axis is parallel to the y-axis. **(Lesson 10-3)** See margin.

38. $608,487.05

38. Finance Mrs. Williams invests $2000 annually in an insurance annuity for 42 years. What will the annuity be worth if it has an APR of 8%? **(Lesson 12-2)**

39. Fifty tickets, numbered consecutively 1 to 50, are placed in a box. Four tickets are drawn without replacement. What is the probability that 4 odd numbers are drawn? **(Lesson 14-5)** $\frac{253}{4606}$

40. College Entrance Exam Choose the best answer. D
The distance between $P(4, 0)$ and Q is 8. The coordinates of point Q could be any of the following except

(A) $(-4, 0)$ **(B)** $(0, 4\sqrt{3})$ **(C)** $(4, 8)$ **(D)** $(8, 0)$ **(E)** $(4, -8)$

EXTENDING THE LESSON

Math Power: Problem Solving

For the dart game pictured at the right, the radii of the concentric circles are 1 in., 2 in., 3 in., and 4 in. The scores you get for landing in a ring are listed on the dart board. Suppose you throw a dart and it lands randomly on the dart board. What is the probability that you score over 20 points?

$\frac{1}{4}$

14-7 Conditional Probability

NCTM Standards: 1–4, 11, 12

Lesson Resources

- Practice Master 14–7
- Enrichment Master 14–7

 Transparency 14–7 contains the 5-Minute Check and a teaching aid for this lesson.

INTRODUCING THE LESSON

 5-Minute Check

(over Lesson 14–6)

1. A card is drawn from a standard deck of 52 cards. Determine if drawing a king or drawing a heart are mutually exclusive or inclusive events. **inclusive**

2. Find the probability of drawing a king or a heart in Exercise 1. $\frac{4}{13}$

3. Allison has 3 pennies, 4 nickels, and 6 quarters in her pocket. She removes one coin at random. What is the probability that it is a nickel or quarter? $\frac{10}{13}$

4. A family of eight went to a restaurant. Three people ordered appetizers, four people ordered dessert, and two people ordered both. Determine the probability that a person ordered an appetizer or a dessert. $\frac{5}{8}$

Motivating the Lesson

Suppose you draw an ace when you are playing cards. What is the probability that the next card you draw will give you a pair of aces? **Actually, it depends on how many cards have already been drawn from the deck. If the first card drawn from a standard deck of 52 cards is an ace, then the probability that the next card will also be an ace is $\frac{3}{51}$, or $\frac{1}{17}$.**

Objective
14–7

After studying this lesson, you should be able to:
- find the probability of an event given the occurrence of another event.

Application

Suppose Jhan draws a card from a standard deck of 52 cards. What is the probability that he picks a queen? By forming the ratio of the number of successful outcomes to the number of all possible outcomes, we know that $P(\text{queen}) = \frac{4}{52}$. But now, suppose Jhan draws the card and tells you that he has drawn a red card. With this new information, what is the probability that he has drawn a queen? When you need to find the probability of an event under the condition that some preceding event has occurred, you are finding the **conditional probability**. The conditional probability of a queen given that it is known to be a red card can be symbolized as $P(\text{queen/red card})$.

Under the conditions of the problem, successful outcomes must be red *and* they must be queens. Therefore, the successful outcomes are red queens. There are two of these. So, $P(\text{queen and red card}) = \frac{2}{52}$. Also, the probability of choosing a red card is $\frac{26}{52}$.

$$P(\text{queen/red}) = \frac{P(\text{queen and red})}{P(\text{red})}$$

$$= \frac{\frac{2}{52}}{\frac{26}{52}} \text{ or } \frac{1}{13}$$

The probability of drawing a queen, given that the card is red, is $\frac{1}{13}$.

Conditional Probability

The conditional probability of event A, given event B, is defined as

$$P(A/B) = \frac{P(A \text{ and } B)}{P(B)} \text{ where } P(B) \neq 0.$$

$P(A/B)$ is read "the probability of A given B."

ALTERNATE TEACHING STRATEGIES

Using Connections

A coin is tossed twice. Have students use a tree diagram to illustrate the probability of showing heads on the second toss if it is known that the first toss also showed heads.

Using Manipulatives

Put 3 red marbles, 2 blue marbles, and 4 white marbles in each of three boxes. Roll a die. If an odd number comes up, pick from the first box. If 2 or 4 comes up, pick from the second box. If 6 comes up, pick from the third box. Find the probability of picking a white marble. $\frac{2}{27}$

Example 1

In the game of Yahtzee®, players toss 5 dice and receive points for certain combinations. To score 25 points in the "Full House" box, three dice must show the same number and two dice must show another number. Suzan tosses the dice. Three of the five dice each show a three. Neither of the other two show a three, and they do not match. Suzan tosses the two dice that do not match. Find the probability that the numbers of the dice match, given that their sum is greater than 7.

Let event A be that the numbers match.

Let event B be that their sum is greater than 7.

$$P(B) = \frac{15}{36} \qquad P(A \text{ and } B) = \frac{3}{36}$$

$$P(A/B) = \frac{P(A \text{ and } B)}{P(B)}$$

$$= \frac{\frac{3}{36}}{\frac{15}{36}} \text{ or } \frac{1}{5}$$

The probability of tossing matching numbers given that their sum is greater than 7 is $\frac{1}{5}$.

The set of all possible outcomes for an event is called the **sample space** for the event. A **reduced sample space** is the subset of a sample space that contains only those outcomes that satisfy a given condition. For example, if a pair of dice is thrown, the sample space would contain 36 outcomes of the form $(1,1)$, $(1,2)$, $(1,3)$, $\cdots$, $(6,6)$. Under the condition that the dice must match, the reduced sample space would contain only 6 outcomes: $(1,1)$, $(2,2)$, $(3,3)$, $(4,4)$, $(5,5)$, $(6,6)$.

Example 2 illustrates how to find conditional probabilities using sample spaces and reduced sample spaces.

Example 2

A pair of dice is thrown. Find the probability that the dice match, given that their sum is greater than five.

Let event A be that the numbers match.

Let event B be that the sum of the dice is greater than 5.

The sample space includes all of the possible outcomes of throwing a pair of dice. These are shown in the box at the right. Using the basic counting principle, there are 36 outcomes.

(1, 1)	(1, 2)	(1, 3)	(1, 4)	(1, 5)	(1, 6)
(2, 1)	(2, 2)	(2, 3)	(2, 4)	(2, 5)	(2, 6)
(3, 1)	(3, 2)	(3, 3)	(3, 4)	(3, 5)	(3, 6)
(4, 1)	(4, 2)	(4, 3)	(4, 4)	(4, 5)	(4, 6)
(5, 1)	(5, 2)	(5, 3)	(5, 4)	(5, 5)	(5, 6)
(6, 1)	(6, 2)	(6, 3)	(6, 4)	(6, 5)	(6, 6)

(continued on the next page)

Chalkboard Examples

For Example 1

Refer to Example 1 in the Student Edition. Find the probability that the numbers of the dice match given that the sum is greater than 8. $\frac{1}{5}$

For Example 2

A pair of dice is rolled. Find the probability that the dice match, given that their sum is greater than 9. $\frac{1}{3}$

Teaching Tip Use Example 2 as an example of the benefit of making a chart as a problem-solving strategy.

The condition that their sum is greater than five causes the reduced sample space to include only pairs in the shaded region. The reduced sample space contains 26 outcomes.

(1, 1)	(1, 2)	(1, 3)	(1, 4)	(1, 5)	(1, 6)
(2, 1)	(2, 2)	(2, 3)	(2, 4)	(2, 5)	(2, 6)
(3, 1)	(3, 2)	(3, 3)	(3, 4)	(3, 5)	(3, 6)
(4, 1)	(4, 2)	(4, 3)	(4, 4)	(4, 5)	(4, 6)
(5, 1)	(5, 2)	(5, 3)	(5, 4)	(5, 5)	(5, 6)
(6, 1)	(6, 2)	(6, 3)	(6, 4)	(6, 5)	(6, 6)

To find the probability of a match given a sum greater than five, circle the number of favorable outcomes in the reduced sample space. There are four such outcomes. Thus, the probability of A given B is $\dfrac{4}{26}$ or $\dfrac{2}{13}$.

(1, 1)	(1, 2)	(1, 3)	(1, 4)	(1, 5)	(1, 6)
(2, 1)	(2, 2)	(2, 3)	(2, 4)	(2, 5)	(2, 6)
(3, 1)	(3, 2)	(3, 3)	(3, 4)	(3, 5)	(3, 6)
(4, 1)	(4, 2)	(4, 3)	(4, 4)	(4, 5)	(4, 6)
(5, 1)	(5, 2)	(5, 3)	(5, 4)	(5, 5)	(5, 6)
(6, 1)	(6, 2)	(6, 3)	(6, 4)	(6, 5)	(6, 6)

In some situations, event A is a subset of event B. When this occurs, the probability that both event A and event B occur is the same as the probability of event A occurring. Thus, in these situations, $P(A/B) = \dfrac{P(A)}{P(B)}$. Consider the following example.

Example 3

One card is drawn from a standard deck of 52 cards. What is the probability that it is a queen if it is known to be a face card?

Let event A be that a queen is drawn.   *There are 4 queens.*

Let event B be that a face card is drawn.   *There are 12 face cards.*

Since a queen is a face card, A is a subset of B.

$$P(A \text{ and } B) = P(A) = \frac{4}{52} \text{ or } \frac{1}{13} \qquad\qquad P(B) = \frac{12}{52} \text{ or } \frac{3}{13}$$

$$P(A/B) = \frac{P(A)}{P(B)}$$

$$= \frac{\frac{1}{13}}{\frac{3}{13}} \text{ or } \frac{1}{3}$$

The probability that a queen is drawn, given that a face card is drawn, is $\dfrac{1}{3}$.

CHECKING FOR UNDERSTANDING

Communicating Mathematics

Read and study the lesson to answer each question. 1–3. See margin.

1. **Explain** what is meant by conditional probability.

2. Are $P(A/B)$ and $P(B/A)$ the same? Illustrate your answer.

3. **Describe** an example of a reduced sample space that is different from Example 2.

4. Under what conditions does $P(A/B) = \dfrac{P(A)}{P(B)}$? *when A is a subset of B*

786   CHAPTER 14   COMBINATORICS AND PROBABILITY

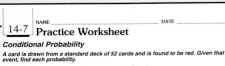

Guided Practice

Identify events A and B in each problem. Then find the probability.

5. Two coins are tossed. What is the probability that one coin shows tails if it is known that at least one coin shows heads? See margin.

6. A city council consists of six Democrats, two of whom are women, and six Republicans, four of whom are men. A member is chosen at random. If the member chosen is a man, what is the probability that he is a Democrat?
See margin.

A card is chosen at random from a standard deck of 52. Find each probability given that the card is red.

7. $P(\text{heart})$ $\frac{1}{2}$

8. $P(\text{ace})$ $\frac{1}{13}$

9. $P(\text{face card})$ $\frac{3}{13}$

10. $P(\text{six of spades})$ 0

11. $P(\text{six of hearts})$ $\frac{1}{26}$

12. $P(\text{red six})$ $\frac{1}{13}$

Identify events A and B in each problem. Then find the probability.

13. Two boys and two girls are lined up at random. What is the probability that the girls are separated if a girl is at an end? See margin.

14. A bag contains 4 red marbles and 4 blue marbles. Another bag contains 2 red marbles and 6 blue marbles. A marble is drawn from one of the bags at random and found to be blue. What is the probability that the marble is from the first bag? See margin.

EXERCISES

Practice

A pair of dice is thrown. Find each probability given that their sum is greater than or equal to 9.

15. $P(\text{sum is 8})$ 0

16. $P(\text{numbers match})$ $\frac{1}{5}$

17. $P(\text{sum is 12})$ $\frac{1}{10}$

18. $P(\text{sum is even})$ $\frac{2}{5}$

19. $P(\text{sum is 9 or 10})$ $\frac{7}{10}$

20. $P(\text{numbers match or sum is even})$ $\frac{2}{5}$

Three coins are dropped. Find the probability that they all land tails up for each known condition.

21. The first coin shows a tail. $\frac{1}{4}$

22. One of the coins is a head. 0

23. At least one coin shows a tail. $\frac{1}{7}$

24. At least two coins show tails. $\frac{1}{4}$

A committee of 3 student council members is randomly selected from Andy, Becky, Cho, Dan, Emily, and Fernando. Draw a sample space to represent all of the possible outcomes. Then find each conditional probability.

25. $P(\text{Fernando was selected, given that Becky was selected})$ $\frac{2}{5}$

26. $P(\text{Emily was not selected, given that Andy and Cho were selected})$ $\frac{3}{4}$

27. $P(\text{Becky and Cho were selected, given that Dan was not selected})$ $\frac{3}{10}$

28. $\frac{1}{2}$

28. $P(\text{Cho and Andy were selected, given that neither Becky nor Emily were selected})$

Additional Answers

35. Sample answer: when the number of possible outcomes becomes so large that it's not easy to list all of them

36. $P(A/B) = \frac{P(A \text{ and } B)}{P(B)}$ by definition. So, if $P(A) = P(A/B)$ then by substitution $P(A) = \frac{P(A \text{ and } B)}{P(B)}$ or $P(A \text{ and } B) = P(A) \cdot P(B)$. Therefore, events A and B are independent.

37. Let event A be that a person buys something. Let event B be that a person asks questions.

$$P(A/B) = \frac{P(A \text{ and } B)}{P(B)}$$

$$= \frac{\frac{48}{200}}{\frac{60}{200}} \text{ or } \frac{4}{5}$$

Four out of five customers who ask questions will make a purchase. Therefore, they are more likely to buy something if they ask questions.

---

29. A five-digit number is formed from the digits 1, 2, 3, 4, and 5. What is the probability that the number ends in the digits 52, given that it is even? $\frac{1}{8}$

30. Two numbers are selected at random from the numbers 1 through 9 without replacement. If their sum is even, what is the probability that both numbers are odd? $\frac{5}{8}$

In an advanced biology class, 60% of the students have brown hair, 30% have brown eyes, and 10% have both brown hair and eyes. A student is excused to go to the state track meet.

31. If the student has brown hair, what is the probability that the student also has brown eyes? $\frac{1}{6}$

32. If the student has brown eyes, what is the probability that the student does not have brown hair? $\frac{2}{3}$

In a card game played with a deck of 52 cards, each face card has a value of 10 points, each ace has a value of 1 point, and each number card has a value equal to the number. Two cards are drawn at random.

33. One card is the queen of hearts. What is the probability that the sum of the cards is greater than 18? $\frac{19}{51}$

34. At least one card is an ace. What is the probability that the sum of the cards is 7 or less? $\frac{23}{198}$

Critical Thinking

35. When would using the sample space/reduced sample space approach for solving a conditional probability problem not be the most advantageous one? See margin.

36. The probability of an event A is equal to the probability of the same event, given that event B has already occurred. Prove that A and B are independent events. See margin.

Applications and Problem Solving

37. Business The manager of a paint supply store wants to know whether people who come in and ask questions are more likely to make a purchase than the average customer. A survey of 200 people exiting the store found that 100 people bought something, 48 asked questions and bought something, and 12 people asked questions but did not buy anything. Based on the survey, determine whether a person who asks questions is more likely to buy something than the average person entering the store. See margin.

38. Medicine To test the effectiveness of a new vaccine, the developers gave 100 volunteers the conventional treatment and gave the new vaccine to another 100 volunteers. The results are shown in the table at the top of the next page.

Treatment	Disease Prevented	Disease Not Prevented
New Vaccine	68	32
Conventional Treatment	62	38

a. What is the probability that the disease is prevented in a volunteer chosen at random? $\frac{13}{20}$

b. What is the probability that the disease is prevented in a volunteer who was given the new vaccine? $\frac{17}{25}$

c. What is the probability that the disease is prevented in a volunteer who was not given the new vaccine? $\frac{31}{50}$

d. What conclusion can the developers of the new vaccine make? See margin.

39. **Money** A dollar-bill changer in a soft drink machine was tested with 100 $1-bills. Twenty-five of the bills were counterfeit. The results of the test are shown in the chart at the right.

Bill	Accepted	Rejected
Legal	69	6
Counterfeit	1	24

a. What is the probability that a bill accepted by the changer is legal? $\frac{69}{70}$

b. What is the probability that a bill is rejected given that it is legal? $\frac{2}{25}$

c. What is the probability that a counterfeit bill is not rejected? $\frac{1}{25}$

Mixed Review

40. Find $f(-2)$ if $f(x) = 2x^2 - 2x + 8$. **(Lesson 1-1)** 20

41. Use synthetic division to divide $x^5 - 3x^2 - 20$ by $x - 2$. **(Lesson 4-3)** See margin.

42. **Finance** What does the state of Illinois need to deposit into an account with an APR of 12% in order for the state to pay $1,000,000 to a single lottery winner in equal annual payments over the next twenty years? **(Lesson 11-2)** $133,878.78

43. Find the first three iterates of the function $f(x) = x^2 + 1$ for an initial value of $x_o = -1$. **(Lesson 13-1)** 2, 5, 26

44. A letter is picked at random from the alphabet. Find the probability that the letter is contained in the word *house* or in the word *phone*. **(Lesson 14-6)** $\frac{7}{26}$

45. **College Entrance Exam** Compare quantities A and B below. C
Write A if quantity A is greater.
Write B if quantity B is greater.
Write C if the two quantities are equal.
Write D if there is not enough information to determine the relationship.
(A) 15% of 1400   **(B)** 14% of 1500

EXTENDING THE LESSON

Math Power: Reasoning

Given the tree diagram at the right, find each probability.
$P(A \text{ and } E)$ 0.24
$P(A \text{ and } F)$ 0.12
$P(A \text{ and } D) + P(B \text{ and } E)$ 0.34

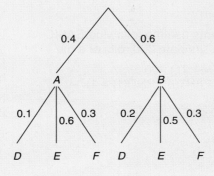

38d. The new vaccine is slightly more effective than the conventional treatment.

41. $x^4 + 2x^3 + 4x^2 + 5x + 10$

Enrichment Masters Booklet, p. 100

14-7 **Enrichment Worksheet**

NAME _____ DATE _____

Probability in Genetics

The Austrian monk and botanist Gregor Mendel discovered the basic laws of genetics during the nineteenth century. Through experiments with pea plants, Mendel found that cells in living organisms contain pairs of units that control traits in the offspring of the organism. We now call these units *genes*. If the genes in a cell are identical, the trait is *pure*. If they are different, the trait is *hybrid*. A trait like *tallness* which masks other traits, preventing them from showing up in offspring, is *dominant*. Otherwise, it is *recessive*. A combination of a dominant gene and a recessive gene will always produce a hybrid displaying the dominant trait.

Example   Two hybrid tall pea plants are crossed. What is the probability that the offspring will be short?

Punnett squares are used to analyze gene combinations. Use capital letters to represent dominant genes and lower-case letters to represent recessive genes.

	T	t
T	TT	Tt
t	Tt	tt

T = tall   t = short

The table shows the four equally possible outcomes. One of the outcomes, TT, is a pure tall plant. Two of the outcomes, Tt and Tt, are hybrid tall plants. Only one of the outcomes, tt, is a short plant. Therefore, the probability that an offspring will be short is $\frac{1}{4}$.

Use Punnett squares to solve.

1. A pure dominant yellow pea plant (Y) is crossed with a pure recessive white plant (w).
a. What are the possible outcomes?   Yw, Yw, Yw, Yw
b. Find the probability that an offspring will be yellow.   1

2. A hybrid tall pea plant is crossed with a short plant. Find the probability that an offspring will be short. $\frac{1}{2}$

3. Brown eyes are dominant over blue eyes in humans. What is the probability that a woman with blue eyes and a man with hybrid brown eyes will have a child with blue eyes? $\frac{1}{2}$

4. What is the probability that the offspring of a hybrid-tall, hybrid-yellow pea plant and a hybrid-tall white plant will be short white? $\frac{1}{8}$

T100
Glencoe Division, Macmillan/McGraw-Hill

NCTM Standards: 1–4, 11, 12

Lesson Resources

- Practice Master 14–8
- Enrichment Master 14–8
- Evaluation Master, Quiz D, p. 178
- Technology Master, p. 28

 Transparency 14–8 contains the 5-Minute Check and a teaching aid for this lesson.

INTRODUCING THE LESSON

5-Minute Check

(over Lesson 14–7)

1. A card is chosen at random from a standard deck of 52 cards. Find the probability of drawing an ace given that the card is black. $\frac{1}{13}$

2. A card is chosen at random from a standard deck of 52 cards. Find the probability of drawing a 7 of spades given that the card is black. $\frac{1}{26}$

3. A pair of dice is rolled. Find the probability that their sum is 10 given that their sum is greater than 8. $\frac{3}{10}$

4. Three coins are dropped. Find the probability that they all land heads up given that the first coin lands heads up. $\frac{1}{4}$

Prerequisite Skills

Students should be familiar with Pascal's triangle.
Show the first seven rows of Pascal's triangle.

```
              1
           1     1
        1     2     1
     1     3     3     1
  1     4     6     4     1
1     5    10    10     5     1
1   6   15   20   15    6    1
```

14-8 The Binomial Theorem and Probability

Objective
14–8

After studying this lesson, you should be able to:
■ find the probability of an event by using the binomial theorem.

Application

Suppose you didn't study for your 20th-century U.S. history quiz, so you decide to guess on all 10 true/false questions. What is the probability that exactly half of your answers are correct? *This problem will be solved in Example 2.*

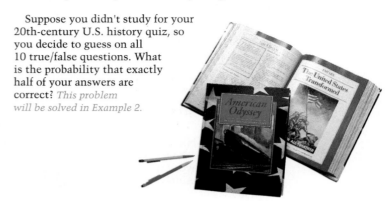

You may wish to review the binomial theorem in Lesson 12-6.

In a simpler case, suppose there are only 5 questions on the quiz. What is the probability that 3 of your answers are correct? The number of ways that this can happen is $C(5, 2)$ or 10. Let p_c represent the probability of guessing the answer correctly, and let p_i represent the probability of guessing the answer incorrectly. The terms of the binomial expansion of $(p_c + p_i)^5$ can be used to find the probabilities of each combination of correct and incorrect answers.

$$(p_c + p_i)^5 = 1p_c^5 + 5p_c^4p_i + 10p_c^3p_i^2 + 10p_c^2p_i^3 + 5p_cp_i^4 + 1p_i^5$$

coefficient	term	meaning
$C(5, 0) = 1$	$1p_c^5$	1 way to have all 5 correct
$C(5, 1) = 5$	$5p_c^4p_i$	5 ways to have 4 correct and 1 incorrect
$C(5, 2) = 10$	$10p_c^3p_i^2$	10 ways to have 3 correct and 2 incorrect
$C(5, 3) = 10$	$10p_c^2p_i^3$	10 ways to have 2 correct and 3 incorrect
$C(5, 4) = 5$	$5p_cp_i^4$	5 ways to have 1 correct and 4 incorrect
$C(5, 5) = 1$	$1p_i^5$	1 way to have all 5 incorrect

 FYI...

On September 22, 1950, Ralph J. Bunche, former professor of political science at Howard University, was the first African-American to receive a Nobel citation and was awarded the Nobel Peace Prize.

On a true/false test, the probability that you guess the correct answer is $\frac{1}{2}$. So, the probability that your guess is incorrect is also $\frac{1}{2}$. To find the probability of guessing exactly 3 out of 5 answers correctly, substitute $\frac{1}{2}$ for p_c and $\frac{1}{2}$ for p_i in the term $10p_c^3p_i^2$. Thus, $10p_c^3p_i^2 = 10\left(\frac{1}{2}\right)^3\left(\frac{1}{2}\right)^2$ or $\frac{5}{16}$. Therefore, the probability that you guess exactly 3 answers correctly is $\frac{5}{16}$.

790   CHAPTER 14   COMBINATORICS AND PROBABILITY

ALTERNATE TEACHING STRATEGIES

Using Computers

Have students use the following BASIC program to simulate 200 rolls of a die.

```
10  FOR D = 1 TO 200
20  LET N = (INT(6 * RND(1) + 1)
30  PRINT N
40  NEXT D
50  END
```

Using Connections

Use the chart below to help students see the probabilities associated with tossing three coins, where p = tossing a head, q = tossing a tail.

Number of Heads	Probability
0 {(T, T, T)}	q^3
1 {(T, T, H), (T, H, T), (H, T, T)}	pq^2
2 {(T, H, H), (H, H, T), (H, T, H)}	p^2q
3 {(H, H, H)}	p^3

Other probabilities can be determined from the expansion on the previous page. For example, what is the probability of guessing at least 3 questions correctly? The first, second, and third terms represent the condition that three or more guesses are correct. Therefore, the probability of this happening is the sum of the probabilities of these terms.

$$P(\text{at least 3 correct}) = 1p_c^5 + 5p_c^4 p_i + 10p_c^3 p_i^2$$

$$= \frac{1}{32} + \frac{5}{32} + \frac{5}{16}$$

$$= \frac{16}{32} \text{ or } \frac{1}{2}$$

The probability that at least 3 guesses are correct is $\frac{1}{2}$.

Problems that can be solved using binomial expansion are called **binomial experiments**.

Conditions of a Binomial Experiment	**A binomial experiment exists *if and only if* these conditions occur.** • **The experiment consists of n identical trials.** • **Each trial results in *one* of two possible outcomes.** • **The trials are independent.**

Example 1

APPLICATION

Sports

While pitching for the Toronto Blue Jays, 4 of every 7 pitches Juan Guzman threw in the first 5 innings were strikes. What is the probability that 3 of the next 4 pitches will be strikes?

There are 4 pitches involved. Let's assume that there are only two possible outcomes, strikes (S) or balls (B), and that the 4 pitches are independent events. This is a binomial experiment.

When $(S + B)^4$ is expanded, the term $S^3 B$ represents 3 strikes and 1 ball. The coefficient of $S^3 B$ is $C(4, 3)$ or 4.

$$P\,(3 \text{ strikes}, 1 \text{ ball}) = 4S^3 B$$

$$= 4\left(\frac{4}{7}\right)^3\left(\frac{3}{7}\right) \text{ or } \frac{768}{2401} \qquad S = \frac{4}{7} \text{ and } B = \frac{3}{7}$$

The probability of 3 strikes and 1 ball is $\frac{768}{2401}$ or about 0.32.

The binomial theorem can be used to find probability when the number of trials makes working with the binomial expansion unrealistic.

LESSON 14-8   THE BINOMIAL THEOREM AND PROBABILITY   791

EVALUATING THE LESSON

Checking for Understanding

Exercises 1–5 are designed to help you assess students' understanding through reading, writing, speaking, and modeling. You should work through Exercises 1–2 with your students and then monitor their work on Exercises 3–5.

Closing the Lesson

Modeling Activity Toss 10 coins 10 times. Find the experimental probability that there will be at least four tails.

Practice Masters Booklet, p. 101

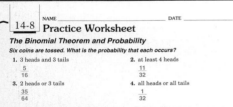

Example 2

APPLICATION

School

In the application at the beginning of the lesson, determine the probability that exactly half of the answers are correct.

Let p_c be the probability that the answer is correct, and let p_i be the probability that the answer is incorrect. Since there are 10 questions, we can use the binomial theorem to find any term in the expansion of $(p_c + p_i)^{10}$.

$$(p_c + p_i)^{10} = \sum_{r=0}^{10} \frac{10!}{r!(10-r)!} p_c^{10-r} p_i^{r}$$

Getting half of the answers correct means that you would get exactly 5 correct and 5 incorrect. So, the probability can be found using the term where $r = 5$, the sixth term.

$$\frac{10!}{5!(10-5)!} p_c^5 p_i^5 = 252 p_c^5 p_i^5$$

$$= 252 \left(\frac{1}{2}\right)^5 \left(\frac{1}{2}\right)^5 \text{ or } \frac{63}{256}$$

The probability that you guess exactly 5 answers correctly is $\frac{63}{256}$ or about $\frac{1}{4}$.

CHECKING FOR UNDERSTANDING

Communicating Mathematics

Read and study the lesson to answer each question.

1. **Explain** how to find the probability of exactly 4 heads showing when 5 coins are tossed. Evaluate $C(5, 4) \left(\frac{1}{2}\right)^4 \left(\frac{1}{2}\right)^1$.

2. **List** the conditions that must be satisfied for a problem to be classified as a binomial experiment. See margin.

Guided Practice

In Exercises 3—5, determine whether each situation represents a binomial experiment. Solve those that represent a binomial experiment.

3. binomial, $\frac{3}{8}$

3. What is the probability of 2 heads and 2 tails if Sergio tosses a coin 4 times?

4. What is the probability of Bianca drawing 4 kings from a deck of cards for each condition? a. binomial, $\frac{1}{28,561}$ b. not binomial

   a. She replaces the card each time.   b. She does not replace the card.

5a. binomial, $\frac{16}{81}$

5b. binomial, $\frac{4}{81}$

5c. binomial, $\frac{1}{9}$

5. There are 8 pennies, 4 nickels, and 6 dimes in an antique coin collection. Two coins are selected with replacement after the first selection. Find each probability.

   a. P(both pennies)   b. P(both nickels)   c. P(both dimes)

   d. P(1 penny, 1 dime)   e. P(1 penny, 1 nickel)   f. P(1 nickel, 1 dime)
     not binomial   not binomial   not binomial

792   CHAPTER 14   COMBINATORICS AND PROBABILITY

RETEACHING THE LESSON

Have students find the probability that if a coin is tossed 5 times, there will be at least 3 heads.

$\frac{1}{2}$

Additional Answer

2. A binomial experiment exists *if and only if* these conditions occur.
   • The experiment consists of *n* identical trials.
   • Each trial results in one of two outcomes.
   • The trials are independent.

EXERCISES

Practice

Find each probability if a coin is tossed three times.

6. P(all heads) $\frac{1}{8}$

7. P(exactly 2 tails) $\frac{3}{8}$

8. P(at least 2 heads) $\frac{1}{2}$

Find each probability if a die is tossed five times.

9. P(only one 4) $\frac{3125}{7776}$

10. P(at least three 4s) $\frac{23}{648}$

11. P(no more than two 4s) $\frac{625}{648}$

12. P(exactly five 4s) $\frac{1}{7776}$

Angie carries tubes of lipstick in a bag in her purse. The probability of pulling out the color she wants is $\frac{2}{3}$. Suppose she uses her lipstick 4 times in a day. Find each probability.

13. P(never the correct color) $\frac{1}{81}$

14. P(correct at least 3 times) $\frac{16}{27}$

15. P(no more than 3 times correct) $\frac{65}{81}$

16. P(correct exactly 2 times) $\frac{8}{27}$

Maroa guesses at all 10 true/false questions on her psychology test. Find each probability.

17. P(7 correct) $\frac{15}{128}$

18. P(all incorrect) $\frac{1}{1024}$

19. P(at least 6 correct) $\frac{193}{512}$

20. P(at least half correct) $\frac{319}{512}$

Jojo MacMahon plays for the Worthington Wolves softball team. She is now batting 0.200 (meaning 200 hits in 1000 at bats). Find each probability for the next 5 times at bat.

21. P(exactly 1 hit) $\frac{256}{625}$

22. P(exactly 3 hits) $\frac{32}{625}$

23. P(at least 4 hits) $\frac{21}{3125}$

Find each probability if three coins are tossed.

24. P(3 heads) $\frac{1}{8}$

25. P(3 tails) $\frac{1}{8}$

26. P(at least 2 heads) $\frac{1}{2}$

27. P(exactly 2 tails) $\frac{3}{8}$

If a thumbtack is dropped, the probability of its landing point up is $\frac{2}{5}$. Miss Hostetler drops 10 tacks while putting up the lunch menus for the week on the bulletin board. Find each probability.

28. P(all point up) $\frac{1024}{9,765,625}$

29. P(exactly 3 point up) $\frac{419,904}{1,953,125}$

30. P(exactly 5 point up) $\frac{1,959,552}{9,765,625}$

31. P(at least 6 point up) $\frac{1,623,424}{9,765,625}$

LESSON 14-8   THE BINOMIAL THEOREM AND PROBABILITY   793

Exercise Note

For Exercises 32–35, encourage students to give a percent approximation of the probability so they can appreciate the meaning of the probability.

Critical Thinking

32. In baseball, the World Series matches the champion from the American League against the champion from the National League in a best of 7 series of games (meaning the first team to win 4 games is the World Series champion).

    a. If the two teams are evenly matched, what is the probability that the World Series will end in exactly 5 games? $\frac{1}{4}$

    b. If the probability that the team from the National League will win is $\frac{3}{5}$ for each game, what is the probability that the National League will win the World Series in exactly 5 games? $\frac{648}{3125}$

Applications and Problem Solving

33. Cooking In cooking class, 1 out of 5 souffles that Sabrina makes will collapse. She is preparing 6 souffles to serve at a party for her parents. What is the probability that exactly 4 of them do not collapse?

33. $\frac{768}{3125}$

34. Skeet Shooting Skeet shooting involves shooting at discs, called clay pigeons, propelled into the air by a machine. Heather usually hits 9 out of 10 clay pigeons. If she shoots 12 times, find each probability.

    a. $P(\text{all misses})$ $\frac{1}{1,000,000,000,000}$

34b. $\frac{3,788,111,448}{1,000,000,000,000}$

    b. $P(\text{exactly 7 hits})$

    c. $P(\text{all hits})$ $\frac{282,429,536,481}{1,000,000,000,000}$ or $\left(\frac{9}{10}\right)^{12}$

34d. $\frac{177,826,004,451}{200,000,000,000}$

    d. $P(\text{at least 10 hits})$

35. Finance A stock broker is researching 13 independent stocks. An investment in each stock will either make money or lose money. The probability that each stock will make money is $\frac{5}{8}$. What is the probability that exactly 10 of the stocks make money? 0.1372

Mixed Review

36. Find the product of A and B if $A = \begin{bmatrix} 4 & 3 \\ 7 & 2 \end{bmatrix}$ and $B = \begin{bmatrix} 8 & 5 \\ 9 & 6 \end{bmatrix}$. **(Lesson 2-2)** $\begin{bmatrix} 59 & 38 \\ 74 & 47 \end{bmatrix}$

37. Find the inner product of $\vec{u}$ and $\vec{v}$ if $\vec{u} = (2, -1, 3)$ and $\vec{v} = (5, 3, 0)$. **(Lesson 8-4)** 7

38. Simplify $\dfrac{x!(x-3)!}{(x-2)!(x-1)!}$. Assume x and y are positive integers, $x > y$, $x > 2$. **(Lesson 12-6)** $\dfrac{x}{x-2}$

39. A pair of dice is tossed. Find the probability that their sum is greater than 7 given that the numbers match. **(Lesson 14-7)** $\frac{1}{2}$

40. College Entrance Exam Choose the best answer. C

    If $a > b$ and $c < 0$, which of the following are true?

    I. $ac < bc$

    II. $a + c > b + c$

    III. $a - c < b - c$

    (A) I only   **(B)** II only   **(C)** I and II only   **(D)** I, II, and III

794 CHAPTER 14 COMBINATORICS AND PROBABILITY

EXTENDING THE LESSON

Math Power: Problem Solving

A basketball player's free-throw percentage changes each time he or she makes a shot. Suppose a player makes 70% of his or her shots. What is the probability that out of the next five shots, four will go into the basket?

$\frac{7203}{20,000}$ or about 0.36

Enrichment Masters Booklet, p. 101

NAME _____ DATE _____

14-8 Enrichment Worksheet

Combinations and Pascal's Triangle

Pascal's triangle is a special array of numbers invented by Blaise Pascal (1623-1662). The values in Pascal's triangle can be found using the combinations shown below.

1. Evaluate the expression in each cell of the triangle

	$C(1, 0)$	$C(1, 1)$	
	1	1	

2. The pattern shows the relationship between $C(n, r)$ and Pascal's triangle. In general, it is true that $C(n, r) + C(n, r + 1) = C(n + 1, r + 1)$. Complete the proof of this property. In each step, the denominator has been given.

T101
Glencoe Division, Macmillan/McGraw-Hill

Technology

Dice Roll Simulation

```
  5 DIM A(12)
 10 INPUT "ENTER NUMBER OF
    ROLLS DESIRED: " ;R
 20 FOR N = 2 TO 12
 30 LET A(N) = 0
 40 NEXT N
 45 PRINT: PRINT
 50 FOR I = 1 TO R
 60 LET D1 = INT(6*RND(1) + 1)
 70 LET D2 = INT(6*RND(1) + 1)
 80 LET T = D1 + D2
 90 PRINT T:" ";
100 LET C = 2
110 IF T = C THEN GOTO 140
120 LET C = C + 1
130 GOTO 110
140 LET A(C) = A(C) + 1
150 NEXT I
155 PRINT: PRINT
160 FOR M = 2 TO 12
170 LET P = INT(((A(M)/R)*1000) + .5)/10
180 LET E = INT((250 * (6 - ABS(7 - M))/9)
    + .5)/10
190 PRINT "#":M:"TIMES ROLLED:":A(M):
    "EXPERIMENTAL PROBABILITY":P:"%"
200 PRINT "THEORETICAL PROBABILITY: ":E:
    "%":PRINT
210 NEXT M
220 END
```

Using Technology

Objective This optional page shows how a BASIC program can be used to simulate rolling dice so that experimental probabilities can be calculated.

Teaching Suggestions

Have the students run the program several times to simulate dice rolls. Have them keep track of the probability in a chart format and then use the chart to make a conjecture about the expected probability in relation to the number of rolls. If a spreadsheet is available, enter the chart into the spreadsheet and have the computer calculate the probability. Then use the spreadsheet to make predictions about the expected probability.

You may wish to follow up this lesson by having groups of students discuss the following questions.
- How does your conjecture about the number of rolls in relation to the theoretical probability compare with those of others in the group?
- What are the advantages of having a computer program simulate rolling dice?
- Does using a computer mean that the experimental probability will be closer to the theoritical probability? If not, why?
- Can the experimetal probability ever equal the theoretical probability?

Probability is used to predict the outcome in games of chance involving rolling dice, tossing coins, selecting cards, or winning sweepstakes or lotteries. A computer program can be used to simulate rolling dice, tossing coins, and so on.

The BASIC program at the left simulates rolling two dice, prints the number of times a sum was rolled, experimental probability, and the theoretical probability. Each time the program is run, the experimental probability may be different due to the random selection of values in lines 60 and 70.

Each random number selected by the computer lies between 0 and 1. Then it is multiplied by 6 to simulate the six faces of a die. Finally, the INT (integer) function eliminates any decimal places, and a result of 0, 1, 2, 3, 4, 5, or 6 is chosen randomly.

Enter the program and run it several times. Notice the changes in the experimental probability. When you use the program for the exercises below, it may take several minutes to complete the large samples.

EXERCISES

1. Run the program once. Enter 20 for the input. 1–3. See students' work.
2. Run the program four more times to simulate 40, 60, 80, and 100 rolls.
3. Run the program to simulate 1000 rolls.
4. Make a conjecture about the number of rolls in relation to the theoretical probability. The greater the number of rolls, the more likely it is that the experimental probability will approach the theoretical probability.

TECHNOLOGY: DICE ROLL SIMULATION 795

Using the Chapter Summary and Review

The Chapter Summary and Review begins with an alphabetical listing of the new terms that were presented in the chapter. Have students define each term and provide an example of it, if appropriate.

The Skills and Concepts presented in the chapter are reviewed using a side-by-side format. Encourage students to refer to the Objectives and Examples on the left as they complete the Review Exercises on the right.

The Chapter Summary and Review ends with exercises that review Applications and Problem Solving.

VOCABULARY

Upon completing this chapter, you should be familiar with the following terms:

basic counting principle	**752**	**779**	mutually exclusive
binomial experiment	**791**	**779**	inclusive
combination	**764**	**769**	odds
combinatorics	**752**	**753**	permutation
complement	**768**	**768**	probability
conditional probability	**784**	**785**	reduced sample space
dependent event	**752**	**785**	sample space
failure	**768**	**768**	success
independent event	**752**	**753**	tree diagram

SKILLS AND CONCEPTS

OBJECTIVES AND EXAMPLES	REVIEW EXERCISES
Upon completing this chapter, you should be able to:	Use these exercises to review and prepare for the chapter test.

- solve problems related to the basic counting principle **(Lesson 14-1)**

  Using the letters from the word *compute*, how many four-letter patterns can be formed?

  $$P(7,4) = \frac{7!}{(7-4)!}$$
  $$= \frac{7 \cdot 6 \cdot 5 \cdot 4 \cdot 3 \cdot 2 \cdot 1}{3 \cdot 2 \cdot 1} \text{ or } 840 \text{ patterns}$$

Find each value.

1. $P(6,3)$ 120   **2.** $P(8,6)$ 20,160

3. $\dfrac{P(4,\ 2) - P(6,\ 3)}{P(5,\ 3)}$ $-\dfrac{9}{5}$

4. How many ways can six different books be placed on a shelf if the only dictionary must be on an end? 240 ways

---

- solve problems involving permutations with repetitions **(Lesson 14-2)**

  How many ways can the letters of *Mississippi* be arranged?

  $$\frac{11!}{4!4!2!} = 34,650 \text{ ways}$$

How many different ways can the letters of each word be arranged?

50,400

5. LEVEL 30   **6.** CINCINNATI

7. GRADUATE 20,160 **8.** BANANA 60

■ **solve problems involving combinations (Lesson 14-3)**

From a standard deck of cards, how many different 4-card hands can have 4 cards of the same suit?

$$4[C(13, 4)] = 4\left(\frac{13!}{(13-4)!4!}\right) \text{ or } 2860 \text{ hands}$$

Find each value.

9. $C(5, 3)$ 10

10. $C(11, 8)$ 165

11. $C(5, 5) \cdot C(3, 2)$ 3

12. From a group of 3 men and 7 women, how many committees of 2 men and 2 women can be formed? 63 committees

■ **find the probability and the odds for the success and failure of an event (Lesson 14-4)**

Find the probability of randomly selecting 3 consonants from the word *algebra* without replacement.

$$P(3 \text{ consonants}) = \frac{C(4, 3)}{C(7, 3)}$$
$$= \frac{\frac{4!}{1!3!}}{\frac{7!}{4!3!}} \text{ or } \frac{4}{35}$$

State the odds of an event occurring given the probability of the event.

13. $\frac{4}{9}$ $\frac{4}{5}$

14. $\frac{1}{12}$ $\frac{1}{11}$

A bag contains 7 pennies, 4 nickels, and 5 dimes. Three coins are selected at random with replacement. What is the probability of each of the following selections?

15. all 3 pennies $\frac{343}{4096}$

16. 2 pennies, 1 nickel $\frac{49}{1024}$

■ **find the probability of independent and dependent events (Lesson 14-5)**

Three yellow and 5 black marbles are placed in a bag. What is the probability of drawing a black marble, not replacing it, then drawing a yellow marble?

$P(\text{black, yellow})$
$= P(\text{black}) \cdot P(\text{yellow following black})$
$= \frac{5}{8} \cdot \frac{3}{7} \text{ or } \frac{15}{56}$

A green die and a red die are thrown. What is the probability that each of the following occurs?

17. The red die shows a 1 and the green die shows any other number. $\frac{5}{36}$

18. Neither die shows a 1. $\frac{25}{36}$

■ **find the probability of mutually exclusive and inclusive events (Lesson 14-6)**

On a school board, 2 of the 4 female members are over 40 years old and 5 of the 6 male members are over 40. If one person didn't attend the meeting, what is the probability that it was a male or a member over 40?

$P(\text{male or over 40}) = P(\text{male}) + P(\text{over 40}) -$
$\qquad\qquad\qquad P(\text{male and over 40})$
$$= \frac{6}{10} + \frac{7}{10} - \frac{5}{10} \text{ or } \frac{4}{5}$$

A box contains slips of paper numbered from 1 to 14. A slip of paper is drawn at random. What is the probability that each of the following occurs?

19. The number is prime or is a multiple of 4. $\frac{9}{14}$

20. The number is a multiple of 2 or a multiple of 3. $\frac{9}{14}$

Alternate Review Strategy

To provide a brief in-class review, you may wish to read the following questions to your students and have them answer verbally.

1. Find $P(7, 4)$. **840**
2. Find $\frac{P(6, 3) - P(4, 1)}{P(4, 2)}$. $\frac{29}{3}$
3. How many ways can 5 books be stacked on a shelf? **120**
4. How many four-letter patterns can be formed for the letters of the word *Ohio*? **12**
5. Find $C(8, 2)$. **28**
6. From a list of 8 books, how many groups of 4 books can be selected? **70**
7. Two cards are drawn at random from a standard deck of 52 cards. What is the probability that both are diamonds? $\frac{1}{17}$
8. State the odds of an event occurring given that the probability of the event is $\frac{3}{5}$. $\frac{3}{2}$
9. A drawer contains 3 red socks and 2 white socks. If you pull out one pair of socks randomly, what is the probability you will select a pair of white socks? $\frac{1}{10}$
10. Joel has 5 pennies, 2 nickels, and 4 dimes in his pocket. He takes one coin from his pocket at random. What is the probability that it is a penny or nickel? $\frac{7}{11}$
11. There are 6 pennies, 3 nickels, and 2 dimes in a coin purse. Two coins are selected with replacement after the first selection. What is the probability that both coins are dimes? $\frac{4}{121}$

For more information on other methods of alternate assessment, you may wish to refer to Glencoe's *Alternate Assessment in the Mathematics Classroom*.

Two multiple-choice tests (Forms 1A and 1B) and two free-response tests (Forms 2A and 2B) are provided in the *Evaluation Masters*. Chapter 14 Test, Form 1A is shown below. Chapter 14 Test, Form 2A is shown on the next page.

Evaluation Masters Booklet, pp. 169–170

■ find the probability of an event given the occurrence of another event **(Lesson 14-7)**

A coin is tossed three times. What is the probability that at the most 2 heads show given that at least 1 head shows?

Let event A be that at most 2 heads show.

Let event B be that at least 1 head shows.

$$P(A/B) = \frac{P(A \text{ and } B)}{P(B)}$$

$$= \frac{\frac{6}{8}}{\frac{7}{8}} \text{ or } \frac{6}{7}$$

■ find the probability of an event by using the binomial theorem **(Lesson 14-8)**

If you guess on all 8 answers of a true/false quiz, what is the probability that exactly 5 of your answers will be correct?

$$(p + q)^8 = \sum_{r=0}^{8} \frac{8!}{r!(8 - r)!} p^{8-r} q^r$$

$$\frac{8!}{5!(8 - 5)!}\left(\frac{1}{2}\right)^5\left(\frac{1}{2}\right)^3 = \frac{56}{256} \text{ or } \frac{7}{32}$$

A green die and a red die are thrown.

21. What is the probability that the sum of the dice is less than 5 if the green die shows a 1? $\frac{1}{2}$

22. What is the probability that the sum of the dice is 9 if the two numbers showing are different? $\frac{2}{15}$

A coin is tossed 4 times. What is the probability that each of the following occurs?

23. exactly 1 head $\frac{1}{4}$

24. no heads $\frac{1}{16}$

25. 2 heads and 2 tails $\frac{3}{8}$

26. at least 3 tails $\frac{5}{16}$

APPLICATIONS AND PROBLEM SOLVING

27. **Employment** Ms. Sommers, the new school custodian, is given 7 keys for the school building. How many ways can she place these keys on a key ring? **(Lesson 14-2)** 360 ways

28. **Tourism** A taxi in The Netherlands can hold 4 passengers safely. A party of 6 people wish to travel by taxi to The Hague. How many different groups can occupy the first taxi if it will be full? **(Lesson 14-3)** 15 ways

29. **Gifts** The Blackburn family is drawing names from a bag for their holiday gift exchange. There are 7 males and 8 females in the family. If family members draw their own name, then they must draw again before replacing their name. **(Lessons 14-4 and 14-5)**

29a. $\frac{7}{15}$

   a. What is the probability that Marie Blackburn will draw a female's name that is not her own?

   b. What is the probability that Marie will draw her own name, not replace it, then draw a male's name? $\frac{1}{30}$

NAME _____ DATE _____

~ Chapter 14 Test, Form 1A

Write the letter for the correct answer in the blank at the right of each problem.

1. Find the value of $P(9, 4)$.
   A. 15,120   B. 5280   C. 3024   D. 120   **1. C**

2. There are 6 finalists in the 100-meter hurdles. In how many ways can gold, silver, and bronze metals be awarded?
   A. 720   B. 120   C. 360   D. 90   **2. B**

3. How many ways can the letters in the word *freeform* be arranged?
   A. 40,320   B. 5040   C. 10,080   D. 6720   **3. B**

4. How many ways can 8 pins be arranged on a circular hat band?
   A. 5040   B. 40,320   C. 720   D. 2540   **4. A**

5. How many ways can 5 people be seated around a circular table with 6 chairs if the chair by the door must be empty?
   A. 720   B. 360   C. 240   D. 120   **5. D**

6. Three men and 3 women are to be selected to represent a group of 10 men and 11 women. How many ways can the representatives be selected?
   A. 1710   B. 59,400   C. 19,800   D. 712,800   **6. C**

7. Evaluate the expression $C(5, 2) \cdot C(7, 3)$.
   A. 4200   B. 350   C. 210   D. 2100   **7. B**

8. The probability that Bob's name will be drawn to win a door prize is 1 in 75. What are the odds that Bob's name will be drawn?
   A. $\frac{1}{74}$ B. $\frac{1}{75}$ C. $\frac{1}{76}$ D. $\frac{7}{6}$ **8. A**

9. Mr. Lim has 6 striped ties, 8 patterned ties, and 5 solid colored ties. If he selects 2 ties at random, what is the probability that both will be striped?
   A. $\frac{5}{57}$ B. $\frac{1}{8}$ C. $\frac{15}{128}$ D. $\frac{9}{64}$ **9. A**

10. If 3 cards are dealt from a standard deck of cards, what are the odds that all of the cards will be face cards?
    A. $\frac{11}{1105}$ B. $\frac{1}{18}$ C. $\frac{27}{2197}$ D. $\frac{2197}{132,600}$ **10. A**

11. A red die and a green die are tossed. What is the probability that both dice will show 4?
    A. $\frac{1}{3}$ B. $\frac{1}{18}$ C. $\frac{1}{6}$ D. $\frac{1}{36}$ **11. D**

NAME _____ DATE _____

~ Chapter 14 Test, Form 1A (continued)

12. There are 5 pens, 6 pencils, and 4 crayons in a jar. Robin selects three without replacement. What is the probability that she selects one of each?
    A. $\frac{1}{8}$ B. $\frac{4}{91}$ C. $\frac{24}{675}$ D. $\frac{91}{2730}$ **12. B**

13. Table-tennis balls numbered 1 to 20 are placed in a box. Three balls are drawn at random. What is the probability of drawing 3 numbers less than 10 if no replacement occurs?
    A. $\frac{7}{95}$ B. $\frac{729}{8000}$ C. $\frac{81}{760}$ D. $\frac{63}{1000}$ **13. A**

14. A card is drawn from a standard deck of cards. What is the probability that the card will be either a diamond or a face card?
    A. $\frac{1}{16}$ B. $\frac{25}{52}$ C. $\frac{11}{26}$ D. $\frac{3}{8}$ **14. C**

15. There are 12 seniors and 10 juniors on the prom committee. If 2 people are selected at random to be in charge of the decorations, what is the probability that at least one of them will be a senior?
    A. $\frac{62}{77}$ B. $\frac{5}{11}$ C. $\frac{11}{60}$ D. $\frac{5}{6}$ **15. A**

16. Jean has 5 blue shirts, 3 red shirts, and 5 white shirts. If she selects one shirt at random, what is the probability the shirt will be red or blue?
    A. $\frac{5}{8}$ B. $\frac{3}{8}$ C. $\frac{4}{5}$ D. $\frac{8}{13}$ **16. D**

17. A card is drawn at random from a standard deck of cards. If the card is black, what is the probability that it is the ace of clubs?
    A. $\frac{1}{52}$ B. $\frac{1}{26}$ C. $\frac{1}{13}$ D. $\frac{1}{4}$ **17. B**

18. 70% of the employees at Acme Wheels graduated from college, 50% have had 5 or more years of business experience, 20% have 5 or more years of business experience and have graduated from college. What is the probability that an employee selected at random has less than 5 years experience if the employee graduated from college?
    A. $\frac{5}{7}$ B. $\frac{1}{5}$ C. $\frac{2}{7}$ D. $\frac{3}{5}$ **18. A**

19. If three coins are tossed, find P(at least 2 tails).
    A. $\frac{3}{8}$ B. $\frac{1}{4}$ C. $\frac{1}{2}$ D. $\frac{5}{8}$ **19. C**

20. The probability that Julie will make a free throw is $\frac{2}{3}$. What is the probability that she will make exactly 4 out of her next 6 free throw shots?
    A. $\frac{4}{15}$ B. $\frac{6}{25}$ C. $\frac{108}{805}$ D. $\frac{432}{3125}$ **20. D**

Bonus

A test has 5 true and false questions and 5 multiple-choice questions. Each multiple-choice question has 4 possible answers. If Maria guesses on all 10 questions, what is the probability that she will get exactly 8 right answers?
A. $\frac{189}{2048}$ B. $\frac{175}{32,768}$ C. $\frac{81}{16,384}$ D. $\frac{243}{1024}$ **Bonus: B**

CHAPTER 14   TEST

Find each value.

1. $P(6,2)$ 30   2. $P(7,5)$ 2520   3. $C(8,3)$ 56   4. $C(5,4)$ 5

5. The letters r, s, t, u, and v are to be used to form five-letter patterns. How many patterns can be formed if repetitions are not allowed? 120 patterns

6. **Employment** There are 5 persons who are applicants for 3 different positions in a store, each person being qualified for each position. In how many ways is it possible to fill the positions? 60 ways

7. How many ways can 7 people be seated at a round table relative to each other? 720 ways

8. **Sports** How many baseball teams can be formed from 15 players if only 3 pitch and the others play the remaining 8 positions? 1485 teams

9. A bag contains 4 red and 6 white marbles. How many ways can 5 marbles be selected if exactly 2 must be red? 120 ways

10. **Geometry** Find the number of possible diagonals in a polygon that has 20 sides. 170 diagonals

11. **Sports** The probability that the Pirates will win a game against the Hornets is $\frac{4}{7}$. What are the odds that the Pirates will beat the Hornets? $\frac{4}{3}$

12. Five cards are drawn from a standard deck of cards. What is the probability that they are all from one suit? $\frac{33}{16,660}$

13. Find the probability of getting a sum of 8 on the first throw of two dice and a sum of 4 on the second throw. $\frac{5}{432}$

14. **Telephones** A new phone is being installed at the Collier residence. What is the probability that the final 3 digits in the telephone number will be odd? $\frac{1}{8}$

15. A bag contains 3 red, 4 white, and 5 blue marbles. If 3 marbles are selected at random, what is the probability that all are red or all are blue? $\frac{1}{20}$

16. A card is drawn from a standard deck of cards. What is the probability of having drawn an ace or a black card? $\frac{7}{13}$

17. Four-digit numbers are formed from the numbers 7, 3, 3, 2, and 2. If a number is odd, what is the probability that the 3s are together? $\frac{5}{18}$

18. Two numbers are selected at random from the numbers 1 through 9. If their product is even, what is the probability that both numbers are even? $\frac{3}{13}$

19. Five bent coins are tossed. The probability of heads is $\frac{2}{3}$ for each of them. What is the probability that no more than 2 will show heads? $\frac{17}{81}$

20. **Archery** While shooting arrows, Akira can hit the center of the target 4 out of 5 times. What is the probability that he will hit it exactly 4 out of the next 7 times? $\frac{1792}{15,625}$

Bonus
A positive integer $n \le 120$ is chosen in such a way that if $n \le 80$, then the probability of choosing n is p, and if $n > 80$, then the probability of choosing n is $2p$. What is the probability that a perfect square is chosen? 0.075

CHAPTER 14   TEST   799

15 STATISTICS AND DATA ANALYSIS

PREVIEWING THE CHAPTER

This chapter begins by reviewing frequency tables, bar graphs, and histograms. Included are back-to-back bar graphs, three-dimensional bar graphs, and frequency polygons. Students analyze data using measures of central tendency (mean, median, and mode). They also encounter measures of variation (quartiles, interquartile range) and the box-and-whisker plots that can be used to represent them. They are introduced to the concepts of mean deviation and standard deviation. Students then explore the properties of a normal distribution. They build on this knowledge to find the standard error of the mean and predict the population mean for a sample set of data within a given level of confidence. Finally they draw scatter plots and their regression lines, determining the goodness of fit.

Lesson Objective Chart

Lesson (Pages)	Lesson Objectives	State/Local Objectives
15-1 (802-810)	**15-1A:** Draw, analyze, and use bar graphs and histograms.	
	15-1B: Orgranize data into a frequency distribution table.	
15-2 (811-819)	**15-2A:** Find the mean, mode, and median of a set of data.	
	15-2B: Find the mean and median of data organized in a stem-and-leaf plot or a frequency distribution table.	
15-3 (820-829)	**15-3A:** Find the mean deviation, semi-interquartile range, and standard deviation of a set of data.	
	15-3B: Organize and compare data using box-and-whisker plots.	
15-4 (830-837)	**15-4:** Use the normal distribution curve.	
15-5 (838-843)	**15-5:** Find the standard error of the mean to predict the true mean of a population with a certain level of confidence.	
15-6 (846-854)	**15-6A:** Draw and analyze scatter plots.	
	15-6B: Draw regression lines.	
	15-6C: Compute correlation values to determine goodness of fit.	

ORGANIZING THE CHAPTER

You may want to refer to the **Course Planning Guide Calendar** on pages T34-T35 for a complete pacing chart.

Lesson Planning Guide

Lesson	Pages	Practice	Enrichment	Evaluation	Graphing Calculator	Computer	Multicultural Activity	Applications	Problem Solving	Case Study Follow-Up	Decision Making	Transparencies
					Technology				Activity Masters			
15-1	802-810	p. 102	p. 102		p. 29							15-1
15-2	811-819	p. 103	p. 103	Quiz A, p. 189					p. 44			15-2
15-3	820-829	p. 104	p. 104	Quiz B, p. 189		p. 30				p. 45		15-3
15-4	830-837	p. 105	p. 105	Quiz C, p. 190 Mid-Chapter Test, p.191								15-4
15-5	838-843	p. 106	p. 106				p. 15	p. 43				15-5
15-6	846-854	p. 107	p. 107	Quiz D, p. 190								15-6
Review	860-862	Multiple Choice Tests, Forms 1A and 1B, pp. 181-184 Free Response Tests, Forms 2A and 2B, pp. 185-188 Standardized Test Questions, p. 192										
Test	863											

(Blackline Masters Booklets — Technology / Activity Masters)

Other Chapter Resources

Student Edition

Case Study Follow-Up, p. 829
Decision Making, p. 810
Technology, p. 855

Other Supplements

Transparency 15-0 for Chapter Opener
Alternate Assessment in the Mathematics Classroom,
    Glencoe Publishing Co., 1993
Cooperative Learning in the Mathematics Classroom,
    Glencoe Publishing Co., 1993

Software

Test and Review Generator Software
    Available for Apple, IBM, and Macintosh
Teacher's Guide for Software Resources

ENHANCING THE CHAPTER

Cooperative Learning

Intervening to Teach Cooperative-Learning Skills

In many of their other activities, both inside and outside of school, students are required to compete more often than to cooperate. Therefore, it may require some time and attention for students to develop positive group skills. Experienced researchers recommend that only a few of these skills be taught each semester. Each new skill should be clearly defined before the session begins and skills that were introduced earlier reviewed. Then, after the session begins, the teacher should monitor the groups and intervene when appropriate. Remember to intervene only when necessary and then in a positive manner. Once students recognize the need for the skill, they only need help with developing it. This involves the teacher including examples of expected behavior when the skill is first defined and then offering appropriate guidance and feedback as students practice the skill during their cooperative-learning sessions. After each session, you also should provide time for the students to discuss and assess their behaviors. To motivate the discussion, you can simply ask each group to list the two things they did better this time than the last time and the one thing they plan to do better the next time.

For more information on cooperative learning, see pages T20-T21. Additional information on using cooperative groups is available in Glencoe's *Cooperative Learning in the Mathematics Classroom,* ©1993.

Multicultural

Multicultural Activity Masters, p. 15

Activity Masters

Applications, p. 43

Problem Solving, p. 44

Case Study Follow-Up, p. 45

Technology

The Technology feature following Lesson 15-6 uses *Data Insights*, a statistical software package from Sunburst. Among the features of the software is the ability to graph two sets of related data as ordered pairs and draw the median-fit line, if it exists. The software also draws other types of statistical graphs, such as bar graph, histograms, box-and-whisker plots, and broken-line graphs, as well as calculating measures of central tendency and variation.

The Exploration in Lesson 15-1 provides instruction for inputting data and then drawing a histogram with a graphing calculator. The Exploration in Lesson 15-2 investigates the mean by using the STAT functions of the calculator. In Lesson 15-3, the calculator is used to find the standard deviation of a set of data and of a frequency distribution. Lesson 15-6A illustrates how to make a scatter plot on a graphing calculator and find the line of regression. Lesson 15-6 shows student how the Pearson Product-Moment Correlation can be found using a graphing calculator. Lesson 15-6B is a detailed lesson on using the graphing calculator to determine the best curve that represents a set of data.

Graphing Calculator Exercises, pp. 808, 845, 853, 859

Outside Resources

Books/Periodicals

Fennema, E. and G.C. Leder, editors. *Mathematics and Gender*, Teachers College Press, New York, 1990.

North Carolina School of Science and Mathematics. *New Topics for Secondary School Mathematics: Data Analysis.*, NCTM: Reston, VA, 1988.

Films/Videotapes/Videodiscs

Mathematics, Probability, and Statistics, Great Plains National, University of Nebraska-Lincoln

Software

Statistics Workshop. Sunburst (Macintosh)

StatExplorer. Scott Foresman (IBM, Macintosh)

Data Models. Sunburst (Macintosh)

Data Insights. Sunburst (Apple II, IBM)

Technology Masters

Graphing Calculator, p. 29

Computer, p. 30

This two-page introduction to the chapter provides students with an opportunity to see how college students use the mathematics presented in this chapter in their chosen majors. It also gives students a glimpse of the college majors that are available to them.

Transparency 15–0, available in the *Advanced Mathematical Concepts* Teaching Transparency Package, provides another full-color visual and motivational activity that you can use to engage your students in the mathematical content of the chapter.

More About
Darlene Rose Helzerman

Darlene Helzerman is required to take a variety of mathematics courses for her major in accounting. The mathematics courses she has taken include calculus, statistics, computer programming, and business information systems. She is attending the University of Michigan, where she is a member of the Michigan Honorary Accounting Society and is treasurer of University Students Against Cancer. Her major gives her the knowledge and experience to take an examination in *certified public accounting*. She wants to work for a public accounting firm where she would audit the accounts of corporations.

CHAPTER 15

STATISTICS AND DATA ANALYSIS

HISTORICAL SNAPSHOT

First pictograph statement of accounts Uruk, Sumer (now Iraq)	Decimal system Aryabhata and Varamibara, India	Binary arithmetic Gottfried Leibnitz Germany	Pencil with attached eraser, Hyman Lipman Philadelphia	Ford Motor Company Detroit, Michigan	School of Business established at University of Michigan	Electronic pocket calculator, Texas Instruments, Dallas
3500 BC	AD 520	1703	1858	1903	1924	1972

800

Chapter Project

Materials   graphing calculators or statistical software

Procedure   Organize students into cooperative groups. Have each group choose an item to survey, such as favorite radio show, favorite athletic shoe, height, age, favorite food, and so on. Have them develop the format for the type of survey questions they will use. The groups should survey at least 50 students in various other subject classes.

Have them organize the data they gather and do a full statistical analysis of the data, including finding the mean, median, mode, and standard deviation. Have them also find the prediction mean and determine confidence intervals for their data. Have them organize the data into charts and graphs, prepare a report, and present their findings to the class.

CHAPTER OBJECTIVES

In this chapter, you will:
- Make and use graphs and plots to analyze data.
- Find measures of central tendency and variability.
- Organize data into frequency distributions.
- Use the normal distribution curve.
- Fit curves to curvilinear data.

CAREER GOAL: Public Accounting

When most people think of accounting, they think of keeping track of account balances in a ledger. But much more is involved, especially for the public accountant. Darlene Helzerman would like to become a certified public accountant because "in public accounting I would gain experience with the operations of several corporations of different sizes and complexity. If I were to work as a corporate accountant, I would only experience the operation of a single corporation."

Darlene was inspired to pursue a career in accounting by her professors. "At the University of Michigan, our professors come from the real world of business. As a result, they are able to relate real-world experiences and opportunities. I would say that my professors have been the greatest inspiration for me."

Darlene emphasizes the role that mathematics plays in accounting. "Mathematics is so analytical that a knowledge of mathematics helps you to analyze and adapt to any new situation," she says. She also uses mathematics in her work. "For manufacturing corporations, we find variances in order to reduce errors. For example, consider the process of manufacturing cereal boxes. If variances related to the size of a cereal box are within a given range, it would be acceptable to continue manufacturing them. If the variances fall outside the given range, however, the process of manufacturing would have to be changed in order to avoid costly errors."

Darlene looks forward to being a positive role model for other young women. "It is important for women to be seen in successful professional roles. I find it exciting to think that I might help change society's view of women."

READ MORE ABOUT IT

Batty, J. *Designing and Presenting Financial Information*. Brookfield, Vermont: Gower Publishing Company, 1988.

Gaylord, Gloria L. and Glenda E. Ried. *Careers in Accounting*. Lincolnwood, Illinois: VGM Career Horizons, 1991.

Levy, Morton. *Accounting Goes Public*. Philadelphia: University of Pennsylvania Press, 1977.

SPOTLIGHT ON...

Darlene Helzerman
Age: 20
Class: Junior
School: University of Michigan
  Ann Arbor, Michigan
Major: Accounting

"I find it exciting to think that I might help change society's view of women."

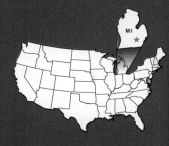

FOR MORE INFORMATION

If you would like more information about accounting, contact:

National Society of Public Accountants (NSPA)
1010 N. Fairfax Street
Alexandria, VA 22314

Applications

Lesson	Application	Examples	Exercises
15–1	Civics	1	
	Health	2	
	Sports		34
	Demographics		35
15–2	Sportswear	1	
	Salaries	2	
	Testing		23
	Sports		24
15–3	Entertainment		13
	Energy		15
	Sports		16, 17
15–4	Quality Control	1, 2	
	Retirement	4	
	Academics	5	
	Obstetrics		34
	Evaluation		35
15–5	Quality Control	3	
	Manufacturing		15
	Business		16
	Employment		17
15–6	Nutrition		23
	Health		24

NCTM Standards: 1-4, 10

Lesson Resources

- Practice Master 15–1
- Enrichment Master 15–1
- Technology Master, p. 29

 Transparency 15–1 contains the 5-Minute Check and a teaching aid for this lesson.

INTRODUCING THE LESSON

 5-Minute Check

(over Chapter 14)

1. How many seven-digit phone numbers can begin with the prefix 93? **100,000**
2. How many five-letter patterns can be formed from the letters of the word *foods*? **60**
3. From a list of seven books, how many groups of four books can be selected? **35**
4. A box contains 3 tennis balls, 6 baseballs, and 5 softballs. What is the probability that a ball selected at random will be a baseball?
   $\frac{6}{14}$ or $\frac{3}{7}$
5. Find the probability of getting a sum of 7 on the first roll of two dice and a sum of 3 on the second roll.
   $\frac{1}{108}$

Motivating the Lesson

How tall are the players on the girls' varsity basketball team and the boys' varsity basketball team? The heights of the members of each team could be displayed in chart form. Ask students to compare the numbers and check their heights against those on the chart.

15-1 The Frequency Distribution

Objectives

After studying this lesson, you should be able to:

15–1A
- draw, analyze, and use bar graphs and histograms, and

15–1B
- organize data into a frequency distribution table.

Application

Compact discs (CDs) first appeared in music stores in 1983. A compact disc is $4\frac{2}{3}$ inches in diameter, and the music on a CD is recorded by sampling sounds from a master tape at a rate of 44,100 times per second. The samples are translated into a binary code that is stored on the disc. A laser in the CD player translates the codes back into musical sounds. How many compact discs do you think are made each year?

The table below shows different types of recording media and how many millions of units were shipped in 1973 compared to 1990. The **back-to-back bar graph** shows the comparisons for each recording medium. A back-to-back bar graph is plotted on a two-quadrant coordinate system with the horizontal scale repeated in each direction from the central axis.

Manufacturers' Shipments of Recording Media (in millions of units)		
Medium	1973	1990
albums	280.0	11.7
45s	228.0	27.6
cassette tapes	15.0	442.2
compact discs	0.0	286.5

You can see from the graph that the popularity of cassettes and compact discs has increased dramatically from 1973 to 1990 while the popularity of albums and 45s has plummeted.

Example 1

APPLICATION

Civics

Make a back-to-back bar graph of the following data which compares the percent of the U. S. population in each age group over the century.

Age (yr)	0—9	10—19	20—29	30—39	40—49	50—59	60—69	70+
1890	25%	22%	18%	14%	9%	6%	4%	2%
1990	16%	14%	16%	17%	12%	9%	8%	8%

Let the age groups be the central axis. Draw a horizontal axis that is scaled from 0 to 20 in each direction. Let the left side of the graph represent the population groups from 1890 and the right side of the graph be those from 1990. Draw bars the appropriate lengths for the data.

802   CHAPTER 15   STATISTICS AND DATA ANALYSIS

ALTERNATE TEACHING STRATEGIES

Using Cooperative Groups

Have students work in groups to make a bar graph of data that they gather by research. Encourage them to check newspapers and almanacs for data.

Using Graphing Calculators

Have students enter data into the statistics mode of a graphing calculator. Have the calculator display the histogram.

FYI...

The census was originally created to determine the number of seats in the House of Representatives according to the population in each state.

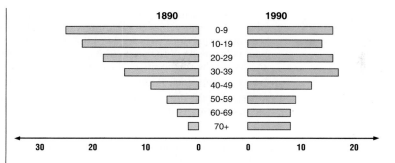

1890   1990

0-9
10-19
20-29
30-39
40-49
50-59
60-69
70+

30   20   10   0   0   10   20

You can see from the graph that a greater percent of the population in 1890 was very young, and very few people lived past the age of 50. In 1990, that trend was very different. 25% of our population was 50 or older.

Wheat, Rice, and Corn Production, 1990
(in millions of metric tons)
Source: U.N. Food and Agriculture Organization

Sometimes it is desirable to show three or more aspects of a set of data at the same time. To present data in this way, a **three-dimensional bar graph** is often used. The graph at the left represents the production of wheat, rice, and corn in several countries. The grid defines the crop and the country. The height of each bar is drawn proportional to the millions of metric tons of the crop produced in each country.

Sometimes the amount of data you wish to represent in a bar graph is too great for each item of data to be considered individually. In this case, a **frequency distribution** is a convenient system for organizing the data. A number of classes are determined, and all values in a class are tallied and grouped together. The intervals are often named by a range of values. In the table, the interval described by 2.0–4.0 means all tree diameters d such that $2.0 \le d < 4.0$. The **class interval** is the range of each class. The class intervals in a frequency distribution should all be equal. In the table at the right, the class interval for each range is 2.0.

The range of a set of data is the difference between the greatest and least values in the set.

Sample Tree Diameters from the Cumberland National Forest, 1992

Tree Diameters (in inches)	Frequency
2.0–4.0	6
4.0–6.0	30
6.0–8.0	38
8.0–10.0	33
10.0–12.0	9
12.0–14.0	4

LESSON 15-1 THE FREQUENCY DISTRIBUTION 803

Teaching Tip After explaining Example 1, have students use the back-to-back bar graph to make other conclusions about the data.

Chalkboard Example

For Example 1

Make a back-to-back bar graph of the following data, which compares the farm population to the nonfarm population.

Age(yr)	Farm	Nonfarm
0–14	0.4%	22.9%
15–24	0.2%	13.9%
25–34	0.2%	17.2%
35–44	0.3%	14.9%
45–54	0.2%	10.1%
55–64	0.2%	8.4%
65–74	0.2%	7.2%
75+	0.1%	4.6%

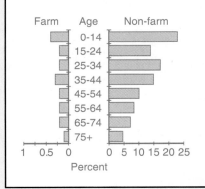

Teaching Tip After explaining the frequency distribution example, emphasize that the intervals in a frequency distribution should all be equal.

The heights (in inches) of 43 girls trying out for basketball at Forest View High School have been tallied in the chart below.

Class Limits	Tally	f
58–62	II	2
62–66	JHT III	8
66–70	JHT JHT JHT I	16
70–74	JHT JHT II	12
74–78	JHT	5

a. Determine if the class intervals of 4 are appropriate for the data. **78 − 58 = 20; Class intervals of 4 are appropriate.**

b. Find the class marks. **60, 64, 68, 72, 76**

c. Draw a histogram of the data.

The **class limits** of a set of data organized in a frequency distribution are the upper and lower values in each interval. The class limits in the tree sample data on the previous page are 2.0, 4.0, 6.0, 8.0, 10.0, 12.0, and 14.0. If an item of data falls on one of the class limits, it is tallied in the higher class. The **class marks** are the midpoints of the classes; that is, the average of the upper and lower limit in each interval. The class mark for 2.0–4.0 is $\frac{2.0 + 4.0}{2}$ or 3.0. Notice that the difference in the consecutive class marks is the same number as the class interval.

The most common way of displaying frequency distributions is by using a histogram. A **histogram** is a type of bar graph in which the width of each bar represents a class interval and the height of the bar represents the frequency in that interval.

Example 2

APPLICATION

Health

A complete frequency distribution includes the class limits, the class marks, the tallies, and the frequency of each class.

The weights of 200 boys trying out for football at Indian Hills High School have been tallied in the chart below. The actual range of weights was from 99 to 253.

Class Limits	Tally	Frequency f
95–110	II	3
110–125	JHT II	7
125–140	JHT JHT	15
140–155	JHT JHT JHT JHT JHT IIII	34
155–170	JHT JHT JHT JHT JHT JHT JHT II	42
170–185	JHT JHT JHT JHT JHT JHT JHT II	38
185–200	JHT JHT JHT JHT IIII	24
200–215	JHT JHT JHT	15
215–230	JHT JHT I	11
230–245	JHT II	7
245–260	IIII	4
	Total	**200**

a. **Determine if the class intervals of 15 are appropriate for this data.**

b. **Find the class marks.**

c. **Draw a histogram of the data.**

a. The actual range of the data is 253 − 99 or 154. Class intervals of 15 pounds, beginning with 95 and ending with 260, seem appropriate.

b. The class marks are the averages of the class limits of each interval. The class marks are 102.5, 117.5, 132.5, 147.5, 162.5, 177.5, 192.5, 207.5, 222.5, 237.5, and 252.5.

c. Label the horizontal axis with the class limits. A jagged line is often used to show the values omitted from 0 to the first limit. The vertical axis should be labeled from 0 to a value that will allow for the greatest frequency. Draw the bars side by side so that the height of each bar corresponds to its interval's frequency.

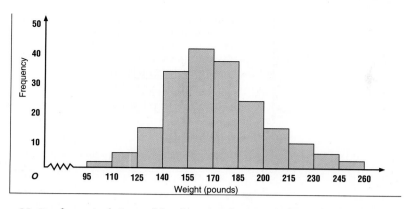

A graphing calculator can be used to create histograms. It is important to clear old data from the memory of the calculator because only one set of data can be stored at a time. Keeping old data in the calculator will alter your results.

Notice that a single item of data loses its identity in a frequency distribution. For example, a weight of 138 is grouped with all the others in the 125–140 class. In working with such a distribution, it is assumed that the data in any class are uniformly distributed over the class.

Usually, only a slight error may be introduced by this assumption.

EXPLORATION: Graphing Calculator

Use a TI-81 graphing calculator to create a histogram of the data in Example 2.

1. Clear the statistical memory.
- Press [2ND] [STAT] [◄] for the STAT DATA Menu.
- Select 2:CLRSTAT.   *CLRSTAT will appear on the home screen.*
- Press [ENTER].   *The home screen will display Done.*

2. Enter the data.
- Press [2ND] [STAT] [◄]. Then select 1:EDIT.
  The screen will show DATA, $X_1 =$, and $Y_1 = 1$.
- The X-value is the class mark and the Y-value is the frequency for the class. Enter each class mark and then press [ENTER]. Enter the number(s) for the frequency and then press [ENTER]. Continue this way until all classes are entered.

  X_1 102.5 [ENTER]
  Y_1 3 [ENTER]
  X_2 117.5 [ENTER]
  Y_2 7 [ENTER] *and so on*
  ⋮
  X_{11} 252.5 [ENTER]
  Y_{11} 4 [ENTER]
- Press [2ND] [CLEAR].   *You will return to the home screen.*

(continued on the next page)

LESSON 15-1   THE FREQUENCY DISTRIBUTION   805

Checking for Understanding

Exercises 1–11 are designed to help you assess students' understanding through reading, writing, speaking, and modeling. You should work through Exercises 1–3 with your students and then monitor their work on Exercises 4–11.

Closing the Lesson

Writing Activity   Have students write a paragraph describing how to organize a set of data in a frequency chart and how to make a histogram.

Additional Answers

1. It is similar to a histogram because it shows the graph of intervals of data. It is not a true histogram because the intervals are not equal.

5. HBO, Cinemax, and Showtime have shown an increase in the number of subscribers. TMC has shown a decrease in the number of subscribers.

Practice Masters Booklet, p. 102

15-1   NAME _____ DATE _____
Practice Worksheet

The Frequency Distribution

The selling prices of a random sample of 30 single-family homes sold in a city during the past year are given below.

67,500	72,000	54,600	38,900	87,400	28,300
105,000	91,600	46,500	62,800	136,600	81,200
59,900	76,200	117,100	64,400	25,500	51,800
88,000	63,900	125,000	70,500	28,200	59,500
118,700	81,100	42,600	57,300	77,700	64,800

1. Make a frequency distribution of the data using six classes from $20,000 to $140,000.

CLASS LIMITS	TALLY	FREQUENCY
$20,000 - 40,000	IIII	4
$40,000 - 60,000	HHT II	7
$60,000 - 80,000	HHT IIII	9
$80,000 - 100,000	HHT	5
$100,000 - 120,000	III	3
$120,000 - 140,000	II	2

2. List the class marks. $30,000, $50,000, $70,000, $90,000, $110,000, $130,000

3. What are the class intervals? $20,000-40,000, $40,000-60,000, $60,000-80,000, $80,000-100,000, $100,000-120,000, $120,000-140,000

4. What are the class limits? $20,000, $40,000, $60,000, $80,000, $100,000, $120,000, $140,000

5. Which class interval had the greatest frequency? $60,000-80,000

The ages of 100 people attending a concert are given below.

Class Limits	10 - 13	13 - 16	16 - 19	19 - 22	22 - 25
Frequency	4	19	28	36	13

6. List the class marks. 11.5, 14.5, 17.5, 20.5, 23.5
7. What is the class interval? 3
8. What are the class limits? 10, 13, 16, 19, 22, 25
9. Which age group had the most people in attendance? 19-22
10. Which age group had the fewest people in attendance? 10-13

T 102
Glencoe Division, Macmillan/McGraw-Hill

---

3. Set the range for your graph.
   • Press RANGE. Set the range as follows:
     XMIN: 95   XMAX: 260   XSCL: 15
     YMIN: 0   YMAX: 50   YSCL: 5   XRES: 1
   • Press 2ND CLEAR to return to the home screen.

4. Graph the histogram.
   • Press 2ND STAT ▶ for the STAT DRAW menu.
   • Select 1: Hist.   *Hist appears on the screen.*
   • Press ENTER.   5. See students' work.

5. Write a sentence to compare this graph to the one in Example 2.

Another type of graph can be created from a histogram. A broken line graph, often called a **frequency polygon**, can be drawn by connecting the class marks on the graph. The class marks are graphed as the midpoints of the top edge of each bar. The frequency polygon for the histogram in Example 2 is shown at the left.

CHECKING FOR UNDERSTANDING

Communicating Mathematics

Read and study the lesson to answer each question.

1. **Explain** why the back-to-back bar graph on page 803 might be considered a variation of a histogram. Why might it not? See margin.

2. **Explain** when you are most likely to use a histogram. to graph frequency distributions

3. **Demonstrate** how you would draw a frequency polygon for the histogram shown at the right.
   Find the midpoint of the top of each bar and connect the midpoints with a broken line graph.

Guided Practice

Use the bar graph to answer each question.

4. Which cable channel has the greatest number of subscribers? the least number of subscribers?
   greatest: HBO, least: TMC

5. What is the trend over time of the number of subscribers? See margin.

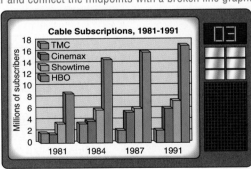

806   CHAPTER 15   STATISTICS AND DATA ANALYSIS

Have groups of students discuss how to interpret the data represented in a histogram.

The table at the right gives the annual earnings of a random sample of 100 U.S. high school teachers.

Annual Salary	Frequency
Less than $26,000	9
$26,000—$32,000	21
$32,000—$38,000	31
$38,000—$44,000	26
$44,000—$50,000	13

7–8, 11.
See margin.

6. State the class interval of the frequency distribution. $6000

7. State the class limits of the frequency distribution.

8. State the class marks of the frequency distribution.

9. What percent of the teachers polled earn $38,000 to $44,000? 26%

10. What percent of the teachers polled earn at least $38,000? 39%

11. Draw a histogram of this data.

EXERCISES

Practice Find the class interval and the class limits for each set of class marks of a frequency distribution. 12–15. See margin.

12. {10, 20, 30, 40, 50}

13. {1.1, 1.2, 1.3, 1.4, 1.5, 1.6, 1.7}

14. {2.5, 5, 7.5, 10, 12.5}

15. {25, 26, 27, 28, 29, 30, 31, 32}

The table at the right lists the salaries of males and females and the corresponding educational backgrounds.

16. See margin.

16. Make a back-to-back bar graph of this information.

17. Write a statement that describes the comparative salaries.

Women make less money than men for the same education.

Average Monthly Earnings, 1992		
Education	Males	Females
Professional Degree	$4,480	$2,311
Master's Degree	$2,901	$1,733
Bachelor's Degree	$2,471	$1,136
Associate Degree	$1,977	$1,022
Vocational School	$1,699	$773
Some College-no degree	$1,483	$710
High School Degree	$1,350	$583
High School Non-graduate	$709	$207

The IQ's of a random sample of 100 seniors are given below. 18–19. See Teacher's Answer Key.

84	120	78	89	107	116	73	88	106	117
144	92	100	124	84	100	115	76	93	112
89	109	110	128	101	109	135	100	112	81
99	119	88	117	110	81	103	127	97	120
93	115	92	116	68	97	66	102	84	108
95	72	104	95	80	85	106	99	87	115
104	100	95	85	121	112	97	106	113	82
104	102	111	103	125	95	102	88	102	97
99	100	103	78	99	99	91	97	99	103
102	110	88	100	90	100	103	92	103	100

18. Make a frequency distribution of the data using a class interval of 10. Then make a histogram of the data.

19. Make a frequency distribution of the data using a class interval of 12. Then make a histogram of the data.

LESSON 15-1   THE FREQUENCY DISTRIBUTION   807

APPLYING THE LESSON

Homework Exercises

Assignment Guide

Average: 12–22, 28, 29, 33, 34, 36–41
Enriched: 20–41

The red A, B, and C flags, printed only in the Teacher's Wraparound Edition, indicate the level of difficulty of the exercises.

Additional Answers

7. $0; $26,000; $32,000; $38,000; $44,000; $50,000

8. $13,000; $29,000; $35,000; $41,000; $47,000

11.

12. interval: 10, limits: 5, 15, 25, 35, 45, 55

13. interval: 0.1, limits: 1.05, 1.15, 1.25, 1.35, 1.45, 1.55, 1.65, 1.75

14. interval: 2.5, limits: 1.25, 3.75, 6.25, 8.75, 11.25, 13.75

15. interval; 1, limits: 24.5, 25.5, 26.5, 27.5, 28.5, 29.5, 30.5, 31.5, 32.5

Additional Answer

16.
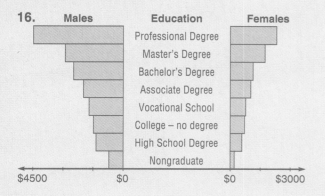

Using Technology

For Exercises 28 through 31, remind students to first organize the data into a frequency table. Then use the Edit Mode to enter the data and the frequency. Choose Hist under the Draw menu to see a histogram.

Additional Answers

28.

29.

30.

31.

20. Make a frequency distribution of the data using 16 classes. Then make a histogram of the data.

20–21. See Teacher's Answer Key.

21. Make a frequency distribution of the data using 10 classes. Then make a histogram of the data.

22. What interval would you use if you wanted to create a histogram to show that the IQ of seniors is higher than average? Sample answer: interval of 20 beginning with class limit of 60.

As an experiment in precision and gathering data, the 24 members of a pre-calculus class were given the assignment of measuring the length of the new driveway into the school's campus. Their measurements, rounded to the nearest tenth of a meter, are listed below. 23–25. See Teacher's Answer Key.

2013.3	2012.6	2012.3	2012.8
2013.5	2011.4	2013.4	2012.4
2012.3	2012.2	2012.1	2011.6
2012.0	2012.6	2012.2	2012.2
2013.9	2012.7	2011.8	2013.7
2012.4	2011.7	2012.8	2012.7

23. Make a frequency distribution of the data using an appropriate class interval.

24. Make a histogram of the data.

25. Make a frequency polygon of the data.

26. How would you handle the data if one student reported a length of 2112.7 meters instead of 2012.7 meters? Probably discard it as a mistake since it is so different from the other measures.

 27. Make a three-dimensional bar graph of the data on the population change of four regions of the United States according to the Census reports of 1970, 1980, and 1990 shown below. See Teacher's Answer Key.

Population Change (in millions)				
Year	Northeast	Midwest	South	West
1970	49	57	63	35
1980	49	59	75	43
1990	51	60	85	53

28–31. See margin.

Graphing Calculator Use a graphing calculator to make a histogram for the data in each exercise.

28. Exercise 18   **29.** Exercise 19   **30.** Exercise 20   **31.** Exercise 21

32. Read the graphing calculator manual to find how you could create a frequency polygon after you have graphed a histogram. Write a paragraph describing the process. See students' work.

Critical Thinking **33.** Find a graph in a newspaper or magazine. See students' work.
   a. Does the graph accurately represent the data?
   b. Could the data have been presented effectively without a graph?
   c. Write a summary of what the graph says to you.

Additional Answer

34a.

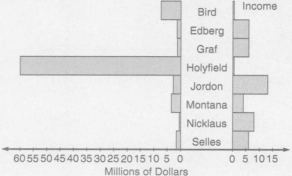

34. Sports The following table lists the yearly incomes in millions of dollars of some of the highest paid athletes in the world in 1991. The *Other Income* category includes endorsements, exhibition fees, and incentive bonuses. (Money made from businesses owned by the athletes is not included.)

Athlete	Sport	Salary	Other Income
Larry Bird	Basketball	$7.4	$0.5
Stefan Edberg	Tennis	1.4	6.0
Steffi Graf	Tennis	1.3	6.0
Evander Holyfield	Boxing	60.0	0.5
Michael Jordan	Basketball	2.8	13.2
Joe Montana	Football	3.5	4.0
Jack Nicklaus	Golf	0.5	8.0
Monica Selles	Tennis	1.6	6.0

a. Make a back-to-back bar graph that compares the salary of each athlete with their other income. See margin.

b. If you were an athlete, which appears to be the most lucrative profession if only salary is considered? boxing

c. If you were an athlete, which appears to be the most lucrative profession if other income is considered? basketball

d. Who has the greatest total salary? the least? greatest: Holyfield, least: Graf

35. Demographics The number of participants to the 1992 Summer Olympics by state are listed below. See margin.

State	Participants	State	Participants	State	Participants
AL	4	LA	8	OH	15
AK	1	ME	2	OK	5
AZ	13	MD	16	OR	12
AR	4	MA	19	PA	18
CA	140	MI	15	RI	6
CO	15	MN	11	SC	4
CT	8	MS	2	SD	1
DE	0	MO	4	TN	4
FL	41	MT	1	TX	43
GA	6	NE	1	UT	3
HI	6	NV	5	VT	2
ID	1	NH	5	VA	13
IL	17	NJ	18	WA	5
IN	8	NM	7	WV	2
IA	6	NY	28	WI	14
KS	5	NC	7	WY	0
KY	3	ND	1		

a. Make a frequency distribution showing the number of states for each interval of participants, excluding California. Use a class interval of 10.

b. Make a histogram using the information in part a. Then draw the frequency polygon.

c. Why do you think California's data was excluded from this distribution? How does the inclusion of California change the distribution?

LESSON 15-1   THE FREQUENCY DISTRIBUTION   809

Additional Answers

35a.

Class Limits	Class Marks	Tally	f
0–10	5	‖‖‖ ‖‖‖ ‖‖‖ ‖‖‖ ‖‖‖ ‖‖‖ III	33
10–20	15	‖‖‖ ‖‖‖ III	13
20–30	25	I	1
30–40	35		0
40–50	45	II	2

35b.

35c. Because it differs greatly from the other data. If it was included, it would skew the intervals and the representation of the majority of the distribution.

Additional Answer

38. $(3, 0)$, $x = -3$

Enrichment Masters Booklet, p. 102

15-1	NAME _____ DATE _____

Enrichment Worksheet

Misuses of Statistics

Statistics can be misleading. Two graphs for the same set of data can look very different from each other. Compare the following graphs.

Notice that the two graphs show the same data, but the spacing in the vertical and horizontal scales differs. Scales can be cramped or spread out to make a graph that gives a certain impression.

1. Which graph would you use to give the impression that the unemployment rate dropped dramatically from 1982 to 1990?
the first graph

2. Suppose that a car company claims, "75% of people surveyed say that our car is better than the competition." If only four people were surveyed, how many people thought that this company's car was better? 3 people

Suppose an advertiser claims that 90% of all the cars of one brand sold in the last 10 years are still on the road.

3. If 10,000 cars were sold, how many are still on the road?
9,000

4. If 1000 cars were sold, how many are still on the road? 900

5. Find an example to show how you think averages could be used in a misleading way. See students' work.

6. A survey of a large sample of people who own small computers revealed that 85% of the people thought the instruction manuals should be better written. A manufacturer of small computers claimed that it surveyed many of the same people and found that all of them liked their manuals. Discuss the possible discrepancy in the results. See students' work.

T102
Glencoe Division, Macmillan/McGraw-Hill

Mixed Review

36. Find the measure of the reference angle for an angle of $-\frac{13\pi}{3}$ radians. $\frac{\pi}{3}$ **(Lesson 5-1)**

37. State whether $\overrightarrow{PQ}$ and $\overrightarrow{RS}$ are *equal, opposite, parallel*, or *none of these* for points $P(8, -7)$, $Q(-2, 5)$, $R(8, -7)$, and $S(7, 0)$. **(Lesson 8-1)** none

38. Find the coordinates of the focus and the equation of the directrix of the parabola with equation $y^2 = 12x$. Then graph the equation. **(Lesson 10-2)** See margin.

39. Form a sequence that has two geometric means between 125 and 216. **(Lesson 12-2)** 125, 150, 180, 216

40. $\frac{59,049}{100,000}$

40. Probability Tess is running a "Wheel of Fortune" booth to raise money for a muscular dystrophy charity. The wheel has the numbers 1 to 10 on it. What is the probability of 7 never coming up in five spins of the wheel? **(Lesson 14-8)**

41. College Entrance Exam Compare quantities A and B below. $(x \neq 0)$ A
Write A if quantity A is greater.
Write B if quantity B is greater.
Write C if the two quantities are equal.
Write D if there is not enough information to determine the relationship.

(A) $\left(\frac{3}{8} + \frac{1}{6} + \frac{5}{12}\right) x^2$ **(B)** $\left(\frac{4}{15} + \frac{2}{25} + \frac{1}{3}\right) x^2$

DECISION MAKING

Safety: Car Airbags

More than 40 states now have laws requiring car passengers to wear seat belts. But because they are not yet readily available, airbags remain a luxury for most Americans. Statistics show that an airbag provides a passenger with a better chance of surviving a serious accident than a seat belt does. Is the amount of added protection great enough to justify the added cost? If airbags become readily available, should people who do not want them in their cars be required to have them? 1–3. See students' work.

1. Research the safety record of cars with airbags. Has enough data been collected to draw any conclusions about their safety relative to the safety of seat belts?

2. What is your opinion of airbags? Would you like to have them installed in your car? Do you think that a date should be set when all new cars should be equipped with airbags?

3. Project Work with your group to complete one of the projects listed at the right based on the information you gathered in Exercises 1–2.

PROJECTS

- *Conduct an interview.*
- *Write a book report.*
- *Write a proposal.*
- *Write an article for the school paper.*
- *Write a report.*
- *Make a display.*
- *Make a graph or chart.*
- *Plan an activity.*
- *Design a checklist.*

EXTENDING THE LESSON

Math Power: Communication

Explain why the bar graph below may be misleading.

Sample answer: It appears that the annual profit has gone up 10 times as much, but has actually doubled.

Decision Making

This activity provides students an opportunity to work together on a given problem. You may wish to refer to pages T20–T21 and page 800c for the various elements of cooperative groups and specific goals and strategies for using them.

15-2 Measures of Central Tendency

Objectives
15–2A
15–2B

After studying this lesson, you should be able to:
- find the mean, mode, and median of a set of data, and
- find the mean and median of data organized in a stem-and-leaf plot or a frequency distribution table.

Application

The tennis shoes sold at Hackett's Racquets are lightweight for playing tennis. Below is a table of various tennis shoes and the weight (in ounces) of men's and women's shoes. Which weight is most representative of the weights of men's tennis shoes?

Company/ Shoe name	Men's Weight	Women's Weight
Adidas Score Lite	10.7	9.1
Avia 758	13.7	11.3
Avia 748	13.5	10.9
Champion Unlimited	15.9	12.3
Converse Light 5000	12.8	11.1
Converse Light 3000	13.4	10.6
Head Radial	15.1	12.5
K-Swiss Si-I8	16.5	13.5
K-Swiss Grancourt Gstaad	16.0	13.0
K-Swiss CT 500	14.0	10.8
Nike Air Tech Challenger	14.0	11.0
Nike Air Supreme Low	12.3	9.7
Nike Air Challenge Pro	12.8	11.0

Company/ Shoe name	Men's Weight	Women's Weight
Nike Air Courtlite	13.6	10.5
Nike Air Tour Challenge	12.8	10.4
Prince FST	15.8	10.0
Reebok Pump Court Victory II	16.0	14.0
Reebok Club Pump Low	14.5	11.5
Reebok Victory LWT Low	15.0	11.5
Reebok Club Low	13.5	10.5
Reebok Victory 7000	14.0	10.5
Wilson Perfecta	12.3	10.3
Wilson Plexus	15.4	11.7
Wilson Pro Staff	14.7	11.6
Wilson Staff	14.5	11.0

The average weight of men's shoes is a value that is the most representative of the entire set of men's shoe data. A **measure of central tendency** is a type of average. It is a number that represents a set of data. The most commonly used averages are the median, mode, and mean. These measures may be used to describe and summarize a set of data, or to compare one set of data with another.

The **arithmetic mean** is symbolized by $\overline{X}$ and is often referred to as the average or, simply, the **mean**. The mean is found by adding the values in the set of data and dividing the sum by the number of values in that set. Every number in a set of data affects the value of the mean. Consequently, the mean is generally a good representative measure of central tendency. However, the mean can be considerably influenced by extreme values.

LESSON 15-2   MEASURES OF CENTRAL TENDENCY   811

ALTERNATE TEACHING STRATEGIES

Using Discussion

Have students discuss the strengths and weaknesses of the mean, median, and mode.   **Sample answer: The mean includes all the data, but is sometimes skewed by extreme values. The median gives the middle of the data, but tells little about the data. The mode tells which data value appears most frequently in the list. It tells little else.**

Using Applications

Have students work in groups to make a list of applications of the uses of central tendency in reporting data. Encourage them to gather data from newspapers or almanacs.

Lesson Resources

- Practice Master 15–2
- Enrichment Master 15–2
- Evaluation Master, Quiz A, p. 189
- Activity Master, p. 44

 Transparency 15–2 contains the 5-Minute Check and a teaching aid for this lesson.

INTRODUCING THE LESSON

5-Minute Check
(over Lesson 15–1)

1. The weights of 76 boys participating in a wrestling competition at Gerald High are tallied in the chart below.

Class Limits	Tally	f
80–90	II	2
90–100	III	3
100–110	JHT I	6
110–120	JHT JHT II	12
120–130	JHT JHT JHT JHT	20
130–140	JHT JHT JHT III	18
140–150	JHT JHT I	11
150–160	IIII	4
160–170	I	1

a. Determine if class intervals of 10 are appropriate for the data. **yes**
b. Find the class marks. **85, 95, 105, 115, 125, 135, 145, 155, 165**
c. Draw a histogram of the data.

Motivating the Lesson

Find the average height (to the nearest $\frac{1}{4}$") and the average age (to the nearest month) of the class.

TEACHING THE LESSON

Teaching Tip   After discussing the application, point out the importance of using data in business to help make decisions that can affect the profit of the company, as well as future decision-making.

Chalkboard Example

For Example 1

The chart below shows what percent of disposable income (income not needed for anything else) is saved. Find the mean percent of savings.   5.05

Year	Percent
1980	6.0
1981	6.7
1982	6.2
1983	5.4
1984	6.1
1985	4.4
1986	4.1
1987	3.2
1988	4.2
1989	4.6
1990	4.6

Example 1

APPLICATION

Sportswear

Notice that the mean is not necessarily a member of the set of data.

Refer to the application at the beginning of the lesson. Find the mean of the weights of the men's tennis shoes.

$$\overline{X} = \frac{\text{sum of the weights of the men's shoes}}{\text{number of weights being added}}$$

$$= \frac{10.7 + 13.7 + 13.5 + 15.9 + \cdots + 15.4 + 14.7 + 14.5}{25}$$

$$= \frac{352.8}{25} \text{ or about } 14.1$$

The mean weight of the men's tennis shoes is about 14.1 ounces.

EXPLORATION: Graphing Calculator

Refer to Example 1. Use a TI-81 graphing calculator to find the mean of the weights of the men's tennis shoes.

1. Clear the statistical memory.
2. Enter the data. The X-value is the weight of the shoe, and the Y-value is the frequency for the weight.
3. Press [2nd] [STAT]. Select 1:VAR to verify the number of data inputs.
4. Press [ENTER] to display the value of n and x, which is the mean.
5. Write a sentence to compare this mean to the one in Example 1.
   See students' work.

Refer to the Exploration in Lesson 15–1 for a review of data input.

A general formula for the mean of any set of data can be written using special notation. If X is a variable used to represent any value in a set of data containing n items, then the arithmetic mean $\overline{X}$ of the n values is given by the formula

$$\overline{X} = \frac{X_1 + X_2 + X_3 + \cdots + X_n}{n}.$$

The numerator of the fraction can be abbreviated using the summation symbol, $\sum$.   *Recall that $\sum$ is the uppercase Greek letter sigma.*

$$\sum_{i=1}^{n} X_i = X_1 + X_2 + X_3 + \cdots + X_n$$

The symbol X_i represents successive values of the set of data as i assumes successive integral values from 1 to n. By substituting the sigma notation into the formula for the mean, the formula becomes

$$\overline{X} = \frac{\sum_{i=1}^{n} X_i}{n} \text{ or } \overline{X} = \frac{1}{n} \sum_{i=1}^{n} X_i.$$

Arithmetic Mean

If a set of data has n values given by X_i such that i is an integer and $1 \leq i \leq n$, then the arithmetic mean, $\overline{X}$, can be found as follows.

$$\overline{X} = \frac{1}{n} \sum_{i=1}^{n} X_i$$

Another measure of central tendency is the **median**, symbolized by M_d. It is the middle value of a set of data. Before the median can be found, the data must be organized in an **array**. An array is formed by arranging the data into an ordered sequence, usually from least to greatest. The median of an odd number of data is the middle value of the array. For example, in $\{2, 3, 4, 6, 7\}$, the median is 4. The median of an even number of data is the mean of the two middle values of the array. For example, in $\{2, 3, 4, 6, 8, 9\}$, $M_d = \frac{4+6}{2}$ or 5. *Notice that the median is not necessarily a member of the set of data.*

The median is preferable to the mean as a measure of central tendency when there are a few extreme values or when some of the values cannot be determined. Unlike the mean, the median is influenced very little by extreme values.

The **mode** of a set of data is the item of data that appears more frequently than any other in the set. Data with two modes are **bimodal**. Sets have no mode when each item of the set has equal frequency. The value of the mode is not affected by extreme values. *Notice that the mode, if it exists, is always a member of the set of data.*

Example 2

APPLICATION

Salaries

Find the mean, median, and mode of the salaries for the corporate employees listed below. State which measures of central tendency seem most representative of the set of data.

Employee	Salary	Employee	Salary
Abner	$54,000	Iron	$65,000
Adams	$75,000	Johnston	$59,000
Conners	$55,000	Jones	$61,000
Harrison	$62,000	Ortez	$162,000
Heiko	$226,000	Newman	$59,000

Since there are 10 salaries, $n = 10$.

$$\sum_{i=1}^{10} X_i = \frac{1}{10}(54{,}000 + 75{,}000 + 55{,}000 + 62{,}000 + 226{,}000 + 65{,}000 + 59{,}000 + 61{,}000 + 162{,}000 + 59{,}000) \text{ or } \$87{,}800$$

To find the median, place the data in an array. Since all of the salaries are multiples of $1000, you can order the set by thousands.

54   55   59   59   61   62   65   75   162   226

Since there are an even number of data, the median is the mean of the two middle numbers, 61,000 and 62,000. The median salary is $61,500.

The mode is $59,000.

Notice that the mean is affected by the extreme values $162,000 and $226,000 and does not accurately represent the data. The median and the mode are more representative measures of central tendency in this case.

When you have a large number of data, it is often helpful to use a **stem-and-leaf plot** to organize your data in an array. In a stem-and-leaf plot, each item of data is separated into two parts that are used to form a stem and a leaf. The parts are organized into two columns. The column on the left shows the **stems**. Stems usually consist of the digits in the greatest common place value of all the data. For example, if the set of data includes the numbers 980 and 1132, the greatest common place value is hundreds. Therefore, the stem of 980 is 9, and the stem of 1132 is 11. The column on the right contains the **leaves**. The leaves consist of the other part of each item of data. The leaves are always one-digit numbers. The leaf of 980 is 8, and the leaf of 1132 is 3. The stems and leaves are usually arranged from least to greatest.

Example 3

Refer to the application at the beginning of the lesson. Make a stem-and-leaf plot of the weights of women's tennis shoes. Then determine the mean, median, and mode.

Since the weights range from 9.1 to 14.0, we will use the units place for the stems. List the stems and draw a vertical line to the right of the stems. Then list the leaves, which in this case will be the tenths digit of each weight. As shown below it is often helpful to list the leaves as you come to them and then rewrite the plot with the leaves in order from least to greatest.

An annotation usually accompanies a stem-and-leaf plot to give meaning to the representation.

stem	leaf
9	1 7
10	9 6 8 5 4 0 5 5 3
11	3 1 0 0 5 5 7 6 0
12	3 5
13	5 0
14	0

stem	leaf
9	1 7
10	0 3 4 5 5 5 6 8 9
11	0 0 0 1 3 5 5 6 7
12	3 5
13	0 5
14	0

10|6 means 10.6 ounces

Find the sum of the weights and divide by 25 to find the mean. The mean is about 11.2 ounces.

Since the median is the middle value, it is the 13th leaf on the plot. The median is about 11.0 ounces.

The stem-and-leaf plot shows the modes by repeated digits for a particular stem. There are three 5s with 10 and three 0s with 11. The set is bimodal with 10.5 ounces and 11.0 ounces as the modes.

In a frequency distribution containing large amounts of data, each individual value in the set of data loses its identity. The data in each class are assumed to be uniformly distributed over the class. Thus, the class mark is assumed to be the mean of the data tallied in its class. For example, the mean of the data in a class with limits 22.5–27.5 is assumed to be 25, the class mark.

In a frequency distribution, the sum of the values in a class is found by multiplying the class mark X, by the frequency, f, of that class. The sum of all the values in a given set of data is found by adding the sums of the values of each class in the frequency distribution. The sum of all values in the set can be represented by $\sum_{i=1}^{k} (f_i \cdot X_i)$, where k is the number of classes in the frequency distribution. Thus, the arithmetic mean of n values in a frequency distribution is found by dividing the sum of the values in the set by n or an expression equivalent to n, such as $\sum_{i=1}^{k} f_i$.

Remember that the measures of central tendency are only representations of the set of data.

Chalkboard Example

For Example 4

Find the mean of the scores of 52 students on an algebra test given the following frequency distribution.

Class Limits	Class Marks(X_i)	f	$f_i \cdot X_i$
92–100	96	14	1344
84–92	88	10	880
76–84	80	18	1440
68–76	72	8	576
60–68	64	2	128

84

Mean of the Data in a Frequency Distribution

If $X_1, X_2, \ldots, X_k$ are the class marks in a frequency distribution with k classes and $f_1, f_2, \ldots, f_k$ are the corresponding frequencies, then the arithmetic mean, $\overline{X}$, can be approximated as follows.

$$\overline{X} = \frac{\sum_{i=1}^{k}(f_i \cdot X_i)}{\sum_{i=1}^{k} f_i}$$

Example 4

Find the mean of the scores of 90 students on a geometry test given in the following frequency distribution.

Class Limits	Class Marks (X)	Frequency (f_i)	f_iX_i
93–101	97	12	1164
85–93	89	19	1691
77–85	81	38	3078
69–77	73	11	803
61–69	65	7	455
53–61	57	3	171

$$\sum_{i=1}^{6} f_i = 90 \qquad \sum_{i=1}^{6}(f_i \cdot X_i) = 7362$$

$\overline{X} \approx \dfrac{7362}{90}$ or 81.8   The mean is approximately 81.8.

Class Limits	Frequency f	Cumulative Frequency
93–101	12	90
85–93	19	78
77–85	38	59
69–77	11	21
61–69	7	10
53–61	3	3

It is often helpful to calculate the cumulative frequency from the last interval to the first.

The median, M_d, of the data in a frequency distribution is found from a cumulative frequency distribution. The chart at the left shows the cumulative frequency for the data in Example 4. The cumulative frequency of each class is the sum of the frequency of the class and the frequencies of the previous classes. So, for the class limit 77–85, the cumulative frequency equals $38 + 11 + 7 + 3$ or 59. This means that 59 geometry test scores fall below the upper class limit of 85.

Since the median is the value below which (50%)of the data lie, the class in which the median lies can be located. This class is called the **median class**. The median can be found by using an estimation technique called *interpolation. This method can also be used to find any percent other than 50%.*

Example 5

Estimate the median of the data in the frequency distribution in Example 4.

Since there are 90 scores in this frequency distribution, 45 scores are below the median and 45 are above. From the chart on the previous page, find the least cumulative frequency that is greater than or equal to 45. That cumulative frequency is 59. So, the median class is 77–85.

You can use a proportion to find the value of M_d by finding the ratios of the differences in the cumulative frequencies and the upper limits of the classes.

$$59 - 21 = 38 \begin{cases} 59 \text{ test scores lie below } 85 \\ 45 \text{ test scores lie below } M_d \end{cases} 85 - 77 = 8$$

$$45 - 21 = 24 \begin{cases} 45 \text{ test scores lie below } M_d \\ 21 \text{ test scores lie below } 77 \end{cases} M_d - 77 = x$$

$$\frac{38}{24} = \frac{8}{x}$$
$$x \approx 5.1$$

$$M_d - 77 = x$$
$$M_d - 77 \approx 5.1 \qquad x \approx 5.1$$
$$M_d \approx 82.1 \qquad \text{The median of the data is approximately 82.1.}$$

CHECKING FOR UNDERSTANDING

Communicating Mathematics

Read and study the lesson to answer each question. 1–3. See margin.

1. **Write** an argument you, as an employee, would use in Example 2 to convince management that you deserve a raise because your salary is so far below the average.

2. **Write** the sigma notation for the mean of a set of data containing 25 values.

3. **Explain** how to make a stem-and-leaf plot for a set of data whose greatest value is 135 and least value is 82.

4. Which measure of central tendency is most affected by extreme values?   mean

Guided Practice

5. **Make** a stem-and-leaf plot of the following ages of people attending a Paula Abdul concert.   See margin.

15	55	35	46	28	35	25	17	30	30	27	35
15	25	25	20	20	15	20	17	15	25	10	

Find the mean, median, and mode(s) for each set of data.

6. $\{3, 3, 6, 12, 3\}$ 5.4, 3, 3

7. $\{10, 45, 58, 10\}$ 30.75, 27.5, 10

8. $\{140, 150, 160, 170\}$ 155, 155, none

9. $\{6, 9, 11, 11, 12, 7, 6, 11, 5, 8, 10, 6\}$ 8.5, 8.5, 6 and 11

RETEACHING THE LESSON

Use cooperative groups to discuss Exercises 15, 23, and 24. Have them compare their values for the mean, median, and mode for the data.

10. The store manager of a discount department store is studying the weekly wages of her employees and the effects of an increase in health insurance. The chart at the right profiles her employees.

Weekly Wages	Frequency
$130—$140	11
$140—$150	24
$150—$160	30
$160—$170	10
$170—$180	13
$180—$190	8
$190—$200	4

a. Find the sum of the wages in each class.

10a. $1485, $3480, $4650, $1650, $2275, $1480, $780

b. Find the sum of all of the wages in the frequency distribution. $15,800

c. Find the number of employees in the frequency distribution. 100

d. Find the mean weekly wage in the frequency distribution. $158

e. Make a column showing the cumulative frequency of the weekly wage classes.

10e. 11, 35, 65, 75, 88, 96, 100

f. Find the median class of the frequency distribution. $150–$160

g. Find the median weekly wage in the frequency distribution. $155

EXERCISES

Practice

11. The table shows the numbers of live births (in millions) in the United States between 1930 and 1990.

Year	1930	'35	'40	'45	'50	'55	'60	'65	'70	'75	'80	'85	'90
Live Births	2.6	2.4	2.6	2.9	3.6	4.1	4.3	3.8	3.7	3.1	3.6	3.8	4.2

b. 3,438,500; 3,600,000; 2,600,000, 3,600,000, and 3,800,000

a. Make a stem-and-leaf plot of this data. See margin.

b. Find the mean, median, and mode of the data.

c. The term "baby boomers" is used to describe people born from 1946 to 1964. Explain how baby boomers are significant in the United States. See margin.

12. Emmanuel has scores of 84, 72, 91, 64, and 83. The class mean for the grading period was 80. How did Emmanuel compare? He was below average with 78.8.

13. Consider the heights of seven students chosen at random: 5'7", 4'8", 6'1", 5'4", 7'0", 6'7", and 5'4". 13b. See margin.

a. Find the mean of this set of data. about $5'9\frac{1}{2}"$

b. How representative of the data is the mean? Explain.

14. Crates of books are being stored for later use. The weights in pounds of the crates are 142, 160, 151, 139, 145, 117, 172, 155, and 124.

a. Find the difference between the mean and the median of their weights. 0

b. If each crate is reinforced with a 5-pound metal strip, how are the mean and median affected? Add 5 pounds to each.

LESSON 15-2 MEASURES OF CENTRAL TENDENCY 817

APPLYING THE LESSON

Homework Exercises

Assignment Guide

Average: 11–19, 22, 23, 25–30
Enriched: 14–22, 24–30

The red A, B, and C flags, printed only in the Teacher's Wraparound Edition, indicate the level of difficulty of the exercises.

Chapter 15, Quiz A, (Lessons 15–1 through 15–2), is available in the *Evaluation Masters*, p. 189.

Additional Answers

1. The mean of the corporate employees' salaries is $87,000.

2. $\frac{1}{25}\sum_{i=1}^{25} x_i$

3. The greatest common place value is tens. So the stems will go from 8 to 13. The leaves will be the units digit for each stem.

5.
```
1 | 0 5 5 5 5 7 7
2 | 0 0 0 5 5 5 5 7 8
3 | 0 0 5 5 5
4 | 6
5 | 5
```
1|0 means 10.

11a.
```
2 | 4 6 6 9
3 | 1 6 6 7 8 8
4 | 1 2 3
```
2|4 means 2.4 million.

11c. These are the years when the most babies were born. This large population is now adults in their 30s and 40s and are an active group in commerce, politics, and other fields.

13b. Answers will vary. The mean may not be very representative because the mean is greater than the median (5'7") and the mode (5'4").

15. The Laketown Fitness Club is keeping a frequency table of how many times its members use the facilities in the club during a typical month. They organized their data into the following chart.

Visits	1–5	5–9	9–13	13–17	17–21	21–25	25–29	29–33
Members	2	8	15	6	38	31	13	7

    a. Find the mean of the data. 19.3
    b. Find the median class of the data. 17–21
    c. Find the median of the data. 20.1

16. Find the value of x so that the mean of $\{2, 4, 5, 8, x\}$ is 7.5. 18.5

17. Find the value of x so that the mean of $\{x, 2x - 1, 2x, 3x + 1\}$ is 6. 3

18. Find the value of x so that the median of $\{11, 2, 3, 3.2, 13, 14, 8, x\}$ is 8. 8

19. The mean height of five boys is 68 inches. If one boy is 5 feet tall and another is 6 feet tall, give an equation to describe the possible heights for the other three boys. Sample answer: $x + y + z = 208$

A 1-meter rod is suspended at its middle so that it balances. Suppose 1-gram weights are hung on the rod at the following distances from one end.

5 cm   20 cm   37 cm   44 cm   52 cm   68 cm   71 cm   85 cm

The rod does not balance at the 50-cm mark.

20. Where must one more 1-gram weight be hung so that the rod will balance at the 50-cm mark? 68 cm from the end

21. Where must a 2-gram weight be hung so that the rod will balance at the 50-cm mark? 34 cm from the end

Critical Thinking

22. The model below is a histogram created by letting coins represent the data. The letters A, B, and C represent the mean, median, and mode, but not necessarily in that order. Determine which is which. A: mode, B: mean, C: median

Applications and Problem Solving

23. Testing The frequency distribution of the Verbal Scores of Females on the 1990 SAT test are shown below.

Scores	Number of Females (in thousands)	Scores	Number of Females (in thousands)
200–250	26.6	500–550	55.1
250–300	43.3	550–600	34.8
300–350	69.3	600–650	20.5
350–400	89.0	650–700	9.9
400–450	98.8	700–750	4.0
450–500	83.1	750–800	0.6

a. Find the mean of the data in the frequency distribution. 424.4

b. Make a column showing the cumulative frequency of the classes. See margin.

c. Find the median class of the frequency distribution. 400–450

d. Find the median of the data. 419.9

e. The published average verbal score for all females taking the SAT in 1990 was 422. Compare this score with your calculations and explain any differences that might exist. Lower; means differ because published average has access to each item of data whereas frequency distributions do not.

24. Sports The table lists the height and weight of the 11 professional basketball players who played on the Dream Team in the 1992 Summer Olympics in Barcelona.

Name	Height	Weight (lb)
Charles Barkley	6'6"	250
Larry Bird	6'9"	220
Clyde Drexler	6'7"	222
Patrick Ewing	7'0"	240
Earvin "Magic" Johnson	6'9"	220
Michael Jordan	6'6"	198
Karl Malone	6'9"	256
Chris Mullin	6'7"	215
Scottie Pippen	6'7"	210
David Robinson	7'1"	235
John Stockton	6'1"	175

24a. 6'7.8", 6'7", 6'7" and 6'9"
24b. 221.91 lb, 220 lb, 220 lb

a. Determine the mean, median, and mode of the heights of the Dream Team.

b. Determine the mean, median, and mode of the weights of the Dream Team.

c. Which measure(s) of central tendency is most representative of the data in parts a and b? See margin.

Mixed Review

25. Simplify $\dfrac{2 + i\sqrt{3}}{2 - i\sqrt{3}}$. **(Lesson 9-5)** $\dfrac{1 + 4i\sqrt{3}}{7}$

26. Evaluate $\log_{10} 0.001$. **(Lesson 11-4)** -3

27. See margin.

28. $\dfrac{59}{143}$

27. Describe what is meant by iteration and give an example. **(Lesson 13-1)**

28. City Planning There are six women and seven men on the committee for city park enhancement. A subcommittee of five members is being selected at random to study the feasibility of redoing the landscaping in one of the parks. What is the probability that the committee will have at least three women? **(Lesson 14-6)**

29. Sports Refer to the application at the beginning of this lesson. Make a histogram of the weights of the women's tennis shoes. Use a class interval of 0.5 ounces. **(Lesson 15-1)** See margin.

30. College Entrance Exam A rectangular sign is cut down by 10% of its height and 30% of its width. What percent of the original area remains? 63%

EXTENDING THE LESSON

Math Power: Reasoning

The mean age of a group of 26 teenagers is 16.8, the median age is 15.5, and the mode age is 16. Suppose a 19-year old joins the group. What are the new mean, median, and mode?
16.9, 16, 16

NCTM Standards: 1-4, 10

Lesson Resources

- Practice Master 15–3
- Enrichment Master 15–3
- Evaluation Master, Quiz B, p. 189
- Technology Master, p. 30
- Activity Master, p. 45

 Transparency 15–3 contains the 5-Minute Check and a teaching aid for this lesson.

INTRODUCING THE LESSON

 5-Minute Check

(over Lesson 15–2)

1. Find the mean, median, and mode(s) for the following set of data. {10, 12, 15, 12, 16, 20, 21, 18, 16}   **mean: 15.6; median: 16; modes 12, 16**
2. Make a stem-and-leaf plot of the data in Exercise 1.
   ```
   1 | 0 2 2 5 6 6 8
   2 | 0 1
   ```
   2|0 means 20.
3. Juan has scores of 84, 72, 91, 87, and 90 in physics. The class average is 88. How does his average compare?   **lower**

Motivating the Lesson

Discuss one of the criteria colleges use to accept applications from students, the quartile that contains the student's grade point average. The upper quartile of students often have *preferred admissions* (a process which often includes early acceptance into the college and choice of housing arrangements and classes).

15-3 Measures of Variability

Objectives

After studying this lesson, you should be able to:

15–3A ■ find the mean deviation, semi-interquartile range, and standard deviation of a set of data, and

15–3B ■ organize and compare data using box-and-whisker plots.

Application

Do you know what's in the food you eat? Today, people are more aware of the importance of eating a well-balanced diet than ever before. The chart below lists some common cereals and the number of calories and the grams of carbohydrates in a single serving of cereal (about $\frac{3}{4}$ cup). *You will use these data in Examples 1 through 4.*

Cereal Name	Calories	Carbohydrates (in grams)	Cereal Name	Calories	Carbohydrates (in grams)
Alpha-Bits	110	24	Alpen Natural Cereal with Raisins	440	80
Apple Jacks	110	26	Quaker 100% Natural Cereal	536	71
Cracklin' Oat Bran	330	57			
Cookie Crisp	200	44	Raisin Bran	200	44
Cheerios	88	16	Rice Krispies	110	25
Kellogg's Corn Flakes	110	24	Shredded Wheat	165	35
Post Corn Flakes	88	19	Special K	88	17
Froot Loops	110	25	Sugar Smacks	147	25
Frosted Flakes	165	39	Trix	110	25
Hearty Life Fruit and Nut Natural 100	390	51	Wheat Chex	165	35
Life	150	33			

Measures of central tendency, such as the mean, median, and mode of these data, are statistics that describe certain important characteristics of data. However, they do not indicate anything about the variability of the data. For example, 40 is the mean of both {35, 40, 45} and {10, 40, 70}. The variability is much greater in the second set of data than in the first since $70 - 10$ is much greater than $45 - 35$.

One measure of variability is the **range**. The range is the difference of the greatest and least values in a set of data. In the table above, the range of calories is $536 - 88$ or 448, and the range of carbohydrates is $80 - 16$ or 64.

ALTERNATE TEACHING STRATEGIES

Using Cooperative Groups

Have students work in groups to create flowcharts to find the mean and standard deviation of the cereal data presented in the application at the beginning of the lesson. Then have the groups compare their flowcharts and choose the best one to present to the class.

Using Computers

Have pairs of students use various statistical software packages to find the measures of central tendency and the standard deviation of the application presented at the beginning of the lesson.

If the median is a member of the set of data, that item of data is excluded when calculating the first and third quartile points.

Suppose a set of data is rewritten in an array and the median is found, which separates the data into two groups. Then the median of each group is found, separating the data into four groups. Each of these groups is called a **quartile**. There are three quartile points, Q_1, Q_2, and Q_3, that denote the breaks in the data for each quartile. The median is the second quartile point Q_2. The medians of the two groups defined by the median are the first quartile point Q_1 and the third quartile point Q_3, respectively.

One fourth of the data is less than the first quartile point, Q_1, and three fourths of the data is less than the third quartile point, Q_3. The difference between the first quartile point and the third quartile point is called the **interquartile range**. When the interquartile range is divided by 2, the quotient is called the **semi-interquartile range**.

Semi-Interquartile Range	If a set of data has first quartile point, Q_1, and third quartile point, Q_3, the semi-interquartile range, Q_R, can be found as follows. $$Q_R = \frac{Q_3 - Q_1}{2}$$

Example 1

Refer to the application at the beginning of the lesson. Find the interquartile range and the semi-interquartile range of the calories in the breakfast cereals.

First, make an array.

$$Q_1 \qquad\qquad \text{median} \qquad\qquad Q_3$$
$$\downarrow \qquad\qquad\qquad \downarrow \qquad\qquad\qquad \downarrow$$

88 88 88 110 110 110 110 110 110 147 150 165 165 165 200 200 330 390 440 536

$$Q_1 = \frac{110 + 110}{2} \text{ or } 110 \qquad M_d = \frac{147 + 150}{2} \text{ or } 148.5 \qquad Q_3 = \frac{200 + 200}{2} \text{ or } 200$$

The interquartile range is $200 - 110$ or 90. This means that half of the cereals are between 110 and 200 calories per serving and are within 90 calories per serving of each other. The semi-interquartile range is $\frac{90}{2}$ or 45. This means that one fourth of the cereals are within 45 calories per serving of each other.

Box-and-whisker plots are used to summarize data and to illustrate the variability of the data. These plots graphically display the median, quartiles, interquartile range, and extreme values in a set of data. They can be drawn vertically, as shown at the left, or horizontally. A box-and-whisker plot consists of a rectangular box with the ends, or **hinges**, located at the first and third quartiles. The segments extending from the ends of the box are called **whiskers**. The whiskers stop at the extreme values of the set, unless the set contains **outliers**. Outliers are extreme values that are more than 1.5 of the interquartile range beyond the upper or lower quartiles. Outliers are represented by single points. If an outlier exists, each whisker is extended to the last value of the data that is not an outlier.

LESSON 15-3 MEASURES OF VARIABILITY 821

The dimensions of the box-and-whisker plot can help you characterize the data. Each whisker and each small box contains 25% of the data. If the whisker or box is short, the data are concentrated over a narrower range of values. The longer the whisker or box, the more diverse the data. Thus, the box-and-whisker is a pictorial representation of the variability of the data.

Example 2

Box-and-whisker plots are sometimes called box plots.

Draw a box-and-whisker plot of the calorie data of the breakfast cereals.

In Example 1, you found that the median is 148.5, Q_1 is 110, and Q_3 is 200. The extreme values are the least value, 88, and the greatest value, 536.

Draw a number line and plot the quartiles, the median, and the extreme values. Draw a box to show the interquartile range. Draw a segment through the median to divide the box into two smaller boxes.

Before drawing the whiskers, determine if there are any outliers.

The interquartile range is $200 - 110$ or 90. An outlier is any value that lies more than 1.5(90) units below Q_1 or above Q_3.

$$Q_1 - 1.5(90) = 110 - 135 \qquad\qquad Q_3 + 1.5(90) = 200 + 135$$
$$= -25 \qquad\qquad\qquad\qquad\qquad = 335$$

The lower extreme, 88, is within the limits. However, 390, 440, and 536 are not within the limits. They are all outliers. Graph these points on the plot. Then draw the left whisker from 88 to 110 and the right whisker from 200 to the greatest value that is not an outlier, 330.

The box-and-whisker plot shows that the three lower quartiles of data are fairly close together in range. However, the upper quartile of data is more diverse.

Another measure of variability can be found by examining deviations from the mean, symbolized by $X_i - \overline{X}$. The sum of the deviations from the mean is zero. That is, $\sum_{i=1}^{n}(X_i - \overline{X}) = 0$. For example, the mean of the data set {13, 20, 17, 12, 38} is 20. The sum of the deviations from the mean is shown in the chart at the right.

X_i	$\overline{X}$	$X_i - \overline{X}$
13	20	-7
20	20	0
17	20	-3
12	20	-8
38	20	18
$\sum(X_1 - \overline{X})$		0

To indicate how far individual items vary from the mean, we use the absolute values of the deviations. The arithmetic mean of the absolute values of the deviations from the mean of a set of data is called the **mean deviation**, symbolized by *MD*.

Mean Deviation	If a set of data has *n* values given by X_i, such that $1 \leq i \leq n$, with arithmetic mean $\overline{X}$, then the mean deviation *MD* can be found as follows. $$MD = \frac{1}{n} \sum_{i=1}^{n} |X_i - \overline{X}|$$

In sigma notation for statistical data, i is always an integer.

Example 3

Find the mean deviation of the grams of carbohydrates found in breakfast cereals.

There are 20 cereals listed and the mean is 35.75 grams of carbohydrates.

$$MD = \frac{1}{20} \sum_{i=1}^{20} |X_i - 35.75|$$

$$= \frac{1}{20}(|24 - 35.75| + |26 - 35.75| + \ldots + |25 - 35.75| + |35 - 35.75|)$$

$$= \frac{1}{20}(|-11.75| + |-13.75| + \ldots + |-10.75| + |-0.75|)$$

$$= 13.575$$

The mean deviation of the grams of carbohydrates is 13.575 grams. This means that the number of grams of carbohydrates per serving is an average of about 13.575 grams above or below the mean of 35.75.

A measure of variability that is often associated with the arithmetic mean is the **standard deviation**. Like the mean deviation, the standard deviation is a measure of the average amount by which individual items of data deviate from the arithmetic mean of all the data. Each individual deviation can be found by subtracting the arithmetic mean from each individual value, $X_i - \overline{X}$. Some of these differences will be negative, but since they are squared, the results are positive. The standard deviation is the square root of the mean of the squares of the deviations from the arithmetic mean. *The square of the standard deviation, called the <u>variance</u>, is often used as a measure of variability.*

Standard Deviation	If a set of data has *n* values, given by X_i such that $1 \leq i \leq n$, with arithmetic mean $\overline{X}$, the standard deviation, σ, can be found as follows. $$\sigma = \sqrt{\frac{1}{n} \sum_{i=1}^{n} (X_i - \overline{X})^2}$$

σ is the Greek lowercase letter sigma.

LESSON 15-3   MEASURES OF VARIABILITY   823

The standard deviation is the most important and widely used measure of variability.

Example 4 **Refer to the application at the beginning of the lesson. Find the standard deviation of the grams of carbohydrates in the breakfast cereals.**

The mean is 35.75 and there are 20 cereals.

$$\sigma = \sqrt{\frac{1}{20}[(24 - 35.75)^2 + (26 - 35.75)^2 + \cdots + (25 - 35.75)^2 + (35 - 35.75)^2]}$$

$$= \sqrt{294.7875}$$

$$\approx 17.169 \quad \textit{Use your calculator.}$$

You can also use a TI-81 graphing calculator to find the standard deviation of this set of data. *Refer to the Exploration in Lesson 15-1 for a review of data input.*

• Clear the data memory.
• Input the new data. The data are not frequency based. The values for X are the data and the value for Y is always 1.
• Press [2nd] [STAT]. Select 1:1 - Var. 1-Var will appear on the home screen. Press [ENTER].
• The calculated mean, $\overline{X}$, appears on the first line.
• The calculated standard deviation, σX, appears on the next to last line.

The mean is 35.75 and the standard deviation is 17.16937681, which agree with the calculations using the formula.

When studying the standard deviation of a set of data, it is important to consider the mean. For example, compare a standard deviation of 50 with a mean of 100 to a standard deviation of 50 with a mean of 10,000. The latter indicates very little variation, while the former indicates a great deal of variation since 50 is 50% of 100 while 50 is only 0.5% of 10,000.

The standard deviation of a frequency distribution is the square root of the mean of the squares of the deviations of the class marks from the frequency.

Standard Deviation of the Data in a Frequency Distribution

If $X_1, X_2, \cdots, X_k$ are the class marks in a frequency distribution with k classes, and $f_1, f_2, \cdots, f_k$ are the corresponding frequencies, then the standard deviation σ of the data in the frequency distribution is found as follows.

$$\sigma = \sqrt{\frac{\sum\limits_{i=1}^{k} \left(X_i - \overline{X}\right)^2 \cdot f_i}{\sum\limits_{i=1}^{k} f_i}}$$

The standard deviation of a frequency distribution is an approximate number.

Additional Answers

2. The non-frequency data is treated as individual pieces of data when finding the sum, mean, and so on. Frequency data is calculated using the products of the class marks and frequencies to find the sums, means, and so on.

3. The median of the data is $\frac{6 + 7}{2}$ or 6.5. $Q_1 = 3.5$ and $Q_3 = 9.5$. Plot these points on a number line and draw two side-by-side boxes that contain these points on their vertical sides. There are no outliers. The least extreme is 1 and the greatest extreme is 12. Plot these points and draw segments from each of these to its nearest quartile point.

Example 5

To use the TI-81 graphing calculator to find the standard deviation of a frequency distribution, let X be the class mark and let Y be the frequency. Then follow the same procedures as in Example 4.

Use the frequency distribution data below to find the arithmetic mean and the standard deviation of the number of home runs scored by the National League home run leaders between 1901 and 1991.

Class Limits	Class Marks	f	$f \cdot X$	$(X - \overline{X})$	$(X - \overline{X})^2$	$(X - \overline{X})^2 \cdot f$
0–10	5	6	30	−29.01	841.5801	5049.4806
10–20	15	12	180	−19.01	361.3801	4336.5612
20–30	25	10	250	− 9.01	81.1801	811.801
30–40	35	26	910	0.99	0.9801	25.4826
40–50	45	31	1395	10.99	120.7801	3744.1831
50–60	55	6	330	20.99	440.5801	2643.4806
		91	3095			1,6610.9891

The mean, $\overline{X}$, is $\dfrac{3095}{91}$ or 34.01.

The standard deviation is $\sqrt{\dfrac{16,610.9891}{91}}$ or approximately 13.51.

Since the mean number of home runs is 34.01 and the standard deviation is 13.51, this indicates a great amount of variability in the data.

CHECKING FOR UNDERSTANDING

Communicating Mathematics

Read and study the lesson to answer each question. 2–3. See margin.

1. **Determine** if there are any outliers for the carbohydrate data in the application at the beginning of the lesson. If they exist, state them. 80

2. **Explain** how calculating the standard deviation of data in a frequency table differs from calculating the standard deviation of data not in a frequency table.

3. **Demonstrate** how to make a box-and-whisker plot for a set containing the numbers 1 through 12.

4. Refer to Example 3. Suppose that the mean deviation of the grams of carbohydrates found in another sample of breakfast cereal was 3.5 with a mean of 37.75. How is this data different from that in Example 3?
It has less variability and is clustered more closely around the mean.

Guided Practice

Use the box-and-whisker plot below for Exercises 5—11.

100 125 150 175 200 225 250 275 300 325 350 375

5. What is the range of the data? 205
6. What is the median of the data? 220
7. What percent of the data is greater than the third quartile point? 25%

Assignment Guide

Average: 13–15, 18, 20–24
Enriched: 15–24

The red A, B, and C flags, printed only in the Teacher's Wraparound Edition, indicate the level of difficulty of the exercises.

Chapter 15, Quiz B, (Lesson 15–3), is available in the *Evaluation Masters*, p. 189.

Additional Answer

13i.

(A box-and-whisker plot on a number line from 5 to 15)

8. What values are outliers of the data? 320, 350
9. What percent of the data is less than 220? 50%
10. What percent of the data is greater than 175? 75%
11. What percent of the data is greater than 175 and less than 230? 50%
12. The table shows the resulting scores of the final exam in history for 90 students at Madrid High School.

Scores	53–61	61–69	69–77	77–85	85–93	93–101
Frequency	3	7	11	38	19	12

a. Find the mean of the test scores. 81.8
b. Find the median class of the distribution. 77–85
c. Find the median of the test scores. 82.1
d. Find the standard deviation of the test scores. about 9.69

EXERCISES

Applications and Problem Solving

13. **Entertainment** The best selling pre-recorded videos of all time as of 1991 are listed in the table. The number of units sold are in millions.

Video	Distributor	Units Sold
E.T. the Extra-Terrestrial	MCA	15.1
Batman	Warner	11.5
Bambi	Disney	10.5
The Little Mermaid	Disney	9.0
Teenage Mutant Ninja Turtles	LIVE	8.8
Who Framed Roger Rabbit?	Disney	8.5
Cinderella	Touchtone	8.5
Peter Pan (animated)	Disney	7.6
Pretty Woman	Paramount	6.2
Honey, I Shrunk the Kids	Disney	5.8

b. 5.95, 2.35, 1.35, –0.15, –0.35, –0.65, –0.65, –1.55, –2.95, –3.35

a. Find the mean of the units sold. 9.15
b. Find the deviation from the mean for each value in the set of data.
c. Find the mean deviation of the units sold. 1.93
d. Find the values of Q_1, Q_2, and Q_3 for the data. 10.5, 8.65, 7.6
e. Find the interquartile range of the data. 2.9
f. Find the semi-interquartile range for the data. 1.45
g. Find the sum of the squares of the individual deviations for the data. 66.065
h. Find the standard deviation of the data. about 2.57
i. Make a box-and-whisker plot of the data. See margin.
j. State any outliers. 15.1

826 CHAPTER 15 STATISTICS AND DATA ANALYSIS

The miles per gallon for city travel and the fuel tank capacity in gallons of twelve 1991-model cars are given below.

Cars	MPG	Fuel Tank Capacity	Cars	MPG	Fuel Tank Capacity
Geo Metro	46	10.6	Eagle Summit	31	13.2
Honda Civic CX	42	11.9	Nissan Sentra E	29	13.0
Hyundai Excel GS	29	11.9	Ford Escort	30	11.9
Mazda 323	29	13.2	Ford Festiva GL	35	10.0
Plymouth Sundance	26	14.0	Subaru Justi GL	33	9.2
Saturn SL	28	12.8	Toyota Tercel	32	11.9

B

14. Energy Let Group 1 = {Geo Metro, Honda Civic CX, Hyundai Excel GS, Mazda 323, Plymouth Sundance, Saturn SL}. Let Group 2 = {Eagle Summit, Nissan Sentra E, Ford Escort, Ford Festiva GL, Subaru Justi GL, Toyota Tercel}.

   a. Find the mean, median, and the standard deviation of the miles per gallon of the cars in Group 1. mean: 33.3, median: 29, SD: 7.7

   b. Find the mean, median, and the standard deviation of the miles per gallon of the cars in Group 2. mean: 31.7, median: 31.5, SD: 1.97

14c. See margin for box-and-whisker plot.

   c. Make a box-and-whisker plot of each group of miles per gallon data.

   (1) How do the means of the two groups of data compare? similar

   (2) How do the standard deviations compare? very different

   (3) Which group of data has the smaller variability in miles per gallon?
   Group 2

15. Energy Let Group 3 = {Geo Metro, Mazda 323, Plymouth Sundance, Eagle Summit, Ford Festiva GL, Subaru Justi GL}. Let Group 4 = {Honda Civic CX, Hyundai Excel GS, Saturn SL, Nissan Sentra E, Ford Escort, Toyota Tercel}.

   a. Find the mean, median, and the standard deviation of the fuel tank capacities of the cars in Group 3. mean: 11.7, median: 11.9, SD: 1.83

   b. Find the mean, median, and the standard deviation of the fuel tank capacities of the cars in Group 4. mean: 12.23, median 11.9, SD: 0.47

   c. Make a box-and-whisker plot of the two groups of data. See margin.

   (1) How do the means of the two groups compare? similar

   (2) How do the standard deviations compare? very different

   (3) Which group has the greater variability in fuel tank capacity? Group 3

C

16. Sports The chart at the right shows the frequency of runs batted in (RBI) by the American League batting leaders between 1907 and 1991.

   a. Find the mean of the data. 129.65

   b. Find the standard deviation. about 23.29

   c. In 1991, the RBI champion in the American League was Cecil Fielder of the Detroit Tigers with 133 RBIs. Write a sentence to compare this number with the mean of the data. It is 3.35 more than the mean, but very close to it considering the standard deviation.

RBI	Frequency
70–90	2
90–110	11
110–130	39
130–150	17
150–170	9
170–190	7

LESSON 15-3   MEASURES OF VARIABILITY   827

Additional Answers

14c.

17. **Sports** The medals won by the top 20 countries at the 1992 Summer Olympics at Barcelona, Spain, are shown below.

Country	Gold	Silver	Bronze	Total
Unified Team	45	38	29	112
United States	37	34	37	108
Germany	33	21	28	82
China	16	22	16	54
Cuba	14	6	11	31
Hungary	11	12	7	30
South Korea	12	5	12	29
France	8	5	16	29
Australia	7	9	11	27
Spain	13	7	2	22
Japan	3	8	11	22
Britain	5	3	12	20
Italy	6	5	8	19
Poland	3	6	10	19
Canada	6	5	7	18
Romania	4	6	8	18
Bulgaria	3	7	6	16
Netherlands	2	6	7	15
Sweden	1	7	4	12
New Zealand	1	4	5	10

a. Find the range, mean, mean deviation, interquartile range, and the standard deviation of the number of gold medals. See margin.

b. Find the range, mean, mean deviation, interquartile range, and the standard deviation of the number of silver medals. See margin.

c. Which set of data demonstrated greater variability: the gold medals or the silver medals? Explain what this means. gold

18. Is it possible for the variance to be less than the standard deviation for a set of data? If so, explain when this would occur. yes, when $\sigma < 1$

19. When would the variance for a set of data be equal to the standard deviation of the set? when both have a value of 1

20. $\pm\frac{1}{2}, \pm 1, \pm\frac{3}{2}, \pm 3$

Mixed
Review

20. Find all possible rational roots of $2x^3 + 3x^2 - 8x + 3 = 0$. **(Lesson 4-4)**

21. Aviation Two airplanes leave an airport at the same time. Each flies at a speed of 110 mph. One flies in the direction 60° east of north. The other flies in the direction 40° east of south. How far apart are the planes after 3 hours? **(Lesson 5-6)** 424.24 miles

22. Find the value of x to the nearest tenth such that $x = e^{0.346}$. **(Lesson 11-3)** 1.4

23. Find the value of x so that the set $\{x, 2x - 1, 2x, 3x + 1\}$ has a mean of 6. **(Lesson 15-2)** 3

24. College Entrance Exam Choose the best answer. C
In the figure at the right, the largest possible circle is cut out of a square piece of tin. The total area of the remaining pieces of tin is approximately

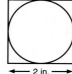

← 2 in. →

(A) 0.14 in² **(B)** 0.75 in² **(C)** 0.86 in² **(D)** 1.0 in² **(E)** 3.14 in²

CASE STUDY FOLLOW-UP

Refer to Case Study 3: *The Legal System*, on pages 962–965.

The Census Bureau reported a United States population of 248.7 million in 1990.

1. About how many of the crimes committed in 1990 occurred in the South? about 5.4 million

2. Approximate the mean annual number of crimes per 100,000 population in the period from 1981 to 1990. about 5500 crimes

3. Find the standard deviation of the above set of data. about 260

4. Research Compile a set of data relating to crime in your city. Use statistics to analyze the data and report your analysis in a 1-page paper. See students' work.

LESSON 15-3 MEASURES OF VARIABILITY 829

EXTENDING THE LESSON

Math Power: Problem Solving

Interpret the following formula. How is it related to the formula for variance?

$$s^2 = \frac{\sum_{i=1}^{k} Xi^2}{k} - \overline{X}^2$$

mean of squares − square of mean; equivalent

Case Study Follow-Up

This activity provides an opportunity to do research and apply mathematics in solving problems related to issues that may face students in their adult lives. Case Study 3 is located on pages 962–965.

Enrichment Masters Booklet, p. 104

NAME _____ DATE _____

15-3 **Enrichment Worksheet**

Percentiles

The table at the right shows test scores and their frequencies. The frequency is the number of people who had a particular score. The cumulative frequency is the total frequency up to that point, starting at the lowest score and adding up.

Score	Frequency	Cumulative Frequency
95	1	50
90	2	49
85	5	47
80	6	42
75	7	36
70	8	29
65	7	21
60	6	14
55	4	8
50	3	4
45	1	1

Example 1 What score is at the 16th percentile?
A score at the 16th percentile means the score just above the lowest 16% of the scores.
16% of the 50 scores is 8 scores.
The 8th score is 55.
The score just above this is 56.
Thus, the score at the 16th percentile is 56.
Notice that no one had a score of 56 points.

Use the table above to find the score at each percentile.

1. 42nd percentile 66
2. 70th percentile 76
3. 33rd percentile 66
4. 90th percentile 86
5. 58th percentile 71
6. 80th percentile 81

Example 2 At what percentile is a score of 75?
There are 29 scores below 75.
Seven scores are at 75. The fourth of these seven is the midpoint of this group.
Adding 4 scores to the 29 gives 33 scores.
33 out of 50 is 66%.
Thus, a score of 75 is at the 66th percentile.

Use the table above to find the percentile of each score.

7. a score of 50 6th
8. a score of 77 72th
9. a score of 85 90th
10. a score of 58 16th
11. a score of 62 28th
12. a score of 81 84th

T104
Glencoe Division, Macmillan/McGraw-Hill

NCTM Standards: 1-4, 10

Lesson Resources

- Practice Master 15–4
- Enrichment Master 15–4
- Evaluation Master, Quiz C, p. 190

 Transparency 15–4 contains the 5-Minute Check and a teaching aid for this lesson.

INTRODUCING THE LESSON

 ### 5-Minute Check

(over Lesson 15–3)

1. Consider the data {12, 15, 22, 14, 6}.
   a. What is the range of the data? **16**
   b. What is the median of the data? **14**
   c. What is the mean of the data? **13.8**
   d. What is the standard deviation of the data? **5.15**
2. The following is a list of college entrance test scores for ten seniors: 490, 560, 620, 580, 599, 740, 600, 620, 680, 500.
   a. What is the range of the data? **250**
   b. What is the mean of the data? **598.9**
   c. What is the interquartile range of the data? **60**
   d. What is the semi-interquartile range of the data? **30**
   e. Draw a box-and-whisker plot of the data.

490 530 570 610 650 690 730

Motivating the Lesson

Have students do a binomial experiment like flipping a coin 10, 20, 30, 40 times, and so on. Have them plot the number of heads they get for each experiment. Note that as the number of trials increases, the plot looks more and more like the normal distribution.

The Normal Distribution

Objective
15–4

After studying this lesson, you should be able to:
- use the normal distribution curve.

Application

One of the many uses of census data is by special interest groups that target certain populations for their particular cause. Suppose a group wanted to know the proportion of the states in the United States (including the District of Columbia) that had large populations of people of Hispanic origin. The table below shows portions of a frequency distribution of data from the 1990 census. The graph beside it shows a histogram and frequency polygon of those states having less than 1,000,000 people of Hispanic origin.

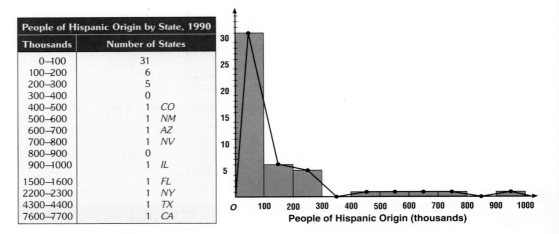

People of Hispanic Origin by State, 1990		
Thousands	**Number of States**	
0–100	31	
100–200	6	
200–300	5	
300–400	0	
400–500	1	CO
500–600	1	NM
600–700	1	AZ
700–800	1	NV
800–900	0	
900–1000	1	IL
1500–1600	1	FL
2200–2300	1	NY
4300–4400	1	TX
7600–7700	1	CA

A frequency polygon displays a limited number of data and does not represent an entire population. To display the frequency of an entire population, a smooth curve is used rather than a polygon.

If the curve is symmetric, then information about the measures of central tendency can be gathered from the graph. Study the graphs below.

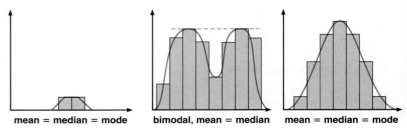

mean = median = mode   bimodal, mean = median   mean = median = mode

ALTERNATE TEACHING STRATEGIES

Using Critical Thinking

Suppose the heights of a senior class of 400 students are normally distributed. If the mean height is 5'4", and the standard deviation is 6", how many students in the senior class are over 6 feet tall? **39**

Using Discussion

Have students discuss any test grades that have ever been *curved*. Ask students what types of curves were used. Find out if any grades fit a *bell-shaped curve*.

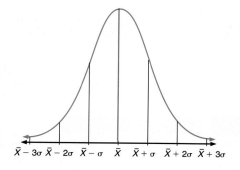

A **normal distribution** is a frequency distribution that often occurs when there is a large number of values in a set of data. The graph of this distribution is a symmetric, bell-shaped curve, shown at the left. This is known as a **normal curve**. The shape of the curve indicates that the frequencies in a normal distribution are concentrated around the center portion of the distribution. A small portion of the population occurs at the extreme values.

Teaching Tip Before discussing normal distribution, emphasize that on the coordinate plane, the mean would be the maximum value of the curve.

In a normal distribution, small deviations are much more frequent than larger ones. Negative deviations and positive deviations occur with the same frequency. The points on the horizontal axis represent values that are a certain number of standard deviations from the mean, $\overline{X}$. In the curve shown above, each interval represents one standard deviation. So, the section from σ to $\overline{X} + \sigma$ represents those values between the mean and one standard deviation greater than the mean, the section from $\overline{X} + \sigma$ to $\overline{X} + 2\sigma$ represents the interval one standard deviation greater than the mean to two standard deviations greater than the mean, and so on. The total area under the normal curve and above the horizontal axis represents the total probability of the distribution, which is 1.

Chalkboard Example

For Example 1

Suppose the scores of 500 college freshmen taking Psychology 101 are normally distributed. The mean score is 60 out of 100, and the standard deviation is 10. Sketch a normal curve that represents the frequency of scores.

Example 1

APPLICATION

Quality Control

The lifetimes of 10,000 watch batteries are normally distributed. The mean lifetime is 500 days. The standard deviation is 60 days. Sketch a normal curve that represents the frequency of lifetimes of the batteries.

First, find the values defined by the standard deviation in a normal distribution.

$\overline{X} - 1\sigma = 500 - 1(60)$ or 440 $\overline{X} + 1\sigma = 500 + 1(60)$ or 560
$\overline{X} - 2\sigma = 500 - 2(60)$ or 380 $\overline{X} + 2\sigma = 500 + 2(60)$ or 620
$\overline{X} - 3\sigma = 500 - 3(60)$ or 320 $\overline{X} + 3\sigma = 500 + 3(60)$ or 680

Sketch the general shape of a normal curve. Then, replace the horizontal scale with the values you have calculated.

FYI...

The longest lasting batteries were made in 1840 by Watlin and Hill of London. These batteries have powered ceaseless ringing of bells inside a bell jar at the Clarendon Laboratory, Oxford, United Kingdom, since the year they were made.

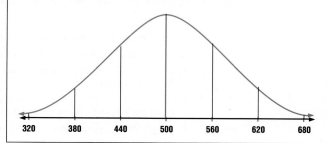

The tables below give the fractional parts of a normally distributed set of data for selected areas about the mean. The letter t represents the number of standard deviations from the mean (that is, $\overline{X} \pm t\sigma$). When $t = 1$, t means 1 standard deviation above and below the mean.

P represents the fractional part of the data that lies in the interval $\overline{X} \pm t\sigma$. The percent of the data within these limits is $100P$.

t	P	t	P	t	P	t	P
0.0	0.000	0.9	0.632	1.7	0.911	2.5	0.988
0.1	0.080	1.0	0.683	1.8	0.928	2.58	0.990
0.2	0.159	1.1	0.729	1.9	0.943	2.6	0.991
0.3	0.236	1.2	0.770	1.96	0.950	2.7	0.993
0.4	0.311	1.3	0.807	2.0	0.955	2.8	0.995
0.5	0.383	1.4	0.838	2.1	0.964	2.9	0.996
0.6	0.451	1.5	0.866	2.2	0.972	3.0	0.997
0.7	0.516	1.6	0.891	2.3	0.979	3.5	0.9995
0.8	0.576	1.65	0.900	2.4	0.984	4.0	0.9999

The P value also corresponds to the probability that a randomly selected member of the sample lies within t standard deviation units of the mean. For example, suppose the mean of a set of data is 60 and the standard deviation is 6.

Boundaries: $\overline{X} - t\sigma$ to $\overline{X} + t\sigma$
$60 - t(6)$ to $60 + t(6)$
$60 - 1(6)$ to $60 + 1(6)$
   54   to   66

$\overline{X} = 60$, $\sigma = 6$

68.3% of the values in this set of data lie within 1 standard deviation of 60, that is, between 54 and 66.

If you randomly select one item from the sample, the probability that the one you pick will be between 54 and 66 is 0.683. If you repeat this process 1000 times, approximately 68.3% (about 683) of those selected will be between 54 and 66.

Thus, normal distributions have the following properties.

1. The maximum point of the curve is at the mean.

2. About 68.3% of the data are within one standard deviation from the mean.

3. About 95.5% of the data are within two standard deviations from the mean.   *When $t = 2.0$, $P = 0.955$.*

4. About 99.7% of the data are within three standard deviations from the mean.   *When $t = 3.0$, $P = 0.997$.*

CHECKING FOR UNDERSTANDING

Communicating Mathematics

Read and study the lesson to answer each question.

1. **Describe** the shape of the graph of a normal distribution. bell-shaped

2. **Explain** in your own words what a normal distribution is. See students' work.

3. **Sketch** a normal distribution curve to describe the scores on a physics test that ranged from 56 to 96 and had an average score of 89. The mode is also the mean and 70% of the scores are in the interval around the mean. See margin.
4–5. See margin.

Guided Practice

4. Sketch a normal curve with a mean of 75 and a standard deviation of 10. Label the points that would be 1, 2, and 3 standard deviations from the mean.

5. Sketch a normal curve with a mean of 75 and a standard deviation of 5. Label the points that would be 1, 2, and 3 standard deviations from the mean.

6. Compare the graphs in Exercises 4 and 5. Which curve displays less variability? Exercise 5

Suppose 200 values in a set of data are normally distributed.

7. How many values are within one standard deviation of the mean? 137

8. How many values are within two standard deviations of the mean? 191

9. How many values fall in the interval between the mean and one standard deviation above the mean? 68

10. How many values are between two and three standard deviations less than the mean? 4

A set of 500 values is normally distributed with a mean of 24 and a standard deviation of 2.

11. What percent of the data is in the interval 22–26? 68.3%

12. What percent of the data is in the interval 20.5–27.5? 92.8%

13. Find the range about the mean that includes 95% of the data. 20.1–27.9

14. Find the range about the mean that includes 50% of the data. 22.6–25.4

EXERCISES

Practice

A set of data is normally distributed with a mean of 140 and a standard deviation of 20. Assume values are selected at random.

15. What percent of the data is in the interval 120–160? 68.3%

16. What percent of the data is between 130 to 150? 38.3%

17. Find the probability that a value from the data lies in the interval 110–170. 86.6%

18. Find the probability that a value from the data is less than 100. 2.25%

19. Find the probability that a value from the data is greater than 160. 15.85%

20. Find the probability that a value from the data lies in the interval 110–200. 93.15%

21. Find the interval about the mean that includes 90% of the data. 107–173

22. Find the limit below which 90% of the data lies. 166

LESSON 15-4   THE NORMAL DISTRIBUTION   835

APPLYING THE LESSON

Homework Exercises

Assignment Guide

Average: 15–22, 23–33 odd, 34, 36–41
Enriched: 16–30 even, 31–41
All: Mid-Chapter Review, 1–7

The red A, B, and C flags, printed only in the Teacher's Wraparound Edition, indicate the level of difficulty of the exercises.

Chapter 15, Quiz C, (Lesson 15–4), is available in the *Evaluation Masters*, p. 190.

Practice Masters Booklet, p. 105

15-4 Practice Worksheet

NAME _____ DATE _____

The Normal Distribution

A set of 1000 values has a normal distribution. The mean of the data is 120, and the standard deviation is 20.

1. How many values are within one standard deviation from the mean? 683

2. What percent of the data is in the range 110 to 130? 38.3%

3. What percent of the data is in the range 90 to 110? 24.15%

4. Find the range about the mean which includes 90% of the data. 87 to 153

5. Find the range about the mean which includes 77% of the data. 96 to 144

6. Find the probability that a value selected at random from the data will be within the limits 100 and 150. 0.7745

7. Find the probability that a value selected at random from the data will be greater than 140. 0.1585

8. Find the point below which 90% of the data lie. 146

T105
Glencoe Division, Macmillan/McGraw-Hill

RETEACHING THE LESSON

Have groups of students shake 50 pennies in a cup and record the number of heads for each of 10 throws. Then have them calculate the mean number of heads in each throw. Determine how many of the throws yielded a number of heads within one standard deviation, two standard deviations, and three standard deviations of the mean. Compare this with the expected number of heads.

40a.

The volumes of the liquid content of soft drink cans are normally distributed. The mean volume is 355 mL with a standard deviation of 2 mL.

23. What percent of the cans contain between 353 mL and 357 mL? 68.3%
24. What percent of the cans contain between 353 and 355 mL? 34%
25. What percent of the cans contain more than 351mL? 97.8%
26. Out of 1000 cans, how many will contain between 349 mL and 363 mL? 998

The lifetimes of a certain type of car tire are normally distributed. The mean lifetime is 40,000 miles, and the standard deviation is 5000 miles. Answer each of the following questions for a sample of 10,000 of these tires.

27. How many tires will last between 35,000 miles and 45,000 miles? 6800
28. How many tires will last between 30,000 and 40,000 miles? 4775
29. How many tires will last less than 40,000 miles? 5000
30. How many tires will last more than 50,000 miles? 225
31. How many tires will last less than 25,000 miles? 15

32. The burning time of a synthetic fireplace log is normally distributed with a mean of 5 hours and a standard deviation of 15 minutes. A store has 1000 logs to sell. How many of these logs will burn longer than 4 hours 30 minutes? 978 logs

Critical Thinking

33. The grading scale at a local university is 90–100 = A, 80 – 89 = B, 70 – 79 = C, 60 – 69 = D, and below 60 = F. The calculus class has just taken a test. Will the grades be normally distributed? Write a paragraph to defend your answer and draw a curve to represent the distribution. Answers will vary.

Applications and Problem Solving

34. **Obstetrics** The longest baby born in the United States was a boy, born to Mrs. Anna Bates in Seville, Ohio, in 1879. The baby weighed 23.75 pounds and was about 30 inches long. However, the lengths of the 2400 babies born at Valley Hospital in the past year were normally distributed. The average length was 19.88 inches and the standard deviation was 1.42 inches.

a. Find the probability that the length of a baby selected at random is less than 17.72 inches. 6.7%

34b. 25.8%

b. What percent of the babies were between 18.9 and 19.88 inches long?

34c. 22.95%

c. What percent of the babies were between 20.47 and 21.65 inches long?

d. How many standard deviations from the mean birth length at Valley Hospital was the length of Mrs. Bates' baby? about 7 standard deviations

35. A: 6.7%,
B: 24.15%,
C: 38.3%,
D: 24.15%
F: 6.7%

35. **Evaluation** Teachers sometimes change the grading scale for a given test because of student performance. At Jennings High School, the physics teacher decided to grade a test "on the curve." The teacher defined the grades in the following way: A(grades above $\overline{X} + 1.5\sigma$), B(grades from $\overline{X} + 0.5\sigma$ to $\overline{X} + 1.5\sigma$), C(grades from $\overline{X} + 0.5\sigma$ to $\overline{X} - 0.5\sigma$), D(grades from $\overline{X} - 0.5\sigma$ to $\overline{X} - 1.5\sigma$), and F(grades below $\overline{X} - 1.5\sigma$). What percent of the class will receive each letter grade if the grades are normally distributed?

836 CHAPTER 15 STATISTICS AND DATA ANALYSIS

37.
$$\sin^2 \phi \cot^2 \phi \stackrel{?}{=} (1 - \sin \phi)(1 + \sin \phi)$$

$$\sin^2 \phi \left(\frac{\cos \phi}{\sin \phi} \right)^2 \stackrel{?}{=} (1 - \sin \phi)(1 + \sin \phi)$$

$$\cos^2 \phi \stackrel{?}{=} (1 - \sin \phi)(1 + \sin \phi)$$

$$1 - \sin^2 \phi \stackrel{?}{=} (1 - \sin \phi)(1 + \sin \phi)$$

$$(1 - \sin \phi)(1 + \sin \phi) = (1 - \sin \phi)(1 + \sin \phi)$$

Additional Answer
Mid-Chapter Review

1.

Class Limits	Class Marks	Tally	f
100–105	102.5	III	3
105–110	107.5	IIII III	8
110–115	112.5	IIII IIII IIII II	17
115–120	117.5	IIII IIII III	13
120–125	122.5	IIII II	7
125–130	127.5	I	1
130–135	132.5	I	1

Mixed Review

36. Find matrix X in $\begin{bmatrix} 3 & 7 \\ 8 & 9 \end{bmatrix} X - \begin{bmatrix} 2 & 7 \\ 6 & 9 \end{bmatrix} = \begin{bmatrix} 3 & 6 \\ 9 & 6 \end{bmatrix}$. **(Lesson 2-3)**

36. $\begin{bmatrix} \dfrac{60}{29} & -\dfrac{12}{29} \\ -\dfrac{5}{29} & \dfrac{59}{29} \end{bmatrix}$

37. See margin.

37. Verify that $\sin^2 \phi \cot^2 \phi = (1 - \sin \phi)(1 + \sin \phi)$ is an identity. **(Lesson 7-2)**

38. Write the equation of a circle that is tangent to the x-axis and has its center at $(2, -4)$. **(Lesson 10-1)** $(x - 2)^2 + (y + 4)^2 = 16$

39. A pair of dice is thrown. Find the probability that their sum is greater than 7 if both dice show the same number. **(Lesson 14-7)** $\dfrac{1}{2}$

40. Nutrition The amounts of sodium, in milligrams, present in the top brands of peanut butter are given below.

```
195 210 180 225 255 225 195 225 203 225 195 195 188 191
210 233 225 248 225 210 240 180 225 240 180 225 240 240
195 189 178 255 225 225 225 194 210 225 195 188 205
```

40b. See students' work.

    a. Make a box-and-whisker plot of the data. See margin.
    b. Write a paragraph describing the variability of the data. **(Lesson 15-3)**

41. College Entrance Exam Choose the best answer. A
The arithmetic mean of a series of numbers is 20 and their sum is 160. How many numbers are in the series?

    (A) 8   **(B)** 16   **(C)** 32   **(D)** 48   **(E)** 80

MID-CHAPTER REVIEW

The following list contains the all-time record high temperature (in degrees Fahrenheit) for each of the 50 states.

```
112 100 127 120 134 118 105 110 109 112 100 118 117
116 118 121 114 114 105 109 107 112 114 115 118 117
118 122 106 110 116 108 110 121 113 120 119 111 104
111 120 113 120 117 105 110 118 112 114 114
```

1–3. See margin.

1. Make a frequency distribution of the data above. **(Lesson 15-1)**

2. Make a histogram of the frequency distribution. **(Lesson 15-1)**

3. Make a stem-and-leaf plot of the data. **(Lesson 15-2)**

4. Find the mean, median, and mode of the data. **(Lesson 15-2)** 113.88, 114, 118

5. Make an array of the data. **(Lesson 15-3)**
    a. Find the upper and lower quartile marks. 118, 110
    b. Find the range of the data. 34
    c. Make a box-and-whisker plot of the data. See margin.

6. Find the standard deviation of the data. **(Lesson 15-3)** 6.427

7. Assume that the data are normally distributed. Find the interval in which you would expect about 68% of the data to lie. **(Lesson 15-4)** 107–120

LESSON 15-4   THE NORMAL DISTRIBUTION   837

EXTENDING THE LESSON

Math Power: Connections

Use a graphing calculator to graph the function

$$y = \frac{1}{2\pi} e^{\frac{-x^2}{2}}.$$ Describe the graph.

It is the standard normal curve.

Mid-Chapter Review

The Mid-Chapter Review provides students with a brief review of the concepts and skills in Lessons 15–1 through 15–4. Lesson numbers are given at the end of problems or instruction lines so students may review concepts not yet mastered.

Additional Answers
Mid-Chapter Review

2.

3.

```
10 | 0 0 4 5 5 5 6 7 8 9 9
11 | 0 0 0 0 1 1 2 2 2 2 3 3 4 4 4
 • | 4 4 5 6 6 7 7 7 8 8 8 8 8 8 9
12 | 0 0 0 0 1 1 2 7
13 | 4
```
$10 | 9$ means 109.

5c.

Enrichment Masters Booklet, p. 105

T 105
Glencoe Division, Macmillan/McGraw-Hill

LESSON 15–4   THE NORMAL DISTRIBUTION   837

Lesson Resources

- Practice Master 15–5
- Enrichment Master 15–5
- Multicultural Activity Master, p. 15
- Activity Master, p. 43

 Transparency 15–5 contains the 5-Minute Check and a teaching aid for this lesson.

INTRODUCING THE LESSON

 5-Minute Check

(over Lesson 15–4)

1. Suppose 300 values in a set of data have a normal distribution. How many values are within one standard deviation of the mean? **204.9**
2. A set of 400 values has a normal distribution with a mean of 82 and a standard deviation of 4.
   a. What percent of the data is in the interval 78 to 82? **34.2%**
   b. What percent of the data is within two standard deviations from the mean? **95.5%**
   c. Find the upper and lower limits of the interval about the mean in which 84% of the values can be found. **76.4 to 87.6**
   d. How many data values can be found in the interval 70–94? **399**

Motivating the Lesson

When pollsters report their findings, they often cite a *margin of error*, ± 3 percentage points for example. Discuss the meaning of this term in relation to data samples.

15-5 Sample Sets of Data

Objective
15–5

After studying this lesson, you should be able to:
- find the standard error of the mean to predict the true mean of a population with a certain level of confidence.

Application

As part of his physiology project, Ward Quan must determine the mean height of all 1285 male high school seniors attending school in his school district. His resources and the amount of time that he has to collect the measurements of the seniors are limited. The 1285 senior males are the total population. The population in a statistical study is all of the items or individuals in the group being considered. Rarely will a researcher find 100% of a population accessible as a source of data. Therefore, a random sample of the population is selected so that it is representative of the entire population.

The characteristics of the population pertinent to the study should be found in the sample in about the same ratio as they exist in the total population. When Ward selects the seniors in the sample, there should be males that are tall, short, and of medium height from each of the senior high schools in his school district. Then, based upon a random sample of the population, certain inferences can be made about the population in general. The major purpose of **inferential statistics** is to use the information gathered in a sample to make predictions about a population.

Ward decides that the number of male seniors in his sample should be 100. So that the sample is a random sample of all of the male seniors in the district, he decides to measure the 100 male seniors that were selected for the All-District Band. All senior high schools are represented in proportion to their enrollment of boys. He assumes that musical talent has no relationship to height, and, therefore, that the sample is random with respect to height.

ALTERNATE TEACHING STRATEGIES

Using Communication

Have students discuss their own experiences with discrepancies in sets of data.

Using Models

Have students work in groups to devise a questionnaire with straightforward questions such as, "What is your favorite brand of athletic shoe?" Then have the groups gather data about each other, organize their results in chart form, and make generalizations from the chart. Have them try to determine any possible errors in their generalizations.

At a band rehearsal, the heights of the 100 males are measured to the nearest tenth of an inch. After tabulating the data, the mean and standard deviation are computed for that sample. Ward found that the mean height of the sample was 69.2 inches with a standard deviation of 2.7 inches.

Ward is not sure that the mean height of this one sample is a truly representative mean height of all male seniors. He knows that there is an Honor Society convention scheduled for the next weekend. There are also 100 senior males from his school district attending the conference in which all senior high schools are represented in proportion to their enrollment of boys. He again measures the 100 seniors, and this time he finds that the mean height of the sample is 68.4 inches with a standard deviation of 2.4.

The discrepancies that Ward found in his two samples are common when taking random samples. Large companies and statistical organizations often take hundreds of samples to find the "average" they are seeking. For this reason, a sample mean is assumed to be near its true population mean, symbolized by μ. The standard deviation of the distribution of the sample means is known as the **standard error of the mean**.

μ is the lowercase Greek letter mu.

Standard Error of the Mean	If a sample set of data has N values and σ is the standard deviation, the standard error of the mean, $\sigma_{\overline{X}}$, is $$\sigma_{\overline{X}} = \frac{\sigma}{\sqrt{N}}.$$

The symbol $\sigma_{\overline{X}}$ is read "sigma sub x bar."

The standard error of the mean is a measurement of how well a sample mean selected at random estimates the true mean. If the standard error of the mean is small, then the sample means are closer to (or approximately the same value as) the true mean. If the standard error of the mean is large, many of the sample means would be far from the true mean. The greater the number of items or subjects in the sample, the closer the sample mean reflects the true mean and the smaller the standard error of the mean.

Example 1

> **Refer to the application at the beginning of the lesson. The mean height of Ward's first sample containing 100 senior males was 69.2 inches and the standard deviation was 2.7 inches. Determine the standard error of the mean.**
>
> For the sample, $N = 100$. Find $\sigma_{\overline{X}}$.
>
> $$\sigma_{\overline{X}} = \frac{2.7}{\sqrt{100}} \text{ or } 0.27$$
>
> The standard error of the mean for Ward's first sample was 0.27.
>
> This standard error is very small and indicates that Ward's first mean is probably very close to the true mean.

Chalkboard Examples

For Example 2

The mean weight of the 36 boys in Chalkboard Example 1 was 136.4 pounds, the standard deviation was 4.1 pounds, and the standard error of the mean was 0.683. Determine the range of weights such that the probability is 80% that the mean weight lies within it.
135.51 lb to 137.29 lb

For Example 3

a. Suppose 54 out of 100 voters polled were in favor of passing an education referendum with standard deviation of 3%. You wish to have a 95% level of confidence that the range containing the sample mean contains the true mean. Determine the range of the sample mean that has a 3% level of confidence.   53.412 to 54.588

b. Suppose 54 out of 1000 voters polled were in favor of passing the referendum with a standard deviation of 3%. Determine the range of the sample mean that has a 3% level of confidence.   54.814 to 54.186

c. Compare parts a and b.   By increasing the number of voters in the sample, the range increased.

The sampling error is the difference between the population mean (μ) and the sample mean ($\overline{X}$).

The sample mean is only an estimate of the true mean of the population. Sample means of various random samples of the same population are normally distributed about the true mean with the standard error of the mean as a measure of their variability. Thus, the standard error of the mean behaves like the standard deviation. Using the standard error of the mean and the sample mean, we can state a range about the sample mean in which we think the true mean lies. Probabilities of the occurrence of sample means and true means may be determined by referring to the tables on page 832.

Example 2

The mean height of Ward's first sample containing 100 senior males was 69.2 inches, the standard deviation was 2.7 inches, and, from Example 1, the standard error of the mean is 0.27. Determine the range of heights such that the probability is 90% that the mean height of the entire population of senior males lies within that range.

When $P = 0.90$ or 90%, the value of $t = 1.65$. *Refer to the tables on page 832.*

To find the range, use a technique similar to finding the interval for a normal distribution.

$$\overline{X} \pm t\sigma_{\overline{X}} = 69.2 \pm (1.65)(0.27)$$
$$= 68.7545 \text{ and } 69.6455$$

The probability is 90% that the true mean, μ, is within the range of about 68.75 to 69.65 inches.

The probability of the true mean being within a certain range of a sample mean may be expressed as a **level of confidence**. The most commonly used levels of confidence are 1% and 5%. A 1% level of confidence means that there is less than a 1% chance that the true mean differs from the sample mean by a certain amount. That is, you are 99% confident that the true mean is within a certain range of the sample mean. A 5% level of confidence means that the probability of the true mean being within a certain range of the sample mean is 95%.

If a higher level of confidence is desired for the same number of values, accuracy must be sacrificed by providing a wider range. However, if the number of values in the sample is larger, the range for a given level of confidence is smaller.

Example 3

APPLICATION
Quality Control

The longevity of light bulbs is normally distributed. It is your job to determine the mean lifetime of the light bulbs being produced in your factory. You are to take a sample of light bulbs, test them, and record how many hours each light bulb lasts. Then you will calculate the mean lifetime. You wish to have a 1% level of confidence that the range containing the mean lifetime of the sample also contains the true mean.

a. **One hundred light bulbs are randomly selected and illuminated. The time for each bulb to burn out is recorded. From this sample, the average life is 350 days with a standard deviation of 45 days. Determine the range of the sample mean that has a 1% level of confidence.**

Additional Answers

1. A population includes all possible items of data. A sample is only a representative portion of the population.

2. Sample answer: Group c, because freshmen usually are required to take beginning composition classes. Few freshmen take advanced physics and many athletes take fewer classes than the average student per year. The students on the third floor of the girls' dormitory may or may not be freshmen.

3. The standard error of the mean is a measure used to give a level of confidence about the sample mean.

b. One thousand light bulbs are randomly selected and their lifetimes are recorded. From this sample, the average life is 350 days with a standard deviation of 45 days. Determine the range of the sample mean that has a 1% level of confidence.

c. Compare the results of parts a and b.

a. A 1% level of confidence is given when $P = 99\%$.

When $P = 0.99$, $t = 2.58$.

Find $\sigma_{\overline{X}}$. $\sigma_{\overline{X}} = \dfrac{45}{\sqrt{100}}$ or 4.5

Find the range. $\overline{X} = 350 \pm (2.58)(4.5)$
$= 338.39$ and 361.61

Thus, the range of the sample means is 338.39 days to 361.61 days, for a 1% level of confidence.

b. Determine the range. As in part a, $t = 2.58$.

Find $\sigma_{\overline{X}}$. $\sigma_{\overline{X}} = \dfrac{45}{\sqrt{1000}}$ or 1.42

Find the range. $\overline{X} = 350 \pm (2.58)(1.42)$
$= 346.34$ and 353.66

Thus, the range of the sample means is 346.34 days to 353.66 days, for a 1% level of confidence.

c. By increasing the number of items in the sample, the range has decreased substantially, from about 23 days to about 8 days.

CHECKING FOR UNDERSTANDING

Communicating Mathematics

Read and study the lesson to answer each question. 1–3. See margin.

1. **Explain** the difference between a population and a sample.

2. **State** which group you might sample if you wished to collect data to determine the average number of hours of classes in which a college freshman enrolls.
   a. students in the advanced physics classes
   b. students who are also on the college football team
   c. students in the Tuesday and Thursday beginning composition classes
   d. students from the third floor of the freshman girls dormitory
   Explain your answer.

3. **Define** the standard error of the mean.

4. **Describe** what a 1% level of confidence means. There is a 99% probability that the true mean is within a certain range of the sample mean.

Guided Practice

Find the standard error of the mean for each sample. Then find the range of the sample mean that has a 1% level of confidence and the range for a 5% level of confidence.

5. $\sigma = 40$, $N = 64$, $\overline{X} = 200$
   5, 187.1–212.91, 190.2–209.8

6. $\sigma = 5$, $N = 36$, $\overline{X} = 45$
   0.83, 42.86–47.14, 43.37–46.63

LESSON 15-5 SAMPLE SETS OF DATA 841

RETEACHING THE LESSON

A newspaper reported that 80% of the registered voters planned to vote in the upcoming election. The figure was based on a survey of 100 voters and there was a 4% margin of error. Discuss how to find the confidence interval for the news article.

Assignment Guide

Average: 8–11, 14–16, 18–22
Enriched: 11–22

The red A, B, and C flags, printed only in the Teacher's Wraparound Edition, indicate the level of difficulty of the exercises.

7. In a random sample of 100 families in Waco, Texas, a television reporter found that children watched an average of 4.6 hours of television programming a day. The standard deviation was 1.4 hours.
   a. Find the standard error of the mean. 0.14   b. 4.239–4.961
   b. Find the range about the sample mean that has a 1% level of confidence.
   c. Find the range about the sample mean that reflects a 50% chance that the true mean lies within that range. 4.506–4.694
   d. Find the range about the sample mean so that a probability of 0.90 exists that the true mean will lie within the range. 4.369–4.831

EXERCISES

Practice

Find the standard error of the mean for each sample. Then find the range for a 1% level of confidence and the range for a 5% level of confidence.

8. $\sigma = 2.4, N = 100, \overline{X} = 24$
   0.24, 23.38–24.62, 23.53–24.47

9. $\sigma = 12, N = 200, \overline{X} = 80$
   0.85, 77.81–82.19, 78.33–81.67

10. Grapefruit were first planted in the United States in 1820. Grapefruit, unlike oranges, are native to the western hemisphere. Suppose 50 grapefruit were gathered at random from a grove of premium grapefruit trees. The mean diameter of the sample is 16.2 cm with a standard deviation of 1.4 cm.
    a. Find the standard error of the mean. 0.20   b. 15.808–16.692
    b. Find the range about the sample mean that has a 5% level of confidence.
    c. Find the range about the sample mean that gives a 99% chance that the true mean lies within that range. 15.684–16.716
    d. Find the range about the sample mean such that the probability is 0.80 that the true mean lies within it. 15.944–16.456

11. The table shows a frequency distribution of the time in minutes required for a shopper to stand in line at a local supermarket. The distribution is a random sample from 2361 shoppers on a given weekend.

Number of Minutes	4	6	8	10	12	14	16	18	20
Number of Shoppers	1	3	5	12	17	13	7	4	2

a. Find the standard deviation of the data in the frequency distribution. 3.4   c. 11.567–13.233
b. Find the standard error of the mean. 0.425
c. Find the range about the sample mean such that the probability is 0.95 that the true mean lies within the range.
d. Find the probability that the mean of the population will be less than one minute from the mean of the sample. 0.982

12. 0.454

12. The standard deviation of the weights of 36 seven-year-olds in the United States is 8 pounds. What is the probability that the mean weight of the random sample will differ by more than one pound from the mean weight of all seven-year-olds?

13. Eighty-one beef cattle were fed a special diet for six weeks. The mean gain in weight was 40 pounds with a standard deviation of 5 pounds. With what level of confidence can it be said that the diet will cause an average gain of between 30 to 50 pounds in a similar group? 4.5%

Critical Thinking

14. Describe an industrial situation in which decreasing the range for a given level of confidence by increasing the sample size would be prohibitive.
Sample answer: when the product sampled is very expensive; for example, jet engines

Applications and Problem Solving

15. **Manufacturing** The tensile strength of a certain type of wire is normally distributed with a mean of 99.8 and a standard deviation of 5.48.
 a. Find the standard error of the mean for a sample of 100 wires. 0.548
 b. What is the probability that the mean of this sample will be between 98.8 and 100.9? 0.9415

16. **Business** A steel manufacturing firm employs 1500 people. During a given year, the mean amount contributed to a charity drive for the homeless was $25.75 per employee with a standard deviation of $5.25. What is the probability that a random sample of 100 employees yields a mean between $25 and $27? 0.911

17. **Employment** An employment agency has found that the mean time required for an applicant to take an aptitude test is 24.5 minutes, with a standard deviation of 4.5 minutes. The time required to take the test is recorded on the applicant's file. If a random sample of 81 applicants' files are pulled, what is the probability that the mean time for test-taking in this sample is greater than 25 minutes?
0.1585

Mixed Review

18. **Manufacturing** Icon, Inc. manufactures two types of computer graphics cards, Model 28 and Model 74. There are three stations, A, B, and C, on the assembly line. The assembly of Model 28 graphics card requires 30 minutes at station A, 20 minutes at station B, and 12 minutes at station C. Model 74 requires 15 minutes at station A, 30 minutes at station B, and 10 minutes at station C. Station A can be operated for no more than 4 hours a day, station B can be operated for no more than 6 hours a day, and station C can be operated for no more than 8 hours. **(Lesson 2-6)**
 a. If the profit on Model 28 is $100 and on Model 74 is $60, how many of each model should be assembled each day to provide maximum profit?
 b. What is the maximum daily profit? $900   a. 3 of Model 28, 10 of Model 74

19. **Transportation** The change in the direction of a highway is given by the central angle θ, subtended by the arc of the curve. A curve on Interstate 64, modeled by an arc of a circle, is 500 feet long. The radius of the circle that the curve follows is 2500 feet. Find the change in direction of the highway in degrees formed by the curve. **(Lesson 5-2)** $11°28'$

20. Find the sum of the first ten terms of the series $1^3 + 2^3 + 3^3 + \cdots$. **(Lesson 12-8)**
3025

21. Find the probability that a value selected at random from a set of data will be greater than 160 if the data are normally distributed, the mean is 140, and the standard deviation is 20. **(Lesson 15-4)** 0.1585

22. **College Entrance Exam** Choose the best answer. E
Which of the following numbers is the least?

(A) $\sqrt{3}$ (B) $\dfrac{1}{\sqrt{3}}$ (C) $\dfrac{\sqrt{3}}{3}$ (D) $\dfrac{1}{3}$ (E) $\dfrac{1}{3\sqrt{3}}$

LESSON 15-5   SAMPLE SETS OF DATA   843

EXTENDING THE LESSON

Math Power: Reasoning

A pollster wants to have a 95% level of confidence that the range containing the mean of the sample is within 1% of the real mean. How large should her sample be?
10,000

Enrichment Masters Booklet, p. 106

NAME _____ DATE _____

15-5 **Enrichment Worksheet**

Binomial Expansion Coefficients

The picture at the right shows a device often used to illustrate a normal probability distribution. The device is filled with small steel marbles. The marbles roll past a series of hexagonal obstacles, collecting at the bottom in each of nine columns.

It can be shown that the number of paths from A to G is 1, A to J is 1, A to H is 3, and A to I is 3. For example, H can be reached by the way of E. Hence the number of paths to H is the sum of the number of paths to D and the number of paths to E. Likewise the number of paths to any point can be found by adding the number of paths to points diagonally above it. This is precisely the method by which the numbers in Pascal's triangle are obtained.

The numbers in Pascal's triangle are the coefficients in the expansion of $(x + y)^n$ where n is any positive integer. Therefore, the probability of a marble falling in any given column is proportional to the coefficient of the corresponding term in the binomial expansion of a power. The power is a whole number equal to the row being considered. For example, in the illustration above the columns are in the *eighth* row. Thus the probability of a marble falling in the *third* column is proportional to the coefficient of the *third* term in the binomial expansion of $(x + y)^8$.

The figure above at the right has equally-spaced vertical segments whose lengths are proportional to the numbers in the eighth row of Pascal's triangle. A smooth curve connecting the tops of these segments suggests the probable distribution of marbles in the column. Notice the similarity of this curve to the normal distribution curve.

Solve.

1. Draw a smooth curve connecting the tops of the segments whose lengths are proportional to the coefficients in the expansion of $(x + y)^{12}$.
2. A teacher decided to mark 64 tests with the grades A, B, C, D, and F (A highest) in proportion to the coefficients in the expansion of $(x + y)^4$. How many tests received each grade?
A = 4, B = 16, C = 24, D = 16, F = 4

T106
Glencoe Division, Macmillan/McGraw-Hill

LESSON 15-5   SAMPLE SETS OF DATA   843

15-6A   Graphing Calculators: Scatter Plots and Regression Lines

Objective   Graph sets of data, find an equation of the line of best fit, and use the equation of the line to solve problems.

Motivating the Lesson

Ask students to think of a situation in which a general statement can be used to describe events or data, even though the description may not address every element in the situation. For example, the statement *Seniors make plans to go to college* may be true for most of the senior class but does not hold true for every senior.

TEACHING THE LESSON

Teaching Tip   Have students plot the ordered pairs from the data set in Example 1 and make a conjecture as to whether a linear relationship exists between the points. Once students have convinced themselves that a linear relationship exists, have them work in groups to determine the line of best fit.

Graphs are often used to organize and display data. We can use information obtained from graphs in many different ways, and we can display the data on many different graphs or plots as well. You have already studied several types of graphs and plots that are used to display data. Yet another type of plot is called a **scatter plot**. A scatter plot is used when data will *almost* form a straight line when the data points are graphed. In this case, a **best-fit line**, or **regression line**, can be drawn and used to approximate solutions to other problems.

Example 1

APPLICATION

Astronomy

Main sequence stars are stars that are in the neighborhood of the sun. Draw a scatter plot and regression line for the data about the radius of eight main sequence stars that are given in the following table.

Stars	MU-1 Scorpii	Sirius A	Altair	Polycon A	Sun	61 Cygni A	Krueger 60	Barnard's Star
Surface Temp. in °C (in thousands)	20.0	10.2	7.3	6.8	5.9	2.6	2.8	2.7
Radius (in Suns)	5.2	1.9	1.6	2.6	1.0	0.7	0.35	0.15

First, set the range parameters. Use the viewing window [0, 25] by [0, 6] with scale factors of 5 for the *x*-axis and 1 for the *y*-axis.

Next, clear any equations from the Y=list, clear the statistical memories, and clear the graphics screen. If you are using a Casio graphing calculator, you will also need to set your calculator to the proper statistical mode.

TI-81:   [2nd] [STAT] [◄] 2 [ENTER] [2nd] [STAT] [◄] [ENTER]
Casio: [SHIFT] [Cls] [EXE] [SHIFT] [MODE] [÷] [SHIFT] [Scl] [EXE]

Now, input your data. The Casio will plot each point as it is entered. The TI-81 will wait until you tell it to graph the scatter plot.

TI-81:   20 [ENTER] 5.2 [ENTER] . . . 2.7 [ENTER] 0.15 [ENTER]
Casio: 20 [SHIFT] [,] 5.2 [DT] . . . 2.7 [SHIFT] [,] 0.15 [DT]

Now draw the scatter plot and regression line.

TI-81:   [2nd] [STAT] [►] 2 [ENTER]   *Draws the scatter plot.*

[2nd] [STAT] 2 [ENTER]   *Calculates the coefficients of the regression line.*

[Y=] [VARS] [►] [►] 4   *Writes the equation of the regression line.*

[GRAPH]   *Graphs the regression line.*

[2nd] [STAT] [►] 2 [ENTER]   *Restores the scatter plot.*

Casio: [Graph] [SHIFT] [Line] 1 [EXE]   *Draws the regression line.*

Additional Answers

1.

2.

Notice that on the TI-81 when you calculated the coefficients of the regression line by pressing [2nd] [STAT] 2 [ENTEP], you were calculating the slope and y-intercept of the regression line. The value a is the y-intercept of the regression equation, and b is the slope of the regression equation. The value r is the correlation value or the value that tells you how well the regression line "fits" the data. In this case, with $r = 0.9534$, this is a good fit and shows a positive correlation. On the Casio, these values can be obtained by pressing [SHIFT] [A] (below the 7 key), [SHIFT] [B] (below the 8 key), and [SHIFT] [r] (below the 9 key).

Example 2

Use the TRACE function on the regression line in Example 1 to predict the radius of a main sequence star that has a surface temperature of 12,500 °C.

First activate the TRACE function.

TI-81: [TRACE]

Casio: [SHIFT] [Trace]

You can use the TRACE function to find that a main sequence star with a surface temperature of about 12,500 °C will have a radius of about 3.1 suns based on the regression line.

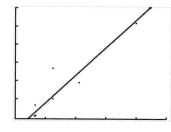

EXERCISES

Use a graphing calculator to draw a scatter plot and a regression line for the data in the following tables. 1-3. See margin.

1.
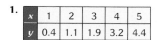

x	1	2	3	4	5
y	0.4	1.1	1.9	3.2	4.4

2.

x	-4	-1	0	0.5	3	3.6
y	20	12.2	4	-0.3	-3	-6.8

3. The following table shows the average heights in feet of 30 men and 30 women at various ages.

Age (yr)	1	3	5	10	12	15	18	20	22
Men	2.4	3.2	3.8	4.5	4.8	5.3	5.7	5.9	6.0
Women	2.5	3.3	3.7	4.4	4.9	5.2	5.3	5.4	5.5

  a. Use a graphing calculator to draw a scatter plot and regression line to show how age is related to the height of the 30 men.
  b. Predict the height of one of the men at age 7.
  c. Use a graphing calculator to draw a scatter plot and regression line to show how age is related to the height of the 30 women.
  d. Predict the height of one of the women at age 17.
  e. What do you think would happen if the data included ages beyond 22?

NCTM Standards: 1-4, 10

Lesson Resources

- Practice Master 15–6
- Enrichment Master 15–6
- Evaluation Master, Quiz D, p. 190

 Transparency 15–6 contains the 5-Minute Check and a teaching aid for this lesson.

INTRODUCING THE LESSON

 5-Minute Check

(over Lesson 15–5)

1. a. Let $\sigma = 8$, $N = 80$, and $\bar{X} = 100$. Find the standard error of the mean. **0.9**
   b. Find the range for a 1% level of confidence. **97.678 to 102.322**
   c. Find the range for a 5% level of confidence. **98.236 to 101.764**
2. Twenty students in Mrs. Garcia's class reported that they watched an average of 3.5 hours of television a day with a standard deviation of 0.5 hours.
   a. Find the standard error of the mean. **0.112 hour**
   b. Determine the range of the sample mean that has a 1% level of confidence. **3.211 to 3.789**

Motivating the Lesson

Discuss how correlations are important to decision-making. For example, income is usually related to the level of education; performance on a test is usually related to how much effort is put in preparing for the test; sales performance is related to marketing strategy in business, and so on.

15-6 Scatter Plots

Objectives	After studying this lesson, you should be able to:
15–6A	▪ draw and analyze scatter plots,
15–6B	▪ draw regression lines, and
15–6C	▪ compute correlation values to determine goodness of fit.

Application

Companies spend hundreds of thousands of dollars each year in focus groups to discover if consumers like their products. Do you ever wonder to what extent you like the same things as someone else? One device that is used to determine how groups of data are related is a **scatter plot**. Such a diagram visually shows the nature of a relationship. The table below shows how five students ranked a list of 10 of the most popular films to rent. Each person ranked the 10 films from 1 to 10, with their favorite film ranked 1.

Rating of Favorite Films					
Film	**Lei**	**Maria**	**Brian**	**Lucia**	**Randy**
Back to the Future III	10	4	10	1	4
Pretty Woman	4	8	5	7	3
Batman	7	7	7	3	10
Dick Tracy	8	1	9	4	9
Die Hard 2	5	10	4	6	2
Ghost	3	5	3	8	6
Home Alone	1	6	2	10	1
Teenage Mutant Ninja Turtles	6	2	6	5	5
Total Recall	9	3	8	2	8
The Hunt for Red October	2	9	1	9	7

As you look at the rankings, it is difficult to make any quick comparisons. A statistician who is looking for relationships among these rankings may construct a scatter plot of the data.

Each scatter plot shown below illustrates the relationship between two people's rankings. The ordered pair for each point represents the rating of a single film by two people. For example, the ordered pair $(1, 2)$ represents Lei and Brian's ranking of *Home Alone*.

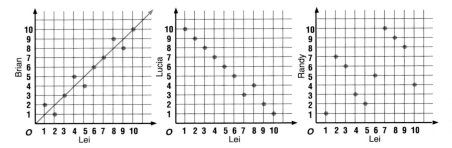

ALTERNATE TEACHING STRATEGIES

Using Computers

Use statistical software packages to plot the data, to find the median fit line, and to find the correlation between data values.

Using Graphing Calculators

Use graphing calculators to show a scatter plot of the data in this lesson. Also encourage students to make use of the other statistical capabilities of the calculator, such as finding the correlation coefficient and the line of best fit.

The left scatter plot on the previous page suggests a linear relationship. Notice that several of the points are on the line, with the rest being very close to it. These rankings are said to have a strong positive relationship, or correlation. In other words, Lei and Brian have similar tastes in films. Note that the slope of the linear pattern in this scatter plot is positive.

The middle scatter plot also has a linear pattern. However, the slope is negative. Thus, the correlation between the ranking is negative, or opposite. It could be said that Lei and Lucia have very different, or opposite, tastes in films. The films that Lei likes are those that Lucia dislikes, and vice versa.

The points in the right scatter plot are very scattered. The points have little or no correlation. Lei and Randy like some of the same movies and dislike some of the same movies. However, they also have differing opinions on other films.

In many cases, the analysis of data involves exactly two variables. When this occurs, the data are said to be **bivariate**. Bivariate data can be examined through the use of scatter plots. When data appear to be linear in a scatter plot, it is often helpful to fit a line to the data in order to define the apparent linear relationship between the two variables. Statisticians often study this relationship in the hope that it may be used to make predictions about one of the variables.

One informal technique used to fit a line is to choose several points on a line that is suggested by the pattern of points in the scatter plot. Then find the equation of that line. This equation is called a **prediction equation** for the relationship. Its graph is often referred to as the **best-fit line**, or the line of best fit. Techniques used to find lines of best fit are called **regression methods.**

Example 1

Find a prediction equation for the line of regression representing the ranking of films by Lei and Brian.

Select the points at $(6, 6)$ and $(10, 10)$.
Determine the slope.

$$m = \frac{y_2 - y_1}{x_2 - x_1} \qquad \text{\textit{Defintion of slope}}$$
$$= \frac{10 - 6}{10 - 6} \qquad \text{\textit{(x$_1$, y$_1$)} = (6, 6), (x$_2$, y$_2$) = (10, 10)}$$
$$= \frac{4}{4} \text{ or } 1$$

Now use one of the ordered pairs, such as $(10, 10)$, and the slope in the point-slope form of an equation.

$$y - y_1 = m(x - x_1) \qquad \text{\textit{Point-slope form of an equation}}$$
$$y - 10 = 1(x - 10) \qquad \text{\textit{(x$_1$, y$_1$) = (10, 10) and m = 1}}$$
$$y = x$$

Thus, a prediction equation is $y = x$. So you may predict that Lei's rating of films will generally be the same as Brian's.

LESSON 15-6   SCATTER PLOTS   847

Teaching Tip   You may want to do a class survey of favorite films and use that data to do the examples in this lesson.

Chalkboard Example

For Example 1

Refer to the application at the beginning of the lesson. Find the prediction equation for the line representing the ranking of films by Lei and Lucia.
$y = -x + 11$, where y represents Lei's rating and x represents Lucia's rating

Chalkboard Example

For Example 2

Consider a company's data about income level and number of years of education at the secondary or college level.

Years	Income
2	$10,000
4	$15,500
6	$26,000
8	$38,000
10	$49,500
12	$62,000

Find the median-fit line for the data. Then make a statement about how representative the line is of the data.

It is representative.

A more accurate method for determining a line of best fit is to find a **median-fit line**. Consider the data about an adult typing class and its graph shown below.

Experience (in weeks)	1	2	3	4	5	6	7	8	9	10
Typing Speed (in wpm)	20	22	30	33	38	40	42	46	52	55

Experience has shown that this trend does not continue much beyond 10 weeks. Some students would go on to excel by reaching speeds of 80 or more words per minute. However, these are exceptions to the results usually found in the typing class. By finding the median-fit line, we can approximate the linear relationship that might exist for this set of data.

Example 2 **Find the median-fit line for the typing data given above. Then make a statement about how representative the line is of the data.**

Step 1 Use two vertical lines to separate the data into three sets of equal size, if possible. The outer sets should have the same number of points in them.

Step 2 Locate a point in each set whose x- and y-coordinates represent the medians of the x- and y- coordinates of all the points in that set. This can be done by examining the points in the set, both vertically and horizontally. Notice that in this example, the middle points in the three sets have been marked with a "+" to indicate the median point.

The points are not necessarily points in the set of data.

Step 3 Take a straightedge and align it with the outer two median points. Then slide it one third of the distance to the median point in the center set of points. Draw the line.

This line is the median-fit line.

These points cluster very closely to the median-fit line, so it is very representative of the data.

Data that are linear in nature will have varying degrees of **goodness of fit** to the lines of fit. Various formulas are often used to find a correlation value that describes the nature of the data. The more closely the data fit a line, the closer the correlation value, r, approaches 1 or –1. Positive correlation values are associated with linear data having positive slopes, and negative correlation values are associated with negative slopes. Thus, the more linear the data, the more closely the correlation value approaches 1 or –1.

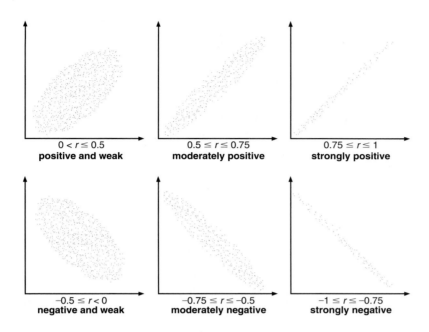

With the aid of technology, correlation values can easily be computed. The TI-81 graphing calculator uses the **Pearson product-moment correlation**. The Pearson product-moment correlation is labeled r and is the ratio of the degree of variation of X and Y together to the degree of the separate variation of X and Y.

The formula that is used to determine the Pearson product-moment correlation is $r = \dfrac{SP}{\sqrt{SS_x SS_y}}$, where $SP = \sum(X - \overline{X})(Y - \overline{Y}) = \sum XY - \dfrac{(\sum X)(\sum Y)}{n}$, $SS_X = \sum(X - \overline{X})^2$, $SS_Y = \sum(Y - \overline{Y})^2$, and n is the number of items being ranked. You can see how software or a graphing calculator that are programmed to compute this formula makes the use of correlation values much easier.

EVALUATING THE LESSON

Checking for Understanding

Exercises 1–12 are designed to help you assess students' understanding through reading, writing, speaking, and modeling. You should work through Exercises 1–2 with your students and then monitor their work on Exercises 3–12.

Closing the Lesson

Writing Activity   Write a short paragraph describing the algorithm used to find the Pearson-product moment correlation .

Additional Answers

1. One method is to select two points typical of the set of data and use the points to find the slope of the line passing through them. Then use the point-slope method to write the equation of the line. Another method is to separate the data into three equivalent sets and find a point that represents the average of the x-coordinates and the average of the y-coordinates for the points in each set. Then connect the three points with a line. The equation of the line can be found by using two of the points.

Example 3

Refer to the application at the beginning of the lesson. Use a graphing calculator to find the Pearson product-moment correlation for the film ratings of Lei and Maria.

Set the calculator in the proper mode and clear the memory.

TI-81:   [2nd] [STAT] [◄] 2 [ENTER]
[2nd] [DRAW] 1 [ENTER]

Casio: [SHIFT] [CLS] [EXE] [MODE] [SHIFT] [÷] [SHIFT] [AC] [EXE]

Set the range.

XMIN: 0   XMAX: 11   XSCL: 1   YMIN: 0   YMAX: 11   YSCL: 1
XRES1   *TI-81 only*

Input the data.

TI-81:   X will be the rankings of Lei, Y will be the rankings of Maria.
X1 10 Press [ENTER]
Y1 4 Press [ENTER]
X2 4 Press [ENTER]
X3 8 Press [ENTER]   *and so on*

Casio: Enter the data as ordered pairs.
10 [SHIFT] [.] 4 [DT]
4 [SHIFT] [.] 8 [DT]
7 [SHIFT] [.] 7 [DT]   *and so on*

After each ordered pair is entered, its graph will appear on the screen.

Find the value of r.

TI-81:   Press [2nd] [STAT]. Select 2: LinReg.   *The home screen will appear.*
Then press [ENTER].

On the screen you will see the display shown at the right.

> A=8.5333333333
> B=−0.5515151515
> R=−0.5515151515

Casio: Press [SHIFT] [r] [EXE] -0.5515151515

The Pearson product-moment correlation value is about –0.55. The correlation between the rankings of Lei and Maria is moderately negative.

10.

11.

12.

CHECKING FOR UNDERSTANDING

Communicating
Mathematics

Read and study the lesson to answer each question. 1. See margin.

1. **Explain** two methods for finding the line of best fit for a given set of paired data.

2. **Explain** what the Pearson product-moment correlation means in relation to the graph of the ordered pairs. Its value will tell you whether the relation is negative or positive and to what degree.

Guided
Practice

Determine whether you would expect the scatter plot of each set of data to show a *positive, negative,* or *no correlation* between the variables.

3. heights of mothers (*m*) and heights of daughters (*d*) positive

4. age of a television set (*a*) and its current value (*v*) negative

5. weight of a person (*w*) and calories consumed (*c*) positive

6. height of a person (*h*) and the person's birth month (*b*) no correlation

7. money spent each week (*m*) and money saved each week (*s*) negative

8. driving skill (*d*) and experience (*e*) positive

9. The Wakeside Deli Corporation was informed by its marketing department that if they spend $5 million on product development, sales will reach $100 million, and if they spend $12 million on product development, sales will be $149 million. The marketing department said they based this information on a prediction equation in which *p* represented product development and *s* represented sales.

b. 65 million

c. $s = 7p + 65,000,000$

d. $86 million

   a. Find the slope of a prediction equation. 7
   b. Find the *s*-intercept of a prediction equation.
   c. Find a prediction equation.
   d. What would you predict sales would be if $3 million is spent on product development?

Make a sketch of bivariate data that has each Pearson product-moment correlation value. 10–12. See margin.

10. near 1.0   11. near –1.0   12. near 0

EXERCISES

13. The number of chirps per minute that one cricket makes as the temperature changed during a period of several hours is recorded below.

Chirps per minute	105	105	125	125	130	149	153	152	164	171	175
Temperature (°C)	18	19	20	21	21	23	24	24	24	26	26

   a. Draw a scatter plot and find a median-fit line for the data. See margin.
   b. Find the equation of the line of regression. $c = 8.93t - 58.3$

(continued on the next page)

RETEACHING THE LESSON

Ask groups of students to discuss how to use a graphing calculator to find the Pearson-product moment correlation for the data representing the ranking of films by Lei and Randy at the beginning of the lesson.
Answers will vary.

Additional Answer

13a.

The red A, B, and C flags, printed only in the Teacher's Wraparound Edition, indicate the level of difficulty of the exercises.

Chapter 15, Quiz D, (Lessons 15–5 through 15–6), is available in the *Evaluation Masters*, p. 190.

Practice Masters Booklet, p. 107

14a.

15a.

16a.

16b. The older the machine, the more expensive maintenance is.

17.

18.

19.

20.

c. What is the Pearson product-moment correlation value? 0.9844291973

d. What does the correlation value in Exercise 13c mean? There is a strongly positive correlation between the temperature and the chirps per minute.

At the regional music festival, ten of the top teenage pianists competed for a music scholarship. The chart below shows how the three judges ranked the ten competitors.

Contestant	A	B	C	D	E	F	G	H	I	J
Judge #1	1	3	5	4	2	9	10	6	8	7
Judge #2	2	4	6	3	1	10	9	5	7	8
Judge #3	9	8	6	7	10	1	2	5	3	4

 14. Consider the scores awarded by judges 1 and 2.

    a. Draw a scatter plot to show how these rankings are related. See margin.

    b. Describe the relationship. strongly positive

    c. Determine the Pearson product-moment correlation value for the data. $0.\overline{93}$

15. Consider the scores awarded by judges 2 and 3.

    a. Draw a scatter plot to show how these rankings are related. See margin.

    b. Describe the relationship. strongly negative

    c. Determine the Pearson product-moment correlation value for the data. $-0.9\overline{63}$

    d. Consider the correlation values in Exercises 14c and 15c. How would you analyze the consistency of the three judges? Judges 1 and 2 seem very close in the scoring while judge 3 is not in synch with their opinions.

 16. A garment manufacturer wants to know the relationship between the age and annual maintenance costs of the sewing machines in their factory. A sample of 16 machines reveals the following information.

Age (years)	8	3	1	9	5	7	5	2
Maintenance Costs ($)	109	75	21	135	67	125	71	52

Age (years)	1	3	6	2	1	2	6	8
Maintenance Costs ($)	25	70	126	58	30	47	120	105

a-b. See margin.

    a. Draw a scatter plot to show how age is related to maintenance cost.

    b. Describe the relationship.

    c. Find an equation for the line of regression. Sample answer: $y = 22.6 + 12.67x$

d.
0.9210450398
    d. Determine the Pearson product-moment correlation value for the data.

    e. What does the correlation value in part d mean? The relationship between age of a machine and the cost of its maintenance is strongly positive.

Use a graphing calculator to draw the scatter plot and line of regression for each of the following exercises. 17–20. See margin.

17. Exercise 13   **18.** Exercise 14   **19.** Exercise 15   **20.** Exercise 16

21. Refer to Example 3. Three values appear on the screen of the TI-81 graphing calculator when you access the linear regression menu. What do the values of *a* and *b* represent? *a* = the *y*-intercept of the line of regression, *b* = its slope

Critical
Thinking

22. Different correlation values are acceptable for different situations. For each situation give a specific example and explain your reasoning. See margin.

a. When would a correlation value less than 0.99 be considered unsatisfactory?

b. When would a correlation value of 0.60 be considered as good?

c. When would a strong negative correlation value be desirable?

Applications
and Problem
Solving

23. Nutrition   The table below deals with the nutritional value of America's favorite snack foods, as reported by the USDA.

Snack Food	% Calories from Fat	% Calories from Carbohydrates
Apple (medium, Delicious)	9%	89%
Bagel (plain)	6%	76%
Banana (medium)	2%	93%
Bran Muffin (large)	40%	53%
Fig Newtons (4 cookies)	18%	75%
PowerBar (any flavor)	8%	76%
Snickers bar (regular size)	42%	51%
Ultra Slim-Fast Bar (one)	30%	63%

a. Draw a scatter plot to show the relationship of the percentage of the calories from fat and the percentage of calories from carbohydrates. See margin.

b. Sample answer:
y = –0.9x + 90

b. Find an equation for the line of regression.

c. extremely
negative

c. Describe the relationship.

d. Find the Pearson product-moment correlation for the data. –0.939240534

e. In your own words, write what this correlation means.
See margin.

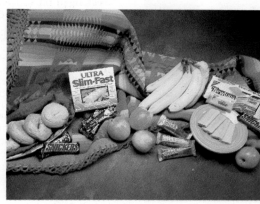

Using Technology

For Exercises 17 through 20, you can also have students draw the curve which fits the data by pressing Y= and then choosing LR under the VARS menu.

Additional Answers

Sample answers are given for Exercises 22a–22c.
22a. the space shuttle, because anything less than perfect may endanger the lives of the passengers
22b. a medication that proves to help AIDS patients, because any positive correlation is better than none or a negative one
22c. comparing a dosage of medicine to the growth factor of cancer cells, because the greater the dosage the fewer cells are produced would be good

23a.

23e. Sample answer: the greater the percentage of calories from fat, the lesser the percentage of calories from carbohydrates

24. Health The table below shows the ideal weight for each body frame for men and women in relationship to their height. 24b-c. See margin.

Ideal Weights for Women				Ideal Weights for Men			
Height	Small Frame	Medium Frame	Large Frame	Height	Small Frame	Medium Frame	Large Frame
4'10"	95	100	111	5'2"	126	134	144
4'11"	98	102	114	5'3"	129	137	147
5'0"	101	107	117	5'4"	132	140	150
5'1"	104	110	120	5'5"	135	143	154
5'2"	106	113	124	5'6"	139	147	157
5'3"	109	115	126	5'7"	143	152	162
5'4"	112	119	129	5'8"	147	156	167
5'5"	115	122	134	5'9"	151	159	171
5'6"	118	127	137	5'10"	155	163	175
5'7"	122	131	141	5'11"	159	168	180
5'8"	126	135	145	6'0"	163	172	185
5'9"	130	139	149	6'1"	167	177	190
5'10"	135	143	154	6'2"	173	181	195
5'11"	139	147	159	6'3"	176	186	199
6'0"	143	151	163	6'4"	180	191	205

a. Draw scatter plots to compare the height to the ideal weight for each frame group for men and women. See Teacher's Answer Key.

b. Find an equation for the line of regression for each plot.

c. Find the Pearson product-moment correlation for each plot.

25. 14, 13.5

Mixed Review

25. Find $[f \circ g](4)$ and $[g \circ f](4)$ for $f(x) = 5x + 9$ and $g(x) = 0.5x - 1$. **(Lesson 1-2)**

26. Photography A photographer observes a 35-foot totem pole that stands vertically on a uniformly-sloped hillside and the shadow cast by it at different times of day. At a time when the angle of elevation of the sun is $37°12'$, the shadow of the pole extends directly down the slope. This is the effect that the photographer is seeking. If the hillside has an angle of inclination of $6°40'$, find the length of the shadow. **(Lesson 5-6)** 54.87 ft

27. See margin.

27. Find the first five iterates for $f(x) = 3x^2 - 10$ for $x_0 = 3.4$. **(Lesson 13-1)**

28. Botany A random sample of fifty acorns from an oak tree in the park reveals a mean diameter of 16.2 mm and a standard deviation of 1.4 mm. Find the range about the sample mean that gives a 99% chance that the true mean lies within it. **(Lesson 15-5)** 15.684–16.716 mm

29. College Entrance Exam Choose the best answer. D
Suppose every letter in the alphabet has a number value that is equal to its place in the alphabet: the letter A has a value of 1, B a value of 2, and so on. The number value of a word is obtained by adding up the values of the letters in the word and then multiplying the sum by the number of letters of the word. The "word" *DFGH* would have a number value of

(A) 22   (B) 44   (C) 66   (D) 100   (E) 108

854   CHAPTER 15   STATISTICS AND DATA ANALYSIS

EXTENDING THE LESSON

Math Power: Connections

An exponential regression equation has the form $y = a \cdot b^x$. Enter each pair, data values found in the table at the right, into the statistical menu of a graphing calculator. Choose exponential regression to find the equation of the exponential curve.
$y = 0.6 \cdot 2^x$

x	y
1	1.2
2	2.4
3	4.8
4	9.6
5	19.2
6	38.4

Technology

Median-Fit Lines

BASIC
Spreadsheets
▶ **Software**

In Lesson 15-6, you learned to graph scatter plots and find the prediction equation that can describe a line of regression for the set of data. *Data Insights*, a software product from Sunburst, Inc., will graph the data you input as ordered pairs and then draw a line suggested by the points, if one exists. *Data Insights* will also give you the equation of the line, which it calls the **median-fit line**.

You can also customize your graph by choosing the scale increments that you want for your axes and the titles that you wish to appear.

The data below include the year and the millions of students in elementary and secondary schools in the United States. The graph done by *Data Insights* shows the graphed data and the median-fit line. Notice that *Data Insights* labels the axes for you.

Data Insights: Scatter Plot

STUDENTS IN U.S. SCHOOLS

$Y = 0.36571X + -686.99609$

Year	Millions of Students
1900	10.6
1910	12.6
1920	16.2
1930	21.3
1940	22.0
1950	22.3
1960	32.5
1970	42.5
1980	38.2
1990	38.0

In the median-fit line equation, $y = 0.36571x + (-686.99609)$, x represents the year and y represents the millions of students.

EXERCISES

1a. 15.9 million
1b. 28.0 million

1. Use the median-fit line given above and your calculator to estimate the number of students in each year.
   a. 1922   b. 1955   c. 1978 → 36.4 million   d. 1991 → 41.1 million   e. 2005 → 46.3 million

2. Use *Data Insights* to enter the data below for the number of calories and grams of fat for certain bread products. What is the equation of the median-fit line comparing calories to grams of fat? $y = 0.00840x + 0.43977$

Item	Calories	Fat (g)	Item	Calories	Fat (g)
Corn tortilla	45	1	Plain bagel	150	1
Croissant	240	14	Pita bread	63	1
English muffin	120	1	Wheat bread	60	1
Flour tortilla	90	2	White bread	60	1
Oat-bran bagel	179	2	Honey wheat bread	70	1

Objective   This optional page shows how graphing software can be used to find the median-fit line for data.

Teaching Suggestions

You may wish to have students form cooperative groups to discuss the role of the median-fit line in making projections from the data. Encourage students to use the software to investigate how outliers in data can affect the equation of the median-fit line. You may also have them predict future values from the data, regraph the data, find the new median-fit line, and determine how it compares to the median-fit line given for fewer data values.

15-6B   Graphing Calculators: Curve Fitting

The table below shows population data from the U. S. Census for the years 1790 through 1990. A scatter plot of the data is shown at the right of the table.

Years since 1780	Population (in millions)	Years since 1780	Population (in millions)
10	3.9	120	76.2
20	5.3	130	92.2
30	7.2	140	106.1
40	9.6	150	123.2
50	12.8	160	132.2
60	17.0	170	151.3
70	23.2	180	179.3
80	31.4	190	203.3
90	38.6	200	226.5
100	50.2	210	248.7
110	63.0		

INTRODUCING THE LESSON

Objective   Graph sets of data, find an exponential or power function to model the data, and use that function to solve problems.

Motivating the Lesson

Discuss with students the population data and scatter plot presented in the introduction to the lesson. Have students discuss what type of function from those they have studied might fit the data. Some students might think of a quadratic function, others an exponential function, and still other might think of a cubic function. Ask student what kinds of functions would not model the data well. Possible answers might include square root functions, step functions, or polynomial functions that have relative maxima and minima.

Rather than a linear scatter plot, a curved plot results. Much of the real-world data that are collected and analyzed are nonlinear in nature. A set of data that best fits a curve is called **curvilinear data**. Since most real-world data are positive, most scatter plots are graphs in the first quadrant. If the points were connected, the graph would resemble that of an exponential graph of the form $y = Ae^{Bx}$, or that of a polynomial graph of the form $y = Ax^B$.

The graphs of exponential functions and polynomial functions have similar characteristics in the first quadrant. As a result, it is difficult to distinguish between a quadratic, cubic, or an exponential function upon casual observation. Since it is too difficult to determine what type of function a scatter plot may resemble simply by looking at the data points, it is best to try both equations and see which one fits best.

The TI-81 graphing calculator will draw exponential and polynomial regression curves. The Casio graphing calculator will not, so we must develop another procedure that will allow us to determine the regression curve function. Because a linear relationship among data is easily recognizable, a technique for determining the type of function that approximates the data can be used. This process is known as **linearizing the data**. The object is to manipulate the original data so that the graph of the manipulated data forms a straight line. After the data has been transformed and is linear, we can use the linear regression techniques learned in Lesson 15-6A.

To linearize exponential data, take the natural log of both sides of the exponential equation $y = Ae^{Bx}$ to obtain a linear equation.

$$y = Ae^{Bx}$$
$$\ln y = \ln Ae^{Bx}$$
$$\ln y = \ln A + \ln e^{Bx}$$
$$\ln y = \ln A + Bx \ln e$$
$$\ln y = \ln A + Bx$$

TEACHING THE LESSON

Teaching Tip   Discuss the development of linearizing the exponential data presented at the bottom of the page. Ask students to analyze the following statements.
- If data is modeled by an exponential function, then $\ln y$ is a linear function of x.
- If the data is modeled by a power function, $\ln y$ is a linear function of x.

To draw the graphs of the line of regression and scatter plot, plot ln y along the vertical axis instead of y. Then ln A is a constant and represents the y-intercept of the line. The coefficient of x is B, which is also the slope of the line of regression. The points plotted are then of the form $(x, \ln y)$.

Example 1

APPLICATION

Population

Use the population data at the beginning of the lesson to determine the exponential equation that best fits the data and describe its goodness of fit.

First, set the range parameters. The values of data suggest that we use the viewing window [0, 225] by [0, 275] with scale factors of 25 for both axes on the TI-81, and [0, 225] by [0, 7] with scale factors of 25 for the x-axis and 1 for the y-axis on the Casio.

Next, set your calculator in the proper statistical mode and clear the statistical memories and the graphics screen. Also clear any equations from the Y= list.

TI-81: [2nd] [STAT] [▶] 2 [ENTER] [2nd] [STAT] [◀] [ENTER]

Casio: [SHIFT] [Cls] [EXE] [SHIFT] [MODE] [÷] [SHIFT] [Scl] [EXE]

Then, input your data. For the Casio graphing calculator, input the natural log of each y-value because ln y is plotted on the vertical axis of the graph.

TI-81: 10 [ENTER] 3.9 [ENTER] . . . 210 [ENTER] 248.7 [ENTER]

Casio: 10 [SHIFT] [,] [ln] 3.9 [DT] . . . 210 [SHIFT] [,] [ln] 248.7 [DT]

Now, draw the scatter plot and regression curve or line.

TI-81: [2nd] [STAT] [▶] 2 [ENTER]

[2nd] [STAT] 4 [ENTER]

[Y=] [VARS] [▶] [▶] 4

[GRAPH]

[2nd] [STAT] [▶] 2 [ENTER]

Casio: [Graph] [SHIFT] [Line] 1 [EXE]

On the TI-81 graphing calculator, the equation for the regression curve is $y = 4.721 \times 1.0210^x$, where $a = A$, and $b = e^B$. Pressing [LN] [VARS] [▶] [▶] 2 will give the value of B. The equation then can be written as $y = 4.721e^{0.0208x}$.

To find the equation for the regression curve on the Casio graphing calculator, press [SHIFT] [A] [EXE] to find the value of ln A, and [SHIFT] [B] [EXE] to find the value of B. Pressing [SHIFT] [e^x] [SHIFT] [A] [EXE] gives the value of A. The equation for the regression curve is then $y = 4.721e^{0.0208x}$.

(continued on the next page)

The list below gives the average distance, x (in millions of kilometers), of each planet from the sun and the number of days, y, it takes for each planet to orbit the sun. Find an appropriate model for the data.

Planet	x	y
Mercury	57.9	88
Venus	108.1	225
Earth	149.5	365
Mars	228.2	687
Jupiter	777.6	4333
Saturn	1426.0	10,759
Uranus	2869.0	30,686
Neptune	4495.0	60,188
Pluto	5921.0	90,737

$y = 0.1995x^{1.5}$

Pressing $\boxed{\text{SHIFT}}$ $\boxed{r}$ on the Casio graphing calculator will give the Pearson product-moment correlation value of $+0.9836$, which is the same correlation value obtained from the TI-81 graphing calculator. From this, we can conclude that the regression curve is an extremely good fit to the data.

To determine if a polynomial equation would better fit the data in Example 1, you can press $\boxed{\text{2nd}}$ $\boxed{\text{STAT}}$ 5 $\boxed{\text{ENTER}}$ and check the value r on the TI-81 graphing calculator. For Example 1, the exponential regression equation gives a better fit to the curve.

To calculate and graph polynomial equations of the form $y = Ax^B$ that can be used to fit data on the Casio graphing calculator, it is again necessary to linearize the data and use a linear regression model to find equations of this form.

$$y = Ax^B$$
$$\ln y = \ln Ax^B$$
$$\ln y = \ln A + B \ln x$$

Rather than plotting y along the vertical axis, you plot $\ln y$. And rather than plotting x along the horizontal axis, you plot $\ln x$. Here, $\ln A$ is a numeric value and represents the y-intercept of the regression line and the coefficient of x is B, which is the slope of the regression line.

Example 2

APPLICATION

Physics

The data in the table at the right were recorded in a physics class at West Chicago High School. The table shows the length of a pendulum (in meters) and the time (in seconds) it took to make the pendulum swing back and forth one time. Find the polynomial equation that best fits the data and describe its goodness of fit.

Time	Length	Time	Length
0.453	0.05	1.419	0.50
0.628	0.10	1.552	0.60
0.776	0.15	1.679	0.70
0.891	0.20	2.005	1.00
1.100	0.30	2.196	1.20
1.270	0.40	2.371	1.40

First, set the range parameters. Use the viewing window [0, 3] by [0, 2] with scale factors of .25 for both axes on the TI-81 and [-1, 1] by [-3, 1] with scale factors of .25 for the both axes on the Casio. Next, clear the statistical memories and the graphics screen. Clear any equations from the Y= list also.

TI-81: $\boxed{\text{2nd}}$ $\boxed{\text{STAT}}$ $\boxed{\blacktriangleleft}$ 2 $\boxed{\text{ENTER}}$ $\boxed{\text{2nd}}$ $\boxed{\text{STAT}}$ $\boxed{\blacktriangleleft}$ $\boxed{\text{ENTER}}$

Casio: $\boxed{\text{SHIFT}}$ $\boxed{\text{Cls}}$ $\boxed{\text{EXE}}$ $\boxed{\text{SHIFT}}$ $\boxed{\text{Scl}}$ $\boxed{\text{EXE}}$

Then, input your data. For the Casio, input the natural log of each x-value and each y-value because these are the values being plotted on the graph.

TI-81: .453 $\boxed{\text{ENTER}}$ .05 $\boxed{\text{ENTER}}$ ... 2.371 $\boxed{\text{ENTER}}$ 1.40 $\boxed{\text{ENTER}}$

Casio: $\boxed{\ln}$ .453 $\boxed{\text{SHIFT}}$ $\boxed{,}$ $\boxed{\ln}$ .05 $\boxed{\text{DT}}$ ... $\boxed{\ln}$ 2.371 $\boxed{\text{SHIFT}}$ $\boxed{,}$ $\boxed{\ln}$ 1.40 $\boxed{\text{DT}}$

Now, draw the scatter plot and regression curve or line.

TI-81: [2nd] [STAT] [▶] 2 [ENTER]
[2nd] [STAT] 5 [ENTER]
[Y=] [VARS] [▶] [▶] 4
[GRAPH]
[2nd] [STAT] [▶] 2 [ENTER]

Casio: [GRAPH] [SHIFT] [LINE] 1 [EXE]

Using the TI-81 graphing calculator, the equation for the regression curve is $y = 0.2488 \times x^{2.0013}$, where $a = A$, and $b = B$.

To find the equation for the regression curve on the Casio graphing calculator, press [SHIFT] [A] [EXE] to find the value of ln A, and [SHIFT] [B] [EXE] to find the value of B. Pressing [SHIFT] [e^x] [SHIFT] [A] [EXE] gives the value of A. The equation for the regression curve is then $y = 0.2488x^{2.0013}$.

Pressing [SHIFT] [r] on the Casio graphing calculator will give the Pearson product-moment correlation value of $+0.9999$, which is the same correlation value obtained from the TI-81 graphing calculator. From this, we can conclude that the regression curve is an extremely good fit to the data.

Remember that since it is difficult to determine whether a scatter plot is best fitted by a polynomial equation or an exponential equation, it is advisable to apply both processes to the data and observe the Pearson product-moment correlation values to determine which one fits the data best.

EXERCISES

Solve each problem using your graphing calculator. 2–4. See margin.

1. A set of data has Pearson product-moment correlation values of $+0.964$ for $(x, \ln y)$ and $+0.962$ for $(\ln x, \ln y)$. Which type of regression equation fits the data best, exponential or polynomial? polynomial

2. Would you use a polynomial regression equation or an exponential regression equation for the data $(2, 121.40)$, $(3, 56.27)$, $(4, 32.11)$, $(5, 23.06)$, $(6, 18.27)$, $(7, 11.14)$? Why?

3. Find the exponential function that best fits the data $(2.2, 6.04)$, $(2.8, 10.65)$, $(3.6, 25.8)$, $(4.1, 43.57)$, $(4.4, 58.21)$, $(5.1, 129.98)$. What is the Pearson product-moment correlation value? Sketch the exponential regression equation and scatter plot, or the linearized regression equation and scatter plot.

4. Find the function of the form $y = Ax^B$ that best fits the data $(27, 2390)$, $(29, 3003)$, $(32, 3875)$, $(35, 4461)$, $(37, 5698)$. What is the Pearson product-moment correlation value? Sketch the polynomial regression equation and scatter plot, or the linearized regression equation and scatter plot.

GRAPHING CALCULATORS: CURVE FITTING   859

Closing the Lesson

Ask students to find other applications of curve fitting that might appear in newspapers, magazines, or in news reports on television. Ask them how what they have learned in this lesson could be applied.

Homework Exercises

Assignment Guide

All: 1–14

Using the Chapter Summary and Review

The Chapter Summary and Review begins with an alphabetical listing of the new terms that were presented in the chapter. Have students define each term and provide an example of it, if appropriate.

The Skills and Concepts presented in the chapter are reviewed using a side-by-side format. Encourage students to refer to the Objectives and Examples on the left as they complete the Review Exercises on the right.

The Chapter Summary and Review ends with exercises that review Applications and Problem Solving.

Additional Answer

3.

VOCABULARY

Upon completing this chapter, you should be familiar with the following terms:

arithmetic mean or mean	**811**	**813**	median
array	**813**	**815**	median class
back-to-back bar graph	**802**	**848**	median-fit line
best-fit line	**847**	**813**	mode
bimodal data	**813**	**831**	normal curve
bivariate data	**847**	**831**	normal distribution
box-and-whisker plot	**821**	**821**	outlier
class interval	**803**	**821**	quartile
class limits	**804**	**849**	Pearson product-moment correlation
class marks	**804**	**847**	prediction equation
frequency distribution	**803**	**820**	range
frequency polygon	**806**	**847**	regression methods
goodness of fit	**849**	**846**	scatter plot
hinges	**821**	**821**	semi-interquartile range
histogram	**804**	**823**	standard deviation
inferential statistics	**838**	**839**	standard error of the mean
interquartile range	**821**	**814**	stem-and-leaf plot
level of confidence	**840**	**803**	three-dimensional bar graph
mean deviation	**823**		

SKILLS AND CONCEPTS

OBJECTIVES AND EXAMPLES	REVIEW EXERCISES
Upon completing this chapter, you should be able to:	Use these exercises to review and prepare for the chapter test.

■ draw, analyze, and use bar graphs and histograms **(Lesson 15-1)**

Draw a histogram of the data below.

Score	Freq.
60—70	2
70—80	8
80—90	11
90—100	6

The table below gives the grade point averages of 500 college freshmen.

Point Average	Frequency
0.0-1.0	54
1.0-2.0	92
2.0-3.0	124
3.0-4.0	145
4.0-5.0	85

1. What are the class marks? 0.5, 1.5, 2.5, 3.5, 4.5

2. Find the class interval. 1.0

3. Draw a histogram of this data. See margin.

OBJECTIVES AND EXAMPLES	REVIEW EXERCISES

OBJECTIVES AND EXAMPLES

■ find the mean, mode, and median of a set of data **(Lesson 15-2)**

Find the mean, mode, and median of the set {46, 47, 48, 49, 50, 53, 54, 56, 58, 58, 64}.

mean = $\dfrac{46 + 47 + \cdots + 58 + 64}{11}$ or 53

mode = 58

median = 53 (the 6th value)

■ find the mean deviation, semi-interquartile range, and standard deviation of a set of data **(Lesson 15-3)**

semi-interquartile range: $Q_R = \dfrac{Q_3 - Q_1}{2}$

mean deviation: $MD = \dfrac{1}{n} \sum_{i=1}^{n} |X_i - \overline{X}|$

standard deviation: $\sigma = \sqrt{\dfrac{1}{n} \sum_{i=1}^{n} (X_i - \overline{X})^2}$

■ use the normal distribution curve **(Lesson 15-4)**

A Normal Distribution

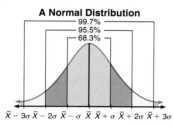

$\overline{X} - 3\sigma \ \overline{X} - 2\sigma \ \overline{X} - \sigma \ \overline{X} \ \overline{X} + \sigma \ \overline{X} + 2\sigma \ \overline{X} + 3\sigma$

■ find the standard error of the mean to predict the true mean of a population with a certain level of confidence **(Lesson 15-5)**

Find the standard error of the mean for $\sigma = 12, N = 100$, and $\overline{X} = 75$. Then find the range for a 1% level of confidence.

$\sigma_{\overline{X}} = \dfrac{12}{\sqrt{100}}$ or 1.2

1% level of confidence: $P = 0.99$, so $t = 2.58$.

$\overline{X} = 75 \pm (2.58)(1.2)$

$= 71.90$ and 78.10

REVIEW EXERCISES

Find the mean, median, and mode(s) for each set of data.

4. {4, 8, 2, 4, 5, 5, 6, 7, 4} 5, 5, 4
5. {19, 11, 13, 15, 16} 14.8, 15, none
6. {6.6, 6.3, 6.8, 6.6, 6.7, 5.9, 6.4, 6.3}
7. {130, 135, 131, 128, 122, 141, 133, 146}
6. 6.45, 6.5, 6.3 and 6.6
7. 133.25, 132, none

A die was tossed 10 times with these results.

5 1 5 4 2 3 6 2 5 1

8. Find the mean deviation of the data. 1.6
9. Find the standard deviation of the data.
10. Find the semi-interquartile range of the data. 1.5   9. 1.74

A set of data has a normal distribution with a mean of 88 and a standard deviation of 5.

11. What percent of the data is in the interval 78–98? 95.5%
12. Find the probability that a value selected at random from the data lies in the interval 86–90. 0.33
13. Find the interval about the mean that includes 90% of the data. 79.75–96.25

In a random sample of 200 adults, it was found that the average number of hours per week spent cleaning their home was 1.8, with a standard deviation of 0.5.

14. Find the standard error of the mean. 0.035
15. Find the range about the mean such that the probability is 0.90 that the true mean lies within the range. 1.742–1.858
16. Find the range about the sample mean that has a 5% level of confidence. 1.7314–1.8686

Answer to Exercise 1
Alternate Review Strategy

45–50	1
50–55	2
55–60	1
60–65	3
65–70	2
70–75	4
75–80	1
80–85	2
85–90	5
90–95	0
95–100	4

Alternate Review Strategy

To provide a brief in-class review, you may wish to read the following questions to your students and have them answer verbally.

Twenty-five students' scores on a chapter test are as follows.

82	89	72	98	100
63	71	97	82	63
58	72	47	72	54
51	98	89	70	70
61	78	89	89	89

1. Make a frequency distribution of the data. See below.
2. Make a histogram of the data.

3. Find the mean of the data.
   76.16
4. Find the median of the data.
   72
5. Find the standard deviation of the data. 15.35
6. Find the mode of the data. 89
7. Find the semi-interquartile range of the data. 13
8. Make a box-and-whisker plot of the data.

9. Find the mean deviation of the data. 13.29
10. Assume that the data are normally distributed. Find the lower and upper limits within which 90% of the data lie. 50.8 to 101.5
11. Find the range about the sample mean that has a 5% level of confidence. 70.1428 to 82.1772

Two multiple-choice tests (Forms 1A and 1B) and two free-response tests (Forms 2A and 2B) are provided in the *Evaluation Masters*. Chapter 15 Test, Form 1A is shown below. Chapter 15 Test, Form 2A is shown on the next page.

Evaluation Masters Booklet, pp. 181–182

NAME _____ DATE _____

Chapter 15 Test, Form 1A

Write the letter for the correct answer in the blank at the right of each problem. Use the data in the table below for Exercises 1-11.

Number of Cars per 1000 People, 1988

Country	Number	Country	Number	Country	Number
United States	559	Sweden	400	Finland	344
Australia	497	France	394	Denmark	321
Canada	454	Austria	370	United Kingdom	318
Switzerland	419	Belgium	349	Spain	263
Italy	408	Netherlands	348	Japan	241

1. What is the range of the data?
   A. 559   B. 318   C. 800   D. 241   1. __B__

2. Which would be an appropriate class interval for displaying the data?
   A. 200   B. 100   C. 30   D. 5   2. __C__

3. What is the mean of the data?
   A. 569   B. 379   C. 370   D. 349   3. __B__

4. Find the mode of the data.
   A. 379   B. 370   C. 349   D. none   4. __D__

5. What is the median of the data?
   A. 370   B. 379   C. 408   D. none   5. __A__

6. What is the deviation from the mean for the number of cars in the United States?
   A. 180   B. 189   C. 270   D. 379   6. __A__

7. Find the mean deviation of the data.
   A. 956   B. 63.1   C. 65.6   D. 63.7   7. __D__

8. What is the upper quartile value of the data?
   A. 413.5   B. 419   C. 408   D. 379   8. __B__

9. What is the lower quartile value of the data?
   A. 344   B. 305.5   C. 348   D. 321   9. __D__

10. What is the interquartile range for the data?
    A. 98   B. 81   C. 140   D. 198   10. __A__

11. What is the semi-interquartile range of the data?
    A. 40.5   B. 99   C. 70   D. 49   11. __D__

NAME _____ DATE _____

Chapter 15 Test, Form 1A (continued)

A set of data has a normal distribution with a mean of 180 and a standard deviation of 20.

12. What percent of the data is in the interval 140-220?
    A. 38.3%   B. 68.3%   C. 95.5%   D. 99.7%   12. __C__

13. Find the probability that a value selected at random is less than 160.
    A. 15.9%   B. 19.1%   C. 2.2%   D. 31.7%   13. __A__

14. Find the limit below which 80% of the data lies.
    A. 216   B. 206   C. 196   D. 154   14. __B__

Suppose each of the families in a sample of 100 purchase an average of 5.4 magazines monthly. The standard deviation of the samples is 1.2 magazines.

15. Find the standard error of the mean.
    A. 1.0   B. 0.12   C. 0.45   D. 0.54   15. __B__

16. Find the interval about the sample mean that has a 5% confidence level.
    A. 5.32–5.48   B. 4.34–6.46   C. 4.2–5.52   D. 5.16–5.64   16. __D__

17. Find the interval about the sample mean that gives a 50% chance that the true mean lies within that interval.
    A. 5.32–5.48   B. 4.34–6.46   C. 4.2–5.52   D. 5.16–5.64   17. __A__

18. Find the interval about the sample mean such that the probability is 0.90 that the true mean lies within the interval.
    A. 5.202–5.598   B. 7.05–3.75   C. 4.5–6.3   D. 4.2–6.6   18. __A__

A study of the deer population in a certain forest yielded the following data.

Year	1964	1968	1972	1976	1980	1984	1988	1992
Number of Deer	756	702	643	512	396	304	235	172

19. Find an equation of the line of regression.
    A. $y = 3x$ B. $y = 22.5 - 449x$ C. $y = 44946 - 22.5x$ D. $y = 22x - 449$ 19. __C__

20. Describe the relationship.
    A. strongly negative   B. moderately negative   C. moderately positive   D. strongly positive   20. __A__

Bonus

Find the Pearson product-moment correlation value for the number of deer.
    A. 0.99368   B. -0.99368   C. 0.00632   D. -0.00632   Bonus: __B__

- draw regression lines **(Lesson 15-6)**

Find the median fit line for the data.

Number of People at the Pool

High Temperature (°F)   High Temperature (°F)

Use the chart to complete Exercises 17—18.

Student	A	B	C	D	E	F	G
Days Absent	0	3	6	1	2	2	4
Final Grade	95	88	69	89	90	86	77

17. Draw a scatter plot and find a median fit line for the data. See Teacher's Answer Key.

18. Find an equation of the line of regression. Sample answer: $y = -4.44x + 96.64$

- compute correlation values to determine goodness of fit **(Lesson 15-6)**

Pearson product-moment correlation:

$$r = \frac{SP}{\sqrt{SS_x SS_y}}, \text{ where } SP = \Sigma(X - \overline{X})(Y - \overline{Y}),$$

$$SS_X = \Sigma(X - \overline{X})^2, \text{ and } SS_Y = \Sigma(Y - \overline{Y})^2,$$

and n is the number of items being ranked.

Use the chart above to complete Exercises 19—20.

19. Determine the Pearson product-moment correlation value for the data. -0.95

20. Describe the relationship between the days absent and the final grade. strongly negative

---

APPLICATIONS AND PROBLEM SOLVING

21. **Safety** The numbers of job-related injuries at a construction site for each month of 1992 are listed below. **(Lesson 15-2)**

    10   13   15   39   21   24   19   16   39   17   23   25

    a. Make a stem-and-leaf plot of the numbers of injuries. See margin.
    b. Find the median, mode, and mean of the numbers of injuries. 20; 39; 21.75

22. **Transportation** The length, in miles, of the eight longest underwater vehicular tunnels in North America are listed below. **(Lesson 15-3)**

    3.60   1.73   1.62   1.56   1.55   1.50   1.45   1.42

    a. Find the mean and median of the tunnel lengths. 1.80; 1.555
    b. Find the mean deviation and the standard deviation of the tunnel lengths. 0.45; 0.69
    c. Make a box-and-whisker plot of the data. Name any outliers. See margin; 3.60.

23. **Recreation** Juan wants to know the relationship between the number of hours students spend watching TV each week and the number of hours students spend reading each week. A sample of 10 students reveals the following. **(Lesson 15-6)**

Student	A	B	C	D	E	F	G	H	I	J
Watching TV	20	32	42	12	5	28	33	18	30	25
Reading	8.5	3.0	1.0	4.0	14.0	4.5	7.0	12.0	3.0	3.0

    a. Draw a scatter plot to see how the data is related. See margin.
    b. Determine the Pearson product-moment correlation value for the data. -0.72
    c. Describe the relationship. moderately negative

Additional Answers

21a.
```
1 | 0 3 5 6 7 9
2 | 1 3 4 5
3 | 9 9

1 | 0 means 10.
```

22c.

23a.

Attendance The days missed for a random sample of 80 high school students at Dover High School in a certain school year are given. 2. See Teacher's Answer Key.

```
 6  16  12   7   7   9  13  12   7   7
19   4   9   6   4  11  13  10  16  20
10  17  11  12   6   9  10  14   3   8
 8  12  13   8   8  11  12   1  11   5
11  16  13   5  10   1  10   8  15  10
13   9  20   5   9  15  11  18  12  14
10  16   8  10   2  11  19  10  12  17
14   6   9  12  10  14   8   9   7   9
```

Use the data below for Exercises 6-12.

Physics A small metal object is weighed on a laboratory balance by each of 15 pupils in a physics class. The weight of the object in grams is reported as 2.341, 2.347, 2.338, 2.350, 2.344, 2.342, 2.345, 2.348, 2.340, 2.345, 2.343, 2.344, 2.347, 2.341, and 2.344.

10. See margin.   12. 0.0031

Assume the data given for Exercises 1–5 are normally distributed.

1. Make a frequency distribution of the data using a class interval of 3. 1. See Teacher's Answer Key.
2. Make a histogram of the data.
3. Find the mean of the data. 10.438
4. Find the median of the data. 10
5. Find the standard deviation of the data. 4.210
6. Find the mean of the data. 2.344
7. Find the median of the data. 2.344
8. Find the mode of the data. 2.344
9. Find the semi-interquartile range of the data. 0.003
10. Make a box-and-whisker plot of the data.
11. Find the mean deviation of the data. 0.0025
12. Find the standard deviation of the data.

13. Find the lower and upper limits within which 90% of the data lie. 3.47–17.33
14. Find the probability that a value selected at random from the data will be between 8 and 12. 0.381
15. Find the standard error of the mean. 0.4707
16. Find the range about the sample mean that has a 5% level of confidence. 9.515–11.361

Grades The table below shows the statistics grades and the economics grades for a group of college students at the end of a semester.

Statistics Grades	95	51	49	27	42	52	67	48	46
Economics Grades	88	70	65	50	60	80	68	49	40

17. Draw a scatter plot and find a median fit line for the data. See Teacher's Answer Key.
18. What is an equation of the line of regression? See margin.
19. Find the Pearson product-moment correlation value. 0.724
20. Describe the relationship between the statistics grades and the economics grades. moderately positive

Bonus The *variance* of a set of data can be found using the formula $\sigma^2 = \frac{1}{n}\sum_{i=1}^{n}(X_i - \overline{X})^2$. How is this formula related to the formula for the standard deviation? Find the variance of the data for Exercises 6–12. See margin.

Test Generator Software is provided in Apple, IBM, and Macintosh versions. You may use this software to create your own tests, based on the needs of your students.

Additional Answers

10.

2.338 2.340 2.342 2.344 2.346 2.348 2.350

18. Let x = statistics grades, and y = economics grades.
$y = 0.59x + 32.06$

Bonus The formula is the radicand of the standard deviation formula, or it is the square of the standard deviation. variance = 0.00000961

This page may be used as a test or as a review. All answers to this test appear in the Selected Answers in the student text.

Standardized Test Questions are also provided in the *Evaluation Masters*.

Evaluation Masters Booklet, pp. 185–186

PREVIEWING THE CHAPTER

This chapter introduces a new definition of graphs as figures composed of vertices and edges. Unlike traditional geometric figures, these graphs have edges that may not be line segments. Students learn to distinguish simple graphs , multigraphs, planar graphs, and digraphs. They determine if graphs contain walks, paths, trails, circuits, and/or cycles. Algorithms for Euler paths and circuits, shortest paths, and minimal distances are presented. Properties of trees and algorithms for finding a spanning tree and minimal spanning tree are also introduced. The chapter concludes by using matrices to represent digraphs. Students then use the matrix theorem and the path theorem to solve problems.

Lesson Objective Chart

Lesson (Pages)	Lesson Objectives		State/Local Objectives
16-1 (866-871)	**16-1A:**	Distinguish between multigraphs and simple graphs.	
	16-1B:	Determine whether a graph is complete.	
16-2 (872-876)	**16-2A:**	Distinguish among walks, trails, paths circuits, and cycles.	
	16-2B:	Determine whether a graph is connected.	
16-3 (877-882)	**16-3:**	Find Euler paths and circuits.	
16-4 (883-889)	**16-4:**	Use the breadth-first search algorithm and Dijkstra's algorithm to find a shortest path.	
16-5 (890-895)	**16-5A:**	Find spanning trees.	
	16-5B:	Find minimal spanning trees.	
16-6 (896-903)	**16-6A:**	Use digraphs to solve problems.	
	16-6B:	Represent digraphs as matrices and vice versa.	

ORGANIZING THE CHAPTER

You may want to refer to the **Course Planning Guide Calendar** on pages T34-T35 for a complete pacing chart.

Lesson Planning Guide

Blackline Masters Booklets

Lesson	Pages	Practice	Enrichment	Evaluation	Technology — Graphing Calculator	Technology — Computer	Technology — Multicultural Activity	Applications	Activity Masters — Problem Solving	Activity Masters — Case Study Follow-Up	Activity Masters — Decision Making	Transparencies
16-1	866-871	p. 108	p. 108						p. 47			16-1
16-2	872-876	p. 109	p. 109	Quiz A, p. 201			p. 16					16-2
16-3	877-882	p. 110	p. 110	Quiz B, p. 201 Mid Chapter Test, p. 203		p. 32						16-3
16-4	883-889	p. 111	p. 111	Quiz C, p. 202							p. 48	16-4
16-5	890-895	p. 112	p. 112									16-5
16-6	896-903	p. 113	p. 113	Quiz D, p. 202	p. 31			p. 46				16-6
Review Test		Multiple Choice Tests, Forms 1A and 1B, pp. 193-196 Free Response Tests, Forms 2A and 2B, pp. 197-200 Standardized Test Questions, p. 204									

Other Chapter Resources

Student Edition
Case Study Follow-Up, p. 889
Decision Making, p. 895
Unit Review, pp. 908-909

Other Supplements
Transparency 16-0 for Chapter Opener
Evaluation Masters, Unit Test, pp. 205-208
Alternate Assessment in the Mathematics Classroom,
    Glencoe Publishing Co., 1993
Cooperative Learning in the Mathematics Classroom,
    Glencoe Publishing Co., 1993

Software
Test and Review Generator Software
    Available for Apple, IBM, and Macintosh
Teacher's Guide for Software Resources

ENHANCING THE CHAPTER

Cooperative Learning

Providing Closure to the Lesson

After each session, ample time should be provided for students to summarize what they have learned. To reinforce their understanding of the academic content acquired during the session, groups should review the major points covered and discuss any additional questions that they may have about the content. Class discussion can be a proper forum for this review. For example, select a member of one group to discuss with the class what his or her group concluded and how they reached these conclusions. Encourage the reporter to be thorough by asking for specific examples or additional details about various points. Do not immediately accept or reject the report, but involve the rest of the class by asking members of other groups if they agree or disagree with the conclusions reached by the reporter's group and if any group used different procedures to arrive at the same conclusions. You can also ask groups to relate this content to content learned earlier and to provide examples of different settings or applications where the content could be utilized. Such sharing of ideas and methods will ensure a greater retention of the academic content learned during the group activities.

For more information on cooperative learning, see pages T20-T21. Additional information on using cooperative groups is available in Glencoe's *Cooperative Learning in the Mathematics Classroom,* ©1993.

Multicultural

Multicultural Activity Masters, p. 16

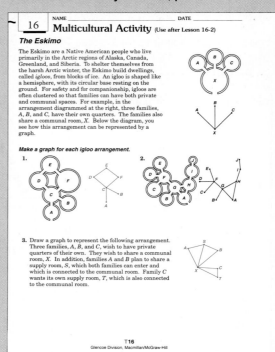

Activity Masters

Applications, p. 46

Problem Solving, p. 47

Decision-Making, p. 48

Technology

Few software products have been developed to deal with graph theory. However, with the growing importance of discrete mathematics, more of these products should appear. Students may be able to use geometric software such as Logo to draw their own graphs to meet given requirements.

In Lesson 16-6, students use their skills with matrices on the TI-81 graphing calculator to enter the edge matrix of a digraph. The matrix theorem is then used to determine the number of two-step paths that exists between vertices. Students can use the matrix features of a graphing calculator to work many of the exercises in the lesson.

Outside Resources

Books/Periodicals

Copes, Wayne, et al. *Graph Theory: Euler's Rich Legacy,* Janson Publications, MA, 1987.

Stewart Ian. *The Problems of Mathematics,* Oxford University Press, 1987.

Films/Videotapes/Videodisc

For All Practical Purposes: Introduction to Contemporary Mathematics, the Anneberg/CPB Project, Washington, DC

Software

Discrete Math. True BASIC (IBM, Macintosh)

Discrete Mathematics. COMAP, Inc. (Macintosh)

Graph Theory (Topics in Discrete Mathematics). Addison-Wesley (Apple II)

Technology Masters

Graphing Calculator, p. 31

Computer, p. 32

CHAPTER 16

GRAPH THEORY

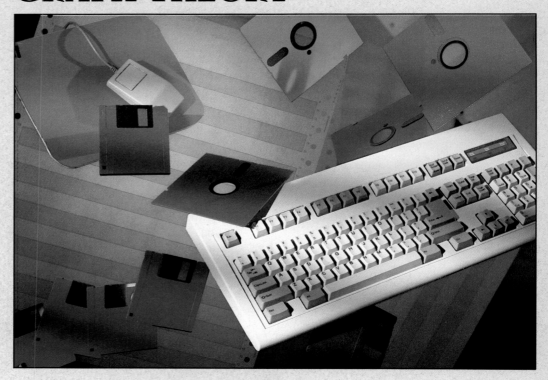

HISTORICAL SNAPSHOT

	First calculating machine Charles Babbage and Ada Byron Lovelace, London		UNIVAC 1 (Universal Automatic Computer) Philadelphia, Pennsylvania		Minicomputer (PDP-5) Digital Corporation Maynard, Massachusetts	
Binary arithmetic Gottfried Leibnitz Germany		First Data-Processing Computer, Dr. Herman Hollerith, New York		FORTRAN (computer programming language) IBM, NYC		Department of Computer Science established at Univ. of Southern California

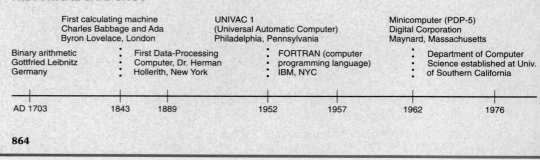

AD 1703	1843	1889	1952	1957	1962	1976

864

CHAPTER OBJECTIVES

In this chapter, you will:
- Define graphs, multigraphs, planar graphs, and digraphs.
- Find walks, paths, and circuits.
- Use matrices to draw graphs.
- Draw and use trees.

CAREER GOAL: Computer Consulting

Computers are used in every phase of every business you can think of. Mary Ann Terrazas says she chose computer science as a career because "I knew that it would be a career that would keep growing and one in which I would be needed."

Mary Ann has already spent time working in her field. "During the summer of 1989, I worked for Pacific Bell, programming with their data base. During the summer of 1990, I worked for the Central Intelligence Agency (CIA) in a computer science position. During the summer of 1992, I am working for Loral Electro-Optics Systems, programming for their Defense Department projects."

Mary Ann is glad that she was able to take algebra, geometry, trigonometry, mathematical analysis, and a full year of calculus in high school. Computer science is closely tied to mathematics. For example, "In order for a computer process to use a piece of hardware, like a monitor, a printer, or a modem, that hardware has to be free. Before a process will release the hardware it has been using, it will first seek out another piece of hardware that is in use. This may create a chain of processes that are waiting on each other for different resources. Such a chain is called *deadlock*. In computer science, we use a *dependency graph* to diagnose problems like deadlock. Once a dependency graph identifies a cycle that would create deadlock, you can eliminate one of the processes to avoid a system crash."

Mary Ann says that she dislikes the repetitive motion and the sitting for long hours that are involved when you work with computers. However, Mary Ann says, "I like the versatility of computer science. It will allow me to get a job almost anywhere, anytime."

READ MORE ABOUT IT

Career Associates. *Career Choices for the 90's for Students of Computer Science.* New York: Walker, 1990.
Jones, Marilyn. *Exploring Computer Careers For the Handicapped.* New York: The Rosen Publishing Group, Inc., 1985.
Stair, Lila B. *Careers in Computers.* Homewood, Illinois: Dow Jones-Irwin, 1984.

SPOTLIGHT ON...

Mary Ann Terrazas
Age: 21
Class: Senior
School: University of Southern California
Los Angeles, California
Major: Computer Science

"A career in computer science will allow me to get a job almost anywhere, anytime."

FOR MORE INFORMATION

If you would like more information about computer science, contact:

Association for Computing Machinery (ACM)
11 W. 42nd Street, 3rd Floor
New York, NY 10036

Applications

Lesson	Application	Examples	Exercises
16–1	Communication	5	29
	BASIC Programming		48
	Airlines		49
16–2	Manufacturing	2	
	Transportation		27
	Design		28
16–3	Interior Design	2	
	Transportation		26
	Tourism		27
16–4	Energy	3	
	Transportation		27
	Communication		28
16–5	Engineering	2	
	Communications		24
	Computer Technology		25
16–6	Fine Arts	1	
	Manufacturing	2	25
	Biology	4	
	Catering		4
	Construction		26
	Sociology		28
	Transportation		29

NCTM Standards: 1–4, 12

Lesson Resources

- Practice Master 16–1
- Enrichment Master 16–1
- Activity Master, p. 47

 Transparency 16–1 contains the 5-Minute Check and a teaching aid for this lesson.

INTRODUCING THE LESSON

5-Minute Check

(over Chapter 15)

The quiz scores for 15 students are shown below.

72	69	82	88	90
69	78	87	89	69
89	88	42	72	54

1. Make a histogram of the data.

2. Find the mean of the data.
   75.9
3. Find the median of the data.
   78
4. Find the standard deviation of the data. 13.67
5. Make a box-and-whisker plot of the data.

Motivating the Lesson

Show students maps given in magazines distributed by many airlines. They show the complex pattern of routes used by airplanes. Each of the routes represents a multigraph.

16-1 Graphs

Objectives
16–1A
16–1B

After studying this lesson, you should be able to:
- distinguish between multigraphs and simple graphs, and
- determine whether a graph is complete.

Application

Airline magazines often include maps of the routes flown by the airline. On these maps, the cities are usually represented by points and the routes by line segments or arcs. The diagram at the right represents a portion of such a map.

The diagram above is a model of the relationship between cities and airline routes. Such a model is called a **graph.** This type of graph is quite different from the graphs of functions with which you are familiar. In this chapter, a graph is a collection of points in which a pair of points called **vertices,** or **nodes,** are connected by a set of segments or arcs, called **edges.**

Definition of Graph	A graph *G* is a finite, nonempty set *V* of vertices, along with a set *E* of edges.

 FYI...

In the 1930s, the early years of commercial air travel, 224 American cities were listed as regular stops, all seats were first class, and all fares were identical.

The simplest graph has one vertex and no edges. There cannot be a graph of edges only, because edges must connect vertices. In a **simple graph,** only one edge is allowed between any two vertices.

Not all situations can be modeled by a simple graph. Consider the bus route maps illustrated below. The map on the left represents the routes of a single bus company. It is an example of a simple graph. The map on the right represents the routes of several bus companies. This map represents another type of graph called a **multigraph.**

A multigraph is a graph with a finite set of vertices and a finite set of edges. Unlike a simple graph, a multigraph may have several edges connecting the same pair of vertices. These are called **parallel edges.** A multigraph may also contain edges that connect a vertex to itself. These are called **loops.** Since simple graphs are by definition multigraphs, all of the properties of multigraphs apply to simple graphs.

ALTERNATE TEACHING STRATEGIES

Using Cooperative Groups

Have students work in groups to make a multigraph of the homes of the students in the group. Have them map out how to travel from one home to the next.

Using Discussion

Have students discuss possible paths from one big city to the next using a road map. Have them tell why the path they have chosen represents a multigraph.

Definitions of Multigraphs and Simple Graphs

Multigraphs can have:
- loops, or edges connecting a vertex to itself, and
- parallel edges, or several edges connecting the same pair of vertices.

Simple graphs have:
- no loops, and
- no parallel edges.

Example 1

In the multigraph at the right, name the parallel edges and loops.

The parallel edges are b and c.
The loops are edges f and h.

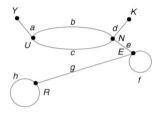

A graph can be described in three ways. One way to describe a graph is by the number of vertices and edges. We will use the notation $G(n, m)$, where n is the number of vertices and m is the number of edges of a graph G. The graph at the right can be described as $G(4, 5)$.

This way of describing a graph is not specific because in some cases, different graphs can be drawn with the same number of vertices and edges. For example, the graphs below also represent $G(4, 5)$.

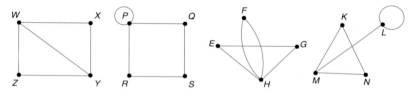

Edge $\{Y, Z\}$ is the same as edge $\{Z, Y\}$.

A more specific way to describe a graph is by listing the vertices and edges. The graph on the left above can be described using the sets $V = \{W, X, Y, Z\}$ and $E = \{\{W, X\}, \{W, Y\}, \{Y, Z\}, \{Z, W\}, \{X, Y\}\}$. This is one way to ensure that the graph drawn more closely represents the correct relationships. Do not assume that when two edges cross, there will be a vertex at their crossing. In the last graph above, $\{M, L\}$ and $\{K, N\}$ cross, but there is no vertex. Unless a vertex is actually indicated and labeled, there is not a vertex where the two edges cross.

LESSON 16-1 GRAPHS 867

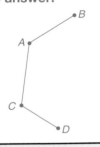
Example 2

Draw a diagram representing a graph with $V = \{R, S, T, M\}$ and $E = \{\{R, S\}, \{S, T\}, \{T, M\}\}$.

Two graphs that satisfy the given conditions are shown below.

Vertices are **connected** or **adjacent** if there is an edge joining them. An edge that is connected to a vertex is **incident** on that vertex. Edges are considered adjacent if they share a vertex. In the graph at the right, vertices D and E are adjacent, but vertices A and C are not. Edge y is incident on vertices D and E, and edge w is adjacent to edge v since they share vertex A.

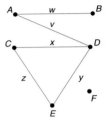

The **degree** of a vertex C, denoted deg (C), is the number of edges incident on C. In the graph above, deg $(C) = 2$ and deg $(B) = 1$. A vertex that has a degree of 0 is **isolated.** In the graph above, vertex F is isolated.

Degree Theorem	For any graph $G(n, m)$, where n is the number of vertices and m is the number of edges, the sum of the degrees of the vertices is twice the number of edges.

In a multigraph, a vertex can have any degree.

You can now describe a graph a third way by indicating the number of vertices and the degrees of each vertex.

Example 3

Draw a graph with five vertices, where deg $(A) = 1$, deg $(B) = 1$, deg $(C) = 2$, deg $(D) = 2$, and deg $(E) = 2$.

Two graphs that satisfy the given conditions are shown below.

A **complete** graph with n vertices, denoted K_n, is a graph in which each pair of vertices is connected by exactly one edge. The graph at the right is an example of a complete graph. You can use a formula to find the number of edges in a complete graph.

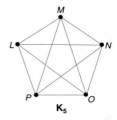

K_5

Complete Graph Theorem

For any complete graph K_n,
1. there are $\dfrac{n(n-1)}{2}$ edges; that is, $G(n, m) = G\left(n, \dfrac{n(n-1)}{2}\right)$, and
2. the maximum degree of every vertex is $n - 1$.

Example 4

Determine if each graph could be complete.
a. $G(7, 21)$
b. $G(6, 12)$

a. $\dfrac{n(n-1)}{2} = \dfrac{7(6)}{2}$
$= 21$

Since $21 = 21$, the graph could be complete.

b. $\dfrac{n(n-1)}{2} = \dfrac{6(5)}{2}$
$= 15$

Since $15 \neq 12$, the graph is not complete.

Properties of complete graphs are often applied in communication relationships.

Example 5

APPLICATION

Communications

The director of sales for Glencoe Publishing Company in Columbus, Ohio, is planning a teleconference with regional vice-presidents from New Jersey, Illinois, South Carolina, Texas, and California. How many telephone lines does the telephone company need to reserve for the teleconference?

Each person in the teleconference can be represented by a vertex of a graph. Since each person will have a direct line with everyone else, a model of this situation would be a complete graph.

$G(n, m) = G(6, m)$ *n = 6, the director plus 5 vice-presidents*

$= G\left(6, \dfrac{6(6-1)}{2}\right)$ *Definition of complete graph*

$= G(6, 15)$

The company needs to reserve 15 lines for the teleconference.

CHECKING FOR UNDERSTANDING

Communicating Mathematics

Read and study the lesson to answer each question.

1. **Describe** the difference between a simple graph and a multigraph. See margin.

2. *True* or *false:* The sum of the degrees of the vertices of a graph equals the number of edges. false

---

RETEACHING THE LESSON

Have each student draw a multigraph representing the various paths that could be taken to get to school from his or her home.

Additional Answer

1. A multigraph can have loops and parallel edges; a simple graph cannot.

Homework Exercises

Assignment Guide

Average: 16–32 even, 33, 35, 40–43,
47, 48, 50–56
Enriched: 17 to 33 odd, 34–56

The red A, B, and C flags, printed only in the Teacher's Wraparound Edition, indicate the level of difficulty of the exercises.

Additional Answers

3. Sample answer:

4. Every pair of vertices is not connected by exactly one edge.

10. It is a multigraph because it has a loop and parallel edges.

Answers for Exercises 13–15 and Exercises 27–28 may vary.

13.

14.

15.

---

3. **Draw** a graph that represents the relationships in Example 5. See margin.

4. **Explain** why the graph used for Exercises 5–12 is not complete. See margin.

Guided Practice

5. t, u, and v
7. B, C, E, and F
8. 2; x and y
9. 1; z

Use the graph at the right to answer each question.

5. Which edges are incident on vertex C?
6. What is deg (E)? 1
7. Which vertices are adjacent to vertex D?
8. How many parallel edges are there?
9. How many loops are there? Name them.
10. Is this a simple graph or a multigraph? Explain. See margin.
11. Name the set of vertices in the graph. $V = \{A, B, C, D, E, F\}$
12. Name the set of edges in the graph. $E = \{q, r, s, t, u, v, w, x, y, z\}$

Draw each graph described below. 13–15. See margin.

13. $G(2, 1)$ 14. $V = \{A, B, C, D\}$, $E = \emptyset$ 15. 5 vertices, each with degree 2

EXERCISES

Practice

A

Draw each graph described below. 16–26. See Teacher's Answer Key.

16. $G(3, 4)$ 17. $G(4, 3)$ 18. $G(2, 0)$ 19. $G(3, 3)$
20. $V = \{M, N, O, P\}, E = \{\{M, O\}, \{O, P\}\}$
21. $V = \{L, M, N\}, E = \{\{L, M\}, \{M, N\}\}$
22. $V = \{R, S, T, U, V\}, E = \{\{R, T\}, \{S, U\}, \{U, V\}, \{S, V\}\}$
23. 3 vertices; deg (A) = 0, deg (B) = 1, deg (C) = 1
24. 4 vertices; deg (A) = 1, deg (B) = 2, deg (C) = 2, deg (D) = 1
25. 5 vertices; deg (A) = 4, deg (B) = 1, deg (C) = 2, deg (D) = 1, deg (E) = 2
26. 6 vertices, each with degree 1

Draw a graph to model each situation. 27–28. See margin.

B

27. Abby, Brenda, Caitlin, Debbie, Evie, and Francine are good friends. Brenda, Debbie, and Evie can only walk to each others' houses because the others are too far. Caitlin can walk to everybody's house but Brenda's.

28. State Route 181 goes from San Antonio to Floresville and Corpus Christi. Route 97 goes through Floresville, Pleasanton, Jourdanton, and Charlotte. Interstate 37 connects San Antonio, Pleasanton, and Corpus Christi.

Draw each graph described below. 30–31. See Teacher's Answer Key.

29. K_2 30. K_4 31. K_6

32. How many edges does the graph of K_5 have? 10
33. How many edges does the graph of K_7 have? 21
34. How many edges does the graph of K_{10} have? 45
35. How many edges does the graph of K_n have? $\dfrac{n(n-1)}{2}$

27.

28.

29.

Determine whether each graph could be complete. Write *yes* or *no*.

36. $G(3, 4)$ no **37.** $G(4, 5)$ no **38.** $G(6, 15)$ yes

39. $G(10, 45)$ yes **40.** $G(14, 91)$ yes **41.** $G(100, 4900)$ no

42. What is the maximum degree of any one vertex in $G(5,2)$? 4, 2 loops on same vertex.

43. Can you draw a graph with exactly 8 vertices, each with a degree of 1? Explain your answer. Yes; see margin.

44. Can you draw a graph with exactly 7 vertices, each with degree 3? Explain your answer. No; the sum of the degrees must be even.

45. How many vertices are there in a graph with 11 edges if each vertex has degree 2? 11 vertices

46. Draw a graph in which each vertex is adjacent to exactly two other vertices and each edge is adjacent to exactly two other edges. K_3

Critical Thinking

47. Could $G\left(x + 3, \dfrac{x^2 + 6x + 9}{2}\right)$ be complete? Why or why not? No; there would be $\dfrac{x^2 + 5x + 6}{2}$ edges, since $\dfrac{n(n-1)}{2} = \dfrac{(x+3)(x+2)}{2}$.

Applications and Problem Solving

Draw a graph to model each situation. Then write a paragraph that completely describes each graph. 48–49. See Teacher's Answer Key.

48. BASIC programming

```
A 10 INPUT N
B 20 IF N = 1000 THEN 80
C 30 IF N > 0 THEN 60
D 40 PRINT N;" IS NEGATIVE"
E 50 GOTO 10
F 60 PRINT N:" IS POSITIVE"
G 70 GOTO 10
H 80 END
```

49. Airlines

A	New York	B	Los Angeles
A	New York	C	Chicago
B	Los Angeles	C	Chicago
B	Los Angeles	D	Dallas
E	Atlanta	D	Dallas
E	Atlanta	C	Chicago
E	Atlanta	A	New York
D	Dallas	C	Chicago

Mixed Review

50. Find an equation of a parabola that contains the points at $(1, 9), (4, 6)$, and $(6, 14)$. **(Lesson 2-4)** $y = x^2 - 6x + 14$

51. Find all rational roots of $x^3 - x^2 - x - 2 = 0$. **(Lesson 4-4)** 2

52. Graph $y = 3\cos(2\theta + 180°)$. **(Lesson 6-3)** See Teacher's Answer Key.

53. Physics Two forces, one of 30 N and the other of 50 N, act on an object. If the angle between the forces is 40°, find the magnitude and the direction of the resultant force. *N is the symbol for the metric unit of force, the newton.* **(Lesson 8-5)** 75.5 N, 14°50′

54. Find an equation of the circle that passes through the points at $(2, -1), (-3, 0)$, and $(1, 4)$. **(Lesson 10-1)** $3x^2 + 3y^2 + x - 7y - 24 = 0$

55. See Teacher's Answer Key.

55. Draw a scatter plot and find a prediction equation to show how study time and test scores are related. Use the data in the table below. **(Lesson 15-6)**

Study time (in minutes)	15	75	60	45	90	60	30	120	10	120
Test scores (percentages)	68	87	92	73	95	83	77	98	65	94

56. College Entrance Exam If $\dfrac{x}{8} = 8$, what would be the value of x? 64

EXTENDING THE LESSON

Math Power: Problem Solving

Have students name the parallel edges and loops of the graph at the right. Then describe the graph in terms of its vertices, edges, and degrees of each vertex. Determine if the graph is complete.
parallel edges: *t, y*; loops: *r, s*; $V: \{A, B, C, D, E\}; E: \{r, s, t, u, v, w, x, y, z\}$; deg($A$) = 5, deg($B$) = 3, deg($C$) = 3, deg($D$) = 5, deg($E$) = 2; It is not complete.

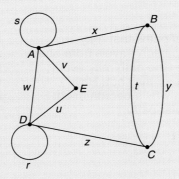

Additional Answer

43. Vertices are connected by edges in pairs. Sample graph:

Enrichment Masters Booklet, p. 108

16-1 Enrichment Worksheet

NAME _____ DATE _____

Graph Coloring

The student council is scheduling a volleyball tournament for teams from all four classes. They want each class team to play every other class team exactly once. How should they schedule the tournament?

If we call the teams A, B, C, and D, all of the possible games among the four teams can be represented as AB, AC, AD, BC, BD, and CD.

Draw a graph to represent the problem. Then color the graph. To **color** a graph means to color the vertices of that graph so that no two vertices connected by an edge have the same color.

Let the vertices represent the possible games. Let the edges represent games that cannot be scheduled at the same time. For example, if team B is playing team C, then team C cannot play team D.

Choose a vertex at which to begin.

• Color AB red. Since CD is not connected to AB, color it red as well. All of the other vertices are connected to AB, so do not color them red.
• Color AC blue. Since BD is not connected to AC, color it blue.
• Color AD green. Since BC is not connected to AD, color it green.

The colored graph shows that pairs of games can be scheduled as follows

AB with CD; AC with BD; AD with BC

The **chromatic number** of a graph is the least number of colors necessary to color the graph. The chromatic number of the graph above is 3.

1. What does the chromatic number of the graph in the example above represent?
the number of game times scheduled

2. Draw and color a graph to represent the same type of tournament, but with 6 teams playing.
See students' graphs.

3. What is the chromatic number for your graph? 5

T108
Glencoe Division, Macmillan/McGraw-Hill

NCTM Standards: 1–4, 12

Lesson Resources

- Practice Master 16-2
- Enrichment Master 16-2
- Evaluation Master, Quiz A, p. 201
- Multicultural Activity Master, p. 16

 Transparency 16–2 contains the 5-Minute Check and a teaching aid for this lesson.

INTRODUCING THE LESSON

🕐 5-Minute Check

(over Lesson 15–1)

1. In the multigraph below, name the parallel edges and loops.

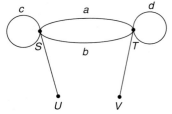

   parallel edges: *a* and *b*
   loops: *c* and *d*

2. Draw a diagram representing the graph with $V = \{R, S, T\}$ and $E = \{\{R, T\}, \{S, T\}\}$.
   Sample answer:

3. Draw a graph with four vertices, where deg(A) = 2, deg(B) = 1, and deg(C) = 3, deg(D) = 2.
   Sample answer:

4. Determine if the graph $G(6, 12)$ is complete.   no

16-2   Walks and Paths

Objectives
16–2A
16–2B

After studying this lesson, you should be able to:
- distinguish among walks, trails, paths, circuits, and cycles, and
- determine whether a graph is connected.

Application

A common problem in graph theory is finding a route that satisfies a given set of conditions.
For example, in some cities it is necessary to develop a spraying route for mosquito abatement. A graph can be used to model the streets of the city. In this case, the intersections would be modeled by vertices, and the streets would be modeled by edges. To minimize cost and resources, the route should include each street only once, if possible. In order to satisfy these conditions, a route is needed that includes each edge exactly once.

In a graph, a **walk** is the course taken from one vertex to another vertex along edges of a graph. For example, a walk from vertex U to vertex V (called a U–V walk) is an alternating sequence of vertices and edges beginning with U and ending with V. This sequence is of the form $V_1, e_1, V_2, e_2, V_3, e_3, \ldots, V_n, e_n, V_{n+1}$, where $V_1 = U$ and $V_{n+1} = V$. The length of this walk is n, the number of edges listed.

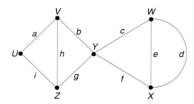

In the graph at the left, W, d, X, e, W, c, Y is a walk of length 3 from W to Y. This W–Y walk can also be written d, e, c. Notice that vertex W appears twice in this walk. Walks may repeat the same edges and vertices. A **trail** is a walk in which no edge is used more than once. In the graph at the left, Y, c, W, d, X, e, W is a Y–W trail. A **path** is a walk in which no vertex nor edge is repeated. Paths also do not contain loops or parallel edges. In the graph at the left, U, a, V, h, Z is a U–Z path.

Example 1

Find a *U–V* walk, a *U–V* trail, and a *U–V* path for the multigraph at the right.

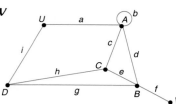

One U–V walk is a, b, c, h, g, f.
One U–V trail is a, d, g, h, e, f.
One U–V path is i, g, f.

ALTERNATE TEACHING STRATEGIES

Using Questioning

There are several paths that may describe how a person travels from one point to another. One path may seem direct while another may not. Have students discuss why a person might choose a particular path.

Using Applications

Have students work in groups to make a list of the various paths through the building that they can take to get to the football field. Have them draw the paths and tell which is the shortest in feet.

In Example 1, another *U–V* path is *a, c, h, g, f*. It can be found in the *U–V* walk given if loop *b* is deleted. This observation leads to the following theorem.

Walks and Paths Theorem	**Every walk contains a path.**

A closed walk starts and ends at the same vertex. In a closed trail, or **circuit,** only vertices may be repeated. In a closed path, or **cycle,** no edges may be repeated and only the beginning and ending vertices may be the same.

Example 2

Suppose a chemical company hires an efficiency expert to create a weekly production schedule of seven chemicals. We'll refer to them as *A, B, C, D, E, F, G*. The schedule must start by producing chemical *A*, include each of the six other chemicals, and end the week in readiness to begin production of *A* the next week. The efficiency expert drew the graph below. The vertices represent the chemicals, and the edges represent the shortest times it takes to change the calibrations for production between each pair of chemicals. What schedule did the efficiency expert recommend?

To create the most efficient schedule, the efficiency expert must find a path where only the beginning and ending vertices are the same. In other words, the efficiency expert must find a cycle that begins and ends with *A*.

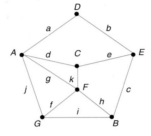

The path *a, b, e, k, h, i, j* satisfies the given condition.

The production schedule would be *A, D, E, C, F, B, G*, and *A*.

A graph is **connected** if there is a path between every two vertices. That is, a graph is connected if it is possible to go from any vertex to any other vertex by following the edges. Complete graphs are always connected. Of the graphs shown below, the graph on the left is connected. The graph on the right is **disconnected.**

 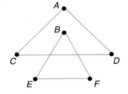

Find several paths, including the "shortest" path, from the nearest shopping center to the school. Discuss possible meanings of *shortest*.

TEACHING THE LESSON

Teaching Tip After discussing the application, point out that finding the route that minimizes cost and resources is the underlying theme of *management science*. That is, find the best method of solving a problem. The best method is called the *optimal solution*.

Chalkboard Examples

For Example 1

Find a *U-V* walk, a *U-V* trail, and a *U-V* path for the multigraph below.
Sample answer: *U-V* walk: *a, h, f, e, c, d, e, g*; *U-V* trail: *a, f, d, c, g*; *U-V* path: *b, g*

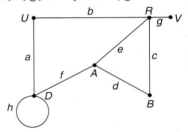

For Example 2

A candidate for president hires a private jet to take him to stops *A*, *B*, *C*, *D*, and *E*, as shown by the graph below. Find a path that will enable him to make each stop and then return to *A*.
Sample answer: *x, y, u, t, w*

For $G(n, m)$ to be connected, there must be at least $n - 1$ edges. However, even if there are at least $n - 1$ edges, they may not be arranged in such a way for the graph to be connected.

Example 3

Determine if each graph is connected.
a. $G(12, 18)$
b. $G(12, 66)$

a. Since there are more than $12 - 1$ or 11 edges, it is possible that $G(12, 18)$ is connected. However, it is not possible to tell if the graph is connected without seeing the graph.

b. This could be a complete graph because $\frac{n(n-1)}{2} = \frac{12(11)}{2}$ or 66. If it is a complete graph, then it is connected.

In a connected graph, a **bridge** is an edge whose removal would cause the graph to no longer be connected. In the graphs shown at the bottom of the previous page, $\{A, B\}$ is a bridge.

CHECKING FOR UNDERSTANDING

Communicating Mathematics

Read and study the lesson to answer each question. 1–2. See margin.

1. **Describe** the differences among walks, trails, and paths.
2. **Explain** why every walk contains a path.
3. **Draw** an example of a graph that is not connected. See students' work.
4. **Explain** the relationship between a connected graph and a bridge. See margin.

Guided Practice

Use the graph at the right to answer each question.

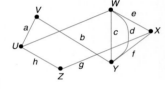

5. Determine whether a, b, c, d, f, g, h is a walk, a trail, or a path. Then state its length. trail, 7
6. What is the length of the shortest U–X path? 2

7. Multigraph; it has parallel edges.

7. Is this a simple graph or a multigraph? Explain.
8. Is the graph connected? yes
9. Does the graph have a bridge? If so, name it. no

EXERCISES

Practice

Use the graph at the right to determine whether each walk is a circuit, cycle, path, trail, or walk. Use the most specific name.

10. a, b, c, k, ℓ, d, c walk
11. a, h, g cycle
12. i, j, c, k, ℓ, e trail
13. k, d, e, f path
14. i, k, d, ℓ, j, b circuit

RETEACHING THE LESSON

Use cooperative groups to have students discover various walks and paths for a given graph by using tracing paper and colored pencils.

Additional Answers

1. In a walk, vertices and edges can be repeated. In a trail, vertices can be repeated but edges cannot be repeated. In a path, you cannot repeat anything.
2. because the set of paths is a subset of the set of walks
4. A bridge is an edge that, if removed, would cause the graph to no longer be connected.

Use the graph at the right to answer each question.

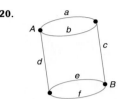

15. How many different *A–E* walks are there in the graph? infinite number

16. How many different *A–E* paths are there in the graph? 3

17. Answers will vary. Sample answer: a, b, g, c, f.

17. Name an *A–E* walk of length 5 in this graph.

18. Name an *A–E* path of length 4 in this graph. a, b, c, f

For each multigraph in Exercises 19–21,
a. list three different walks from *A* to *B* and state the length of each,
b. list all of the paths from *A* to *B* and state the length of each, and
c. for each walk in part a, find a path from *A* to *B* that is contained in it.

19–21. See margin

19.

20.

21.

22. What is the greatest number of edges possible in a disconnected simple graph with 5 vertices? 6

23. What is the greatest number of edges possible in a disconnected simple graph with 8 vertices? 21

24. What is the least number of edges possible in a connected graph with 5 vertices? 4

25. What is the least number of edges possible in a connected graph with 8 vertices? 7

Critical Thinking

26. Is every complete graph a connected graph?
No, K_1 is not connected, since it has no edges.

Applications and Problem Solving

27. **Transportation** An agricultural chemical supplier needs to ship six chemicals from a refinery to a processing plant. We'll refer to the chemicals as *U, V, W, X, Y,* and *Z.* Environmental Protection Agency rail shipping regulations require that certain chemicals must be shipped in separate tank cars due to the possibility of explosion. In the graph at the right, chemicals linked by an edge may not be shipped together. What is the minimum number of tank cars needed to ship equal quantities of each chemical, and what chemicals will be in each car? 3 cars; Sample answer: *U, Z; V, X; W, Y*

LESSON 16-2 WALKS AND PATHS 875

Homework Exercises

Assignment Guide

Average: 10–16, 19, 20, 22, 26, 27, 29–33
Enriched: 14–18, 21–33

The red A, B, and C flags, printed only in the Teacher's Wraparound Edition, indicate the level of difficulty of the exercises.

Chapter 16, Quiz A, (Lessons 16–1 through 16–2), is available in the *Evaluation Masters,* p. 201.

Additional Answers

19a. Sample answer: *d*; 1; *b, c*; 2; *a, d*; 2
19b. *d*; 1; *b, c*; 2
19c. *d*; *b, c*; *d*
20a. Sample answer: *a, c*; 2; *d, e*; 2; *a, b, d, f*; 4
20b. *a, c*; 2; *b, c*; 2; *d, e*; 2; *d, f*; 2
20c. *a, c*; *d, e*; *d, f*
21a. Sample answer: *a*; 1; *b*; 1; *c*; 1
21b. *a*; 1; *b*; 1; *c*; 1; *d*; 1
21c. *a*; *b*; *c*

Additional Answer

28a.

NAME _____ DATE _____

16-2 Enrichment Worksheet

Isomorphic Graphs

We say two graphs are **isomorphic** if they have the same structure. The definition below will help you determine whether two graphs are isomorphic.

> A graph G' is isomorphic to a graph G if the following conditions hold.
> 1. G and G' have the same number of vertices and edges.
> 2. The degree of each vertex in G is the same as the degree of each corresponding vertex in G'.
> 3. If two vertices in G are joined by k ($k \geq 0$) edges, then the two corresponding vertices in G' are also joined by k edges.

Example In the graphs below $HIJKLMN \leftrightarrow TUVWXYZ$. Determine whether the graphs are isomorphic.

Number of vertices in G: 7   Number of vertices in G': 7
Number of edges in G: 10   Number of edges in G': 10
deg (H): 3   deg (I): 3   deg (T): 1   deg (U): 3
deg (J): 3   deg (K): 3   deg (V): 3   deg (W): 3
deg (L): 4   deg (M): 3   deg (X): 4   deg (Y): 3
deg (N): 1   deg (Z): 3

Since there are the same number of vertices and the same number of edges and there are five vertices of degree 3, one vertex of degree 4, and one vertex of degree 1 in both graphs, we can assume they are isomorphic.

Each graph in Column A is isomorphic to one graph in column B. Match the graphs that are isomorphic.

Column A		Column B
1. L	b	a. W
2. Z	a	b. C
3. T	c	c. G

T 109
Glencoe Division, Macmillan/McGraw-Hill

---

28. **Design**   Jack Hanna, the director emeritus for the Columbus Zoo, wishes to provide enclosures for 10 new animals. We'll refer to them as $A, B, C, D, E, F, J, K, L$, and M. Because some animals are natural enemies, they must be kept in different enclosures. The table at the right lists the enemies of each animal.

    a. Represent the information in the table with a graph. Let the animals represent the vertices and let the edges represent animals that may *not* be enclosed together. Try to position the vertices so that edges cross as few times as possible. See margin.

28b. 3 enclosures;
Sample answer:
C, J, K, L; B,
D, E, F; A, M

    b. How many enclosures does Mr. Hanna need and what animals will be in each enclosure?

Animal	Enemies
A	D, F, J, L
B	C, K
C	B, D
D	A, C, L
E	K, M
F	A, J, K
J	A, F
K	B, E, F, M
L	A, D
M	E, K

30. $\dfrac{5}{\sqrt{34}} =$

$r\cos(\theta - 121°)$

Mixed Review

29. Find the critical points of the graph of $f(x) = x^4 - 8x^2 + 16$. Then, determine whether each point represents a maximum, minimum, or a point of inflection. **(Lesson 3-7)**   (0,16), maximum; $(\pm 2, 0)$, minima; $\left(\pm\dfrac{2\sqrt{3}}{3}, \dfrac{64}{9}\right)$, pts. of inflection

30. Write $3x - 5y + 5 = 0$ in polar form.   **(Lesson 9-4)**

31. **Food**   Classic Pizza offers pepperoni, mushrooms, sausage, onions, peppers, and olives as toppings for their seven-inch pizza. How many different 3-topping pizzas can be made?   **(Lesson 14-3)** 20

32. List the vertices adjacent to A and state the degree of A in the figure at the right.   **(Lesson 16-1)** F, H, J; 3

33. **College Entrance Exam**   Choose the best answer. E
    If $x^2 = 36$, then 2^{x-1} could equal

    (A) 4   (B) 6   (C) 8   (D) 16   (E) 32

EXTENDING THE LESSON

Math Power: Problem Solving

The graph represents the walkways in an estate garden. Can the gardener sweep all the walkways without walking over a section twice?
no

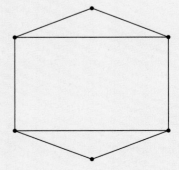

16-3 Euler Paths and Circuits

Objective
16–3

After studying this lesson, you should be able to:
- find Euler paths and circuits.

Application

Before World War II, the city of Kaliningrad, in the former Soviet Union, was known as Königsberg. The Pregel River flowed through the city, and there were seven bridges that connected two islands and the shore. In the early 1700s, the residents of Königsberg tried to solve a problem that is now considered one of the oldest problems involving graph theory. The problem, known as the Königsberg bridge problem, asked whether it was possible to walk through the city while crossing each bridge exactly once. Consider the illustration of the city shown below.

NCTM Standards: 1–4, 12

Lesson Resources

- Practice Master 16–3
- Enrichment Master 16–3
- Evaluation Master, Quiz B, p. 201
- Technology Master, p. 32

Transparency 16–3 contains the 5-Minute Check and a teaching aid for this lesson.

FYI...

Kaliningrad has been almost entirely rebuilt after near total destruction in World War II.

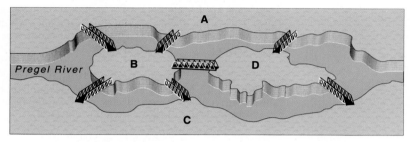

Pregel River

Tracing the graph is similar to walking the path.

In 1736, Leonhard Euler solved this problem by using the graph shown at the right. Each vertex represents a land mass and each edge represents a bridge. Euler showed that walking through Königsberg while crossing each bridge exactly once was equivalent to tracing the graph without retracing any edge.

EXPLORATION: Modeling

Materials: different colored opaque markers

1. Copy the graph modeling the Königsberg bridge problem.
2. Choose a starting vertex and try to trace the graph without retracing any edge.
3. Using the same starting vertex and different color markers, repeat the process starting with each different edge.
4. Repeat the process, with each vertex as a starting point.
5. Use the results of your tracings to answer the questions below.
   a. In how many different ways did you start your tracings? 14 ways
   b. Were you able to trace all of the edges of the graph without retracing any edges? no   It is impossible.
   c. What was Euler's solution to the Königsberg bridge problem?

INTRODUCING THE LESSON

5-Minute Check
(over Lesson 16–2)

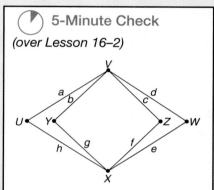

1. a. Use the graph above to determine whether h, g, b is a walk, a trail, or a path from U to V. **walk, trail, path**
   b. List two different walks from U to Z. **Sample answer: a, c or h, f**
   c. Determine whether the walk a, d, e, h is a circuit, path, trail, or walk. Use the most specific name. **circuit**
2. Determine if each graph is connected.
   a. G(11, 55) **yes**
   b. G(11, 25) **maybe**

Motivating the Lesson

Ask students whether they could walk through the closest mall or shopping center without passing through a particular store more than once.

ALTERNATE TEACHING STRATEGIES

Using Models

Have students work in groups to construct models of other bridge problems. Have them predict whether they could walk through the "city" while crossing each bridge exactly once. Then have them share their models with other groups and have them make the same prediction.

Using Problem Solving

Have students add edges to transform the circuit below to an Euler circuit.

In honor of Euler's work, two important characteristics of a connected multigraph bear his name. A path that includes each edge exactly once and has the same starting and ending vertex is called an **Euler circuit**. A path that includes each edge exactly once, but has different starting and ending vertices is called an **Euler path**.

Example 1

Determine whether each graph contains an Euler circuit or an Euler path. If so, name the circuit or path.

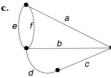

a. The path a, b, c, d, e is an Euler circuit since it contains all of the edges exactly once and returns to the starting vertex.
b. This graph contains neither an Euler circuit nor an Euler path.
c. The path c, d, b, a, e, f is an Euler path since it contains all the edges exactly once and ends at a vertex that is different from the starting vertex.

While working on the Königsberg bridge problem, Euler discovered that for a path to include each edge exactly once and return to the starting vertex, the degree of each vertex must be even.

Euler Circuit Test	**A connected multigraph contains an Euler circuit if and only if the degree of each vertex is even.**

Example 2

APPLICATION

Interior Design

The figure at the right is a floor plan for a house. Is it possible for a person starting at A to take a tour of the house and walk through each doorway exactly once? If so, state the path.

First, develop a multigraph to model the floor plan. Let each vertex represent a room and let each edge represent a doorway.

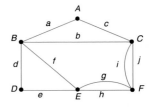

Since each vertex has even degree, the Euler circuit test is satisfied. Thus, it is possible for a person to tour the house and walk through each doorway exactly once.

One possible path is $a, d, e, h, g, f, b, i, j, c$.

Once it has been determined that a connected multigraph does contain an Euler circuit, the circuit can be found. Sometimes the circuit is easily found through observation, but often this is not possible in a more complicated graph. As is the case with any complex problem, a systematic process is helpful. An **algorithm** is a sequence of instructions that solves all cases of a certain type of problem. **Fleury's algorithm** gives a method for finding an Euler circuit in a connected multigraph that has a large number of vertices, all of even degree.

Teaching Tip After explaining Example 2, have students draw a floor plan of one floor of their house. Have them describe the path to walk through each doorway exactly once, if possible.

Fleury's Algorithm

If a connected multigraph contains an Euler circuit, the circuit can be located by the following process.

Step 1 Choose a starting vertex and walk the edges. Mark off the edges walked as you go.

Step 2 Do not choose a bridge, unless not choosing a bridge will disconnect the circuit.

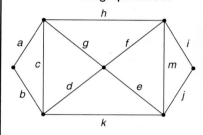

Chalkboard Example

For Example 3

Find an Euler circuit in the connected multigraph below.

Sample answer: *a, h, i, j, k, d, e, m, f, g, c, b*

Example 3

Find an Euler circuit in the connected multigraph at the right.

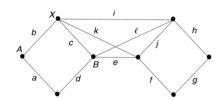

Using Fleury's algorithm, begin at vertex *A* and walk edge *b*. At vertex *X*, you can choose among edges *c, k,* and *i*. Since none of these edges are bridges, any one can be chosen. Let's choose *c*.

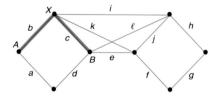

At vertex *B*, the choices include *l, e,* and *d*. Edges *b* and *c* have been eliminated, so *d* is now a bridge back to *A*. Since there are other choices, do *not* choose *d*. Choose *e*. Then choose *j* and *h*.

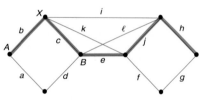

Continue to check for bridges at each vertex. To complete the circuit, choose *g, f, k, i, l, d,* and *a*, respectively.

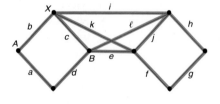

An Euler circuit for this multigraph is *b, c, e, j, h, g, f, k, i, l, d, a*.

LESSON 16-3   EULER PATHS AND CIRCUITS   879

Checking for Understanding

Exercises 1–10 are designed to help you assess students' understanding through reading, writing, speaking, and modeling. You should work through Exercises 1–3 with your students and then monitor their work on Exercises 4–10.

Closing the Lesson

Speaking Activity Have students describe the difference between an Euler path and an Euler circuit.

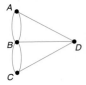

Since the degree of every vertex in the multigraph that models the city of Königsberg is odd, the entire city of Königsberg could not be explored without crossing one bridge at least twice. That is, no Euler circuit could be found. The following test will help you determine whether a graph has an Euler path.

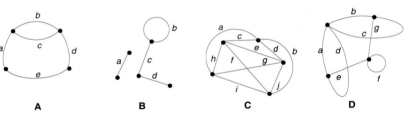

Euler Path Test	A connected multigraph has an Euler path if and only if each vertex has even degree, except for exactly two. Euler paths always start with one of the vertices of odd degree and end with the other.

To find an Euler path from one vertex of odd degree to the other, you can add a temporary edge connecting the two vertices. Then, find an Euler circuit using Fleury's Algorithm. When the temporary edge is removed from the circuit, the result is an Euler path.

CHECKING FOR UNDERSTANDING

Communicating Mathematics

Read and study the lesson to answer each question. 1–3. See margin.

1. **Explain** why a graph must be connected in order to contain an Euler path or an Euler circuit.

2. **Describe** the difference between an Euler circuit and an Euler path.

3. **Describe** the conditions under which a connected graph will contain an Euler circuit.

Guided Practice

Use the figures below to answer Exercises 4–10.

A   B   C   D

4. Which of the figures are connected multigraphs? *A, C, D*

5. Which of the multigraphs contain Euler circuits? *C*

6. Which of the multigraphs contain Euler paths? *A, D*

7. Name an Euler circuit in *C*. Sample answer: *a, d, e, f, j, g, h, c, b, i*

8. Is *C* a complete graph? yes

9. Name an Euler path in *D*. Sample answer: *a, b, g, f, e, d, c*

10. What could you do to make *B* a connected multigraph?
    Connect edge *a* to the rest of the graph.

Practice Masters Booklet, p. 110

RETEACHING THE LESSON

Have students use pipe cleaners (or parts of them) to represent each edge of a given graph. Label each edge with masking tape, writing the letter on the tape. Have students recreate the graph using the edges in order of the circuit they are seeking.

Additional Answers

1. If the graph is not connected, at least one vertex will always be excluded from the path or circuit.

2. An Euler circuit is a path that includes each edge exactly once and has the same starting and ending vertex. An Euler path also includes each edge once and has different starting and ending vertices.

EXERCISES

Practice

Determine whether each multigraph is a simple graph. Write *yes* or *no*.

11.
yes

12.
no

13.
yes

14.
no

15.
yes

16.
yes

17. Which of the multigraphs in Exercises 11–16 are connected? 11, 12, 14, 16

18. Which of the multigraphs in Exercises 11–16 have an Euler circuit? 11, 16

19. Which of the multigraphs in Exercises 11–16 have an Euler path? 12

20. Does the graph below have an Euler circuit? Why or why not?
No; it is not connected.
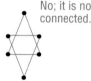

21. Does the graph below have an Euler circuit? Why or why not?
Yes; each vertex has even degree.

22. Draw a graph with 5 vertices that contains an Euler circuit. 22–24. See margin.

23. Draw a graph with 6 vertices that contains an Euler circuit.

24. Draw a graph with 7 vertices that contains an Euler circuit.

Critical Thinking

25. Do all graphs of the form K_n, where $n \geq 2$, contain an Euler circuit? Explain. See margin.

Applications and Problem Solving

26. Transportation Ed Bailey drives a snowplow for Harrison Township. Using the road map of the township shown at the right, his supervisor wants him to find a route that goes over each roadway once. Is such a route possible? If so, find a route that begins and ends at the township office, T. yes; sample route: $y, k, b, m, n, h, a, c, d, e, s, i, q, z, j, p, r, f, g, o, w$

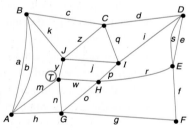

LESSON 16-3 EULER PATHS AND CIRCUITS 881

Enrichment Masters Booklet, p. 110

---

27. **Tourism** Staten Island, New York, is connected to New Jersey by three bridges and to Brooklyn, New York, by one bridge. Can a tour bus from New Jersey cross all four bridges exactly once and end the tour back in New Jersey? If not, what is the least number of additional bridges needed to complete the tour and where should they be located?

No; one, between New Jersey and Brooklyn.

Mixed Review

28. Find the distance between the points with coordinates $(3, -5)$ and $(-1, 2)$. Then find the slope of the line containing these points. **(Lesson 1-4)** $\sqrt{65}, -\dfrac{7}{4}$

29. Without using a calculator, find the value of sin 450°. **(Lesson 5-4)** 1

30. Use the ratio test to determine whether the following series is *convergent* or *divergent:* $1 + \dfrac{1}{2^2} + \dfrac{1}{3^3} + \dfrac{1}{4^4} + \cdots + \dfrac{1}{n^n} + \cdots.$ **(Lesson 12-4)** convergent

31. For the multigraph at the right, list three different walks from *A* to *B* and state the length of each.
(Lesson 16-2)
Sample answer: f, 1; a, b, c, d, e, 5; a, b, c, g, b, c, d, e, 8.

32. **College Entrance Exam** Compare quantities A and B below. C
Write A if quantity A is greater.
Write B if quantity B is greater.
Write C if the two quantities are equal.
Write D if there is not enough information to determine the relationship.

   (A) $\dfrac{8a + 12}{2}$ (B) $4a + 6$

MID-CHAPTER REVIEW

Use the graph at the right to answer each question.

1. Is the figure a multigraph? **(Lesson 16-1)** yes
2. Is the figure a complete graph? **(Lesson 16-1)** no
3. What is deg (E)? **(Lesson 16-1)** 4
4. Which edges are incident on *D*? **(Lesson 16-1)** 4–5. See margin.
5. Which vertices are adjacent to *D*? **(Lesson 16-1)**
6. Is r, x, z, t, v, w a path, a circuit, or a cycle? **(Lesson 16-2)** circuit
7. Is the figure a connected graph? **(Lesson 16-2)** no
8. Does the graph contain an Euler circuit? If so, name it. **(Lesson 16-3)**
   yes; sample answer: $r, s, u, t, z, x, y, v, w$

EXTENDING THE LESSON

Math Power: Problem Solving

Add one or more edges to the graph below to produce a graph that contains an Euler circuit.   Sample:

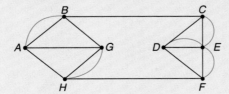

Mid-Chapter Review

The Mid-Chapter Review provides students with a brief review of the concepts and skills in Lessons 16–1 through 16–3. Lesson numbers are given at the end of problems or instruction lines so students may review concepts not yet mastered.

16-4 Shortest Paths and Minimal Distances

Objective
16–4

After studying this lesson, you should be able to:
- use the breadth-first search algorithm and Dijkstra's algorithm to find a shortest path.

Application

Ohio Electric has a fossil fuel powered generating plant in northeastern Ohio that serves several surrounding communities. Some of the electrical power is sent along older transmission lines that have a problem of power loss due to their deteriorating condition. Based on resistance tests, electrical engineers determined the percent of power lost along each line between these communities as shown in the graph below.

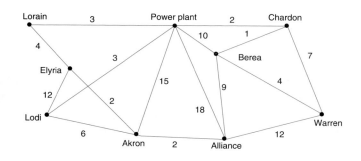

The engineers' final task is to determine the best electrical power route, that is, one with the least power loss, between any two cities. Can you find such a route and the minimum power lost between the power plant and Alliance? *This problem will be solved in Example 3.*

In this lesson, you will explore ways to find the shortest paths, or paths with the fewest edges, and the minimal paths, or paths with the least total weight, in multigraphs and weighted multigraphs. **Weighted multigraphs** are multigraphs in which a value is assigned to each edge.

To find the shortest path in a multigraph means to find the path that contains the fewest edges. One way to find the shortest path is to list all of the possible paths and then choose the shortest one. However, since some graphs are very complex, an algorithm called the **breadth-first search algorithm** can be used that will ensure finding the shortest path. In this algorithm, each vertex is assigned a number followed by a letter. An example is $3(F)$, where 3 is the sum of the fewest edges to this vertex and F represents the preceding vertex in this path.

LESSON 16-4 SHORTEST PATHS AND MINIMAL DISTANCES 883

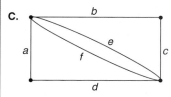

Have students describe the shortest path from your mathematics classroom to the main office.

TEACHING THE LESSON

Chalkboard Example

For Example 1

Find the shortest path and distance from *A* to *K* in the multigraph below.

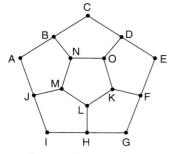

Sample answer:
A, J, M, L, K; 4

Breadth-First Search Algorithm

Step 1 Assign *U*, the starting vertex, the label 0(–). The (–) means that there is no preceding vertex in the path. Then label the vertices adjacent to *U* as 1(*U*).

Step 2 Label all of the vertices adjacent to the already labeled vertices. Assign these vertices a number, $n + 1$, based on the preceding vertex having been assigned the number *n*, followed by the name of the preceding vertex. If one of the unlabeled vertices is adjacent to more than one labeled vertex, then choose one of them at random.

Step 3 If you have reached *V*, then stop (if not, go back to Step 2). The label assigned to *V* describes the distance from *U* to *V*. Listing the sequence of preceding vertices produces one of the shortest paths from *U* to *V*.

Example 1

Find the shortest path and the distance from *A* to *K* in the multigraph at the right.

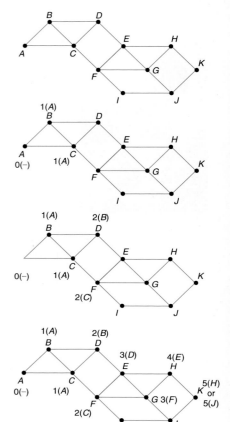

Step 1 Assign *A* the label 0(–). Assign vertices *B* and *C* the label 1(*A*) because they are adjacent to 0(–).

Step 2 Since vertex *D* is adjacent to labeled vertices *B* and *C*, vertex *D* is assigned either label 2(*B*) or 2(*C*) at random. Since vertex *F* is adjacent to labeled vertex *C*, assign *F* the label 2(*C*).

Step 3 Repeat this process until *K* is reached.

Two of the possible shortest paths are *A, B, D, E, H, K* and *A, C, F, G, J, K*. Both have a distance of 5.

In a weighted graph, the value assigned to each edge is called the **weight of the edge**. The **weight of a path** is the sum of the weights of the edges along a path. The path with the minimum weight is called the **minimal path**. The weight of the minimal path is called the **minimal distance**.

In a weighted multigraph, **Dijkstra's algorithm** can help to determine the minimal path and distance from any vertex to all others. In this algorithm, each vertex is assigned a label, sometimes temporarily. An example is $4(A)$, where 4 is the sum of the weights of all previous edges and A represents the preceding vertex in the path. When a label becomes permanent, a check (✓) is placed next to it.

Dijkstra's Algorithm

Step 1 Assign U, the starting vertex, the label $0(-)$. Place a check beside it.

Step 2 Assign all vertices adjacent to U the temporary label $w(U)$, where w is the weight of the edge from U, the only permanently labeled vertex.

Step 3 Of all the vertices with temporary labels, choose the one with the least weight (if there are more than one, choose one at random). Make this label permanent by placing a check beside it. Then, assign (or revise, if necessary) temporary labels to each vertex adjacent to the latest permanently labeled vertex. Assign the vertex the label $w(X)$, where w is the sum of the weights of the preceding permanently labeled vertex and the weight of the new edge connected to X, the preceding vertex. Do not change the label of any temporarily labeled vertex if its current weight is less than what the new weight would be.

Step 4 Continue Step 3 until all of the vertices are permanently labeled with a check. The weight on a vertex is the minimal distance from vertex U. The list of preceding vertices will provide the minimal path from U.

Example 2

Find the minimal path and distance in the weighted multigraph at the right from A to D.

Step 1 Assign vertex A the permanent label $0(-)$.

Step 2 Assign vertices $B, G,$ and F temporary labels since they are adjacent to vertex A.

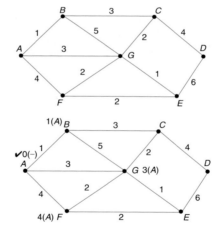

(continued on the next page)

LESSON 16-4   SHORTEST PATHS AND MINIMAL DISTANCES   885

Step 3 Since vertex B has the least weight among B, G, and F, place a check beside it. Then, since vertices C and G are adjacent to B, assign label $4(B)$ to vertex C and leave label $3(A)$ on vertex G, since $3 < 1 + 5$ (the distance from A to B to G). Now G has the least weight of vertices C, G, and F, so mark vertex G with a check. Then repeat Step 3.

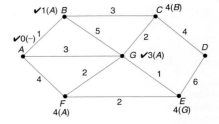

Step 4 Since vertices C, E, and F have the same weight, choose a vertex with which to continue. Let's choose F. Mark vertex F with a check, then repeat Step 3.

Investigate the labels next to C and E next. Repeat Step 3.

Finally, do vertex D.

The minimal distance from vertex A to vertex D is 8. The minimal path is A, B, C, D.

Example 3

APPLICATION

Energy

Find the route with the least power loss from the power plant to Alliance, using the weighted multigraph shown in the application at the beginning of the lesson. Also state the route.

Using Dijkstra's Algorithm resulted in the figure at the right.

There are two possible routes of least power loss. The route *power plant, Lorain, Elyria, Akron, Alliance* and the route *power plant, Lodi, Akron, Alliance* both have power losses of 11%.

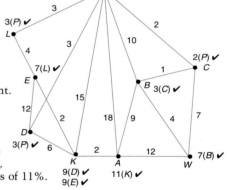

CHECKING FOR UNDERSTANDING

Communicating Mathematics

Read and study the lesson to answer each question. 1–2. See margin.

1. **Explain** why a shortest path is not necessarily a minimal path.
2. **Describe** the difference between a multigraph and a weighted multigraph.
3. **Describe** the conditions under which a path of a weighted multigraph is the minimal path. When the sum of the weights of the edges is the minimum weight.

Guided Practice

Applying the breadth-first search algorithm to a multigraph resulted in the figure at the right. Use this figure to answer each question.

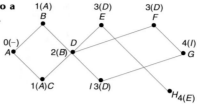

4. What is the distance from *A* to *H*? 4
5. What is the distance from *A* to *F*? 3

6. *A, B, D, I, G;*
A, C, D, I, G;
A, B, D, F, G;
or *A, C, D, F, G*

7. *C, D, F, G,*
or *C, D, I, G*

6. What is the shortest path from *A* to *G*?
7. What is the shortest path from *C* to *G*?
8. Could vertex *D* have been labeled 2(*C*)? yes

Applying Dijkstra's algorithm to a weighted multigraph resulted in the figure at the right. Use this figure to answer each question.

9. 6

9. What is the minimal distance from *P* to *E*?
10. What is the minimal path from *P* to *E*? *P, B, C, D, E*

11. Because the path *P, B, A* is shorter.
12. 6

11. Why does vertex *A* not have permanent label 3(*P*)?
12. What is the minimal distance from *E* to *P*?
13. Which vertex, *C* or *D*, is closer to *P*? C

EXERCISES

Practice

Determine the distance and a shortest path from *A* to *Z* in the graphs below by using the breadth-first search algorithm.

14.
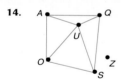
None; *A* and *Z* are not connected.

15.
3; one path is *A, G, K, M, I, Z.*

16.

3; one path is *A, F, I, Z.*

17.
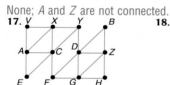
4; one path is *A, C, Y, D, Z.*

18.

4; one path is *A, K, I, B, Z.*

19.

7; one path is *A, B, I, L, N, Q, F, Z.*

LESSON 16-4 SHORTEST PATHS AND MINIMAL DISTANCES **887**

Additional Answers

1. Since the minimal paths are weighted, the shortest path is not necessarily the minimal path.
2. Weighted multigraphs have values or weights assigned to their edges, multigraphs do not.

Practice Masters Booklet, p. 111

Determine the minimal distance from A to all of the other vertices. Then find a minimal path and the minimal distance from A to Z by using Dijkstra's algorithm.

20.

6; A, B, Z

21.

7; A, G, K, Z

22.

6; A, C, S, Z

23.

5; A, B, C, Z

24.

13; A, G, K, M, I, Z

25.

3; A, E, Z

Critical Thinking

26. Eileen Snow needs to leave Salt Lake City, visit 3 cities exactly once, and return to Salt Lake City. It takes Ms. Snow 6 minutes to find the shortest route possible. When two more cities are added to the itinerary, it takes her 2 hours to find the shortest route from Salt Lake City through the other 5 cities and back to Salt Lake City. How long would it take Ms. Snow to find the shortest route from Salt Lake City through 9 cities and back to Salt Lake City?
252 days

Applications and Problem Solving

27b. Buffalo, Cleveland, Charleston, Nashville, Atlanta

27c. Mobile, Birmingham, Nashville; 469 miles

27. Transportation A truck driver makes deliveries to the cities listed in the mileage table below. She wants to develop a schedule where no city-to-city trip exceeds 450 miles.

a. On the basis of the mileages given in the table, draw a graph with vertices representing cities and edges representing trips not exceeding 450 miles. If your initial graph has edge crossings, reposition the vertices and redraw the graph to eliminate edge crossings. See margin.

b. Using your graph, find the shortest path from Buffalo to Atlanta.

c. Using your graph, find the minimal path and distance from Mobile to Nashville.

	Atlanta	Birmingham	Buffalo	Charleston	Cleveland	Memphis	Mobile	Nashville	Norfolk
Atlanta	—	161	896	515	774	394	345	250	572
Birmingham	161	—	901	535	718	244	274	195	789
Buffalo	896	901	—	864	200	922	1246	721	657
Charleston	515	535	864	—	256	609	808	395	407
Cleveland	774	718	200	256	—	731	1030	530	571
Memphis	394	244	922	609	731	—	402	208	924
Mobile	345	274	1246	808	1030	402	—	467	893
Nashville	250	195	721	395	530	208	467	—	708
Norfolk	572	789	657	407	571	924	893	708	—

Additional Answers

27a.

29.

Kalispell
Havre
Great Falls
Missoula
Helena
Butte
Billings
Bozeman

31. See Teacher's Answer Key.

Mixed Review

28. **Communication** A telephone company in a mountainous region of Montana is looking for ways to improve the efficiency of their communications system. Based on an analysis of the set-up costs to provide direct communications between several cities, they set the costs (in cents) for a three-minute call between the cities as shown on the graph at the left. Find the minimum cost of a three-minute call from Kalispell to Bozeman. Also state the switching path for routing this telephone call. 30¢; Kalispell, Missoula, Helena, Bozeman

29. Graph $y = \dfrac{4x}{x-1}$. **(Lesson 3-4)** See margin.

30. If $\sin \theta = \dfrac{3}{4}$, find $\sec \theta$ for values of θ between $0°$ and $360°$. **(Lesson 7-1)** $\dfrac{4\sqrt{7}}{7}$

31. Use mathematical induction to prove that the following formula is valid for all positive integral values of n: $2 + 2^2 + 2^3 + \cdots + 2^n = 2^{n+1} - 2$. **(Lesson 12-8)**

32. Find an Euler path in the graph at the left. **(Lesson 16-3)** a, b, c, e, f, d

33. **College Entrance Exam** Choose the best answer. D
If $x = -7$ and $\dfrac{1}{2y} = -14$, what is the value of y in terms of x?

(A) $x - 7$ 　　(B) $2x - 7$ 　　(C) $\dfrac{1}{2x}$ 　　(D) $\dfrac{1}{4x}$ 　　(E) $\dfrac{2x}{7}$

CASE STUDY FOLLOW-UP

Refer to Case Study 2: *Trashing the Planet*, on pages 959–961.

John Meadows is a planner for the Middleboro Waste Management System (MWMS). In addition to trash pickup, MWMS offers curbside recycling for newspapers, aluminum cans, plastics, and glass bottles. Mr. Meadows handles the recycling pickup for the new Montreal Park subdivision, whose streets are illustrated at the right. 1–2. See margin.

1. Middleboro has a 95% participation rate for curbside recycling. How does this compare with the national average of households that recycle at least one item?

2. Mr. Meadows wants to create a route that goes down each street exactly once.
   a. Is this possible? Explain.
   b. Find a route that begins and ends at the regional recycling center at R.

3. **Research** ways in which glass, newspapers, aluminum cans, or plastics are recycled. Write a 1-page paper that describes the process. See students' work.

LESSON 16-4 SHORTEST PATHS AND MINIMAL DISTANCES 889

EXTENDING THE LESSON

Math Power: Communication

Describe how to find the minimal path from A to Z. Give the distance.

Graph is drawn to scale.

Use as many horizontal segments as possible. 10

Case Study Follow-Up

This activity provides an opportunity to do research and apply mathematics in solving problems related to issues that may face students in their adult lives. Case Study 2 is located on pages 959–961.

NCTM Standards: 1–4, 12

Lesson Resources

- Practice Master 16–5
- Enrichment Master 16–5

 Transparency 16–5 contains the 5-Minute Check and a teaching aid for this lesson.

INTRODUCING THE LESSON

 5-Minute Check

(over Lesson 16–4)

Determine the minimal path and distance from *A* to *Z* in the graphs below.

1.

none

2.

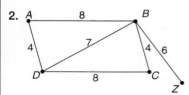

A, B, Z; 14

3.

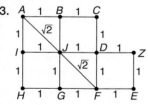

Sample answer: *A, J, D, Z;*
2 + √2

4.

A, B, C, Z; 43

16-5 Trees

Objectives
16–5A
16–5B

After studying this lesson, you should be able to:
- find spanning trees, and
- find minimal spanning trees.

Application

The graph on the left below is a model of all of the possible communication lines linking seven cities in Colorado. Due to the enormous cost of building such a network, the communications company is seeking a more efficient way to link all seven cities together. The graph on the right accomplishes this task at a much lower cost. This graph is called a **tree**.

 FYI...

Today's VCR Plus+™, a device that automatically programs a VCR, operates by using a coding tree invented in 1951 by a 25-year-old MIT student, David A. Huffman.

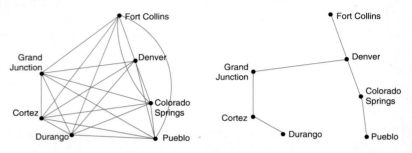

Properties of Trees

Trees are connected graphs that have the following properties.
1. They contain no cycles.
2. There is exactly one path between any two vertices.
3. If a tree contains more than one vertex, then it will have at least two vertices of degree 1.
4. A tree with n vertices will always have $n - 1$ edges.

A tree diagram, which you used in Chapter 14, is a type of tree.

Of the figures shown below, only the graph in the center is a tree. The graph on the left contains a cycle, so it is not a tree. The graph on the right has 7 vertices and 7 edges, so it is also not a tree.

A **subgraph** is a graph that contains a subset of the edges and vertices of a larger graph. A tree that is a subgraph of a connected graph and includes all of the vertices of that graph is called a **spanning tree**. Graphs may contain more than one spanning tree.

ALTERNATE TEACHING STRATEGIES

Using Communication

Have students discuss their own experiences with being part of communication trees, like telephone trees.

Using Models

Have the entire class make a "human spanning tree" in the following way: The first person whispers a code such as "Arnold Schwarzenegger" to the next person or persons in the tree. Then these student(s) whisper to the next group, and so on. Everyone in the class must hear the code within six steps of whispering.

Two different spanning trees are shown below for the same graph.

Since finding spanning trees in a large graph could be difficult, an algorithm exists to help you find them.

Spanning Tree Algorithm

To find a spanning tree in a graph, use the following process.
Step 1 Locate a cycle in the graph.
Step 2 Remove an edge from the cycle that will not disconnect the graph.
Step 3 If there are cycles left, then repeat Step 2. Otherwise, stop.

Example 1

Find a spanning tree in the graph at the right.

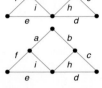

Remove g from cycle a, b, g.

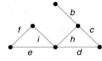

Remove a from cycle a, b, h, i.

Remove f from cycle f, i, e.

Remove c from cycle c, d, h.

No cycles remain, so the result is a spanning tree.

Since there are often several spanning trees for each graph, one of them must have a weight that is less than or equal to the weight of all the rest. This tree is called the **minimal spanning tree**. There may be more than one minimal spanning tree for a graph, but their weights will be the same.

LESSON 16-5 TREES 891

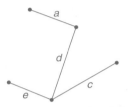

Chalkboard Example

For Example 2

Suppose the graph below represents the miles on a road map connecting 5 homes. A cable company wants to connect all the homes on the map. Find the least number of miles connecting all of the locations. **26 miles**

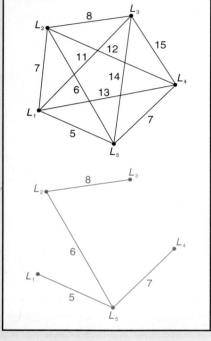

Additional Answers

Answers for Exercises 1–4 may vary. Sample answers are given.

1.

2.

3.

4.

You can use **Kruskal's algorithm** to find a minimal spanning tree.

Kruskal's Algorithm

To find a minimal spanning tree in a weighted graph, use the following process.

Step 1 Choose the edge with the least weight.

Step 2 Choose the next edge with the least weight, as long as it does not create a cycle.

Step 3 Continue as in Step 2 until all of the vertices are connected.

Example 2

At a campsite in northern Michigan, there are seven main areas: 2 lodges, 2 cabin areas, a restaurant, the caretaker's home, and a recreation center. Tired of driving on dirt roads, the owner decides to put in paved roads. The owner must decide the most economical way to put the roads in so that people can get from one location to another. The firm that will do the paving has drawn the weighted graph at the right to show the roads that are possible. The cost to put in each road is indicated on the graph in thousands of dollars. Find the least expensive way to build the roads and still connect all of the main areas.

Since we can begin at any vertex, let's start at CH. Choose the edge of least weight incident on CH, the edge between CH and C_2. Next, choose the edge of least weight incident on C_2, the edge between C_2 and R.

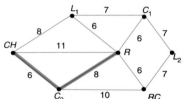

Since there are 3 edges incident on R with weight 6, choose one at random. Let's choose the edge between R and L_1. Since the edge between R and C_1 has less weight than the edge between L_1 and C_1, choose it.

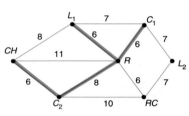

FYI...

Joseph B. Kruskal (1928–), is a member of the technical staff at Bell Laboratories. He discovered his algorithm, however, when he was a second-year graduate student.

The next edge of least weight is the edge between R and RC, so choose it. Finally, choose the edge between L_2 and RC.

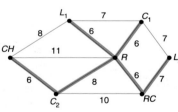

892   CHAPTER 16   GRAPH THEORY

The roads to be constructed are shown at the right, at a minimal cost of $39,000.

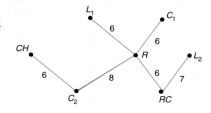

CHECKING FOR UNDERSTANDING

Communicating Mathematics

Read and study the lesson to answer each question. 1–4. See margin.

1. **Draw** a graph with a cycle.
2. **Draw** a graph without a cycle that is not a tree.
3. **Draw** a graph that is a tree.
4. **Draw** graph that does not have a spanning tree.
5. **Design** a telephone tree for you and five of your closest friends. Is your tree a spanning tree? See students' work.

Guided Practice

6. How many vertices are there in a tree with 21 edges? 22 vertices
7. How many edges are there in a tree with 18 vertices? 17 edges
8. How many vertices of a graph does its spanning tree contain? all
9. How many edges will a spanning tree have if the graph in which it is contained has 7 vertices? 6 edges

10. at least 2 vertices

10. How many vertices of degree 1 does a tree of 2 or more vertices have?

11. Find a spanning tree for the graph below. Sample answer: *a, c, g, f, e.*

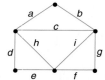

12. Find a minimal spanning tree for the weighted graph below.

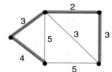

EXERCISES

Practice

A

Determine whether each graph is a tree. Write *yes* or *no*. If no, explain.

13.

No; contains a cycle.

14.

No; not connected.

15.
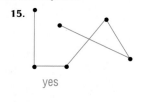
yes

RETEACHING THE LESSON

Have students model the graph below by using sticks, pipe cleaners, or other objects. Then have students find all of the spanning trees in the graph by removing the appropriate edge(s).

EVALUATING THE LESSON

Checking for Understanding

Exercises 1–12 are designed to help you assess students' understanding through reading, writing, speaking, and modeling. You should work through Exercises 1–5 with your students and then monitor their work on Exercises 6–12.

Closing the Lesson

Writing Activity Have students write a short paragraph explaining how to find a spanning tree in a graph.

APPLYING THE LESSON

Homework Exercises

Assignment Guide

Average: 13–17, 19, 22, 24, 26–30
Enriched: 15–21, 23, 24–30

The red A, B, and C flags, printed only in the Teacher's Wraparound Edition, indicate the level of difficulty of the exercises.

Practice Masters Booklet, p. 112

Additional Answers

Sample answers are given:

16. {V, X}, {X, Y}, {Y, D}, {D, B},
    {B, Z}, {Z, H}, {H, G}, {G, F},
    {F, C}, {E, A}, {A, V}

17. {Z, I}, {I, F} {F, A}, {A, B},
    {B, D}, {D, H}, {D, C}, {D, E},
    {G, H}

18. {A, B}, {B, I}, {I, L}, {L, C},
    {C, D}, {D, E}, {E, N}, {N, Q},
    {Q, F}, {F, Z}, {Z, M}, {M, S},
    {S, R}, {R, T}, {T, K}, {K, J},
    {J, P}, {P, O}, {O, H}, {H, G}

22. Sample Answer:

23.

Find a spanning tree for each graph. 16–18. See margin.

B 16. 17. 18.

Find a minimal spanning tree for each weighted graph. State the weight of the tree.

C 19.
7

20.

14

21.
15

22–23. See margin.

Critical Thinking

22. Draw a tree with at least 7 vertices that has exactly 2 vertices of degree 1.

23. Draw a weighted graph in which the minimal spanning tree must contain the edge of greatest weight.

Applications and Problem Solving

24. **Communications**
A new fiber optics communication system is to be installed that will serve the cities in the map at the right. The communications company has determined that the costs to connect each pair of cities are those that are shown on the map (weights are in millions of dollars). Find the minimal cost to establish such a system and show its design.
$66,000,000; See students' work.

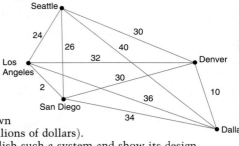

25. **Computer Technology** The mathematics editorial department of Glencoe Publishing Company plans to network fifteen computers to the same laser printer. How might this be done using the fewest communications lines possible?
See students' work; any spanning tree with fifteen vertices will satisfy the conditions.

Mixed Review

26. Determine if $\text{Tan}^{-1}x = \dfrac{1}{\text{Tan } x}$ for all x. If false, give a counterexample.
(Lesson 6-6) false; sample answer: $x = 90°$

27. $\sqrt{46}$; 6.78

27. Find the length of the tangent segment from the point with coordinates $(4, -1)$ to the graph of a circle with the equation $(x + 3)^2 + y^2 - 4 = 0$. **(Lesson 10-8)**

28. **Business** A buyer for a department store will accept a carton containing 10 clocks if neither of two samples, chosen at random, is defective. What is the probability that she will accept a carton of 10 if it contains 4 defective clocks? (**Lesson 14-8**) $\frac{1}{3}$

29. Find a minimal path and the minimal distance from *A* to *D* in the weighted multigraph at the right. (**Lesson 16-4**) *A, B, C, D*; 8

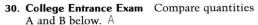

30. **College Entrance Exam** Compare quantities A and B below. A
    Write A if quantity A is greater.
    Write B if quantity B is greater.
    Write C if the two quantities are equal.
    Write D if there is not enough information to determine the relationship.
    (A) $(-8)^{62}$ **(B)** $(-8)^{75}$

DECISION MAKING

Planning a Party

In the movie *Father of the Bride,* the title character, played by Steve Martin, was ridiculed for being reluctant to spend $50,000 on his daughter's wedding. Martin had good reasons for balking, but he was quickly talked out of them. How can you decide on the right amount of money to spend on a party and then, keep your expenses under the limit you have set? What arrangements can you take care of yourself and which ones should you leave to professionals?
1–4. See students' work.

1. Describe the ideal party. Where would you hold it? What food and entertainment would you provide? How many people would be on your guest list? List all of the ingredients you think are important.

2. Decide on the amount of money you can spend on a party. Then go back to the list in Exercise 1 and decide how you can hold the best possible party for the money. Which elements of the perfect party must you eliminate? Which ones can you provide at a level that is slightly less than "perfect?"

3. Plan your party, keeping within your budget. Include such factors as location, food, entertainment, number of people, and other essential details.

4. **Project** Work with your group to complete one of the projects listed at the right based on the information you gathered in Exercises 1–3.

PROJECTS

- *Conduct an interview.*
- *Write a book report.*
- *Write a proposal.*
- *Write an article for the school paper.*
- *Write a report.*
- *Make a display.*
- *Make a graph or chart.*
- *Plan an activity.*
- *Design a checklist.*

EXTENDING THE LESSON

Math Power: Problem Solving

How many spanning trees can be made from the graph below? 8

Decision Making

This activity provides students an opportunity to work together on a given problem. You may wish to refer to pages T20–T21 and page 864c for the various elements of cooperative groups and specific goals and strategies for using them.

Enrichment Masters Booklet, p. 112

Lesson Resources

- Practice Master 16–6
- Enrichment Master 16–6
- Evaluation Master, Quiz D, p. 202
- Technology Master, p. 31
- Activity Master, p. 46

 Transparency 16–6 contains the 5-Minute Check and a teaching aid for this lesson.

INTRODUCING THE LESSON

 5-Minute Check

(over Lesson 16–5)

1. How many vertices are there in a tree with 12 edges?   **13**
2. Find a spanning tree for the graph below.

sample answer:

3. Find a minimal spanning tree for the weighted graph below.

sample answer:

4. Determine whether each graph is a tree. Write *yes* or *no*. If no, explain.

a.

no, contains a cycle

b.

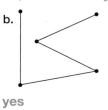

yes

16-6 Graphs and Matrices

Objectives
16–6A
16–6B

After studying this lesson, you should be able to:
- use digraphs to solve problems, and
- represent digraphs as matrices and vice versa.

Application

Biologists use graphs called food webs to model the predatory relationships among members of a particular ecosystem. In the food web below, arrows point from each member of the ecosystem to its predator.

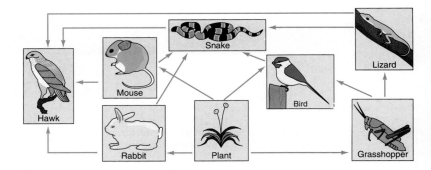

The graph at the right represents the food web relationships. Notice that arrowheads have been placed along the edges to represent the direction of each relationship. A graph with arrowheads on the edges is called a **directed graph,** or **digraph.**

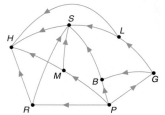

In a simple graph, you counted the number of incident edges to describe the degree of a vertex. Similarly, arrowheads are counted to describe a vertex in a digraph. The **indegree** of a vertex in a digraph is the number of edges pointing into the vertex. The **outdegree** of a vertex is the number of edges pointing away from the vertex. In the digraph above, the indegree of vertex G is 1 and the outdegree is 2.

Digraphs are often used to determine whether a location is **reachable.** In the graph above, H is reachable from P because there is a **directed path** from P to H. One such path is $\{P,M\}, \{M,H\}$. A directed path occurs when you can walk each edge in the direction of the arrows.

ALTERNATE TEACHING STRATEGIES

Using Communication

Have students to recall if they have followed a detour while on a road trip. Ask them to describe how following detour signs is related to a digraph.

Using Graphing Calculators

Use graphing calculators to perform the matrix operations in this lesson. Have students enter the matrices and then find powers of the matrices by using the power key of the calculator.

Example 1

The **Beaumont Museum of Art** is being renovated. In order to remain open during the renovation, one-way corridors will be used to control the flow of visitors. The digraph at the right represents the floor plan of the museum's corridors.

a. Are all of the exhibits reachable?
b. If not, modify the graph to make each exhibit reachable and simplify traffic flow.

a. Currently, Exhibit 6 is not reachable, because it has indegree 0.
b. To solve the problem, change the direction of the edge between Exhibit 6 and Exhibit 4.

Digraphs can also be used in scheduling a complex task. Suppose you are planning to cook dinner for friends, but you only have one hour in which to prepare. The tasks that you need to complete are shown in the chart at the right.

Task	Time Required
U: Set Table	5 minutes
V: Marinate Steaks	15 minutes
W: Grill Steaks	8 minutes
X: Bake Potatoes	40 minutes
Y: Make Salad	10 minutes
Z: Change Clothes	10 minutes

If you did one task at a time, it would take you 88 minutes to prepare. However, some of the tasks could be done simultaneously. For example, you could marinate the steaks, bake the potatoes, and set the table at the same time. However, you can't grill the steaks until you have marinated them. The digraph below is one way to model the situation.

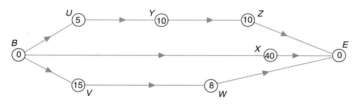

Notice that the times required are shown inside the vertices. Two vertices B and E have been added to signify when the tasks begin and end. You want to find the shortest time to complete all of the tasks. That time is shown by the longest path from B to E. This is called the **critical path.** There are three paths from B to E. The longest path from B to E is $B \rightarrow X \rightarrow E$, which requires 40 minutes. That means that the least amount of time needed to prepare the meal is 40 minutes.

LESSON 16-6   GRAPHS AND MATRICES   897

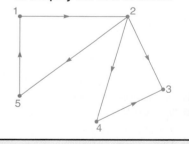

Chalkboard Example

For Example 2

Suppose tasks *T* through *Y* are required to manufacture compact discs. The tasks, the time each task requires, and the tasks that must precede each task are given in the chart below.

Task	Time required	Prerequisite tasks
T	10 minutes	none
U	12 minutes	*T*
V	9 minutes	*U*
W	15 minutes	*T*
X	14 minutes	*U, W*
Y	9 minutes	*T, V, X*

Draw a digraph to model this situation and find the critical path. Then find the minimum number of minutes needed to complete the tasks.

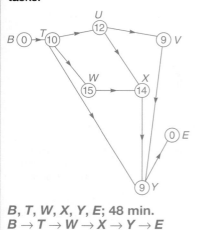

B, T, W, X, Y, E; 48 min.
$B \to T \to W \to X \to Y \to E$

Teaching Tip You may wish to review operations with matrices before continuing to Example 3.

Example 2

APPLICATION

Manufacturing

Suppose tasks *T* through *Z* are required to manufacture athletic shoes. The tasks, the time each task requires, and the tasks that must precede each task are given in the chart below.

Task	Time Required	Prerequisite Tasks
T	11 minutes	none
U	6 minutes	none
V	8 minutes	none
W	16 minutes	*T, U*
X	4 minutes	*U*
Y	3 minutes	*V, W, X*
Z	9 minutes	*W*

Draw a digraph to model this situation and find the critical path. Then find the minimum amount of time needed to complete all of the tasks.

One view of the digraph is shown below.

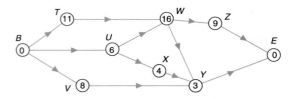

The critical path is $B \to T \to W \to Z \to E$. The minimum amount of time needed is 36 minutes.

In many situations, graphs can be very complex and difficult to analyze. Therefore, it is advantageous to describe a graph numerically so you could use a calculator or a computer. This can be done by using a matrix. Since we can count the number of edges joining the vertices of a graph, a matrix of a graph can be formed. This matrix is called an **adjacency matrix**.

Definition of Adjacency Matrix

For any graph $G(n, m)$,
1. the adjacency matrix representing it, denoted $M(G)$, is an $n \times n$ matrix, and
2. the entry in the *i*th row and the *j*th column of the matrix represents the number of edges from V_i to V_j.

If the graph is a digraph, then the (i, j)th entry describes the number of <u>directed edges</u> *from V_i to V_j.*

Example 3

Find $M(G)$ for each graph.

a.

b.

a. Since there are 4 vertices, the adjacency matrix will have 4 rows and 4 columns. There are no edges from R to R, so the entry in row 1, column 1 is 0. There are 2 edges from R to S, so the entry in row 1, column 2 is 2. Continuing the process gives the matrix below.

$$\begin{array}{c} \\ R \\ S \\ T \\ U \end{array} \begin{array}{cccc} R & S & T & U \\ \left[\begin{array}{cccc} 0 & 2 & 0 & 1 \\ 2 & 0 & 0 & 0 \\ 0 & 0 & 0 & 1 \\ 1 & 0 & 1 & 0 \end{array}\right] \end{array}$$

b. Since there are 3 vertices, the adjacency matrix will have 3 rows and 3 columns. There is 1 directed edge from X to X, so the entry in row 1, column 1 is 1. There is 1 directed edge from X to Y, so the entry in row 1, column 2 is 1. Continuing the process gives the matrix below.

$$\begin{array}{c} \\ X \\ Y \\ Z \end{array} \begin{array}{ccc} X & Y & Z \\ \left[\begin{array}{ccc} 1 & 1 & 0 \\ 1 & 0 & 1 \\ 1 & 1 & 0 \end{array}\right] \end{array}$$

You can use matrices and the theorems below to solve problems.

Matrix Theorem

If G is a digraph and $M(G)$ is its matrix, and if n is a positive integer, then the (i, j)th entry of $[M(G)]^n$ is the number of directed paths in G that go from V_i to V_j in exactly n steps.

If we look at $[M(G)]^2$, that will tell us how many 2-step paths there are between vertices. $[M(G)]^3$ will tell us how many 3-step paths there are, and so on. But how do we know the maximum number of steps that can be checked? The theorem below determines how many powers of $M(G)$ we need to check.

Path Theorem

In a digraph that has n vertices, if two distinct vertices can be joined by a path, then they can be joined by a path that is no longer than $n - 1$ edges.

Example 4

APPLICATION

Biology

The digraph at the right is a subgraph of the food web shown at the beginning of the lesson. Suppose this ecosystem is accidently contaminated by a poisonous substance, like a pesticide. When this occurs, one species becomes contaminated and then others that prey on that species also become contaminated, and so on. If the plant is contaminated, will the contamination spread to all of the others in two steps or less?

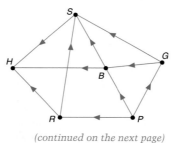

(continued on the next page)

LESSON 16-6 GRAPHS AND MATRICES 899

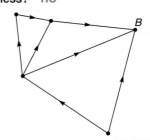

Checking for Understanding

Exercises 1–10 are designed to help you assess students' understanding through reading, writing, speaking, and modeling. You should work through Exercises 1–3 with your students and then monitor their work on Exercises 4–10.

Closing the Lesson

Writing Activity   Have students write a paragraph describing how to find $M(G)$ for a graph.

Additional Answers

1. Possible answers: friendship patterns, authority structure in an organization, communication patterns, and cause-and-effect relationships.
2. Choose the longest path from the start.
3.

$$\begin{array}{c}\\A\\B\\C\\D\end{array}\begin{array}{cccc}A & B & C & D\\\left[\begin{array}{cccc}0 & 0 & 1 & 1\\1 & 0 & 0 & 0\\1 & 1 & 0 & 0\\1 & 0 & 1 & 0\end{array}\right]\end{array}$$

Practice Masters Booklet, p. 113

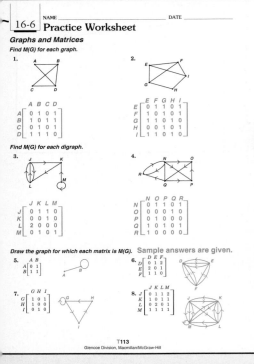

Since there are 6 vertices, the adjacency matrix will have 6 rows and 6 columns. Label the rows and columns with the vertex names. To fill the entries, count the number of directed edges from a row to a column. For example, there are no edges from H to H, so the entry in row 1, column 1 is 0. The entire adjacency matrix is shown at the right.

$$\begin{array}{c}\\H\\S\\B\\G\\P\\R\end{array}\begin{array}{cccccc}H & S & B & G & P & R\\\left[\begin{array}{cccccc}0 & 0 & 0 & 0 & 0 & 0\\1 & 0 & 0 & 0 & 0 & 0\\1 & 1 & 0 & 0 & 0 & 0\\0 & 1 & 1 & 0 & 0 & 0\\0 & 0 & 1 & 1 & 0 & 1\\1 & 1 & 0 & 0 & 0 & 0\end{array}\right]\end{array}$$

Using a TI-81 graphing calculator, enter the above values in matrix [A]. You want to determine whether the contamination will spread to all the members in two steps or less. The sum $M(G) + M(G)^2$ represents the total number of paths of length less than or equal to 2.

To find $M(G) + M(G)^2$, press
2nd [A] + 2nd [A] x^2 ENTER.

$M(G) + M(G)^2$ is shown at the right. Notice that the row corresponding to the plant (P) shows paths to every member of the ecosystem except itself. Therefore, the contamination can spread from the plant to all the other members of the ecosystem in two steps or less.

$$\begin{array}{c}\\H\\S\\B\\G\\P\\R\end{array}\begin{array}{cccccc}H & S & B & G & P & R\\\left[\begin{array}{cccccc}0 & 0 & 0 & 0 & 0 & 0\\1 & 0 & 0 & 0 & 0 & 0\\2 & 1 & 0 & 0 & 0 & 0\\2 & 2 & 1 & 0 & 0 & 0\\2 & 3 & 2 & 1 & 0 & 1\\2 & 1 & 0 & 0 & 0 & 0\end{array}\right]\end{array}$$

CHECKING FOR UNDERSTANDING

Communicating Mathematics

Read and study the lesson to answer each question. 1–3. See margin.

1. **Describe** a situation that was not discussed in this lesson that may be modeled by a digraph.

2. **Explain** how to find the critical path in a digraph.

3. **Construct** an adjacency matrix to describe the airline service digraph shown at the right.

Guided Practice

4. **Catering**   JoAnn's Catering is catering a retirement party. JoAnn's employees will have to complete the following tasks.

Task	Time Required
P: Decide on menu	30 minutes
Q: Purchase food	60 minutes
R: Set up kitchen on site	15 minutes
S: Cook food	50 minutes
T: Set tables	10 minutes
U: Serve food	40 minutes

Draw a digraph to model the situation. Then find its critical path and the minimum amount of time needed to complete all of the tasks. You may decide which activities should precede others. See margin.

RETEACHING THE LESSON

Ask students to draw digraphs for moves on a checkerboard or chessboard.

Additional Answer

4.

Find $M(G)$ for each graph. 5–7. See margin.

5.

6.

7.

Draw the graph for which each matrix is $M(G)$. 8–10. See margin.

8.

	S	T
S	0	1
T	1	0

9.

	P	Q	R
P	0	1	1
Q	1	0	0
R	1	0	0

10.

	A	B	C	D
A	0	1	2	1
B	1	0	1	0
C	2	1	0	1
D	1	0	1	0

EXERCISES

Practice

Draw a digraph to represent each situation. 11–12. See margin.

11. In a volleyball tournament, the Lions defeated the Tigers and the Bulls, the Bulls defeated the Tigers and the Rams, the Rams defeated the Lions, and the Tigers defeated the Rams.

12. Kama knows the locker number of Ursula. Beth knows the locker numbers of Sam and Kama. Sam knows the locker numbers of Ursula and Tammy. Tammy knows the locker number of Ursula, who knows the locker numbers of Kama and Ray.

Find $M(G)$ for each graph. 13–15. See Teacher's Answer Key.

13.

14.

15.

Find $M(G)$ for each digraph. 16–18. See Teacher's Answer Key.

16.

17.

18.

LESSON 16-6   GRAPHS AND MATRICES   901

10.

11.

12.

19.

20.

21.

22.

23.

24.

25. sample answer:

The path $B \rightarrow R \rightarrow U \rightarrow W \rightarrow X \rightarrow E$ and $B \rightarrow S \rightarrow V \rightarrow E$ are both critical. The minimum amount of time needed is 6 weeks.

Draw the graph for which each matrix is $M(G)$. 19–21. See margin.

19.

$$\begin{array}{c} \\ A \\ B \\ C \end{array}\begin{array}{ccc} A & B & C \\ \begin{bmatrix} 0 & 1 & 1 \\ 1 & 0 & 1 \\ 1 & 1 & 0 \end{bmatrix} \end{array}$$

20.

$$\begin{array}{c} \\ D \\ E \\ F \\ G \end{array}\begin{array}{cccc} D & E & F & G \\ \begin{bmatrix} 0 & 1 & 0 & 1 \\ 1 & 0 & 1 & 1 \\ 0 & 1 & 0 & 1 \\ 1 & 1 & 1 & 0 \end{bmatrix} \end{array}$$

21.

$$\begin{array}{c} \\ J \\ K \\ L \\ M \\ N \end{array}\begin{array}{ccccc} J & K & L & M & N \\ \begin{bmatrix} 0 & 2 & 1 & 0 & 1 \\ 2 & 0 & 1 & 0 & 2 \\ 1 & 1 & 0 & 2 & 1 \\ 0 & 0 & 2 & 0 & 1 \\ 1 & 2 & 1 & 1 & 0 \end{bmatrix} \end{array}$$

Draw the digraph for which each matrix is $M(G)$. 22–24. See margin.

22.

$$\begin{array}{c} \\ X \\ Y \\ Z \end{array}\begin{array}{ccc} X & Y & Z \\ \begin{bmatrix} 0 & 1 & 1 \\ 1 & 0 & 1 \\ 1 & 1 & 0 \end{bmatrix} \end{array}$$

23.

$$\begin{array}{c} \\ A \\ B \\ C \\ D \end{array}\begin{array}{cccc} A & B & C & D \\ \begin{bmatrix} 0 & 1 & 1 & 1 \\ 0 & 0 & 1 & 1 \\ 1 & 0 & 0 & 0 \\ 0 & 0 & 1 & 0 \end{bmatrix} \end{array}$$

24.

$$\begin{array}{c} \\ R \\ S \\ T \\ U \end{array}\begin{array}{cccc} R & S & T & U \\ \begin{bmatrix} 0 & 1 & 0 & 1 \\ 1 & 0 & 1 & 0 \\ 1 & 1 & 0 & 1 \\ 0 & 1 & 0 & 0 \end{bmatrix} \end{array}$$

Draw a digraph to model each situation. Then find its critical path and the minimum time needed to complete all of the tasks. If precedence is not given, you may decide which tasks should precede others. 25–26. See margin.

25. Manufacturing A clothing manufacturer uses the schedule below to introduce a new line of sportswear.

Task	Time Required
R: Decide on the pieces in the new collection	1 week
S: Get a celebrity to endorse the line	2 weeks
T: Create advertising copy, plan commercials, and so on	4 weeks
U: Set manufacturer's suggested prices	1 week
V: Plan and hold fashion shows for buyers and the press	4 weeks
W: Choose department stores that will sell the line	1 week
X: Ship the line to retail outlets	3 weeks

26. Construction Canarsie Builders builds homes using the schedule below.

Task	Time	Prerequisite Tasks
L: Site preparation	5 days	none
M: Laying the foundation	8 days	Site preparation
N: Drains and utilities	3 days	Site preparation
O: Framing	12 days	Laying the foundation
P: Roofing and gutters	3 days	Framing
Q: Windows and exterior doors	2 days	Roofing and gutters
R: Heating and cooling system	4 days	Windows and exterior doors
S: Plumbing	4 days	Windows and exterior doors
T: Electrical wiring	4 days	Heating, cooling, and plumbing
U: Insulation and drywall	12 days	Electrical wiring
V: Siding and painting exterior	8 days	Windows and exterior doors
W: Interior painting and finishing	24 days	Insulation and drywall
X: Landscaping	3 days	Siding and painting exterior

26. The path $B \rightarrow L \rightarrow M \rightarrow O \rightarrow P \rightarrow Q \rightarrow S \rightarrow T \rightarrow U \rightarrow W \rightarrow E$ is a critical path. The minimum amount of time needed is 74 days.

27. Suppose G is a connected graph. If you are given $M(G)$, how can you tell whether G contains an Euler circuit without drawing it? See margin.

28. Sociology Suppose the digraph at the right is a model for the way rumors spread among a group of friends in the Drama Club.

a. Represent the data in the graph in matrix form. See margin.

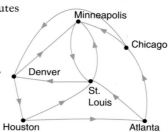

b. If you wanted to start a rumor, what one person in this group could you tell and expect the rumor to spread to all the others? Ben

29. Transportation Suppose an airline's service routes are represented in the digraph at the right.

a. Represent the data in the digraph in matrix form. See margin.   29b. 3

b. In how many ways can a traveller get from Denver to St. Louis in three or fewer flights?

c. Is it possible for a traveller to get from Chicago to Houston? If so, what is the minimum number of flights needed to accomplish this? yes; 2 flights

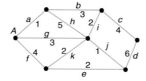

30. Find the distance from the line $3x - 7y - 1 = 0$ to the point with coordinates $(-1, 4)$. **(Lesson 7-7)** 4.2

31. Use logarithms to evaluate $\dfrac{\sqrt[4]{0.0063}}{6.73}$. **(Lesson 11-5)** 0.042

32. Find a set of numbers with a mean of 6, a median of 5.5, and a mode of 9. **(Lesson 15-2)** Sample answer: {3, 4, 5, 6, 9, 9}

33. Sample answer:
a, b, c, i, j, e

33. Find a minimal spanning tree for the weighted graph at the right. **(Lesson 16-5)**

34. College Entrance Exam Choose the best answer. D
If $(a - b)^2 = 64$, and $ab = 3$, find $a^2 + b^2$.
(A) 58   **(B)** 61   **(C)** 67   **(D)** 70   **(E)** 75

LESSON 16-6   GRAPHS AND MATRICES   903

EXTENDING THE LESSON

Math Power: Connections

Predict how many paths are in the digraph below. Explain how you made your prediction.   12, counted the paths

Additional Answers

27. If the sum of each row and the sum of each column are even then G contains an Euler circuit.

28a.

	A	B	C	D	E	F
A	0	0	0	0	0	1
B	1	0	1	1	0	0
C	0	0	0	1	0	0
D	0	0	0	0	0	0
E	1	0	0	1	0	0
F	0	0	0	0	1	0

29a.

	A	C	D	H	M	S
A	0	1	0	0	0	1
C	0	0	1	0	1	0
D	0	0	0	1	1	0
H	1	0	0	0	0	1
M	0	0	0	0	0	1
S	0	0	1	0	1	0

Enrichment Masters Booklet, p. 113

16-6 Enrichment Worksheet

Number of Paths

For the figure and adjacency matrix shown at the right, the number of paths or circuits of length 2 can be found by computing the following product.

$$A = \begin{matrix} & V_1\ V_2\ V_3\ V_4 \\ V_1 \\ V_2 \\ V_3 \\ V_4 \end{matrix}\begin{bmatrix} 0 & 1 & 1 & 1 \\ 1 & 0 & 1 & 1 \\ 1 & 1 & 0 & 0 \\ 1 & 1 & 0 & 0 \end{bmatrix}$$

$$A^2 = AA = \begin{bmatrix} 0 & 1 & 1 & 1 \\ 1 & 0 & 1 & 1 \\ 1 & 1 & 0 & 0 \\ 1 & 1 & 0 & 0 \end{bmatrix} \cdot \begin{bmatrix} 0 & 1 & 1 & 1 \\ 1 & 0 & 1 & 1 \\ 1 & 1 & 0 & 0 \\ 1 & 1 & 0 & 0 \end{bmatrix} = \begin{bmatrix} 3 & 2 & 1 & 1 \\ 2 & 3 & 1 & 1 \\ 1 & 1 & 2 & 2 \\ 1 & 1 & 2 & 2 \end{bmatrix}$$

In row 3 column 4, the entry 2 in the product matrix means that there are 2 paths of length 2 between V_3 and V_4. The paths are $V_3 \to V_1 \to V_4$ and $V_3 \to V_2 \to V_4$. Similarly, in row 1 column 3, the entry 1 means there is only 1 path of length 2 between V_1 and V_3.

Name the paths of length 2 between the following.

1. V_1 and V_2 V_1, V_3, V_2; V_1, V_4, V_2
2. V_1 and V_3 V_1, V_2, V_3
3. V_1 and V_1 V_1, V_2, V_1; V_1, V_3, V_1; V_1, V_4, V_1

For Exercises 4-6, refer to the figure below.

4. The number of paths of length 3 is given by the product $A \cdot A \cdot A$ or A^3. Find the matrix for paths of length 3. $\begin{bmatrix} 4 & 5 & 5 & 5 \\ 5 & 4 & 5 & 5 \\ 5 & 5 & 2 & 2 \\ 5 & 5 & 2 & 2 \end{bmatrix}$

5. How many paths of length 3 are there between Atlanta and St. Louis? Name them. 2; A, D, C, S and A, C, D, S

6. How would you find the number of paths of length 4 between the cities? Find Matrix A^4.

VOCABULARY

Upon completing this chapter, you should be familiar with the following terms:

adjacency matrix	**898**	**868**	isolated
adjacent	**868**	**892**	Kruskal's algorithm
algorithm	**879**	**866**	loops
breadth-first search algorithm	**883**	**885**	minimal distance
bridge	**874**	**885**	minimal path
circuit	**873**	**891**	minimal spanning tree
complete graph	**869**	**866**	multigraph
connected	**868, 873**	**896**	outdegree
critical path	**897**	**866**	parallel edges
cycle	**873**	**872**	path
degree	**868**	**896**	reachable
digraph	**896**	**866**	simple graph
Dijkstra's algorithm	**885**	**890**	spanning tree
directed path	**896**	**890**	subgraph
disconnected	**873**	**872**	trail
edges	**866**	**890**	tree
Euler circuit	**878**	**866**	vertex
Euler path	**878**	**872**	walk
Fleury's algorithm	**879**	**885**	weight
graph	**866**	**885**	weight of a path
incident	**868**	**883**	weighted multigraph
indegree	**896**		

SKILLS AND CONCEPTS

OBJECTIVES AND EXAMPLES	REVIEW EXERCISES
Upon completing this chapter, you should be able to:	Use these exercises to review and prepare for the chapter test.
■ determine whether a graph is complete **(Lesson 16-1)**	**Use the graph below to answer each question.** 3–4. See margin.
Is a graph with 4 vertices and 6 edges a complete graph?	**1.** Is it a complete graph? no
$$\frac{n(n-1)}{2} = \frac{4(3)}{2}$$ $$= 6$$	**2.** What is $\deg(E)$? 4
Since $6 = 6$, the graph is complete.	**3.** Which edges are incident on A?
	4. Which vertices are adjacent to D?
	5. Is the figure a multigraph? yes

OBJECTIVES AND EXAMPLES

- distinguish among walks, paths, trails, closed walks, circuits, and cycles **(Lesson 16-2)**

Find an $A-E$ walk, an $A-E$ trail, and an $A-E$ path for the multigraph below.

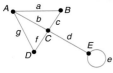

One $A-E$ walk is $a, c, b, g, f, b, a, c, d$.
One $A-E$ trail is g, f, b, a, c, d.
One $A-E$ path is b, d.

- find Euler paths and circuits **(Lesson 16-3)**

Determine whether the graph below contains an Euler circuit or an Euler path. If so, name the circuit or path.

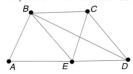

This graph does not contain an Euler circuit because the degree of each vertex is not even. The path $C, D, B, E, C, B, A, E, D$ is an Euler path since it contains all of the edges exactly once and ends at a vertex that is different from the starting vertex.

- use the breadth-first search algorithm and Dijkstra's algorithm to find a shortest path **(Lesson 16-4)**

Find a shortest path from A to E in the graph below. Then state its length.

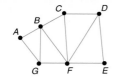

Paths A, G, F, E and A, B, F, E have length 3.

REVIEW EXERCISES

Use the graph below to determine whether each walk is a circuit, cycle, path, trail, or walk. Use the most specific name.

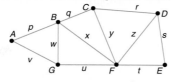

6. p, q, y, x, q, r, s walk
7. p, w, u, z, s, t trail
8. p, q, r, s, t, u, v cycle
9. x, y, r, s, t, u, v, p circuit

10. Find an Euler path in the graph below.
    u, w, v, x, z, y

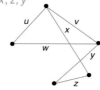

11. How could you alter the graph in Exercise 10 so it would contain an Euler circuit? Add a temporary edge parallel to v.

12. Find the minimal path and minimal distance from A to E in the weighted multigraph below.

Path is A, D, E; distance is 40.

For more information on other methods of alternate assessment, you may wish to refer to Glencoe's *Alternate Assessment in the Mathematics Classroom*.

Alternate Review Strategy

To provide a brief in-class review, you may wish to read the following questions to your students and have them answer verbally.

1. In the multigraph below, name the parallel edges and loops.

   loops: x, u; parallel edges: z, w

2. Draw a graph with four vertices, where deg(A) = 1, deg(B) = 2, deg(C) = 3, and deg (D) = 2. Sample answer:

3. Find a $U-V$ walk, $U-V$ trail, and a $U-V$ path for the multigraph below.

   Sample answer: walk: a, d; trail: b, c, d; path: a, d

4. The figure below is a floor plan. Can a person starting at point A take a tour of the house and walk through each doorway exactly once? If so, state the path.

   no

5. Find an Euler circuit in the connected multigraph below.

   a, c, d, f, h, g, b

6. Find the shortest path and the distance from A to H.

   Sample answer: A, B, I, H; 6

Two multiple-choice tests (Forms 1A and 1B) and two free-response tests (Forms 2A and 2B) are provided in the *Evaluation Masters*. Chapter 16 Test, Form 1A is shown below. Chapter 16 Test, Form 2A is shown on the next page.

Enrichment Masters Booklet, pp. 193–194

NAME _____ DATE _____

Chapter 16 Test, Form 1A

Write the letter for the correct answer in the blank at the right of each problem.

1. Which statement is *not* true of a simple graph?
   A. A simple graph has no loops.
   B. A simple graph can have parallel edges.
   C. A simple graph does not have edges connecting a vertex to itself.
   D. A simple graph can be described by the number of its vertices and the number of its edges.   1. **B**

2. Which diagram represents a graph with 4 vertices, each with degree 2?
   A.   B.   C.   D.   2. **D**

3. Determine how many edges K_9 has.
   A. 45   B. 40   C. 36   D. 31   3. **C**

4. Which graph is not complete?
   A. $G(6, 15)$ B. $G(12, 66)$ C. $G(8, 28)$ D. $G(25, 325)$ 4. **D**

5. Determine the most specific name of the walk $a, b, g, f, e,$ in the graph to the right.
   A. circuit   B. path
   C. trail   D. cycle   5. **D**

6. Which statement best describes $G(9, 36)$?
   A. The graph is disconnected.
   B. The graph may be connected.
   C. The graph is connected.
   D. The graph is both connected and complete.   6. **D**

For Exercises 7–9, refer to the multigraphs below.
   A.   B.   C.   D.

7. Identify any simple graphs.
   A. A, C   B. B   C. A, C, D   D. There are none.   7. **D**

8. Which path in graph C is an Euler circuit?
   A. a, e, d, c, b, a B. a, b, c, d, e
   C. c, d, e, a, e, b D. There are none.   8. **B**

T 193
Glencoe Division, Macmillan/McGraw-Hill

NAME _____ DATE _____

Chapter 16 Test, Form 1A (continued)

9. Identify any graph with an Euler path.
   A. B   B. A and D   C. C   D. There are none.   9. **B**

10. Use the breadth-first search algorithm to determine the distance of the shortest path from A to Z in the multigraph at the right.
    A. 5   B. 4
    C. 3   D. 2   10. **C**

11. Use Dijkstra's algorithm to find the minimal distance from A to Z in the multigraph at the right.
    A. 6   B. 7
    C. 10   D. 11   11. **A**

12. Find a spanning tree for the graph at the right.
    A. g, e, h B. a, b, c, d, e, f
    C. a, g, e, d, f D. g, e, d, h, i, b 12. **D**

13. Which number represents the weight of a minimal spanning tree from vertex B for the graph at the right?
    A. 15   B. 12
    C. 19   D. 11   13. **D**

14. Find the entry in the second column of the third row of $M(G)$ for the digraph at the right.
    A. 0   B. 1
    C. 2   D. 3   14. **A**

15. Find the number of directed edges from Z to Y in the digraph described by the matrix below.
$$\begin{array}{c} \\ W \\ X \\ Y \\ Z \end{array}\begin{array}{c}\begin{array}{cccc} W & X & Y & Z \end{array}\\ \begin{bmatrix} 0 & 0 & 1 & 2 \\ 0 & 1 & 2 & 1 \\ 2 & 0 & 0 & 1 \\ 1 & 1 & 3 & 0 \end{bmatrix}\end{array}$$
    A. 0   B. 1   C. 2   D. 3   15. **D**

Bonus
How many edges are there in K_{2x-1}?

   A. $2x^2 + x$ B. $\dfrac{4x^2 + 5x + 2}{2}$

   C. $4x^2 + 2x$ D. $\dfrac{2x^2 + 4x + 1}{2}$ Bonus: **A**

T 194
Glencoe Division, Macmillan/McGraw-Hill

■ find minimal spanning trees
(Lesson 16-5)

Find a minimal spanning tree and its weight for the graph below.

One minimal spanning tree is $\{S, P\}, \{P, Q\},$ $\{Q, T\}, \{T, V\},$ $\{V, W\}, \{W, U\},$ $\{T, R\}$ with a weight of $5 + 5 + 7 + 6 + 4 + 3 + 5$ or 35.

■ represent digraphs as matrices and vice versa **(Lesson 16-6)**

Find $M(G)$ for the digraph at the right.

Since there are 4 vertices, the matrix will have 4 rows and 4 columns. There are no edges from P to P, so the entry in row 1, column 1 is 0. There is 1 edge from P to Q, so the entry in row 1, column 2 is 1. Continuing the process gives the matrix at the right.

$$\begin{array}{c} \\ P \\ Q \\ R \\ S \end{array}\begin{array}{c}\begin{array}{cccc} P & Q & R & S \end{array}\\ \begin{bmatrix} 0 & 1 & 0 & 0 \\ 0 & 0 & 1 & 0 \\ 2 & 0 & 0 & 0 \\ 1 & 0 & 1 & 0 \end{bmatrix}\end{array}$$

13. Find a spanning tree for the graph below.
    See margin.

14. Find a minimal spanning tree and its weight for the graph below.
    See margin.

Find $M(G)$ for each graph or digraph below. 15–16. See Teacher's Answer Key.

15.   16.

Draw the graph for which each matrix is $M(G)$. 17–18. See Teacher's Answer Key.

17. $A\ B\ C\ D\ E$
$$\begin{array}{c} A \\ B \\ C \\ D \\ E \end{array}\begin{bmatrix} 0 & 0 & 0 & 1 & 0 \\ 1 & 0 & 1 & 0 & 1 \\ 0 & 0 & 0 & 0 & 0 \\ 0 & 0 & 1 & 0 & 2 \\ 2 & 1 & 2 & 0 & 0 \end{bmatrix}$$

18. $F\ G\ H\ I\ J\ K$
$$\begin{array}{c} F \\ G \\ H \\ I \\ J \\ K \end{array}\begin{bmatrix} 0 & 1 & 0 & 0 & 0 & 0 \\ 1 & 0 & 0 & 0 & 0 & 0 \\ 0 & 0 & 0 & 1 & 0 & 1 \\ 0 & 0 & 1 & 0 & 1 & 0 \\ 0 & 0 & 0 & 1 & 0 & 1 \\ 0 & 0 & 1 & 0 & 1 & 0 \end{bmatrix}$$

19. See Teacher's Answer Key.

APPLICATIONS AND PROBLEM SOLVING

19. **Transportation** The Lopez family is moving to a new city. They need to do the things in the chart to make the move. Draw a digraph to model the situation and find a critical path. Then find the minimum amount of time needed to complete all of the tasks. **(Lesson 16-6)**

Task	Time Required
G: Get packing boxes	1 day
H: Secure a new home	30 days
I: Pack	7 days
J: Sell current home	30 days
K: Buy clothing appropriate for new climate	3 days
L: Send boxes to new address	5 days
M: Secure a moving company	3 days

Additional Answers

13. Sample answer:

14.

The weight is 75.

CHAPTER 16 TEST

Use the graph to complete Exercises 1–1.

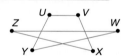

1. Is this a simple graph or a multigraph? Explain.   *1. See margin.*
2. What is deg (I)?   5
3. Which edges are incident on D? m, y, w, n, z, v
4. Is this a complete graph?   no
5. Which vertices are adjacent to A? B, C, D
6. Is this graph connected?   yes
7. Determine whether l, m, n, s, t, u, v, y is a walk, trail, path, circuit, or cycle.   circuit
8. Determine whether the graph contains an Euler circuit or an Euler path. If so, name it.   Euler path: $o, p, q, r, s, t, k, n, z, u, v, w, x, y, m, l$
9. Find a shortest path from A to K. y, n, o, p
10. Find a spanning tree for the graph.   See margin.
11. Find $M(G)$ for the graph.   See Teacher's Answer Key.
12. What is the difference between a graph and a multigraph?   See margin.
13. Draw K_6.   *13–14. See Teacher's Answer Key.*
14. Draw a connected graph with four vertices, two of even degree and two of odd degree.
15. What is the minimum number of edges in a connected graph that has six vertices?   5
16. *True or false:* Every $U-V$ walk contains a $U-V$ path.   true
17. What is the difference between a path and an Euler path?   See margin.
18. If a graph contains an Euler path, where does it begin and end?   at the vertices of odd degree
19. **Recreation** The honors club is planning a trip to a nearby amusement park. Their faculty sponsor wants to make sure that only boys who are friends go in the same car. If the list below names the boys and their friends, what is the least number of cars needed?   3 cars

   Adam: Bob, Frank, Ho-Chin   Evan: Dave, Greg
   Bob: Adam, Carlos, Dave, Ho-Chin   Frank: Adam, Carlos, Dave, Greg, Ho-Chin
   Carlos: Bob, Frank   Greg: Evan, Frank
   Dave: Bob, Evan, Frank   Ho-Chin: Adam, Bob, Frank

20. **Telecommunications** A telecommunications company wants to develop a network to connect six cities. The table below lists the cities and the cost (in thousands of dollars) to connect each pair. What is the minimum cost, and which cities should be connected?   See margin.

City	Sarasota	St. Augustine	Lakeland	Jacksonville	Daytona Beach
St. Augustine	18				
Lakeland	9	35			
Jacksonville	12	14	11		
Daytona Beach	16	9	6	19	
Bunnell	23	4	18	26	14

Bonus Find the value of k when
$m\angle U + m\angle V + m\angle W + m\angle X + m\angle Y + m\angle Z = 45k.$ 8

This page may be used as a test or as a review. All answers to this test appear in the Selected Answers in the student text.

Standardized Test Questions are also provided in the *Evaluation Masters*.

Enrichment Masters Booklet, pp. 197–198

NAME _____ DATE _____

Chapter 16 Test, Form 2A

1. True or false? A multigraph must have more than one edge connecting the same pair of vertices.   1. false

2. Draw a graph with 3 vertices such that $\deg(A) = 1$, $\deg(B) = 0$, and $\deg(C) = 2$.   2. See students' graphs.

3. How many edges does K_{20} have?   3. 190

4. Determine whether $G(15, 105)$ is complete. Write *yes* or *no*.   4. yes

5. Refer to the graph at the right to determine whether the walk g, h, d, c, a is a circuit, a cycle, a path, or a trail. Use the most specific name.   5. path

6. Is $G(10, 8)$ connected? Write *yes* or *no*.   6. no

For Exercises 7-9, refer to the multigraph below.

7. Is the graph a simple graph? Write *yes* or *no*.   7. no   Sample answer: a, b, e, f, g, c, d

8. If possible, find an Euler circuit.   8. h, i No, no vertices have an odd degree.

9. Is there an Euler path? Why or why not?   9. degree.

T197
Glencoe Division, Macmillan/McGraw-Hill

NAME _____ DATE _____

Chapter 16 Test, Form 2A (continued)

10. Determine the distance and a shortest path from A to Z in the graph at the right by using the breadth-first search algorithm.   10. 6; one path is A, O, E, F, G, H, Z.

11. Find a minimal path and the minimal distance from A to Z for the graph at the right by using Dijkstra's algorithm.   11. A, H, F, Z; 8

12. Find a spanning tree for the graph below.   12. Sample answer: a, b, c, i, k, e

13. Find a minimal spanning tree for the graph below. Then state the weight of the tree.   13. 11

14. Find $M(G)$ for the digraph below.   MISSING ART16-2A-7   14.
$$\begin{array}{c} & A\ B\ C\ D \\ A & \begin{bmatrix} 0 & 0 & 0 & 1 \\ 3 & 0 & 0 & 0 \\ 0 & 1 & 0 & 0 \\ 0 & 0 & 1 & 1 \end{bmatrix} \\ B \\ C \\ D \end{array}$$

15. Draw a graph for which $M(G)$ is
$$\begin{array}{c} & R\ S\ T \\ R & \begin{bmatrix} 1 & 0 & 2 \\ 0 & 0 & 1 \\ 1 & 0 & 1 \end{bmatrix} \\ S \\ T \end{array}$$ 15. See students' graphs.

Bonus
Draw a graph with 5 vertices that contains an Euler path.   Bonus: See students' graphs.

T198
Glencoe Division, Macmillan/McGraw-Hill

Test Generator Software is provided in Apple, IBM, and Macintosh versions. You may use this software to create your own tests, based on the needs of your students.

Additional Answers

1. simple graph; no loops or parallel edges
10. $\{A, C\}, \{C, D\}, \{D, B\}, \{D, I\}, \{I, F\}, \{F, E\}, \{I, G\}, \{I, J\}, \{J, K\}, \{I, H\}$
12. A multigraph may contain loops and/or parallel edges; a graph may not.

17. A path may include any number of edges; an Euler path must include all of the edges.
20. $39,000; Sarasota, Lakeland; Lakeland, Jacksonville; Lakeland, Daytona Beach; Daytona Beach, St. Augustine; St. Augustine, Bunnell

Using the Unit Review

These two pages review the skills and concepts presented in Unit 4. In addition, a four-page unit test, shown below and on the next page, is provided in the *Evaluations Masters Booklet*.

Evaluation Masters Booklet, pp. 205–206

NAME _____ DATE _____

Unit Test, Chapters 12-16

1. Determine whether the Julia set for the function $f(z) = z^2 + (-0.2 + 0i)$ is connected or disconnected. — **connected**

2. A set of data has a normal distribution with a mean of 16 and a standard deviation of 0.3. What percent of the data is in the interval $15.2 - 16$? — **49.6%**

3. Is the multigraph at the right a simple graph? Write *yes* or *no*. — **no**

4. Find the twelfth term of the geometric sequence $\frac{1}{16}, \frac{1}{8}, \frac{1}{4}, \cdots$. — **128**

5. There are 21 wrapped packages in a grab bag at an office holiday party. Five of the packages contain $20 bills, 7 packages contain $5 bills, and 9 packages contain $1 bills. What is the probability that the first two people choose packages with $20 bills inside them? — **$\frac{1}{21}$**

6. Write $1 + i$ in exponential form. — **$\sqrt{2} e^{i\frac{\pi}{4}}$**

7. Find the coordinates of the vertex of the graph of the logistic function $f(x) = 1.9x(1 - x)$. — **(0.5, 0.475)**

8. *True* or *false*: Choosing an entrée and choosing an appetizer from a dinner menu are independent events. — **true**

9. Find a minimal path and the minimal distance from A to Z in the graph at the right by using Dijkstra's algorithm. — **7; A, G, E, Z**

10. Graph the functions $f(x) = -5x$ and $f(x) = x$ on the same set of axes. Then perform graphical iteration for $x_0 = 1$. State the type of path that the iteration forms. — **See students' graphs; spiral out**

T **205**
Glencoe Division, Macmillan/McGraw-Hill

NAME _____ DATE _____

Unit Test, Chapters 12-16 (continued)

11. The marketing manager for a company that sells office equipment recorded the amount spent on advertising and the amount of sales for 12 consecutive quarters. His results are recorded in the chart below. Draw a scatter plot to show how the expenditures for advertising are related to the income from sales. Describe the relationship.

Quarter	Advertising	Sales
1	$900	$20,000
2	$1000	$28,000
3	$1600	$22,000
4	$2000	$25,000
5	$2200	$34,000
6	$2700	$20,000
7	$3000	$30,000
8	$3000	$38,000
9	$4000	$30,000
10	$4000	$40,000
11	$4000	$50,000
12	$4600	$46,000

See students' graphs; significantly positive

12. How many different ways can the letters of the word *circular* be arranged? — **10,080**

13. Use the ratio test to determine whether the series $\frac{1}{3} + \frac{1}{3^2} + \frac{1}{3^3} + \cdots$ is convergent or divergent. — **convergent**

14. Find the first three iterates of the function $f(z) = z^2 + (z - i)$ if $z_0 = i$. — **$-1, -i, -1 - 2i$**

15. How many edges does the graph of K_{11} have? — **81**

16. Eight out of ten people surveyed prefer to observe Veterans Day on November 11 rather than on the second Monday of November. Use the binomial theorem to determine the probability that each of the first 3 people surveyed preferred to observe Veterans Day on November 11. — **$\frac{64}{125}$**

17. Use the binomial theorem to expand $(x - 2y)^3$. — **$x^3 - 6x^2y + 12xy^2 - 8y^3$**

18. Find a spanning tree for the graph at the right. — **Sample answer: b, k, l, d, n, g, f**

T **206**
Glencoe Division, Macmillan/McGraw-Hill

Solve. (Lessons 12-1 and 12-2)

1. Find the 20th term of the arithmetic sequence for which $a_1 = 3$ and $d = -2$. **–35**

2. Find the sum of the first nine terms of the geometric series $2 + 4 + 8 + \cdots$. **1022**

Evaluate each limit, or state that the limit does not exist. (Lesson 12-3)

3. $\lim\limits_{n \to \infty} \frac{4n + 1}{3n}$ **$\frac{4}{3}$**

4. $\lim\limits_{n \to \infty} \frac{n^2 - 1}{n}$ **does not exist**

Determine whether each series is *convergent* or *divergent*. (Lesson 12-4)

5. $1 + 4 + 7 + 10 + \cdots$ **divergent**

6. $6 + 2 + \frac{2}{3} + \frac{2}{9} + \cdots$ **convergent**

7. $\frac{3}{1^1} + \frac{3}{2^2} + \frac{3}{3^3} + \cdots$ **convergent**

Write each expression in expanded form and find the sum. (Lesson 12-5)

8. $\sum\limits_{a=2}^{8} (3a - 6)$ **63**

9. $\sum\limits_{k=0}^{6} 7 \left(\frac{1}{2}\right)^k$ **$\frac{889}{64}$**

Find the designated term of each binomial expansion. (Lesson 12-6)

10. 4th term of $(x + 1)^9$ **$84x^6$**

11. 7th term of $(x - 2y)^{12}$ **$59{,}136x^6y^6$**

Find the first three iterates of each function using the given initial value. If necessary, round your answers to the nearest hundredth. (Lesson 13-1)

12. $f(x) = 3x + 1, x_0 = 1$ **4, 13, 40**

13. $f(x) = x^2 - 5, x_0 = -2$ **–1, –4, 11**

Find the x-coordinate of the fixed point for each function. Is it a repeller or an attractor? (Lesson 13-2)

14. $f(x) = 1.5x + 2$ **(–4, –4); repeller**

15. $f(x) = -0.5x + 3$ **(2, 2); attractor**

Find the first three iterates of the function $f(z) = 2z + 3i$ for each initial value. (Lesson 13-4)

16. $z_0 = -i$ **$i, 5i, 13i$**

17. $z_0 = 3 - i$ **$6 + i, 12 + 5i, 24 + 13i$**

Determine whether the graph of each value is in the prisoner set or the escape set for the function $f(z) = z^2$. (Lesson 13-5)

18. $-0.5 + 0.5i$ **prisoner set**

19. $2 + i$ **escape set**

Solve. (Lessons 14-1, 14-2, 14-3)

20. The letters $a, b, c, d,$ and e are to be used to form five letter patterns. How many patterns can be formed if repetitions are not allowed?   **120 patterns**

21. How many ways can the letters of the word *COLOR* be arranged?   **60 ways**

22. From a group of 3 men and 5 women, how many committees of 2 men and 2 women can be formed?   **30 committees**

State the odds of an event occurring given the probability of the event. (Lesson 14-4)

23. $\frac{2}{7}$ **$\frac{2}{5}$**

24. $\frac{1}{14}$ **$\frac{1}{13}$**

Solve. (Lessons 14-5, 14-6, 14-7, and 14-8)

25. Three cards are drawn at random from a standard deck of 52 cards. What is the probability that all are clubs?   **$\frac{11}{850}$**

26. Find the probability of getting a sum of 6 on the first throw of two dice and a sum of 2 on the second throw.   **$\frac{5}{1296}$**

27. Find the probability of a sum of 7 or 9 on a single throw of two dice.   **$\frac{5}{18}$**

28. One card is drawn from a standard deck of 52 cards. What is the probability that it is a king if it is known to be a face card?   **$\frac{1}{3}$**

Additional Answer

29. 42 65 65 66 69 70 72 76 77
77 77 80 82 82 86 89 89 91
95 99

The test scores for Mrs. Humphrey's math class are listed.   (Lessons 15-2 and 15-3)

89	95	65	70	77	82	66
69	91	82	77	99	65	89
72	80	42	76	86	77

29. Make an array of the data. See margin.

30. Find the range of the data. 57

31. Find the mean of the data. 77.45

32. Find the median of the data. 77

33. Find the mode of the data. 77

34. Find the mean deviation of the data. 9.595

35. Find the semi-interquartile range of the data. 9

36. Find the standard deviation of the data. 12.65

Solve.   (Lessons 15-4 and 15-5)

37. A value is selected at random from a normally distributed set of data. Suppose the mean, $\bar{x}$, is 70 and the standard deviation, σ, is 6. What is the probability that the selected value lies within the limits 65 and 75? about 0.595

38. The mean height of a random sample of 169 junior girls is 65.2 inches, and the standard deviation is 2.2 inches. Find the range of the sample mean that has a 5% level of confidence. 64.9 inches to 65.5 inches

The table below shows the calculus grades and the physics grades for a group of college students at the end of a quarter.   (Lesson 15-6)

Student	A	B	C	D	E	F	G	H
Calculus Grade	90	78	56	32	45	69	75	79
Physics Grade	85	65	78	60	72	62	70	85

39. Draw a scatter plot relating calculus grades to physics grades and find a median-fit line for the data.

40. Use a graphing calculator to plot the data and draw a line of regression.
    39–40. See margin.

Use the graph at the right to answer each question.   (Lesson 16-1)

41. Is it a complete graph? no

42. What is deg (D)? 3

43. Which edges are incident on A?
    $\{A, D\}, \{A, C\}, \{A, B\}$

Use the graph below to determine whether each walk is a _circuit, cycle, path, trail,_ or _walk_. Use the most specific name. (Lesson 16-2)

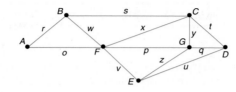

44. p, q, t, s, r path

45. v, u, t, y, p cycle

46. w, s, x, v, u trail

Solve.   (Lessons 16-3 and 16-4)

47. Does the multigraph below contain an Euler Circuit? Explain. No; the degrees of vertices A and C are not even.

48. Use the breadth-first search algorithm to find a shortest path from A to E in the graph below. State its length.
    Paths A, B, I, E; A, F, I, E; and A, F, G, E have length 3.

Additional Answers

39.
(scatter plot with line, axes labeled to 100)

40.
(calculator regression plot)

The key theme of Unit 5 is the relationship between differential and integral calculus. Some of the concepts are extensions of topics from algebra, geometry, and early units in this text. The exploration of limits, derivatives, and integrals is fundamental to the study of calculus.

Connections to Other Units

The concepts developed in this unit are related to concepts in Units 1, 2, and 4. The concept of maximum and minimum of a functions, presented in Units 1 and 2, is further explored in this unit. The concept of limits applied to sequences and series in Unit 4 is extended to functions in this unit.

Multicultural Notes

Iran   Over 160,000 miles of an ancient water system called *qanats* are still in use in Iran today. A qanat channels underground mountain water downhill through a series of tunnels to desired locations. This system, which relies on basic hydraulic principals, was developed in Iran and spread east to Afghanistan and west to Egypt.

Japan   The Japanese build and use the greatest number of robots in the world. These robots are most often employed in manufacturing to position and join parts. They are usually equipped with sensors to aid in positioning. Light sensors locate position for robot welders who join the steel plates of Japanese-built oil tankers. The design of the mechanical structure of a robot addresses measures, such as degrees of movement, velocity and acceleration, structure strength, amount of vibration, and degree of accuracy.

UNIT 5

AN INTRODUCTION TO CALCULUS

Chapter 17   Limits, Derivatives, and Integrals

For many of you, calculus will be largely uncharted territory. However, calculus is one of the most important areas of mathematics. There are two branches of calculus, *differential* calculus and *integral* calculus. Differential calculus deals mainly with variable, or changing, quantities. In this chapter, you will study problems of optimization, where you will find the maximum or minimum value, and problems of motion, where you will study acceleration and velocity.

Integral calculus deals mainly with finding sums of infinitesimally small quantities. This generally involves finding a limit. German astronomer Johannes Kepler used this method to calculate the area of the ellipses formed by the orbits of the planets. In this chapter, you will use calculus to find the areas and volumes of many objects.

The relationship between differential and integral calculus is not obvious, but it does exist. Differentiation and integration are actually inverse operations, which you studied in algebra. In order to succeed in your study of calculus, you will need to use your knowledge of algebra and geometry. Upon completion of your study of calculus, however, you will be ready to embark on studies of many different fields in mathematics. It is our hope that you will enjoy learning about this wondrous field of mathematics.

910

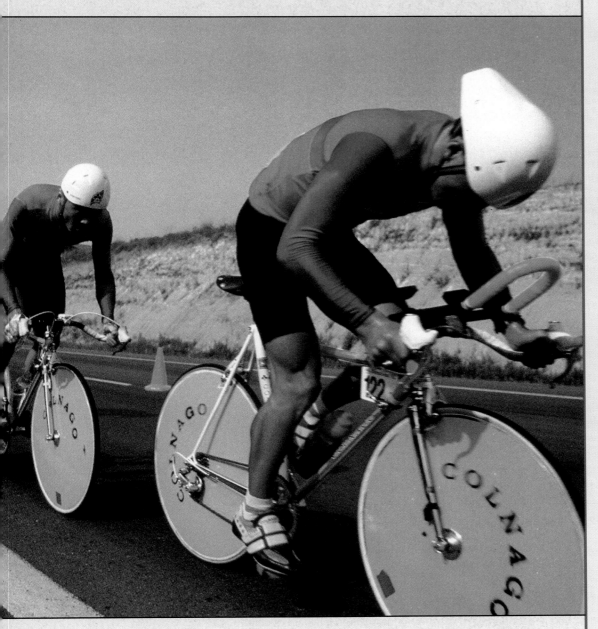

Cooperative Learning

The **Decision Making** activity offers students an opportunity to explore real-world questions while working in cooperative groups. These questions require students to do research and come to a viable conclusion.

Problem Solving

The **Case Study Follow-Up** provides an arena for problem solving, applying mathematics, and becoming more aware of issues that may face students in their adult lives. These questions require research and applications of the mathematics of the chapter.

Using Technology

Computer and calculator literacy is a growing part of our everyday lives. The features in this unit give students exposure to different technology tools available to facilitate their study of mathematics.

911

CHAPTER 17 LIMITS, DERIVATIVES, AND INTEGRALS

PREVIEWING THE CHAPTER

This chapter extends the concept of limits introduced in Chapter 12 to include limits of functions. Theorems that define operations involving limits are presented and students use them to evaluate limits. Derivatives were first introduced in Chapter 3. In this chapter, students deepen their understanding of the derivative by using different differentiation techniques to find the derivatives of functions. The area under a curve is defined using limits. Students use this definition to compute the area between a curve and the x-axis. Finally, students find integrals and use the fundamental theorem of calculus to evaluate definite integrals and to find areas under a curve.

Lesson Objective Chart

Lesson (Pages)	Lesson Objectives	State/Local Objectives
17-1 (914-922)	**17-1:** Use limit theorems to evaluate the limit of a polynomial function.	
17-2 (923-930)	**17-2:** Find the derivative of a function.	
17-3 (931-937)	**17-3:** Find the area between a curve and the x-axis by using the limit of areas of rectangles.	
17-4 (939-944)	**17-4:** Use integration formulas.	
17-5 (945-951)	**17-5:** Use the fundamental theorem of calculus to evaluate definite integrals and to find area.	

ORGANIZING THE CHAPTER

You may want to refer to the **Course Planning Guide Calendar** on pages T34-T35 for a complete pacing chart.

Lesson Planning Guide

Blackline Masters Booklets

Lesson	Pages	Practice	Enrichment	Evaluation	Technology: Graphing Calculator	Technology: Computer	Technology: Multicultural Activity	Applications	Activity Masters: Problem Solving	Activity Masters: Case Study Follow-Up	Activity Masters: Decision Making	Transparencies
17-1	914-922	p. 114	p. 114		p. 33		p. 17	p. 49				17-1
17-2	923-930	p. 115	p. 115	Quiz A, p. 117		p. 34			p. 50			17-2
17-3	931-937	p. 116	p. 116	Quiz B, p. 117 Mid-Chapter Test, p. 119								17-3
17-4	939-944	p. 117	p. 117	Quiz C, p. 118							p. 51	17-4
17-5	945-951	p. 118	p. 118	Quiz D, p. 118								17-5
Review	952-954	Multiple Choice Tests, Forms 1A and 1B, pp. 209-212 Free Response Tests, Forms 2A and 2B, pp. 213-216 Standardized Test Questions, p. 220										
Test	955											

Other Chapter Resources

Student Edition
Case Study Follow-Up, p. 930
Decision Making, p. 951
Technology, p. 938

Other Supplements
Transparency 17-0 for Chapter Opener
Alternate Assessment in the Mathematics Classroom,
    Glencoe Publishing Co., 1993
Cooperative Learning in the Mathematics Classroom,
    Glencoe Publishing Co., 1993

Software
Test and Review Generator Software
    Available for Apple, IBM, and Macintosh
Teacher's Guide for Software Resources

ENHANCING THE CHAPTER

Cooperative Learning

Assessing How Well the Group Functioned

To ensure improved performance in cooperative-learning sessions, it is important to process what students have learned about groups skills after each session. Whole-class discussions can be a valuable way to do this since groups can learn from the experiences of other groups. Such discussions should concentrate on how well the groups functioned during the session, what things were done well, and what things could be improved. To begin the processing, select one member from a group to discuss with the class one or two things that they did well during the session. Encourage the reporter to provide details and examples. Ask about specific actions taken by group members that helped, such as encouraging each other to participate, keeping one another focused on the task, paraphrasing or expanding on contributions, and so on. If you wish, you can also ask a reporter to discuss something that the group could have done better or would like to work harder on. The reporter need not use names but should be as specific as possible. The emphasis should be on improving the effectiveness of students in cooperating with and assisting other members of their group. This sharing of ideas and experiences will promote improved group behavior in future sessions.

For more information on cooperative learning, see pages T20-T21. Additional information on using cooperative groups is available in Glencoe's *Cooperative Learning in the Mathematics Classroom,* ©1993.

Multicultural

Multicultural Activity Masters, p. 17

17 **Multicultural Activity** (Use after Lesson 17-1)

The Fascination with π

Since ancient times, mathematicians throughout the world have been fascinated with the question, "What is the value of π?" The list of dates below gives you just a brief glimpse of the many attempts to determine a rational value of π.

20th century B.C. The Egyptians used $\pi \approx \left(\frac{4}{3}\right)^4$.

The Babylonians used $\pi \approx 3\frac{1}{8}$.

2nd century A.D. Hou Han Shu of China used $\pi \approx 3.1622$, which is close to $\sqrt{10}$.

4th century A.D. The Hindus of India used $\pi = 3\frac{177}{1250} = 3.1416$.

In modern times, mathematicians realized that π was irrational and could only be approximated to a greater degree of precision by using a finite number of terms of infinite expressions.

17th century A.D. The English mathematician John Wallis calculated:

$$\pi = 2 \cdot \left[\frac{2 \times 2 \times 4 \times 4 \times 6 \times 6 \times \dots}{3 \times 3 \times 5 \times 5 \times 7 \times 7 \times \dots} \right]$$

The English mathematician John Gregory and the German mathematician Wilhem Leibniz found:

$$\pi = 4\left(1 - \frac{1}{3} + \frac{1}{5} - \frac{1}{7} + \dots\right)$$

The complete decimal representation of π will always elude us. However, computers have given us incredibly precise approximations.

20th century A.D. Using a supercomputer, David and Gregory Chudnovsky at Columbia University approximated π to 2,160,000,000 places.

Refer to the Gregory-Leibniz series for π.

a. Write a BASIC computer program to evaluate the sum for the first *n* terms.

b. Test your program by using *n* = 100. How long did it take to get an approximation for π?
See students' work.

Sample answer:
```
10 INPUT N
20 S = 0
30 FOR I = 1 TO N
40 T = (-1)^(I-1)/(2*I - 1)
50 S = S + T
60 NEXT I
70 R = 4*S
80 PRINT R
```

T17
Glencoe Division, Macmillan/McGraw-Hill

Activity Masters

Applications, p. 49

CHAPTER **17** NAME _____ DATE _____
Applications (Use after Lesson 17-2)

Instantaneous Velocity

Consider an object moving along a number line. Let $s(t)$ be its distance from 0 at time t.

The average velocity of the object from time t_1 to time t_2 is $\frac{s(t_2) - s(t_1)}{t_2 - t_1}$. Let $h = t_2 - t_1$ so that $s(t_2) = s(t_1 + h)$. The instantaneous velocity $v(t)$ of the object at time t_1 is the limit of the average velocity as $h \to 0$.

$$v(t) = \lim_{h \to 0} \frac{s(t_1 + h) - s(t_1)}{h}$$

Notice that the expression on the right side of the equation is the definition of the derivative of $s(t_1)$. Since t_1 was an arbitrary choice of t, the instantaneous velocity of the object at any time t is given by $v(t) = s'(t)$. The instantaneous velocity is a directed measure. For the orientation shown above, a positive velocity means the object is moving to the right and a negative velocity means the object is moving to the left. The object is instantaneously stationary when $v(t) = 0$.

Example An object is moving along a line according to the distance function $s(t) = t^2 - 3t$ where t is seconds and $s(t)$ is centimeters. Find its instantaneous velocity at $t = 1, 1.5$, and 3 seconds.

$$v(t) = s'(t) = 2t - 3$$
$$v(1) = 2(1) - 3 = -1 \text{ cm/second}$$
$$v(1.5) = 2(1.5) - 3 = 0 \text{ cm/second}$$
$$v(3) = 2(3) - 3 = 3 \text{ cm/second}$$

Example A ball is thrown straight up. Its distance above the ground is given by $s(t) = -16t^2 + 30t$ where t is seconds and $s(t)$ is feet. Find the maximum height of the ball.

At the maximum height the ball is instantaneously stationary. Therefore, find t such that $v(t) = 0$.

$$v(t) = s'(t) = -32t + 30$$

From $-32t + 30 = 0$, $t = \frac{15}{16}$ seconds. The maximum height is

$$s\left(\frac{15}{16}\right) = -16\left(\frac{15}{16}\right)^2 + 30\left(\frac{15}{16}\right) = 14\frac{1}{16} \text{ feet.}$$

Solve.

1. An object is moving along a number line according to the distance function $s(t) = 3t^3 - 4t$, where $t \ge 0$. For what time interval is the object moving to the left? **for $t = 0$ to $t = \frac{2}{3}$ seconds**

2. A ball is thrown straight up so that its height in feet above the ground after t seconds is given by $s(t) = -16t^2 + 48t$. What is its maximum height? What is its velocity when it strikes the ground? **maximum height: 36 ft; velocity; –48 ft/second**

T49
Glencoe Division, Macmillan/McGraw-Hill

Problem Solving, p. 50

CHAPTER **17** NAME _____ DATE _____
Problem Solving (Use after Lesson 17-4)

Working Backward

Lesson 17-4 lists formulas that are useful in finding integrals. While the formulas are invaluable, you should always keep the relationship between the integral and the derivative in mind when you are finding integrals. This relationship, together with the problem-solving strategy *work backward*, can often help you find integrals even if you forget the formulas.

Example Find $\int 2x^3\, dx$.

By the definition of an integral, we need to find the function $F(x)$ such that $F'(x) = 2x^3$. Work backward to find F. Think: Differentiation reduces the degree of a monomial by one. Since the degree of $F'(x)$ is 3, the degree of $F(x)$ must be 4, and $F(x)$ must have the form $F(x) = nx^4 + C$.

$$F'(x) = 4nx^3 = 2x^3$$
$$n = \frac{1}{2}$$
$$F(x) = \frac{1}{2}x^4 + C$$

Work backward to find each integral.

1. $\int 12x\, dx$ $6x^2 + C$

2. $\int 6x^3\, dx$ $\frac{3}{2}x^4 + C$

3. $\int \sqrt[3]{x^2}\, dx$ $\frac{3}{5}x^{\frac{5}{3}} + C$

4. $\int (2x^5 - 5x^2 + 3)\, dx$ $\frac{1}{3}x^6 - \frac{5}{3}x^3 + 3x + C$

5. $\int (14x^{10} - 8x^{12})\, dx$ $\frac{14}{11}x^{11} - \frac{8}{13}x^{13} + C$

6. $\int (x^{\frac{8}{5}} - 13x^{\frac{4}{9}})\, dx$ $\frac{5}{13}x^{\frac{13}{5}} - 9x^{\frac{13}{9}} + C$

T50
Glencoe Division, Macmillan/McGraw-Hill

Decision Making, p. 51

CHAPTER **17** NAME _____ DATE _____
Decision Making (Use after Lesson 17-5)

Protecting Freedom of Speech

All Americans know and most are proud of the fact that they live in a country that protects a citizen's freedom of speech. The First Amendment of the Constitution of the United States specifically prohibits Congress from making any law that abridges freedom of speech or freedom of the press.

Nevertheless, few Americans are willing to grant freedom of speech completely without restriction. Recent polls establish that 60% of Americans believe that the government should have the right to ban records with lyrics that encourage drug use, 51% believe the government should prohibit hateful speech that demeans a person's race, sex, national origin, or religion, 40% believe the government should have the right to deny First Amendment privileges to artists, musicians, filmmakers, and photographers, and 50% believe that books with "dangerous ideas" should be banned from school libraries. The results of the polls suggest that while Americans favor the idea of freedom of speech, most find certain types of speech unacceptable.

Research freedom of speech. Decide if the freedom should be granted unconditionally or if there are certain areas where it should be restricted. Use the following questions to guide you. Answers will vary.

1. What is "speech" according to the law? Does it include film, photographs, clothing, behavior, or anything other than written or spoken words?

2. The Supreme Court has decided that speech that is likely to endanger people's lives, such as falsely crying "Fire!" in a crowded theater, should not be protected by the First Amendment. Do you agree?

3. In 1798, because of fear of foreign influences in the United States, the federal government passed the Alien and Sedition Acts, which attempted to silence critics of President John Adams' policies. During times of war or during great national crises, such as the current epidemic of illegal drug use, should the government have the right to suspend the First Amendment?

4. Should teenagers be exempt from the privileges and responsibilities of the First Amendment? Should the editor of the school newspaper have the right to print anything he or she desires? Should parents and teachers have the right to inspect school libraries and to remove books they believe to be dangerous to students?

5. In what ways, if at all, can words, photographs, or ideas harm a person?

6. After you have completed your research, decide whether you believe that all forms of speech should be protected unconditionally, or whether some forms should be prohibited, either permanently or under certain conditions. Write a 1-page paper outlining your decision and explaining the reasons behind it.

T51
Glencoe Division, Macmillan/McGraw-Hill

The Technology feature following Lesson 17-3 shows students how to use IBM's *MET (Mathematics Exploration Toolkit)* to calculate Riemann sums.

The Graphing Calculator Exploration in Lesson 17-1 demonstrates how to use the TRACE feature of a graphing calculator to estimate the value of the limit of a graphed function. Students also use the calculator in the exercises to verify values of limits. Lesson 17-3 contains a graphing calculator program that will approximate the area between the graphs of two functions.

Graphing Calculator Exercises, p. 921
Graphing Calculator Program, p. 936

Outside Resources

Books/Periodicals

Steen, Lynn et al., editors. *Calculus for a New Century: A Pump Not a Filter,* MAA Notes, No. 8, Mathematical Association of America, Washington, D.C., 1988.

McLeod & Stolze. *Topics in Precalculus,* Kendall-Hunt, 1990.

Films/Videotapes/Videodiscs

Mathematics: Calculus, Great Plains National, University of Nebraska-Lincoln

Software

IBM Mathematics Exploration Toolkit (MET). IBM

A Graphic Approach to the Calculus. Wings for Learning/Sunburst (IBM)

Calculus 4.0. True BASIC (IBM, Macintosh)

Cactusplot. PC Consultants (Apple II, IBM)

MathTools for Precalculus/Calculus. (from *MacNumerics* by Spring Branch Software, Inc.) William K. Bradford Publishing (Macintosh)

Technology Masters

Graphing Calculator, p. 33

Computer, p. 34

This two-page introduction to the chapter provides students with an opportunity to see how college students use the mathematics presented in this chapter in their chosen majors. It also gives students a glimpse of the college majors that are available to them.

Transparency 17–0, available in the *Advanced Mathematical Concepts* Teaching Transparency Package, provides another full-color visual and motivational activity that you can use to engage your students in the mathematical content of the chapter.

More About Robert Wickwire

One of the things that helped Robert Wickwire decide on manufacturing engineering as a major is the cooperative program set up between 27 companies and the professors in the department at Oregon State University. This program has allowed Robert to gain a full year of experience in his chosen field while studying for his degree. He is excited at the prospect of going to work for a company and making an immediate impact in terms of productivity and efficiency as well as enhancing the quality of the workplace and its safety for the workers.

Chapter Project

Materials   a simple manufactured item for each group having only a few parts; for example, a spring-type clothespin, a yo-yo, or a sauce pan

Procedure   Organize students into cooperative groups. Each group will be given a simple manufactured item and be asked to model the process by which it is manufactured. The group will begin by examining its assigned item and making a flowchart showing the steps used to produce it. They should draw a sketch of the plant layout used and mark on the flowchart where each of the item's parts are in the plant at each step in the manufacturing process. Next, they should analyze the time frame involved in the production and include the relative time

CHAPTER 17

LIMITS, DERIVATIVES, AND INTEGRALS

HISTORICAL SNAPSHOT

	Mass production of 10,000 muskets in 15 months Eli Whitney, Connecticut		Nation's oldest salmon cannery Astoria, Oregon			Primitive industrial robot, Unimation, Inc. Danbury, Massachusetts	
"Fluxions" (methods of calculus) Sir Isaac Newton, England		Oregon State University established at Corvallis		Moving assembly line Ford's "Tin Lizzie" Detroit, Michigan		Robotic manufacture of robots Yamazaki, Japan	
AD 1666	1798		1868	1881	1914	1962	1983

912

coordinates of each step on their flowchart. Finally, the group will select one particular part of the manufactured item and using the information on the plant layout and flowchart, write equations that show its position and velocity as functions of time. Each group will report on its results to the class, explaining their flowchart and plant layout.

CHAPTER OBJECTIVES

In this chapter, you will:
- Define the limit of a function.
- Find the derivative of a function.
- Find the integral of a function by finding the area under the curve.
- Develop and use the fundamental theorem of calculus.

CAREER GOAL: Manufacturing Engineering

Robert Wickwire began his working life by selling heavy equipment for a mill supply company, but soon decided that he wanted to be an engineer. "When customers would call with problems or needing information, I would have to refer them to the engineering department of the company that manufactured the equipment. I wanted to be a problem-solver myself, so I decided to become a manufacturing engineer."

"Manufacturing engineering deals with production processes," Robert explains. "It's such a broad field that there are a lot of opportunities and different directions that I can pursue. During one internship, for example, I worked for a company that makes dental equipment, from small tools to dental chairs. I redesigned work centers where people make cabinetry. I also worked to reduce carpal tunnel syndrome, a wrist disorder that affects people who use their hands all day."

Robert took algebra, geometry, trigonometry, and pre-calculus in high school, but wishes he had also taken a full year of calculus. "Manufacturing engineering uses calculus a lot to control time-dependent operations and positioning. Whenever objects are in motion, like on a production line, their position, velocity, and acceleration are time-dependent, and require calculus for measuring each accurately."

Robert hopes to use his skills in manufacturing engineering to help revive the American economy. "Many people believe that the United States will become a totally service-oriented country. I don't agree with that; many areas of manufacturing need to improve to compete more effectively internationally. People in manufacturing engineering will be the people who give United States manufacturing back its competitive edge in the world market. That's something I want to be a part of."

READ MORE ABOUT IT

Jones, John Taylor. *Engineering For You, A Career Guide*. Ames, Iowa: Iowa State University Press, 1991.

Kiplinger, Austin H. and A. *America in the Global '90s*. Washington D.C.: Kiplinger Books, 1989.

Plossl, George W. *Managing in the New World of Manufacturing, How Companies Can Improve Operations to Compete Globally*. New York: Prentice-Hall, 1991.

SPOTLIGHT ON...

Robert Wickwire
Age: 32
Class: Senior
School: Oregon State University Corvallis, Oregon
Major: Manufacturing Engineering

"Manufacturing engineers will give the U.S. back its competitive edge in the world market."

FOR MORE INFORMATION

If you would like more information about manufacturing engineering, contact:

Society of Manufacturing Engineers (SME)
P.O. Box 930
1 SME Drive
Dearborn, MI 48121

Applications

Lesson	Application	Examples	Exercises
17–1	Hydraulics	2	
	Physics		49
	Chemistry		50
	Demographics		51
17–2	Business	4	44
	Physics		45
	Economics		46
	Research		47
17–3	Physics	3	
	Business		24
	Sports		25
17–4	Demographics	4	
	Physics		28
	Business		29, 30
17–5	Business	2	39
	Medicine		40
	Hydraulics		41

NCTM Standards: 1–4, 6, 13

Lesson Resources

- Practice Master 17–1
- Enrichment Master 17–1
- Multicultural Activity Master, p. 17
- Technology Master, p. 33
- Activity Master, p. 49

 Transparency 17–1 contains the 5-Minute Check and a teaching aid for this lesson.

INTRODUCING THE LESSON

 5-Minute Check

(over Chapter 16)

1. Draw the graph represented by $M(G)$. Let $M(G) =$

$$\begin{array}{c|ccccc} & A & B & C & D & E \\ \hline A & 0 & 1 & 0 & 0 & 2 \\ B & 1 & 0 & 0 & 1 & 0 \\ C & 0 & 0 & 0 & 1 & 1 \\ D & 0 & 1 & 1 & 0 & 1 \\ E & 2 & 0 & 1 & 1 & 0 \end{array}.$$

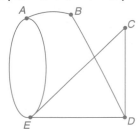

2. Find an A–D trail and an A–D path for the graph in Exercise 1.   Sample answers: *A, E, A, B, D*; *A, E, D*
3. Determine whether the graph in Exercise 1 has an Euler circuit or an Euler path. If so, name the circuit or path.   Euler path; sample answer: *A, B, D, C, E, A, E, D*
4. Determine the shortest path and the distance from A to Z in the graph below.   6; *A, B, C, E, J, K, Z*

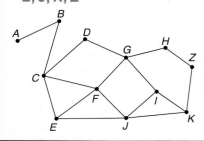

17-1   Limits

Objective
17–1

After studying this lesson, you should be able to:
- use limit theorems to evaluate the limit of a polynomial function.

Application

If a pendulum is moved from its equilibrium position and released, it will oscillate back and forth. Each swing will be shorter than the last as the forces of friction and gravity slow the pendulum. Assume that the length of the first swing was $\frac{1}{2}$ unit and each subsequent swing was half as long as the one before. Let ℓ_n represent the length of the nth swing. Find the lengths of the first five swings.

$$\ell_1 = \frac{1}{2}$$

$$\ell_2 = \left(\frac{1}{2}\right)\frac{1}{2} \text{ or } \frac{1}{2^2}$$

$$\ell_3 = \frac{1}{2}\left(\frac{1}{2^2}\right) \text{ or } \frac{1}{2^3}$$

$$\ell_4 = \frac{1}{2}\left(\frac{1}{2^3}\right) \text{ or } \frac{1}{2^4}$$

$$\ell_5 = \frac{1}{2}\left(\frac{1}{2^4}\right) \text{ or } \frac{1}{2^5}$$

The length of the nth swing, ℓ_n, will be $\frac{1}{2^n}$ unit.

Some of the terms of the sequence of swing lengths are graphed on the number line below.

As n increases without limit, the points representing the length of the swing become closer and closer to 0, but always remain greater than 0. Thus, the limit of $\frac{1}{2^n}$ as n increases without bound is 0.

In Chapter 12, we found the limits of sequences such as the one above and limits of series. The concept of a limit can be extended to a function. What is the limit of $5x - 3$ as x approaches 0? What is the limit as x approaches 6? The limit of a function $f(x)$ as x approaches a is represented by $\lim_{x \to a} f(x)$. So $\lim_{x \to 0} (5x - 3)$ is $5(0) - 3$ or -3, and $\lim_{x \to 6} (5x - 3)$ is $5(6) - 3$ or 27.

914   CHAPTER 17   LIMITS, DERIVATIVES, AND INTEGRALS

ALTERNATE TEACHING STRATEGIES

Using Connections

Have students consider how continuity and limit are related. If $f(x)$ is continuous at $x = a$, what is true of $\lim_{x \to a} f(x)$? $\lim_{x \to a} f(x) = f(a)$ If $f(x)$ is not continuous at $x = a$, what happens to $\lim_{x \to a}$?   If $f(x)$ has a removable discontinuity at $x = a$, then the limit exists and equals the value that would "plug the hole."

Using Discussion

Have students consider the functions
$$f(x) = \begin{cases} x, & \text{if } x \le 0 \\ x + 1, & \text{if } x > 0 \end{cases}$$
$$g(x) = \begin{cases} x, & \text{if } x \le 0 \\ x^2, & \text{if } x > 0. \end{cases}$$

Graph each function and use a chart of values to consider their limits at 0.

$\lim_{x \to 0} f(x)$ is undefined; $\lim_{x \to 0} g(x) = 0.$

Example 1

Show that $\lim\limits_{x\to 3}(x^2+1)=10$ by selecting replacements for x near 3.

Replace x with values close to 3 and observe the patterns of x^2+1.

x	2.8	2.9	2.99	2.999
x^2+1	8.84	9.41	9.9401	9.994001

x	3.1	3.01	3.001	3.0001
x^2+1	10.61	10.0601	10.006001	10.00060001

The limit of x^2+1 as x approaches 3 is 10.

Consider any polynomial function with real coefficients of the form $P(x)=a_0x^n+a_1x^{n-1}+a_2x^{n-2}+\cdots+a_{n-1}x+a_n$. Let the domain of P be the set of all real numbers. Then, for any real number r, there exists a real number $P(r)$. The limit of such a polynomial function as x approaches r is $P(r)$. For example, the limit of $P(x)=x^2+2x-4$ as x approaches 2 is $P(2)=2^2+2(2)-4$ or 4.

Limit of a Polynomial Function	**The limit of a polynomial function, $P(x)$, as x approaches r, is $P(r)$.** $$\lim_{x\to r}P(x)=P(r)$$

Example 2

The velocity of a molecule of liquid flowing through a pipe varies depending upon the distance that the molecule is from the center of the pipe. The velocity in inches per second of a certain molecule is given by the function $v(r)=k(R^2-r^2)$, where r is the distance the molecule is from the center of the pipe in inches, R is the radius of the pipe in inches, and k is a constant. Suppose $k=0.65$ and $R=0.5$ for a certain situation.
a. Use a limit to find the velocity of a molecule at the center of the pipe.
b. What is the limiting velocity of a molecule as the molecule approaches the wall of the pipe?

a. If the molecule is at the center of the pipe, then $r=0$. Evaluate $\lim\limits_{r\to 0}v(r)$ to find the velocity of a molecule at the center.

$$v(r)=0.65(0.5^2-r^2) \qquad \text{\small $k=0.65$ and $R=0.5$}$$
$$\lim_{r\to 0}v(r)=v(0)$$
$$=0.65(0.5^2-0^2) \qquad \text{\small $r=0$}$$
$$=0.1625$$

The limit of the function as r approaches 0 is 0.1625. Thus, the velocity of a molecule at the center of the pipe is 0.1625 inches per second.

(continued on the next page)

LESSON 17-1   LIMITS   915

---

b. If the molecule is approaching the wall of the pipe, then *r* is approaching
0.5. Find $\lim\limits_{r \to 0.5} v(r)$ to find the velocity of the molecule.

$$v(r) = 0.65(0.5^2 - r^2) \qquad k = 0.65 \text{ and } R = 0.5$$

$$\lim_{r \to 0.5} v(r) = v(0.5)$$

$$= 0.65(0.5^2 - 0.5^2) \qquad r = 0.5$$

$$= 0$$

The limit of the function as *r* approaches 0.5 is 0. Thus, the limiting
velocity of a molecule that is approaching the wall of the pipe is 0 inches
per second.

Now consider the rational function
$f(x) = \dfrac{x^3}{x}$. Find the limit of this function as *x*
approaches 2. Let *r* = 2.

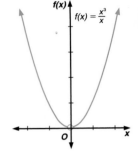

$$\lim_{x \to r} f(x) = f(r)$$

$$\lim_{x \to 2} \frac{x^3}{x} = f(2)$$

$$= \frac{8}{2} \text{ or } 4$$

What is $\lim\limits_{x \to 0} \dfrac{x^3}{x}$? Then *r* = 0. In this case, *f*(*r*) is undefined. It appears from
the graph above that $\lim\limits_{x \to 0} \dfrac{x^3}{x} = 0$. Replace *x* with values closer and closer to
zero to observe the behavior of $\dfrac{x^3}{x}$.

x	1	0.1	0.01	0.001	0.0001
$\dfrac{x^3}{x}$	1	0.01	0.0001	0.000001	0.00000001

It appears that $\lim\limits_{x \to 0} \dfrac{x^3}{x} = 0$. Even though the function is undefined at zero,
the limit of the function exists as *x* approaches zero. The limit is zero.

*Change rational
functions to
polynomial functions
whenever possible.*

You can also show that $\lim\limits_{x \to 0} \dfrac{x^3}{x} = 0$ by transforming $\dfrac{x^3}{x}$ into x^2, since the
two functions are equal for all values of *x* except for *x* = 0. Since x^2 is a
polynomial, $\lim\limits_{x \to 0} x^2 = 0$. This method will work whenever a function can
be simplified, even if the given function is *not* defined for the value that *x*
approaches.

916   CHAPTER 17   LIMITS, DERIVATIVES, AND INTEGRALS

Example 3

Find $\lim\limits_{x \to 4} \dfrac{x^2 - 16}{x - 4}$.

$$\lim_{x \to 4} \frac{x^2 - 16}{x - 4} = \lim_{x \to 4} \frac{(x-4)(x+4)}{x-4} \qquad \text{\textit{Factor.}}$$

$$= \lim_{x \to 4} (x + 4)$$

$$= 8$$

Note that $\dfrac{x^2 - 16}{x - 4} = x + 4$ for all real values of x <u>except</u> 4. However, the fact that the function is not defined for x = 4 does <u>not</u> affect the value of the limit as x approaches 4.

The limit of $\dfrac{x^2 - 16}{x - 4}$ as x approaches 4 is 8.

Chalkboard Example

For Example 3

Find $\lim\limits_{x \to 2} \dfrac{x^2 - 7x + 10}{x + 2}$. 0

It is useful to have principles that define operations involving limits when attempting to find the limits of some functions. These operations include addition, subtraction, multiplication, and division, as well as using powers and roots. The principles are stated as theorems without proofs and are shown in the table below.

The following theorems are given for $f(x)$ and $g(x)$, where $\lim\limits_{x \to a} f(x) = F$, $\lim\limits_{x \to a} g(x) = G$, a and c are real numbers, and n is a positive integer.

Limit of a Constant Function	If $f(x) = c$, then $\lim\limits_{x \to a} f(x) = c$.	Theorem 1
Addition	$\lim\limits_{x \to a} [f(x) + g(x)] = \lim\limits_{x \to a} f(x) + \lim\limits_{x \to a} g(x) = F + G$	Theorem 2
Subtraction	$\lim\limits_{x \to a} [f(x) - g(x)] = \lim\limits_{x \to a} f(x) - \lim\limits_{x \to a} g(x) = F - G$	Theorem 3
Multiplication	$\lim\limits_{x \to a} [f(x) \cdot g(x)] = \left[\lim\limits_{x \to a} f(x)\right] \left[\lim\limits_{x \to a} g(x)\right] = F \cdot G$	Theorem 4
Division	$\lim\limits_{x \to a} \dfrac{f(x)}{g(x)} = \dfrac{\lim\limits_{x \to a} f(x)}{\lim\limits_{x \to a} g(x)} = \dfrac{F}{G} \ (G \neq 0)$	Theorem 5
Product of a Constant and a Limit	$\lim\limits_{x \to a} [c \cdot g(x)] = c \lim\limits_{x \to a} g(x) = cG$	Theorem 6
Powers	$\lim\limits_{x \to a} [f(x)^n] = \left[\lim\limits_{x \to a} f(x)\right]^n = F^n$	Theorem 7
Roots	$\lim\limits_{x \to a} \sqrt[n]{f(x)} = \sqrt[n]{\lim\limits_{x \to a} f(x)} = \sqrt[n]{F}$ ($F > 0$ if n is even.)	Theorem 8

The limit theorems make it easy to find the limit of almost any function.

Example 4   **Use the limit theorems to evaluate** $\lim\limits_{x \to -1} \dfrac{\sqrt[3]{x^2 + 6x - 22}}{\sqrt{10x^4 - 1}}$.

$$\lim_{x \to -1} \frac{\sqrt[3]{x^2 + 6x - 22}}{\sqrt{10x^4 - 1}} = \frac{\lim\limits_{x \to -1} \sqrt[3]{x^2 + 6x - 22}}{\lim\limits_{x \to -1} \sqrt{10x^4 - 1}} \qquad \textit{Theorem 5}$$

$$= \frac{\sqrt[3]{\lim\limits_{x \to -1}(x^2 + 6x - 22)}}{\sqrt{\lim\limits_{x \to -1}(10x^4 - 1)}} \qquad \textit{Theorem 8}$$

$$= \frac{\sqrt[3]{-27}}{\sqrt{9}} \text{ or } -1$$

Recall that if $f(x)$ and $g(x)$ are two functions of x, the composite of f and g is defined to be $f(g(x))$. For example, if $f(x) = x^2$ and $g(x) = x + 2$, $f(g(x)) = f(x + 2)$ or $(x + 2)^2$. In general, composition of functions is *not* a commutative operation. In other words, the value of $f(g(x))$ is usually not the same as $g(f(x))$.

Theorem 9

Given functions $f(x)$ and $g(x)$, $\lim\limits_{x \to a} g(x) = G$, f is continuous at $x = G$, and any real number a, the limit of the composite of functions $f(x)$ and $g(x)$ is as follows.

$$\lim_{x \to a} f[g(x)] = f\left(\lim_{x \to a} g(x)\right) = f(G)$$

Example 5   **Evaluate** $\lim\limits_{x \to 4} f[g(x)]$ **if** $f(x) = x^2$ **and** $g(x) = 6 - x$.

$$\lim_{x \to 4} f[g(x)] = f\left[\lim_{x \to 4} g(x)\right]$$

$$= f\left[\lim_{x \to 4}(6 - x)\right]$$

$$= f(2)$$

$$= 2^2 \text{ or } 4 \qquad f(x) = x^2$$

You can also evaluate limits of trigonometric functions.

Theorem 10

$$\lim_{x \to 0} \frac{\sin x}{x} = 1, \text{ where } x \text{ is the radian measure of an angle.}$$

Theorem 10 can be demonstrated as follows. Suppose $0 < x < \frac{\pi}{2}$. Arc AB is part of a circle with center O and radius of 1 unit. As x approaches 0, the length of $\overline{AD}$ approaches the length of $\widehat{AB}$. Thus, $\dfrac{AD}{\text{measure of } \widehat{AB}}$ approaches 1 as x approaches 0. But, $AD = \sin x$ and the measure of $\widehat{AB} = x$, so $\lim\limits_{x \to 0} \dfrac{\sin x}{x} = 1$.

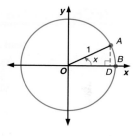

Example 6

Evaluate $\lim\limits_{x \to 0} \dfrac{\sin 2x}{x}$.

$\lim\limits_{x \to 0} \dfrac{\sin 2x}{x} = \lim\limits_{x \to 0} \dfrac{2 \cdot \sin 2x}{2x}$ *Multiply the numerator and denominator by 2.*

$\qquad\qquad = 2 \cdot \lim\limits_{x \to 0} \dfrac{\sin 2x}{2x}$ *Theorem 6*

Let $y = 2x$. Then $\lim\limits_{x \to 0} \dfrac{\sin 2x}{2x} = \lim\limits_{y \to 0} \dfrac{\sin y}{y}$ because as x approaches 0, y also approaches 0.

Since $\lim\limits_{y \to 0} \dfrac{\sin y}{y} = 1, \lim\limits_{x \to 0} \dfrac{\sin 2x}{2x} = 1$.

Then $2 \cdot \lim\limits_{x \to 0} \dfrac{\sin 2x}{2x} = 2 \cdot 1$ or 2.

EXPLORATION: Graphing Calculator

A graphing calculator can be helpful when you are evaluating the limit of a function. You can graph the function and use the TRACE function to estimate the value of the limit.   1. $\lim\limits_{x \to 0} \dfrac{\cos x - 1}{x} = 0$

1. Use Theorem 10 to evaluate $\lim\limits_{x \to 0} \dfrac{\cos x - 1}{x}$.

2. Graph $y = \dfrac{\cos x - 1}{x}$ on a graphing calculator.

3. Use the TRACE function to estimate the value of $\lim\limits_{x \to 0} \dfrac{\cos x - 1}{x}$. Does the estimate support the conclusion you made using Theorem 10?   yes

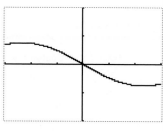

Using Technology

Just as in Example 6, the function in the Exploration, $y = \dfrac{\cos x - 1}{x}$, is undefined at $x = 0$, so there will be no point on the graph having 0 as its x-coordinate. Students need to check the y-values for x-values near 0.

Checking for Understanding

Exercises 1–19 are designed to help you assess students' understanding through reading, writing, speaking, and modeling. You should work through Exercises 1–6 with your students and then monitor their work on Exercises 7–19.

Closing the Lesson

Modeling Activity Have students think of everyday uses of the word "limit" and compare and contrast them to the mathematical concept of limit.

Communicating Mathematics

Read and study the lesson to answer each question. 4–6. See margin.

1. **Define** the limit of a function. See margin.

2. **Sketch** the graph of $y = \dfrac{x^2 - 16}{x - 4}$. Does the graph confirm that $\lim\limits_{x \to 4} \dfrac{x^2 - 16}{x - 4} = 8$? yes

3. **Explain** the steps you follow to find $\lim\limits_{x \to s} f(x)$. See margin.

4. A student in your class says, "The limit of the sum of two functions is the sum of the limits of the functions." When is the statement *not* correct?

5. **Show** that $\lim\limits_{x \to 0} x^2 = 0$ by using the fact that $x \cdot x = x^2$.

6. **Express** $\lim\limits_{x \to 3} (x - 1)^3$ in two different ways.

Guided Practice

Evaluate each limit.

7. $\lim\limits_{x \to 2} 6x$ 12

8. $\lim\limits_{x \to 3} (x^2 + 4x - 5)$ 16

9. $\lim\limits_{x \to 1} \dfrac{x - 2}{x + 2}$ $-\dfrac{1}{3}$

10. $\lim\limits_{x \to 5} \sqrt{25 - x^2}$ 0

11. $\lim\limits_{x \to 3} \dfrac{x - 4}{x + 1}$ $-\dfrac{1}{4}$

12. $\lim\limits_{x \to -2} \dfrac{x^2 - 4}{x^2 + 4}$ 0

13. $\lim\limits_{x \to 3} \dfrac{x^2 - x - 6}{x - 3}$ 5

14. $\lim\limits_{x \to 0} \dfrac{2x^3}{x}$ 0

15. $\lim\limits_{x \to -1} \dfrac{x^2 + 3x + 2}{x^2 + 4x + 3}$ $\dfrac{1}{2}$

Evaluate the limit of $f(g(x))$ as x approaches 0 for each $f(x)$ and $g(x)$.

16. $f(x) = 4x - 4$
    $g(x) = 8x + 1$ 0

17. $f(x) = 5x + 2$
    $g(x) = x^2 - 1$ -3

Use Theorem 10 to evaluate each limit.

18. $\lim\limits_{x \to 0} \dfrac{\sin^2 x}{x}$ 0

19. $\lim\limits_{x \to 0} \dfrac{\sin 3x}{5x}$ $\dfrac{3}{5}$

APPLYING THE LESSON

Homework Exercises

Assignment Guide

Average: 20–34, 38–42 even, 47–49, 52–61
Enriched: 31–46, 48–61

The red A, B, and C flags, printed only in the Teacher's Wraparound Edition, indicate the level of difficulty of the exercises.

Practice Masters Booklet, p. 114

EXERCISES

Practice

Evaluate each limit.

A

20. $\lim\limits_{x \to 2} (x^2 - 4x + 1)$ -3

21. $\lim\limits_{x \to 0} (4x + 1)$ 1

22. $\lim\limits_{x \to 2} x^2$ 4

23. $\lim\limits_{x \to 1} \dfrac{x + 1}{x + 2}$ $\dfrac{2}{3}$

24. $\lim\limits_{x \to 6} (7x - 22)$ 20

25. $\lim\limits_{x \to 1} (x^2 + 4x + 3)$ 8

B

26. $\lim\limits_{n \to 0} \left(5^n + \dfrac{1}{5^n}\right)$ 2

27. $\lim\limits_{x \to 3} \dfrac{x^2 - 9}{x + 3}$ 0

RETEACHING THE LESSON

Let $f(x) = 3x + 4$, $g(x) = \sqrt{2x} + 1$, and $a = 4$. Have students write out the specific result of theorems 2 through 8 for this pair of functions.

28. $\lim\limits_{n\to 3}\dfrac{n^2-9}{n-3}$ 6

29. $\lim\limits_{x\to 2}\dfrac{x^2-4}{x^3-8}$ $\dfrac{1}{3}$

30. $\lim\limits_{x\to 4}\dfrac{x-4}{x^2-16}$ $\dfrac{1}{8}$

31. $\lim\limits_{x\to -2}(x^4-x^2+x-2)$ 8

32. $\lim\limits_{x\to 2}\dfrac{x^3-8}{x-2}$ 4

33. $\lim\limits_{x\to 2}\dfrac{x^2-x-2}{x^2-4}$ $\dfrac{3}{4}$

34. $\lim\limits_{x\to 0}\dfrac{(1+x)^2-1}{x}$ 2

35. $\lim\limits_{n\to 0}\dfrac{n^2}{n^4+1}$ 0

36. $\lim\limits_{x\to -1}\sqrt{x^2-1}$ 0

37. $\lim\limits_{x\to 1}\sqrt{\dfrac{2x+1}{2x-1}}$ $\sqrt{3}$

Evaluate the limit of $f[g(x)]$ as x approaches 1 for each $f(x)$ and $g(x)$.

38. $f(x)=2x+1$
$g(x)=x-3$ –3

39. $f(x)=7x-2$
$g(x)=9x+2$ 75

40. $f(x)=3x-4$
$g(x)=2x+5$ 17

41. $f(x)=x^2+3$
$g(x)=2x-1$ 4

Use Theorem 10 to evaluate each limit.

42. $\lim\limits_{x\to 0}\dfrac{\sin(-x)}{x}$ –1

43. $\lim\limits_{x\to 0}\dfrac{1-\cos x}{x^2}$ $\dfrac{1}{2}$

44. $\lim\limits_{x\to 0}\dfrac{\sin\sqrt[3]{x}}{\sqrt[3]{x}}$ 1

Graphing
Calculator

Evaluate each limit. Then use a graphing calculator to verify your answer.

45. $\lim\limits_{x\to \frac{1}{2}}\dfrac{6x-3}{x(1-2x)}$ –6

46. $\lim\limits_{x\to 0}\dfrac{\sin 6x}{x}$ 6

47. $\lim\limits_{x\to 4}\dfrac{\sqrt{x}-2}{4-x}$ $-\dfrac{1}{4}$

Critical
Thinking

48. A function is **bounded** if there is a real number M such that $|f(x)| < M$ for all x in the domain of $f(x)$. Suppose a certain function $f(x)$ is defined for all real numbers and is bounded. See margin.

   a. Do you think that $f(x)$ has a limit as x approaches infinity? If so, what could the value of that limit be? Explain.

   b. If $f(x)$ is strictly increasing, do you think that $f(x)$ has a limit as x approaches infinity? If so, what could the value of that limit be? Explain.

Applications
and Problem
Solving

49. Physics Refer to the application at the beginning of the lesson. The limit of the sum of the lengths of the pendulum swings as n approaches infinity is the distance the pendulum will travel before it comes to rest. Find that limit. 1

50. Chemistry Acetylcholine is a chemical that is released at automatic nerve endings to transmit nerve impulses. The chemical is formed in body tissue and one of its many functions is to slow the heart rate. It has been found that the effect of acetylcholine on a frog's heart is given by the formula $f(x)=\dfrac{x}{a+bx}$ for $0\le x\le 1$, where a and b are positive constants, x is the concentration of acetylcholine, and $f(x)$ is a measure of the degree of response. Find $\lim\limits_{x\to \frac{2}{3}}f(x)$ when $a=8$ and $b=6$. $\dfrac{1}{18}$

Using Technology

You may want your students to review the procedures presented in the Exploration on page 919 before attempting Exercises 45–47.

Additional Answers

1. The limit of a function is the value of the function as the variable approaches a given value.

3. Substitute s for x in $f(x)$. Then solve.

4. when the limit of one of the functions does not exist

5. $\lim\limits_{x\to 0} x^2 = \lim\limits_{x\to 0} x\cdot x$

$\qquad = \lim\limits_{x\to 0} x\cdot \lim\limits_{x\to 0} x$

$\qquad = 0\cdot 0$

$\qquad = 0$

6. $\lim\limits_{x\to 3}(x-1)^3 = \left[\lim\limits_{x\to 3}(x-1)\right]^3$

$\lim\limits_{x\to 3}(x-1)^3 = \left[\lim\limits_{x\to 3}(x-1)\right]\cdot$

$\left[\lim\limits_{x\to 3}(x-1)\right]\cdot\left[\lim\limits_{x\to 3}(x-1)\right]$

48a. The function may have a limit of any number L such that $|L| < M$.

48b. If $f(x)$ is strictly increasing, then the limit of the function is M.

Additional Answers

54. $\sin \theta = -\dfrac{2\sqrt{5}}{5}$, $\cos \theta = \dfrac{\sqrt{5}}{5}$,

$\tan \theta = -2$, $\sec \theta = \sqrt{5}$,

$\csc \theta = -\dfrac{\sqrt{5}}{2}$, $\cot \theta = -\dfrac{1}{2}$

60.

Enrichment Masters Booklet, p. 114

---

51. **Demographics** The population of a certain small city is predicted to be given by $P(t) = 30,000 + \dfrac{15,000}{(t+3)^2}$, t years from now. Determine the population in the long run. That is, find $\lim\limits_{t\to\infty} P(t)$. 30,000

Mixed Review

52. Solve the matrix equation $\begin{bmatrix} 5 & -3 \\ -1 & 0 \end{bmatrix} \cdot \begin{bmatrix} x \\ y \end{bmatrix} = \begin{bmatrix} 9 \\ -2 \end{bmatrix}$. **(Lesson 2-3)** $\left(2, \dfrac{1}{3}\right)$

53. $f'(x) = 8x - 8$

53. Find the derivative of the function $f(x) = 4x^2 - 8x + 9$. **(Lesson 3-6)**

54. Find the values of the six trigonometric functions of an angle in standard position if the point at $(2, -4)$ is on its terminal side. **(Lesson 5-3)** See margin.

55. $\dfrac{41\sqrt{10}}{20} \approx 6.48$

55. Find the distance between $P(8, -3)$ and the line $6x + 2y - 1 = 0$. **(Lesson 7-7)**

56. Evaluate $\left(6^{\frac{2}{3}}\right)^3$. **(Lesson 11-1)** 36

57. Use the first five terms of the exponential series $e^x = 1 + x + \dfrac{x^2}{2!} + \dfrac{x^3}{3!} + \dfrac{x^4}{4!} + \cdots$ and a calculator to approximate $e^{3.3}$ to the nearest hundredth. **(Lesson 12-7)** 20.68

58. **Management** The Foxtrail Condominium Association is electing board members. How many groups of four board members can be chosen from the ten candidates who are running? **(Lesson 14-3)** 210

59. Find the mean, median, and mode of the set $\{7.3, 8.6, 5.4, 8.6, 8.9, 10.1, 6.4\}$. **(Lesson 15-2)** 7.9, 8.6, 8.6

60. For any graph $G(n, m)$ the matrix representing it, $M(G)$, is an $n \times m$ matrix. Draw a graph for which the matrix $\begin{bmatrix} 0 & 1 & 1 \\ 1 & 0 & 0 \\ 1 & 0 & 0 \end{bmatrix}$ is $M(G)$. **(Lesson 16-6)** See margin.

61. **College Entrance Exam** Choose the best answer. C
Triangle ABC has sides that are 6, 8, and 10 inches long. A rectangle that has area equal to that of the triangle has a width of 3 inches. Find the perimeter of the rectangle in inches.

(A) 30   (B) 24   (C) 22   (D) 16   (E) 11

922   CHAPTER 17   LIMITS, DERIVATIVES, AND INTEGRALS

EXTENDING THE LESSON

Math Power: Connections

What is meant by $\lim\limits_{x\to\infty} f(x)$?

Where have we seen this type of limit before? Can you name a function $f(x)$ such that $\lim\limits_{x\to\infty} f(x) = 0$?

$\lim\limits_{x\to\infty} f(x)$ is used to describe the end behavior of $f(x)$ as x approaches infinity. An example where $\lim\limits_{x\to\infty} f(x) = 0$ would be $f(x) = \dfrac{1}{x}$.

17-2 Derivatives and Differentiation Techniques

NCTM Standards: 1–4, 6, 13

Lesson Resources

- Practice Master 17–2
- Enrichment Master 17–2
- Evaluation Master, Quiz A, p. 117
- Technology Master, p. 34
- Activity Master, p. 50

 Transparency 17–2 contains the 5-Minute Check and a teaching aid for this lesson.

Objective 17–2	After studying this lesson, you should be able to:

■ find the derivative of a function.

Application

Howell Hosiery makes panty hose and stockings to be sold in department stores. The total cost function for Howell is $C(q) = -10,484.69 + 6.750q - 0.000328q^2$, where q is the number of dozens of pairs of stockings made and $C(q)$ is the cost in dollars. The marginal cost function indicates the rate at which the cost changes with respect to the number of units produced. Find the marginal cost function and evaluate it when $q = 4500$. *This problem will be solved in Example 4.*

Recall that in Chapter 3, a derivative was defined as the slope of the line tangent to a curve at a given point.

To solve this problem, we need to find the derivative of the function. The process of finding derivatives is called **differentiation**. A function is **differentiable** at a if the derivative of the function exists at a and is finite.

Recall from Chapter 3 that the definition of the derivative of a function $f(x)$ at $x = a$ is $f'(a) = \lim_{h \to 0} \frac{f(a+h) - f(a)}{h}$. The symbol h in the definition is often replaced with Δx, read "delta x", to show the change in x. Then, the difference quotient is $\frac{f(x + \Delta x) - f(x)}{\Delta x}$. But, $f(x + \Delta x) - f(x)$ can be denoted as Δy since it is actually the change in y. Thus, the derivative of $f(x)$ may be written with delta notation as follows.

$f'(x) = \frac{dy}{dx} = \lim_{\Delta x \to 0} \frac{\Delta y}{\Delta x}$

$$f'(x) = \lim_{\Delta x \to 0} \frac{f(x + \Delta x) - f(x)}{\Delta x} \text{ or } \lim_{\Delta x \to 0} \frac{\Delta y}{\Delta x}$$

$\frac{dy}{dx}$ *is the notation for a derivative. It is not a fraction.*

When the function is written in the form $y = f(x)$, the derivative is sometimes written as $\frac{dy}{dx}$. Thus, $\frac{dy}{dx} = \lim_{\Delta x \to 0} \frac{f(x + \Delta x) - f(x)}{\Delta x}$ or $\lim_{\Delta x \to 0} \frac{\Delta y}{\Delta x}$.

The notation $\frac{dy}{dx}$ is called **derivative notation** and is read "the derivative of y with respect to x."

Example 1

If $y = 5x^2 + 1$, find $\frac{dy}{dx}$ at $x = 3$.

First, find $\frac{\Delta y}{\Delta x}$.

$\frac{\Delta y}{\Delta x} = \frac{f(x + \Delta x) - f(x)}{\Delta x}$

$= \frac{[5(x + \Delta x)^2 + 1] - (5x^2 + 1)}{\Delta x}$

(continued on the next page)

INTRODUCING THE LESSON

5-Minute Check

(over Lesson 17–1)

Evaluate each limit.

1. $\lim_{x \to 4} (2x^2 - 4x - 1)$ 15

2. $\lim_{x \to -3} \frac{x^2 + 4x + 3}{x^2 - 9}$ $\frac{1}{3}$

3. $\lim_{x \to 0} \frac{(x-2)^2 - 4}{x}$ −4

4. $\lim_{x \to 0} \frac{\sin 3x}{4x}$ $\frac{3}{4}$

5. Evaluate the limit of $f[g(x)]$ as x approaches 2 for $f(x) = 3 - x^2$ and $g(x) = \sqrt{x + 2}$.   −1

Motivating the Lesson

In Chapter 3, we used the derivative as a tool for graphing functions. Derivatives help in locating critical points and the intervals where a function is increasing or decreasing. This lesson will extend our knowledge of derivatives to include a broader class of functions we can differentiate and a broader range of questions that we can use derivatives to answer.

ALTERNATE TEACHING STRATEGIES

Using Critical Thinking

Let $f(x) = \frac{3x^2 - 6}{x^3 + 4x}$. Have the students find $f'(x)$, first using the quotient rule and then using the product rule. Ask students which method seems easier, and why.

Using Communication

Have students form small groups and assign each group one of the theorems 11 through 16. Have students practice using their theorem, and then present it to the class along with a demonstration of its use in finding the derivative of an appropriate function.

Teaching Tip   Since $f'(x)$ is the slope of the tangent line to the graph of $f(x)$ at $x = a$, if $f(x)$ is a constant function or other non-vertical line, the value of the derivative at each point is the same as the slope of the line.

$$= \frac{5(x^2 + 2x\Delta x + \Delta x^2) + 1 - 5x^2 - 1}{\Delta x}$$

$$= \frac{10x\Delta x + 5\Delta x^2}{\Delta x}$$

$$= 10x + 5\Delta x$$

Then, find $\frac{dy}{dx}$.

$$\frac{dy}{dx} = \lim_{\Delta x \to 0} \frac{\Delta y}{\Delta x}$$

$$= \lim_{\Delta x \to 0} (10x + 5\Delta x)$$

$$= 10x$$

Thus, $\frac{dy}{dx}$ is $10(3)$ or 30 at $x = 3$.

The slope of the line tangent to the graph of $y = 5x^2 + 1$ at $x = 3$ is 30.

As you can see from Example 1, the process of finding the derivative of a function by setting up a difference quotient and then finding its limit can be rather involved. To shorten this process, formulas can be used to find derivatives of functions. You learned some of these formulas when you studied the tangents of a curve in Chapter 3.

Consider the function $f(x) = c$, where c is a constant.

$$f'(x) = \lim_{h \to 0} \frac{f(x+h) - f(x)}{h}$$

$$= \lim_{h \to 0} \frac{c - c}{h} \text{ or } 0$$

Thus, the derivative of a constant function, $f(x) = c$, is zero. For example, if $f(x) = 6$, then $f'(x) = 0$.

One of the most important differentiation formulas is the power formula.

Theorem 11 *Power Formula*	If $f(x) = cx^n$, where n is a real number and c is a constant, then $f'(x) = cnx^{n-1}$.

Example 2

Find the derivative of each function.
a. $f(x) = x^4$ b. $f(x) = 4x^6 - 4$

a. $f(x) = x^4$
   $f'(x) = 4x^{4-1}$ or $4x^3$

b. $f(x) = 4x^6 - 4$
   $f'(x) = 4 \cdot 6x^{6-1} - 0$
   $\qquad = 24x^5$

The notation $\frac{dy}{dx}$ is used in the statement of the following theorem. This notation can be used with other functions of x. For example, $\frac{du}{dx}$ is the derivative of u with respect to x.

Theorem 12	If $u = f(x)$ and $v = g(x)$ are differentiable functions of x, then $$\frac{d(u+v)}{dx} = \frac{du}{dx} + \frac{dv}{dx}.$$

Example 3

Find the derivative of $f(x) = x^4 + (x^2 - 3)$.

Use $\dfrac{d(u+v)}{dx} = \dfrac{du}{dx} + \dfrac{dv}{dx}$.

$$\frac{d}{dx}[x^4 + (x^2 - 3)] = \frac{d}{dx}x^4 + \frac{d}{dx}(x^2 - 3) \qquad u = x^4 \text{ and } v = x^2 - 3$$
$$= (4x^3) + (2x - 0)$$
$$= 4x^3 + 2x$$

The derivative of a function can be thought of as the rate of change of the function when $x = a$. In business, the derivative is found in order to determine the rate of change of a company's cost or revenue. Suppose the equation $y = f(x)$ denotes the total cost or total revenue of a company when x units are produced or sold. Then the rate at which the cost or revenue changes with respect to the number of units produced or sold is $\frac{dy}{dx}$, called the **marginal cost function** or **marginal revenue function**.

Example 4

APPLICATION

Business

Refer to the application at the beginning of the lesson. Find the marginal cost function and evaluate it for $q = 4500$.

The total cost function is $C(q)$. To find the marginal cost function, we must find the derivative of the total cost function. Use Theorem 12.

$$\frac{d}{dq}C(q) = \frac{d}{dq}(-10{,}484.69 + 6.750q - 0.000328q^2)$$
$$= \frac{d}{dq}(-10{,}484.69) + \frac{d}{dq}(6.750q) - \frac{d}{dq}(0.000328q^2)$$
$$= 0 + 6.750 - 0.000656q$$
$$= 6.750 - 0.000656q$$

The marginal cost function is $\frac{dC(q)}{dq} = 6.750 - 0.000656q$. When $q = 4500$, the marginal cost is $6.750 - 0.000656(4500)$ or 3.798. This means that when production is at 4500 dozens of pairs, making an additional dozen will cost \$3.798.

FYI...

Modern panty hose and stockings are made of nylon, a man-made fiber invented by DuPont chemist Wallace Carothers in 1935. The chemicals used to make nylon come from petroleum, natural gas, and agricultural byproducts.

Theorem 13	If $u = f(x)$ is a differentiable function of x and c is a constant, then $$\frac{d(cu)}{dx} = c\frac{du}{dx}.$$

LESSON 17-2 DERIVATIVES AND DIFFERENTIATION TECHNIQUES 925

Teaching Tip Theorem 15 is a special case of the chain rule, one of the most important differentiation rules. It may help students to refer to this theorem as the chain rule. Having a special name for it should help to remind them to apply it every time they differentiate a power function.

Example 5 | **Find the derivative of $f(x) = 5(x^2 + 5x - 4)$.**

Use $\dfrac{d(cu)}{dx} = c\dfrac{du}{dx}$.

$\dfrac{d}{dx}[5(x^2 + 5x - 4)] = 5\dfrac{d}{dx}(x^2 + 5x - 4)$ $\qquad c = 5$ and $u = x^2 + 5x - 4$

$= 5(2x + 5)$

$= 10x + 25$

The formulas for the derivatives of the sum of two functions and for a multiple of a function were relatively simple. The formula for the derivative of the product of two functions is more complicated.

Theorem 14
Product Rule

If $u = f(x)$ and $v = g(x)$ are differentiable functions of x, then
$$\dfrac{d(uv)}{dx} = u\dfrac{dv}{dx} + v\dfrac{du}{dx}.$$

Example 6 | **Find the derivative of $f(x) = (x^4 + 7x)(x^5)$.**

Use $\dfrac{d(uv)}{dx} = u\dfrac{dv}{dx} + v\dfrac{du}{dx}$. $\qquad$ *You could also find the product before differentiating.*

$\dfrac{d}{dx}[(x^4 + 7x)(x^5)] = (x^4 + 7x)\dfrac{d}{dx}x^5 + x^5\dfrac{d}{dx}(x^4 + 7x)$ $\qquad u = x^4 + 7x$ and $v = x^5$

$= (x^4 + 7x)(5x^4) + (x^5)(4x^3 + 7)$

$= 5x^8 + 35x^5 + 4x^8 + 7x^5$

$= 9x^8 + 42x^5$

Theorem 15

If $u = f(x)$ is a differentiable function of x and n is a nonzero rational number, then $\dfrac{d(u^n)}{dx} = nu^{n-1}\dfrac{du}{dx}$.

Example 7 | **Find the derivative of each function.**

a. $f(x) = \sqrt{x^2 + 2x - 1}$

a. Use $\dfrac{d(u^n)}{dx} = nu^{n-1}\dfrac{du}{dx}$. Remember, $\sqrt{x^2 + 2x - 1} = (x^2 + 2x - 1)^{\frac{1}{2}}$.

$\dfrac{d}{dx}(\sqrt{x^2 + 2x - 1}) = \dfrac{1}{2}(x^2 + 2x - 1)^{-\frac{1}{2}}(2x + 2)$ $\qquad u = x^2 + 2x - 1$ and $n = \dfrac{1}{2}$

$= \dfrac{2x + 2}{2\sqrt{x^2 + 2x - 1}}$

$= \dfrac{2(x + 1)}{2\sqrt{x^2 + 2x - 1}}$

$= \dfrac{x + 1}{\sqrt{x^2 + 2x - 1}}$

b. $f(x) = x^3(x^2 - 3)^{-4}$

b. Use $\dfrac{d(uv)}{dx} = u\dfrac{dv}{dx} + v\dfrac{du}{dx}$ and $\dfrac{d(u^n)}{dx} = nu^{n-1}\dfrac{du}{dx}$.

$$\frac{d}{dx}[x^3(x^2-3)^{-4}] = x^3\frac{d}{dx}[(x^2-3)^{-4}] + [(x^2-3)^{-4}]\frac{d}{dx}(x^3)$$

$$u = x^3,$$
$$v = (x^2-3)^{-4}$$

$$= x^3[-4(x^2-3)^{-5}(2x)] + [(x^2-3)^{-4}](3x^2)$$

$$\frac{du}{dx} = 3x^2,$$

$$= -8x^4(x^2-3)^{-5} + 3x^2(x^2-3)^{-4}$$

$$\frac{dv}{dx} = -4(x^2-3)^{-5}(2x)$$

$$= \frac{-8x^4}{(x^2-3)^5} + \frac{3x^2}{(x^2-3)^4}$$

$$= \frac{-8x^4 + 3x^2(x^2-3)}{(x^2-3)^5}$$

$$= \frac{-5x^4 - 9x^2}{(x^2-3)^5}$$

Theorem 16
Quotient Rule

If $u = f(x)$ and $v = g(x)$ are differentiable functions of x at a point where $v \neq 0$, then $\dfrac{d\left(\frac{u}{v}\right)}{dx} = \dfrac{v\frac{du}{dx} - u\frac{dv}{dx}}{v^2}$.

Example 8

Find the derivative of each function.

a. $f(x) = \dfrac{4x^2 - 2x + 3}{2x - 1}$

a. Use $\dfrac{d\left(\frac{u}{v}\right)}{dx} = \dfrac{v\frac{du}{dx} - u\frac{dv}{dx}}{v^2}$. Let $u = 4x^2 - 2x + 3$ and $v = 2x - 1$. Then $\dfrac{du}{dx} = 8x - 2$ and $\dfrac{dv}{dx} = 2$.

$$\frac{d}{dx}\left(\frac{4x^2 - 2x + 3}{2x - 1}\right) = \frac{(2x-1)(8x-2) - (4x^2 - 2x + 3)(2)}{(2x-1)^2}$$

$$= \frac{(16x^2 - 12x + 2) - (8x^2 - 4x + 6)}{4x^2 - 4x + 1}$$

$$= \frac{8x^2 - 8x - 4}{4x^2 - 4x + 1}$$

b. $f(x) = \dfrac{(x+1)^2}{(x-1)^2}$

b. Use Theorems 15 and 16. Let $u = (x+1)^2$ and $v = (x-1)^2$. Then $\dfrac{du}{dx} = 2(x+1)(1)$ and $\dfrac{dv}{dx} = 2(x-1)(1)$.

(continued on the next page)

LESSON 17-2   DERIVATIVES AND DIFFERENTIATION TECHNIQUES   927

Teaching Tip   Some students may find the product rule and quotient rule easier to learn in the forms $\dfrac{d(uv)}{dx} = uv' + u'v$

and $\dfrac{d\left(\frac{u}{v}\right)}{dx} = \dfrac{vu' - uv'}{v^2}$.

Chalkboard Example

For Example 8

Find the derivative of each function.

a. $f(x) = \dfrac{2x - 1}{\sqrt{x + 1}}$ $\dfrac{2x + 5}{2(x+1)^{\frac{3}{2}}}$

b. $f(x) = \dfrac{x^2 - 1}{(x-2)^2}$ $\dfrac{2 - 4x}{(x-2)^3}$

$$\frac{d}{dx}\frac{(x+1)^2}{(x-1)^2} = \frac{(x-1)^2(2)(x+1) - (x+1)^2(2)(x-1)}{(x-1)^4}$$

$$= \frac{(x^2-2x+1)(2x+2) - (x^2+2x+1)(2x-2)}{(x-1)^4}$$

$$= \frac{-4(x^2-1)}{(x-1)^4} \text{ or } \frac{-4(x+1)}{(x-1)^3} \qquad x^2-1 = (x+1)(x-1)$$

Checking for Understanding

Exercises 1–19 are designed to help you assess students' understanding through reading, writing, speaking, and modeling. You should work through Exercises 1–5 with your students and then monitor their work on Exercises 6–19.

Closing the Lesson

Writing Activity Have students explain what the quotient $\frac{\Delta y}{\Delta x}$ is and how it is related to the derivative.

APPLYING THE LESSON

Homework Exercises

Assignment Guide

Average: 20–37, 43, 44, 48–56
Enriched: 27–56

The red A, B, and C flags, printed only in the Teacher's Wraparound Edition, indicate the level of difficulty of the exercises.

Chapter 17, Quiz A, (Lessons 17–1 through 17–2), is available in the *Evaluation Masters*, p. 117.

Practice Masters Booklet, p. 115

CHECKING FOR UNDERSTANDING

Communicating Mathematics

Read and study the lesson to answer each question. 1–5. See margin.

1. **Explain** how the formula $\frac{f(a+h)-f(a)}{h}$ is related to the tangent line of a function at a point $(a, f(a))$.

2. Write three different expressions for the derivative of $y = f(x)$.

3. **Explain** the product rule for differentiation in your own words.

4. Find the derivative of $x^4(3x^5 - 2x^3)$ using two different methods.

5. What does the symbol $\frac{du}{dx}$ represent?

Guided Practice

Find the derivative of each function.

6. $f(x) = 2x$ 2
7. $f(x) = 7x - 3$ 7
8. $f(x) = -x$ -1
9. $f(x) = 2x^2$ 4x
10. $f(x) = x^3$ $3x^2$
11. $f(x) = 6x^2$ 12x

13. $18x^2 - 26x - 5$

12. $f(x) = (2x-3)(x+5)$ 4x + 7
13. $f(x) = (3x+1)(2x^2 - 5x)$

15. $\frac{-2x(2x^2-1)}{(x^2+1)^4}$

14. $f(x) = (x - 2x^2)^2$ $2x(2x-1)(4x-1)$
15. $f(x) = x^2(x^2+1)^{-3}$

16. $\frac{4x}{\sqrt{4x^2-1}}$

16. $f(x) = \sqrt{4x^2 - 1}$
17. $f(x) = \frac{2x+3}{4x-1}$ $-\frac{14}{(4x-1)^2}$

18. $f(x) = \frac{x^3-1}{x^4+1}$ $-\frac{x^2(x^4-4x-3)}{(x^4+1)^2}$
19. $f(x) = -3x - \frac{6}{x+2}$ $-3 + \frac{6}{(x+2)^2}$

EXERCISES

Practice

Find the derivative of each function. 26–42. See margin.

A

20. $f(x) = x$ 1
21. $f(x) = 6x - 4$ 6
22. $f(x) = -4x - 2$ -4

23. $10x - 1$
24. $4x^3 - 4x$

23. $f(x) = 5x^2 - x$
24. $f(x) = x^4 - 2x^2$
25. $f(x) = x^5 + 3$ $5x^4$

26. $f(x) = x^{\frac{1}{2}}$
27. $f(x) = \sqrt[3]{x}$
28. $f(x) = x^2(x^2 - 3)$

B

29. $f(x) = (x^3 - 2x)(3x^2)$
30. $f(x) = 8x^4(1 - 9x^2)$

31. $f(x) = (x^2 + 4)^3$
32. $f(x) = (x^3 - 2x + 1)^4$

33. $f(x) = \sqrt{x^2 - 1}$
34. $f(x) = x^2(x+1)^{-1}$

35. $f(x) = (x^2 - 4)^{-\frac{1}{2}}$
36. $f(x) = \frac{x+1}{x^2-4}$

C

37. $f(x) = \left(\frac{x+1}{x-1}\right)^2$
38. $f(x) = x\sqrt{1 - x^3}$

RETEACHING THE LESSON

The product and quotient rules for differentiation are somewhat complicated. Have students work some examples of each, explicitly writing out $f(x) = u \cdot v$ (or $\frac{u}{v}$), filling out a chart with the headings:

$u =$	$\frac{du}{dx} =$	$v =$	$\frac{dv}{dx} =$

and then applying the appropriate formula for the derivative of $f(x)$.

Additional Answers

1. The limit of $\frac{f(a+h)-f(a)}{h}$ as h approaches 0 is the slope of the tangent through $(a, f(a))$.

2. $f'(x), \frac{dy}{dx}, \lim_{\Delta x \to 0} \frac{\Delta y}{\Delta x}$

3. See students' work.

---

39. $f(x) = 2x^3 + \dfrac{2}{x^3}$

40. $f(x) = \sqrt{2x} - \sqrt{2}x$

41. $f(x) = \left(1 + \dfrac{1}{x}\right)\left(2 - \dfrac{1}{x}\right)$

42. $f(x) = 3x - \dfrac{\frac{2}{x} - \frac{3}{x-1}}{x-2}$

Critical Thinking

43. Suppose $v = f(x)$ is a differentiable function such that $v \neq 0$. Derive a formula

for $\dfrac{d\left(\frac{1}{v}\right)}{dx}$. $-\dfrac{\frac{dv}{dx}}{v^2}$

Applications and Problem Solving

44. Business The total cost function for an electric company is estimated to be $C(t) = 32.07 - 0.79t + 0.02142t^2 - 0.0001t^3$, where t is the total output and $C(t)$ is total fuel cost in dollars.

  a. Find the marginal cost function. $C'(t) = -0.79 + 0.04284t - 0.0003t^2$

  b. Evaluate the marginal cost function when $t = 70$. 0.7388

  c. If possible, find the number of units produced when the marginal cost is 0.6. 50 or 93

45. Physics Suppose a ball has been shot upward with an initial velocity of 96 feet per second. Then the equation $h(t) = 256 + 96t - 16t^2$ gives the height of the ball in feet after t seconds.

  a. The derivative of the function for the height of the ball gives the rate of change of the height, or the velocity of the ball. Find the velocity function. $h'(t) = 96 - 32t$

  b. Find the velocity of the ball after 2 seconds. 32 ft/s

  c. Is the velocity increasing or decreasing? decreasing

  d. What is the velocity of the ball when it hits the ground? −160 ft/s

46. Economics The consumption function expresses the relationship between the national income, I, and the national consumption, $C(I)$. The marginal propensity to consume, $\dfrac{dC}{dI}$, is the rate of change of consumption with respect to income. For a certain period of time, the consumption function for the United States was $C(I) = \dfrac{5(2\sqrt{I^3} + 3)}{I + 10}$, where C and I are measured in billions of dollars.

  a. Write a formula for the marginal propensity to consume for this time. See margin.

  b. What was the marginal propensity to consume at this time if the national income was 100 billion dollars? ≈ 0.536

  c. The marginal propensity to save, $\dfrac{dS}{dI}$, indicates how fast savings change with respect to income. The formula for the marginal propensity to save is $1 - \dfrac{dC}{dI}$. What was the marginal propensity to save for the given consumption function if the national income was 150 billion dollars? 0.570

LESSON 17-2 DERIVATIVES AND DIFFERENTIATION TECHNIQUES 929

Exercise Note

The derivation of the formula in Exercise 43 is as follows.

Use $= \dfrac{d\left(\frac{u}{v}\right)}{dx} = \dfrac{v\frac{du}{dx} - u\frac{dv}{dx}}{v^2}$ for $u = 1$. Then $\dfrac{du}{dx} = 0$.

$\dfrac{d\left(\frac{u}{v}\right)}{dx} = \dfrac{v\frac{du}{dx} - u\frac{dv}{dx}}{v^2} = \dfrac{v(0) - (1)\frac{dv}{dx}}{v^2} = \dfrac{-\frac{dv}{dx}}{v^2}$

Additional Answers

4. Answers may vary. A sample answer is given.

Use $\dfrac{d(uv)}{dx} = u\dfrac{dv}{dx} + v\dfrac{du}{dx}$.

$\dfrac{d(x^4(3x^5 - 2x^3))}{dx}$,

$= x^4(15x^4 - 6x^2) + (3x^5 - 2x^3)(4x^3)$
$= (15x^8 - 6x^6) + (12x^8 - 8x^6)$
$= 27x^8 - 14x^6$

Simplify the expression first.

$x^4(3x^5 - 2x^3) = 3x^9 - 2x^7$

$\dfrac{d(3x^9 - 2x^7)}{dx}$

$= 9(3x^{9-1}) - 7(2x^{7-1})$
$= 27x^8 - 14x^6$

5. The derivative of expression u with respect to x.

26. $\dfrac{1}{2\sqrt{x}}$

27. $\dfrac{1}{3\sqrt[3]{x^2}}$

28. $4x^3 - 6x$

29. $15x^4 - 18x^2$

30. $32x^3 - 432x^5$

31. $6x(x^2 + 4)^2$

32. $(12x^2 - 8)(x^3 - 2x + 1)^3$

33. $\dfrac{x}{\sqrt{x^2 - 1}}$

34. $\dfrac{x^2 + 2x}{(x + 1)^2}$

35. $\dfrac{-x}{\sqrt{(x^2 - 4)^3}}$

36. $\dfrac{-x^2 - 2x - 4}{(x^2 - 4)^2}$

37. $\dfrac{-4(x + 1)}{(x - 1)^3}$

38. $\dfrac{-3x^3}{2\sqrt{1 - x^3}} + \sqrt{1 - x^3}$

39. $6x^2 - \dfrac{6}{x^4}$

40. $\dfrac{1}{\sqrt{2x}} - \sqrt{2}$

41. $-\dfrac{1}{x^2} + \dfrac{2}{x^3}$

42. $3 - \dfrac{2x^3 + 3x^2 - 12x + 4}{[x(x - 1)(x - 2)]^2}$

46a. $\dfrac{dC}{dI} =$

$\dfrac{(I + 10)(15\sqrt{I}) - 5(2\sqrt{I^3} + 3)}{(I + 10)^2}$

LESSON 17–2 DERIVATIVES AND DIFFERENTIATION TECHNIQUES 929

47. **Research** The notation for a derivative $\frac{dy}{dx}$ is often called *Leibniz notation* after German mathematician Gottfried Wilhelm Leibniz. Some claim that Leibniz was the inventor of calculus, while others credit Isaac Newton with the invention. Research the controversy and its effects on the development of mathematics. Write a one-page paper on your findings. See students' work.

Mixed Review

48. **Geometry** Determine whether the figure with vertices at $(0, 3), (8, 4), (2, -5),$ and $(10, -4)$ is a parallelogram. **(Lesson 1-4)** yes

49. $\pm 1, \pm 2,$ $\pm \frac{1}{2}, \pm \frac{1}{4}, \pm \frac{1}{8}$

49. List all possible rational roots of the function $f(x) = 8x^3 + 3x - 2$. **(Lesson 4-4)**

50. Use Hero's formula to find the area of $\triangle ABC$ if $a = 2.1, b = 3.2,$ and $c = 4.4$. Round your answer to the nearest tenth. **(Lesson 5-8)** 3.1 units^2

51. Sample answer: $y = 12 \sin \frac{\pi t}{2}$

51. Write an equation with phase shift 0 to represent simple harmonic motion if the initial position is 0, the amplitude is 12, and the period is 4. **(Lesson 6-7)**

52. Find the quotient of $16\left(\cos \frac{\pi}{8} + i \sin \frac{\pi}{8}\right)$ divided by $4\left(\cos \frac{\pi}{4} + i \sin \frac{\pi}{4}\right)$. **(Lesson 9-7)** $4\left(\cos \frac{15\pi}{8} + i \sin \frac{15\pi}{8}\right)$

53. The first term of a geometric sequence is 9, and the common ratio is $-\frac{1}{3}$. Find the sixth term of the sequence. **(Lesson 12-2)** $-\frac{1}{27}$

54. Shawn guessed on all of the five multiple choice questions on a quiz. If there were four choices for each question, what is the probability that he got all five questions correct? **(Lesson 14-8)** $\frac{1}{1024}$

55. Evaluate $\lim\limits_{x \to -1} \sqrt{x^2 - 1}$. **(Lesson 17-1)** 0

56. **College Entrance Exam** If $2^n = 8$, what is the value of 3^{n+2}? 243

CASE STUDY FOLLOW-UP

Refer to Case Study 4, *The U.S. Economy*, on pages 966–969.

To approximate unemployment figures for the years 1980–1985, an economist used the function $f(x) = -0.42x^2 + 2.1x + 7.2$, where x is the number of years since 1980 and $f(x)$ is the percent of Americans unemployed. 1–2. See margin.

1. How well does the function approximate the unemployment curve?
2. The derivative of a function is the rate of change of a function $f(x)$ when $x = a$. Find the derivative of the function used to describe the unemployment curve.
3. Find the rate of change of the unemployment rate for the year 1982. Explain what the rate of change means. 0.42; The unemployment rate is growing.
4. **Research** Use an economics text to find one aspect of the economy that can be analyzed by using calculus. Write about your findings in a 1-page paper.

4. See students' work.

930 CHAPTER 17 LIMITS, DERIVATIVES, AND INTEGRALS

EXTENDING THE LESSON

Math Power: Reasoning

Differentiate the function $f(x) = \frac{1}{x}$ and then go on to differentiate each successive derivative up to the fifth derivative. Observe the pattern. Can you find a formula for the nth derivative of $f(x)$?

$-\frac{1}{x^2}, \frac{2}{x^3}, -\frac{6}{x^4}, \frac{24}{x^5}, \ldots; \frac{(-1)^n n!}{x^{n+1}}$

Case Study Follow-Up

This activity provides an opportunity to do research and apply mathematics in solving problems related to issues that may face students in their adult lives. Case Study 4 is located on pages 966–969.

17-3 Area Under a Curve

Objective
17-3

After studying this lesson, you should be able to:
- find the area between a curve and the x-axis by using the limit of areas of rectangles.

Application

Traci is stopped at the traffic light at High Street and Wilson-Bridge Road. When the light turns green, Traci accelerates for the first 8 seconds. The velocity of the car in feet per second can be described by the equation $v(t) = 16t - t^2$, where t is time in seconds. How far will Traci's car travel in 8 seconds? *This problem will be solved in Example 3.*

When $f(x)$ is a function in terms of x, it is often useful to be able to find the area of a region bounded by the graph of $f(x)$. Consider the area between the graph of a function $f(x)$ and the x-axis for an interval from $x = a$ to $x = b$. We don't know a formula for the area of a figure with a curved edge, but we can approximate the area by drawing rectangles. Suppose the interval from a to b is separated into n subintervals of equal width, and vertical lines are drawn at each subinterval to form rectangles, as shown below. The sum of the areas of the rectangles drawn under the curve, A_u, must be less than the area of the region. The sum of the areas of the rectangles drawn above the curve, A_o, must be greater than the area of the region. A_u and A_o are called the **lower** and **upper sums**, respectively.

The area of a rectangle is length times width. The length of each of these rectangles is f(x), and the width is $x_{i+1} - x_i$.

Rectangles under curve, A_u

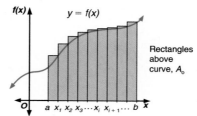

Rectangles above curve, A_o

area of 1st rectangle $= f(a)(x_1 - a)$
area of 2nd rectangle $= f(x_1)(x_2 - x_1)$
area of 3rd rectangle $= f(x_2)(x_3 - x_2)$
⋮
area of $(i + 1)$th rectangle
   $= f(x_i)(x_{i+1} - x_i)$
⋮
area of nth rectangle $= f(x_{n-1})(b - x_{n-1})$

A_u = *sum of areas of the rectangles*

area of 1st rectangle $= f(x_1)(x_1 - a)$
area of 2nd rectangle $= f(x_2)(x_2 - x_1)$
area of 3rd rectangle $= f(x_3)(x_3 - x_2)$
⋮
area of $(i + 1)$th rectangle
   $= f(x_{i+1})(x_{i+1} - x_i)$
⋮
area of nth rectangle $= f(b)(b - x_{n-1})$

A_o = *sum of areas of the rectangles*
$A_o = f(x_1)(x_1 - a) + f(x_2)(x_2 - x_1) +$
   $f(x_3)(x_3 - x_2) + \cdots +$
   $f(x_{i+1})(x_{i+1} - x_i) + \cdots +$
   $f(b)(b - x_{n-1})$

LESSON 17-3 AREA UNDER A CURVE 931

NCTM Standards: 1–4, 6, 13

Lesson Resources

- Practice Master 17–3
- Enrichment Master 17–3
- Evaluation Master, Quiz B, p. 117

 Transparency 17–3 contains the 5-Minute Check and a teaching aid for this lesson.

INTRODUCING THE LESSON

 5-Minute Check

(over Lesson 17–2)

Find the derivative of each function.
1. $f(x) = 4x^2 - 6x + 1$ $8x - 6$
2. $f(x) = 4x^2 + 14 - \frac{1}{x^2}$ $8x + \frac{2}{x^3}$
3. $f(x) = \sqrt{3x^5 - 4x^2}$
   $\frac{15x^4 - 8x}{2\sqrt{3x^5 - 4x^2}}$
4. $f(x) = \frac{x^2}{x^2 + 1}$ $\frac{2x}{(x + 1)^2}$
5. $f(x) = (x - 1)^2(x^3 + 4x + 5)$
   $(x - 1)(5x^3 - 3x^2 + 12x + 6)$

Motivating the Lesson

If a car travels 60 feet per second for 8 seconds, how far has it gone? $d = rt$, so we multiply $60 \cdot 8$ and come up with 480 feet. But what if the car is accelerating or decelerating over those 8 seconds so that its speed is changing? Then we need to modify our method to find the distance traveled.

ALTERNATE TEACHING STRATEGIES

Using Cooperative Groups

Assign the class a problem like the following. Find the area under the curve $y = 2x^2$ from $x = 0$ to $x = 1$. Have students break up into small groups and assign each group a value of n; for example, $n = 8$, 10, and so on. Have each group find the sum A_a. List the values of n and A_a on the chalkboard and have students guess the value of the area.

Using Models

Have students graph $f(x) = 4 - x^2$ over the interval [0, 2]. Have students cut out this area, fold the paper accordion-style to partition it into 16 equal subintervals, and then cut it into 16 strips along the folds, and mark them according to what part would be included in the calculation of A_a. Then calculate both A_a and A itself.

Thus, the actual area, A, is between A_u and A_o. We can write this as $A_u \le A \le A_o$. As the number of subintervals, n, is increased, the areas A_u and A_o approach the actual area A. So, A is the limit of A_o as n increases without bound. The area A_o may be written using summation notation.

$$A_o = \sum_{i=1}^{n} f(x_i)(x_i - x_{i-1})$$

Area Under a Curve

The area A between the graph of $y = f(x)$ and the x-axis from $x = a$ to $x = b$ is as follows:

$$A = \lim_{n \to \infty} \sum_{i=1}^{n} f(x_i)(x_i - x_{i-1}),$$

where the width of each rectangle, $x_i - x_{i-1}$, approaches zero, $x_0 = a$, and $x_n = b$.

Example 1 **Find the area of the region between the graph of $y = x^3$ and the x-axis from $x = 0$ to $x = 1$.**

Form n equal intervals on the x-axis such that

$$0 < \frac{1}{n} < \frac{2}{n} < \frac{3}{n} < \cdots < \frac{i}{n} < \cdots < \frac{n-1}{n} < 1.$$

The area of each rectangle can be represented by

$f\left(\dfrac{i}{n}\right)(x_i - x_{i-1})$ or $\left(\dfrac{i}{n}\right)^3 \left(\dfrac{1}{n}\right).$ *Why is $(x_i - x_{i-1}) = \dfrac{1}{n}$?*

Use the definition of the area under a curve.

$$A = \lim_{n \to \infty} \sum_{i=1}^{n} f(x_i)(x_i - x_{i-1})$$

$$= \lim_{n \to \infty} \sum_{i=1}^{n} \left(\frac{i}{n}\right)^3 \left(\frac{1}{n}\right)$$

$$= \lim_{n \to \infty} \sum_{i=1}^{n} \left(\frac{1}{n}\right)^4 \cdot (i^3)$$

$$= \lim_{n \to \infty} \frac{1}{n^4}(1^3 + 2^3 + \cdots + n^3)$$

$$= \lim_{n \to \infty} \frac{1}{n^4} \cdot \left(\frac{n^2(n+1)^2}{4}\right)$$ *Recall that $1^3 + 2^3 + \cdots + n^3 = \dfrac{n^2(n+1)^2}{4}$.*

$$= \lim_{n \to \infty} \frac{(n+1)^2}{4n^2}$$

$$= \lim_{n \to \infty} \frac{1}{4}\left(\frac{n^2 + 2n + 1}{n^2}\right)$$

$$= \lim_{n \to \infty} \frac{1}{4}\left(1 + \frac{2}{n} + \frac{1}{n^2}\right) \text{ or } \frac{1}{4}$$

Thus, the area of the region under the curve is $\dfrac{1}{4}$ square unit.

When finding the area under a curve from $x = a$ to $x = b$, it may be simpler to find the area under the curve for $x = 0$ to $x = b$ and then subtract the area under the curve from $x = 0$ to $x = a$.

Example 2

Find the area of the region between the graph of $y = x^2$ and the x-axis from $x = 2$ to $x = 5$.

First, find the area under the curve from $x = 0$ to $x = 5$. Form n equal subintervals on the x-axis such that

$$0 < \frac{5 \cdot 1}{n} < \frac{5 \cdot 2}{n} < \frac{5 \cdot 3}{n} < \cdots < \frac{5 \cdot i}{n} < \cdots$$
$$< \frac{5(n-1)}{n} < \frac{5n}{n} \text{ or } 5.$$

The area of each rectangle can be represented as follows.

$$f\left(\frac{5 \cdot i}{n}\right)(x_i - x_{i-1}) \text{ or } \left(\frac{5i}{n}\right)^2\left(\frac{5}{n}\right)$$

$$A = \lim_{n \to \infty} \sum_{i=1}^{n} \left(\frac{5i}{n}\right)^2\left(\frac{5}{n}\right)$$

$$= \lim_{n \to \infty} \frac{125}{n^3}(1^2 + 2^2 + 3^2 + \cdots + n^2)$$

$$= \lim_{n \to \infty} \frac{125}{n^3}\left(\frac{n(n+1)(2n+1)}{6}\right) \quad \begin{array}{l}\textit{Recall that } 1^2 + 2^2 + 3^2 + \cdots + n^2 = \\ \frac{n(n+1)(2n+1)}{6}.\end{array}$$

$$= \lim_{n \to \infty} \frac{125}{6}\left(\frac{2n^3 + 3n^2 + n}{n^3}\right)$$

$$= \lim_{n \to \infty} \frac{125}{6}\left(2 + \frac{3}{n} + \frac{1}{n^2}\right)$$

$$= \frac{125}{6} \cdot 2 \text{ or } \frac{125}{3}$$

Now, find the area under the curve from $x = 0$ to $x = 2$.

$$A = \lim_{n \to \infty} \sum_{i=1}^{n} \left(\frac{2i}{n}\right)^2\left(\frac{2}{n}\right)$$

$$= \lim_{n \to \infty} \frac{8}{n^3}(1^2 + 2^2 + 3^2 + \cdots + n^2)$$

$$= \lim_{n \to \infty} \frac{8}{n^3}\left(\frac{n(n+1)(2n+1)}{6}\right)$$

$$= \lim_{n \to \infty} \frac{8}{6}\left(2 + \frac{3}{n} + \frac{1}{n^2}\right)$$

$$= \frac{8}{6} \cdot 2 \text{ or } \frac{8}{3}$$

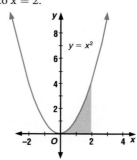

Thus, the area of the region between $y = x^2$ and the x-axis from $x = 2$ to $x = 5$ is $\frac{125}{3} - \frac{8}{3}$ or 39 square units.

LESSON 17-3   AREA UNDER A CURVE   933

EVALUATING THE LESSON

Checking for Understanding

Exercises 1–8 are designed to help you assess students' understanding through reading, writing, speaking, and modeling. You should work through Exercises 1–2 with your students and then monitor their work on Exercises 3–8.

Closing the Lesson

Writing Activity Have students write an explanation as to what area $\lim_{n\to\infty} \sum_{i=1}^{n} \left(\frac{2i}{n}\right)^3 \frac{2i}{n}$ refers?

the area under the curve $y = x^3$ from $x = 0$ to $x = 2$

Additional Answers

1. The upper sum is the sum of the areas of the rectangles above the curve and the lower sum is the sum of the areas of the rectangles below the curve. The sums give the interval in which the area of the region must fall.

2. The interval from 0 to 1 was divided into n rectangles, so each rectangle would be $\frac{1}{n}$ units wide.

3. $A = \lim_{n\to\infty} \sum_{i=1}^{n} \left(\frac{i}{n}\right)^2 \left(\frac{1}{n}\right)$

4. $A = \lim_{n\to\infty} \sum_{i=1}^{n} \left(\frac{4i}{n}\right)^2 \left(\frac{4}{n}\right)$

5. $A = \lim_{n\to\infty} \sum_{i=1}^{n} \left(\frac{i}{n}\right)\left(\frac{1}{n}\right)$

In physics, when the velocity of an object is graphed with respect to time, the area under the curve represents the displacement of the object.

Example 3

APPLICATION

Physics

Refer to the application at the beginning of the lesson. Find the area between the graph of $v(t) = 16t - t^2$ and the x-axis to find the distance that the car traveled in the first 8 seconds after the light turned green.

In order to find the distance the car traveled, find the area under the curve from $x = 0$ to $x = 8$. Form n equal intervals on the x-axis such that
$$0 < \frac{8 \cdot 1}{n} < \frac{8 \cdot 2}{n} < \frac{8 \cdot 3}{n} < \cdots < \frac{8 \cdot i}{n} < \cdots < \frac{8(n-1)}{n} < \frac{8n}{n} \text{ or } 8.$$ Then the area of each rectangle is $f\left(\frac{8 \cdot i}{n}\right)\left(\frac{8}{n}\right)$.

$$A = \lim_{n\to\infty} \sum_{i=1}^{n} \left(16\left(\frac{8i}{n}\right) - \left(\frac{8i}{n}\right)^2\right)\left(\frac{8}{n}\right)$$

$$= \lim_{n\to\infty} \sum_{i=1}^{n} \left(\frac{1024i}{n^2} - \frac{512i^2}{n^3}\right)$$

$$= \lim_{n\to\infty} \frac{1024}{n^2}\left(\frac{n(n+1)}{2}\right) - \frac{512}{n^3}\left(\frac{n(n+1)(2n+1)}{6}\right) \quad 1+2+3+\cdots+n = \frac{n(n+1)}{2}$$

$$= \lim_{n\to\infty} \frac{1024n^2 + 1024n}{2n^2} - \frac{1024n^3 + 1536n^2 + 512n}{6n^3}$$

$$= \lim_{n\to\infty} 512 + \frac{512}{n} - \frac{512}{3} - \frac{256}{n} - \frac{256}{3n^2}$$

$$= \lim_{n\to\infty} \frac{1024}{3} + \frac{256}{n} - \frac{256}{3n^2}$$

$$= \frac{1024}{3} \text{ or } 341\frac{1}{3}$$

Traci's car traveled $341\frac{1}{3}$ feet in the first 8 seconds after the traffic light turned green.

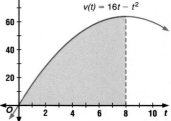

You may find the following formulas for the sums of series helpful when solving the problems in the exercises.

Mathematical induction can be used to prove these formulas.

$$1 + 2 + 3 + \cdots + n = \frac{n(n+1)}{2}$$

$$1^2 + 2^2 + 3^2 + \cdots + n^2 = \frac{n(n+1)(2n+1)}{6}$$

$$1^3 + 2^3 + 3^3 + \cdots + n^3 = \frac{n^2(n+1)^2}{4}$$

$$1^4 + 2^4 + 3^4 + \cdots + n^4 = \frac{6n^5 + 15n^4 + 10n^3 - n}{30}$$

$$1^5 + 2^5 + 3^5 + \cdots + n^5 = \frac{2n^6 + 6n^5 + 5n^4 - n^2}{12}$$

---

6. $A = \lim_{n\to\infty} \sum_{i=1}^{n} \left(\frac{4i}{n}\right)^2\left(\frac{4}{n}\right) - \lim_{n\to\infty} \sum_{i=1}^{n} \left(\frac{i}{n}\right)^2\left(\frac{1}{n}\right)$

7. $A = \lim_{n\to\infty} \sum_{i=1}^{n} \left(\frac{5i}{n}\right)\left(\frac{5}{n}\right) - \lim_{n\to\infty} \sum_{i=1}^{n} \left(\frac{2i}{n}\right)\left(\frac{2}{n}\right)$

8. $A = \lim_{n\to\infty} \sum_{i=1}^{n} \left(\frac{2i}{n}\right)^3\left(\frac{2}{n}\right)$

9. $A = \lim_{n\to\infty} \sum_{i=1}^{n} \left(\frac{A}{2i}\right)^2\left(\frac{2}{n}\right)$

10. $A = \lim_{n\to\infty} \sum_{i=1}^{n} \left(\frac{10i}{n}\right)\left(\frac{10}{n}\right)$

11. $A = \lim_{n\to\infty} \sum_{i=1}^{n} \left(\frac{i}{n}\right)^5\left(\frac{1}{n}\right)$

12. $A = \lim_{n\to\infty} \sum_{i=1}^{n} \left(\frac{ai}{n}\right)^2\left(\frac{a}{n}\right)$

13. $A = \lim_{n\to\infty} \sum_{i=1}^{n} \left(\frac{7i}{n}\right)^4\left(\frac{7}{n}\right) - \lim_{n\to\infty} \sum_{i=1}^{n} \left(\frac{4i}{n}\right)^4\left(\frac{4}{n}\right)$

14. $A = \lim_{n\to\infty} \sum_{i=1}^{n} \left(\frac{ai}{n}\right)^3\left(\frac{a}{n}\right)$

CHECKING FOR UNDERSTANDING

Communicating
Mathematics

Read and study the lesson to answer each question. 1–2. See margin.

1. **Describe** the upper and lower sums used to find the area under a curve. How are they similar and how are they different?

2. **Explain** why the width of the rectangles considered in Example 1 was $\frac{1}{n}$.

Guided
Practice

Write a limit to find the area between each curve and the x-axis for the given interval. Then find the area. 3–8. See margin for limits. Areas are in square units.

3. $y = x^2$ from $x = 0$ to $x = 1$ $\frac{1}{3}$

4. $y = x^2$ from $x = 0$ to $x = 4$ $\frac{64}{3}$

5. $y = x$ from $x = 0$ to $x = 1$ $\frac{1}{2}$

6. $y = x^2$ from $x = 1$ to $x = 4$ 21

7. $y = x$ from $x = 2$ to $x = 5$ $\frac{21}{2}$

8. $y = x^3$ from $x = 0$ to $x = 2$ 4

EXERCISES

Practice

Write a limit to find the area between each curve and the x-axis for the given interval. Then find the area. 9–17. See margin for limits. Areas are in square units.

9. $y = x^2$ from $x = 0$ to $x = 2$ $\frac{8}{3}$

10. $y = x$ from $x = 0$ to $x = 10$ 50

11. $y = x^5$ from $x = 0$ to $x = 1$ $\frac{1}{6}$

12. $y = x^2$ from $x = 0$ to $x = a, a > 0$ $\frac{a^3}{3}$

13. $y = x^4$ from $x = 4$ to $x = 7$ $3156\frac{3}{5}$

14. $y = x^3$ from $x = 0$ to $x = a, a > 0$ $\frac{a^4}{4}$

15. $y = x^2$ from $x = a$ to $x = b, 0 < a < b$ $\frac{b^3 - a^3}{3}$

16. $y = x^2$ from $x = -3$ to $x = 2$ $\frac{35}{3}$

17. $y = |x|$ from $x = -2$ to $x = 4$ 10

Find the area of each shaded region.

18.

$\frac{1}{6}$

19.

$\frac{1}{4}$

Write a formula for the area between each curve and the x-axis for the given interval. Assume that $0 < a < b$.

20. $y = x$ from $x = a$ to $x = b$ $\frac{b^2 - a^2}{2}$

21. $y = x^3$ from $x = a$ to $x = b$ $\frac{b^4 - a^4}{4}$

LESSON 17-3   AREA UNDER A CURVE   **935**

RETEACHING THE LESSON

Students may have more success with these problems by using a chart to organize the information. Set up a chart with columns labeled $y = f(x)$, $x_i - x_{i-1} = \frac{b}{n}$, $f(x_i)$,

$f(x_i)(x_i - x_{i-1})$, and $\sum_{i=1}^{n} f(x_i)(x_i - x_{i-1})$.

Filling out one row of this chart for each problem will help to set up the limit needed to find the area.

Additional Answers

15. $A = \lim\limits_{n \to \infty} \sum\limits_{i=1}^{n} \left(\frac{bi}{n}\right)^2 \left(\frac{b}{n}\right) - $

$\lim\limits_{n \to \infty} \sum\limits_{i=1}^{n} \left(\frac{ai}{n}\right)^2 \left(\frac{a}{n}\right)$

16. $A = \lim\limits_{n \to \infty} \sum\limits_{i=1}^{n} \left(\frac{3i}{n}\right)^2 \left(\frac{3}{n}\right) + $

$\lim\limits_{n \to \infty} \sum\limits_{i=1}^{n} \left(\frac{2i}{n}\right)^2 \left(\frac{2}{n}\right)$

17. $A = \lim\limits_{n \to \infty} \sum\limits_{i=1}^{n} \left(\frac{2i}{n}\right) \left(\frac{2}{n}\right) + $

$\lim\limits_{n \to \infty} \sum\limits_{i=1}^{n} \left(\frac{4i}{n}\right) \left(\frac{4}{n}\right)$

APPLYING THE LESSON

Homework Exercises

Assignment Guide

Average: 9–15, 16–20 even, 23–30
Enriched: 12–30
All: Mid-Chapter Review, 1–16

The red A, B, and C flags, printed only in the Teacher's Wraparound Edition, indicate the level of difficulty of the exercises.

Chapter 17, Quiz B, (Lesson 17–3), is available in the *Evaluation Masters*, p. 117.

Exercise Note

For Exercises 18 and 19, students should start by drawing a typical rectangle used in the summation and writing the formula for its length and width.

Practice Masters Booklet, p. 116

17-3	NAME _____ DATE _____

Practice Worksheet

Area Under a Curve

Write a limit to find the area between each curve and the x-axis for the given interval. Then find the area.

1. $y = x^2$ from $x = 1$ to $x = 6$

$A = \lim\limits_{n \to \infty} \sum\limits_{i=1}^{n} \left(\frac{6i}{n}\right)^2 \left(\frac{6}{n}\right) - $

$\lim\limits_{n \to \infty} \sum\limits_{i=1}^{n} \left(\frac{i}{n}\right)^2 \left(\frac{1}{n}\right);$

$71\frac{2}{3}$ square units

2. $y = x^3$ from $x = 1$ to $x = 5$

$A = \lim\limits_{n \to \infty} \sum\limits_{i=1}^{n} \left(\frac{5i}{n}\right)^3 \left(\frac{5}{n}\right) - $

$\lim\limits_{n \to \infty} \sum\limits_{i=1}^{n} \left(\frac{i}{n}\right)^3 \left(\frac{1}{n}\right);$

156 square units

3. $y = x^4$ from $x = 1$ to $x = 3$

$A = \lim\limits_{n \to \infty} \sum\limits_{i=1}^{n} \left(\frac{3i}{n}\right)^4 \left(\frac{3}{n}\right) - $

$\lim\limits_{n \to \infty} \sum\limits_{i=1}^{n} \left(\frac{i}{n}\right)^4 \left(\frac{1}{n}\right);$

$48\frac{2}{5}$ square units

4. $y = x^5$ from $x = 2$ to $x = 5$

$A = \lim\limits_{n \to \infty} \sum\limits_{i=1}^{n} \left(\frac{5i}{n}\right)^3 \left(\frac{5}{n}\right) - $

$\lim\limits_{n \to \infty} \sum\limits_{i=1}^{n} \left(\frac{2i}{n}\right)^5 \left(\frac{2}{n}\right);$

$2593\frac{1}{2}$ square units

T116
Glencoe Division, Macmillan/McGraw-Hill

Using Technology

The program given in Exercise 22 is for use with a TI-81 graphing calculator. For other programmable calculators, have students consult their owner's manual for commands similar to those presented here.

Programming

22. The following program will approximate the area between the graphs of two functions by dividing the region into rectangles. Store the two functions as Y_1 and Y_2 in the Y= list. The program requires you to input the lower and upper bounds and the number of rectangles to use for the calculations.

```
Prgm 17: AreaCrve
:ClrHome                        Clears the text screen.
:"abs (Y₁-Y₂)"→Y₃               Finds the average height of a rectangle.
:Disp "LOWER BOUND ="           Displays the message.
:Input L                        Accepts a value for L.
:Disp "UPPER BOUND ="
:Input U
:Disp "NUMBER OF RECTANGLES"
:Input R
:(U-L)/R→ W                     Finds the width of each rectangle.
:L→X                            Sets the first value of X equal to L.
:Y₃→C                           Stores height of rectangle at X = L as C.
:0→N                            Sets rectangle counter to 0.
:0→A                            Sets area to 0.
:Lbl 1                          Sets a marker at position 1.
:N + 1→N                        Increases the rectangle counter by 1.
:X + W→X                        Adds width to X to determine next X
:A + WY₃→A                      Adds area to current total area.
:If N = R                       Tests whether all rectangles were added.
:Goto 2                         Sends program to line Lbl 2".
:Goto 1
:Lbl 2
:U→X                            Sets X to value of upper bound.
:Y₃→D                           Stores height at X + U in D.
:A + WC-WD→B                    Calculates area using left endpoints.
:(A + B)/2→E                    Averages two areas.
:Disp "AREA = "
:Disp E
:End
```

Find the area between the graphs of each pair of functions for the given interval.

a. $y = x^2$
   $y = 0$
   $x = 0$ to $x = 4$
   ≈ 21.33 units^2

b. $y = x^4$
   $y = x$
   $x = 1$ to $x = 3$
   44.4 units^2

c. $y = 4x^5$
   $y = 12x^2$
   $x = 0.5$ to $x = 1.5$
   5.60 units^2

Critical Thinking

23. For what type of function would the upper and lower sums be equal?
    a constant function

Applications and Problem Solving

24. **Business** If $f(x)$ is the marginal cost function for a company, then the area under the curve from $x = a$ to $x = b$ is the amount it would cost to increase production from a units to b units. The Penguin Umbrella Company has a marginal cost function of $f(x) = 3 + 0.1x$ for $x < 30$ umbrellas. If they are now producing 20 umbrellas each day, how much would it cost to increase production to 30? $25

25. Sports A bicyclist accelerates from a resting position to a velocity of 18 feet per second in 6 seconds. His velocity over that time is given by $v(t) = 0.5t^2$. Find the distance that the bicyclist traveled in the first 6 seconds. 36 feet

Mixed Review

26. Find the inner product of the vectors $(-3, 9)$ and $(2, 1)$. Are the vectors perpendicular? Explain. **(Lesson 8-4)** 3, no

27. Write an equation of the parabola that has a horizontal axis and passes through $(0, 0)$, $(2, -1)$, and $(4, -4)$. **(Lesson 10-2)** $y^2 + 3x + 7y = 0$

28. Determine whether the point $0.3 + 0.4i$ is in the prisoner set or the escape set for the function $f(z) = z^2$. Explain. **(Lesson 13-5)** prisoner set

29. Find the derivative of $f(x) = \left(1 + \frac{1}{x}\right)\left(2 - \frac{1}{x}\right)$. **(Lesson 17-2)** $-\frac{1}{x^2} + \frac{2}{x^3}$

30. College Entrance Exam Compare quantities A and B below. B
Write A if quantity A is greater.
Write B if quantity B is greater.
Write C if the quantities are equal.
Write D if there is not enough information to determine the relationship.
(A) The area of a square with sides s units long
(B) The area of an equilateral triangle with sides $2s$ units long

MID-CHAPTER REVIEW

Evaluate each limit. (Lesson 17-1)

1. $\lim\limits_{x \to 5}(x^2 - 4x + 1)$ 6

2. $\lim\limits_{n \to 3}\dfrac{n^2 - 3n + 2}{n - 1}$ 1

3. $\lim\limits_{x \to -3}\dfrac{x^2 - 9}{x + 3}$ -6

4. $\lim\limits_{n \to \infty}\dfrac{5n^2 - 1}{n^2}$ 5

5. $\lim\limits_{x \to \infty}\dfrac{(x - 4)(x + 1)}{x^2}$ 1

6. $\lim\limits_{x \to 0}\dfrac{(x + 2)^2 - 4}{x}$ 4

7. $\lim\limits_{n \to \frac{1}{2}}\dfrac{2x^2 + 5x - 3}{x^2 - x}$ 0

8. $\lim\limits_{n \to 3}\sqrt{\dfrac{2n + 3}{3n - 5}}$ $\frac{3}{2}$

9. $\lim\limits_{x \to 1}\dfrac{x^2}{\sqrt[3]{(x^2 - 2)^2}}$ 1

Find the derivative of each function. (Lesson 17-2) 14. $\dfrac{6}{(x + 5)^2}$ 15. $\dfrac{1}{x^2\sqrt{x^2 - 1}}$

10. $f(x) = 4x^2$ $8x$

11. $f(x) = (x - 1)^2$ $2x - 2$

12. $f(x) = \dfrac{5}{1 - 3x}$ $\dfrac{15}{(1 - 3x)^2}$

13. $f(x) = -\dfrac{4}{x^9}$ $\dfrac{36}{x^{10}}$

14. $f(x) = \dfrac{x^2 - 5x + 4}{x^2 + x - 20}$

15. $f(x) = \dfrac{\sqrt{x^2 - 1}}{x}$

16. Sports A walker accelerates from a resting position to a velocity of 10.8 feet per second in 6 seconds. Her velocity is given by $v(t) = 0.3t^2$. Find the distance that the walker traveled in the first 6 seconds. **(Lesson 17-3)** 21.6 feet

LESSON 17-3 AREA UNDER A CURVE 937

EXTENDING THE LESSON

Math Power: Problem Solving

Have students estimate the area under the curve $f(x) = \dfrac{1}{x}$ from $x = 1$ to $x = 2$ using rectangles and a partition of the interval as shown in the lesson. Can they guess what the actual value of the area is? In 2

Mid-Chapter Review

The Mid-Chapter Review provides students with a brief review of the concepts and skills in Lessons 17–1 through 17–3. Lesson numbers are given at the end of problems or instruction lines so students may review concepts not yet mastered.

Objective This optional page shows how graphing software can be used to approximate the area between the x-axis and a curve.

Teaching Suggestions

Encourage students to experiment with varying the number of rectangles used to find the upper and lower sums. As they increase the number of rectangles, have them predict an approximate value for the integral. Use the program to check and refine their predictions.

Exercise Note

Some students may want to use a chart to help them make a conjecture for Exercise 3. Have them list the functions used, the number of rectangles used to make the approximations, and the upper and lower sums for the functions.

Technology

Riemann Sums

Riemann is pronounced REE mahn.

There are several methods used to approximate the area between the x-axis and a curve on some interval $x = a$ to $x = b$. One method involves partitioning the area into several rectangles and calculating the sum of the areas of these rectangles. This sum is called a **Riemann sum** for the nineteenth-century German mathematician Georg Bernhard Riemann. The upper and lower sums that were described in Lesson 17-3 are two special Riemann sums. IBM's *Mathematics Exploration Toolkit (MET)* has a defer sequence that calculates Riemann sums. We will use this defer sequence to examine the upper and lower sums for the function $f(x) = \frac{1}{5}x^2$ on the interval $x = 0$ to $x = 5$.

Enter	Result
load numint	*Pulls up the defer sequence.*
run start	*Begins running the defer sequence.*
1/5 x ∧ 2	*Enters the function*
go	$f(x) = \frac{1}{5}x^2$.
0	*Enters the limits of the*
5	*interval.*
go	
10	*Determines the number*
go	*of rectangles.*
run r	*Starts the calculations.*
lims 0 5 0 5	*Sets the range of the*
go	*viewing window.*

The program will draw rectangles and find the upper sum. Press ENTER. After lower sum is displayed, the program will find the actual area of the region, called the **definite integral.** Press ENTER to return to the menu.
1. 8.9688, 7.7188; 8.585, 8.085; 8.4588, 8.2088; They are closer approximations of the area.

EXERCISES

1. Find the upper and lower sums for the function $f(x) = \frac{1}{5}x^2$ on the interval $x = 0$ to $x = 5$ using 20, 50 and 100 rectangles. As the number of rectangles is increased, what happens to the upper and lower sums?

2. Is the upper or the lower sum a better approximation of the area of a region for this function? Try different numbers of rectangles and different intervals. Is this sum always the better approximation? lower; yes

3. The graph of $f(x) = \frac{1}{5}x^2$ is concave up. Find upper and lower sums for other functions that are concave up. Which sum is the better approximation of the area for these functions? Make a conjecture as to which sum gives the better approximation for the area under a curve that is concave down. lower; upper

17-4 Integration

Objective
17-4

After studying this lesson, you should be able to:
■ use integration formulas.

Application

"Seven out of ten American families own their own homes." "People in the District of Columbia purchase 1.3 newspapers each day." "On the average, each American spends 5¢ of each food dollar at a vending machine." Demographers study the habits and trends of populations to produce statistics like these. The statistics are used by businesses to identify the number and habits of their potential customers.

College Connections Inc. is a scholarship-search service that helps high school students find college scholarships. In developing their marketing plan for the next year, the marketing manager of College Connections needs to determine the number of people that will be in the college-age bracket in this year. They will use a life table function, a function ℓ such that $\ell(x)$ is the number of people in the population who reach the age of x years at any time during the year, to find this population. Life table functions involve **integrals**.

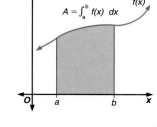

The integral of a function $f(x)$ is the area of the region bounded by the graph of $f(x)$, the x-axis and the lines $x = a$ and $x = b$. The area is symbolized as follows.

The expression dx in the integral notation tells you to integrate with respect to x.

$$A = \int_a^b f(x)\ dx$$

The notation is read the "integral of f, with respect to x, from a to b." By definition, $\int_a^b f(x)\ dx$ is equal to $\lim_{n\to\infty} \sum_{i=1}^{n} f(x_i)(x_i - x_{i-1})$.

To understand the concept of an integral, consider the function $f(x)$ in the following equation.

$$\frac{dy}{dx} = f(x),\ \text{where } a < x < b$$

Is it possible to find a function $y = F(x)$ for which $f(x)$ is the derivative? This is the "anti" or inverse problem of finding the derivative. Thus, the function $F(x)$ is called an **antiderivative** of $f(x)$ if and only if $F'(x) = f(x)$.

LESSON 17-4   INTEGRATION   939

ALTERNATE TEACHING STRATEGIES

Using Logical Reasoning
Write a list of functions, such as $f(x) = 2x$, $f(x) = 3x^2$, $f(x) = 2x + 1$, and $f(x) = x^2 + x$ on the chalkboard, and challenge students to find an antiderivative for each one. After they have found the answers, encourage them to formulate some general rules, perhaps for powers of x and sums of terms.

Using Charts
Have students make a chart with three columns headed $f'(x)$, $f(x)$, and $F(x)$. Have them list x^{-2}, x^{-1}, c, x, x^2, x^3, and x^4 in the $f(x)$ column, then fill in the derivatives in the first column. Next, use the first two columns to find the antiderivatives for each entry and fill in the third column.

NCTM Standards: 1–4, 6, 13
Lesson Resources
- Practice Master 17–4
- Enrichment Master 17–4
- Evaluation Master, Quiz C, p. 118
- Activity Master, p. 51

 Transparency 17–4 contains the 5-Minute Check and a teaching aid for this lesson.

INTRODUCING THE LESSON

5-Minute Check
(over Lesson 17–3)

Write a limit to find the area between each curve and the x-axis for the given interval. Then find the area.
1. $y = x^3$, from $x = 0$ to $x = 3$
$$\lim_{n\to\infty} \sum_{i=1}^{n} \left(\frac{3i}{n}\right)^3\left(\frac{3}{n}\right);\ \frac{81}{4}$$
2. $y = x^2$, from $x = 1$ to $x = 4$
$$\lim_{n\to\infty} \sum_{i=1}^{n} \left(\frac{4i}{n}\right)^2\left(\frac{4}{n}\right) -$$
$$\lim_{n\to\infty} \sum_{i=1}^{n} \left(\frac{i}{n}\right)^2\left(\frac{1}{n}\right);\ 21$$

Motivating the Lesson
After working through the exercises in Lesson 17–3, students will probably have noticed that the "limit-of-a- sum" process is rather long and tedious, and that it was only applied to finding areas for the simplest power functions. In order to apply this idea and explore some of its uses and applications, it is necessary to find some way to streamline the process itself. This lesson introduces such a method.

Is it possible to find an antiderivative of $f(x)$, represented by $F(x)$, if $f(x) = 3x^2$? A few possibilities are $F(x) = x^3 + 3$, $F(x) = x^3 + \pi$, and $F(x) = x^3 - 5$. These are all valid answers and can be summarized as $F(x) = x^3 + C$, where C is a constant.

The following definition makes the connection between the antiderivative and the integral.

Definition of an Integral	**The function $F(x)$ is an integral of $f(x)$ with respect to x if and only if $F(x)$ is an antiderivative of $f(x)$. That is,** $$F(x) = \int f(x)\,dx \text{ if and only if } F'(x) = f(x).$$

Thus, in the previous example, $\int 3x^2\,dx = x^3 + C$ since $F'(x^3 + C) = 3x^2$.

Example 1

Find each integral.

a. $\int 1\,dx$

b. $\int x^2\,dx$

a. Since $F'(x) = 1$ when $F(x) = x + C$, then $\int 1\,dx = x + C.$

b. Since $F'(x) = x^2$ when $F(x) = \dfrac{x^3}{3} + C$, then $\int x^2\,dx = \dfrac{x^3}{3} + C.$

Some of the formulas that are useful in finding integrals are listed below.

1. If k is a constant, $\int k\,dx = kx + C$.

2. If $n \neq -1$, $\int u^n\,du = \dfrac{u^{n+1}}{n+1} + C$ where u is a differentiable function.

3. By definition, $\int x^{-1}dx = \ln|x| + C$.

4. The integral of a sum of functions is the sum of the integrals of the functions.
$$\int (f(x) + g(x))\,dx = \int f(x)\,dx + \int g(x)\,dx$$

5. The integral of the product of a constant, a, and a function, $f(x)$, is the product of the constant and the integral of the function.
$$\int af(x)\,dx = a\int f(x)\,dx$$

Example 2

Find each integral.

a. $\int (4x + 7)\,dx$

a. Use the formula that says the integral of a sum of functions is the sum of the integrals.

$$\int (4x+7)\,dx = \int 4x\,dx + \int 7dx$$

$$= 4\int x\,dx + \int 7dx \qquad \textit{Use the fifth formula.}$$

$$= 4\left(\frac{x^2}{2}+C_1\right)+7x+C_2 \qquad \begin{array}{l}\textit{Use the second and first}\\ \textit{formulas respectively.}\end{array}$$

$$= 2x^2 + 4C_1 + 7x + C_2 \qquad \textit{Let } C = 4C_1 + C_2.$$

$$= 2x^2 + 7x + C$$

Thus, $\int (4x+7)\,dx = 2x^2 + 7x + C.$

b. $\int (3x^2 + 6x + 1)\,dx$

b. $\int (3x^2 + 6x + 1)\,dx = \int 3x^2\,dx + \int 6x\,dx + \int 1\,dx$

$$= 3\int x^2\,dx + 6\int x\,dx + \int 1\,dx$$

$$= 3\left(\frac{x^3}{3}+C_1\right)+6\left(\frac{x^2}{2}+C_2\right)+(x+C_3)$$

$$= x^3 + 3x^2 + x + C \qquad \textit{Let } C = 3C_1 + 6C_2 + C_3.$$

Thus, $\int (3x^2 + 6x + 1)\,dx = x^3 + 3x^2 + x + C.$

Sometimes it is possible to rewrite the integral by using u and $\dfrac{du}{dx}$. To do this, use the formula $\int f(x)\,dx = \int u\dfrac{du}{dx}\cdot dx = \int u\,du.$

Example 3

Find $\int (x^2 + 1)2x\,dx.$

Let $u = (x^2+1)$. Then $du = 2x\,dx.$

$$\int (x^2+1)2x\,dx = \int u\,du$$

$$= \frac{u^2}{2}+C \qquad \textit{Use the formula } \int u^n du = \frac{u^{n+1}}{n+1}+C.$$

$$= \frac{(x^2+1)^2}{2}+C \qquad \textit{Substitute.}$$

Therefore, $\int (x^2+1)2x\,dx = \dfrac{(x^2+1)^2}{2}+C.$

Integration is used often in the sciences and in business.

Chalkboard Example

For Example 4

A nonnegative function $f(x)$ is a probability density function if the total area under its graph is equal to 1. The antiderivative of $f(x)$ is the cumulative distribution function and is used to calculate the probabilities of particular events. Let $f(x) = 3(1 - x)^2$ for $0 < x < 1$ and 0 for all other x. Find the integral of $f(x)$.
$3x - 3x^2 + x^3 + C$

EVALUATING THE LESSON

Checking for Understanding

Exercises 1–8 are designed to help you assess students' understanding through reading, writing, speaking, and modeling. You should work through Exercises 1–2 with your students and then monitor their work on Exercises 3–8.

Closing the Lesson

Speaking Activity Have students compare and contrast the rules for integration and differentiation of $f(x) = x^n$.

Practice Masters Booklet, p. 117

NAME _____ DATE _____

17-4 Practice Worksheet

Integration
Find each integral.

1. $\int 8\,dx$
   $8x + C$

2. $\int (2x + 6)\,dx$
   $x^2 + 6x + C$

3. $\int (6x^2 - 12x + 8)\,dx$
   $2x^3 - 6x^2 + 8x + C$

4. $\int (9x^2 + 12x - 9)\,dx$
   $3x^3 + 6x^2 - 9x + C$

5. $\int (x - 2)^{10}\,dx$
   $\frac{(x-2)^{11}}{11} + C$

6. $\int 2(2x - 3)^4\,dx$
   $\frac{(2x-3)^5}{5} + C$

7. $\int (5 - x)^6\,dx$
   $-\frac{(5-x)^7}{7} + C$

8. $\int (3x - 1)^4\,dx$
   $\frac{(3x-1)^5}{15} + C$

9. $\int \frac{1}{x+2}\,dx$
   $\ln |x + 2| + C$

10. $\int \frac{3}{x-4}\,dx$
    $3\ln |x - 4| + C$

11. $\int 3x^2\sqrt{x^3 + 5}\,dx$
    $\frac{2}{3}\sqrt{(x^3 + 5)^3} + C$

12. $\int x\sqrt{x^2 - 5}\,dx$
    $\frac{3}{8}\sqrt[3]{(x^2 - 5)^4} + C$

13. $\int \frac{10}{x^2}\,dx$
    $-\frac{10}{x} + C$

14. $\int \frac{4}{x^3}\,dx$
    $-\frac{2}{x^2} + C$

T117
Glencoe Division, Macmillan/McGraw-Hill

Example 4

APPLICATION
Demographics

Refer to the application at the beginning of the lesson. The marketing manager for College Connections, Inc. has determined that the life table function for the region of the country that she is considering is $\ell(t) = 12{,}000\sqrt{100 - t}$. Under the appropriate conditions, the integral of the life table function gives a function that can be used to determine the number of people in the population that are t years old or younger. Find the integral of $\ell(t)$.

$$\int 12{,}000\sqrt{100 - t}\,dt = 12{,}000 \int \sqrt{100 - t}\,dt$$

Let $u = (100 - t)$, then $\frac{du}{dt} = -1$.

$$12{,}000 \int \sqrt{100 - t}\,dt = 12{,}000 \int \sqrt{u} \cdot -\frac{du}{dt} \cdot dt \qquad \sqrt{100 - t} = \sqrt{u},$$
$$\qquad\qquad\qquad\qquad\qquad 1 = -(-1) \text{ or } -\frac{du}{dt}$$

$$= 12{,}000 \int -\sqrt{u}\,du \qquad\qquad \text{Simplify.}$$

$$= 12{,}000 \int -u^{\frac{1}{2}}\,du \qquad\qquad \sqrt{u} = u^{\frac{1}{2}}$$

$$= 12{,}000 \left(-\frac{u^{\frac{1}{2}+1}}{\frac{1}{2} + 1} \right) + C \qquad \text{Use the second formula.}$$

$$= 12{,}000 \left(-\frac{2}{3}u^{\frac{3}{2}} \right) + C$$

$$= -8000u^{\frac{3}{2}} + C$$

$$= -8000(100 - t)^{\frac{3}{2}} + C$$

The integral of the life table function is $-8000(100 - t)^{\frac{3}{2}} + C$.

CHECKING FOR UNDERSTANDING

Communicating Mathematics

Read and study the lesson to answer each question. 1–2. See margin.

1. **Explain** what the notation $\int_a^b f(x)\,dx$ means in relation to $f(x)$.

2. **Describe** the relationship between integration and differentiation.

Guided Practice

Find each integral.

3. $\int 5\,dx$ $5x + C$

4. $\int 2x\,dx$ $x^2 + C$

5. $\int 3x^2\,dx$ $x^3 + C$

6. $\int (2x - 3)\,dx$ $x^2 - 3x + C$

7. $\int (5x^4 + 2x)\,dx$ $x^5 + x^2 + C$

8. $\int \sqrt{2x}\,dx$ $\frac{2}{3}\sqrt{(2x)^3} + C$

942 CHAPTER 17 LIMITS, DERIVATIVES, AND INTEGRALS

RETEACHING THE LESSON

The following exercises may help students recognize the appropriate expressions for u and du when substitution is required to evaluate an integral.
Given the function u and the value of n, find $\frac{du}{dx}$, write out $\int u^n \frac{du}{dx}\,dx$, and find the antiderivative.

1. $u = x^2 + 1, n = \frac{1}{2}$

$2x; \int \sqrt{x^2 + 1}\,2x\,dx; \frac{2}{3}(x^2 + 1)^{\frac{3}{2}} + C$

2. $u = x^3 + 2x, n = 3$ $3x^2 + 2;$
$\int (x^3 + 2x)^3(3x^2 + 2)dx;$
$\frac{1}{4}(x^3 + 2x)^4 + C$

3. $u = x^2 - x + 1, n = -1$ $2x - 1;$
$\int \frac{2x - 1}{x^2 - x + 1}\,dx;$
$\ln |x^2 - x + 1| + C$

4. $u = x^3 - 8, n = -2$ $3x^2; \int \frac{3x^2}{(x^3 - 8)^2}\,dx;$
$-\frac{1}{(x^3 - 8)} + C$

EXERCISES

Practice   **Find each integral.** 11. $x^3 - 2x^4 + x^5 + C$

9. $\int 10\, dx$ $10x + C$ **10.** $\int (2x - 12)\, dx$ $x^2 - 12x + C$

11. $\int (3x^2 - 8x^3 + 5x^4)\, dx$ **12.** $\int (x^4 - 5)\, dx$ $\frac{1}{5}x^5 - 5x + C$

13. $\int 5x^3\, dx$ $\frac{5}{4}x^4 + C$ **14.** $\int (\pi x + \sqrt{x})\, dx$ $\frac{\pi x^2}{2} + \frac{2\sqrt{x^3}}{3} + C$

15. $\int (x + 5)^{20}\, dx$ $\frac{(x+5)^{21}}{21} + C$ **16.** $\int \sqrt{1 + x}\, dx$ $\frac{2\sqrt{(1+x)^3}}{3} + C$

17. $\int (-2x + 3)\, dx$ $-x^2 + 3x + C$ **18.** $\int \frac{-2x}{\sqrt{1 - x^2}}\, dx$ $2\sqrt{1 - x^2} + C$

19. $\int \frac{1}{x - 1}\, dx$ $\ln |x - 1| + C$ **20.** $\int \left(\frac{x + 1}{\sqrt[3]{x^2 + 2x + 2}} \right) dx$

                                                   $\frac{3}{4}\sqrt[3]{(x^2 + 2x + 2)^2} + C$

Find the antiderivative of each function.

21. $f(x) = 8x^4$ $\frac{8}{5}x^5 + C$ **22.** $f(x) = 4\sqrt[3]{x}$ $3\sqrt[3]{x^4} + C$

23. $f(x) = x^5 - \frac{1}{x^4}$ $\frac{x^6}{6} + \frac{1}{3x^3} + C$ **24.** $f(x) = \frac{2}{x^3}$ $-\frac{1}{x^2} + C$

25. $f(x) = \frac{2}{\sqrt{x}}$ $4\sqrt{x} + C$ **26.** $f(x) = \frac{2}{1 - 4x}$ $-\frac{1}{2} \ln |1 - 4x| + C$

Critical Thinking   **27.** Find $\int \frac{1}{x^2} \left(\frac{x + 1}{x} \right)^{\frac{1}{3}} dx$. $\left(\textit{Hint: Substitute } u = \frac{x + 1}{x}. \right)$ $-\frac{3}{4} \left(\frac{x + 1}{x} \right)^{\frac{4}{3}} + C$

Applications and Problem Solving   **28. Physics**   If a function $v(t)$ describes the velocity of a moving object at time t, then the function $s(t)$ that describes the distance from a given point to the object at time t can be found by integrating $v(t)$.

a. A car is moving at a constant velocity of 45 miles per hour. Write an equation that describes the distance that the car has traveled after t hours. $s(t) = 45t + C$

b. If the car described in part a is 104 miles from the given point at time $t = 2$, write an equation that describes the position of the car at time t. $s(t) = 45t + 14$

c. The velocity of a rocket is given by $v(t) = -32t + 100$. If the rocket is launched from a point 50 feet above the ground, write an equation that describes the distance the rocket has traveled after t seconds. $s(t) = -16t^2 + 100t + 50$

LESSON 17-4   INTEGRATION   943

The red A, B, and C flags, printed only in the Teacher's Wraparound Edition, indicate the level of difficulty of the exercises.

Chapter 17, Quiz C, (Lesson 17–4), is available in the *Evaluation Masters*, p. 118.

Exercise Note

Encourage students to rewrite expressions with fractional or negative exponents where appropriate before applying the integration formulas.

Additional Answers

1. the area under the curve $f(x)$ between $x = a$ and $x = b$
2. Integration is finding the antiderivative of a function.

29. **Business** For Suds Inc., the marginal revenue from the sale of the xth pound of soap is found by $m(x) = 4 - 0.02x$ when $0 \le x \le 400$. If Suds sells no soap, they will lose \$300. Write an equation that describes the total revenue for Suds Inc. $r(x) = 4x - 0.01x^2 - 300$

30. **Business** The buyer for Food King Grocery has found that the marginal daily demand for their home made French bread can be described by the function $D'(x) = -3.2x + 20$ where x is the price charged for a loaf of bread and $D'(x)$ is the number of loaves.

a. Find a daily demand function for this product. $D(x) = -1.6x^2 + 20x + C$

b. If the daily demand for French bread is 65 loaves when the price is 85¢ per loaf, what will the daily demand be if the price is increased to 95¢ per loaf? 67 loaves

Mixed Review

31. Michael Thomas, the manager of the paint department at Builder's Headquarters, is mixing paint for a spring sale. There are 32 units of yellow dye, 54 units of brown dye, and an unlimited supply of base paint available. Mr. Thomas plans to mix as many gallons as possible of Autumn Wheat and Harvest Brown paint. Each gallon of Autumn Wheat requires 4 units of yellow dye and 1 unit of brown dye. Each gallon of Harvest Brown paint requires 1 unit of yellow dye and 6 units of brown dye. Find the maximum number of gallons of paint that Mr. Thomas could mix. **(Lesson 2-6)** 14 gallons

32. Verify that $1 + \sin 2x = (\sin x + \cos x)^2$ is an identity. **(Lesson 7-4)**

32. See Teacher's Answer Key.

33. Simplify $7^{\log_7 2x}$. **(Lesson 11-4)** $2x$

34. Find the first three iterates of the function $f(x) = 0.5x - 1$ using $x_0 = 8$. **(Lesson 13-1)** $3, 0.5, -0.75$

35. How many vertices are there in a graph with 15 edges if each vertex has degree 2? **(Lesson 16-1)** 15

36. Find the area between the graph of $y = x^2$ and the x-axis for the interval from $x = 2$ to $x = 7$. **(Lesson 17-3)**. $111\frac{2}{3}$ units^2

37. **College Entrance Exam** Choose the best answer. A

Sherry mixes a pounds of peanuts that cost b cents per pound with c pounds of rice crackers that cost d cents per pound to make Oriental Peanut Mix. What should the price in cents for a pound of Oriental Peanut Mix be if Sherry is to make a profit of 10¢ per pound?

(A) $\dfrac{ab + cd}{a + c} + 10$

(B) $\dfrac{b + d}{a + c} + 10$

(C) $\dfrac{ab + cd}{a + c} + 0.10$

(D) $\dfrac{b + d}{a + c} + 0.10$

(E) $\dfrac{b + d + 10}{a + c}$

944   CHAPTER 17   LIMITS, DERIVATIVES, AND INTEGRALS

EXTENDING THE LESSON

Math Power: Connections

What is $\dfrac{d}{dx}$ (ln x), and thinking of it as the slope of the tangent line, what information does it give us about the graph of $y = \ln x$?

$\dfrac{1}{x}$; $\dfrac{1}{x} > 0$ for all x in the domain of ln x, so $y = \ln x$ is always increasing.

Enrichment Masters Booklet, p. 117

The Fundamental Theorem of Calculus

Objective
17–5

After studying this lesson, you should be able to:
■ use the fundamental theorem of calculus to evaluate definite integrals and to find area.

NCTM Standards: 1–4, 6, 13

Lesson Resources

- Practice Master 17–5
- Enrichment Master 17–5
- Evaluation Master, Quiz D, p. 118

Transparency 17–5 contains the 5-Minute Check and a teaching aid for this lesson.

Application

Magic Memories Inc. (MMI) makes photo albums and scrapbooks. Their marginal cost function is $m(x) = \frac{1}{\sqrt{x}} + 2$, where x is thousands of books produced and $m(x)$ is measured in thousands of dollars. MMI has the opportunity to bid on a contract for producing senior memory books for a company that sells high school rings, key chains, and jackets. The contract would require MMI to produce between 1000 and 4000 scrapbooks. Producing the scrapbooks would require a fixed cost of $1000. Their sales manager would like to find the average cost for producing the scrapbooks in order to make the bid accurate. *This problem will be solved in Example 2.*

The derivative has been defined as the limit of the difference quotients.

$$f'(x) = \lim_{h \to \infty} \frac{f(x+h) - f(x)}{h}$$

The integral has been defined as the limit of the sum of the areas.

$$A = \lim_{n \to \infty} \sum_{i=1}^{n} f(x_i)(x_i - x_{i-1}), \text{ where } (x_i - x_{i-1}) \text{ approaches zero}$$

The **fundamental theorem of calculus** formally states that these limiting processes are inverse operations.

Fundamental Theorem of Calculus	If the function $f(x)$ is continuous and $F(x)$ is such that $F'(x) = f(x)$, then $\int_a^b f(x)\,dx = F(b) - F(a)$.

a and b are called the lower and upper limits or bounds of the integration.

The fundamental theorem of calculus provides a way to evaluate the **definite integral** $\int_a^b f(x)\,dx$ if an antiderivative $F(x)$ can be found. A vertical line on the right side is used to abbreviate $F(b) - F(a)$. Thus, the principal statement of the theorem may be written as follows.

$$\int_a^b f(x)\,dx = F(x)\Big|_a^b = F(b) - F(a)$$

INTRODUCING THE LESSON

🕐 5-Minute Check
(over Lesson 17–4)

Find each integral.

1. $\int (9 - 4x)\,dx$

   $9x - 2x^2 + C$

2. $\int \frac{2x}{(x^2 - 1)^3}\,dx$

   $-\frac{1}{2(x^2 - 1)^2} + C$

Find the antiderivative of each function.

3. $f(x) = x^2 + \frac{1}{\sqrt{x}}$

   $\frac{x^3}{3} + 2\sqrt{x} + C$

4. $f(x) = \frac{1}{x + 3}$

   $\ln |x + 3| + C$

Motivating the Lesson

In Lesson 17–4, students learned the definition of the antiderivative studied a number of formulas to help them find antiderivatives for particular functions. How can this knowledge be used to calculate quantities such as the area under the curve or the distance traveled by an accelerating car? The fundamental theorem of calculus in this lesson provides the connection.

ALTERNATE TEACHING STRATEGIES

Using Problem Solving

Have students suggest a few specific antiderivatives for $f(x) = x^2 - 4x + 9$.
Ask them to apply the formula $\int_a^b f(x)\,dx = F(b) - F(a)$ to evaluate $\int_0^3 (x^2 - 4x + 9)\,dx$ by using each of the antiderivatives they suggested. This will show how the constant terms cancel each other so that every antiderivative gives the same result.

Using Connections

Refer to Lesson 17–3. List the area problems from Exercises 9–16, 18 and 19 on the chalkboard. For each problem, have students find an antiderivative for $f(x)$, calculate $F(b) - F(a)$, and compare the results of this calculation with the value of the area found previously.

Teaching Tip
The fundamental theorem of arithmetic states that every integer greater than one has a unique prime factorization, and is the basis of much of the branch of mathematics known as number theory. The fundamental theorem of algebra was presented in Chapter 4. It is foundational to the study of modern algebra. In the same way, the fundamental theorem of calculus is of major importance to the study of the calculus.

Teaching Tip
The definite integral of a function over a specific interval is a number. The fundamental theorem of calculus tells us how to use an antiderivative of the function to calculate this number.

Chalkboard Examples

For Example 1

Evaluate $\int_{2}^{7} (x-1)^3 \, dx$.   **323.75**

For Example 2

The marginal cost function for a toy company's production of yo-yos is given by $f(x) = -1.8x + 72$, where x is the number of lots of 100 yo-yos each produced. Find the average cost of producing each yo-yo if between 1000 and 1500 yo-yos are produced.
$0.495

Example 1

Evaluate $\int_{1}^{4} (5x+1)^2 \, dx$.

$$\int_{1}^{4} (5x+1)^2 \, dx = \int_{1}^{4} (25x^2 + 10x + 1) \, dx \qquad \textit{Expand } (5x+1)^2.$$

$$= \frac{25}{3}x^3 + 5x^2 + x \Big|_{1}^{4} \qquad \textit{Integrate.}$$

$$= \left(\frac{25}{3}(4^3) + 5(4^2) + 4\right) - \left(\frac{25}{3}(1^3) + 5(1^2) + 1\right) \quad \begin{array}{l} F(x)\big|_{a}^{b} = \\ F(b) - F(a) \end{array}$$

$$= 603$$

Since $F(x)$ is any antiderivative of $f(x)$, the constant C is omitted when using the integration formulas to find a definite integral. Therefore, the area between the x-axis and the graph of $f(x) = (5x+1)^2$ for the interval $x = 1$ to $x = 4$ is 603 units^2.

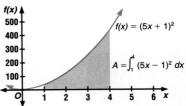

Definite integrals can be used to find the average value of a function over an interval. If $\bar{f}$ is the average value of the function $f(x)$, then

$$\bar{f} = \left(\frac{1}{b-a}\right) \int_{a}^{b} f(x) \, dx.$$

Example 2

Notice that C(x) is defined as the number of thousands of dollars to produce x thousands of scrapbooks.

Refer to the application at the beginning of the lesson. Find the average cost of producing each scrapbook if between 1000 and 4000 scrapbooks are produced.

The marginal cost function is $m(x) = \frac{1}{\sqrt{x}} + 2$, so the cost function is $\int m(x) dx$ or $2\sqrt{x} + 2x + C$. The fixed cost is $1000, so the cost function for this contract would be $C(x) = 2\sqrt{x} + 2x + 1$.

Now use the formula $\bar{f} = \left(\frac{1}{b-a}\right) \int_{a}^{b} f(x) \, dx$ for $f(x) = C(x)$.

$$\overline{C(x)} = \left(\frac{1}{b-a}\right) \int_{a}^{b} C(x) \, dx$$

$$= \left(\frac{1}{4-1}\right) \int_{1}^{4} (2\sqrt{x} + 2x + 1) \, dx \qquad a = 1, b = 4, C(x) = 2\sqrt{x} + 2x + 1$$

$$= \frac{1}{3}\left(\frac{4}{3}x^{\frac{3}{2}} + x^2 + x\right)\Big|_{1}^{4} \qquad \textit{Integrate.}$$

$$= \frac{1}{3}\left(\frac{4}{3}(4)^{\frac{3}{2}} + (4)^2 + (4)\right) - \frac{1}{3}\left(\frac{4}{3}(1)^{\frac{3}{2}} + (1)^2 + (1)\right)$$

$$= \frac{92}{9} - \frac{10}{9} \text{ or } \frac{82}{9}$$

It will cost an average of $\frac{82}{9}$ or about 9.11 thousands of dollars to produce one thousand scrapbooks if between 1000 and 4000 scrapbooks are produced. Therefore, it will cost about $9.11 to produce each scrapbook.

The definite integral will produce a negative value if $f(x) < 0$ in the interval from $x = a$ to $x = b$. It will produce a positive value if $f(x) > 0$ in the same interval. Therefore, if the integral is being used to find the area between a curve and the x-axis, the absolute value of the integral is used.

Example 3

Find the area between the x-axis and the graph of the function $f(x) = x^2 - 9$ from $x = -3$ to $x = 3$.

Use the absolute value of the definite integral since we are finding an area.

$$A = \left| \int_{-3}^{3} (x^2 - 9)\, dx \right|$$

$$= \left| \frac{x^3}{3} - 9x \right|_{-3}^{3}$$

$$= \left| \left[\frac{27}{3} - 9(3) \right] - \left[\frac{-27}{3} - 9(-3) \right] \right|$$

$$= |-36|$$

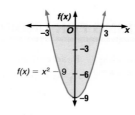

$f(x) = x^2 - 9$

The area is 36 square units.

When a function is both positive and negative in the interval from $x = a$ to $x = b$, and the area is to be found, the limits of integration must be split at the zeros of the function.

Example 4

Find the area between the x-axis and the function $f(x) = x^3 - 3x^2 + 2x$ from $x = 0$ to $x = 2$.

The area is the sum of the areas of A_1 and A_2.

$$f(x) = x^3 - 3x^2 + 2x$$

$$= x(x - 1)(x - 2)$$

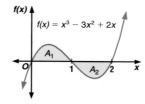

$f(x) = x^3 - 3x^2 + 2x$

The zeros of the function are 0, 1, and 2. So evaluate the integral for the intervals $x = 0$ to $x = 1$ and $x = 1$ to $x = 2$.

$$A_1 = \left| \int_{0}^{1} (x^3 - 3x^2 + 2x)\, dx \right|$$

$$= \left| \frac{1}{4}x^4 - x^3 + x^2 \right|_{0}^{1}$$

$$= \left| \left(\frac{1}{4}(1)^4 - (1)^3 + (1)^2 \right) - \left(\frac{1}{4}(0)^4 - (0)^3 + (0)^2 \right) \right| \text{ or } \left| \frac{1}{4} \right|$$

$$A_2 = \left| \int_{1}^{2} (x^3 - 3x^2 + 2x)\, dx \right|$$

$$= \left| \frac{1}{4}x^4 - x^3 + x^2 \right|_{1}^{2}$$

$$= \left| \left(\frac{1}{4}(2)^4 - (2)^3 + (2)^2 \right) - \left(\frac{1}{4}(1)^4 - (1)^3 + (1)^2 \right) \right| \text{ or } \left| -\frac{1}{4} \right|$$

(continued on the next page)

LESSON 17-5   THE FUNDAMENTAL THEOREM OF CALCULUS   947

Teaching Tip   In Example 3, point out that we could use the symmetry of the parabola to write $A = 2 \left| \int_{0}^{3} (x^2 - 9)\, dx \right| = 2 \left| (x^3 - 9x) \right|_{0}^{3} = 36$. Note that the use of such symmetry simplifies the computation.

$A = A_1 + A_2$

$= \left|\frac{1}{4}\right| + \left|-\frac{1}{4}\right|$

$= \frac{1}{2}$

The area is $\frac{1}{2}$ square unit.

CHECKING FOR UNDERSTANDING

Communicating Mathematics

Read and study the lesson to answer each question. 1–3. See margin.

1. What relationship does the fundamental theorem of calculus establish for differentiation and integration?

2. When you find an indefinite integral of a function, a constant C is added to the function. Why is it not necessary to add the constant when you are finding a definite integral?

3. **Explain** why you must take the absolute value when finding the area between a curve and the x-axis.

Guided Practice

Use integration to find each area.

4.
10 sq units

5.
12 sq units

6.
12.5 sq units

7.
$2\frac{2}{3}$ sq units

8.
18 sq units

9.
4 sq units

Evaluate each definite integral.

10. $\int_{0}^{1} (2x + 3) \, dx$ 4

11. $\int_{0}^{1} (3x^2 + 6x + 1) \, dx$ 5

12. $\int_{0}^{3} \left(\frac{1}{2}x - 4\right) dx$ $-\frac{39}{4}$

13. $\int_{-4}^{-1} (5x + 14) \, dx$ $\frac{9}{2}$

RETEACHING THE LESSON

Have students apply the fundamental theorem of calculus to evaluate $\int_{0}^{2} x^3 \, dx$ and $\int_{-2}^{2} x^3 \, dx$. Which of these integrals represents an area?
the first

How can we use integration to find the area between $y = x^3$ and the x-axis over the interval [–2, 2]?

$A = 2 \int_{0}^{2} x^3 \, dx$

Have students find the area between the x-axis and $y = f(x)$ over the stated interval and compare it with $\int f(x) \, dx$.

1. $f(x) = x$, [–1, 4]   8.5, 7.5
2. $f(x) = x^3 - 3x^2 - 4x$, [–1, 4]
   32.75, –31.25
3. $f(x) = x^2 - 4$, [–2, 2] $\frac{32}{3}$, $-\frac{32}{3}$

Graph each function. Then, find the area between the function and the *x*-axis for the given interval using integration. 14–15. See margin for graphs.

14. $f(x) = 2x + 3$ for $x = 1$ to $x = 4$
24 sq units

15. $f(x) = x^2$ for $x = -2$ to $x = 2$
$\frac{16}{3}$ sq units

EXERCISES

 Practice   Use integration to find the area of each shaded region.

 A

16. 8 sq units

$y = 3 - x$

17.

$y = x + 3$

18.

$y = \frac{x}{2} - 3$
$16\frac{1}{2}$ sq units
9 sq units

19. $1\frac{1}{3}$ sq units

$y = 2x - x^2$

20.

$y = x^2 - 4$
$10\frac{2}{3}$ sq units

21.

$y = \frac{1}{2}x^2$
$4\frac{1}{3}$ sq units

Evaluate each definite integral.

 B

22. $\int_0^3 x\, dx$ $\frac{9}{2}$

23. $\int_{-1}^1 (x + 1)^2\, dx$ $2\frac{2}{3}$

24. $\int_{-1}^1 (4x^3 + 3x^2)\, dx$ 2

25. $\int_1^4 \left(x^2 + \frac{2}{x^2}\right) dx$ $22\frac{1}{2}$

26. $\int_{-1}^1 12x(x + 1)(x - 1)\, dx$ 0

27. $\int_4^5 (x^2 + 6x - 7)\, dx$ $40\frac{1}{3}$

28. $\int_0^2 (x - 4x^2)\, dx$ $-8\frac{2}{3}$

29. $\int_{-1}^0 (1 - x^2)\, dx$ $\frac{2}{3}$

30. $\int_1^4 (3x^2 - 6x)\, dx$ 18

31. $\int_{-2}^3 (x + 2)(x - 3)\, dx$ $-20\frac{5}{6}$

Graph each function. Then, find the area between the graph of the function and the *x*-axis for the given interval by integrating. 32–37. See Teacher's Answer Key for graphs.

C

32. $f(x) = -x$ for $x = 1$ to $x = 4$ $7\frac{1}{2}$ sq units

33. $f(x) = x^3$ for $x = -1$ to $x = 2$ $\frac{17}{4}$ sq units

34. $f(x) = -x^2$ for $x = 0$ to $x = 5$ $\frac{125}{3}$ sq units

35. $f(x) = -x^3$ for $x = -4$ to $x = 0$ 64 sq units

36. $f(x) = \frac{3x^2 - 18x + 15}{5}$ for $x = 0$ to $x = 6$ $9\frac{1}{5}$ sq units

37. $f(x) = 9 - 3x^2$ for $x = 0$ to $x = 3$ about 20.8 sq units

LESSON 17-5   THE FUNDAMENTAL THEOREM OF CALCULUS   949

Critical Thinking

38. a. Use integration and the fundamental theorem of calculus to prove that for any numbers a and b, $\int_a^b x^3 \, dx = \frac{1}{4}(b^4 - a^4)$.

b. Find a formula for $\int_a^b x^n \, dx$ that would hold for any integer n.

38. See margin.

Applications and Problem Solving

39. Business The life table function of a population is a function ℓ such that $\ell(x)$ is the number of people in the population who reach the age of x years at any time during the year. Under the appropriate conditions, $\int_a^b \ell(x) \, dx$ gives the number of people in the populations between the exact ages of a and b years, inclusive. The marketing manager for College Connections Inc. has determined that the life table function for the region of the country she is considering is $\ell(x) = 12,000\sqrt{100 - x}$.

a. Find the number of people in the region that are between 18 and 21 years old. 322,994

b. A sister company, Career Connections Inc., finds jobs for clients and also finds people to fill jobs at local companies. Their largest market is recent college graduates. The marketing manager at Career Connections would like to know the number of people in this region that are between the ages of 21 and 23. Find this number. 211,961

40. Medicine Arteries carry blood away from the heart to the other parts of the body. Let r represent the radius of a cylindrical artery that is 1 unit long. A certain blood cell is x units from the center of a cross section of the artery. Then, the volume of blood that can flow through the artery in a unit of time is given by $V = \int_0^r \frac{k}{\ell}x(r^2 - x^2) \, dx$, where k is a constant depending on the difference in pressure at the two ends of the artery and on the viscosity of the blood. Find V. $\frac{kr^4}{4\ell}$

41. Hydraulics A cylindrical water tank is 100 feet high and has a diameter of 100 feet. The work, W, in foot-pounds that is required to pump all the water out of the tank is given by $W = (156,250\pi)\int_0^{100} (100 - y) \, dy$. How much work is required? $781,250,000\pi$ or 2,454,369,261 foot-pounds

Mixed Review

42. Find the inverse of $y = 7 - x^2$. **(Lesson 3-3)** $y = \pm\sqrt{7 - x}$

43. Write the polynomial equation of least degree with roots of $-3, 0.5, 6$, and 2. **(Lesson 4-1)** $2x^4 - 11x^3 - 19x^2 + 84x - 36 = 0$

44. Write an equation of the line with parametric equations $x = -5t - 1$ and $y = 2t + 10$ in slope-intercept form. **(Lesson 8-6)** $y = -\frac{2}{5}x + \frac{48}{5}$

45. Write the equation $2x^2 - y^2 - 16x + 4y + 24 = 0$ in standard form. Then find the coordinates of the center, the foci, the vertices, and the equations of the asymptotes of the graph and sketch the graph. **(Lesson 10-4)** See margin.

46. Use the binomial theorem to expand $(5x - 1)^3$. **(Lesson 12-6)** See margin.

47. Education The scores of a national achievement test are normally distributed with a mean of 500 and a standard deviation of 100. What percentage of those who took the test had a score more than 100 points above or below the mean? **(Lesson 15-4)** 31.7%

48. Find $\int x^3(2 - 5x^4)^7 \, dx$. **(Lesson 17-4)**

$48. -\frac{1}{160}$
$(2 - 5x^4)^8 + C$

49. College Entrance Exam Choose the best answer. C
Triangle ABC is inscribed in circle O, and $\overleftrightarrow{CD}$ is tangent to $\odot O$ at point C. If $m\angle BCD = 40°$, find $m\angle A$.

(A) 60°   (B) 50°   (C) 40°
(D) 30°   (E) 20°

DECISION MAKING

Planning a Move

The average American moves 10 times in a lifetime. Every move brings with it new hopes and opportunities, but also some outlay of money, loss of friends and security, and temporary feelings of dislocation and confusion. The key to a successful move is careful planning to assure that the confusion is brief and the expense is minimal. What can you do to accomplish these goals? 1–3. See students' work.

1. Describe a place, other than where you live now, where you think you would like to live. What advantages does that place have over your present home? What disadvantages are there?

2. Plan a move to the place described in Exercise 1. What services will you have to have cut off in your present home and which ones will you have to arrange for your new home? How will you pack and transport your belongings? As you draw up your plan, look for ways you can cut expenses, minimize your feelings of dislocation, and pave the way for a smooth transition to life in your new home.

3. **Project** Work with your group to complete one of the projects listed at the right based on the information you gathered in Exercises 1–2.

PROJECTS

- *Conduct an interview.*
- *Write a book report.*
- *Write a proposal.*
- *Write an article for the school paper.*
- *Write a report.*
- *Make a display.*
- *Make a graph or chart.*
- *Plan an activity.*
- *Design a checklist.*

EXTENDING THE LESSON

Math Power: Reasoning

Let $f(x)$ be a continuous function and $F(x)$ be an antiderivative of f. Prove that $\int_b^a f(x)\, dx = -\int_a^b f(x)\, dx$ and $\int_a^b f(x)\, dx + \int_b^c f(x)\, dx = \int_a^c f(x)\, dx$.

$\int_b^a f(x)\, dx = F(a) - F(b) = -[F(b) - F(a)] = -\int_a^b f(x)\, dx$

$\int_a^b f(x)\, dx + \int_b^c f(x)\, dx = [F(b) - F(a)] + [F(c) - F(b)] = F(c) - F(a) = \int_a^c f(x)\, dx$

Decision Making

This activity provides students an opportunity to work together on a given problem. You may wish to refer to pages T20–T21 and page 912c for the various elements of cooperative groups and specific goals and strategies for using them.

Additional Answers

45. equation:
$\frac{(x - 4)^2}{2} - \frac{(y - 2)^2}{4} = 1$
center: (4, 2)
foci: $(4 \pm \sqrt{6}, 2)$
vertices: $(4 \pm \sqrt{2}, 2)$
asymptotes:
$y = 2 \pm \sqrt{2}(x - 4)$

(4, 2)
$(4 - \sqrt{2}, 2)$ $(4 + \sqrt{2}, 2)$

46. $125x^3 - 75x^2 + 15x - 1$

Enrichment Masters Booklet, p. 118

17-5 Enrichment Worksheet

Chain Rule

An alternate way to define a derivative is
$\frac{dy}{dx} = \lim_{\triangle x \to 0} \frac{\triangle y}{\triangle x}$, where $\triangle y$ is $f(x + h) - f(x)$ and $\triangle x = h$.

Suppose $y = f(u)$ and $u = g(x)$. If both $\triangle x$ and $\triangle u \to 0$,
$\frac{dy}{dx} = \lim_{\triangle x \to 0} \frac{\triangle y}{\triangle u} \cdot \frac{\triangle u}{\triangle x} = \lim_{\triangle u \to 0} \frac{\triangle y}{\triangle u} \cdot \lim_{\triangle x \to 0} \frac{\triangle u}{\triangle x} = \frac{dy}{du} \cdot \frac{du}{dx}$.

This is known as the chain rule. It provides a short cut for finding some derivatives.

Example If $y = (x^2 - 2x)^2$, find $\frac{dy}{dx}$ by the chain rule.

Let $u = x^2 - 2x$, then $f(u) = u^2$.
$\frac{dy}{dx} = 2u \cdot (2x - 2)$ or $\frac{dy}{dx} = 2(x^2 - 2x)(2x - 2) = 4x^3 - 12x^2 + 8x$

Check: $y = (x^2 - 2x)^2 = x^4 - 4x^3 + 4x^2$
$\frac{dy}{dx} = 4x^3 - 12x^2 + 8x$ ✓

Use the chain rule to find the derivative of each function. If possible, check by expansion or multiplication.

1. $y = (x^2 - 1)^2$
$2(x^2 - 1)(2x) = 4x(x^2 - 1)$

2. $y = (\sqrt{x} + 2)^3$
$3(\sqrt{x} + 2)^2(\frac{x^{-\frac{1}{2}}}{2}) = \frac{3x^{-\frac{1}{2}}}{2}(\sqrt{x} + 2)^2$

3. $y = (x + \frac{1}{x})^2$
$2(x + \frac{1}{x})(1 - x^{-2})$

4. $y = (x^2 - 3x + 2)^2$
$2(x^2 - 3x + 2)(2x - 3) = 4x^3 - 18x^2 + 26x - 12$

5. $y = \sqrt{2x + 3}$
$\frac{1}{2}(2x + 3)^{-\frac{1}{2}}(2) = (2x + 3)^{-\frac{1}{2}}$

6. $y = (3x - 1)^{-\frac{1}{2}}$
$\frac{-1}{2}(3x - 1)^{-\frac{3}{2}}(3) = \frac{-3}{2}(3x - 1)^{-\frac{3}{2}}$

7. $y = \frac{1}{2x - 5}$
$-(2x - 5)^{-2}(2) = -2(2x - 5)^{-2}$

8. $y = \frac{2}{x^2 - 1}$
$-2(x^2 - 1)^{-2}(2x) = -4x(x^2 - 1)^{-2}$

T118
Glencoe Division, Macmillan/McGraw-Hill

VOCABULARY

Upon completing this chapter, you should be familiar with the following terms:

antiderivative	**939**	**939**	integral
definite integral	**945**	**931**	lower sums
derivative notation	**923**	**925**	marginal cost function
differentiable	**923**	**925**	marginal revenue function
differentiation	**923**	**938**	Riemann sum
fundamental theorem of calculus	**945**	**931**	upper sums

SKILLS AND CONCEPTS

OBJECTIVES AND EXAMPLES	REVIEW EXERCISES

Upon completing this chapter, you should be able to:

- use limit theorems to evaluate the limit of a function. **(Lesson 17-1)**

Evaluate $\lim\limits_{n\to\infty} \dfrac{n^2+n-6}{n^2}$.

$$\lim_{n\to\infty} \frac{n^2+n-6}{n^2} = \lim_{n\to\infty}\frac{n^2}{n^2} + \lim_{n\to\infty}\frac{n}{n^2} - \lim_{n\to\infty}\frac{6}{n^2}$$
$$= \lim_{n\to\infty} 1 + \lim_{n\to\infty}\frac{1}{n} - \lim_{n\to\infty}\frac{6}{n^2}$$
$$= 1$$

Use Theorem 10 to evaluate $\lim\limits_{x\to 0}\dfrac{\sin x}{2x}$.

$$\lim_{x\to 0}\frac{\sin x}{2x} = \lim_{x\to 0}\frac{1}{2}\cdot\lim_{x\to 0}\frac{\sin x}{x}$$
$$= \frac{1}{2}\cdot 1 \text{ or } \frac{1}{2}$$

Use these exercises to review and prepare for the chapter test.

Evaluate each limit.

1. $\lim\limits_{x\to 0}\left(4^x + \dfrac{1}{4^x}\right)$ 2
2. $\lim\limits_{x\to 0}\dfrac{\sqrt{x+4}-2}{x}$ $\frac{1}{4}$
3. $\lim\limits_{x\to 0}\dfrac{3x^3-2x}{2x^2-3x}$ $\frac{2}{3}$
4. $\lim\limits_{x\to 0}\dfrac{\sqrt{3x^2+x+1}}{\sqrt[3]{3x^3-x+8}}$ $\frac{1}{2}$

Evaluate the limit of $f[g(x)]$ as x approaches 1 for each $f(x)$ and $g(x)$.

5. $f(x)=x+2$ $g(x)=-3x$ –1
6. $f(x)=x^2-1$ $g(x)=2x+1$ 8

Use Theorem 10 to evaluate each limit.

7. $\lim\limits_{x\to 0}\dfrac{1-\cos^2 x}{x^2}$ 1
8. $\lim\limits_{x\to 0}\left(x-\dfrac{\sin 3x}{x}\right)$ –3

Alternate Review Strategy

To provide a brief in-class review, you may wish to read the following questions to the class and have them answer verbally.

- find the derivative of a function (**Lesson 17-2**)

Find the derivative of
$f(x) = (2x^3)(x^2 + 1)$.

$\dfrac{d}{dx}[2x^3(x^2 + 1)]$

$= 2x^3 \dfrac{d}{dx}(x^2 + 1) + (x^2 + 1)\dfrac{d}{dx}2x^3$

$= (2x^3)(2x) + (x^2 + 1)(6x^2)$

$= 4x^4 + 6x^4 + 6x^2$

$= 10x^4 + 6x^2$

Find the derivative of each function.

9. $f(x) = x^6 \quad 6x^5$

10. $f(x) = 4x^3 \quad 12x^2$

11. $f(x) = 3x + 4x^2 \quad 3 + 8x$

12. $f(x) = (x^4 - 3x^2)(5x^3) \quad 35x^6 - 75x^4$

13. $f(x) = \sqrt{2x^3 - 6x} \quad \dfrac{3x^2 - 3}{\sqrt{2x^3 - 6x}}$

14. $f(x) = 4x + \dfrac{(x-1)^2}{2x} \quad \dfrac{9}{2} - \dfrac{1}{2x^2}$

Evaluate each limit.

1. $\displaystyle\lim_{x \to 2} \dfrac{x^2 - 5x + 6}{x^2 - 4} \quad -\dfrac{1}{4}$

2. $\displaystyle\lim_{x \to 0} (1 - 4^x) \quad 0$

3. What differentiation formula might be used to evaluate
$\dfrac{d}{dx}\left(5x^2 \sqrt{3x^3 - 2}\right)$?

$\dfrac{d}{dx}(uv) = u\dfrac{dv}{dx} + v\dfrac{du}{dx}$

- find the area between a curve and the x-axis by using the limit of areas of rectangles (**Lesson 17-3**)

Find the area of the region between the graph of $y = 3x^2$ and the x-axis from $x = 0$ to $x = 1$.

$A = \displaystyle\lim_{n \to \infty} \sum_{i=1}^{n} f(x_i)(x_i - x_{i-1})$

$= \displaystyle\lim_{n \to \infty} \sum_{i=1}^{n} 3\left(\dfrac{i}{n}\right)^2 \left(\dfrac{1}{n}\right)$

$= \displaystyle\lim_{n \to \infty} \dfrac{3}{n^3}(1^2 + 2^2 + \ldots + n^2)$

$= \displaystyle\lim_{n \to \infty} \dfrac{3}{n^3}\left(\dfrac{n(n+1)(2n+1)}{6}\right)$

$= \displaystyle\lim_{n \to \infty} \dfrac{1}{2}(2 + \dfrac{3}{n} + \dfrac{1}{n^3})$

$= 1$

Write a limit to find the area between each curve and the x-axis for the given interval. Then find the area.

15. $y = 2x$ from $x = 0$ to $x = 2$ $\quad 4 \text{ unit}^2$

16. $y = x^3$ from $x = 0$ to $x = 1$ $\quad \dfrac{1}{4} \text{ unit}^2$

17. $y = x^2$ from $x = 3$ to $x = 4$ $\quad \dfrac{37}{3} \text{ unit}^2$

18. $y = 6x^2$ from $x = 1$ to $x = 2$ $\quad 14 \text{ unit}^2$

4. If the derivative of $f(x)$ is a quadratic polynomial, what can you conclude about the function f? **It is a cubic polynomial.**

5. What limit is used to calculate the area between the curve $y = x^2$ and the x-axis from $x = 0$ to $x = 4$?

$\displaystyle\lim_{n \to \infty} \sum_{i=1}^{n} \left(\dfrac{4}{n}\right)\left(\dfrac{4i}{n}\right)^2$

6. List two different antiderivatives of $f(x) = 6x^2 - 6x + 4$.
Sample answer: $2x^3 - 3x^2 + 4x - 5$; $2x^3 - 3x^2 + 4x + 1$

7. According to the fundamental theorem of calculus, what does $\int_a^b F'(x)\, dx$ equal? $\quad F(b) - F(a)$

- use integration formulas (**Lesson 17-4**)

Find $\int (6x - 4)\, dx$.

$\int (6x - 4)\,dx = \int 6x\, dx - \int 4\, dx$

$= 6\int x\, dx - \int 4\, dx$

$= 6\left(\dfrac{x^2}{2}\right) + C_1 - (4x + C_2)$

$= 3x^2 - 4x + C$

Find each integral.

19. $\int \dfrac{4}{x^2}\, dx \quad -\dfrac{4}{x} + C$

20. $\int 5x^3\, dx \quad \dfrac{5x^4}{4} + C$

21. $\int (1 - x)\, dx \quad x - \dfrac{x^2}{2} + C$

22. $\int \dfrac{1}{\sqrt{x + 3}}\, dx \quad 2\sqrt{x + 3} + C$

Find the antiderivative of each function.

23. $f(x) = 5(x + 3)^9 \quad \dfrac{(x+3)^{10}}{2} + C$

24. $f(x) = 1 - \dfrac{1}{x^2} \quad x + \dfrac{1}{x} + C$

8. Find the integral
$\int \left(x^2 - \dfrac{1}{x + 2}\right)dx$.

$\dfrac{1}{3}x^3 - \ln|x + 2| + C$

For more information on other methods of alternate assessment, you may wish to refer to Glencoe's *Alternate Assessment in the Mathematics Classroom*.

Two multiple-choice tests (Forms 1A and 1B) and two free-response tests (Forms 2A and 2B) are provided in the *Evaluation Masters*. Chapter 17 Test, Form 1A is shown below. Chapter 17 Test, Form 2A is shown on the next page.

Evaluation Masters Booklet,
pp. 209–210

OBJECTIVES AND EXAMPLES	REVIEW EXERCISES

■ use the fundamental theorem of calculus to evaluate definite integrals and to find area   **(Lesson 17-5)**

Evaluate $\int_4^7 (x^2 - 3)\,dx$.

$$\int_4^7 (x^2 - 3)\,dx = \frac{x^3}{3} - 3x \Big|_4^7$$
$$= \left(\frac{7^3}{3} - 3(7)\right) - \left(\frac{4^3}{3} - 3(4)\right)$$
$$= 84$$

Evaluate each definite integral.

25. $\int_2^4 6x\,dx$ 36

26. $\int_{-3}^2 3x^2\,dx$ 35

27. $\int_{-2}^2 (3x^2 - x + 5)\,dx$ 36

28. $\int_0^4 (x-2)(2x+3)\,dx$ $10\frac{2}{3}$

APPLICATIONS AND PROBLEM SOLVING

29. **Physics**   The kinetic energy of an object with mass m is given by the formula $k(t) = \frac{1}{2}m[v(t)]^2$, where $v(t)$ is the velocity of the object at time t. Suppose $v(t) = \frac{50}{1 + t^2}$ for all $t \geq 0$. What does the measure of the kinetic energy of an object approach as time approaches 100?   **(Lesson 17-1)**   0.0000125 m

30. **Business**   The controller for the AMC Electronics Company has used the production figures for the last few months to determine that the function $c(x) = -9x^5 + 135x^3 + 10{,}000$ approximates the cost of producing x thousands of one of their products. Find the marginal cost per unit production if they are now producing 2600 units.   **(Lesson 17-2)** $681.41

31. **Automobile Industry**   An advertisement for a new sports car claims that the car can accelerate from 0 to 50 miles per hour in 7 seconds.   **(Lesson 17-4)**
    a. Find the acceleration of the sports car in feet per second squared.   10.48 ft/s^2
    b. Write an equation for the velocity of the sports car at t seconds. $v(t) = 10.48t + C_1$
    c. Write an equation for the distance traveled in t seconds. $d(t) = 5.24t^2 + C_1 t + C_2$

32. **Geometry**   Find the area inside the parabola with equation $f(x) = 3x^2 - 2x + 1$ between $x = -1$ and $x = 2$.   **(Lesson 17-5)**
    13.5 units^2

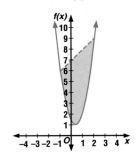

Evaluate each limit.

1. $\lim\limits_{x\to 3}\dfrac{x^2 - 9}{x^3 - 27}$ $\dfrac{2}{9}$

2. $\lim\limits_{x\to 1}\dfrac{x^2 - 2x + 3}{3x^2 - 5}$ -1

3. $\lim\limits_{x\to\infty}\dfrac{(x - 2)(x + 1)}{x^2}$ 1

4. $\lim\limits_{x\to 4}\sqrt{x}(x - 1)^2$ 18

5. $\lim\limits_{x\to 0}\dfrac{\sin(-2x)}{3x}$ $-\dfrac{2}{3}$

6. $\lim\limits_{x\to 1}\dfrac{x - 1}{x^3 - 1}$ $\dfrac{1}{3}$

7. Evaluate the limit of $f[g(x)]$ as x approaches 1 for $f(x) = x^3$ and $g(x) = 3x^2$. 27

Find the derivative of each function.

8. $f(x) = 4x^3 - 4$ $12x^2$

9. $f(x) = (x + 3)^2$ $2(x + 3)$

10. $f(x) = 6(x^4 - 5)$ $24x^3$

11. $f(x) = (2x^4)(x^3 + 3x^2)$ $14x^6 + 36x^5$

12. $f(x) = \dfrac{2x}{1 + x^2}$ $\dfrac{2 - 2x^2}{1 + 2x^2 + x^4}$

13. $f(x) = \sqrt{4x^2 - 1}$ $\dfrac{4x}{\sqrt{4x^2 - 1}}$

Write a limit to find the area between each curve and the x-axis for the given interval. Then find the area.

14. $y = x^3$ from $x = 0$ to $x = 2$

$\lim\limits_{n\to\infty}\sum\limits_{i=1}^{n}\left(\dfrac{2i}{n}\right)^3\left(\dfrac{2}{n}\right)$; 4 unit^2

15. $y = 3x^2$ from $x = 1$ to $x = 3$

$\lim\limits_{n\to\infty}\sum\limits_{i=1}^{n}3\left(\dfrac{3i}{n}\right)^2\left(\dfrac{3}{n}\right) - \lim\limits_{n\to\infty}\sum\limits_{i=1}^{n}3\left(\dfrac{i}{n}\right)^2\left(\dfrac{1}{n}\right)$; 26 unit^2

Find each integral.

16. $\displaystyle\int(1 - 2x)\,dx$ $x - x^2 + C$

17. $\displaystyle\int(3x^2 + 4x + 7)\,dx$ $x^3 + 2x^2 + 7x + C$

18. $\displaystyle\int\dfrac{1}{x^2}\,dx$ $-\dfrac{1}{x} + C$

Find the antiderivative of each function.

19. $f(x) = \sqrt[3]{x^2}$ $\dfrac{3}{5}\sqrt[3]{x^5} + C$

20. $f(x) = \dfrac{1}{2x^3}$ $-\dfrac{1}{4x^2} + C$

Evaluate each definite integral.

21. $\displaystyle\int_0^1(2x + 3)\,dx$ 4

22. $\displaystyle\int_1^3(-x^2 - x + 3)\,dx$ $-\dfrac{20}{3}$

23. $\displaystyle\int_1^4\left(x^2 + \dfrac{2}{x^2}\right)dx$ $22\dfrac{1}{2}$

24. **Physics** The period of a simple pendulum is given by the formula $T(\ell) = 2\pi\sqrt{\dfrac{\ell}{g}}$, where ℓ is the length of the pendulum and g is the acceleration due to gravity. When ℓ is measured in feet, g is 32 ft/s^2. Find a formula for the rate of change of the period of a pendulum with respect to the length of the pendulum. $T'(\ell) = \dfrac{\pi}{\sqrt{32\ell}}$

25. **Geometry** The volume of a sphere is given by $V = \pi\displaystyle\int_{-r}^{r}(r^2 - x^2)\,dx$, where r is the radius. Use this formula to find the volume of a sphere with a radius of 2 units. $\dfrac{32\pi}{3}$

Bonus Evaluate $\lim\limits_{x\to 0}\dfrac{\tan x}{x}$. 1

Evaluation Masters Booklet, pp. 213–214

Case Study 1

Buying a Home

Owning a home has always been part of the American dream. In recent years, however, as the cost of buying a home has risen markedly in comparison with personal income, the dream has begun to fade. During the 1980s, the median price of a new single-family house in the United States rose from $64,600 to $123,000, a 90.4% increase. New home prices in 1990 were highest in the Northeast, averaging $157,000, and lowest in the South, averaging $99,000. Average monthly mortgage payments rose from $599 in 1980 to $1054 in 1989.

Figure 1–1 Median sales price of single-family houses, 1970–1990

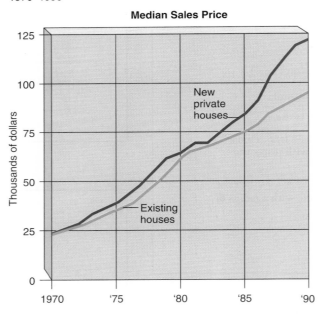

While housing costs were soaring, the after-tax income of low- and middle-income families remained almost unchanged. Only the top one fifth of income earners gained substantially during the 1980s. Yet even the average after-tax rise in income posted by that group—34%—paled in comparison with the overall increase in housing prices.

One reason for the huge rise in prices was a steadily increasing demand for existing houses. Sales of existing houses fell off between 1978 and 1982. But beginning in 1982, when 1,990,000 houses were sold, annual sales rose steadily, peaking at 3,594,000 in 1988. Prices have leveled off since then, although in selected areas they continue to skyrocket. In Honolulu, for example, the median price of a new home rose from $215,000 in 1988 to $345,000 in 1990, a 60% increase in just two years.

Figure 1–2 Single-family houses sold, 1970–1990

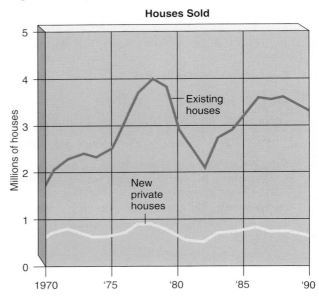

Homes and Homeowners

U.S. Census Bureau figures show that there were 105.8 million housing units in the United States in 1990. Of these, 60.0 million were occupied by their owners, 33.7 million were occupied by renters, and 12.2 million were vacant. Only 8% of all home owners are African-American, and 4% are Hispanic. This compares unfavorably to the general population that is 12% African-American and 9% Hispanic.

The great majority of American homes—72%, including mobile homes—are traditional single-unit structures. The typical home has 4 to 7 rooms (only 12% have 8 or more rooms; about the same number have 3 or fewer rooms). In 1989, the median age of all houses was 27 years. Only 10% of all houses are 70 or more years of age.

Along with price, several other features of new homes have changed greatly in recent years. Between 1970 and 1990, the average size of new single-family dwellings increased from 1500 square feet to 2080 square feet, a 38.7% increase. During the same period, the percent of homes with central air conditioning increased from 34% to 76%, and those with one or more fireplaces increased from 35% to 66%. By contrast, the portion with one or no bathrooms decreased from 32% to 8%.

Figure 1–3 Gas was the heating fuel of choice in single-family homes in 1990.

Home Heating Fuels, 1990

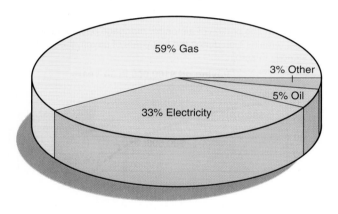

A House As an Investment

For those who can afford it, a house is one of the best investments they can make. Even in weak economic climates, home values tend to *appreciate* (increase) steadily. At a modest 5% rate of appreciation, a new home purchased for $120,000 will be worth $153,000 in only five years, a $33,000 profit should the owner decide to sell.

Since few people have the cash to purchase a home outright, most make only a down payment in cash, financing the balance with a loan, called a *mortgage*. Borrowers agree to pay back the loan, with interest, in monthly installments over a

specified period of time, usually 15, 20, or 30 years. The down payment may be as low as 5% of the selling price, but is generally higher. In 1989, the average down payment for first-time buyers was 15.8% of the sales price; for repeat buyers it was 30.3%. The advantage of a high down payment is that it will lower the monthly mortgage payments. But it carries a risk, too: the higher the down payment, the less cash the buyer will have on hand to deal with emergencies like illness or job loss.

Two principal types of mortgages are available. A *fixed-rate mortgage* (FRM) is paid off at a fixed rate of interest. Monthly payments remain the same throughout the period of repayment regardless of fluctuations in interest rates.

In the beginning, an *adjustable-rate mortgage* (ARM) is paid off at an interest rate that is lower than that of a fixed-rate mortgage. The rate, however, may be raised or lowered several times during the life of the loan. An agreed-upon *cap* limits the total amount the rate may be raised and also limits the yearly rate increase. Home owners with ARMs have the advantage of initially lower monthly payments than those of FRM holders who borrowed the same amount to begin with. In later years, however, ARM monthly payments will increase steadily, eventually surpassing FRM payments. ARMs are tailored for young buyers with relatively low incomes who expect their incomes to increase steadily through the years. The risk is that if, due to unforeseen circumstances, incomes do not increase, borrowers carrying ARMs may be unable to make their higher monthly payments and could lose their homes. ARMs are also a good alternative if a buyer plans to move within a short period of time, for example, 5 years.

A Case History

George and Melinda Bauer have decided to buy their first home. They are each 30 years old, the average age of first-time buyers in the United States, and have a combined gross annual income of $42,000. The home they want to buy is on the market for $128,000, but through a series of offers and counter-offers, they are able to negotiate a price of $120,000 with the owner. They make a $20,000 down payment ($16\frac{2}{3}$%), leaving $100,000 to be financed by a mortgage lender.

With the help of their realtor, the Bauers are able to find a mortgage company offering a 30-year, 9% FRM. Before they can obtain the money, however, they must provide the company with tax records, banking records, proof of employment, credit histories, and a myriad of other records to prove that they are good credit risks.

Figure 1–4 Monthly payments on 9% fixed rate mortgages

	9% Annual Percent Rate				
	Monthly Payments (Payments and Interest)*				
Amount Financed	10 Years	15 Years	20 Years	25 Years	30 Years
$ 25,000	316.69	253.57	224.93	209.80	201.16
30,000	380.03	304.28	269.92	251.76	241.39
35,000	443.36	354.99	314.90	293.72	281.62
40,000	506.70	405.71	359.89	335.68	321.85
45,000	570.04	466.42	404.88	377.64	362.08
50,000	633.38	507.13	449.86	419.60	402.31
60,000	760.05	608.56	539.84	503.52	482.77
70,000	886.73	709.99	629.81	587.44	563.24
80,000	1013.41	811.41	719.78	671.36	643.70
90,000	1140.08	912.84	809.75	755.28	724.16
100,000	1266.76	1014.27	899.73	839.20	804.62
120,000	1520.10	1217.12	1079.68	1007.04	965.54
140,000	1773.46	1419.98	1259.62	1174.88	1126.48
160,000	2026.82	1622.82	1439.56	1342.72	1297.40
180,000	2280.16	1825.68	1619.50	1510.56	1448.32
200,000	2533.52	2028.54	1799.46	1678.40	1609.24

Mortgage companies require that borrowers earn enough so that monthly payments do not exceed 28% of their gross income. Twenty-eight percent of the Bauers' monthly income of $3500 is $980, well above the calculated $804.62 monthly mortgage payment. Therefore, they easily meet the 28% requirement. Furthermore, they are judged excellent risks by the company because of their credit history. Five weeks after applying for the loan, they learn that, like 85% of those who apply for mortgages, they have been approved for the loan. One-time costs relating to the purchase of the house, called *closing costs*, amount to $2645. Moving into their new home from their apartment costs $1580. Lastly, the mortgage company charges 1 *point* (1 percent of the loan), or $1000, for its services.

Cost to Purchase a Home

Down payment	$20,000
Closing costs	2,645
Moving costs	1,580
Mortgage fee	1,000
Total	$25,225

Is It Worth It?

Home owners face substantially greater operating costs than renters face. Furthermore, the cost of borrowing money is enormous. Over 30 years, the Bauers will pay a whopping $189,663.20 in interest on their $100,000 loan, repaying a total of $289,663.20 to the mortgage company.

On the other hand, most Americans move long before they pay off their mortgages. Through the sale of their homes they are able to repay mortgage lenders and earn a profit, which most then reinvest as down payments on more expensive homes. Renters never earn profits and can afford more expensive housing only if their financial situation improves markedly.

In addition, mortgage holders have an enormous tax advantage over renters. Mortgage interest payments are not subject to federal income taxes. The result is large tax savings to the mortgage holder, especially in the early years of repayment on a loan, when almost the entire monthly installment consists of interest.

Figure 1–5 The portion of a monthly mortgage payment that is interest remains high during the first years of payoff, then drops off steadily to zero.

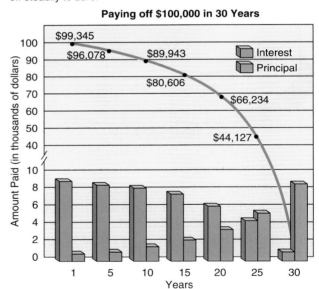

The major reasons that people want to own their own homes, however, are probably intangible. Home ownership conveys a sense of pride, security, and independence to the owner. Even if prices of new homes continue to skyrocket, owning one will remain an essential part of the American dream.

Case Study 2

Trashing the Planet

Can you imagine the archaeologists of the future digging into the ruins of the late 1900s to analyze what civilization was like then? Instead of buried cities, the memorials to American society would be its landfills. For example, between 1960 and 1986, the amount of plastic in trash in the United States increased by a factor of 26, effectively describing our lifestyle as that of a "throwaway" society.

Trash (technically, *municipal solid waste*) is becoming more problematic to the American public than air and water pollution. In reality, trash also affects air and water. Nearly one half of all landfills are within one mile of a drinking-water resource. Emissions escaping from decaying materials can contain 20 different toxic synthetic organic chemicals, some of which are carcinogens, such as vinyl chloride and carbon tetrachloride.

Americans dispose of 450,000 tons of residential and commercial trash per day. Landfills receive about 80% of the trash generated in the United States. We are running out of places to dump this trash. In 1986, there were approximately 6000 active trash landfills in the United States. In 1993, the number had been reduced by half, and by 2006, it is estimated that only about 20% of the 6000 will still be in operation.

Recycling to Reduce Waste

Experts estimate that ideally, 85–90% of the trash generated by households could be recycled. However, less than 65% of U.S. households participate in the recycling effort in some way. Only a few industries recycle materials to any great extent.

Recycling programs require a great deal of education, training, and up-front money to become effective. It's just too easy to throw everything away. Some basic separation of your trash can make recycling efficient and economical for your community. However, recycling does not solve all trash problems.

Not everything can be recycled effectively. Some items such as glass, aluminum, and steel can be recycled again and again without degeneration of the quality of the product. However, when paper is recycled, about 10% of the fibers are lost during processing and the end product is of lesser quality than the original material. The fibers in the highest quality of paper can usually last through 10 generations of recycling before the fibers are useless. Plastic products have the shortest recyclable life. The chemical properties of plastics change in the recycling process.

Figure 2–1 Experts estimate that 85–90% of household trash can be recycled. However, larger cities, like New York City, recycle only about 6% of their residential solid waste.

Average Composition of US. Trash

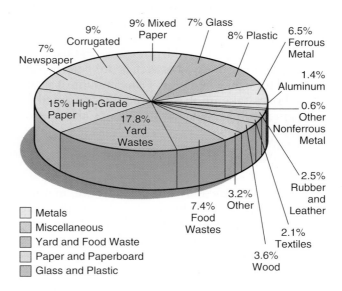

Metals
Miscellaneous
Yard and Food Waste
Paper and Paperboard
Glass and Plastic

Another drawback to the recycling effort is the actual cost of recycling the materials. Unlike aluminum, the market for some types of materials,

Figure 2–2 The data below illustrate how wasteful Americans have become.

- Every two weeks, we throw away enough glass bottles and jars to fill the 1350-foot twin towers of the World Trade Center in New York.

- Americans use 2.5 million plastic bottles every hour, of which only a small portion are recycled.

- Households and industries throw away enough aluminum to rebuild the entire commercial airfleet every three months.

- Americans throw away enough iron and steel to continuously supply all of the nation's auto makers.

- Each year, we dispose of 24 million tons of leaves and grass clippings, which could be composted instead of taking up space in landfills.

- More than 500,000 trees are used each week to produce the newspapers that are never recycled.

like newspaper, is so glutted that the newspaper itself has little monetary value (less than $0.05 per ton). The storage, handling, and processing of these materials often cost the recycling company more than they yield. This is why many centers no longer accept some materials for recycling.

We as consumers can help the recycling effort by buying products made from recycled materials. In this way, our demands make recycled materials more attractive to manufacturers, causing a greater need for the supply of recycled materials. For example, McDonald's restaurants used to package all of their sandwiches in polystyrene boxes. Through awareness of the amount of space these boxes take up in landfills, they returned to wrapping their sandwiches in paper products.

International Environmental Concerns

While Americans may think they are making great strides toward saving the planet, they lag behind other countries in recycling efforts. The U.S. recycles about 10% of its glass and 27% of its paper. In Europe and Japan, an average of 31% of the glass and 40% of the paper is recycled. European countries are much more advanced in the effort to compost organic materials. For example, nearly one million tons of compost is produced in France each year and used in their vineyards.

While trash is not a great environmental concern in Europe and Asia, water and air pollution is. Until recently, there have been few regulations on industrial pollution and safety procedures. This has often meant that people near industrial plants and the workers in those plants have been exposed to toxic materials at levels not permitted in the United States. You may think, "Well, that doesn't affect me." Remember that the winds of Earth blow everywhere. Thus, what happens in one place does affect the world environmentally.

Scientists are closely watching the effects of the fires and oil spills in Kuwait as a result of the Gulf War in 1991. Many scientists feared the smoke from these fires would affect the weather worldwide. On November 6, 1991, the last of the 650 fires was extinguished. The task was accomplished much more quickly than experts had estimated. Even though the worldwide environmental effects of the smoke are not known, we do know of the trouble faced by the people of Kuwait. The acid rain resulting from water mixing with the toxic smoke has harmed much of the vegetation in the area. Because of the smoke cloud, the temperatures in Kuwait were often 20° below normal. The particles in the air have hampered breathing for many. Some experts estimate that as many as 1000 Kuwaitis died in 1992 from the polluted air.

Figure 2–3 About 350 miles of Saudi Arabia's coastline is oil-soaked and because the waters of the Gulf move so slowly, it may be a long time before the water is safe.

In addition to air pollution, the war brought about water pollution as well. The Persian Gulf is slowly recovering from a spill of 250 million gallons of oil—more than 20 times larger than the spill created near Alaska by the *Exxon Valdez* in 1989. The oil from the burning wells has also formed pools that are sinking into the sands of Kuwait, affecting the plant and animal life as well as the drinking water in the subterranean levels.

Only observations of future global weather patterns and studies of atmospheric conditions will determine if the Gulf War affected the far regions of Earth.

Protecting the Ozone Layer

Coal miners used to carry canaries with them into the mines to determine if there were toxic gases building up in the areas where they were working. If the canary died, they knew that the buildup of gases was dangerous. The hole in the ozone layer over the Antarctic has been the world's canary for the past two decades. The greater the hole grows, the more dangerous are the global effects of a thinner ozone layer.

Man-made chemicals, such as chlorofluorocarbons (CFCs), are attacking the ozone layer. While the effects are most dramatic over the Antarctic, the rest of Earth's atmosphere is also being affected. Because of wind patterns, pollutants, and atmospheric ice, the region over the Antarctic is most sensitive to the depletion of the ozone layer.

But why is the ozone so important? The ozone layer acts as a sunscreen for Earth. It protects the planet from the sun's harmful ultraviolet (UV) rays. With more UV rays being let through the at-

mosphere, there is a greater possibility for seasonal damage leading to reduced crop yields and increased skin cancer in humans. The Environmental Protection Agency (EPA) has estimated that the number of deaths due to skin cancer will increase from 9300 to 200,000 per year in the next 50 years.

Figure 2–4 The photos of the ozone layer above the Antarctic shown below show the increase in the hole over the last few years.

1989

1992

How can this be reversed? If we dramatically reduce the use of products containing CFCs, the damaging elements can be reduced in the atmosphere. Public awareness and demand have forced manufacturers to produce products without the use of CFCs.

Some proponents say emission controls are the best way to save the ozone layer. For example, the invention of the catalytic converter in cars was intended to reduce emissions of carbon monoxide by 90% and nitrogen oxide by 70% from 1975–1985. However, the carbon monoxide levels decreased only 19% in that period and nitrogen oxide increased by 4%. Thus, auto emissions are not the only contributor to the air pollution problem. Today, the EPA suggests that rather than concentrating on controlling the result of air pollution, we put our efforts toward avoiding the source of the pollution.

Case Study 3
The Legal System

*L*aw is a set of rules by which a society governs itself. Through most of history, laws were set down by the king or queen or by the state. But beginning 200 years ago with the adoption of the United States Constitution and the Bill of Rights, the concept of law written and agreed to by the *citizens* of the state was established in this country. This is the foundation of a democratic society. Since, in general, it is not possible for all citizens to participate directly in the writing of law, the people of a democratic society elect *legislators*, or lawmakers, who create the law and are responsible to the people who elected them. Because a democracy operates on the rule of the majority of its citizens, the people may remove from office legislators whose performance is judged unsatisfactory. At the national level in the United States, this is rarely done, since more than 95% of legislators are routinely reelected by the voters.

Figure 3–1 The U.S. Capitol Building in Washington, D.C., is the symbol of the American legal system.

A Brief History

The law never stands still. Society changes constantly and each change brings with it the need for new laws. Congress considers more than 20,000 laws during every session. Legislative bodies at the state and local level consider thousands more. Only a fraction of these *bills*, or proposals, are enacted into law, but the large number that are proposed suggests that the law is a dynamic, constantly evolving system.

Some laws, like the law that makes murder illegal, are based on universally-accepted moral and ethical principles. They prescribe unvarying standards of behavior that are necessary for the smooth functioning of society. At the other extreme are laws that address minor problems temporarily affecting citizens' lives. Some of these remain in effect long after they have outlived their usefulness. One community in the United States still has a law stating that any family owning a bathtub must keep it in the yard rather than in the house. While most laws fall somewhere between these two extremes, all are derived from an understanding of how civilized people should behave that traces its roots back at least 4000 years.

The earliest law that has been preserved is the Code of Hammurabi, set down by Hammurabi, the ruler of the Sumerians, about 2000 B.C. It spelled out in great detail laws and penalties relating to business, real estate, wages, military service, loans, family rights, and many other areas. The code was based on the revolutionary premises that the individual has rights and that the strong shall not injure the weak.

Around 1200 B.C., the Hebrew leader Moses gave the world the Ten Commandments, which codified basic principles of human behavior and have been adopted by almost every succeeding civilized society. Eight hundred years later, the Greeks developed the concept of democracy and the idea that a nation should be governed by law rather than by rulers. The Greeks introduced the important notion that people can write their own laws and change them if the need arises.

At about the same time, the Romans published the Law of the Twelve Tables, which specified customary behavior in great detail. Modern American law is derived directly from Roman law, or *canon law*, which governed the Roman Catholic church during the Middle Ages, and from *common law*, a legal system used by the English and brought to America by the first colonists. Common law is based on customs and traditions relating to human behavior, rather than on written law.

The Need for Law

Laws would not be necessary if everyone agreed on proper behavior. No matter how strongly most people agree on what is acceptable practice, however, there are always some who disagree and who violate that practice. For that reason, laws need to be put into writing and enforced.

The clearest evidence of this is that violation of laws in the United States is widespread and, for most offenses, on the rise. Between 1981 and 1990, the overall crime rate rose 7.8%. The biggest increases during that period were in violent crimes, up 33.7%, and forcible rape, up 24.3%. (Greater willingness by women to report rape and by law enforcement agencies to prosecute the crime, compared with earlier years, partially explains the increase.) Burglary—breaking and entering to commit a felony—was the only crime to register a decrease during the same period.

The total number of crimes is huge and practically incomprehensible. In 1990, there were 14,475,630 crimes committed in the United States. These included 1,820,130 violent crimes and 12,655,500 property crimes. The violent crimes consisted of 23,440 murders, 102,560 forcible rapes, 639,270 robberies, and 1,054,860 aggravated assaults. The property crimes consisted of 3,073,900 burglaries, 7,945,700 larceny-thefts, and 1,635,900 motor vehicle thefts. Perhaps these numbers can best be grasped by considering their frequencies. In 1990, there were, on average:
• one violent crime every 17 seconds,
• one property crime every 2 seconds,
• one murder every 22 minutes,
• one forcible rape every 5 minutes,
• one robbery every 49 seconds,
• one aggravated assault every 30 seconds,
• one larceny (theft) every 4 seconds,
• one burglary every 10 seconds, and
• one motor vehicle theft every 19 seconds.

Figure 3–2 The Department of Justice collects statistics on the number and distribution of crimes in the United States.

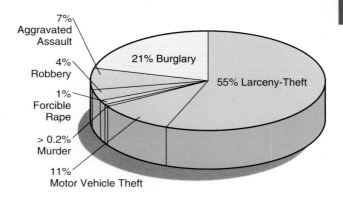

Crime Index Offenses, 1990
Percent Distribution

7% Aggravated Assault
4% Robbery
1% Forcible Rape
> 0.2% Murder
11% Motor Vehicle Theft
21% Burglary
55% Larceny-Theft

In 1990, an estimated 5820 crimes were committed for every 100,000 people in the United States. The figure was highest in the south, with 6334 crimes per 100,000 people, and lowest in the northeast, with 5194 per 100,000 people. With a population of 85,446,000, more crimes—37% of the total—were committed in the southern states than in any other region. The western states, with a population of 52,786,000, were second, with 23% of the total, followed by the midwestern states (59,669,000; 21%) and the northeastern states (50,809,000; 18%).

Figure 3–3 The number of crimes per 100,000 people reached its lowest point in recent history in 1984.

Crime Rate, 1981-1990

Crimes per 100,000 people

1981 '82 '83 '84 '85 '86 '87 '88 '89 '90

Teenagers are victimized by crime more than other age groups. In a given year, about 6% of teenagers, on average, experience violent crimes, compared with about 3% of persons age 20 or older. About half of violent crimes against teenagers occur in school buildings, on school property, or on the street.

Figure 3–4 There were nearly 8 million incidents of personal property larceny-theft in the United States in 1990.

Larceny-Theft 1990
Percent Distribution by Type of Theft

Purse-Snatching 1%
Pocket-Picking 1%
Coin Machines 1%
Shoplifting 16%
Bicycles 6%
From Motor Vehicles 22%
From Buildings 14%
Motor Vehicle Accessories 15%
All Others 24%

Gangs are responsible for much of the teenage crime in America. A 1989 survey turned up evidence of some 1500 youth gangs nationwide, with a total of more than 120,000 members. The rate of violent crimes by gang members is three times as high as that of non-gang delinquents. In 1990 in Los Angeles, the city with the most highly publicized gang violence, there were 329 murders committed by gang members, 34% of the total homicides committed in the city that year. The average age of the murderers was nineteen.

The Justice System

There are two principal branches of the law. *Criminal law* addresses acts that are considered harmful to society as a whole. *Civil law* protects individual citizens in their dealings with other citizens.

Crimes can also be classified according to whether they violate federal or state laws. Federal laws apply to and generally affect the entire country. Alleged violators of federal law are tried in federal court. State laws apply only in the state in which they are passed. Generally they address crimes such as murder, robbery, drunken driving, assault, and other offenses that do not affect the entire nation or take place across state lines. Alleged violators of state law are tried in state court.

Like the number of crimes, the number of arrests and convictions in the United States and the number of inmates in the nation's prisons is on the rise. In 1990, there were about 14 million arrests in the United States. The largest numbers were for property crimes (2.2 million), larceny (1.6 million), drunken driving (1.8 million), and drug abuse violations (1.1 million). Of those arrested, 82% were males and 13% were under the age of 18.

The United States imprisons a greater proportion of its population than any other nation. Of every 100,000 Americans, 426 were in prison in 1990, a total of just over 1 million inmates. The state with the greatest imprisonment rate is South Carolina, followed by Nevada and Louisiana. The western states showed a 203% increase in the number of prisoners between 1980 and 1989, the biggest jump of any region. California's prison population increased by 11,000 in just one year, 1989. The annual cost of operating America's prisons is estimated at $16 billion.

Among foreign nations, South Africa has the second highest imprisonment rate behind the United States (333 per 100,000 people). European and Asian countries generally range from 20 to 140 prisoners per 100,000 people.

Efforts to use the prison system to rehabilitate criminals and prepare them to become contributing members of society upon their release have been only marginally successful. *Recidivism* is the tendency of criminals to return to crime after serving their prison sentences. The Bureau of Justice Statistics studied 108,000 men and women released from prison in 1983. Within three years,

31.9% of the burglars had been rearrested for burglary, 24.8% of the drug offenders had been rearrested for drug offenses, and 19.6% of the robbers had been rearrested for robbery.

Of all the former inmates, 62.5% had been rearrested for a felony or serious misdemeanor by 1986, 46.8% had been reconvicted, and 41.4% were back in prison. Released rapists were ten times more likely than nonrapists to be rearrested for rape. Released murderers were five times more likely than other offenders to be rearrested for homicide.

Trial by Jury

Television and movies have greatly exaggerated the drama of the courtroom. In reality, most trials are slow, meticulous, and sometimes boring, characterized more by tedious legal maneuvering than by startling developments or witnesses breaking down on the stand. While this may diminish the drama and excitement of a trial, it is necessary to assure that the accused receives the fair trial guaranteed by the Constitution.

Figure 3–5 The Constitution guarantees the right to a fair and speedy trial.

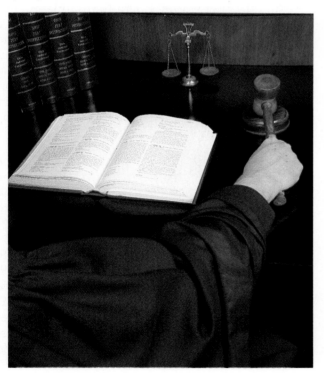

Before a trial begins, the prosecution and the defense choose a jury that faithfully represents the local community. The jury's duty is to listen to the arguments of both sides in the case and then to decide whether the defendant is innocent or guilty.

The trial begins with an opening statement by the prosecutor describing the evidence collected against the defendant and outlining the case the prosecution will make during the trial. This is followed by a statement by the defense attorney summarizing the evidence supporting the defendant's position.

The prosecution makes its case by presenting detailed evidence to the jury and calling witnesses to testify against the defendant. After the witnesses testify, the defense lawyer may *cross-examine* them to try to break down their testimony or turn it to the defendant's advantage. If the prosecution cannot establish a strong case, the judge can end the trial at this point in favor of the defendant.

If the case continues, the defense presents its evidence and witnesses, which the prosecutor may cross-examine. Then the prosecutor makes a *summation*, a closing statement summing up the case against the defendant. The defense attorney follows with the defense summation. The prosecution is entitled to make a final closing argument after the defense summation.

Then the judge presents the *charge* to the jury, an explanation of the relevant laws and a description of how the jury is to conduct its deliberations. The jury retires and discusses the case in seclusion. In a criminal case, the jury usually must agree unanimously on a verdict. If the members cannot agree, the result is a *hung jury*. A new trial, with a new jury, may be held.

If the jury comes to an agreement, they return to the courtroom and announce their verdict—guilty or not guilty. If the verdict is guilty, the judge will sentence the defendant to pay a fine, go to prison, or both. The judge also has the discretion to *suspend* the sentence, allowing the defendant to go free. Under a suspended sentence, a convicted criminal must obey all laws and conditions of the suspension, or else go directly to prison.

Case Study 4

The U.S. Economy

The state of a nation's economy is a measure of the nation's health. If employment and personal income are high, if interest rates and inflation are low, if the nation is paying its bills at home and selling its goods abroad, if manufacturers are producing quality goods and selling them at prices that attract buyers, then the economy is healthy.

In practice, few national economies are ever so strong that they meet all of these goals at once or for an extended period of time. An economy is an enormously complex mixture of factors, each of which influences the others. Economists cannot always say with certainty how a change in one element of the economy—the amount of money in circulation, for example—will affect other key elements, such as unemployment or interest rates. Economics is not an exact science, but rather a dynamic system that changes constantly due to individual economic decisions of millions of people, all acting on their own self-interest. For this reason, most national economies follow cyclical patterns of growth, remaining relatively strong for a period of years, reaching a point of maximum strength, then falling into a period of relative weakness before beginning a new cycle.

Measuring the U.S. Economy

The United States has experienced its share of hard economic times, but overall, has remained one of the world's great economic powers throughout the twentieth century. There are a number of ways to measure the U.S. economy, both internally and in relation to that of other nations.

The Gross National Product The Gross National Product (GNP) is the market value of all goods and services that have been bought for use during a year. It measures the value of purchases of everything from the services of baby-sitters and loaves

of bread by 250 million individual Americans, to fighter planes and land for new parks by the government, to factories and machinery by manufacturers. Because the amount of money spent is an excellent indicator of the strength of an economy, the GNP is considered the most comprehensive measure of U.S. economic activity.

Figure 4–1 In 1990, the U.S. GNP amounted to about $22,000 in purchases of goods and services for every man, woman, and child in America.

Growth of GNP, 1980-1990

Inflation In 1920, it was possible to buy a new car for $400. Today the average new car costs almost forty times that much. In general, the price of goods does not remain constant. While the prices of some goods may decrease occasionally, most increase over time. An increase in the price of goods is called *inflation*.

In a strong economy, inflation is kept low. Consumers can count on stable price levels, allowing them to plan more easily for the future. This in turn gives them confidence in the economy, an intangible but extremely important component of a nation's economic strength. Suppose you found a CD player you liked that retailed for $200. Three months later, after saving $200, you discover that the CD now sells for $600. This is precisely the situation in some nations, where prices can multiply many times over in a single year. An extreme example of out-of-control prices occurred in 1989 in Argentina, when inflation reached 6000% that year. A quart of milk that cost $1.00 (in U.S. currency) in January cost $61.00 by year's end. How much confidence would you have in such an economy?

In the United States, the *Consumer Price Index* (CPI) measures the rate of inflation. The CPI is based on average prices of food, clothing, shelter, fuel, transportation, health care costs, and a variety of other goods and services. Index figures are given in relation to average prices for 1982–84, which are set at 100.0. Thus, the 1989 CPI for shoes, 114.4, means that, on average, a pair of shoes in 1989 cost $\frac{114.4}{100}$ as much as a pair of shoes in 1982–84. In other words, the price of shoes inflated 14.4% during that period. By 1990, the CPI for shoes had increased to 117.4. That means that shoe prices went up $\frac{117.4 - 114.4}{114.4}$ or about 2.6% from 1989 to 1990.

Figure 4–2 Energy prices have shown the most volatility in recent years.

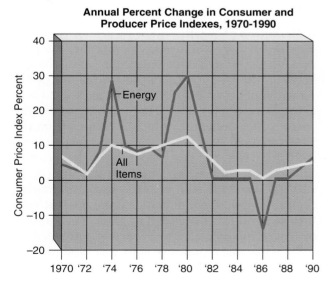

The CPI occasionally shows a drop in prices. For example, during 1986, the price of gasoline was 21.9% lower than in 1985 and the 1990 cost of televisions was 1.5% lower than in 1989. In general, however, prices have increased steadily since the 1982–84 base period began. The major categories showing the smallest changes during those years have been transportation, up 20.5% by 1990, wearing apparel, up 24.1%, and housing, up 28.5%. Two of the greatest changes from 1984 to 1990 were in the cost of personal and educational expenses, up 70.2% and in the cost of medical care, up 62.8%. Both of these expenses represent an annual inflation rate of more than 10%.

The CPI is calculated for geographical regions as well as for the entire country. The index shows that of the four principal regions, the northeast showed the greatest rate of inflation, followed by the west, the south, and the north central region. In 1990, prices in the northeast averaged about 9% higher than in the north central states.

Employment A strong economy will offer good jobs and decent wages to workers, and unemployment will be low. U.S. unemployment reached its highest point during the Depression, when for a period of four years (1929–1933), more than one out of five workers was unable to find a job. In 1933, unemployment peaked at 24.9%. More than 12 million Americans were unable to find work.

Bureau of Labor Statistics figures show that workers earned an average of $23,602 annually in the United States in 1990. The states whose workers received the highest pay were Alaska ($29,946) and Connecticut ($28,995). The states with the lowest rates of pay were South Dakota ($16,430) and North Dakota ($17,626). In general, men received significantly higher salaries than women, an average of 39% more according to the U.S. Census Bureau.

Congress specifies the minimum amount an employee can be paid. Beginning in 1991, the minimum wage was $4.25 per hour. An employee working 40 hours per week, 50 weeks a year, will earn $8,500 per year at minimum wage.

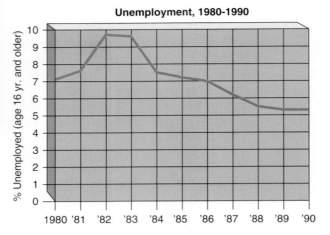

Figure 4–3 In recent years, unemployment has fluctuated between 5% and 10% of the work force.

Unemployment, 1980-1990

Receipts versus Outlays The graphs below show how the U.S. government makes its money and how it spends it. When the government makes more than it spends, it has a net *surplus* of funds. When outlays exceed receipts, there is a *deficit*. Since 1961, the government has registered a surplus only once, in 1969. This means that for more than thirty years the government has been falling further and further into debt. In 1990, the total national debt surpassed $3 trillion, which averages out to $13,000 for every person in the country.

Figure 4–4 Federal revenues and expenditures, 1988–89

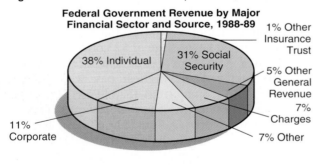

Federal Government Revenue by Major Financial Sector and Source, 1988-89

38% Individual

31% Social Security

1% Other Insurance Trust

5% Other General Revenue

7% Charges

7% Other

11% Corporate

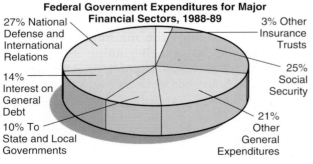

Federal Government Expenditures for Major Financial Sectors, 1988-89

27% National Defense and International Relations

14% Interest on General Debt

10% To State and Local Governments

3% Other Insurance Trusts

25% Social Security

21% Other General Expenditures

There are numerous problems associated with the federal deficit. The greater the deficit, the less likely the government will be able to provide needed services for its citizens. A huge amount of money—$265 billion in 1990—must be spent simply to pay the *interest* on the steadily increasing debt. The confidence of citizens, other nations, and foreign investors in the ability of the government to operate in a fiscally responsible manner erodes.

In 1982, the yearly federal deficit topped $100 billion for the first time. It has remained above that figure every succeeding year, several times topping $200 billion. Only through vastly increased revenues (taxes) and/or decreased expenditures will the government be able to bring the deficit under control. Both solutions require sacrifices that the American people have so far shown themselves unwilling to make.

A second problem of receipts versus outlays occurs when a nation sells less of its products abroad than it purchases from foreign nations. This relative dependency on goods produced by other countries is called a *trade deficit*. In 1990, U.S. companies sold $394 billion worth of goods abroad. That same year, American consumers purchased $495 billion in foreign-made products. This resulted in a trade deficit of $101 billion. The largest portion of the deficit—$41 billion—resulted from our trade imbalance with Japan. One of the world's most powerful economies and a leader in innovative technologies, Japan produces a wealth of goods desired by American consumers, especially cars and electronic equipment.

Distribution of Wealth A strong economy should provide for the basic needs of everyone, the poor as well as the rich. During recent years, the gap between the two groups in the United States has grown wider by the year. In 1990, the top 20% of earners collected 45% of the income, while the bottom 20% collected only 5%. Figures from the Congressional Budget Office show that between 1977 and 1988, the yearly income of the wealthiest 1% of Americans rose, on average, from $203,000 to $451,000, a 122% increase. During the same period, the income of the poorest one-fifth of Americans declined by 10%. The amount of federal taxes paid by the top 1% dropped by 18%, while the amount paid by low- and middle-income families remained about the same.

In 1990, the *poverty line*—the minimum annual income needed to secure basic needs—was $13,359 for a family of four. The Census Bureau estimated that 33.6 million Americans—13.5% of the population—lived below the poverty line and that the number increased by 2.1 million persons during 1990. Children registered a poverty rate of 20.6%.

Figure 4–5 The overall poverty level was lowest in the early 1970s.

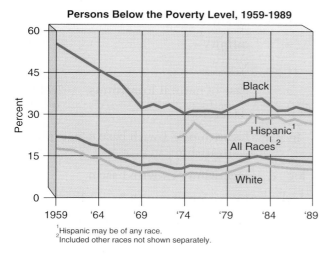

Persons Below the Poverty Level, 1959-1989

¹Hispanic may be of any race.
²Included other races not shown separately.

The Economy in the 1990s

By most measures, the U.S. economy was extremely weak during the early years of the 1990s. On the positive side, inflation and interest rates remained low, although inflation showed signs of inching upward. The GNP continued to grow, but at a diminished rate.

Figure 4–6 The cost of borrowing money has dropped steadily in recent years.

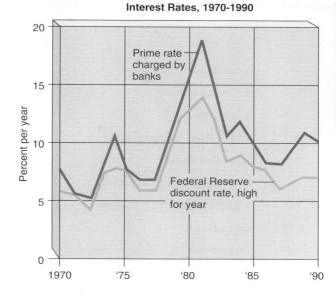

Interest Rates, 1970-1990

On the negative side, unemployment, the federal deficit, the trade deficit, and poverty remained high throughout the period. The Index of Leading Economic Indicators, a monthly figure published by the Commerce Department and designed to assess the overall economic health of the country, indicated that the nation had entered a *recession*, a period of general economic stagnation. The cyclical nature of economic health suggested that at some point in the future, the country would once again experience a robust economy. Exactly when that would occur neither economists nor anyone else could say with certainty.

Figure 4–7 The state of the economy was a major issue in the 1992 presidential campaign.

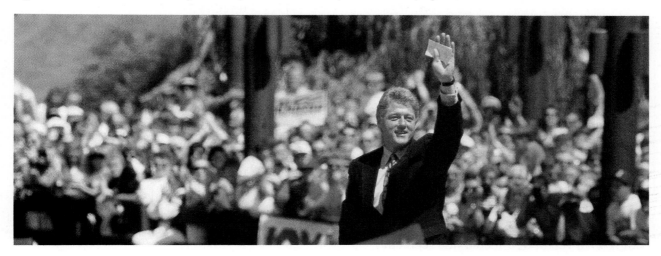

SYMBOLS

$=$	is equal to		$\lvert \vec{\mathbf{v}} \rvert$	magnitude of the vector $\mathbf{v}$
$\neq$	is not equal to		$\vec{\mathbf{a}} \cdot \vec{\mathbf{b}}$	inner product of dot product of vectors $\mathbf{a}$ and $\mathbf{b}$
$<$	is less than		$\vec{\mathbf{a}} \times \vec{\mathbf{b}}$	cross product of vectors $\mathbf{a}$ and $\mathbf{b}$
$\leq$	is less than or equal to		$\sin^{-1} x$	arcsin x
$>$	is greater than		∞	infinity
$\geq$	is greater than or equal to		i	$\sqrt{-1}$
$\approx$	is approximately equal to		e	base of natural logarithms; ≈ 2.718
$\{\ \}$	set notation		$n!$	n factorial
$\pm$	plus or minus		$\ln x$	logarithm of x with base e; natural logarithm
$\mp$	minus or plus		$\log_a x$	logarithm of x with base a
$f(x)$	f of x or the value of function f at x		$\log x$	logarithm of x with base 10
$f'(x)$	f prime of x or the derivative of f at x		$P(n, r)$	permutation of n objects, taken r at a time
$f''(x)$	the second derivative of $f(x)$		$C(n, r)$	combination of n objects, taken r at a time
$f \circ g$ or $f(g(x))$	composite of functions f and g		$\overline{X}$	X bar or arithmetic mean
$\lim\limits_{x \to a}$	the limit as x approaches a		M_d	median
$\triangle ABC$	triangle ABC		σ_X	standard error of the mean
$\overset{\frown}{RTS}$	arc RTS		MD	mean deviation
$\angle ABC$	angle ABC		$\dfrac{dy}{dx}$	the derivative of y with respect to x
$m\angle ABC$	measure of angle ABC		$\int$	integral
AB	measure of line segment AB		α	alpha
$\overline{AB}$	line segment AB		β	beta
$\lvert n \rvert$	the absolute value of n		Δ or δ	delta
x^n	the nth power of x		ϵ	epsilon
$\sqrt{x}$	the square root of x		θ	theta
$\sqrt[n]{x}$ or $x^{\frac{1}{n}}$	the nth root of x		λ	lambda
$[x]$	greatest integer not greater than x		π	pi
A^{-1}	inverse of A		σ	sigma; standard deviation
a_{ij}	the element of the ith row and the jth column		$\sum$	sigma; summation symbol
$\begin{vmatrix} a_1 & b_1 \\ a_2 & b_2 \end{vmatrix}$	the determinant $a_1 b_2 - a_2 b_1$		ϕ	phi
$\deg (A)$	the degree of A			
$\vec{\mathbf{v}}$ or $\overrightarrow{AB}$	a vector or directed line segment			

FORMULAS

Chapter 1
Distance Formula for Two Points (30)
$$d = \sqrt{(x_2 - x_1)^2 + (y_2 - y_1)^2}$$

Chapter 4
Quadratic Formula (188)
$$x = \frac{-b \pm \sqrt{b^2 - 4ac}}{2a}$$

Chapter 5
Degree/Radian Conversion Formulas (242)

1 radian $= \dfrac{180}{\pi}$ degrees

1 degree $= \dfrac{\pi}{180}$ radians

Length of an Arc (248)
$$s = r\theta$$

Linear and Angular Velocity (249)
$$v = r\frac{\theta}{t}$$

Area of a Circular Sector (250)
$$A = \frac{1}{2}r^2\theta$$

Area of a Triangle
$$K = \frac{1}{2}bc \sin A \quad (288)$$
$$K = \frac{1}{2}c^2 \frac{\sin A \sin B}{\sin C} \quad (289)$$

Hero's Formula (290)
$$K = \sqrt{s(s-a)(s-b)(s-c)}$$

Area of a Circular Segment (292)
$$S = \frac{1}{2}r^2(\alpha - \sin \alpha)$$

Chapter 7
Distance from a Point to a Line (399)
$$d = \frac{Ax_1 + By_1 + C}{\pm\sqrt{A^2 + B^2}}$$

Chapter 9
Conversion from Polar Coordinates to Rectangular Coordinates (483)
$$x = r \cos\theta, \; y = r \sin\theta$$

Conversion from Rectangular Coordinates to Polar Coordinates (484)
$$r = \sqrt{x^2 + y^2}$$
$$\theta = \text{Arctan} \frac{y}{x} \text{ when } x > 0$$
$$\theta = \text{Arctan} \frac{y}{x} + \pi \text{ when } x < 0$$

Chapter 10
Length of a Segment Tangent to a Circle
$$t = \sqrt{(x_1 - h)^2 + (y_1 - k)^2 - r^2} \quad (588)$$

Chapter 11
Compound Interest Formulas
$$A = P\left(1 + \frac{r}{n}\right)^{nt} \quad (614)$$
$$A = Pe^{rt} \quad (615)$$

Change of Base Formula (638)
$$\log_a n = \frac{\log_b n}{\log_b a}$$

Chapter 12
nth Term of an Arithmetic Sequence (657)
$$a_n = a_1 + (n-1)d$$

Sum of an Arithmetic Sequence (659)
$$S_n = \frac{n}{2}(a_1 + a_n)$$

nth Term of a Geometric Sequence (664)
$$a_n = a_1 r^{a-1}$$

Sum of a Geometric Sequence (666)
$$S_n = \frac{a_1 - a_1 r^n}{1 - r}$$

Sum of an Infinite Geometric Series (674)
$$S_n = \frac{a_1}{1 - r}$$

Euler's Formula (698)
$$e^{1\alpha} = \cos \alpha + i \sin \alpha$$

Chapter 13
Verhulst Population Model (712)
$$p_{n+1} = p_n + rp_n(1 - p_n)$$

Chapter 14
Definitions of Permutation (754)
$$P(n, n) = n!, \; P(n, r) = \frac{n!}{(n-r)!}$$

Definition of Combination (764)
$$C(n, r) = \frac{n!}{(n-r)!r!}$$

Chapter 15
Arithmetic Mean (812)
$$\overline{X} = \frac{1}{n}\sum_{i=1}^{n} X_i$$

Mean of the Data in a Frequency Distribution (815)
$$\overline{X} = \frac{\sum\limits_{i=1}^{k} f_i \cdot X_i}{\sum\limits_{i=1}^{k} f_i}$$

Semi-Interquartile Range (821)
$$Q_R = \frac{Q_3 - Q_1}{2}$$

Mean Deviation (823)
$$MD = \frac{1}{n}\sum_{i=1}^{n} |X_i - \overline{X}|$$

Standard Deviation (823)
$$\sigma = \sqrt{\frac{1}{n}\sum_{i=1}^{n} (X_i - \overline{X})^2}$$

Standard Deviation of the Data in a Frequency Distribution (824)
$$\sigma = \sqrt{\frac{\sum\limits_{i=1}^{k} (X_i - \overline{X})^2 \cdot f_i}{\sum\limits_{i=1}^{k} f_i}}$$

Standard Error of the Mean (839)
$$\sigma_{\overline{x}} = \frac{\sigma}{\sqrt{N}}$$

Pearson Product-Moment Correlation (849)
$$r = \frac{SP}{\sqrt{SS_x SS_y}}$$

Chapter 17
Limit of a Polynomial Function (915)
$$\lim_{x \to r} P(x) = P(r)$$

Limit of a Trigonometric Function (918)
$$\lim_{x \to 0} \frac{\sin x}{x} = 1$$

Power Formula (924)
$$f'(x) = cnx^{n-1}$$

Area Under a Curve (932)
$$A = \lim_{n \to \infty} \sum_{i=1}^{n} f(x_i)(x_i - x_{i-1})$$

Fundamental Theorem of Calculus (945)
$$\int_a^b f(x)dx = F(b) - F(a)$$

GLOSSARY

A

adjacency matrix   a square matrix whose entries are the number of edges from one vertex of a graph to another   (898)

adjacent vertices   vertices that are joined by an edge   (868)

algorithm   a sequence of instructions that solves all cases of a certain type of problem   (879)

alternate optimal solutions   When there are two or more optimal solutions for a linear programming problem, the problem is said to have alternate optimal solutions.   (93)

amplitude $|A|$ for functions in the form $y = A \sin k\alpha$ or $y = A \cos k\alpha$ (309)

amplitude of a complex number   the angle θ when a complex number is written in the form $r (\cos \theta + i \sin \theta)$ (501)

amplitude of a vector   the directed angle between the positive x-axis and the vector   (412)

analytic geometry   the study of coordinate geometry from an algebraic perspective   (31)

angle of depression   the angle between a horizontal line and the line of sight from the observer to an object at a lower level   (272)

angle of elevation   the angle between a horizontal line and the line of sight from an observer to an object at a higher level   (272)

angular velocity   the change in the central angle with respect to time as an object moves along a circular path   (249)

annual percentage rate   interest rate per year   (609)

annuity   a series of payments made at equal intervals of time   (609)

antiderivative $F(x)$ is an antiderivative of $f(x)$ if and only if $F'(x) = f(x)$.   (939)

antilogarithm   If $\log x = a$, then x is called the antilogarithm of a, abbreviated antilog a.   (631)

arcsine   the inverse of $y = \sin x$ (329)

arithmetic mean   1. the terms between any two nonconsecutive terms of an arithmetic sequence   (658) 2. a measure of central tendency found by dividing the sum of all values by the number of values   (811)

arithmetic sequence   a sequence in which the difference between successive terms is a constant   (656)

arithmetic series   the indicated sum of the terms of an arithmetic sequence   (658)

array   statistical data arranged in an ordered sequence   (813)

asymptote   lines that a curve approaches   (134)

asymptote of a hyperbola   the lines that the hyperbola approaches as it recedes from the center   (551)

attractor   the x-coordinate of the fixed point to which a path generated by iteration staircases or spirals   (718)

augmented matrix   an array of the coefficients and constants of a system of equations   (79)

axis   See axis of symmetry.

axis of symmetry   a line about which a figure is symmetric   (534)

B

back-to-back bar graph   a graph plotted on a two-quadrant coordinate system with the horizontal scale repeated in each direction from the central axis used to show comparisons   (802)

best-fit line   the graph of a prediction equation   (847)

bimodal data   data with two modes   (813)

binomial experiment   a problem that can be solved using binomial expansion   (791)

bivariate data   data that involve exactly two variables   (847)

boundary   a line or curve that separates the coordinate plane into two regions   (23)

box-and-whisker plot   a diagram that graphically displays the median, quartiles, extreme values, and outliers in a set of data   (821)

bridge   an edge of a connected graph whose removal would cause the graph to no longer be connected   (874)

C

center of a circle   See circle.

central angle   an angle whose vertex lies at the center of a circle   (247)

characteristic   the part of the logarithm of a number which is the exponent of 10 used to write the number in scientific notation   (630)

circle   the locus of all points in a plane at a given distance, called the radius, from a fixed point on the plane, called the center   (524)

circuit   a trail that starts and ends at the same vertex   (873)

circular functions   functions defined using a unit circle   (255)

class interval   the range of each class in a frequency distribution   (803)

class limits   the upper and lower values in each class in a frequency distribution   (804)

class marks   the means of the class limits in a frequency distribution   (804)

classic curves   special curves formed by graphing polar equations   (475)

column matrix   a matrix that has only one column   (64)

combination   an arrangement of objects where the order is not a consideration   (764)

combinatorics   the investigation of the different possibilities for the arrangement of objects   (752)

common difference   the difference between the successive terms of an arithmetic sequence   (656)

common logarithms   logarithms that use 10 as the base   (629)

common ratio   the ratio of successive terms of a geometric sequence   (663)

complements   Two events are complements if and only if the sum of their probabilities is 1.   (768)

complete graph   a graph in which each pair of vertices is connected by exactly one edge   (869)

complex number   any number that can be written in the form $a + bi$, where a and b are real numbers and i is the imaginary unit   (179)

components of a vector   two or more vectors whose sum is a given vector   (415)

composite   Given functions f and g, the composite function $f \circ g$ can be described by $[f \circ g](x) = f(g(x))$.   (13)

composition   See composite.   (13)

compound function   a function consisting of sums or products of trigonometric functions   (324)

compound interest   interest computed on the sum of the original principal and any previously earned interest   (614)

concentric circles   circles with the same center   (524)

conditional probability   the probability of an event under the condition that some preceding event has occurred   (784)

confidence interval   an interval about the sample mean in which the population mean lies within a certain confidence level   (840)

conic section   a curve determined by the intersection of a plane with a double right cone   (561)

conjugate axis   the segment perpendicular to the transverse axis of a hyperbola through its center   (551)

conjugate of a complex number   The conjugate of the complex number $a + bi$ is $a - bi$.   (190, 496)

connected graph   a graph in which there is a path along an edge between each pair of two vertices   (873)

connected vertices   See adjacent vertices.

consistent system   a system of equations that has at least one solution   (57)

constant function   a function of the form $f(x) = b$ (23)

constraints   conditions given to variables, often expressed as linear inequalities   (91)

continuous   A function is said to be continuous at point (x_1, y_1) if it is defined at that point and passes through that point without a break.   (164)

converge   If a sequence has a limit, then the related infinite series is said to converge.   (679)

coterminal angles   two angles in standard position that have the same terminal side   (242)

critical path   the longest path between two vertices   (897)

critical points   points at which the nature of a graph changes   (157)

cross product   The cross product of $\vec{a}$ and $\vec{b}$ if $\vec{a} = (a_1, a_2, a_3)$ and $\vec{b} = (b_1, b_2, b_3)$ is defined as follows.   (431)

$$\vec{a} \times \vec{b} = \begin{vmatrix} a_2 & a_3 \\ b_2 & c_2 \end{vmatrix} \vec{i} - \begin{vmatrix} a_1 & a_3 \\ b_1 & b_3 \end{vmatrix} \vec{j} + \begin{vmatrix} a_1 & a_2 \\ b_1 & b_2 \end{vmatrix} \vec{k}$$

cycle   a path in which only the beginning and ending vertices are the same   (873)

D

definite integral   an integral that has lower and upper bounds   (945)

degenerate case   the intersection of a plane with a double right cone resulting in a point, a line, or two intersecting lines   (561)

degree   the measure of an angle that is $\frac{1}{360}$ of a complete rotation in the positive direction   (241)

degree of a polynomial in one variable   the greatest exponent of the variable of the polynomial   (178)

degree of a vertex   the number of edges incident on the vertex   (868)

dependent events   events that affect each other   (752)

dependent system   a system of equations that has infinitely many solutions   (57)

depressed polynomial   the quotient when a polynomial is divided by one of its binomial factors   (197)

derivative notation $\frac{dy}{dx}$, read "the derivative of y with respect to x"   (923)

derivative of $f(x)$ the function $f'(x)$, which is defined as follows.   (150)

$$f'(x) = \lim_{h \to 0} \frac{f(x + h) - f(x)}{h}$$

determinant   a square array of numbers having a numerical value; the numerical value of the square array of numbers   (71)

differentiable   A function is differentiable at a if the derivative of the function exists at a and is finite.   (923)

differentiation   the process of finding derivatives   (923)

digraph   a graph with arrowheads on the edges to represent the direction of each relationship; a directed graph   (896)

dimensions of a matrix   the number of rows, m, and the number of columns, n, of the matrix written as $m \times n$ (64)

directed path   a path in a digraph that can be walked in the direction of the arrows   (896)

direction vector   a vector used to describe the slope of a line   (442)

directrix   See parabola.

disconnected graph   a graph in which there is not a path along an edge between at least two vertices   (873)

discontinuous   A function is said to be discontinuous at point (x_1, y_1) if there is a break in the graph of the function at that point.   (164)

discriminant   in the quadratic formula, the expression under the radical sign, $b^2 - 4ac$ (189)

diverge   If a sequence does not have a limit, then the related infinite series is said to diverge.   (679)

domain   the set of all abscissas of the ordered pairs of a relation   (6)

dust   a disconnected Julia set   (737)

E

eccentricity   the ratio of the distance between any point of a conic section and a fixed point to the distance between the same point of the conic section to a fixed line   (563)

edge of a graph   a line segment or arc that connects a pair of vertices of a graph   (866)

element of a matrix   any value in the array of values   (64)

ellipse   the locus of all points in a plane such that the sum of the distances from two given points in the plane, called foci, is constant   (542)

end behavior   the behavior of $f(x)$ as $|x|$ becomes very large   (166)

equilateral hyperbola   a hyperbola with perpendicular asymptotes   (555)

escape set   the set of initial values for which the iterates of a function approach infinity   (736)

Euler circuit a path that includes each edge of a graph exactly once and has the same starting and ending vertex (878)

Euler path a path that includes each edge of a graph exactly once, but has different starting and ending vertices (878)

even function a function whose graph is symmetric with respect to the y-axis (112)

exponential curve the graph of a function of the form $y = a^x$ (606)

exponential equation an equation in which variables appear as exponents (636)

exponential function an function in the form $y = a^x$, where a is a positive real number (608)

exponential series the series by which e^x may be approximated;

$$e^x = 1 + x + \frac{x^2}{2!} + \frac{x^3}{3!} + \frac{x^4}{4!} + \frac{x^5}{5!} + \cdots \quad (607)$$

F

failure any outcome other than the desired outcome of an event (768)

Fibonacci sequence a sequence in which the first two terms are 1 and each of the additional terms is generated by adding the two previous terms (696)

fixed points the points where the graph of the function $g(x)$ intersects the graph of the line $f(x) = x$ (717)

foci See ellipse, hyperbola.

focus See parabola.

fractal a complex geometric structure generated by the iteration of complex numbers through a quadratic equation having self-similarity (736)

fractal geometry the study of the properties of fractals and their application to natural phenomena (734)

frequency the number of cycles per unit of time (347)

frequency distribution a system of organizing data by determining classes and the frequency of values in each class (803)

frequency polygon a broken line graph drawn by connecting the class marks on a histogram (806)

function a relation in which each element of the domain is paired with exactly one element in the range (7)

future value of an annuity the sum of all of the annuity payments plus any accumulated interest (609)

G

geometric mean the terms between any two nonconsecutive terms of a geometric sequence (665)

geometric sequence a sequence in which the ratio between successive terms is a constant (663)

geometric series the indicated sum of the terms of a geometric sequence (665)

geometric transformation a transformation in which a nonlinear graph is stretched or shrunk (120)

goodness of fit the degree to which data fits a regression line (849)

graph in graph theory, a finite, nonempty set of points connected by a set of segments or arcs (866)

graphical iteration a process used to find the values of the iterates of a function and their path for a given initial value by graphing (717)

greatest integer function a step function, written as $f(x) = [x]$, where $f(x)$ is the greatest integer not greater than x (119)

H

hinges in a box-and-whisker plot, the ends of the rectangular box which are located at the first and third quartiles (821)

histogram a type of bar graph in which the width of each bar represents a class interval and the height of the bar represents the frequency in that interval (804)

hole Whenever the denominator and numerator of a rational function contain a common factor, a hole appears in the graph of the function. (138)

horizontal asymptote The line $y = b$ is a horizontal asymptote for a function $f(x)$ if $f(x) \to b$ as $x \to \infty$ or as $x \to -\infty$. (135)

hyperbola the locus of all points in the plane such that the absolute value of the difference of the distances from two given points in the plane, called foci, is constant (551)

I

identity a statement of equality between two expressions that is true for all values of the variables for which the expressions are defined (358)

imaginary number a complex number of the form $a + bi$ where $b \neq 0$ and i is the imaginary unit (179)

incident An edge that connects a vertex to another vertex is incident on each vertex. (868)

inclusive events two events whose outcomes may be the same (779)

inconsistent system a system of equations that has no solutions (57)

indegree of a vertex the number of edges pointing into a vertex in a digraph (896)

independent events events that do not affect each other (752)

independent system a system of equations that has exactly one solution (57)

index of summation the variable used with the summation symbol (686)

infeasibility When the constraints of a linear programming problem cannot be satisfied simultaneously, then infeasibility is said to occur. (92)

inferential statistics statistics based on information gathered in a sample to make predictions about a population (838)

infinite sequence a sequence which has infinitely many terms (671)

infinite series the indicated sum of the terms of an infinite sequence (674)

inner product If $\vec{a}$ and $\vec{b}$ are two vectors, (a_1, a_2, a_3) and (b_1, b_2, b_3), then the inner product of $\vec{a}$ and $\vec{b}$ is defined as follows. (430)
$$\vec{a} \cdot \vec{b} = a_1 b_1 + a_2 b_2 + a_3 b_3$$

integral the area between the curve of a function, the x-axis, and lines $x = a$ and $x = b$ (939)

interquartile range the difference between the first quartile point and the third quartile point (821)

inverse function   Two functions are inverse functions if and only if $[f \circ g](x) = [g \circ f](x) = x$ for all values of x.   (15)

inverse relations   Two relations are inverse relations if and only if one relation contains the element (b, a), whenever the other relation contains the element (a, b).   (126)

isolated vertex   a vertex that has a degree of 0   (868)

iterate   the output of the composition of a function with itself   (713)

iteration   1. the composition of a function to itself   (15)
2. the repeated composition of a function with itself   (713)

J

Julia set   the boundary between the escape set and the prisoner set for the iteration of complex numbers through the quadratic equation $f(z) = z^2 + c$ where c is a complex number   (736)

L

line symmetry   Two distinct points P and P' are symmetric with respect to a line ℓ if and only if ℓ is the perpendicular bisector of $\overline{PP'}$. A point P is symmetric to itself with respect to a line ℓ if and only if P is on ℓ.   (108)

linear equation   an equation of the form $Ax + By = 0$ where A and B are not both 0   (22)

linear function   a function defined by $f(x) = mx + b$, where m and b are real numbers   (22)

linear inequality   a relation whose boundary is a straight line   (23)

linear programming   a procedure for finding the maximum or minimum value of a function in two variables subject to given constraints on the variables   (91)

linear transformation   a relocation of a graph on the coordinate plane that does not change the graph's size or shape   (118)

linear velocity   distance traveled per unit of time   (249)

locus   a set of points and only those points that satisfy a given set of conditions   (524)

logarithm   In the function $x = a^y$, y is called the logarithm, base a, of x.   (622)

logarithmic function $y = \log_a x$, $a > 0$ and $a \neq 1$ which is the inverse of the exponential function $y = a^x$ (622)

logistic function   the function $f(x) = ax(1 - x)$ (722)

loop   an edge that connects a vertex to itself   (866)

lower bound   the integer less than or equal to the least real zero of the polynomial $P(x)$ (212)

lower sum   a Riemann sum for rectangles which are always below the curve   (931)

M

$m \times n$ matrix   a matrix with m rows and n columns   (64)

magnitude of a vector   the length of the directed line segment   (412)

major axis   the axis of symmetry of an ellipse which contains the foci   (543)

Mandelbrot set   a complex mathematical picture generated by iterating the function $f(z) = z^2 + c$ where $z_0 = 0 + 0i$ and c is allowed to vary   (740)

mantissa   the common logarithm of a number between 1 and 10   (630)

marginal cost function   the rate at which the cost changes with respect to the number of units produced   (925)

marginal revenue function   the rate at which the revenue changes with respect to the number of units sold   (925)

mathematical induction   a method of proof that depends on a recursive process   (702)

matrix   any rectangular array of terms called elements   (64)

maximum   a critical point of a graph where the curve changes from an increasing curve to a decreasing curve   (157)

mean deviation   the arithmetic mean of the absolute value of the deviations from the mean of a set of data   (823)

median   the middle value of a set of data that has been arranged into an ordered sequence   (813)

median class   in a frequency distribution, the class in which the median of the data is located   (815)

median-fit line   a line drawn by using the medians of the x- and y-coordinates of groups of points in a scatter plot   (848)

minimal distance   the weight of the minimal path in a weighted graph   (885)

minimal path   the path with minimal weight in a weighted graph   (885)

minimal spanning tree   the spanning tree having a weight that is less than or equal to the weight of all other spanning trees in a graph   (891)

minimum   a critical point of a graph where the curve changes from a decreasing curve to an increasing curve   (157)

minor   The minor of an element of an nth-order matrix is the determinant of $(n - 1)$th order found by deleting the row and column containing the element.   (71)

minor axis   the axis of symmetry of an ellipse which does not contain the foci   (543)

minute   a unit of angle measure that is $\frac{1}{60}$ of a degree   (241)

mixing   the outcome of an iteration which fills the entire interval from 0 to 1   (723)

mode   the item of data that appears more frequently than any other in the set   (813)

modulus   the number r when a complex number is written in the form $r(\cos \theta + i \sin \theta)$ (501)

multigraph   a graph having loops or parallel edges   (866)

mutually exclusive events   two events whose outcomes can never be the same   (779)

N

n factorial   written $n!$, for n, an integer greater than zero, the product $n(n - 1)(n - 2) \cdots 1$ (687)

natural logarithm   logarithms that use e as the base, written $\ln x$ (641)

normal   1. a line that is perpendicular to another line, curve, or surface   (392)   2. the line that is perpendicular to the tangent of a curve at the point of tangency   (589)

normal curve   a symmetric bell-shaped graph of a normal distribution   (831)

normal distribution   a frequency distribution that often occurs when there is a large number of values in a set of data: about 68% of the values are within one standard deviation of the mean, 95% of the values are within two standard deviations of the mean, and 99% of the values are within three standard deviations   (831)

normal form   the equation of a line that is written in terms of the length of the normal from the line to the origin   (392)

nth order matrix   a square matrix with n rows and n columns   (64)

O

odd function   a function whose graph is symmetric with respect to the origin   (112)

odds   the ratio of the probability of the success of an event to the probability of its complement   (769)

opposite vectors   two vectors that have the same magnitude and opposite directions   (414)

orbit   the graph of the sequence of successive iterates   (731)

outdegree of a vertex   the number of edges pointing away from a vertex in a digraph   (896)

outlier   a value of a set of data that is more than 1.5 interquartile ranges beyond the upper or lower quartiles   (821)

P

parabola   the locus of all points in a given plane that are the same distance from a given point, called the focus, and a given line, called the directrix   (534)

parallel edges   two edges that connect the same pair of vertices   (866)

parallel lines   nonvertical coplanar lines that have equal slopes; any two coplanar vertical lines   (42)

parallel vectors   two vectors that have the same or opposite directions   (414)

parameter   the independent variable t in the vector equation of a line   (443)

parametric equation of a line   the vector equation $(x - x_1, y - y_1) = t(a_1, a_2)$ written as the two equations $x = x_1 + ta_1$ and $y = y_1 + ta_2$ (443)

parent graph   an anchor graph from which other graphs in the family are derived   (117)

partial fraction   one of the fractions that were added or subtracted to result in a given rational expression   (217)

Pascal's triangle   a triangular array of numbers such that the $(n + 1)^{th}$ row is the coefficient of the terms of the expansion $(x + y)^n$ for $n = 0, 1, 2 \cdots$ (691)

path   a walk in which no vertex nor edge is repeated   (872)

Pearson product-moment correlation   a method of determining the goodness of fit   (849)

period of a trigonometric function   the least positive value of α for which $f(x) = f(x + \alpha)$ (311)

period-n attractor   If the iterates repeat every n steps, the function $f(x) = ax(1 - x)$ is said to have a period-n attractor.   (725)

permutation   the arrangement of objects in a certain order   (753)

perpendicular lines   any two nonvertical lines the product of whose slopes is -1; any vertical line and any horizontal line   (43)

phase shift   the least value of $|k\theta + c|$, for which the trigonometric function $f(k\theta + c) = 0$ (312)

point of inflection   a critical point of a graph where the graph changes its curvature from concave down to concave up or vice versa   (157)

point symmetry   Two distinct points P and P' are symmetric with respect to a point, M, if and only if M is the midpoint of $\overline{PP'}$. Point M is symmetric to itself.   (106)

point-slope form   the equation of the line that contains the point with coordinates (x_1, y_1) and having slope m written in the form $y - y_1 = m(x - x_1)$ (37)

polar axis   a ray whose initial point is the pole   (466)

polar coordinate system   a grid of concentric circles and their center, which is called the pole, whose radii are integral multiples of 1   (466)

polar equation   an equation that uses polar coordinates   (469)

polar form   the complex number $x + yi$ written as $r(\cos \theta + i \sin \theta)$ where $r = \sqrt{x^2 + y^2}$ and $\theta = \text{Arctan} \frac{y}{x}$ when $x > 0$ and $\theta = \text{Arctan} \frac{y}{x} + \pi$ when $x < 0$ (502)

polar graph   the representation of the solution set which is the set of points whose coordinates (r, θ) satisfy a given polar equation   (469)

pole   See polar coordinate system.

polygonal convex set   the solution of a system of linear inequalities   (87)

polynomial equation   a polynomial that is set equal to zero   (179)

polynomial function   a function $y = P(x)$ where $P(x)$ is a polynomial in one variable   (179)

polynomial in one variable   an expression of the form $a_0x^n + a_1x_{n-1} + \cdots + a_{n-1}x + a_n$ where the coefficients $a_0, a_1, \cdots, a_n$ represent complex numbers, a_0 is not zero, and n represents an nonnegative integer   (178)

prediction equation   an equation suggested by the points of a scatter plot used to predict other points   (847)

present value of an annuity   the sum of the present values of all the periodic payments   (609)

principal values   the unique solutions of a trigonometric equation if the values of the function is restricted to two adjacent quadrants   (334, 387)

prisoner set   the set of initial values for which the iterates of a function do not approach infinity   (736)

probability   the measure of the chance of a desired outcome happening   (768)

Q

quadrantal angle   an angle in standard position whose terminal side coincides with one of the axes   (240)

quadratic formula   the formula $x = \frac{-b \pm \sqrt{b^2 - 4ac}}{2a}$, that gives the roots of the quadratic equation of the form $ax^2 + bx + c = 0$ with $a \neq 0$ (188)

quadratic inequality   an inequality of the form $y > ax^2 + bx + c$, $y < ax^2 + bx + c$, $y \geq ax^2 + bx + c$, $y \leq ax^2 + bx + c$, where $a \neq 0$ (191)

quartile   one of four groupings of a set of data determined by the median of the set and the medians of the sets determined by the median   (821)

R

radian the measure of a central angle whose sides intercept an arc that is the same length as the radius of the circle (241)

radius See circle.

range the difference of the greatest and least values in a set of data (820)

range of a relation the set of all ordinates of the ordered pairs of a relation (6)

rational equation an equation that consists of one or more rational expressions (216)

rational function the quotient of two polynomials in the form $f(x) = \frac{g(x)}{h(x)}$, where $h(x) \neq 0$ (134)

reachable Point A is reachable from point B if there is a directed path from B to A. (896)

rectangular form a complex number written as $x + yi$ where x is the real part and yi is the imaginary part (501)

recursive a formula for determining the next term of a sequence using one or more of the previous terms (657)

reduced sample space the subset of a sample space that contains only those outcomes that satisfy a given condition (785)

reference angle the acute angle formed by the terminal side of an angle in standard position and the x-axis (243)

reflection a linear transformation that flips a figure over a line called the line of symmetry (118)

regression methods techniques used to find lines of best fit (847)

relation a set of ordered pairs (6)

relative maximum a point that represents the maximum for a certain interval (157)

relative minimum a point that represents the minimum for a certain interval (157)

repeller the x-coordinate of the fixed point from which a path generated by iteration staircases or spirals (718)

resultant of vectors the sum of two or more vectors (413)

Riemann sum a sum of the areas of rectangles formed by partitioning the area between the x-axis and a curve on some interval $x = a$ to $x = b$ (938)

root a solution of the equation $P(x) = 0$ (179)

row matrix a matrix that has only one row (64)

S

sample space the set of all possible outcomes of an event (785)

scalar a real number (66)

scientific notation the expression of a number in the form $a \times 10^n$, where $1 \leq a < 10$ and n is an integer (598)

secant line a line that intersects a curve at two or more points (149)

second a unit of angle measure that is $\frac{1}{60}$ of a minute (241)

sector of a circle a region bounded by a central angle and the intercepted arc (250)

segment of a circle the region bounded by an arc and its chord (291)

self-similarity Self-similar objects contain replicas of the entire shape or object imbedded over and over again inside the object in different sizes. (736)

semi-interquartile range one-half the interquartile range of a set of data (821)

semi-major axis one of the two segments into which the center of an ellipse divides the major axis (543)

semi-minor axis one of the two segments into which the center of an ellipse divides the minor axis (543)

sequence a set of numbers in a specific order (656)

simple graph a graph having no loops or parallel edges (866)

simple harmonic motion the rhythmic motion of an object when friction and other factors affecting such motion are ignored (345)

slant asymptote The oblique line ℓ is a slant asymptote for a function $f(x)$ if the graph of $f(x)$ approaches ℓ as $x \to \infty$ or as $x \to -\infty$. (137)

slope of a line the value $m = \frac{y_2 - y_1}{x_2 - x_1}$, where (x_1, y_1) and (x_2, y_2), $x_2 \neq x_1$, are two points of the line (30)

slope-intercept form the equation of a line with slope, m, and y-intercept, b, written in the form $y = mx + b$ (36)

spanning tree a tree that is a subgraph of a connected graph and includes all of the vertices of that graph (890)

square matrix a matrix with the same number of rows as columns (64)

standard deviation a measure of the average amount by which individual items of data deviate from the arithmetic mean of all the data (823)

standard error of the mean the standard deviation of the distribution of a sample mean (839)

standard form a linear equation written in the form $Ax + By + C = 0$, where A, B, and C are real numbers and A and B are not both zero (42)

standard position an angle with its vertex at the origin and its initial side along the positive x-axis (240)

standard position of a vector If a vector has its initial point at the origin, it is in standard position. (412)

stem-and-leaf plot a display of numerical data for which each value is separated into two numbers (814)

subgraph a graph that contains a subset of the edges and vertices of a larger graph (890)

success the desired outcome of an event (768)

system of equations a set of equations with the same variables (56)

system of linear inequalities a set of inequalities with the same variables (86)

T

tangent a line that intersects a curve at exactly one point (149)

term of a sequence a number in a sequence (656)

trail a walk in which no edge is used more than once (872)

translation a linear transformation that slides the graph vertically and/or horizontally on the coordinate plane, but does not change the shape (118)

translation matrix the matrix used to represent the translation of a set of points with respect to (h, k) which is equal to $\begin{bmatrix} h & h & h & h \\ k & k & k & k \end{bmatrix}$ (570)

transverse axis the line segment that has as its endpoints the vertices of a hyperbola (551)

tree   a connected graph in which there are no cycles, there is exactly one path between any two vertices, there are at least two vertices of degree 1 if the graph contains more than one vertex, and there is one less edge than vertices   (890)

tree diagram   a diagram used to show the total number of possible outcomes of an event   (753)

trigonometric equation   an equation involving a trigonometric function that is true for some, but not all, values of the variable   (387)

trigonometric form   See polar form.

trigonometric functions   For any angle with measure α, a point $P(x, y)$ on its terminal side, and $r = \sqrt{x^2 + y^2}$, the trigonometric functions of α are as follows.   (258)

$$\sin \alpha = \frac{y}{r} \qquad \cos \alpha = \frac{x}{r} \qquad \tan \alpha = \frac{y}{x}$$

$$\csc \alpha = \frac{r}{y} \qquad \sec \alpha = \frac{r}{x} \qquad \cot \alpha = \frac{x}{y}$$

trigonometric identity   an equation involving a trigonometric function that is true for all values of the variable   (358)

trigonometric series   infinite series that define the trigonometric functions sine and cosine   (697)

U

unbounded   The solution of a linear programming problem is unbounded if the region defined by the constraints is infinitely large.   (93)

unit circle   a circle of radius 1 unit whose center is at the origin of a rectangular coordinate system   (241)

unit vector   a vector of length 1 that is parallel to the x-, y-, or z-axis   (422)

upper bound   the integer greater than or equal to the greatest zero of the polynomial $P(x)$ (212)

upper sum   a Riemann sum for rectangles which are always above the curve   (931)

V

vector   a quantity, or directed distance, that has both magnitude and direction   (412)

vertex of a conic section   a point at which a conic section intersects its axis of symmetry   (534, 543, 551)

vertex   in graph theory, a point of a graph; a node   (866)

vertical asymptote   The line $x = a$ is a vertical asymptote for a function $f(x)$ if $f(x) \to \infty$ or $f(x) \to -\infty$ as $x \to a$ from either the left or the right.   (135)

vertical displacement   the distance the graph of a function has been translated vertically represented by h in $y = A\,f(k\theta + c) + h$ when $y = f(\theta)$ is a trigonometric function   (322)

W

walk   the course taken from one vertex to another along an edge   (872)

weight of an edge   the value assigned to each edge in a weighted graph   (885)

weight of a path   the sum of the weights of the edges along a path   (885)

weighted multigraph   a multigraph in which a value is assigned to each edge   (883)

X

x-intercept   the x-coordinate of the point at which the graph of an equation crosses the x-axis   (22)

Y

y-intercept   the y-coordinate of the point at which the graph of an equation crosses the y-axis   (36)

Z

zero   a value of x for which $f(x) = 0$ (22, 179)

zero matrix   a matrix whose elements are all zero   (65)

CHAPTER 1 LINEAR RELATIONS AND FUNCTIONS

Pages 10-11 Lesson 1-1
5. yes **7.** yes **9.** -9 **11.** -114 **13.** -6.69
15. $-29 - 12n - n^2$ **17.** $x \le 4$ **19.** {-3, 0, 1, 2}, {-6, 0, 2, 4}, yes
21. {-2}, {7, 8, 9}, no **23.** {1, 2, 3, 4}, {5, 6, 7, 8}, yes
25. {6, 7, 8}, {-3, 3}, yes **27.** {(4, 10), (5, 12.5), (6, 15),
(7, 17.5), (8, 20)}, yes **29.** {(11, 3), (11, -3)}, no **31.** {(-2, 0.5),
(-1, -0.5), (0, -1.5), (1, -0.5), (2, 0.5), (3, 1.5)}, yes **33.** 6
35. 5 **37.** 7 **39.** $[q] + 5$ **41.** 3 **43.** 9 **45.** $10\frac{3}{4}$
47. $|25m^2 - 13|$ **49.** -5 **51.** $\pm 4\frac{1}{2}$ **53.** $-\sqrt{7} \le x \le \sqrt{7}$
59. If the x-coordinate represents the pounds of aluminum
produced and the y-coordinate represents the number of cans
recycled, the relation is a function. If the x-coordinate
represents the number of cans recycled and the y-coordinate
represents the pounds of aluminum produced, the relation is
not a function because the x-coordinate 75,000 would be
paired with 2 y-coordinates, 3000 and 3100.

Pages 17-18 Lesson 1-2
5. $\frac{-x^3 - x^2 + 2x + 1}{x + 1}$, $x \ne -1$ **7.** $\frac{x}{x^3 + x^2 - x - 1}$, $x \ne 1$
9. $x^2 + 8x + 7, x^2 - 5$ **11.** no **13.** $\frac{-x^3 - 2x^2 - 35x - 3}{x - 7}$, $x \ne 7$
15. $\frac{3}{x^3 - 2x^2 - 35x}$, $x \ne -5, 0, 7$ **17.** $3x^2 - 24x + 48, 3x^2 - 4$
19. $5x^4 - 10x^2 + 5, 25x^4 - 1$ **21.** $x^2 + 7x + 12, x^2 + 5x + 7$
23. yes **25.** no **27.** yes **29.** $f^{-1}(x) = \sqrt[3]{x}$, function
37. $65 **39.** {(-3, 14), (-2, 13), (-1, 12), (0, 11)}, yes
41. $\pm\sqrt{6}$

Pages 25-27 Lesson 1-3
3. 2 **5.** none **7.** all points **9.** $x > 2$ **11.** $y \le x + 2$
13.
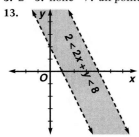
15. $1 \le y \le 4$ **17.** -12
19. $-\frac{5}{9}$ **21.** none

23.

27.

31.

35.
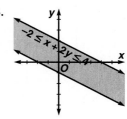

41a.

$y = 0.82x + 24$

b. $24 billion **c.** If the
nation had no disposable
income, personal
consumption expenditures
would be $24 billion.
43. $8 - 6a - 6a^2 - a^3$
45. $16x - 4$ **47.** A

Page 27 Mid-Chapter Review
1a. domain: {2, 3, 5, 6}, range: {-1, 0, 1, 2, 3} **b.** No, the
element 5 in the domain is paired with both 2 and -1 in the
range. **3.** -1 **5.** $4 + 18k - 27k^3$ **7.** $\frac{1}{x^2}, \frac{1}{x^2}$
9.

$2x - 4y = 8$

Pages 33-35 Lesson 1-4
5. 10, undefined **7.** 5, $\frac{3}{4}$ **9.** $2\sqrt{2}$, 1 **11.** 12 **13.** 30
15. (1, 1), (-2, -1), (2, -2) **17.** $6\sqrt{2}$, -1 **19.** $8\sqrt{5}$, -2 **21.** 3,
undefined **23.** $\sqrt{1 + 9n^2}$, -3n **25.** no **27.** yes **29.** 8
31. -5 **33.** Prove that $DE = \frac{1}{2}AB = \frac{1}{2}a$.
$D = \left(\frac{b + 0}{2}, \frac{c + 0}{2}\right) = \left(\frac{b}{2}, \frac{c}{2}\right)$
$E = \left(\frac{a + b}{2}, \frac{0 + c}{2}\right) = \left(\frac{a + b}{2}, \frac{c}{2}\right)$
$DE = \sqrt{\left(\frac{b}{2} - \frac{a + b}{2}\right)^2 + \left(\frac{c}{2} - \frac{c}{2}\right)^2} = \sqrt{\left(-\frac{a}{2}\right)^2} = \frac{a}{2}$
37a. 0.2 **b.** $361 **39.** -4 **41.** $x^5 - 3x^4 + 7x^3, \frac{x^3}{x^2 - 3x + 7}$

43.

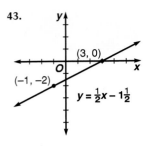

(3, 0)
(−1, −2)
$y = \frac{1}{2}x - 1\frac{1}{2}$

Pages 39-41   Lesson 1-5

7. $y = 4x + \frac{1}{2}, 4, \frac{1}{2}$ **9.** $y = 4x - 10$ **11.** $y = -6x - 22$

13. $y - 0 = -1(x + 2), y = -x - 2$ **15.** $y = 8x + 50$

17. $y = -3x + 14$ **19.** $y = -\frac{1}{4}x + \frac{5}{4}$ **21.** Point-slope form

is undefined, $x = -1$ **23.** $y - 2 = \frac{7}{2}(x - 5), y = \frac{7}{2}x - \frac{31}{2}$

25. $y - 1 = -\frac{3}{5}(x - 3), y = -\frac{3}{5}x + \frac{14}{5}$ **27.** The graphs are all lines. When m is positive, the graph slopes up to the right. When m is negative, the graph slopes down to the right. All three graphs cross the y-axis at (0, -1).   **29.** The graphs are all lines. When m is positive, the graph slopes up to the right. When m is negative, the graph slopes down to the right. All three graphs cross the y-axis at (0, 2).

33a. $C(x) = 0.5x + 1000$ **b.** $1000, $0.50

c.

Cost
$ 500
500
Boxes Produced

35a. $y = \frac{7}{2}x + 83$

b. 21.286 cm

37. $4x^2 - 7, 4x^2 - 7$

39. 76,650 people per year

Pages 45-47   Lesson 1-6

5. 3, -3, neither   **7.** 1, -1, perpendicular   **9.** -4, -4, parallel
11. $2x - y - 6 = 0, x + 2y - 8 = 0$ **13.** $2x - y - 18 = 0,$
$x + 2y - 4 = 0$

15.

X(3, 6)
W(-1, 3)
Y(6, 2)
Z(2, −1)

$WZ = \sqrt{(2 + 1)^2 + (-1 - 3)^2} = 5$
$YZ = \sqrt{(2 - 6)^2 + (-1 - 2)^2} = 5$
$XY = \sqrt{(6 - 3)^2 + (2 - 6)^2} = 5$
$WX = \sqrt{(3 + 1)^2 + (6 - 3)^2} = 5$
Thus, $WXYZ$ is a rhombus. The slope of $\overline{WX} = \frac{6 - 3}{3 + 1} = \frac{3}{4}$, and the slope of $\overline{WZ} = \frac{3 + 1}{-1 - 2} = -\frac{4}{3}$.
Thus $\overline{WZ}$ is perpendicular to $\overline{WX}$ and $WXYZ$ is a square.
17. $3x - y + 6 = 0$

19. $6x - y - 3 = 0$ **21.** $2x + 3y - 16 = 0$ **23.** $x - 2y - 6 = 0$ **25.** $5x + 4y + 43 = 0$ **27.** $2x + 3y - 40 = 0$

29. $4, -\frac{49}{4}$ **31.** slope of $\overline{AB} = \frac{2 - (-3)}{-1 - 4} = \frac{5}{-5} = -1$

slope of $\overline{BC} = \frac{-1 - (-3)}{-2 - 4} = \frac{2}{-6} = -\frac{1}{3}$

slope of $\overline{CA} = \frac{-1 - 2}{-2 - (-1)} = \frac{-3}{-1} = 3$

The slopes of $\overline{BC}$ and $\overline{CA}$ have a product of -1, so the lines are perpendicular. Therefore, $\triangle ABC$ is a right triangle.

35. No, they are riding along parallel lines or the same line, 5 miles apart.

37.

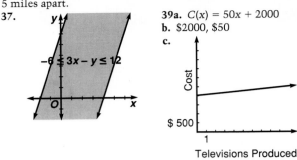

$-6 \le 3x - y \le 12$

39a. $C(x) = 50x + 2000$
b. $2000, $50
c.

Cost
$ 500
1
Televisions Produced

Pages 48-50   Chapter 1 Summary and Review

1. {(0, -7), (1, -2), (2, 3), (3, 8)}, yes   **3.** {(5, 1), (5, -1), (6, 2), (6, -2)}, no   **5.** 0   **7.** -3   **9.** $3x + 1, 3x - 3$ **11.** $x^2 + 4x + 6, x^2 + 2x + 4$ **13.** $f^{-1}(x) = \pm\sqrt{x + 12}$, no   **15.** $f^{-1}(x) = \frac{1}{2}\sqrt[3]{x}$, yes   **17.** $\frac{8}{3}$ **19.** 20   **21.** 13   **23.** 5   **25.** $y = 2x - 5$

27. $y = \frac{3}{5}x$ **29.** $y = x + 4$ **31.** $y = \frac{7}{2}x - 10$

33. $4x - y + 11 = 0$ **35.** $x + 3y - 12 = 0$ **37a.** 10 m, 40 m, 90 m, 160 m, 250 m   **b.** Yes, each element of the domain is paired with exactly one element of the range.
39. $y = 0.1x + 140; $140, $0.10

Page 51   Chapter 1 Test

1. {(2, 5), (1, 2), (0, -1), (-1, -4), (-2, -7)}, yes   **2.** {(4, 13), (3, 11), (2, 9), (1, 7), (0, 5), (4, -13), (3, -11), (2, -9), (1, -7), (0, -5)}, no
3. 0   **4.** -44   **5.** -114   **6.** -144.13   **7.** $\sqrt{2x^2 - 5}, 2x - 5$
8. $50x^2 + 120x + 72, 10x^2 + 6$ **9.** $3x - 7, 3x + 21$
10. $f^{-1}(x) = \pm\sqrt{3x - 5}$, no   **11.** $f^{-1}(x) = 4x - 4$, yes
12. $f^{-1}(x) = \sqrt[3]{-\frac{x}{2} + 1}$, yes

13.

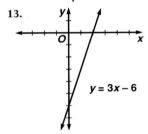

$y = 3x - 6$

14.

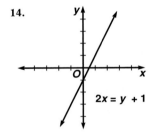

$2x = y + 1$

15.

$y + 4x \le 12$

16.

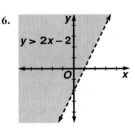

$y > 2x - 2$

17. $\sqrt{17}, -\frac{1}{4}$ **18.** $5\sqrt{2}, \frac{1}{7}$ **19.** $\sqrt{k^2 + 4}, \frac{2}{k}$
20. $y = \frac{5}{3}x + \frac{14}{3}$ **21.** $y = -\frac{3}{4}x + 4$ **22.** $3x + 2y - 17 = 0$
23. $5x + y = 0$

24.

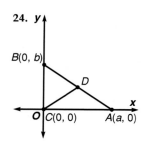

D is the midpoint of hypotenuse $\overline{AB}$. The coordinates of D are $\left(\frac{a}{2}, \frac{b}{2}\right)$. $BD = \sqrt{\left(0 - \frac{a}{2}\right)^2 + \left(b - \frac{b}{2}\right)^2} = \sqrt{\frac{a^2}{4} + \frac{b^2}{4}}$

$AD = \sqrt{\left(a - \frac{a}{2}\right)^2 + \left(0 - \frac{b}{2}\right)^2} = \sqrt{\frac{a^2}{4} + \frac{b^2}{4}}$

$CD = \sqrt{\left(\frac{a}{2} - 0\right)^2 + \left(\frac{b}{2} - 0\right)^2} = \sqrt{\frac{a^2}{4} + \frac{b^2}{4}}$

$BD = AD = CD$ **25a.** 9.5 1m/m² **b.** d cannot be negative or zero. **BONUS** -2

CHAPTER 2 SYSTEMS OF EQUATIONS AND INEQUALITIES

Pages 59-61   Lesson 2-1

5. yes **7.** no **9.** no **11.** (1, 2) **13.** I **15.** CI **17.** (0, 4)
19. (-2, 0) **21.** (4, 2) **23.** (-2, 3) **25.** (12, 2)
27. (5.25, 0.75) **31.** 70 soybeans, 30 corn **33.** {16}, {-4, 4}; no
35. $y = \frac{3}{4}x + 3\frac{1}{4}$ **37.** D

Pages 68-70   Lesson 2-2

5. $\begin{bmatrix} 8 & 1 \\ -4 & 9 \end{bmatrix}$ **7.** $\begin{bmatrix} 2 & 1 \\ -2 & -1 \end{bmatrix}$ **9.** $\begin{bmatrix} -15 & -3 \\ 9 & -12 \end{bmatrix}$ **11.** $\begin{bmatrix} 15 & 3 \\ -20 & 19 \end{bmatrix}$ **13.** $\begin{bmatrix} 22 & 9 \\ -27 & 13 \end{bmatrix}$

15. (7, 9) **17.** $\begin{bmatrix} 7 & 14 & 3 \\ -6 & 15 & -14 \\ 23 & 4 & -4 \end{bmatrix}$ **19.** $\begin{bmatrix} 4 & 20 & -6 \\ -2 & 12 & -14 \\ 31 & 2 & -1 \end{bmatrix}$ **21.** $\begin{bmatrix} 9 & 3 & 5 \\ -15 & 16 & -8 \\ 12 & 6 & -5 \end{bmatrix}$

23. $\begin{bmatrix} 5 & 4 & -11 \\ -16 & 11 & -2 \\ 17 & 4 & 0 \end{bmatrix}$ **25.** (7, 2) **27.** (4, 0) **29.** $\begin{bmatrix} 21 & 0 \\ 15 & 9 \end{bmatrix}$

31. $\begin{bmatrix} 6 & -6 & 12 \\ 10 & 8 & -4 \end{bmatrix}$ **33.** $\begin{bmatrix} 34 & 12 \\ 36 & -12 \\ 16 & 18 \end{bmatrix}$ **35.** $\begin{bmatrix} -30 & 60 \\ 46 & -8 \end{bmatrix}$ **37.** $\begin{bmatrix} 49 & 0 \\ 50 & 9 \end{bmatrix}$

39. $\begin{bmatrix} 162 & -54 & 180 \\ 48 & -156 & 240 \\ 138 & 24 & 60 \end{bmatrix}$ **41.** $\begin{bmatrix} 14 & -29 \\ 3 & 7 \end{bmatrix}$

43. Let $A = \begin{bmatrix} a_{11} & a_{12} \\ a_{21} & a_{22} \end{bmatrix}$, $B = \begin{bmatrix} b_{11} & b_{12} \\ b_{21} & b_{22} \end{bmatrix}$, and $C = \begin{bmatrix} c_{11} & c_{12} \\ c_{21} & c_{22} \end{bmatrix}$.

$(A + B) + C = \begin{bmatrix} a_{11}+b_{11} & a_{12}+b_{12} \\ a_{21}+b_{21} & a_{22}+b_{22} \end{bmatrix} + \begin{bmatrix} c_{11} & c_{12} \\ c_{21} & c_{22} \end{bmatrix}$

$= \begin{bmatrix} (a_{11}+b_{11})+c_{11} & (a_{12}+b_{12})+c_{12} \\ (a_{21}+b_{21})+c_{21} & (a_{22}+b_{22})+c_{22} \end{bmatrix}$

$= \begin{bmatrix} a_{11}+(b_{11}+c_{11}) & a_{12}+(b_{12}+c_{12}) \\ a_{21}+(b_{21}+c_{21}) & a_{22}+(b_{22}+c_{22}) \end{bmatrix}$

$= \begin{bmatrix} a_{11} & a_{12} \\ a_{21} & a_{22} \end{bmatrix} + \begin{bmatrix} b_{11}+c_{11} & b_{12}+c_{12} \\ b_{21}+c_{21} & b_{22}+c_{22} \end{bmatrix}$

$= A + (B + C)$

45. Let $A = \begin{bmatrix} a_{11} & a_{12} \\ a_{21} & a_{22} \end{bmatrix}$, $B = \begin{bmatrix} b_{11} & b_{12} \\ b_{21} & b_{22} \end{bmatrix}$, and $C = \begin{bmatrix} c_{11} & c_{12} \\ c_{21} & c_{22} \end{bmatrix}$.

$(AB)C = \begin{bmatrix} a_{11}b_{11}+a_{12}b_{21} & a_{11}b_{12}+a_{12}b_{22} \\ a_{21}b_{11}+a_{22}b_{21} & a_{21}b_{12}+a_{22}b_{22} \end{bmatrix} \begin{bmatrix} c_{11} & c_{12} \\ c_{21} & c_{22} \end{bmatrix}$

$= \begin{bmatrix} a_{11}b_{11}c_{11}+a_{12}b_{21}c_{11}+a_{11}b_{12}c_{21}+a_{12}b_{22}c_{21} \\ a_{21}b_{11}c_{11}+a_{21}b_{12}c_{21}+a_{22}b_{21}c_{11}+a_{22}b_{22}c_{21} \end{bmatrix}$

$a_{11}b_{11}c_{12}+a_{12}b_{21}c_{12}+a_{11}b_{12}c_{22}+a_{12}b_{22}c_{22}$
$a_{21}b_{11}c_{12}+a_{22}b_{21}c_{12}+a_{21}b_{12}c_{22}+a_{22}b_{22}c_{22}$

$A(BC) = \begin{bmatrix} a_{11} & a_{12} \\ a_{21} & a_{22} \end{bmatrix} \begin{bmatrix} b_{11}c_{11}+b_{12}c_{21} & b_{11}c_{12}+b_{12}c_{22} \\ b_{21}c_{11}+b_{22}c_{21} & b_{21}c_{12}+b_{22}c_{22} \end{bmatrix}$

$= \begin{bmatrix} a_{11}b_{11}c_{11}+a_{11}b_{12}c_{21}+a_{12}b_{21}c_{11}+a_{12}b_{22}c_{21} \\ a_{21}b_{11}c_{11}+a_{21}b_{12}c_{21}+a_{22}b_{21}c_{11}+a_{22}b_{22}c_{21} \end{bmatrix}$

$a_{11}b_{11}c_{12}+a_{11}b_{12}c_{22}+a_{12}b_{21}c_{12}+a_{12}b_{22}c_{22}$
$a_{21}b_{11}c_{12}+a_{22}b_{21}c_{12}+a_{21}b_{12}c_{22}+a_{22}b_{22}c_{22}$

Therefore, $(AB)C = A(BC)$.
47. PG, \$8218; LW3, \$18,422; BR, \$31,736
49. $[f \circ g] x = x^2 + x$, $[g \circ f] x = x^2 + 3x + 1$ **51.** $5|t|, \frac{4}{3}$
53. (45, 60)

Pages 75-77   Lesson 2-3

5. 62 **7.** -50 **9.** $\frac{1}{10}\begin{bmatrix} 1 & -3 \\ 4 & -2 \end{bmatrix}$ **11.** $\left(\frac{3}{4}, \frac{1}{2}\right)$ **13.** 8 **15.** 1

17. -93 **19.** $\begin{bmatrix} -1 & 2 \\ 0 & -1 \end{bmatrix}$ **21.** $-\frac{1}{5}\begin{bmatrix} -3 & -1 \\ -2 & 1 \end{bmatrix}$ **23.** $\frac{1}{7}\begin{bmatrix} 1 & -1 \\ 4 & 3 \end{bmatrix}$ **25.** (7, -9)

27. $\left(\frac{2}{3}, 1, -\frac{4}{3}\right)$ **29.** -109 **31.** 3411 **35.** 80 mL of the 60% solution, 120 mL of the 40% solution **37.** 24, 16 **39.** (3, 1)
41. B

Page 77   Mid-Chapter Review

1. (1, 2) **3.** (3, -1) **5.** $\begin{bmatrix} 8 & 1 \\ -4 & 9 \end{bmatrix}$ **7.** $\begin{bmatrix} 15 & 3 \\ -20 & 19 \end{bmatrix}$ **9.** (19, -11)

Pages 82-83   Lesson 2-4

3. Multiply row 2 by 5 and add it to row 1. Multiply row 1 by -2 and add it to row 2. **5.** Multiply row 1 by 2. Add row 2 to row 1. Multiply row 1 by -3 and row 2 by 5. Add row 1 to row 2. **7.** (-1, 5, -2) **9.** (3, 2) **11.** $\left(-\frac{97}{19}, \frac{155}{19}\right)$ **13.** (-1, 2, -3)
15. (7, 1, -2) **17.** (1, -1, 2, -2) **19.** $y = 2x^2 - 7x + 9$
23. blouse, \$28; skirt, \$32; jeans, \$36 **25.** (7, 2) **27.** 0

Pages 89-90   Lesson 2-5

3. 14 **5.** 4.5 **7.** 32, 0 **9.** (-2, 0), (0, 3), (4, 2), (2, -4); maximum at (2, -4) = 8, minimum at (0, 3) = -1 **11.** (0, 0), (0, 4), (2, 0); maximum at (0, 4) = 4, minimum at (2, 0) = -2
13. (0, 1), (0, 4), (3, 1); maximum at (3, 1) = 21, minimum at (0, 1) = 9 **15.** (0, 0), (5, 0), (5, 1), (0, 2), (2, 4); maximum at (5, 0) = 15, minimum at (2, 4) = -14
17. $y \geq \frac{1}{5}x, y \leq -\frac{2}{5}x + \frac{32}{5}, y \geq 3x - 14, y \leq 6x$
21.

23. consistent and dependent **25.** -1, yes **27.** B

Pages 94-97   Lesson 2-6

5. $x \geq 200$ **7.** $P(x, y) = 20x + 30y$ **9.** (200, 600), (500, 300), (200, 300) **11.** \$22,000 **13.** infeasible **15.** alternate optimal **17.** $9\frac{2}{3}$ of Y and 0 of X **19.** unbounded
21. 1960 of #1, 1840 of #2 **23.** infeasible **25.** $\begin{bmatrix} 6 & -\frac{21}{4} \\ -3 & 0 \end{bmatrix}$
27. Multiply row 2 by -3 and add it to row 1. Multiply row 1 by 2 and row 2 by 3 and add row 1 to row 2. **29.** A

Pages 98-100 Chapter 2 Summary and Review

1. $(2, -4)$ **3.** $\left(-\frac{5}{11}, -\frac{2}{11}\right)$ **5.** $\begin{bmatrix} 4 & 3 \\ 2 & -6 \end{bmatrix}$ **7.** $\begin{bmatrix} -9 & -15 \\ 6 & -6 \end{bmatrix}$ **9.** $\begin{bmatrix} -5 & -51 \\ -8 & 8 \end{bmatrix}$

11. -1 **13.** 0 **15.** $(13, -5)$ **17.** $(-7, -4)$ **19.** $\left(-1, 3, \frac{1}{2}\right)$

21. $(0, 9)$, $(4, 7)$, $(6, 5)$, $(6, 4)$, $(0, 4)$; maximum at $(4, 7) = 25$, minimum at $(0, 4) = 8$ **23.** infeasible **25.** 39 inches, 31 inches, 13 inches

Page 101 Chapter 2 Test

1. $(4, 0)$ **2.** $(2, 7)$ **3.** $(-1, 5)$ **4.** $\left(\frac{3}{4}, \frac{1}{2}\right)$ **5.** $\begin{bmatrix} 5 & -10 \\ 0 & 20 \\ -15 & 20 \end{bmatrix}$

6. $\begin{bmatrix} 9 & 6 \\ 3 & 0 \end{bmatrix}$ **7.** $\begin{bmatrix} -7 & -8 \\ 11 & 10 \end{bmatrix}$ **8.** $\begin{bmatrix} -20 & 44 \\ 8 & -42 \end{bmatrix}$ **9.** $\begin{bmatrix} -5 & 50 \\ -1 & -48 \end{bmatrix}$ **10.** 7

11. -1 **12.** -4 **13.** -64 **14.** $\left(-2, -\frac{3}{4}\right)$ **15.** $(-2, 1, 3)$

16. $(1, 6, -1)$ **17.** $(0, 0)$, $(0, 3)$, $\left(\frac{5}{3}, \frac{14}{3}\right)$, $(4, 0)$; $28\frac{1}{3}$; 0

17.

18.

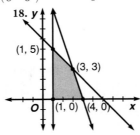

18. $(1, 5)$, $(3, 3)$, $(1, 0)$, $(4, 0)$; 28; 3
19. $\left(-\frac{5}{2}, 5\right)$, $(3, 5)$, $(3, 1)$, $\left(\frac{2}{3}, -\frac{4}{3}\right)$; 34, $-4\frac{2}{3}$
19.

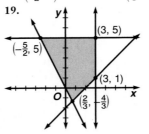

20. $\$460$ **BONUS** pentagon

CHAPTER 3 THE NATURE OF GRAPHS

Pages 113-116 Lesson 3-1

5. both **7.** point **9.** line **11.** $x = 2$ **13.** $x = 2, y = -2$
15a. $(-2, 5)$ **b.** $(2, -5)$ **c.** $(-5, -2)$ **d.** $(5, 2)$ **17.** $P'(4, 4)$
19. $P'(-3, -5)$

21a.

b.

c.

d.

25a.

b.

c.

d.

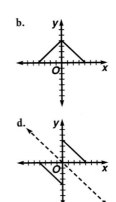

27. neither **29.** even **31.** odd **33.** y-axis **35.** no symmetry **43.** x-intercept: $(2, 0)$; other points: $(-3, 4.5)$, $(3, -4.5)$, $(-3, -4.5)$ **45.** $1, 3$ **47.** Parallel; the lines have the same slope. **49.** $\left(\frac{3}{4}, -\frac{2}{3}, \frac{1}{2}\right)$ **51.** 10

Pages 122-124 Lesson 3-2

5a. shrunk vertically **b.** moved 2 units up **c.** shrunk horizontally **7.** $f(x) + 2$ **9.** $-f(x - 4)$ **11.** $f(x + 5) - 2$

13.

17.

21a. narrower than the parent **b.** narrower and reflected over the x-axis **c.** narrower and moved 2 units right **d.** wider and moved 1 unit left **e.** narrower and moved 5 units down **23a.** moved up 6 units **b.** moved right 4 units **c.** wider **d.** narrower, moved 3 units left, and 8 units down **e.** inverted, moved 3 units right and 6 units up

25.

27.

Selected Answers

33a.

33b.

33c. $125   **35.** not a function
37. -78, yes   **39.** B

Pages 129-131   Lesson 3-3
5. $P'(5, -4)$ **7.** $P'(8, -2)$ **9.** yes   **11.** no   **13.** $y = \frac{x-3}{2}$
15. $y = \pm\frac{1}{3}\sqrt{3(4-x)}$ **17.** $y = \sqrt[3]{x} + 2$ **19.** $y = \pm\sqrt{x-2}$;
no   **21.** $y = \pm\sqrt[4]{x} + 4$; no   **23.** $y = \sqrt[3]{x-6} + 3$; yes
25a. reflection   **b.** reflection, moved 3 units right
c. reflection, moved 6 units up   **d.** narrower version of the
reflection   **e.** wider version of the reflection, moved 4 units
up   **f.** reflection, moved 5 units right, and 3 units up
31. 93%
35. both   **37.** A

33.

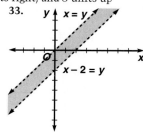

Pages 139-142   Lesson 3-4
5. $f(x) = \frac{1}{x-1}$ **7.** $f(x) = \frac{1}{x} + 5$ **9.** $f(x) = -\frac{1}{x}$ **11.** $x = -1$,
$y = 0$ **13.** $x = -5$ **15.** $x = 2, x = -3, y = 0$
17. $y = \frac{3}{2}x, x = 0$ **19a.** translated 1 unit down
b. translated 5 units left   **c.** closer to the axes   **d.** wider,
translated 8 units up   **e.** translated 3 units right, 7 units up

25.

$y = \frac{x-5}{x+1}$

29.

$y = \frac{-2}{(x-3)^2}$

33.

$y = \frac{3}{(x-4)^2}$

37.

$y = \frac{-x}{x^2-4}$

41a. x- and y-axes   **b.** It increases.   **c.** It is half.   **45.** $-\frac{4}{3}$
47. $y = \pm\sqrt{x+9}$

Pages 147-148   Lesson 3-5
3. yes   **5.** no

7.

11.

15.

19.

23. ϕ **25.** $\{x \mid x \geq 0\}$ **27.** all real numbers   **35.** 31.7% < v
< 38.3%   **37.** $\frac{1}{2}$, -2   **39.** (-6, -3)   **41.** B

Page 148   Mid-Chapter Review
1. y-axis
5. $x = 1$

3.

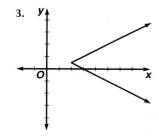

Pages 153-154   Lesson 3-6
5. $f'(x) = 2x$ **7.** $f'(x) = 2x^3$ **9.** $f'(x) = 2.4x^3 - 0.8x$ **11.** 6
13. 0   **15.** $f'(x) = 3x^2 - 4x + 4$ **17.** $f'(x) = 0.9x^2 - 8x$
19. $f'(x) = -20x^4 + 21x^2 + 1$ **21.** -8   **23.** -1   **25.** $1\frac{1}{6}$
27. -11   **29.** $y = 6x - 12$ **31.** $y = -2x + 2.25$
33. $y = -3x - 9$ **35.** (-3, 1)   **37.** (2, -2), (-2, 2)   **45a.** 16π in³
b. For each inch of increase in the radius, the volume
increases 16π or about 50.3 cubic inches.   **47.** (-1, 2)
49. -42

Pages 162-163   Lesson 3-7
5. $\left(-\frac{3}{2}, \frac{19}{2}\right)$, max   **7.** (0, 0), inflection   **9.** x: 0, 1; y: 0
11. (-1, -16), min   **13.** $\left(\frac{2}{3}, -\frac{1}{3}\right)$, min   **15.** $\left(\frac{1}{3}, \frac{26}{27}\right)$, min;
(0, 1), max; $\left(\frac{1}{6}, \frac{53}{54}\right)$, inflection   **17.** (0, -28), inflection

19. x: $-\frac{3}{2}, -\frac{5}{2}$; y: 15   **21.** x: 0, 5, 7; y: 0   **23.** x: 2, -2, 3, -3; y: 36

983

25.

33. 500 ft by 250 ft

35. P lies on $\overline{AB}$.
$$AP \stackrel{?}{=} PB$$
$$\sqrt{(9-4)^2 + (3-2)^2} \stackrel{?}{=} \sqrt{(4+1)^2 + (2-1)^2}$$
$$\sqrt{26} = \sqrt{26}$$
$$AP = PB$$

37. 0, no   **39.** $y = -7x - 2$

Pages 169-171   Lesson 3-8

5. point discontinuity; As $x \to \infty$, $y \to -\infty$. As $x \to -\infty$, $y \to -\infty$.
7. infinite discontinuity; As $x \to \infty$, $y \to \pm\infty$. As $x \to -\infty$, $y \to \pm\infty$.
9. infinite discontinuity; As $x \to \infty$, $y \to 0$. As $x \to -\infty$, $y \to 0$.
11. all reals: increasing   **13.** $x < 0$: decreasing, $x > 0$: increasing   **15.** point discontinuity   **17.** continuous
19. continuous   **21.** infinite discontinuity   **23.** infinite discontinuity   **25.** $x \to \infty$, $f(x) \to \infty$; $x \to -\infty$, $f(x) \to \infty$ **27.** -3, 4   **29.** 64, 4   **35.** $r = 3.6$ cm, $h = 7.4$ cm, $S = 248.8$ cm^2
37. 14   **39.** $f^{-1}(x) = \pm\sqrt{x} + 9$ **41.** max: (0, 3), min: (0.67, 2.85), inflection: (0.33, 2.93)

Pages 172-174   Chapter 3 Summary and Review

1. origin, $y = \pm x$, odd   **3.** none, neither   **5.** reflect across x-axis   **7.** translate left 5 units   **9.** $y = \frac{6-x}{2}$; yes
11. $y = \sqrt[3]{x+2} - 1$; yes   **13.** $x = -3, 4, y = 0$
15.

17.

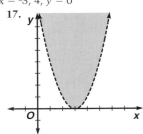

19. $y = 7x - 3$ **21.** $y = 10x - 5$ **23.** $\left(\frac{1}{2}, \frac{17}{4}\right)$, max
25. (0, -4), min; (-2, 0), max; (-1, -2), inflection   **27.** infinite
29. continuous   **31a.** 30.74 m/s   **b.** 6 m/s^2

Page 175   Chapter 3 Test

1. The graph is moved 5 units right.

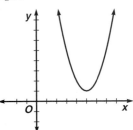

2. The graph is reflected over the x-axis and moved 2 units up.

3.

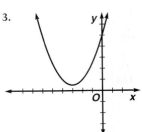

3. wider, shifted left 3 units
4. $y = \pm\sqrt{x} + 4$, no
5. $y = \frac{\sqrt[3]{x-1}}{2}$, yes
6. $y = \pm\sqrt[4]{x+7} - 3$, no
7. $x = -1, 3, y = 0$; neither
8. $x = \pm 2, y = 0$; odd
9. no asymptotes; neither

10.

11.

12. $y = -2x$ **13.** $y = 10x - 11$ **14.** (4, -12), min   **15.** (0, 3), max; (-2, -1), min; (-1, 1), inflection   **16.** point   **17.** jump
18. x: -1, 0, $\frac{5}{3}$; y: 0   **19.** $x \to \infty$, $y \to \infty$; $x \to -\infty$, $y \to \infty$

18.

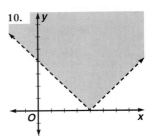

$y = 3x^3 - 2x^2 - 5x$

20a.

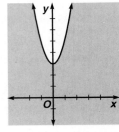

$m_1 = -7$

$v_f = 5\left(\dfrac{m_1 - 7}{m_1 + 7}\right)$

b. 0.83 m/s   **BONUS** $b = -3, c = 4$

CHAPTER 4   POLYNOMIAL AND RATIONAL FUNCTIONS

Pages 181-184   Lesson 4-1

5. yes, 3   **7.** yes, 7   **9.** yes   **11.** no   **13.** $x^4 - 5x^2 + 4 = 0$
15. 1; 2   **17.** 2; 7   **19.** 2; $\frac{5}{6}, -\frac{3}{2}$ **21.** 3; 0, 3, -2.5
23. $x^2 + x - 6 = 0$ **25.** $x^5 - 10x^4 + 25x^3 + 20x^2 - 80x - 64 = 0$ **27.** $x^4 - 2x^3 + x^2 + 2x - 2 = 0$ **29.** 4, $1 \pm i$
31. -1, 1, $\pm i\sqrt{2}$

33a.

33c.

33e.

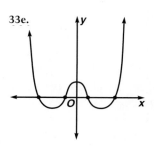

41a. $f(x) = 30,000x^3 + 55,000x^2 + 75,000x$; $198,266.41
b. $178,495.86; $19,770.55 less   **43.** $x^2 - 1$ **45.** (-5, -2)
47.

49. B

Pages 192-194   Lesson 4-2

5. $\frac{1}{4}$ **7.** $\frac{-5 \pm i\sqrt{11}}{2}$ **9.** -364, 2 imaginary roots

11. $5 + i\sqrt{2}$ **13.** $\frac{5 \pm i\sqrt{83}}{6}$ **15.** -8, 11   **17.** $\frac{3}{2}$, -7

19. 6, -4   **21.** $\frac{1}{4}$, -5   **23.** $\frac{-3 \pm i\sqrt{15}}{4}$ **25.** $\frac{3}{2}$, 5

27.

31.

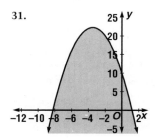

33. (4.1, -108.2), rel min; (-2.8, 60.4), rel max; (0.7, -24.3), pt. of inf.   **35.** (4.2, -3.1), rel min; (1.8, 3.1), rel max; (3, 0), pt. of inf.   **37a.** (-6, 0), (9, 0)

37b.

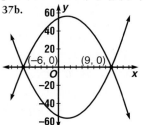

c. The two graphs have the same shape and x-intercepts. However, they are reflections of each other over the x-axis.   **43.** 18 ft by 24 ft   **45.** 5 seconds
47. -2x + y + 6 = 0
49. y-axis
51. $x^3 + x^2 - 80x - 300 = 0$

Pages 199-200   Lesson 4-3

5. 0, yes   **7.** 88, no   **9.** $(x + 1)(x - 1)(x + 7)$ **11.** $x + 1$, R6
13. $x^3 + 3x^2 + 6x + 12$, R23   **15.** $2x^2 + 2x$, R-3   **17.** 0, yes
19. 0, yes   **21.** -2, no   **23.** 0, yes   **25.** 190, no   **27.** 4
29. twice   **33.** $r \approx 1$ inch, $h \approx 5$ inches   **35.** (0, -32), inflection   **37.** 8 or -12

Pages 205-207   Lesson 4-4

5. ±1, ±2, ±3, ±6; -3, -1, 2   **7.** 1 pos; 2 or 0 neg; -3, -1, 2
9. 2 or 0 pos; 1 neg; -1.5, $\frac{1}{3}$, 3   **11.** ±6, ±3, ±2, ±1; -3, -1, 1, -2
13. ±20, ±10, ±5, ±4, ±2, ±1; 2, -2, 5   **15.** ±2, ±1; 1, 2
17. 1 pos and 1 neg; 0, 4, -2   **19.** 2 or 0 pos and 1 neg;
$\frac{1}{4}$, $-\frac{3}{2}$, 2   **21.** 1 pos and 2 or 0 neg; -0.5, -3, $\frac{1}{3}$ **23.** 2 or 0 pos and 2 or 0 neg; -2, 2, -1, 1
31a.

b. 0, 23.5   **33.** The three types of discontinuity are point, jump, and infinite. Point discontinuity means the function displays all the characteristics of continuity except for one point. Jump discontinuity occurs when a function is defined for all values of x, but at one point the graph jumps from (x, a) to (x, b). Infinite discontinuity occurs for functions whose graphs have asymptotes.   **35.** -95, 2 imaginary roots   **37.** B

Page 207   Mid-Chapter Review

1. 0, -10, 8   **3.** 113; 2 real roots; $\frac{13 \pm \sqrt{113}}{14}$ **5.** ±12, ±6, ±4, ±3, ±2, ±1, $\pm\frac{3}{2}$, $\pm\frac{1}{2}$; no rational zero

Pages 213-214   Lesson 4-5

5. 3 zeros; between -2 and -1, at 1, between 3 and 4; UB: 4
7. -0.4 and -2.6   **9.** 4 and 5, -1 and 0   **11.** 1 and 2   **13.** at 2, at -1   **15.** -2, -1   **17.** -2.5   **19.** 1, -1   **21.** 2, -5   **23.** 1, 0
25. 3 complex zeros; 1 positive and 2 or 0 negative zeros; zeros: -4.9, -1.8, 2.2; relative max: (-3.6, 26.5); relative min: (0.6, -43.5)   **29.** 2 meters   **31.** $-\frac{8}{3}$

33.

35. 30

Pages 220-222   Lesson 4-6

5. $2m^2$; -34   **7.** $12(a + 1)(a - 1)$; 3 and $-\frac{1}{2}$ **9.** 31
11. $\frac{2}{x - 1} - \frac{3}{x + 1}$ **13.** -1, 5   **15.** -3   **17.** all reals except 1
19. $\frac{1 \pm \sqrt{145}}{4}$ **21.** $x < 0, x > 3$ **23.** $a < 1, a > 31$
25. $0 \le x \le 2, x \ge 9$ **27.** $\frac{2}{p + 1} + \frac{1}{p - 1}$
29. $\frac{1}{m + 1} + \frac{1}{m}$ **31.** $x < -4, -1 < x < 4, x > 5$
35. $\frac{2}{5}$ or 10   **37.** 3.75 min   **39.** 24 multiple choice, 6 essay
41. ±1, ±2, $\pm\frac{1}{6}$, $\pm\frac{1}{2}$, $\pm\frac{1}{3}$, $\pm\frac{2}{3}$ **43.** E

Pages 228-229   Lesson 4-7

5. 17   **7.** $\frac{16}{3}$ **9.** $-\frac{3}{4}$ **11.** -20   **13.** no real solution
15. 15   **17.** -1   **19.** no real solution   **21.** $x \ge 16$
23. $1.8 \le x \le 5$ **25.** $\frac{3}{2}$ **27.** 0.64 meters   **29.** 7x + y = 2
31. max: (-1, 7), min: (1, 3), inflection: (0, 5)   **33.** E

Pages 230-232   Chapter 4 Summary and Review

1. -4   **3.** $\frac{1}{2}, -\frac{2}{3}$ **5.** 81; 2 distinct real roots; 4, $-\frac{1}{2}$ **7.** -63; no real roots; $\frac{-1 \pm 3i\sqrt{7}}{8}$ **9.** 0; yes   **11.** 4; no   **13.** 3; 1 pos; 2 or 0 neg; -2, -4, 7   **15.** 4; 2 or 0 pos, 2 or 0 neg; 2, -2, 3, -3   **17.** -1 and 0, 3 and 4   **19.** -2 and -1, 0 and 1, 1 and 2   **21.** -6, 1   **23.** $x \le -1, x \ge \frac{4}{3}$ **25.** 23   **27.** 1   **29.** Substitute values for x and $h(x)$; $30 \ne -460.3$; the ball hits the ground about 337 feet from the plate.

Page 233   Chapter 4 Test

1. 1, 4   **2.** $-\frac{1}{3}$, 0, $\frac{3}{2}$ **3.** $\frac{5 \pm i\sqrt{7}}{4}$ **4.** $\frac{80}{7}$ **5.** $-3 \le y \le \frac{5}{3}$
6. $x < -17, -2 < x < 0$ **7.** 11   **8.** 7   **9.** $m < -7$
10.

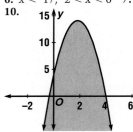

11. $2x^2 + x + 5$, R6
12. $x^3 - 6x^2 - 7x + 60$
13. 9; no   **14.** 0; yes
15. 3; 1 pos, 2 or 0 neg; $\frac{1}{2}, -\frac{1}{3}$, -2
16. 4; 1 pos, 3 or 1 neg; -1, -1
17. 4; 1 pos, 2 or 0 neg; 0, 9
18. 3; 2 or 0 pos, 1 neg; $-\frac{1}{2}, \frac{3}{2}, \frac{7}{2}$ **19.** $\frac{3}{z+2} - \frac{1}{2z-3}$
20. $\frac{6}{x+1} - \frac{3}{x+2} + \frac{4}{x-1}$

21. 3.8, -0.8   **22.** -1.3   **23.** -5   **24.** 5 cm by 12 cm by 2 cm
25. 40 km/h   **BONUS** $3 < k < 20$

Pages 234-235   Unit 1 Review

1. {(-1, -2), (0, 1), (1, 4), (2, 7), (3, 10)}; yes   **3.** $2x + 5, 2x + 2$
5. $4x^2 - 16x - 9, 2x^2 - 54$ **7.** 0

9.

11.

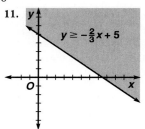

$y \ge -\frac{2}{3}x + 5$

$4 - 3x = y$

13. $\sqrt{58}$, $y = -\frac{7}{3}x - 5$ **15.** $3x - y + 7 = 0$ **17.** (1, -4)
19. (2, -2)   **21.** $\begin{bmatrix} 16 & -2 \\ 1 & -13 \end{bmatrix}$ **23.** $\begin{bmatrix} 9 & 45 \\ -90 & 20 \end{bmatrix}$ **25.** 19   **27.** 1, $\frac{5}{12}, \frac{1}{4}$
29. (0, 0), $\left(0, \frac{1}{2}\right)$, (1, 0); -2; -5   **31.** odd   **33.** neither

35.

35. moved 2 units right
37. $y = \sqrt[3]{x - 2} + 1$; yes
39. hole: $x = -3$

41.

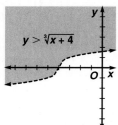

$y > \sqrt[3]{x + 4}$

43. $y = 9x + 3$ **45.** (1, 2), min; (-1, 6), max; (0, 4), inf
47. jump   **49.** $\frac{1 \pm \sqrt{11}}{2}$ **51.** $x < \frac{1}{3}, x > 1$ **53.** $-8 \le x \le 1$
55. 11   **57.** 3 or 1; 1; none   **59.** -1, -3.6, 0.6

986

CHAPTER 5   THE TRIGONOMETRIC FUNCTIONS

Pages 244-246   Lesson 5-1

5. IV   **7.** II   **9.** II   **11.** II   **13.** $\frac{\pi}{10}$ **15.** $\frac{\pi}{180}$ **17.** 180°
19. -210°   **21.** yes   **23.** yes   **25.** III   **27.** III   **29.** IV   **31.** IV
33. $-\frac{5\pi}{6}$ **35.** $\frac{7\pi}{12}$ **37.** $-\frac{5\pi}{2}$ **39.** $-\frac{125\pi}{18}$ **41.** -200°32'
43. -90°   **45.** -105°   **47.** 510°   **53.** $\frac{2\pi}{5}$ **55.** 30°   **57.** 60°
59. $\frac{\pi}{3}$ **61.** -1.935   **65a.** 3700 revolutions per minute
b. 7400π radians per minute   **67.** $\frac{5}{8}$ **69.** (1, 3)   **71.** 50 bicycles, 75 tricycles   **73.** yes   **75.** 23

Pages 251-254   Lesson 5-2

7. $\frac{5\pi}{2}$ **9.** 88   **11.** 2   **13.** 9.6 m²   **15.** 530.1 cm²   **17.** $\frac{20\pi}{3}$ cm
19. 4π cm   **21.** $\frac{5\pi}{12}$ in.   **23.** $\frac{191\pi}{40}$ in.   **25.** 100.3°   **27.** 89.5°
29. 17.0 in²   **31.** 38.1 km²   **33.** 20.5 yd²   **35.** 157.5 m
37. 12.2 in., 2.4 in.   **41.** 8 feet   **43.** A, 0.39 ft²; B, 1.18 ft²; C, 1.96 ft²   **45.** 5.23 mi   **47a.** B, clockwise; C, counterclockwise   **b.** 180 rpm, 75 rpm   **49.** 0, no   **51.** $-\frac{1}{2}, -\frac{2}{3}$
53. 3   **55.** A

Pages 260-262   Lesson 5-3

7. $\sin\theta = \frac{\sqrt{2}}{2}$, $\cos\theta = \frac{\sqrt{2}}{2}$, $\tan\theta = 1$, $\csc\theta = \sqrt{2}$, $\sec\theta = \sqrt{2}$, $\cot\theta = 1$ **9.** $-\frac{\sqrt{3}}{2}$ **11.** $-\frac{2\sqrt{3}}{3}$ **13.** II, IV   **15.** III
23. $\sin\alpha = \frac{8}{17}$, $\cos\alpha = \frac{15}{17}$, $\tan\alpha = \frac{8}{15}$, $\csc\alpha = \frac{17}{8}$, $\sec\alpha = \frac{17}{15}$, $\cot\alpha = \frac{15}{8}$ **25.** $\sin\alpha = -\frac{8\sqrt{65}}{65}$, $\cos\alpha = \frac{\sqrt{65}}{65}$, $\tan\alpha = -8$, $\csc\alpha = -\frac{\sqrt{65}}{8}$, $\sec\alpha = \sqrt{65}$, $\cot\alpha = -\frac{1}{8}$
27. $\sin\alpha = \frac{\sqrt{2}}{2}$, $\cos\alpha = -\frac{\sqrt{2}}{2}$, $\tan\alpha = -1$, $\csc\alpha = \sqrt{2}$, $\sec\alpha = -\sqrt{2}$, $\cot\alpha = -1$ **29.** $\sin\alpha = 1$, $\cos\alpha = 0$, $\tan\alpha = $ undefined, $\csc\alpha = 1$, $\sec\alpha = $ undefined, $\cot\alpha = 0$
31. $\sin\theta = \frac{\sqrt{3}}{2}$, $\tan\theta = -\sqrt{3}$, $\csc\theta = \frac{2\sqrt{3}}{3}$, $\sec\theta = -2$, $\cot\theta = -\frac{\sqrt{3}}{3}$ **33.** $\sin\theta = -\frac{\sqrt{6}}{3}$, $\cos\theta = \frac{\sqrt{3}}{3}$, $\tan\theta = -\sqrt{2}$, $\csc\theta = -\frac{\sqrt{6}}{2}$, $\cot\theta = -\frac{\sqrt{2}}{2}$ **35.** +   **37.** −   **39.** undefined
41. −   **49.** $\tan 35° = \frac{d}{250}$ **51.** $\pm\sqrt{5}$ **53.** 4, $-\frac{5}{3}$
55. $x^2 + 2x + 6$ R15   **57.** 3.14 m/s

Page 262   Mid-Chapter Review

1. -135°   **5.** 6.1 cm   **7.** 8700 ft²

Pages 267-268   Lesson 5-4

5. $\sqrt{3}$ **7.** $-\frac{\sqrt{2}}{2}$ **9.** $\frac{2\sqrt{3}}{3}$ **11.** 0.7431   **13.** 0.5774   **15.** 1
17. $\frac{\sqrt{3}}{2}$ **19.** 2   **21.** undefined   **23.** $-\frac{1}{2}$ **25.** 0
27. -0.1763   **29.** -2.6695   **31.** -0.1584   **33.** -2.0809
35. 0.8288   **37.** 1.52   **39.** $y = -\frac{1}{2}x + 6$ **41.** $\frac{9}{2}$ **43.** 25π m/h
45. C

Pages 273-275   Lesson 5-5

5. $\tan 76° = \frac{a}{13}$ **7.** $\tan A = \frac{21.2}{9}$ **9.** $\tan 49°13' = \frac{10}{b}$
11. $\tan A = \frac{7}{12}$ **13.** 7.0 cm, 5.9 cm   **15.** $B = 49°$, $c = 9.9, a = 6.5$ **17.** $B = 67°38', c = 23.8, a = 9.1$
19. $B = 45°, a = 7, b = 7$ **21.** $B = 52°45', a = 8.4, c = 13.8$

23. $B = 34°$, $a = 13.3$, $b = 9.0$ **25.** 10.80 cm, 9.18 cm
27. 10.57 cm **29.** 4.47 m **31.** about 40° **33.** 60°28'
35. no **37.** I, III **39.** C

Pages 280-281 Lesson 5-6

5. $\dfrac{2.8}{\sin 61°} = \dfrac{a}{\sin 53°}$ **7.** $\dfrac{16}{\sin 42°} = \dfrac{12}{\sin C}$ **9.** one;
$A = 15°25'$, $B = 147°35'$, $b = 20.2$ **11.** none **13.** two;
$B = 50°19'$ or $129°41'$, $C_1 = 91°41'$, $c_1 = 13.0$, $C_2 = 12°19'$,
$c_2 = 2.8$ **15.** none **17.** one; $C = 80°$, $a = 13.1$, $b = 17.6$
19. none **21.** none **23.** none

25.
$$\frac{\sin A}{a} = \frac{\sin C}{c}$$
$$\frac{\sin A}{\sin C} = \frac{a}{c}$$
$$\frac{\sin A}{\sin C} - 1 = \frac{a}{c} - 1$$
$$\frac{\sin A - \sin C}{\sin C} = \frac{a - c}{c}$$

27.
$$\frac{\sin A}{a} = \frac{\sin B}{b}$$
$$\frac{a}{\sin A} = \frac{b}{\sin B}$$
$$\frac{a}{b} = \frac{\sin A}{\sin B}$$

31. 201.1 feet **33.** $45° + 360k°$, where k is an integer
35. 12.7 meters

Pages 286-287 Lesson 5-7

5. cosines; $A = 53°35'$, $B = 59°33'$, $C = 66°52'$ **7.** sines;
$C = 30°57'$, $B = 109°3'$, $b = 14.7$ **9.** cosines; $b = 18.5$,
$C = 79°3'$, $A = 40°57'$ **11.** sines; $A = 30°13'$, $C = 104°19'$,
$c = 23.1$ **13.** 247.3 miles **15.** $a = 7.8$, $B = 44°13'$,
$C = 84°47'$ **17.** $A = 44°25'$, $B = 57°7'$, $C = 78°28'$
19. $A = 21°47'$, $B = 120°$, $C = 38°13'$ **21.** $A = 51°50'$,
$B = 70°53'$, $C = 57°17'$ **23.** $b = 12.3$, $A = 39°19'$,
$C = 20°41'$ **25.** 101.1 cm, 76.9 cm **27.** 349.7 nautical
miles **29.** $\dfrac{5}{8}$ **31.** 30° **33.** 172.7 yd

Pages 293-295 Lesson 5-8

5. $K = \dfrac{1}{2} \cdot 20^2 \cdot \dfrac{\sin 45° \cdot \sin 30°}{\sin 105°}$; 73.2
7. $K = \dfrac{1}{2} \cdot 16 \cdot 12 \sin 43°$; 65.5
9. $K = \dfrac{1}{2} \cdot 12^2 \cdot \dfrac{\sin 30° \cdot \sin 15°}{\sin 135°}$; 13.2 **11.** 238.3 **13.** 6.4
15. 11,486.3 **17.** 21.1 **19.** 13,533.9 **21.** 474.9 **23.** 1.1
25. 13.6 **27.** 83.1 cm² **29.** 116.5 cm² **33a.** 302 in²
b. 1208 ft² **35a.** 17 ft² **b.** 146 ft³ **37.** y-axis
39. 139,000 cm/s **41.** A

Pages 296-298 Chapter 5 Summary and Review

1. 60° **3.** 240° **5.** $-\dfrac{7\pi}{4}$ **7.** $\dfrac{\pi}{4}$ **9.** $\dfrac{\pi}{3}$ **11.** $\dfrac{\pi}{6}$ **13.** $\dfrac{45\pi}{4}$
15. $\dfrac{25\pi}{4}$ **17.** $\dfrac{\sqrt{2}}{2}$ **19.** -4 **21.** $-\dfrac{\sqrt{2}}{2}$ **23.** $\dfrac{2\sqrt{3}}{3}$ **25.** 1
27. $B = 27°$, $c = 10.9$, $b = 4.9$ **29.** $A = 7°$, $c = 5.6$, $a = 0.7$
31. two; $C = 47°33'$, $B = 93°45'$, $b = 274.5$; $C = 132°27'$,
$B = 8°51'$, $b = 42.3$ **33.** two; $B = 37°18'$, $C = 113°42'$,
$c = 22.7$; $B = 142°42'$, $C = 8°18'$, $c = 3.6$ **35.** $a = 36.9$,
$B = 57°24'$, $C = 71°36'$ **37.** $A = 30°31'$, $B = 36°53'$,
$C = 112°36'$ **39.** 471.7 **41.** 78.1 **43.** 4.3 mph

Page 299 Chapter 5 Test

1. $\dfrac{3\pi}{4}$ **2.** -36° **3.** $\dfrac{8\pi}{3}$ **4.** 105° **5.** 16.5 cm **6.** 52.0 cm²
7. 42.0 cm² **8.** $\dfrac{1}{2}$ **9.** $\sqrt{3}$ **10.** $-\sqrt{2}$ **11.** $\dfrac{\sqrt{3}}{2}$ **12.** 1
13. $B = 13°$, $c = 186.7$, $a = 181.9$ **14.** $A = 67°23'$,
$B = 22°37'$, $b = 5$ **15.** $A = 58°$, $b = 7.4$, $a = 11.9$ **16.** one;
$A = 44°46'$, $B = 37°14'$, $b = 55.0$ **17.** none **18.** one;
$A = 60°$, $B = 27°48'$, $C = 92°12'$ **19.** one; $b = 17.9$,
$C = 78°41'$, $A = 54°19'$ **20.** 172.7 **21.** 27.5 **22.** 656
hours or 27.3 days **23.** 61.1 meters **24.** 183.0 miles
25. 93.2 cm **BONUS** 30° or $\dfrac{\pi}{6}$

CHAPTER 6 GRAPHS AND INVERSES OF THE TRIGONOMETRIC FUNCTIONS

Pages 305-307 Lesson 6-1

5. 0 **7.** 0 **9.** 0 **11.** 0 **13.** -1 **15.** $45° + 180k°$, k is any
integer **17.** $90° + 180k°$, k is any integer **19.** 1 **21.** 1
23. -1 **25.** 0 **27.** undefined **29.** $180° + 360k°$, k is any
integer **31.** $135° + 180k°$, k is any integer **33.** $135° + 180k°$, k is any integer **35.** real numbers; $-1 \le y \le 1$
37. real numbers, except $\theta = k \cdot 180° + 90°$; $y \le -1$, $y \ge 1$,
k is any integer **39.** real numbers, except $\theta = k \cdot 180°$;
$y \le -1$, $y \ge 1$, k is any integer

41.

45.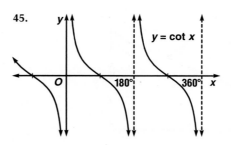

53a. $I_{eff} = 110\sqrt{2} \sin (120\pi t)$

53b.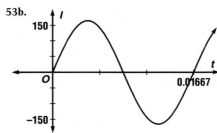

c. $t = \dfrac{1}{30}k$, where k is any integer **55.** $y = -\dfrac{1}{3}x + \dfrac{11}{3}$
57. x-axis **59.** $x = -9$ **61.** No solution exists. **63.** 108
square units

Pages 315-318 Lesson 6-2

5. 2, 72°, 0° **7.** none, 90°, 90° **9.** 3, 360°, 90° **11.** 243,
24°, $2\dfrac{2}{3}°$ **13.** $y = \pm 4 \cos\left(\dfrac{1}{2}\theta - \dfrac{\pi}{4}\right)$ **15.** 2, 360°, 0°
17. 110, 18°, 0° **19.** 7, 60°, 0° **21.** $\dfrac{1}{4}$, 720°, 0°
23. 6, -360°, 180° **25.** $y = \pm 5 \sin(x - 60°)$
27. $y = \pm 17 \sin(8x + 480°)$ **29.** $y = \pm 7 \sin\left(\dfrac{8}{5}x + 144°\right)$
31. $y = \pm 3 \cos(2x - 240°)$ **33.** $y = \pm \dfrac{7}{3} \cos\left(\dfrac{12}{5}x + 648°\right)$

35.

39.

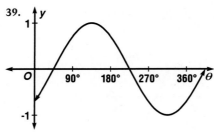

43a. $x = 135°$ **b.** $x = 30°$ **c.** $x = 90°$ **d.** $x = \left(\frac{90 + c}{k}\right)°$

47a. 323, 1388

47b.

49a.

b. 7500 **51.** $\begin{bmatrix} 2 & -1 & 0 \\ 3 & -1 & 1 \\ 2 & 8 & -5 \end{bmatrix}$ **53.** 1.0 **55.** $\sin \alpha = -\frac{3\sqrt{58}}{58}$,

$\cos \alpha = \frac{7\sqrt{58}}{58}$, $\tan \alpha = -\frac{3}{7}$, $\csc \alpha = -\frac{\sqrt{58}}{3}$, $\sec \alpha = \frac{\sqrt{58}}{7}$,

$\cot \alpha = -\frac{7}{3}$ **57.** C

Pages 326–327   Lesson 6-3

5.

9.

13.

17.

21.

25.

29.

$y = 2x \sin 2x$

33. There is a 45° phase difference. **35.** (1.4, -0.04)
37a. 10π radians per second **b.** 15.7 ft/s
39. $y = \pm 4 \cos(2x - 40°)$

Pages 331-333   Lesson 6-4

3. $\theta = \arcsin x$ **5.** $y = \arctan -3$ **7.** $x = \arccos y$ **9.** 0°, 180°, 360° **11.** 60°, 120° **13.** 1 **15.** $\theta = \arcsin n$
17. $\delta = \arctan \frac{3}{2}$ **19.** $\theta = \arccos y$ **21.** 90°, 270° **23.** 30°, 210° **25.** 0°, 180° **27.** 25°, 205° **29.** 90°, 270° **31.** $\frac{5}{4}$
33. 2 **35.** $\sqrt{3}$ **37.** $\frac{\sqrt{2}+1}{2}$ **39.** $\frac{\sqrt{3}}{3}$
41. $\arccos \frac{\sqrt{3}}{2} + \arcsin \frac{\sqrt{3}}{2} \stackrel{?}{=} \arctan 1 + \text{arccot } 1$
$$30° + 60° \stackrel{?}{=} 45° + 45°$$
$$90° = 90°$$
43. $\tan^{-1} 1 + \cos^{-1} \frac{\sqrt{3}}{2} \stackrel{?}{=} \sin^{-1} \frac{1}{2} + \sec^{-1} \sqrt{2}$
$$45° + 30° \stackrel{?}{=} 30° + 45°$$
$$75° = 75°$$
45. $\arcsin \frac{3}{5} + \arccos \frac{15}{17} \stackrel{?}{=} \arctan \frac{77}{36}$
$$36.9° + 28.1° \stackrel{?}{=} 65°$$
$$65° = 65°$$
47a. 82° **b.** 0 km; It is the north or south pole. **49.** about 11.5° **51.** -11 **53.** 2 or $\frac{1}{3}$ **55.** $a = 11.9$, $B = 70°$, $b = 32.9$
57.

$y = 2 \sin x - \frac{1}{2} \cos x$

Page 333   Mid-Chapter Review

1. $n \cdot 180°$ **3.** $n \cdot 360° + 90°$ **5.** none, 180°, -60°
7.

$y = x - \sin x$

9.

$y = 2x + 2 \sin x$

Pages 337-338   Lesson 6-5

5. -60° **7.** 0° **9.** 30° **11.** 90° **13.** $-\frac{4}{3}$ **15.** $-\frac{24}{25}$ **17.** 150°
19. 36°52' **21.** 60° **23.** 0° **25.** $\frac{1}{2}$ **27.** $\frac{\sqrt{3}}{2}$ **29.** $\frac{\sqrt{3}}{2}$
31. $-\frac{\sqrt{3}}{2}$ **33.** $\frac{\sqrt{3}}{2}$ **35.** 0.2669 **37.** $-\frac{1}{2}$ **39.** not possible
41. $-\frac{1}{2}$ **43.** $\frac{33}{56}$ **45.** about 85.4° **47.** no **49.** As $x \to \infty$, $y \to \infty$, as $x \to -\infty$, $y \to -\infty$. **51.** no solution **53.** $\frac{\sqrt{3}}{2}$

Pages 342-344   Lesson 6-6

5. all real numbers except $90° + n \cdot 180°$; all real numbers
7. $-1 \leq x \leq 1$; all real numbers **9.** all real numbers; $-90° < y < 90°$ **11.** true **13.** all real numbers; $-1 \leq y \leq 1$
15. $-90° < x < 90°$; all real numbers **17.** $-1 \leq x \leq 1$; $-90° \leq y \leq 90°$ **19.** $y = \text{Tan } x$ **21.** $y = \text{Arcsin } x$
23. $y = \frac{1}{2} \text{Tan } x$ **25.** true **27.** false, $x = 1$
29. false, $x = \frac{x}{2}$ **31.**

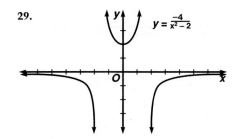

$y = x$

35a. about -5.43 **b.** about 63°, about -63°
37. $27x^3 - 1$; $3x^3 - 3$ **39.** $\frac{37}{8}$ **41.** $\frac{\sqrt{3}}{2}$

Pages 348-351   Lesson 6-7

5. $8, \frac{\pi}{2}, \frac{2}{\pi}, \frac{\pi}{4}$ **7.** $4, \frac{2\pi}{3}, \frac{3}{2\pi}, -\frac{\pi}{4}$ **9.** $y = 5 \sin \pi t$
11. $y = 7 \cos \frac{\pi t}{5}$ **13.** $y = -5 \cos \frac{\pi t}{6}$ **15.** $15, 6, \frac{1}{6}, 0$
17. $150, \frac{1}{40}, 40, 0$ **19.** $25, \frac{\pi}{4}, \frac{4}{\pi}, 0$ **21.** $y = 0.5 \sin 2\pi t$
23. $y = 10 \cos 4\pi t$ **25a.** $\frac{30}{7}$ seconds **b.** $\left[3.5 \cos\left(\frac{7}{15}\pi t\right), 3.5 \sin\left(\frac{7}{15}\pi t\right)\right]$ **c.** (3.20, -1.42) **d.** (-3.50, 0.18)
e. $\left[3.5 \cos\left(\frac{7}{15}\pi t + \frac{\pi}{2}\right), 3.5 \sin\left(\frac{7}{15}\pi t + \frac{\pi}{2}\right)\right]$ **f.** ± 2.72
27a. pulled down **b.** 8 ft **c.** 2 ft **d.** $t = \frac{1}{2}$ second
e. 8 ft **f.** 2 seconds **g.** 3 ft **h.** $\frac{1}{2}$ cycle/second **i.** 5 ft

29.

$y = \frac{-4}{x^2 - 2}$

31. yes **33.** 21

Pages 352-354   Chapter 6 Summary and Review
1. 0   **3.** undefined
5.

7.

9. 15, 240°, -60°
11. none, 36°, 0°
13.

17. $\alpha = \arcsin y$
19. $\theta = \arccos n$
21. $\frac{1}{2}$ **23.** $\frac{\sqrt{2}}{2}$
25. $\frac{\sqrt{3}}{2}$ **27.** $\frac{\sqrt{3}}{2}$
29. 0
31. $y = \text{Arccsc } x$

31.

 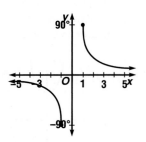

$y = \text{Csc } x$

33. $y = \sec x$

33.

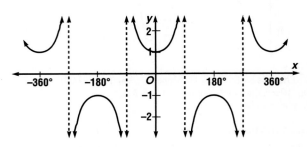

35. 4 cycles/second   **37a.** $y = -38 \cos \frac{\pi}{3} t$
b. $y = -38 \cos \frac{\pi}{3} t - 84$ **c.** 122 feet below the ledge

Page 355   Chapter 6 Test
1. $180k°$, k is any integer   **2.** $270° + 360k°$, k is any integer
3. $45° + 360k°$ and $315° + 360k°$, k is any integer
4.

5.

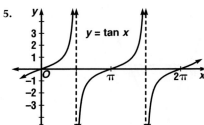

$y = \tan x$

6. 3, 90°, 0°
7. 110, 24°, $2\frac{2}{3}°$
8. 10, 360°, 180°

9.

990

10.

11.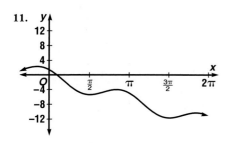

12. $\frac{1}{2}$ **13.** $\frac{12}{5}$ **14.** 0 **15.** $\frac{\sqrt{3}}{2}$ **16.** $\frac{3\sqrt{10}}{10}$ **17.** $\frac{2\sqrt{5}}{5}$

18. $y = \text{Csc } x$

 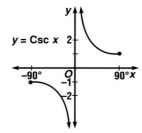

19. $y = \arctan x$

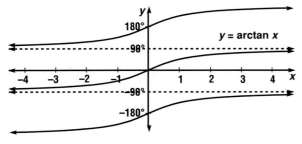

20. $x = 10 \cos 2t$ **21.** $y = \sin 2t$ **22.** 10 **23.** $\frac{1}{\pi}$
24. 3-foot mark **25.** 13.3° **BONUS** even

Pages 362-363   Lesson 7-1
5. $\frac{4}{3}$ **7.** $\frac{1}{3}$ **9.** $\frac{\sqrt{5}}{2}$ **11.** $\sin 40°$ **13.** $-\cos 40°$ **15.** $\sec^2 x$
17. 1 **19.** $\sec A$ **21.** undefined **23.** 1 **25.** $\frac{\sqrt{7}}{2}$ **27.** $\frac{\sqrt{15}}{2}$
29. $\frac{3\sqrt{5}}{5}$ **31.** $\frac{\sqrt{53}}{2}$ **33.** $\frac{\sqrt{5}}{5}$ **35.** $-\cos 22°$ **37.** $-\sin 72°$
39. $-\sec 30°$ **41.** $1 + \sin \theta$ **43.** $\cos A$ **45.** 1 **47.** $1 - \sin A$
49. $\sin^2 A$ **51.** 1 **53.** $\pm\sqrt{1 - \sin^2 \theta}$ **55.** $\pm\frac{\sqrt{1 - \cos^2 \theta}}{\cos \theta}$
61. neither **63.** 1; 3 or 1 **65.** 25.4 units and 54.4 units
67. 23.1 units^2 **69.** 15

Pages 366-368   Lesson 7-2
3. $\tan^2 x \cos^2 x \overset{?}{=} 1 - \cos^2 x$ **5.** $\tan \beta \csc \beta \overset{?}{=} \sec \beta$
$\frac{\sin^2 x}{\cos^2 x} \cdot \cos^2 x \overset{?}{=} 1 - \cos^2 x$ $\qquad \frac{\sin \beta}{\cos \beta} \cdot \frac{1}{\sin \beta} \overset{?}{=} \sec \beta$
$\sin^2 x \overset{?}{=} 1 - \cos^2 x$ $\qquad\qquad \frac{1}{\cos \beta} \overset{?}{=} \sec \beta$
$1 - \cos^2 x = 1 - \cos^2 x$ $\qquad\qquad \sec \beta = \sec \beta$

7. $\sin \theta \sec \theta \cot \theta \overset{?}{=} 1$ **9.** $\sec x = 1$ **11.** $\tan x = 2$
$\sin \theta \cdot \frac{1}{\cos \theta} \cdot \frac{\cos \theta}{\sin \theta} \overset{?}{=} 1$
$\frac{\sin \theta \cos \theta}{\sin \theta \cos \theta} \overset{?}{=} 1$
$1 = 1$

13. $\frac{1}{\sec^2 \theta} + \frac{1}{\csc^2 \theta} \overset{?}{=} 1$ **15.** $\frac{\sin A}{\csc A} + \frac{\cos A}{\sec A} \overset{?}{=} 1$
$\frac{1}{\frac{1}{\cos^2 \theta}} + \frac{1}{\frac{1}{\sin^2 \theta}} \overset{?}{=} 1$ $\qquad \frac{\sin A}{\frac{1}{\sin A}} + \frac{\cos A}{\frac{1}{\cos A}} \overset{?}{=} 1$
$\cos^2 \theta + \sin^2 \theta \overset{?}{=} 1$ $\qquad\qquad \sin^2 A + \cos^2 A \overset{?}{=} 1$
$1 = 1$ $\qquad\qquad\qquad 1 = 1$

17. $\frac{1 + \tan \gamma}{1 + \cot \gamma} \overset{?}{=} \frac{\sin \gamma}{\cos \gamma}$
$\frac{1 + \frac{\sin \gamma}{\cos \gamma}}{1 + \frac{\cos \gamma}{\sin \gamma}} \overset{?}{=} \frac{\sin \gamma}{\cos \gamma}$
$\frac{\frac{\sin \gamma + \cos \gamma}{\cos \gamma}}{\frac{\sin \gamma + \cos \gamma}{\sin \gamma}} \overset{?}{=} \frac{\sin \gamma}{\cos \gamma}$
$\frac{\sin \gamma + \cos \gamma}{\cos \gamma} \cdot \frac{\sin \gamma}{\sin \gamma + \cos \gamma} \overset{?}{=} \frac{\sin \gamma}{\cos \gamma}$
$\frac{\sin \gamma}{\cos \gamma} = \frac{\sin \gamma}{\cos \gamma}$

19. $\cos^2 x + \tan^2 x \cos^2 x \overset{?}{=} 1$
$\cos^2 x + \frac{\sin^2 x}{\cos^2 x} \cdot \cos^2 x \overset{?}{=} 1$
$\cos^2 x + \sin^2 x \overset{?}{=} 1$
$1 = 1$

21. $1 - \cot^4 x \overset{?}{=} 2\csc^2 x - \csc^4 x$
$1 - \cot^4 x \overset{?}{=} \csc^2 x(2 - \csc^2 x)$
$1 - \cot^4 x \overset{?}{=} (1 + \cot^2 x)(2 - (1 + \cot^2 x))$
$1 - \cot^4 x \overset{?}{=} (1 + \cot^2 x)(1 - \cot^2 x)$
$1 - \cot^4 x = 1 - \cot^4 x$

23. $\frac{\sec x - 1}{\sec x + 1} + \frac{\cos x - 1}{\cos x + 1} \overset{?}{=} 0$
$\frac{\frac{1}{\cos x} - 1}{\frac{1}{\cos x} + 1} + \frac{\cos x - 1}{\cos x + 1} \overset{?}{=} 0$
$\frac{1 - \cos x}{1 + \cos x} + \frac{\cos x - 1}{\cos x + 1} \overset{?}{=} 0$
$\frac{1 - \cos x + \cos x - 1}{1 + \cos x} \overset{?}{=} 0$
$0 = 0$

Selected Answers

25.
$$\frac{\cos x}{1 + \sin x} + \frac{\cos x}{1 - \sin x} \overset{?}{=} 2 \sec x$$
$$\frac{\cos x(1 - \sin x) + \cos x(1 + \sin x)}{1 - \sin^2 x} \overset{?}{=} 2 \sec x$$
$$\frac{\cos x(1 - \sin x) + \cos x(1 + \sin x)}{\cos^2 x} \overset{?}{=} 2 \sec x$$
$$\frac{(1 - \sin x) + (1 + \sin x)}{\cos x} \overset{?}{=} 2 \sec x$$
$$\frac{2}{\cos x} \overset{?}{=} 2 \sec x$$
$$2 \sec x = 2 \sec x$$

27. $1 + \sec^2 x \sin^2 x \overset{?}{=} \sec^2 x$
$$1 + \frac{1}{\cos^2 x} \cdot \sin^2 x \overset{?}{=} \sec^2 x$$
$$1 + \tan^2 x = \sec^2 x$$
$$\sec^2 x = \sec^2 x$$

39a.

highway

horizontal

A

41. 74, no   **43.** 54.9°   **45.** E

Pages 375-376   Lesson 7-3

5. $\frac{1}{2}$ **7.** $-\frac{\sqrt{3}}{2}$ **9.** 1

11. $\sin \theta \overset{?}{=} \sin (180° - \theta)$
$$\sin \theta \overset{?}{=} \sin 180° \cos \theta - \cos 180° \sin \theta$$
$$\sin \theta \overset{?}{=} 0 \cdot \cos \theta - (-1) \sin \theta$$
$$\sin \theta = \sin \theta$$

13. $\cot x \overset{?}{=} \tan (270° - x)$
$$\cot x \overset{?}{=} \frac{\sin (270° - x)}{\cos (270° - x)}$$
$$\cot x \overset{?}{=} \frac{\sin 270° \cos x - \sin x \cos 270°}{\cos 270° \cos x + \sin 270° \sin x}$$
$$\cot x \overset{?}{=} \frac{-1 \cdot \cos x - \sin x \cdot 0}{0 \cdot \cos x + (-1) \sin x}$$
$$\cot x \overset{?}{=} \frac{-\cos x}{-\sin x}$$
$$\cot x = \cot x$$

15. $\frac{\sqrt{2} - \sqrt{6}}{4}$ **17.** $2 + \sqrt{3}$ **19.** $\sqrt{3} - 2$ **21.** $\sqrt{3} - 2$

23. $\frac{-\sqrt{6} - \sqrt{2}}{4}$ **25.** $-\frac{16}{65}$ **27.** $\frac{416}{425}$ **29.** $\frac{87}{425}$

31.
$$\cos (90° + \theta) \overset{?}{=} -\sin \theta$$
$$\cos 90° \cos \theta - \sin 90° \sin \theta \overset{?}{=} -\sin \theta$$
$$0 - 1 \cdot \sin \theta \overset{?}{=} -\sin \theta$$
$$-\sin \theta = -\sin \theta$$

33.
$$\sin \left(\frac{\pi}{2} + x\right) \overset{?}{=} \cos x$$
$$\sin \frac{\pi}{2} \cos x + \cos \frac{\pi}{2} \sin x \overset{?}{=} \cos x$$
$$1 \cdot \cos x + 0 \cdot \sin x \overset{?}{=} \cos x$$
$$\cos x = \cos x$$

35.
$$\tan (\pi - \theta) \overset{?}{=} -\tan \theta$$
$$\frac{\tan \pi - \tan \theta}{1 + \tan \pi \tan \theta} \overset{?}{=} -\tan \theta$$
$$\frac{0 - \tan \theta}{1 + 0 \cdot \tan \theta} \overset{?}{=} -\tan \theta$$
$$-\tan \theta = -\tan \theta$$

37.
$$\frac{\sin (\beta - \alpha)}{\sin \alpha \sin \beta} \overset{?}{=} \cot \alpha - \cot \beta$$
$$\frac{\sin \beta \cos \alpha - \cos \beta \sin \alpha}{\sin \alpha \sin \beta} \overset{?}{=} \cot \alpha - \cot \beta$$
$$\frac{\cos \alpha}{\sin \alpha} - \frac{\cos \beta}{\sin \beta} \overset{?}{=} \cot \alpha - \cot \beta$$
$$\cot \alpha - \cot \beta = \cot \alpha - \cot \beta$$

39. $\cos (30° - x) + \cos (30° + x) \overset{?}{=} \sqrt{3} \cos x$
$$(\cos 30° \cos x + \sin 30° \sin x) +$$
$$(\cos 30° \cos x - \sin 30° \sin x) \overset{?}{=} \sqrt{3} \cos x$$
$$\frac{\sqrt{3}}{2} \cdot \cos x + \frac{\sqrt{3}}{2} \cdot \cos x \overset{?}{=} \sqrt{3} \cos x$$
$$\sqrt{3} \cos x = \sqrt{3} \cos x$$

41. $\cot (\alpha + \beta) = \frac{1}{\tan(\alpha + \beta)}$
$$= \frac{1 - \tan \alpha \tan \beta}{\tan \alpha + \tan \beta}$$

$$= \frac{1 - \frac{1}{\cot \alpha \cot \beta}}{\frac{1}{\cot \alpha} + \frac{1}{\cot \beta}}$$
$$= \frac{\cot \alpha \cot \beta - 1}{\cot \beta + \cot \alpha}$$

45. $\tan \theta = \frac{m_2 - m_1}{1 - m_1 m_2}$

47. $y = 2x - 7$ **49.** -1

51. $2 \sec^2 x \overset{?}{=} \frac{1}{1 + \sin x} + \frac{1}{1 - \sin x}$
$$2 \sec^2 x \overset{?}{=} \frac{(1 - \sin x) + (1 + \sin x)}{(1 + \sin x)(1 - \sin x)}$$
$$2 \sec^2 x \overset{?}{=} \frac{2}{1 - \sin^2 x}$$
$$2 \sec^2 x \overset{?}{=} \frac{2}{\cos^2 x}$$
$$2 \sec^2 x = 2 \sec^2 x$$

Pages 381-383   Lesson 7-4

5. $\frac{24}{7}$ **7.** $\frac{\sqrt{10}}{10}$ **9.** $\frac{1}{3}$ **11.** $\frac{\sqrt{2 + \sqrt{2}}}{2}$

13. $\frac{1}{2} \cdot \sin 2A \overset{?}{=} \frac{\tan A}{1 + \tan^2 A}$
$$\frac{1}{2} \cdot \sin 2A \overset{?}{=} \frac{\frac{\sin A}{\cos A}}{\sec^2 A}$$
$$\frac{1}{2} \cdot \sin 2A \overset{?}{=} \frac{\sin A}{\cos A} \cdot \cos^2 A$$
$$\frac{1}{2} \cdot \sin 2A \overset{?}{=} \frac{2 \sin A \cos A}{2}$$
$$\frac{1}{2} \cdot \sin 2A = \frac{1}{2} \cdot \sin 2A$$

15. $\sin 2x \overset{?}{=} 2 \cot x \sin^2 x$
$$\sin 2x \overset{?}{=} \frac{2 \cos x}{\sin x} \cdot \sin^2 x$$
$$\sin 2x \overset{?}{=} 2 \cos x \sin x$$
$$\sin 2x = \sin 2x$$

17. $\frac{120}{169}$ **19.** $\frac{5\sqrt{26}}{26}$ **21.** -5   **23.** $\frac{\sqrt{2 + \sqrt{3}}}{2}$ **25.** $2 - \sqrt{3}$

27. $\frac{\sqrt{2 - \sqrt{2}}}{2}$ **29.** $1 + \cos 2A \overset{?}{=} \frac{2}{1 + \tan^2 A}$
$$1 + \cos 2A \overset{?}{=} \frac{2}{\sec^2 A}$$
$$1 + \cos 2A \overset{?}{=} 2 \cos^2 A$$
$$1 + \cos 2A \overset{?}{=} 1 + 2 \cos^2 A - 1$$
$$1 + \cos 2A = 1 + \cos 2A$$

31. $\csc A \sec A \overset{?}{=} 2 \csc 2A$
$$\frac{1}{\sin A \cos A} \overset{?}{=} 2 \csc 2A$$
$$\frac{2}{2 \sin A \cos A} \overset{?}{=} 2 \csc 2A$$
$$\frac{2}{\sin 2A} \overset{?}{=} 2 \csc 2A$$
$$2 \csc 2A = 2 \csc 2A$$

33. $\cot X \overset{?}{=} \frac{\sin 2X}{1 - \cos 2X}$
$$\cot X \overset{?}{=} \frac{2 \sin X \cos X}{1 - (1 - 2 \sin^2 X)}$$
$$\cot X \overset{?}{=} \frac{2 \sin X \cos X}{2 \sin^2 X}$$
$$\cot X \overset{?}{=} \frac{\cos X}{\sin X}$$
$$\cot X = \cot X$$

35.
$$\sin 2B(\cot B + \tan B) \overset{?}{=} 2$$
$$2 \sin B \cos B\left(\frac{\cos B}{\sin B} + \frac{\sin B}{\cos B}\right) \overset{?}{=} 2$$
$$2 \sin B \cos B\left(\frac{\cos^2 B + \sin^2 B}{\sin B \cos B}\right) \overset{?}{=} 2$$
$$2 = 2$$

37.
$$\cot \frac{\alpha}{2} \overset{?}{=} \frac{\sin \alpha}{1 - \cos \alpha}$$
$$\frac{1}{\tan \frac{\alpha}{2}} \overset{?}{=} \frac{\sin \alpha}{1 - \cos \alpha}$$

$$\frac{1}{\sqrt{\dfrac{1-\cos\alpha}{1+\cos\alpha}}} \overset{?}{=} \frac{\sin\alpha}{1-\cos\alpha}$$

$$\frac{1}{\sqrt{\dfrac{(1-\cos\alpha)^2}{1-\cos^2\alpha}}} \overset{?}{=} \frac{\sin\alpha}{1-\cos\alpha}$$

$$\frac{1}{\sqrt{\dfrac{(1-\cos\alpha)^2}{\sin^2\alpha}}} \overset{?}{=} \frac{\sin\alpha}{1-\cos\alpha}$$

$$\frac{1}{\dfrac{1-\cos\alpha}{\sin\alpha}} \overset{?}{=} \frac{\sin\alpha}{1-\cos\alpha}$$

$$\frac{\sin\alpha}{1-\cos\alpha} = \frac{\sin\alpha}{1-\cos\alpha}$$

39.
$$\frac{\cos 2A}{1+\sin 2A} \overset{?}{=} \frac{\cot A - 1}{\cot A + 1}$$

$$\frac{\cos 2A}{1+\sin 2A} \overset{?}{=} \frac{\dfrac{\cos A}{\sin A} - 1}{\dfrac{\cos A}{\sin A} + 1}$$

$$\frac{\cos 2A}{1+\sin 2A} \overset{?}{=} \frac{\cos A - \sin A}{\cos A + \sin A}$$

$$\frac{\cos 2A}{1+\sin 2A} \overset{?}{=} \frac{\cos A - \sin A}{\cos A + \sin A}$$

$$\frac{\cos 2A}{1+\sin 2A} \overset{?}{=} \frac{\cos^2 A - \sin^2 A}{\cos^2 A + 2\sin A \cos A + \sin^2 A}$$

$$\frac{\cos 2A}{1+\sin 2A} \overset{?}{=} \frac{\cos 2A}{1+2\sin A \cos A}$$

$$\frac{\cos 2A}{1+\sin 2A} = \frac{\cos 2A}{1+\sin 2A}$$

41.
$$\sin 3\alpha = \sin(2\alpha + \alpha)$$
$$= \sin 2\alpha \cos\alpha + \sin\alpha \cos 2\alpha$$
$$= (2\sin\alpha\cos\alpha)\cos\alpha + \sin\alpha\cos\alpha(1 - 2\sin^2\alpha)$$
$$= 2\sin\alpha\cos^2\alpha + \sin\alpha - 2\sin^3\alpha$$
$$= 2\sin\alpha(1 - \sin^2\alpha) + \sin\alpha - 2\sin^3\alpha$$
$$= 2\sin\alpha - 2\sin^3\alpha + \sin\alpha - 2\sin^3\alpha$$
$$= 3\sin\alpha - 4\sin^3\alpha$$

45.
$$n = \frac{\sin\left(\dfrac{\alpha+\beta}{2}\right)}{\sin\left(\dfrac{\alpha}{2}\right)}$$

$$= \frac{\sqrt{\dfrac{1-\cos(\alpha+\beta)}{2}}}{\sqrt{\dfrac{1-\cos\alpha}{2}}}$$

$$= \frac{\sqrt{\dfrac{1-(\cos\alpha\cos\beta - \sin\alpha\sin\beta)}{2}}}{\sqrt{\dfrac{1-\cos\alpha}{2}}}$$

$$= \frac{\sqrt{\dfrac{1-\cos\alpha\cos\beta + \sin\alpha\sin\beta}{2}}}{\sqrt{\dfrac{1-\cos\alpha}{2}}}$$

$$= \sqrt{\dfrac{1-\cos\alpha\cos\beta + \sin\alpha\sin\beta}{1-\cos\alpha}}$$

47. $3x - y - 2 = 0$ **49.** no triangle **51.** $-\dfrac{\sqrt{3}}{3}$

Page 383 Mid-Chapter Review

1. $\dfrac{3}{5}$ **3.** $\cot^2\alpha$ **5.** $\csc\theta \overset{?}{=} \sin\theta(1+\cot^2\theta)$
$$\csc\theta \overset{?}{=} \sin\theta(\csc^2\theta)$$
$$\csc\theta \overset{?}{=} \frac{1}{\csc\theta}(\csc^2\theta)$$
$$\csc\theta = \csc\theta$$

7. $-\cos\theta \overset{?}{=} \cos(180° - \theta)$
$$-\cos\theta \overset{?}{=} \cos 180°\cos\theta + \sin 180°\sin\theta$$
$$-\cos\theta \overset{?}{=} (-1)\cos\theta + (0)\sin\theta$$
$$-\cos\theta \overset{?}{=} -\cos\theta$$

9. $\sin^2\theta \overset{?}{=} \dfrac{1}{2}(1 - \cos 2\theta)$
$$\sin^2\theta \overset{?}{=} \frac{1}{2}[1 - (1 - 2\sin^2\theta)]$$
$$\sin^2\theta \overset{?}{=} \frac{1}{2}(2\sin^2\theta)$$
$$\sin^2\theta = \sin^2\theta$$

Pages 390-391 Lesson 7-5

3. -30° **5.** 45° **7.** 30° **9.** 20°, 100°, 140° **11.** 0° + 120k°
13. 0° + 180k° **15.** 90° + 180k°, 120° + 360k°, 240° + 360k°
17. 60°, 120° **19.** 150° **21.** 30°, 90°, 150° **23.** 30°, 90°, 150°
25. 135° **27.** 120° **29.** 180° **31.** 0° **33.** 60° **35.** 30°, 150°
37. 45° + 90k° **39.** 270° + 360k° **41.** 0° + 180k°, 90° + 360k°
43. 60° + 360k°, 300° + 360k° **47a.** ≈ 6.6° **b.** ≈ 7.5° **c.** 10°
49. yes, yes, no **51.** $\left(\dfrac{2}{3}, 7\dfrac{5}{27}\right)$ max, (2, 6) min, $\left(\dfrac{4}{3}, 6\dfrac{16}{27}\right)$

pt of inf **53.** $\dfrac{5}{2}$ **55.** $\dfrac{\sqrt{2 + \sqrt{2 + \sqrt{3}}}}{2}$

Pages 395-397 Lesson 7-6

3. $x + y - 11\sqrt{2} = 0$ **5.** $x - y = 0$ **7.** $\sqrt{3}x + y - 4 = 0$ **9.** $-y - 4 = 0$ **11.** $\dfrac{3x}{\sqrt{10}} - \dfrac{y}{\sqrt{10}} - \dfrac{4}{\sqrt{10}} = 0$;
$\dfrac{4}{\sqrt{10}} \approx 1.3; \approx 342°$ **13.** $x + y - 5\sqrt{2} = 0$
15. $x + y + 25\sqrt{2} = 0$ **17.** $x + \sqrt{3}y + 16 = 0$
19. $-\dfrac{x}{\sqrt{2}} + \dfrac{y}{\sqrt{2}} - \dfrac{6}{\sqrt{2}} = 0$; $\dfrac{6}{\sqrt{2}} \approx 4.24$; 135°
21. $\dfrac{x}{\sqrt{2}} + \dfrac{y}{\sqrt{2}} - \dfrac{8}{\sqrt{2}} = 0$; $\dfrac{8}{\sqrt{2}} \approx 5.66$; 45°
23. $\dfrac{x}{\sqrt{10}} - \dfrac{3y}{\sqrt{10}} - \dfrac{2}{\sqrt{10}} = 0$; $\dfrac{2}{\sqrt{10}} \approx 0.63$; -71°34'
25. $x - y + 8 = 0$ **27.** $x + \sqrt{3}y + 2 = 0$ and $x + \sqrt{3}y - 2 = 0$
31a.

b. $x - y - 1.25\sqrt{2} = 0$
33. no **37.** D

Pages 402-405 Lesson 7-7

3. 0.9 **5.** $\dfrac{16\sqrt{58}}{29} \approx 4.2$ **11.** $27x - 99y + 161 = 0$
13. $x - (1 + \sqrt{2})y + 2 + 5\sqrt{2} = 0$ **15.** $\dfrac{7\sqrt{2}}{5} \approx 1.98$
17. 0; the point is on the line **19.** 2.4 **21.** $\dfrac{4\sqrt{13}}{13} \approx 1.11$
23. $(2\sqrt{2} + \sqrt{5})x + (\sqrt{5} - \sqrt{2})y - 4\sqrt{2} - 8\sqrt{5} = 0$
25. $(\sqrt{2} - \sqrt{17})x + (4\sqrt{2} + \sqrt{17})y - 4\sqrt{17} + 6\sqrt{2} = 0$
27. $(1 - \sqrt{2})x + y - 5 + 5\sqrt{2} = 0$
29. $(6\sqrt{10} - \sqrt{37})x + (\sqrt{10} - 3\sqrt{37})y - 3\sqrt{10} - \sqrt{37} = 0$
31. $x - 5y + 10 + 3\sqrt{26} = 0$, $x - 5y + 10 - 3\sqrt{26} = 0$
35a. $\dfrac{2\sqrt{10}}{5} \approx 1.26$ units; $\dfrac{\sqrt{10}}{5} \approx 0.63$ units; 0 units
b. (16, 76) **c.** (16, 72) **37.** $y = \dfrac{x-2}{x(x+2)(x-2)}$ **39.** $\cot^2\alpha$
41. A

Pages 406-408 Chapter 7 Summary and Review

1. 2 **3.** $\dfrac{4}{5}$ **5.** $\cos^2 x + \tan^2 x \cos^2 x \overset{?}{=} 1$
$$\cos^2 x + \left(\frac{\sin^2 x}{\cos^2 x}\right)\cos^2 x \overset{?}{=} 1$$
$$\cos^2 x + \sin^2 x \overset{?}{=} 1$$
$$1 = 1$$

7. $\dfrac{\sec\theta+1}{\tan\theta} \overset{?}{=} \dfrac{\tan\theta}{\sec\theta-1}$ **9.** $-\dfrac{1}{2}$ **11.** $\dfrac{\sqrt{6}+\sqrt{2}}{4}$

$\dfrac{\sec\theta+1}{\tan\theta} \overset{?}{=} \dfrac{\tan\theta(\sec\theta+1)}{\sec^2\theta-1}$

$\dfrac{\sec\theta+1}{\tan\theta} \overset{?}{=} \dfrac{\tan\theta(\sec\theta+1)}{\tan^2\theta}$

$\dfrac{\sec\theta+1}{\tan\theta} = \dfrac{\sec\theta+1}{\tan\theta}$

13. $\cos(90°-\theta) \overset{?}{=} \sin\theta$ **15.** $\dfrac{24}{25}$

$\cos 90° \cos\theta + \sin 90° \sin\theta \overset{?}{=} \sin\theta$

$(0)\cdot\cos\theta + (1)\cdot\sin\theta \overset{?}{=} \sin\theta$

$\sin\theta = \sin\theta$

17. $\dfrac{\sqrt{5}}{5}$ **19.** $-\dfrac{24}{7}$ **21.** $360k°$ **23.** $180k°$ **25.** $\dfrac{7x}{\sqrt{58}} +$
$\dfrac{3y}{\sqrt{58}} - \dfrac{8}{\sqrt{58}} = 0;\ \dfrac{8}{\sqrt{58}} \approx 1.1;\ \approx 23°$ **27.** $\dfrac{9x}{\sqrt{106}} +$
$\dfrac{5y}{\sqrt{106}} - \dfrac{3}{\sqrt{106}} = 0;\ \dfrac{3}{\sqrt{106}} \approx 0.3;\ \approx 29°$ **29.** 1.7 units
31. 4.6 units   **33.** $(3\sqrt{5}+\sqrt{10})x + (\sqrt{5}+2\sqrt{10})y - 2\sqrt{5} - 3\sqrt{10} = 0$ **35.** The formulas are equivalent.

Page 409   Chapter 7 Test

1. $\dfrac{\sqrt{3}}{2}$ **2.** $\dfrac{4}{5}$ **3.** $2\sqrt{2}$ **4.** $\dfrac{5}{3}$

5. $\tan\theta(\cot\theta+\tan\theta) \overset{?}{=} \sec^2\theta$

$\tan\theta\cot\theta + \tan^2\theta \overset{?}{=} \sec^2\theta$

$1 + \tan^2\theta \overset{?}{=} \sec^2\theta$

$\sec^2\theta = \sec^2\theta$

6. $\sin^2 A \cot^2 A \overset{?}{=} (1-\sin A)(1+\sin A)$

$\sin^2 A \cdot \dfrac{\cos^2 A}{\sin^2 A} \overset{?}{=} (1-\sin A)(1+\sin A)$

$\cos^2 A \overset{?}{=} (1-\sin A)(1+\sin A)$

$1 - \sin^2 A \overset{?}{=} (1-\sin A)(1+\sin A)$

$(1-\sin A)(1+\sin A) = (1-\sin A)(1+\sin A)$

7. $\dfrac{\sec x}{\sin x} - \dfrac{\sin x}{\cos x} \overset{?}{=} \cot x$

$\dfrac{\sec x\cos x - \sin^2 x}{\sin x\cos x} \overset{?}{=} \cot x$

$\dfrac{1-\sin^2 x}{\sin x\cos x} \overset{?}{=} \cot x$

$\dfrac{\cos^2 x}{\sin x\cos x} \overset{?}{=} \cot x$

$\dfrac{\cos x}{\sin x} \overset{?}{=} \cot x$

$\cot x = \cot x$

8. $\dfrac{\cos x}{1+\sin x} + \dfrac{\cos x}{1-\sin x} \overset{?}{=} 2\sec x$ **9.** $\dfrac{-\sqrt{6}-\sqrt{2}}{4}$

$\dfrac{\cos x - \cos x\sin x + \cos x + \sin x\cos x}{1-\sin^2 x} \overset{?}{=} 2\sec x$

$\dfrac{2\cos x}{1-\sin^2 x} \overset{?}{=} 2\sec x$

$\dfrac{2\cos x}{\cos^2 x} \overset{?}{=} 2\sec x$

$\dfrac{2}{\cos x} \overset{?}{=} 2\sec x$

$2\sec x = 2\sec x$

10. $\dfrac{-\sqrt{2}-\sqrt{6}}{4}$ **11.** $\dfrac{\sqrt{6}-\sqrt{2}}{4}$ **12.** $-\dfrac{3\sqrt{7}}{8}$ **13.** $-\dfrac{\sqrt{14}}{4}$
14. $-3\sqrt{7}$ **15.** 45°   **16.** 30°, 90°, 150°   **17.** 0°, 60°, 180°
18. 30°, 150°   **19.** $-\dfrac{x}{\sqrt{2}} + \dfrac{y}{\sqrt{2}} - \dfrac{3}{\sqrt{2}} = 0;\ \dfrac{3}{\sqrt{2}} \approx 2.1; 135°$
20. $\dfrac{x}{\sqrt{5}} + \dfrac{2y}{\sqrt{5}} - \dfrac{7}{3\sqrt{5}} = 0;\ \dfrac{7}{3\sqrt{5}} \approx 1.0;\ \approx 63°$
21. $\dfrac{2x}{\sqrt{5}} - \dfrac{y}{\sqrt{5}} - \dfrac{1}{\sqrt{5}} = 0;\ \dfrac{1}{\sqrt{5}} \approx 0.4;\ \approx 333°$
22. 3.6 units   **23.** 3.2 units   **24.** $(25+3\sqrt{29})x + (10+4\sqrt{29})y - 35 - 4\sqrt{29} = 0$ **25.** 232.32 feet
BONUS $\dfrac{x^2+y^2}{x^2-y^2}$

CHAPTER 8   VECTORS AND PARAMETRIC EQUATIONS

Pages 417-418   Lesson 8-1

5.

1 cm / 50°

9.

18 mm / 45°

13.

15. about 14.8 km   **17.** 3.4 cm, 85°   **19.** 5.0 cm, 3°
21. 8.1 cm, 60°   **23.** 0.7 cm, 306°   **25.** 2.7 cm, 14°
27. 2.9 cm, 286°   **29.** 2.3 cm, 1.4 cm   **31.** 1.8 cm, 1.8 cm
33. about 11.4 m   **35.** the difference
37a.   **b.** about 100.12 m/s
$\downarrow$ 5 m/s
100 m/s

39a.
165 N
30°
185 N
300°
195 N

b. 436.7 N at 193°
41. $y = 12x - 12$
43. 20.42 ft²   **45.** D

Pages 422-424   Lesson 8-2

5. $5, 4\vec{i}+3\vec{j}$ **7.** $\sqrt{13}, -2\vec{i}-3\vec{j}$ **9.** $(-2, 6); 2\sqrt{10} \approx 6.325$
11. $(5, 9); \sqrt{106} \approx 10.296$ **13.** $(6, 6)$ **15.** $(-9, 1)$ **17.** $(1, 1)$
19. $(5, 7)$ **21.** $(-9, -9); 9\sqrt{2} \approx 12.728$ **23.** $(-5, -5);$
$5\sqrt{2} \approx 7.071$ **25.** $(1, 1); \sqrt{2} \approx 1.414$ **27.** $(1, 0); 1$
29. $(-2, -1)$ **31.** $(12, -9)$ **33.** $(-14, 8)$ **35.** $(-10, 0)$
37. $(-44, 18)$ **39.** $(0, 0)$ **41.** 81.7 N, 73.6 N   **43.** The
magnitude of the horizontal component will increase and
the magnitude of the vertical component will decrease.
45. $\dfrac{4 \pm 2i\sqrt{11}}{5}$ **47.** 63°26'   **49.** D

Pages 427-429   Lesson 8-3

5. $\sqrt{14} \approx 3.742$ **7.** $\sqrt{69} \approx 8.307$ **9.** $3\sqrt{3} \approx 5.196$
11. $(4, -8, -14); 4\vec{i} - 8\vec{j} - 14\vec{k}$ **13.** $(7, 3, -1); 7\vec{i} + 3\vec{j} - \vec{k}$
15. $(2, 0, 3); \sqrt{13} \approx 3.606$ **17.** $(-1, 1, -5); 3\sqrt{3} \approx 5.196$
19. $(15, -24, 4); \sqrt{817} \approx 28.583$ **21.** $3\vec{i} + \vec{k}$
23. $-5\vec{i} - 8\vec{j} + \vec{k}$ **25.** $8\vec{i} - 3\vec{j} + 11\vec{k}$ **27.** $(2, 12, 7)$
29. $(-5, -21, -6)$ **31.** $(1, 33, 38)$ **33.** If $\vec{a} = (-a_1, -a_2, -a_3)$,
then $|\vec{a}| = \sqrt{(a_1)^2 + (a_2)^2 + (a_3)^2}$. If $-\vec{a} = (-a_1, -a_2, -a_3)$, then
$|\vec{a}| = \sqrt{(-a_1)^2 + (-a_2)^2 + (-a_3)^2}$. Since $a_1^2 = (-a_1)^2$, $a_2^2 = (-a_2)^2$,
and $a_3^2 = (-a_3)^2$, $|-\vec{a}| = |\vec{a}|$.   **37a.** $(-132, -3454, 0)$
b. $(-9, 0, -9)$ **39.** no   **41.** $\cos 20°$ **43.** $(1, 1); \sqrt{2} \approx 1.414$

5. 32, no **7.** 0, yes **9.** -1, no **11.** 0, yes **13.** (9, 6, 0)
15. (-8, 19, -2) **17.** 0, yes **19.** 5, no **21.** 0, yes **23.** -10,
no **25.** 68, no **27.** (5, -4, -3), yes **29.** (2, 14, 4), yes

33. $\vec{a} \cdot \vec{b} = (a_1, a_2, a_3) \cdot (b_1, b_2, b_3)$
$= a_1b_1 + a_2b_2 + a_3b_3$
$= b_1a_1 + b_2a_2 + b_3a_3$
$= (b_1, b_2, b_3) \cdot (a_1, a_2, a_3)$
$= \vec{b} \cdot \vec{a}$

35.
$$\vec{a} \times (\vec{b} + \vec{c}) = \begin{vmatrix} \vec{i} & \vec{j} & \vec{j} \\ a_1 & a_2 & a_3 \\ (b_1 + c_1) & (b_2 + c_2) & (b_3 + c_3) \end{vmatrix}$$

$= \begin{vmatrix} a_2 & a_3 \\ (b_2 + c_2) & (b_3 + c_3) \end{vmatrix} \vec{i}$
$- \begin{vmatrix} a_1 & a_3 \\ (b_1 + c_1) & (b_3 + c_3) \end{vmatrix} \vec{j}$
$+ \begin{vmatrix} a_1 & a_2 \\ (b_1 + c_1) & (b_2 + c_2) \end{vmatrix} \vec{k}$

$= [a_2(b_3 + c_3) - a_3(b_2 + c_2)] \vec{i}$
$- [a_1(b_3 + c_3) - a_3(b_1 + c_1)] \vec{j}$
$+ [a_1(b_2 + c_2) - a_2(b_1 + c_1)] \vec{k}$

$= [(a_2b_3 + a_2c_3) - (a_3b_2 + a_3c_2)] \vec{i}$
$- [(a_1b_3 + a_1c_3) - (a_3b_1 + a_3c_1)] \vec{j}$
$+ [(a_1b_2 + a_1c_2) - (a_2b_1 + a_2c_1)] \vec{k}$

$= [(a_2b_3 - a_3b_2) + (a_2c_3 - a_3c_2)] \vec{i}$
$- [(a_1b_3 - a_3b_1) + (a_1c_3 - a_3c_1)] \vec{j}$
$+ [(a_1b_2 - a_2b_1) + (a_1c_2 - a_2c_1)] \vec{k}$

$= (a_2b_3 - a_3b_2) \vec{i} + (a_2c_3 - a_3c_2) \vec{i}$
$- (a_1b_3 - a_3b_1) \vec{j} - (a_1c_3 - a_3c_1) \vec{j}$
$+ (a_1b_2 - a_2b_1) \vec{k} + (a_1c_2 - a_2c_1) \vec{k}$

$= [(a_2b_3 - a_3b_2) \vec{i} - (a_1b_3 - a_3b_1) \vec{j} + (a_1b_2 - a_2b_1) \vec{k}]$
$+ [(a_2c_3 - a_3c_2) \vec{i} - (a_1c_3 - a_3c_1) \vec{j} + (a_1c_2 - a_2c_1) \vec{k}]$

$= \left[\begin{vmatrix} a_2 & a_3 \\ b_2 & b_3 \end{vmatrix} \vec{i} - \begin{vmatrix} a_1 & a_3 \\ b_1 & b_3 \end{vmatrix} \vec{j} + \begin{vmatrix} a_1 & a_2 \\ b_1 & b_2 \end{vmatrix} \vec{k} \right]$
$+ \left[\begin{vmatrix} a_2 & a_3 \\ c_2 & c_3 \end{vmatrix} \vec{i} - \begin{vmatrix} a_1 & a_3 \\ c_1 & c_3 \end{vmatrix} \vec{j} + \begin{vmatrix} a_1 & a_2 \\ c_1 & c_2 \end{vmatrix} \vec{k} \right]$

$= (\vec{a} \times \vec{b}) + (\vec{a} \times \vec{c})$

39a. (0, 71.5, 0) **b.** 71.5 lb/ft **c.** the y-axis
41. as $x \to +\infty$, $y \to -\infty$; as $x \to -\infty$, $y \to +\infty$ **43.** $\frac{4}{7}$ **45.** B

Page 435 Mid-Chapter Review

1.
1 cm
≈ 0.4 cm; ≈ 0.9 cm

3.
0.8 cm
≈ 0.4 cm; ≈ 0.7 cm

5. (-8, 1); $\sqrt{65} \approx 8.062$ **7.** (-10, 12); $2\sqrt{61} \approx 15.620$
9. (-8, -6, -1); $\sqrt{101} \approx 10.050$ **11.** (-32, 54) **13.** (-3, 0, 8)
15. (-4, -4, 20) **17.** 0, yes

Pages 438-441 Lesson 8-5

3.
16 knots
25°
current

5.
18 N
45°
51 N

7. 33.5 km/h, 333°26' **9.** 220.5 km/h, 16°42' **11.** 14.1 lb

13. 7.65 lb **15.** 0 lb **17.** 49.86 ft/s² **19.** 74 N, 253°
21. 800.8 lb, 323.5 lb **23.** 34 N, 223° **25.** 261.7 km,
21°3' SE **27.** 19°28' **29.** 171.5 N, 28°7' **31.** 132.4 lb
33. 66 **35.** 2, -1, $\frac{1}{3}$ **37.** -6, no

Pages 446-447 Lesson 8-6

5a. $(x + 1, y + 5) = t(3, 7)$ **b.** $x = -1 + 3t$, $y = -5 + 7t$
c. $y = \frac{7}{3}x - \frac{8}{3}$ **7a.** $(x - 5, y + 9) = t(3, 7)$ **b.** $x = 5 + 3t$,
$y = -9 + 7t$ **c.** $y = \frac{7}{3}x - \frac{62}{3}$ **9a.** $(x - 11, y + 4) = t(3, 7)$
b. $x = 3t + 11$, $y = 7t - 4$ **c.** $y = \frac{7}{3}x - \frac{89}{3}$ **11.** $x = t$;
$y = 3t + 11$ **13.** $(x + 4, y + 11) = t(-3, 8)$; $x = -3t - 4$,
$y = 8t - 11$ **15.** $(x + 1, y) = t(3, 2)$; $x = 3t - 1$, $y = 2t$
17. $x = t$, $y = -2t + 3$ **19.** $x = t$, $y = -\frac{3}{2}t + \frac{5}{2}$ **21.** $y = -x + 8$
23. $y = \frac{1}{4}x + \frac{23}{4}$ **25.** $x = 8$

27.
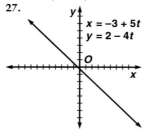
$x = -3 + 5t$
$y = 2 - 4t$

33a. 13.5 hours **b.** 675 miles
c. 9:30 A.M., 8:50 A.M.
d. at least 1.53 mph
35. $\begin{bmatrix} 28 & 20 \\ 10 & 14 \end{bmatrix}$
37. 8, 360°, 30° **39.** A

Pages 453-455 Lesson 8-7

7a. $x = 75t \cos 25°$, $y = 5 + 75t \sin 25° - 16t^2$ **c.** 145 ft
d. 20.7 ft **e.** no **9.** 46.07 ft/s **11a.** ≈ 107 ft, 1.1 s
b. ≈ 270 ft, 3.1 s **c.** ≈ 313 ft, 4.4 s **d.** ≈ 271 ft, 5.4 s
e. ≈ 107 ft, 6.2 s **f.** ≈ 0 ft, 6.25 s **13.** The range is the
same for projectiles fired at angles of $\alpha°$ and $(90 - \alpha)°$. But
the time in the air is greater when the angle is greater.
17a. $x = 155t \cos 22°$, $y = 155t \sin 22° - 16t^2 + 3$ **b.** about
36.12 feet, it will clear the fence **c.** 528.87 ft **19.** No, the
projectile will travel four times as far. **21a.** 127 ft/s
b. about 114.8 yards

23.

$y \le |x + 4|$

25. $5x - 4y - 33 = 0$

Pages 456-458 Chapter 8 Summary and Review

1. 4.1 cm, 25° **3.** 7.3 cm, 357° **5.** 1 cm, 0.8 cm **7.** (5, 12); 13
9. (-2, 12); $2\sqrt{37}$ **11.** (5, -6) **13.** (12, -17) **15.** (4, -1, -3),
$4\vec{i} - \vec{j} - 3\vec{k}$ **17.** (6, 2, 7), $6\vec{i} + 2\vec{j} + 7\vec{k}$ **19.** -16
21. (7, 22, 2) **23.** 43.95 lb, 35°52' **25.** $(x - 3, y + 5) = t(4, 2)$;
$x = 3 + 4t$, $y = -5 + 2t$ **27.** $(x - 4, y) = t(3, -6)$; $x = 4 + 3t$,
$y = -6t$ **29.** $x = 30t \cos 28°$, $y = 30t \sin 28° - 16t^2$
31. 25 lb/ft **33.** 10.2 feet

Page 459 Chapter 8 Test

1. ≈ 3.1 cm, ≈ 69° **2.** ≈ 9.5 cm, ≈ -8°
3. ≈ 1.5 cm, ≈ 2.5 cm **4.** 1.4 cm, 1.4 cm **5.** (-4, 3)
6. (5, 3) **7.** (7, 1, 2) **8.** (-4, -2, 4) **9.** (-5, 0, 10)
10. (14, 3, -26) **11.** (11, 12, -14) **12.** $\sqrt{26}$

13. $\sqrt{61}$ **14.** $-\vec{i} + 3\vec{j} + 4\vec{k}$ **15.** $4\vec{i} + 3\vec{j} - 6\vec{k}$ **16.** -19
17. (-30, 10, -15)   **18.** no   **19.** $x = 3 + 2t$, $y = 11 - 5t$
20. $x = -2 + t$, $y = 9t$ **21.** $x = 12 - 4t$, $y = -8 - 7t$
22. $y = -\frac{9}{2}x + 19$ **23a.** 13.7 knots   **b.** 277.7 m
24. 82.5 lb/ft   **25.** 23 feet   **BONUS** $90° < \theta < 270°$ or $\cos \theta < 0$

Pages 460-461   Unit 2 Review
1. 90°   **3.** 630°   **5.** 6.28 inches   **7.** $\frac{1}{5}$ **9.** 1   **11.** $\frac{\sqrt{3}}{3}$
13. $-\frac{2\sqrt{3}}{3}$ **15.** $A = 30°58'$, $B = 59°2'$, $c = 5.8$
17. no solution   **19.** One; $a = 40.1$, $c = 28.1$, $C = 42°$
21. 78.2   **23.** none, 36°, 0°

25.

$y = \frac{1}{2} \text{Cos } 2x$

27.

$y = x + 2 \sin 3x$

29. $\frac{2\sqrt{5}}{5}$ **31.** $\frac{1}{2}$ **33.** $\frac{\sqrt{3}}{2}$
35.

$y = \cot x$

$y = \text{arccot } x$

37.

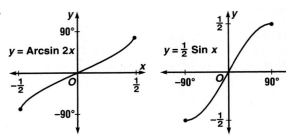

$y = \text{Arcsin } 2x$

$y = \frac{1}{2} \text{Sin } x$

39. $\frac{2\sqrt{2}}{3}$
41. Sample answer: $\tan x + \tan x \cot^2 x \overset{?}{=} \sec x \csc x$
$$\tan x(1 + \cot^2 x) \overset{?}{=} \sec x \csc x$$
$$\tan x(\csc^2 x) \overset{?}{=} \sec x \csc x$$
$$\left(\frac{\sin x}{\cos x}\right)\left(\frac{1}{\sin^2 x}\right) \overset{?}{=} \sec x \csc x$$
$$\left(\frac{1}{\cos x}\right)\left(\frac{1}{\sin x}\right) \overset{?}{=} \sec x \csc x$$
$$\sec x \csc x = \sec x \csc x$$

43. $\frac{\sqrt{2} + \sqrt{6}}{4}$ **45.** $\frac{\sqrt{2} + \sqrt{6}}{4}$ **47.** $\frac{17}{25}$ **49.** $\sqrt{\frac{5 - \sqrt{21}}{5 + \sqrt{21}}}$

51. 0°, 90°, 180°   **53.** 120°   **55.** $\frac{5x}{\sqrt{29}} + \frac{2y}{\sqrt{29}} - \frac{8}{\sqrt{29}} = 0$;
$\frac{8}{\sqrt{29}} \approx 1.49$, $\approx 22°$ **57.** 1.1   **59.** 1.5   **61.** 1 cm, 1.8 cm
63. (1, 1)   **65.** (-1, 7)   **67.** (13, -3, -7); $\vec{u} = 13\vec{i} - 3\vec{j} - 7\vec{k}$
69. (22, 0, -10); $\vec{u} = 22\vec{i} - 10\vec{k}$ **71.** 22   **73.** $(x, y - 5) = t(-1, 5)$; $x = -t$, $y = 5 + 5t$

CHAPTER 9   POLAR COORDINATES AND COMPLEX NUMBERS

Pages 470-472   Lesson 9-1

5.

$\left(12.8, -\frac{11\pi}{6}\right)$, $\left(-12.8, \frac{7\pi}{6}\right)$, $\left(-12.8, -\frac{5\pi}{6}\right)$

9.

13.

17.

996

21.

25.

45.

29.

33.

41. 1.25, 1   **43.** cos 20° + sin 50°   **45.** ≈ 15 feet horizontally, ≈ 22 feet vertically

Pages 491-493   Lesson 9-4

3. $\frac{2x}{\sqrt{13}} + \frac{3y}{\sqrt{13}} - \frac{5}{\sqrt{13}} = 0$ **5.** $\frac{2\sqrt{10}}{5} = r\cos(\theta + 72°)$

7.

11.

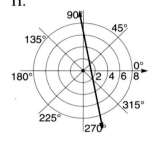

15. $12 = r\cos\theta$ **17.** $\frac{2\sqrt{10}}{5} = r\cos(\theta - 162°)$ **19.** $y = 0$
21. $x = 3$ **23.** $\sqrt{2} = r\cos(\theta - 8°)$
25. $\frac{10\sqrt{34}}{17} = r\cos(\theta - 121°)$ **31.** Leonhard Euler   **33.** 0.5
35.   **37.** B

Pages 480-481   Lesson 9-2

3.

5. cardioid   **7.** spiral of Archimedes   **9.** rose
11. limaçon   **13.** lemniscate
15. cardioid   **17.** rose
19. $(\sqrt{3}, 60°), (-\sqrt{3}, 240°)$
21. (2.1, 0.8)   **23.** (3.0, -0.9), (1.8, 0.3), (3.0, 0.9), (2.2, -1.2)

27. a rose with 10 petals

31. $\frac{-\sqrt{6} - \sqrt{2}}{4}$
33. (10, 340°), (-10, -200°), (-10, 160°)

Page 493   Mid-Chapter Review

1.

3.

(6, 135°), (6, -225°), (6, 315°)   cardioid

5. (2, 60°) or $\left(2, \frac{\pi}{3}\right)$

Pages 498-500   Lesson 9-5

5. 7 + 7*i*   **7.** 11 + 2*i*   **9.** $\frac{5 + i}{13}$ **11.** $-\frac{7}{5}$ or $-1\frac{2}{5}$ **13.** 7 + 2*i*
15. -7 + 9*i*√7   **17.** 3 + 69*i*   **19.** 17 + 17*i*   **21.** -7 − 24*i*
23. 75   **25.** -8 + 6*i*√2   **27.** $\frac{7 + i}{5}$ **29.** -2 ± 5*i*   **31.** $x = 2\sqrt{3}$,

Pages 486-487   Lesson 9-3

3. $\frac{\pi}{4} \approx 0.79$ **5.** 1.18   **7.** $(2\sqrt{2}, 3.93)$ **9.** (0, 3)
11. (-1.04, 2.27)   **13.** $x^2 + y^2 = 49$ **15.** $\left(3, \frac{\pi}{2}\right)$ **17.** (2, 0)
19. $\left(2, \frac{5\pi}{4}\right)$ **21.** (2.99, 4.01)   **23.** (-0.45, -1.34)   **25.** (-1.72, 3.01)
27. $r = 10\sec\theta$ **29.** $r = \frac{5}{2}\sin\theta$ **31.** $y = -x$ **33.** $x = -2$
35. $x^2 + y^2 = x + y$ **39.** about 219 meters   **41.** $y = \frac{x^4(x + 2)}{x(x + 2)}$
43. equal

$y = -\frac{2}{7}$ **33.** $x = -3, y = -2$ **35.** $50 - 125i$ **37.** $\frac{27 + 10i\sqrt{3}}{147}$
39. $\frac{-1 + 2i}{2}$ **41a.** 3 volts   **b.** $0.75(1 - j\sqrt{3})$ ohms
43. $22.28 + 7.96j$ amps   **45.** $y = -\frac{2}{5}x + 2, m = -\frac{2}{5}$,
y-intercept $= 2$ **47a.** 18 SA, 2 essay for a score of 120
b. 12 SA, 8 essay for a score of 180 points
49.
$$\sin^4 A + \cos^2 A \stackrel{?}{=} \cos^4 A + \sin^2 A$$
$$(\sin^2 A)^2 + \cos^2 A \stackrel{?}{=} \cos^4 A + \sin^2 A$$
$$(1 - \cos^2 A)^2 + \cos^2 A \stackrel{?}{=} \cos^4 A + \sin^2 A$$
$$(1 - 2\cos^2 A + \cos^4 A) + \cos^2 A \stackrel{?}{=} \cos^4 A + \sin^2 A$$
$$\cos^4 A + 1 - \cos^2 A \stackrel{?}{=} \cos^4 A + \sin^2 A$$
$$\cos^4 A + \sin^2 A = \cos^4 A + \sin^2 A$$
51. $r = 5$ or $r = -5$ **53.** B

Pages 504-505   Lesson 9-6
5. $\sqrt{2}\left(\cos \frac{3\pi}{4} + i \sin \frac{3\pi}{4}\right)$ **7.** $\sqrt{70}\left(\cos \frac{\pi}{2} + i \sin \frac{\pi}{2}\right)$

9. $2\sqrt{3}\left(\cos \frac{11\pi}{6} + i \sin \frac{11\pi}{6}\right)$

11. 4   **13.** $3i$
15. $\sqrt{2}\left(\cos \frac{5\pi}{4} + i \sin \frac{5\pi}{4}\right)$
17. $10\left(\cos \frac{\pi}{2} + i \sin \frac{\pi}{2}\right)$
19. $5(\cos 0.64 + i \sin 0.64)$
21. $2\left(\cos \frac{\pi}{3} + i \sin \frac{\pi}{3}\right)$
23. $5(\cos \pi + i \sin \pi)$
25. $12 - 12i\sqrt{3}$
27. $-1.25 + 2.73i$ **29.** $\sqrt{3} + i$ **31.** $\frac{-5\sqrt{3}}{2} + \frac{5}{2}i$
35. $I = 22.28 + 7.96j$; $E = 236.59(\cos 1.27 + i \sin 1.27)$, $Z = 10(\cos 0.93 + i \sin 0.93)$, $I = 23.66(\cos 1.34 + i \sin 1.34)$
37. No, the height of the building is approximately 61.9 feet, making a total of 101.9 feet with the tower, which is over the city's limit.
39. $(-1, -1, -10)$, $-\vec{i} - \vec{j} - 10\vec{k}$ **41.** $15i$ ohms

Pages 508-509   Lesson 9-7
3. $30(\cos 3\pi + i \sin 3\pi)$, -30 **5.** $3(\cos \pi + i \sin \pi)$, -3 **7.** $-2i$
9. $-\frac{3}{2}i$ **11.** $6(\cos 90° + i \sin 90°)$, $6i$
13. $2\sqrt{2}\left(\cos \frac{\pi}{12} + i \sin \frac{\pi}{12}\right)$, $\approx 2.7 + 0.7i$
15. $18\left(\cos \frac{4\pi}{3} + i \sin \frac{4\pi}{3}\right)$, $-9 - 9i\sqrt{3}$
17. $6\left(\cos \frac{3\pi}{4} + i \sin \frac{3\pi}{4}\right)$, $-3\sqrt{2} + 3i\sqrt{2}$
19. $2.98(\cos 1.1 + i \sin 1.1)$, $\approx 1.35 + 2.66i$
21. $\sqrt{3}\left(\cos \frac{5\pi}{8} + i \sin \frac{5\pi}{8}\right)$, $\approx -0.66 + 1.60i$
23. $10(\cos \pi + i \sin \pi)$, -10 **25.** Since $\cos \frac{\pi}{4} = \frac{\sqrt{2}}{2}$,
$\sin \frac{\pi}{4} = \frac{\sqrt{2}}{2}$, $\cos\left(-\frac{\pi}{4}\right) = \frac{\sqrt{2}}{2}$, $\sin\left(-\frac{\pi}{4}\right) = -\frac{\sqrt{2}}{2}$,
$s_1 = 4\sqrt{2}\left(\frac{\sqrt{2}}{2} + i \frac{\sqrt{2}}{2}\right)$ or $4 + 4i$ and $s_2 = 4\sqrt{2}\left(\frac{\sqrt{2}}{2} - i \frac{\sqrt{2}}{2}\right)$

or $4 - 4i$. $s_1 + s_2 = 4 + 4i + 4 - 4i$ or 8. $\frac{-b}{a} = \frac{8}{1} = 8$.
$s_1 s_2 = (4 + 4i)(4 - 4i) = 16 - 16i^2$ or 32. $\frac{c}{a} = \frac{32}{1} = 32$.
27. ≈ 1434 ft, $\approx 86{,}751$ ft²   **29.** $44 - 58i$ **31.** A

Pages 516-517   Lesson 9-8
5. $-\frac{9}{2} + \frac{9\sqrt{3}}{2}i$ **7.** $-i$ **9.** $-\frac{1}{2} - \frac{\sqrt{3}}{2}i$ **11.** $-527 - 336i$
13. -1024 **15.** $-119 - 120i$ **17.** $0.72 + 1.08i$
19. $\frac{\sqrt{3}}{2} + \frac{1}{2}i$ or $0.87 + 0.5i$ **21.** $1.22 + 0.71i$
23. $1, 0.31 \pm 0.95i, -0.81 \pm 0.59i$ **25.** $\pm i$, $\frac{\sqrt{3}}{2} \pm \frac{1}{2}i$,
$-\frac{\sqrt{3}}{2} \pm \frac{1}{2}i$ **27.** $0.81 \pm 0.59i, -1, -0.31 \pm 0.95i$ **35.** -1
37a. 800.8 kg   **b.** 278.2 kg   **39.** $10\left(\cos \frac{17\pi}{12} + i \sin \frac{17\pi}{12}\right)$,
$-2.59 - 9.66i$

Pages 518-520   Chapter 9 Summary and Review
1. $(-3, -310°)$, $(3, 230°)$,   **5.**
$(3, -130°)$

9. rose

13. $(3\sqrt{2}, 3\sqrt{2})$
15. $(1.33, -1.49)$
17. $\left(2\sqrt{3}, \frac{4\pi}{3}\right)$
19. $(3.61, -0.59)$
21. $\frac{3\sqrt{5}}{5} = r \cos(\theta - 207°)$
23. $x + \sqrt{3}y - 6 = 0$
25. $6 - i$ **27.** $-i$ **29.** 50
31. $\frac{5\sqrt{2} + 20i}{18}$
33. $4\left(\cos \frac{2\pi}{3} + i \sin \frac{2\pi}{3}\right)$
35. $-2\sqrt{3} + 2i$
37. $-4 + 4i\sqrt{3}$ **39.** $-4i$ **41.** $0.31 + 0.39i$
43. $-64\sqrt{3} + 64i$ **45.** 64   **47.** $1.24 + 0.22i$
49. $-\frac{1}{2} \pm \frac{\sqrt{3}}{2}i, \frac{1}{2} \pm \frac{\sqrt{3}}{2}i, \pm 1$ **51.** $(22.44 + 16.95j)$ amps

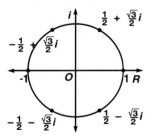

Page 521   Chapter 9 Test
1. $\left(-2, -\frac{3\pi}{4}\right), \left(2, \frac{\pi}{4}\right), \left(2, -\frac{7\pi}{4}\right)$ **2.** $\left(3, \frac{11\pi}{6}\right), \left(-3, -\frac{7\pi}{6}\right), \left(-3, \frac{5\pi}{6}\right)$

1.

2.

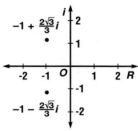

3. (2.5, -220°), (-2.5, -40°), (-2.5, 320°)

4. (-1.7, -335°), (1.7, -155°), (1.7, 205°)

5.

6.

7.

8.

9.

10.

11. $\left(-\frac{3\sqrt{2}}{2}, \frac{3\sqrt{2}}{2}\right)$ **12.** (-0.68, -3.94) **13.** (2, 2)

14. $\frac{3\sqrt{61}}{61} = r\cos(\theta - 230°)$ **15.** $\frac{\sqrt{5}}{10} = r\cos(\theta + 63°)$

16. $\frac{3\sqrt{10}}{5} = r\cos(\theta - 72°)$ **17.** i **18.** $-i$ **19.** $-8 + 3i$

20. $19 + 9i$ **21.** $48 + 14i$ **22.** $2 - 2i$

23. $4\sqrt{2}\left(\cos\frac{3\pi}{4} + i\sin\frac{3\pi}{4}\right)$ **24.** $5(\cos\pi + i\sin\pi)$

25. $12\left[\cos\left(-\frac{\pi}{3}\right) + i\sin\left(-\frac{\pi}{3}\right)\right]$ **26.** $12\left(\cos\frac{7\pi}{4} + i\sin\frac{7\pi}{4}\right)$; $6\sqrt{2} - 6i\sqrt{2}$ **27.** $6 - 2i\sqrt{3}$ **28.** $2\left(\cos\frac{\pi}{2} + i\sin\frac{\pi}{2}\right)$; $2i$

29. 16 **30.** $-\sqrt{3} - i$ or $-1.73 - i$ **31.** $1, \frac{\sqrt{2}}{2} + \frac{i\sqrt{2}}{2}$, $i, -\frac{\sqrt{2}}{2} + \frac{i\sqrt{2}}{2}, -1, -\frac{\sqrt{2}}{2} - \frac{i\sqrt{2}}{2}, -i, \frac{\sqrt{2}}{2} - \frac{i\sqrt{2}}{2}$

32. $160(\cos 62° + j\sin 62°)$

33. $-1 \pm \frac{2i\sqrt{3}}{3}$

BONUS

CHAPTER 10   CONICS
Pages 529-532   Lesson 10-1

5. $x^2 + y^2 = 81$ **7.** $(x - 2)^2 + (y + 7)^2 = 100$ **9.** 3, (4, 3)

11. $\frac{\sqrt{10}}{2}$, (3, 2) **13.** $(x - 1.4)^2 + (y - 3.75)^2 = 16.02$

15. $(x - 7)^2 + (y - 4)^2 = 5$ **17.** $\left(x + \frac{1}{2}\right)^2 + y^2 = 1$

19. $x^2 + y^2 = 9$ **21.** $(x + 0.25)^2 + (y - 1)^2 = 9$

23. $\left(x - \frac{3}{2}\right)^2 + \left(y + \frac{1}{4}\right)^2 = 7$ **25.** $(x + 7)^2 + (y + 12)^2 = 36$

27. $(x - 3)^2 + (y - 4)^2 = 5$, (3, 4), $\sqrt{5}$ **29.** $(x - 4)^2 + (y - 2)^2 = 18$, (4, 2), $3\sqrt{2}$ **31.** $\left(x + \frac{1}{6}\right)^2 + \left(y - \frac{7}{6}\right)^2 = \frac{169}{18}$, $\left(-\frac{1}{6}, \frac{7}{6}\right)$, $\frac{13\sqrt{2}}{6}$ **33.** $(x + 3)^2 + (y - 4)^2 = 25$

35. $(x + \frac{1}{2})^2 + (y - \frac{5}{2})^2 = \frac{34}{4}$ **37.** $(x - 5)^2 + (y - 12)^2 = \frac{1}{5}$

47. 1608.5 m/s **49.** $\sin 100°$ **51.** D(-8, 1) **53.** $1.31 + 0.14i$

Pages 539-541   Lesson 10-2

5. (9, -12), 5, right **7.** (6, -8), 0.5, up **9.** vertex: (2, -1), focus: (2, 1), directrix: $y = -3$ **11.** $(y - 3)^2 = 4x$

13a. $(y - 2)^2 = x - 7$ **b.** vertex: (7, 2), focus: (7.25, 2), directrix: $x = 6.75$, axis: $y = 2$ **15a.** $(x + 4)^2 = -4(y - 2)$

b. vertex: (-4, 2), focus: (-4, 1), directrix: $y = 3$, axis: $x = -4$

17a. $y^2 = -2x$ **b.** vertex: (0, 0), focus: $\left(-\frac{1}{2}, 0\right)$, directrix: $x = \frac{1}{2}$, axis: $y = 0$ **19a.** $(x - 3)^2 = 10(y + 1)$ **b.** vertex: (3, -1), focus: $\left(3, \frac{3}{2}\right)$, directrix: $y = -\frac{7}{2}$, axis: $x = 3$

21a. $(y - 3)^2 = -3(x - 3)$ **b.** vertex: (3, 3), focus: $\left(\frac{9}{4}, 3\right)$, directrix: $x = \frac{15}{4}$, axis: $y = 3$ **23.** $y^2 = -12x$

25. $(x - 4)^2 = -1(y - 3)$ **27.** $(x - 2)^2 = -8(y + 4)$

29. $(y - 2)^2 = 4(x + 1)$ **31a.** The opening becomes narrower. **b.** The opening becomes wider. **39a.** $7 **b.** $2450

41.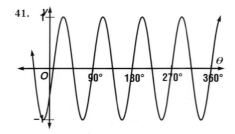

43. $(-1, -3)$ **45.** $(x - 7)^2 + (y - 4)^2 = 2$

Pages 548-550 Lesson 10-3
5. center: $(0, 0)$, foci: $(0, \pm\sqrt{5})$, vertices: $(0, \pm 3)$, $(\pm 2, 0)$
7. center: $(-2, 0)$, foci: $(-2 \pm 4\sqrt{2}, 0)$, vertices: $(-11, 0)$, $(7, 0)$, $(-2, \pm 7)$ **9.** center: $(0, -9)$, foci: $(0, -9 \pm 4\sqrt{3})$, vertices: $(0, -1)$, $(0, -17)$, $(\pm 4, -9)$ **11.** $\frac{x^2}{9} + \frac{y^2}{36} = 1$ **13.** $\frac{x^2}{49} + \frac{(y + 5)^2}{25} = 1$
15. center: $(3, 4)$, foci: $(6, 4)$, $(0, 4)$, vertices: $(8, 4)$, $(-2, 4)$, $(3, 0)$, $(3, 8)$ **17.** center: $(0, 0)$, foci: $(\pm\sqrt{5}, 0)$, vertices: $(-3, 0)$, $(3, 0)$, $(0, -2)$, $(0, 2)$ **19.** center: $(3, 1)$, foci: $(3, 1 \pm \sqrt{5})$, vertices: $(3, 4)$, $(3, -2)$, $(1, 1)$, $(5, 1)$ **21.** center: $(7, -6)$, foci: $(7 \pm \sqrt{5}, -6)$, vertices: $(10, -6)$, $(4, -6)$, $(7, -4)$, $(7, -8)$
23. $\frac{y^2}{64} + \frac{x^2}{36} = 1$ **25.** $\frac{x^2}{36} + \frac{y^2}{16} = 1$ **27.** $\frac{x^2}{49} + \frac{y^2}{45} = 1$
29. ellipse; two squared terms, $A \neq C$ **31.** parabola; one squared term **33.** ellipse; two squared terms, $A \neq C$
35. $\frac{(y - 2)^2}{18} + \frac{(x - 1)^2}{9} = 1$
37. $49x^2 + 9y^2 + 294x - 126y + 441 = 0$ **43.** 116 million km

45.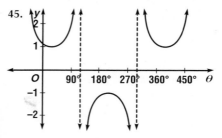

47. 334.3 mph, 9°28'SW **49.** $(x + 5)^2 + (y - 3)^2 = 169$
51. 4

Pages 556-559 Lesson 10-4
5. center: $(-3, 4)$, foci: $(-3 \pm \sqrt{74}, 4)$, vertices: $(2, 4)$, $(-8, 4)$, asymptotes: $y - 4 = \pm\frac{7}{5}(x + 3)$ **7.** center: $(8, 5)$, foci: $(8, 5 \pm \sqrt{104})$, vertices: $(8, 7)$, $(8, 3)$, asymptotes: $y - 5 = \pm\frac{1}{5}(x - 8)$ **9.** center: $(-11, -7)$, foci: $(-11 \pm 6\sqrt{5}, -7)$, vertices: $(1, -7)$, $(-23, -7)$, asymptotes: $y + 7 = \pm\frac{1}{2}(x + 11)$
11. $\frac{(y - 3)^2}{16} - \frac{(x - 4)^2}{9} = 1$ **13.** $\frac{x^2}{9} - \frac{y^2}{9} = 1$ **15.** center: $(0, 0)$, foci: $(\pm\sqrt{41}, 0)$, vertices: $(5, 0)$, $(-5, 0)$, asymptotes: $y = \pm\frac{4}{5}x$ **17.** center: $(0, 0)$, foci: $(\pm\sqrt{117}, 0)$, vertices: $(6, 0)$, $(-6, 0)$, asymptotes: $y = \pm\frac{3}{2}x$ **19.** center: $(3, -5)$, foci: $(3 \pm\sqrt{13}, -5)$, vertices: $(5, -5)$, $(1, -5)$, asymptotes: $y + 5 = \pm\frac{3}{2}(x - 3)$ **21.** center: $(5, -3)$, foci: $(5 \pm \sqrt{13}, -3)$, vertices: $(7, -3)$, $(3, -3)$, asymptotes: $y + 3 = \pm\frac{3}{2}(x - 5)$
23. ellipse **25.** circle **27.** ellipse

29. **33.**

37. $\frac{y^2}{16} - \frac{x^2}{9} = 1$ **39.** $\frac{(x - 3)^2}{9} - \frac{(y - 3)^2}{16} = 1$
41. $\frac{2y^2}{25} - \frac{2x^2}{25} = 1$ **43.** $\frac{(y - 2)^2}{9} - \frac{(x - 4)^2}{16} = 1$
45. $\frac{5(y - 1)^2}{64} - \frac{5(x - 1)^2}{16} = 1$
53a.
b. 116 cm^3 **c.** 58 cm^3
d. $V = 0.5$(original V)
55a. 9.77×10^4 hours or 4070 days **b.** May, 1983 (actual: June 13, 1983)

57.
$$\frac{\sin 2X}{1 - \cos 2X} \stackrel{?}{=} \cot X$$
$$\frac{2 \sin X \cos X}{1 - \cos^2 X + \sin^2 X} \stackrel{?}{=} \cot X$$
$$\frac{2 \sin X \cos X}{2 \sin^2 X} \stackrel{?}{=} \cot X$$
$$\frac{\cos X}{\sin X} \stackrel{?}{=} \cot X$$
$$\cot X = \cot X$$
59. $0 = r \cos(\theta - 135°)$ **61.** $(y + 1)^2 = 4(x - 1)$ **63.** C

Page 559 Mid-Chapter Review
1. $(x - 2)^2 + (y + 7)^2 = 81$ **3.** vertex: $(0, 3)$, focus: $(1, 3)$, directrix: $x = -1$ **5.** center: $(3, 2)$, foci: $(3 \pm \sqrt{15}, 2)$, 8 units, 2 units **7.** $40{,}000x^2 + 90{,}000y^2 = 3{,}600{,}000{,}000$

9.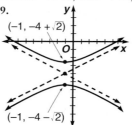

Pages 565-567 Lesson 10-5
5. parabola **7.** hyperbola **9.** circle, $(x - 4)^2 + y^2 = 5$
11. parabola, $\left(y + \frac{1}{2}\right)^2 = -2(x - 2)$ **13.** $\frac{y^2}{4} + \frac{x^2}{1.75} = 1$
15. $\frac{\sqrt{5}}{3}$ **17.** 0 **19.** $\sqrt{2}$ **21.** hyperbola, $xy = \frac{4}{9}$
23. parabola, $x^2 = 4(y + 7)$ **25.** hyperbola, $\frac{(x - 2)^2}{5} - \frac{(y + 2)^2}{5} = 1$ **27.** parabola, $(x - 4)^2 = y$
29. point, $(2, 3)$ **31.** $\frac{(x - 2)^2}{16} + \frac{(y - 5)^2}{15} = 1$
33. $\frac{y^2}{36} - \frac{x^2}{28} = 1$ **35.** $\frac{y^2}{100} + \frac{(x - 3)^2}{51} = 1$

37. $\frac{(y-2)^2}{18} + \frac{(x-1)^2}{9} = 1$ **39.** 1.5 **41a.** 2095.2 miles, 424.8 miles **b.** $\frac{x^2}{27,248,400} + \frac{y^2}{26,550,840.96} = 1$

43. 3.05 cm **45.** 0° **47.** $\frac{(y+1)^2}{4} - \frac{(x-3)^2}{5} = 1$

Pages 575-576   Lesson 10-6

5. circle, $3x^2 + 3y^2 + 30x - 36y + 167 = 0$ **7.** parabola, $x^2 + 16x - 4y + 88 = 0$ **9.** $21x^2 + 2\sqrt{3}xy + 23y^2 = 120$
11. $x^2 + 16\sqrt{3}x - 2\sqrt{3}xy + 16y + 3y^2 = 0$ **13.** circle, $x^2 + y^2 - 4x - 6y + 7 = 0$ **15.** parabola, $2x^2 + 5x - y - 2 = 0$ **17.** $2xy = 9$ **19.** $x^2 - y^2 = 12$
21. hyperbola, 11° **23.** ellipse, -37° **25.** parabola, -30°
27. point **29.** line

39a.

b. $\frac{(x+12)^2}{169} + \frac{y^2}{25} = 1$
c. $25y^2 - 600y + 169x^2 = 625$ **41.** no triangle
43. **45.** $(x-4)^2 + y^2 = 5$, circle

Pages 583-584   Lesson 10-7

5. 4 **7.** 3 **9.** 1 **11.** no solution **13.** (4.0, 0.5), (-2.8, -2.9)
15. **17.** no solution **19.** (3, 3), (-1, -1) **21.** (±2, 1.7), (±2, -1.7) **23.** (±1, 5), (±1, -5) **25.** (±2, 0)
27. $\left(3, -\frac{4}{3}\right)$, (4, -1), $\left(-3, \frac{4}{3}\right)$, (-4, 1)

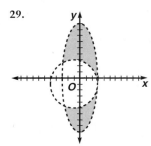

29. **33.**

37. 12 ft by 18 ft **39.** 214.9 meters **41.** (2, 0, 3)
43. (-7, 8)

Pages 589-591   Lesson 10-8

3. 1, -1 **5.** 0, undefined **7.** 1, -1
9. $9x - 8y - 145 = 0, 9y + 8x = 0$ **11.** $4x + 5y - 25 = 0, 25x - 20y - 64 = 0$ **13.** $2x + \sqrt{21}y - 25 = 0, y - \frac{\sqrt{21}}{2}x = 0$ **15.** $10x + 4y + 116 = 0, 5y - 2x = 0$
17. $x + 5y + 14 = 0, 5x - y - 8 = 0$
19. $2x - \sqrt{5}y + 13 = 0, \sqrt{5}x + 2y + 2\sqrt{5} = 0$
21. $x + y - 8 = 0, x - y - 6 = 0$ **23.** $x = -4, y = -3$
25. $\sqrt{3}$ or 1.73 **27.** $\sqrt{33}$ or 5.74 **29.** $y = \pm 5$ **31.** $y = \pm 8$
33. $y = -\frac{3}{4}x + 10, y = -\frac{3}{4}x - 10$ **35.** $a = 4$

41a. **b.** $4y - 3x - 6 = 0$

43. **45.** $16 + 30i$

47.

Pages 592-594   Chapter 10 Summary and Review

1. $x^2 + y^2 = 27$ **3.** $\left(x + \frac{3}{2}\right)^2 + \left(y + \frac{1}{2}\right)^2 = \frac{29}{2}$

5. **7.**

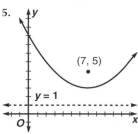

vertex: (7, 3), focus: (7, 5), directrix: $y = 1$

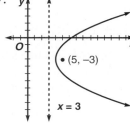

vertex: (4, -3), focus: (5, -3), directrix: $x = 3$

9. center: $(3, -1)$, foci: $(3 \pm \sqrt{21}, -1)$, vertices: $(-2, -1)$, $(8, -1)$, $(3, -3)$, $(3, 1)$ **11.** center: $(4, 6)$, foci: $(4 \pm 3\sqrt{3}, 6)$, vertices: $(10, 6)$, $(-2, 6)$, $(4, 3)$, $(4, 9)$ **13.** center: $(0, 0)$, foci: $(\pm 2\sqrt{3}, 0)$, vertices: $(2, 0)$, $(-2, 0)$, asymptotes: $y = \pm\sqrt{2}x$
15. center: $(2, 0)$, foci: $(2, 6)$, $(2, -6)$, vertices: $(2, \pm\sqrt{30})$, asymptotes: $y = \pm\sqrt{5}(x - 2)$ **17.** ellipse, $\dfrac{(x-1)^2}{4} + \dfrac{y^2}{16} = 1$
19. circle, $(x - 4)^2 + (y - 1)^2 = 4$
21. $(x + 3)^2 + (y - 2)^2 = 3$
23. $21x^2 - 10\sqrt{3}xy + 31y^2 = 144$ **25.** $(3, 3)$, $(-1, -1)$
27.

29. $x = 1$, $y = 1$
31. $8x - y + 12 = 0$, $2x + 8y + 34 = 0$
33. 1.5 feet from the center

Page 595   Chapter 10 Test

1. parabola, $(x + 3)^2 = 8(y + 2)$ **2.** degenerate hyperbola, $4x^2 - y^2 = 0$ **3.** hyperbola, $\dfrac{y^2}{\frac{5}{13}} - \dfrac{x^2}{\frac{5}{2}} = 1$ **4.** ellipse, $\dfrac{(x-3)^2}{81} + \dfrac{(y+4)^2}{16} = 1$ **5.** parabola, $(y + 5)^2 = 2(x - 1)$
6. hyperbola, $\dfrac{(x-4)^2}{36} - \dfrac{(y-5)^2}{4} = 1$ **7.** ellipse, $\dfrac{(x+1)^2}{8} + \dfrac{(y-3)^2}{4} = 1$ **8.** circle, $(x + 2)^2 + y^2 = 10$
9. $(x + 8)^2 + (y - 3)^2 = 53$ **10.** $(x - 3)^2 = -6\left(y + \dfrac{7}{2}\right)$
11. $x^2 + \dfrac{4y^2}{3} = 1$ **12.** $\dfrac{(x-1)^2}{4} - \dfrac{(y+5)^2}{5} = 1$
13. $4(x - 2)^2 + (y + 2)^2 = 36$ **14.** $-x^2 + 6\sqrt{3}xy + 5y^2 = 32$
15. $(2, 0)$, $\left(\dfrac{2}{3}, \dfrac{2\sqrt{2}}{3}\right)$, $\left(\dfrac{2}{3}, -\dfrac{2\sqrt{2}}{3}\right)$
16.

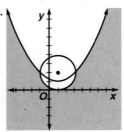

17. $x + 3y - 5 = 0$, $3x - y - 5 = 0$
18. $x + 4\sqrt{2}y - 9\sqrt{2} = 0$, $4\sqrt{2}x - y - 6 = 0$
19. $(x - 1)^2 + (y - 4)^2 = 10$ **20.** $(-3, -9)$ **BONUS** $\dfrac{1}{2}$

CHAPTER 11   EXPONENTIAL AND LOGARITHMIC FUNCTIONS

Pages 602-604   Lesson 11-1

5. 9 **7.** 49 **9.** $x^{\frac{1}{2}}y^{\frac{3}{2}}$ **11.** $\sqrt[5]{15}$ **13.** $\sqrt[4]{a^3y}$ **15.** 81
17. 125 **19.** 2 **21.** $\dfrac{9}{4}$ **23.** 4 **25.** 3 **27.** $b^{\frac{1}{2}}$ **29.** $5a^{\frac{2}{3}}b$
31. $24^{\frac{1}{4}}a^3b^4$ **33.** $2xy^{\frac{8}{5}}$ **35.** $\sqrt[5]{64}$ or 2 **37.** $y\sqrt[3]{4a^2y}$
39. $\sqrt[5]{rt^2v^3}$ **41.** $\sqrt[3]{x}$ **43.** $x^2\sqrt[5]{y^2a^2}$ **45.** x^5 **47.** $125x$
49. $8y^6$ **51.** $a^{-2}b^8c^{-5}$ or $\dfrac{b^8}{a^2c^5}$ **55.** ≈ 254 km

57.

59. $-2, -\dfrac{1}{2}, 2$
61. about 346 m/s
63. $28 - 96i$
65. $4\sqrt{2}$ units

Pages 611-613   Lesson 11-2

5. 5.4622 **7.** 0.0317
11. The graph of Exercise 9 is the graph of Exercise 8 reflected over the x-axis. The graph of Exercise 10 is the graph of Exercise 8 reflected across the y-axis.
13. $11,689.59 **15.** 36.6604

9.

17.

21.

25.

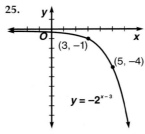

27. They have similar shape, but the graph of Exercise 19 is steeper.

29.

33.

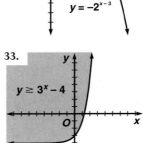

35. They are reflections over the x-axis. **39.** $34,426.47
41. over 30 years, #2 is better; over 5 years, #1 is better **43.** $13,257.20
45. 78 **47.** $-\dfrac{17}{32}$

49. $6\sqrt{2}\left(\cos\dfrac{3\pi}{4} + i\sin\dfrac{3\pi}{4}\right)$ **51.** C

Pages 617-619   Lesson 11-3

5. 27.1 **7.** 1.6 **9.** 114.5 **11.** $1671.38 **13.** 73.6998
15. 4.2340 **17.** 1.0000 **25.** $1489.35 **27.** $892.69

1002

29.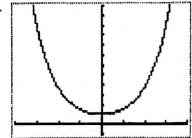

31. ≈ 3.786%   **33a.** 131   **b.** 39   **c.** 2050; No, this is 85 years and the legislator would have to be more than 100 years old then.   **35.** The graph is a logarithmic graph that approaches 0 as x approaches $-\infty$. It has a y-intercept of approximately 9.5 and curves sharply upward for the positive values of x.   **39.** 18 rps   **41.** $15 = r \sin \theta$ **43.** \$891.26

Pages 626-628   Lesson 11-4

5. $\log_6 \left(\frac{1}{36} \right) = -2$ **7.** $27^{\frac{1}{3}} = 3$ **9.** $9^{\frac{3}{2}} = 27$ **11.** 3   **13.** 6
15. 3
19. $\log_2 16 = 4$
21. $\log_3 \left(\frac{1}{27} \right) = -3$
23. $\log_8 \frac{1}{4} = -\frac{2}{3}$
25. $2^3 = 8$ **27.** $10^4 = 10{,}000$
29. $8^{\frac{1}{3}} = 2$ **31.** 6   **33.** 5
35. 5   **37.** 10   **39.** 16   **41.** -2
43. 12   **45.** 3   **47.** 24
49. 4   **51.** 5   **53.** 12

17.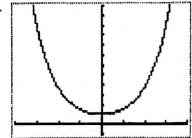
$y = \log_3 (x + 1)$

55.
$y = \log_4 x$

59.
$y \leq \log_6 x$

63a. 100 units   **b.** 5 ft/s   **65.** 300 ft of A, 600 ft of B
67. $y = -8x + 3$ **69.** 0   **71.** -2, no   **73.** $\frac{(x-2)^2}{4} - \frac{y^2}{1} = 1$; hyperbola   **75.** D

Page 628   Mid-Chapter Review

1. 27   **3.** $\sqrt{3}$ **5.** \$211,752.24   **7.** 14.2783   **9.** 444 mm of mercury   **11.** 2

Pages 632-633   Lesson 11-5

5. 2.6274   **7.** 354.73   **9.** 0.01   **11.** 10,000 and 100,000
13. 2809.0   **15.** 1802.8   **17.** 2.9515   **19.** -2.2676
21. 4.3597   **23.** 1.81   **25.** 0.01   **27.** 84,004.01   **29.** 236.5
31. 5213.4   **33.** 13.1   **35.** 2.6   **37.** 5.2   **41a.** 6.3
b. 10 times   **43.** $\begin{bmatrix} 8 & 8 & -1 \\ 2 & -8 & -3 \end{bmatrix}$

45.
$$\frac{\sin^2 x}{\cos^4 x + \cos^2 x \sin^2 x} \overset{?}{=} \tan^2 x$$
$$\frac{\sin^2 x}{\cos^2 x(\cos^2 x + \sin^2 x)} \overset{?}{=} \tan^2 x$$
$$\frac{\sin^2 x}{\cos^2 x} \overset{?}{=} \tan^2 x$$
$$\tan^2 x = \tan^2 x$$
47. $\frac{(x-2)^2}{4} + \frac{(y-6)^2}{3} = 1$ **49.** B

Pages 639-640   Lesson 11-6

5. $x = \frac{\log 98}{\log 7}$; 2.36   **7.** $x = \frac{\log 121}{\log 5}$; 2.98   **9.** $x = \frac{\log 16}{\log 3}$; 2.52
11. $x = -\frac{\log 18}{\log 3}$; -2.63   **13.** $x > 3.807$ **15.** $x \geq 4.716$
17. 4.75   **19.** 7.83   **21.** 0.82   **23.** 2.14   **25.** 1244.84
27. -7.74   **29.** 5.58   **31.** $1 < x < 6$ **33.** -7.64   **35.** 0.37
43. 7.48 yr
47. $y = \pm 17 \sin (8x + 480°)$
49. (-0.25, 0)   **51.** 6.89

45.
$x + 4y < 9$

Pages 643-645   Lesson 11-7

3. 2.2322   **5.** -1.5606   **7.** 2.1882   **9.** 2.1972   **11.** 0.6957
13. 4.0395   **15.** 6.8876   **17.** 0   **19.** 146.4963   **21.** 1.8589
23. 1   **25.** 133.14   **27.** 48.52   **29.** 17.63   **31.** -0.000385
33a. -0.0211   **b.** 81%   **c.** 2037   **35a.** about 12.4 years
37a. 0.713   **b.** about 46 minutes   **39a.** 0.08 g   **b.** 0.055 g
43. (-8, 9)
49. D

47.

Pages 646-648   Chapter 11 Summary and Review

1. $\frac{1}{2}$ **3.** 3   **5.** $\frac{1}{3}$ **7.** $\frac{1}{8}x^{12}$

9.

11.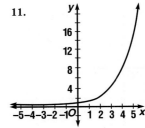

13. 10.3812   **15.** 6.3510   **17.** 3   **19.** 15   **21.** 3
23. 1.6314   **25.** 0.70   **27.** 21.41   **29.** 117.35   **31.** 1.99
33. 2.45   **35.** -4.82   **37.** 5.9989   **39.** 1226.7210   **41.** 2.91
43. 3.32   **45a.** 45 words per minute   **b.** 64 words per minute   **c.** at 3.5 weeks   **47.** 3561 years old

Page 649 Chapter 11 Test

1. 49 **2.** 2.5 **3.** $343\frac{1}{7}$ **4.** $\frac{1}{64a^6}$ **5.** $x^6y^8a^5$ **6.** $a^{\frac{5}{2}}b^3$

7.

8.

9. 8 **10.** 4 **11.** 2 **12.** 3.34 **13.** -0.66 **14.** 1.54
15. 1.4778 **16.** 0.7459 **17.** 2.7340 **18.** -1.3943
19. 3.0701 **20.** 0.0123 **21.** $4825.31 **22.** $7627.49
23. 168 gaps **24.** 11 hours, 21 minutes **25.** 2.66 meters
BONUS a^9

Pages 650-651 Unit 3 Review

1. (2, -300°), (-2, -120°), (-2, 240°)

5.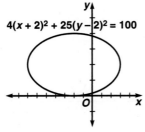

9. (2.83, 3.93) **11.** (3.61, -0.98) **13.** $y = 2$ **15.** i
17. $3 + 3i$ **19.** $\frac{1 + 8i}{13}$ **21.** $3\left(\cos\frac{3\pi}{2} + i\sin\frac{3\pi}{2}\right)$
23. $\sqrt{5}(\cos 2.03 + i\sin 2.03)$ **25.** -8 **27.** $8 - 8i$
29. (0, 0); $\frac{7}{2}$ **31.** $\left(-\frac{9}{2}, 4\right)$, $\frac{\sqrt{129}}{2}$
33. vertex: (3.4, -1), focus: **35.** center: (-2, 2),
(4.65, -1), directrix: $x = 2.15$, foci: $(-2 \pm \sqrt{21}, 2)$, vertices:
axis: $y = -1$ (-7, 2), (3, 2), (-2, 4), (-2, 0)

$4(x + 2)^2 + 25(y - 2)^2 = 100$

37. center: (-1, -3), foci: $(-1, -3 \pm \sqrt{13})$, vertices: (-1, 0),
(-1, -6), asymptotes: $y + 3 = \pm\frac{4}{9}(x + 1)$
(See art in next column.)

37. 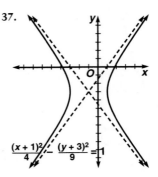 **39.** hyperbola;
$\frac{(x - 1)^2}{25} - \frac{(y + 3)^2}{4} = 1$

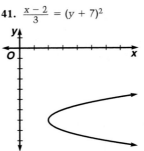 $\frac{(x + 1)^2}{4} - \frac{(y + 3)^2}{9} = 1$

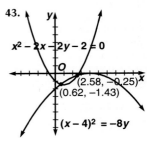 $4(x - 1)^2 = 25(y + 3)^2 + 100$

41. $\frac{x - 2}{3} = (y + 7)^2$ **43.**

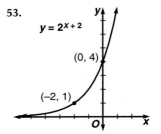
$x^2 - 2x - 2y - 2 = 0$
(2.58, -0.25)
(0.62, -1.43)
$(x - 4)^2 = -8y$

45. $x + y - 1 = 0$,
$x - y - 3 = 0$
47. $y - 8 = 0$, $x - 2 = 0$
49. $3abc^2\sqrt[3]{2ac^2}$ **51.** $\frac{1}{x^2}$
55. 2.7912 **57.** 0.0091
59. $\frac{27}{2}$ **61.** 10,028.573
63. 5.496 **65.** 2 **67.** 3.83
69. 147.24

53.
$y = 2^{x + 2}$
(0, 4)
(-2, 1)

CHAPTER 12 SEQUENCES AND SERIES

Pages 660-662 Lesson 12-1

5. 17, 21, 25, 29, 33 **7.** -13, -19, -25, -31, -37 **9.** 6, 7.5, 9,
10.5, 12 **11.** 2n, 3n, 4n, 5n, 6n **13.** -5b, -7b, -9b, -11b, -13b
15. 227 **17.** 12, 16.5, 21 **19.** -25 **21.** 11 **23.** 15 **25.** 6
27. $3 - 4\sqrt{3}$ **29.** 149 **35.** 77 **37.** 8 **41.** 231 cans **43a.** 31
b. 496 **45.** 1, 3 **47.** 31.68 cm² **49.** 20 + 15i **51.** D

Pages 668-669 Lesson 12-2

7. 1.75, 0.875, 0.4375, 0.21875 **9.** yes **11.** yes **13.** $\frac{3}{2}$
15. $201\frac{2}{3}$ **17.** 12, 18, 27 **19.** 10^{-9} **21.** 0.3125, 0.625, 1.25
25. 41.5625 **27.** $31(1 + \sqrt{2})$ **29.** $585,350.73,
$2,170,024.72, $8,044,761.88, $29,823,712.71, $110,563,103.40
31. 1.258×10^9, 2.111×10^{16} **33a.** 0.020 cm, 0.040 cm
b. $0.005(2)^{n-1}$ **c.** 2.56 cm, 3.169×10^{27} cm
35. 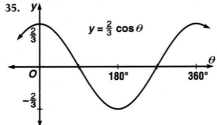 $y = \frac{2}{3}\cos\theta$

37a. 80, 75, 70, ... **b.** $T = 80 - 5n$ **c.** 75°F

Pages 676-678   Lesson 12-3

5. 2^{n-1} **7.** $3 \cdot \left(\frac{2}{3}\right)^{n-1}$ **9.** $-\frac{2}{5}$ **11.** 3 **13.** $\frac{1}{10}$ **15.** $\frac{8}{9}$
17. 0 **19.** does not exist **21.** 1 **23.** $\frac{4}{3}$ **25.** 0 **27.** $\frac{3}{11}$
29. $\frac{7}{22}$ **31.** $2\frac{205}{999}$ **33.** $\frac{3}{2}(\sqrt{3} + 1)$ **35.** $\frac{2}{9}$ **37.** does not
exist **39.** 4 strokes **41.** $2\sqrt{2}$ units **43.** $k = \frac{-3 \pm i\sqrt{15}}{6}$
45. 181.3 **47.** C

Pages 683-684   Lesson 12-4

5. N, C **7.** A, D **9.** G, C **11.** C **13.** C **15.** cannot tell
17. C **19.** C **21.** D **23.** C **25.** C **29.** 380 feet
31. 109.63 ft **33.** 1

Page 684   Mid-Chapter Review

1. $5, 6\frac{1}{2}, 8, 9\frac{1}{2}, 11, 12\frac{1}{2}, 14, 15\frac{1}{2}, 17$ **3.** $2, \pm 1, \frac{1}{2}, \pm\frac{1}{4}, \frac{1}{8}$
5. does not exist **7.** $\frac{4}{11}$ **9.** $608,487.05

Pages 688-690   Lesson 12-5

5. 18 **7.** 60 **9.** 18 **11.** $\sum\limits_{n=1}^{5} \frac{32}{2^n}$ **13.** $\sum\limits_{n=2}^{\infty} \frac{n}{5}$ **15.** 2160
17. 362,880 **19.** 144 **21.** 90 **23.** -3 **25.** -40 **27.** 68
29. 1084 **31.** 42 **33.** 4 **35.** $\sum\limits_{k=1}^{5} 10k$ **37.** $\sum\limits_{k=0}^{4} 3 \cdot 2^k$
39. $\sum\limits_{k=2}^{10} \frac{1}{k}$ **41.** $\sum\limits_{k=0}^{3} (11 - 2k)$ **43.** $\sum\limits_{k=1}^{\infty} 2k$ **45.** $\sum\limits_{k=3}^{\infty} \frac{2}{k}$
47. $\sum\limits_{k=0}^{\infty} \frac{k!}{k+1}$ **49.** $x(x-1)$ **51.** $x - y$ **59.** $360,110.31
61a. 2 weeks **b.** $58.80 per tree **63.** $-\frac{\sqrt{2}}{2}$
65. $(y + 1)^2 = -12(x - 6)$ **67.** $\frac{2}{9}$ **69.** A

Pages 694-695   Lesson 12-6

5. $a^7 + 7a^6b + 21a^5b^2 + 35a^4b^3 + 35a^3b^4 + 21a^2b^5 + 7ab^6 + b^7$
7. $256 - 256b + 96b^2 - 16b^3 + b^4$ **9.** $35a^4b^3$
11. $x^5 + 5x^4y + 10x^3y^2 + 10x^2y^3 + 5xy^4 + y^5$
13. $x^7 - 14x^6 + 84x^5 - 280x^4 + 560x^3 - 672x^2 + 448x - 128$
15. $x^6 + 18x^5 + 135x^4 + 540x^3 + 1215x^2 + 1458x + 729$
17. $64x^6 + 192x^5y + 240x^4y^2 + 160x^3y^3 + 60x^2y^4 + 12xy^5 + y^6$
19. $16x^4 + 32\sqrt{3}x^3 + 72x^2 + 24\sqrt{3}x + 9$ **21.** $4032x^5y^4$
23. $\frac{105}{32}x^4y^6$ **25.** 43,046,721 **27.** 57 **29.** 50%, 25%,
1.56%, $100[1 - (0.5)^d]$% **31.** undefined **33.** 1.5

Pages 699-701   Lesson 12-7

7. $\frac{1}{1} = 1, \frac{2}{1} = 2, \frac{3}{2} = 1.5, \frac{5}{3} = 1.667, \frac{8}{5} = 1.6, \frac{13}{8} = 1.625,$
$\frac{21}{13} = 1.615, \frac{34}{21} = 1.619, \frac{55}{34} = 1.618$; They approach 1.618.
9. 2.99 **11.** 2.58 **13.** $5e^{i\frac{5\pi}{3}}$ **15.** $12e^{i\frac{\pi}{6}}$ **17.** $6e^{i\frac{\pi}{2}}$
19. $i\pi - 4.8036$ **21.** 1.57 **23.** 9.14 **25.** 6.39 **27.** -0.9760; -1
29. $e^{i\frac{\pi}{4}}$ **31.** $4\sqrt{2}e^{i\frac{7\pi}{4}}$ **33.** $6e^{i\frac{\pi}{3}}$ **35.** $i\pi + 1.9459$
37. $i\pi + 1.6544$ **39.** $i\pi - 3.3242$ **43a.** neither **b.** 21, 28, 36,
45, 55 **c.** $\frac{n(n+1)}{2}$ **d.** 1275 **45.** 0° **47.** $285.77 **49.** A

Pages 704-705   Lesson 12-8

5. 3725 **7.** 969 **9.** Step 1: Verify that the formula is valid
for $n = 1$. Since $S_1 = 2$ and $1(1 + 1) = 2$, the formula is valid
for $n = 1$.
Step 2: Assume that the formula is valid for $n = k$ and derive
a formula for $n = k + 1$.
$2 + 4 + 6 + \cdots + 2k + 2(k + 1) = k(k + 1) + 2(k + 1)$
$2 + 4 + 6 + \cdots + 2k + 2(k + 1) = (k + 1)(k + 2)$

Apply the original formula for $n = k + 1$.
$S_{k+1}: (k + 1)[(k + 1) + 1] = (k + 1)(k + 2)$
The formula gives the same result as adding the $(k + 1)$ term
directly. Thus, if the formula is valid for $n = k$, it is also valid
for $n = k + 1$. Since the formula is valid for $n = 1$, it is also
valid for $n = 2$. Since it is valid for $n = 2$, it is also valid for
$n = 3$, and so on, indefinitely. Thus, the formula is valid for
all positive integral values of n.
11. Step 1: Verify that the formula is valid for $n = 1$. Since
$S_1 = \frac{1}{2}$ and $1 - \frac{1}{2^1} = \frac{1}{2}$, the formula is valid for $n = 1$.
Step 2: Assume that the formula is valid for $n = k$ and derive
a formula for $n = k + 1$.
$$\frac{1}{2} + \frac{1}{2^2} + \frac{1}{2^3} + \cdots + \frac{1}{2^k} = 1 - \frac{1}{2^k}$$
$$\frac{1}{2} + \frac{1}{2^2} + \frac{1}{2^3} + \cdots + \frac{1}{2^k} + \frac{1}{2^{k+1}} = 1 - \frac{1}{2^k} + \frac{1}{2^{k+1}}$$
$$= 1 - \frac{2}{2 \cdot 2^k} + \frac{1}{2^{k+1}}$$
$$= 1 - \frac{1}{2^{k+1}}$$
When the original formula is applied for $n = k + 1$, the same
result is obtained. Thus, if the formula is valid for $n = k$, it is
also valid for $n = k + 1$. Since the formula is valid for $n = 1$,
it is also valid for $n = 2$. Since it is valid for $n = 2$, it is also
valid for $n = 3$, and so on, indefinitely. Thus, the formula is
valid for all positive integral values of n.
13. Step 1: Verify that the formula is valid for $n = 1$. Since
$S_1 = 1$ and $\frac{1^2(1 + 1)^2}{4} = 1$, the formula is valid for $n = 1$.
Step 2: Assume that the formula is valid for $n = k$ and derive
a formula for $n = k + 1$.
$$1^3 + 2^3 + 3^3 + \cdots + k^3 = \frac{k^2(k + 1)^2}{4}$$
$$1^3 + 2^3 + 3^3 + \cdots + k^3 + (k + 1)^3 = \frac{k^2(k + 1)^2}{4} + (k + 1)^3$$
$$= \frac{(k + 1)^2(k + 2)^2}{4}$$
When the original formula is applied for $n = k + 1$, the same
result is obtained. Thus, if the formula is valid for $n = k$, it is
also valid for $n = k + 1$. Since the formula is valid for $n = 1$,
it is also valid for $n = 2$. Since it is valid for $n = 2$, it is also
valid for $n = 3$, and so on, indefinitely. Thus, the formula is
valid for all positive integral values of n.
15. Step 1: Verify that the formula is valid for $n = 1$. Since
$S_1 = 1$ and $2^1 - 1 = 1$, the formula is valid for $n = 1$.
Step 2: Assume that the formula is valid for $n = k$ and derive
a formula for $n = k + 1$.
$$1 + 2 + 4 + \cdots + 2^{k-1} = 2^k - 1$$
$$1 + 2 + 4 + \cdots + 2^{k-1} + 2^k = 2^k - 1 + 2^k$$
$$= 2(2^k) - 1 \text{ or } 2^{k+1} - 1$$
When the original formula is applied for $n = k + 1$, the same
result is obtained. Thus, if the formula is valid for $n = k$, it is
also valid for $n = k + 1$. Since the formula is valid for $n = 1$,
it is also valid for $n = 2$. Since it is valid for $n = 2$, it is also
valid for $n = 3$, and so on, indefinitely. Thus, the formula is
valid for all positive integral values of n.
17. Step 1: Verify that the formula is valid for $n = 1$. Since
$S_1 = 1$ and $\frac{6 + 15 + 10 - 1}{30} = 1$, the formula is valid for $n = 1$.
Step 2: Assume that the formula is valid for $n = k$ and derive
a formula for $n = k + 1$.
$$1^4 + 2^4 + 3^4 + \cdots + k^4 = \frac{6k^5 + 15k^4 + 10k^3 - k}{30}$$
$$1^4 + 2^4 + 3^4 + \cdots + k^4 + (k + 1)^4$$
$$= \frac{6k^5 + 15k^4 + 10k^3 - k}{30} + (k + 1)^4$$
$$= \frac{6(k + 1)^5 + 15(k + 1)^4 + 10(k + 1)^3 - (k + 1)}{30}$$

When the original formula is applied for $n = k + 1$, the same result is obtained. Thus, if the formula is valid for $n = k$, it is also valid for $n = k + 1$. Since the formula is valid for $n = 1$, it is also valid for $n = 2$. Since it is valid for $n = 2$, it is also valid for $n = 3$, and so on, indefinitely. Thus, the formula is valid for all positive integral values of n.

19. Step 1: Verify that the formula is valid for $n = 1$. Since $S_1 = \frac{1}{2}$ and $\frac{1}{1+1} = \frac{1}{2}$, the formula is valid for $n = 1$.

Step 2: Assume that the formula is valid for $n = k$ and derive a formula for $n = k + 1$.

$$\frac{1}{1 \cdot 2} + \frac{1}{2 \cdot 3} + \frac{1}{3 \cdot 4} + \cdots + \frac{1}{k(k+1)} = \frac{k}{k+1}$$

$$\frac{1}{1 \cdot 2} + \frac{1}{2 \cdot 3} + \frac{1}{3 \cdot 4} + \cdots + \frac{1}{k(k+1)} + \frac{1}{(k+1)(k+2)}$$

$$= \frac{k}{k+1} + \frac{1}{(k+1)(k+2)}$$

$$= \frac{k+1}{k+2}$$

When the original formula is applied for $n = k + 1$, the same result is obtained. Thus, if the formula is valid for $n = k$, it is also valid for $n = k + 1$. Since the formula is valid for $n = 1$, it is also valid for $n = 2$. Since it is valid for $n = 2$, it is also valid for $n = 3$, and so on, indefinitely. Thus, the formula is valid for all positive integral values of n. **21a.** arithmetic **b.** 156 times **23a.** geometric **b.** 1.718×10^{10} **25.** no solution **27.** $(0, 3)$, $(0, 3 + \sqrt{7})$, $(0, 3 - \sqrt{7})$; $(0, 7)$, $(0, -1)$, $(3, 3)$, $(-3, 3)$ **29.** A

Pages 706-708   Chapter 12 Summary and Review

1. 6.9, 8.2, 9.5, 10.8, 12.1 **5.** 140.8 **7.** $\frac{2}{5}$ **9.** does not exist **11.** divergent **13.** divergent **15.** $\frac{2}{3}$ **17.** $\sum_{k=1}^{9} (k^2 + 1)$ **19.** $16r^4 + 96r^3s + 216r^2s^2 + 216rs^3 + 81s^4$ **21.** $262,440x^3y^7$ **23.** $2\sqrt{2}e^{i\frac{7\pi}{4}}$ **25.** $6e^{i\frac{\pi}{6}}$ **27.** Step 1: Verify that the formula is valid for $n = 1$. Since $S_1 = 1(1 + 2) = 1(3) = 3$ and since $\frac{1(1+1)(2 \cdot 1 + 7)}{6} = \frac{1(2)(2 + 7)}{6} = \frac{1(2)(9)}{6} = \frac{18}{6} = 3$, the formula is valid for $n = 1$.

Step 2: Assume that the formula is valid for $n = k$ and derive a formula for $n = k + 1$.

$$3 + 8 + 15 + \cdots + k(k + 2) = \frac{k(k+1)(2k+7)}{6}$$

$$3 + 8 + 15 + \cdots + k(k + 2) + (k+1)(k+3)$$

$$= \frac{k(k+1)(2k+7)}{6} + (k+1)(k+3)$$

$$= \frac{(k+1)[(k+1)+1][2(k+1)+7]}{6}$$

When the original formula is applied for $n = k + 1$, the same result is obtained. Thus, if the formula is valid for $n = k$, it is also valid for $n = k + 1$. Since the formula is valid for $n = 1$, it is also valid for $n = 2$. Since it is valid for $n = 2$, it is also valid for $n = 3$, and so on, indefinitely. Thus, the formula is valid for all positive integral values of n.

29. 193.75 feet

Page 709   Chapter 12 Test

1. 7.5, 9, 10.5, 12, 13.5 **2.** $\frac{4}{625}$, $\frac{8}{3125}$, $\frac{16}{15,625}$, $\frac{32}{78,125}$ **3.** -4, -1, 2, 5, 8 **4.** Sample answer: 16, 8, 4, 2, 1 **5.** 109 **6.** $\frac{2187}{256}$ **7.** 10 **8.** $2557\frac{1}{2}$ **9.** does not exist **10.** $\frac{1}{2}$ **11.** convergent **12.** divergent **13.** $\sum_{k=1}^{19} 5k$ **14.** $\sum_{k=4}^{\infty} (2k - 1)$ **15.** $8064a^5$ **16.** $5670x^4y^4$ **17.** $2\sqrt{2}e^{i\frac{3\pi}{4}}$ **18.** Step 1: Verify that the formula is valid for $n = 1$. Since

$S_1 = 6$ and $\frac{1(1+1)(4+5)}{3} = 6$, the formula is valid for $n = 1$.

Step 2: Assume the formula is valid for $n = k$ and derive a formula for $n = k + 1$.

$$2 \cdot 3 + 4 \cdot 5 + 6 \cdot 7 + \cdots + 2k(2k+1) = \frac{k(k+1)(4k+5)}{3}$$

$$2 \cdot 3 + 4 \cdot 5 + \cdots + 2k(2k+1) + 2(k+1)(2k+3)$$

$$= \frac{k(k+1)(4k+5)}{3} + 2(k+1)(2k+3)$$

$$= \frac{(k+1)(k+2)(4k+9)}{3}$$

When the original formula is applied for $n = k + 1$, the same result is obtained. Thus, if the formula is valid for $n = k$, it is also valid for $n = k + 1$. Since the formula is valid for $n = 1$, it is also valid for $n = 2$. Since it is valid for $n = 2$, it is also valid for $n = 3$, and so on, indefinitely. Thus, the formula is valid for all positive integral values of n.

19. \$12,080.40 **20.** $\sum_{n=1}^{6} 2^n$; 126 ancestors **BONUS** 0.625

CHAPTER 13   ITERATION AND FRACTALS

Pages 715-716   Lesson 13-1

5. 5, 11, 23 **7.** 0, -1, 0 **9.** -1, -7, 647 **11.** -8, -29, -92, -281, -848, -2549, -7652, -22,961, -68,888, -206,669 **13.** 1, 1, 1 **15.** 2.33, 13.65, 2544.30 **17.** 0.45, 0.69, 0.60, 0.67, 0.62, 0.66, 0.63, 0.65, 0.64, 0.65 **19.** 0.25, 0.53, 0.70, 0.59, 0.68, 0.61, 0.67, 0.62, 0.66, 0.63 **21.** 0.50, 0.78, 0.53, 0.77, 0.55, 0.77, 0.55, 0.77, 0.55, 0.77 **23.** 0.28, 0.62, 0.73, 0.61, 0.74, 0.60, 0.74, 0.60, 0.74, 0.60 **25a.** 2, 1, 2, 1, 2, 1, 2, 1, 2, 1 **b.** $\frac{1}{2}$, 4, $\frac{1}{2}$, 4, $\frac{1}{2}$, 4, $\frac{1}{2}$, 4, $\frac{1}{2}$, 4 **c.** $\frac{2}{a}$, a, $\frac{2}{a}$, a, $\frac{2}{a}$, a, $\frac{2}{a}$, a, $\frac{2}{a}$, a **d.** They repeat in pairs. **e.** yes, $\pm\sqrt{2}$ **29a.** $p_{n+1} = p_n + 1.75p_n(1 - p_n)$ **b.** 458, 525, 479, 514, 489, 508, 494, 505, 496, 503, 498, 501, 499, 501, 499

29c.

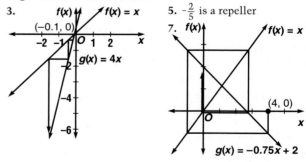

31. $-7 - 24i$ **33.** 0.6, -0.6, -1.2, -1.8 **35.** A

Pages 720-721   Lesson 13-2

3. $f(x)$, $f(x) = x$; $(-0.1, 0)$; $g(x) = 4x$ **5.** $-\frac{2}{5}$ is a repeller **7.** $f(x)$, $f(x) = x$; $(4, 0)$; $g(x) = -0.75x + 2$

9. 4, staircase out **11.** -2, spiral out **13.** -0.75, spiral in **15.** -6, spiral out **19.** $-1 < m < 0$ **21.** $0 < m < 1$ **23.** $\left(-2\frac{2}{3}, -2\frac{2}{3}\right)$; repeller **25.** $(-20, -20)$; attractor **27.** $f(x) = -3x + 2$ and $f(x) = -0.8x - 18$ **33a.** $\left(\frac{12p}{r}, \frac{12p}{r}\right)$;

the interest for a term is equal to the payment, so the principal is never reduced.   **b.** repeller   **35.** $\frac{1}{4}$, $-\frac{4}{3}$ **37.** $26\frac{39}{128}$ **39.** 3%

Pages 726-728   Lesson 13-3
5. (0.5, 0.75)   **7.** (0, 0), (0.5, 0.5); attractor   **9.** (0, 0), $\left(\frac{1}{6}, \frac{1}{6}\right)$; attractor   **11.** fixed point attractor   **13.** (0.5, 0.6)   **15.** (0.5, 1)   **17.** (0, 0), $\left(\frac{3}{8}, \frac{3}{8}\right)$; attractor   **19.** (0, 0), $\left(\frac{11}{16}, \frac{11}{16}\right)$; repeller   **21.** period-2 attractor   **23.** chaos   **25.** period-5 attractor   **27a.** $a \approx 3$ **b.** $a \approx 3.4495$ **c.** $a \approx 3.5441$ **d.** chaos   **29a.** 41, 39, 40, 40, 40, 40, 40, 40, 40, 40   **b.** fixed point attractor   **c.** period-4 attractor   **31.** -6, 2   **33.** $\frac{(x-2)^2}{4} + \frac{(y-5)^2}{25} = 1$; ellipse   **35.** $\left(-\frac{50}{9}, -\frac{50}{9}\right)$; repeller

Page 728   Mid-Chapter Review
1. 37, 182, 907   **3.** -2, 14, 142   **5.** staircase out   **7.** spiral out   **9.** fixed point attractor

Pages 731-733   Lesson 13-4
5. $3 - 4i$, $1.8 - 0.4i$, $1.08 + 1.76i$ **7.** $-4 - 3i$, $7 + 21i$, $-392 + 291i$ **9.** $1 - 3i$, $-8 - 9i$, $-17 + 141i$ **11.** $2 + 5i$, $4 + 11i$, $8 + 23i$ **13.** $6 + i$, $12 + 3i$, $24 + 7i$ **15.** $1 + \frac{1}{2}i$, $2 + 2i$, $4 + 5i$ **17.** $5 + 3i$, $17 + 6i$, $53 + 15i$ **19.** 14, $44 - 3i$, $134 - 12i$ **21.** $3.5 - 6i$, $12.5 - 21i$, $39.5 - 66i$ **23.** $1 + 2i$, $-2 + 6i$, $-31 - 22i$, $478 + 1366i$ **25.** $-1 + i$, $2 - 5i$, $-19 - 23i$, $-166 + 871i$

27.

29.

33. -4   **35.** $3xy^{\frac{1}{4}}z^{\frac{1}{4}}$ **37.** fixed point attractor

Pages 738-739   Lesson 13-5
5. escape set   **7.** Julia set   **9.** Julia set   **11.** escape set   **13.** prisoner set   **15.** escape set   **17.** connected   **19.** connected   **21.** disconnected   **23.** connected   **25.** disconnected   **35.** $\frac{7}{25}$ **37.** $1 - 3i$, $-7 - 9i$, $-31 + 123i$, $-14,167 - 7629i$

Pages 743-745   Lesson 13-6
5a. disconnected   **b.** outside   **c.** orange   **7a.** disconnected   **b.** outside   **c.** light blue   **9a.** disconnected   **b.** outside   **c.** light blue   **11a.** disconnected   **b.** outside   **c.** light blue   **13a.** connected   **b.** inside   **c.** black   **15a.** connected   **b.** inside   **c.** black   **17a.** disconnected   **b.** outside   **c.** light blue   **19a.** disconnected   **b.** outside   **c.** purple   **21a.** disconnected   **b.** outside   **c.** light blue   **23a.** disconnected   **b.** outside   **c.** light blue   **25.** outside the set   **31.** (-3, 2)   **33.** 27   **35.** escape set

Pages 746-748   Chapter 13 Summary and Review
1. -1, 7, -9   **3.** 0.34, 12.81, 3248.37   **5.** $-\frac{1}{2}$ is a repeller   **7.** $\frac{5}{7}$ is a repeller   **9.** (0, 0), (0.630, 0.630); attractor

11. (0, 0), (0.687, 0.687); repeller   **13.** period-2 attractor   **15.** period-4 attractor   **17.** 4, $6 - 2i$, $7 - 3i$ **19.** $2 + i$, $5 - 1.5i$, $6.5 - 2.75i$ **21.** escape   **23.** escape   **25.** disconnected   **27.** disconnected   **29.** orange   **31.** red   **33a.** $b_n = 1.00792b_{n-1} - 714.73$ **b.** $84,958.48, $84,916.63, $84,874.45, $84,831.94

Page 749   Chapter 13 Test
1. 3, 7, 23   **2.** 0.81, 1.42, 0.34   **3.** -1, 6, 223   **4.** (5, 5); repeller   **5.** (-2.5, -2.5); attractor   **6.** (0.133, 0.133); repeller   **7.** $-1 < m < 0$ **8.** (0.5, 0.4); (0, 0), (0.375, 0.375); fixed point attractor   **9.** (0.5, 0.87); (0, 0), (0.713, 0.713); period-4 attractor   **10.** (0.5, 0.97); (0, 0), (0.742, 0.742); chaos   **11.** $3 + 3i$, $9 + 5i$, $21 + 9i$ **12.** $1 + 3i$, $5 + 5i$, $13 + 9i$ **13.** $4 + i$, $11 + i$, $25 + i$ **14.** escape   **15.** prisoner   **16.** escape   **17.** disconnected   **18.** connected   **19.** connected   **20.** outside; 15   **21.** outside; 11   **22.** outside; 7   **23.** outside; 6   **24.** inside the Mandelbrot set   **25.** 137, 96, 136, 97, 136   **BONUS** $3 - 2i$

CHAPTER 14   COMBINATORICS AND PROBABILITY

Pages 755-757   Lesson 14-1
5. independent   **7.** independent   **9.** false   **11.** false   **13.** 12   **15.** 120   **17.** 120   **19.** 39,916,800   **21.** 72   **23.** 8   **25.** 17,576,000   **27.** 14   **29.** 4   **31.** 24   **33.** 72   **35.** 480   **37.** 57,600,000   **39.** 62,500,000   **41.** 42   **43.** 12   **47.** 6,744,109,680   **49.** -4   **51.** $-7 + 24i$ **53.** disconnected; outside

Pages 761-763   Lesson 14-2
7. circular, not reflective, 120   **9.** linear, not reflective, 3,628,800   **11.** linear, not reflective   **13.** circular, not reflective   **15.** 2520   **17.** 90,720   **19.** 6720   **21.** 453,600   **23.** 360   **25.** 2520   **27.** 4200   **29.** 14,440   **31.** 12   **33.** 72   **35.** 72   **37.** 15   **39.** 30% beef, 20% pork; $76   **41.** $c = 9.5$, $A = 38°20'$, $B = 36°22'$ **43.** $\frac{(y+1)^2}{4} - \frac{(x-3)^2}{5} = 1$ **45.** B

Pages 766-767   Lesson 14-3
5. combination   **7.** permutation   **9.** 792   **11.** 168   **13.** 1960   **15.** 267,696   **17.** 3570   **19.** 2940   **21a.** 5148   **b.** 28,561   **23.** 14   **25.** 12   **27.** 126   **29.** 2808   **31.** 2520   **33.** 252   **37.** 233,376   **39.** (5, 4, -11)   **41.** 120

Page 767   Mid-Chapter Review
1. 24   **3.** 24   **5.** 715

Pages 771-773   Lesson 14-4
5. $\frac{1}{1}$ **7.** $\frac{7}{8}$ **9.** $\frac{3}{7}$ **11.** $\frac{4}{13}$ **13.** $\frac{2}{7}$ **15.** $\frac{4}{7}$ **17.** $\frac{1}{3}$ **19.** $\frac{18}{95}$ **21.** $\frac{9}{38}$ **23.** $\frac{11}{25}$ **25.** $\frac{5}{68}$, $\frac{5}{63}$ **27.** $\frac{35}{68}$, $\frac{35}{33}$ **29.** $\frac{99}{16,722,971}$ **31.** $\frac{4719}{9,000,011}$ **35a.** $\frac{46}{125}$ **b.** $\frac{11}{100}$ **c.** $\frac{9}{92}$ **37.** $-\frac{33}{65}$ **39.** 126

Pages 776-778   Lesson 14-5
5. independent, $\frac{25}{81}$ **7.** dependent, $\frac{8}{195}$ **9.** independent, $\frac{3}{10}$ **11.** $\frac{25}{441}$ **13.** $\frac{1}{8}$ **15.** $\frac{5}{48}$ **17.** $\frac{25}{36}$ **19.** $\frac{5}{6}$ **21a.** $\frac{1}{24}$

b. $\frac{35}{1024}$ **23.** $\frac{69,343,957}{2,373,046,875} \approx 0.029$ **25.** $\frac{1}{29,170,800}$

27. $\frac{4}{635,013,559,600}$ **29.** 0   **33.** $\frac{435,643}{560,175}$ **35.** origin

37. $\sum\limits_{k=1}^{\infty} 3^k$ **39.** B

Pages 781-783   Lesson 14-6

5a. exclusive, $\frac{1}{4}$ **b.** inclusive, $\frac{11}{36}$ **7.** inclusive, $\frac{4}{5}$

9. inclusive, $\frac{20}{27}$ **11.** $\frac{2}{3}$ **13.** $\frac{2}{11}$ **15.** $\frac{14}{33}$ **17.** $\frac{12}{221}$

19. $\frac{188}{663}$ **21.** $\frac{35}{64}$ **23.** $\frac{21}{64}$ **25.** $\frac{2}{429}$ **27.** $\frac{175}{429}$ **29.** $\frac{1}{525}$

31. $\frac{3}{35}$ **35.** $\frac{9979}{10,000}$ **37.** $\frac{(y-1)^2}{36} + \frac{(x-3)^2}{36} = 1$ **39.** $\frac{253}{4606}$

Pages 787-789   Lesson 14-7

5. Event A: one coin shows tails; Event B: at least one coin shows heads; $\frac{2}{3}$ **7.** $\frac{1}{2}$ **9.** $\frac{3}{13}$ **11.** $\frac{1}{26}$ **13.** Event A: the girls are separated; Event B: a girl is on an end; $\frac{3}{5}$

15. 0   **17.** $\frac{1}{10}$ **19.** $\frac{7}{10}$ **21.** $\frac{1}{4}$ **23.** $\frac{1}{7}$ **25.** $\frac{2}{5}$

27. $\frac{3}{10}$ **29.** $\frac{1}{8}$ **31.** $\frac{1}{6}$ **33.** $\frac{19}{51}$ **37.** Let event A be that a person buys something. Let event B be that a person asks questions.

$P(A/B) = \dfrac{P(A \text{ and } B)}{P(B)}$ Four out of five customers who ask questions will make a purchase. Therefore, they are more likely to buy something if they ask questions.

$= \dfrac{\frac{48}{200}}{\frac{60}{200}}$ or $\frac{4}{5}$

39a. $\frac{69}{70}$ **b.** $\frac{2}{25}$ **c.** $\frac{1}{25}$ **41.** $x^4 + 2x^3 + 4x^2 + 5x + 10$ **43.** 2, 5, 26   **45.** C

Pages 792-794   Lesson 14-8

3. binomial, $\frac{3}{8}$ **5a.** binomial, $\frac{16}{81}$ **b.** binomial, $\frac{4}{81}$

c. binomial, $\frac{1}{9}$ **d.** not binomial   **e.** not binomial   **f.** not binomial   **7.** $\frac{3}{8}$ **9.** $\frac{3125}{7776}$ **11.** $\frac{625}{648}$ **13.** $\frac{1}{81}$ **15.** $\frac{65}{81}$

17. $\frac{15}{128}$ **19.** $\frac{193}{512}$ **21.** $\frac{256}{625}$ **23.** $\frac{21}{3125}$ **25.** $\frac{1}{8}$ **27.** $\frac{3}{8}$

29. $\frac{419,904}{1,953,125}$ **31.** $\frac{1,623,424}{9,765,625}$ **33.** $\frac{768}{3125}$ **35.** 0.1372

37. 7   **39.** $\frac{1}{2}$

Pages 796-798   Chapter 14 Summary and Review

1. 120   **3.** $-\frac{9}{5}$ **5.** 30   **7.** 20,160   **9.** 10   **11.** 3   **13.** $\frac{4}{5}$

15. $\frac{343}{4096}$ **17.** $\frac{5}{36}$ **19.** $\frac{9}{14}$ **21.** $\frac{1}{2}$ **23.** $\frac{1}{4}$ **25.** $\frac{3}{8}$

27. 360 ways   **29a.** $\frac{7}{15}$ **b.** $\frac{1}{30}$

Page 799   Chapter 14 Test

1. 30   **2.** 2520   **3.** 56   **4.** 5   **5.** 120 patterns   **6.** 60 ways
7. 720 ways   **8.** 1485 teams   **9.** 120 ways   **10.** 170 diagonals
11. $\frac{4}{3}$ **12.** $\frac{33}{16,660}$ **13.** $\frac{5}{432}$ **14.** $\frac{1}{8}$ **15.** $\frac{1}{20}$ **16.** $\frac{7}{13}$
17. $\frac{5}{18}$ **18.** $\frac{3}{13}$ **19.** $\frac{17}{81}$ **20.** $\frac{1792}{15,625}$ **BONUS** 0.075

CHAPTER 15   STATISTICS AND DATA ANALYSIS

Pages 806-810   Lesson 15-1
5. HBO, Cinemax, and Showtime have shown an increase in the number of subscribers. TMC has shown a decrease in the number of subscribers.   **7.** $0; $26,000; $32,000; $38,000; $44,000; $50,000   **9.** 26%

11.

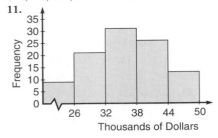

13. interval: 0.1, limits: 1.05, 1.15, 1.25, 1.35, 1.45, 1.55, 1.65, 1.75   **15.** interval: 1, limits: 24.5, 25.5, 26.5, 27.5, 28.5, 29.5, 30.5, 31.5, 32.5   **17.** Women make less money than men for the same education.

19.

21.

Population Change (in millions)

27.

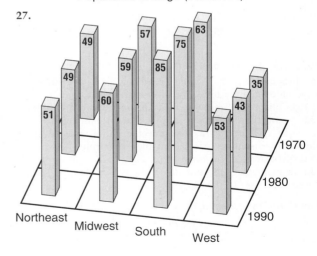

35a.

Class Limits	Class Marks	Tally	Frequency
0–10	5	JHT JHT JHT JHT JHT JHT III	33
10–20	15	JHT JHT III	13
20–30	25	I	1
30–40	35		0
40–50	45	II	2

35b.

c. Because it differs greatly from the other data. If it was included, it would skew the intervals and the representation of the majority of the distribution. **37.** none **39.** 125, 150, 180, 216 **41.** A

Pages 816-819 Lesson 15-2

5.
```
1 | 0 5 5 5 5 7 7
2 | 0 0 0 5 5 5 5 7 8
3 | 0 0 5 5 5
4 | 6
5 | 5      1|0 means 10.
```
7. 30.75, 27.5, 10
9. 8.5, 8.5, 6 and 11

11a.
```
2 | 4 6 6 9
3 | 1 6 6 7 8 8
4 | 1 2 3
2|4 means 2.4 million.
```
b. 3,438,500; 3,600,000; 2,600,000, 3,600,000, and 3,800,000

c. These are the years when the most babies were born. This large population is now adults in their 30s and 40s. They are an active group in commerce, politics, and other fields.
13a. about 5'9$\frac{1}{2}$" **13b.** Answers will vary. The mean may not be representative because the mean is greater than the median (5'7") and the mode (5'4"). **15a.** 19.3 **b.** 17–21 **c.** 20.1 **17.** 3 **21.** 34 cm from the end **23a.** 424.4

b.
26.6	
69.9	
139.2	
228.2	
327.0	
410.1	
465.2	
500.0	
520.5	
530.4	
534.4	
535.0	

c. 400–450
d. 419.9
e. Lower; means differ because published average has access to each item of data whereas frequency distributions do not.
25. $\frac{1 + 4i\sqrt{3}}{7}$

27. Iteration is the process of repeated evaluation of a function using the result of the previous evaluation. Example: Let $f(x) = x^2$. Let $x_1 = 2$. Results: 4, 16, 256, . . .

29.

Pages 825-829 Lesson 15-3

5. 205 **7.** 25% **9.** 50% **11.** 50% **13a.** 9.15 **b.** 5.95, 2.35, 1.35, -0.15, -0.35, -0.65, -0.65, -1.55, -2.95, -3.35 **c.** 1.93 **d.** 10.5, 8.65, 7.6 **e.** 2.9 **f.** 1.45 **g.** 66.065 **h.** about 2.57 **j.** 15.1 **15a.** mean: 11.7, median: 11.9, SD: 1.83 **b.** mean: 12.23, median: 11.9, SD: 0.47 **c.** (1) similar (2) very different (3) Group 3 **17a.** range: 44, mean: 12.21, MD: 8.95, IQ range: 10.5, SD: 12.2 **b.** range: 35, mean: 10.8, MD: 7.3, IQ range: 5.5, SD: 9.74 **c.** gold **19.** when both have a value of 1 **21.** 424.24 miles **23.** 3

Pages 835-837 Lesson 15-4

5.

7. 137 **9.** 68 **11.** 68.3%
13. 20.1–27.9 **15.** 68.3%
17. 86.6% **19.** 15.85%
21. 107–173 **23.** 68.3%
25. 97.5% **27.** 6800
29. 5000 **31.** 15 **35.** A: 6.7%, B: 24.15%, C: 38.3%, D: 24.15%, F: 6.7%

37.
$$\sin^2 \Phi \cot^2 \Phi \overset{?}{=} (1 - \sin \Phi)(1 + \sin \Phi)$$
$$\sin^2 \Phi \left(\frac{\cos \Phi}{\sin \Phi}\right)^2 \overset{?}{=} (1 - \sin \Phi)(1 + \sin \Phi)$$
$$\cos^2 \Phi \overset{?}{=} (1 - \sin \Phi)(1 + \sin \Phi)$$
$$1 - \sin^2 \Phi \overset{?}{=} (1 - \sin \Phi)(1 + \sin \Phi)$$
$$(1 - \sin \Phi)(1 + \sin \Phi) = (1 - \sin \Phi)(1 + \sin \Phi)$$

39. $\frac{1}{2}$ **41.** A

Page 837 Mid-Chapter Review

1.
Class Limits	Class Marks	Tally	Frequency
100–105	102.5	III	3
105–110	107.5	JHT III	8
110–115	112.5	JHT JHT JHT II	17
115–120	117.5	JHT JHT III	13
120–125	122.5	JHT II	7
125–130	127.5	I	1
130–135	132.5	I	1

3.
```
10 | 0 0 4 5 5 5 6 7 8 9 9
11 | 0 0 0 0 1 1 2 2 2 2 3 3 4 4 4
 · | 4 4 5 6 6 7 7 7 8 8 8 8 8 8 9
12 | 0 0 0 0 1 1 2 7
13 | 4
10|9 means 109.
```
5a. 118, 110 **b.** 34
5c.

7. 107–120

Pages 841-843 Lesson 15-5

5. 5, 187.1–212.9, 190.2–209.8 **7a.** 0.14 **b.** 4.239–4.961 **c.** 4.506–4.694 **d.** 4.369–4.831 **9.** 0.85, 77.81–82.19, 78.33–81.67 **11a.** 3.4 **b.** 0.425 **c.** 11.547–13.213

d. 0.982 **13.** 4.5% **15a.** 0.548 **b.** 0.9415 **17.** 0.1585
19. 11°28' **21.** 0.1585

Pages 851-854 Lesson 15-6
3. positive **5.** positive **7.** negative **9a.** 7 **b.** 65 million
c. $s = 7p + 65,000,000$ **d.** $86 million

11.

13a.

13b. $c = 9t - 59$ **c.** 0.9844291973 **d.** There is a strongly
positive correlation between the temperature and the chirps
per minute.
15b. strongly negative **c.** $-0.9\overline{63}$
d. Judges 1 and 2 seem very
close in the scoring while
judge 3 is not in synch with
their opinions.

15a.

Judge 3 / Judge 2

23a.
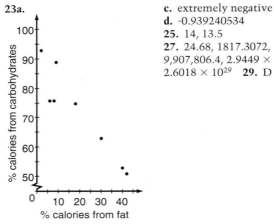
% calories from carbohydrates / % calories from fat

c. extremely negative
d. -0.939240534
25. 14, 13.5
27. 24.68, 1817.3072,
9,907,806.4, 2.9449×10^{14},
2.6018×10^{29} **29.** D

Pages 860-862 Chapter 15 Summary and Review
1. 0.5, 1.5, 2.5, 3.5, 4.5
3.
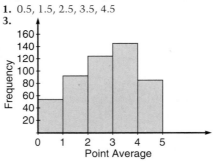
Frequency / Point Average

5. 14.8, 15, none **7.** 133.25, 132, none **9.** 1.74 **11.** 95.5%

13. 79.75–96.25 **15.** 1.742–1.858
17.
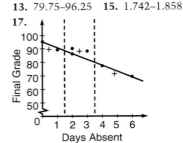
Final Grade / Days Absent

21a.
```
1 | 0 3 5 6 7 9
2 | 1 3 4 5
3 | 9 9
1|0 means 10.
```
b. 20; 39; 21.75

23a.

Reading (h/wk) / Watching TV (h/wk)

b. -0.72 **c.** moderately negative

Page 863 Chapter 15 Test

1.

Class Limits	Class Marks	Tally	Frequency
0–3	1.5	|||	3
3–6	4.5	ⅢH		6
6–9	7.5	ⅢH ⅢH ⅢH		16
9–12	10.5	ⅢH ⅢH ⅢH ⅢH ⅢH	25
12–15	13.5	ⅢH ⅢH ⅢH ||	17
15–18	16.5	ⅢH |||	8
18–21	19.5	ⅢH	5

2.
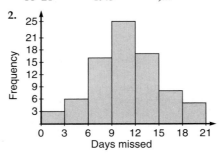
Frequency / Days missed

3. 10.438 **4.** 10 **5.** 4.210 **6.** 2.344 **7.** 2.344 **8.** 2.344
9. 0.003
10.

2.338 2.340 2.342 2.344 2.346 2.348 2.350

11. 0.0025 **12.** 0.0031 **13.** 3.47–17.33 **14.** 0.381

15. 0.4707   **16.** 9.515–11.361
17.

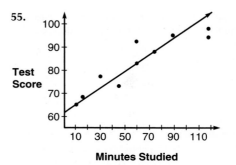

18. Let x = statistics grades and let
y = economics grades;
$y = 0.59x + 32.06$.
19. 0.724   **20.** moderately positive   **BONUS**   The formula
is the radicand of the standard deviation formula, or it is the
square of the standard deviation. variance = 0.00000961

CHAPTER 16   GRAPH THEORY

Pages 870-871   Lesson 16-1
5. t, u, and v **7.** B, C, E, and F **9.** $1: z$
11. $V = \{A, B, C, D, E, F\}$ **13.**

17.

21.

25.

29.

33. 21   **35.** $\dfrac{n(n-1)}{2}$
37. no   **39.** yes   **41.** no

43. Yes; vertices are connected by edges in pairs. Sample graph:

45. 11 vertices   **49.**

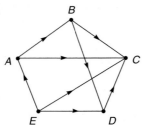

51. 2   **53.** 75.5 N, 14°50'

55.

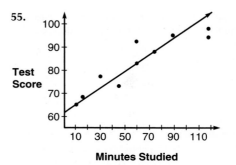

Minutes Studied

Pages 874-876   Lesson 16-2
5. trail, 7   **7.** Multigraph; it has parallel edges.   **9.** no
11. cycle   **13.** path   **15.** an infinite number   **19b.** d; 1; b,
c; 2   **19c.** d; b, c; d **21b.** a; 1; b; 1; c; 1; d; 1   **21c.** a; b; c
23. 21   **25.** 7   **27.** 3 cars   **29.** (0, 16), maximum; (±2, 0),
minima; $\left(\pm\dfrac{2\sqrt{3}}{3}, \dfrac{64}{9}\right)$, pts of inflection   **31.** 20   **33.** E

Pages 880-882   Lesson 16-3
5. C   **11.** yes   **13.** yes   **15.** yes   **17.** 11, 12, 14, 16
19. 12   **21.** Yes; each vertex has even degree.   **27.** No; one,
between New Jersey and Brooklyn   **29.** 1

Page 882   Mid-Chapter Review
1. yes   **3.** 4   **5.** B, C, and E **7.** no

Pages 887-889   Lesson 16-4
5. 3   **7.** C, D, F, G or C, D, I, G **9.** 6   **11.** because the
path P, B, A is shorter   **13.** C **15.** 5; one path is A, G, K,
M, I, Z.   **17.** 4; one path is A, C, Y, D, Z.   **19.** 7; one path is
A, B, I, L, N, Q, F, Z **21.** 7; A, G, K, Z **23.** 5; A, B, C, Z
25. 3; A, E, Z
27a.

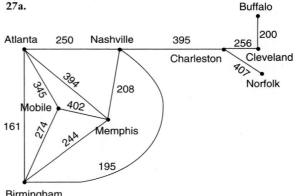

b. Buffalo, Cleveland, Charleston, Nashville, Atlanta
c. Mobile, Birmingham, Nashville; 469 miles
29.

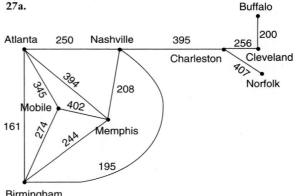

31. Since $S_1 = 2$ and $2^{1+1} - 2 = 2$, the formula is valid for $n = 1$. Assume the formula is valid for $n = k$ and derive a formula for $n = k + 1$.

$$2 + 2^2 + 2^3 + \cdots + 2^k = 2^{k+1} - 2$$
$$2 + 2^2 + 2^3 + \cdots + 2^k + 2^{k+1} = 2^{k+1} - 2 + 2^{k+1}$$
$$= 2(2^{k+1}) - 2$$
$$= 2^{k+2} - 2$$

33. D

Pages 893-895 Lesson 16-5

7. 17 edges **9.** 6 edges **13.** No; contains a cycle. **15.** yes
17. {Z, I}, {I, F}, {F, A}, {A, B}, {B, D}, {D, H}, {D, C}, {D, E}, {G, H}
19. {B, A}, {A, E}, {E, F}, {F, D}, {D, C}, {C, Z}; 7 **21.** {H, G}, {G, A}, {A, B}, {B, E}, {E, C}, {C, D}, {D, Z}, {D, K}; 15
27. $\sqrt{46}$; 6.78 **29.** A, B, C, D; 8

Pages 901-903 Lesson 16-6

5.

	A	B	C	D
A	0	1	1	1
B	1	0	1	1
C	1	1	0	1
D	1	1	1	0

7.

	Q	R	S	T	U	V
Q	0	1	1	1	1	1
R	1	0	1	0	0	0
S	1	1	0	1	0	0
T	1	0	1	0	1	0
U	1	0	0	1	0	1
V	1	0	0	0	1	0

9.

11.
Lions Tigers Rams Bulls

13.

	A	B	C	D
A	0	1	0	1
B	1	0	1	1
C	0	1	0	1
D	1	1	1	0

15.

	X	Y	Z
X	0	2	0
Y	2	0	2
Z	0	2	0

17.

	Q	R	S	T	U	V	W	X	Y
Q	0	0	0	0	0	0	0	1	1
R	0	0	1	0	0	0	0	0	0
S	0	0	0	0	0	0	0	1	0
T	0	0	0	0	0	0	0	1	0
U	0	0	0	1	0	0	0	0	0
V	0	0	0	0	0	0	0	0	0
W	0	0	0	0	0	1	0	0	0
X	0	1	0	0	1	1	1	0	1
Y	0	0	0	0	0	0	0	0	0

19.

23.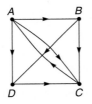

25. The paths $B \to R \to U \to W \to X \to E$ and $B \to S \to V \to E$ are both critical. The minimum amount of time needed is 6 weeks.

29a.

	A	C	D	H	M	S
A	0	1	0	0	0	1
C	0	0	1	0	1	0
D	0	0	0	1	1	0
H	1	0	0	0	0	1
M	0	0	0	0	0	1
S	0	0	1	0	1	0

b. 3 **c.** yes; 2 flights

31. 0.042

Pages 904-906 Chapter 16 Summary and Review

1. no **3.** {A, B}, {A, C}, {A, E} **5.** yes **7.** trail **9.** circuit
11. Add a temporary edge parallel to v.

13.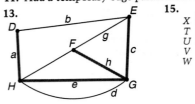

15.

	X	T	U	V	W
X	0	1	1	0	0
T	0	0	0	0	0
U	0	1	0	0	0
V	1	0	1	0	0
W	1	0	0	1	0

19. Critical path is $B \to H \to L \to E$; 35 days.

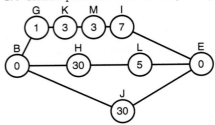

Page 907 Chapter 16 Test

1. simple graph; no loops or parallel edges **2.** 5 **3.** m, y, w, n, z, v **4.** no **5.** B, C, D **6.** yes **7.** circuit
8. Euler path; o, p, q, r, s, t, k, n, z, u, v, w, x, y, m, l
9. y, n, o, p **10.** {A, C}, {C, D}, {D, B}, {D, I}, {I, F}, {F, E}, {I, G}, {I, J}, {J, K}, {I, H}

11.

	A	B	C	D	E	F	G	H	I	J	K
A	0	1	1	1	0	0	0	0	0	0	0
B	1	0	0	1	0	0	0	0	0	0	0
C	1	0	0	1	0	0	0	0	0	0	0
D	1	1	1	0	1	1	0	0	1	0	0
E	0	0	0	1	0	1	0	0	0	0	0
F	0	0	0	1	1	0	1	0	1	0	0
G	0	0	0	0	0	1	0	0	1	0	0
H	0	0	0	0	0	0	0	0	1	0	1
I	0	0	0	1	0	1	1	1	0	1	0
J	0	0	0	0	0	0	0	0	1	0	1
K	0	0	0	0	0	0	0	1	0	1	0

12. A multigraph may contain loops and/or parallel edges; a graph may not.

13.

14. Sample answer:

15. 5 **16.** true **17.** A path may include any number of edges; an Euler path must include all of the edges. **18.** at the vertices of odd degree **19.** 3 cars **20.** $39,000; Sarasota, Lakeland; Lakeland, Jacksonville; Lakeland, Daytona Beach; Daytona Beach, St. Augustine; St. Augustine, Bunnell
BONUS 8

Pages 908-909 Unit 4 Review

1. -35 **3.** $\frac{4}{3}$ **5.** divergent **7.** convergent **9.** $\frac{889}{64}$
11. $59{,}136x^6y^6$ **13.** -1, -4, 11 **15.** (2, 2); attractor
17. $6 + i$, $12 + 5i$, $24 + 13i$ **19.** escape set **21.** 60 ways

23. $\frac{2}{5}$ **25.** $\frac{11}{850}$ **27.** $\frac{5}{18}$ **29.** 42, 65, 65, 66, 69, 70, 72, 76, 77, 77, 77, 80, 82, 82, 86, 89, 89, 91, 95, 99 **31.** 77.45 **33.** 77 **35.** 9 **37.** about 0.595
39.

41. no **43.** {A, D}, {A, C}, {A, B} **45.** cycle **47.** No; the degrees of vertices A and C are not even.

CHAPTER 17 LIMITS, DERIVATIVES, AND INTEGRALS

Pages 920-922 Lesson 17-1

7. 12 **9.** $-\frac{1}{3}$ **11.** $-\frac{1}{4}$ **13.** 5 **15.** $\frac{1}{2}$ **17.** -3 **19.** $\frac{3}{5}$
21. 1 **23.** $\frac{2}{3}$ **25.** 8 **27.** 0 **29.** $\frac{1}{3}$ **31.** 8 **33.** $\frac{3}{4}$ **35.** 0
37. $\sqrt{3}$ **39.** 75 **41.** 4 **43.** $\frac{1}{2}$ **45.** 6 **47.** $-\frac{1}{4}$ **49.** 1
51. 30,000 **53.** $f'(x) = 8x - 8$ **55.** $\frac{41\sqrt{10}}{20} \approx 6.48$
57. 20.68 **59.** 7.9, 8.6, 8.6 **61.** C

Pages 928-930 Lesson 17-2

7. 7 **9.** $4x$ **11.** $12x$ **13.** $18x^2 - 26x - 5$
15. $\frac{-2x(2x^2 - 1)}{(x^2 + 1)^4}$ **17.** $-\frac{14}{\sqrt{(4x - 1)^2}}$ **19.** $-3 + \frac{6}{(x + 2)^2}$
21. 6 **23.** $10x - 1$ **25.** $5x^4$ **27.** $\frac{1}{3\sqrt[3]{x^2}}$ **29.** $15x^4 - 18x^2$
31. $6x(x^2 + 4)^2$ **33.** $\frac{x}{\sqrt{x^2 - 1}}$ **35.** $\frac{-x}{\sqrt{(x^2 - 4)^3}}$ **37.** $\frac{-4(x + 1)}{(x - 1)^3}$
39. $6x^2 - \frac{6}{x^4}$ **41.** $-\frac{1}{x^2} + \frac{2}{x^3}$ **45a.** $h'(t) = 96 - 32t$ **b.** 32 ft/s **c.** decreasing **d.** -160 ft/s **49.** $\pm 1, \pm 2, \pm\frac{1}{2}, \pm\frac{1}{4}, \pm\frac{1}{8}$ **53.** $-\frac{1}{27}$
55. 0

Pages 935-937 Lesson 17-3

3. $A = \lim\limits_{n\to\infty}\sum\limits_{i=1}^{n} \left(\frac{i}{n}\right)^2\left(\frac{1}{n}\right); \frac{1}{3}$ **5.** $A = \lim\limits_{n\to\infty}\sum\limits_{i=1}^{n} \left(\frac{i}{n}\right)\left(\frac{1}{n}\right); \frac{1}{2}$
7. $A = \lim\limits_{n\to\infty}\sum\limits_{i=1}^{n} \left(\frac{5i}{n}\right)\left(\frac{5}{n}\right) - \lim\limits_{n\to\infty}\sum\limits_{i=1}^{n} \left(\frac{2i}{n}\right)\left(\frac{2}{n}\right); 10\frac{1}{2}$
9. $A = \lim\limits_{n\to\infty}\sum\limits_{i=1}^{n} \left(\frac{2i}{n}\right)^2\left(\frac{2}{n}\right); \frac{8}{3}$ **11.** $A = \lim\limits_{n\to\infty}\sum\limits_{i=1}^{n} \left(\frac{i}{n}\right)^5\left(\frac{1}{n}\right); \frac{1}{6}$
13. $A = \lim\limits_{n\to\infty}\sum\limits_{i=1}^{n} \left(\frac{7i}{n}\right)^4\left(\frac{7}{n}\right) - \lim\limits_{n\to\infty}\sum\limits_{i=1}^{n} \left(\frac{4i}{n}\right)^4\left(\frac{4}{n}\right); \frac{15783}{5}$
15. $A = \lim\limits_{n\to\infty}\sum\limits_{i=1}^{n} \left(\frac{ai}{n}\right)^2\left(\frac{a}{n}\right) - \lim\limits_{n\to\infty}\sum\limits_{i=1}^{n} \left(\frac{bi}{n}\right)^2\left(\frac{b}{n}\right); \frac{b^3 - a^3}{3}$
17. $A = \lim\limits_{n\to\infty}\sum\limits_{i=1}^{n} \left(\frac{2i}{n}\right)\left(\frac{2}{n}\right) + \lim\limits_{n\to\infty}\sum\limits_{i=1}^{n} \left(\frac{4i}{n}\right)\left(\frac{4}{n}\right); 10$ **19.** $\frac{1}{4}$
21. $\frac{b^3 - a^3}{3}$ **25.** 36 feet **27.** $y^2 + 3x + 7y = 0$ **29.** $-\frac{1}{x^2} + \frac{2}{x^3}$

Page 937 Mid-Chapter Review

1. 6 **3.** -6 **5.** 1 **7.** 0 **9.** 1 **11.** $2x - 2$ **13.** $\frac{36}{x^{10}}$
15. $\frac{1}{x^2\sqrt{x^2 - 1}}$

Pages 942-944 Lesson 17-4

3. $5x + C$ **5.** $x^3 + C$ **7.** $x^5 + x^2 + C$ **9.** $10x + C$
11. $x^3 - 2x^4 + x^5 + C$ **13.** $\frac{5}{4}x^4 + C$ **15.** $\frac{(x + 5)^{21}}{21} + C$
17. $-x^2 + 3x + C$ **19.** $\ln|x - 1| + C$ **21.** $\frac{8}{5}x^5 + C$
23. $\frac{x^6}{6} + \frac{1}{3x^3} + C$ **25.** $4\sqrt{x} + C$
29. $r(x) = 4x - 0.01x^2 - 300$ **31.** 14 gallons **33.** $2x$
35. 15 **37.** A

Pages 948-951 Lesson 17-5

5. 12 sq units **7.** $2\frac{1}{3}$ sq units **9.** 4 sq units **11.** 5 **13.** $\frac{9}{2}$
15. $\frac{16}{3}$ sq units **17.** $16\frac{1}{2}$ sq units **19.** $1\frac{1}{3}$ sq units
21. $4\frac{1}{3}$ sq units **23.** $2\frac{2}{3}$ **25.** $22\frac{1}{2}$ **27.** $40\frac{1}{3}$ **29.** $\frac{2}{3}$
31. $-20\frac{5}{6}$ **33.** $4\frac{1}{4}$ sq units **35.** 64 sq units **37.** about 20.8 sq units **39a.** 322,994 **b.** 211,961 **41.** 781,250,000π or 2,454,369,261 foot-pounds
43. $2x^4 - 11x^3 - 19x^2 + 84x - 36 = 0$
45. equation: $\frac{(x - 4)^2}{2} - \frac{(y - 2)^2}{4} = 1$; center: (4, 2); foci: $(4 \pm \sqrt{6}, 2)$; vertices: $(4 \pm \sqrt{2}, 2)$; asymptotes: $y = 2 \pm \sqrt{2}(x - 4)$

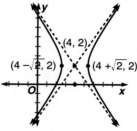

47. 31.7% **49.** C

Pages 952-954 Chapter 17 Summary and Review

1. 2 **3.** $\frac{2}{3}$ **5.** -1 **7.** 1 **9.** $6x^5$ **11.** $3 + 8x$
13. $\frac{3x^2 - 3}{\sqrt{2x^3 - 6x}}$ **15.** 4 unit² **17.** $\frac{37}{3}$ unit² **19.** $-\frac{4}{x} + C$
21. $x - \frac{x^2}{2} + C$ **23.** $\frac{(x + 3)^{10}}{2} + C$ **25.** 36 **27.** 36
29. 0.0000125 **31a.** 10.48 ft/s² **b.** $v(t) = 10.48t + C_1$ **c.** $d(t) = 5.24t^2 + C_1 t + C_2$

Pages 955 Chapter 17 Test

1. $\frac{2}{9}$ **2.** -1 **3.** 1 **4.** 18 **5.** $-\frac{2}{3}$ **6.** $\frac{1}{3}$ **7.** 27
8. $12x^2$ **9.** $2(x + 3)$ **10.** $24x^3$ **11.** $14x^6 + 36x^5$
12. $\frac{2 - 2x^2}{1 + 2x^2 + x^4}$ **13.** $\frac{4x}{\sqrt{4x^2 - 1}}$ **14.** $\lim\limits_{n\to\infty}\sum\limits_{i=1}^{n} \left(\frac{2i}{n}\right)^3\left(\frac{2}{n}\right); 4$ unit²
15. $\lim\limits_{n\to\infty}\sum\limits_{i=1}^{n} 3\left(\frac{3i}{n}\right)^2\left(\frac{3}{n}\right) - \lim\limits_{n\to\infty}\sum\limits_{i=1}^{n} 3\left(\frac{i}{n}\right)^2\left(\frac{1}{n}\right); 26$ unit²
16. $x - x^2 + C$ **17.** $x^3 + 2x^2 + 7x + C$ **18.** $-\frac{1}{x} + C$
19. $\frac{3}{5}\sqrt[3]{x^5} + C$ **20.** $-\frac{1}{4x^2} + C$ **21.** 4 **22.** $-\frac{20}{3}$ **23.** $22\frac{1}{2}$
24. $T'(\ell) = \frac{\pi}{\sqrt{32\ell}}$ **25.** $\frac{32\pi}{3}$ **BONUS** 1

INDEX

Index

Index

Index

Index

894–895, 903, 921–922, 929–930,
936–937, 943–944, 950–951
Projectiles, 449–454
Proofs
by mathematical induction, 702–705
Pure imaginary number, 495
Pythagorean identities, 359–362
Pythagorean Theorem, 256, 283–286,
416, 468, 525, 581

Q

Quadratic equations
applications, 187, 188, 190, 193
parabolas, 534–541
solutions, 185–186
Quadratic formula, 188–189, 191–193,
230, 496, 574
Quadratic functions
graphing, 185–186
Quadratic inequalities, 191–192, 194
Quadratic systems
solving, 577–578
Quotient identities, 359–362

R

Radian conversion formula, 242
Radians, 241–245
Radical equations, 225–229
applications, 225, 229
solving, 223–224
Radical functions
graphing, 125
Radical inequalities, 227–229
applications, 228, 229
Radicals
simplifying, 601–603
Range, 6, 13, 14, 18, 27, 107, 305, 329,
449–454
of arccosine, 340
class interval, 803–804
interquartile, 821–822, 826
semi-interquartile, 821, 826
Rational equations, 216–222
application, 216, 217, 222
Rational exponents, 598–604
applications, 598–599, 603
definition of, 600
Rational functions, 134–142, 916
applications, 134, 137, 141–142
discontinuous, 132–133
graphing, 132–133
Rational inequalities, 218
Rational Root Theorem, 201–207
application, 201, 202, 205, 206–207
Real numbers, 496
iterations of, 712–716
Reciprocal identities, 358–362
Rectangles

area of, 931–933
sum of areas, 931–933
Rectangular coordinates, 483–487
applications, 483
converting to polar coordinates,
484–487
Rectangular form
of complex numbers, 501–504
Recursive formula, 657, 712
Reduced sample space, 785–786
Reference angle rule, 243–244
Reflections, 118, 121–123
Regression methods, 847–848
Relations, 2, 6–7, 11, 27
arcsine, 329–332
inverse, 126–131
programming, 26
Relative maxima, 157–160, 214
Relative minima, 157–160, 214
Relative position of the origin, 401–403
Remainder Theorem, 195–198, 200
applications, 195, 200
Repeller, 718–720
fixed point, 729
Resultant of vectors, 413, 416
Revenue equation, 56
Riemann sums, 938
Right triangles, 269–274
applications of, 269, 271–272,
274–275
solving, 269–274
trigonometric functions, 269–275
Roots
complex, 180, 182, 203
complex conjugates theorem, 190
of complex numbers, 512–516
integral root theorem, 203
nature of, 189–193
of polynomial equation, 201–206
of polynomial functions, 179–183
rational, 201–206
real, 182
zeros, 203–206
Rotation matrices, 571–573

S

Sample sets of data
applications, 838, 840, 843
Sample space, 785–786
Scalar multiplication
of vectors, 420–423
Scatter plots, 844–852
analyzing, 846–852
applications, 846, 853–854
bivariate data, 847
Scientific notation, 598
Secant, 258–260, 264, 267, 269–270
Secant line, 149–150
Second-degree equations, 546,
562–566, 579–581
discriminant, 573

Second-degree systems
applications, 579, 581, 584
Second-order determinants, 71–72
inverses, 73–75
Segment, 291
Self-similarity, 736
Semi-interquartile range, 821, 826
Semi-major axes, 543, 546, 549
Semi-minor axes, 543, 546, 549
Series
arithmetic, 658–661
comparison test, 682–683
convergent, 679–683, 697
divergent, 679–683
exponential, 697–698, 700
geometric, 665–668
infinite, 674–677
for reference, 682–683
in sigma notation, 686–690
trigonometric, 697–701
Sequences
arithmetic, 656–661
defer, 729
Fibonacci, 696
geometric, 663–665, 667–668
infinite, 671–677
iteration, 713
limits of, 672–674
nth terms, 656–661, 671–674
of successive iterates, 731
Sets
escape, 734–739
Julia, 736–739
Mandelbrot, 740–744
prisoner, 734–739
Sigma notation, 685–690
applications, 685, 690
Simple graphs, 866–869
Simple harmonic motion, 345–349
application, 345–346, 349–350
Simple interest, 11
Sine, 255–261, 264–267, 269–271,
273–275, 276–281, 282, 284–286,
388–391, 421
amplitude of, 310–317
graphs of, 302–305, 329
identities, 373, 375, 377–382
inverse of, 329–332
period, 311–317
principle values of, 334
Slant asymptote, 137–138, 140–141
Slope, 30, 34, 150
of linear functions, 720
negative, 847, 849
of parallel lines, 42, 45–46
of perpendicular lines, 43–46
positive, 847, 849
of a tangent, 151–154
Slope-intercept form, 36–40, 49–50
Snell's law, 268, 391
SOH-CAH-TOA, 269
Solutions
of quadratic functions, 185–186
radical equations, 223–224
radical inequalities, 224
quadratic systems, 577–578
Spanning tree algorithm, 891

1020   INDEX

Index

Cover, H. Ross/H. Armstrong Roberts

vi, Andy Sacks/Tony Stone Worldwide; **vii,** (l) Mark J. Wilson, (r) Stephen Webster; **viii,** Elaine Shay; **ix,** (l) Stephen Webster, (r) NASA/Photo Researchers, Inc.; **x,** (l) Ed Degginger, (r) Barry Bomzer/Tony Stone Worldwide; **xi,** Elaine Shay; **xii,** (t) David L. Brown/The Stock Market, (c) Stephen Webster, (b) Aaron Haupt Photography; **xiii,** (l) Stephen Webster, (r) Brownie Harris/The Stock Market; **1,** Elaine Shay; **2–3,** Mak-I Photo Design; **4,** Andy Sacks/Tony Stone Worldwide; **5,** ©1992 Dede Hatch; **6,** NASA/Peter Arnold, Inc.; **11, 12, 14, 18,** Stephen Webster; **19,** Platinum Productions; **24,** Robert Landau/Westlight; **26,** (l) Daniel Wilson/Westlight, (r) Kenneth Garrett/Westlight; **29,** Tom Martin/The Stock Market; **35,** Rod Joslin/Kaplan Graphics; **38,** file photo; **39,** Platinum Productions; **40,** Howard Sochurek/Medichrome; **41,** Wes Thompson/The Stock Market; **42,** Ken Rogers/Westlight; **43,** Matt Meadows; **46,** Gail Meese; **52,** Kristian Hilson/Tony Stone Worldwide; **53,** Jim Lyle/Texas A&M University; **56, 58,** Matt Meadows; **61,** Aaron Haupt Photography; **64,** Larry Lefever from Grant Heilman; **67,** Elaine Shay; **74,** Chris Jones/The Stock Market; **76,** Tim Courlas; **79,** Lowell Georgia/Photo Researchers; **83,** Elaine Shay, courtesy Peasant on the Lane Restaurant; **86,** Platinum Productions; **90,** William Finch/Stock Boston; **91,** Brent Bear/Westlight; **93,** Stephen Webster; **94,** Superstock; **95,** Les Losego/Crown Studios; **96,** Stephen Webster; **102,** P. Petersen/Custom Medical Stock Photo; **103,** courtesy Les Todd, Duke University; **106,** (l) E. R. Degginger, (r) Superstock; **111,** Tracy I. Borland; **117,** Garrett H. Jones, Jr., C.P.C.; **124,** Stephen Webster; **126,** Paul Light/Lightwave; **131,** Mark Stephenson/Westlight; **134,** Mark Fortenberry/Transparencies; **137,** NASA; **141,** Platinum Productions; **142,** Earl Glass/Stock Boston; **144,** Manfred Kage/Peter Arnold, Inc.; **146,** file photo; **147,** Platinum Productions; **148,** Matthew McVay/Stock Boston; **149,** Superstock; **152,** courtesy Daniel L. Feicht, Cedar Point Amusement Park; **154,** Stephen Webster; **156,** AP/Wide World Photos; **160,** Elaine Shay; **162,** Randall L. Schieber; **171,** Chuck O'Rear/Westlight; **176, 177,** Mark J. Wilson; **178,** ©Cindy Lewis; **181,** Platinum Productions; **183,** Mark D. Phillips/Science Source/Photo Researchers; **187,** Aaron Haupt Photography; **190,** Stephen Webster; **193,** G & G Design/The Stock Market; **195,** Duomo; **199,** Superstock; **200,** NASA; **201,** Superstock; **205,** Matt Meadows; **207,** Superstock; **209, 210,** Platinum Productions; **214,** file photo; **216,** Superstock; **217,** file photo; **221,** Elaine Shay; **222,** Mak-I Photo Design; **222,** Stephen Webster; **225,** Comstock; **228,** Stock Montage, Inc.; **236–237,** Derek Bayes/The Stock Market; **238,** Superstock; **239,** courtesy Jerome Crump, Multimedia, University of California, Berkeley; **241,** file photo; **246,** Stephen Webster; **250,** Les Losego/Crown Studios; **251,** Gerard Vandystadt/Photo Researchers; **254, 255, 261,** Doug Martin; **262,** Les Losego/Crown Studios; **266, 268,** Superstock; **268,** Walter Hodges/Westlight; **269,** courtesy Carolyn S. Garcia, Dallas TX Fire Dept.; **274,** Superstock; **281,** Harvey Lloyd/The Stock Market; **286,** Doug Martin, courtesy Rickenbacher Air Force Base, Ohio Port Authority; **287,** E. R. Degginger; **289,** Culver Pictures; **292,** Craig Hammell/The Stock Market; **295,** Bill Gallery/Stock Boston; **300,** Stephen Webster; **301,** Gale Zucker; **302,** Mark J. Wilson; **306,** Platinum Productions; **307,** Comstock; **309,** NASA; **317,** Animals Animals/Mike Andrews; **317,** Bob Daemmrich/Stock Boston; **321,** Clyde H. Smith/Peter Arnold, Inc.; **324,** Les Losego/Crown Studios; **327,** Rod Joslin; **328,** Malcolm S. Kirk/Peter Arnold, Inc.; **330,** NASA; **333,** Royce Bair/The Stock Market; **334,** B. Ross/Westlight; **336, 338,** Les Losego/Crown Studios; **340,** file photo; **342,** Al Francekevich/The Stock Market; **343,** Stephen Webster; **345,** Animals Animals/Johnny Johnson; **347,** Culver Pictures; **348,** Les Losego/Crown Studios; **349,** Art Gingert/Comstock; **351,** Superstock; **356,** Stephen Webster; **357,** courtesy Brigham Young University; **358,** Superstock; **363,** Harvey Lloyd/The Stock Market; **364,** Les Losego/Crown Studios; **368,** George C. Anderson; **368,** Superstock; **376,** Les Losego/Crown Studios; **377,** AP/Wide World Photos; **380,** file photo; **382,** Comstock; **387,** file photo; **388,** Myron J. Dorf/The Stock Market; **391,** file photo; **392, 393,** Superstock; **398, 400,** file photo; **404,** Alvin E. Staffan; **405,** Elaine Shay; **410,** Mark M. Lawrence/The Stock Market; **411,** Doug Martin; **412, 414,** Mark E. Gibson; **416,** file photo; **418,** Platinum Productions; **419, 421,** Mark E. Gibson; **423,** David Madison/Duomo; **425,** Mark E. Gibson; **426,** Audrey Gibson; **428,** Bob Wahlgren/Pictorial History Research; **429,** Stephen Webster; **432,** Platinum Studios; **434,** Rod Joslin; **436,** David Madison/Duomo; **438,** file photo; **439, 440,** Mark E. Gibson; **442,** courtesy Daytona International Speedway; **445,** Richard Dole/Duomo; **447,** Superstock; **449,** file photo; **451,** Al Tielemans/Duomo; **452,** Aaron Haupt Photography; **452,** Dan Helms/Duomo; **454,** Al Tielemans/Duomo; **455,** Mark E. Gibson; **462–463,** Chris Bjornberg/Photo Researchers; **464,** NASA/Photo Researchers; **465,** Gale Zucker; **468,** Les Losego/Crown Studios; **471,** Tom Stack & Associates; **475,** Jeffry W. Myers/The Stock Market; **475,** Manfred Kage/Peter Arnold, Inc.; **481,** Les Losego/Crown Studios; **485,** Tony Stone Worldwide; **487,** courtesy Daniel L. Feicht, Cedar Point Amusement Park; **493,** Mark E. Gibson; **493,** Superstock; **494,** ©1992 R. F. Voss/IBM Research; **494,** Dietmer Saupe; **497,** Les Losego/Crown Studios; **501,** Ann Ronan Picture Library; **505,** Superstock; **506,** ©1991(2) R.F. Voss/IBM Research; **509,** D. Seawell/Westlight; **510,** courtesy the Royal Society; **517,** Superstock; **522,** Ed Degginger or NASA; **523,** John A. Miller; **524,** Mark E. Gibson; **528,** Roger Ressmeyer/Starlight; **531,** Frank P. Rossotto/The Stock Market; **534, 537,** Mark E. Gibson; **539,** file photo; **541,** Mark E. Gibson; **542,** NASA; **550,** Chris Butler/Astrostock; **556,** file photo; **558,** NASA; **564,** John Sanford/Astrostock; **567,** Mark E. Gibson; **570,** courtesy GM Powertrain; **576,** Matt Meadows; **579,** Paul Trent/J. Allen Hynek Center for UFO Studies; **581,** Elaine Shay; **584,** Mark E. Gibson; **584,** Matt Meadows; **585,** NASA; **586, 591,** Mark E. Gibson; **596,** Barry Bomzer/Tony Stone Worldwide; **597,** Colorado State University Photo-

Photo Credits

CHAPTER 1   LINEAR RELATIONS AND FUNCTIONS

Page 20,   Lesson 1-3A

7.

8.

9.

10.

11.

12.

Pages 24-27,   Lesson 1-3

12.

13.

23.

24.

25.

26.

27.

28.

29.

$x < 5$

30.

$y > -x$

31.

$x - y < 5$

32.
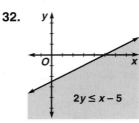
$2y \leq x - 5$

33.
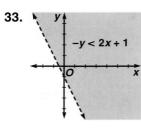
$-y < 2x + 1$

34.
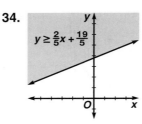
$y \geq \frac{2}{5}x + \frac{19}{5}$

35.
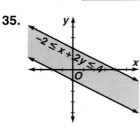
$-2 \leq x + 2y \leq 4$

36.

$y > |x|$

37.
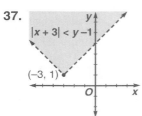
$|x + 3| < y - 1$
$(-3, 1)$

Pages 45-47,   Lesson 1-6

37.

$-6 \leq 3x - y \leq 12$

39c.

Cost
$ 500
1
Televisions Produced

Pages 48-50,   Chapter 1 Summary and Review

17.

$f(x) = 3x - 8$

18.

$f(x) = 19$

19.
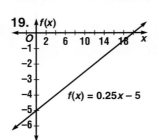
$f(x) = 0.25x - 5$

20.

$f(x) = 7x + 1$

Page 51,   Chapter 1 Test

13.

$y = 3x - 6$

14.
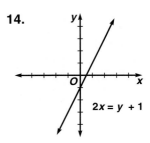
$2x = y + 1$

15.

$y + 4x \leq 12$

16.
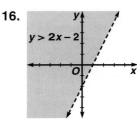
$y > 2x - 2$

24.
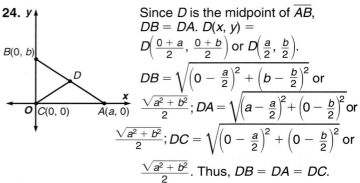
$B(0, b)$ D $C(0, 0)$ $A(a, 0)$

Since D is the midpoint of $\overline{AB}$, $DB = DA$. $D(x, y) = D\left(\frac{0 + a}{2}, \frac{0 + b}{2}\right)$ or $D\left(\frac{a}{2}, \frac{b}{2}\right)$.

$DB = \sqrt{\left(0 - \frac{a}{2}\right)^2 + \left(b - \frac{b}{2}\right)^2}$ or $\frac{\sqrt{a^2 + b^2}}{2}$; $DA = \sqrt{\left(a - \frac{a}{2}\right)^2 + \left(0 - \frac{b}{2}\right)^2}$ or $\frac{\sqrt{a^2 + b^2}}{2}$; $DC = \sqrt{\left(0 - \frac{a}{2}\right)^2 + \left(0 - \frac{b}{2}\right)^2}$ or $\frac{\sqrt{a^2 + b^2}}{2}$. Thus, $DB = DA = DC$.

CHAPTER 2   SYSTEMS OF EQUATIONS AND INEQUALITIES

Pages 59-61,   Lesson 2-1

11.
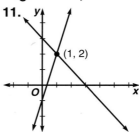
$(1, 2)$

Pages 68-70,   Lesson 2-2

16. $\begin{bmatrix} -2 & 11 & -2 \\ 9 & -1 & -6 \\ 11 & -2 & -1 \end{bmatrix}$

17. $\begin{bmatrix} 7 & 14 & 3 \\ -6 & 15 & -14 \\ 23 & 4 & -4 \end{bmatrix}$

18. $\begin{bmatrix} 3 & 15 & -13 \\ -7 & 10 & -8 \\ 28 & 2 & 1 \end{bmatrix}$

19. $\begin{bmatrix} 4 & 20 & -6 \\ -2 & 12 & -14 \\ 31 & 2 & -1 \end{bmatrix}$

20. $\begin{bmatrix} -4 & 1 & -16 \\ -1 & -5 & 6 \\ 5 & -2 & 5 \end{bmatrix}$

21. $\begin{bmatrix} 9 & 3 & 5 \\ -15 & 16 & -8 \\ 12 & 6 & -5 \end{bmatrix}$

22. $\begin{bmatrix} -9 & -3 & -5 \\ 15 & -16 & 8 \\ -12 & -6 & 5 \end{bmatrix}$ **23.** $\begin{bmatrix} 5 & 4 & -11 \\ -16 & 11 & -2 \\ 17 & 4 & 0 \end{bmatrix}$ **24.** $\begin{bmatrix} -4 & 1 & -16 \\ -1 & -5 & 6 \\ 5 & -2 & 5 \end{bmatrix}$

42. Let $A = \begin{bmatrix} a_{11} & a_{12} \\ a_{21} & a_{22} \end{bmatrix}$ and $B = \begin{bmatrix} b_{11} & b_{12} \\ b_{21} & b_{22} \end{bmatrix}$.

$A + B = \begin{bmatrix} a_{11} & a_{12} \\ a_{21} & a_{22} \end{bmatrix} + \begin{bmatrix} b_{11} & b_{12} \\ b_{21} & b_{22} \end{bmatrix}$

$= \begin{bmatrix} a_{11} + b_{11} & a_{12} + b_{12} \\ a_{21} + b_{21} & a_{22} + b_{22} \end{bmatrix}$

$= \begin{bmatrix} b_{11} + a_{11} & b_{12} + a_{12} \\ b_{21} + a_{21} & b_{22} + a_{22} \end{bmatrix}$

$= \begin{bmatrix} b_{11} & b_{12} \\ b_{21} & b_{22} \end{bmatrix} + \begin{bmatrix} a_{11} & a_{12} \\ a_{21} & a_{22} \end{bmatrix}$

$= B + A$

43. Let $A = \begin{bmatrix} a_{11} & a_{12} \\ a_{21} & a_{22} \end{bmatrix}$, $B = \begin{bmatrix} b_{11} & b_{12} \\ b_{21} & b_{22} \end{bmatrix}$, and $C = \begin{bmatrix} c_{11} & c_{12} \\ c_{21} & c_{22} \end{bmatrix}$.

$(A + B) + C = \begin{bmatrix} a_{11} + b_{11} & a_{12} + b_{12} \\ a_{21} + b_{21} & a_{22} + b_{22} \end{bmatrix} + \begin{bmatrix} c_{11} & c_{12} \\ c_{21} & c_{22} \end{bmatrix}$

$= \begin{bmatrix} (a_{11} + b_{11}) + c_{11} & (a_{12} + b_{12}) + c_{12} \\ (a_{21} + b_{21}) + c_{21} & (a_{22} + b_{22}) + c_{22} \end{bmatrix}$

$= \begin{bmatrix} a_{11} + (b_{11} + c_{11}) & a_{12} + (b_{12} + c_{12}) \\ a_{21} + (b_{21} + c_{21}) & a_{22} + (b_{22} + c_{22}) \end{bmatrix}$

$= \begin{bmatrix} a_{11} & a_{12} \\ a_{21} & a_{22} \end{bmatrix} + \begin{bmatrix} b_{11} + c_{11} & b_{12} + c_{12} \\ b_{21} + c_{21} & b_{22} + c_{22} \end{bmatrix}$

$= A + (B + C)$

44. Let $A = \begin{bmatrix} a_{11} & a_{12} \\ a_{21} & a_{22} \end{bmatrix}$ and $B = \begin{bmatrix} b_{11} & b_{12} \\ b_{21} & b_{22} \end{bmatrix}$.

$AB = \begin{bmatrix} a_{11}b_{11} + a_{12}b_{21} & a_{11}b_{12} + a_{12}b_{22} \\ a_{21}b_{11} + a_{22}b_{21} & a_{21}b_{12} + a_{22}b_{22} \end{bmatrix}$

$BA = \begin{bmatrix} b_{11}a_{11} + b_{12}a_{21} & b_{11}a_{12} + b_{12}a_{22} \\ b_{21}a_{11} + b_{22}a_{21} & b_{21}a_{12} + b_{22}a_{22} \end{bmatrix}$

Thus, $AB \neq BA$, since $a_{12}b_{21} \neq b_{12}a_{21}$.

45. Let $A = \begin{bmatrix} a_{11} & a_{12} \\ a_{21} & a_{22} \end{bmatrix}$, $B = \begin{bmatrix} b_{11} & b_{12} \\ b_{21} & b_{22} \end{bmatrix}$, and $C = \begin{bmatrix} c_{11} & c_{12} \\ c_{21} & c_{22} \end{bmatrix}$.

$(AB)C = \begin{bmatrix} a_{11}b_{11} + a_{12}b_{21} & a_{11}b_{12} + a_{12}b_{22} \\ a_{21}b_{11} + a_{22}b_{21} & a_{21}b_{12} + a_{22}b_{22} \end{bmatrix} \begin{bmatrix} c_{11} & c_{12} \\ c_{21} & c_{22} \end{bmatrix}$

$= \begin{bmatrix} a_{11}b_{11}c_{11} + a_{11}b_{12}c_{21} + a_{12}b_{21}c_{11} + a_{12}b_{22}c_{21} \\ a_{21}b_{11}c_{11} + a_{21}b_{12}c_{21} + a_{22}b_{21}c_{11} + a_{22}b_{22}c_{21} \end{bmatrix}$

$\begin{matrix} a_{11}b_{11}c_{12} + a_{11}b_{12}c_{22} + a_{12}b_{21}c_{12} + a_{12}b_{22}c_{22} \\ a_{21}b_{11}c_{12} + a_{21}b_{12}c_{22} + a_{22}b_{21}c_{12} + a_{22}b_{22}c_{22} \end{matrix}$

$A(BC) = \begin{bmatrix} a_{11} & a_{12} \\ a_{21} & a_{22} \end{bmatrix} \begin{bmatrix} b_{11}c_{11} + b_{12}c_{21} & b_{11}c_{12} + b_{12}c_{22} \\ b_{21}c_{11} + b_{22}c_{21} & b_{21}c_{12} + b_{22}c_{22} \end{bmatrix}$

$= \begin{bmatrix} a_{11}b_{11}c_{11} + a_{11}b_{12}c_{21} + a_{12}b_{21}c_{11} + a_{12}b_{22}c_{21} \\ a_{21}b_{11}c_{11} + a_{21}b_{12}c_{21} + a_{22}b_{21}c_{11} + a_{22}b_{22}c_{21} \end{bmatrix}$

$\begin{matrix} a_{11}b_{11}c_{12} + a_{11}b_{12}c_{22} + a_{12}b_{21}c_{12} + a_{12}b_{22}c_{22} \\ a_{21}b_{11}c_{12} + a_{21}b_{12}c_{22} + a_{22}b_{21}c_{12} + a_{22}b_{22}c_{22} \end{matrix}$

Therefore, $(AB)C = A(BC)$.

11.

12.

13.

14.

15.

16.

21.

22.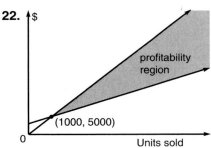

Pages 88-90, Lesson 2-5

9.

10.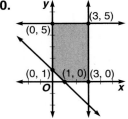

Pages 98-100, Chapter 2 Summary and Review

22.

23.

Page 101, Chapter 2 Test

17.

$(0, 3)$
$(1\frac{2}{3}, 4\frac{2}{3})$
$(4, 0)$
O x

18.

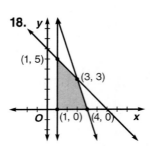

$(1, 5)$
$(3, 3)$
$(1, 0)$ $(4, 0)$
O x

19.

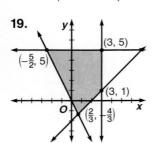

$(3, 5)$
$(-\frac{5}{2}, 5)$
$(3, 1)$
O $(\frac{2}{3}, -\frac{4}{3})$ x

4.

5.

6.

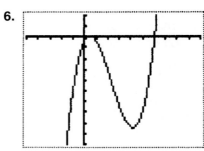

CHAPTER 3 THE NATURE OF GRAPHS

Page 105, Lesson 3-1A

1.

2.

3.

7.

8.

9.

10.

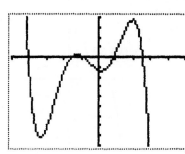

26.
$p(x) = 0.33(x + 2)^3 + 2$

27.
$q(x) = -(x + 2)^2 + 5$

28.

Pages 122-124,   Lesson 3-2

13.
$g(x) = (x + 1)^2$

14.
$h(x) = (x - 2)^2 - 4$

29.

15.
$j(x) = -(x - 2)^2$

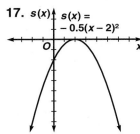

16.
$k(x) = 3(x - 2)^2$

30.

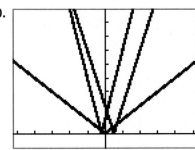

17.
$s(x) = -0.5(x - 2)^2$

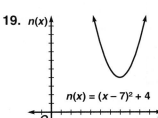

18.
$m(x) = 2(x - 2)^2 + 3$

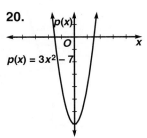

19.
$n(x) = (x - 7)^2 + 4$

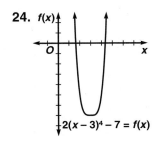

20.
$p(x) = 3x^2 - 7$

33a.

hours

33b.

hours

24.
$2(x - 3)^4 - 7 = f(x)$

25.
$h(x) = -4|x - 5| - 1$

34b.
$V(w) = w^3 + w^2 - 6w$

34c.
$V(w) = (w + 2)^3 + (w + 2)^2 - 6(w + 2)$

Page 125, Lesson 3-3A

1.

2.

3.

4.

5.

6.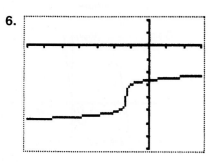

Pages 129-131, Lesson 3-3

19.

20.

21.

22.

23.

24.

27.

28.

29.

Page 133, Lesson 3-4A

1.

2.

3.

4.

5.

6.

7.

8.

9.

10.

Pages 139-142, Lesson 3-4

19. $y = \frac{1}{x}$

a. $y = \frac{1}{x} - 1$

b. $y = \frac{1}{x + 5}$

c. $y = \frac{1}{4x}$

d. $y = \frac{1}{0.2x} + 8$

e. $y = \frac{1}{x - 3} + 7$

20.
$y = \frac{1}{x^2}$

a.
$y = \frac{1}{x^2} + 3$

b.
$y = \frac{1}{(x-9)^2}$

c.
$y = \frac{1}{0.4x^2}$

d.
$y = \frac{1}{(x+5)^2} - 1$

e.
$y = \frac{-1}{(x-2)^2} + 4$

Pages 147-148,   Lesson 3-5

7.

8.

9.

10.

11.

12.

13.

14.

15.

16.

17.

18.

19.

20.

21.

28.

29.

30.

31.

33.

34.

39.
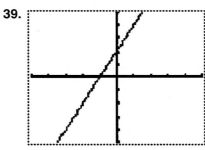

Page 148,   Mid-Chapter Review

3.

4.

40.

5.

6.

41.

Pages 153-154,   Lesson 3-6

29.

30.

Page 155,   Lesson 3-7A

1.

31.

32.

2.

TEACHER'S ANSWER KEY   T1033

3.

4.

5.

6.

7.

8.

Pages 161-163,   Lesson 3-7

27.

28.

29.

30.

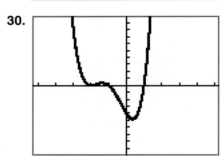

Pages 169-171,   Lesson 3-8

14.

15.

16.

17.

18.

19.

9.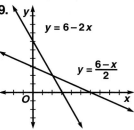

$y = 6 - 2x$

$y = \dfrac{6 - x}{2}$

10.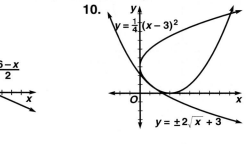

$y = \frac{1}{4}(x - 3)^2$

$y = \pm 2\sqrt{x} + 3$

20.

21.

11.

$y = (x + 1)^3 - 2)$

$y = \sqrt[3]{x + 2} - 1$

12.

22.

23.

13.

14.

31.

15.

16.

32.

17.

18.

33.

27.

28.

29.

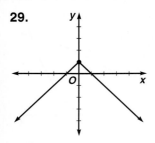

Page 175, Chapter 3 Test

1.

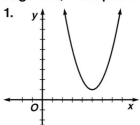

The graph is moved
5 units right.

2.

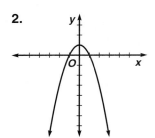

The graph is reflected over
the x-axis and moved up
2 units.

3.

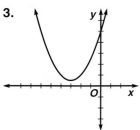

Wider, shifted left 3 units

4. $y = \pm\sqrt{x} + 4$, no

$y = (x - 4)^2$

$y = \pm\sqrt{x} + 4$

5. $y = \dfrac{\sqrt[3]{x-1}}{2}$, yes

$y = 8x^3 + 1$

$y = \dfrac{\sqrt[3]{x-1}}{2}$

6. $y = \pm\sqrt[4]{x+7} - 3$, no

$y = (x + 3)^4 - 7$

$y = \pm\sqrt[4]{x+7} - 3$

10.

11.

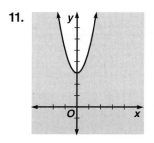

CHAPTER 4 POLYNOMIAL AND RATIONAL FUNCTIONS

Pages 181-184, Lesson 4-1

15.

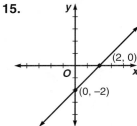

(2, 0)

(0, −2)

16.

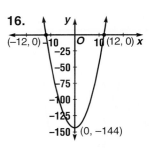

(−12, 0) −10 O 10 (12, 0) x

−25

−50

−75

−100

−125

−150 (0, −144)

16.

17.

17.

(0, 49)

(7, 0)

18.

(0, 25)

19.

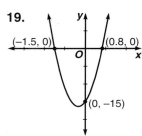

(−1.5, 0) (0.8, 0)

(0, −15)

20.

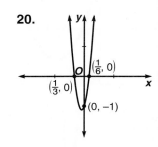

$\left(\frac{1}{6}, 0\right)$

$\left(\frac{1}{3}, 0\right)$

(0, −1)

21.

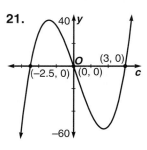

40

(3, 0)

(−2.5, 0) (0, 0) c

−60

22.

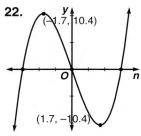

(−1.7, 10.4)

(1.7, −10.4)

29.

30.

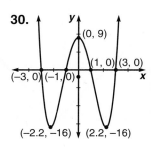

(0, 9)

(1, 0) (3, 0)

(−3, 0) (−1, 0)

(−2.2, −16) (2.2, −16)

31.

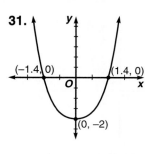

(−1.4, 0)   (1.4, 0)
O
(0, −2)

32.

3.

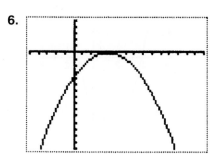

4.

5.

6.

For Exercises 33a-33e, sample answers are given.

33a.

33b.

33c.

33d.

33e.

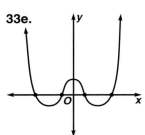

33f. not possible

Page 186,   Lesson 4-2A

1.

2.

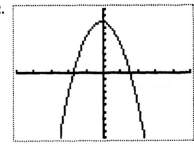

Pages 192-194,   Lesson 4-2

7.

f(x)
O   x

8.

f(z)
O   z

15.

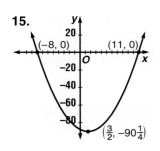

y
20
(−8, 0)   (11, 0)
O   x
−20
−40
−60
−80
$\left(\frac{3}{2}, -90\frac{1}{4}\right)$

16.

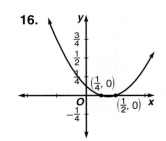

y
$\frac{3}{4}$
$\frac{1}{2}$
$\frac{1}{4}$ $\left(\frac{1}{4}, 0\right)$
O $\left(\frac{1}{2}, 0\right)$ x
$-\frac{1}{4}$

Teacher's Answer Key

17.

18.

19.

20.

21.

22.

23.

24.

25.

26.

27.

28.

29.

30.

31.

32.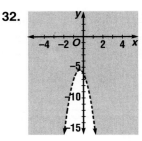

42.
$$ax^2 + bx + c = 0 \qquad (a \neq 0)$$
$$x^2 + \frac{b}{a}x + \frac{c}{a} = 0$$
$$x^2 + \frac{b}{a}x = -\frac{c}{a}$$
$$x^2 + \frac{b}{a}x + \left(\frac{b}{2a}\right)^2 = -\frac{c}{a} + \left(\frac{b}{2a}\right)^2$$
$$\left(x + \frac{b}{2a}\right)^2 = -\frac{c}{a} + \frac{b^2}{4a^2}$$
$$\left(x + \frac{b}{2a}\right)^2 = \frac{b^2 - 4ac}{4a^2}$$
$$\left|x + \frac{b}{2a}\right| = \sqrt{\frac{b^2 - 4ac}{4a^2}}$$
$$x + \frac{b}{2a} = \pm\frac{\sqrt{b^2 - 4ac}}{2a}$$
$$x = -\frac{b}{2a} \pm \frac{\sqrt{b^2 - 4ac}}{2a}$$
$$x = \frac{-b \pm \sqrt{b^2 - 4ac}}{2a}$$

Pages 213-214,   Lesson 4-5

28a.

32.

33.

34. zeros: -4, 1, 7; rel max: (-1.8, 54.2), rel min: (4.5, -74.4), pt of infl: (1.3, -9.1)

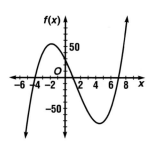

Page 224,   Lesson 4-7A

1.

2.

3.

4.

5.

6.

7.

8.

9.

10.

11.

12.

47.

$$y = \begin{cases} x-1, & \text{if } x < 0 \\ x-3, & \text{if } x \geq 0 \end{cases}$$

Pages 242-243,   Unit 1 Review

9.

$4 - 3x = y$

10.

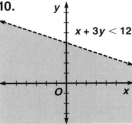

$x + 3y < 12$

11.

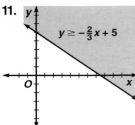

$y \geq -\frac{2}{3}x + 5$

36.

$y = 2(x + 5)$

$y = \frac{1}{2}x - 5$

37.

$y = (x - 1)^3 + 2$

$y = \sqrt[3]{x - 2} + 1$

38.

$y = \dfrac{x}{(2x + 1)(x + 2)}$

39.

$y = \dfrac{x^2 - 9}{x + 3}$

40.

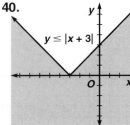

$y \leq |x + 3|$

41.

$y > \sqrt[3]{x + 4}$

46.

$y = \dfrac{x^2 - 1}{x + 1}$

CHAPTER 5   THE TRIGONOMETRIC FUNCTIONS

Pages 280-281,   Lesson 5-6

8. none   **9.** one; $A = 15°25'$, $B = 147°35'$, $b = 20.2$
10. one; $B = 90°$, $C = 60°$, $c = 6.9$ **11.** none   **12.** one;
$B = 90°$, $C = 30°$, $c = 1$ **13.** two; $B = 50°19'$, $C = 91°41'$,
and $c = 13.0$, or $B = 129°41'$, $C = 12°19'$, and $c = 2.8$
14. one; $C = 74°$, $b = 8.9$, $c = 10.2$ **15.** none   **16.** two;
$B = 71°4'$, $C = 50°56'$, and $c = 23.8$, or $B = 108°56'$,
$C = 13°4'$ and $c = 6.9$ **17.** one; $C = 80°$, $a = 13.1$,
$b = 17.6$ **18.** one; $A = 52°$, $b = 100.2$, $c = 90.4$
19. none   **20.** two; $B = 30°28'$, $C = 124°32'$, and
$c = 243.7$, or $B = 149°32'$, $C = 5°28'$, and $c = 28.2$ **21.** none

25.
$$\frac{\sin A}{a} = \frac{\sin C}{c}$$
$$\frac{\sin A}{\sin C} = \frac{a}{c}$$
$$\frac{\sin A}{\sin C} - 1 = \frac{a}{c} - 1$$
$$\frac{\sin A - \sin C}{\sin C} = \frac{a - c}{c}$$

26. By the results in Exercise 25, $\dfrac{\sin B - \sin C}{\sin C} = \dfrac{b - c}{c}$, so

$\dfrac{\sin B - \sin C}{b - c} = \dfrac{\sin C}{c}$. Also, $\dfrac{\sin B}{b} = \dfrac{\sin C}{c}$, so $\dfrac{\sin B}{\sin C} = \dfrac{b}{c}$. Thus,

$\dfrac{\sin B}{\sin C} + 1 = \dfrac{b}{c} + 1$ and $\dfrac{\sin B + \sin C}{\sin C} = \dfrac{b + c}{c}$.

$\dfrac{\sin B + \sin C}{b + c} = \dfrac{\sin C}{c}$, therefore,

$\dfrac{\sin B + \sin C}{b + c} = \dfrac{\sin B - \sin C}{b - c}$ and $\dfrac{b + c}{b - c} = \dfrac{\sin B + \sin C}{\sin B - \sin C}$.

27. $\dfrac{\sin A}{a} = \dfrac{\sin B}{b}$

$\dfrac{a}{\sin A} = \dfrac{b}{\sin B}$

$\dfrac{a}{b} = \dfrac{\sin A}{\sin B}$

28. $\dfrac{\sin B}{b} = \dfrac{\sin A}{a}$

$\dfrac{a}{b} = \dfrac{\sin A}{\sin B}$

$\dfrac{a}{b} + 1 = \dfrac{\sin A}{\sin B} + 1$

$\dfrac{a + b}{b} = \dfrac{\sin A + \sin B}{\sin B}$

$\dfrac{b}{a + b} = \dfrac{\sin B}{\sin A + \sin B}$

29. Let $\angle A \cong \angle X$, $\angle B \cong \angle Y$, and $\angle C \cong \angle Z$. Applying the
law of sines, $\dfrac{a}{\sin A} = \dfrac{b}{\sin B} = \dfrac{c}{\sin C}$ and $\dfrac{x}{\sin X} = \dfrac{y}{\sin Y} = \dfrac{z}{\sin Z}$.
Thus, $\sin A = \dfrac{a \sin B}{b}$ and $\sin X = \dfrac{x \sin Y}{y}$. Since $A = X$,
$\dfrac{a \sin B}{b} = \dfrac{x \sin Y}{y}$. However, $B = Y$ so $\dfrac{a}{b} = \dfrac{x}{y}$ or $\dfrac{a}{x} = \dfrac{b}{y}$.
Similar proportions can be derived for c and z.

CHAPTER 6 GRAPHS AND INVERSES OF THE TRIGONOMETRIC FUNCTIONS

Pages 304-307, Lesson 6-1

40.
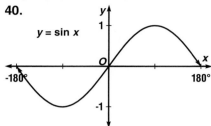
$y = \sin x$

41.
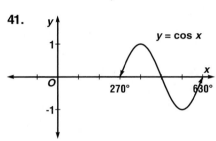
$y = \cos x$

42.
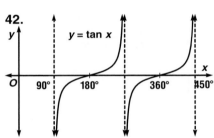
$y = \tan x$

43.
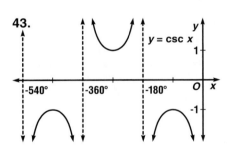
$y = \csc x$

44.
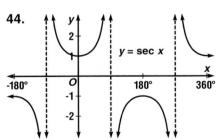
$y = \sec x$

45.
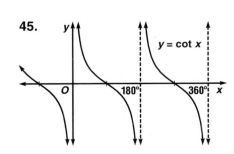
$y = \cot x$

46.

47.

48.

49.

50.

51.

Page 320, Lesson 6-3A

1.

2.

3.

4.

5.

6.

7.

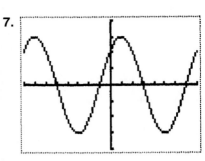

13. $y = \sin(\theta + 90°)$

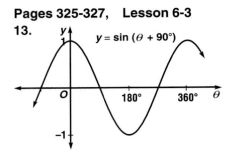

19. $y = \tan(\theta + 90°)$

8.

14. $y = \sin(\theta - 180°)$

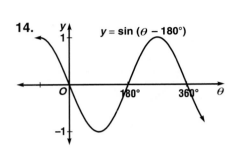

20. $y = \cot(\theta - 90°)$

9.

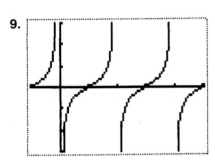

15. $y = -3\sin(\theta - 45°)$

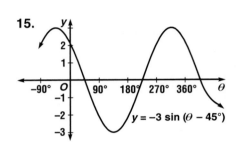

21. $\frac{1}{2}y = \sin(3\theta + 180°)$

10.

16. $y = 3\cos(\theta - 90°)$

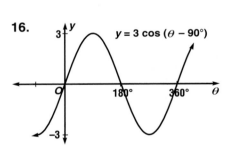

22. $2y = 10\sin\left(\frac{\theta}{2} + 90°\right)$

11.

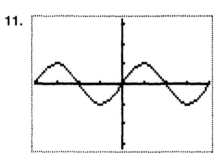

17. $y = \frac{1}{2}\cos\left(\frac{\theta}{2} - 180°\right)$

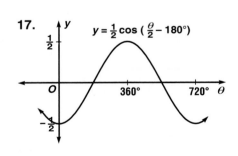

23. $y = \sin x + \sin 2x$

12.

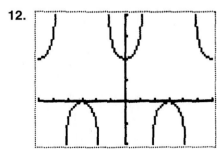

18. $y = -\frac{1}{3}\sin(2\theta + 45°)$

24. $y = \cos x - \sin x$

25.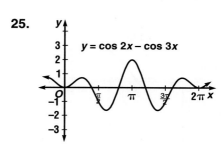
$y = \cos 2x - \cos 3x$

26.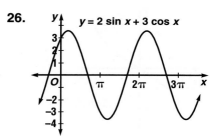
$y = 2\sin x + 3\cos x$

27.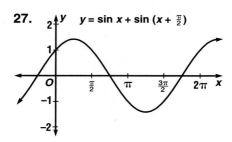
$y = \sin x + \sin\left(x + \frac{\pi}{2}\right)$

28.
$y = \frac{1}{2}\sin x - \cos 3x$

29.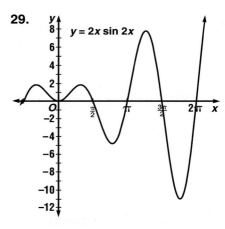
$y = 2x \sin 2x$

30.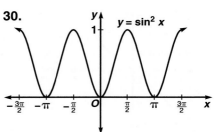
$y = \sin^2 x$

Pages 331-333, Lesson 6-4

40. $\sin^{-1}\frac{\sqrt{2}}{2} + \cos^{-1}\frac{\sqrt{2}}{2} \overset{?}{=} \tan^{-1}\frac{\sqrt{3}}{3} + \tan^{-1}\sqrt{3}$
$$45° + 45° \overset{?}{=} 30° + 60°$$
$$90° = 90°$$

41. $\arccos\frac{\sqrt{3}}{2} + \arcsin\frac{\sqrt{3}}{2} \overset{?}{=} \arctan 1 + \text{arccot } 1$
$$30° + 60° \overset{?}{=} 45° + 45°$$
$$90° = 90°$$

42. $\arcsin\frac{2}{5} + \arccos\frac{2}{5} \overset{?}{=} 90°$
$$23.6° + 66.4° \overset{?}{=} 90°$$
$$90° = 90°$$

43. $\tan^{-1}1 + \cos^{-1}\frac{\sqrt{3}}{2} \overset{?}{=} \sin^{-1}\frac{1}{2} + \sec^{-1}\sqrt{2}$
$$45° + 30° \overset{?}{=} 30° + 45°$$
$$75° = 75°$$

44. $\tan^{-1}\frac{3}{4} + \tan^{-1}\frac{5}{12} \overset{?}{=} \tan^{-1}\frac{56}{33}$
$$36.9° + 22.6° \overset{?}{=} 59.5°$$
$$59.5° = 59.5°$$

45. $\arcsin\frac{3}{5} + \arccos\frac{15}{17} \overset{?}{=} \arctan\frac{77}{36}$
$$36.9° + 28.1° \overset{?}{=} 65°$$
$$65° = 65°$$

Page 339, Lesson 6-6A

1.

2.

3.

4.

5.

6.

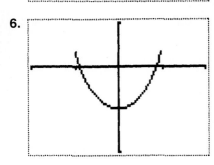

Pages 342-344,   Lesson 6-6

19.

20.

21.

22.

23.

24.

31.

32.

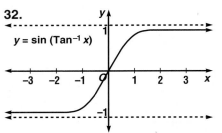

Pages 352-354,   Chapter 6 Summary and Review

30.

31.

$y = \text{Csc } x$

32.

$y = \cot x$

$y = \text{arccot } x$

33.

Page 355, Chapter 6 Test

4.

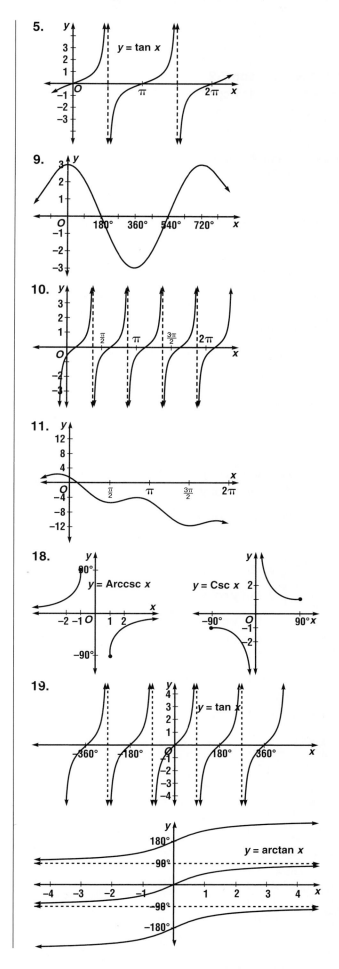

5.

$y = \tan x$

9.

10.

11.

18.

$y = \text{Arccsc } x$ $y = \text{Csc } x$

19.

$y = \tan x$

$y = \text{arctan } x$

CHAPTER 7 TRIGONOMETRIC IDENTITIES AND EQUATIONS

Pages 366-368, Lesson 7-2

3. $\tan^2 x \cos^2 x \overset{?}{=} 1 - \cos^2 x$

$\dfrac{\sin^2 x}{\cos^2 x} \cdot \cos^2 x \overset{?}{=} 1 - \cos^2 x$

$\sin^2 x \overset{?}{=} 1 - \cos^2 x$

$1 - \cos^2 x = 1 - \cos^2 x$

4. $\csc A \sec A \overset{?}{=} \cot A + \tan A$

$\csc A \sec A \overset{?}{=} \dfrac{\cos A}{\sin A} + \dfrac{\sin A}{\cos A}$

$\csc A \sec A \overset{?}{=} \dfrac{\sin^2 A + \cos^2 A}{\sin A \cos A}$

$\csc A \sec A \overset{?}{=} \dfrac{1}{\sin A \cos A}$

$\csc A \sec A = \csc A \sec A$

5. $\tan \beta \csc \beta \overset{?}{=} \sec \beta$

$\dfrac{\sin \beta}{\cos \beta} \cdot \dfrac{1}{\sin \beta} \overset{?}{=} \sec \beta$

$\dfrac{1}{\cos \beta} \overset{?}{=} \sec \beta$

$\sec \beta = \sec \beta$

6. $\csc \alpha \cos \alpha \tan \alpha \overset{?}{=} 1$

$\dfrac{1}{\sin \alpha} \cdot \cos \alpha \cdot \dfrac{\sin \alpha}{\cos \alpha} \overset{?}{=} 1$

$\dfrac{\sin \alpha \cos \alpha}{\sin \alpha \cos \alpha} \overset{?}{=} 1$

$1 = 1$

7. $\sin \theta \sec \theta \overset{?}{=} 1$

$\sin \theta \cdot \dfrac{1}{\cos \theta} \cdot \dfrac{\cos \theta}{\sin \theta} \overset{?}{=} 1$

$\dfrac{\sin \theta \cos \theta}{\sin \theta \cos \theta} \overset{?}{=} 1$

$1 = 1$

8. $\sec^2 y - \tan^2 y \overset{?}{=} \tan y \cot y$

$\dfrac{1}{\cos^2 y} - \dfrac{\sin^2 y}{\cos^2 y} \overset{?}{=} \tan y \cot y$

$\dfrac{1 - \sin^2 y}{\cos^2 y} \overset{?}{=} \tan y \cot y$

$\dfrac{\cos^2 y}{\cos^2 y} \overset{?}{=} \tan y \cot y$

$\dfrac{\cos y}{\cos y} \overset{?}{=} \tan y \cot y$

$\dfrac{\cos y}{\cos y} \cdot \dfrac{\sin y}{\sin y} \overset{?}{=} \tan y \cot y$

$\dfrac{\sin y}{\cos y} \cdot \dfrac{\cos y}{\sin y} \overset{?}{=} \tan y \cot y$

$\tan y \cot y = \tan y \cot y$

13. $\dfrac{1}{\sec^2 \theta} + \dfrac{1}{\csc^2 \theta} \overset{?}{=} 1$

$\dfrac{1}{\frac{1}{\cos^2 \theta}} + \dfrac{1}{\frac{1}{\sin^2 \theta}} \overset{?}{=} 1$

$\cos^2 \theta + \sin^2 \theta \overset{?}{=} 1$

$1 = 1$

14. $\dfrac{\tan x \cos x}{\sin x} \overset{?}{=} 1$

$\tan x \cdot \dfrac{\cos x}{\sin x} \overset{?}{=} 1$

$\dfrac{\sin x}{\cos x} \cdot \dfrac{\cos x}{\sin x} \overset{?}{=} 1$

$1 = 1$

15. $\dfrac{\sin A}{\csc A} + \dfrac{\cos A}{\sec A} \overset{?}{=} 1$

$\dfrac{\sin A}{\frac{1}{\sin A}} + \dfrac{\cos A}{\frac{1}{\cos A}} \overset{?}{=} 1$

$\sin^2 A + \cos^2 A \overset{?}{=} 1$

$1 = 1$

16. $\dfrac{1 + \tan^2 \theta}{\csc^2 \theta} \overset{?}{=} \tan^2 \theta$

$\dfrac{\sec^2 \theta}{\csc^2 \theta} \overset{?}{=} \tan^2 \theta$

$\dfrac{\frac{1}{\cos^2 \theta}}{\frac{1}{\sin^2 \theta}} \overset{?}{=} \tan^2 \theta$

$\dfrac{1}{\cos^2 \theta} \cdot \sin^2 \theta \overset{?}{=} \tan^2 \theta$

$\tan^2 \theta = \tan^2 \theta$

17. $\dfrac{1 + \tan \gamma}{1 + \cot \gamma} \overset{?}{=} \dfrac{\sin \gamma}{\cos \gamma}$

$\dfrac{1 + \frac{\sin \gamma}{\cos \gamma}}{1 + \frac{\cos \gamma}{\sin \gamma}} \overset{?}{=} \dfrac{\sin \gamma}{\cos \gamma}$

$\dfrac{\frac{\sin \gamma + \cos \gamma}{\cos \gamma}}{\frac{\sin \gamma + \cos \gamma}{\sin \gamma}} \overset{?}{=} \dfrac{\sin \gamma}{\cos \gamma}$

$\dfrac{\sin \gamma + \cos \gamma}{\cos \gamma} \cdot \dfrac{\sin \gamma}{\sin \gamma + \cos \gamma} \overset{?}{=} \dfrac{\sin \gamma}{\cos \gamma}$

$\dfrac{\sin \gamma}{\cos \gamma} = \dfrac{\sin \gamma}{\cos \gamma}$

18. $\dfrac{\sec \alpha}{\sin \alpha} - \dfrac{\sin \alpha}{\cos \alpha} \overset{?}{=} \cot \alpha$

$\dfrac{\frac{1}{\cos \alpha}}{\sin \alpha} - \dfrac{\sin \alpha}{\cos \alpha} \overset{?}{=} \cot \alpha$

$\dfrac{1}{\sin \alpha \cos \alpha} - \dfrac{\sin^2 \alpha}{\sin \alpha \cos \alpha} \overset{?}{=} \cot \alpha$

$\dfrac{1 - \sin^2 \alpha}{\sin \alpha \cos \alpha} \overset{?}{=} \cot \alpha$

$\dfrac{\cos^2 \alpha}{\sin \alpha \cos \alpha} \overset{?}{=} \cot \alpha$

$\dfrac{\cos \alpha}{\sin \alpha} \overset{?}{=} \cot \alpha$

$\cot \alpha = \cot \alpha$

19. $\cos^2 x + \tan^2 x \cos^2 x \overset{?}{=} 1$

$\cos^2 x + \dfrac{\sin^2 x}{\cos^2 x} \cdot \cos^2 x \overset{?}{=} 1$

$\cos^2 x + \sin^2 x \overset{?}{=} 1$

$1 = 1$

20. $\tan^2 \theta - \sin^2 \theta \overset{?}{=} \tan^2 \theta \sin^2 \theta$

$\dfrac{\sin^2 \theta}{\cos^2 \theta} - \sin^2 \theta \overset{?}{=} \tan^2 \theta \sin^2 \theta$

$\dfrac{\sin^2 \theta}{\cos^2 \theta} - \dfrac{\cos^2 \theta \sin^2 \theta}{\cos^2 \theta} \overset{?}{=} \tan^2 \theta \sin^2 \theta$

$\dfrac{\sin^2 \theta - \cos^2 \theta \sin^2 \theta}{\cos^2 \theta} \overset{?}{=} \tan^2 \theta \sin^2 \theta$

$\dfrac{\sin^2 \theta (1 - \cos^2 \theta)}{\cos^2 \theta} \overset{?}{=} \tan^2 \theta \sin^2 \theta$

$\dfrac{\sin^2 \theta}{\cos^2 \theta} \cdot \sin^2 \theta \overset{?}{=} \tan^2 \theta \sin^2 \theta$

$\tan^2 \theta \sin^2 \theta = \tan^2 \theta \sin^2 \theta$

21. $1 - \cot^4 x \overset{?}{=} 2\csc^2 x - \csc^4 x$

$1 - \cot^4 x \overset{?}{=} \csc^2 x \cdot (2 - \csc^2 x)$

$1 - \cot^4 x \overset{?}{=} (1 + \cot^2 x)(2 - (1 + \cot^2 x))$

$1 - \cot^4 x \overset{?}{=} (1 + \cot^2 x)(1 - \cot^2 x)$

$1 - \cot^4 x = 1 - \cot^4 x$

22. $\sin \theta + \cos \theta \overset{?}{=} \dfrac{1 + \tan \theta}{\sec \theta}$

$\sin \theta + \cos \theta \overset{?}{=} \dfrac{1 + \frac{\sin \theta}{\cos \theta}}{\frac{1}{\cos \theta}}$

$\sin \theta + \cos \theta \overset{?}{=} \dfrac{\frac{\sin \theta + \cos \theta}{\cos \theta}}{\frac{1}{\cos \theta}}$

$\sin \theta + \cos \theta \overset{?}{=} \dfrac{\sin \theta + \cos \theta}{\cos \theta} \cdot \cos \theta$

$\sin \theta + \cos \theta = \sin \theta + \cos \theta$

23. $\dfrac{\sec x - 1}{\sec x + 1} + \dfrac{\cos x - 1}{\cos x + 1} \overset{?}{=} 0$

$$\frac{\dfrac{1}{\cos x} - 1}{\dfrac{1}{\cos x} + 1} + \frac{\cos x - 1}{\cos x + 1} \stackrel{?}{=} 0$$

$$\frac{1 - \cos x}{1 + \cos x} + \frac{\cos x - 1}{\cos x + 1} \stackrel{?}{=} 0$$

$$\frac{1 - \cos x + \cos x - 1}{1 + \cos x} \stackrel{?}{=} 0$$

$$0 = 0$$

24. $\sec^4 \alpha - \sec^2 \alpha \stackrel{?}{=} \dfrac{1}{\cot^4 \alpha} + \dfrac{1}{\cot^2 \alpha}$

$\sec^4 \alpha - \sec^2 \alpha \stackrel{?}{=} \tan^4 \alpha + \tan^2 \alpha$

$\sec^4 \alpha - \sec^2 \alpha \stackrel{?}{=} \tan^2 \alpha (\tan^2 \alpha + 1)$

$\sec^4 \alpha - \sec^2 \alpha \stackrel{?}{=} \tan^2 \alpha(\sec^2 \alpha)$

$\sec^4 \alpha - \sec^2 \alpha \stackrel{?}{=} (\sec^2 \alpha - 1)\sec^2 \alpha$

$\sec^4 \alpha - \sec^2 \alpha = \sec^4 \alpha - \sec^2 \alpha$

25. $\dfrac{\cos x}{1 + \sin x} + \dfrac{\cos x}{1 - \sin x} \stackrel{?}{=} 2\sec x$

$\dfrac{\cos x(1 - \sin x) + \cos x(1 + \sin x)}{1 - \sin^2 x} \stackrel{?}{=} 2\sec x$

$\dfrac{\cos x(1 - \sin x) + \cos x(1 + \sin x)}{\cos^2 x} \stackrel{?}{=} 2\sec x$

$\dfrac{(1 - \sin x) + (1 + \sin x)}{\cos x} \stackrel{?}{=} 2\sec x$

$\dfrac{2}{\cos x} \stackrel{?}{=} 2\sec x$

$2\sec x \stackrel{?}{=} 2\sec x$

26. $\dfrac{\sec B}{\cos B} - \dfrac{\tan B}{\cot B} \stackrel{?}{=} 1$

$\dfrac{\sec B}{\dfrac{1}{\sec B}} + \dfrac{\tan B}{\dfrac{1}{\tan B}} \stackrel{?}{=} 1$

$\sec^2 B - \tan^2 B \stackrel{?}{=} 1$

$(\tan^2 B + 1) - \tan^2 B \stackrel{?}{=} 1$

$1 = 1$

27. $1 + \sec^2 x \sin^2 x \stackrel{?}{=} \sec^2 x$

$1 + \dfrac{1}{\cos^2 x} \cdot \sin^2 x \stackrel{?}{=} \sec^2 x$

$1 + \tan^2 x \stackrel{?}{=} \sec^2 x$

$\sec^2 x = \sec^2 x$

28. $\dfrac{1 - 2\cos^2 \theta}{\sin \theta \cos \theta} \stackrel{?}{=} \tan \theta - \cot \theta$

$\dfrac{1 - 2\cos^2 \theta}{\sin \theta \cos \theta} \stackrel{?}{=} \dfrac{\sin \theta}{\cos \theta} - \dfrac{\cos \theta}{\sin \theta}$

$\dfrac{1 - 2\cos^2 \theta}{\sin \theta \cos \theta} \stackrel{?}{=} \dfrac{\sin^2 \theta - \cos^2 \theta}{\cos \theta \sin \theta}$

$\dfrac{1 - 2\cos^2 \theta}{\sin \theta \cos \theta} \stackrel{?}{=} \dfrac{1 - \cos^2 \theta - \cos^2 \theta}{\cos \theta \sin \theta}$

$\dfrac{1 - 2\cos^2 \theta}{\sin \theta \cos \theta} \stackrel{?}{=} \dfrac{1 - 2\cos^2 \theta}{\sin \theta \cos \theta}$

Pages 374-376,   Lesson 7-3

30. $\sin (270° + x) \stackrel{?}{=} -\cos x$

$\sin 270° \cos x + \cos 270° \sin x \stackrel{?}{=} -\cos x$

$-1 \cdot \cos x + 0 \cdot \sin x \stackrel{?}{=} -\cos x$

$-\cos x = -\cos x$

31. $\cos (90° + \theta) \stackrel{?}{=} -\sin \theta$

$\cos 90° \cos \theta - \sin 90° \sin \theta \stackrel{?}{=} -\sin \theta$

$0 - 1 \cdot \sin \theta \stackrel{?}{=} -\sin \theta$

$-\sin \theta \stackrel{?}{=} -\sin \theta$

32. $\tan (90° + \theta) \stackrel{?}{=} -\cot \theta$

$\dfrac{\sin (90° + \theta)}{\cos (90° + \theta)} \stackrel{?}{=} -\cot \theta$

$\dfrac{\sin 90° \cos \theta + \cos 90° \sin \theta}{\cos 90° \cos \theta - \sin 90° \sin \theta} \stackrel{?}{=} -\cot \theta$

$\dfrac{1 \cdot \cos \theta + 0 \cdot \sin \theta}{0 \cdot \cos \theta - 1 \cdot \sin \theta} \stackrel{?}{=} -\cot \theta$

$\dfrac{\cos \theta}{-\sin \theta} \stackrel{?}{=} -\cot \theta$

$-\cot \theta = -\cot \theta$

33. $\sin \left(\dfrac{\pi}{2} + x\right) \stackrel{?}{=} \cos x$

$\sin \dfrac{\pi}{2} \cos x + \cos \dfrac{\pi}{2} \sin x \stackrel{?}{=} \cos x$

$1 \cdot \cos x + 0 \cdot \sin x \stackrel{?}{=} \cos x$

$\cos x = \cos x$

34. $-\cos \theta \stackrel{?}{=} \cos (\pi + \theta)$

$-\cos \theta \stackrel{?}{=} \cos \pi \cos \theta - \sin \pi \sin \theta$

$-\cos \theta \stackrel{?}{=} -1 \cdot \cos \theta - 0 \cdot \sin \theta$

$-\cos \theta = -\cos \theta$

35. $\tan (\pi - \theta) \stackrel{?}{=} -\tan \theta$

$\dfrac{\tan \pi - \tan \theta}{1 + \tan \pi \tan \theta} \stackrel{?}{=} -\tan \theta$

$\dfrac{0 - \tan \theta}{1 + 0 \cdot \tan \theta} \stackrel{?}{=} -\tan \theta$

$-\tan \theta = -\tan \theta$

36. $-\sin \theta \stackrel{?}{=} \cos \left(\dfrac{\pi}{2} + \theta\right)$

$-\sin \theta \stackrel{?}{=} \cos \dfrac{\pi}{2} \cos \theta - \sin \dfrac{\pi}{2} \sin \theta$

$-\sin \theta \stackrel{?}{=} 0 \cdot \cos \theta - 1 \cdot \sin \theta$

$-\sin \theta = -\sin \theta$

37. $\dfrac{\sin (\beta - \alpha)}{\sin \alpha \sin \beta} \stackrel{?}{=} \cot \alpha - \cot \beta$

$\dfrac{\sin \beta \cos \alpha - \cos \beta \sin \alpha}{\sin \alpha \sin \beta} \stackrel{?}{=} \cot \alpha - \cot \beta$

$\dfrac{\cos \alpha}{\sin \alpha} - \dfrac{\cos \beta}{\sin \beta} \stackrel{?}{=} \cot \alpha - \cot \beta$

$\cot \alpha - \cot \beta = \cot \alpha - \cot \beta$

38. $\sin^2 \alpha - \sin^2 \beta \stackrel{?}{=} \sin (\alpha + \beta) \sin (\alpha - \beta)$

$\sin^2 \alpha - \sin^2 \beta \stackrel{?}{=} (\sin \alpha \cos \beta + \cos \alpha \sin \beta)$
$(\sin \alpha \cos \beta - \cos \alpha \sin \beta)$

$\sin^2 \alpha - \sin^2 \beta \stackrel{?}{=} \sin^2 \alpha \cos^2 \beta - \sin^2 \beta \cos^2 \alpha$

$\sin^2 \alpha - \sin^2 \beta \stackrel{?}{=} \sin^2 \alpha(1 - \sin^2 \beta) - \sin^2 \beta(1 - \sin^2 \alpha)$

$\sin^2 \alpha - \sin^2 \beta \stackrel{?}{=} \sin^2 \alpha - \sin^2 \alpha \sin^2 \beta - \sin^2 \beta + \sin^2 \beta \sin^2 \alpha$

$\sin^2 \alpha - \sin^2 \beta = \sin^2 \alpha - \sin^2 \beta$

39. $\cos(30° - x) + \cos(30° + x) \stackrel{?}{=} \sqrt{3} \cos x$

$(\cos 30° \cos x + \sin 30° \sin x) +$
$(\cos 30° \cos x - \sin 30° \sin x) \stackrel{?}{=} \sqrt{3} \cos x$

$\dfrac{\sqrt{3}}{2} \cdot \cos x + \dfrac{\sqrt{3}}{2} \cos x \stackrel{?}{=} \sqrt{3} \cos x$

$\sqrt{3} \cos x = \sqrt{3} \cos x$

40. $\cos (\alpha + \beta) + \cos(\alpha - \beta) \stackrel{?}{=} 2 \cos \alpha \cot \beta$

$(\cos \alpha \cos \beta - \sin \alpha \sin \beta) +$
$(\cos \alpha \cos \beta + \sin \alpha \sin \beta) \stackrel{?}{=} 2 \cos \alpha \cos \beta$

$2 \cos \alpha \cos \beta = 2 \cos \alpha \cos \beta$

44. $n = \dfrac{\sin\left[\dfrac{1}{2}(\alpha + \beta)\right]}{\sin\left(\dfrac{\beta}{2}\right)}$

$n = \dfrac{\sin\left[\dfrac{1}{2}(\alpha + 60°)\right]}{\sin\left(\dfrac{60°}{2}\right)}$

$n = \dfrac{\sin\left(\dfrac{\alpha}{2} + 30°\right)}{\sin 30°}$

$n = \dfrac{\sin \dfrac{\alpha}{2} \cos 30° + \cos \dfrac{\alpha}{2} \sin 30°}{\dfrac{1}{2}}$

$n = 2\left(\dfrac{\sqrt{3}}{2} \sin \dfrac{\alpha}{2} + \dfrac{1}{2} \cos \dfrac{\alpha}{2}\right)$

$n = \sqrt{3} \sin\left(\dfrac{\alpha}{2}\right) + \cos\left(\dfrac{\alpha}{2}\right)$

51. $2 \sec^2 x \stackrel{?}{=} \dfrac{1}{1 + \sin x} + \dfrac{1}{1 - \sin x}$

$2 \sec^2 x \stackrel{?}{=} \dfrac{(1 - \sin x) + (1 + \sin x)}{(1 + \sin x)(1 - \sin x)}$

$2 \sec^2 x \stackrel{?}{=} \dfrac{2}{1 - \sin^2 x}$

$2 \sec^2 x \stackrel{?}{=} \dfrac{2}{\cos^2 x}$

$2 \sec^2 x = 2 \sec^2 x$

29. $1 + \cos 2A \overset{?}{=} \dfrac{2}{1 + \tan^2 A}$

$1 + \cos 2A \overset{?}{=} \dfrac{2}{\sec^2 A}$

$1 + \cos 2A \overset{?}{=} 2\cos^2 A$

$1 + \cos 2A \overset{?}{=} 1 + 2\cos^2 A - 1$

$1 + \cos 2A = 1 + \cos 2A$

30. $\cos^2 2x + 4\sin^2 x \cos^2 x \overset{?}{=} 1$

$\cos^2 2x + (2\sin x \cos x)^2 \overset{?}{=} 1$

$\cos^2 2x + (\sin 2x)^2 \overset{?}{=} 1$

$\cos^2 2x + \sin^2 2x \overset{?}{=} 1$

$1 = 1$

31. $\csc A \sec A \overset{?}{=} 2 \csc 2A$

$\dfrac{1}{\sin A \cos A} \overset{?}{=} 2 \csc 2A$

$\dfrac{2}{2 \sin A \cos A} \overset{?}{=} 2 \csc 2A$

$\dfrac{2}{\sin 2A} \overset{?}{=} 2 \csc 2A$

$2 \csc 2A = 2 \csc 2A$

32. $\dfrac{1 - \tan^2 \theta}{1 + \tan^2 \theta} \overset{?}{=} \cos 2\theta$

$\dfrac{1 + \dfrac{\sin^2 \theta}{\cos^2 \theta}}{\sec^2 \theta} \overset{?}{=} \cos 2\theta$

$\cos^2 \theta \left(1 - \dfrac{\sin^2 \theta}{\cos^2 \theta}\right) \overset{?}{=} \cos 2\theta$

$\cos^2 \theta - \sin^2 \theta \overset{?}{=} \cos 2\theta$

$\cos 2\theta = \cos 2\theta$

33. $\cot X \overset{?}{=} \dfrac{\sin 2X}{1 - \cos 2X}$

$\cot X \overset{?}{=} \dfrac{2 \sin X \cos X}{1 - (1 - 2\sin^2 X)}$

$\cot X \overset{?}{=} \dfrac{2 \sin X \cos X}{2 \sin^2 X}$

$\cot X \overset{?}{=} \dfrac{\cos X}{\sin X}$

$\cot X \overset{?}{=} \cot X$

34. $\dfrac{1 + \cos x}{\sin x} \overset{?}{=} \cot \dfrac{x}{2}$

$\dfrac{1 + \cos x}{\sin x} \overset{?}{=} \dfrac{\cos \dfrac{x}{2}}{\sin \dfrac{x}{2}}$

$\dfrac{1 + \cos x}{\sin x} \overset{?}{=} \dfrac{\sqrt{\dfrac{1 + \cos x}{2}}}{\sqrt{\dfrac{1 - \cos x}{2}}}$

$\dfrac{1 + \cos x}{\sin x} \overset{?}{=} \sqrt{\dfrac{1 + \cos x}{1 - \cos x}}$

$\dfrac{1 + \cos x}{\sin x} \overset{?}{=} \sqrt{\dfrac{(1 + \cos x)^2}{1 - \cos^2 x}}$

$\dfrac{1 + \cos x}{\sin x} \overset{?}{=} \sqrt{\dfrac{(1 + \cos x)^2}{\sin^2 x}}$

$\dfrac{1 + \cos x}{\sin x} = \dfrac{1 + \cos x}{\sin x}$

35. $\sin 2B(\cot B + \tan B) \overset{?}{=} 2$

$2 \sin B \cos B \left(\dfrac{\cos B}{\sin B} + \dfrac{\sin B}{\cos B}\right) \overset{?}{=} 2$

$2 \sin B \cos B \left(\dfrac{\cos^2 B + \sin^2 B}{\sin B \cos B}\right) \overset{?}{=} 2$

$2 = 2$

36. $1 - \sin A \overset{?}{=} \left(\sin \dfrac{A}{2} - \cos \dfrac{A}{2}\right)^2$

$1 - \sin A \overset{?}{=} \sin^2 \dfrac{A}{2} - 2 \sin \dfrac{A}{2} \cos \dfrac{A}{2} + \cos^2 \dfrac{A}{2}$

$1 - \sin A = 1 - \sin A$

37. $\cot \dfrac{\alpha}{2} \overset{?}{=} \dfrac{\sin \alpha}{1 - \cos \alpha}$

$\dfrac{1}{\tan \dfrac{\alpha}{2}} \overset{?}{=} \dfrac{\sin \alpha}{1 - \cos \alpha}$

$\dfrac{1}{\sqrt{\dfrac{1 - \cos \alpha}{1 + \cos \alpha}}} \overset{?}{=} \dfrac{\sin \alpha}{1 - \cos \alpha}$

$\dfrac{1}{\sqrt{\dfrac{(1 - \cos \alpha)^2}{1 - \cos^2 \alpha}}} \overset{?}{=} \dfrac{\sin \alpha}{1 - \cos \alpha}$

$\dfrac{1}{\sqrt{\dfrac{(1 - \cos \alpha)^2}{\sin^2 \alpha}}} \overset{?}{=} \dfrac{\sin \alpha}{1 - \cos \alpha}$

$\dfrac{1}{\dfrac{1 - \cos \alpha}{\sin \alpha}} \overset{?}{=} \dfrac{\sin \alpha}{1 - \cos \alpha}$

$\dfrac{\sin \alpha}{1 - \cos \alpha} = \dfrac{\sin \alpha}{1 - \cos \alpha}$

38. $\dfrac{\sin \dfrac{x}{2}}{\cos \dfrac{x}{2}} \overset{?}{=} \dfrac{\sin x}{1 + \cos x}$

$\dfrac{\sqrt{\dfrac{1 - \cos x}{2}}}{\sqrt{\dfrac{1 + \cos x}{2}}} \overset{?}{=} \dfrac{\sin x}{1 + \cos x}$

$\sqrt{\dfrac{1 - \cos x}{1 + \cos x}} \overset{?}{=} \dfrac{\sin x}{1 + \cos x}$

$\sqrt{\dfrac{1 - \cos^2 x}{(1 + \cos x)^2}} \overset{?}{=} \dfrac{\sin x}{1 + \cos x}$

$\sqrt{\dfrac{\sin^2 x}{(1 + \cos x)^2}} \overset{?}{=} \dfrac{\sin x}{1 + \cos x}$

$\dfrac{\sin x}{1 + \cos x} = \dfrac{\sin x}{1 + \cos x}$

39. $\dfrac{\cos 2A}{1 + \sin 2A} \overset{?}{=} \dfrac{\cot A - 1}{\cot A + 1}$

$\dfrac{\cos 2A}{1 + \sin 2A} \overset{?}{=} \dfrac{\dfrac{\cos A}{\sin A} - 1}{\dfrac{\cos A}{\sin A} + 1}$

$\dfrac{\cos 2A}{1 + \sin 2A} \overset{?}{=} \dfrac{\cos A - \sin A}{\cos A + \sin A}$

$\dfrac{\cos 2A}{1 + \sin 2A} \overset{?}{=} \dfrac{\cos^2 A - \sin^2 A}{\cos^2 A + 2\sin A \cos A + \sin^2 A}$

$\dfrac{\cos 2A}{1 + \sin 2A} \overset{?}{=} \dfrac{\cos 2A}{1 + 2\sin A \cos A}$

$\dfrac{\cos 2A}{1 + \sin 2A} \overset{?}{=} \dfrac{\cos 2A}{1 + \sin 2A}$

40. $\dfrac{\sin \alpha + \sin 3\alpha}{\cos \alpha + \cos 3\alpha} \overset{?}{=} \tan 2\alpha$

$\dfrac{\sin \alpha + \sin(2\alpha + \alpha)}{\cos \alpha + \cos(2\alpha + \alpha)} \overset{?}{=} \tan 2\alpha$

$\dfrac{\sin \alpha + \sin 2\alpha \cos \alpha + \cos 2\alpha \sin \alpha}{\cos \alpha + \cos 2\alpha \cos \alpha - \sin 2\alpha \sin \alpha} \overset{?}{=} \tan 2\alpha$

$\dfrac{\sin \alpha + 2\sin \alpha \cos \alpha \cos \alpha + \sin \alpha (2\cos^2 \alpha - 1)}{\cos \alpha + (2\cos^2 \alpha - 1)\cos \alpha - 2\sin \alpha \cos \alpha \sin \alpha} \overset{?}{=} \tan 2\alpha$

$\dfrac{\sin \alpha(1 + 2\cos^2 \alpha + 2\cos^2 \alpha - 1)}{\cos \alpha(1 + 2\cos^2 \alpha - 1 - 2\sin^2 \alpha)} \overset{?}{=} \tan 2\alpha$

$\dfrac{\sin \alpha(4 \cos^2 \alpha)}{\cos \alpha(2)(\cos^2 \alpha - \sin^2 \alpha)} \overset{?}{=} \tan 2\alpha$

$\dfrac{2 \cos \alpha \sin \alpha}{\cos^2 \alpha - \sin^2 \alpha} \overset{?}{=} \tan 2\alpha$

$\dfrac{\sin 2\alpha}{\cos 2\alpha} \overset{?}{=} \tan 2\alpha$

$\tan 2\alpha = \tan 2\alpha$

Page 383, Mid-Chapter Review

5. $\sin \theta(1 + \cot^2 \theta) \overset{?}{=} \csc \theta$

$$\sin \theta(\csc^2 \theta) \stackrel{?}{=} \csc \theta$$
$$\frac{1}{\csc \theta}(\csc^2 \theta) \stackrel{?}{=} \csc \theta$$
$$\csc \theta = \csc \theta$$

6. $\cos^2 A \stackrel{?}{=} (1 - \sin A)(1 + \sin A)$
$\cos^2 A \stackrel{?}{=} 1 - \sin^2 A$
$\cos^2 A = \cos^2 A$

7. $-\cos \theta \stackrel{?}{=} \cos(180° - \theta)$
$-\cos \theta \stackrel{?}{=} \cos 180° \cos \theta + \sin 180° \sin \theta$
$-\cos \theta \stackrel{?}{=} (-1)\cos \theta + (0)\sin \theta$
$-\cos \theta = -\cos \theta$

8.
$$\frac{\cos A + \sin A}{\cos A - \sin A} \stackrel{?}{=} \frac{1 + \sin 2A}{\cos 2A}$$
$$\frac{\cos A + \sin A}{\cos A - \sin A} \cdot \frac{\cos A + \sin A}{\cos A + \sin A} \stackrel{?}{=} \frac{1 + \sin 2A}{\cos 2A}$$
$$\frac{\cos^2 A + 2\sin A \cos A + \sin^2 A}{\cos^2 A - \sin^2 A} \stackrel{?}{=} \frac{1 + \sin 2A}{\cos 2A}$$
$$\frac{1 + 2\sin A \cos A}{\cot^2 A - \sin^2 A} \stackrel{?}{=} \frac{1 + \sin 2A}{\cos 2A}$$
$$\frac{1 + \sin 2A}{\cos 2A} = \frac{1 + \sin 2A}{\cos 2A}$$

9. $\sin^2 \theta \stackrel{?}{=} \frac{1}{2}(1 - \cos 2\theta)$

$\sin^2 \theta \stackrel{?}{=} \frac{1}{2}[1 - (1 - 2\sin^2 \theta)]$

$\sin^2 \theta \stackrel{?}{=} \frac{1}{2}(2\sin^2 \theta)$

$\sin^2 \theta = \sin^2 \theta$

10. $\sin 2x \stackrel{?}{=} 2\cot x \sin^2 x$

$\sin 2x \stackrel{?}{=} 2 \cdot \frac{\cos x}{\sin x} \cdot \sin^2 x$

$\sin 2x \stackrel{?}{=} 2\cos x \sin x$

$\sin 2x \stackrel{?}{=} 2\sin x \cos x$

$\sin 2x = \sin 2x$

Page 386, Lesson 7-5A

1.

2.

3.

4.

5.

6.

7.

8.

9.

10.

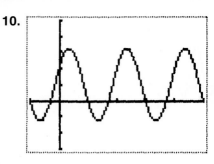

Page 409, Chapter 7 Test

5. $\tan \theta (\cot \theta + \tan \theta) \stackrel{?}{=} \sec^2 \theta$

$\tan \theta \cot \theta + \tan^2 \theta \stackrel{?}{=} \sec^2 \theta$

$1 + \tan^2 \theta \stackrel{?}{=} \sec^2 \theta$

$\sec^2 \theta = \sec^2 \theta$

6. $\sin^2 A \cot^2 A \stackrel{?}{=} (1 - \sin A)(1 + \sin A)$

$\sin^2 A \cdot \dfrac{\cos^2 A}{\sin^2 A} \stackrel{?}{=} (1 - \sin A)(1 + \sin A)$

$\cos^2 A \stackrel{?}{=} (1 - \sin A)(1 + \sin A)$

$1 - \sin^2 A \stackrel{?}{=} (1 - \sin A)(1 + \sin A)$

$(1 - \sin A)(1 + \sin A) = (1 - \sin A)(1 + \sin A)$

7. $\dfrac{\sec x}{\sin x} - \dfrac{\sin x}{\cos x} \stackrel{?}{=} \cot x$

$\dfrac{\sec x \cos x - \sin^2 x}{\sin x \cos x} \stackrel{?}{=} \cot x$

$\dfrac{1 - \sin^2 x}{\sin x \cos x} \stackrel{?}{=} \cot x$

$\dfrac{\cos^2 x}{\sin x \cos x} \stackrel{?}{=} \cot x$

$\dfrac{\cos x}{\sin x} \stackrel{?}{=} \cot x$

$\cot x = \cot x$

8. $\dfrac{\cos x}{1 + \sin x} + \dfrac{\cos x}{1 - \sin x} \stackrel{?}{=} 2 \sec x$

$\dfrac{\cos x - \cos x \sin x + \cos x + \sin x \cos x}{1 - \sin^2 x} \stackrel{?}{=} 2 \sec x$

$\dfrac{2 \cos x}{1 - \sin^2 x} \stackrel{?}{=} 2 \sec x$

$\dfrac{2 \cos x}{\cos^2 x} \stackrel{?}{=} 2 \sec x$

$\dfrac{2}{\cos x} \stackrel{?}{=} 2 \sec x$

$2 \sec x = 2 \sec x$

CHAPTER 8 VECTORS AND PARAMETRIC EQUATIONS

Pages 427-429, Lesson 8-3

4.

$(3, 4, 9)$

5.

$(-2, 1, 3)$

6.

$(-1, 0, 4)$

7.

$(7, 2, 4)$

8.

$(4, 1, -3)$

9.

$(-1, -1, 5)$

Pages 433-435, Lesson 8-4

34. $\vec{a} \times \vec{a} = \begin{vmatrix} a_2 & a_3 \\ a_2 & a_3 \end{vmatrix} \vec{i} - \begin{vmatrix} a_1 & a_3 \\ a_1 & a_3 \end{vmatrix} \vec{j} + \begin{vmatrix} a_1 & a_2 \\ a_1 & a_2 \end{vmatrix} \vec{k}$

$= (a_2 a_3 - a_2 a_3)\vec{i} - (a_1 a_3 - a_1 a_3)\vec{j} + (a_1 a_2 - a_1 a_2)\vec{k}$

$= 0$

35. $\vec{a} \times (\vec{b} + \vec{c}) = \begin{vmatrix} \vec{i} & \vec{j} & \vec{k} \\ a_1 & a_2 & a_3 \\ (b_1 + c_1) & (b_2 + c_2) & (b_3 + c_3) \end{vmatrix}$

$= \begin{vmatrix} a_2 & a_3 \\ (b_2 + c_2) & (b_3 + c_3) \end{vmatrix} \vec{i} - \begin{vmatrix} a_1 & a_3 \\ (b_1 + c_1) & (b_3 + c_3) \end{vmatrix} \vec{j}$

$\quad + \begin{vmatrix} a_1 & a_2 \\ (b_1 + c_1) & (b_2 + c_2) \end{vmatrix} \vec{k}$

$= [a_2(b_3 + c_3) - a_3(b_2 + c_2)] \vec{i}$

$\quad - [a_1(b_3 + c_3) - a_3(b_1 + c_1)] \vec{j}$

$\quad + [a_1(b_2 + c_2) - a_2(b_1 + c_1)] \vec{k}$

$= [(a_2 b_3 + a_2 c_3) - (a_3 b_2 + a_3 c_2)] \vec{i}$

$\quad - [(a_1 b_3 + a_1 c_3) - (a_3 b_1 + a_3 c_1)] \vec{j}$

$\quad + [(a_1 b_2 + a_1 c_2) - (a_2 b_1 + a_2 c_1)] \vec{k}$

$= [(a_2 b_3 - a_3 b_2) + (a_2 c_3 - a_3 c_2)] \vec{i}$

$\quad - [(a_1 b_3 - a_3 b_1) + (a_1 c_3 - a_3 c_1)] \vec{j}$

$\quad + [(a_1 b_2 - a_2 b_1) + (a_1 c_2 - a_2 c_1)] \vec{k}$

$= (a_2 b_3 - a_3 b_2) \vec{i} + (a_2 c_3 - a_3 c_2) \vec{i}$

$\quad - (a_1 b_3 - a_3 b_1) \vec{j} - (a_1 c_3 - a_3 c_1) \vec{j}$

$\quad + (a_1 b_2 - a_2 b_1) \vec{k} + (a_1 c_2 - a_2 c_1) \vec{k}$

$= [(a_2 b_3 - a_3 b_2) \vec{i} - (a_1 b_3 - a_3 b_1) \vec{j}$

$\quad + (a_1 b_2 - a_2 b_1) \vec{k}]$

$\quad + [(a_2 c_3 - a_3 c_2) \vec{i} - (a_1 c_3 - a_3 c_1) \vec{j}$

$\quad + (a_1 c_2 - a_2 c_1) \vec{k}]$

$= \begin{vmatrix} a_2 & a_3 \\ b_2 & b_3 \end{vmatrix} \vec{i} - \begin{vmatrix} a_1 & a_3 \\ b_1 & b_3 \end{vmatrix} \vec{j} + \begin{vmatrix} a_1 & a_2 \\ b_1 & b_2 \end{vmatrix} \vec{k}$

$\quad + \begin{vmatrix} a_2 & a_3 \\ c_2 & c_3 \end{vmatrix} \vec{i} - \begin{vmatrix} a_1 & a_3 \\ c_1 & c_3 \end{vmatrix} \vec{j} + \begin{vmatrix} a_1 & a_2 \\ c_1 & c_2 \end{vmatrix} \vec{k}$

$= (\vec{a} \times \vec{b}) + (\vec{a} \times \vec{c})$

38. $\vec{a} \cdot \vec{b} = \vec{a} \cdot \vec{c}$

$\vec{a} \cdot \vec{b} - \vec{a} \cdot \vec{c} = 0$

$\vec{a} \cdot (\vec{b} - \vec{c}) = 0$

So $\vec{a} \perp (\vec{b} - \vec{c})$.

$\vec{a} \times \vec{b} = \vec{a} \times \vec{c}$

$\vec{a} \times \vec{b} - \vec{a} \times \vec{c} = 0$

$\vec{a} \times (\vec{b} - \vec{c}) = 0$

So $\vec{a} = (\vec{b} - \vec{c})$, $\vec{a} = 0$, or $(\vec{b} - \vec{c}) = 0$.

Since the inner products were equal, we concluded that $\vec{a} \perp (\vec{b} - \vec{c})$, so it cannot be that $\vec{a} = (\vec{b} - \vec{c})$. We are given that $\vec{a} \neq 0$, so it must be that $(\vec{b} - \vec{c}) = 0$.

$\vec{b} - \vec{c} = 0$

$\vec{b} = \vec{c}$ Yes, $\vec{b} = \vec{c}$.

Pages 460-461, Unit 2 Review

25.
$y = \frac{1}{2}$ Cos $2x$

26.
$y = 3\tan(2x - 90°)$

27.
$y = x + 2\sin 3x$

34.
$y = \arccos x$

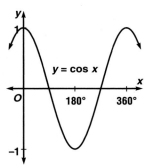
$y = \cos x$

35.
$y = \cot x$

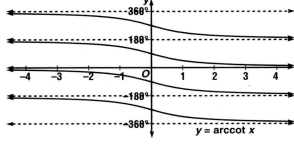
$y = \text{arccot } x$

36.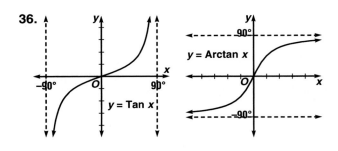
$y = \text{Tan } x$

$y = \text{Arctan } x$

37.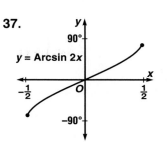
$y = \text{Arcsin } 2x$

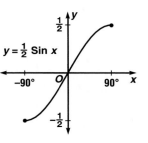
$y = \frac{1}{2}$ Sin x

41. $\tan x + \tan x \cot^2 x \overset{?}{=} \sec x \csc x$

$\tan x(1 + \cot^2 x) \overset{?}{=} \sec x \csc x$

$\tan x(\csc^2 x) \overset{?}{=} \sec x \csc x$

$\left(\dfrac{\sin x}{\cos x}\right)\left(\dfrac{1}{\sin^2 x}\right) \overset{?}{=} \sec x \csc x$

$\left(\dfrac{1}{\cos x}\right)\left(\dfrac{1}{\sin x}\right) \overset{?}{=} \sec x \csc x$

$\sec x \csc x = \sec x \csc x$

42. $\sin(180° - \theta) \overset{?}{=} \tan\theta\cos\theta$

$\sin 180°\cos\theta - \cos 180°\sin\theta \overset{?}{=} \tan\theta\cos\theta$

$0(\cos\theta) - (-1)\sin\theta \overset{?}{=} \tan\theta\cos\theta$

$\sin\theta \overset{?}{=} \tan\theta\cos\theta$

$\sin\left(\dfrac{\cos\theta}{\cos\theta}\right) \overset{?}{=} \tan\theta\cos\theta$

$\dfrac{\sin\theta}{\cos\theta} \cdot \cos\theta \overset{?}{=} \tan\theta\cos\theta$

$\tan\theta\cos\theta = \tan\theta\cos\theta$

CHAPTER 9 POLAR COORDINATES AND COMPLEX NUMBERS

Pages 470-472, Lesson 9-1

4.
(100, 50°)

5.
$(12.8, \frac{\pi}{6})$

6.
(1.2, 70°)

7.

8.

9.

10.

11.

12.

13.

14.

15.

16.

17.

18.

19.

20.

21.

25.

26.

27.

28.

29.

30.

31.

32.

33.

34.

35.

36.

Page 474, Lesson 9-2A

1.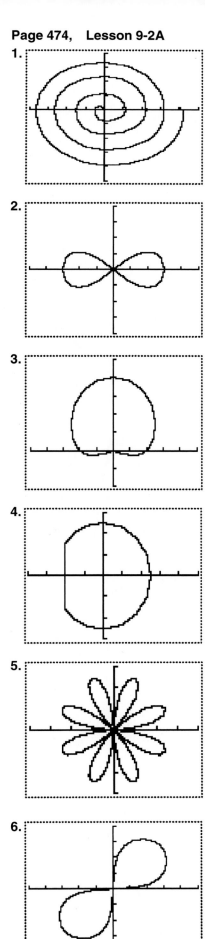

2.

3.

4.

5.

6.

7.

8.

Pages 479-481, Lesson 9-2

6.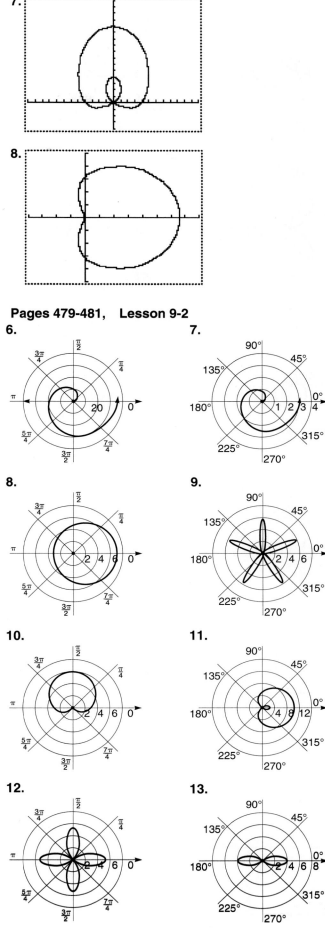

7.

8.

9.

10.

11.

12.

13.

14.

15.

23.

16.

17.

Pages 492-493, Lesson 9-4

9.

10.

18.

19.

11.

12.

20.

13.

14.

21.

Page 493, Mid-Chapter Review

1.

2.

22.

3.

Page 500, Lesson 9-5

49.

$$\sin^4 A + \cos^2 A \overset{?}{=} \cos^4 A + \sin^2 A$$
$$(\sin^2 A)^2 + \cos^2 A \overset{?}{=} \cos^4 A + \sin^2 A$$
$$(1 - \cos^2 A)^2 + \cos^2 A \overset{?}{=} \cos^4 A + \sin^2 A$$
$$(1 - 2\cos^2 A + \cos^4 A) + \cos^2 A \overset{?}{=} \cos^4 A + \sin^2 A$$
$$\cos^4 A + 1 - \cos^2 A \overset{?}{=} \cos^4 A + \sin^2 A$$
$$\cos^4 A + \sin^2 A = \cos^4 A + \sin^2 A$$

Pages 504-505, Lesson 9-6

5.

$$\sqrt{2}\left(\cos \frac{3\pi}{4} + i \sin \frac{3\pi}{4}\right)$$

6.

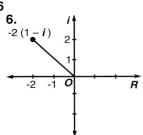

$$2\sqrt{2}\left(\cos \frac{3\pi}{4} + i \sin \frac{3\pi}{4}\right)$$

7.

$$70\left(\cos \frac{\pi}{2} + i \sin \frac{\pi}{2}\right)$$

8.

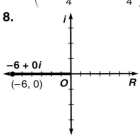

$$6(\cos \pi + i \sin \pi)$$

9.

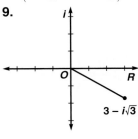

$$2\sqrt{3}\left(\cos \frac{11\pi}{6} + i \sin \frac{11\pi}{6}\right)$$

10.

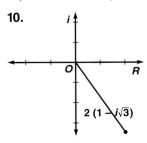

$$4\left(\cos \frac{5\pi}{3} + i \sin \frac{5\pi}{3}\right)$$

11.

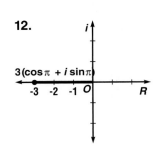

$4(\cos 0 + i \sin 0)$

12.

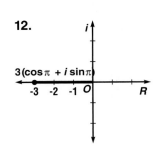

$3(\cos \pi + i \sin \pi)$

13.

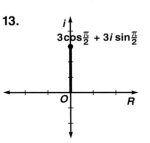

$3\cos\frac{\pi}{2} + 3i \sin\frac{\pi}{2}$

14.

$0.5 \left(\cos \frac{5\pi}{6} + i \sin \frac{5\pi}{6}\right)$

15. $\sqrt{2}\left(\cos \frac{5\pi}{4} + i \sin \frac{5\pi}{4}\right)$ **16.** $6\left(\cos \frac{\pi}{2} + i \sin \frac{\pi}{2}\right)$

17. $10\left(\cos \frac{\pi}{2} + i \sin \frac{\pi}{2}\right)$ **18.** $\sqrt{26}\ (\cos 3.34 + i \sin 3.34)$

19. $5(\cos 0.64 + i \sin 0.64)$

20. $\sqrt{21}[\cos (-0.71) + i \sin (-0.71)]$

21. $2\left(\cos \frac{\pi}{3} + i \sin \frac{\pi}{3}\right)$ **22.** $4\left(\cos \frac{3\pi}{2} + i \sin \frac{3\pi}{2}\right)$

23. $5(\cos \pi + i \sin \pi)$

34.

40.

Pages 515-517, Lesson 9-8

22.

23.

24.

25.

26.

27.

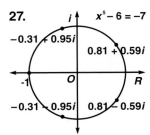

Pages 518-520, Chapter 9 Summary and Review

1.

(-3, -310°), (3, 230°), (3, -130°)

2.

(1.5, 250°), (-1.5, 70°), (-1.5, -290°)

3.

$\left(2, -\frac{7\pi}{4}\right), \left(-2, \frac{5\pi}{4}\right), \left(-2, -\frac{3\pi}{4}\right)$

4.

$\left(-3, \frac{3\pi}{2}\right), \left(3, \frac{\pi}{2}\right), \left(3, -\frac{3\pi}{2}\right)$

5.

6.

7.

8.

48.

2, 0.62 ± 1.90*i*, -1.62 ± 1.18*i*

49.

$\pm 1, \frac{1}{2} \pm \frac{\sqrt{3}}{2}i, -\frac{1}{2} \pm \frac{\sqrt{3}}{2}i$

Page 521, Chapter 9 Test

1.

$\left(-2, -\frac{3\pi}{4}\right), \left(2, \frac{\pi}{4}\right), \left(2, -\frac{7\pi}{4}\right)$

2.

$\left(3, \frac{11\pi}{6}\right), \left(-3, -\frac{7\pi}{6}\right), \left(-3, \frac{5\pi}{6}\right)$

3.

(2.5, -220°), (-2.5, -40°), (-2.5, 320°)

4.

(-1.7, -335°), (1.7, -155°), (1.7, 205°)

5.

6.

7.

8.

9.

10.

33.

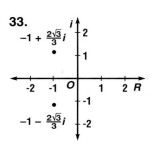

$-1 + \frac{2\sqrt{3}}{3}i$

$-1 - \frac{2\sqrt{3}}{3}i$

Bonus

20.

21.

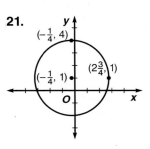

CHAPTER 10   CONICS

Pages 529-532,   Lesson 10-1

22.

23.

9.

10.

24.

25.

11.

12.

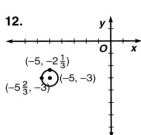

Pages 539-541,   Lesson 10-2

14.

15.

8.

9.

16.

17.

10.

13c.

18.

19.

14c.

15c.

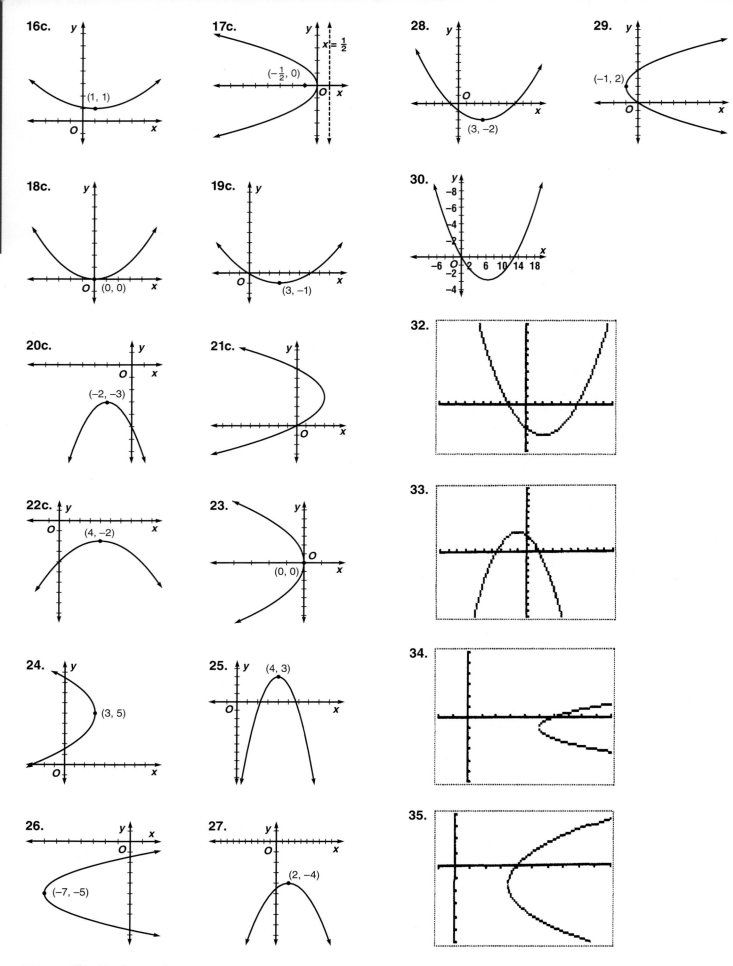

16c. (1, 1)

17c. $x = \frac{1}{2}$, $(-\frac{1}{2}, 0)$

28. (3, −2)

29. (−1, 2)

18c. (0, 0)

19c. (3, −1)

30.

20c. (−2, −3)

21c.

32.

22c. (4, −2)

23. (0, 0)

33.

24. (3, 5)

25. (4, 3)

34.

26. (−7, −5)

27. (2, −4)

35.

40a.

41.

17.

18.

19.

20.

21.

22.

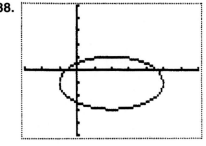

Pages 548-550, Lesson 10-3

5.

6.

7.

8.

37.

9.

10.

38.

15.

16.

39.

40.

41.

Pages 556-559,   Lesson 10-4

4. center: (0, 0), foci:
(0, 0 ± √85), vertices: (0, 6),
(0, -6), asymptotes: $y = \pm\frac{6}{7}x$

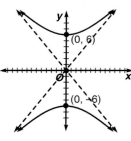

5. center: (-3, 4), foci:
(-3 ± √74, 4), vertices:
(2, 4), (-8, 4), asymptotes:
$y - 4 = \pm\frac{7}{5}(x + 3)$

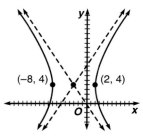

6. center: (0, 5), foci:
(±√97, 5), vertices: (4, 5),
(-4, 5), asymptotes:
$y - 5 = \pm\frac{9}{4}x$

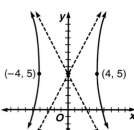

7. center: (8, 5), foci:
(8, 5 ± √104), vertices:
(8, 7), (8, 3), asymptotes:
$y - 5 = \pm\frac{1}{5}(x - 8)$

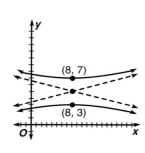

8. center: (-12, 0), foci:
(-12, ±√458), vertices:
(-12, 13), (-12, -13),
asymptotes: $y = \pm\frac{13}{17}(x + 12)$

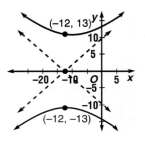

9. center (-11, -7), foci:
(-11 ± 6√5, -7), vertices:
(1, -7), (-23, -7), asymptotes:
$y + 7 = \pm\frac{1}{2}(x + 11)$

14.

15.

16.

17.

18.

19.

20.

21.

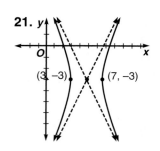

T1060   TEACHER'S ANSWER KEY

22.

29.

10.

30.

31.

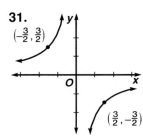

Pages 565-567, Lesson 10-5

20.

21.

32.

33.

22.

23.

34.

35.

24.

25.

Page 559, Mid-Chapter Review

2.

4.

26.

27.

6.

9.

28.

29.

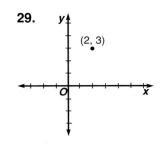

TEACHER'S ANSWER KEY   T1061

Pages 568-569,   Lesson 10-6A

1.

2.

3.

4.

5.

6.

Pages 574-576,   Lesson 10-6

4.

5.

6.

7.

13.

14.

15.

16.

27.

28.

29.

30.

31.

32.

33.

34.

35.

36.

38a.

38b.

38c.

38d.

Pages 582-584, Lesson 10-7

11.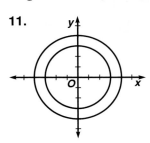

12. (−1, 6.9) (−1, −6.9)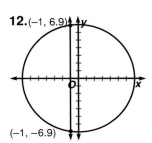

13. (4.0, 0.5) (−2.8, −2.9)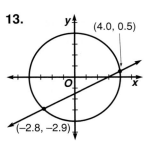

16. (8, 6) (−6, −8)

17.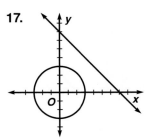

18. (−4.6, 5) (4.6, 5)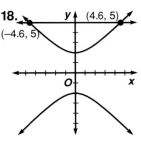

19. (3, 3) (−1, −1)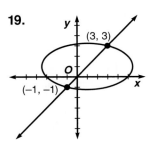

20. (2, 1) (−2, −1)

21.

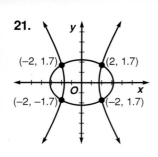

(−2, 1.7) (2, 1.7) O (−2, −1.7) (−2, 1.7)

22.

33.

34.

35.

23.

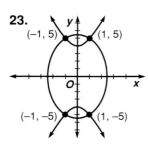

(−1, 5) (1, 5) O (−1, −5) (1, −5)

24.

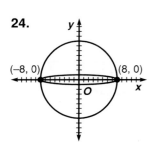

(−8, 0) (8, 0) O

Pages 592-594, Chapter 10 Summary and Review

1.

2.

3.

4.

25.

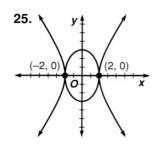

(−2, 0) (2, 0) O

26.

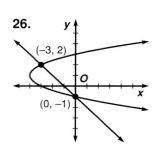

(−3, 2) O (0, −1)

27.

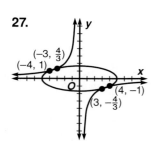

(−3, 4/3) (−4, 1) O (4, −1) (3, −4/3)

28.

5.

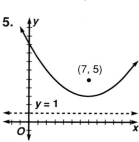

(7, 5) y = 1 O

vertex: (7, 3), focus: (7, 5), directrix: $y = 1$

6.

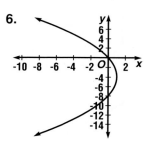

vertex: (1, −4), focus: (−3, −4), directrix: $x = 5$

29.

30.

31.

32.

7.

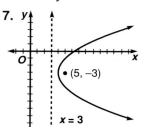

(5, −3) x = 3

vertex: (4, −3), focus: (5, −3), directrix: $x = 3$

8.

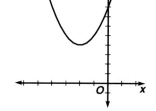

vertex: (−2, 4), focus: $(-2, 4\frac{1}{4})$, directrix: $y = 3\frac{3}{4}$

9.

center: (3, -1), foci: (3 ± √21, -1), vertices: (8, -1), (-2, -1), (3, 1), (3, -3)

10.

center: (5, 2), foci: (5, 2 ± 2√5), vertices: (5, 8), (5, -4), (1, 2), (9, 2)

11.

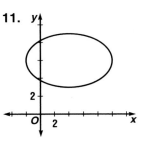

center: (4, 6), foci: (4 ± 3√3, 6), vertices: (10, 6), (-2, 6), (4, 3), (4, 9)

12.

center: (-3, 4), foci: (-3, 4 ± √2), vertices: (-3, 4 ± √6), (-1, 4), (-5, 4)

13.

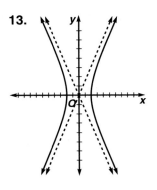

center: (0, 0), foci: (±2√3, 0), vertices: (±2, 0), asymptotes: $y = ±√2x$

14.

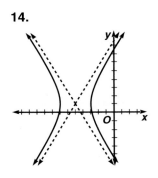

center: (-5, 1), foci: (-5 ± 2√3, 1), vertices: (-3, 1), (-7, 1), asymptotes: $y - 1 = ±√2(x + 5)$

15.

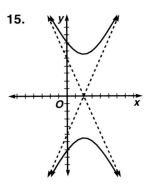

center: (2, 0), foci: (2, ±6), vertices: (2, ±√30), asymptotes: $y = ±√5(x - 2)$

16.

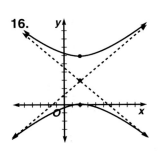

center: (2, 3), foci: (2, 8), (2, -2), vertices: (2, 6), (2, 0), asymptotes: $y - 3 = ±\frac{3}{4}(x - 2)$

17.

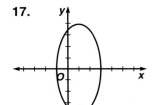

$$\frac{y^2}{16} + \frac{(x - 1)^2}{4} = 1$$

18.

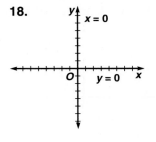

$x = 0, y = 0$

19.

$(x - 4)^2 + (y - 1)^2 = 4$

20.

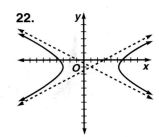

$(x - 4)^2 = 6y$

21.

22.

23.

24.

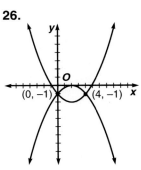

25.

(3, 3)

(-1, -1)

26.

(0, -1)   (4, -1)

27.

28.

(0, 2)

1.

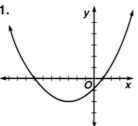

$(x + 3)^2 = 8(y + 2)$

2.

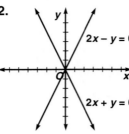

$2x - y = 0$

$2x + y = 0$

$4x^2 - y^2 = 0$

3.

$$\frac{y^2}{\frac{5}{13}} - \frac{x^2}{\frac{5}{2}} = 1$$

4.

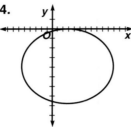

$$\frac{(x - 3)^2}{81} + \frac{(y + 4)^2}{16} = 1$$

5.

$(y + 5)^2 = 2(x - 1)$

6.

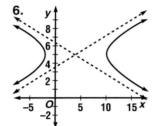

$$\frac{(x - 4)^2}{36} - \frac{(y - 5)^2}{4} = 1$$

7.

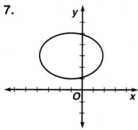

$$\frac{(x + 1)^2}{8} + \frac{(y - 3)^2}{4} = 1$$

8.

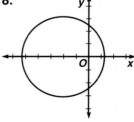

$(x + 2)^2 + y^2 = 10$

13.

14.

15.

$(\frac{2}{3}, \frac{2\sqrt{2}}{3})$

$(2, 0)$

$(\frac{2}{3}, -\frac{2\sqrt{2}}{3})$

16.

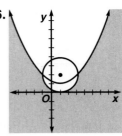

Page 605,   Lesson 11-2A

1.

2.

3.

4.

5.

6.

7.

8.

9.

12.
$y < 2^x + 1$

17.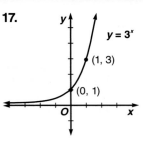
$y = 3^x$
(1, 3)
(0, 1)

18.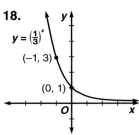
$y = \left(\frac{1}{3}\right)^x$
(−1, 3)
(0, 1)

19.
(−1, 5)
$y = 5^{-x}$
(0, 1)

20.
$y = 3^{-x}$

21.
$y = -3^x$

22.
$y = \left(\frac{1}{5}\right)^x$

23.
$y = 2^{x+3}$
(0, 8)
(−3, 1)

24.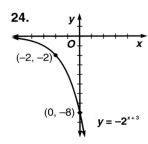
(−2, −2)
(0, −8)
$y = -2^{x+3}$

25.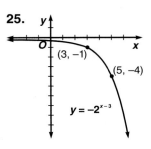
(3, −1)
(5, −4)
$y = -2^{x-3}$

Pages 612-614,   Lesson 11-2

8.
$y = 2^x$
(2, 4)
(0, 1)

9.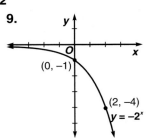
(0, −1)
(2, −4)
$y = -2^x$

10.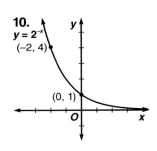
$y = 2^{-x}$
(−2, 4)
(0, 1)

11. The graph of Exercise 9 is the graph of Exercise 8 reflected over the *x*-axis. The graph of Exercise 10 is the graph of Exercise 8 reflected across the *y*-axis.

Page 621,   Lesson 11-4A

1.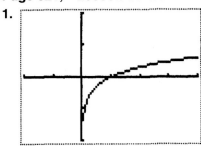
domain: $x > 0$
range: all reals

2.

domain: $x > -2$
range: all reals

3.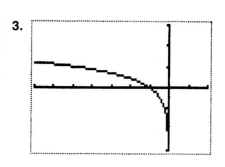

domain: $x < 0$
range: all reals

4.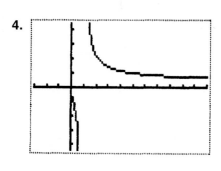

domain: $x > 0$
range: all reals

5.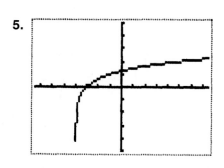

domain: $x > -4$
range: all reals

6.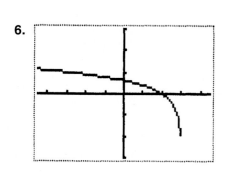

domain: $x < 3$
range: all reals

7.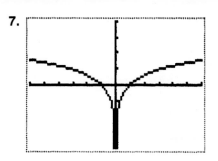

domain: all reals
except 0
range: all reals

8. cannot be graphed

Pages 626-628,   Lesson 11-4

55.

$y = \log_4 x$

56.

$y = \log_{10} x$

57.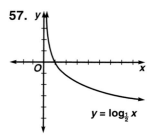

$y = \log_{\frac{1}{2}} x$

58.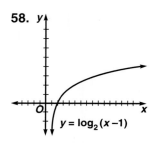

$y = \log_2 (x - 1)$

59.

$y \le \log_6 x$

60.

$y > \log_{10} (x + 1)$

Pages 650-651,   Unit Review 3

1.

$(2, -300°)$, $(-2, -120°)$,
$(-2, 240°)$

2.

$(-4, -315°)$, $(4, -135°)$,
$(4, 225°)$

3.

4.

$\left(1.5, \frac{-11\pi}{6}\right), \left(-1.5, \frac{-5\pi}{6}\right), \left(-1.5, \frac{7\pi}{6}\right)$ $\left(-2, \frac{4\pi}{3}\right), \left(2, \frac{\pi}{3}\right), \left(2, \frac{-5\pi}{3}\right)$

5.

6.

7.

8.

32.

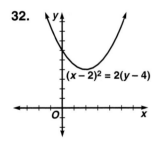

vertex: (2, 4), focus: (2, 4.5), directrix: $y = 3.5$, axis: $x = 2$

33.

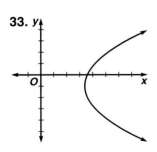

vertex: (3.4, -1), focus: (4.65, -1), directrix: $x = 2.15$, axis: $y = -1$

34.

center: (1, 3), foci: $\left(1 \pm \frac{5\sqrt{2}}{2}, 3\right)$, vertices: (6, 3), (-4, 3), (1, -0.54), (1, 6.54)

35.

center: (-2, 2), foci: $(-2 \pm \sqrt{21}, 2)$, vertices: (-7, 2), (3, 2), (-2, 4), (-2, 0)

36.

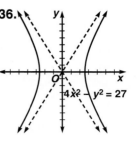

center: (0,0), foci: $\left(\pm\frac{3\sqrt{15}}{2}, 0\right)$, vertices: $\left(\frac{\pm 3\sqrt{3}}{2}, 0\right)$, asymptotes: $y = \pm 2x$

37.

$\frac{(x+1)^2}{4} - \frac{(y+3)^2}{9} = 1$

center: (-1, -3), foci: $(-1, -3 \pm \sqrt{13})$, vertices: (-1, 0), (-1, -6), asymptotes: $y + 3 = \pm\frac{4}{9}(x + 1)$

38.

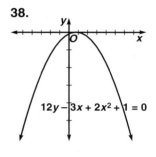

$\left(x - \frac{3}{4}\right)^2 = -6\left(y - \frac{1}{96}\right)$

39.

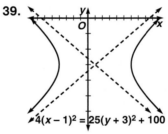

$\frac{(x-1)^2}{25} - \frac{(y+3)^2}{4} = 1$

40.

$(x + 2)^2 + (y - 6)^2 = 36$

41.

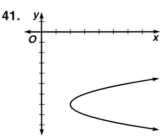

$\frac{x-2}{3} = (y + 7)^2$

42.

$13x^2 + 34\sqrt{3}xy + 47y^2 - 64 = 0$

43.

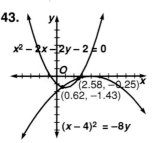

$x^2 - 2x - 2y - 2 = 0$

(2.58, −0.25)

(0.62, −1.43)

$(x - 4)^2 = -8y$

44.

52.

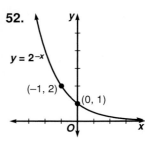

$y = 2^{-x}$

(−1, 2)

(0, 1)

53.

$y = 2^{x+2}$

(0, 4)

(−2, 1)

CHAPTER 12   SEQUENCES AND SERIES

Pages 687–690,   Lesson 12-5

53. $\sum\limits_{k=0}^{5} a^k = a^0 + a^1 + \cdots + a^5$

$\sum\limits_{n=6}^{10} a^n = a^6 + a^7 + \cdots + a^{10}$

$\sum\limits_{k=0}^{5} a^k + \sum\limits_{n=6}^{10} a^n = \sum\limits_{b=0}^{10} a^b$

54. $\sum\limits_{r=3}^{7} 3^r = 3^3 + 3^4 + \cdots + 3^7$

$\sum\limits_{a=7}^{9} 3^a = 3^7 + 3^8 + 3^9$

Since there are two 3^7 terms, $\sum\limits_{r=3}^{7} 3^r + \sum\limits_{a=7}^{9} 3^a \neq \sum\limits_{j=3}^{9} 3^j$.

55. $\sum\limits_{n=1}^{10} (5 + n) = 6 + 7 + \cdots + 15 = 105$

$\sum\limits_{m=0}^{9} (4 + m) = 4 + 5 + \cdots + 13 = 85$

Since $105 \neq 85$, $\sum\limits_{n=1}^{10} (5 + n) \neq \sum\limits_{m=0}^{9} 4 + m$.

56. $\sum\limits_{r=2}^{8} (2r - 3) = 1 + 3 + \cdots + 13 = 49$

$\sum\limits_{s=3}^{9} (2s - 5) = 1 + 3 + \cdots + 13 = 49$

Since $49 = 49$, $\sum\limits_{r=2}^{8} 2r - 3 = \sum\limits_{s=3}^{9} 2s - 5$.

57. $2\sum\limits_{k=3}^{7} k^2 = 18 + 32 + \cdots + 98 = 270$

$\sum\limits_{k=3}^{7} 2k^2 = 18 + 32 + \cdots + 98 = 270$

Since $270 = 270$, $2\sum\limits_{k=3}^{7} k^2 = \sum\limits_{k=3}^{7} 2k^2$.

58. $3\sum\limits_{n=1}^{5} (n + 3) = 12 + 15 + \cdots + 24 = 90$

$\sum\limits_{n=1}^{15} (n + 3) = 4 + 5 + \cdots + 18 = 165$

Since $90 \neq 165$, $3\sum\limits_{n=1}^{5} (n + 3) \neq \sum\limits_{n=1}^{15} (n + 3)$.

Pages 699–701,   Lesson 12-7

42b. Use the table below to follow the growth of the rabbit population.

Month	Pairs of Newborn Rabbits	Pairs of Adult Rabbits	Total Pairs of Rabbits
1	1	0	1
2	0	1	1
3	1	1	2
4	1	2	3
5	2	3	5
6	3	5	8
7	5	8	13
8	8	13	21
9	13	21	34
10	21	34	55
11	34	55	89
12	55	89	144

Notice that the Fibonacci sequence occurs in each population column above.

Pages 704–705,   Lesson 12-8

9. Step 1: Verify that the formula is valid for $n = 1$.
Since $S_1 = 2$ and $1(1 + 1) = 2$, the formula is valid for $n = 1$.
Step 2: Assume that the formula is valid for $n = k$ and derive a formula for $n = k + 1$.
$2 + 4 + 6 + \cdots + 2k + 2(k + 1) = k(k + 1) + 2(k + 1)$
$2 + 4 + 6 + \cdots + 2k + 2(k + 1) = (k + 1)(k + 2)$
Apply the original formula for $n = k + 1$.
$S_{k+1}: (k + 1)[(k + 1) + 1] = (k + 1)(k + 2)$
The formula gives the same result as adding the $(k + 1)$ term directly. Thus, if the formula is valid for $n = k$, it is also valid for $n = k + 1$. Since the formula is valid for $n = 1$, it is also valid for $n = 2$. Since it is valid for $n = 2$, it is also valid for $n = 3$, and so on, indefinitely. Thus, the formula is valid for all positive integral values of n.

10. Step 1: Verify that the formula is valid for $n = 1$.
Since $S_1 = 1$ and $\dfrac{1(1 + 1)(1 + 2)}{6} = 1$, the formula is valid for $n = 1$.
Step 2: Assume that the formula is valid for $n = k$ and derive a formula for $n = k + 1$.

$1 + 3 + 6 + \cdots + \dfrac{k(k + 1)}{2} = \dfrac{k(k + 1)(k + 2)}{6}$

$1 + 3 + 6 + \cdots + \dfrac{k(k + 1)}{2} + \dfrac{(k + 1)(k + 2)}{2}$

$= \dfrac{k(k + 1)(k + 2)}{6} + \dfrac{(k + 1)(k + 2)}{2}$

$= \dfrac{k(k + 1)(k + 2) + 3(k + 1)(k + 2)}{6}$

$= \dfrac{(k + 1)(k + 2)(k + 3)}{6}$

Apply the original formula for $n = k + 1$.
$S_{k+1}: \dfrac{(k + 1)[(k + 1) + 1][(k + 2) + 1]}{6} = \dfrac{(k + 1)(k + 2)(k + 3)}{6}$

The formula gives the same result as adding the $(k + 1)$ term directly. Thus, if the formula is valid for $n = k$, it is also valid for $n = k + 1$. Since the formula is valid for $n = 1$, it is also valid for $n = 2$. Since it is valid for $n = 2$, it is also valid for $n = 3$, and so on, indefinitely. Thus, the formula is valid for all positive integral values of n.

11. Step 1: Verify that the formula is valid for $n = 1$.
Since $S_1 = \dfrac{1}{2}$ and $1 - \dfrac{1}{2^1} = \dfrac{1}{2}$, the formula is valid for $n = 1$.
Step 2: Assume that the formula is valid for $n = k$ and derive a formula for $n = k + 1$.

$$\frac{1}{2} + \frac{1}{2^2} + \frac{1}{2^3} + \cdots + \frac{1}{2^k} = 1 - \frac{1}{2^k}$$

$$\frac{1}{2} + \frac{1}{2^2} + \frac{1}{2^3} + \cdots + \frac{1}{2^k} + \frac{1}{2^{k+1}} = 1 - \frac{1}{2^k} + \frac{1}{2^{k+1}}$$

$$= 1 - \frac{2}{2 \cdot 2^k} + \frac{1}{2^{k+1}}$$

$$= 1 - \frac{2}{2^{k+1}} + \frac{1}{2^{k+1}}$$

$$= 1 - \frac{1}{2^{k+1}}$$

When the original formula is applied for $n = k + 1$, the same result is obtained. Thus, if the formula is valid for $n = k$, it is also valid for $n = k + 1$. Since the formula is valid for $n = 1$, it is also valid for $n = 2$. Since it is valid for $n = 2$, it is also valid for $n = 3$, and so on, indefinitely. Thus, the formula is valid for all positive integral values of n.

12. Step 1: Verify that the formula is valid for $n = 1$.
Since $S_1 = 1$ and $\frac{1(1+1)(2 \cdot 1 + 1)}{6} = 1$, the formula is valid for $n = 1$.
Step 2: Assume that the formula is valid for $n = k$ and derive a formula for $n = k + 1$.

$$1^2 + 2^2 + 3^2 + \cdots + k^2 = \frac{k(k+1)(2k+1)}{6}$$

$$1^2 + 2^2 + 3^2 + \cdots + k^2 + (k+1)^2 = \frac{k(k+1)(2k+1)}{6} + (k+1)^2$$

$$= \frac{k(k+1)(2k+1) + 6(k+1)(k+1)}{6}$$

$$= \frac{(k+1)[k(2k+1) + 6(k+1)]}{6}$$

$$= \frac{(k+1)(2k^2 + 7k + 6)}{6}$$

$$= \frac{(k+1)(k+2)(2k+3)}{6}$$

Apply the original formula for $n = k + 1$.
$$S_{k+1}: \quad \frac{(k+1)[(k+1)+1][2(k+1)+1]}{6} = \frac{(k+1)(k+2)(2k+3)}{6}$$
The formula gives the same result as adding the $(k + 1)$ term directly. Thus, if the formula is valid for $n = k$, it is also valid for $n = k + 1$. Since the formula is valid for $n = 1$, it is also valid for $n = 2$. Since it is valid for $n = 2$, it is also valid for $n = 3$, and so on, indefinitely. Thus, the formula is valid for all positive integral values of n.

13. Step 1: Verify that the formula is valid for $n = 1$.
Since $S_1 = 1$ and $\frac{1^2(1+1)^2}{4} = 1$, the formula is valid for $n = 1$.
Step 2: Assume that the formula is valid for $n = k$ and derive a formula for $n = k + 1$.

$$1^3 + 2^3 + 3^3 + \cdots + k^3 = \frac{k^2(k+1)^2}{4}$$

$$1^3 + 2^3 + 3^3 + \cdots + k^3 + (k+1)^3 = \frac{k^2(k+1)^2}{4} + (k+1)^3$$

$$= \frac{k^2(k+1)^2 + 4(k+1)^3}{4}$$

$$= \frac{(k+1)^2[k^2 + 4(k+1)]}{4}$$

$$= \frac{(k+1)^2(k^2 + 4k + 4)}{4}$$

$$= \frac{(k+1)^2(k+2)^2}{4}$$

When the original formula is applied for $n = k + 1$, the same result is obtained. Thus, if the formula is valid for $n = k$, it is also valid for $n = k + 1$. Since the formula is valid for $n = 1$, it is also valid for $n = 2$. Since it is valid for $n = 2$, it is also valid for $n = 3$, and so on, indefinitely. Thus, the formula is valid for all positive integral values of n.

14. Step 1: Verify that the formula is valid for $n = 1$.
Since $S_1 = 1$ and $\frac{1(2 \cdot 1 - 1)(2 \cdot 1 + 1)}{3} = 1$, the formula is valid for $n = 1$.
Step 2: Assume that the formula is valid for $n = k$ and derive a formula for $n = k + 1$.

$$1^2 + 3^2 + 5^2 + \cdots + (2k-1)^2 = \frac{k(2k-1)(2k+1)}{3}$$

$$1^2 + 3^2 + 5^2 + \cdots + (2k-1)^2 + (2k+1)^2$$

$$= \frac{k(2k-1)(2k+1)}{3} + (2k+1)^2$$

$$= \frac{k(2k-1)(2k+1) + 3(2k+1)^2}{3}$$

$$= \frac{[k(2k-1) + 3(2k+1)](2k+1)}{3}$$

$$= \frac{(2k^2 + 5k + 3)(2k+1)}{3}$$

$$= \frac{(2k+3)(k+1)(2k+1)}{3}$$

When the original formula is applied for $n = k + 1$, the same result is obtained. Thus, if the formula is valid for $n = k$, it is also valid for $n = k + 1$. Since the formula is valid for $n = 1$, it is also valid for $n = 2$. Since it is valid for $n = 2$, it is also valid for $n = 3$, and so on, indefinitely. Thus, the formula is valid for all positive integral values of n.

15. Step 1: Verify that the formula is valid for $n = 1$.
Since $S_1 = 1$ and $2^1 - 1 = 1$, the formula is valid for $n = 1$.
Step 2: Assume that the formula is valid for $n = k$ and derive a formula for $n = k + 1$.

$$1 + 2 + 4 + \cdots + 2^{k-1} = 2^k - 1$$

$$1 + 2 + 4 + \cdots + 2^{k-1} + 2^k = 2^k - 1 + 2^k$$

$$= 2(2^k) - 1$$

$$= 2^{k+1} - 1$$

When the original formula is applied for $n = k + 1$, the same result is obtained. Thus, if the formula is valid for $n = k$, it is also valid for $n = k + 1$. Since the formula is valid for $n = 1$, it is also valid for $n = 2$. Since it is valid for $n = 2$, it is also valid for $n = 3$, and so on, indefinitely. Thus, the formula is valid for all positive integral values of n.

16. Step 1: Verify that the formula is valid for $n = 1$.
Since $S_1 = -\frac{1}{2}$ and $\frac{1}{2^1} - 1 = -\frac{1}{2}$, the formula is valid for $n = 1$.
Step 2: Assume that the formula is valid for $n = k$ and derive a formula for $n = k + 1$.

$$-\frac{1}{2} - \frac{1}{4} - \frac{1}{8} - \cdots - \frac{1}{2^k} = \frac{1}{2^k} - 1$$

$$-\frac{1}{2} - \frac{1}{4} - \frac{1}{8} - \cdots - \frac{1}{2^k} + \frac{1}{2^{k+1}} = \frac{1}{2^k} - 1 + \frac{1}{2^{k+1}}$$

$$= \frac{2}{2 \cdot 2^k} - 1 - \frac{1}{2^{k+1}}$$

$$= \frac{2}{2^{k+1}} - 1 - \frac{1}{2^{k+1}}$$

$$= \frac{1}{2^{k+1}} - 1$$

When the original formula is applied for $n = k + 1$, the same result is obtained. Thus, if the formula is valid for $n = k$, it is also valid for $n = k + 1$. Since the formula is valid for $n = 1$, it is also valid for $n = 2$. Since it is valid for $n = 2$, it is also valid for $n = 3$, and so on, indefinitely. Thus, the formula is valid for all positive integral values of n.

17. Step 1: Verify that the formula is valid for $n = 1$.
Since $S_1 = 1$ and $\frac{6 + 15 + 10 - 1}{30} = 1$, the formula is valid for $n = 1$.
Step 2: Assume that the formula is valid for $n = k$ and derive a formula for $n = k + 1$.

$$1^4 + 2^4 + 3^4 + \cdots + k^4 = \frac{6k^5 + 15k^4 + 10k^3 - k}{30}$$

$$1^4 + 2^4 + 3^4 + \cdots + k^4 + (k+1)^4$$

$$= \frac{6k^5 + 15k^4 + 10k^3 - k}{30} + (k+1)^4$$

$$= \frac{(k+1)(6k^4 + 9k^3 + k^2 - k) + 30(k+1)(k^3 + 3k^2 + 3k + 1)}{30}$$

$$= \frac{(k+1)(6k^4 + 9k^3 + k^2 - k + 30k^3 + 90k^2 + 90k + 30)}{30}$$

(continued on next page)

$$= \frac{(k+1)[6(k^4 + 4k^3 + 6k^2 + 4k + 1) + 15(k^3 + 3k^2 + 3k + 1) + 10(k^2 + 2k + 1) - 1]}{30}$$

$$= \frac{(k+1)[6(k+1)^4 + 15(k+1)^3 + 10(k+1)^2 - 1]}{30}$$

$$= \frac{6(k+1)^5 + 15(k+1)^4 + 10(k+1)^3 - (k+1)}{30}$$

When the original formula is applied for $n = k + 1$, the same result is obtained. Thus, if the formula is valid for $n = k$, it is also valid for $n = k + 1$. Since the formula is valid for $n = 1$, it is also valid for $n = 2$. Since it is valid for $n = 2$, it is also valid for $n = 3$, and so on, indefinitely. Thus, the formula is valid for all positive integral values of n.

18. Step 1: Verify that the formula is valid for $n = 1$.
Since $S_1 = a$ and $\frac{1}{2}[2a + (1 - 1)d] = a$, the formula is valid for $n = 1$.
Step 2: Assume that the formula is valid for $n = k$ and derive a formula for $n = k + 1$.

$$a + (a + d) + (a + 2d) + \cdots + [a + (k - 1)d]$$
$$= \frac{k}{2}[2a + (k - 1)d]$$
$$a + (a + d) + (a + 2d) + \cdots + [a + (k - 1)d] + (a + kd)$$
$$= \frac{k}{2}[2a + (k - 1)d] + (a + kd)$$
$$= \frac{k[2a + (k - 1)d] + 2a + 2kd}{2}$$
$$= \frac{2ak + k(k - 1)d + 2a + 2kd}{2}$$
$$= \frac{(k + 1)(2a) + [k(k - 1) + 2k]d}{2}$$
$$= \frac{(k + 1)(2a) + (k^2 + k)d}{2}$$
$$= \frac{(k + 1)(2a) + k(k + 1)d}{2}$$
$$= \frac{(k + 1)}{2}(2a + kd)$$

When the original formula is applied for $n = k + 1$, the same result is obtained. Thus, if the formula is valid for $n = k$, it is also valid for $n = k + 1$. Since the formula is valid for $n = 1$, it is also valid for $n = 2$. Since it is valid for $n = 2$, it is also valid for $n = 3$, and so on, indefinitely. Thus, the formula is valid for all positive integral values of n.

19. Step 1: Verify that the formula is valid for $n = 1$.
Since $S_1 = \frac{1}{2}$ and $\frac{1}{1 + 1} = \frac{1}{2}$, the formula is valid for $n = 1$.
Step 2: Assume that the formula is valid for $n = k$ and derive a formula for $n = k + 1$.

$$\frac{1}{1 \cdot 2} + \frac{1}{2 \cdot 3} + \frac{1}{3 \cdot 4} + \cdots + \frac{1}{k(k + 1)} = \frac{k}{k + 1}$$
$$\frac{1}{1 \cdot 2} + \frac{1}{2 \cdot 3} + \frac{1}{3 \cdot 4} + \cdots + \frac{1}{k(k + 1)} + \frac{1}{(k + 1)(k + 2)}$$
$$= \frac{k}{k + 1} + \frac{1}{(k + 1)(k + 2)}$$
$$= \frac{k(k + 2) + 1}{(k + 1)(k + 2)}$$
$$= \frac{k^2 + 2k + 1}{(k + 1)(k + 2)}$$
$$= \frac{(k + 1)^2}{(k + 1)(k + 2)}$$
$$= \frac{k + 1}{k + 2}$$

When the original formula is applied for $n = k + 1$, the same result is obtained. Thus, if the formula is valid for $n = k$, it is also valid for $n = k + 1$. Since the formula is valid for $n = 1$, it is also valid for $n = 2$. Since it is valid for $n = 2$, it is also valid for $n = 3$, and so on, indefinitely. Thus, the formula is valid for all positive integral values of n.

20. Step 1: Verify that $S_n: (x + y)^n = x^n + nx^{n-1}y + \frac{n(n - 1)}{2!}x^{n-2}y^2 + \frac{n(n - 1)(n - 2)}{3!}x^{n-3}y^3 + \cdots + y^n$ is valid for $n = 1$.
Since $S_1 = (x + y)^1 = x^1 + 1x^0y^1$, or $x + y$, S_n is valid for $n = 1$.

Step 2: Assume that the formula is valid for $n = k$ and derive a formula for $n = k + 1$.

$$S_k: (x + y)^k = x^k + kx^{k-1}y + \frac{k(k - 1)}{2!}x^{k-2}y^2 +$$
$$\frac{k(k - 1)(k - 2)}{3!}x^{k-3}y^3 + \cdots + y^k$$

$$S_{k+1}: (x + y)^k(x + y) =$$
$$(x + y)\left(x^k + kx^{k-1}y + \frac{k(k - 1)}{2!}x^{k-2}y^2 + \cdots + y^k\right)$$
$$(x + y)^{k+1} = x\left(x^k + kx^{k-1}y + \frac{k(k - 1)}{2!}x^{k-2}y^2 + \cdots + y^k\right) +$$
$$y\left(x^k + kx^{k-1}y + \frac{k(k - 1)}{2!}x^{k-2}y^2 + \cdots + y^k\right)$$
$$= x^{k+1} + kx^ky + \frac{k(k - 1)}{2!}x^{k-1}y^2 + \cdots + xy^k +$$
$$x^ky + kx^{k-1}y^2 + \frac{k(k - 1)}{2!}x^{k-2}y^3 + \cdots + y^{k+1}$$
$$= x^{k+1} + (k + 1)x^ky + kx^{k-1}y^2 +$$
$$\frac{k(k - 1)}{2!}x^{k-1}y^2 + \cdots + y^{k+1}$$
$$= x^{k+1} + (k + 1)x^ky + \frac{k(k + 1)}{2!}x^{k-1}y^2 + \cdots + y^{k+1}$$

When the original formula is applied for $n = k + 1$, the same result is obtained. Thus, if the formula is valid for $n = k$, it is also valid for $n = k + 1$. Since the formula is valid for $n = 1$, it is also valid for $n = 2$. Since it is valid for $n = 2$, it is also valid for $n = 3$, and so on, indefinitely. Thus, the formula is valid for all positive integral values of n.

Pages 706-708   Chapter 12 Summary and Review

26. Step 1: Verify that the formula is valid for $n = 1$.
Since $\frac{1(1 + 1)}{2} = \frac{1(2)}{2} = \frac{2}{2} = 1$, the formula is valid for $n = 1$.
Step 2: Assume that the formula is valid for $n = k$ and derive a formula for $n = k + 1$.

$$1 + 2 + 3 + \cdots + k = \frac{k(k + 1)}{2}$$

$$1 + 2 + 3 + \cdots + k + (k + 1) = \frac{k(k + 1)}{2} + \frac{2(k + 1)}{2}$$
$$= \frac{k^2 + k}{2} + \frac{2k + 2}{2}$$
$$= \frac{k^2 + k + 2k + 2}{2}$$
$$= \frac{k^2 + 3k + 2}{2}$$
$$= \frac{(k + 1)(k + 2)}{2}$$
$$= \frac{(k + 1)((k + 1) + 1)}{2}$$

When the original formula is applied for $n = k + 1$, the same result is obtained. Thus, if the formula is valid for $n = k$, it is also valid for $n = k + 1$. Since the formula is valid for $n = 1$, it is also valid for $n = 2$. Since it is valid for $n = 2$, it is also valid for $n = 3$, and so on, indefinitely. Thus, the formula is valid for all positive integral values of n.

27. Step 1: Verify that the formula is valid for $n = 1$.
Since $1(1 + 2) = 1(3) = 3$, and since $\frac{1(1 + 1)(2 \cdot 1 + 7)}{6} = \frac{1(2)(2 + 7)}{6} = \frac{1(2)(9)}{6} = \frac{18}{6} = 3$, the formula is valid for $n = 1$.
Step 2: Assume that the formula is valid for $n = k$ and derive a formula for $n = k + 1$.

$$3 + 8 + 15 + \cdots + k(k + 2) = \frac{k(k + 1)(2k + 7)}{6}$$
$$3 + 8 + 15 + \cdots + k(k + 2) + (k + 1)(k + 3)$$
$$= \frac{k(k + 1)(2k + 7)}{6} + (k + 1)(k + 3)$$
$$= \frac{k(k + 1)(2k + 7)}{6} + \frac{6(k + 1)(k + 3)}{6}$$
$$= \frac{k(k + 1)(2k + 7) + 6(k + 1)(k + 3)}{6}$$

$$= \frac{(k + 1)[k(2k + 7) + 6(k + 3)]}{6}$$

$$= \frac{(k + 1)(2k^2 + 7k + 6k + 18)}{6}$$

$$= \frac{(k + 1)(2k^2 + 13k + 18)}{6}$$

$$= \frac{(k + 1)(k + 2)(2k + 9)}{6}$$

$$= \frac{(k + 1)[(k + 1) + 1][2(k + 1) + 7]}{6}$$

When the original formula is applied for $n = k + 1$, the same result is obtained. Thus, if the formula is valid for $n = k$, it is also valid for $n = k + 1$. Since the formula is valid for $n = 1$, it is also valid for $n = 2$. Since it is valid for $n = 2$, it is also valid for $n = 3$, and so on, indefinitely. Thus, the formula is valid for all positive integral values of n.

Page 709,   Chapter 12 Test

18. Since $S_1 = 6$, and $\frac{1(1 + 1)(4 + 5)}{3} = 6$, the formula is valid for $n = 1$. Assume the formula is valid for $n = k$ and derive a formula for $n = k + 1$.

$$2 \cdot 3 + 4 \cdot 5 + 6 \cdot 7 + \cdots + 2k(2k + 1) = \frac{k(k + 1)(4k + 5)}{3}$$

$$2 \cdot 3 + 4 \cdot 5 + \cdots + 2k(2k + 1) + 2(k + 1)(2k + 3)$$

$$= \frac{k(k + 1)(4k + 5)}{3} + 2(k + 1)(2k + 3)$$

$$= \frac{k(k + 1)(4k + 5) + 6(k + 1)(2k + 3)}{3}$$

$$= \frac{(k + 1)(k(4k + 5) + 6(2k + 3))}{3}$$

$$= \frac{(k + 1)(4k^2 + 17k + 18)}{3}$$

$$= \frac{(k + 1)(k + 2)(4k + 9)}{3}$$

When the original formula is applied for $n = k + 1$, the same result is obtained. Thus, if the formula is valid for $n = k$, it is also valid for $n = k + 1$. Since the formula is valid for $n = 1$, it is also valid for $n = 2$. Since it is valid for $n = 2$, it is also valid for $n = 3$, and so on, indefinitely. Thus, the formula is valid for all positive integral values of n.

CHAPTER 13   ITERATION AND FRACTALS

Pages 714-716,   Lesson 13-1

34. Show that for $n \in \{1, 2, 3, \cdots\}$, $n^3 + (n + 1)^3 + (n + 2)^3$ is divisible by 9. Let S equal the set of natural numbers for which the statement is true.
Suppose $n = 1$. Then $n^3 + (n + 1)^3 + (n + 2)^3 = 1^3 + 2^3 + 3^3$ or 36. 36 is divisible by 9, so $1 \in S$.
Assume that $k \in S$. Then $k^3 + (k + 1)^3 + (k + 2)^3$ is divisible by 9. Prove that $k + 1 \in S$.
$(k + 1)^3 + ((k + 1) + 1)^3 + ((k + 1) + 2)^3$
$\quad = (k + 1)^3 + (k + 2)^3 + k^3 + 9k^2 + 27k + 27$
$\quad = k^3 + (k + 1)^3 + (k + 2)^3 + 9(k^2 + 3k + 3)$
The expressions $[k^3 + (k + 1)^3 + (k + 2)^3]$ and $9(k^2 + 3k + 3)$ are each divisible by 9. So their sum must be also.
Therefore, if $k \in S$, $(k + 1) \in S$ also. The assertion is proved.

Pages 731-733,   Lesson 13-4

10.

CHAPTER 15   STATISTICS AND DATA ANALYSIS

Pages 806-810,   Lesson 15-1

18.

Class Limits	Class Marks	Tally	Frequency
65-75	70	IIII	4
75-85	80	IIII IIII	10
85-95	90	IIII IIII IIII I	16
95-105	100	IIII IIII IIII IIII IIII IIII IIII III	38
105-115	110	IIII IIII IIII	15
115-125	120	IIII IIII II	12
125-135	130	III	3
135-145	140	II	2

19.

Class Limits	Class Marks	Tally	Frequency
63-75	69	IIII	4
75-87	81	IIII IIII II	12
87-99	93	IIII IIII IIII IIII III	23
99-111	105	IIII IIII IIII IIII IIII IIII IIII IIII	39
111-123	117	IIII IIII IIII I	16
123-135	129	IIII	4
135-147	141	II	2

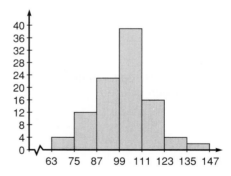

20.

Class Limits	Class Marks	Tally	Frequency
65-70	67.5	II	2
70-75	72.5	II	2
75-80	77.5	III	3
80-85	82.5	IIII II	7
85-90	87.5	IIII IIII	9
90-95	92.5	IIII II	7
95-100	97.5	IIII IIII IIII	2
100-105	102.5	IIII IIII IIII IIII III	23
105-110	107.5	IIII II	7
110-115	112.5	IIII III	8
115-120	117.5	IIII III	8

(continued on next page)

120-125	122.5	IIII		4
125-130	127.5	III		3
130-135	132.5			0
135-140	137.5	I		1
140-145	142.5	I		1

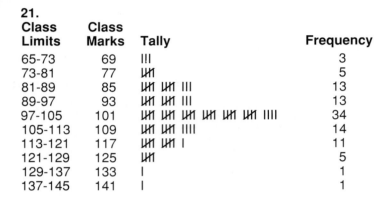

21.

Class Limits	Class Marks	Tally	Frequency
65-73	69	III	3
73-81	77	ЦНІ	5
81-89	85	ЦНІ ЦНІ III	13
89-97	93	ЦНІ ЦНІ III	13
97-105	101	ЦНІ ЦНІ ЦНІ ЦНІ ЦНІ ЦНІ IIII	34
105-113	109	ЦНІ ЦНІ IIII	14
113-121	117	ЦНІ ЦНІ I	11
121-129	125	ЦНІ	5
129-137	133	I	1
137-145	141	I	1

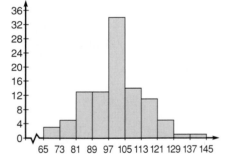

23-25. Sample answers are given. Since all data begin with 20, the first two digits have been ignored.

23.

Class Limits	Class Marks	Tally	Frequency
11.4-11.9	11.65	IIII	4
11.9-12.4	12.15	ЦНІ II	7
12.4-12.9	12.65	ЦНІ III	8
12.9-13.4	13.15	I	1
13.4-13.9	13.65	IIII	4

24–25.

27. Population Change (in millions)

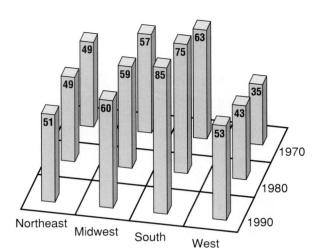

Pages 844-845,   Lesson 15-6A

1.

2.

3a.

Pages 860-862,   Chapter 15 Summary and Review

17.

Page 863, Chapter 15 Test

1.

Class Limits	Class Marks	Tally	Frequency
0-3	1.5	III	3
3-6	4.5	IIII I	6
6-9	7.5	IIII IIII IIII I	16
9-12	10.5	IIII IIII IIII IIII IIII	25
12-15	13.5	IIII IIII IIII II	17
15-18	16.5	IIII III	8
18-21	19.5	IIII	5

2.

17.

CHAPTER 16   GRAPH THEORY

Pages 869-871,   Lesson 16-1

16.

17.

18.

L   M

19.

20.

21.

22.

23.

24.

25.

26.

30.

31.

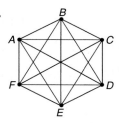

For Exercises 48 and 49, descriptions may vary.

48.   **49.**

52.

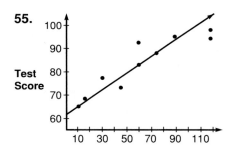

$$y = 3\cos(2\theta + 180°)$$

55.

If x = minutes studied and y = test scores, a prediction equation is $y = 0.36x + 61.4$.

Pages 887-889,   Lesson 16-4

31. Since $S_1 = 2$ and $2^{1+1} - 2 = 2$, the formula is valid for $n = 1$. Assume the formula is valid for $n = k$ and derive a formula for $n = k + 1$.

$2 + 2^2 + 2^3 + \cdots + 2^k = 2^{k+1} - 2$

$2 + 2^2 + 2^3 + \cdots + 2^k + 2^{k+1} = 2^{k+1} - 2 + 2^{k+1}$

$$= 2\left(2^{k+1}\right) - 2$$

$$= 2^{k+2} - 2$$

When the original formula is applied for $n = k + 1$, the same result is obtained. Thus, if the formula is valid for $n = k$, it is also valid for $n = k + 1$. Since the formula is valid for $n = 1$, it is also valid for $n = 2$. Since it is valid for $n = 2$, it is also valid for $n = 3$, and so on indefinitely.

Pages 900-903, Lesson 16-6

13.

	A	B	C	D
A	0	1	0	1
B	1	0	1	1
C	0	1	0	1
D	1	1	1	0

14.

	H	I	J	K	L
H	0	1	0	0	1
I	1	0	1	1	1
J	0	1	0	1	0
K	0	1	1	0	0
L	1	1	0	0	0

15.

	X	Y	Z
X	0	2	0
Y	2	0	2
Z	0	2	0

16.

	E	F	G	H	I	J	K
E	0	1	0	0	0	0	0
F	0	0	0	1	0	0	0
G	0	1	0	1	0	0	0
H	0	0	0	0	1	0	0
I	0	0	0	0	0	0	1
J	0	0	0	1	0	0	0
K	1	1	0	0	0	1	0

17.

	Q	R	S	T	U	V	W	X	Y
Q	0	0	0	0	0	0	0	1	1
R	0	0	1	0	0	0	0	0	0
S	0	0	0	0	0	0	0	1	0
T	0	0	0	0	0	0	0	1	0
U	0	0	0	1	0	0	0	0	0
V	0	0	0	0	0	0	0	0	0
W	0	0	0	0	0	1	0	0	0
X	0	1	0	0	1	1	1	0	1
Y	0	0	0	0	0	0	0	0	0

18.

	L	M	N	O	P
L	0	1	0	0	1
M	0	0	0	0	0
N	1	1	0	1	0
O	0	1	0	0	1
P	0	0	0	0	0

Pages 904-906, Chapter 16 Summary and Review

15.

	X	T	U	V	W
X	0	1	1	0	0
T	0	0	0	0	0
U	0	1	0	0	0
V	1	0	1	0	0
W	1	0	0	1	0

16.

	H	I	J	K	L	M
H	0	1	0	0	1	1
I	1	0	2	1	1	0
J	0	2	0	1	0	1
K	0	1	1	0	1	0
L	1	1	0	1	0	2
M	1	0	1	0	2	0

17. sample answer:

18. sample answer:

19.

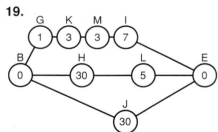

Critical path is *B, H, L, E*; 35 days.

Page 907, Chapter 16 Test

11.

	A	B	C	D	E	F	G	H	I	J	K
A	0	1	1	1	0	0	0	0	0	0	0
B	1	0	0	1	0	0	0	0	0	0	0
C	1	0	0	1	0	0	0	0	0	0	0
D	1	1	1	0	1	1	0	0	1	0	0
E	0	0	0	1	0	1	0	0	0	0	0
F	0	0	0	1	1	0	1	0	1	0	0
G	0	0	0	0	0	1	0	0	1	0	0
H	0	0	0	0	0	0	0	0	1	0	1
I	0	0	0	1	0	1	1	1	0	1	0
J	0	0	0	0	0	0	0	1	0	1	0
K	0	0	0	0	0	0	1	0	1	0	0

13.

14. sample answer:

CHAPTER 17 LIMITS, DERIVATIVES, AND INTEGRALS

Pages 942-944, Lesson 7-4

32.
$$1 + \sin 2x \overset{?}{=} (\sin x + \cos x)^2$$
$$1 + 2 \sin x \cos x \overset{?}{=} \sin^2 x + 2 \sin x \cos x + \cos^2 x$$
$$1 + 2 \sin x \cos x \overset{?}{=} (\sin^2 x + \cos^2 x) + 2 \sin x \cos x$$
$$1 + 2 \sin x \cos x = 1 + 2 \sin x \cos x$$

Pages 948-951, Lesson 7-5

32.

$f(x) = -x$

33.

$f(x) = x^3$

34.

$f(x) = -x^2$

35.

$f(x) = -x^3$

36.

$f(x) = \dfrac{3x^2 - 18x + 15}{5}$

37.

$f(x) = 9 - 3x^2$